Interactive General Chemistry

Lead Author

Jessica White

Coauthors

Brian Anderson

Brandon Green

Mildred Hall

macmillan learning

New York

Interactive General Chemistry was designed as a digital-first experience. However, we understand some adopters will require a print companion. The print version you have here is intended to demonstrate the print option we have available through our Freeman Select publishing division. Our goal was to save students money, which is why we provide this print version with a paperback binding and two-column format. For the best experience please visit www.saplinglearning.com!

VICE PRESIDENT, STEM: Daryl Fox
EDITORIAL DIRECTOR, PHYSICAL SCIENCES: Brooke Suchomel
SENIOR PROGRAM MANAGER: Jeff Howard
SENIOR DEVELOPMENT EDITOR: Debbie Hardin
CONTRACT DEVELOPMENT EDITORS: John Murdzek, Evelyn Dahlgren
DIRECTOR OF CONTENT: Kristen Ford
CONTENT CONTRIBUTORS: Stacy Benson, Kris Hiebner, Heather Southerland
MEDIA AND SUPPLEMENTS EDITORS: Lee Hershey, Kevin Davidson
MARKETING MANAGER: Maureen Rachford
INTERNS: Aislyn Fredsall, Paola Garcia-Muniz, Amanda McHugh
MEDIA PROJECT MANAGER: Daniel Comstock
EXECUTIVE MEDIA PRODUCER: Keri deManigold
MEDIA PERMISSIONS MANAGER: Christine Buese
DIRECTOR, CONTENT MANAGEMENT ENHANCEMENT: Tracey Kuehn
SENIOR MANAGING EDITOR: Lisa Kinne
PROJECT MANAGERS: Bharathi Sriram and Vanavan Jayaraman, Lumina Datamatics, Inc.
SENIOR WORKFLOW MANAGER: Susan Wein
PRODUCTION SUPERVISOR: Lawrence Guerra
DIRECTOR OF DESIGN, CONTENT MANAGEMENT: Diana Blume
COVER DESIGN MANAGER: John Callahan
PHOTO COVER CREDIT: Sheri Neva/AGE Fotostock
INTERIOR DESIGN: Lumina Datamatics, Inc.
ART DEVELOPMENT MANAGER: Alexandra Gordon
ILLUSTRATIONS: Clarissa Cochran, Sara Egner, Alexandra Gordon, Cheryl McCutchan, Thomas Turner
COMPOSITION: Lumina Datamatics, Inc.
PRINTING AND BINDING: King Printing

Library of Congress Control Number: 2018942999

ISBN-13: 978-1-319-25201-4
ISBN-10: 1-319-25201-X

Printed in the United States of America

1 2 3 4 5 6 23 22 21 20 19 18

Macmillan Learning/W. H. Freeman and Company
One New York Plaza
Suite 4500
New York, NY 10004-1562
www.macmillanlearning.com

Contents

Chapters 8–11 in the standard version are Chapters 4–7 in the Atoms-First version.

Acknowledgments

Lead Video Presenter:
Tyler DeWitt

Video Co-Presenters:
Jason Bourgeois
Joanna Chen
Rebecca Hogan

Advisors:
Betsy Granger
Erin Inks
Katherine Koen
Regis Komperda
Kelly Lancaster
Becca Runyon
Erin Scully

Copyeditors:
Anthony Calcara
Karen Carriere
Katharine Munz

Reviewers:
Hanan Abdou, *Blinn College, Bryan Campus*
Binyomin Abrams, *Boston University*
Ken Adair, *Case Western Reserve University*
Soheila Adl, *Laguardia Community College*
D. Glen Akridge, *Northwest Arkansas Community College*
Lourdes C. Alba, *St. Philip's College*
Ian Alberts, *LaGuardia Community College*
Dragos Albinescu, *Northeastern State University*
Zahra Alghoul, *California Polytechnic State University*
Sarah Alvanipour, *Houston Community College*
Premilla Arasasingham, *Moorpark College, El Camino College*
Abdurrahman C. Atesin, *University of Texas-Rio Grande Valley*
Tulay Atesin, *University of Texas Rio Grande Valley*
Pamela Auburn, *Lone Star College*
Kaveh Azimi, *Tarrant County College-South*
Jon E. Baldvins, *Normandale Community College*
Ali Bazzi, *University of Michigan-Dearborn*
John Bellizzi, *The University of Toledo*
Stacey-Ann Benjamin, *Broward College*
David M. Benson, *Bainbridge State College*
Kyle A. Beran, *University of Texas of the Permian Basin*
Mary Ellen Biggin, *Augustana College*
Lisa Y. Blue, *University of Kentucky*
Alison Bray, *Texas Lutheran University*
Drew R. Brodeur, *Worcester Polytechnic Institute*
Davida J. Ankeny Brown, *George Fox University*
Mark Bryant, *Manchester University*
Gary Buckley, *Cameron University*
Drew Budner, *Coastal Carolina University*
Stuart Burris, *Western Kentucky University*
Priscilla Burrow, *Colorado University, Denver*
Katherine Burton, *Northern Virginia Community College*
Kristin Butterworth, *East Texas Baptist University*
Roger Campbell, *University of West Alabama*
David A. Carter, *Angelo State University*
Mihaela Chamberlin, *Northern Virginia Community College*
Liheng Chen, *Aquinas College*
Edward Chikwana, *Franklin College*
Emma Chow, *Palm Beach State College*
Kristin Clark, *Ventura College*
Michael J. Claus, *Adrian College*
Wheeler Conover, *Southeast Kentucky Community and Technical College*
John A Conrad, *University of Nebraska, Omaha*
Paul Cooper, *George Mason University*
Patrick Crawford, *Augustana College*
Michael F. Cuddy, *Northwest College*
Ximena Da Silva Tavares, *Bakersfield College*
Darwin B. Dahl, *Western Kentucky University*
Christine Dalton, *Carson-Newman University*
Joel G. Davis, *Wisconsin Lutheran College*
Phillip Davis, *University of Tennessee at Martin*
J. De Anda, *Long Beach City College*
Nipa Deora, *Borough of Manhattan Community College*
Christopher M. Dettmar, *California Polytechnic University, San Luis Obispo*
Ajit S. Dixit, *Wake Technical Community College*
Greg Domski, *Augustana College*
Victoria Dougherty, *The University of Texas at San Antonio*
Joyce B. Easter, *Virginia Wesleyan University*
Sarah Edwards, *Western Kentucky University*
Barrett Eichler, *Augustana University*
Michael J. Elliott, *Florida Memorial University*
Elliot Ennis, *Clemson University*
David Erickson, *Bowling Green State University*
Sylvia Esjornson, *Southwestern Oklahoma State University*
Michael Evans, *Georgia Institute of Technology*
Caryn Evilia, *Idaho State University*
Farkhondeh Fathi, *Mount Allison University*
David B. Fenske, *University of the Fraser Valley*
Carl Fictorie, *Dordt College*
Steve Froelicher, *Saginaw Valley State University*
Gija Geme, *Southern Arkansas University*
Stephen Z. Goldberg, *Adelphi University*
Bridget Gourley, *DePauw University*
Marlyn Goya, *Vaughn College*
Joel William Gray, *Texas State University*
Elizabeth C. Griffith, *University of Maryland, College Park*
Ozcan Gulacar, *University of California, Davis*

Stephen Habay, *Salisbury University*
Julian Haigh, *Linfield College*
Baocheng Han, *University of Wisconsin, Whitewater*
Patrick M. Hare, *Northern Kentucky University*
W. Hill Harman, *University of California, Riverside*
Jerry D. Harris, *Northwest Nazarene University*
Tony Hascall, *Northern Arizona University*
Cathy Haustein, *Central College*
James A. Hebda, *Austin College*
Destin Heilman, *Worcester Polytechnic Institute*
Susan Hendrickson, *University of Colorado at Boulder*
Mohammad Hossain, *St. Cloud State University*
Jason M. Hudzik, *County College of Morris*
Alan J. Jircitano, *Pennsylvania State Erie, The Behrend College*
Lori Jones, *University of Guelph*
George K. Kaufman, *Columbia College*
Robert K. Killin, *Arizona Western College*
Kathleen Knierim, *University of Louisiana at Lafayette*
Bryan Knuckley, *University of North Florida*
Benjamin Knurr, *Assumption College*
Sophia Koziatek, *St. Charles Community College*
Keith Michael Krise, *Gannon University*
Steve Kroner, *The Ohio State University*
Allison C. Lamanna, *Boston University*
Christos Lampropoulos, *University of North Florida*
Onica Le Gendre, *LaGuardia Community College*
Hoitung Leung, *University of Virginia*
Wei Lin, *University of Texas Rio Grande Valley*
Douglas Linder, *Southwestern Oklahoma State University*
Yujuan Liu, *University of South Florida*
Dongning Lu, *Houston Community College*
Xiang Ma, *Idaho State University*
Mary Mackey, *William Carey University*
Nicholas Madhiri, *Southwestern Adventist University*
Bernard Majdi, *South Georgia State College*
Blain Mamiya, *Texas State University*
Arnulfo Mar, *University of Texas-Rio Grande Valley*
Ben Martin, *Texas State University*
Carol A. Martinez, *Central New Mexico Community College*
Heather M. McDonald, *University of West Alabama*
Thomas D. McGrath, *Baylor University*
Adango Miadonye, *Cape Breton University*
David W. Millican, *Guilford College*
Troy Milliken, *Holmes Community College*
Katherine A. Moga, *Ohio State University*
Chris Monson, *Southern Utah University*
Luis D. Montes, *University of Central Oklahoma*
Sherif Moussa, *Virginia Commonwealth University*
Guillermo Muhlmann, *Capital Community College*
Therese M. Myers, *Northern Arizona University*
Kimberly Naber, *University of Wisconsin, Whitewater*
Megan Nagel, *Pennsylvania State, Greater Allegheny*
Matthew J. Nee, *Western Kentucky University*
Donald Neu, *Saint Cloud State University*
Llanie Nobile, *Marquette University*
Ann Omollo, *Community College of Rhode Island*
Lea Padgett, *Armstrong State University*
Hector Palencia, *University of Nebraska at Kearney*
Han J. Park, *University of Tennessee at Chattanooga*
Lilly Parr-Robino, *Clovis Community College*
James E. Patterson, *Brigham Young University*
M.J. Patterson, *Texas State University*
Thomas Pentecost, *Grand Valley State University*
Chris Petrie, *Eastern Florida State College*
Julie A. Pigza, *University of Southern Mississippi*
Kathryn Plath, *University of Colorado, Boulder*
John Pollard, *University of Arizona*
Ramin Radfar, *Wofford College*
Bhavna Rawa, *Houston Community College*
Christian R. Ray, *University of Illinois at Urbana-Champaign*
Gary D. Rayson, *New Mexico State University*
Carrie G. Read Spray, *Eastern Nazarene College*
Jimmy Reeves, *University of North Carolina, Wilmington*
Ruth Robinson, *Normandale Community College*
Mary C. Roslonowski, *Eastern Florida State College*
Paul A. Rupar, *University of Alabama*
Tiffiny Rye-McCurdy, *Ohio State University Marion*
Deepika Saikrishnan, *Central New Mexico Community College*
Halimah Sayahi, *University at Albany*
Jeffrey Schwarz, *University of the Cumberlands*
Ray Scolavino, *University of Wisconsin, Milwaukee*
Louis Scudiero, *Washington State University*
John P. Selegue, *University of Kentucky*
Neeta Sharma, *Berkeley City College*
Vasudha Sharma, *Valencia College*
Supriya Sihi, *Houston Community College*
Gabriela Smeureanu, *Hunter College*
Julie Smist, *Springfield College*
Michele L. Smith, *Georgia Southwestern State University*
Kevin R. Smith, *Southern Illinois University*
Jie Song, *University of Michigan, Flint*
Allison Soult, *University of Kentucky*
Anna Spaulding, *North Seattle College*
Andrew Steele, *Lenoir Rhyne University*
Charles Taylor, *Florence-Darlington Technical College*
Dennis Taylor, *Clemson University*
Brandon Tenn, *Merced College*
Emanuel G. Terezakis, *Community College of Rhode Island*
Kara Tierney, *Monroe Community College*
Wei Lin, *University of Texas, Rio Grande Valley*
Eric M. Villa, *Creighton University*
Elena Viltchinskaia, *New Mexico Military Institute*
John B. Vincent, *University of Alabama*
Jordan T. Walk, *College of William & Mary*
Keith Walters, *Northern Kentucky University*

Elizabeth M. Walters, *University of North Carolina at Wilmington*
Patricia Warner, *Northwest Missouri State University*
Nathan S. Werner, *Southern Utah University*
Joseph Williams, *Eastern Nazarene College*
Amanda Wilmsmeyer, *Augustana College*
Katharine Winans, *University of New Hampshire*
Todd Windman, *Arizona State University*
Neil M. Wolfman, *Boston College*
Kimberly Woznack, *California University of Pennsylvania*
Mingming Xu, *West Virginia University*
Jeannie Yang, *California Lutheran University*
Chad Yuen, *Augustana College*
Chen Zhou, *University of Central Missouri*
Lin Zhu, *Indiana University, Purdue University at Indianapolis*

CHEMISTRY

Whether a student's learning path starts with problem solving or with reading, *Interactive General Chemistry* delivers the learning experience he or she needs to succeed in general chemistry. Built from the ground up as a digital learning program, *Interactive General Chemistry* combines the Sapling Learning homework platform with a robust e-book with seamlessly embedded, multimedia-rich learning resources. This flexible learning environment helps students effectively and efficiently tackle chemistry concepts and problem solving.

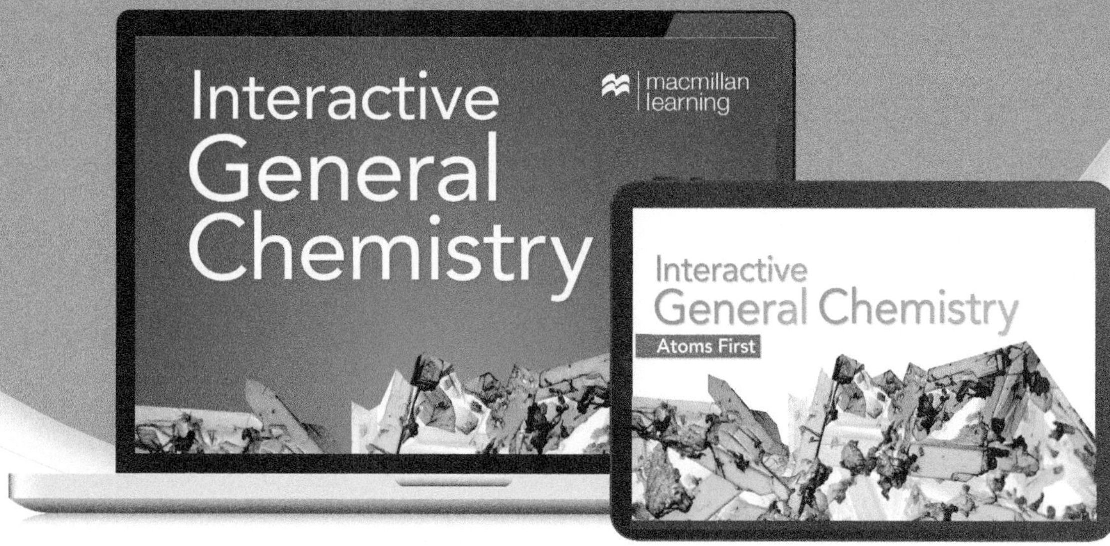

Macmillan Learning

Student-centered development

In addition to Macmillan's standard rigorous peer review process, student involvement was critical to the development and design of *Interactive General Chemistry*. Using extensive research on student study behavior and data collection on the resources and tools that most effectively promote understanding, we crafted this complete course solution to intentionally embrace the way that students learn. Photo credit: Kristen Ford/Lee Hershey, Macmillan Learning

Digital-first experience

Interactive General Chemistry was built from the ground up to take full advantage of the digital learning environment. High-quality multimedia resources—including Sapling interactives, PhET simulations, and new whiteboard videos by Tyler DeWitt—are seamlessly integrated into a streamlined, uncluttered e-book. Embedded links provide easy and efficient navigation, enabling students to link to review material and definitions as needed. Photo credit: Macmillan Learning

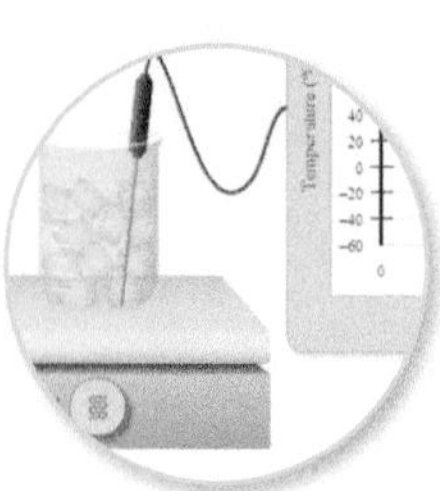

Problems drive purposeful study

Our research into students' study behavior showed that students learn best by **doing**—so with *Interactive General Chemistry,* homework problems are designed to be a front door for learning. Expanding upon the acclaimed Sapling homework—where every problem contains hints, targeted feedback, and detailed step-by-step solutions—embedded resources link problems directly to the multimedia-rich e-book, providing just-in-time support at the section and chapter level.

for the way students learn

PRINT OPTION

FREEMAN SELECT
macmillanlearning.com/freemanselect

Though intended to be a digital-first experience, we understand there will be adopters who require a printed text. Through Freeman Select, our custom book-building site, a print version can be created to suit your individual needs. Choose to print the full text or selected chapters—it's up to you, and you can modify your personalized Freeman Select text every term!

STANDARD AND ATOM-FIRST OPTIONS

In both versions of *Interactive General Chemistry,* we have taken care to include molecular-level representations of reactions in addition to macroscopic and symbolic representations. In the atoms-first arrangement, these molecular-level representations serve to reinforce earlier topics to provide understanding. In the reactions-first arrangement, these representations may be unfamiliar to the student the first time through, but serve to tie concepts together when referencing these topics at a later time.

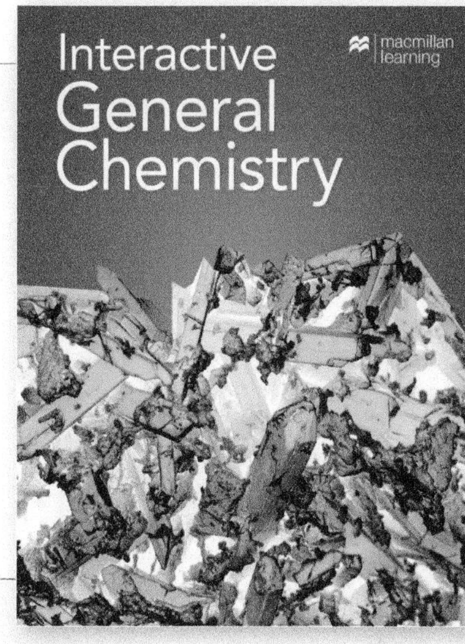

Standard Version:
Single-term Access Code: 978-1-319-10921-9
Multi-term Access Code: 978-1-319-20661-1

Atoms-First Version:
Single-term Access Code: 978-1-319-26370-6
Multi-term Access Code: 978-1-319-26372-0

Stand-alone General Chemistry
Readiness: 978-1-319-07917-8

Contributing Voices and Vision

Interactive General Chemistry is the result of collaboration among teachers with diverse backgrounds and a shared passion for improving the learning experience of chemistry students.

Jessica White • Lead Author
M.A. Chemical Education, University of Texas at Austin
As the author of the original question bank for Sapling Learning General Chemistry and longtime educational consultant for its users, Jessica has consulted with hundreds of chemistry instructors from around the country. She taught general chemistry, introductory chemistry, and labs at Austin Community College.

Brian Anderson • Author
Ph.D. Chemistry, University of Texas at Austin
Brian is a science education consultant. He previously worked as a chemistry lecturer at the University of Texas.

Brandon Green • Author
Ph.D. Chemistry, Purdue University
Brandon is a science education consultant, and he is also a higher education program evaluator for the state of Oregon. Previously Brandon spent several years teaching chemistry at the university and community college levels.

Mildred Hall • Author
D.A. Chemistry, Middle Tennessee State University
Midge is currently a chemistry lecturer for Northern Kentucky University. She previously worked as a professor of chemistry for Clark State Community College.

Tyler DeWitt • Lead Video Presenter
Ph.D. Microbiology, Massachusetts Institute of Technology
Tyler is a digital content author and presenter, research scientist, and instructor. He is the creator of a popular educational channel on YouTube and lectures frequently on how to engage students in STEM subjects.

Co-presenters: Jason Bourgeois, Joanna Chen, Rebecca Hogan

Advisors: Betsy Granger, Erin Inks, Katherine Milligan, Regis Komperda, Kelly Lancaster, Becca Runyon, Erin Scully

Student-Centered Development

In addition to our rigorous academic peer review process, we made the student experience central to the development of *Interactive General Chemistry.* The goal was to create a learning environment that reflects the way students truly study. During the development process, we focused on creating and curating resources and tools that students said they were most likely to use and that contributed to their understanding of chemistry concepts.

Our research with students served as the foundation to everything included in *Interactive General Chemistry*. We tested, iterated, and made changes based on student feedback, which came to us in a variety of ways:

Kristen Ford/Lee Hershey, Macmillan Learning

Student Interviews

Interviews enabled us to ask students specific questions about how they approach studying for their general chemistry course and provided insight into how the different components of *Interactive General Chemistry* could contribute to overall learning.

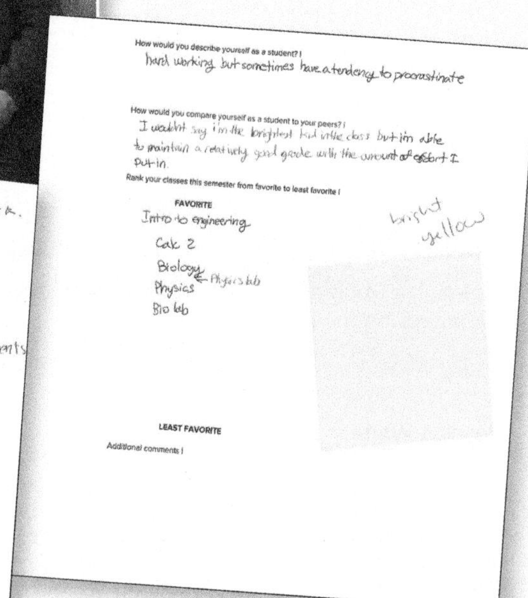

How would you describe yourself as a student? I

hard working but sometimes have a tendency to procrastinate

How would you compare yourself as a student to your peers? I

I wouldn't say I'm the brightest kid in the class but I'm able to maintain a relatively good grade with the amount of effort I put in.

Rank your classes this semester from favorite to least favorite I

FAVORITE

Intro to engineering

Calc 2

Biology ← Physics lab

Physics

Bio lab

bright yellow

LEAST FAVORITE

Additional comments I

Kristen Ford/Lee Hershey, Macmillan Learning

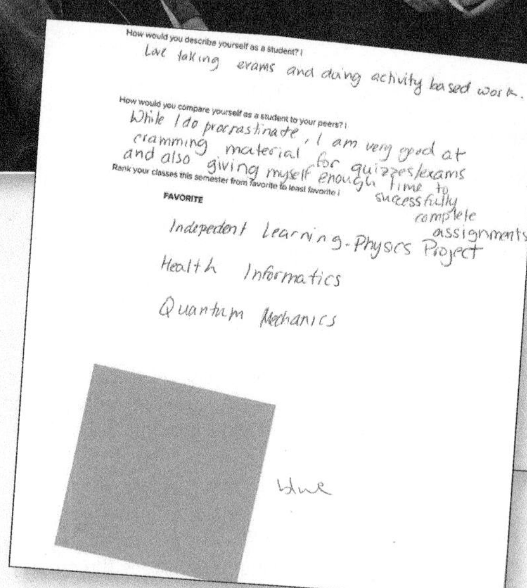

How would you describe yourself as a student? I

Love taking exams and doing activity based work.

How would you compare yourself as a student to your peers? I

While I do procrastinate, I am very good at cramming material for quizzes/exams and also giving myself enough time to successfully complete assignments

Rank your classes this semester from favorite to least favorite I

FAVORITE

Independent Learning - Physics Project

Health Informatics

Quantum Mechanics

blue

Kristen Ford/Lee Hershey, Macmillan Learning

"I think it's a really good idea to incorporate students' feedback into the

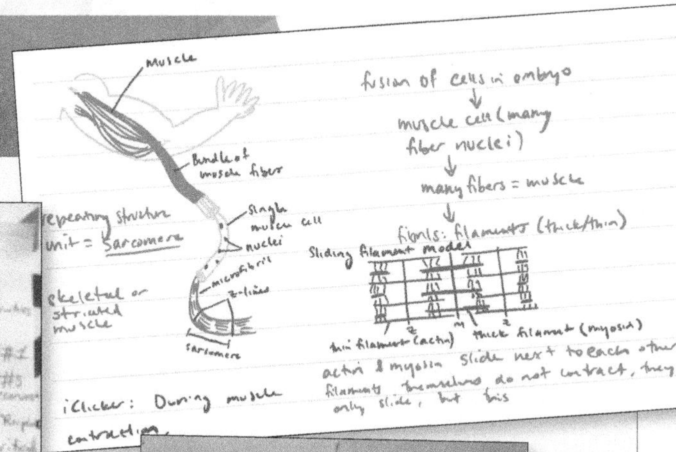

Natalie Gilmore, Student/Macmillan Learning

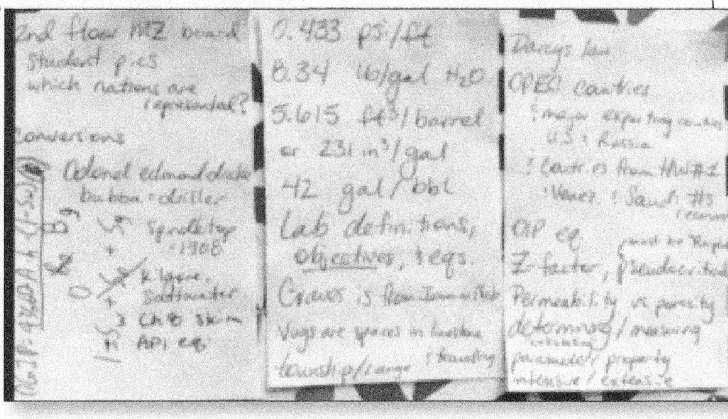

Sam Leshikar, Student/Macmillan Learning

Student Journals

Journals gave us a revealing look at how students work—problem to problem, topic to topic.

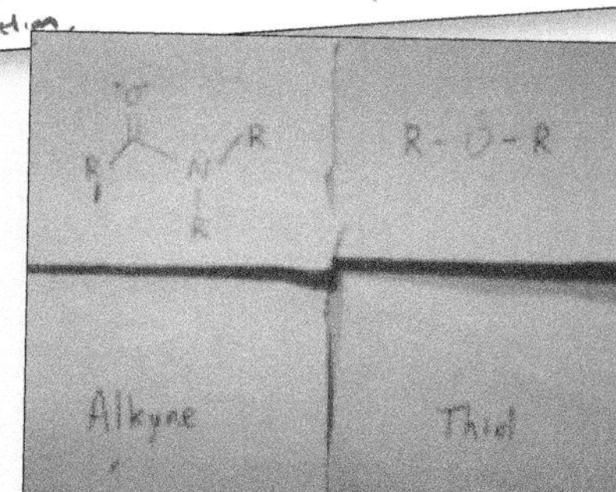

Jessica Chen, Student/Macmillan Learning

Brenda Nguyen, Student/Macmillan Learning

Student Video Diaries

Video diaries let students provide spontaneous observations about their experiences with the material.

Kristen Ford/Lee Hershey, Macmillan Learning

Student Workshops

Workshops gave us the opportunity to work with students firsthand, and understand their study habits and other important behaviors relevant to learning chemistry.

development of products they will be using and purchasing." —Anonymous Student Reviewer

A Digital-First Experience

Built from the ground up as a digital product, *Interactive General Chemistry* was designed to integrate narrative, multimedia resources, and student interaction into a seamless e-book and homework system, for an all-in-one learning experience.

A Flexible Framework offers easy navigation at the section level. Students can quickly access background information as needed, as well as link to content mapped to the chapter's learning objectives.

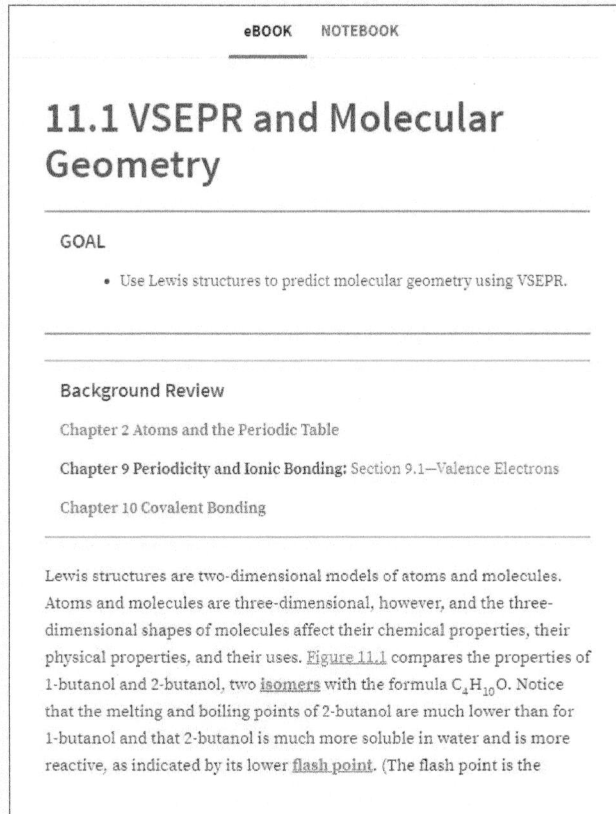
eBOOK NOTEBOOK

11.1 VSEPR and Molecular Geometry

GOAL

- Use Lewis structures to predict molecular geometry using VSEPR.

Background Review

Chapter 2 Atoms and the Periodic Table

Chapter 9 Periodicity and Ionic Bonding: Section 9.1—Valence Electrons

Chapter 10 Covalent Bonding

Lewis structures are two-dimensional models of atoms and molecules. Atoms and molecules are three-dimensional, however, and the three-dimensional shapes of molecules affect their chemical properties, their physical properties, and their uses. Figure 11.1 compares the properties of 1-butanol and 2-butanol, two isomers with the formula $C_4H_{10}O$. Notice that the melting and boiling points of 2-butanol are much lower than for 1-butanol and that 2-butanol is much more soluble in water and is more reactive, as indicated by its lower flash point. (The flash point is the

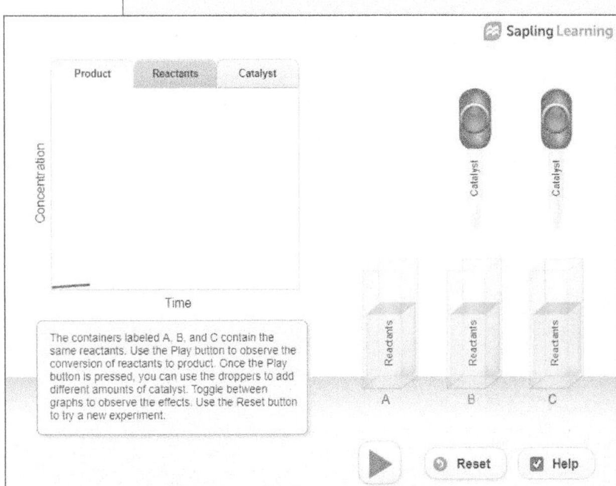
Sapling Learning
Product
Reactants
Catalyst
Concentration
Time
The containers labeled A, B, and C contain the same reactants. Use the Play button to observe the conversion of reactants to product. Once the Play button is pressed, you can use the droppers to add different amounts of catalyst. Toggle between graphs to observe the effects. Use the Reset button to try a new experiment.
Catalyst
Catalyst
Reactants
Reactants
Reactants
A
B
C
Reset
Help

Embedded Interactive Simulations created by Sapling provide students with a way to interact with the material, promoting the idea of learning by doing.

PhET Simulations from the University of Colorado at Boulder help students gain a visual understanding of concepts. Corresponding Sapling tutorial questions further encourage this quantitative exploration, while addressing specific problem-solving needs.

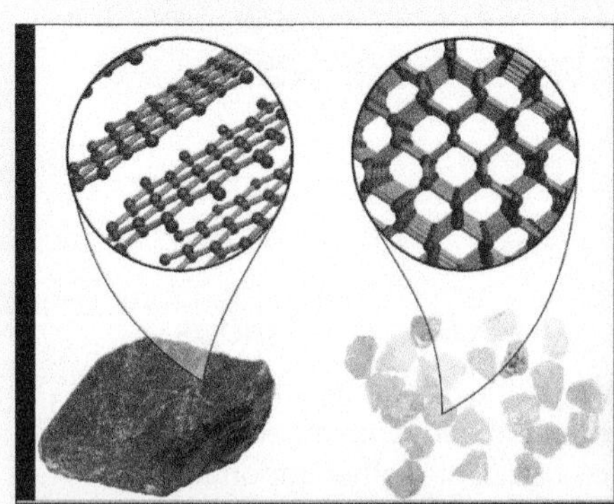

Animations and Videos help students visualize the molecular world, illustrate difficult concepts, and present live representations of lab activities.

"I love the fact that it's digital – it makes it easier to reference as I go

Practice Problems throughout *Interactive General Chemistry* simulate the Sapling experience with hints and detailed solutions hidden until needed, encouraging students to first attempt the problem before looking up the answer.

PRACTICE PROBLEM 7.7

Q: Calculate the volume of a sample of hydrogen gas that occupies 575 mL at 734 torr and 22°C if its temperature and pressure are changed to 85°C and 1.55 atm, respectively.

Show Hint

Show Answer

Hide Hint

Use the combined gas law (Equation 7.3) when there are changes in the temperature, pressure, and volume of a sample of gas.

Hide Answer

First, tabulate the given data and convert to consistent, appropriate units:

Initial Conditions	Final Conditions
$T_1 = 22^\circ C + 273 = 295\ K$	$T_2 = 85^\circ C + 273 = 358\ K$
$V_1 = 575\ mL$	$V_2 = ?$
$P_1 = 737\ torr \left(\frac{1\ atm}{760\ torr}\right) = 0.970\ atm$	$P_2 = 1.55\ atm$

This is another example of opposing effects on the volume, because the increase in the temperature causes the volume to *increase*, while the increase in the pressure causes the volume to *decrease*. To find out which effect is greater, rearrange the combined gas law (Equation 7.3) to isolate V_2, then plug in the values from the table.

$$\frac{P_1V_1}{T_1} = \frac{P_2V_2}{T_2}$$

$$V_2 = \frac{P_1V_1T_2}{T_1P_2}$$

$$V_2 = \frac{(0.970\ atm)(575\ mL)(358\ K)}{(295\ K)(1.55\ atm)} = 437\ mL$$

The value for V_2 tells you that, in this case, the change in pressure had a greater impact on the volume than the change in temperature.

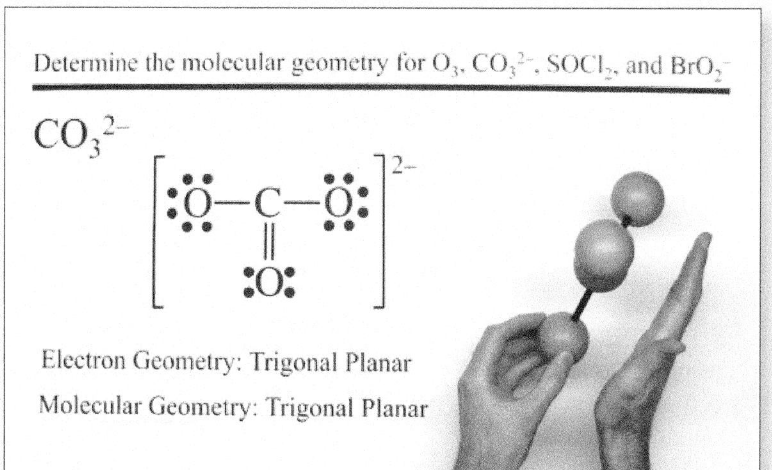

Determine the molecular geometry for O_3, CO_3^{2-}, $SOCl_2$, and BrO_2^-
CO_3^{2-}
Electron Geometry: Trigonal Planar
Molecular Geometry: Trigonal Planar

Steve Lemon, Macmillan Learning

Video Examples from master teacher and popular YouTube video author Tyler DeWitt make chemistry concepts clear and understandable through the effective use of whiteboard videos.

At least one whiteboard video example is included per section in *Interactive General Chemistry.*

"The video was really great. I liked that the narrator talked slowly, drew out the math, identified what was happening, and pointed out which numbers and variables he was using with his hands..." —Anonymous Student Reviewer

through the homework and lab assignments." —Crystle Sheppard-Hrichena, Fergus Falls Community College

Problems Drive Purposeful Study

Interactive General Chemistry ensures that homework problems serve as a front door to a true student learning experience. Students can either answer a question immediately or study further before answering. The new Resources tab directs students to material in the multimedia-rich e-book that will help them solve the problem. Each problem also offers Sapling's hallmark hints, targeted feedback, and detailed solutions.

Answer straight away.

Students can begin to solve problems immediately and take advantage of the hints, targeted feedback, and detailed solutions.

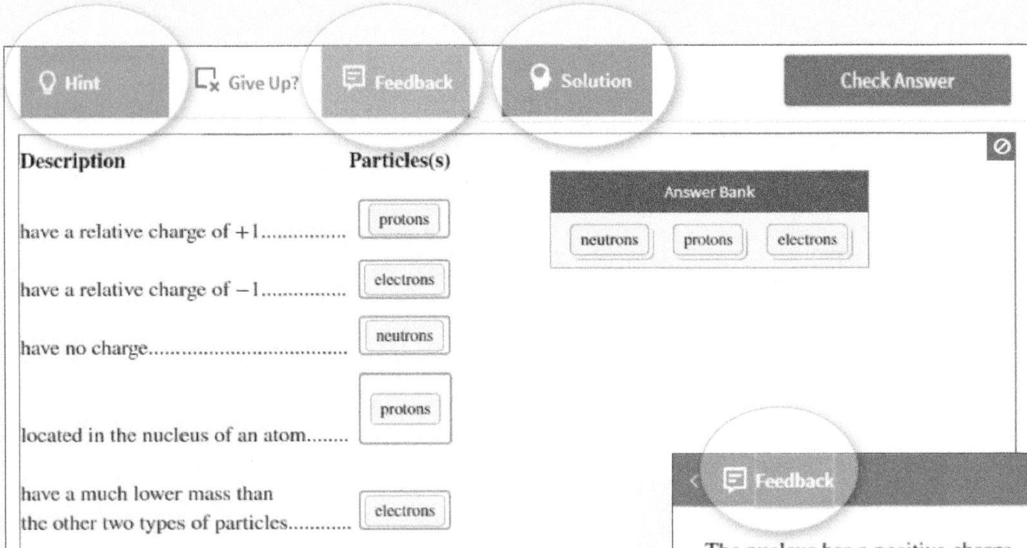

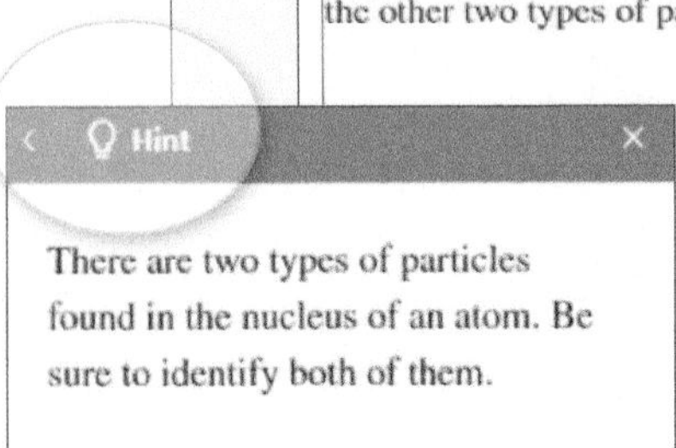

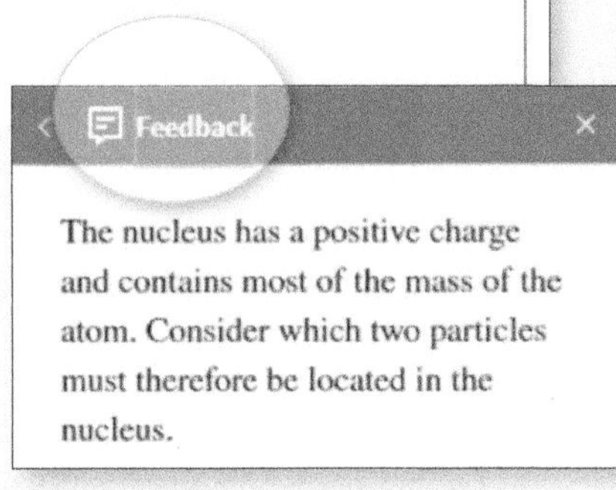

Targeted feedback

When a student selects or inputs an incorrect answer they receive targeted feedback or can choose to give up and see a detailed step-by-step solution.

Hints

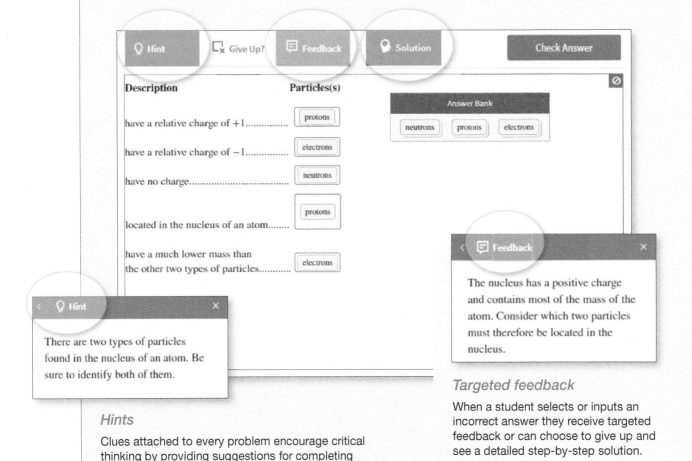

Clues attached to every problem encourage critical thinking by providing suggestions for completing the problem, without giving away the answer.

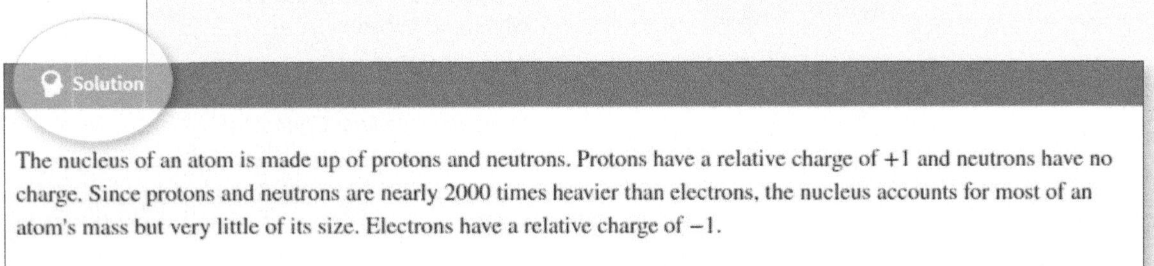

Detailed solutions

Fully worked solutions reinforce concepts and provide an in-product study guide for every problem in the Sapling Learning system.

"I am a visual learner, so the fact that I could interact with the figures, animations, videos,

Study further, then answer.

If students are unsure about an answer, they can explore the underlying concept of the problem further, taking advantage of the Resources tab in addition to Sapling Learning's signature hints, feedback, and solutions.

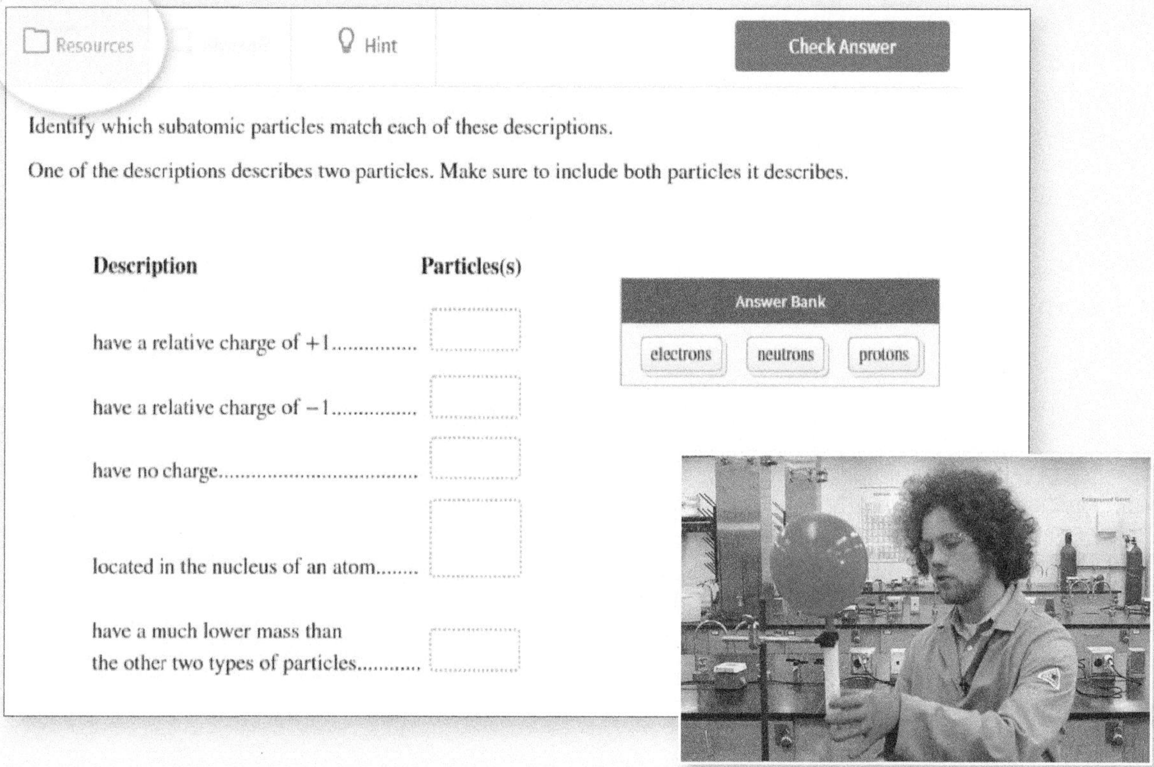

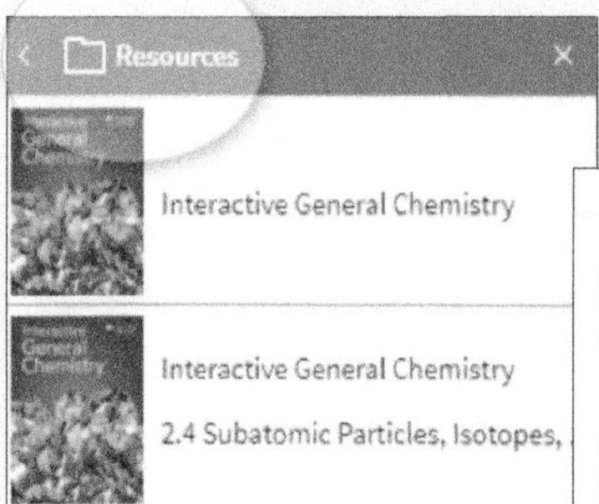

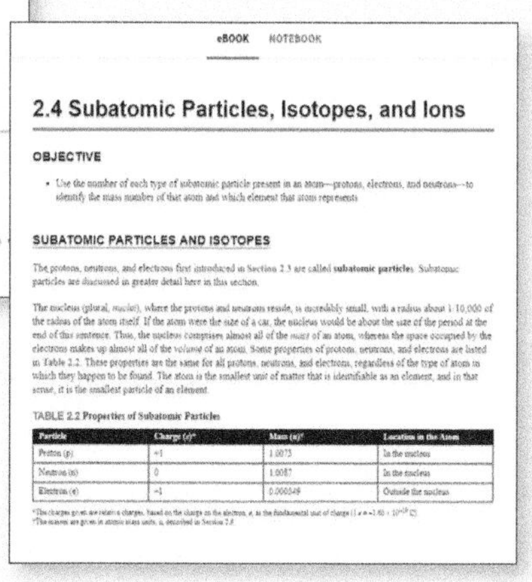

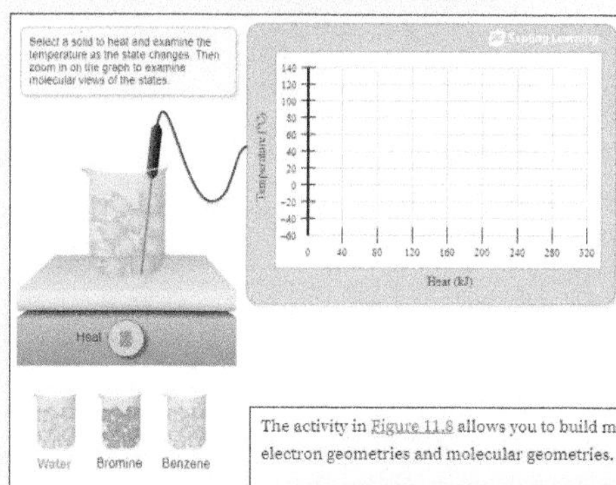

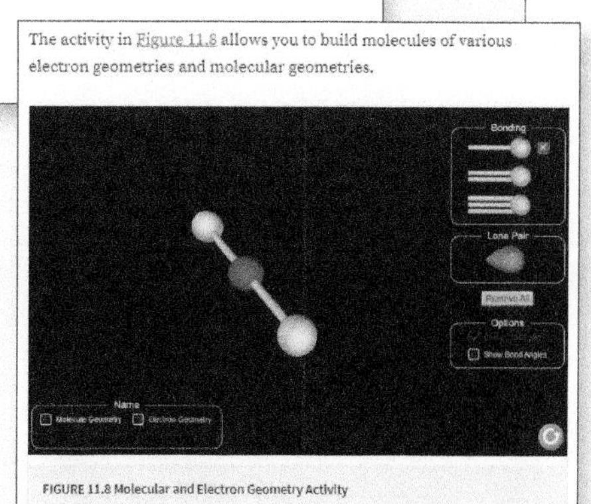

Resources

The Resources tab takes students directly to the place in the e-book they need to study to be able to solve the problem. Embedded multimedia resources contribute to just-in-time learning.

and interactives, helps me to better understand the content." —Cristina Throckmorton, Western Kentucky University

General Chemistry Readiness

General Chemistry Readiness serves up a diagnostic practice test to identify each individual student's level of preparedness for general chemistry. A student's performance on the diagnostic test generates a personalized student plan to help him or her acquire the foundational skills he or she needs to succeed in general chemistry. Students see progress bars as they work through core math topics, problem-solving skills, and basic chemistry content, building a sense of accomplishment. Both students and instructors can view analytics after a final post-test, empowering students to target specific areas for continued practice and giving instructors an at-a-glance class view of student preparedness.

Personalized Learning Path

Each student takes a practice test, which generates a personalized study plan (if necessary) and is followed by a final test.

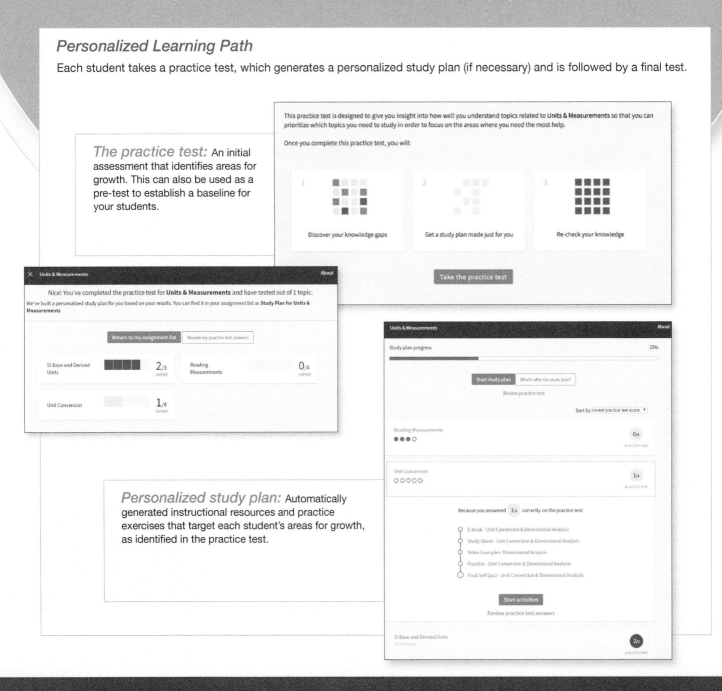

The practice test: An initial assessment that identifies areas for growth. This can also be used as a pre-test to establish a baseline for your students.

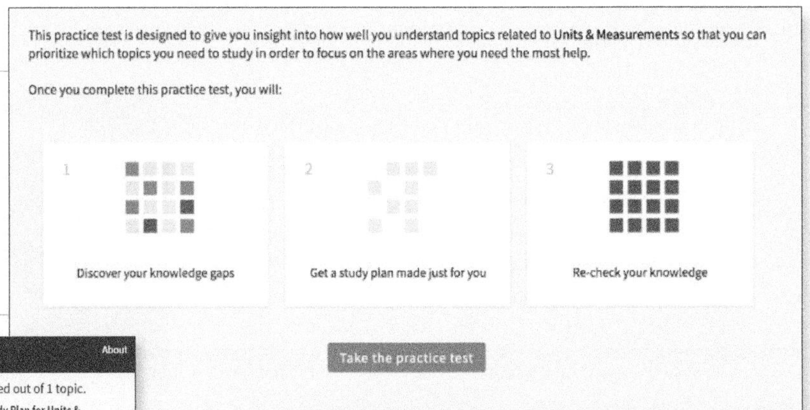

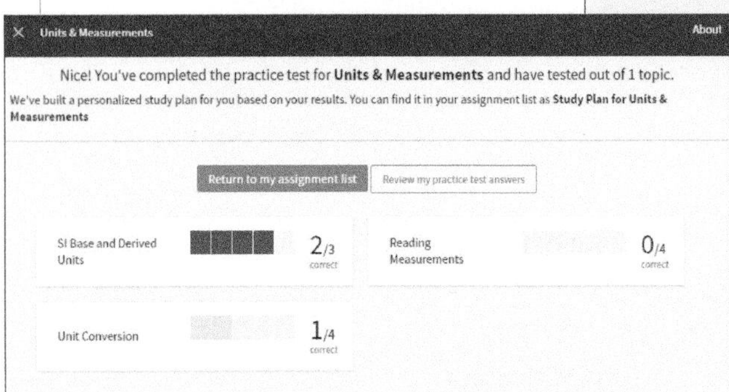

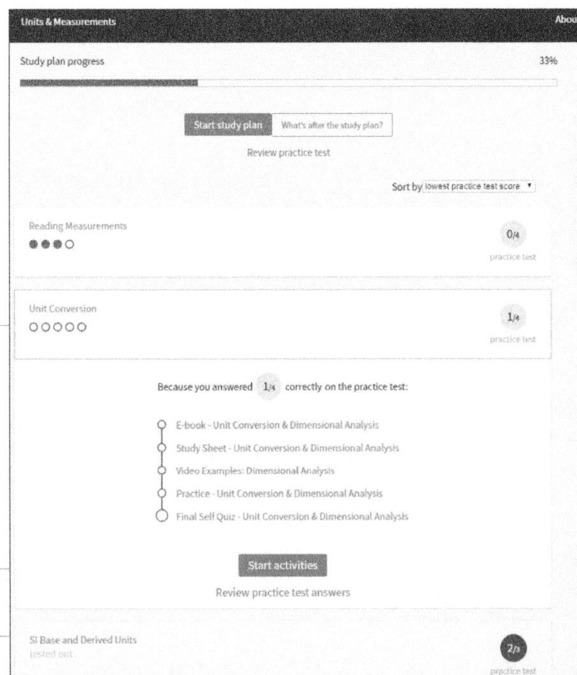

Personalized study plan: Automatically generated instructional resources and practice exercises that target each student's areas for growth, as identified in the practice test.

"This is an easy painless way to assess class knowledge base, flag students that are at risk and proactively advise. Less work

Get started on the right path!

Included with Interactive General Chemistry!

The final test: A summative assessment that measures students' growth and identifies any further areas that require remediation. You can also use this as a post-test to compare against the baseline established on the practice test.

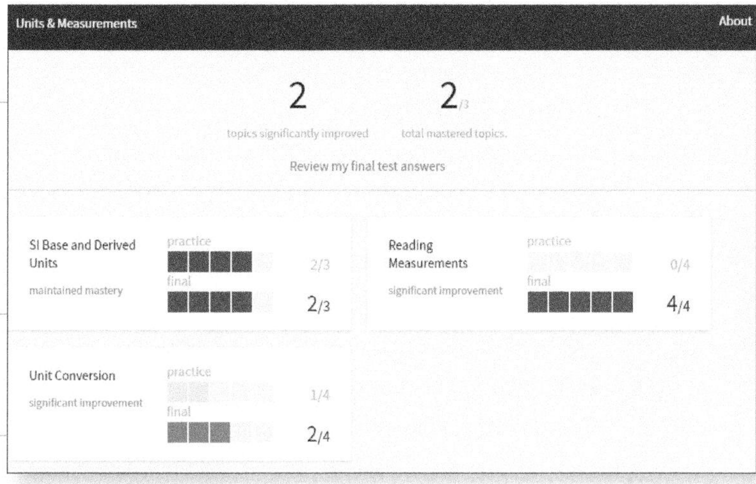

Insightful Reporting

Student Reports help students overcome the challenges of low metacognition. Upon completion of their practice test, students see a summary of their performance highlighting areas for growth. A prominent progress bar on the study plan builds confidence on completed topics and provides motivation for remaining topics. After the final test, students see a performance summary, highlighting their progress, as well as areas for continued improvement.

Instructor Reports provide insight into strengths and weaknesses at both the class and individual student level. Reports enable monitoring of progress from the practice test through the study plan to the final test.

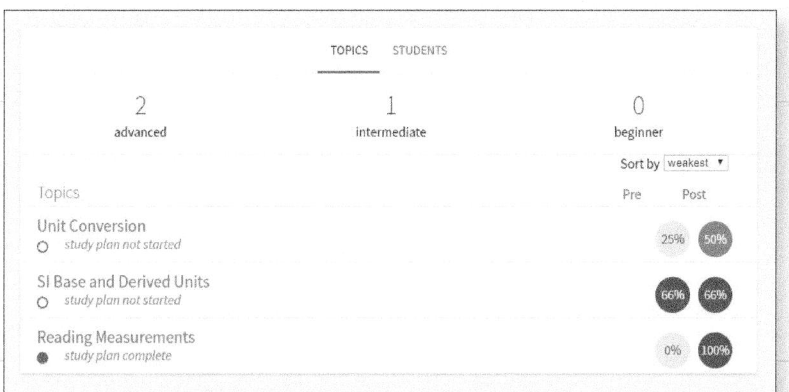

Topics/Subtopics List:

Expressions
- Simplifying Expressions
- Exponents and Exponent Laws
- Fraction Operations

Equations
- Linear Equations
- Isolating an Unknown
- Solving Systems of Linear Equations Analytically and Graphically

Units & Measurements
- SI Base and Derived Units
- Reading Measurements
- Unit Conversion

Reporting Measurements & Data
- Significant Figures in Calculations
- Scientific Notation
- Mean and Median
- Linear Correlation in Scatterplots

Word Problems
- Word Problem to Equation
- Direct Linear Variation
- Mixtures and Weighted Averages
- Choosing and Rearranging Formulae
- Using Units for Inference and Justification

Basic Chemistry
- States of Matter
- Potential and Kinetic Energy
- Chemical Formulas

on faculty from a review and assessment perspective and lets the students own their success." —Maria Pacheco, Buffalo State University

For the Chemistry Classroom

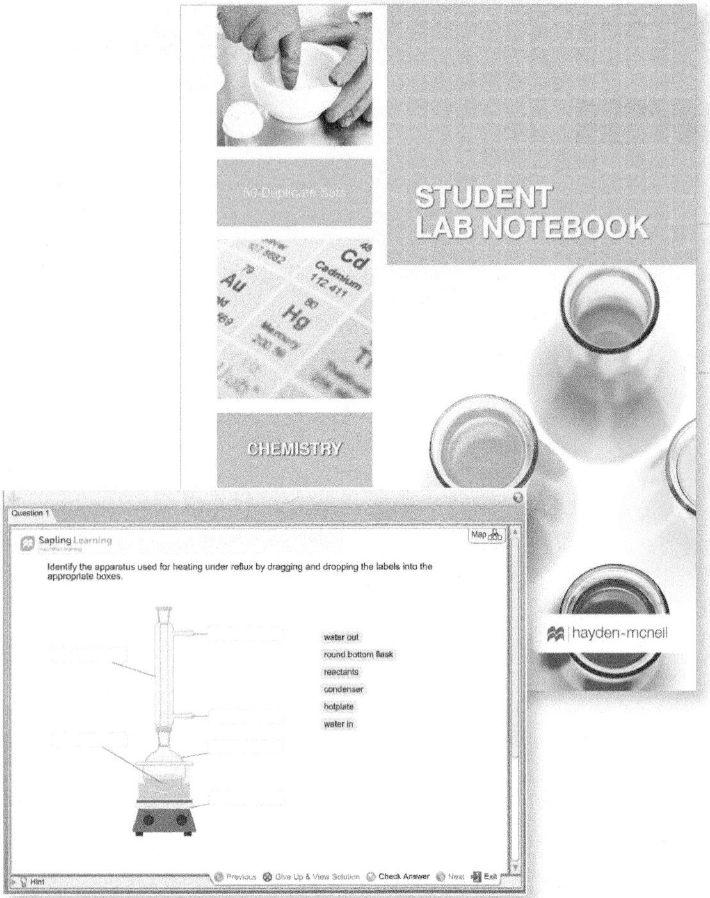

HAYDEN-MCNEIL LAB SOLUTIONS

haydenmcneil.com

Hayden-McNeil Lab Solutions provides the resources to build a seamless, comprehensive, lab experience for your students.

Print Solutions

Hayden-McNeil Carbonless Student Lab Notebook

Hayden-McNeil Custom Lab Manuals

Digital Solutions

LabPartner Chemistry Database

Hayden-McNeil Custom e-Manuals & eBooks

Full Custom Digital Course Site

Custom Digital Interactives, Tutorials, & Videos

Sapling Learning Labs Pre- and Post-Lab Assignments

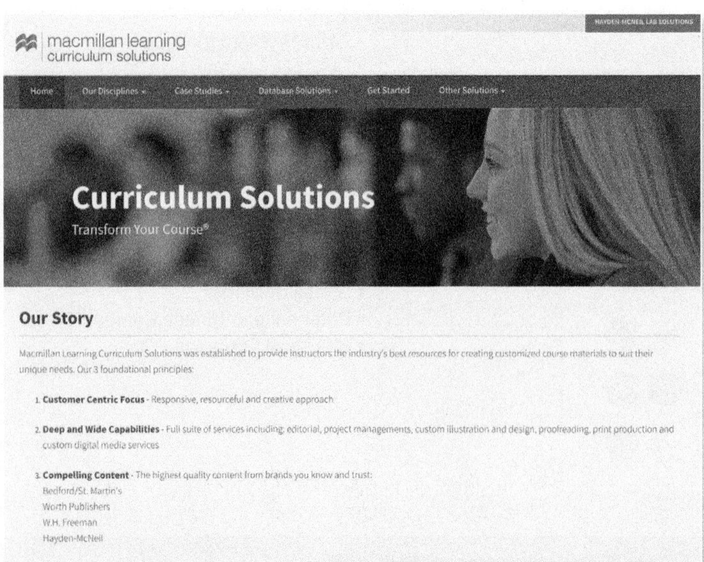

CURRICULUM SOLUTIONS

macmillanlearning.com/curriculumsolutions

Whether you are looking to create a customized version of one of our textbooks, author your own text, or incorporate our content with your own, we are uniquely poised to help you achieve your distinct curriculum objectives. Talk to your rep about creating a fully customized digital course solution.

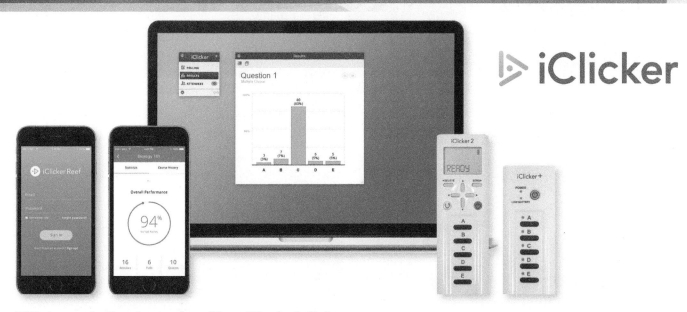

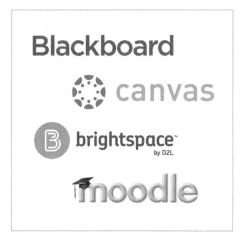

CHAPTER 0

Math Review

MPanchenko/Shutterstock

The study of chemistry is full of numerical measurements that reveal patterns about the physical world around us. Manipulating these measurements often requires math, and sometimes a scientific calculator, as shown above. For most students, the math involved in this course will be something you have seen before, although you may be rusty, so this is your opportunity to review these concepts and practice some skills to refresh your memory.

Your instructor may opt to cover this chapter fully before proceeding to Chapter 1, as a preview of what you will encounter in this course. Alternatively, this chapter may be used solely as a reference when these topics are applied in later chapters. Either way, this chapter links ahead to the relevant chemistry topics, and the later chapters link back to the relevant math topics for easy reference both ways.

Chapter Outline

GOALS

- Use a scientific calculator to perform operations that are necessary in science, such as entering numbers in scientific notation and calculating logarithms.
- Represent repeated multiplication with an exponent.
- Translate between scientific notation and standard notation.
- Perform calculations in the proper order when multiple operations are grouped together.
- Manipulate equations to isolate a variable using various techniques, such as the distributive property.
- Evaluate logarithms and antilogs.
- Manipulate equations involving logarithms.
- Compute percentages.
- Translate word problems involving percentages into mathematical equations.
- Interpret graphical data.
- Describe graph axes in terms of dependent and independent variables.
- Describe the relationship between quantities that are directly proportional or inversely proportional.
- Calculate weighted averages.
- Distinguish weighted averages from standard averages.
- Solve equations that include an x^2 term using the quadratic formula.

0.1 Using a Calculator

GOAL

- Use a scientific calculator to perform operations that are necessary in science, such as entering numbers in scientific notation and calculating logarithms.

SCIENTIFIC NOTATION

For chemistry, you will need a **scientific calculator**. The best way to verify that your calculator is "scientific" is to enter scientific notation (Section 0.2 and Section 1.6). On the Web 2.0 calculator shown in Figure 0.1, the e key represents $\times 10^{?}$ (e stands for *exponent*), so the number 2×10^{-5} would be entered as $2e^{-5}$. On some calculators, the exponent function button may be labeled E, EE, or EXP. Additionally, on some calculators, the button to change the sign of the exponent may be labeled as $+/-$ (or something other than a plain minus sign, which is only used for subtraction). *Do not* press the 10^x button on your calculator to enter a number in scientific notation—that key is the inverse log function (Section 0.5).

FIGURE 0.1 Web 2.0 Scientific Calculator

If you do not have a scientific calculator handy, use this one found at web2.0calc.com.

BUTTON ORDER

Many calculators expect you to enter a value before pressing the button for an operation. For example, to evaluate a quantity such as log(100), you may need to enter the number 100 first, then press the log or LOG button. Other calculators may require that you press the log or LOG button first. Knowing that log(100) = 2, you can experiment on your calculator to see what works.

SECOND FUNCTIONS

Symbols above a button usually indicate what that button will do if you first press 2nd. For example, notice that if you press the 2nd button on the Web 2.0 calculator, the function of the e button changes to i. On some calculators, the button is labeled INV for "inverse" instead of 2nd.

Example 0.1

Evaluate $\dfrac{5.8}{3.2 \times 10^{-4}}$ using a calculator.

Solution

If you got 18,125, then you are using your calculator correctly for scientific notation.

$$\frac{5.8}{3.2 \times 10^{-4}} = 18{,}125$$

If you got a different answer, you may need more practice with your calculator to identify which buttons to press and in which order. For example, if you got 0.00018125, you likely typed the $\times 10$ directly, rather than using your calculator's built-in exponential function (e, EE, or exp).

PRACTICE PROBLEM 0.1

Evaluate $\frac{9750}{5 \times 10^5}$ using a calculator.

Hint: Use your calculator's built-in exponential function for scientific notation. To do this on the Web 2.0 calculator, enter the denominator as 5 e 5. The exponent key e represents $\times 10^?$, where the number that follows the e key becomes the ? exponent. The exponent key on your calculator might be labeled differently, such as EE or EXP, but the order of key presses will be the same.

0.2 Exponents and Scientific Notation

GOALS

- Represent repeated multiplication with an exponent.
- Translate between scientific notation and standard notation.

An **exponent**, sometimes called a **power**, represents repeated multiplication of the same number. For example, $5^3 = 5 \times 5 \times 5 = 125$. In this example, 5 is the **base** (the number that is being multiplied by itself repeatedly), and 3 is the exponent (the number of times the base is multiplied by itself).

A negative exponent means repeated multiplication of the reciprocal. For example,

$$5^{-3} = \frac{1}{5 \times 5 \times 5} = \frac{1}{125}$$

Any number raised to the power of 0 is equal to 1. For example, $5^0 = 1$, and $10{,}000^0 = 1$.

Powers of 10 are particularly useful in science. In chemistry, you will work with extremely large numbers, such as Avogadro's number (Section 3.7), 602,200,000,000,000,000,000,000, and very small numbers, such as the autoionization constant for water (Section 16.4), 0.00000000000010.

Scientific notation uses powers of 10 to consolidate very large or very small numbers into a more manageable form. A number written in scientific notation has the following parts:

$$1.73 \times 10^3$$

Coefficient: 1.73; Base: 10; Exponent: 3; Exponential part: 10^3

The **coefficient** is an ordinary number that may or may not include a decimal point. In scientific notation, the coefficient is always greater than or equal to 1 and less than 10. The coefficient always has exactly one digit before the decimal point but may have any number of digits after the decimal point. The coefficient is multiplied by 10 raised to an integer exponent. Thus, 1.73×10^3 means that 1.73 is multiplied three times by 10.

$$1.73 \times 10^3 = 1.73 \times 10 \times 10 \times 10 = 1730$$

Table 0.1 lists some of the exponentials of 10 that are commonly used in chemistry, along with their decimal equivalents. The table includes both the exponential part and its meaning. One million, for example, can be written in exponential notation as

$$1{,}000{,}000 = 1 \times 10 \times 10 \times 10 \times 10 \times 10 \times 10 = 1 \times 10^6$$

TABLE 0.1 Common Exponentials of Ten and Their Meanings

Exponential Part	Value	Meaning
10^{-12}	0.000000000001	One-trillionth
10^{-9}	0.000000001	One-billionth
10^{-6}	0.000001	One-millionth
10^{-3}	0.001	One-thousandth
10^{-2}	0.01	One-hundredth
10^{-1}	0.1	One-tenth
10^{0}	1	One
10^{1}	10	Ten
10^{2}	100	One hundred
10^{3}	1000	One thousand
10^{6}	1,000,000	One million
10^{9}	1,000,000,000	One billion
10^{12}	1,000,000,000,000	One trillion

You can see from Table 0.1 that positive exponents indicate a number greater than 1, while negative exponents indicate a number less than 1 but greater than zero. A negative exponent (e.g., 1.73×10^{-3}) is different from a negative coefficient (e.g., -1.73×10^{3}):

$$1.73 \times 10^{-3} = 1.73 \times 10^{-1} \times 10^{-1} \times 10^{-1}$$
$$= 1.73 \times 0.1 \times 0.1 \times 0.1 = 0.00173$$
$$-1.73 \times 10^{3} = -1.73 \times 10 \times 10 \times 10 = -1730$$

> In scientific notation, the coefficient is equal to or greater than 1 but less than 10, and the exponent is an integer.

To convert a number in standard format into scientific notation, simply move the decimal point as many places to the right or left as necessary to result in exactly one (nonzero) digit to the left of the decimal point. The number of places you move the decimal point will be the magnitude of the exponent. If you start with a large number and are moving the decimal point to the left, your exponent will be positive. If you are starting with a number that is less than 1 and are moving the decimal point to the right, your exponent will be negative.

For example, to convert Avogadro's number, 602,200,000,000,000,000,000,000, into scientific notation, you would need to move the decimal point 23 places to the left, resulting in 6.022×10^{23}. To convert the autoionization constant for water, 0.000000000000010, into scientific notation, you would move the decimal point 14 places to the right, resulting in 1.0×10^{-14}.

Some numbers in standard notation have a number of *leading zeros* or *trailing zeros* (the zeros that occur before the first nonzero number in a decimal less than 1, and the zeros that come after the last nonzero digit in a number greater than 1, respectively). When converting these numbers into scientific notation, leave out all of the leading zeros or trailing zeros unless you are instructed otherwise. For example, 150,000 written in scientific notation would be 1.5×10^{5}, not 1.50000×10^{5}. (The rules for when to include additional zeros in a number written in scientific notation are discussed further in Section 1.8.)

Example 0.2

Convert the following numbers from standard notation to scientific notation.

a. 1450 mL
b. 0.0000218 g
c. 29,029

Solution

a. The decimal point must be moved three places to the *left* so that the coefficient is 1 or greater but less than 10. Moving the decimal point three places to the left *increases* the exponent from 10^{0} to 10^{3}: 1.45×10^{3} mL. The trailing 0 is dropped.
b. The decimal point must be moved five places to the *right* so that the coefficient is 1 or greater but less than 10. Moving the decimal point five places to the right *decreases* the exponent from 10^{0} to 10^{-5}: 2.18×10^{-5} g.
c. This number lacks a decimal point, but you can mentally place one to the right of the number (29,029.). The decimal point must be moved four places to the *left* so that the coefficient is 1 or greater, but less than 10. Moving the decimal point four places to the left *increases* the exponent from 10^{0} to 10^{4}: 2.9029×10^{4}.

PRACTICE PROBLEM 0.2

Convert the following values from standard notation to scientific notation.

a. 10,911 mg
b. 19,964,000,000,000 atoms
c. 0.0000000000106 m^3

Hint: The coefficient must be 1 or greater but less than 10, and the exponent must be an integer. The magnitude of the integer will be the number of places you have to move the decimal point.

On most calculators, if you enter a number in an exponential form that is not in correct scientific notation and then press the = or ENTER key, the calculator will automatically move the decimal point and change the exponent, and will display the number in correct scientific notation. For example, if you enter 22.4e7 and press = or ENTER, the calculator will move the decimal point and change the exponent, and will display the number in correct scientific notation, 2.24e8.

0.3 Order of Operations

GOAL

- Perform calculations in the proper order when multiple operations are grouped together.

Do you remember the mnemonic PEMDAS (Please Excuse My Dear Aunt Sally)? If not, here is a refresher.

Parentheses

Exponents

Multiplication and Division

Addition and Subtraction

These steps are called the **order of operations** and indicate the order in which you should evaluate multiple steps within a mathematical expression.

But even students who remember PEMDAS often struggle with the following concept:

> Even though M comes before D in the acronym, multiplication does not take precedence over division!

For example, $2 \times 3/2 \times 3 = 9$ (if you thought the answer was 1, then you may be making this mistake). Similarly, addition does not take precedence over subtraction. When you see a series of multiplication and division operations or a series of addition and subtraction operations, you simply do them in the order in which they appear. However, all of the multiplication and division operations should be done before any of the addition and subtraction operations.

Example 0.3

Evaluate $15 - 2^2 \times 3$.

Solution

First, evaluate the exponent.

$$2^2 = 4\text{: } 15 - 4 \times 3$$

Next, perform the multiplication.

$$4 \times 3 = 12\text{: } 15 - 12$$

Finally, perform the subtraction.

$$15 - 12 = 3$$

PRACTICE PROBLEM 0.3

Evaluate $12/2 \times 3$.

Hint: In the order of operations, neither multiplication nor division takes precedence over the other, so when a problem involves only multiplication and division and has no parentheses, carry out the multiplication and division operations in the order in which they appear.

0.4 Algebra

GOAL

- Manipulate equations to isolate a variable using various techniques, such as the distributive property.

Algebra is a method for rearranging the numbers and variables in a mathematical equation to simplify the equation or make it easier to solve. An equation always has an equals sign that separates the two sides. The basic rule of algebra is that whatever you do to one side of the equation, you must also do to the other side. For example, if you multiply one side of the equation by 5, you must also multiply the other side by 5 so that the two sides of the equation remain equal.

REARRANGING NUMBERS AND VARIABLES IN EQUATIONS

In chemistry, you will often be solving a mathematical equation to determine the value of one of the variables. When doing so, you always want to rearrange the equation so that the variable for which you are solving is isolated all by itself on one side of the equation, with all the other numbers and variables on the other side of the equals sign. For example, suppose you were given this equation and were asked to solve for temperature, T.

$$PV = nRT$$

To isolate T, you must remove n and R from that side of the equation. Since n and R are being multiplied by T, to remove them you divide that side of the equation by nR. You must also divide the other side of the equation by nR because whatever you do to one side of the equation, you must also do to the other.

$$\frac{PV}{nR} = \frac{nRT}{nR}$$

Since nR is in both the numerator and the denominator of the right side of the equation, it can be canceled out,

$$\frac{PV}{nR} = \frac{\cancel{nR}T}{\cancel{nR}}$$

leaving

$$\frac{PV}{nR} = T$$

T is now isolated by itself on one side of the equation. By substituting (plugging in) the known values for P, V, n, and R, you can solve for T.

> To solve an algebraic equation, there can be only one unknown variable. All of the other variables in the equation will be given to you, or else you will be able to determine them through a prior calculation.

If the variable for which you are solving is in the denominator of the equation, you can move it to the numerator on the other side of the equation by multiplying both sides of the equation by that variable. If the variable for which you are solving is already isolated in the denominator on one side, you can simply flip both sides of the equation. For example, if you are solving for V in the equation

$$\frac{D}{m} = \frac{1}{V}$$

V can be moved to the numerator by flipping both sides of the equation.

$$\frac{m}{D} = V$$

Sometimes, an equation will involve addition or subtraction as well as multiplication or division. In that case, you will want to rearrange the pieces of the equation one by one until the desired variable is isolated. For example, if you are solving for z in the equation

$$a = (b - c)\left(\frac{1}{z} + 3\right)$$

you would first divide both sides by $(b - c)$.

$$\frac{a}{(b - c)} = \left(\frac{1}{z} + 3\right)$$

At that point, 3 can be subtracted from both sides, resulting in

$$\frac{a}{(b - c)} - 3 = \frac{1}{z}$$

When taking the inverse (reciprocal) of an equation to bring the variable you are solving for into the numerator, remember to flip the entire other side of the equation as one piece. Flipping each piece individually does not produce the same mathematical result. The final equation to solve for z is

$$z = \frac{1}{\dfrac{a}{(b - c)} - 3} \quad \text{not} \quad z = \frac{(b - c)}{a} - \frac{1}{3}$$

Example 0.4

Rearrange the following equations to solve for the indicated variable.

a. $\nu\lambda = c$. Solve for ν.

b. $\dfrac{A}{B} = \dfrac{X}{Y}$. Solve for B.

Solution

a. The variable ν is being multiplied by λ, so to isolate ν, you have to divide both sides of the equation by λ.

$$\nu = \frac{c}{\lambda}$$

b. When the variable for which you are solving is in the denominator, start by flipping both sides of the equation to bring that variable into the numerator.

$$\frac{B}{A} = \frac{Y}{X}$$

Then multiply both sides by A to isolate B.

$$B = \frac{YA}{X}$$

PRACTICE PROBLEM 0.4

Rearrange the following equations to solve for the indicated variable.

a. $E = h\nu$. Solve for ν.

b. $\dfrac{X}{Y} = \dfrac{5}{Z}$. Solve for Z.

Hint: Rearrange the equation using algebra to isolate ν by itself on one side of the equals sign. If the variable for which you are solving is in the denominator, start by flipping both sides of the equation to bring that variable into the numerator.

Two other situations often arise in chemistry calculations where a little bit of algebra can greatly simplify the math. These situations are addressed by the distributive property and fractions within fractions.

THE DISTRIBUTIVE PROPERTY

Whenever you have an equation that includes a term such as $a(b + c - d)$, the multiplier a can be "distributed" across each term inside the parentheses to yield $ab + ac - ad$. The reverse operation is also valid; that is, if you have two or more terms that are multiplied by a common term, the common term can be factored out. For example, $xy + xz$ is the same as $x(y + z)$.

Example 0.5

a. Distribute the factor of 5 across the terms inside the parentheses.

$$5\left(a + 3b + \frac{1}{5}c\right)$$

b. Factor the following expression.

$$6x + 2y$$

Solution

a. $5 \times a + 5 \times 3b + 5 \times \frac{1}{5}c = 5a + 15b + c$

b. The largest common factor between the 6 and 2 coefficients is 2.

$$2(3x + y)$$

PRACTICE PROBLEM 0.5

a. Distribute the factor of 8 across the terms inside the parentheses.

$$8\left(\frac{1}{4}x + y + 2z\right)$$

b. Factor the following expression.

$$20b + 50c$$

Hint: a. Multiply each of the coefficients inside the parentheses by 8, and then simplify. If a variable has no coefficient, the coefficient is 1.
b. Factor out the largest common factor from the coefficients within the parentheses and place it outside the parentheses, and leave the remaining factors as coefficients on the variables inside the parentheses.

FRACTIONS WITHIN FRACTIONS

Complex fractions are fractions that contain other fractions within them, such as this one.

$$\frac{\frac{1}{4}}{\frac{2}{3}}$$

You can simplify complex fractions if you know that *dividing by a fraction* is the same operation as *multiplying by the inverse of that same fraction*. To simplify the above complex fraction, start by writing the fraction in the numerator, and then multiply by the flipped version (inverse) of the fraction that was originally in the denominator.

$$\frac{\frac{1}{4}}{\frac{2}{3}} = \frac{1}{4} \times \frac{3}{2} = \frac{3}{8}$$

Example 0.6

Simplify the following complex fraction.

$$\frac{\frac{2a}{3}}{\frac{x}{6}}$$

Solution

Write the fraction in the numerator, and then multiply it by the inverse of the fraction in the denominator.

$$\frac{\frac{2a}{3}}{\frac{x}{6}} = \left(\frac{2a}{3} \times \frac{6}{x}\right) = \frac{12a}{3x} = \frac{4a}{x}$$

PRACTICE PROBLEM 0.6

Simplify the following complex fraction.

$$\frac{\frac{2a}{3y}}{\frac{4x}{z}}$$

Hint: Rewrite the complex fraction as two separate fractions to be multiplied—the fraction from the numerator times the inverse of the fraction from the denominator—and then carry out the multiplication.

0.5 Logarithms and Antilogs

GOALS

- Evaluate logarithms and antilogs.
- Manipulate equations involving logarithms.

Just as any ordinary number can be represented in scientific notation, logarithms are another way of representing a number. In this course, logarithms will only be used in pH calculations (Section 16.4), but they are widely used throughout science. For example, the Richter scale for measuring the strength of earthquakes and the decibel scale for loudness are both logarithmic scales. The benefit of using logarithms is that an extremely wide range of very large to very small numbers can be represented over a smaller, more easily managed range of values. In Figure 0.2, the numbers printed on the 14 different colors of the pH paper key can be used to estimate the acid content of a solution over an extremely wide concentration range.

LOGARITHMS

The **logarithm** of a number, often referred to as the log or log value, is the exponent of 10 that would be equal to the original number. For example, 100 is equal to 10^2, so the logarithm of 100 is 2. This is written as $\log(100) = 2$. Log values do not have units.

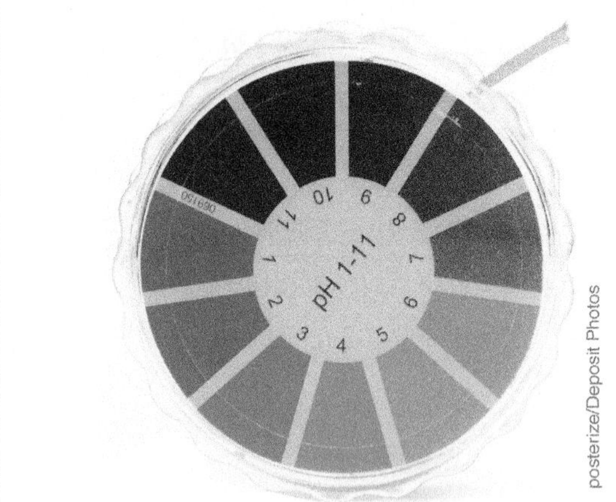

posterize/Deposit Photos

FIGURE 0.2 pH Paper

pH paper is used in chemistry laboratories to measure the pH of a liquid or solution.

For powers of 10, calculating the logarithm of a number is simple since it is just the exponent of 10 that results in that number. For example,

Number	Exponent of 10	log(Number)
10,000	10^4	4
1000	10^3	3
100	10^2	2
10	10^1	1
1	10^0	0
0.1	10^{-1}	−1
0.01	10^{-2}	−2
0.001	10^{-3}	−3

Notice that each increase by 1 on a log scale reflects an increase by a factor of 10 in the original number. In this table, values from 0.001 to 10,000 (a range covering a factor of 10 million) can be represented by numbers from −3 to 4 using logarithms. Any positive number can be represented by a logarithm.

Logarithms are different from ordinary numbers in an important way: the log scale is nonlinear. For example, going from a 2 on the log scale to a 3 represents an increase in the original number by a factor of 10 (from 100 to 1000), and going from a 2 to a 4 on the log scale is an increase by a factor of 100.

Because the log scale is nonlinear, it usually requires a calculator to determine log values that are not simple powers of 10. For example, 55 is halfway between 10 and 100, so you might expect log(55) to be halfway between 1 and 2, but log(55) = 1.74.

When you calculate a log, keep as many digits after the decimal place in the log value as there were significant digits (Section 1.8) in the original value.

$$\underbrace{\log(4.5}_{\text{2 digits in the original number in scientific notation}} \times 10^{-7}) = \underbrace{-6.35}_{\text{2 digits after the decimal point in the log value}}$$

Example 0.7

a. What is the log of 0.0000001?
b. What is the log of 0.0000005?

Solution

a. $0.0000001 = 1 \times 10^{-7}$. Since the coefficient is 1, the log of 1×10^{-7} is the exponent −7.0. (There is one digit after the decimal place because there is one digit in the coefficient of the original number.)
b. $0.0000005 = 5 \times 10^{-7}$. This number lies between 1×10^{-6} and 1×10^{-7}, so the log value will fall somewhere between −6 and −7, but determining the exact value requires a calculator. $\text{Log}(5 \times 10^{-7}) = -6.3$.

PRACTICE PROBLEM 0.7

a. What is the log of 1,000,000,000?
b. What is the log of 8,000,000,000?

Hint: For simple powers of 10, the log value is the exponent. For values that contain a coefficient other than 1, use the log function of your calculator, remembering to match the number of decimal places in the log value to the number of significant figures in the original number.

Suppose you needed to solve for x in the following equation.

$$\log(x) = -4.76$$

To convert a log value to an ordinary number, the log value is placed as the exponent on 10, and anything you do to one side of the equation you also do to the other side.

$$10^{\log(x)} = 10^{-4.76}$$

Raising something to a power of 10 is the **inverse log** function, also called the **antilog**. So, on the left side of the equation, the antilog and the log function cancel each other out, leaving only the x.

$$x = 10^{-4.76} = 1.7 \times 10^{-5}$$

When you take an inverse log, keep as many digits in your calculated answer as there are decimal places in the original log value.

$$\overbrace{10^{-1.2}}^{\text{only 1 digit after the decimal point in the log value}} = \underbrace{6}_{\text{only 1 digit in the coefficient in scientific notation}} \times 10^{-2}$$

The logarithms described here, which have the antilog function 10^x, are known as log base 10, or simply log 10, and are sometimes written as $\log_{10}$. There are other log systems based on other numbers, most notably the natural log system, written as $\ln(x)$, but in this course only $\log_{10}$ will be used.

Example 0.8

Solve for x in $\log(x) = 2.53$.

Solution

$x = 10^{2.53} = 339$. Since the log value (2.53) has two digits after the decimal place, the calculated antilog should have two digits when expressed in scientific notation, so the final answer is 3.4×10^2, or 340.

PRACTICE PROBLEM 0.8

Solve for x in $\log(x) = -6.59$.

Hint: Use the 10^x function on your calculator. Remember to match the number of significant figures in your answer to the number of decimal places in the log value.

Natural Logarithm

The **natural logarithm** is a type of logarithm represented as $\ln x$ in equations (as opposed to $\log x$ for a standard logarithm). On a calculator, it is designated with the ln or LN button. (On the Web 2.0 calculator, you can access the natural logarithm button from the dropdown menu below "log" or "10^x.") The difference between ln and log is that ln is a logarithm with base e instead of base 10. The symbol e represents a constant equal to 2.71828 (just as the symbol π represents a constant equal to 3.14159). So, to "undo" a natural log, you would raise it as a power of e, $x = e^{\ln x}$, just as you can "undo" a standard log by raising it as a power of 10, $x = 10^{\log x}$.

Example 0.9

Determine the value of x.

a. $x = \ln(2.00)$
b. $\ln(x) = 2.00$

Solution

a. Use a calculator to compute $\ln(2.00) = 0.693$.
b. Use a calculator to compute the inverse natural log function, $e^{2.00} = 7.39$.

PRACTICE PROBLEM 0.9

Determine the value of x.

a. $x = \ln(1.81)$
b. $\ln(x) = 1.81$

Hint: On the Web 2.0 calculator, click the small triangle under the log button to reveal the ln and e^x buttons.

0.6 Percentage

GOALS

- Compute percentages.
- Translate word problems involving percentages into mathematical equations.

A percentage expresses the amount of a certain component within the total. For example, oxygen is just one component of air, so the amount of oxygen in air can be expressed as percentage of the whole (Figure 0.3).

The word *per* implies division, and *cent* means 100. So the word **percent** literally means "divided by 100." That is why 50% is equal to $50/100 = 0.5$, or one half. Word problems involving percentage can often be "translated" to formulas using a few simple rules.

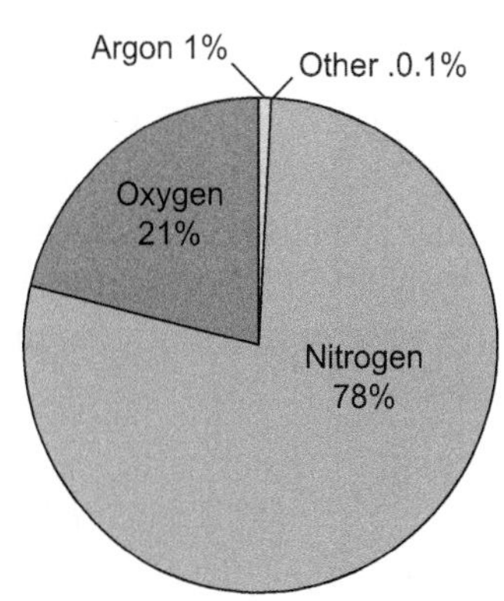

FIGURE 0.3 Percentage as a Fraction of the Whole
Air on Earth is 21% oxygen.

Word or Phrase	Mathematical Translation
percent (or %)	÷ 100
of	× or · (multiplication)
what	x (the unknown quantity)
is	=

For example, here are some word problems and their equivalent mathematical formulas.

Word Problem	Formula	Answer
What is 15% of 60?	$x = \frac{15}{100} \times 60$	$x = 9$
8 is what percent of 40?	$8 = \frac{x}{100} \times 40$	$x = 20$
2 is 25% of what number?	$2 = \frac{25}{100} \times x$	$x = 8$

Example 0.10

Sucrose, also called table sugar, is 42.1% carbon by mass. If you had a 5.0 lb bag of sugar, how many pounds of carbon would it contain?

Solution

This question is asking, "What is 42.1% of 5 lb?"

$$x = \frac{42.1}{100} \times 5.0 \text{ lb} = 2.1 \text{ lb of carbon}$$

PRACTICE PROBLEM 0.10

Table sugar is 51.4% oxygen by mass. If you had a 5.0 lb bag of sugar, how many pounds of oxygen would it contain?

Hint: This question is asking, "What is 51.4% of 5 lb?" To convert this question into a mathematical formula, consult the above chart of word problems and their corresponding formulas.

The percentages of all of the components of something always add up to 100%, so if you knew that table sugar is made up only of carbon, oxygen, and hydrogen, you could calculate the percent hydrogen in sugar by subtracting the percent carbon and oxygen from 100%.

$$\begin{aligned} \% \text{ hydrogen} &= 100\% - (42.1\% \text{ carbon}) \\ &\quad - (51.4\% \text{ oxygen}) \\ \% \text{ hydrogen in sucrose} &= 6.5\% \end{aligned}$$

If you are familiar with the factor label method of doing unit conversions (Section 1.5), you may prefer to think of a percentage as a conversion factor. Since percentages are often used to express the amount of a certain component within the total, percentages can be used to convert between a component and the total. For example, a certain type of rock might be 25% iron by mass. In other words, there is 25 g of iron in 100 g of the rock (or 25 oz of iron in 100 oz of rock, or whatever mass unit you prefer to use). Now if you were asked to predict the amount of iron in a rock weighing 72 g, you could use the percentage as a conversion factor between the amounts of iron and rock.

$$72 \text{ g rock}\left(\frac{25 \text{ g iron}}{100 \text{ g rock}}\right) = 18 \text{ g iron}$$

Areas of this course where percentage is particularly important are atomic mass (Section 2.7), percent composition of compounds (Section 3.8), reaction yields (Section 5.4), and solution concentration (Section 13.3).

0.7 Graphs

GOALS

- Interpret graphical data.
- Describe graph axes in terms of dependent and independent variables.

INTERPRETING A GRAPH

Oftentimes in science, you will need to interpret a graph. The most common type of graph used in science is a line graph that relates two quantities. Line graphs show how changing one of the two quantities creates a change in the second one. For example, a graph can be used to show how quickly the temperature of a liquid sample increases as heat energy is added to it (Section 6.5). The variable that is being controlled (the amount of heat added) is plotted on the horizontal axis of the graph (the x-axis), and the variable that changes in response is plotted on the vertical axis (the y-axis). The quantity that is being controlled and is plotted on the x-axis is known as the **independent variable**, and the quantity that changes in response and is plotted on the y-axis is known as the **dependent variable**.

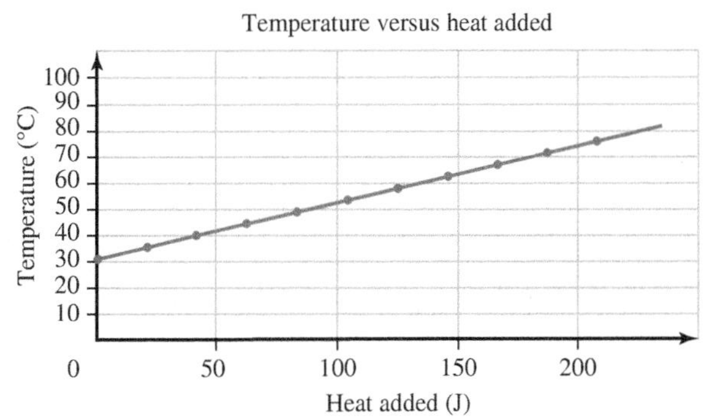

FIGURE 0.4 A Line Graph

A line graph relates a dependent variable on the *y*-axis (temperature) to an independent variable on the *x*-axis (heat added).

A typical line graph is shown in Figure 0.4. On this graph, *heat added* is the independent variable, plotted on the *x*-axis, and *temperature* is the dependent variable, plotted on the *y*-axis. The axis labels include the units for both the heat added and the temperature, and the title of the graph is written as *dependent variable* versus *independent variable.*

Each data point on the graph is made up of a pair of numbers, listed in order of *x*, *y*. For example, the first data point on the graph corresponds to 0 on the *x*-axis and 30 on the *y*-axis; that is, it corresponds to the *x*, *y* pair (0, 30). This data point tells you that when no heat had been added (heat added = 0 joules, J), the temperature of the sample was 30°C. The final measurement taken in this experiment was a temperature of 75°C after 210 J of heat was added and corresponds to the data point at (210, 75).

Graphs can also be used to determine (*x*, *y*) pairs that lie between the measured data points. For example, you can determine what the temperature of the sample was when 50 J of heat was added, even though no measurement was taken at that time. To do this, locate 50 J on the *x*-axis, and then follow a vertical line until it intersects the straight line going through the data points. This intersection occurs at a point that is at about 42 on the *y*-axis, so when 50 J of heat was added, the temperature of the sample was about 42°C.

This process of determining (*x*, *y*) pairs that lie between the actual data points is called **interpolation**. You could also determine (*x*, *y*) pairs that lie beyond the highest data points by extending the line through the data points all the way to 250 J, for example, and then reading the corresponding temperature. Determining (*x*, *y*) values that lie outside the range of actual data points is called **extrapolation**. Extrapolation can lead to errors, however, and the farther you extrapolate outside of the data range, the greater those errors are likely to be. For this reason, extrapolation is generally avoided whenever possible.

Example 0.11

A scientist carried out a chemical reaction and monitored how much product was formed as the reaction progressed. She then graphed her results as shown below.

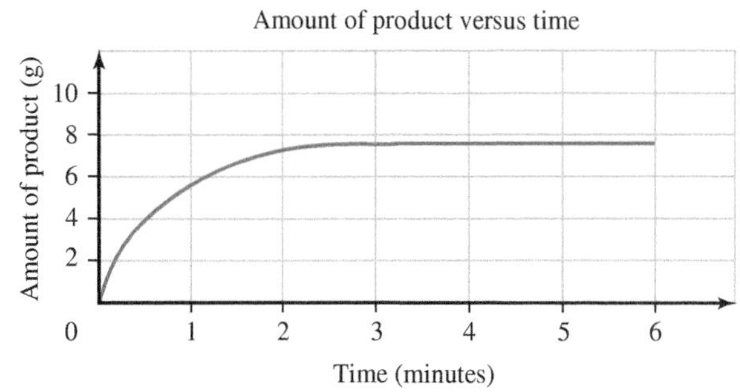

From this graph, determine the following.

a. How many grams of product was present when the reaction began?
b. How many grams of product was formed by the time the reaction was over?
c. How long did the scientist allow the reaction to proceed?
d. At what point in time was the reaction essentially complete (no more product was being formed)?

Solution

a. At the beginning of the experiment ($x = 0$), the value of *y* (the amount of product formed) is also 0, so there was 0 g of product present when the reaction began.
b. The highest value on this graph for amount of product formed (the highest *y* value) is about 7.5 g, so 7.5 g of product was formed.
c. The graph runs on the *x*-axis from 0 to 6 minutes, min, so she stopped the experiment after 6 min had passed.
d. The amount of product formed reaches 7.5 g at about 2.5 min and stays there, so at that point no additional product is being formed.

PRACTICE PROBLEM 0.11

On the next page is a graph that relates temperature on the Celsius scale to temperature on the Fahrenheit scale.

a. If each point on the graph represents two temperature measurements (one in Celsius and one in Fahrenheit), how many measurements were made to construct this graph?

b. What Fahrenheit temperature corresponds to 50°C?

c. What Celsius temperature corresponds to 200°F?

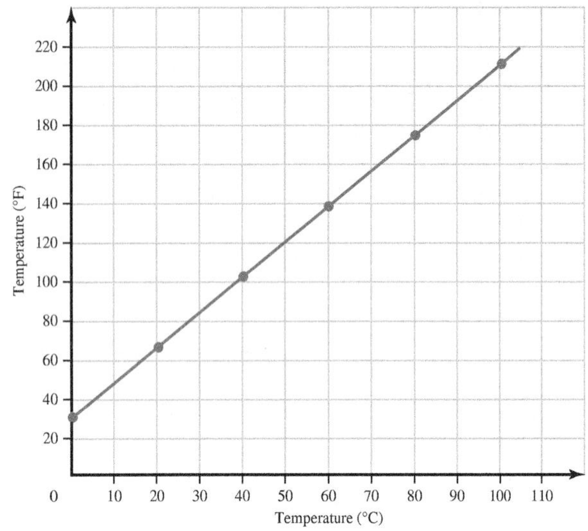

Hint: Take note of the number of points shown on the graph and pay special attention to the labels on each axis.

FINDING SLOPE FOR LINEAR DATA

A data set is said to be **linear** if the points form a straight line when plotted on a graph. A straight-line plot has a **slope, *m***, which is a number that describes the steepness of its incline. Slope is defined as "rise over run" (Figure 0.5).

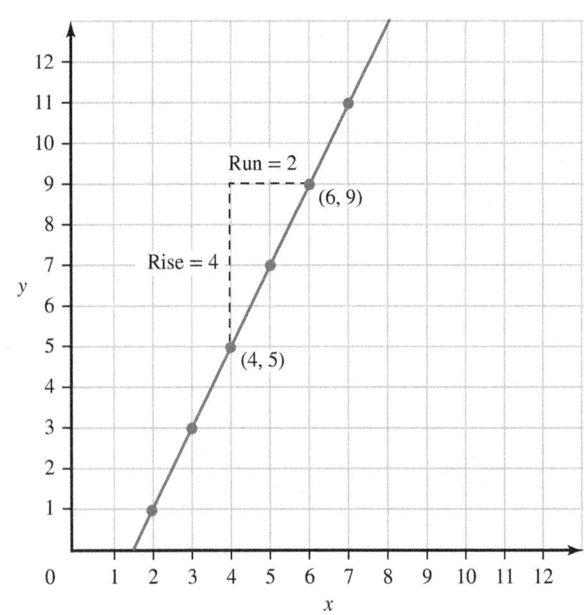

FIGURE 0.5 Rise and Run

The steepness of a line can be quantified by the lengths of the vertical rise and the horizontal run.

The equation for slope is

$$m = \frac{y_2 - y_1}{x_2 - x_1} \tag{0.1}$$

where (x_1, y_1) and (x_2, y_2) are two arbitrary points along the line. For the line shown in Figure 0.5, the selected points are (4, 5) and (6, 9), so the slope calculation is as follows.

$$m = \frac{9 - 5}{6 - 4} = \frac{4}{2} = 2$$

Notice that any other combination of points on this line will yield the same result for m. This is because the slope is a constant for linear data.

The equation for a straight line is

$$y = mx + b \tag{0.2}$$

where m is the slope, b is the y-intercept, and all x, y coordinate pairs on the line satisfy the equation. The **y-intercept, b,** is the y value when $x = 0$ (where the line crosses the y-axis). For the line in Figure 0.5, you can plug values into Equation 0.2 and solve for b, using the x and y values for any point on the line. This calculation uses the point (4, 5), so $x = 4$, $y = 5$, and $m = 2$.

$$b = y - mx$$
$$b = 5 - (2 \times 4)$$
$$b = 5 - 8 = -3$$

This value for b tells us that if the line were extended downward, it would cross the y-axis at -3.

Example 0.12

Determine the slope and y-intercept for the straight line formed from these data.

x	y
2.2	4.2
3.8	6.6
5.4	9.0

Solution

Choose any two points and substitute their x and y values into Equation 0.1. This calculation happens to use the first two points (2.2, 4.2) and (3.8, 6.6).

$$m = \frac{y_2 - y_1}{x_2 - x_1}$$

$$m = \frac{6.6 - 4.2}{3.8 - 2.2} = \frac{2.4}{1.6} = 1.5$$

Now plug this value of m and the x and y values for any point into Equation 0.2 and solve for b. This calculation happens to use the first point, where $x = 2.2$ and $y = 4.2$.

$$y = mx + b$$
$$b = y - mx$$
$$b = 4.2 - (1.5 \times 2.2) = 0.9$$

PRACTICE PROBLEM 0.12

Determine the slope and y-intercept for the line shown here.

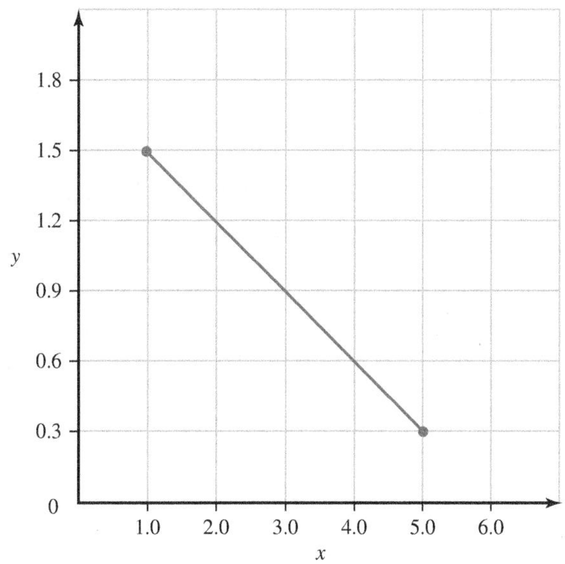

Hint: Start by reading the x and y values of each point.

Finding the slope and y-intercept for linear data are skills that apply to vapor pressure calculations in Section 12.4 and activation energy calculations in Section 14.4.

0.8 Proportionality

GOAL

- Describe the relationship between quantities that are directly proportional or inversely proportional.

A direct relationship means that two quantities increase and decrease together. More specifically, two quantities are said to be **directly proportional** if they both increase or both decrease by the same factor. For example, if you make more money when you work more hours and less money when you work fewer hours, that is a direct relationship between money earned and hours worked (Figure 0.6). More specifically, if you make double the money by working double the number of hours and half the money for working half the number of hours, money earned is directly proportional to the number of hours worked.

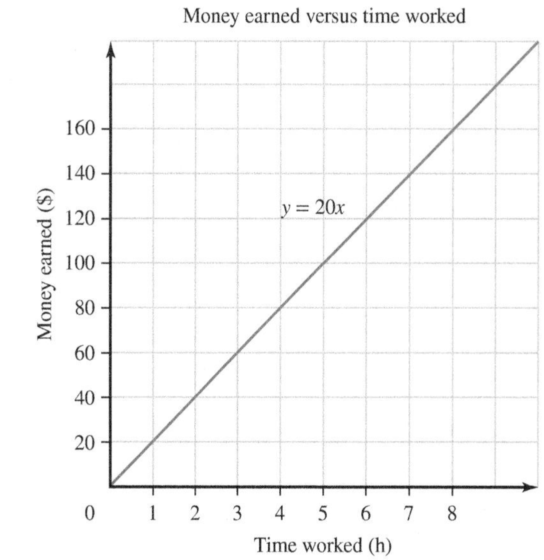

FIGURE 0.6 Direct Proportionality
This graph shows the relationship between money and time for a worker who earns $20 an hour.

In contrast, two quantities have an inverse relationship if one quantity decreases when the other increases and are **inversely proportional** if they do so by the same factor. For example, the time it takes to get somewhere is inversely related to the speed at which you travel because a higher speed leads to a shorter travel time, and a lower speed leads to a longer travel time. More specifically, travel time is inversely proportional to travel speed because doubling the speed leads to half the travel time and halving the speed leads to double the travel time. Figure 0.7 is a graph of the inversely proportional relationship between travel time and speed.

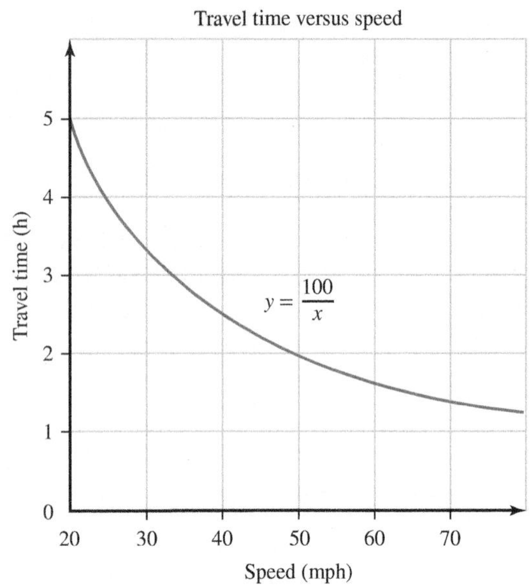

FIGURE 0.7 Inverse Proportionality

This graph shows the relationship between time and speed over a distance of 100 miles. Note that the graph of an inverse proportionality is not linear. For an inversely proportional relationship, a linear relationship exists when one of the variables is *inverse*, so a plot of $1/y$ versus x or a plot of y versus $1/x$ would be linear, but a plot of y versus x would not be.

You will encounter proportionality in many places in this course, particularly when discussing weight and mass in Section 1.3, properties of light in Section 8.1, properties of gases in Chapter 7, and colligative properties of solutions in Section 13.7.

Example 0.13

Suppose that it takes you 33 min to paddle a canoe from one side of a lake to another. Given that travel speed is inversely proportional to travel time, how long would it take if you could triple your speed by traveling in a motorboat?

Solution

Because these quantities are inversely proportional, increasing the speed by a factor of 3 (tripling) will *decrease* the time by a factor of 3. In other words, the new travel time will be one third of the original travel time.

$$\frac{1}{3}(33 \text{ min}) = 11 \text{ min}$$

Notice that you did not need to know the speed or the distance, only the factor by which one of them changed.

PRACTICE PROBLEM 0.13

Suppose that a child's allowance is directly proportional to the number of hours he spends doing chores. Last week, he earned \$4.00 in allowance. But this week, he spends 1.5 times the amount of time doing chores as he spent last week. How much money does he earn this week?

Hint: Direct proportionality tells you that when the child spends twice the amount of time on chores, he will earn twice as much allowance.

0.9 Weighted Average

GOALS

- Calculate weighted averages.
- Distinguish weighted averages from standard averages.

If you were asked to average two numbers, a and b, you would likely sum them and then divide by 2. That operation is equivalent to first dividing each value by 2 and then summing the results.

$$\frac{a+b}{2} = \frac{1}{2}a + \frac{1}{2}b = (50\%)a + (50\%)b$$

In this case, the percentage (or weight) applied to each value is equal. A real-world example might be if your teacher wanted to average two exam scores that each count equally toward your overall grade.

In contrast, now suppose your teacher wanted to average an exam score and a quiz score, but the exam counts for 80% of the overall grade and the quiz counts for only 20% of the overall grade. In this case, your teacher would multiply the exam score by 80%, the quiz score by 20%, and then sum the results.

$$\text{overall grade} = \frac{80}{100}(\text{exam score}) + \frac{20}{100}(\text{quiz score})$$

Weighted averages are used whenever you are calculating an overall average, but the things you are averaging are not of the same type. In general, a weighted average is found by multiplying each value by its weight (expressed as a percentage) and then summing the results. In this course, weighted averages are particularly important in determining atomic masses (Section 2.7).

Example 0.14

Suppose that you drive 60 miles per hour, mph, for 83% of a road trip and 70 mph for 17% of the trip. What was your average speed?

Solution

To calculate the weighted average, multiply each speed by its weight and then sum the results. Recall that 83% means $83/100 = 0.83$ and that 17% means $17/100 = 0.17$.

$$0.83(60 \text{ mph}) + 0.17(70 \text{ mph}) = 61.7 \text{ mph}$$

Although the average of 60 and 70 is 65, the weighted average, taking into account the percentage of time spent at each speed, is closer to 60 than to 70.

PRACTICE PROBLEM 0.14

Suppose that 45% of the students in a particular elementary school are 6 years old, 35% are 7 years old, and the remaining 20% are 8 years old. What is the average age of the students in this school?

Hint: Multiply each percentage (expressed as a fraction or decimal) by its appropriate value (age of student) and sum the results.

0.10 The Quadratic Formula

GOAL

- Solve equations that include an x^2 term using the quadratic formula.

Most of the relationships used in general chemistry involve variables raised to the first power. These *linear* equations can be solved using basic algebra. However, the equilibrium concept, introduced in Chapter 15 and applied in Chapter 16 and Chapter 17, frequently involves variables raised to the second power in **quadratic equations**. Because the variables are squared in quadratic equations, they will always have two solutions. Solving quadratic equations can be done using the **quadratic formula**. To use this method, the first step is to express the equation in **standard format**,

$$ax^2 + bx + c = 0 \quad (0.3)$$

where a, b, and c are numerical coefficients and a is not equal to zero.

To solve any quadratic equation for x, identify the coefficients from the standard format version of the quadratic equation and place them into the quadratic formula, given here.

$$x = \frac{-b \pm \sqrt{b^2 - 4ac}}{2a} \quad (0.4)$$

The plus or minus, $\pm$, operation found in the numerator of the quadratic formula produces two different answers, called roots. Some scientific calculators come with a preprogrammed quadratic formula function. If your calculator has this function, simply enter the a, b, and c values to identify the roots. Otherwise, follow the steps in the next example.

Example 0.15

Use the quadratic formula to determine the values of x for this quadratic equation.

$$5.1x^2 - 1.7x = 3.2$$

Solution

Start by rearranging this equation into the standard format for a quadratic equation.

$$5.1x^2 - 1.7x = 3.2$$
$$5.1x^2 - 1.7x - 3.2 = 0$$

Identify the coefficients, which are $a = 5.1$, $b = -1.7$, and $c = -3.2$, and place them into the quadratic formula.

$$x = \frac{-b \pm \sqrt{b^2 - 4ac}}{2a}$$
$$x = \frac{-(-1.7) \pm \sqrt{(-1.7)^2 - 4(5.1)(-3.2)}}{2(5.1)}$$

Determine the value of the radical next.

$$\sqrt{(-1.7)^2 - 4(5.1)(-3.2)} = 8.257$$

Determine the value of one root of x using the addition option. Add the value of the radical to $-b$ and then divide by $2a$.

$$\frac{1.7 + 8.257}{10.2} = 0.9762$$

Determine the value of the second root of x using the subtraction option. Subtract the value of the radical from $-b$ and then divide by $2a$.

$$\frac{1.7 - 8.257}{10.2} = -0.6428$$

In chemical applications, the coefficients in quadratic equations are based on measurements and include significant figures. Therefore, the values for the roots of x must be rounded to the appropriate number of significant figures. For this example, $x = 0.98$ or -0.64.

PRACTICE PROBLEM 0.15

Use the quadratic formula to determine the values of x for these quadratic equations.

a. $7.06x^2 = 9.85x - 1.92$
b. $422x^2 - 506x = 347$

Hint: Rearrange the equation into standard format, identify the coefficients, and place them into the quadratic formula. Then, determine the value of the radical and use the addition and subtraction options to solve for the two roots of x.

Although the quadratic formula always provides two mathematical solutions to the original equation, in chemical applications one of the answers is usually not realistic (e.g., a negative value for mass), and only one of the solutions will be the correct answer to the problem.

Key Terms, Symbols, and Equations

KEY TERMS

algebra (0.4): A method for rearranging the numbers and variables in a mathematical equation to simplify the equation or make it easier to solve.

antilog (0.5): The inverse of the logarithm function in which 10 is raised to the power of the original number. Also known as an inverse logarithm.

base (0.2): The number that is being multiplied by itself in an exponential expression. In scientific notation, the base is always 10.

coefficient (0.2): A number by which a quantity is multiplied. In a scientific notation, the coefficient is the number that comes before $\times 10^x$.

complex fractions (0.4): Fractions that contain other fractions within them.

dependent variable (0.7): The quantity that changes in response to the dependent variable and is measured on the y-axis.

directly proportional (0.8): Two quantities with a fixed quotient. When one quantity increases, the other will also increase by the same factor, and vice versa.

exponent (0.2): A superscript that represents repeated multiplication of the same number.

extrapolation (0.7): Determining a value from a graph when that value lies outside the range of the data plotted on the graph.

independent variable (0.7): The quantity that is being controlled and is measured on the x-axis.

interpolation (0.7): Determining a value from a graph when that value lies between two of the plotted data points.

inverse logarithm (0.5): The inverse of the logarithm function in which 10 is raised to the power of the original number. Also known as an antilog.

inversely proportional (0.8): Two quantities with a fixed product. When one quantity increases, the other will decrease by the same factor, and vice versa.

linear (0.7): Describes a data set in which the points form a straight line when plotted on a graph.

logarithm (0.5): The exponent of 10 that would be equal to the original number.

natural logarithm (0.5): A type of logarithm with base e.

order of operations (0.3): Indicates the order in which you should evaluate multiple steps within a mathematical expression.

percent (0.6): The amount of a certain component in 100 units of the total.

power (0.2): Another word for exponent, also used to identify the value of the exponent, as in "2^3 is two to the third power".

quadratic equation (0.10): An algebraic equation involving a variable raised to the second power.

quadratic formula (0.10): A formula used to solve for the variables in quadratic equations: $x = \dfrac{-b \pm \sqrt{b^2 - 4ac}}{2a}$.

scientific calculator (0.1): A type of electronic calculator with keys for functions, such as scientific notation, logarithms, and exponents, that are necessary for solving problems in science and related disciplines.

scientific notation (0.2): A format that uses powers of 10 to consolidate very large or very small numbers into a more manageable form.

slope, *m* (0.7): The steepness of a line on a straight-line graph. A higher slope is a steeper line, and a lower slope is a flatter line.

standard format (0.10): An arrangement of a quadratic equation that provides coefficient values to solve for the variable: $ax^2 + bx + c = 0$.

weighted average (0.9): The average value of several types of items, taking into account the number of individual items of each type.

***y*-intercept, *b* (0.7):** The value of the y variable on a graph when the value of the x variable is 0.

SYMBOLS AND ABBREVIATIONS

e (2.71828) (0.5)

log (base 10 logarithm) (0.5)

ln (natural log) (0.5)

PEMDAS (parentheses exponents multiplication division addition subtraction) (0.3)

% (percent) (0.6)

m (slope) (0.7)

b (y-intercept) (0.7)

EQUATIONS

$m = \dfrac{y_2 - y_1}{x_2 - x_1}$ (0.1)

$y = mx + b$ (0.2)

$ax^2 + bx + c = 0$ (0.3)

$x = \dfrac{-b \pm \sqrt{b^2 - 4ac}}{2a}$ (0.4)

Chapter Summary

A scientific calculator is an important tool in science, engineering, and mathematics. Knowing how to properly use your calculator is an important skill for solving the types of problems you will encounter in this course (Section 0.1).

Exponents represent repeated multiplication of the same number. Negative exponents are repeated multiplication of the reciprocal of that number. Exponents of 10 are particularly useful in science because they allow for scientific notation, where very large or very small numbers can be expressed more succinctly (Section 0.2).

When evaluating mathematical expression involving multiple steps, it is important to follow the order of operations, sometimes abbreviated PEMDAS.

1. Parentheses
2. Exponents
3. Multiplication and Division
4. Addition and Subtraction

Following a different order can lead to a completely different (and incorrect) answer. Keep in mind that a series of multiplication and division operations or a series of addition and subtraction operations should be done in the order in which they appear. However, all of the multiplication and division operations should be done before any of the addition and subtraction operations (Section 0.3).

Formulas are a set of mathematical operations written using variables instead of just numbers. You will often need to rearrange formulas to isolate a particular variable using algebra. Once the unknown variable is isolated on one side of the equation and all the known variables are on the other side, you can substitute (plug in) those known values and solve for the unknown variable. Algebra is a technique for rearranging equations whereby whatever you do to one side of the equation, you must also do to the other (Section 0.4).

Logarithms are the inverse operation of exponentiation, sometimes called an antilog. Most of the time, you will compute logs and antilogs using a calculator. However, it is still useful to understand the general meaning of a logarithmic scale, where each step up by 1 on a log is an increase by a factor of 10 in the original number. The natural logarithm function, ln, is similar to the logarithm function, log, but with a base of e instead of 10 (Section 0.5).

Percentage is a way to express the amount of one component in 100 units of the total. Keep in mind that percent, symbolized as %, literally means *per 100*, so notation such as 7% means 7/100. Additionally, translating word problems involving percentage into mathematical expressions is easy once you know a few tricks, such as "of" means multiplication, "is" means equals, and "what" means x, the unknown variable for which you are solving (Section 0.6).

Graphs are useful tools for expressing how a dependent variable, shown on the y-axis, changes with an independent variable, shown on the x-axis. The shape of the plot indicates the relationship between the variables—for example, whether the dependent variable increases or decreases, and by how much, when the independent variable increases. A line has the formula $y = mx + b$, where m is the slope (the steepness of the line) and b is the y-intercept (where the line crosses the y-axis). To calculate slope for linear data, find the difference between y values (the rise) and divide by the difference between x values (the run) for the same two points (Section 0.7).

Just as graphs depict the relationship between two quantities visually, proportionality is a verbal expression of how two quantities are related. Two quantities are said to be directly proportional if increasing one of them by some factor causes the other to increase by the same factor, and decreasing one of them by some factor causes the other to decrease by the same factor. Two quantities are said to be inversely proportional if *increasing* one of them causes the other to *decrease* by the same factor, and *decreasing* one of them causes the other to *increase* by the same factor (Section 0.8).

The average of two numbers is the midpoint of the two values. Similarly, the weighted average of two numbers will be somewhere between the two numbers but not necessarily at the exact midpoint of their values. Instead, it is closer to the number with the greater weight, such as in a case where a test counts more than a quiz toward your course grade. Mathematically, the weighted average of any number of values is calculated by multiplying each value by its weight and then summing the results. Weights are typically expressed as a percentage. Keep in mind that a weighted average is typically used when averaging values of different types, such as quiz scores and exam scores (Section 0.9).

Equations involving variables raised to the second power (x^2), known as quadratic equations, can be solved using the quadratic formula. The standard format is $ax^2 + bx + c = 0$. The coefficients a, b, and c from the standard format are then placed in the quadratic formula, $x = \dfrac{-b \pm \sqrt{b^2 - 4ac}}{2a}$. Obtain the two answers, called roots, by either adding or subtracting the radical. In most cases in chemistry, only one of the two solutions is realistic; the other is a mathematical possibility but not realistic physically (Section 0.10).

END OF CHAPTER QUESTIONS

0.1 Using a Calculator

1. Use a calculator to evaluate these fractions, which contain numbers in scientific notation.
 a. $\frac{344}{7.9 \times 10^{-3}}$
 b. $\frac{5.033 \times 10^{-8}}{2.66 \times 10^{3}}$
 c. $\frac{0.006449}{7.119 \times 10^{-7}}$
 d. $\frac{7.5332 \times 10^{2}}{0.00335}$

2. Use a calculator to evaluate these fractions, which contain numbers in scientific notation.
 a. $\frac{0.002488}{9.224 \times 10^{5}}$
 b. $\frac{3.72 \times 10^{8}}{8.75 \times 10^{-4}}$
 c. $\frac{5.720 \times 10^{1}}{2.61 \times 10^{-3}}$
 d. $\frac{6.5 \times 10^{-2}}{3.52 \times 10^{-4}}$

3. Use a calculator to evaluate these fractions, which contain numbers in scientific notation.
 a. $\frac{0.025}{8.26 \times 10^{3}}$
 b. $\frac{66{,}320}{5.43 \times 10^{-1}}$
 c. $\frac{4.178 \times 10^{-6}}{6.93 \times 10^{2}}$
 d. $\frac{56.91}{1.89 \times 10^{-2}}$

4. Use a calculator to evaluate these fractions, which contain numbers in scientific notation.
 a. $\frac{2.975}{9.42 \times 10^{5}}$
 b. $\frac{0.000348}{8.31 \times 10^{-6}}$
 c. $\frac{5.285 \times 10^{2}}{9.32 \times 10^{4}}$
 d. $\frac{88{,}942}{7.643 \times 10^{2}}$

0.2 Exponents and Scientific Notation

5. Convert the following numbers into scientific notation.
 a. 13,250
 b. 0.2558
 c. 52,867,000
 d. 0.000000337

6. Convert the following numbers into scientific notation.
 a. 451
 b. 0.0229
 c. 95,314,000,000
 d. 0.0000275

7. Convert the following numbers into standard notation.
 a. 4.55×10^{-7}
 b. 7.815×10^{5}
 c. 3.65×10^{2}
 d. 8.62×10^{-3}

8. Convert the following numbers into standard notation.
 a. 5.69×10^{6}
 b. 2.005×10^{-4}
 c. 6.82×10^{-6}
 d. 7.214×10^{3}

0.3 Order of Operations

9. Use the correct order of operations to evaluate:
 a. $(3 + 2)6^3 - 25$
 b. $\frac{(3 + 2)}{6^3} - 25$
 c. $(3 + 2)6^3 \div 25$
 d. $(3 + 2)6^3 \times 25$

10. Use the correct order of operations to evaluate:
 a. $\frac{42}{3} - 17(2^3)$
 b. $(42 \times 3) - 17 \times 2^3$
 c. $42 \times (3 - 17) \times 2^3$
 d. $\frac{42}{3 - 17} \times 2^3$

11. Use the correct order of operations to evaluate:
 a. $27 - 6 \div 3 + 15$
 b. $(27 - 6) \div 3 + 15$
 c. $27 - 6 \div (3 + 15)$
 d. $(27 - 6 \div 3) + 15$

12. Use the correct order of operations to evaluate:
a. $(4 \times 2)^2 - 5 \times 8$
b. $(4 \times 2)^2 \div (5 \times 8)$
c. $4 \times (2 - 5)^2 \times 8$
d. $4 + 2 \times 5 - 8$

0.4 Algebra

13. Boyle's law, $P_1V_1 = P_2V_2$, describes the mathematical relationship between the pressure and volume of an ideal gas. Rearrange Boyle's law to solve for:
a. P_1
b. V_1
c. P_2
d. V_2

14. The ideal gas law, $PV = nRT$, describes the mathematical relationship between pressure, volume, temperature, and amount of a gas and includes the gas constant, R. Rearrange the ideal gas law to solve for:
a. the gas constant, R
b. amount of gas, n
c. pressure, P
d. volume, V

15. Rearrange the equation to solve for x.

$$y = (z + 2x)(a - 3)$$

16. Rearrange the equation to solve for c.

$$a = b\left(\frac{1}{c} - \frac{1}{d}\right)$$

17. Rearrange the equation to solve for w.

$$p - 2l = 2w$$

18. Rearrange the equation to solve for a.

$$s = ut + \frac{at^2}{2}$$

19. Rearrange the equation to solve for c.

$$b(2c + 4) = d(8 - c)$$

20. Rearrange this equation to solve for x.

$$\frac{a}{b} = \frac{c}{2x}$$

Determine the effect on the value of x when
a. the value of a is doubled.
b. the value of b is doubled.
c. the value of c is tripled.
d. the value of c is tripled and the value of a is doubled.

21. Distribute the number outside the parentheses across the terms within the parentheses.
a. $3\left(2x + y + \frac{c}{3}\right)$
b. $2\left(\frac{a}{2} + 3b + \frac{1}{z}\right)$
c. $5(0.2p + 2.4r + 13)$

22. Distribute the number outside the parentheses across the terms within the parentheses.
a. $4\left(\frac{1}{2}x + 3y + c\right)$
b. $6\left(2a + \frac{1}{3}b + 4z\right)$
c. $8(6 + 3.2p + 0.5r)$

23. Factor each of the expressions.
a. $5p + 30$
b. $9x^2 + 45y - 3$

24. Factor each of the expressions.
a. $-7n - 70$
b. $4 - 16x + 36y$

25. Simplify these complex fractions.
a. $\dfrac{\frac{3x}{2}}{\frac{y}{4}}$
b. $\dfrac{\frac{q}{2p}}{\frac{3}{8}}$
c. $\dfrac{\frac{12}{y}}{\frac{2x}{3}}$

26. Simplify these complex fractions.
a. $\dfrac{\frac{1x}{4}}{\frac{3y}{8}}$
b. $\dfrac{\frac{2}{3y}}{\frac{5}{7x}}$
c. $\dfrac{\frac{7y}{8x}}{\frac{2}{3}}$

0.5 Logarithms and Antilogs

27. *Without using your calculator,* ***estimate*** the log of the following numbers. For example, when estimating the log of 200, you know that 200 is greater than 100 (log of 2) and less than 1000 (log of 3), so the log value must be between 2 and 3.
    a. 4100
    b. 325
    c. 675,000
    d. 0.0498
    e. 0.00008366

28. This time, use your calculator to determine the log of the following numbers.
    a. 4100
    b. 325
    c. 675,000
    d. 0.0498
    e. 0.00008366

29. *Without using your calculator,* ***estimate*** the log of the following numbers. For example, when estimating the log of 200, you know that 200 is greater than 100 (log of 2) and less than 1000 (log of 3), so the log value must be between 2 and 3.
    a. 276
    b. 987,000,000
    c. 23,631
    d. 0.00869
    e. 0.0000004287

30. This time, use your calculator to determine the log of the following numbers.
    a. 276
    b. 987,000,000
    c. 23,631
    d. 0.00869
    e. 0.0000004287

31. *Without using your calculator,* ***estimate*** the antilog of the following numbers. For example, when estimating the antilog of -2.5, you know it must be between $10^{-2}(0.01)$ and $10^{-3}(0.001)$.
    a. 4.25
    b. -3.6
    c. 1.82
    d. -5.77
    e. -12.7

32. This time, use your calculator to determine the antilogs of the following numbers.
    a. 4.25
    b. -3.6
    c. 1.82
    d. -5.77
    e. -12.7

33. *Without using your calculator,* ***estimate*** the antilog of the following numbers. For example, when estimating the antilog of -2.5, you know it must be between $10^{-2}(0.01)$ and $10^{-3}(0.001)$.
    a. -11.5
    b. 8.95
    c. 2.73
    d. -3.87
    e. -1.94

34. This time, use your calculator to determine the antilogs of the following numbers.
    a. -11.5
    b. 8.95
    c. 2.73
    d. -3.87
    e. -1.94

35. Using a calculator, find the natural logarithms of the following numbers.
    a. 0.250
    b. 4.00
    c. 9.12
    d. 3.31
    e. 0.107

36. Using a calculator, find the inverse natural logarithm of the following numbers.
    a. 1.47
    b. -1.47
    c. -0.242
    d. 0.0839
    e. 2.65

0.6 Percentage

37. A 15.73 g rock sample contains 6.44 g of silicon, 7.52 g of oxygen, and 1.77 g of water. Determine the percent composition by mass of
    a. silicon
    b. oxygen
    c. water

38. A gas sample contains 1.559 g of nitrogen, 0.205 g of oxygen, and 0.111 g of water vapor. Determine the percent composition by mass of
    a. nitrogen
    b. oxygen
    c. water vapor

39. Carbon dioxide contains carbon and oxygen and is 27.3% carbon by mass.
    a. How many grams of carbon are present in 65.4 g of carbon dioxide?

b. How many grams of oxygen are present in 125 g of carbon dioxide?

40. Water contains hydrogen and oxygen and is 11.2% hydrogen by mass.
   a. How many grams of water do you need to provide 32.7 g of hydrogen?
   b. How much oxygen is present in 4392 g of water?

41. A mixture of oxygen and nitrogen contains 22.21% oxygen by mass.
   a. How many grams of the gas sample are needed to provide 5.00 g of oxygen?
   b. How many grams of nitrogen are present in 725 g of the gas sample?

42. You have a solution of sodium hydroxide and water that contains 25% sodium hydroxide by mass.
   a. How many grams of that solution do you need to provide 1.425 g of sodium hydroxide?
   b. How many grams of sodium hydroxide are present in 2.55 g of the solution?

43. You have a solution of sodium chloride and water that contains 1.9% sodium chloride by mass.
   a. How many grams of sodium chloride are in 515 g of that solution?
   b. How many grams of solution are needed to provide 0.328 g of sodium chloride?

44. The hydrogen peroxide solution used to clean minor injuries contains 3% hydrogen peroxide by mass, with the rest being water.
   a. What mass of solution is needed to provide 0.0576 g of hydrogen peroxide?
   b. How many grams of hydrogen peroxide are present in 17.5 g of the solution?

45. One type of iron ore is 69.94% iron by mass.
   a. How many grams of iron ore would be needed to make a 862 g steel pan for cooking, assuming that the pan is close to 100% iron?
   b. How many grams of iron are present in 75.0 kg (75,000 g) of this iron ore?

0.7 Graphs

46. An ice sample is removed from the freezer and placed on a lab bench. Its Celsius temperature is measured at one-minute intervals.

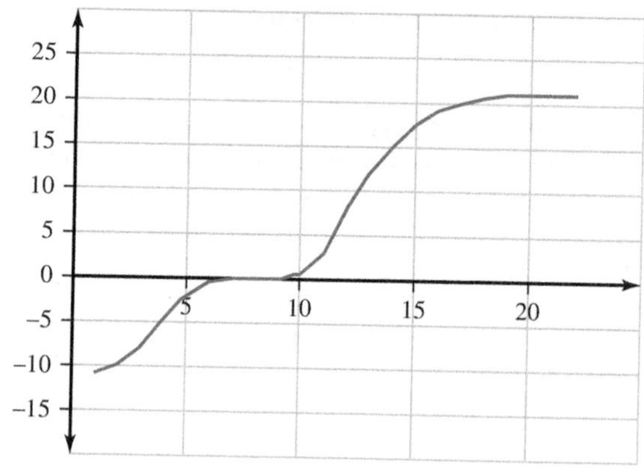

   a. Identify the dependent and independent variables.
   b. Label the axes of the graph, including units.
   c. What is the temperature of the freezer?
   d. At what time interval(s) is the change in temperature (ΔT) equal to 0?
   e. What is the temperature of the lab?

47. The average monthly temperatures for a Midwestern U.S. city are shown in the graph.

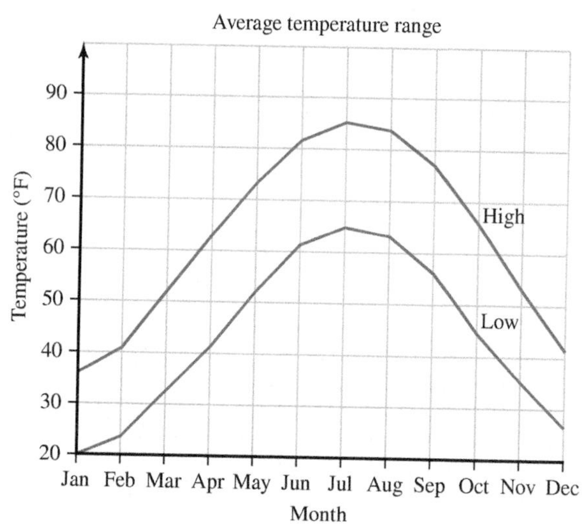

   a. What is the average low temperature in September?
   b. What is the average high temperature in February?
   c. What month has the highest average low temperature?
   d. What month has the lowest average high temperature?

48. The fraction of O_2 molecules is plotted versus the molecular speed of the molecules at two different temperatures.

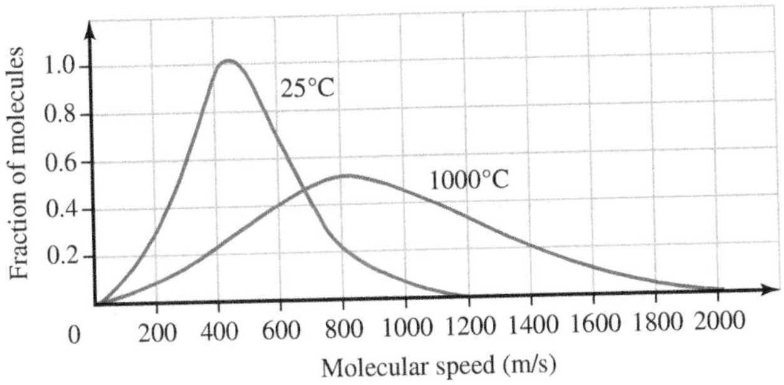

a. Identify the dependent and independent variables.
b. What is the proper title of this graph in __________ versus __________ format?
c. At what temperature is the average molecular speed of the O_2 molecules the greatest?
d. At 25°C, what fraction of the O_2 molecules have a molecular speed of 200 m/s?
e. At 1000°C, what fraction of the O_2 molecules have a molecular speed of 1400 m/s?

49. For the following linear data,

x	y
9.4	3.3
9.9	4.0

a. Calculate the slope.
b. Calculate the y-intercept.

50. For the following linear data,

x	y
0.187	6.22
0.503	7.62

a. Calculate the slope.
b. Calculate the y-intercept.

51. For a line with a slope of 4.0 and a y-intercept of 1.8,
a. determine the equation for the line.
b. find the value of y when $x = 0.75$.

52. For the following data set,

x	y
3.52	1.09
4.63	1.72
5.74	2.35

a. calculate the slope of the line formed between the first two points.
b. calculate the slope of the line formed between the second two points.
c. Is the data set linear? How can you tell?

0.8 Proportionality

53. Describe the following relationships as being directly or inversely related.
a. If you double the amount of air in a balloon, it gets twice as big. The amount of air and volume are __________ proportional.
b. In the checkout line at the grocery story, the number of people in line ahead of you and the time you wait to pay for your groceries are __________ related.
c. Again at the grocery store, the number of working checkout lines and the time you wait to pay for your groceries are __________ related.

54. The speed of a certain chemical reaction is found to be directly proportional to the amount of substance A present at the start of the process. If you increase the amount of A by a factor of 1.5, what happens to the rate of the reaction?

55. A student typically walks from her apartment to campus at a fairly slow pace (as she checks her cell phone for messages), taking 22 min. She decides to use this walk as a part of her daily fitness activity, but wants to increase the pace gradually. Given that travel speed is inversely proportional to travel time, by what factor will she need to increase her walking pace to get to campus in
a. 20 min?
b. 18 min?
c. 15 min?

56. The amount of money a professional soccer player makes in a season is directly proportional to the number of games he plays. Last year, due to injuries, he missed several games and made $2 million. If he plays in four times the number of games this season, how much money will he make?

57. Suppose it takes you 50 min to commute to work each morning from your home due to traffic. One day the traffic is lighter than usual and you are able to drive five times faster than you normally do. Given that travel speed is inversely proportional to travel time, how long will it take you to commute to work on this light traffic day?

58. The amount of money a landscaping company makes is directly proportional to the number of lawns the workers mow. In one week they mowed 30 lawns and made $900.
   a. How many lawns would they need to mow the next week to make $1200?
   b. If they mowed only 20 lawns the next week, how much many would they make?

59. It takes you 80 min to run a 10K (10 kilometer, km, footrace) at a speed of 0.125 km per minute. The speed at which you run the 10K is inversely proportional to the amount of time it takes you to run the 10K.
   a. How long would it take you to run the 10K if you increased your speed to 0.150 km per minute?
   b. What would your speed be if you ran the 10K in 55 min?

0.9 Weighted Average

60. Find the weighted average of these values:

Value	Weight
42	25%
36	65%
27	10%

61. Students in a middle school class have counted the different types of marbles in their collection and measured the masses of the different marbles, with their observations shown in the table. What is the average mass of a marble in their collection?

Type of Marble	Mass in Grams	Number in Collection
blue	4.8	12
cat's eye	7.3	5
green	4.4	15
red	5.1	18

62. Find the weighted average of these values:

Value	Weight
3.55	24.3%
3.67	67.6%
3.88	8.1%

63. Calculate the average height of a group of people, given that 5 of them are 167 cm tall, 2 of them are 183 cm tall, and 1 is 164 cm tall.

64. Find the weighted average of these values:

Value	Weight
4820	54.8%
6370	27.3%
5220	17.9%

65. Calculate the average mass of a group of kindergarten children, given that 5 of the girls have a mass of 16.0 kg, 2 girls have a mass of 18.3 kg, 3 boys have a mass of 16.4 kg, and 4 boys have a mass of 18.7 kg.

66. Find the weighted average of these values:

Value	Weight
563	24.8%
558	47.3%
555	27.9%

67. Use the student scores listed below to determine the average score on the quiz.

Number of Students	Score
2	5
3	6
9	7
8	9
5	10

68. Find the weighted average of these values:

Value	Weight
0.00367	34.3%
0.00442	37.5%
0.00395	28.2%

69. Use the student scores listed below to determine the average score on the exam.

Number of Students	Score
12	55
13	65
19	75
18	95
5	100

0.10 The Quadratic Formula

70. Rearrange these equations into the standard format for quadratic equations, $ax^2 + bx + c = 0$.
    a. $53 + 2x^2 = 14.2x$
    b. $3.8 + 7x = 43x^2$
    c. $3x^2 + 28x = -4.9$
    d. $1.5x - 6x^2 = 9$
    e. $45 = 23x + 17x^2$

71. Use the quadratic formula to determine the values of x in these equations. Hint: Use the a, b, and c values from the previous question.
    a. $5.3 + 2x^2 = 14.2x$
    b. $3.8 + 7x = 43x^2$
    c. $3x^2 + 28x = -4.9$
    d. $1.5x - 6x^2 = -9$
    e. $45 = 23x + 17x^2$

72. Rearrange these equations into the standard format for quadratic equations, $ax^2 + bx + c = 0$.
    a. $x^2 + 3x = 75$
    b. $10 - x = 24x^2$
    c. $12x^2 + 8x = 15$
    d. $-64x + 4x^2 = 0$
    e. $4 = -12x + 9x^2$

73. Use the quadratic formula to determine the values of x in these equations. Hint: Use the a, b, and c values from the previous question.
    a. $x^2 + 3x = 75$
    b. $10 - x = 24x^2$
    c. $12x^2 + 8x = 15$
    d. $-64x + 4x^2 = 0$
    e. $4 = -12x + 9x^2$

74. Resolve these equations into the standard format for quadratic equations, $ax^2 + bx + c = 0$.
    a. $3x^2 - 10x = -5$
    b. $2 - 3x = -x^2$
    c. $9x^2 + 30x = -25$
    d. $-8x + 15x^2 = -1$
    e. $14 = 19x + 3x^2$

75. Use the quadratic formula to determine the values of x in these equations. Hint: Use the a, b, and c values from the previous question.
    a. $3x^2 - 10x = -5$
    b. $2 - 3x = -x^2$
    c. $9x^2 + 30x = -25$
    d. $-8x + 15x^2 = -1$
    e. $14 = 19x + 3x^2$

PRACTICE PROBLEM SOLUTIONS

Practice Problem 0.1 Solution

$$\frac{9750}{5 \times 10^5} = 0.0195$$

Practice Problem 0.2 Solution

a. The decimal point must be moved four places to the *left* so that the coefficient is 1 or greater but less than 10. Moving the decimal point four places to the left *increases* the exponent from 10^0 to 10^4: 1.0911×10^4 mg.

b. The decimal point must be moved 13 places to the *left* so that the coefficient is 1 or greater but less than 10. Moving the decimal point 13 places to the right *increases* the exponent from 10^0 to 10^{13}: 1.9964×10^{13} atoms. The trailing zeroes are dropped.

c. The decimal point must be moved 11 places to the *right* so that the coefficient is 1 or greater but less than 10. Moving the decimal point 11 places to the right *decreases* the exponent from 10^0 to 10^{-11}: 1.06×10^{-11} m^3.

Practice Problem 0.3 Solution

Since this term is made up entirely of multiplication and division, evaluate the terms in the order in which they appear.

$$12/2 \times 3 = 6 \times 3 = 18$$

Practice Problem 0.4 Solution

a. Divide both sides by h to isolate ν all by itself on one side of the equals sign.

$$\nu = \frac{E}{h}$$

b. Z is in the denominator, so flip both sides of the equation to bring Z into the numerator.

$$\frac{Z}{5} = \frac{Y}{X}$$

Then multiply both sides by 5 to isolate Z.

$$Z = \frac{5Y}{X}$$

Practice Problem 0.5 Solution

a. $\frac{8}{4}x + 8y + 8 \times 2z = 2x + 8y + 16z$

b. The largest common factor between 20 and 50 is 10 ($20 = 10 \times 2$ and $50 = 10 \times 5$), so place the 10 as a factor outside the parentheses, and leave the remaining factors (2 and 5) as coefficients on the variables:

$$10(2b + 5c)$$

Practice Problem 0.6 Solution

Write the fraction in the numerator, and then multiply it by the inverse of the fraction in the denominator.

$$\frac{\frac{2a}{3y}}{\frac{4x}{z}} = \left(\frac{2a}{3y} \times \frac{z}{4x}\right) = \frac{2az}{12xy} = \frac{az}{6xy}$$

Practice Problem 0.7 Solution

a. $1{,}000{,}000{,}000 = 1 \times 10^9$, and the log of 1×10^9 is 9.0.

b. $8{,}000{,}000{,}000 = 8 \times 10^9$. This number lies between 1×10^9 and 1×10^{10}, so the log value will fall somewhere between 9 and 10, but determining the exact value requires a calculator. $\text{Log}(8 \times 10^9) = 9.9$.

Practice Problem 0.8 Solution

$10^{-6.59} = 2.57 \times 10^{-7}$. Since the log value ($-6.59$) has two digits after the decimal place, the calculated antilog should have two digits when expressed in scientific notation, so the final answer is 2.6×10^{-7}.

Practice Problem 0.9 Solution

a. Use a calculator to compute $\ln(1.81) = 0.588$.

b. Use a calculator to compute the inverse natural log function, $e^{1.81} = 6.11$.

Practice Problem 0.10 Solution

"What is 51.4% of 5 lb?" is the equivalent of

$$x = \frac{51.4}{100} \times 5.0 \text{ lb} = 2.6 \text{ lb of oxygen}$$

Practice Problem 0.11 Solution

a. Twelve measurements were made to construct six (x, y) data points for the graph.

b. 50°C on the x-axis intersects the line through the data points just above $y = 120$. (The actual value is 122°F.)

c. 200°F on the y-axis intersects the line through the data points between the vertical lines for 90°C and 95°C, at about 93°C.

Practice Problem 0.12 Solution

The points are (1.0, 1.5) and (5.0, 0.3). Plug these values into the slope equation (Equation 0.1).

$$m = \frac{y_2 - y_1}{x_2 - x_1}$$

$$m = \frac{0.3 - 1.5}{5.0 - 1.0} = \frac{-1.2}{4.0} = -0.30$$

Notice that the slope is negative, which is characteristic of lines that slant backward (such as this one) as opposed to forward (such as the one in Figure 0.5).

Now plug this value of m and the x and y values for either point into the equation for a line (Equation 0.2) and solve for b.

$$y = mx + b$$

$$b = y - mx$$

$$b = 1.5 - (-0.30 \times 1.0) = 1.8$$

If the line were extended upward, it would cross the y-axis at 1.8.

Practice Problem 0.13 Solution

Because these quantities are directly proportional, the money earned will increase by the same factor by which the hours increased.

$$1.5(\$4.00) = \$6.00$$

Practice Problem 0.14 Solution

Each percentage corresponds to a fraction of 100 or the decimal equivalent (Section 0.6), so the decimal equivalent of 45%, for example, is 0.45. Multiply each age by the percentage of students who are that age to find the weighted average of the ages of the students in the school:

$$0.45(6 \text{ years}) + 0.35(7 \text{ years}) + 0.20(8 \text{ years}) = 6.75 \text{ years}$$

Practice Problem 0.15 Solution

a. Start by rearranging this equation into the standard format.

$$7.06x^2 = 9.85x - 1.92$$

$$7.06x^2 - 9.85x + 1.92 = 0$$

Identify the coefficients, which are $a = 7.06$, $b = -9.85$, and $c = 1.92$, and place them into the quadratic formula.

$$x = \frac{-b \pm \sqrt{b^2 - 4ac}}{2a}$$

$$x = \frac{-(-9.85) \pm \sqrt{(-9.85)^2 - 4(7.06)(1.92)}}{2(7.06)}$$

Determine the value of the radical next.

$$\sqrt{(-9.85)^2 - 4(7.06)(1.92)} = 6.542$$

Determine the value of the two roots of x by either adding or subtracting the radical from $-b$ and then dividing by $2a$. Round the final values to match the number of significant figures in the coefficients.

$$\frac{9.85 + 6.542}{14.12} = 1.161, \text{ or } 1.16 \text{ rounded to three significant figures}$$

$$\frac{9.85 - 6.542}{14.12} = 0.2343, \text{ or } 0.234 \text{ rounded to three significant figures}$$

b. Start by rearranging the equation into standard format.

$$422x^2 - 506x = 347$$

$$422x^2 - 506x - 347 = 0$$

Place the coefficients, which are $a = 422$, $b = -506$, and $c = -347$, into the quadratic formula.

$$x = \frac{-b \pm \sqrt{b^2 - 4ac}}{2a}$$

$$x = \frac{-(-506) \pm \sqrt{(-506)^2 - 4(422)(-347)}}{2(422)}$$

Determine the value of the radical next.

$$\sqrt{(-506)^2 - 4(422)(-347)} = 917.48$$

Determine the value of the two roots of x by either adding or subtracting the radical from $-b$ and then dividing by $2a$. Round the final values to match the number of significant figures in the coefficients.

$$\frac{-506 + 917.48}{844} = 0.48754, \text{ or } 0.488 \text{ rounded to three significant figures}$$

$$\frac{-506 - 917.48}{844} = -1.6866, \text{ or } -1.69 \text{ rounded to three significant figures}$$

CHAPTER 1

Science and Measurement

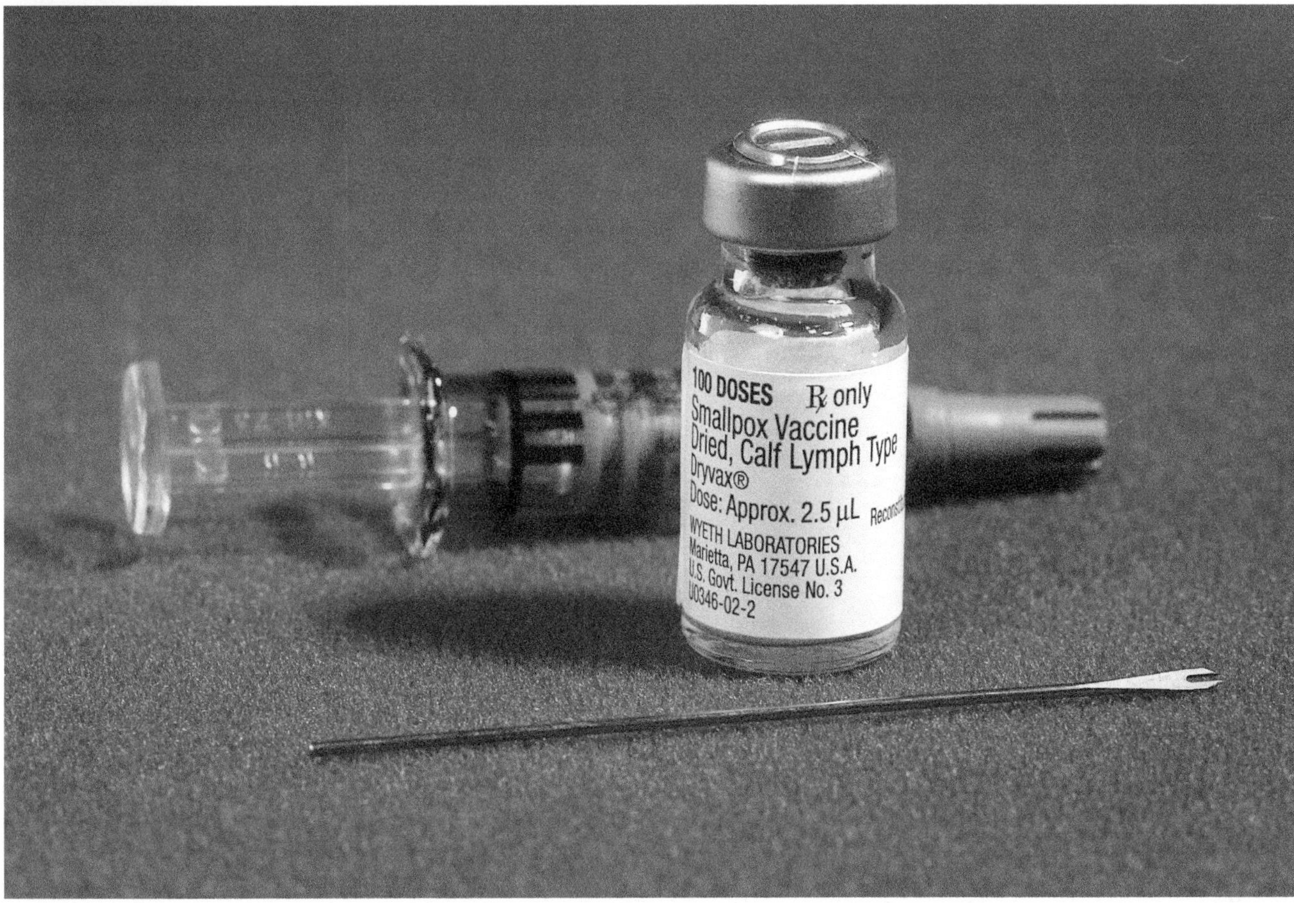

James Gathany/CDC

Chemistry, like all sciences, involves observing and measuring the world around us. The techniques of science are central to everyday life in ways that are often overlooked. Vaccines, for example, are a product of the scientific method, and proper dosages are administered through careful measurement.

Chapter Outline

GOALS

- Classify matter into types based on its composition.
- Recognize different types of properties and use these properties to help identify substances.
- Differentiate between physical and chemical changes.
- Explain the difference between matter, mass, and weight.
- Differentiate between matter and energy.
- Describe the scientific method.
- Distinguish between hypotheses, theories, and laws.
- Recognize SI units and prefixes to convert measurements between units.
- Determine the correct number of digits to indicate the precision of a measurement or a calculated result.
- Use the units of a measurement as a guide in setting up calculations.
- Calculate density, volume, or mass when two of three values are given.
- Identify substances using density.
- Distinguish between the Fahrenheit, Celsius, and Kelvin temperature scales.
- Convert temperature values between scales.

1.1 Classification of Matter

GOAL

- Classify matter into types based on its composition.

Chemistry is the study of matter and energy. **Matter** is anything that has mass and occupies space. All the matter on Earth is composed of about a hundred elements. **Elements** are the simplest form of matter that has distinct physical and chemical properties (discussed in Section 1.2) and cannot be broken down chemically into simpler, stable substances. Elements can be thought of as building blocks for everything in the universe. The same elements that make up matter on Earth, and that make up Earth itself, also make up the Moon, as shown by analysis of lunar rock samples. Moreover, analysis of light from distant stars shows that the rest of the universe is composed of the same elements that are found on Earth.

If you had a sample of any element, such as iron, and you were able to repeatedly divide that sample in half again and again and again, discarding half of the sample each time, you would eventually reach a point where all you had left was a single particle of iron that could not be divided any further without breaking it into pieces that would no longer be iron. That smallest iron particle is called an atom. An **atom** is the smallest amount of an element that still has the characteristics of that element. You would be unable to see your iron sample long before dividing it into a single atom, however. An iron sample the size of a grain of sand contains about a billion iron atoms. Atoms of different elements can form attractions called **chemical bonds** that hold the atoms together. These bonds can then be broken and new bonds formed with different atoms. (Atoms are discussed in more detail in Chapter 2, while bonding is discussed in Chapter 9 and Chapter 10.)

A **compound** is a chemical combination of elements that has its own set of properties and a **definite composition**. For example, pure water obtained from any natural source always contains the same two elements, oxygen and hydrogen, in the same proportion—88.8% oxygen and 11.2% hydrogen by mass. Compounds can be separated into their constituent elements only through chemical reactions. Elements and compounds are the two types of **pure substances**.

Two or more pure substances can be physically combined to produce a **mixture**. The components of a mixture are not chemically bonded to each other and can be separated from one another by physical means, such as filtering by size, melting or boiling one or more of the components away, or separating based on density differences (sinking or floating).

Figure 1.1 illustrates elements, compounds, and mixtures on a particle level. In an element, the atoms may be single or bound together in any number, but all of the atoms are the same type. In a compound, there are at least two different types of atoms bound together in a specific ratio, and all of the compound particles have exactly the same composition. A mixture can be made up of any combination of elements

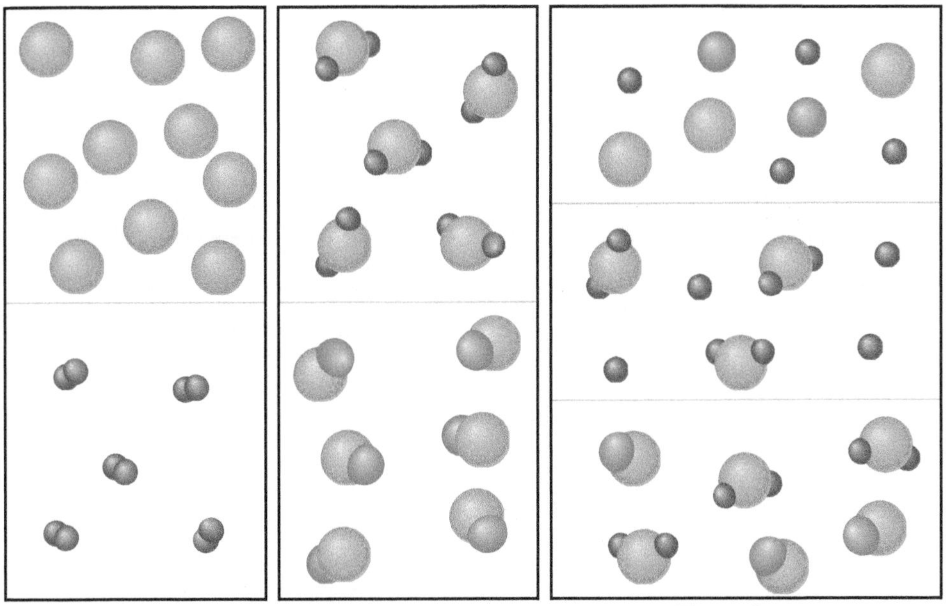

Two elements Two compounds Three mixtures

FIGURE 1.1 Elements, Compounds, and Mixtures

In an element, all atoms are the same type. In a compound, different kinds of atoms are bound together to form new particles. In a sample of a single element or a single compound, all of the particles are the same type, but in a sample of a mixture, multiple types of particles are present. In a mixture, elements and compounds may be jumbled together in any combination, but they are not bonded to one another.

or compounds. In a mixture, the particles are not all the same type and are not bonded to one another. The ratio of one type of particle to another is variable in a mixture.

Example 1.1

Identify the components of each of the three different mixtures in Figure 1.1 as elements or compounds.

Solution

The top mixture consists of elements because none of the atoms is bonded to a different kind of atom.

The middle mixture consists of atoms and compounds.

The bottom mixture consists of compounds.

PRACTICE PROBLEM 1.1

Identify the pure substances in Figure 1.1.

Hint: There are only two types of pure substances. What are they?

Mixtures do not have definite compositions and can be either **heterogeneous** or **homogeneous**. In heterogeneous mixtures, the substances that make up the mixture are not uniformly mixed, so two samples taken from the same mixture might have different compositions. Heterogeneous mixtures can be physically separated into their constituent components. Homogeneous mixtures, also called solutions, do have uniform compositions, so every sample taken from the same homogeneous mixture will have the same composition. It is more difficult to physically separate homogeneous mixtures into their constituent components. Although the word "solution" is most commonly associated with homogeneous liquid mixtures, in chemistry a **solution** is any homogeneous mixture, including one made up of two or more gases or two or more solids. An example of a solution made up of two or more gases is the atmosphere, which is a homogeneous mixture made up mostly of nitrogen, oxygen, and argon gases. Brass, a metal alloy made up of a homogeneous mixture of copper and zinc, is an example of a solid solution. The most familiar solutions both in chemistry and in everyday life are homogeneous mixtures in water, which include things like seawater, coffee, and tea, as well as any laboratory chemicals that are dissolved in water. A solution in water is known as an **aqueous solution**.

TABLE 1.1 Classification of Matter

Classification	Subclassification	Examples
Pure Substances	Element	Hydrogen, sodium
	Compound	Water, table salt
Mixtures	Heterogeneous mixture	Oil and water mixture, chicken noodle soup
	Homogeneous mixture	Brass, vodka

The word *homogeneous* does not necessarily refer to a mixture. Most samples of pure substances are also homogeneous, but some, such as ice water, are heterogeneous.

The entire classification scheme for matter discussed in this section is outlined in Table 1.1 and Figure 1.2.

Example 1.2

The percentage of carbon in a small box of the pure substance sucrose (table sugar) is 42.1%.

a. Is sucrose an element or a compound?
b. What is the percentage of carbon in a large box of sucrose?

Solution

a. Sucrose is a compound—it contains more than one element. If it contained just carbon, then the percentage of carbon would be 100%, not 42.1%.
b. The larger box also contains 42.1% carbon because a given compound always contains the same percentage of each of its elements, no matter what the size of the sample.

PRACTICE PROBLEM 1.2

Determine whether the following mixtures are homogeneous or heterogeneous.

a. Mud (a mixture of dirt and water that settles out over time)
b. Carbonated water (a mixture of water and carbon dioxide) before the bottle is opened
c. Carbonated water (a mixture of water and carbon dioxide) immediately after the bottle is opened

Hint: Consider whether each of these mixtures has a uniform composition. If you can see each of the different components in the mixture, then it is most likely heterogeneous.

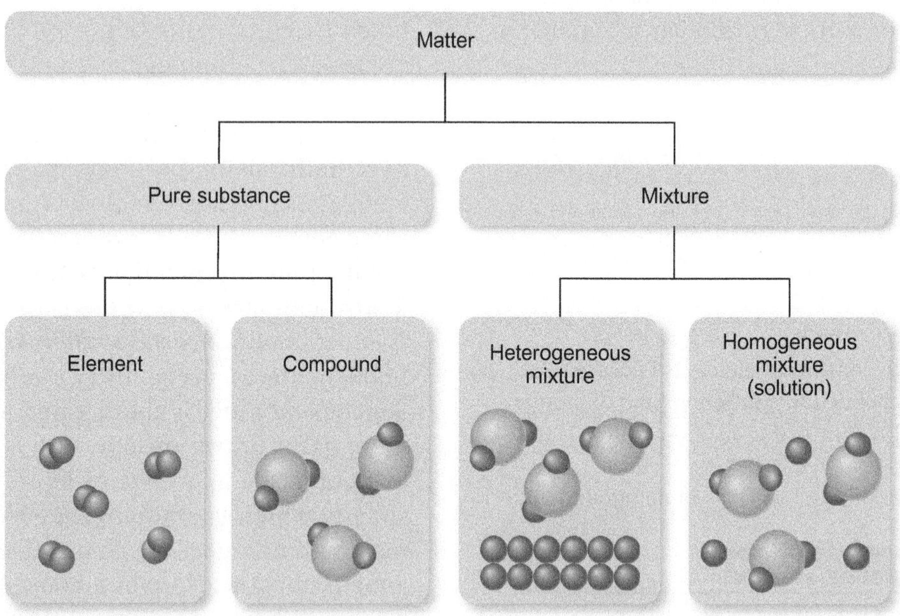

FIGURE 1.2 Classification of Matter

Matter can be classified as pure substances or mixtures. Elements and compounds are pure substances, whereas mixtures are made up of two or more pure substances. Heterogeneous mixtures do not have the same composition throughout, and their components can be physically separated. A homogeneous mixture, also called a solution, has a uniform composition. It is more difficult to physically separate the constituent components of a homogeneous mixture than those of a heterogeneous mixture.

EVERYDAY CONNECTION

One example of the difference between elements and compounds can be found in nutritional minerals. In the field of nutrition, about 20 elements are called *minerals*. The minerals known to be essential for good health are calcium, phosphorus, potassium, sulfur, sodium, chlorine, magnesium, iron, manganese, copper, iodine, cobalt, fluorine, and zinc. Traces of silicon, boron, arsenic, strontium, aluminum, bromine, molybdenum, selenium, and nickel may also be required for the body to function. However, these elements are actually eaten in the form of their compounds, not as pure elements. For example, magnesium supplements often use the compounds magnesium citrate or magnesium carbonate as the source of magnesium. Elemental magnesium, in contrast, is a metal that reacts violently when exposed to stomach acid (as shown in the video below) and would be extremely dangerous to consume.

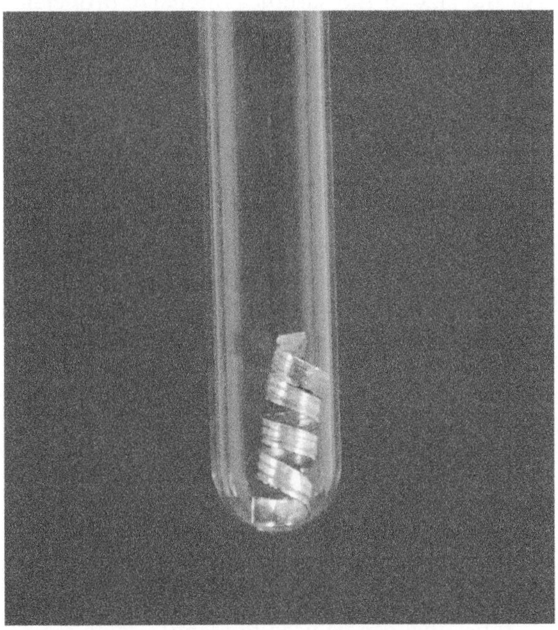

NOTE: You need to be online to access this video.

Example 1.3

If you stir a teaspoon of sugar into a glass of water and a teaspoon of mud into another glass of water, the sugar will eventually dissolve into the water, but the mud will not. Which mixture is a solution?

Solution

The mud and water form a heterogeneous mixture (a). The sugar forms a solution, a homogeneous mixture, with the water (b). Particles of mud can be seen in the mud–water mixture, but seeing any sugar particles in the sugar–water solution is impossible, no matter how hard you look (even with a microscope). If enough sugar is added that the solution becomes saturated and no more sugar can dissolve, then undissolved solid sugar will accumulate at the bottom of the test tube, resulting in a heterogeneous mixture.

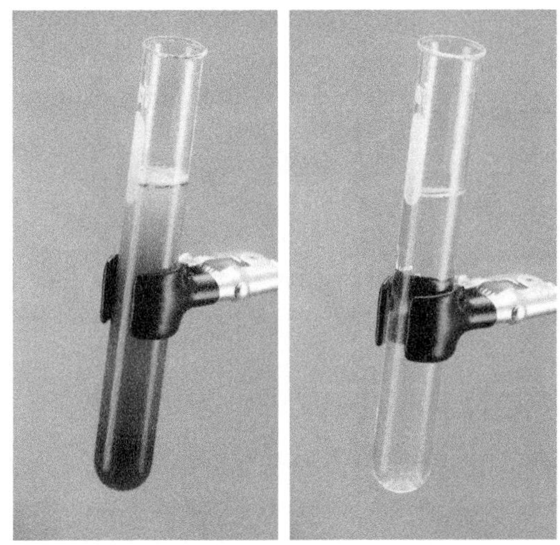

(a) (b)

Steve Lemon, Macmillan Learning

PRACTICE PROBLEM 1.3

When iodine (a purple solid) is added to ethyl alcohol (a colorless liquid), a uniform, transparent liquid mixture with a brown color is formed. Is the iodine–ethyl alcohol mixture homogeneous or heterogeneous?

Hint: Consider whether solutions that are uniform in composition are homogeneous or heterogeneous.

Example 1.4

Indicate whether each of the following statements is true or false.

a. Every compound is a pure substance.
b. Every compound contains two or more elements.
c. Every mixture contains two or more compounds.
d. Every pure substance is a compound.
e. All mixtures are homogeneous.

Solution

a. True
b. True
c. False: Mixtures may contain elements or compounds or both.
d. False: Some pure substances, such as oxygen gas, are elements.
e. False: Some mixtures, such as iron metal and solid sulfur, are heterogeneous.

PRACTICE PROBLEM 1.4

Indicate whether each of the following statements is true or false.

a. Every mixture contains two or more elements.
b. All mixtures are heterogeneous.
c. Every pure substance contains two or more elements.
d. All homogeneous samples are solutions.

Hint: A mixture must contain more than one substance. Also, both pure substances and solutions are homogeneous.

SECTION REVIEW

- Matter has mass and occupies space.
- An element is the simplest form of matter that has distinct physical and chemical properties (see Section 1.2). There are about 100 different chemical elements.
- Elements can be combined chemically to form compounds.
- Elements and compounds are pure substances.
- All pure substances have definite compositions.
- Mixtures do not have definite compositions.
- Homogeneous mixtures have a uniform composition.
- Heterogeneous mixtures do not have a uniform composition.

1.2 Properties of Matter

GOALS

- Recognize different types of properties and use these properties to help identify substances.
- Differentiate between physical and chemical changes.

Every substance has a definite set of properties. **Properties** are the characteristics by which something can be identified. For example, pure water is a colorless, odorless, and tasteless substance that is a liquid at room temperature. Salt has a different set of properties than does water, and sugar has yet another set of properties.

Physical properties are the ways that a substance can be described or identified without changing its chemical composition. For example, elemental iron is a gray solid at room temperature that conducts heat and electricity, and melts at 1538°C. Iron's color, conductivity, and melting point are all physical properties of iron. **Chemical properties** are the characteristic ways that a substance can chemically react with another substance. For example, iron can react with oxygen in the air to form rust. That reactivity with oxygen is a chemical property of iron (Figure 1.3).

Chemists distinguish between properties that are extensive and properties that are intensive. **Extensive properties** depend on the quantity of the sample. For example, the weight of a solid sample depends on how much of the substance is present. Other properties, such as color and boiling point, are **intensive properties** because they remain unchanged, regardless of the size of the sample. Intensive properties are much more useful for identifying the chemical composition of a substance.

Example 1.5

a. If sample A weighs twice as much as sample B, is it possible to tell which sample is iron and which is powdered sugar?
b. If sample A is attracted by a magnet and sample B is a white powder, is it possible to tell which sample is iron and which is powdered sugar?

Solution

a. No. The weight of a sample is an extensive property that does not tell anything about the material's identity.
b. Yes. The magnetism of sample A and the physical appearance of sample B are intensive properties that can be used to identify sample A as iron and sample B as powdered sugar.

PRACTICE PROBLEM 1.5

a. Ethanol is a colorless, flammable liquid. If you have two 1 gallon containers labeled sample A and sample B, and each is filled with a colorless liquid, is it possible to tell which sample is water and which is ethanol just by looking at them?
b. When liquid from sample A is splashed onto a small wood fire, the fire is extinguished. When

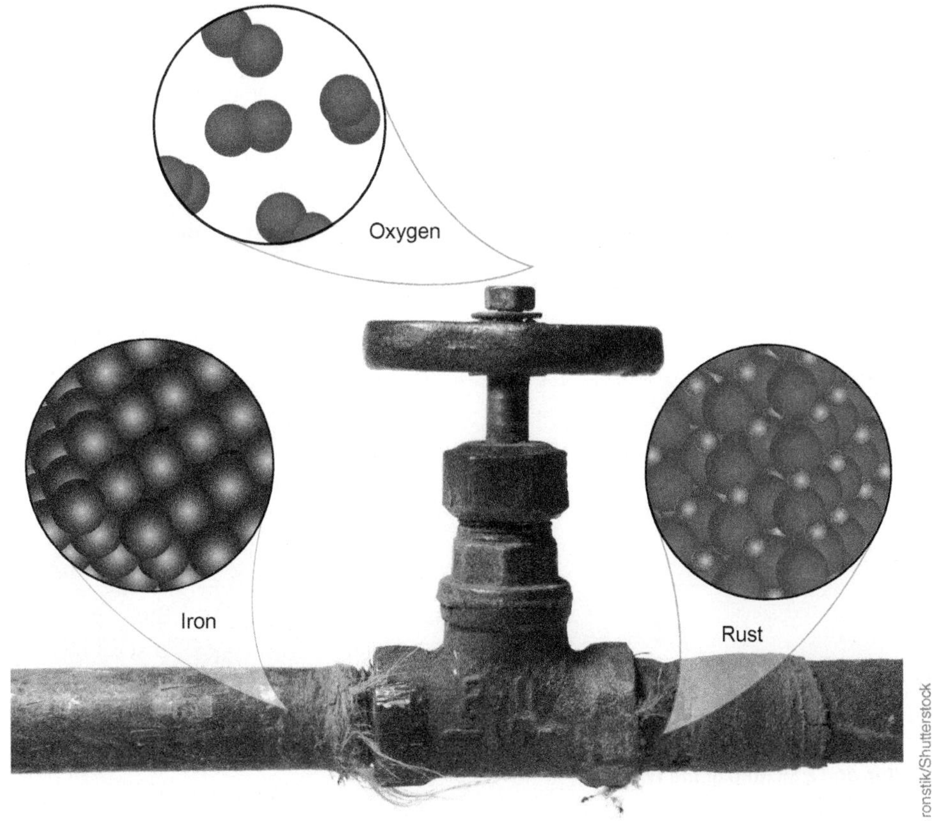

FIGURE 1.3 Properties of Iron

Physical properties of iron include the fact that it is gray and a solid at room temperature. A chemical property of iron is that it can react with oxygen in the air to form rust.

liquid from sample B is splashed onto a small wood fire, the fire grows larger. Based on these observations, is it possible to tell which sample is water and which is ethanol?

Hint: The flammability of ethanol is a chemical property.

The properties of *compounds* are constant and typically are different from the properties of the elements that compose them. For example, hydrogen and oxygen are both colorless gases at room temperature, whereas water, in which hydrogen and oxygen are chemically combined, is a colorless liquid at room temperature. The properties of *mixtures*, on the other hand, are similar to the properties of the components that make up the mixture, and these properties change depending on the amount of each component in the mixture. Thus, dissolving one spoonful of sugar in a glass of water yields a solution (a homogeneous mixture) that is sweet, but dissolving three spoonsful of sugar in the same amount of water yields a solution that is even sweeter.

The experiment shown in the video Figure 1.4 demonstrates how physical and chemical properties can be used to distinguish between a compound and a mixture. Small samples of iron filings and powdered sulfur are prepared on separate watch glasses. Both are solids. If you had large pieces of each element and pounded them with a hammer, you would find that the sulfur is brittle and is easily crushed into powder, whereas the iron is **malleable**, which means it can be pounded into various shapes without breaking. In the experiment, the iron filings and powdered sulfur samples are first placed into separate test tubes. When a magnet is held beside the tube containing the iron filings, the iron is attracted to the magnet. When the magnet is held next to the tube containing the sulfur, nothing happens; the sulfur is not attracted to the magnet.

Next, some iron filings and some powdered sulfur are poured into a large test tube and stirred together to create a mixture. The sample appears to be a dirty yellow, but if you look closely, you can see yellow specks and black specks, indicating that this is a heterogeneous mixture. When a magnet is held next to the test

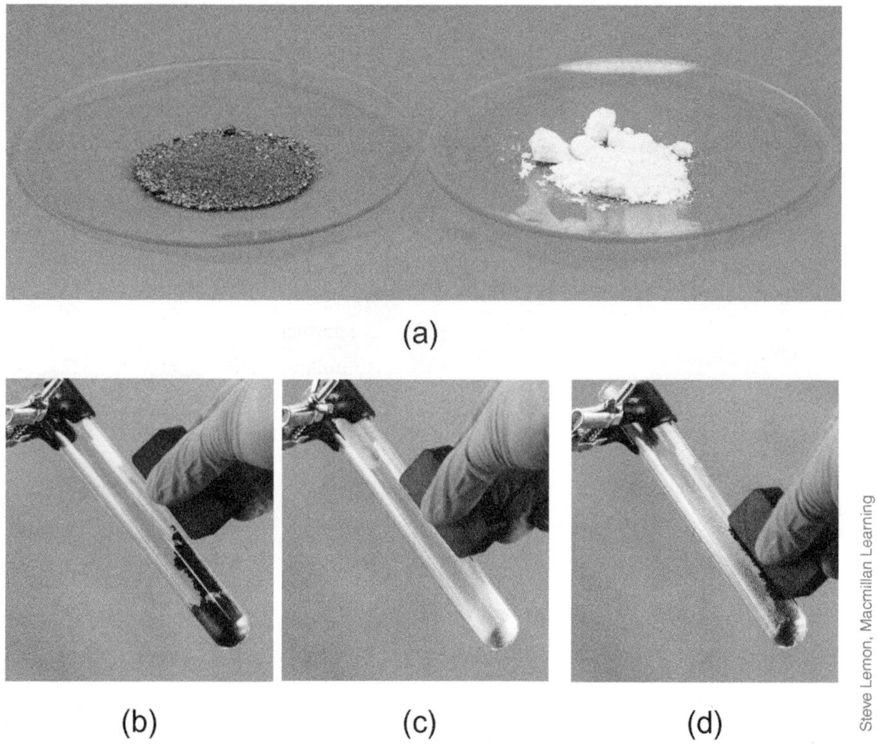

FIGURE 1.4 Iron, Sulfur, and a Mixture of the Two

NOTE: You need to be online to access this video.

Elemental iron is attracted to a magnet, but sulfur is not. When iron filings are mixed with sulfur powder, specks of black and yellow are visible, indicating that a heterogeneous mixture was made. The iron in the mixture is attracted to the magnet. Some of the powdered sulfur sticks to the iron, but the sulfur itself is not attracted to the magnet. The components of the mixture retain the same properties they had when they were pure substances.

tube, the black particles, with some yellow particles clinging to them, are attracted by the magnet.

Because the sulfur sticks to the iron, you cannot completely separate the iron from the sulfur using a magnet. However, if you were to pour some carbon disulfide—a colorless, flammable liquid—on the pure sulfur sample, you would see that the solid sulfur **dissolves**, forming a yellow solution with the carbon disulfide. If you pour carbon disulfide on the iron, nothing happens; the iron remains solid, and the liquid carbon disulfide remains colorless. Sulfur is **soluble** in carbon disulfide and iron is not, so you can separate the sulfur from the iron based on this difference in their solubility, a physical property. (Caution: Carbon disulfide is poisonous and explosive in air and should not be handled without appropriate safety precautions.)

If you were to pour carbon disulfide onto the mixture of sulfur and iron, you would again see the liquid turn yellow as the sulfur dissolved, while the iron filings remain unchanged. If you poured off that yellow solution and evaporated the carbon disulfide away in a fume hood, you would be left with a yellow solid again. If you placed a magnet next to the black material that was left behind in the test tube, you would find that it is attracted to the magnet. Mixing the iron and sulfur together did not change their properties. The sulfur is still yellow and still soluble in carbon disulfide; the iron filings are still black and still attracted by a magnet. The two elements have retained their properties and their identities; they are still elements. This combination of the two is a mixture, but a mixture does not have a definite composition, and its properties depend on the properties of its component elements and/or compounds.

When matter undergoes a change, the starting material is known as the **reactant** and the resulting material is the **product**. **Physical changes** do not alter the chemical composition of matter. As an example, boiling water changes the phase (physical state) of water from a liquid to a gas (water vapor), but throughout the change from liquid to gas, the water does not change its chemical composition.

FIGURE 1.5 Physical Change

NOTE: You need to be online to access this video.

In a physical change, the product you end up with is the same substance as the reactant with which you started. The substance might change its shape or its physical state, but the reactant and product in a physical change are always the same substance—they are just in different forms.

It is still water with a chemical composition made up of one oxygen atom and two hydrogen atoms bonded together. Another example of a physical change is separating a mixture into its components. A mixture of elements and compounds might be separated into pure substances, but the pure substances that result are the same ones that were in the mixture to begin with. No new pure substances were formed by separating a mixture into its components, so it was a physical change. This video (Figure 1.5) shows a physical change.

Now suppose that instead of simply mixing random amounts of sulfur and iron together, you placed two carefully measured samples of iron filings, Fe, and powdered sulfur, S, into a large test tube and heated

FIGURE 1.6 Reaction of Iron and Sulfur

NOTE: You need to be online to access this video.

When a mixture of iron and sulfur is heated, a chemical reaction occurs. The product of the reaction is a brittle black solid that does not dissolve in carbon disulfide and is not attracted to a magnet. The properties of the black solid are not the same as those of either iron or sulfur.

TABLE 1.2 Some Properties of Iron, Sulfur, and an Iron–Sulfur Compound

	Iron	Sulfur	Iron–Sulfur Compound
Phase	Solid	Solid	Solid
Luster	Shiny	Dull	Dull
Magnetic Properties	Magnetic	Not magnetic	Not magnetic
Color	Black	Yellow	Dull black
Mechanical Properties	Malleable	Brittle	Brittle
Solubility	Insoluble in carbon disulfide	Soluble in carbon disulfide	Insoluble in carbon disulfide

the mixture with a Bunsen burner (Figure 1.6). A black solid forms in the test tube as a result of a chemical reaction between iron and sulfur. If you removed the solid from the test tube, you would find that it is brittle and that you can pulverize it with a hammer. If you added carbon disulfide to the material, it would *not* dissolve. If you brought the magnet close to the material, it would not be attracted. Unlike the iron and sulfur mixture you saw earlier, whose properties were similar to the properties of elemental iron and sulfur, this material has its own set of properties—a dull black color, brittleness, insolubility in carbon disulfide, and lack of attraction to a magnet. It is the new compound iron sulfide, FeS, a chemical combination of iron and sulfur.

Table 1.2 compares the properties discussed earlier for iron, sulfur, and the iron–sulfur compound. The properties of the iron–sulfur compound are not exactly like those of either iron or sulfur.

Chemical changes, also called chemical reactions, change the composition, or chemical structure, of a substance by breaking and/or forming chemical bonds. Every time a chemical bond is broken, energy is absorbed from the surroundings, and every time a new chemical bond is formed, energy is released to the surroundings. Therefore, chemical changes always involve an overall absorption or release of energy.

As another example of a chemical reaction, burning charcoal in air in a backyard grill forms carbon dioxide and other products. Charcoal is made up mostly of carbon atoms bonded together, air contains oxygen atoms bonded together in pairs, and the carbon dioxide gas that is formed is a combination of carbon atoms from the charcoal chemically bonded to oxygen atoms from the air. The video in Figure 1.7 shows another chemical change.

FIGURE 1.7 Chemical Change

NOTE: You need to be online to access this video.

In a chemical change, the products with which you end up are different substances from the reactants with which you started. In this video, vinegar reacts with baking soda to produce carbon dioxide gas and other products.

EVERYDAY CONNECTION

Preparing food can involve both chemical and physical changes. Melting butter and dissolving salt are examples of physical changes encountered in food preparation. Cooking processes that change the food's texture, taste, and color, however, are typically chemical changes. Cooking an egg, for example, denatures the proteins in the egg.

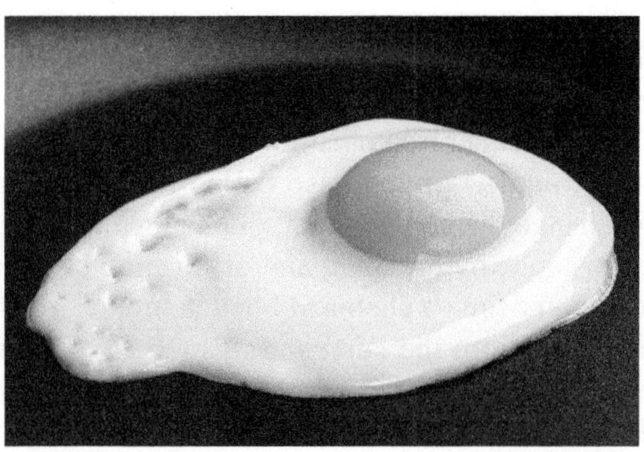

Valentina Proskurina/Shutterstock

Example 1.6

a. A pure substance is heated in air until no further reaction takes place. A different pure substance is produced that has a mass that is 58.5% of that of the original substance. Can you tell whether each substance in this reaction is an element or a compound?

b. After a different pure substance is heated in air, a new pure substance is formed that has a mass of 138% of that of the original substance. Can you tell whether each substance in these reactions is an element or a compound?

Solution

a. The first substance (the reactant) is a compound. When it is heated, it decomposes into a different material that is left behind and some gaseous product that escapes into the air. Because the mass of the new material is less than the mass of the original substance, the original substance must have decomposed—in which case, it cannot be an element. The new product might or might not be decomposable, so you cannot tell from the information given whether it is an element or a compound.

b. The second substance (the product) gained mass, so it must have combined with something in the air. The product is therefore a combination of substances and cannot be an element. You do not know if the original substance (the reactant) can be decomposed (it was not decomposed in this experiment), so you cannot tell if it is an element or a compound.

PRACTICE PROBLEM 1.6

A sample of a shiny substance is heated in air, yielding a white powder with twice the mass. Is the change a chemical reaction? Is the powder an element?

Hint: A new substance is created when the shiny substance is heated in air. Consider whether the original substance can be an element if its mass increases after it is heated.

SECTION REVIEW

- Every substance has its own characteristic set of properties.
- Physical properties describe a substance. Color, mass, volume, freezing point, boiling point, solubility, taste, texture, and hardness are all examples of physical properties.
- Chemical properties describe whether or not a substance undergoes a chemical change. For example, flammability and reactivity with acids are chemical properties.
- Extensive properties, such as mass and volume, depend on how much sample is present; intensive properties, such as color and malleability, do not.

- Intensive properties are useful for identifying substances.
- Physical changes do not alter the chemical composition of a substance, although they may change its size or its physical state. The product(s) of a physical change always have the same chemical composition as the reactant(s).
- Chemical changes result in products that are chemically different from the reactants. Chemical changes occur when chemical bonds between atoms break and/or new chemical bonds form.

1.3 Matter and Energy

GOALS

- Explain the difference between matter, mass, and weight.
- Differentiate between matter and energy.

What do the following five processes have in common?

1. Your cell phone battery recharging
2. Fireworks exploding in the night sky
3. Penicillin destroying a bacterial infection
4. A batch of cookies baking in an oven
5. A log burning in a campfire

The answer is *chemistry*. Each of these processes is an example of how interactions between matter and energy on the smallest scale create a desired effect on a much larger scale. Chemistry is the study of the interaction of matter and energy and the changes that matter undergoes. Understanding interactions between matter and energy is the first step toward being able to control them to improve the quality of everyday life.

Your cell phone battery contains chemicals that react in a way that results in the release of electrical energy. As these chemicals are used up, your battery indicator drops, but never fear. By plugging your phone into an electrical outlet, the interaction is reversed, returning the original chemicals to their starting levels and restoring your battery to 100% capacity. The variety of dazzling colors in a fireworks display is the result of energy being given off during interactions between different chemicals in the fireworks. Penicillin is a drug that interacts with a specific enzyme in certain bacteria and causes the bacteria to burst open and die. When cookie dough is placed on a tray in a hot oven, the ingredients in the dough interact with one another and form a different substance altogether. When burning a log, what began as a heavy piece of brown wood gives off heat and light as it burns, resulting in the production of gases and gray ashes.

In each of these interactions, just as in all chemical interactions, you end up with different materials from those with which you started. Sometimes, such as in the case of the rechargeable phone battery, the interaction is reversible, but more often it is not. The baked cookies, for example, cannot be restored to their original ingredients, nor can the ashes and gases be reformed into the piece of wood.

As mentioned in Section 1.1, matter is anything that has mass and occupies space. All the material things in the universe are composed of matter, including all the solids, liquids, and gases on Earth, the other planets, and the stars. Even individual atoms are made up of smaller pieces of matter.

The **mass** of an object measures how much matter is in the object. Mass is directly proportional to weight at any given place in the universe. If you leave the surface of Earth, your weight changes, but your mass remains the same. An astronaut positioned between two celestial bodies such that their gravitational attractions pull equally in opposite directions is weightless, but the astronaut's mass remains the same as it is on Earth. Because chemists ordinarily work on Earth's surface and because mass and weight are directly proportional, many chemists use the terms *mass* and *weight* interchangeably, but it is important to remember that they differ.

Energy is the capacity to do work. You cannot hold a sound or a beam of light in your hands because they are forms of energy, not matter. Some of the many forms of energy are outlined in the following list. Energy cannot be created or destroyed, but energy can be converted from one form to another. This statement is known as the **law of conservation of energy**.

Forms of Energy

- Heat
- Chemical
- Nuclear
- Mechanical
  - Kinetic (energy of motion)
  - Potential (energy of position)
- Electrical
- Sound

- Electromagnetic radiation
  - Gamma rays
  - X-rays
  - Ultraviolet
  - Visible light
  - Infrared
  - Microwaves
  - Radio waves

Example 1.7

Which energy conversions are exhibited by (a) using the flashlight app on your cell phone and (b) recharging your cell phone battery by plugging it into a wall outlet?

Solution

a. Chemical energy in your cell phone battery is converted to electrical energy, which is converted to light.
b. Electrical energy from the wall outlet is converted to chemical energy in your phone's battery.

PRACTICE PROBLEM 1.7

Which energy conversions are exhibited by (a) a firework exploding and (b) a loud motorcycle accelerating up a hill?

Hint: Chemical energy is involved in any chemical reaction, including explosions and the combustion of gasoline in an engine.

SECTION REVIEW

- Mass is a measure of the quantity of matter in a sample.
- Energy exists in many different forms and can be converted between forms, but it can never be created or destroyed.

1.4 The Scientific Method, Hypotheses, Theories, and Laws

GOALS

- Describe the scientific method.
- Distinguish between hypotheses, theories, and laws.

In this section, you will learn about the scientific method, hypotheses, theories, and laws—what they *are* and what they are *not*.

There is a widespread misconception that science is a massive collection of facts. Science, though, is far more than the facts you know—it is also a procedure for figuring out what you do *not* know. The process of conducting experimental science is guided by a procedure called the scientific method.

THE SCIENTIFIC METHOD

Imagine that you walk out into your backyard one day and there in the grass is a frog. It's not moving and you can't see it breathing. Is it dead? You already have some information from your initial observations—namely, the frog is not moving and you can't see it breathing—so you might reasonably think the frog is dead. How can you check to see if you are right?

You might not want to touch the frog, so perhaps you find a stick and use that to poke the frog, knowing that a dead frog will not respond. You gently poke the frog, and it does not move. You probably then poke it harder, or try to flip it over with the stick. When you do, the frog quickly hops away from you through the grass. You conclude (hopefully) that the frog is alive.

That process of determining information about the frog parallels the steps followed in the scientific method. The **scientific method** is a process that combines observation, hypothesis, and experimentation. For the frog, you started with an observation that led to a *question*: Is the frog dead? *Observation* that the frog was not moving and might not be breathing led to a *hypothesis* (an initial explanation of the facts based on all available evidence) that the frog was dead. An *experiment* (an interaction with the object being studied, in this case, poking the frog with a stick) provided new evidence, which led to the correct *conclusion* that the frog is alive. This conclusion might not have been reached based on observation alone.

Only experimental science is guided by the scientific method, and there are other types of science that do not involve experimentation but still answer questions about the world. For example, if a field biologist wants to know the size of the giraffe population of a particular savannah, he would count them. That process involves a question, observation, and conclusion. Similarly, if an astrophysicist thinks she may have discovered a new exoplanet, there is no experiment she can perform—no interaction with the object being studied—that can verify whether it really is an exoplanet or perhaps some other phenomenon affecting the signal. She can only continue to observe and collect data. Because the scientific method applies only to experimental science, it is applicable only to questions that can be answered through some form of experiment. In addition, the hypothesis should be testable through experimentation. If you have two similar pieces of iron but one has noticeably more rust on it than does the other, you might hypothesize that one piece got wet at some point in the past, accelerating the rusting process. That is certainly a reasonable explanation for the difference, but it is a poor hypothesis because there is no way to experimentally test the iron to determine whether your explanation is correct.

Another way to think about the scientific method is to ask yourself the following three questions:

1. What background information, data, or observations do you have?
2. What is your initial explanation for the background information and data? (This is your hypothesis, which should be supported by your initial observations and any other available data.)
3. How can you check? (This is the experiment, where you interact with the subject being studied.)

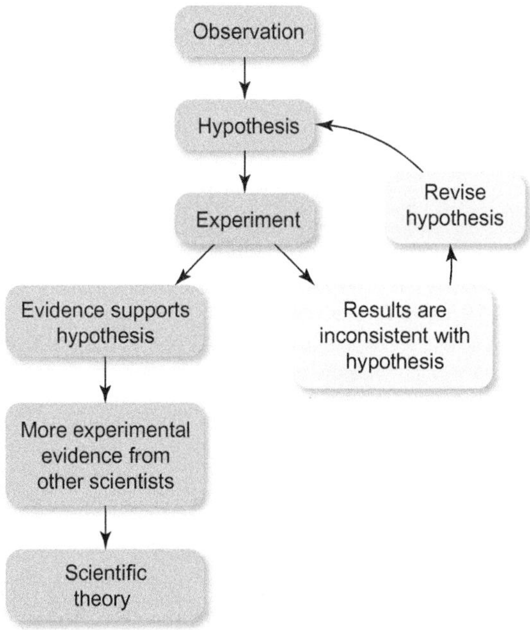

FIGURE 1.8 The Scientific Method

In the scientific method, the scientist first makes observations and develops a hypothesis to explain the observations. The scientist then conducts experiments to test the hypothesis. The hypothesis may then be modified based on the results of additional experiments. If a hypothesis is supported by repeated observation and experimentation, and no evidence arises to contradict the hypothesis, the hypothesis may become a theory.

HYPOTHESES, THEORIES, AND LAWS

There may be no terms in science more widely misunderstood than *hypothesis*, *theory*, and *law*. To better understand them, you need to know what they are and what they are not.

The following describes what hypotheses, theories, and laws *are*:

- A **hypothesis** is the initial explanation for some observed fact or facts. It is based on observation and evidence, and it is intended to be tested through experimentation.
- When a hypothesis has been tested through continued observations and repeated experiments and is never contradicted, it becomes more widely accepted as a valid explanation—something scientists call a **theory** (Figure 1.8). Theories are typically broader in scope than are hypotheses and are able to explain and predict many different observations that are linked by the same underlying phenomena. Hypotheses normally do not emerge unscathed from repeated testing but instead are continually revised as new evidence becomes known, but the theory that eventually results is supported by all of the prior experimentation and evidence. Of all scientific explanations, theories have withstood the most scrutiny and are the most reliable.
- Unlike hypotheses and theories, **scientific laws** are not explanations. Laws are simply scientific observations that are always seen to be that way, with no exceptions. For example, the law of gravity describes the mutual forces exerted by masses on other masses. The gravitational interaction always follows the same laws, whether you are talking about a dropped pencil in a laboratory or the supermassive black hole in the center of the Milky Way galaxy. The law of gravity does not explain how gravity works because a law is not an explanation. Some scientific laws can be expressed quantitatively in the form of mathematical equations, but others are simply statements that describe the observed phenomenon.

The following describes what hypotheses, theories, and laws are *not*:

- A hypothesis is *not* a guess or even an educated guess. It is a tentative explanation for observed facts, based on reason and evidence.

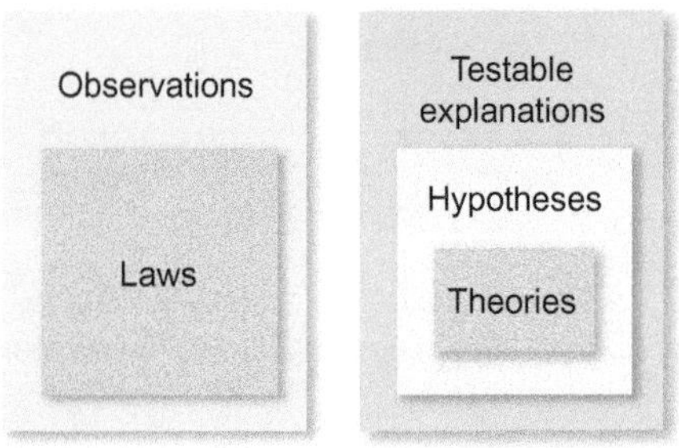

FIGURE 1.9 Laws Versus Theories
Laws are scientific observations that have always been seen to be true, but they are not explanations for *why* the observation is always that way. Theories are scientific explanations that so far have never been proven wrong. A theory and a law are two entirely different things. A hypothesis can become a theory, but a theory can never become a law.

- A theory is *not* a hunch or an explanation made up out of thin air. Outside of science, the word *theory* is often used to describe an idea that is based on few facts, but within science, a theory is an explanation that has never been contradicted by evidence. That does not necessarily mean that the theory is correct—it only means that no evidence has been discovered yet that refutes it.
- A law is *not* a theory that has been proven correct (Figure 1.9). Laws are observations and theories are explanations, so a theory can never become a law.

The **law of conservation of mass** states that, in any chemical reaction or physical change, the total mass present after the change is equal to the total mass present before the change. This law was discovered before there was a theory of the atom to explain it, but as discussed in Chapter 3, the first theory of the atom was able to explain why the law of conservation of mass was true (it also explained some other laws in chemistry). Note that the law of conservation of mass does *not* apply to nuclear reactions, where the mass of the reactants and products differ somewhat. But when the law was first introduced, nuclear reactions had not yet been discovered. This underscores the fact that even scientific laws need to be revised at times.

Example 1.8

A scientist conducts a few experiments in her lab and comes up with an initial explanation for her observations.

a. What is the proper term for this initial explanation?
b. Suppose that the scientist and several of her colleagues conduct numerous additional experiments and that none of the new results contradict the original explanation. What is the proper term for the explanation at this point?

Solution

a. The scientist's initial explanation for her observations is known as a hypothesis.
b. After numerous additional experiments are performed and none of the results contradicts the original hypothesis, the explanation may become a scientific theory.

PRACTICE PROBLEM 1.8

Is it possible for a scientific law to be proven incorrect or in need of refinement?

Hint: Scientific laws are observations that do not *appear* to have exceptions.

SECTION REVIEW

- Experimental science generally follows the scientific method.
- A scientific law is an observation that is always seen to be true.
- A hypothesis is a tentative explanation for the observation, based on available evidence.
- If many additional experiments support the hypothesis and no evidence is found to contradict it, the hypothesis becomes generally accepted and is upgraded to a theory.
- A hypothesis can become a theory, but a theory can never become a law because laws are simply observations, whereas hypotheses and theories are explanations.

1.5 The International System of Units

GOAL

- Recognize SI units and prefixes to convert measurements between units.

Background Review

Chapter 0 Math Review: Section 0.2—Exponents and Scientific Notation

In 1960, an international committee published a set of standard units of measure called the **International System of Units SI** (or Système International d'Unités). This system of units, a modern form of the metric system, is based on the meter, kilogram, and second. Units from this system are collectively called SI units.

SI units can be used to describe many different kinds of quantities. Some of these quantities can be described in terms of a single unit such as length of time. Others, such as area or density, must be described in terms of compound units.

SI BASE UNITS

Length, mass, time, electric current, temperature, amount of substance, and luminous intensity are fundamental quantities that can be combined to describe every other quantity. Scientists selected a specific unit to associate with each of these fundamental quantities. These units are defined by a particular physical measurement, such as the length of a path of light, and are collectively called **base units**, or fundamental units (Table 1.3). Of these seven quantities, the ones studied most in chemistry are length, mass, time, temperature, and amount of substance.

The **meter, m**, is the SI base unit for length (distance). For shorter distances, the centimeter, cm (1/100 of a meter) is commonly used. There are exactly 2.54 cm in 1 inch, in. Longer distances are typically given in kilometers, km, where 1 km is 1000 m, approximately 0.62 miles, mi.

The **kilogram, kg**, is the SI base unit of mass. One kilogram is equal to 1000 **grams, g**. The gram is a suitable unit when measuring out solid chemicals in a chemistry lab, but for larger masses encountered on a daily basis, the kilogram is more commonly used instead. One kilogram is equal to approximately 2.2 pounds, lb (Figure 1.10).

FIGURE 1.10 One-Kilogram Samples
One-kilogram masses of cubes of sugar, water, grapes, screws, and pennies have different volumes.

TABLE 1.4 SI Prefixes

Prefix	Abbreviation	Meaning
Tera-	T	10^{12}
Giga-	G	10^{9}
Mega-	M	10^{6}
Kilo-	k	10^{3}
Deci-	d	10^{-1}
Centi-	c	10^{-2}
Milli-	m	10^{-3}
Micro-	μ	10^{-6}
Nano-	n	10^{-9}
Pico-	p	10^{-12}
Femto-	f	10^{-15}
Atto-	a	10^{-18}

TABLE 1.3 SI Base Units

Quantity	Unit	Symbol
Length	Meter	m
Mass	Kilogram	kg
Time	Second	s
Temperature	Kelvin	K
Amount of substance	Mole	mol
Electric current	Ampere	A
Luminous intensity	Candela	cd

The SI base unit of temperature, the kelvin, is discussed in detail in Section 1.8.

SI prefixes can be added to a unit to describe a very large or very small measurement. These prefixes, shown in Table 1.4, indicate powers of 10 by which the unit is multiplied. For example, the prefix *kilo-*, k, multiplies the unit by 10^3, or 1000. Thus, 1 km = 1000 m. Similarly, the prefix *centi-*, c, multiplies the unit by 10^{-2}, so 1 cm = 10^{-2} m. For a review of scientific notation, see Section 0.2.

Example 1.9

Which is larger: 1 mg or 1 Mg?

Solution

Use the definitions of *milli-* and *mega-* from Table 1.4 to define a milligram and a megagram in terms of grams.

$$1 \text{ mg} = 0.001 \text{ g}$$
$$1 \text{ Mg} = 1{,}000{,}000 \text{ g}$$

1 Mg (megagram) is considerably larger than 1 mg (milligram).

PRACTICE PROBLEM 1.9

Which is smaller: 10 μg or 10 ng?

Hint: Use the definitions of *micro-* and *nano-* in Table 1.4 to define a microgram and a nanogram in terms of grams.

DERIVED SI UNITS—AREA AND VOLUME

The meter is the SI base unit for length, a one-dimensional quantity. To calculate the **area** of a square, however, such as the one in Figure 1.11, multiply the length by the width. The area will be in units of length squared.

$$3 \text{ cm} \times 3 \text{ cm} = 9 \text{ cm}^2$$

Volume, *V*, is the amount of space occupied by a three-dimensional object. The volume of a rectangular prism is the product of the length, width, and height of

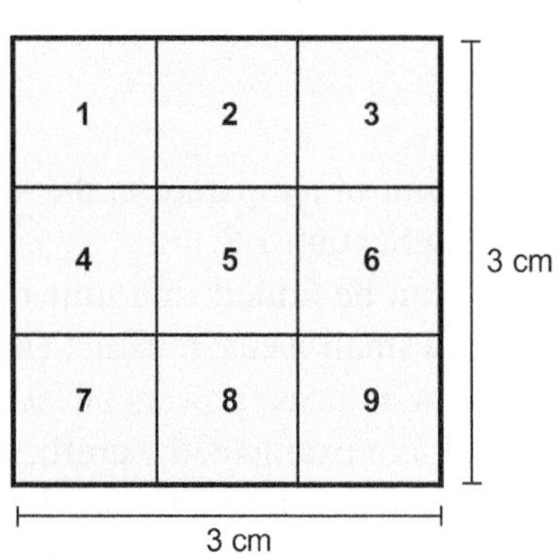

FIGURE 1.11 The Area of a Square
The area of this square is 9 cm^2.

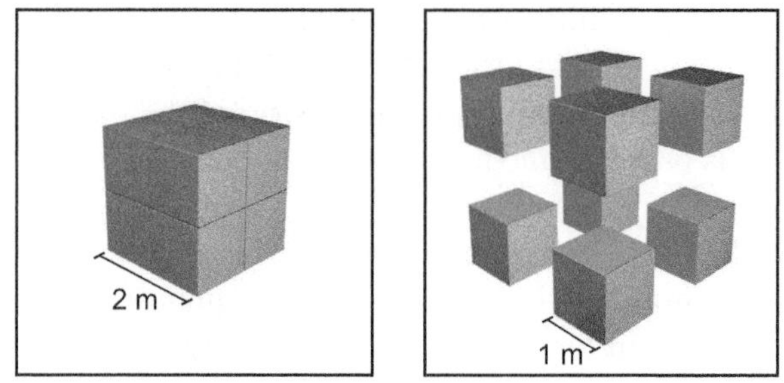

FIGURE 1.12 The Volume of a Cube
Each side of the large cube measures 2 m, so the volume of this cube is 8 m^3.

TABLE 1.5 SI Derived Units

Quantity	Unit	Abbreviation	Derivation
Volume	Cubic meter	m^3	
Speed	Meter per second	m/s	
Acceleration	Meter per second squared	m/s^2	
Density	Kilogram per cubic meter	kg/m^3	
Frequency	Hertz	Hz	s^{-1}
Force	Newton	N	$kg \cdot m/s^2$

the object. A cubic meter is the volume of a cube with side lengths of 1 m. Figure 1.12 represents a cube that is made of several smaller cubes. Notice again how the units of each measurement are multiplied together. The volume of the cube in Figure 1.12 is

$$2 \text{ m} \times 2 \text{ m} \times 2 \text{ m} = 8 \text{ m}^3$$

The square centimeter (Figure 1.11) and the cubic meter (Figure 1.12) are both **derived units**. A derived unit is the product of one or more base units. Although the base units combined to express the area and volume are the same, the base units that make up a derived unit can be different. For example, the unit of density is kg/m^3, a combination of mass and volume.

Table 1.5 lists some common quantities used in chemistry and physics that are derived from SI base units. The table shows the derivations specifically from the SI base units. For example, an object's speed is the distance it travels per unit of time. The SI units of length and time (meters and seconds, respectively) are used to create the unit for speed, m/s. Acceleration is the change in speed per unit of time, or m/s^2.

Some derived units have special names. For example, the hertz, Hz, is a unit that describes frequency and is derived from the SI unit for time. Frequency

TABLE 1.6 SI–English Conversions

Length	Mass	Volume
1 m = 39.37 in	1 kg = 2.2046 lb	1 L = 1.057 qt
2.54 cm = 1 in (exact)	453.6 g = 1 lb	29.57 mL = 1 fl oz
1.609 = 1 mi = 1760 yd = 5280 ft.	28.35 g = 1 oz	3.785 L = 1 U.S. gal
	1 metric ton = 2204.5 lb	0.473 L = 1 U.S. pint

measures the number of complete cycles of a wave per unit of time. Therefore, 1 Hz is equal to one cycle per second, or $1\text{ Hz} = 1/\text{s} = 1\text{ s}^{-1}$. Force is calculated as a mass, kg, times acceleration, m/s^2, and these units make up the newton, $1\text{ N} = 1\text{ kg}\cdot\text{m/s}^2$.

The English measurement system is primarily used in the United States. In contrast with SI units, the English measurement system has no pattern among the conversion factors—there are 12 in "in" 1 ft, 5280 ft in 1 mi, and so on. SI calculations, therefore, tend to be easier than calculations using the English system and can more often be done without a calculator. Some common SI–English conversions are shown in Table 1.6.

Example 1.10

Determine which of the following values are given in SI base units, SI derived units, or English units.

a. 1.5 gal
b. $2.04\text{ kg}\cdot\text{m/s}^2$
c. 298 K
d. 8.25 s^{-1}

Solution

a. The gallon is an *English* unit (Table 1.6).
b. The kilogram, kg, meter, m, and second, s, are all SI base units (Table 1.3). Therefore, $\text{kg}\cdot\text{m/s}^2$ is a SI *derived* unit.
c. The kelvin is a SI *base* unit (Table 1.3).
d. The second, s, is a SI base unit (Table 1.3), but the inverse second, s^{-1}, is a SI *derived* unit known as the hertz (Table 1.5).

PRACTICE PROBLEM 1.10

Determine which of the following values are given in SI base units, SI derived units, or English units.

a. 6.50 mol of iron
b. 16 oz of beer
c. 825 N of force
d. 250 A of current

Hint: Consult Table 1.3 and Table 1.6 to determine whether the value is given in SI or English units, respectively. Some derived SI units are given in Table 1.5.

SECTION REVIEW

- The standard units of measurement in chemistry are the International System of Units, SI units.
- There are seven SI base units, and the ones used most often in chemistry are the meter (length), kilogram (mass), second (time), kelvin (temperature), and mole (amount of substance).
- SI prefixes can be added to a unit to describe a very large or very small measurement. The prefixes differ by powers of 10.
- SI derived units are the products or powers of one or more base units. SI derived units include units of area, volume, speed, and acceleration.
- English–metric conversions are presented in this book only to give you an idea of the size of the metric unit. English units are rarely used in a chemistry lab.

1.6 Significant Digits

GOAL

- Determine the correct number of digits to indicate the precision of a measurement or a calculated result.

Measurement is the heart of modern science. Measurements make identifications of substances more precise and enable more scientific generalities to be made. In the world of chemistry, **qualitative** descriptions refer to the identity or form of a substance present. Thus, the qualitative analysis of a water sample may show the presence of iron compounds, but it would not determine the *amount* of substance present. Experiments that determine the amount of a substance present are known as **quantitative** measurements.

ACCURACY AND PRECISION

Scientific measurements are usually repeated three or more times. The average value of the measurements is probably closer to the true value than any individual measurement. The **accuracy** is the closeness of the average of a set of measurements to the true value. The **precision** is the closeness of all of a set of measured values to one another. Figure 1.13 uses a dartboard to illustrate the difference between precision and accuracy. In the lab, a set of measurements may

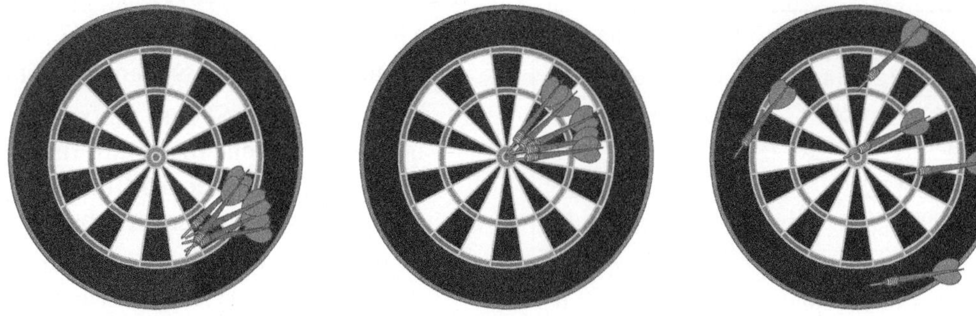

(a) (b) (c)

FIGURE 1.13 Precision and Accuracy

Precision is how close together repeated measurements are. Accuracy is how close the measurements are to the true value (the true value must be known to know how accurate a measurement is). If the bull's eye is the intended target, the darts in (a) are precise but not accurate, the darts in (b) are both precise and accurate, and the darts in (c) are neither precise nor accurate.

be precise without being accurate or accurate without being precise (if the measurer is very lucky), but the best measurements are both accurate and precise.

Example 1.11

Suppose a bathroom scale registers 2 lb with no load.

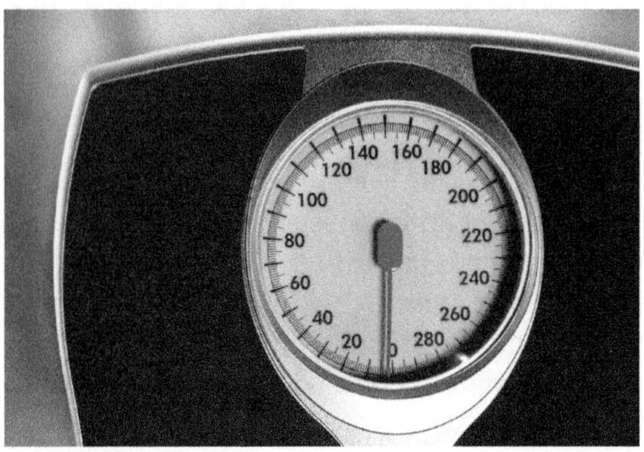

Steve Lemon, Macmillan Learning

An object is weighed repeatedly on this bathroom scale, and each results in a reading of 117 lb.

a. Are the measurements precise?
b. Are the measurements accurate?
c. What is the probable true weight of the person?

Solution

If a bathroom scale is not adjusted to read zero when no load is on it, the results it yields with a load may be precise but probably not accurate. For example, if it reads 2 lb with no load, each time a person uses the scale, it will probably read 2 lb heavier than the person's true weight.

a. The measurements are precise because exactly the same weight value (to the precision of the device) was obtained each time.
b. They are not accurate because the no-load value was incorrect.
c. Since the scale reads 2 lb with no load, it is likely giving readings that are falsely high by 2 lb. Therefore, the true weight is probably 117 lb − 2 lb = 115 lb.

PRACTICE PROBLEM 1.11

Answer the following questions and explain your answers.

a. Is it possible to obtain high precision without high accuracy?
b. Is it possible to obtain relatively high accuracy without high precision?

Hint: For part (a), think about the darts in Figure 1.13. Does one of these three scenarios represent high precision but low accuracy? For part (b), imagine a result that is similar to the arrangement of darts in Figure 1.13 (c), but the darts all land inside the inner circle of the board.

In addition to describing how close together replicate measurements are, the word *precision* has another meaning that is used when referring to a single measurement. The precision of a measurement is how exact, or how specific, the measurement is. This will usually depend on the tool that is being used to make the measurement. For example, an object whose length is measured using a ruler marked in millimeters can be measured to a greater precision than the same object measured using a ruler marked

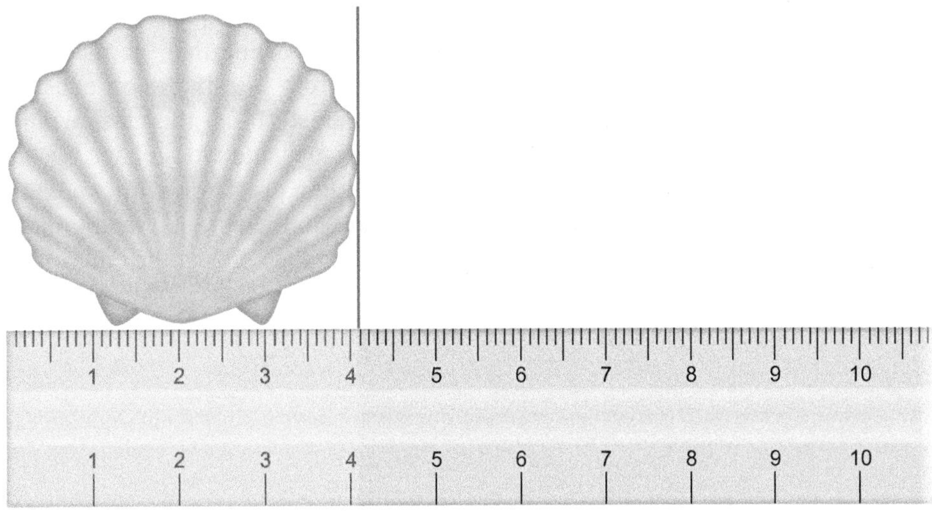

FIGURE 1.14 Measurements of Different Precision

The smallest scale divisions on the upper ruler are millimeters. The ones on the lower ruler are centimeters.

in centimeters. You cannot get an accurate measurement of the thickness of a piece of paper using a ruler that is marked in centimeters or an accurate measurement of the weight of a grain of rice using a bathroom scale because these tools are not precise enough to make a measurement on the scale of the object they are trying to measure.

When making a measurement, estimate to one digit beyond the smallest scale division, if possible. For example, if the shell in Figure 1.14 is measured with the bottom markings, calibrated in centimeters, the shell is between 4 cm and 5 cm long, and you can estimate that it extends 0.1 cm past 4 cm, for a reading of 4.1 cm. In contrast, if the top markings are used, calibrated in tenths of centimeters—that is, millimeters—the shell is between 4.0 cm and 4.1 cm. You can estimate that it is 4.08 cm. The precision of the measurement is therefore indicated in the reported number itself, and the last decimal place in the measurement goes one place beyond the narrowest markings on the measuring device.

If the shell extended exactly to the 4.1 line on the millimeter ruler, you should report 4.10 cm. If you omit the zero, someone reading the result will think that you used a ruler calibrated only in centimeters. The third digit indicates that the result was obtained using the more precise ruler but just happened to be a value ending in zero.

Example 1.12

Determine the length of this screw, not including the screw head.

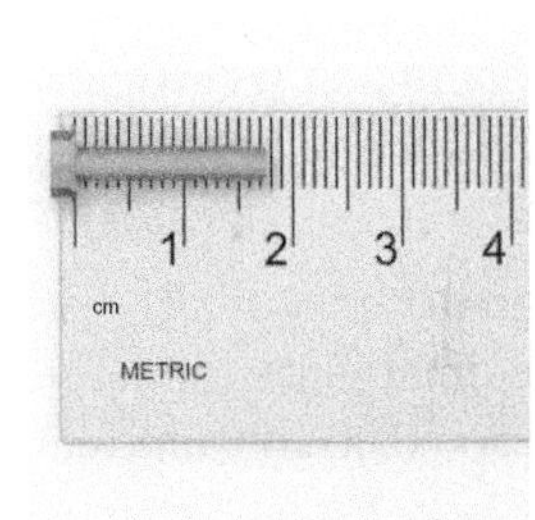

Solution

The length is somewhere between 1.7 cm and 1.8 cm. You should estimate the value of the third decimal place. The end of the screw appears to be exactly halfway between 1.7 cm and 1.8 cm, so a reasonable determination of this value is 1.75 cm. The last decimal place in the measurement goes one place beyond the narrowest markings on the ruler.

PRACTICE PROBLEM 1.12

Approximately what fraction of measurements reported should be values ending in a zero?

Hint: The last digit in a measurement has an equal probability of being 0–9. Given that, determine the probability of the last digit being zero.

SIGNIFICANT DIGITS

Scientists report the precision of their measurements every time they write down a result. The number of digits they use consists of the absolutely certain digits plus one estimated digit. Every digit that reflects the precision of the measurement, including the estimated digit at the end, is called a **significant digit** or **significant figure**. The word *significant* has a different meaning here than in everyday conversation, where it means "important." The word *significant* as used here refers to the precision of the measurement and does not mean "important."

All nonzero numbers in a properly reported measurement are significant, but sometimes zeros are used merely to indicate the magnitude of a number (how big or small the number is). If the purpose of a zero is *only* to establish the magnitude of the number, that zero is not significant. Determining which zeros are significant in a properly reported measurement is important for understanding how precisely the measurement was made.

The following rules enable you to tell whether zeros in a number are significant or not:

1. Any zeros to the left of all nonzero digits, such as in 0.03, are not significant, so 0.03 contains only one significant digit.
2. Any zeros between significant digits, such as in 903, are significant, so 903 contains three significant digits.
3. Any zeros to the right of all nonzero digits in a number with decimal-place digits, such as in 70.00, are significant, so 70.00 contains four significant digits.
4. Any zeros to the right of all nonzero digits in an integer, such as in 4000, are uncertain. If no further information is given, assume that those zeros are not significant, so 4000 would have only one significant digit.
5. All the digits in the coefficient of a number in scientific notation are significant.

Sometimes, however, a measurement can result in zeros that are significant. For example, if an object was weighed to the nearest 1 g and the mass turned out to be exactly 4000 g, those zeros are part of the measurement and are therefore significant digits. In that case, the result would be reported with a decimal point, but with no digits following the decimal point (4000.). The decimal point after the number is an indicator that the zero in the ones place is significant and, therefore, the other zeros are as well.

Alternatively, the most precise significant zero can be underlined, so the mass could also be reported as $400\underline{0}$ g, showing that the measurement was made to the nearest 1 g. If the object had been weighed to the nearest 100 g, the mass would be reported as $4\underline{0}00$ g instead and would have two significant digits, reflecting the precision with which the measurement was made. In the absence of any indication, however, assume that the zeros at the end of a number that does not have a decimal are *not* significant.

Example 1.13

Underline the significant digits in each of the following measurements. If a digit is uncertain, place a question mark under it.

a. 0.0020 m
b. 1.200 m
c. 10.002 m
d. 6000 m

Solution

a. $0.00\underline{20}$ m
The zeros to the left of the 2 are not significant (rule 1), but the one to the right is (rule 3).

b. $\underline{1.200}$ m
The zeros to the right of the 2 are significant (rule 3).

c. $\underline{10.002}$ m
Zeros between significant digits are significant (rule 2).

d. $\underline{6}000$ m
The 6 is significant because all nonzero digits are significant. The zeros to the right of all other digits in an integer are uncertain; they may reflect the precision or just the magnitude of the number. Without further information, it is impossible to tell (rule 4), so you would conclude that they are *not* significant.

PRACTICE PROBLEM 1.13

Underline the significant digits in each of the following measurements.

a. 35.00 cm
b. 203.50 cm
c. 0.02030 cm
d. 30 cm

Hint: Trailing zeros after the decimal point are significant digits, but zeros to the left of nonzero digits are not. Also, zeros to the right of nonzero digits in an integer have ambiguous uncertainty.

SIGNIFICANT DIGITS IN CALCULATED RESULTS

Calculators are frequently used to solve arithmetic problems, but calculators usually fill the entire display with digits and do not give the correct number of significant digits. A calculator may give the correct number of significant digits just by chance, but it is up to the user to make sure that the number of significant digits in a calculated answer is correct.

Not only must the original data reflect the precision of the measurements, but any results calculated from the data must also reflect that precision. Two rules govern how many significant digits are permitted in calculated results.

Addition and Subtraction

In the answers to addition and subtraction problems, the estimated digit that is farthest to the left is the last digit that can be retained:

Estimated digits

$$\begin{array}{r} 6.2\ \text{cm} \\ +\ 9.203\ \text{cm} \\ \hline 15.403\ \text{cm} \longrightarrow 15.4\ \text{cm} \end{array}$$

Last digit that can be retained in the answer

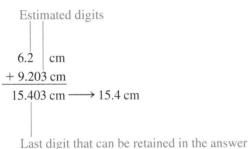

The digit 2 in 6.2 cm is an estimated digit; it has some uncertainty in it. Therefore, the digit 4 in the answer is also uncertain, and the 0 and 3 from the more precise measurement cannot be retained after being added to the less precise measurement. The value cannot be reported as 15.403 cm, or the reader will believe that 3 is the only uncertain digit. The number of digits in the answer must be limited to leave 4 as the last digit because that is the decimal place where the uncertainty lies. As a result, the value 15.403 is **rounded** to 15.4 to express it with the correct number of significant digits. In general, *if the first digit to be dropped is 5 or greater, the final digit reported is rounded up by one; otherwise, the last digit is left unchanged.* (Note that some texts and instructors use a different rule for this.)

Thus, for addition or subtraction, retain the digits in an answer only as far to the right as the leftmost uncertain digit in any of the numbers being added or subtracted. Note that the *number* of significant digits does not matter for addition or subtraction; what matters is *where the last digits lie.* In the previous calculation, there are two significant digits in the first number and four in the second, and the answer happens to have three. The final answer has the same number of decimal places as the value with the fewest number of decimal places.

> In addition and subtraction, the answer is rounded to the fewest number of decimal places that are present in the added or subtracted values.

Example 1.14

Calculate the sum of 10.10 cm + 1.332 cm + 6.4 cm. Report the answer with the correct number of significant digits.

Solution

$$\begin{array}{r} 10.10\ \text{cm} \\ 1.332\ \text{cm} \\ +\ 6.4\ \text{cm} \\ \hline 17.832\ \text{cm} \longrightarrow 17.8\ \text{cm} \end{array}$$

Of the values added, 6.4 has only one decimal place, so the final answer is rounded to one decimal place.

PRACTICE PROBLEM 1.14

Calculate the answer to the proper precision:

$$62.44\ \text{cm} - 7.145\ \text{cm} + 27.7\ \text{cm}$$

Hint: In addition and subtraction problems, the answer is rounded to the fewest number of decimal places that are present in the values that are added or subtracted.

Multiplication and Division

For multiplication and division, the number of significant digits in the measurement with the fewest significant digits limits the number of significant digits in the answer:

$$4.1\ \text{cm} \times 21.07\ \text{cm} = 86.387\ \text{cm}^2 = 86\ \text{cm}^2$$

Reporting the answer as 86.387 cm^2 would indicate that the measurement had been carried out with a precision of 1 part in 86,387, which is not true. The number of significant digits in the final answer must be reduced to two because the measurement with the fewest significant digits (4.1 cm) only has two.

> In multiplication and division, the answer is rounded to the fewest number of *significant figures* that are present in the multiplied or divided values. This is different from the rule for addition and subtraction.

Example 1.15

Perform the following calculations and report the answers to the correct number of significant digits.

a. $2.171 \text{ cm} \times 4.20 \text{ cm}$
b. $4.92 \text{ g}/1.64 \text{ cm}^3$

Solution

a. $2.171 \text{ cm} \times 4.20 \text{ cm} = 9.1182 \text{ cm}^2 = 9.12 \text{ cm}^2$
9.1182 cm^2 must be rounded to three significant digits because the second factor (4.20 cm) has only three significant digits.
b. $(4.92 \text{ g}/1.64 \text{ cm}^3) = 3.00 \text{ g/cm}^3$
It must have three significant digits because both the dividend (4.92 g) and the divisor (1.64 cm^3) have only three significant digits. In this case, the division comes out to be exactly 3, so despite the fact that your calculator shows only a 3, you have to add two zeros to the answer given by the calculator to get the correct number of significant digits. Since the units were different in the dividend and the divisor, the final answer has units from both the original values.

PRACTICE PROBLEM 1.15

Perform the following calculations and limit the answers to the correct number of significant digits.

a. $1.27 \text{ cm} \times 6.220 \text{ cm} \times 4.10 \text{ cm}$
b. $9.030 \text{ g}/(3.01 \text{ cm} \times 1.414 \text{ cm} \times 7.500 \text{ cm})$
c. $(0.71 \text{ cm})^3$

Hint: In multiplication and division, the final answer is rounded to the fewest number of significant figures that are present in the multiplied or divided values.

Numbers that are definitions and not measurements, such as the number of centimeters in a meter (100) or the number of radii in the diameter of a circle (2), are exact numbers. They do not limit the number of significant digits in a calculated result. Counted items, such as 12 books on a shelf or 500 sheets of paper in a ream, are also exact values and do not limit the number of significant digits. Significant digits are limited only by measurements and by inexact estimates. For example, using the value 3.14 for pi, π, would limit your answer to no more than three significant digits, but using 3.1416 as π would allow you up to five significant digits in your answer, provided you had that many significant digits in your measurements.

Conversion factors that are exact do not limit significant figures. Unit conversions within the metric system that only involve changing a prefix are always exact. Unit conversions within the English system such as 16 pt in 1 gal are also exact. Conversions between metric and English measurements are typically not exact, except for the conversion factor between centimeters and inches (2.54 cm = 1 in), which is exact. Any conversion factor that is based on an actual measurement will always be inexact and can therefore limit the number of significant digits in the final answer.

In summary, exact numbers result from

- defined quantities, such as the number of feet in a mile or the number of quarts in a gallon;
- counting—for example, you can count the number of wheels on a vehicle and report that value with no error; and
- integers within formulas, such as the 2 in the formula for diameter, $d = 2r$.

Example 1.16

The radius of a circle is 13.7 cm. Calculate the diameter of the circle to the correct number of significant digits.

Solution

The diameter of a circle is twice the radius.

$$d = 2r = 2(13.7 \text{ cm}) = 27.4 \text{ cm}$$

The *measurement* with the fewest significant digits is 13.7 cm. It is the only measurement in the problem.

PRACTICE PROBLEM 1.16

Calculate the circumference of the circle in Example 1.16 to the correct number of significant digits. The circumference of a circle is equal to $2\pi r$, where $\pi = 3.14159$.

Hint: Determine the value in the calculation that has the fewest number of significant digits.

If a problem has both addition or subtraction and multiplication or division, the part that is done first must have its significant digits noted before the next operation is performed because the rules are different for determining which digits are retained. You must follow the *order of operations* rules, which are as follows:

1. First, perform any calculations that are in parentheses.
2. Perform any exponential calculations.

Steve Lemon, Macmillan Learning

FIGURE 1.15 Video Tutorial: Significant Figures

NOTE: You need to be online to access this video.

This video shows how to perform a multistep calculation and to round the answer to the proper number of significant figures.

3. Perform any multiplication or division calculations, going from left to right.
4. Lastly, perform any addition or subtraction calculations, going from left to right.

If addition or subtraction is done first, the *number* of significant digits in the sum or difference is used to determine the number in the multiplication or division operation to follow. If multiplication or division is done first, the *position* of the last significant digit is noted to help determine the last significant digit in the next answer resulting from addition or subtraction. In multipart problems in the rest of this text, to avoid excessive round-off errors, at least one extra digit will be retained (if it is nonzero) until the final answer.

Figure 1.15 is a video that shows the strategy behind solving a multistep calculation.

Example 1.17

Find the result of each of the following calculations to the proper number of significant digits.

a. $\dfrac{(80.21\text{g} - 79.93\text{ g})}{65.22\text{ cm}^3}$

b. $(92.12\text{ mL})(0.912\text{ g/mL}) + 223.02\text{ g}$

Solution

a. Following the order of operations, perform the calculation inside the parentheses first, which gives an answer with two digits after the decimal point. It also happens to have two significant digits, which will be important to keep track of for later.

$$80.21\text{ g} - 79.93\text{ g} = 0.28\text{ g}$$

Now perform the division step:

$$\frac{0.28\text{ g}}{65.22\text{ cm}^3} = 0.0043\text{ g/cm}^3$$

The two significant digits in the numerator limit the final number of significant digits to two.

b. Following the order of operations, do the multiplication first. This gives a value with three significant digits (and one significant digit after the decimal point).

$$(92.12\text{ mL})(0.912\text{ g/mL}) = 84.01\text{ g}$$

The 1 in 84.01 is *not* significant, but it is carried through the calculation to prevent round-off errors. Now do the addition step:

$$84.01\text{ g} + 223.02\text{ g} = 307.03\text{ g}$$
$$307.03\text{ g} \rightarrow 307.0\text{ g}$$

Round the final answer to one decimal place because the result of the first calculation (84.0 g) was limited to three significant figures, and only one of those significant digits followed the decimal point.

PRACTICE PROBLEM 1.17

Calculate the result of each of the following problems to the correct number of significant digits.

a. $1.41 \times 10^7\text{ g} - 5.98 \times 10^6\text{ g}$

b. $\dfrac{(2.50 \times 10^2\text{ g} + 3.75 \times 10^3\text{ g})}{255\text{ cm}^3}$

Hint: When adding or subtracting values that have different powers of 10, it often helps to convert one of the values so that it has the same power of 10 as the other. This makes it easier to determine the number of significant digits in the final answer.

Logarithms

Logarithms (Section 0.5) will not appear again in this course until Chapter 12, but the relevant significant digit rules are given here for reference.

- The number of digits after the decimal point of $\log(x)$ should be equal to the number of significant figures of x; for example, $\log(3.5 \times 10^5) = 5.54$.
- For an inverse log of x (10^x), the number of significant figures in the answer is equal to the number of digits after the decimal point in x; for example, $10^{-3.421} = 3.79 \times 10^{-4}$.

SECTION REVIEW

- The precision that was used to make a measurement is reflected in the number of significant digits reported.

- The rules for significant digits in addition and subtraction are different from those in multiplication and division.
- Significant digits and decimal-place digits (such as the tenths place and hundredths place) are not the same. There is no necessary relationship between the two.
- In general, calculators do not give the proper number of significant digits.
- All the digits in the coefficient of a number in scientific notation are significant.

1.7 Dimensional Analysis

GOAL

- Use the units of a measurement as a guide in setting up calculations.

Background Review

Chapter 0 Math Review: Section 0.1—Using a Calculator

Every measurement results in a number and a **unit**. Reporting the unit is just as important as reporting the number. There is an enormous difference, for example, between a snake that is 6 *inches* long and a snake that is 6 *feet* long! The units are an important part of any measurement, and the units should be stated for every measured quantity and for every quantity calculated from measured data. Always use full spellings or standard abbreviations for all units.

> Use units in reporting all measurements and the results of calculations using them. Use either full spellings or standard abbreviations for all units.

In many cases, the units provide a clue to which operation—multiplication or division—should be performed in calculations. The units of measurement can be treated as algebraic quantities in calculations. For example, the total wages of a student aide who has earned exactly $9 per hour for exactly 30 h of work is $270:

$$\text{Total wages} = 30\,\cancel{\text{h}}\left(\frac{\$9}{\cancel{\text{h}}}\right) = \$270$$

Time worked (in hours) × Hourly rate (in dollars/hour) = Total wages (in dollars)

The unit *hours* in the time cancels the unit *hour* in the rate, leaving the unit *dollars* in the answer. This canceling is indicated by crossing out the units of hours in both terms. For the units to cancel, it does not matter if the unit is singular (such as hour) or plural (such as hours). If you did not know the equation to calculate the total wages, you could have put down the time with the unit *hours* and multiplied by the rate of pay, which has the unit *hour* in its denominator. The units tell you that you must multiply.

Because money can be counted rather than measured, the monetary values in these examples are treated as exact (e.g., having infinite significant figures).

The calculation of the student's wages used **dimensional analysis**, also called unit analysis or the factor label method. In the dimensional analysis, a quantity is multiplied by a conversion factor that is written as a fraction or ratio. The numerator and denominator in the conversion factor are equal or equivalent to one another, so the overall conversion factor is equal to 1. In the previous example, $9 is equivalent to 1 h because those are the wages given in this problem, and the calculation changes the number of hours worked to the equivalent number of dollars. The units included in the conversion factor are the labels. In dimensional analysis, you always write down the units along with the numbers when doing calculations. To use dimensional analysis, first put down the given quantity (30 h), then multiply by a **conversion factor**, a rate or ratio that will change the units given to the units desired for the answer (in this case, $9 per hour). The conversion factor may be a known constant, such as 100 cents/dollar, or it may be a value that is given in the problem, such as $9 per hour.

To summarize the steps of dimensional analysis:

1. Write down the *quantity* given or, occasionally, a ratio to be converted.
2. Multiply the quantity by one or more conversion factors (rates or ratios), which will change the units *given* to those *required* for the answer. The conversion factors may be given in the problems, or they may be constants of known value.

> To use dimensional analysis effectively, you must know the units of all the quantities being dealt with and write them down as part of the calculation.

Diagrams that depict the initial units and the final units connected by the conversion factor are used in many places in this book to show how to change a quantity from one of the units to the other. To calculate the student aide's total wages, for example, use the following diagram:

$$30 \text{ hours} \left(\frac{9 \text{ dollars}}{1 \text{ hour}}\right) = 270 \text{ dollars}$$

Diagrams like this will accompany many of the solutions to the in-text examples in this chapter. To solve the practice problems, make your own diagrams if necessary.

Example 1.18

Convert 5445 min to hours.

Solution

Write down the quantity given and then multiply it by a factor, which in this case is known, that changes minutes to hours. The appropriate conversion factor would be that 1 h is equivalent to 60 min. The factor should have the unit *minutes* in the denominator to cancel the *minutes* in the quantity given. It should also have the unit *hour* in the numerator so that the answer is in hours:

$$5445 \cancel{\text{min}} \times \left(\frac{1 \text{ h}}{60 \cancel{\text{min}}}\right) = 90.75 \text{ h}$$

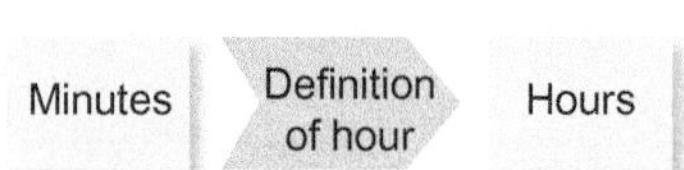

Any units in the denominator are divided into units in the numerator, just as any number in the denominator is. Any units and any numbers in the numerator are multiplied. (If a quantity, such as 5445 min, is given with no denominator, the quantity is considered to be in a numerator.)

PRACTICE PROBLEM 1.18

Convert 5445 min to seconds.

Hint: The conversion factor between minutes and seconds is $\left(\frac{1 \text{ min}}{60 \text{ s}}\right)$ or $\left(\frac{60 \text{ s}}{1 \text{ min}}\right)$. Arrange this conversion factor so that the units of minutes cancel.

Example 1.19

Calculate the time required for a student aide to earn \$378 at \$9 per hour.

Solution

First, write down the quantity given, and then multiply it by a factor involving the rate:

$$378 \cancel{\text{dollars}} \left(\frac{1 \text{ h}}{9 \cancel{\text{dollars}}}\right) = 42 \text{ h}$$

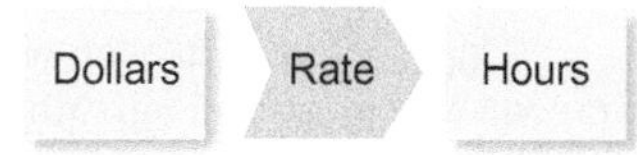

In this case, the inverse of the rate of pay, the factor used previously to calculate total wages, is required. Rates or ratios can be used either right side up or upside down; getting the units to cancel properly will indicate which form to use. Just be sure that the number in the rate, such as 9.00, stays with the proper unit (i.e., dollars).

PRACTICE PROBLEM 1.19

Calculate the time required to travel 15.0 mi at 60.0 mph in units of (a) hours and (b) minutes.

Hint: For part (a), use 15.0 mi and the conversion factor given in the problem statement: $\left(\frac{60 \text{ mi}}{1 \text{ h}}\right)$. Be sure that the units of miles cancel. For part (b), you will have to use an analogous conversion factor to convert the time to minutes.

Example 1.20

a. How many meters are in 5.200 km?
b. How many meters are in 5.200 μm?

Solution

a. According to Table 1.4, the SI prefix k (for *kilo-*) is equal to 10^3. Multiply 5.200 km by the relationship $\left(\frac{10^3 \text{ m}}{1 \text{ km}}\right)$:

$$5.200 \cancel{\text{km}} \left(\frac{10^3 \text{ m}}{1 \cancel{\text{km}}}\right) = 5.200 \times 10^3 \text{ m}$$

b. According to Table 1.4, the SI prefix μ (for *micro-*) is equal to 10^{-6}. Multiply 5.200 μm by the relationship $\left(\frac{10^{-6} \text{ m}}{1 \ \mu\text{m}}\right)$:

$$5.200 \cancel{\mu\text{m}} \left(\frac{10^{-6} \text{ m}}{1 \cancel{\mu\text{m}}}\right) = 5.200 \times 10^{-6} \text{ m}$$

In both parts (a) and (b), the relationships between the SI prefixes have infinite significant digits. As a result, the given quantities determine the number of significant digits in the answer.

PRACTICE PROBLEM 1.20

Determine the number of meters in (a) 525 nm and (b) 175 dm.

Hint: Use Table 1.4 to identify the SI prefixes. For each part, multiply the given value by the relevant relationship, as was done in Example 1.20.

USING MULTIPLE CONVERSION FACTORS

Sometimes it is necessary to use more than one factor to get a desired answer. The factors may be used in separate steps, or they may be combined in a single step.

Example 1.21

Calculate the number of seconds in 5.175 h.

Solution

To convert hours to seconds, first convert hours to minutes.

$$5.175\ \cancel{h}\left(\frac{60\ \text{min}}{1\ \cancel{h}}\right) = 310.5\ \text{min}$$

Hours → Definition of hour → Minutes

Then, convert minutes to seconds.

$$310.5\ \cancel{\text{min}}\left(\frac{60\ \text{s}}{1\ \cancel{\text{min}}}\right) = 18{,}630\ \text{s}$$

Minutes → Definition of minute → Seconds

Alternatively, dimensional analysis can be used to combine these two steps into one calculation. You should get the same answer either way.

Hours → Definition of hour → Minutes → Definition of minute → Seconds

$$5.175\ \text{hours}\left(\frac{60\ \text{minutes}}{1\ \text{hour}}\right) = 310.5\ \text{minutes}\left(\frac{60\ \text{seconds}}{1\ \text{minute}}\right) = 18{,}630\ \text{seconds}$$

or

$$5.175\ \text{hours}\left(\frac{60\ \text{minutes}}{1\ \text{hour}}\right)\left(\frac{60\ \text{seconds}}{1\ \text{minute}}\right) = 18{,}630\ \text{seconds}$$

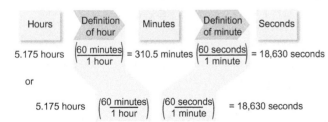

In multistep calculations such as this, it is important to keep all the digits from the intermediate answers and round only the final answer at the end.

PRACTICE PROBLEM 1.21

Calculate the number of seconds in exactly 7 weeks.

Hint: Begin by using the conversion factor between days and weeks, $\left(\frac{7\ \text{days}}{1\ \text{week}}\right)$, and then convert from days to hours, hours to minutes, and minutes to seconds. In each step, be sure that the conversion factors are set up so that the proper units cancel.

Example 1.22

Convert 755 mm to inches. There are exactly 2.54 cm in 1 in.

Solution

First, convert 755 mm to meters and meters to centimeters. Then convert centimeters to inches.

$$755\ \cancel{\text{mm}}\left(\frac{1\ \cancel{\text{m}}}{10^3\ \cancel{\text{mm}}}\right)\left(\frac{10^2\ \cancel{\text{cm}}}{1\ \cancel{\text{m}}}\right)\left(\frac{1\ \text{in}}{2.54\ \cancel{\text{cm}}}\right) = 29.7\ \text{in}$$

PRACTICE PROBLEM 1.22

Determine the number of centimeters in (a) 215 nm and (b) 575 km.

Hint: Use Table 1.4 to identify the SI prefixes. For each part, first convert the given value to meters, and then convert it to the desired unit.

Example 1.23

To give you some idea of how large the number one billion is, calculate the number of years it would take to spend \$1 billion (\$1,000,000,000) if you spent \$1000 per day.

Solution

To solve this problem, the rate of dollars spent per day converts dollars to days, which can then be converted to years.

Dollars → Daily rate → Days → Days/year → Years

$$1{,}000{,}000{,}000\ \cancel{\text{dollars}}\left(\frac{1\ \cancel{\text{day}}}{1000\ \cancel{\text{dollars}}}\right)\left(\frac{1\ \text{year}}{365\ \cancel{\text{days}}}\right) = 2740\ \text{years}$$

It would take more than 2,700 years to spend \$1 billion by spending \$1,000 a day. Just think how large the number 100 billion is. Many numbers that are commonly used in science are even larger than these.

PRACTICE PROBLEM 1.23

The distance from Earth to Mars is 225 million km (2.25×10^8 km). If the Space Shuttle is able to travel at a speed of 28,000 km/h, how many days would it take the Space Shuttle to reach Mars?

Hint: Combining the distance from Earth to Mars with the conversion factor provided by the speed of the Space Shuttle can be used to determine the number of hours it takes the Space Shuttle to reach Mars. The number of hours can then be converted to days because there are exactly 24 hours in a day.

FIGURE 1.16 Video Tutorial: Dimensional Analysis

NOTE: You need to be online to access this video.
This video shows how to use dimensional analysis to convert a pay rate from dollars per hour to cents per minute.

CONVERTING RATIOS

A ratio may be changed to an equivalent ratio with different units by applying dimensional analysis. The video in Figure 1.16 shows how dimensional analysis can be used to convert from a pay rate in dollars per hour to a pay rate in cents per minute.

Example 1.24

A student is offered two summer jobs. Job A pays \$500 per week, whereas job B pays \$11.25 per hour. Both jobs are 40 h per week. Which job pays more money?

Solution

In order to compare the two jobs, the pay rates must be in the same units. You can either convert the first job from dollars per week to dollars per hour and then compare it with the second pay rate, or you can convert the second pay rate to dollars per week and compare it with the first. In either case, the conversion factor you will use to convert between hours and work weeks is 1 week = 40 h.

To convert the pay rate of job A to an hourly wage and compare it to job B's hourly wage of \$11.25 per hour, put weeks in the numerator of the conversion factor so that it cancels with weeks in the denominator of the pay rate:

$$\frac{\$500}{\cancel{\text{week}}} \times \frac{1\ \cancel{\text{week}}}{40\text{ h}} = \frac{\$12.50}{1\text{ h}}$$

The wage of job A (\$12.50 per hour) is higher than that of job B (\$11.25 per hour).

Alternatively, to convert job B's pay rate to a weekly rate and compare the result with the rate of \$500 per week of job A, you would use the reciprocal of the conversion factor in order to cancel the hours in the denominator of the pay rate:

$$\frac{\$11.25}{1\ \cancel{\text{h}}} \times \frac{40\ \cancel{\text{h}}}{1\text{ week}} = \frac{\$450}{1\text{ week}}$$

Again, job B's wage (\$450 per week) is lower than job A's (\$500 per week). Both calculations show that the student will earn more money by accepting job A.

PRACTICE PROBLEM 1.24

Jim is paid \$750 per week, whereas Phil earns a yearly salary of \$45,000. Given that there are 52 weeks in a year, which person earns more money in a year?

Hint: Use dimensional analysis to convert one of the salaries to units that match the other salary.

Example 1.25

A cheetah can reach a top speed of 75 mph. Convert 75 mph to units of feet per second. *Hint:* There are 5280 ft in 1 mi.

Solution

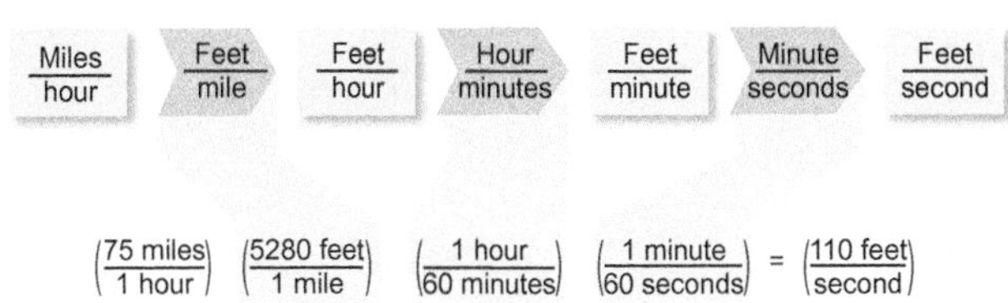

PRACTICE PROBLEM 1.25

The top speed ever recorded for a human runner occurred when Usain Bolt covered a distance of 65.6 ft in 1.61 s during the 100 m dash in 2009. Calculate his top speed in units of miles per hour.

Hint: Begin with the ratio of $\left(\frac{65.6\text{ ft}}{1.61\text{ s}}\right)$ and use the appropriate conversion factors to obtain a result in $\left(\frac{\text{miles}}{\text{hour}}\right)$. There are 5280 ft in 1 mi.

UNITS RAISED TO A POWER

A conversion factor will sometimes have to be raised to a power for the units in the calculation to cancel properly. When a ratio in parentheses is raised to a power, *all the numbers* and *all the units* within the parentheses must be raised to that power.

Example 1.26

Calculate the number of square feet, ft^2, that are in 12.0 square yards, yd^2.

Solution

There are 3 ft in 1 yd. This relationship is squared when multiplied by 12.0 yd^2.

$$12.0\text{ yd}^2\left(\frac{3\text{ ft}}{1\text{ yd}}\right)^2$$

$$12.0\,\cancel{\text{yd}^2}\left(\frac{9\text{ ft}^2}{1\,\cancel{\text{yd}^2}}\right) = 108\text{ ft}^2$$

Square yards → Square of factor → Square feet

Thus, there are 3 ft in 1 yd but 9 ft^2 in 1 yd^2. This is shown graphically below.

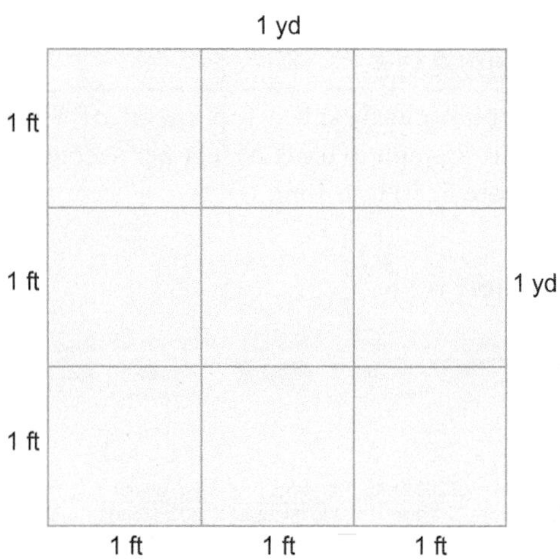

PRACTICE PROBLEM 1.26

How many cubic feet, ft^3, of cement can be held in a cement mixer with a capacity of 7.34 yd^3?

Hint: Use the conversion factor of $\left(\frac{3\text{ ft}}{1\text{ yd}}\right)$. You will need to cube this factor in the calculation: $\left(\frac{3\text{ ft}}{1\text{ yd}}\right)^3$

Example 1.27

Earth's volume is $1.08 \times 10^{12}\text{ km}^3$. What is this volume in units of cubic centimeters?

Solution

According to Table 1.4, there are 10^3 m in 1 km and 10^{-2} m in 1 cm. First, convert cubic kilometers to cubic meters, and then convert cubic meters to cubic centimeters.

$$1.08 \times 10^{12}\text{ km}^3\left(\frac{10^3\text{ m}}{1\text{ km}}\right)^3\left(\frac{1\text{ cm}}{10^{-2}\text{ m}}\right)^3 = 1.08 \times 10^{27}\text{ cm}^3$$

PRACTICE PROBLEM 1.27

Calculate the volume of a 623 L container in cubic meters.

Hint: Begin with $\left(\frac{1\text{ cm}^3}{1\text{ mL}}\right)$, and then convert cubic centimeters to cubic meters. When doing so, you will use the relationship $\left(\frac{1\text{ m}}{100\text{ cm}}\right)$ and cube the entire term.

SECTION REVIEW

- In dimensional analysis, units may be canceled like variables in algebra. Placing the units so that they cancel to give the desired units will help you set up the calculation correctly.
- Some conversion factors are constant, such as the number of cents in a dollar. Others are variable, such as the number of miles traveled by a car per hour, and these must be given in the problem.

1.8 Density

GOALS

- Calculate density, volume, or mass when two of three values are given.
- Identify substances using density.

Background Review

Chapter 0 Math Review: Section 0.4—Algebra

Density is a measure of how much mass something has relative to how much space it takes up (its volume). A golf ball and a ping pong ball are about the same size, but the golf ball is denser because it contains much more mass in the same volume. Objects that are less dense float in fluids that are denser. Oil is less dense than water, and oil and water do not mix, so an oil spill in the ocean spreads out across the surface of the water instead of sinking below the surface. Weather is the result of air masses with different densities interacting with one another. Earthquakes result from the movement of Earth's tectonic plates as the crust floats on the moving mantle beneath. The tectonic plates are less dense than is the mantle.

Density is defined as mass per unit volume:

$$\text{Density} = \frac{\text{Mass}}{\text{Volume}}$$

In symbols,

$$d = \frac{m}{V} \qquad (1.1)$$

The dimensions (combination of units) of density involve a mass unit divided by a volume unit, such as grams per milliliter, g/mL, or grams per cubic centimeter, g/cm^3. Thus, to get the density of an object, simply divide the mass of the object by its volume. Problems involving density usually involve finding one of the variables—d, m, or V—having been given the other two. In problems of this type, density is a conversion factor that allows you to calculate an object's volume when you know its mass, or its mass when you know its volume.

Example 1.28

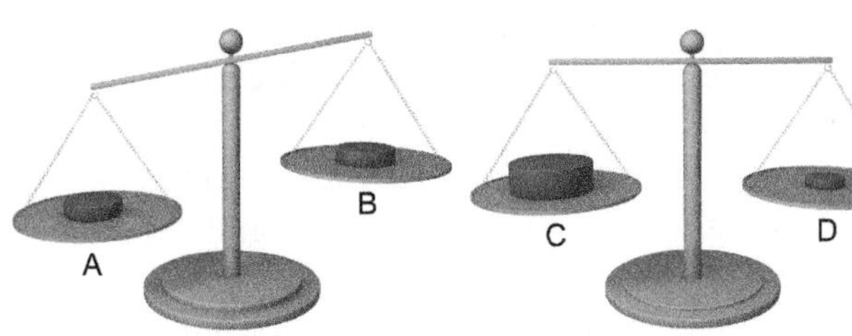

(a) (b)

a. Objects A and B have the same volume, but A has a greater mass. Which is denser?
b. Objects C and D have the same mass, but C is larger. Which is denser?

Solution

a. Object A is denser because it has more mass per unit volume.
b. Object D is denser because it has more mass per unit volume.

PRACTICE PROBLEM 1.28

A piece of lead has a mass of 5.55 g and occupies a volume of 0.491 mL. Calculate the density of lead.

Hint: Density is mass divided by volume.

The video in Figure 1.17 shows how to calculate density, as well as how to find mass from volume or volume from mass using density as a conversion factor.

Density is an intensive physical property (Section 1.2), which means it is independent of the size of the sample. For example, a large piece of aluminum and a small piece of aluminum will have different masses and different volumes, but the ratio of mass to volume for any size piece of aluminum will be the same. This means density can be used to identify substances. For example, gold can be distinguished from iron pyrite by their different densities—19.3 g/mL for gold, but only 5.0 g/mL for iron pyrite. Iron pyrite is known as "fool's gold" because of its striking visual resemblance

Steve Lemon, Macmillan Learning

FIGURE 1.17 Video Tutorial: Density

NOTE: You need to be online to access this video.

This video shows how to calculate density and use density as a conversion factor between mass and volume.

TABLE 1.7 Densities of Some Common Substances at 25°C

Substance	Density (g/mL)
Aluminum	2.70
Copper	8.96
Gold	19.3
Iron	7.87
Lead	11.3
Magnesium	1.74
Mercury	13.53
Platinum	21.5
Silver	10.5
Tin	7.26
Octane	0.7025
Salt (NaCl)	2.165
Sugar (sucrose)	1.56
Water (at 25°C)	0.997
Water (at 4°C)	1.000

to gold. Many prospectors in the western United States in gold-rush days were terribly disappointed when the test in the assay office showed that they had found iron pyrite rather than gold.

Densities of some common substances are listed in Table 1.7.

Example 1.29

Calculate the mass of 41.0 mL of mercury (density = 13.53 g/mL).

Solution

$$41.0\,\cancel{\text{mL}}\left(\frac{13.53\text{ g}}{1\,\cancel{\text{mL}}}\right) = 555\text{ g}$$

Milliliters → Density → Grams

PRACTICE PROBLEM 1.29

Calculate the volume of 12.7 g of mercury (density 13.53 g/mL).

Hint: Use density as the conversion factor and arrange it so that the units of grams cancel.

Relative densities determine whether an object will float in a given liquid in which it does not dissolve. An object will float if its density is less than the density of the liquid. For example, the density of liquid water at 4°C is 1.0 g/mL and that of a particular kind of wood is 0.831 g/mL. The wood will float in the water because it has a lower density.

Example 1.30

Calculate the density of the wood in a certain desk if its mass is 41.6 kg and its volume is 51.3 L. Give your answer in both kilograms per liter and grams per milliliter. Would this desk float in water?

Solution

The density in kilograms per liter is

$$d = \frac{m}{V} = \frac{41.6\text{ kg}}{51.3\text{ L}} = 0.811\text{ kg/L}$$

Now, convert the density to units of grams per milliliter and compare it with the density of water.

$$\left(\frac{0.811\text{ kg}}{1\text{ L}}\right)\left(\frac{1\text{ L}}{1000\text{ mL}}\right)\left(\frac{1000\text{ g}}{1\text{ kg}}\right) = 0.811\text{ g/mL}$$

The density of 0.811 g/mL is less than the density of water (1.0 g/mL), so the desk would float in water.

Note that 0.811 kg/L is equal to 0.811 g/mL.

PRACTICE PROBLEM 1.30

Calculate the density of a rectangular metal bar that is 7.00 cm long, 4.00 cm wide, and 1.00 cm thick and has a mass of 220.0 g. Compare your answer with the densities listed in Table 1.7 and identify the metal.

Hint: Begin by calculating the volume of the metal bar. The answer will be in units of cubic centimeters. Then use the mass of the bar to calculate its density.

In a laboratory setting, the density of a substance can be determined by first measuring the mass and the volume of a sample. Mass is typically measured by placing the sample on a digital balance. If the sample sinks in water, its volume can be measured by the volume of water that it displaces. If the sample has a regular shape (such as a sphere or a cube), its volume can be calculated from its dimensions (such as radius or edge length), which can be measured with a ruler.

Use the density activity (Figure 1.18) to calculate the densities of various substances and identify an unknown substance.

Substances expand or contract when heated or cooled, and the resulting change in volume causes

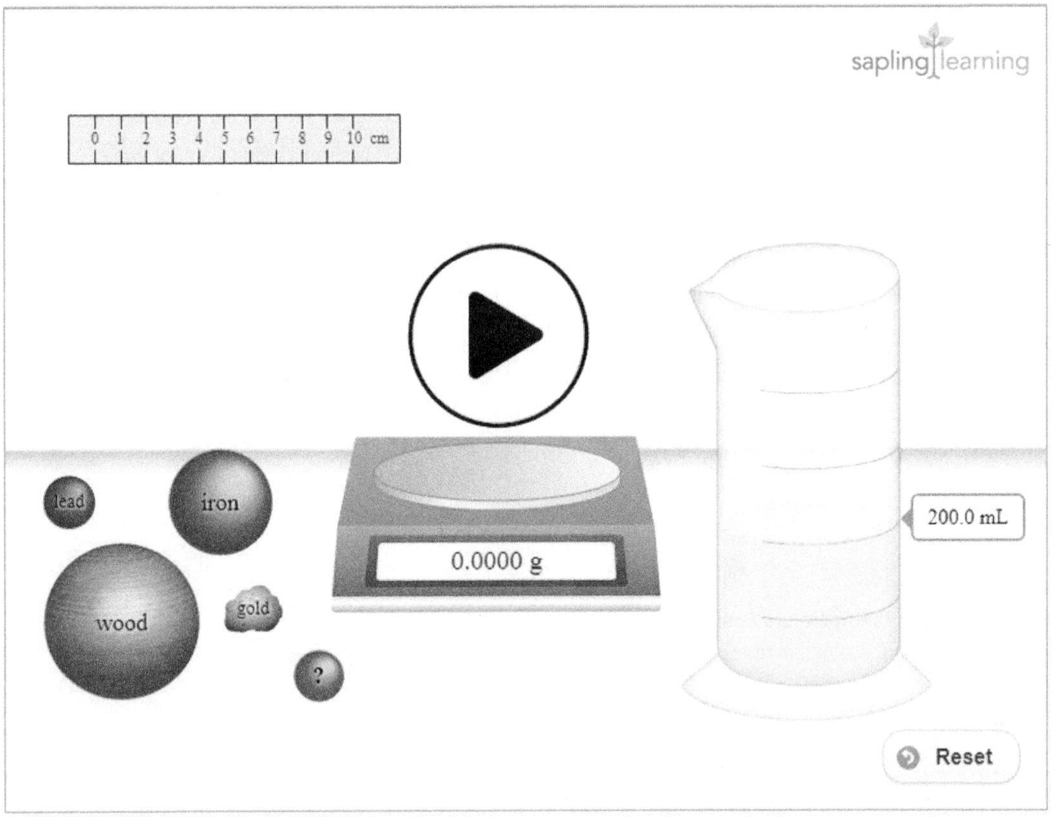

FIGURE 1.18 Density Activity

NOTE: You need to be online to access this activity.

Measure the mass and volume of each sample, and then calculate its density. The mass of a sample is measured by placing it on the balance. The volume of a sample can be measured by the amount of liquid it displaces. Alternatively, for a spherical sample, $V = \frac{4}{3}\pi r^3$. Use Table 1.7 to identify the unknown sample from its density value.

some change in density. However, within reasonable temperature ranges, the density of a substance is relatively constant. For example, water varies from its maximum density of 1.0000 g/mL at 4°C to 0.9584 g/mL at 100°C. Such slight differences are usually ignored, especially since you will work most often with densities measured to only three significant digits.

SECTION REVIEW

- Density is equivalent to mass divided by volume. Mass and volume are measured, and density is calculated.
- Density may be used as a conversion factor, with either mass units or volume units in the numerator, to calculate the mass or volume of a sample.
- Density is an intensive property, so it can be used to identify substances.

1.9 Temperature Scales

GOALS

- Distinguish between the Fahrenheit, Celsius, and Kelvin temperature scales.
- Convert temperature values between scales.

Background Review

Chapter 0 Math Review: Section 0.4—Algebra

Scientists in the United States need to know the three different temperature scales depicted in Figure 1.19—Fahrenheit, Celsius, and Kelvin. On the **Fahrenheit scale**, water freezes at 32°F, and it boils at 212°F.

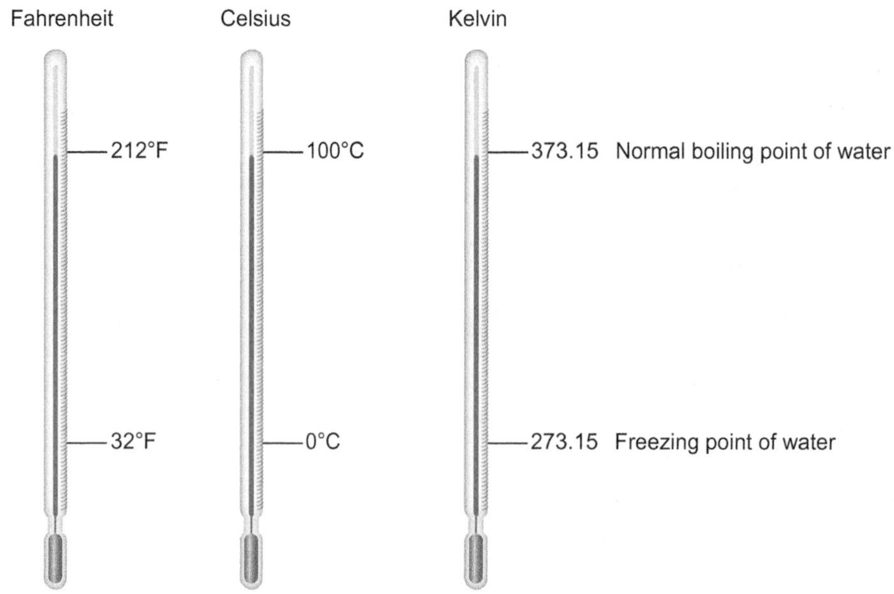

FIGURE 1.19 Comparison of Temperature Scales

On the Fahrenheit temperature scale, the freezing point of water is defined as 32°, and the boiling point is defined as 212°. These same two temperatures are defined as 0° and 100°, respectively, on the Celsius scale, and 273.15 K and 373.15 K, respectively, on the Kelvin scale. Temperature values on the Kelvin scale are equal to the Celsius value plus 273.15. Values on the Kelvin scale have units of kelvins, not *degrees* kelvin.

On the **Celsius scale**, formerly called the centigrade scale, water freezes at 0°C and it boils at 100°C. The **Kelvin scale** is the SI unit for temperature and is used for calculations with gases (Chapter 12) and in other advanced work. On the Kelvin scale, water freezes at 273.15 K, and it boils at 373.15 K. The degree sign (°) is not used with the Kelvin scale, and the units are called kelvins, rather than degrees. The coldest possible temperature is known as absolute zero, which is 0 K (−459.67°F or −273.15°C).

To convert from degrees Fahrenheit (T_F) to degrees Celsius (T_C), or vice versa, use these equations.

$$T_C = \frac{5}{9}(T_F - 32) \qquad (1.2)$$

$$T_F = \frac{9}{5}T_C + 32 \qquad (1.3)$$

The 32°F and 0°C freezing points of water are definitions, not measurements, so they are exact values. That means they do not limit the number of significant digits in temperature conversion calculations. To convert from degrees Celsius to kelvins (T_K or just T), use

$$T_K = T_C + 273.15 \qquad (1.4)$$

Example 1.31

What is 98.6°F (normal body temperature) on the Celsius scale?

Solution

Use the equation that converts T_C to T_F:

$$T_C = \frac{5}{9}(T_F - 32) = \frac{5}{9}(98.6°F - 32) = 37.0°C$$

PRACTICE PROBLEM 1.31

The hottest reliably recorded air temperature on Earth was 134°F at the Death Valley National Park in 1934. What is this temperature on the Kelvin scale?

Hint: First, convert °F to °C, then convert °C to K.

SECTION REVIEW

- T_F denotes a temperature given in degrees Fahrenheit, T_C refers to degrees Celsius, and T_K is a temperature given in kelvins. When units are not specified, assume that T means the Kelvin temperature.

- The following equations make it possible to convert between these three temperature scales:

$$T_C = \frac{5}{9}(T_F - 32)$$

$$T_F = \frac{9}{5}T_C + 32$$

$$T_K = T_C + 273.15$$

Putting It Together

The example problems in earlier sections of this chapter focus on just the new skills acquired in each section of the chapter, but homework and exam questions in chemistry often require more than just one skill at a time. In fact, you will likely be expected to apply knowledge from across the entire chapter, or even multiple chapters in a single problem. This final example and problem are meant to help you prepare for these types of multiconcept questions. Additional examples can be found in the end-of-chapter exercises.

Example 1.32

One hundred grams of pure solid substance X was heated for 1 h. Afterward, 56 g of a new solid Y was present, and 44 g of colorless gas Z was produced. None of substance X remained after heating.

a. Is the original solid an element or a compound?
b. Does the heating of the solid substance to produce less solid material and a gas describe a physical or chemical change in the original substance?
c. The solid material present after the original substance was heated is light gray in color. Is the gray color a physical or chemical property of the material?

Solution

a. The solid substance lost mass when it was heated, which means that it was transformed into two substances of lower mass. Therefore, the solid substance must be a compound.
b. The process of heating a solid substance to generate a gas and a new solid material describes a chemical change. This result describes a chemical property of substance X, where substance X can chemically react with another substance. In contrast, the physical properties of a substance are demonstrated *without* changing the composition of the substance.
c. The gray color of the solid material left at the end of the chemical reaction is a physical property of that material. Physical properties can be identified (visually, in this case) without changing the chemical composition of the substance of interest.

PRACTICE PROBLEM 1.32

The world's oceans have a combined volume of 1.335 billion km^3 (1.335×10^9 km^3). Answer the following questions and be sure to include the correct number of significant digits in your answers.

a. What is the volume of the world's oceans in units of liters? Recall that 1 mL = 1 cm^3.
b. The Atlantic Ocean has a volume of 3.1×10^8 km^3, and the Pacific Ocean has a volume of 6.6×10^8 km^3. What is the volume of the rest of the world's oceans in units of cubic kilometers?
c. If the average density of ocean water is 1.027 kg/m^3, what is the mass of the Pacific Ocean in units of kilograms?
d. The world's oceans have an average depth of 3688 m. What is this depth in units of miles and units of inches? See Table 1.6 for the relevant conversion factors.

Hint: For part (a), convert cubic kilometers to cubic meters and then cubic meters to cubic centimeters. Use the relationship between cubic centimeters and milliliters to convert the volume to liters. In part (b), recall that the significant figures rules for addition/subtraction are different from those for multiplication/division. In part (c), recall the definition of density and its use for converting volume to mass. There are multiple ways to solve part (d). The relationship between a mile and kilometer would be a good place to start.

Key Terms, Symbols, and Equations

KEY TERMS

accuracy (1.6): The closeness of a measurement or set of measurements to the correct or known value.

aqueous solution (1.1): A solution in water.

area (1.5): The amount of space occupied by a two-dimensional object.

atom (1.1): A single particle of any element—the smallest possible amount of an element that retains the properties of that element.

base units (1.5): The fundamental SI quantities (i.e., length, mass, time, electric current, temperature, amount of substance, and luminous intensity) that can be combined to describe every other quantity.

Celsius scale (1.9): The temperature scale in which the freezing point of water is defined as 0°C and the normal boiling point of water is defined as 100°C; formerly the centigrade scale.

chemical bond (1.1): An attraction between any two atoms that holds them together.

chemical change (1.2): A chemical reaction. The products of a chemical change are different materials than the reactants.

chemical property (1.2): A property having to do with possible changes in the composition of a substance.

chemistry (1.1): The study of the interaction of matter and energy and the changes that matter undergoes.

compound (1.1): A chemical combination of elements that has a definite composition and its own set of properties.

conversion factor (1.7): A ratio equal to 1 that can be multiplied by a quantity to change the form of the quantity without changing its value.

definite composition (1.1): The given ratio by mass of each element in a compound to any other element in the compound.

density, *d* (1.8): The mass per unit volume of a sample of matter.

derived units (1.5): The product or powers of one or more base units.

dissolve (1.2): To go into solution, thus making a homogeneous mixture.

dimensional analysis (1.7): A system that involves the use of units to indicate the proper arithmetic operation to perform; also called unit analysis or the factor label method.

element (1.1): A substance that cannot be broken down into simpler substances by chemical means; one of the basic building blocks of which all matter is composed.

energy (1.3): The capacity to do work.

extensive property (1.2): A characteristic that depends on the quantity of the sample.

Fahrenheit scale (1.9): A temperature scale in which the freezing point of water is defined as 32°F and the normal boiling point of water is defined as 212°F.

gram, g (1.5): The primary unit of mass in the metric system; one-thousandth of the kilogram, the SI standard unit of mass.

heterogeneous mixture (1.1): A physical combination of substances that is not uniform throughout, so different samples taken from the same mixture might have different compositions from one another.

homogeneous mixture (1.1): A physical combination of substances that is uniform throughout, so different samples taken from the same mixture always have identical compositions; a solution.

hypothesis (1.4): A proposed explanation for a body of observed facts.

intensive property (1.2): A characteristic, such as color, that does *not* depend on the quantity of material present.

International System of Units, SI (1.5): Système International d'Unités; the modern form of the metric system.

Kelvin scale (1.9): The temperature scale with 273.15 K as the freezing point of water and 373.15 K as the normal boiling point of water; the scale required for gas law and many other scientific calculations.

kilogram, kg (1.5): 1000 g; the standard SI unit of mass.

law of conservation of energy (1.3): Energy can be neither created nor destroyed in any chemical or physical process.

law of conservation of mass (1.4): The amount of mass present at the end of a chemical or physical change is equal to the amount of mass present before the change.

malleable (1.2): Capable of being pounded into various shapes.

mass, *m* (1.3): A measure of how much matter is in a sample. When a mass is acted on by an attracting force like gravity, the downward force exerted by the mass is measured as weight.

matter (1.1): Anything that has mass and occupies space.

meter, m (1.5): The primary unit of length in the metric system and SI.

mixture (1.1): A physical combination of substances that has a nondefinite composition and properties characteristic of its components.

physical change (1.2): A process in which no change in chemical composition occurs.

physical property (1.2): Property unrelated to possible changes in the chemical composition of a substance.

product (1.2): The substance or substances that result from a chemical or physical change.

property (1.2): A characteristic of a substance.

pure substance (1.1): A substance in which all of the particles that make up that substance are of exactly the same kind. Elements and compounds are pure substances, but mixtures are not.

precision (1.6): The degree to which measurements are reproducible.

qualitative (1.6): Without a numeric measurement of any kind. A qualitative description might include things like color and shape, or subjective terms like *heavy* or *tall* that do not involve making a numeric measurement.

quantitative (1.6): Based on a numerical measurement of some kind.

reactant (1.2): The starting material that undergoes a change in a physical or chemical change.

rounding (1.6): Reducing the number of digits in a calculated result to the proper number of significant digits.

scientific law (1.4): A scientific observation that is always seen to be that way, with no exceptions.

scientific method (1.4): A process that combines observation, hypothesis, and experimentation.

significant digit (1.6): Any digit that reflects the precision with which a measurement was made.

significant figure (1.6): A significant digit.

soluble (1.2): Able to be dissolved.

solution (1.1): A homogenous mixture.

theory (1.4): An explanation that has been thoroughly tested and widely accepted.

unit (1.7): A standard division of measure having a certain value; for example, the meter is the SI base unit of length.

volume, *V* (1.5): The extent of space occupied by a sample of matter.

SYMBOLS AND ABBREVIATIONS

c (centi-) (1.5)
d (density) (1.8)
g (gram) (1.5)
k (kilo-) (1.5)
h (hour) (1.7)
L (liter) (1.5)
m (mass) (1.8)
m (meter) (1.5)
m (milli-) (1.5)
min (minute) (1.7)
s (second) (1.5)
T_C (Celsius temperature) (1.9)
T_K or T (Kelvin temperature) (1.9)
T_F (Fahrenheit temperature) (1.9)
V (volume) (1.5)

EQUATIONS

$$d = \frac{m}{V} \quad (1.1)$$

$$T_C = \frac{5}{9}(T_F - 32) \quad (1.2)$$

$$T_F = \frac{9}{5}T_C + 32 \quad (1.3)$$

$$T_K = T_C + 273.15 \quad (1.4)$$

Chapter Summary

Matter includes everything in the universe that has mass and takes up space. Matter can be divided into pure substances and mixtures. Pure substances are elements or compounds. Elements are the fundamental building blocks of matter and cannot be broken down into simpler substances with the same properties by chemical or physical means. Compounds are chemical combinations of elements; they have their own sets of properties different from the elements and have definite compositions. A physical combination of substances results in a mixture whose components retain most of their original properties. Mixtures do not have definite compositions and may be either heterogeneous or homogeneous. Homogeneous mixtures, called solutions, look alike throughout; some parts of a heterogeneous mixture can be seen to be different from other parts (Section 1.1).

Properties are the characteristics used to identify samples of matter. Physical properties, such as color, mass, or freezing point, are characteristics that do not involve changing the substance into a different substance. Physical properties can be further divided into intensive properties and extensive properties. Intensive properties, such as color and brittleness, do not depend on the size of the sample, whereas extensive properties, such as mass and volume, do. Intensive properties are more useful for identifying substances because they do not change as the size of the sample changes. Chemical properties always refer to a chemical change that a substance is able to undergo, such as flammability, which changes the substance into a different substance (Section 1.2).

In physical changes, the chemical composition of the products is the same as that of the reactants. In chemical changes, such as when a lump of charcoal burns or a piece of iron rusts, the chemical composition of the materials does change, and the products with which you end up have a different chemical composition from the reactants with which you started. You can determine whether a combination of substances is a mixture or a compound by its properties. Whether combining substances to create something new or breaking down a sample into its components, the total mass of all the components before the change is equal to the total mass of all the components. This is the law of conservation of mass (Section 1.2).

Chemistry is the study of the interaction of matter and energy and the changes that matter undergoes. Mass is a measure of the quantity of matter in a sample. The mass of an object does not change with its position in the universe. On the surface of Earth, mass is directly proportional to weight, and the mass of an object is determined by "weighing" it. Energy is the ability to do work and comes in many forms. Energy cannot be created or destroyed, but it can be converted from one form to another. This is the law of conservation of energy (Section 1.3).

A statement that summarizes observations that are always seen to be true and enables scientists to predict what will happen in a certain type of situation is called a law. For example, the law of gravity enables you to predict that if you drop something, it will fall downward. This law resulted from innumerable observations. An explanation that is proposed to explain why an observation or law works is called a hypothesis. If the explanation is supported through repeated experimentation and is not contradicted by any known evidence, it becomes accepted by the scientific community and is known as a theory (Section 1.4).

The International System of Units, SI, is an internationally recognized units system based on the meter, kilogram, and second. Units from this system are collectively called SI units. The SI is the modern form of the metric system. SI units can be used to describe many different kinds of quantities. Some of these quantities, known as SI base units, can be described in terms of a single unit such as length of time. Others, such as area or density, must be described in terms of compound units known as SI derived units. SI prefixes use multiples of units that are equal to powers of 10, and they also use the same prefixes to mean certain fractions or multiples, no matter what primary unit is being modified. For example, the prefixes *centi-* (0.01), *milli-* (0.001), and *kilo-* (1000) can be used with any SI unit (Section 1.5).

The number of digits reported for a measurement or for the result of a calculation involving measurements is a way to show how precisely the measurements were made. The last digit of reported measurements is usually an estimate based on tenths of the smallest scale division of the measuring instrument. Any digit from 1 through 9 in a properly reported result is significant. The word *significant* as used here refers to the precision of the measurement and does not mean "important." Zeros may or may not be significant; if they merely show the magnitude of the number, they are not significant.

When measurements are added or subtracted, the measurement that has the fewest significant digits to the right of the decimal point is the one that limits the number of significant digits in the answer. When measurements are multiplied or divided, the measurement with the fewest significant digits overall limits the number of significant digits in the answer. If too many digits are present in a calculated answer, the answer must be rounded off. While a calculator gives the correct magnitude when used properly, you must understand the calculation processes to be able to determine the number of significant figures to report. All digits in the coefficients of numbers in scientific notation are significant (Section 1.6).

The results of every measurement must include both a numeric value and a unit or set of units. Dimensional analysis is used to convert a quantity from one set of units to another without changing its value. The original quantity is multiplied by a factor equal to 1. The numerator and denominator of the factor have equal value but different units. To use dimensional analysis: (1) write down the quantity given, including the units; (2) multiply by a factor that will yield the desired units; (3) cancel the units; and (4) multiply all numbers in the numerator and divide by all numbers in the denominator. When a problem requires you to multiply by more than one factor, you can solve for the intermediate answers after each multiplication operation or just carry out all of the mathematical operations and record the final result (Section 1.7).

Density, an intensive property, is defined as mass per unit volume. It can be calculated by dividing the mass of a sample by its volume:

$$d = \frac{m}{V}$$

If a density is given, you can use it as a conversion factor to solve for the substance's mass or volume. Density may be used to help identify a substance. Samples of lower density float in fluids of higher density (Section 1.8).

The Fahrenheit (T_F) and Celsius (T_C) temperature scales are related to one another as follows:

$$T_C = \frac{5}{9}(T_F - 32°)$$

$$T_F = \frac{9}{5}T_C + 32°$$

The relationship between the Celsius (T_C) and Kelvin (T_K) temperature scales is

$$T_K = T_C + 273.15$$

(Section 1.9)

END OF CHAPTER QUESTIONS

1.1 Classification of Matter

1. Which of the following are pure substances?
   a. elements
   b. compounds
   c. homogeneous mixtures
   d. heterogeneous mixtures

2. Classify each of the following as a compound or a mixture. If it is impossible to tell, explain why.
   a. a solid combination of iron and oxygen, no part of which is attracted to a magnet
   b. a material containing 88.8% oxygen and 11.2% hydrogen
   c. a material that is explosive and that contains 88.8% oxygen and 11.2% hydrogen
   d. a material that consists of blue particles and red particles
   e. a material containing only hydrogen and oxygen that is a gas under ordinary room conditions

3. Classify each of the following as a compound or a mixture.
   a. bubbling carbonated water
   b. salt water
   c. iced tea
   d. the liquid formed by a certain combination of hydrogen and oxygen gases

4. Bromine melts at −7.2°C and sodium melts at 97.81°C. A certain combination of the two melts at 747°C. Is the combination a mixture or a compound?

5. Classify each of the following as an element, a compound, or a mixture.
   a. solid iodine (a dark violet solid)
   b. a homogeneous combination of sodium and iodine that is a white solid
   c. a homogeneous combination of iodine and alcohol (tincture of iodine), which retains a dark color and the liquid state of the alcohol

6. If three dozen donuts costs $15.00 and 10 dozen donuts costs $50.00, is the price of donuts intensive or extensive?

7. Classify the following materials as homogeneous or heterogeneous.
   a. white paint
   b. milk
   c. household ammonia (ammonia gas dissolved in water)
   d. a glass of pure water holding an ice cube (also pure water)
   e. a teaspoon of sugar in a glass of warm water after having been stirred thoroughly
   f. a cola drink with no bubbles
   g. a cola drink with bubbles

8. Electricity is passed through 14.40 g of a pure substance, and 5.66 g of one material and 8.74 g of another material are produced. Is the original substance an element or a compound?

9. Elemental nitrogen and hydrogen are both odorless.
   a. What is the odor of a mixture of the two gases?
   b. Explain why ammonia, a compound of nitrogen and hydrogen only, smells so strongly.

10. When pure water is cooled below 0°C (32°F), it freezes. When the solid is warmed above that temperature, it melts again. Its composition does not change during the entire process. Are these physical changes or chemical changes?

11. When gaseous ethylene is treated with a small quantity of a certain other substance, it solidifies. It is difficult to cause the resulting solid to re-form a gas. Is the solidification a chemical or a physical change?

12. What kind of change—chemical or physical—accompanies each of the following?
    a. the conversion of two elements to a compound
    b. the conversion of two compounds into a solution
    c. the combinations of an element and a compound into another compound
    d. the conversion of a compound to an element and another compound
    e. the separation of a mixture into its components

13. In a certain experiment, two separate samples of matter are mixed and a great deal of heat is generated. Is this more likely to be a chemical or a physical change?

1.2 Properties of Matter

14. Which of the following properties are intensive and which are extensive?
    a. length
    b. color

c. price per unit
d. total cost

15. Which of the following properties are intensive and which are extensive?
a. volume
b. mass
c. boiling point
d. speed

16. Classify each of the following as a chemical change or a physical change.
a. melting ice by spreading salt on an icy sidewalk
b. striking a match
c. breaking a piece of metal by bending it back and forth
d. baking a cake

17. Classify each of the following as a chemical change or a physical change.
a. rubbing your hands together to get them warm
b. cooking a hamburger
c. boiling water

18. When some salt is added to water, a solution is formed. State several ways in which you can tell that the combination is a solution rather than a new compound.

19. List four properties you could use to distinguish between iron and aluminum. State which of them are chemical properties.

20. List four properties you could use to distinguish between water and gasoline. State which of them are chemical properties.

21. A sample of a liquid is homogeneous. When it is cooled to 7°C, part of the liquid solidifies. The solid part is removed, and the liquid part is cooled further, but no other change takes place. Is the original liquid a compound or a solution?

22. A sample of a solid substance is heated under a stream of hydrogen gas, and the solid that remains after the treatment has a mass 63% of that of the original substance. Further treatment with hydrogen causes no further change. Is the original substance an element or a compound?

23. In the iron-sulfur experiment described in section 1.2, heat was used to start a chemical reaction, which gave off more heat. Give another example of a reaction that is started by heating and then gives off more heat.

24. When dinitrogen tetroxide, a colorless liquid, is warmed, a brown gas is formed. Is this change a physical change or a chemical change?

1.3 Matter and Energy

25. List as many types of energy as you can think of.

26. What is the mass of a 101 kg astronaut on the surface of the Moon, where gravity is 17% of that on Earth?

27. For a given quantity of energy, the electricity produced by a battery is much more expensive than that provided by the electric company. Why do we still use batteries?

28. Explain the advantages and disadvantages of house current versus batteries for use in a home smoke detector.

29. What is wrong with the following statement and how might you correct it? "Energy is created when coal is burned."

30. What two changes of energy occur when you turn on a flashlight?

31. Name a device commonly found on a car that changes
a. chemical energy to electrical energy.
b. electrical energy to sound.
c. mechanical energy to heat.
d. electrical energy to chemical energy.
e. chemical energy to mechanical energy.
f. electrical energy to mechanical energy.
g. electrical energy to heat.

32. Name one common device, not on a car, that performs each of the following conversions.
a. electrical energy to light
b. electrical energy to sound
c. chemical energy to heat
d. chemical energy to mechanical energy

1.4 The Scientific Method, Hypotheses, Theories, and Laws

33. Would an accepted generalization that explains why active metals react with acids be referred to as a law, a hypothesis, or a theory?

34. Suppose you are a consultant to the National Science Foundation, an agency with the U.S.

government. In a proposal for a \$10 million grant, a claim is made that a method will be developed to make 20 ounces of gold from 10 ounces of gold and no other ingredients. Would you recommend that government money be spent on this proposed research? Explain your reasoning.

35. Suppose you are a consultant to the National Science Foundation. In a proposal for a \$100 million grant, a claim is made that a method will be developed to make a machine that produces twice as much energy as it uses up, with no permanent changes in matter. Would you recommend that government money be spent on this proposed research? Explain your reasoning.

36. Many people use the steps in the scientific method in their everyday lives. For example, Rob is unable to start his car and tries to identify the problem by following the steps below. Identify each statement as indicating a hypothesis, an experiment, or an observation.
   a. When the key is placed in the car ignition and turned, nothing happens.
   b. The battery is dead.
   c. Recharge the battery in the car.
   d. After recharging the battery, the car still does not start.
   e. The original battery no longer holds a charge.
   f. Replace the battery with a new one.
   g. The car starts with a new battery.
   h. My experimental results indicate the original battery was unable to hold a charge.

37. Karen's toaster won't work and she identifies the issue by following the steps below. Identify each statement as indicating a hypothesis, an experiment, or an observation.
   a. A toaster does not work when plugged in.
   b. The toaster is broken.
   c. The electric outlet has malfunctioned.
   d. The toaster does not work when plugged into a different outlet.
   e. The toaster works in any outlet when the cord is held a certain way.
   f. The toaster cord needs to be repaired.

1.5 The International System of Units

38. Calculate the following.
   a. How many milligrams are in 6.21 g?
   b. How many centimeters are in 6.21 m?
   c. How many kilograms are in 6.21 g?

39. How many milligrams are in 12.1 kg?

40. Convert
   a. 6.96 m to millimeters.
   b. 6.96 L to milliliters.
   c. 6.96 g to milligrams.
   d. 6.96 watts to milliwatts.

41. Convert
   a. 21.3 m to centimeters.
   b. 21.3 m to millimeters.
   c. 21.3 m to kilometers.

42. Calculate the number of
   a. millimeters in 6.03 m.
   b. milliliters in 6.03 L.
   c. milligrams in 6.03 g.

43. Calculate the number of
   a. feet in 6.03 miles.
   b. short tons (2000 lb per ton) in 6.03 lb.
   c. fluid ounces in 6.03 gal.

44. Express the following measurements as a decimal value.
   a. 7.00×10^{-3} L
   b. 7.0×10^{-3} L
   c. 7×10^{-3} L

45. Calculate the number of cubic centimeters in a rectangular box that is 0.0722 m by 3.39 cm by 7.013 mm.

46. Calculate the length of each edge of a cube that has a volume of 2.57 cm^3.

47. The edge of a cube is 3.000×10^{-1} cm. What is the volume of the cube in cubic meters?

48. Which of the following is the smallest container that would hold 1 m^3 of liquid?
   a. swimming pool
   b. drinking glass
   c. soda bottle
   d. thimble

49. Convert
   a. 1.09×10^{-4} kg to milligrams.
   b. 6.03×10^{-4} m^3 to milliliters and express the answer in scientific notation.

50. Calculate the number of liters in
   a. 0.0117 m^3.
   b. 808 m^3.
   c. 290.2 mL.
   d. 1.43×10^3 mm^3.

51. How many liters are in 6.11×10^{-2} m^3?

52. How many cubic millimeters are in 0.117 mL?

53. What is the volume of a rectangular solid that is 0.0622 m wide, 7.15 cm long, and 0.0000560 km thick?

54. Calculate the number of liters in 7.05×10^{-2} m^3.

55. Convert each of the following numbers to centimeters, and express the answer in scientific notation.
   a. 6133 mm
   b. 1.733 m
   c. 20.2 km
   d. 6.191×10^4 mm

56. Change 3.50×10^4 cm to
   a. meters.
   b. millimeters.
   c. kilometers.

1.6 Significant Digits

57. Underline the significant digits in each of the following measurements. If any digit is uncertain, place a question mark below it.
   a. 67.00 km
   b. 0.0013 kg
   c. 690 m
   d. 209 L

58. Underline the significant digits in each of the following measurements. If any digit is uncertain, place a question mark below it.
   a. 5.0×10^2 cm
   b. 5.02×10^2 cm
   c. 7.00×10^2 cm
   d. 5.000×10^{-2} m

59. Convert each of the following values to decimal notation.
   a. 6.000×10^3 cm
   b. 6.00×10^3 cm
   c. 6.0×10^3 cm
   d. 6×10^3 cm

60. Express the following volumes in milliliters.
   a. 8.00×10^{-3} L
   b. 8.0×10^{-3} L
   c. 8×10^{-3} L

61. Express each of the following measurements in liters.
   a. 3.00×10^3 mL
   b. 3.0×10^3 mL
   c. 3×10^3 mL

62. Underline the significant digits in each of the following measurements. If any digit is uncertain, place a question mark below it.
   a. 1.000 mm
   b. 0.0040 cm
   c. 4000 m
   d. 40.00 km

63. Round each of the following measurements to three significant digits.
   a. 0.0637425 cm
   b. 0.637425 cm
   c. 6.37425 cm
   d. 63.7425 cm
   e. 6374.25 cm

64. Round each of the following measurements to three significant digits.
   a. 0.02316 cm
   b. 0.2316 cm
   c. 23.16 cm
   d. 2316 cm

65. Perform the following calculations and report your answer with the proper number of significant digits.
   a. 6.17 cm $\times$ 3.722 cm
   b. 3.09 cm $-$ 122.7 cm
   c. 7.07 g/1.81 mL

66. Express each of the following lengths in centimeters with the proper number of significant digits.
   a. 4×10^{-3} m
   b. 4.0×10^{-3} m
   c. 4.00×10^{-3} m
   d. 4.000×10^{-3} m

67. Convert each of the following distances to meters and express the results in standard numbers, not scientific notation.
   a. 1.00×10^5 mm
   b. 1.00×10^5 cm
   c. 1.00×10^{-3} km

68. How many significant digits are present in each of the following measurements? How many decimal place digits?
   a. 127.900 kg
   b. 12.88 cm^3
   c. 0.3930 mL
   d. 2.002 m

69. Underline the significant digits in each of the following measurements. If any digit is uncertain, place a question mark below it.
    a. 1.630 cm
    b. 8.090 cm
    c. 0.022 cm
    d. 4000 cm

70. Underline the significant digits in each of the following measurements. If any digit is uncertain, place a question mark below it.
    a. 41.07 km
    b. 6050 cm
    c. 400.0 mm
    d. 0.00120 m
    e. 220 mm

71. How many significant digits are present in each of the following measurements? How many decimal place digits?
    a. 0.020 kg
    b. 33.0 mL
    c. 403 mL
    d. 1.0 mm

72. Perform the following calculations and report your answer with the proper number of significant digits.
    a. 219 g + 17.39 g
    b. 6.11 mL + 0.012 mL
    c. 1.102 mL + 0.013 mL
    d. 42.7 mm + 61.4 mm

73. Round off each measurement to three significant digits.
    a. 110.9 mL
    b. 1109 mL
    c. Are the answers the same? Explain.

74. Express each measurement as a decimal value. State how many significant digits are in each answer.
    a. 9.00×10^3 mL
    b. 9.0×10^3 mL
    c. 9×10^3 mL

75. Perform the following calculations and report your answer with the proper number of significant digits.
    a. $(3.08 \times 10^3 \text{ g})/(6.912 \text{ m}^3)$
    b. $(9.39 \text{ cm}^2)/(3.13 \times 10^{-1} \text{ cm})$
    c. $(6.93 \times 10^3 \text{ cm}^3)/(30 \text{ cm})$
    d. $(6.66 \times 10^4 \text{ g})/(2.22 \times 10^1 \text{ cm})^3$

76. Perform the following calculations and report your answer with the proper number of significant digits.
    a. $5.10 \text{ cm} \times (1.40 \times 10^2 \text{ cm})$
    b. $0.0115 \text{ cm} \times (9.2 \times 10^{-2} \text{ cm})$
    c. $(2.505 \times 10^{-2} \text{ mm})(40.00 \text{ mm})$
    d. $(1.03 \times 10^3 \text{ m})(6.88 \times 10^2 \text{ m})$

77. Perform the following calculations and report your answer with the proper number of significant digits.
    a. $(3.00 \times 10^{-3} \text{ g}) + (7.0 \times 10^1 \text{ mg})$
    b. $(4.00 \times 10^{-1} \text{ g}) + (8.88 \times 10^{-4} \text{ kg})$

78. Solve the problem and report your answer with the proper number of significant digits.
    $(101.1 \text{ g} - 98.31 \text{ g})/(38.92 \text{ mL} - 1.97 \text{ mL})$

79. Perform the following calculations and report your answer with the proper number of significant digits.
    a. $(7.11 \times 10^3 \text{ mm})(23.7 \text{ mm})$
    b. $(9.02 \times 10^{-6} \text{ m})(4.9 \times 10^{-3} \text{ mm})$
    c. $(6.13 \text{ kg})/(6.8 \times 10^3 \text{ mL})$
    d. $(1.627 \text{ g})/(0.1122 \text{ L})$
    e. $(2.004 \times 10^4 \text{ mm})(6.98 \times 10^4 \text{ cm})$
    f. $(22.3 \text{ g}) + (1.0 \times 10^{-4} \text{ g})$

80. Perform the following calculations and report your answer with the proper number of significant digits.
    a. $(4.66 \times 10^2 \text{ mm}^2)/(23.3 \text{ mm})$
    b. $(3.18 \times 10^{-5} \text{ m}^3)/(6.929 \times 10^{-3} \text{ m})$
    c. $(215 \text{ g})/(3.5 \times 10^2 \text{ mL})$
    d. $(19.55 \text{ g})/(21.21 \text{ mL})$
    e. $(6.172 \times 10^5 \text{ m}^2)(7.17 \times 10^2 \text{ m})$
    f. $(6.33 \text{ g}) + (12.3 \times 10^{-2} \text{ g})$

81. Perform the following calculations and report your answer with the proper number of significant digits.
    a. $(8.14 \times 10^3 \text{ cm})^3$
    b. $3.38 \times 10^{-3} \text{ g} - 1.902 \times 10^{-1} \text{ g}$
    c. $1.173 \times 10^6\ \mu\text{m} - 9.09 \times 10^4\ \mu\text{m}$

82. Perform the following calculations and report your answer with the proper number of significant digits.
    a. $1.72 \text{ kg} + (3.44 \times 10^2 \text{ g})$
    b. $0.0115 \text{ kg} + (6.96 \times 10^{-1} \text{ g})$
    c. $9.42 \text{ mg} + (3.72 \times 10^{-3} \text{ g})$
    d. $(9.00 \times 10^4 \text{ mm}^2) + (1.14 \times 10^4 \text{ m})^2$

1.7 Dimensional Analysis

83. Calculate the number of minutes in 5.150 h.

84. Assume that donuts are \$5.00 per dozen.
   a. How much do 2.50 dozen donuts cost?
   b. How many dozen donuts can you buy with \$32.50?
   c. How many donuts can you buy with \$32.50?

85. Determine the cost of 540 pencils if the price is \$1.15 per dozen.

86. Calculate the pay earned by a student who worked 18 h per week for 32 weeks at \$9.00 per hour.

87. Calculate the pay received for 1.00 h of work by a junior executive who works 40 h per week and earns \$48,250 per year for 50 weeks of work.

88. There is 60.0% oxygen by mass in a certain compound of sulfur and oxygen. Percent by mass is a ratio of the number of grams of a particular component to 100 g of the total sample. How many grams of sulfur are in a 14.6 g sample of the compound?

89. Calculate the number of hours in 8676 seconds.

90. Calculate the cost of a carpet required to cover a living room floor that is 15.3 ft wide and 18.3 ft long if the price is \$29.00 yd^2.

1.8 Density

91. What quantity is obtained in each of the following cases?
   a. Density is multiplied by volume.
   b. Mass is divided by density.
   c. Mass is divided by volume.

92. Calculate the volume of lead (density = 11.3 g/mL) having a mass of 4.145 kg.

93. Calculate the mass of water that occupies 9.10 L.

94. Calculate the density of an object that has a volume of 7.05 L and a mass of 52.6 kg.

95. Calculate the volume of a rectangular box with the dimensions 42.6 cm by 4.41 cm by 1.932 cm. Then calculate the number of kilograms of mercury (density = 13.63 g/mL) that can fit into that box.

96. Using the data from Table 1.7, give one reason why magnesium might be preferable to steel (mostly iron) for building airplanes. What other metal might be useful for building airplanes?

97. Which of the metals in Table 1.7 has a mass of 225 g in a volume of 50.02 mL?

98. Calculate the number of milliliters of mercury having a mass of 1.213 kg.

99. Does lead (d = 11.3 g/mL) float in mercury (d = 13.53 g/mL)? Explain.

100. Explain why gasoline floats on water. Is water useful for putting out gasoline fires?

101. Calculate the volume in milliliters of an object with a density of 4.15 g/mL and a mass of 673 g.

102. Express the density 11.7 kg/L in grams per milliliter.

103. Convert the density 2.05×10^3 kg/m^3 to grams per milliliter.

104. Calculate the number of kilograms of mercury occupying 747 mL.

105. Calculate the density in grams per milliliter of an object that has a volume of 7.81 mL and a mass of 44.9 g.

1.9 Temperature Scales

106. Calculate the temperature in degrees Celsius of each of the temperatures.
   a. 212°F
   b. 32.0°F
   c. 60°F
   d. 98.6°F
   e. 0°F
   f. −40.0°F
   g. 35.0°F

107. Calculate the temperature in degrees Fahrenheit of each of the temperatures.
   a. 0°C
   b. 100°C
   c. 27.0°C
   d. 50.0°C
   e. −15°C
   f. 75°C
   g. −273°C

108. Calculate the temperature in kelvins of each of the following.
   a. 25°C
   b. 19.2°C
   c. −273°C
   d. 42°C
   e. 100°C

109. Calculate the temperature in degrees Celsius of each of the following.
  a. 295 K
  b. 373 K
  c. 273 K
  d. 0 K

Putting It Together

110. Properties that are ratios of two units are generally intensive. Explain why.

111. Is it possible to predict the color of the following substances? Explain your answers.
  a. a solution made by dissolving a blue substance in a yellow substance
  b. a compound made from the chemical reaction of a blue substance with a yellow substance

112. Typical density units for solid materials are given as g/cm^3, for liquids are given as g/mL, and for gases are given as g/L. Use the properties of the different states of matter to explain why these different density units are appropriate.

113. A shiny, silvery solid is heated in a flame, resulting in a very bright white light and a grayish powder. Careful measurements show that the mass of the grayish powder is 1.7 times greater than the mass of the silvery solid.
  a. Is it possible to identify the reactant as an element or a compound? Explain.
  b. Is it possible to identify the product as an element or a compound? Explain.
  c. What form of energy was released during the reaction?

114. A white solid is heated to form another white solid with a loss of almost 40% of the mass.
  a. Is it possible to identify the reactant as an element or a compound? Explain.
  b. Is it possible to identify the product as an element or a compound? Explain.
  c. What form of energy was involved in this reaction? Was it absorbed or released?

115. In January 2014, a massive rockfall in New Zealand reduced the height of Aoraki, or Mt. Cook, from the previously measured 12,316 feet to 12,218 feet.
  a. Determine the difference, in meters, of the height of Mt. Cook before and after the rockfall.
  b. Determine the percent of height lost by Mt. Cook due to the rockfall.

PRACTICE PROBLEM SOLUTIONS

Practice Problem 1.1 Solution

By definition, the elements and compounds in Figure 1.1 are pure substances.

Practice Problem 1.2 Solution

a. Mud is heterogeneous. After mud settles over time into dirt and water, its nonuniform composition is revealed.

b. Before the bottle is opened, you cannot see the bubbles, which suggests a homogeneous mixture.

c. Immediately after opening the bottle, the gas bubbles can be seen within the liquid, which suggests a heterogeneous mixture.

Practice Problem 1.3 Solution

The mixture is homogeneous because it is uniform in composition.

Practice Problem 1.4 Solution

a. True, although the elements may be combined into compounds.

b. False: Some mixtures, such as table salt and water, are homogenous.

c. False: A pure substance may be a single element, such as gold.

d. False: Pure substances are homogeneous, but they are not solutions.

Practice Problem 1.5 Solution

a. No. The physical properties that are being compared—physical state and color—are the same for both water and ethanol, so they cannot be distinguished from one another based on this information alone.

b. Yes. The chemical property that is being compared—flammability—is different for water and ethanol, so they can be distinguished based on these observations. Water is nonflammable, and sample A extinguished the fire, so sample A is water. Ethanol is flammable, and sample B caused the fire to grow, so sample B is ethanol.

Practice Problem 1.6 Solution

A chemical reaction takes place, creating a new substance with definite properties of its own. The powder is not an element; it is a compound (a chemical combination of the shiny substance—a metal—and something else).

Practice Problem 1.7 Solution

a. Chemical energy in the firework is converted to sound, light, heat, and kinetic energy as the paper shreds go flying.

b. Chemical energy in the gasoline that fuels the motorcycle is converted to potential energy as the motorcycle goes up the hill, to kinetic energy as it accelerates, and to heat and sound in the engine.

Practice Problem 1.8 Solution

Yes. Recall that scientific laws are observations that are always seen to be that way, with no exceptions. However, if an exception is found, the scientific law must be revised accordingly. One example is the law of conservation of mass, which was originally thought to be universal. The discovery of nuclear energy showed, however, that mass could be converted to energy in nuclear reactions (Chapter 20). Therefore, the law of conservation of mass had to be refined to apply only to chemical and physical processes.

Practice Problem 1.9 Solution

According to Table 1.4, 1 μg = 10^{-6} g and 1 ng = 10^{-9} g. Since a nanogram is smaller than a microgram, 10 ng is smaller than 10 μg.

Practice Problem 1.10 Solution

a. The mole, mol, is an *SI base* unit (Table 1.3).

b. The ounce, oz, is an *English* unit (Table 1.6).

c. The newton, N, is an *SI derived* unit equal to one $kg \cdot m/s^2$ (Table 1.5).

d. The ampere, A, is an *SI base* unit (Table 1.3).

Practice Problem 1.11 Solution

a. Figure 1.13 (a) shows that it is possible to obtain high precision without high accuracy.

b. It is possible to obtain a reasonable degree of accuracy without high precision. An example would be the gunshots arranged in a circle around the bull's eye as shown below. The gunshots are in different locations (low precision), but are all somewhat close to the bull's eye (relatively accurate). That said, high precision is generally required for high accuracy.

Practice Problem 1.12 Solution

About 1 time in 10, the last digit of a reported measurement should be a zero. There is an equal possibility of each digit, 0–9, being the last, so one-tenth of the time it should be a 0, one-tenth of the time it should be a 1, one-tenth of the time a 2, and so on.

Practice Problem 1.13 Solution

a. <u>35.00</u> cm

b. <u>23.050</u> cm

c. 0.0<u>2030</u> cm

d. <u>3</u>0 cm

In part (d), the significance of the zero in 30 is not known. Trailing zeros *after* the decimal point are significant, but trailing zeros *before* the decimal point are uncertain unless specified otherwise. In this case, you invoke rule 4 and assume that the zero is *not* significant.

Practice Problem 1.14 Solution

$$62.44\text{ cm} - 7.145\text{ cm} + 27.7\text{ cm} = 82.995\text{ cm}$$
$$82.995\text{ cm} \rightarrow 83.0\text{ cm}$$

The value 27.7 cm has the least number of decimal places (one), so the final answer is rounded to one decimal place. The first digit to be dropped is 9, which is greater than 5, so the final digit is rounded up by one (82.9 becomes 83.0).

Practice Problem 1.15 Solution

a. $1.27\text{ cm} \times 6.220\text{ cm} \times 4.10\text{ cm} = 32.3875\text{ cm}^3 \rightarrow 32.4\text{ cm}^3$

This is a multiplication problem and the values that are multiplied have three, four, and three significant figures, respectively. Therefore, the final answer has three significant figures. The third significant digit is rounded up from 3 to 4 because the following number (8) is greater than 5.

b. $9.030\ \text{g}/(3.01\ \text{cm} \times 1.414\ \text{cm} \times 7.500\ \text{cm}) =$
$9.030\ \text{g}/(31.921\ \text{cm}^3) = 0.282885\ \text{g}/\text{cm}^3$

$0.282885\ \text{g}/\text{cm}^3 \rightarrow 0.283\ \text{g}/\text{cm}^3$

This problem combines multiplication and division, and the value with the least number of significant figures is 3.01 (three significant figures). Therefore, the final answer has three significant figures. The third significant digit is rounded up from 2 to 3 because the following number (8) is greater than 5.

c. $(0.71\ \text{cm})^3 = 0.3579\ \text{cm}^3 \rightarrow\ = 0.36\ \text{cm}^3$

There is only one measured value (the cubed term is an exact number), and it has two significant figures. Since this is effectively a multiplication ($0.71^3 = 0.71 \times 0.71 \times 0.71$), the final answer also has two significant figures. The second significant digit is rounded from 5 to 6 because the following number (7) is greater than 5.

Practice Problem 1.16 Solution

The circumference of the circle is calculated as follows:

$$c = 2\pi r = 2(3.14159)(13.7\ \text{cm}) = 86.1\ \text{cm}$$

The measurement with the fewest significant digits is 13.7 cm. Pi was given with six significant digits, and 2 has infinite significant digits.

Practice Problem 1.17 Solution

a. $(1.41 \times 10^7\ \text{g} - 5.98 \times 10^6\ \text{g}) = (14.1 \times 10^6\ \text{g} - 5.98 \times 10^6\ \text{g}) = 8.12 \times 10^6\ \text{g}$

$$8.12 \times 10^6\ \text{g} \rightarrow 8.1 \times 10^6\ \text{g}$$

The final answer is rounded to one decimal place because 14.1×10^6 g only has one decimal place.

b. Following the order of operations, the addition in the numerator is performed first. The second mass value is converted to units of 10^2 g.

$2.50 \times 10^2\ \text{g} + 37.5 \times 10^2\text{g} = 40.0 \times 10^2\text{g}$
(three significant figures)

$$\frac{40.0 \times 10^2\ \text{g}}{255\ \text{cm}^3} = 15.686\ \text{g}/\text{cm}^3$$

$$15.686\ \text{g}/\text{cm}^3 \rightarrow 15.7\ \text{g}/\text{cm}^3$$

The final answer has three significant figures.

Practice Problem 1.18 Solution

There are exactly 60 s in 1 min, so arrange this conversion factor with minutes in the denominator (where they will cancel) and seconds in the numerator (where they will be retained):

$$5445\ \cancel{\text{min}}\left(\frac{60\ \text{s}}{1\ \cancel{\text{min}}}\right) = 326{,}700\ \text{s}$$

Practice Problem 1.19 Solution

a. $15.0\ \cancel{\text{mi}}\left(\frac{1\ \text{h}}{60\ \cancel{\text{mi}}}\right) = 0.250\ \text{h}$

b. $0.250\ \cancel{\text{h}}\left(\frac{60\ \text{min}}{1\ \cancel{\text{h}}}\right) = 15.0\ \text{min}$

Practice Problem 1.20 Solution

a. According to Table 1.4, 1 nm = 10^{-9} m.

$$525\cancel{\text{nm}}\left(\frac{10^{-9}\ \text{m}}{1\cancel{\text{nm}}}\right) = 5.25 \times 10^{-7}\ \text{m}$$

b. According to Table 1.4, 1 dm = 10^{-1} m.

$$175\ \cancel{\text{dm}}\left(\frac{10^{-1}\ \text{m}}{1\ \cancel{\text{dm}}}\right) = 1.75 \times 10^1\ \text{m}$$

Practice Problem 1.21 Solution

This problem can be solved in a single step. Using the appropriate conversion factors, weeks are converted to days, days are converted to hours, hours are converted to minutes, and minutes are converted to seconds. The denominator of each conversion factor cancels out in each step.

$$7\ \cancel{\text{weeks}}\left(\frac{7\ \cancel{\text{days}}}{1\ \cancel{\text{week}}}\right)\left(\frac{24\ \cancel{\text{h}}}{1\ \cancel{\text{day}}}\right)\left(\frac{60\ \cancel{\text{min}}}{1\ \cancel{\text{h}}}\right)\left(\frac{60\ \text{s}}{1\ \cancel{\text{min}}}\right)$$
$$= 4{,}233{,}600\ \text{s}$$

Practice Problem 1.22 Solution

a. According to Table 1.4, 1 nm = 10^{-9} m and 1 cm = 10^{-2} m.

$$215\ \cancel{\text{nm}}\left(\frac{10^{-9}\ \cancel{\text{m}}}{1\ \cancel{\text{nm}}}\right)\left(\frac{1\ \text{cm}}{10^{-2}\ \cancel{\text{m}}}\right) = 2.15 \times 10^{-5}\ \text{cm}$$

b. According to Table 1.4, 1 km = 10^3 m and 1 cm = 10^{-2} m.

$$575\ \cancel{\text{km}}\left(\frac{10^3\ \cancel{\text{m}}}{1\ \cancel{\text{km}}}\right)\left(\frac{1\ \text{cm}}{10^{-2}\ \cancel{\text{m}}}\right) = 5.75 \times 10^7\ \text{cm}$$

Practice Problem 1.23 Solution

To solve this problem, begin with the distance from Earth to Mars and use the ratio of $\left(\frac{1\text{ h}}{28{,}000\text{ km}}\right)$ to convert to units of hours. Then convert from hours to days:

$$2.25 \times 10^8\ \cancel{\text{km}}\left(\frac{1\ \cancel{\text{h}}}{28{,}000\ \cancel{\text{km}}}\right)\left(\frac{1\text{ day}}{24\ \cancel{\text{h}}}\right) = 335\text{ days}$$

Thus, it would take almost a full Earth year to travel to Mars. Also, given that the Space Shuttle would not have adequate propellant to leave Earth's orbit, it could not realistically make the journey from Earth to Mars.

Practice Problem 1.24 Solution

One way to solve this problem is to convert Jim's weekly salary to a yearly salary:

$$\frac{\$750}{1\ \cancel{\text{week}}} \times \frac{52\ \cancel{\text{weeks}}}{1\text{ year}} = \frac{\$39{,}000}{1\text{ year}}$$

Jim's yearly salary ($39,000) is less than Phil's ($45,000).

Practice Problem 1.25 Solution

The speed of 65.6 ft per 1.61 s is converted to units of miles per hour by changing the denominator from units of seconds to units of hours and then converting the numerator from units of feet to miles. This can be done in one step:

$$\left(\frac{65.6\ \cancel{\text{ft}}}{1.61\ \cancel{\text{s}}}\right)\left(\frac{60\ \cancel{\text{s}}}{1\ \cancel{\text{min}}}\right)\left(\frac{60\ \cancel{\text{min}}}{1\text{ h}}\right)\left(\frac{1\text{ mi}}{5280\ \cancel{\text{ft}}}\right) = \frac{27.8\text{ mi}}{\text{h}}$$

Practice Problem 1.26 Solution

One yard = 3 feet, so this relationship is cubed when multiplied by 7.34 yd^3.

$$7.34\text{ yd}^3\left(\frac{3\text{ ft}}{1\text{ yd}}\right)^3 = 7.34\ \cancel{\text{yd}^3}\left(\frac{27\text{ ft}^3}{1\ \cancel{\text{yd}^3}}\right) = 198\text{ ft}^3$$

Practice Problem 1.27 Solution

First, determine the number of cubic meters in 1 L. Begin by using the relationship 1 cm^3 = 1 mL:

$$\left(\frac{1\text{ cm}^3}{1\text{ mL}}\right)\left(\frac{1000\text{ mL}}{1\text{ L}}\right)\left(\frac{1\text{ m}}{100\text{ cm}}\right)^3 = \left(\frac{1\text{ cm}^3}{1\text{ mL}}\right)$$

$$\left(\frac{1000\text{ mL}}{1\text{ L}}\right)\left(\frac{1\text{ m}^3}{1 \times 10^6\text{ cm}^3}\right) = \frac{0.001\text{ m}^3}{1\text{ L}}$$

Now, use this relationship to convert 623 L to cubic meters:

$$623\text{ L}\left(\frac{0.001\text{ m}^3}{1\text{ L}}\right) = 0.623\text{ m}^3$$

Practice Problem 1.28 Solution

$$d = \frac{m}{V} = \frac{5.55\text{ g}}{0.491\text{ mL}} = 11.3\text{ g/mL}$$

Practice Problem 1.29 Solution

Use the inverse of density to convert mass to volume.

$$12.7\ \cancel{\text{g}}\left(\frac{1\text{ mL}}{13.53\ \cancel{\text{g}}}\right) = 0.939\text{ mL}$$

Practice Problem 1.30 Solution

First, calculate the volume of the metal bar:

$$(7.00\text{ cm})(4.00\text{ cm})(1.00\text{ cm}) = 28.0\text{ cm}^3$$

Now calculate the density (recall that 1 cm^3 = 1 mL):

$$d = \frac{m}{V} = \frac{220.0\text{ g}}{28.0\text{ mL}} = 7.86\text{ g/mL}$$

According to Table 1.7, iron has a density of 7.87 g/mL, so the metal bar in this problem is most likely iron.

Practice Problem 1.31 Solution

First, convert the given temperature in °F to °C:

$$T_C = \frac{5}{9}(T_F - 32) = \frac{5}{9}(134°\text{F} - 32) = 57.0°\text{C}$$

Then, convert this temperature in °C to K:

$$T_K = T_C + 273.15 = 57.0 + 273.15 = 330.15\text{ K} = 330\text{ K}$$

Practice Problem 1.32 Solution

a. First, convert cubic kilometers to cubic centimeters, and then convert milliliters to liters:

$$1.335 \times 10^9\ \cancel{\text{km}^3}\left(\frac{1000\ \cancel{\text{m}}}{1\ \cancel{\text{km}}}\right)^3\left(\frac{100\ \cancel{\text{cm}}}{1\ \cancel{\text{m}}}\right)^3\left(\frac{1\ \cancel{\text{mL}}}{1\ \cancel{\text{cm}^3}}\right)\left(\frac{1\text{ L}}{1000\ \cancel{\text{mL}}}\right) = 1.335 \times 10^{21}\text{ L}^3$$

These conversion factors have unlimited significant digits, so the number of digits in the final answer is determined by the number in the original, measured value, 1.335 × 10^9 km^3.

b. (Total ocean volume) − (Atlantic Ocean volume) − (Pacific Ocean volume) = (Remaining ocean volume)

To make it easier to keep track of significant figures, convert the total ocean volume to units of 10^8 km^3:

$$(13.35 \times 10^8\ \text{km}^3) - (3.1 \times 10^8\ \text{km}^3) - (6.6 \times 10^8\ \text{km}^3) = 3.7 \times 10^8\ \text{km}^3$$

c. Convert the volume of the Pacific Ocean (6.6×10^8 km^3) to cubic meters, and then use the given density to calculate the mass:

$$6.6 \times 10^8\ \cancel{\text{km}^3}\left(\frac{1000\ \cancel{\text{m}}}{1\ \cancel{\text{km}}}\right)^3\left(\frac{1.027\ \text{kg}}{\cancel{\text{m}^3}}\right) = 6.8 \times 10^{17}\ \text{kg}$$

d. According to Table 1.6, 1 mi = 1.609 km and 1 in = 2.54 cm.

$$3688\ \cancel{\text{m}}\left(\frac{1\ \cancel{\text{km}}}{1000\ \cancel{\text{m}}}\right)\left(\frac{1\ \text{mi}}{1.609\ \cancel{\text{km}}}\right) = 2.292\ \text{mi}$$

$$3688\ \cancel{\text{m}}\left(\frac{100\ \cancel{\text{cm}}}{1\ \cancel{\text{m}}}\right)\left(\frac{1\ \text{in}}{2.54\ \cancel{\text{cm}}}\right) = 1.452 \times 10^5\ \text{in}$$

The number of significant figures for the value in inches is not limited by the 1 in = 2.54 cm conversion factor because that conversion is exact.

CHAPTER 2

Atoms and the Periodic Table

The notion that matter is made up of tiny particles dates back surprisingly far in human history. The ancient Greek philosopher Democritus first proposed the idea of a smallest unit of matter around 400 BCE. In fact, the word "atom" comes from the Greek word *atomos*, meaning indivisible.

Chapter Outline

GOALS

- Recognize the symbols for commonly used elements.
- Write the names of commonly used elements from their symbols.
- Calculate some of the quantities involved in chemical combinations of elements using the classical laws known during John Dalton's time.
- Explain the classical laws of chemical combination using Dalton's atomic theory.
- Outline the series of experiments that culminated in Rutherford's nuclear model of the atom.
- Identify the mass number of an atom using the number of each type of subatomic particle—protons, electrons, and neutrons—present in that atom, and vice versa.
- Identify which element an atom represents using the mass number of that atom, and vice versa.
- Calculate the atomic mass of any element from the masses and abundances of its naturally occurring mixture of isotopes.
- Discuss the contributions of Mendeleev and Meyer that led to the development of the periodic table.
- Classify the elements in a systematic manner based on their location in the periodic table.
- Identify periods, groups, and sections of the periodic table by name and number.

2.1 Chemical Symbols

GOALS

- Recognize the symbols for commonly used elements.
- Write the names of commonly used elements from their symbols.

Each chemical element is identified by an internationally recognized **symbol** consisting of one or two letters, such as C for carbon and He for helium. The first letter of an element's symbol is always capitalized. If the symbol has a second letter, it is always lowercase. The symbol is an abbreviation of the element's name, but some symbols represent names in languages other than English. The 10 elements whose symbols and English names have different first letters are listed in Table 2.1. In most cases, these symbols derive from older Latin names for these elements. A periodic table with the names and symbols of the 118 known elements, along with some other information, is given in Appendix A.1.

> Be sure to use the correct symbols for elements with proper capitalization throughout your study of chemistry.

Chemists write chemical symbols together in chemical **formulas** to identify compounds. Chemical formulas give each of element present in a compound.

TABLE 2.1 Elements Whose English Names and Symbols Begin with Different Letters

English Name	Symbol	Basis for the Symbol
Antimony	Sb	Stibium
Gold	Au	Aurum
Iron	Fe	Ferrum
Lead	Pb	Plumbum
Mercury	Hg	Hydrargyrum
Potassium	K	Kalium
Silver	Ag	Argentum
Sodium	Na	Natrium
Tin	Sn	Stannum
Tungsten	W	Wolfram

For example, the letters CO represent carbon monoxide, a compound made up of carbon and oxygen. Do not confuse the chemical formula CO for the chemical symbol Co, which represents the element cobalt.

Chemical formulas use subscripts to indicate the relative proportions of the elements present. For example, H_2O represents water, which has two atoms of hydrogen for every one atom of oxygen present. A subscript of 1 is never used in chemical formulas.

When parentheses appear in a chemical formula, multiply the number of each atom inside the parentheses by the subscripted number outside of the parentheses. For example, $Ca(NO_3)_2$ has $1 \times 2 = 2$ atoms of nitrogen and $3 \times 2 = 6$ atoms of oxygen for every one atom of calcium. A more thorough discussion of chemical formulas is presented in Chapter 3.

Example 2.1

What are the names of the elements that correspond to the following symbols?

a. C
b. Br
c. Hg
d. Sr

Solution

The periodic table in Appendix A.1 indicates the name of an element when you click on its symbol.

a. Carbon
b. Bromine
c. Mercury
d. Strontium

PRACTICE PROBLEM 2.1

What are the symbols of the following elements?

a. Manganese
b. Arsenic
c. Germanium
d. Plutonium

Hint: The periodic table in Appendix A.1 indicates the name of an element when you click on its symbol.

Example 2.2

Determine the relative number of each type of element in the following compounds.

a. CO_2
b. PCl_3
c. $Fe(OH)_3$

Solution

a. CO_2 has two atoms of oxygen, O, for every atom of carbon, C.
b. PCl_3 has three atoms of chlorine, Cl, for every atom of phosphorus, P.
c. $Fe(OH)_3$ has three atoms of oxygen, O, and three atoms of hydrogen, H, for every atom of iron, Fe.

PRACTICE PROBLEM 2.2

Determine the relative number of each type of element in the following compounds.

a. Na_2S
b. B_2H_6
c. $Ni(ClO_4)_2$

Hint: The subscript after the element symbol gives the number of that type of element. If parentheses are present, multiply the number of each element inside the parentheses by the number outside of the parentheses.

SECTION REVIEW

- The first letter in a symbol for an element is always capitalized; the second letter, if any, is lowercase.
- Not all element symbols start with the same letter as the English element name.
- Compounds are represented by the combination of chemical symbols in chemical formulas.
- Chemical formulas give the relative number of each type of element in a compound.

2.2 The Laws of Chemical Combination

GOAL

- Calculate some of the quantities involved in chemical combinations of elements using the classical laws known during John Dalton's time.

Background Review

Chapter 1 Science and Measurement:
Section 1.1—Classification of Matter

THE LAW OF CONSERVATION OF MASS

In Section 1.3, burning a log in a campfire was presented as one example of a chemical change, also referred to as a chemical reaction (Section 1.2). In that reaction, the heavy log is turned into a pile of ashes that has considerably less mass than the log had to begin with. Based on these data alone, some may conclude that the total amount of mass present at the beginning and at the end of a chemical reaction does not have to be the same.

An open campfire is a poorly controlled experiment, however, because mass can freely enter or leave the reaction site. What if the log could be burned in a closed container so that no mass could enter or leave? If the total mass of everything in the container—including the log, the ashes, the smoke, and even the air in the container—could be measured before and after the log burned, would the total mass still change during the reaction?

To find out, Antoine Lavoisier (1743–1794), the father of modern chemistry, carried out an experiment

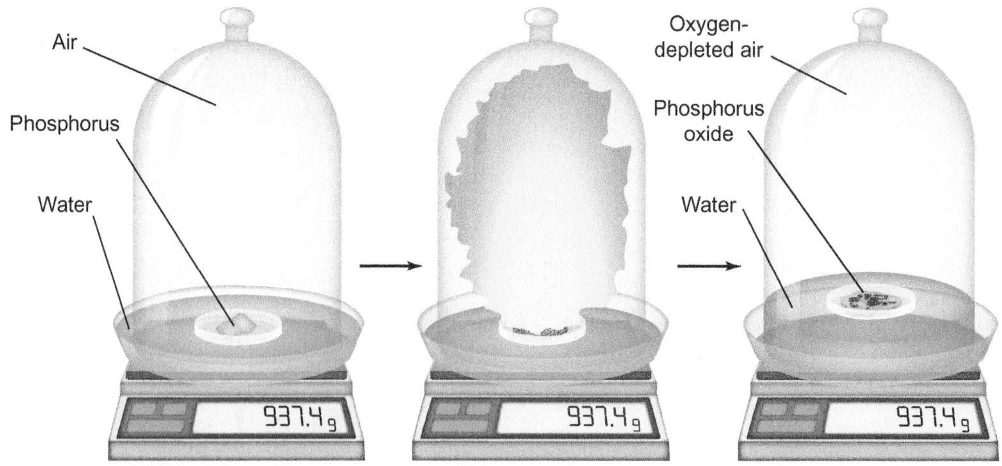

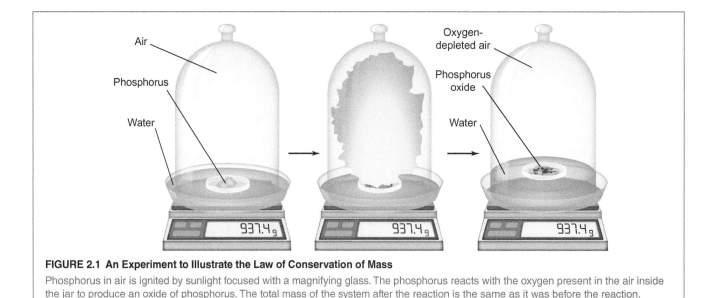

FIGURE 2.1 An Experiment to Illustrate the Law of Conservation of Mass
Phosphorus in air is ignited by sunlight focused with a magnifying glass. The phosphorus reacts with the oxygen present in the air inside the jar to produce an oxide of phosphorus. The total mass of the system after the reaction is the same as it was before the reaction.

similar to the one shown in Figure 2.1. In this experiment, a sample of phosphorus is placed on a flat surface that is floating in a pan of water, and the sample is then covered with a glass jar. The entire apparatus is placed on a balance, and the mass is measured. The phosphorus is ignited using sunlight focused through a magnifying glass, and it is allowed to burn in the air inside the glass jar. When the reaction is over, the mass is measured again.

The total mass of the system does not change over the course of the reaction. Alone, the solid product at the end of the experiment actually has more mass than the phosphorus sample did to begin with, but the increase in the water level at the end of the experiment compared with the beginning reveals that there is less air in the jar at the end than there was at the beginning. In fact, the mass of oxygen that is missing from the air inside the jar is exactly equal to the solid mass gained when the phosphorus was combusted to form a compound containing both phosphorus and oxygen.

Lavoisier's experiments were quantitative (Section 1.7 and Section 17.9)—they involved making careful measurements, which enabled him to conclude that the mass of the products generated during a chemical reaction is the same as the mass of the reactants that were used up. As a result of his work, Lavoisier proposed the law of conservation of mass (Section 1.4), which states that during a chemical reaction, mass is neither gained nor lost.

Lavoisier's work led other chemists to measure the masses of their reactants and products to confirm his conclusions and to see if they could make other quantitative observations. Two important laws—the law of definite proportions and the law of multiple proportions—arose from this work and, together with the law of conservation of mass, laid the groundwork for a new theory explaining how atoms combine to form other substances.

Figure 2.2 is an activity that allows you to perform an experiment similar to those performed by Lavoisier and his peers to test the law of conservation of mass. Note that one of the products of the reaction is a gas, which gets collected in the balloon so that its mass can be taken into account.

THE LAW OF DEFINITE PROPORTIONS

The **law of definite proportions**, also known as the **law of constant composition**, emerged after careful work by many investigators. In these experiments, the early chemists would take a compound such as water, which was known to contain oxygen and hydrogen; break it down into its constituent elements; and then compare the masses of each element in the compound. When this was done with water, the result was always the same—no matter where the water came from, the mass of the oxygen was always eight times the mass of the hydrogen. The 8 to 1 mass ratio of oxygen to hydrogen was constant for any sample of water. The law of definite proportions states that any given compound is composed of definite proportions by mass of its elements.

This law was difficult to establish because many samples of compounds contain impurities of other

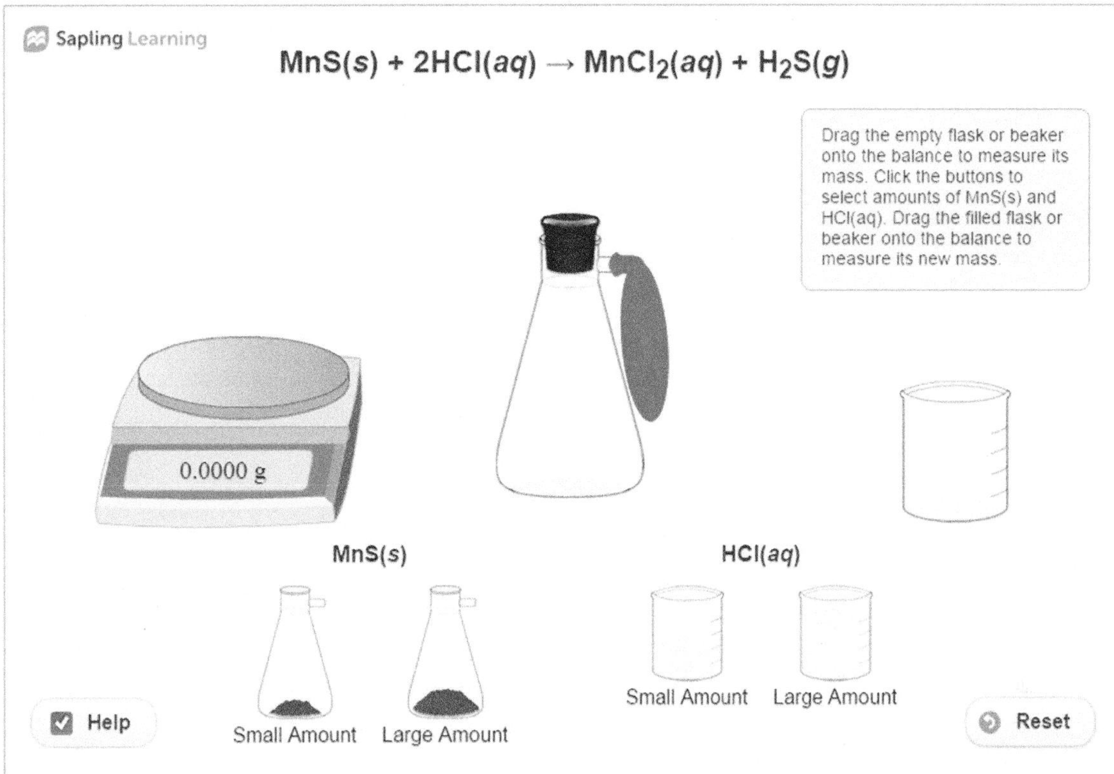

FIGURE 2.2 Conservation of Mass Activity

NOTE: You need to be online to access this activity.

Carry out the simulated chemical reaction between manganese(II) sulfide, MnS, and hydrochloric acid, HCl. Record the mass of the solid MnS in the flask and the mass of the HCl solution in the beaker and predict the final mass of the system when the reaction is complete. Does it make a difference how much of each reactant you use?

compounds composed of the same elements. For example, nitrogen monoxide, NO, an air pollutant, and dinitrogen monoxide, N_2O, known as laughing gas, are two different compounds, but each is composed of only nitrogen and oxygen. In a sample of NO gas, the mass of the oxygen is always 1.14 times the mass of the nitrogen—for every 1 g of nitrogen in a sample of NO gas, there is 1.14 g of oxygen. In N_2O, however, the ratio of oxygen to nitrogen is only half that of NO—for every 1 g of nitrogen in a sample of N_2O gas, there is only 0.57 g of oxygen. These two gases can form a homogeneous mixture in any proportion. Analysis of an impure sample of either gas could lead to a mass ratio of oxygen to nitrogen anywhere between that of pure N_2O (0.57 to 1) and that of pure NO (1.14 to 1). A pure sample of NO or N_2O, not a mixture of the two, is necessary to determine an accurate mass ratio. Once chemists were able to isolate and work on pure compounds, it was apparent that the law of definite proportions applied to all pure substances (Section 1.4).

Instead of comparing the mass of one element in a compound with the mass of another, it is often more useful to compare the mass of each element in a compound to the total mass of the compound itself. The **proportion** by mass of an element in a compound is the ratio of the mass of the element to the total mass of the compound. The **percent** by mass of the element in the compound is just the proportion of the element multiplied by 100%. For example, sucrose, also known as table sugar, $C_{12}H_{22}O_{11}$, is made up of carbon, hydrogen, and oxygen. A 342 g sample of sucrose is analyzed and is found to contain 144 g of carbon, 22 g of hydrogen, and 176 g of oxygen. The proportion by mass of each element in sucrose is calculated by dividing the mass of each element by the total mass of the entire sample:

$$\text{Carbon: } \frac{144\text{ g}}{342\text{ g}} = 0.421 \qquad \text{Hydrogen: } \frac{22\text{ g}}{342\text{ g}} = 0.064$$

$$\text{Oxygen: } \frac{176\text{ g}}{342\text{ g}} = 0.515$$

The proportion of each element in a compound when calculated this way is always a number between 0 and 1. The percent by mass of each element in sucrose is calculated by multiplying the proportion of each element by 100%:

$$\text{Carbon: } 0.421 \times 100\% = 42.1\%$$
$$\text{Hydrogen: } 0.064 \times 100\% = 6.4\%$$
$$\text{Oxygen: } 0.515 \times 100\% = 51.5\%$$

In other words, a little more than half of the mass of any sample of table sugar (51.5%) is made up of oxygen atoms, most of the rest is made up of carbon, and hydrogen atoms make up only 6.4% of the mass of the sample. All pure samples of sucrose will have this same percent composition by mass. For a review of calculating and using percentages, see Section 0.6.

Example 2.3

a. A 4.33 g sample of dinitrogen monoxide, N_2O, is composed of 63.65% nitrogen and 36.35% oxygen by mass. What is the percent composition of a 14.9 g sample of N_2O?
b. Nitrogen monoxide, NO, has a percent composition of 46.68% nitrogen and 53.32% oxygen by mass. What possible percentages of nitrogen could be in a *mixture* of N_2O and NO?

Solution

a. The 14.9 g sample is 63.65% nitrogen and 36.35% oxygen by mass. According to the law of definite proportions, *all* pure samples of N_2O have the same percent composition.
b. The possible percentages of nitrogen in the N_2O/NO mixture would be between 63.65% (the percentage of nitrogen in N_2O) and 46.68% (the percentage of nitrogen in NO).

PRACTICE PROBLEM 2.3

A sample of 15.50 g of dinitrogen monoxide, N_2O, decomposes into 9.866 g of nitrogen and 5.364 g of oxygen. A sample of 25.50 g N_2O decomposes into 16.23 g of nitrogen and 9.269 g of oxygen. Show that the amount of nitrogen and oxygen obtained in each decomposition is consistent with the law of definite proportions.

Hint: For the decomposition results to be consistent with the law of definite proportions, the mass percentages of nitrogen and oxygen in each N_2O sample must be the same.

Example 2.4

Calculate the mass of nitrogen in a 4.75 g sample of nitrogen monoxide, NO, using the percentages given in Example 2.3.

Solution

The percentage by mass of each element is the mass of that element divided by the total mass of the sample, times 100%:

$$\% \text{ by mass} = \frac{\text{Mass of element}}{\text{Mass of sample}} \times 100\%$$

Rearrange this equation to solve for the mass of the element:

$$\text{Mass of element} = \frac{\% \text{ by mass}}{100\%} \times \text{Mass of sample}$$

$$\text{Mass of N} = \frac{46.68\%}{100\%}(4.75 \text{ g}) = 2.22 \text{ g}$$

PRACTICE PROBLEM 2.4

Given that NO is 46.68% nitrogen by mass, calculate the mass of NO that contains 100.0 g of nitrogen.

Hint: Think of the 46.68% nitrogen by mass in NO as equivalent to $\left(\frac{46.68 \text{ g N}}{100 \text{ g NO}}\right)$. Use this relationship and dimensional analysis to determine the mass of NO that contains 100 g of N.

THE LAW OF MULTIPLE PROPORTIONS

The **law of multiple proportions** states that for any two (or more) compounds that are composed of the same elements, such as carbon monoxide, CO, and carbon dioxide, CO_2, for a given mass of one of the elements, the ratio of the masses of any other element in the compounds is a small, whole-number ratio. For example, for every 1 g of carbon in CO, there is 1.33 g of oxygen, and for every 1 g of carbon in CO_2, there is 2.66 g of oxygen. The ratio 2.66 to 1.33 is equal to 2 to 1. In nitrogen monoxide, NO, the mass ratio of oxygen to nitrogen (1.14 to 1) is exactly twice what it is in dinitrogen monoxide, N_2O (0.57 to 1).

Sometimes the mass ratio of one element to another in a compound does not appear at first to be a whole number. For example, the compound iron(II) oxide, FeO, contains 3.49 g of iron for every 1.00 g of oxygen, and the compound iron(III) oxide (rust),

Fe_2O_3, contains 2.32 g of iron for every 1.00 g of oxygen. The ratio of 3.49 to 2.32 is equal to 1.5 to 1, which is not a small whole number. However, if you multiply both values by 2, the ratio becomes 3 to 2, which is a small whole-number ratio as predicted by the law of multiple proportions.

Example 2.5

A sample of nitrogen monoxide, NO, consists of 14.01 g of nitrogen and 16.00 g of oxygen, whereas a sample of nitrogen dioxide, NO_2, consists of 14.01 g of nitrogen and 32.00 g of oxygen. Show that NO and NO_2 follow the law of multiple proportions.

Solution

Calculate the nitrogen-to-oxygen (N:O) ratios for both compounds:

$$\text{For NO: } \frac{14.01 \text{ g N}}{16.00 \text{ g O}} = 0.8756$$

$$\text{For NO}_2\text{: } \frac{14.01 \text{ g N}}{32.00 \text{ g O}} = 0.4378$$

The N:O mass ratios of these two compounds can now be compared. It is easiest to divide the larger value by the smaller value:

$$\frac{\text{N:O ratio for NO}}{\text{N:O ratio for NO}_2} = \frac{0.8756}{0.4378} = 2.000$$

The ratio of N:O mass ratios for these compounds is a whole number, 2, so NO and NO_2 follow the law of multiple proportions.

PRACTICE PROBLEM 2.5

A sample of sulfur dioxide, SO_2, consists of 16.04 g of sulfur and 16.00 g of oxygen, whereas a sample of sulfur trioxide, SO_3, consists of 16.04 g of sulfur and 24.00 g of oxygen. Show that SO_2 and SO_3 follow the law of multiple proportions.

Hint: Follow the same strategy that was used in Example 2.5. If the S:O ratio does not appear to be a whole number at first, see if it can be multiplied by another whole number to give an S:O ratio that is consistent with the law of multiple proportions.

Although early chemists were able to determine experimentally that compounds obeyed the law of definite proportions and the law of multiple proportions, they did not yet have an underlying theory to explain why this behavior occurred. The theory that explains these and many other phenomena is discussed in Section 2.3.

SECTION REVIEW

- Careful measurements of the masses of reactants and products in chemical reactions led to the development of the laws of conservation of mass, definite proportions, and multiple proportions.
- These three laws of chemical composition formed the basis for the theoretical development of chemistry.

2.3 The History of the Atom

GOALS

- Explain the classical laws of chemical combination using Dalton's atomic theory.
- Outline the series of experiments that culminated in Rutherford's nuclear model of the atom.

Background Review

Chapter 1 Science and Measurement:
Section 1.4—The Scientific Method, Hypotheses, Theories, and Laws

DALTON'S ATOMIC THEORY

From 1803–1807, John Dalton (Figure 2.3) formulated his atomic theory to explain the laws of chemical combination discussed in Section 2.2. **Dalton's atomic theory** included the following hypotheses:

1. Matter is made up of very tiny, indivisible particles called **atoms**.
2. Each atom of a particular element has the same mass, but the mass of an atom of one element is different from the mass of an atom of any other element.
3. Atoms combine to form what we now call **molecules**. When they do so, they combine in small, whole-number ratios.
4. Atoms of some pairs of elements can combine with each other in different small, whole-number ratios to form different compounds.

Note that some of these hypotheses have been revised in modern atomic theory. For example, the discovery of subatomic particles and nuclear reactions corrected the notion that atoms are indivisible. Also, the discovery of isotopes (Section 2.4) disproved the second hypothesis.

FIGURE 2.3 John Dalton (1766–1844)
English scientist John Dalton proposed a set of rules that govern how atoms combine to form molecules and also came up with the first set of relative atomic weights based on a hydrogen atom having a relative mass of 1.

FIGURE 2.4 Joseph John Thomson (1856–1940)
Thomson discovered the electron and won the 1906 Nobel Prize in Physics for his experiments on passing electricity through gases.

Dalton's atomic theory explained the three laws of chemical combination that had emerged from experiments by early chemists. Section 2.2 introduced these three laws.

1. The law of conservation of mass: Because atoms merely exchange "partners" during a chemical reaction and are not created or destroyed, their mass is also neither created nor destroyed. Thus, mass is always conserved during a chemical reaction.
2. The law of definite proportions: All samples of a given chemical compound will be composed of the same elements in the same proportion. For example, water is always H_2O whether you have a little or a lot, so the hydrogen-to-oxygen mass ratio in water is definite (it never changes).
3. The law of multiple proportions: When atoms of the same two elements are able to form more than one compound, they do so by combining with one another in different small, whole-number ratios.

Dalton's work explained the laws of chemical combination known at the time, and they stimulated research activity among scientists, which led to more generalizations and further advances in chemistry.

THE DISCOVERY OF THE ELECTRON

In the late 1800s, there was no evidence that particles existed that were smaller than atoms. Atoms were considered to be indivisible—they were the smallest particles of matter in the universe. In 1897, English physicist Joseph John (J. J.) Thomson (Figure 2.4) constructed a cathode-ray tube and observed how a beam of particles known as **cathode rays** passed through the tube. Thomson used an experimental setup similar to that shown in Figure 2.5, with an electrode containing a hole through which the rays were allowed to pass, a fluorescent screen at the other end of the tube for detection, and a magnet and electrically charged plates around the beam path. Thomson discovered that the cathode ray traveled from the negatively charged electrode of the cathode-ray tube to the positively charged electrode. Based on this result, he concluded that cathode rays had a negative charge. He also found that the cathode rays traveled in straight lines and that cathode-ray tubes constructed of different materials produced identical cathode rays. Interestingly, Thomson found that the beam of cathode rays could be deflected if an external electrical or magnetic field was applied. By adjusting the magnetic and electrical field strengths so that the beam traveled in a straight line, Thomson measured a charge-to-mass ratio of $-1.76 \times 10^8\ C/g$. (The coulomb, C, is the SI unit of electrical charge.) The cathode rays that Thomson studied are now known to be beams of **electrons**.

In 1909, American physicist Robert Millikan (1868–1953) succeeded in measuring the charge of a single electron. He did this by spraying small drops of oil into an apparatus that contained oppositely charged

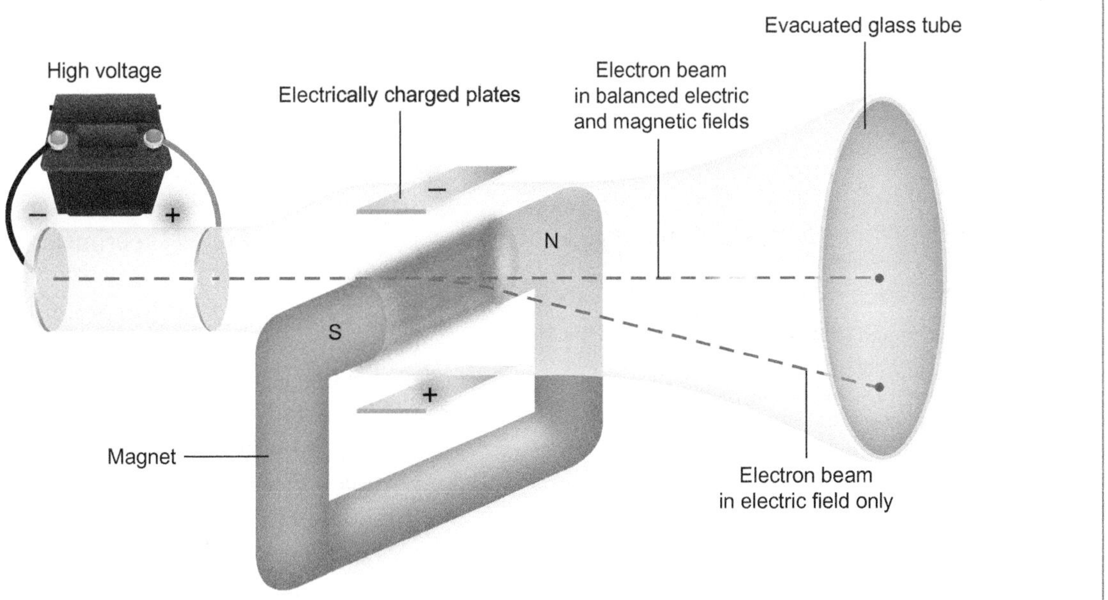

FIGURE 2.5 A Cathode-Ray Tube

In an electrical field, the cathode ray (electron beam) is deflected. In both a balanced electrical field and a magnetic field, the beam travels in a straight line.

electrical plates (Figure 2.6). The area in near the plates was irradiated with X-rays to give the oil drops extra negative charge. Since the lower plate was negatively charged, it repelled the negatively charged oil drops; adjusting the magnitude of the electric field would either slow or completely stop the falling drops. Millikan viewed the falling drops through a scope and determined the field strength required to stop the drops from falling. He then calculated the mass of each drop.

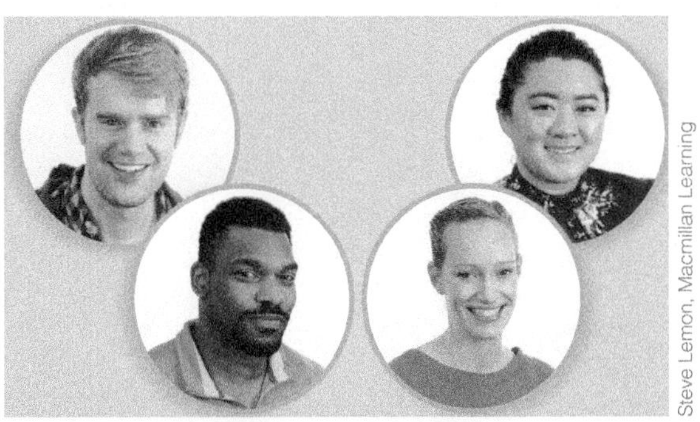

FIGURE 2.6 Millikan's Oil-Drop Experiment

NOTE: You need to be online to access this video.
Millikan measured the charge of the electron (-1.60×10^{-19} C) by determining the electrical field strength necessary to suspend a charged drop of oil. With this information and Thomson's measurement of the electron's charge-to-mass ratio, Millikan calculated the mass of the electron (9.10×10^{-28} g).

Millikan also found that the total charge of each drop was a multiple of a particular number: -1.60×10^{-19} C: Millikan had discovered the charge of an electron. From this value and Thomson's charge-to-mass ratio of the electron (-1.76×10^{8} C/g), Millikan was able to calculate the mass of an electron:

$$\text{Mass} = \text{Charge} \times \frac{\text{Mass}}{\text{Charge}}$$

$$\text{Mass of an electron} = (-1.60 \times 10^{19}\ \text{C})\left(\frac{1\ \text{g}}{-1.76 \times 10^{8}\ \text{C}}\right)$$
$$= 9.10 \times 10^{28}\ \text{g}$$

Thomson's discovery of the electron and the combined work of Thomson and Millikan in determining the mass of the electron fundamentally changed how scientists viewed the atom. Dalton had previously hypothesized that the atom was an indivisible sphere (Figure 2.7a), but it was now clear that electrons existed as part of the atom. And, because atoms are neutral in charge overall, the nonelectron portion of the atom must have a positive charge equal to the negative charge of the electrons. Since the newly measured mass of the electron was just 1/1836 the mass of the lightest element, hydrogen, Thomson proposed a model of the atom that consisted of a sphere of positive charge in which negatively charged electrons were suspended (Figure 2.7b). This was known as the plum-pudding model of the atom (named after a popular English dessert).

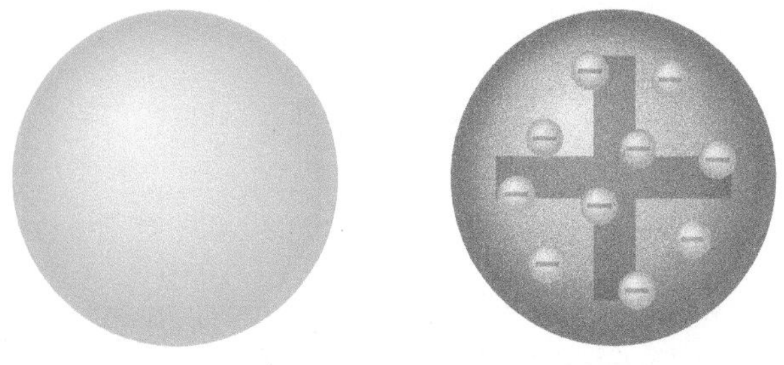

FIGURE 2.7 Dalton and Thomson's Early Models of the Atom

(a) Dalton's model of the atom consisted of an indivisible sphere. (b) Thomson's plum-pudding model consisted of negatively charged electrons suspended in a larger sphere of positive charge.

THE NUCLEAR MODEL OF THE ATOM

In 1896, French scientist Henri Becquerel (1852–1908) discovered that uranium emitted high-energy radiation. This phenomenon, known as **radioactivity**, was further studied by Marie Curie (1867–1934). By the early 1900s, three types of radioactivity had been discovered: alpha, α, particles; beta, β, particles; and gamma, γ, particles. Alpha particles were known to have a positive charge, while beta particles had a negative charge. (A more detailed account of radioactivity is given in Section 20.1.)

One of the most accomplished researchers in radioactivity in the late 1800s and early 1900s was Ernest Rutherford (1871–1937), a British scientist and former student of Thomson. In 1909, Rutherford's students, Hans Geiger and Ernest Marsden, carried out an experiment that Rutherford believed would substantiate Thomson's plum-pudding model of the atom (Figure 2.7b). In this experiment, a radioactive source was used to bombard a very thin piece of gold foil with α particles. The gold foil was surrounded by a fluorescent screen, a material that would detect the impact of α particles (Figure 2.8). In Thomson's model, the positive and negative charges are spread throughout the atom, in which case the positively charged α particles should have gone through the gold foil with minimal deflection. The vast majority of the α particles did travel through the foil, but a substantial number of them were deflected. Some were even deflected directly backward, toward the source. From these results, Rutherford concluded that Thomson's model of the atom was incorrect and that the atom must contain a concentration of positive charge in a relatively small area.

Given the results of his gold foil experiment and subsequent experimentation, Rutherford proposed a nuclear model of the atom:

1. The atom's positive charge and the majority of its mass are located in a relatively small area, which he later named the **nucleus** (plural, *nucleii*).

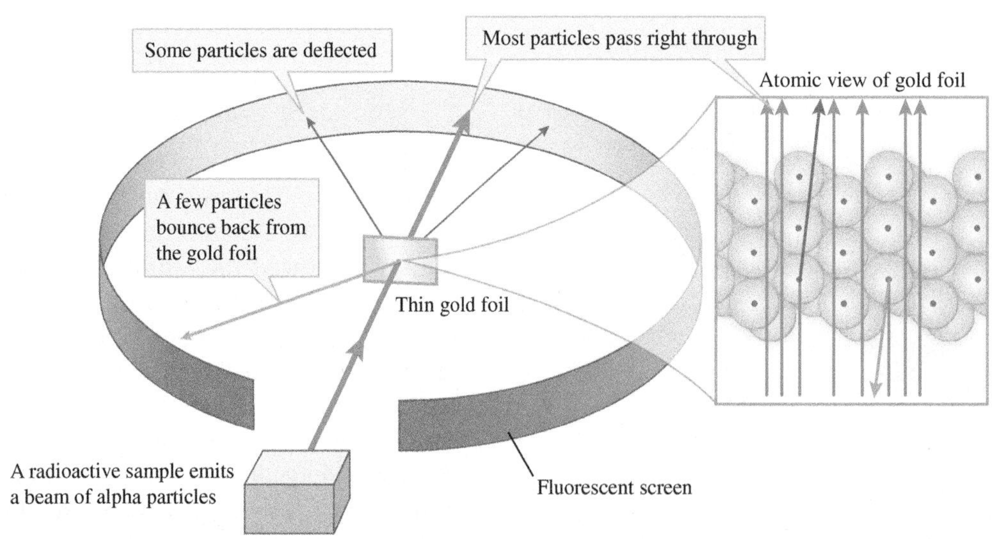

FIGURE 2.8 Rutherford's Gold Foil Experiment

In Rutherford's experiment, positively charged α particles were allowed to bombard a thin piece of gold foil. A larger-than-expected number of α particles were deflected or bounced backward, suggesting that there is a concentration of mass and positive charge in a relatively small area of the atom.

2. The vast majority of the atom is empty space. Small, negatively charged electrons are spread throughout this empty space.
3. The number of negatively charged electrons is equal to the number of positively charged particles called **protons** inside the nucleus.

Building on point 3 of Rutherford's model, the charge of the proton (+1) is *equal in magnitude, but opposite in sign* from the charge of the electron (−1). This is why an electrically neutral atom has the same number of protons and electrons. These charges are relative and based on Millikan's measured charge of the electron (-1.60×10^{-19} C).

In Rutherford's model of the atom, a core of positively charged protons lies at the center, while negatively charged electrons exist in the empty space around the nucleus.

Because helium has only one more proton than does hydrogen but four times the mass, Rutherford hypothesized the existence of another particle to account for this difference in mass. This missing particle was discovered in 1932, when Rutherford's student, James Chadwick (1891–1974), demonstrated the existence of neutral particles, now called **neutrons**, in the nucleus. Neutrons have approximately the same mass as protons. The presence of two neutrons and two protons in a helium atom explains why it is four times heavier than a hydrogen atom, which contains one proton and zero neutrons.

> Protons and neutrons exist in the nucleus of an atom, whereas electrons exist in the mostly empty space that surrounds the nucleus.

While Rutherford's model of the atom was later refined by Niels Bohr and others (Section 8.2), Rutherford's model is largely consistent with the currently recognized structure of the atom (Figure 2.9).

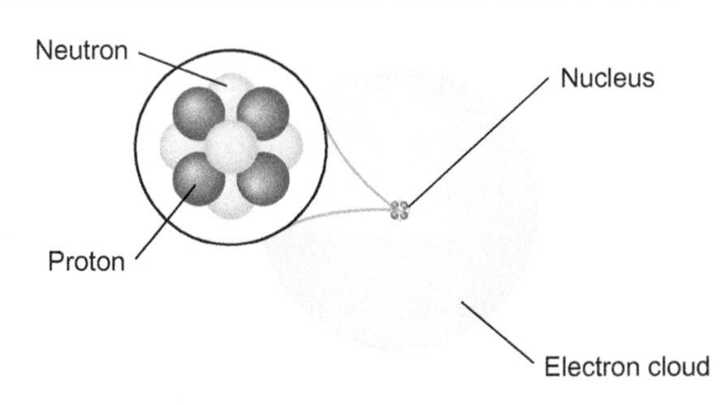

FIGURE 2.9 Model of the Atom
Atoms have a small, dense, positively charged nucleus made up of protons and neutrons. Negatively charged electrons are found outside of the nucleus. Most of the atom is empty space.

Example 2.6

Dalton concluded that matter was made up of atoms. What additional insight about atoms did Thomson's experiments reveal?

Solution

Thomson's experiments showed that cathode rays have a negative charge and that the atom is composed of smaller particles. This led Thomson to propose the plum-pudding model of the atom.

PRACTICE PROBLEM 2.6

How did our model of the atom change after Rutherford's experiment?

Hint: How does the distribution of positive charge in Thomson's model of the atom compare with that in Rutherford's?

SECTION REVIEW

- Dalton's atomic theory was an explanation for why the three laws of chemical combination (the law of conservation of mass, the law of definite proportions, and the law of multiple proportions) worked, and it provided the theoretical background for the entire future development of chemistry.
- Experiments demonstrated that the atom is not indivisible but consists of a nucleus made up of protons and neutrons that is surrounded by a cloud of electrons.
- The charges on protons and electrons are equal in magnitude, and atoms are electrically neutral, so atoms contain equal numbers of protons and electrons.

2.4 Subatomic Particles, Isotopes, and Ions

GOALS

- Identify the mass number of an atom using the number of each type of subatomic particle—protons, electrons, and neutrons—present in that atom, and vice versa.
- Identify which element an atom represents using the mass number of that atom, and vice versa.

SUBATOMIC PARTICLES AND ISOTOPES

The protons, neutrons, and electrons first introduced in Section 2.3 are called **subatomic particles**. Subatomic particles are discussed in greater detail in this section.

The nucleus, where the protons and neutrons reside, is incredibly small, with a radius about 1/10,000 of the radius of the atom itself. If the atom were the size of a car, the nucleus would be about the size of the period at the end of this sentence. Thus, the nucleus accounts for almost all of the *mass* of an atom, whereas the space occupied by the electrons makes up almost all of the *volume* of an atom. Some properties of protons, neutrons, and electrons are listed in Table 2.2. These properties are the same for all protons, neutrons, and electrons,

TABLE 2.2 Properties of Subatomic Particles

Particle	Charge (e)*	Mass (u)†	Location in the Atom
Proton (p)	+1	1.0073	In the nucleus
Neutron (n)	0	1.0087	In the nucleus
Electron (e)	−1	0.000549	Outside the nucleus

*The charges given are relative charges, based on the charge on the electron, e, as the fundamental unit of charge ($1\ e = -1.60 \times 10^{-19}$ C).

†The masses are given in atomic mass units, u, described in Section 2.5.

EVERYDAY CONNECTION

Protons and neutrons are significantly heavier than electrons. If an electron had the mass of a marble, then a proton or neutron would have the mass of a bowling ball. If you were carrying a bowling ball in a bag, and then someone added a marble to that bag, you might not even notice. Similarly, the mass of the electrons in an atom is negligible compared to the mass of the nucleus.

TOMO/Shutterstock

In terms of size, however, the nucleus takes up very little of the space of an atom. If the nucleus were the size of a marble, then the atom would be the size of a stadium.

regardless of the type of atom in which they happen to be found. The atom is the smallest unit of matter that is identifiable as an element, and in that sense, it is the smallest particle of an element.

As you learned in Section 2.3, atoms are electrically **neutral** because the number of positively charged protons, p, equals the number of negatively charged electrons, e:

$$\text{Number of protons} = \text{Number of electrons (for a neutral atom)}$$

Neutrons are electrically neutral (Table 2.2), so the number of neutrons, n, does not affect the charge on the atom.

The **atomic number, Z**, is the number of protons in an atom's nucleus.

$$Z = \mathrm{p} \quad (2.1)$$

In the periodic table in Appendix A.1, the atomic numbers are the whole numbers that are shown above the element symbols. All atoms that have the same number of protons (the same atomic number) are atoms of the same element, whereas atoms that have different numbers of protons are atoms of different elements. For example, all atoms with one proton ($Z = 1$) are hydrogen atoms, and all atoms with eight protons ($Z = 8$) are oxygen atoms.

> The atomic number is equal to the number of protons in the atom and determines its identity.

The number of neutrons in the nuclei of atoms of the same element can differ. If two atoms have the same number of protons but different numbers of neutrons, they are said to be **isotopes** of each other. Isotopes are still atoms of the same element because they have the same atomic number, but they have different masses because of the different numbers of neutrons.

Each isotope of an element is usually identified by its **mass number, A**, which is the sum of the number of protons and the number of neutrons in the atom.

$$A = \mathrm{p} + \mathrm{n} = Z + \mathrm{n} \quad (2.2)$$

The number of neutrons is thus the difference between the mass number and the atomic number.

$$\mathrm{n} = A - Z \quad (2.3)$$

Individual isotopes can be represented using their isotopic symbol, which includes the symbol for the element (Section 2.1) as well as the mass number. For example, the isotope of hydrogen with $A = 1$ is ^{1}H or H-1, and its name is hydrogen-1, whereas the isotope of hydrogen with $A = 2$ is ^{2}H or H-2, and its name is hydrogen-2. Thus, isotopes are identified by the symbol

Steve Lemon, Macmillan Learning

FIGURE 2.10 Video Tutorial: Subatomic Particles

NOTE: You need to be online to access this video.
This video demonstrates how to determinate the number of protons, neutrons, and electrons in an atom of an isotope.

of the element, with the mass number added as a superscript on the left side or after the symbol following a dash.

The number of protons (the atomic number) may be shown as a subscript on the left, if desired, as in $^{1}_{1}H$. This symbol means that this hydrogen atom has one proton and a mass number of one and therefore no neutrons. However, the element's identity determines the atomic number, and vice versa, so giving both the symbol and the atomic number is redundant—it identifies the element twice:

$$\text{p} + \text{n} = A \rightarrow {}^{1}_{1}\text{H} \qquad \text{(Optional) p} = Z \rightarrow {}^{1}_{1}\text{H}$$

The video in Figure 2.10 demonstrates how to determine the number of protons, neutrons, and electrons in a neutral atom of a given isotope when given the elemental symbol and the mass number of an isotope.

Example 2.7

How many protons, neutrons, and electrons are in a neutral atom of each of the following isotopes?

a. S-32
b. ^{19}F
c. A neon atom with equal numbers of protons and neutrons in its nucleus
d. $^{238}_{92}U$

Solution

a. Sulfur has an atomic number of 16, so it has 16 protons in the nucleus. The mass number of this isotope is given as 32, so the number of neutrons in the nucleus is $n = A - Z = 32 - 16 = 16$. A neutral atom always has the same number of electrons as protons, so an atom of S-32 contains 16 protons, 16 neutrons, and 16 electrons.

b. Fluorine has $Z = 9$, so it has 9 protons in its nucleus. Since it is a neutral atom, it must have an equal number of electrons. The mass number of this isotope is 19, so the number of neutrons in the nucleus is equal to $n = A - Z = 19 - 9 = 10$. Therefore, an atom of F-19 contains 9 protons, 10 neutrons, and 9 electrons.

c. Neon is atomic number 10, so this neon atom has 10 protons in the nucleus and 10 electrons. Since the number of neutrons in this case is equal to the number of protons, this isotope has 10 neutrons in its nucleus, too.

d. Uranium has $Z = 92$, which is indicated in this notation by the subscript on the left. The mass number of this isotope is 238, so the number of neutrons in the nucleus is equal to $n = A - Z = 238 - 92 = 146$. Since it is a neutral atom, it must have 92 electrons to balance the charge of the 92 protons. Altogether, this atom has 92 protons, 146 neutrons, and 92 electrons.

PRACTICE PROBLEM 2.7

Write symbols for each of the following isotopes by using an elemental symbol with a superscript.

a. A helium atom with a mass number of 3
b. An oxygen atom with 7 neutrons in the nucleus
c. A boron atom with equal numbers of protons and neutrons in the nucleus
d. A carbon atom that has one more neutron than protons in its nucleus

Hint: Your answers should include the element symbol with the mass number ($A = Z + n$) as a superscript on the left.

The notation used here omits the atomic number as a subscript on the left. However, if you included the atomic number in your answers, such as $^{3}_{2}He$ instead of ^{3}He, then your answers are equally correct.

Example 2.8

Assuming the element symbols are correct, which of the following isotopic symbols are correct? Explain why.

a. $^{6}_{14}C$
b. O-17
c. $_{2}H$
d. $^{14}_{6}N$
e. S-6

Solution

a. Incorrect. Carbon has an atomic number of 6, not 14. Carbon can have a mass number of 14, though, so the atomic and mass numbers must be switched: $^{14}_{6}C$. If the atomic number were correct, making this an isotope of silicon, Si ($Z = 14$), it would still be incorrect because it is impossible for an atom to have a mass number that is less than its atomic number.

b. O-17 is correct. This is an isotope of oxygen ($Z = 8$) that has 8 protons and 9 neutrons.

c. Incorrect. Hydrogen ($Z = 1$) has 1 proton, not 2. Hydrogen can have a mass number of 2, however, so the "2" should be a superscript instead: ^{2}H.

d. Incorrect. The atomic number given as a subscript does not match the element symbol. Assuming the element symbol is correct, this isotope should be $^{14}_{7}N$. (If the subscript were correct, then the isotope would be $^{14}_{6}C$.)

e. Incorrect. Sulfur has an atomic number of 16, so a mass number of 6 is impossible. The mass number can never be less than the atomic number.

PRACTICE PROBLEM 2.8

Write the isotopic symbol that correctly represents each of the following.

a. A hydrogen isotope with 2 neutrons
b. An iodine isotope with 78 neutrons
c. A polonium isotope with 42 more neutrons than protons

Hint: In an isotopic symbol for an element X, $^{A}_{Z}X$, the mass number, A, is the number of protons + neutrons. The atomic number, Z, is the number of protons. Writing the atomic number is optional because the element symbol already identifies the atomic number.

Example 2.9

Two atoms have 17 protons each, but the first atom contains 18 neutrons, whereas the second contains 20 neutrons. Show that their atomic numbers are the same but that their mass numbers differ.

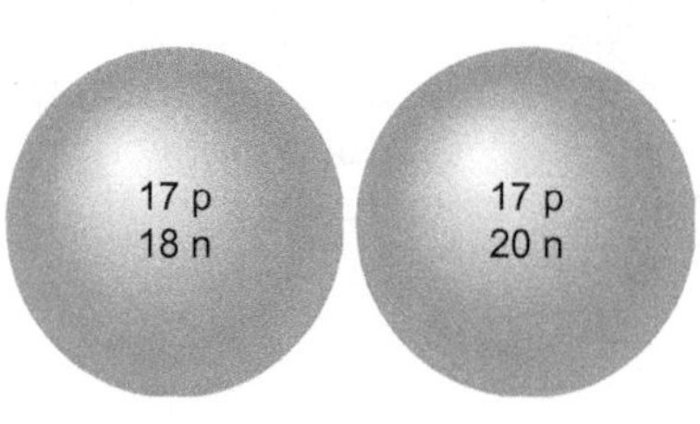

Solution

The atomic number, Z, is the number of protons in an atom. Both of these atoms have 17 protons, so both are the same element, chlorine. To determine the mass numbers, A, of these atoms, add the number of protons and the number of neutrons. For the first atom, $A = 17 + 18 = 35$; for the second atom, $A = 17 + 20 = 37$. The atoms have the same atomic number but different mass numbers, so they are isotopes of each other, ^{35}Cl and ^{37}Cl.

PRACTICE PROBLEM 2.9

Two atoms have $A = 119$, but one has 69 neutrons and the other has 70 neutrons. Are they isotopes of each other? If not, what elements do they represent?

Hint: How many protons are in each atom? The number of protons determines which element it is.

Example 2.10

How many electrons are associated with each of the neutral atoms in Example 2.9?

Solution

In a neutral atom, the number of electrons equals the number of protons. Each chlorine atom has 17 protons, so each must have 17 electrons, too.

PRACTICE PROBLEM 2.10

How many electrons does each of the atoms in Practice Problem 2.9 have?

Hint: Protons have a +1 charge, whereas electrons have a −1 charge. No overall charge was specified for these atoms, so assume that they are neutral, with equal amounts of positive and negative charge.

IONS

Although atoms have the same number of protons and electrons, they can gain or lose electrons. The resulting particle is charged and is known as an **ion**. Ions are commonly formed in chemical reactions. For example, sodium can react to *lose* an electron, e^-. The result is the sodium ion, Na^+:

$$Na \rightarrow Na^+ + e^-$$

In this reaction, the sodium atom reactant has 11 protons and 11 electrons, whereas the Na^+ ion product has 11 protons and 10 electrons, resulting in an overall charge of +1. Positively charged ions such as Na^+ are known as **cations**.

When an atom gains one or more electrons, a negatively charged ion called an **anion** is formed. For example, oxygen can react to *gain* two electrons, forming O^{2-}:

$$O + 2e^- \rightarrow O^{2-}$$

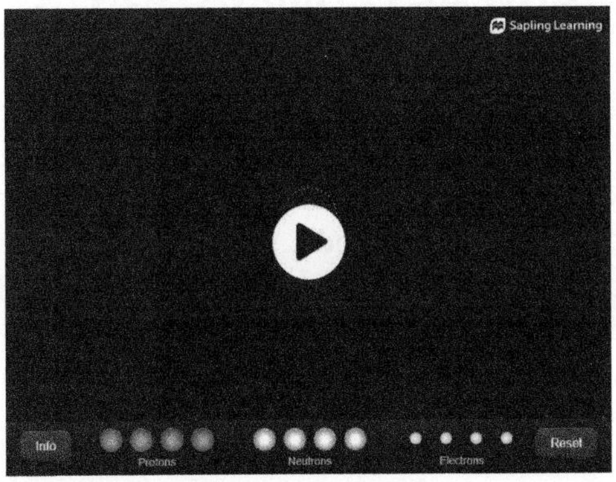

FIGURE 2.11 Build an Atom Activity

NOTE: You need to be online to access this activity.
Drag and drop the subatomic particles to create two different stable and neutral isotopes each of hydrogen, helium, and lithium.

In this reaction, the oxygen atom reactant has 8 protons and 8 electrons, whereas the O^{2-} ion product has 8 protons and 10 electrons, resulting in an overall charge of -2.

Some isotopes are stable and others are unstable. Unstable isotopes are discussed in detail in Chapter 20. The Build an Atom activity (Figure 2.11) allows you to combine subatomic particles and get information about the resulting atom or ion such as element, charge, and whether it is stable or unstable.

Example 2.11

How many protons and electrons are in each of the following ions?

a. F^-
b. Mg^{2+}
c. N^{3-}
d. W^{6+}

Solution

a. Fluorine ($Z = 9$) has 9 protons, so a neutral fluorine atom has 9 electrons, too. F^- has a charge of -1, so it has one *extra* electron: F^- has 9 protons and 10 electrons.
b. Magnesium ($Z = 12$) has 12 protons, so a neutral magnesium atom has 12 electrons, too. Mg^{2+} has a charge of $+2$, so it must have two *fewer* electrons than it has protons: Mg^{2+} has 12 protons and 10 electrons.
c. Nitrogen ($Z = 7$) has 7 protons, so a neutral nitrogen atom has 7 electrons, too. N^{3-} has a charge of -3, so it must have three *extra* electrons: N^{3-} has 7 protons and 10 electrons.
d. Tungsten ($Z = 74$) has 74 protons, so a neutral tungsten atom would have 74 electrons, too. W^{6+} has a charge of $+6$, so it must have six *fewer* electrons than it has protons: W^{6+} has 74 protons and 68 electrons.

PRACTICE PROBLEM 2.11

Write symbols for each of the following isotopes by using an elemental symbol with a superscript and the charge, if appropriate. Then determine the number of protons, neutrons, and electrons in each.

a. A hydrogen atom with a mass number of 3
b. An oxygen ion with 7 neutrons and a charge of -2
c. A selenium ion with a mass number of 78 and a charge of -2
d. A manganese ion with 30 neutrons and a charge of $+4$

Hint: An ion with a negative charge (an anion) has more electrons than it has protons, whereas an ion with a positive charge (a cation) has fewer electrons than it has protons.

SECTION REVIEW

- Atoms are composed of subatomic particles: protons (p), neutrons (n), and electrons (e).
- Protons and neutrons are both found in the nucleus and account for essentially all of the mass of the atom; protons are positively charged, whereas neutrons are electrically neutral. The mass number, A, is the total number of protons and neutrons in the atom.
- Electrons are found outside the nucleus and make up essentially all of the volume of the atom; electrons are negatively charged.
- The atomic number, Z, is equal to the number of protons in the nucleus and determines which element the atom is identified as.
- Atoms with different numbers of neutrons but the same number of protons are isotopes of each other.
- Ions are formed when an atom gains or loses electrons.
- Positively charged ions are called cations, whereas negatively charged ions are called anions.

2.5 Atomic Masses

GOAL

- Calculate the atomic mass of any element from the masses and abundances of its naturally occurring mixture of isotopes.

Steve Lemon, Macmillan Learning

FIGURE 2.12 The Problem with Weighing Atoms

If you try to weigh one grain of rice on a bathroom scale, you get a sense of the much more difficult task of weighing atoms.

Atoms are so tiny that, until recently, the masses of individual atoms could not be measured directly (Figure 2.12). However, because mass was so important in Dalton's theory, some measure of atomic masses was necessary. Therefore, a **relative scale**—the **atomic mass scale**—was developed. On this scale, the mass of one isotope of one element is assigned a value, and the masses of all other atoms are measured relative to the mass of that standard.

HISTORIC DETERMINATION OF ATOMIC MASS

The early pioneers of chemistry, trying to verify Dalton's atomic theory, could not measure the mass of individual atoms. The best they could do was to measure the masses of equal numbers of atoms or other known ratios of atoms of two or more elements at a time to determine their relative masses. They established one element as a standard, gave it an arbitrary value of atomic mass, and used that value to establish the atomic mass scale. The naturally occurring mixture of oxygen isotopes was defined as having an atomic mass of exactly 16 **atomic mass units, u**, also abbreviated as amu. That standard was replaced in 1961 with a new standard that is based on the mass of a single carbon isotope, and the current SI symbol for atomic mass unit is u. The atomic mass unit is tiny; it takes 6.022×10^{23} u to make 1.00 g.

> The symbol of the atomic mass unit, amu, is u.
>
> Atoms have masses between 1 and 250 atomic mass units, nowhere near as large as 1 g. Be careful to use the correct units for the masses of individual atoms and for the masses of weighable samples.

MODERN DETERMINATION OF ATOMIC MASS

The modern method of determining **atomic mass** uses the ^{12}C isotope as the standard, with the mass of a single ^{12}C atom defined as exactly 12 u. However, as you can see in the periodic table (Appendix A.1), the atomic mass of carbon on this scale is 12.011 u and that of oxygen is 15.9994 u. This is because the atomic mass of an element is defined as the **weighted average** of the actual masses of its naturally occurring isotopes. A weighted average (Section 0.9) is the average taking into account the relative numbers of atoms of each type of isotope. The concept of weighted average may be understood using an analogy to a situation in everyday life, presented in Example 2.12.

Example 2.12

In a particular class, exams are worth 50% of the overall grade, quizzes are worth 25% of the overall grade, homework is worth 20% of the overall grade, and class participation is worth 5% of the overall grade. A particular student has earned an average score of 80.2% on the exams, 77.3% on the quizzes, 87.8% on the homework assignments, and 100.0% on class participation. What is this student's overall grade in the course?

Solution

To calculate the weighted average, multiply the student's score on each component by its weight, expressed as a fraction, and then sum the values. Recall that to change a percentage to a fraction, divide by 100, which is equivalent to moving the decimal two places to the left (Section 0.6):

$$\text{Grade} = 0.50(\text{Exam }\%) + 0.25(\text{Quiz }\%) + 0.20(\text{Homework }\%) + 0.05(\text{Participation }\%)$$

$$\text{Grade} = 0.50(80.2\%) + 0.25(77.3\%) + 0.20(87.8\%) + 0.05(100\%)$$

$$\text{Grade} = 40.10\% + 19.33\% + 17.56\% + 5.00\%$$

$$\text{Grade} = 82.0\%$$

PRACTICE PROBLEM 2.12

Suppose that you go on a road trip where your car averages a fuel economy of 37.2 mpg for 65% of the trip, 24.2 mpg for 23% of the trip, and 8.8 mpg for 12% of the trip. Determine the car's average fuel economy for the trip.

Hint: Convert each percentage into a fraction by dividing by 100. Multiply each fraction by its corresponding fuel economy and sum the resulting values.

Steve Lemon, Macmillan Learning

FIGURE 2.13 Video Tutorial: Average Atomic Mass

NOTE: You need to be online to access this video.

This video shows how to calculate the average atomic mass of an element from isotope masses and abundance data.

As mentioned earlier in this chapter, elements often exist as a mixture of multiple isotopes that have different isotope masses. The atomic mass of an element is the weighted average of the masses of the naturally occurring isotopes (the Σ operator means "sum of"):

$$\text{Atomic mass} = \Sigma(\text{Fraction of isotope}) \times (\text{Mass of isotope}) \qquad (2.4)$$

A video showing the calculation of the average atomic mass of an element is presented in Figure 2.13.

Example 2.13

Naturally occurring copper consists of 69.17% ^{63}Cu, which has an isotope mass of 62.9396 u, and 30.83% ^{65}Cu, which has an isotope mass of 64.9278 u. What is the atomic mass of copper?

Solution

The weighted average is given by the sum of the fraction of ^{63}Cu times its isotope mass and the fraction of ^{65}Cu and its isotope mass. To convert a percentage to a fraction, divide by 100 (Section 0.6). For ^{63}Cu:

$$69.17\% = \frac{69.17}{100} = 0.6917$$

Similarly, for ^{65}Cu, 30.83% = 30.83/100 = 0.3083. The weighted average mass of copper is

$$(0.6917)(62.9396\text{ u}) + (0.3083)(64.9278\text{ u}) = 63.55\text{ u}$$

Note that this atomic mass is much closer to the isotope mass of ^{63}Cu (62.9396 u) than to the isotope mass of ^{65}Cu (64.9278 u). This happens because ^{63}Cu (69%) is far more abundant than is ^{65}Cu (31%).

PRACTICE PROBLEM 2.13

Naturally occurring potassium consists of the following isotopes in the percentages listed:

^{39}K: 38.9637 u (93.258%)
^{40}K: 39.9640 u (0.0117%)
^{41}K: 40.9618 u (6.7302%)

What is the atomic mass of potassium?

Hint: Convert each percentage into a fraction by dividing by 100. Multiply each fraction by its corresponding mass and sum the resulting values.

Isotopes of atoms are identified by an instrument known as a *mass spectrometer*. In a mass spectrometer, atoms are vaporized and then ionized. The instrument detects each isotope based on its mass-to-charge ratio, and the relative intensity of each isotope is proportional to the natural abundance of the isotopes.

Example 2.14

The most abundant naturally occurring isotope of chlorine is ^{35}Cl, which has an isotope mass of 34.9689 u. Its natural abundance is 75.76%, and ^{37}Cl is the only other chlorine isotope that has a measurable abundance. Given that the atomic mass of chlorine is 35.453 u, calculate the isotope mass and abundance of ^{37}Cl.

Solution

Because ^{35}Cl and ^{37}Cl are the only two isotopes that have a measurable abundance, the natural abundance of ^{37}Cl is simply 100.00% − 75.76% = 24.24%.

Use the following equation to solve for the isotope mass of ^{37}Cl, which is represented as x.

$$\text{Atomic mass of Cl} = (\text{Fraction of }^{35}\text{Cl})(\text{Mass of }^{35}\text{Cl}) + (\text{Fraction of }^{37}\text{Cl})(\text{Mass of }^{37}\text{Cl})$$

$$35.453\text{ u} = (0.7576)(34.9689\text{ u}) + (0.2424)(x)$$

$$35.453\text{ u} = (26.492\text{ u}) + (0.2424)(x)$$

$$8.961\text{ u} = (0.2424)(x)$$

$$x = {}^{37}\text{Cl mass} = 36.97\text{ u}$$

PRACTICE PROBLEM 2.14

The most abundant naturally occurring isotope of boron is ^{11}B, which has an isotope mass of 11.0093 u. Its natural abundance is 80.1%, and ^{10}B is the only other boron isotope that has a measurable abundance. Given that the atomic mass of boron is 10.811 u, calculate the isotope mass and abundance of ^{10}B.

Hint: The natural abundance of ^{10}B and the natural abundance of ^{11}B should sum to 100.0%. Once you have the natural abundances, convert them to fractions and set the atomic mass of boron equal to the sum of each isotope mass multiplied by its natural abundance fraction.

Atomic masses of naturally occurring elements are listed in the periodic table (Appendix A.1). Because atomic mass is the weighted average of *naturally occurring* isotopes, artificial elements by definition do not have atomic masses. Instead, the mass number of the most stable isotope of each artificial element is placed in parentheses in the box for the element in the table. For example, uranium (atomic number 92) is the heaviest naturally occurring element, so all elements with an atomic number greater than 92 list a mass number in parentheses, rather than an atomic mass in the periodic table. Naturally occurring samples of an element have almost exactly the same mixture of isotopes, no matter what the source. Thus, Dalton's hypothesis of a constant mass for the atoms of an element explained the laws of chemical combination because there is a constant *average* mass.

Atomic mass and mass number are *not* the same. Atomic mass refers to the naturally occurring mixture of isotopes, whereas mass number refers to an individual isotope. Atomic mass is an average and is never an exact integer, whereas mass number is the sum of the number of protons plus the number of neutrons of an individual isotope and is always an integer. The mass number is essentially the isotope mass rounded to an integer.

SECTION REVIEW

- Historically, atomic mass was determined from mass ratios, such as those used to develop the law of definite proportions. Today, the mass and percent occurrence of each isotope are used.
- Atomic mass is the weighted average of the masses of the naturally occurring mixture of isotopes of an element. Do not confuse the atomic mass with the *mass number*, *A*, which is the total number of protons and neutrons in the atom.

2.6 The Periodic Table

GOALS

- Discuss the contributions of Mendeleev and Meyer that led to the development of the periodic table.
- Classify the elements in a systematic manner based on their location in the periodic table.
- Identify periods, groups, and sections of the periodic table by name and number.

Background Review

Chapter 1 Science and Measurement:
Section 1.4—The Scientific Method, Hypotheses, Theories, and Laws

DEVELOPMENT OF THE PERIODIC TABLE

Section 1.2 explained a few of the properties of sulfur and of iron. For more than 140 years, chemists have arranged the elements into groups with similar chemical characteristics. This grouping of the elements has been refined to a high degree, and the **periodic table** is the result. A full periodic table is available in Appendix A.1. The elements in the periodic table are numbered sequentially from left to right, and top to bottom. The elements numbered 104 and greater have only recently been synthesized and are so unstable that their chemical properties are unmeasured. Therefore, they will be almost totally ignored for the remainder of this text.

In the periodic table, the elements are arranged so that their atomic numbers, *Z*, are in increasing order horizontally and grouped vertically so that elements with similar chemical properties are in the same group (vertical column).

Many atomic masses were determined as a direct result of work that was inspired by Dalton's hypotheses (Section 2.3). Additionally, scientists attempted to relate the atomic masses of the elements to the elements' properties. This research culminated in the independent development of the periodic table by Dmitri Mendeleev (Figure 2.14) and Lothar Meyer (1830–1895). Because Mendeleev used his periodic table to predict the existence and properties of as yet unknown elements, he is often given sole credit for its development.

FIGURE 2.14 Dmitri Mendeleev (1834–1907)

In 1869, Russian chemist Dmitri Mendeleev arranged the 63 known elements at the time into a table based on their masses and properties. Based on his table, he successfully predicted the existence and properties of four elements that had not yet been discovered.

Mendeleev put the elements known in the 1860s in ascending order according to their atomic masses. (Atomic numbers had not yet been defined because protons had not yet been discovered.) When he did this, Mendeleev noticed that, in general, the properties of every seventh known element were similar. He arranged the elements in a table, with elements having similar properties in the same group. At several points where an element did not seem to fit well in the position its atomic mass called for, he hypothesized that there was an undiscovered element for that position. For example, the next known element after zinc, Zn, by atomic mass was arsenic, As. However, because arsenic's properties were much more similar to those of phosphorus, P, than to those of aluminum, Al, or silicon, Si, Mendeleev predicted that two elements that fit the positions between zinc and arsenic in the periodic table had not yet been discovered (Figure 2.15). He described their expected properties from those of the elements above and below them in the table. His predictions helped other chemists discover these elements, now known as gallium, Ga, and germanium, Ge.

ОПЫТЪ СИСТЕМЫ ЭЛЕМЕНТОВЪ

ОСНОВАННОЙ НА ИХЪ АТОМНОМЪ ВѢСѢ И ХИМИЧЕСКОМЪ СХОДСТВѢ

			Ti = 50	Zr = 90	? = 180.
			V = 51	Nb = 94	Ta = 182
			Cr = 52	Mo = 96	W = 186.
			Mn = 55	Rh = 104,4	Pt = 197,4.
			Fe = 56	Ru = 104,4	Ir = 198
			Ni = Co = 59	Pl = 106,6	Os = 199.
H = 1			Cu = 63,4	Ag = 108	Hg = 200
	Be = 9,4	Mg = 24	Zn = 65,2	Cd = 112	
	B = 11	Al = 27,4	? = 68	Ur = 116	Au = 197?
	C = 12	Si = 28	? = 70	Sn = 118	
	N = 14	P = 31	As = 75	Sb = 122	Bi = 210?
	O = 16	S = 32	Se = 79,4	Te = 128?	
	F = 19	Cl = 35	Br = 80	I = 127	
Li = 7	Na = 23	K = 39	Rb = 85,4	Cs = 133	Tl = 204
		Ca = 40	Sr = 87,6	Ba = 137	Pb = 207
		? = 45	Ce = 92		
		?Er = 56	La = 94		
		?Yt = 60	Di = 95		
		?In = 75,6	Th = 118?		

Д. Менделѣевъ

FIGURE 2.15 Mendeleev's Periodic Table

Mendeleev's periodic table was laid out sideways compared with the modern version, but you can still recognize the vertical groups from the modern periodic table as horizontal rows in Mendeleev's table. Because the chemical properties of arsenic were similar to those of phosphorus, Mendeleev placed arsenic in the same group as phosphorus in the table and left two open spots between zinc and arsenic for elements that had not yet been discovered. His table also predicted undiscovered elements where scandium and hafnium would later be placed. Red boxes have been added to call attention to these open spots.

Several other elements seemed out of order. For example, based on their atomic masses, iodine, I (126.9 u) should have gone before tellurium, Te (127.6 u), but their chemical properties suggested the opposite order, with tellurium in the same family as selenium, Se, and iodine in the same family as bromine, Br. Mendeleev concluded that the atomic masses must have been determined incorrectly and put these two elements in the positions consistent with their properties. The periodic properties of the elements are based on their atomic numbers, not their atomic masses, which explains Mendeleev's difficulty placing certain elements based solely on their atomic masses.

> The periodic table is based on the atomic numbers, *Z*, of the elements, not their atomic masses.

Example 2.15

In the modern periodic table, locate two pairs of naturally occurring elements besides iodine and tellurium that are out of order, based on their atomic masses. You can use the periodic table in Appendix A.1.

Solution

Based on their atomic masses, the elements argon ($Z = 18$; 39.95 u) and potassium ($Z = 19$; 39.10 u) and the elements cobalt ($Z = 27$; 58.93 u) and nickel ($Z = 28$; 58.69 u) are in reverse order. This illustrates the challenge of trying to construct a periodic table in the days before the discovery of atomic numbers and Mendeleev's insight in recognizing the importance of chemical properties over atomic mass.

PRACTICE PROBLEM 2.15

Are any elements in the periodic table out of order according to their atomic numbers?

Hint: Atomic masses depend on the individual masses of the naturally occurring isotopes.

EVERYDAY CONNECTION

Noble gases are not very reactive, but they glow in distinctive colors when given an electrical discharge.

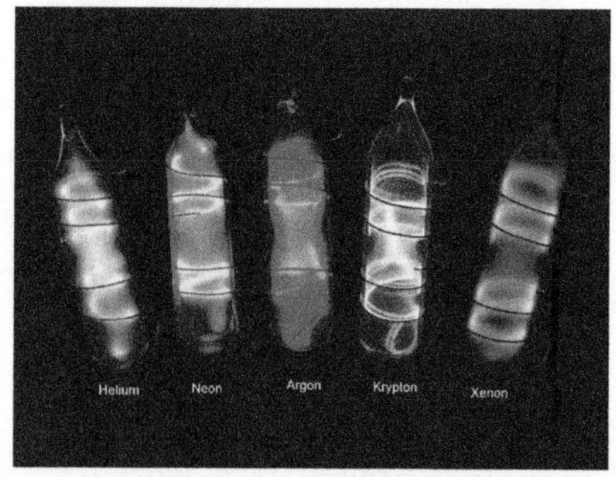

smart-elements®

This is the phenomenon behind neon signs.

iStockphoto/ Thinkstock

An entire group of elements—the noble gases—was discovered after the periodic table was first formulated. These elements are colorless, odorless gases, and almost totally inert. Their lack of combining capacity means that they are not found in any naturally occurring compounds. If some compound had had a percentage of its mass unaccounted for, chemists would have known to look for the missing elements, but because the noble gases do not combine spontaneously with substances that they come into contact with in nature, there was no clue to their existence. Helium was first discovered by its emission lines in sunlight, which did not match those of any known element. The other noble gases were discovered after scientists realized that the density of air was different from calculated values.

At this point, every atomic number between 1 and 118 is accounted for, so there are no "missing" elements, and there is no evidence for any more undiscovered naturally occurring elements. Any new elements that are added to the periodic table will be artificial elements with very high atomic numbers that are yet to be synthesized.

The periodic table is a tremendous source of information once it is understood. Chapter 8 describes how to use the periodic table to predict the arrangement of electrons around the nucleus in the atoms of each element. Chapter 10 shows how to use the periodic table to predict the number of chemical bonds an atom is likely to form, based on the arrangement of the outermost electrons in the atom. The periodic table's numerical data are used in Chapter 4 in chemical formula calculations and again in Chapter 5 to calculate the masses of chemicals produced or consumed in chemical reactions.

USING THE MODERN PERIODIC TABLE

All of the elements in any horizontal row of the periodic table are said to be in the same **period**. There are seven periods, the first consisting of just hydrogen and helium. The second and third periods contain eight elements each, and the next two periods contain 18 elements each. The sixth and seventh periods each have 32 elements (including the inner transition elements, which are usually located at the bottom of the table for space-saving reasons). The periods are conventionally numbered 1 through 7 going down the left-hand side of the periodic table at the start of each period (Figure 2.16).

The elements in any vertical column in the periodic table are in the same **group**, or **family**. They have similar chemical properties, which change gradually from each one to the one below it. In some groups, the elements are very similar; in others, less so.

> The elements in a given group of the periodic table have similar properties.

> Some periodic tables place hydrogen above fluorine in group 17 (7A) in addition to its position above lithium in group 1 (1A). The properties of hydrogen, however, do not resemble those of the elements in either of those two groups.

Two different sets of group numbers are shown in Figure 2.16. In the older classical group numbering system, the groups are numbered 1 through 8, followed by a letter A or B. Groups 1A and 2A are the two columns on the far left of the periodic table, and groups 3A–8A are the six columns on the far right. Groups 1B–8B cover a total of 10 columns in the middle of the periodic table. The classical group numbers are a holdover from an earlier version of the periodic table, but they are still included on most modern periodic tables (often using Roman numerals I through VIII followed by an A or B). In the modern group numbering system, the columns are simply numbered 1–18 going across the top of the periodic table. In this book, the modern group numbers will typically be used. Occasionally, the classical group numbers will also be included in parentheses.

metal | metalloid | nonmetal

	1 1A	2 2A	3 3B	4 4B	5 5B	6 6B	7 7B	8	9 8B	10	11 1B	12 2B	13 3A	14 4A	15 5A	16 6A	17 7A	18 8A
1	1 H 1.008																	2 He 4.0026
2	3 Li 6.94	4 Be 9.0122											5 B 10.81	6 C 12.011	7 N 14.007	8 O 15.999	9 F 18.998	10 Ne 20.18
3	11 Na 22.99	12 Mg 24.305											13 Al 26.982	14 Si 28.085	15 P 30.974	16 S 32.06	17 Cl 35.45	18 Ar 39.948
4	19 K 39.098	20 Ca 40.078	21 Sc 44.956	22 Ti 47.867	23 V 50.942	24 Cr 51.996	25 Mn 54.938	26 Fe 55.845	27 Co 58.933	28 Ni 58.693	29 Cu 63.546	30 Zn 65.38	31 Ga 69.723	32 Ge 72.63	33 As 74.922	34 Se 78.971	35 Br 79.904	36 Kr 83.798
5	37 Rb 85.468	38 Sr 87.62	39 Y 88.906	40 Zr 91.224	41 Nb 92.906	42 Mo 95.95	43 Tc (98)	44 Ru 101.07	45 Rh 102.91	46 Pd 106.42	47 Ag 107.87	48 Cd 112.41	49 In 114.82	50 Sn 118.71	51 Sb 121.76	52 Te 127.6	53 I 126.9	54 Xe 131.29
6	55 Cs 132.91	56 Ba 137.33	57 La 138.91	72 Hf 178.49	73 Ta 180.95	74 W 183.84	75 Re 186.21	76 Os 190.23	77 Ir 192.22	78 Pt 195.08	79 Au 196.97	80 Hg 200.59	81 Tl 204.38	82 Pb 207.2	83 Bi 208.98	84 Po (209)	85 At (210)	86 Rn (222)
7	87 Fr (223)	88 Ra (226)	89 Ac (227)	104 Rf (267)	105 Db (268)	106 Sg (271)	107 Bh (270)	108 Hs (269)	109 Mt (278)	110 Ds (281)	111 Rg (282)	112 Cn (285)	113 Nh (286)	114 Fl (289)	115 Mc (289)	116 Lv (293)	117 Ts (294)	118 Og (294)

Lanthanoids	58 Ce 140.12	59 Pr 140.91	60 Nd 144.24	61 Pm (145)	62 Sm 150.36	63 Eu 151.96	64 Gd 157.25	65 Tb 158.93	66 Dy 162.5	67 Ho 164.93	68 Er 167.26	69 Tm 168.93	70 Yb 173.05	71 Lu 174.97
Actinoids	90 Th 232.04	91 Pa 231.04	92 U 238.03	93 Np (237)	94 Pu (244)	95 Am (243)	96 Cm (247)	97 Bk (247)	98 Cf (251)	99 Es (252)	100 Fm (257)	101 Md (258)	102 No (259)	103 Lr (266)

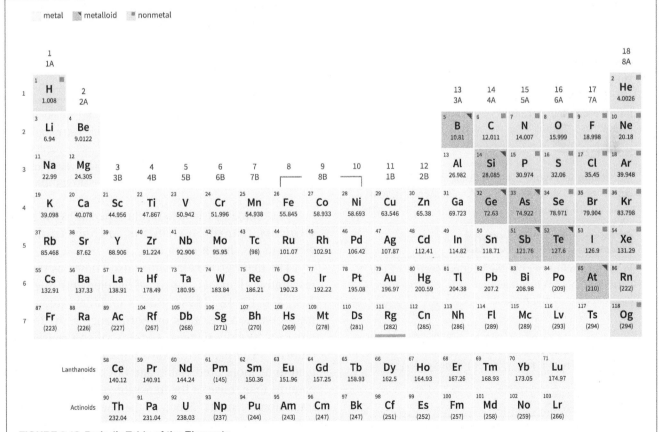

FIGURE 2.16 Periodic Table of the Elements

NOTE: You need to be online to access this activity.

Notice the group numbers across the top of the table and the period numbers along the left side. Click on the image to open an interactive version of the table, where clicking any individual element will allow you to see its name.

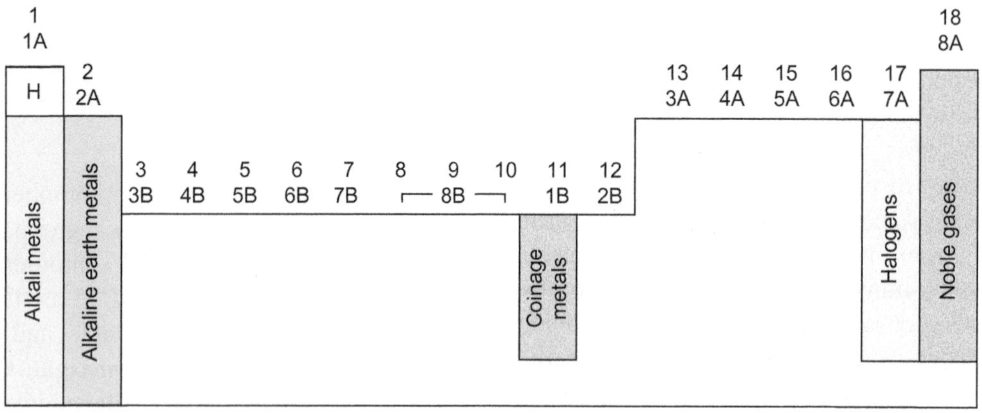

FIGURE 2.17 Group Names

Some groups are known by a name as well as a number. Some of the more commonly used group names are shown here.

Some groups have family names and are typically referred to by these names rather than by their group numbers (Figure 2.17). The **alkali metals** include all the elements of group 1 (1A), except hydrogen. The **alkaline earth metals** are the elements of periodic group 2 (2A), and the **coinage metals** (copper, silver, and gold) are in group 11 (1B). The **halogens** form group 17 (7A), and the **noble gases** constitute group 18 (8A).

Example 2.16

Which element begins the fourth period of the periodic table? Which element ends it? How many elements are in that period?

Solution

According to Figure 2.16, potassium, K ($Z = 19$), begins period 4; krypton, Kr ($Z = 36$), ends it; and there are 18 elements in the period.

PRACTICE PROBLEM 2.16

Which element begins the second period of the periodic table? Which element ends it? How many elements are in that period?

Hint: Use Figure 2.16. Recall that periods are the horizontal rows, and they are numbered on the left side of the periodic table.

Example 2.17

a. Select the period and group where each of the following elements is located: neon, Ne; rubidium, Rb; tungsten, W; and francium, Fr.
b. Which of the elements in (a) have similar chemical properties?

Solution

a. According to Figure 2.16:
   Ne is in period 2, group 18 (8A)
   Rb is in period 5, group 1 (1A)
   W is in period 6, group 6 (6B)
   Fr is in period 7, group 1 (1A)
b. Elements that are in the same group (family) have similar chemical properties, so Rb and Fr (both in group 1) should have similar chemical properties.

PRACTICE PROBLEM 2.17

Sodium reacts violently with water. Which element—fluorine, F; aluminum, Al; palladium, Pd; or potassium, K—is likely to react violently with water, too?

Hint: Elements that are in the same group (vertical column) have similar chemical properties.

The elements can also be classified as **main group elements, transition elements,** or **inner transition elements,** as shown in Figure 2.18.

The main group elements, also known as the representative elements, consist of the elements in groups 1, 2, and 13–18. These groups include some of the most common elements on Earth, such as hydrogen, nitrogen, carbon, oxygen, sodium, silicon, sulfur, and chlorine. The properties of the main group elements tend to be more predictable and fall more reliably into patterns than those of the transition elements and inner transition elements. Much of the chemistry described in this course will deal with the main group elements.

The transition elements consist of groups 3–11, which include some of the most common metals used in our everyday lives, such as iron, nickel, chromium, cobalt, and copper. Since all of the transition elements

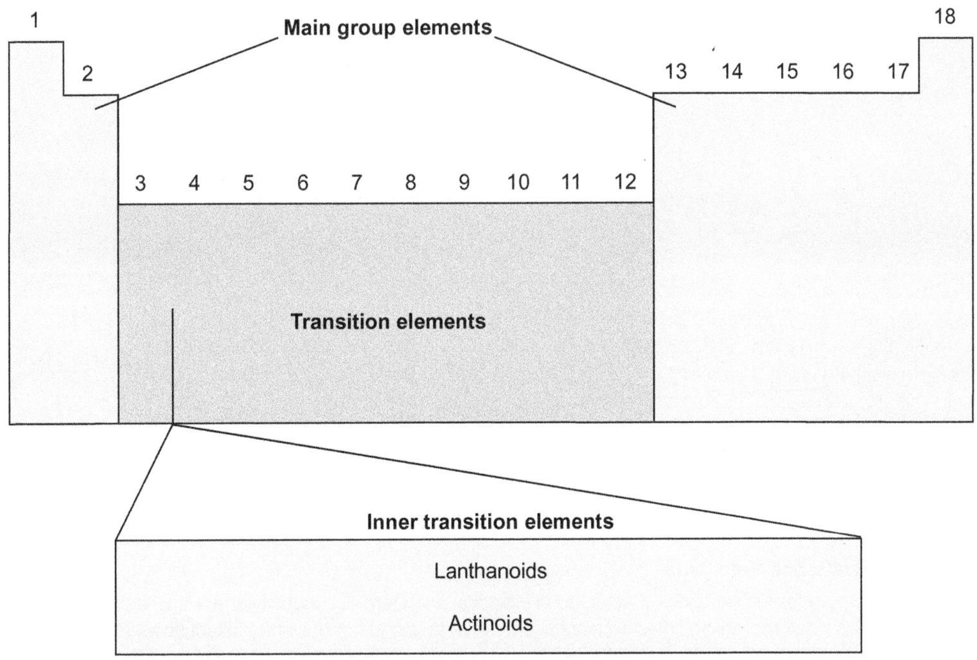

FIGURE 2.18 Main Group Elements, Transition Elements, and Inner Transition Elements

The main group elements are those in the two columns on the far left of the periodic table and the six columns on the right side. The transition elements, also known as the transition metals, make up the four rows in the center of the table. The inner transition elements, or rare earth elements, are the two rows shown separately at the bottom of the periodic table.

are metals, they are also known as the **transition metals**. The group 12 (2B) elements (zinc, cadmium, and mercury) are technically not considered transition metals and are often called *post-transition metals* instead.

The inner transition elements fit into the periodic table in periods 6 and 7, right after lanthanum, La, and actinium, Ac, respectively. Elements 58–71 (cerium, Ce, through lutetium, Lu) are called the lanthanoids (also known as the lanthanide series), after lanthanum, the element that precedes cerium. Elements 90–103 (thorium, Th, through lawrencium, Lr) are similarly called the actinoids (also known as the actinide series), after actinium, the element that precedes thorium. The inner transition elements are also known as the rare earth elements, but some of them, such as cerium, lanthanum, and dysprosium, are fairly common in Earth's crust; however, they tend to be found more spread out rather than in rich deposits the way many other elements are. Many of the inner transition metals have common uses. For example, cerium is often used in water purifiers. Lanthanum is used in rechargeable batteries and camera lenses. Dysprosium has strong magnetic properties when combined with other elements and is used to construct motors for wind turbines and hybrid car batteries. The inner transition metals are conventionally placed below the others to make the width of the periodic table more manageable. All of the inner transition elements belong to group 3 (3B).

Example 2.18

Classify the following elements as main group, transition elements, or inner transition elements.

a. Cs
b. In
c. U

Solution

Use Figure 2.16 and Figure 2.18 to locate these elements in the periodic table.

a. Cs (group 1, period 6) is a main group element.
b. In (group 13, period 5) is a main group element.
c. U ($Z = 92$) is an inner transition element—an actinoid. All of the elements after U in the periodic table are artificial and radioactive (Chapter 20).

PRACTICE PROBLEM 2.18

In which period are the lanthanoid elements found? In which period are the actinoid elements found?

Hint: The lanthanoids and actinoids are the inner transition elements that are placed below the main periodic table.

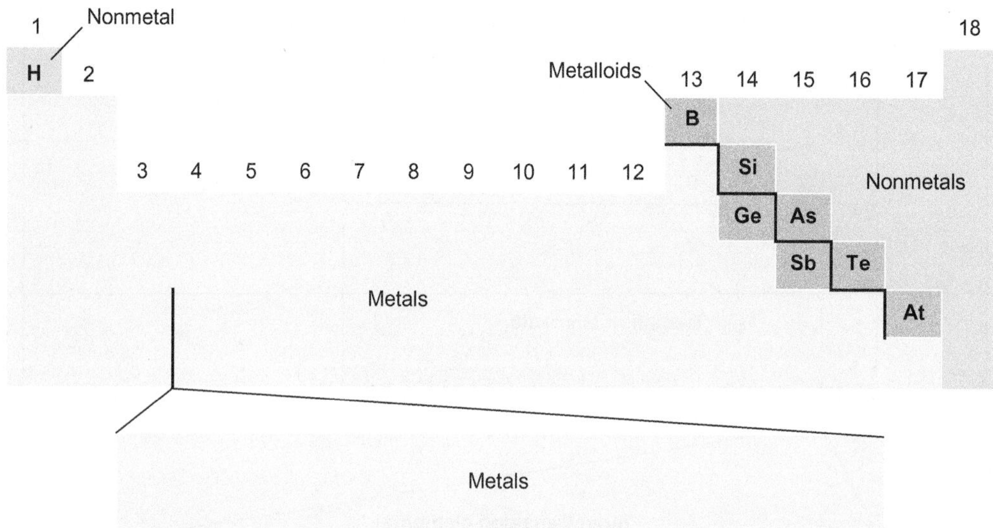

FIGURE 2.19 Metals, Nonmetals, and Metalloids

The metals all share certain properties, such as a shiny luster, good electrical and thermal conductivity, and malleability. The nonmetals also share certain properties, such as a dull (not shiny) color, nonconductivity of heat and electricity, and brittleness as solids. The seven elements shaded in green, adjacent to the stepped line, are the metalloids. They have some properties of metals and some properties of nonmetals.

FIGURE 2.20 Video Tutorial: Classifying Elements

NOTE: You need to be online to access this video.

This video shows how to classify elements as metal, nonmetal, or metalloid, and also as main group, transition metal, or inner transition metal.

Figure 2.19 shows how the elements can also be classified as **metals**, **nonmetals**, and **metalloids**. The metals, which make up the majority of the elements, are located to the left of a stepped line starting to the left of boron, B, and continuing downward and to the right, ending to the left of astatine, At. The nonmetals consist of hydrogen and most of the elements to the right of the stepped line. The metalloids consist of the seven elements shown in Figure 2.19 that appear along the step.

Metals generally have a glossy or shiny appearance called a metallic luster and are mostly malleable (can be pounded into thin sheets) and **ductile** (can be drawn into a wire). Nonmetals, when found in the solid phase, are generally brittle. Metals conduct electricity, whereas most nonmetals do not. Metalloids have some properties of metals and some of nonmetals. The video in Figure 2.20 discusses the classification of the elements.

Example 2.19

Which of the following elements are metals and which are nonmetals?

a. Calcium, Ca
b. Phosphorus, P
c. Nickel, Ni
d. The carbon in a diamond, C

Solution

According to Figure 2.19:

a. Calcium is a metal.
b. Phosphorus is a nonmetal.
c. Nickel is a metal.
d. Carbon is a nonmetal.

PRACTICE PROBLEM 2.19

Classify each of the following as a metal or a nonmetal:

a. The carbon (graphite) in a "lead" pencil, C
b. Silver, Ag

Hint: Locate carbon and silver in the periodic table in Figure 2.17, and then determine to which regions these correspond in the periodic table in Figure 2.19.

Example 2.20

Use the periodic table to identify each of the following.

a. The fifth element in the first row of transition metals
b. The element of the fourth period that is also in group 6
c. The seventh transition element
d. The first element of group 8
e. The third halogen
f. The first alkaline earth metal
g. The first coinage metal

Solution

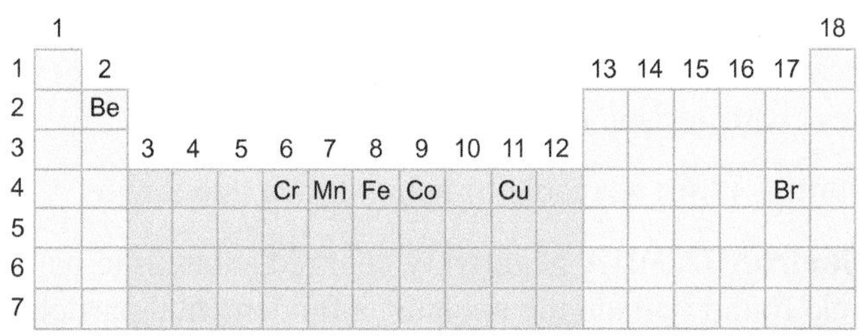

a. Mn
b. Cr
c. Co
d. Fe
e. Br
f. Be
g. Cu

PRACTICE PROBLEM 2.20

Given the properties of the following elements, determine whether the element is most likely a metal, nonmetal, or metalloid.

a. Shiny, malleable, conducts electricity
b. Shiny, brittle, conducts electricity
c. Dull, brittle, does not conduct electricity

Hint: Metalloids have properties of both metals and nonmetals.

SECTION REVIEW

- The periodic table was originally developed using atomic masses and the chemical and physical properties of the elements, but it is now known that atomic numbers, not atomic masses, are the basis for the properties of an element.
- The modern periodic table is arranged in order of increasing atomic number.
- The organization of elements in the periodic table makes it easier to identify the similarities and differences among different elements.
- Elements in the same group in the periodic table generally have similar chemical properties.

Putting It Together

The example problems in earlier sections of this chapter focus on just the new skills acquired in that section, but homework and exam questions in chemistry often require more than just one skill at a time. In fact, you will likely be expected to apply knowledge from across the entire chapter, or even multiple chapters, in a single problem. This final example problem is meant to help you prepare for these types of multiconcept questions. Additional examples can be found in the end-of-chapter exercises.

Example 2.21

Provide the following information about the elements hydrogen, H; yttrium, Y; and arsenic, As.

a. Determine the period and group of each element.
b. Classify each element as a main group element, a transition element, or an inner transition element.
c. Classify each element as a metal, a metalloid, or a nonmetal.

Solution

a. There are seven horizontal rows, or periods, in the periodic table. They are labeled 1–7, as shown in Figure 2.16. There are also 18 columns (or groups or families) in the periodic table. There are two different sets of numbering systems for groups.

   Hydrogen is in period 1 and group 1 (1A).
   Yttrium is in period 5 and group 3 (3B).
   Arsenic is in period 4 and group 15 (5A).

b. The locations of the main group, transition metals, and inner transition elements are shown in Figure 2.18.

   Elements in groups 1 (1A) and 2 (2A) are main group elements, so hydrogen (group 1/1A) is a main group element. Yttrium is located in row 5 of group 3 (3B), so it is a transition element. Arsenic is located in group 15 (5A), so it is a main group element.

c. The locations of the metals, nonmetals, and metalloids in the periodic table are shown in Figure 2.19.

Despite being placed above the group 1 (1A) metals in most periodic tables, hydrogen is a nonmetal. Yttrium is located in the middle of the periodic table (group 3/3B), far to the left of the stepped line, so it is a metal (a transition metal, in fact). Arsenic (period 4, group 15/5A) is one of the seven metalloid elements located immediately to the left and right of the stepped line.

PRACTICE PROBLEM 2.21

Ga-69 and Ga-71 are the only two naturally occurring isotopes of gallium.

a. How many protons, neutrons, and electrons are there in each isotope?
b. Give the isotopic symbols for Ga-69 and Ga-71.
c. The isotope mass of ^{69}Ga is 68.926 u, and its natural abundance is 60.11%. What is the isotope mass and abundance of ^{71}Ga?

Hint: The numbers in Ga-69 and Ga-71 are the mass numbers, which are the sum of the protons and neutrons in those isotopes. Gallium contains 31 protons. The isotopic symbols will have the form ^{A}Ga, where A is the mass number. According to the periodic table, the atomic mass of gallium is 69.723 u. Set the atomic mass of gallium equal to the sum of each isotope mass multiplied by its natural abundance fraction. You can determine the natural abundance of ^{71}Ga based on the fact that ^{69}Ga is the only other gallium isotope of appreciable natural abundance.

Key Terms, Symbols, and Equations

KEY TERMS

alkali metal (2.6): A metal in group 1 (1A) of the periodic table—Li, Na, K, Rb, Cs, or Fr.

alkaline earth metal (2.6): A metal in group 2 (2A) of the periodic table—Be, Mg, Ca, Sr, Ba, or Ra.

anion (2.4): A negatively charged ion.

atom (2.3): The smallest particle that retains the characteristic composition of an element.

atomic mass (2.5): The weighted average of the masses of the naturally occurring mixture of isotopes of an element, compared with one-twelfth of the mass of a ^{12}C atom.

atomic mass scale (2.5): A relative scale of masses based on the mass of ^{12}C being the standard and having a mass defined as exactly 12 u.

atomic mass unit, u (2.5): A mass equal to one-twelfth of the mass of a ^{12}C atom; also abbreviated as amu.

atomic number, *Z* (2.4): The number of protons in the nucleus of each atom of an element.

cathode ray (2.3): A beam of electrons.

cation (2.4): A positively charged ion.

coinage metal (2.6): An element of periodic group 11 (1B)—Cu, Ag, or Au.

Dalton's atomic theory (2.3): The theory that matter is made up of small particles (atoms) that have properties characteristic of an element.

ductile (2.6): Capable of being drawn into a wire.

electron (2.3): A negatively charged subatomic particle found outside the nucleus; a fundamental particle of nature.

family (2.6): In the periodic table, a column that includes elements with similar chemical properties; a periodic group.

formula (2.1): A combination of symbols, subscripts, and possibly superscripts that identifies the composition of an element, compound, or ion.

group (2.6): In the periodic table, a column that includes elements with similar chemical properties; a family.

halogen (2.6): An element of periodic group 17 (7A)—F, Cl, Br, I, or At.

inner transition elements (2.6): A collective term for the lanthanoids and actinoids.

ion (2.4): A charged atom or molecule that has either lost or gained one or more electrons.

isotope (2.4): A form of an element whose atoms have the same number of protons but different numbers of neutrons.

law of constant composition (2.2): The composition of a compound is fixed; also called *law of definite proportions*.

law of definite proportions (2.2): The composition of a compound is fixed; also called *law of constant composition*.

law of multiple proportions (2.2): When two or more elements combine to form more than one compound, for a fixed mass of one element, the masses of each of the other elements in the compounds occur in a small, whole-number ratio.

main group element (2.6): An element in groups 1, 2, and 13–18 (1A–8A) in the periodic table.

mass number, *A* (2.4): The sum of the number of protons and the number of neutrons in an atom; the distinguishing difference among isotopes of a given element.

metal (2.6): An element on the left of the stepped line in the periodic table, or a mixture of such elements. Metals tend to be solids at room temperature, conduct heat and electricity, and are malleable and ductile.

metalloid (2.6): An element near the stepped line between metals and nonmetals in the periodic table. Metalloids have some properties of both metals and nonmetals.

molecule (2.3): A group of atoms bonded by shared electrons.

neutral (2.4): Neither positively nor negatively charged.

neutron (2.3): A subatomic particle found in the nucleus that has no charge and a mass slightly greater than 1 u.

nucleus (2.3): The center (core) of an atom, consisting of the protons and neutrons. It accounts for almost all of the mass, but almost none of the volume, of an atom.

noble gas (2.6): An element in the far-right column of the periodic table, group 18 (8A)—He, Ne, Ar, Kr, Xe, or Rn.

nonmetal (2.6): Hydrogen or any element to the right of the stepped line in the periodic table. When nonmetals are solid at room temperature, they tend to be brittle and nonconducting. Many nonmetals are gases at room temperature.

percent (2.2): Parts per hundred parts.

period (2.6): One of the seven horizontal rows of the periodic table.

periodic table (2.6): An organization of elements by increasing atomic number, with elements having similar chemical properties being aligned in vertical columns.

proportion (2.2): The ratio of the number of a certain item divided by the total number of items (compare to percent).

proton (2.3): A subatomic particle found in the nucleus with a mass slightly greater than 1 u and a charge of 1+.

radioactivity (2.3): The emission of particles during nuclear decay.

relative scale (2.5): A scale based on an arbitrarily chosen standard; the atomic mass scale is a relative scale of masses based on the mass of ^{12}C.

subatomic particle (2.4): A proton, neutron, or electron.

symbol (2.1): The abbreviation for an element consisting of a capital letter, which may sometimes be followed by a lowercase letter.

transition element (2.6): Any element in groups 3–12 that start in the fourth period of the periodic table, having atomic numbers 21–30, 39–48, 57, 72–80, or 104–112, and designated with B in the classical group naming system.

transition metal (2.6): Another term for transition element, because all of the transition elements are metals.

weighted average (2.5): The average value of several types of items, taking into account the number of individual items of each type.

SYMBOLS AND ABBREVIATIONS

A (mass number) (2.4)

n (number of neutrons) (2.4)

p (number of protons) (2.4)

u (atomic mass unit) (2.5)

Z (atomic number) (2.4)

EQUATIONS

Atomic mass = Σ(Fraction of isotope) × (Mass of isotope) (2.4)

$A = \text{p} + \text{n} = Z + \text{n}$ (2.2)

$\text{n} = A - Z$ (2.3)

$Z = \text{p}$ (2.1)

Chapter Summary

Each element has a chemical symbol consisting of one or two letters. The first letter (or the only one) is always capitalized; the second, if present, is always lowercase (Section 2.1).

Lavoisier's careful measurements of mass during chemical reactions led him to propose the law of conservation of mass, which states that matter cannot be created or destroyed during chemical reactions or physical changes. This generalization encouraged chemists to measure the masses of elements in compounds more carefully and resulted in the laws of definite proportions and multiple proportions. The law of definite proportions states that the percentage of each element in a sample of any pure compound is always the same. The law of multiple proportions states that if the mass of one of the elements in two or more compounds of the same elements is held constant, then the masses of each of the other elements form a small, whole-number ratio (Section 2.2).

Dalton suggested that the elements are composed of indivisible atoms and that the atoms of each element have a characteristic mass, different from the mass of any other element. He stated that atoms combine to form molecules when the elements combine to form compounds. These hypotheses explained the laws of chemical combination known at that time, but most of them have been amended in light of later discoveries. While the atom is still considered to be the fundamental particle of an element, subsequent work in the early 1900s showed the existence of subatomic particles. Thomson discovered the electron and Chadwick discovered the neutron. Rutherford proposed the nuclear model of the atom, where protons occupy the nucleus, a small volume at the center of the atom (Section 2.3).

The nucleus does not change during a chemical reaction. The number of electrons in the neutral atom matches the number of protons, called the atomic number, Z. All atoms of a given element have the same atomic number, which differs from the atomic numbers of other elements. The sum of the numbers of protons and neutrons is called the mass number, A. Different atoms of the same element may have different numbers of neutrons and thus different mass numbers. Those that do are isotopes of one another. An isotope is identified by the symbol of the element, with the mass number as a superscript to the left. Ions are formed when an atom gains or loses electrons. Positively charged ions are known as cations and negatively charged ions are called anions (Section 2.4).

The naturally occurring mixture of isotopes in any sample of a given element has almost exactly the same percentage of each isotope as any other sample. Therefore, the average mass of all the atoms in any sample of the element is constant to four or more significant digits. That weighted average is called the atomic mass, which is not the same as the mass number or the mass of an atom. Atomic masses are reported on a relative scale, with an atom of the ^{12}C isotope being defined as having a mass of exactly 12 u. The symbol u is the atomic mass unit (Section 2.5).

When arranged in order of increasing atomic mass, the various elements, with a few exceptions, have periodically recurring properties. Mendeleev produced a periodic table based on this ordering. Later, it was learned that the atomic number is the basis for the chemical properties of an element, so the modern periodic table arranges the elements in order of increasing atomic number. Elements with similar properties are arranged in vertical groups.

The periodic table consists of 118 elements, arranged in 7 periods and 18 groups. The groups that have special names are the alkali metals, alkaline earth metals, coinage metals, halogens, and noble gases. The elements can be classified as metals, nonmetals, or metalloids. They can also be classified as main group elements, transition elements, or inner transition elements (Section 2.6).

END OF CHAPTER QUESTIONS

Refer to the periodic table as needed.

2.1 Chemical Symbols

1. Write the symbol for each element.
   a. hydrogen
   b. helium
   c. lithium
   d. carbon
   e. nitrogen
   f. oxygen

2. Write the symbol for each element.
   a. mercury
   b. argon
   c. copper
   d. zinc
   e. strontium
   f. sodium

3. Write the symbol for each element.
   a. palladium
   b. gallium
   c. antimony
   d. iron
   e. lead
   f. Bromine

4. Write the symbol for each element.
   a. gold
   b. fluorine
   c. tungsten
   d. neon
   e. potassium
   f. silver

5. Write the symbol for each element.
   a. carbon, cadmium, and calcium
   b. boron, barium, and bismuth
   c. iron and iodine
   d. tin and titanium

6. Give the name for each element.
   a. Mg and Mn
   b. K and P
   c. Na and S
   d. Cu and Co

7. Give the name for each element.
   a. Fe and F
   b. Ag and Au
   c. Na and Ne
   d. Sn and S
   e. P and K

8. Give the name of each element.
   a. Ag
   b. Pb
   c. As
   d. Se
   e. W
   f. Ni

9. Give the name of each element.
   a. Au
   b. C
   c. Kr
   d. Sb
   e. Nd
   f. Hg

10. How many elements are present in each of the following?
    a. $OsSO_4$
    b. BN
    c. NI_3
    d. $Sc(SCN)_3$
    e. HF
    f. Nb

11. How many elements are present in each of the following?
    a. $CoCl_2$
    b. $W(CO)_6$
    c. CCl_4
    d. HCN
    e. PH_3
    f. $(NH_4)_2SO_4$

12. Determine the relative number of atoms of each type of element in the following compounds.
    a. $OsSO_4$
    b. BN
    c. NI_3
    d. $Sc(SCN)_3$
    e. $CoCl_2$
    f. $W(CO)_6$
    g. CCl_4
    h. HCN
    i. PH_3
    j. $(NH_4)_2SO_4$

2.2 The Laws of Chemical Combination

13. When 31.9 mg of a compound containing only carbon and hydrogen is burned completely in oxygen, it yields 87.7 mg of carbon dioxide and 71.8 mg of water. How much oxygen is used up?

14. When 7.80 mg of a compound containing only carbon and hydrogen was burned completely in 28.3 mg of oxygen, 23.3 mg of carbon dioxide and some water were formed. Calculate the mass of water formed.

15. A 7.33 g sample of mercury(I) oxide was decomposed into mercury and oxygen, yielding 7.05 g of mercury.
    a. What mass of oxygen was obtained?
    b. What fraction of the compound was oxygen?
    c. What percentage of the compound was oxygen?

16. An 18.6 g sample of a compound contains 39.35% sodium and 60.65% chlorine.
    a. Calculate the mass of chlorine present.
    b. Calculate the mass of chlorine present in a 30.0-g sample of the same compound.

17. Sodium and chlorine react to form one compound only. In a certain reaction, 20.0 g of sodium reacts completely with 3.454 g of chlorine to produce sodium chloride.
    a. How much chlorine would react with 15.44 g of sodium?
    b. How much sodium would react with 0.7206 g of chlorine?

18. Sodium and chlorine react to form one compound only. In a certain reaction, 20.0 g of sodium and 30.8 g of chlorine react completely. How much chlorine would remain unreacted if 20.0 g of sodium and 50.0 g of chlorine were allowed to react?

19. A compound is formed between elements A and B in which two atoms of B combine with each atom of A. Each atom of B has a mass of 127 u, and each atom of A has a mass of 24.3 u.
    a. Calculate the mass ratio.
    b. Which ratio is an integer: the ratio of atoms, or masses, or both?

20. The ratio of masses of sulfur and oxygen in sulfur dioxide is 1.0 g to 1.0 g. Is this fact a proof of the law of multiple proportions?

21. The ratio of the mass of carbon to the mass of oxygen in carbon monoxide is about 3 g to 4 g. Does this fact confirm the law of multiple proportions?

22. A sample of a compound of only carbon and hydrogen contains 79.89% carbon. Show that this compound obeys the law of multiple proportions.

23. Show that the following set of data obeys the law of multiple proportions.

	First Compound	**Second Compound**
Element 1	92.26%	85.63%
Element 2	7.74%	14.37%

24. Show that the following set of data obeys the law of multiple proportions.

	First Compound	**Second Compound**
Element X	103.1 g	96.23 g
Element Y	7.96 g	14.87 g

25. Two compounds are each composed of elements A and B. The first contains 2.468 g of B for every gram of A. Of the following possibilities, which could be the correct number of grams of B per gram of A of the second compound?
    a. 1.234 g
    b. 4.936 g
    c. 2.512 g
    d. 2.468 g

2.3 The History of the Atom

26. What happens to a scientific hypothesis if experiments show it to be incorrect? To which of Dalton's postulates did this first happen?

27. According to Dalton's atomic theory, all atoms of the same element have the same mass. An atom of zinc has a mass of 65.4 u and an atom of sulfur has a mass of 32.1 u.
    a. What is the mass ratio of one atom of zinc to one atom of sulfur?
    b. What is the total mass of 100 atoms of zinc? What is the total mass of 100 atoms of sulfur?
    c. What is the ratio of masses of 100 atoms of zinc to 100 atoms of sulfur?
    d. Choose an arbitrary, large number of atoms of zinc. Then calculate the mass of that number and the mass of an equal number of sulfur atoms. Calculate the ratio of the total masses.
    e. What can you conclude about the ratio of masses of equal numbers of zinc and sulfur atoms?

28. All naturally occurring samples of boron trifluoride, when purified, contain the same percentage of boron and the same percentage of fluorine.

Naturally occurring fluorine consists of only one isotope. What do the constant percentages say about the two naturally occurring isotopes of boron?

29. The atoms of element Z each have about 12 times the mass of a ^{9}Be atom. Another element, X, has atoms whose mass is about one-fourth the mass of Z atoms. A third element, Q, has atoms with $1\,^{1}/_{3}$ the mass of X atoms.
   a. Make a table of relative atomic masses based on ^{9}Be as 9 u.
   b. Identify the elements Z, X, and Q.

30. Restate Dalton's first three postulates in amended form, based on modern information.

31. Match the names of the scientists with their contribution to the understanding of the atom.

Scientist	Contribution
a) Dalton	1) Discovered radioactivity
b) Thomson	2) Nuclear atom model
c) Rutherford	3) Solid-sphere atom model
d) Chadwick	4) Plum-pudding model
e) Becquerel	5) Discovered the neutron

32. What part of Dalton's atomic theory was challenged by Thomson's work with cathode rays?

33. Analyze Rutherford's gold-foil experiment for use of the scientific method.
   a. What was the hypothesis at the start of the experiment?
   b. How was the hypothesis tested?
   c. What were the results? Did the results support the hypothesis?
   d. How did Rutherford use his results to modify his hypothesis?

34. Rutherford knew that atoms were made up of negatively and positively charged particles, now called electrons and protons. What evidence led him to propose that another, neutral particle must exist?

2.4 Subatomic Particles, Isotopes, and Ions

35. Identify the only stable isotope that contains no neutrons. Hint: Use Figure 2.11.

36. Isotopes of which element have the following?
   a. the smallest mass number
   b. the smallest atomic number
   c. exactly 100 protons
   d. the largest number of protons

37. Of the isotopes of elements 104–118 listed in the periodic table, which one has the greatest number of neutrons?

38. Complete the table for neutral atoms of specific isotopes.

	Isotopic Symbol	Atomic Number	Mass Number	No. of Protons	No. of Neutrons	No. of Electrons
a.	^{112}Cd					
b.		49	115			
c.		81			122	
d.			80	34		
e.	$^{128}_{52}?$					
f.					54	42
g.				45	58	

39. Write the symbol for an isotope for each of the following requirements:
   a. containing one proton and two neutrons
   b. for which the atomic number is 1 and there is one neutron
   c. for which the atomic number is 1 and the mass number is 1
   d. with a mass number of 3 and containing one neutron
   e. with a mass number of 3 and containing two neutrons

40. Complete the table for neutral atoms of specific isotopes.

	Isotopic Symbol	Atomic Number	Mass Number	No. of Protons	No. of Neutrons	No. of Electrons
a.				50	66	
b.		44			56	
c.			174	70		
d.		56	138			

41. Complete the table for neutral atoms of specific isotopes.

	Isotopic Symbol	Atomic Number	Mass Number	No. of Protons	No. of Neutrons	No. of Electrons
a.	^{134}Xe					
b.		27	60			
c.					165	106
d.			126	52		

42. Deuterium, symbol: ^2D, is a special name for the isotope that contains one proton and one neutron.
a. Deuterium is an isotope of which element?
b. Write the more familiar symbol for this isotope.

2.5 Atomic Masses

43. Which element has atoms with average mass about 10 times those of the fluorine atom?

44. Which element has atoms with average mass about 35 times those of the average helium atom?

45. If 37.40% of naturally occurring rhenium atoms have an atomic mass of 184.953 u and the rest have an atomic mass of 186.956 u, what is the atomic mass of rhenium?

46. After a calculation, a student reported the atomic mass of an element as 2.2×10^{-3} u. The student later changed the value to $2.2 \times 10^{+3}$ u. Which value, if either, is more probably correct?

47. One can guess the mass number of the predominant isotope for many elements from the atomic mass of the element, but not in all cases. The mass numbers of the isotopes of selenium are 74, 76, 77, 78, 80, and 82. Explain why the atomic mass is so close to 79 u.

48. ^{80}Br does not occur naturally. Explain how bromine gets its atomic mass of 79.909 u.

49. ^{108}Ag does not occur naturally. Explain how silver gets its atomic mass of 107.87 u.

50. Calculate the atomic mass of rubidium if 72.17% of naturally occurring rubidium atoms have a mass of 84.9118 and 27.83% have a mass of 86.9092 u.

51. Which of the following represent(s) the mass of one atom (to three significant figures)?
a. 0.500 u
b. 12.0 g
c. 6.02×10^{23} u
d. 2.11×10^{3} u
e. 74.9 u

52. A compound contains almost equal masses of fluorine and selenium. Using their atomic masses, determine the formula of the compound.

53. The mass of iodine in a certain compound is almost exactly twice that of the only other element in the compound—copper. Using their atomic masses, determine the formula of the compound.

2.6 The Periodic Table

54. How important was it to the work of Mendeleev that atomic mass generally increases as atomic number increases? Explain.

55. Identify the element:
a. third period, group 15
b. first period, group 3
c. fifth period, group 7
d. sixth period, group 18

56. The general term for a compound formed by an element reacting with oxygen is an oxide. The table below gives you the formulas of oxides of several fourth-period elements. Use your knowledge of periodic trends to predict the formulas of oxides of the elements that are directly above these in the periodic table.

Predicted formulas							
Example formulas	K_2O	CaO	Ga_2O_3	GeO_2	As_2O_3	SeO_2	Br_2O

57. The general term for a compound formed by an element reacting with sulfur is a sulfide. Predict the formulas for sulfides of the same fourth-period elements as in the preceding problem.

Predicted formulas							
Example formulas	K_2O	CaO	Ga_2O_3	GeO_2	As_2O_3	SeO_2	Br_2O

58. The general term for a compound formed by an element reacting with fluorine is a fluoride. The following are the formulas for certain fluorides of fourth-period elements. Predict the formula for a fluoride of each of the elements directly above these in the periodic table.

Predicted formulas							
Example formulas	KF	CaF_2	GaF_3	GeF_4	AsF_3	SeF_2	BrF

59. The general term for a compound formed by an element reacting with chlorine is a chloride. Predict the formulas of chlorides of the same fourth-period elements as in the preceding problem.

60. From the following properties of chlorine and iodine and from the positions of these three elements on the periodic table, predict the corresponding properties of bromine.

Chlorine	**Iodine**	**Bromine**
Gas under normal conditions	Solid under normal conditions	
Light yellow	Deep violet	
Reacts with metals	Reacts with metals	
Reacts with oxygen	Reacts with oxygen	
Does not conduct electricity	Does not conduct electricity	

Putting It Together

61. Could you use the average number of neutrons, instead of atomic number, to build a periodic table as useful as that of Mendeleev?

62. Two compounds of carbon, hydrogen, and oxygen have the following percent compositions. Show that these compounds obey the law of multiple proportions.
a. 62.1% C, 10.3% H, 27.6% O
b. 52.2% C, 13.0% H, 34.8% O

63. In a certain compound, 8.761 g of element B is combined with 15.55 g of element A. In another compound of A and B, 15.55 g of A could possibly be combined with which of the following masses of B?
a. 4.381 g
b. 2.920 g
c. 17.52 g
d. 5.841 g
e. 8.761 g

64. The law of multiple proportions applies to two or more compounds of the same two or more elements. Show that the following data support the law.

	%H	**%S**	**%O**
Compound 1	2.44	39.02	58.54
Compound 2	5.88	84.12	
Compound 3	2.04	32.65	65.31

65. The law of multiple proportions applies to two or more compounds of the same two or more elements. Show that the following data support the law.

	%C	**%H**	**%O**
Compound 1	52.2	13.0	34.8
Compound 2	74.9	25.1	

66. A 14.9 g sample of element A reacts incompletely with a 7.11 g sample of element B. What is the total mass of the product plus the portion of A that did not react?

67. Explain why Mendeleev could predict the existence of germanium but missed the entire group of noble gases.

68. Naturally occurring sulfur consists of 95.0% ^{32}S, which has a mass of 31.97207 u; 0.76% ^{33}S, which has a mass of 32.97146 u; and 4.22% ^{34}S, which has a mass of 33.96786 u. Calculate the atomic mass of sulfur to the proper number of significant digits.

69. Calculate the atomic mass of selenium using the following data.

Isotope	Natural Abundance (%)	Relative Mass (u)
^{74}Se	0.87	73.9205
^{76}Se	9.02	75.9192
^{77}Se	7.58	76.9199
^{78}Se	23.52	77.9173
^{80}Se	49.82	79.9165
^{82}Se	9.19	81.9167

70. The atomic mass of chlorine is 35.453 u. Does any atom of any isotope of chlorine have a mass of 35.453 u? Explain.

71. If you considered the faces of a six-sided die (plural, *dice*) to be "isotopes," then a die would have six isotopes with equal abundances and with masses of 1, 2, 3, 4, 5, and 6. What would the average "atomic mass" of these isotopes be? Would there be any isotopes that have that actual mass?

72. Plot mass number versus atomic number for ^{1}H, ^{16}O, ^{56}Fe, ^{96}Mo, ^{138}Ba, ^{197}Au, and ^{238}U.
   a. Are atomic number and mass number directly proportional?
   b. What can you say about the relationship of these two quantities?

73. The masses of the atoms of the only two naturally occurring isotopes of boron are 10.013 u and 11.009 u, and boron's atomic mass is 10.811 u. Calculate the percentage of each isotope. (Hint: Let x equal the fraction of one of the isotopes, and $(1 - x)$ equal the fraction of the other.)

74. Calculate the atomic mass of lithium from the following data.

Isotope	Natural Abundance (%)	Relative Mass (u)
^{6}Li	7.5	6.0151
^{7}Li	92.5	7.0160

75. Sodium and iodine react to form only one product, sodium iodide. In a certain reaction, 10.00 g of sodium and 55.17 g of iodine react completely.
   a. How much sodium iodide is produced?
   b. When 10.00 g of sodium is mixed with 75.00 g of iodine, only 55.17 g of iodine reacts, producing the same amount of sodium iodide as in part a. Which law(s) of chemical composition explain this phenomenon?

76. Naturally occurring silicon consists of 92.2% ^{28}Si, which has a mass of 27.9769 u; 4.67% ^{29}Si, which has a mass of 28.9765 u; and 3.18% ^{30}Si, which has a mass of 29.9738 u. Calculate the atomic mass of silicon.

PRACTICE PROBLEM SOLUTIONS

Practice Problem 2.1 Solution

The periodic table in Appendix A.1 indicates the name of an element when you click on its symbol.

a. Mn

b. As

c. Ge

d. Pu

Practice Problem 2.2 Solution

The names that correspond to the symbols are given in Appendix A.1.

a. Na_2S has two atoms of sodium, Na, for each atom of sulfur, S.

b. B_2H_6 has six atoms of hydrogen, H, for every two atoms of boron, B.

c. $Ni(ClO_4)_2$ has $1 \times 2 = 2$ atoms of chlorine, Cl, and $4 \times 2 = 8$ atoms of oxygen, O, for each atom of nickel, Ni.

Practice Problem 2.3 Solution

According to Example 2.3, N_2O consists of 63.65% nitrogen by mass and 36.35% oxygen by mass. You can use the reported masses of nitrogen and oxygen to confirm these percentages.

For the 15.50 g sample:

$$\frac{9.866\text{ g N}}{15.50\text{ g N}_2\text{O}} \times 100\% = 63.65\%\text{ N}$$

$$\frac{5.634\text{ g O}}{15.50\text{ g N}_2\text{O}} \times 100\% = 36.35\%\text{ O}$$

For the 25.50 g sample:

$$\frac{16.23 \text{ g N}}{25.50 \text{ g N}_2\text{O}} \times 100\% = 63.65\% \text{ N}$$

$$\frac{9.269 \text{ g O}}{25.50 \text{ g N}_2\text{O}} \times 100\% = 36.35\% \text{ O}$$

The percentages are the same for both samples, which is consistent with the law of definite proportions. Percent composition by mass is independent of the total mass of the sample.

Practice Problem 2.4 Solution

Recall that 46.68% nitrogen by mass means that there is 46.68 g of nitrogen in every 100.0 g NO. Use this relationship and dimensional analysis (Section 1.7) to calculate the mass of NO that contains 100.0 g N:

$$100.0 \text{ g N}\left(\frac{100.0 \text{ g NO}}{46.68 \text{ g N}}\right) = 214.2 \text{ g NO}$$

Practice Problem 2.5 Solution

Calculate the sulfur-to-oxygen, S:O, ratios for both compounds:

$$\text{For SO}_2\text{: } \frac{16.04 \text{ g S}}{16.00 \text{ g O}} = 1.003$$

$$\text{For SO}_3\text{: } \frac{16.04 \text{ g S}}{24.00 \text{ g O}} = 0.6683$$

The S:O mass ratios of these two compounds can now be compared. Dividing the larger value by the smaller value gives

$$\frac{\text{S:O ratio for SO}_2}{\text{S:O ratio for SO}_3} = \frac{1.003}{0.6683} = 1.501$$

Multiplying 1.501 by 2 gives a ratio of 3.002.

The ratio of S:O mass ratios for these compounds is a whole number, 3, so SO_2 and SO_3 follow the law of multiple proportions.

Practice Problem 2.6 Solution

Rutherford showed that the positive charge of the atom was not dispersed throughout the atom but was instead concentrated in a small area (the nucleus). This led Rutherford to propose the nuclear model of the atom.

Practice Problem 2.7 Solution

For each element symbol, the mass number (A) is the superscript on the left side.

a. ^{3}He (The mass number is 3.)

b. ^{15}O (Oxygen has 8 protons, and this isotope has 7 neutrons, so $A = 15$.)

c. ^{10}B (Boron has 5 protons and the same number of neutrons, so $A = 10$.)

d. ^{13}C (Carbon has 6 protons and, in this isotope, $6 + 1 = 7$ neutrons. So, $A = 6 + 7 = 13$.)

Practice Problem 2.8 Solution

a. Hydrogen ($Z = 1$) has one proton, and this isotope of hydrogen has 2 neutrons. The mass number, A, is the sum of the protons and neutrons: $1 + 2 = 3$. The isotope symbol is ^{3}H or $^{3}_{1}$H.

b. Iodine ($Z = 53$) has 53 protons, and this isotope of iodine has 78 neutrons. The mass number, A, is the sum of the protons and neutrons: $53 + 78 = 131$. The isotope symbol is ^{131}I or $^{131}_{53}$I.

c. Polonium ($Z = 84$) has 84 protons. If this isotope has 42 more neutrons than protons, then it has $42 + 84 = 126$ neutrons. The mass number, A, is the sum of the protons and neutrons: $84 + 126 = 210$. The isotope symbol is ^{210}Po or $^{210}_{84}$Po.

Practice Problem 2.9 Solution

$A = \text{p} + \text{n} = Z + \text{n}$, so $Z = A - \text{n}$. For the first atom, $Z = 119 - 69 = 50$, which corresponds to the element tin, Sn. For the second atom, $Z = 119 - 70 = 49$, which corresponds to the element indium, In. Thus, these two atoms are *not* isotopes of the same element.

Practice Problem 2.10 Solution

The first atom, $^{119}_{50}$Sn, has 50 protons and a mass number of 119. It must also have 50 electrons.

The second atom, $^{119}_{49}$In, has 49 protons and a mass number of 119. It must also have 49 electrons.

Practice Problem 2.11 Solution

a. ^{3}H has one proton, two neutrons, and one electron.

b. $^{15}O^{2-}$ has 8 protons, 7 neutrons, and 10 electrons. There are two more electrons than there are protons because the anion has a charge of −2.

c. $^{78}Se^{2-}$ has 34 protons, $78 - 34 = 44$ neutrons, and 36 electrons. There are two more electrons than there are protons because the anion has a charge of −2.

d. $^{55}Mn^{4+}$ has 25 protons, 30 neutrons, and 21 electrons. There are four fewer electrons than there are protons because the cation has a charge of +4.

Practice Problem 2.12 Solution

$$\text{Fuel economy} = 0.65(37.2 \text{ mpg}) + 0.23(24.2 \text{ mpg}) + 0.12(8.8 \text{ mpg})$$

$$\text{Fuel economy} = 24.18 \text{ mpg} + 5.57 \text{ mpg} + 1.06 \text{ mpg}$$

$$\text{Fuel economy} = 30.8 \text{ mpg}$$

Practice Problem 2.13 Solution

The atomic mass is the sum of the fraction of each isotope (i.e., each percentage value divided by 100) multiplied by its isotope mass:

$$\begin{aligned}\text{Atomic mass} &= (0.93258)(38.9637\text{ u})\\ &\quad + (0.000117)(39.9640\text{ u})\\ &\quad + (0.067302)(40.9618\text{ u})\\ \text{Atomic mass} &= (36.33677\text{ u}) + (0.0046758\text{ u})\\ &\quad + (2.75681\text{ u})\\ \text{Atomic mass} &= 39.0983\text{ u}\end{aligned}$$

Practice Problem 2.14 Solution

The problem is solved in the same way as in Example 2.14.

The natural abundance of ^{10}B is 100.0% − 80.1% = 19.9%.

The following equation can be used to solve for the isotope mass of ^{10}B, which is represented as x:

$$\begin{aligned}\text{Atomic mass of B} &= (\text{Fraction of }^{11}\text{B})(\text{Mass of }^{11}\text{B})\\ &\quad + (\text{Fraction of }^{10}\text{B})(\text{Mass of }^{10}\text{B})\\ 10.811\text{ u} &= (0.801)(11.0093\text{ u}) + (0.199\text{ u})(x)\\ 10.811\text{ u} &= 8.818\text{ u} + (0.199)(x)\\ 1.993 &= (0.199)(x)\\ x &= {}^{10}\text{B mass} = 10.0\text{ u}\end{aligned}$$

Practice Problem 2.15 Solution

No elements are out of order according to atomic number.

Practice Problem 2.16 Solution

Lithium, Li ($Z = 3$), begins period 2; neon, Ne ($Z = 10$), ends it; and there are eight elements in the period.

Practice Problem 2.17 Solution

Potassium also reacts violently with water because both potassium and sodium, Na, are in group 1 (1A).

Practice Problem 2.18 Solution

The lanthanoids are elements 58–71, so they are found in period 6. The actinoids are elements 90–103, so they are found in period 7.

Practice Problem 2.19 Solution

a. Carbon is a nonmetal in all of its forms.

b. Silver is a metal.

Practice Problem 2.20 Solution

a. Elements that are shiny, malleable, and conduct electricity tend to be metals.

b. Elements that are shiny and conduct electricity tend to be metals. Elements that are brittle tend to be nonmetals. An element that has properties of both metals and nonmetals is most likely a metalloid.

c. Elements that are dull, brittle, and do not conduct electricity tend to be nonmetals.

Practice Problem 2.21 Solution

a. Gallium has an atomic number of 31, so Ga-69 has 31 protons and 38 neutrons to give a total mass number of 69. Ga-71 has 31 protons and 40 neutrons to give a total mass number of 71. Both isotopes are neutral, so both contain 31 electrons to offset the charge of the 31 protons.

b. An isotopic symbol consists of the element symbol with the mass number as a superscript on the left side. The atomic number is sometimes included as a subscript on the left side, but it is not necessary.

For Ga-69, the isotopic symbol is ^{69}Ga (or $^{69}_{31}Ga$).

For Ga-71, the isotopic symbol is ^{71}Ga (or $^{71}_{31}Ga$).

c. The natural abundance of ^{71}Ga is 100.00% − 60.11% = 39.89%.

Use the following equation to solve for the isotope mass of ^{71}Ga, which is represented as x:

$$\begin{aligned}\text{Atomic mass of Ga} &= (\text{Fraction of }^{69}\text{Ga})(\text{Mass of }^{69}\text{Ga})\\ &\quad + (\text{Fraction of }^{71}\text{Ga})(\text{Mass of }^{71}\text{Ga})\end{aligned}$$

According to the periodic table in Appendix A.1, the atomic mass of gallium is 69.723 u. Thus:

$$\begin{aligned}69.723\text{ u} &= (0.6011)(68.926\text{ u}) + (0.3989\text{ u})(x)\\ 69.723\text{ u} &= 41.431\text{ u} + (0.3989\text{ u})(x)\\ 28.292 &= (0.3989)(x)\\ x &= \text{mass of }^{71}\text{Ga} = 70.93\text{ u}\end{aligned}$$

Since the atomic mass of gallium is 69.723 u and only about 40% of naturally occurring gallium is ^{71}Ga, it makes sense that ^{69}Ga (68.926 u) is closer in mass to 69.723 u than is ^{71}Ga.

CHAPTER 3 Compounds and the Mole

Sara Egner, Macmillan Learning

As you will learn in this chapter, a mole is a specific number of particles (e.g., atoms, molecules). This photo shows a mole of various familiar substances, along with their names, formulas, and masses in grams. For example, 26.982 g of aluminum contains the same total number of Al atoms as there are H_2O molecules in 18.015 g of water.

Chapter Outline

GOALS

- Interpret chemical formulas.
- Write chemical formulas to represent chemical compounds.
- Name binary compounds of nonmetals from formulas.
- Write formulas for binary compounds of nonmetals from names.
- Determine the formulas of ionic compounds from the charges of the ions that make up the compound.
- Name cations and anions from symbols.
- Write symbols for cations and anions from names.
- Name ionic compounds from formulas.
- Write formulas for ionic compounds from names.
- Name acids from formulas.
- Write formulas for acids from names.
- Identify the appropriate naming system for a given compound.
- Calculate the number of moles from the number of particles and vice versa.
- Calculate the mass of 1 mol of a substance based on its chemical formula and atomic masses from the periodic table.
- Calculate the percent composition by mass of a compound based on its chemical formula and atomic masses from the periodic table.
- Determine the empirical formula of a compound from percent composition or other mass-ratio data.
- Determine the molecular formula of a compound from its percent composition and molar mass data.
- Determine the molecular formula of a compound from its empirical formula and molar mass data.
- Determine the empirical formula for a compound based on data from a combustion analysis, in which the carbon in the compound is converted to carbon dioxide and the hydrogen is converted to water.

3.1 Chemical Formulas

GOALS

- Interpret chemical formulas.
- Write chemical formulas to represent chemical compounds.

Background Review

Chapter 1 Science and Measurement:
Section 1.1—Classification of Matter

Chemical nomenclature is a systemic approach to naming chemical compounds. **Chemical formulas** combine elemental symbols and subscripts to represent compounds, such as Fe_2O_3 for rust or O_2 for elemental oxygen. In doing so, a chemical formula provides information about the relative number of atoms of each element contained in a compound. Some chemical formulas are also written in a way that provides information about how the atoms are arranged in the compound.

> Writing a chemical formula implies bonding of some type.

FORMULA UNITS AND MOLECULES

The group of atoms represented by a chemical formula is called a **formula unit**. A chemical formula is made up of the symbols of element(s), with **subscripts** that tell how many atoms of each element are present per formula unit. The subscript follows the symbol of the element it multiplies. If there is no subscript, then one atom of that element is present. For example, one formula unit of H_2O contains two hydrogen, H, atoms and one oxygen, O, atom.

Sometimes one formula unit for a compound might contain more than one of the same grouping of atoms, such as the (PO_4) part of the formula $Ba_3(PO_4)_2$. Parentheses are placed around the group, and a subscript after the closing parenthesis indicates the number of groups present in each formula unit. As a result, one formula unit of $Ba_3(PO_4)_2$ contains three barium, Ba, atoms, two phosphorus, P, atoms, and eight oxygen, O, atoms.

> A subscript multiplies the number of atoms of the *preceding* element, or the number of preceding groups if the subscript follows a closing parenthesis.

Example 3.1

How many atoms of each element are present in one formula unit of each of the following substances?

a. $Mg(ClO_3)_2$
b. $(NH_4)_2SO_3$
c. CH_3CH_2OH
d. S_8

Solution

The subscript that follows each chemical symbol tells how many atoms of that element are present. If the same element appears in more than one place in the chemical formula, add all of that atom type together to get the total. If a chemical symbol has no subscript, then there is one atom of that type. A subscript outside a set of parentheses multiplies all of the subscripts within the parentheses.

a. 1 Mg, $2 \times 1 = 2$ Cl, $2 \times 3 = 6$ O
b. $2 \times 1 = 2$ N, $2 \times 4 = 8$ H, 1 S, 3 O
c. $1 + 1 = 2$ C, 3 H $+ 2$ H $+ 1$ H $= 6$ H, 1 O
d. 8 S

PRACTICE PROBLEM 3.1

How many atoms of each element are present in one formula unit of each of the following substances?

a. Hg_2Cl_2
b. $NH_4H_2PO_4$

Hint: The subscript that follows each chemical symbol tells how many atoms of that element are present. If the same element appears in more than one place in the chemical formula, add all of that atom type together to get the total. If a chemical symbol has no subscript, then there is one atom of that type.

A formula unit represents the ratio of the atoms in a compound, but compounds can exist in different forms (Figure 3.1). Some compounds exist as individual particles made up of bonded atoms. These individual particles of compounds are called **molecules**, and for these compounds, one formula unit is the same as one molecule. Molecules are formed when nonmetal atoms bond to other nonmetal atoms through an interaction called covalent bonding (Chapter 10), so compounds that exist as individual molecules are also called **molecular compounds** or **covalent compounds**.

Other compounds exist not as individual particles, but as an extended three-dimensional **lattice structure**, or network, of atoms that are bonded together in repeating patterns. A single crystal of one of these compounds can easily contain a thousand billion billion identical repeating patterns of bonded atoms. In compounds of this type, one formula unit is one of the repeating patterns of bonded atoms. Compounds that exist in the form of extended lattice networks are known as **ionic compounds**. Ionic compounds are held together by a different type of attraction called an ionic bond (Chapter 9), which occurs between metal atoms and nonmetal atoms (or between metal atoms and clusters of nonmetal atoms that are covalently bonded together). Ionic compounds are discussed in more detail in Section 3.3.

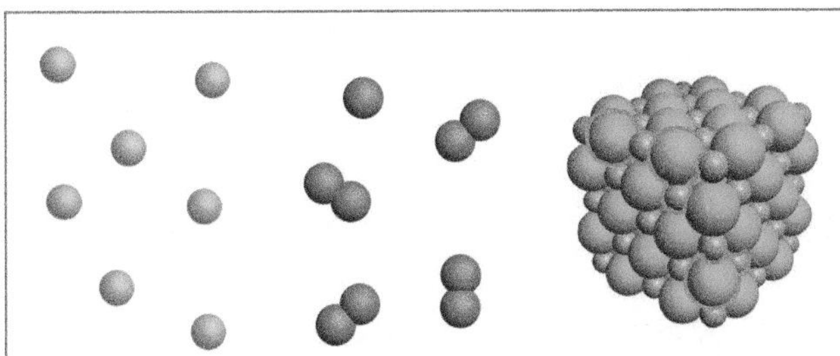

FIGURE 3.1 Atoms, Molecules, and Formula Units
(a) Atoms of argon, Ar; (b) molecules of bromine, Br_2; and (c) a sodium chloride, NaCl, lattice with some formula units circled.

Example 3.2

Classify the following compounds as ionic or covalent (molecular).

a. $CaCl_2$
b. CCl_4
c. H_2O
d. Fe_2O_3

Solution

Use the periodic table to determine whether each element is a metal or a nonmetal. A metal and a nonmetal form an ionic compound. Two nonmetals form a covalent (molecular) compound.

a. Ca is a metal and Cl is a nonmetal so $CaCl_2$ is an ionic compound.
b. C and Cl are both nonmetals so CCl_4 is a covalent (molecular) compound.
c. H and O are both nonmetals so H_2O is a covalent (molecular) compound.
d. Fe is a metal and O is a nonmetal so Fe_2O_3 is an ionic compound.

PRACTICE PROBLEM 3.2

Classify the following compounds as ionic or covalent (molecular).

a. NaBr
b. NH_3
c. $AlCl_3$
d. CO_2

Hint: Use the periodic table to determine whether each element is a metal or a nonmetal. A metal and a nonmetal form an ionic compound. Two nonmetals form a covalent (molecular) compound.

MOLECULES OF ELEMENTS

Some elements are never found in nature as individual atoms and instead occur as small molecules containing two or more of the same kind of atom bonded together. The elements that are found only in molecular form are hydrogen, H_2, nitrogen, N_2, oxygen, O_2, fluorine, F_2, chlorine, Cl_2, bromine, Br_2, and iodine, I_2, as well as phosphorus, P_4, and sulfur, S_8 (Figure 3.2).

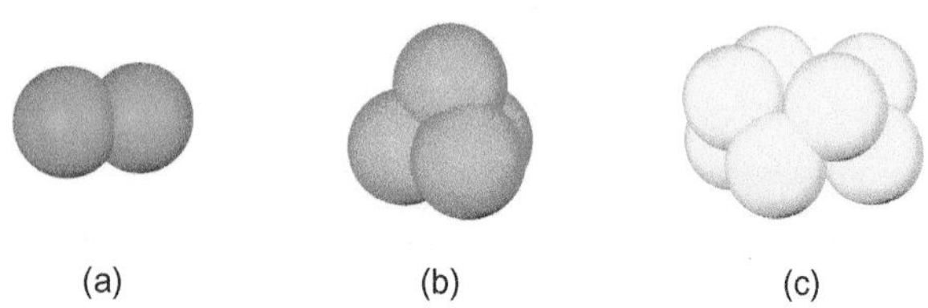

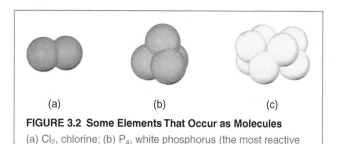

FIGURE 3.2 Some Elements That Occur as Molecules
(a) Cl_2, chlorine; (b) P_4, white phosphorus (the most reactive form of elemental phosphorus); (c) S_8, rhombic sulfur (the most stable form of elemental sulfur).

Seven elements occur as **diatomic molecules** (molecules consisting of two atoms) when they are in their elemental form. With the exception of H, these elements form a shape like a seven in the periodic table, starting at N, the element with atomic number 7 (Figure 3.3).

> Seven elements occur as diatomic molecules (H_2, N_2, O_2, F_2, Cl_2, Br_2, and I_2) when they are in their elemental form.

Some elements can be found in more than one molecular form. These different molecular forms for the same element are called **allotropes**. O_2 and O_3 are allotropes of O. Allotropes of C consist of diamond and graphite, as well as C nanotubes and fullerenes. Even though allotropes are different physical forms of the same element, they can have remarkably different physical and chemical properties from one another. For example, diamond is hard and colorless, whereas graphite is soft and gray.

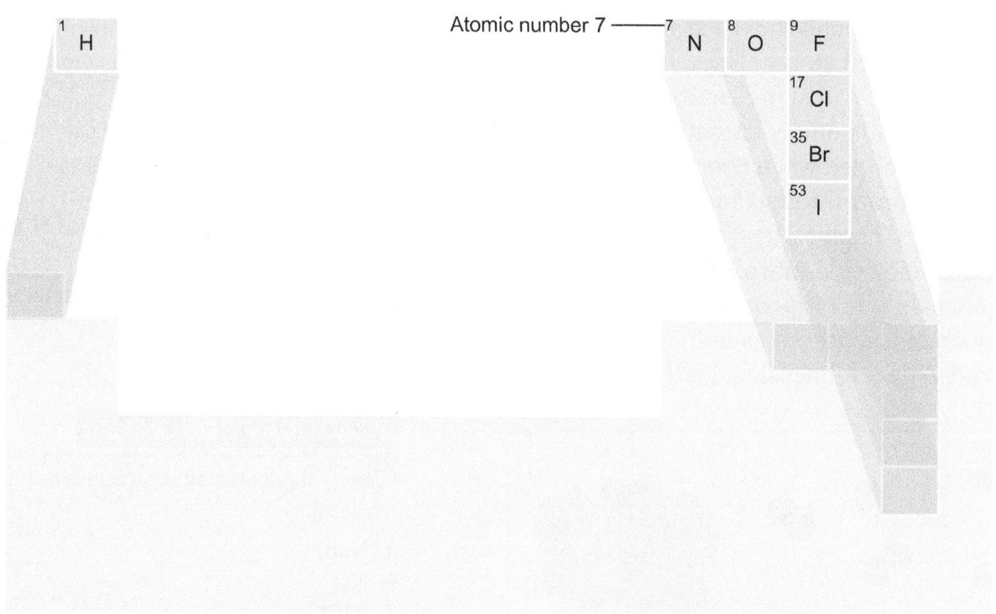

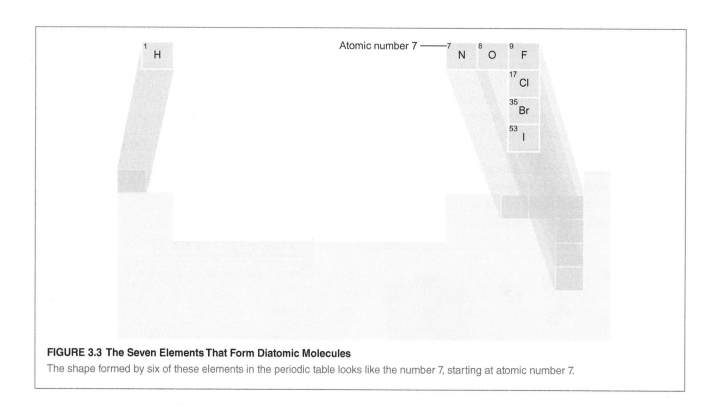

FIGURE 3.3 The Seven Elements That Form Diatomic Molecules
The shape formed by six of these elements in the periodic table looks like the number 7, starting at atomic number 7.

EVERYDAY CONNECTION

Molecular oxygen gas, O_2, is essential to most life on Earth, but ozone, O_3, is toxic. O_3 is formed in the upper atmosphere when high-energy rays from outer space bombard O_2 molecules. The O_3 molecules in the upper atmosphere absorb harmful ultraviolet light from the Sun. This prevents some of that light from reaching Earth's surface, where it could injure humans and other animals.

But O_3 is also formed in the lower atmosphere by chemical reactions between air pollutants, such as those found in car exhaust and power plant emissions. Breathing in O_3 can contribute to a variety of health problems, especially in children, the elderly, and people who already have lung diseases such as asthma. Many cities in the United States now have "ozone alert" days when the O_3 concentration in the atmosphere rises to levels that can be harmful to people. On ozone alert days, residents are advised to avoid driving if possible and to limit their outdoor activities to minimize exposure to O_3.

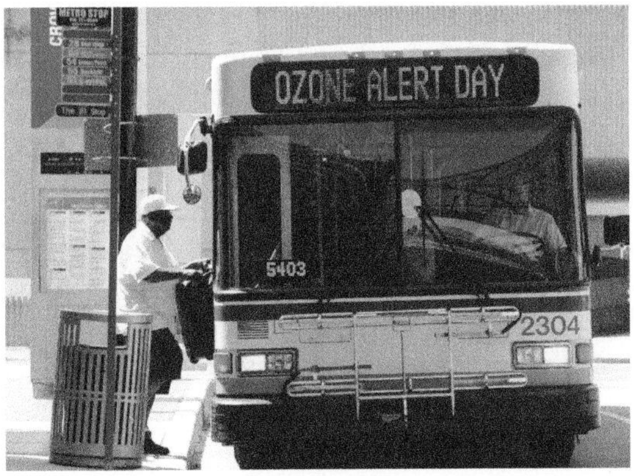

REUTERS/Dave Kaup

SECTION REVIEW

- The chemical formula for a molecular compound indicates the number of atoms of each type in a molecule. The chemical formula for an ionic compound indicates the ratio of the atoms of each type.
- A subscript after a chemical symbol in a chemical formula indicates how many atoms of that type are in one formula unit of that compound. If there is no subscript, the number 1 is implied.
- Subscripts outside of parentheses in a chemical formula are multipliers that apply to each element inside the parentheses.
- Ionic compounds contain metal atoms bonded to nonmetal atoms.
- Covalent (molecular) compounds contain only nonmetal atoms.
- There are seven diatomic elements: H_2, N_2, O_2, F_2, Cl_2, Br_2, and I_2.

3.2 Naming Binary Covalent Compounds

GOALS

- Name binary compounds of nonmetals from formulas.
- Write formulas for binary compounds of nonmetals from names.

Background Review

Chapter 2 Atoms and the Periodic Table:
Section 2.1—Chemical Symbols; Section 2.6—The Periodic Table

Binary compounds are compounds that are made up of exactly two elements. A binary covalent compound is made up of exactly two nonmetals, such as hydrosulfuric acid, H_2S, or silicon(IV) dioxide, SiO_2.

PREFIXES IN BINARY COVALENT COMPOUND NAMES

When nonmetals or metalloids bond together in covalent compounds, the same two elements are often able to bond together in different ratios, thus forming different compounds. C and O can combine in a 1:1 ratio to form CO, or in a 1:2 ratio to form CO_2. To distinguish between these two compounds, the number of atoms of each type must be specified in the name. Covalent compound names therefore use prefixes (Table 3.1) to indicate the number of atoms of each type present. The prefix indicating the number of oxygen atoms in each molecule is how carbon *mono*xide, CO, which has only a single O atom, is distinguished from carbon *di*oxide, CO_2, which has two O atoms.

TABLE 3.1 Prefixes Used in Naming Binary Covalent Compounds

Number of Atoms	Prefix*
1	mon(o)-
2	di-
3	tri-
4	tetr(a)-
5	pent(a)-
6	hex(a)-
7	hept(a)-
8	oct(a)-
9	non(a)-
10	dec(a)-

*The last *o* or *a* of the prefix is usually dropped when the element name begins with *o*.

When naming covalent compounds, the name of the first element is simply the element name, with a prefix added if there is more than one atom of that element in the formula, as in *di*nitrogen *mon*oxide, N_2O. The second element in the formula is given a prefix to indicate how many atoms of that element are in the chemical formula, and that element name is modified to end with the suffix *-ide* (Figure 3.4).

To name a binary covalent compound:

- Write the full name of the first element.
- Use the root of the second element with the ending changed to *-ide*.
- If there is more than one atom of the first element, add a prefix to indicate the number of atoms. The prefixes are given in Table 3.1.
- Add a prefix to indicate the number of atoms of the second element, no matter how many atoms there are.

Example 3.3

Name the compound whose molecules contain the following elements.

a. One atom of silicon and four atoms of chlorine
b. One atom of sulfur and three atoms of oxygen
c. One atom of sulfur and two atoms of bromine
d. Two atoms of phosphorus and three atoms of sulfur

Assume that the element listed first comes first in the name.

Solution

a. Silicon tetrachloride. Silicon comes first, so the element name is used, and there is only one, so no prefix is applied. Chlorine comes second, so the suffix *-ide* is used, and there are four chlorine atoms, so the prefix *tetra-* is applied.
b. Sulfur trioxide. Sulfur comes first, so the element name is used, and there is only one, so no prefix is applied. Oxygen comes second, so the suffix *-ide* is used, and there are three oxygen atoms, so the prefix *tri-* is applied.
c. Sulfur dibromide. Sulfur comes first, so the element name is used, and there is only one, so no prefix is applied. Bromine comes second, so the suffix *-ide* is used, and there are two bromine atoms, so the prefix *di-* is applied.
d. Diphosphorus trisulfide. The prefix *di-* is needed for the first element because there is more than one atom of phosphorus. Sulfur comes second, so the suffix *-ide* is used, and there are three sulfur atoms, so the prefix *tri-* is applied.

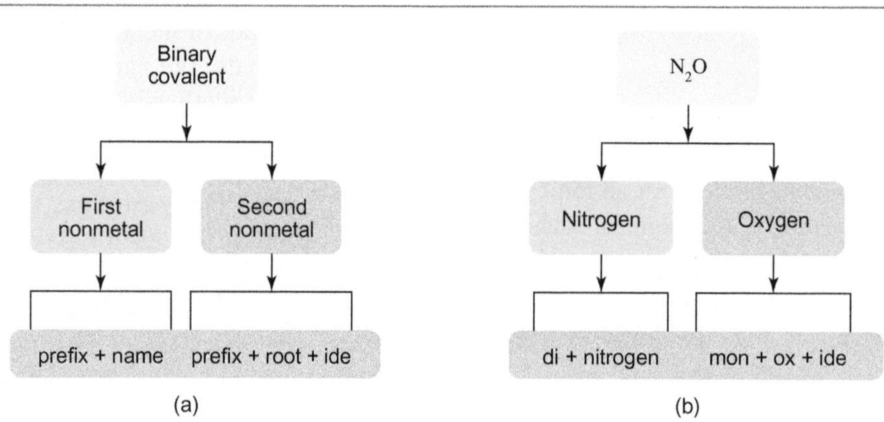

FIGURE 3.4 Naming a Binary Covalent Compound

The system for naming a binary covalent compound (a) in general and (b) N_2O in particular. The first element is given a prefix only if there is more than one atom of it in the chemical formula.

PRACTICE PROBLEM 3.3

Name the compound whose molecules contain the following elements.

a. Two atoms of chlorine and three atoms of oxygen
b. Four atoms of sulfur and four atoms of nitrogen
c. Two atoms of phosphorus and five atoms of sulfur
d. One atom of sulfur and two atoms of fluorine

Assume that the element listed first comes first in the name.

Hint: Add prefixes to the element names to indicate how many of each type of atom is present, and change the ending of the second element to *-ide*. See Figure 3.4 and Table 3.1 for details.

The video in Figure 3.5 demonstrates how to name a binary covalent compound when given its formula.

Example 3.4

Name each of the following compounds.

a. NI_3
b. NO
c. N_2O_4
d. As_2O_5
e. CBr_4
f. S_4N_4

Solution

All six compounds consist entirely of nonmetals, so they are all binary covalent (molecular) compounds.

a. Nitrogen triiodide. Nitrogen is named first, so the ending of *iodine* is changed to *-ide*. The prefix *tri-* is added to *iodide* because there are three iodine atoms in the chemical formula. The *mono-* prefix is *not* added to nitrogen because it comes first in the name.
b. Nitrogen monoxide. Nitrogen is named first, so the ending of *oxygen* is changed to *-ide*. The last *o* of the prefix *mono-* is dropped before adding it to *oxide* because *oxide* starts with *o*. The *mono-* prefix is *not* added to nitrogen because it comes first in the name.
c. Dinitrogen tetroxide. Nitrogen is named first, so the ending of *oxygen* is changed to *-ide*. There are two nitrogen atoms, so the *di-* prefix is added to *nitrogen*. The *a* in the prefix *tetr*(*a*)- is not used with *oxide* because *oxide* starts with *o*.
d. Diarsenic pentoxide. Arsenic is named first, so the ending of *oxygen* is changed to *-ide*. There are two arsenic atoms in the formula, so the *di-* prefix is added to *arsenic*. The *a* in the prefix *pent*(*a*)- is not used with *oxide* because *oxide* starts with *o*.
e. Carbon tetrabromide. Carbon is named first, so the ending of *bromine* is changed to *-ide*. The prefix *tetra-* is added to *bromide* because there are four bromine atoms in the chemical formula. The *mono-* prefix is *not* added to carbon because it comes first in the name.
f. Tetrasulfur tetranitride. Sulfur is named first, so the ending of *nitrogen* is changed to *-ide*. There are four sulfur atoms in the formula, so the *tetra-* prefix is added to *sulfur*. There are four nitrogen atoms, too, so the *tetra-* prefix is added to *nitride*.

Steven Lemon, Macmillan Learning

FIGURE 3.5 Video Tutorial: Binary Covalent Compound Names

NOTE: You need to be online to access this video.
This video shows how to name binary covalent compounds given their formulas.

PRACTICE PROBLEM 3.4

Name each of the following compounds.

a. P_4O_6
b. B_2O_3
c. N_2O
d. ICl_5
e. IF_7
f. PCl_3

Hint: These are all binary covalent (molecular) compounds. Add prefixes to the element names to indicate how many of each type of atom is present, and use the *-ide* ending on the second element. See Figure 3.4 and Table 3.1 for details.

Example 3.5

Write formulas for the following compounds.

a. Dinitrogen pentoxide
b. Diboron trioxide
c. Chlorine dioxide

Solution

The prefixes in the names tell you how many of each type of atom are present (Table 3.1).

a. N_2O_5: *di-* = 2 nitrogen atoms, followed by *pent-* = 5 oxygen atoms
b. B_2O_3: *di-* = 2 boron atoms, followed by *tri-* = 3 oxygen atoms
c. ClO_2: no prefix = 1 chlorine atom, followed by *di-* = 2 oxygen atoms

PRACTICE PROBLEM 3.5

Write formulas for the following compounds.

a. Disulfur decafluoride
b. Iodine trioxide
c. Tetraarsenic hexoxide

Hint: The prefixes used for each element in the name indicate what the subscript for that element is in the formula. See Table 3.1 for the subscript that corresponds to each prefix.

Binary compounds of H are named using a different system from other binary covalent compounds. Many binary H compounds are acids. Acids have chemical formulas that begin with H and are typically named according to the system used for naming acids (Section 3.5). Binary compounds of H whose chemical formulas end with H are not acids, but these compounds are given special names, such as **ammonia** for NH_3 (Figure 3.6). Other examples include phosphine for PH_3 and arsine for AsH_3.

Steve Lemon, Macmillan Learning

FIGURE 3.6 Household Ammonia
Household NH_3 is a solution of gaseous NH_3 dissolved in water. It is normally colorless, but many manufacturers add soap and a coloring agent.

SECTION REVIEW

- Binary covalent compounds are made up of two different nonmetal elements.
- Binary covalent compounds use prefixes to denote the number of atoms of each element in a molecule. The prefix for the first element is omitted if there is only one atom of that element.
- If the element is named first in a compound, its symbol is written first in the formula, and vice versa.

3.3 Formulas for Ionic Compounds

GOAL

- Determine the formulas of ionic compounds from the charges of the ions that make up the compound.

Background Review

Chapter 2 Atoms and the Periodic Table:
Section 2.1—Chemical Symbols; Section 2.6—The Periodic Table

An **ion** is an atom or group of atoms that has gained or lost electrons and therefore has a net negative or positive charge (Section 2.4). Positive ions are known as **cations**, and negative ions are known as **anions**. A single atom that has gained or lost electrons, such as Mg^{2+} or Cl^-, is called a **monatomic ion**.

Binary ionic compounds form when metal atoms combine with nonmetal atoms. When this happens, the metal atoms each give one or more of their electrons to the nonmetal atoms. The loss of electrons by the metal atoms leaves them with a positive charge, and the gain of electrons by the nonmetal atoms leaves them with a negative charge. Thus, metals tend to form cations, whereas nonmetals tend to form anions.

The periodic table in Figure 3.7 shows the most common monatomic ions with their charges. The group 1 elements form only +1 ions, the group 2

1 1A	2 2A	3	4	5	6	7	8	9	10	11	12	13 3A	14 4A	15 5A	16 6A	17 7A	18 8A
H +1, −1																	
Li +1	Be +2													N −3	O −2	F −1	
Na +1	Mg +2											Al +3		P −3	S −2	Cl −1	
K +1	Ca +2		Ti +2, +3	V +2, +3	Cr +2, +3	Mn +2, +3	Fe +2, +3	Co +2, +3	Ni +2, +3, +4	Cu +1, +2	Zn +2				Se −2	Br −1	
Rb +1	Sr +2								Pd +2, +4	Ag +1	Cd +2		Sn +2, +4			I −1	
Cs +1	Ba +2								Pt +2, +4	Au +1, +3	Hg +2		Pb +2, +4				
Fr +1	Ra +2																

FIGURE 3.7 Charges on Common Monatomic Ions

The nonmetals and the elements of groups 1 and 2, along with Al (group 13), form only one type of ion. Most other metals can form more than one type of cation.

elements form only +2 ions, and aluminum, Al, in group 13 forms only a +3 ion. You will never find an Al ion that is +1 or +2, and every ionic compound that contains Al contains Al^{3+} ions. Some common nonmetals, such as the ones shown in groups 15–17 in Figure 3.7, also form only one type of monatomic anion. Many of the metals in groups 4–12, on the other hand, can form more than one type of ion.

Some nonmetals do not form monatomic anions, so no ionic charges are shown for these elements in Figure 3.7. H commonly forms a +1 ion, but it can react with very active metals to form the hydride ion, H^-.

CHEMICAL FORMULAS FOR BINARY IONIC COMPOUNDS

All compounds are electrically neutral overall, so the total positive charge on the cations in the formula for an ionic compound must balance the total negative charge of the anions in the formula.

$$\text{Total positive charge} = \text{Total negative charge} \quad (3.1)$$

For example, Al forms only a +3 ion and Cl forms only a −1 ion, so an ionic compound made up of Al and Cl must have three Cl ions for every Al ion to balance the charges. The formula for the compound is therefore $AlCl_3$.

Example 3.6

Use the monatomic ion charges shown in Figure 3.7 to determine the chemical formulas for binary ionic compounds made up of the following pairs of elements.

a. Al and O
b. Na and Br
c. Ba and F
d. Pb^{4+} and O

Solution

a. Al_2O_3: Each aluminum, Al, ion has a +3 charge, whereas each oxygen ion has a −2 charge. The compound cannot be AlO because the overall charge would be +1, not 0. To obtain the correct number of Al^{3+} and O^{2-} ions, find the smallest number that is a multiple of both 3 and 2. That number is 6. Therefore, the compound will have an overall charge of zero if it has two Al^{3+} ions [$2(+3) = +6$] and three O^{2-} ions [$3(-2) = -6$].
b. NaBr: Each sodium cation has a charge of +1, and each bromine anion has a −1 charge, so a simple 1:1 ratio will balance the charges and result in an electrically neutral compound.
c. BaF_2: Each barium cation has a +2 charge, whereas each fluorine anion has a −1 charge. The charges will balance when there are two fluorine ions for every barium ion.
d. PbO_2: Oxygen forms a −2 anion, so there must be two oxygen, O, ions for every Pb^{4+} ion.

PRACTICE PROBLEM 3.6

Use the monatomic ion charges shown in Figure 3.7 to determine the chemical formulas for binary ionic compounds made up of the following pairs of elements.

a. Al and Cl
b. Ca and P
c. Ba and O
d. Fe^{3+} and O

Hint: Each pair of ions must be combined in a ratio such that the total positive charge equals the total negative charge.

Although some ionic compounds contain more than one type of cation or anion, all of the ionic compounds considered in this book are composed of only one type of cation and one type of anion.

Example 3.7

Determine the formula of the ionic compound formed from calcium and oxygen.

Solution

Ca forms a +2 ion, and O forms a −2 ion, so a 1:1 ratio of Ca to O balances the positive and negative charges. The formula for calcium oxide is CaO.

PRACTICE PROBLEM 3.7

Determine the formula of the ionic compound formed from strontium and nitrogen.

Hint: Use the periodic table in Figure 3.7 to determine the charges on the Sr and N ions, and then combine them in a ratio such that the total positive charge equals the total negative charge.

Because all compounds have an overall charge of zero, the charge on some metal cations can be deduced from the total charge on the anions bonded to them. According to Figure 3.7, copper, Cu, can form cations having a charge of either +1 or +2, but which is it? In CuCl, the charge on the copper ion is +1 because a +1 charge is needed to balance the −1 charge on the one Cl^- ion. In $CuCl_2$, however, the charge on the copper ion is +2 because a +2 charge is needed to balance the −1 charge on each of *two* Cl^- ions.

Example 3.8

What is the charge on each cation in the following compounds?

a. Cu_2O
b. CuO

Solution

a. The charge on each cation must be +1 because two copper cations are required to balance the charge on one O^{2-} ion.
b. The charge on the copper cation must be +2 to balance the −2 charge on one O^{2-} ion.

PRACTICE PROBLEM 3.8

What is the charge on each cation in the following compounds?

a. $FeCl_3$
b. SnO_2

Hint: Use Figure 3.7 to determine the total *negative* charge from the anions, and then divide the total positive charge necessary for an overall neutral compound by the number of cations in the formula to get the charge on the cation.

IONIC FORMULAS WITH POLYATOMIC IONS

A **polyatomic ion** is a group of two or more bonded atoms that have gained or lost electrons, resulting in an overall net charge. For example, the phosphate ion, PO_4^{3-}, consists of one P atom and four O atoms bonded together; the group of five atoms has gained three extra electrons and therefore carries a −3 charge. Table 3.2 lists a few of the most common polyatomic ions. All but the ammonium ion, NH_4^+, are anions. Some additional polyatomic ions will be introduced in the next section.

The chlorate anion, ClO_3^-, appears twice in magnesium chlorate, $Mg(ClO_3)_2$, because two −1 anions are needed to balance the charge of the Mg^{2+} cation. As a result, the polyatomic ion is enclosed in parentheses and the subscript "2" is written outside the closing

TABLE 3.2 Some Common Polyatomic Ions

Name	Formula
Ammonium ion	NH_4^+
Acetate ion	$C_2H_3O_2^-$ or CH_3COO^-
Bromate ion	BrO_3^-
Carbonate ion	CO_3^{2-}
Chlorate ion	ClO_3^-
Cyanide ion	CN^-
Hydroxide ion	OH^-
Nitrate ion	NO_3^-
Phosphate ion	PO_4^{3-}
Sulfate ion	SO_4^{2-}

A more comprehensive list of polyatomic ions is found in Table 3.4.

Steven Lemon, Macmillan Learning

FIGURE 3.8 Video Tutorial: Ionic Formulas

NOTE: You need to be online to access this video.
This video shows how to write formulas for ionic compounds with polyatomic ions by balancing the charges on the ions.

parenthesis to indicate that the "2" applies to all the atoms within the parentheses. When writing the formula for *any* ionic compound (whether it contains monatomic or polyatomic ions), make sure that all the positive and negative charges sum to zero, as demonstrated in Figure 3.8.

Example 3.9

Determine the formula of the compound containing the following pairs of ions.

a. Cr^{2+} and SO_4^{2-}
b. Cr^{3+} and CO_3^{2-}

Solution

a. One Cr^{2+} ion can balance the charge on one SO_4^{2-} ion, so the ions combine in a 1:1 ratio to form $CrSO_4$.
b. It takes three CO_3^{2-} ions $[3 \times (-2) = -6]$ to balance the charge on two Cr^{3+} ions $[2 \times (+3) = +6]$, so the formula is $Cr_2(CO_3)_3$.

PRACTICE PROBLEM 3.9

Determine the formula of the compound containing the following pairs of ions.

a. Cu^{2+} and OH^-
b. Cr^{2+} and PO_4^{3-}

Hint: Balance the overall positive and negative charges, and be sure to enclose polyatomic ions in parentheses before applying the subscript.

SECTION REVIEW

- Ions are formed when atoms lose or gain electrons. Cations have a net positive charge, whereas anions have a net negative charge.
- The net charge on the formula of a neutral compound must be zero, so the total magnitudes of the positive and negative charges in an ionic compound must be equal.
- The smallest integer numbers of cations and anions needed to achieve an overall charge of zero give the formula of the ionic compound.
- Most main-group cations and all monatomic anions have characteristic charges that can be used to deduce the charges on the other ions in ionic compounds.

3.4 Naming Ionic Compounds

GOALS

- Name cations and anions from symbols.
- Write symbols for cations and anions from names.
- Name ionic compounds from formulas.
- Write formulas for ionic compounds from names.

Background Review

Chapter 2 Atoms and the Periodic Table:
Section 2.1—Chemical Symbols

The majority of ionic compounds are made up of one type of cation and one type of anion. The names of these compounds consist of the name of the cation first, followed by the name of the anion. How, then, do you name the various cations and anions?

NAMING CATIONS

There are three main types of cations, each with a different naming convention:

1. Polyatomic cations (primarily the ammonium cation, NH_4^+)
2. Monatomic metal cations with constant charge (metals in groups $1-2$ and a few others shown in Figure 3.9)
3. Monatomic metal cations with variable charge (most group 3–16 metals, as shown in Figure 3.9)

The name of a *polyatomic* ion must be either memorized or looked up in a table such as Table 3.2. The ammonium ion, NH_4^+, is the only polyatomic cation you are likely to encounter in compounds in general chemistry, so it is worth memorizing.

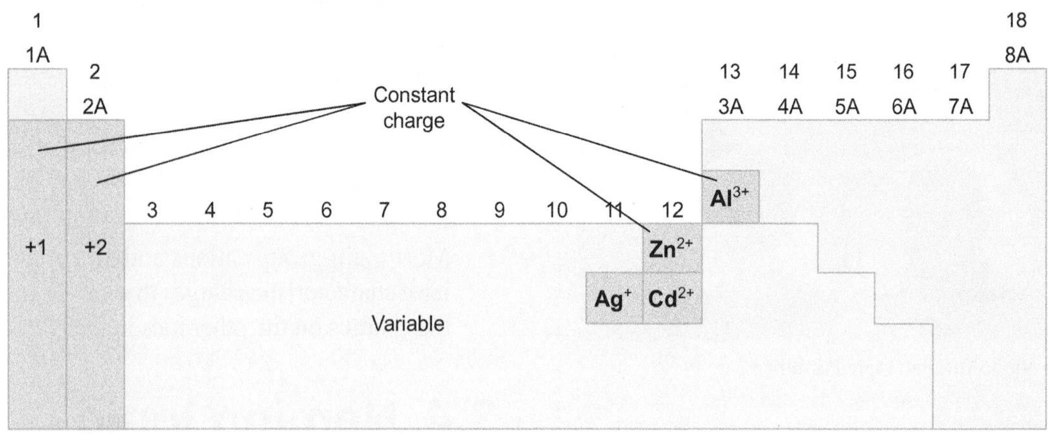

FIGURE 3.9 Monatomic Cations

Elements in groups 1–2 and a few other metals form monatomic cations of constant charge. Most other metals form monatomic cations of variable charge.

The name of a *constant-charge* cation is simply the name of the element followed by the word *ion*. For example, K^+ is the potassium ion, Ba^{2+} is the barium ion, and Al^{3+} is the aluminum ion. The alkali metals (group 1); the alkaline earth metals (group 2); zinc, Zn; cadmium, Cd; aluminum, Al; and silver, Ag, are common metals that form ions of constant charge (Figure 3.9). Each of these metals forms the same ion in all its compounds.

The name of a *variable-charge* cation is the name of the element followed by a Roman numeral in parentheses to indicate the charge. Thus, the Fe^{2+} ion can be distinguished from the Fe^{3+} ion by calling Fe^{2+} the iron(II) ion and Fe^{3+} the iron(III) ion. This system of nomenclature is called the **Stock system** after its inventor, Alfred Stock.

Example 3.10

What are the names of the following cations?

a. Ba^{2+}
b. Ag^{+}
c. Co^{2+}
d. Co^{3+}
e. Li^{+}

Solution

According to Figure 3.9, Ba^{2+}, Ag^+, and Li^+ are constant-charge cations, so they are named by stating the element name followed by the word *ion*. The charge on the cobalt cation can vary, so use a Roman numeral to indicate the charge.

a. Barium ion
b. Silver ion
c. Cobalt(II) ion
d. Cobalt(III) ion
e. Lithium ion

PRACTICE PROBLEM 3.10

What are the names of the following cations?

a. Sr^{2+}
b. Sn^{2+}
c. Sn^{4+}
d. Al^{3+}
e. Zn^{2+}

Hint: Use Figure 3.9 to distinguish constant-charge cations from variable-charge cations. If the charge is variable, use a Roman numeral after the element name to specify the charge.

Example 3.11

Name the cation in $CrCl_2$.

Solution

The cation is chromium(II) because the charge on the Cr cation is +2. As a group 17 element, chlorine always forms −1 ions (Section 3.3), so the chromium ion in this case must have a +2 charge to balance the charge on the two chlorine ions.

PRACTICE PROBLEM 3.11

Name the cation in MnO.

Hint: Oxygen is a group 16 element, so it always forms −2 ions. Use the charge on the oxygen anion to determine the charge on the Mn cation.

A Roman numeral in the name of a compound indicates the *charge on the cation*. The numbers appearing as subscripts in formulas indicate the *number of atoms* of that element present per formula unit.

EVERYDAY CONNECTION

Ferric oxide is another name for iron(III) oxide (rust), and *stannous fluoride* is another name for tin(II) fluoride (the active ingredient in some toothpastes). These names come from an older naming system that used *-ous* and *-ic* suffixes instead of Roman numerals. This older naming system was used for covalent compounds as well, where the suffix was based on the oxidation state (Section 4.6) of the element. For example, N_2O, the laughing gas anesthetic used in dentists' offices, is still commonly known as *nitrous oxide*, and the highly reactive air pollutant NO is still known as *nitric oxide*. The older naming system is now obsolete and is not used in this text, but it still lingers on in the common names of a few compounds.

Example 3.12

Name the cation in each of the following compounds.

a. CuS
b. Cu_2S

Solution

Sulfur, S, is a group 16 element, so it forms ions with a −2 charge.

a. In CuS, only one copper ion is present to balance the −2 charge on the sulfur ion, so the charge on the copper ion must be +2. This cation is copper(II).
b. In Cu_2S, *two* copper ions combine with one S^{2-} anion, so the charge on each copper ion must be +1. The ion is copper(I).

PRACTICE PROBLEM 3.12

Name the cation in each of the following compounds.

a. FeO
b. Fe_2O_3

Hint: The charge on an iron cation can vary, so name it using the Stock system. Determine the positive charge on the iron ion in each formula by balancing the total negative charge on the oxygen ions, O^{2-}.

NAMING ANIONS

Just as different types of cations are named using different naming systems, there are also different types of anions for naming purposes:

1. Monatomic anions (ions of the group 5–7 nonmetals)
2. Polyatomic anions (these anions can be further classified as oxyanions if they contain oxygen)

All monatomic anions are named by changing the ending of the element's name to *-ide*. For example, I^- is the iodide ion, O^{2-} is the oxide ion, and N^{3-} is the nitride ion. Recall that the charges on monatomic anions are −3, −2, and −1 for elements in groups 15, 16, and 17, respectively. Two polyatomic ions, hydroxide, OH^-, and cyanide, CN^-, are named using the *-ide* suffix as though they were monatomic anions.

Oxyanions are a class of anions that contain one atom of a nonmetal element along with a variable number of oxygen atoms. All anions in the same oxyanion series have the same charge. For example, the chlorate ion, ClO_3^-, and the chlorite ion, ClO_2^-, are oxyanions. The suffix *-ate* is used for the oxyanion with more oxygen atoms, and the suffix *-ite* is used for the oxyanion with fewer oxygen atoms. Other examples of oxyanion pairs include nitrate, NO_3^-, and nitrite, NO_2^-; and sulfate, SO_4^{2-}, and sulfite, SO_3^{2-}.

Oxyanion series of the halogens have two additional anions in the series. ClO_4^- is one oxygen atom "above," or "hyper," chlorate and is given the prefix *per-*, making it the *perchlorate* ion. ClO^- is one oxygen atom "under," or "hypo," chlorite and is given the prefix *hypo-*, making it the *hypochlorite* ion.

Table 3.3 summarizes the names of some oxyanions. Each ion has a root that is determined by the central nonmetal atom, along with a suffix that depends on the number of oxygen atoms in the ion. The halogen oxyanion series have two additional ions that are distinguished by the added *per-* and *hypo-* prefixes.

Polyatomic anions with a charge of −2 or −3, such as CO_3^{2-} or PO_4^{3-}, can add an H^+ ion and still be polyatomic anions. The names of these ions are simply *hydrogen* followed by the ion name. If there are two hydrogens on the anion, the word *dihydrogen* is used. For example, HCO_3^- is the hydrogen carbonate ion,

TABLE 3.3 Common Oxyanions

	Chlor-	Brom-	Iod-	Sulf-	Nitr-	Phosph-	Carbon-
Per___ate	ClO_4^-	BrO_4^-	IO_4^-				
___ate	ClO_3^-	BrO_3^-	IO_3^-	SO_4^{2-}	NO_3^-	PO_4^{3-}	CO_3^{2-}
___ite	ClO_2^-	BrO_2^-	IO_2^-	SO_3^{2-}	NO_2^-		
Hypo___ite	ClO^-	BrO^-	IO^-				

TABLE 3.4 Polyatomic Ions

Name	Formula	Name	Formula
Ammonium ion	NH_4^+	Perchlorate ion	ClO_4^-
Hydroxide ion	OH^-	Chlorate ion	ClO_3^-
Cyanide ion	CN^-	Chlorite ion	ClO_2^-
Acetate ion	$C_2H_3O_2^-$ or CH_3COO^-	Hypochlorite ion	ClO^-
Nitrite/Nitrate	NO_2^-/NO_3^-	Perbromate ion	BrO_4^-
Sulfite/Sulfate	SO_3^{2-}/SO_4^{2-}	Bromate ion	BrO_3^-
Phosphate	PO_4^{3-}	Bromite ion	BrO_2^-
Carbonate	CO_3^{2-}	Hypobromite ion	BrO^-
Hydrogen sulfite ion	HSO_3^-	Periodate ion	IO_4^-
Hydrogen sulfate ion	HSO_4^-	Iodate ion	IO_3^-
Hydrogen phosphite ion	HPO_3^{2-}	Iodite ion	IO_2^-
Dihydrogen phosphite ion	$H_2PO_3^-$	Hypoiodite ion	IO^-
Hydrogen phosphate ion	HPO_4^{2-}	Chromate ion	CrO_4^{2-}
Dihydrogen phosphate ion	$H_2PO_4^-$	Dichromate ion	$Cr_2O_7^{2-}$
Hydrogen carbonate ion, or bicarbonate ion*	HCO_3^-	Permanganate ion	MnO_4^-

* The *bi-* prefix on bicarbonate ion is left over from an obsolete naming system and indicates a −2 ion (in this case, CO_3^{2-}) that has added one H^+ ion to become a −1 ion, HCO_3^-. *Bicarbonate* is not the preferred nomenclature, but it persists in common usage.

HPO_4^{2-} is the hydrogen phosphate ion, and $H_2PO_4^-$ is the dihydrogen phosphate ion.

Table 3.4 lists the names and formulas of the common polyatomic ions that are used in this text. Understanding the naming systems described previously makes learning the names of these ions easier.

Example 3.13

If SeO_4^{2-} is named selenate, then what is the name of SeO_3^{2-}?

Solution

With one fewer oxygen atom in the formula than selenate, the name of the SeO_3^{2-} ion is selenite.

PRACTICE PROBLEM 3.13

In *The Empire Strikes Back*, Han Solo is frozen in a fictional substance called "carbonite." If carbonite existed and was named systematically as an oxyanion, what would its formula be?

Hint: In an oxyanion series, the *-ite* ion has one fewer oxygen atoms than the *-ate* ion. You can find the formula for carbonate in Table 3.4.

NAMING IONIC COMPOUNDS

The names of covalent compounds require prefixes to distinguish a compound, such as CO, carbon monoxide, from CO_2, carbon dioxide (Section 3.2). The formulas of ionic compounds, on the other hand, always represent the lowest whole-number ratio of cations to anions that results in a neutral compound. Therefore, the names of ionic compounds do not need to specify the number of cations and anions per formula unit. Naming an ionic compound is simply a matter of stating the name of the cation followed by the name of the anion (Figure 3.10). The subscripts (if any) on the ions are

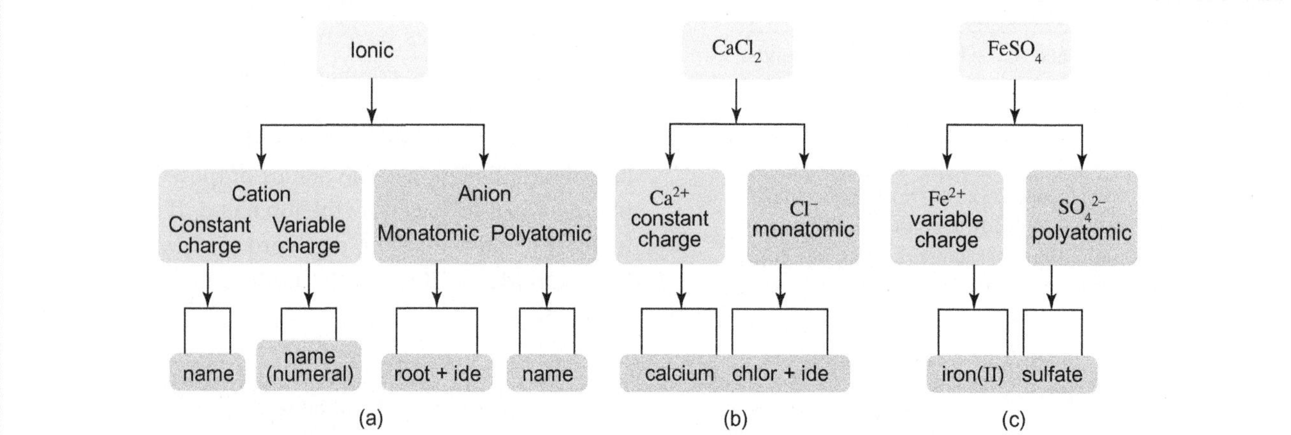

FIGURE 3.10 How to Name Ionic Compounds

(a) A flowchart depicting the general strategy for naming ionic compounds. Applying the strategy to (b) $CaCl_2$ and (c) $FeSO_4$. Recall that names for polyatomic ions such as sulfate must be memorized or looked up in a table, such as Table 3.4.

Steven Lemon, Macmillan Learning

FIGURE 3.11 Video Tutorial: Ionic Compound Names with Roman Numerals

NOTE: You need to be online to access this video.

This video shows how to name and write formulas for ionic compounds that require a Roman numeral in the name because the cation has a variable charge.

not included in the name of the compound because the subscripts can be deduced from the charges on the ions.

The video in Figure 3.11 shows how to use the Stock system to name and write the formulas of ionic compounds containing cations with variable charges.

Example 3.14

Name the following compounds.

a. $NaNO_3$
b. Cu_2S
c. $(NH_4)_2SO_4$

Solution

a. The cation is Na^+, sodium ion, and the anion is NO_3^-, nitrate. The name of the compound is sodium nitrate.
b. The cation is Cu^+, copper(I), and the anion is S^{2-}, sulfide. Cu is a variable-charge cation, which is why the name of the ion includes a Roman numeral. The compound is copper(I) sulfide.
c. The cation is NH_4^+, ammonium ion, and the anion is SO_4^{2-}, sulfate. The compound is ammonium sulfate. No prefix is needed to specify the number of ammonium ions because that can be deduced from the charges on the cations and anion.

PRACTICE PROBLEM 3.14

Name the following compounds.

a. $BaSO_4$
b. $Al(C_2H_3O_2)_3$
c. $Co(ClO_3)_3$

Hint: Barium and aluminum form Ba^{2+} and Al^{3+} cations only, whereas cobalt forms Co^{2+} and Co^{3+} cations. As a result, the name for the cobalt compound will require a Roman numeral. Polyatomic ion names are given in Table 3.4.

Example 3.15

Write formulas for the following compounds.

a. Zinc nitrate
b. Cobalt(III) hypochlorite

Solution

a. The zinc ion is Zn^{2+}; the nitrate ion is NO_3^-. The formula of the compound is $Zn(NO_3)_2$ because it takes the negative charge from two nitrate ions to balance the positive charge from one zinc ion.
b. The cobalt(III) ion is Co^{3+}; the hypochlorite ion is ClO^-. The compound is $Co(ClO)_3$.

PRACTICE PROBLEM 3.15

Write the formula for the following compounds.

a. Lead(IV) sulfate
b. Aluminum sulfide

Hint: Determine the charges on the cation and on the anion, and then combine them in the smallest ratio such that the total positive charge is equal to the total negative charge.

EVERYDAY CONNECTION

The differences in the names of compounds can mean the difference between life and death. For example, physicians sometimes prescribe a barium sulfate, $BaSO_4$, slurry or enema for patients who are about to have a stomach or intestinal X-ray film taken. The $BaSO_4$ is opaque to X-rays and outlines the stomach or colon clearly as in the X-ray shown here. The Ba ion is poisonous to humans, however, but $BaSO_4$ is safe to ingest because it does not dissolve, so the harmful Ba^{2+} is never released. If barium *sulfite*, $BaSO_3$, were given instead of barium *sulfate*, $BaSO_4$, the compound would dissolve in the stomach or colon, and the patient might die.

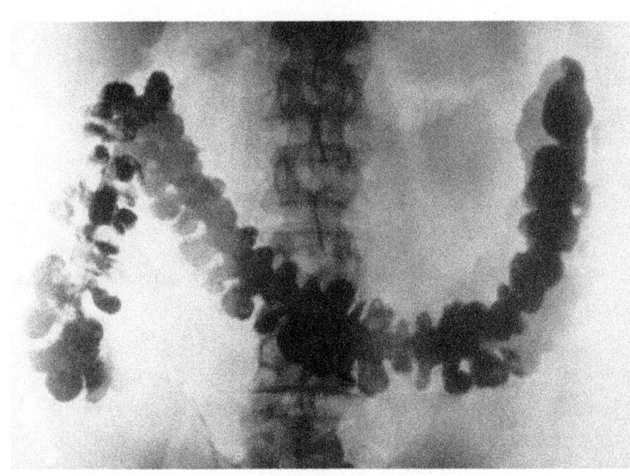

CDC/ Dr. Mae Melvin; Dr. E. West of Mobile, AL

NAMING HYDRATES

When copper(II) sulfate, $CuSO_4$, is crystallized from water, it forms a beautiful blue solid with the formula $CuSO_4 \cdot 5\,H_2O$, copper sulfate pentahydrate (Figure 3.12a). This formula indicates that there are five H_2O molecules included in each formula unit of $CuSO_4 \cdot 5\,H_2O$. These five water molecules are referred to as **waters of hydration**, and the compound is called a **hydrate**. If $CuSO_4 \cdot 5\,H_2O$ is heated sufficiently, the water molecules can be driven off to yield a white solid with the formula $CuSO_4$ (Figure 3.12b). $CuSO_4$ is said to be **anhydrous**, meaning "without water." Although hydrates such as $CuSO_4 \cdot 5\,H_2O$ contain H_2O in their chemical formulas, they are solids at room temperature—the specific number of H_2O molecules included in the chemical formula indicates that these molecules are part of the formula unit for the compound itself and does *not* mean that the compound is dissolved in water.

When reading the formula of a hydrate aloud, the centered dot is read "dot," so the formula for $CuSO_4 \cdot 5\,H_2O$ would be spoken as "C-U-S-O-four dot five-H-two-O."

To name hydrates, simply name the ionic compound first and then combine a prefix from Table 3.1 that identifies the number of water molecules with the word *hydrate* to indicate the presence of the water molecules. For example, $CuSO_4 \cdot 5\,H_2O$ is called copper(II) sulfate pentahydrate, and $MgSO_4 \cdot H_2O$ is called magnesium sulfate monohydrate. Solid $CuSO_4$ without any water molecules in its crystal structure is called copper(II) sulfate or *anhydrous* copper(II) sulfate, if it is important to emphasize that the ionic compound has no water molecules incorporated into its structure.

(a) (b)

Sara Egner, Macmillan Learning

FIGURE 3.12 Copper Sulfate Pentahydrate and Anhydrous Copper Sulfate

(a) Copper sulfate pentahydrate, $CuSO_4 \cdot 5\,H_2O$. (b) Anhydrous copper sulfate, $CuSO_4$. The presence of water molecules in the lattice changes physical properties such as color, but the hydrate and anhydrate have the same chemical properties and will react the same way in chemical reactions.

Example 3.16

Write the formulas for the following compounds.

a. Anhydrous zinc sulfate
b. Zinc sulfate heptahydrate

Solution

a. Zinc forms a cation with a +2 charge, and the sulfate ion, SO_4^{2-}, has a charge of −2, so the formula is $ZnSO_4$.
b. The prefix *hepta-* means seven (Table 3.1), so there are seven H_2O molecules in the formula of this hydrate: $ZnSO_4 \cdot 7\,H_2O$.

PRACTICE PROBLEM 3.16

Determine the names of the following compounds.

a. $MgCl_2$
b. $MgCl_2 \cdot 6\,H_2O$

Hint: To name ionic compounds, first name the cation and then the anion. For a hydrate, add the hydrate suffix using the prefixes in Table 3.1.

SECTION REVIEW

- Constant-charge cations are monatomic metal ions that always have the same charge. The charge on these ions is not included in the name of the ion.
- Variable-charge cations are monatomic metal ions that do not always have the same charge. The charges on these ions are indicated in the name with a Roman numeral.
- Polyatomic ions are given special names, which must either be memorized or looked up in a table.
- Monatomic anions are anions made up of only one atom with a negative charge. These are named using the root of the element name with the suffix *-ide*.
- Oxyanions are a type of polyatomic anion containing oxygen along with another element. They are named using a system that includes the suffixes *-ate* and *-ite*, and in some cases, the prefixes *per-* and *hypo-*, depending on the relative number of oxygen atoms in the ion.
- Ionic compound names result from writing the cation name, followed by the anion name.
- Hydrates are ionic compounds with water molecules incorporated into their structures.
- Hydrates are named like ordinary ionic compounds, with the addition of a prefix from Table 3.1 attached to the word *hydrate* to denote the number of water molecules per formula unit.

3.5 Naming Acids

GOALS

- Name acids from formulas.
- Write formulas for acids from names.

Background Review

Chapter 2 Atoms and the Periodic Table:
Section 2.1—Chemical Symbols

Acids are a special group of hydrogen-containing covalent compounds that, when dissolved in water, can react with water molecules and release one or more H^+ ions. The remainder of the acid molecule becomes an anion with a -1 charge for each hydrogen ion that was released. For example, when sulfurous acid, H_2SO_3, releases an H^+ ion, the remainder of the molecule is the -1 ion HSO_3^-, hydrogen sulfite. This ion can release a second H^+ ion and become the sulfite ion, SO_3^{2-}. In this way, acids are a special type of covalent compound where, when dissolved in water, hydrogen behaves as a cation.

The hydrogen atoms that are released as H^+ ions are called **ionizable hydrogen atoms**. The ionizable hydrogen atoms are always written first in the chemical formula for an acid. Thus, hydrochloric acid, HCl, is an acid with one ionizable H atom per molecule, whereas H_2SO_3 is an acid with two ionizable H atoms per molecule. An acid that has only one ionizable H atom is called a **monoprotic acid**, whereas one that has two or more ionizable H atoms is called a **polyprotic acid**. The H atoms in methane, CH_4, and ammonia, NH_3, are not ionizable, so CH_4 and NH_3 are not acids, and the H atoms in their formulas are not written first. In this text, all of the chemical compounds whose chemical formula begins with H, except for water, H_2O, and hydrogen peroxide, H_2O_2, are acids when dissolved in water. Acids are covered in detail in Chapter 16.

The appearance of hydrogen first in a chemical formula typically indicates that the compound is an acid.

Example 3.17

How many hydrogen atoms per molecule of acetic acid, $HC_2H_3O_2$, are ionizable?

Solution

Acetic acid has one ionizable hydrogen atom. It is represented by the first H in the formula. The three hydrogen atoms in $C_2H_3O_2$ are *not* ionizable, which is why they are written after the carbon atoms in the formula.

PRACTICE PROBLEM 3.17

How many hydrogen atoms per molecule of $H_2C_8H_4O_4$ are ionizable?

Hint: The ionizable hydrogens in an acid are written first in the chemical formula. Any hydrogens written after that do not ionize in water.

Though acids are covalent compounds, they have a special set of naming rules and do not use prefixes like other covalent compounds. There are three types of acid for naming purposes—binary, oxy-, and organic—and each has its own naming system. *Binary acids* are made up of H and one other element, as in hydrogen chloride, HCl, hydrogen fluoride, HF, and hydrosulfuric acid, H_2S. *Oxyacids* are made up of H bonded to oxyanions (discussed in Section 3.5), as in nitric oxide, HNO_3, sulfuric acid, H_2SO_4, and hypochlorous acid, HClO. *Organic acids* are made up of C, H, and O (and sometimes other elements as well), such as those seen in Example 3.17 and Practice Problem 3.17. How to name organic acids is discussed in Chapter 22, so the discussion here is limited to naming binary acids and oxyacids.

BINARY ACIDS

A binary acid always consists of one or two H atoms bonded to a monatomic anion of a nonmetal element from group 16 or 17. The number of H atoms in an acid is equal to the number of negative charges on the anion it is paired with. A flowchart for naming a binary acid is presented in Figure 3.13. The process consists of taking the root portion of the monatomic anion's name and adding the prefix *hydro-* and the suffix *-ic* and then adding the word acid (Figure 3.13).

All binary acid names begin with *hydro-* and end with *-ic acid.*

Example 3.18

Name the following binary acids.

a. HF
b. H_2S
c. HI

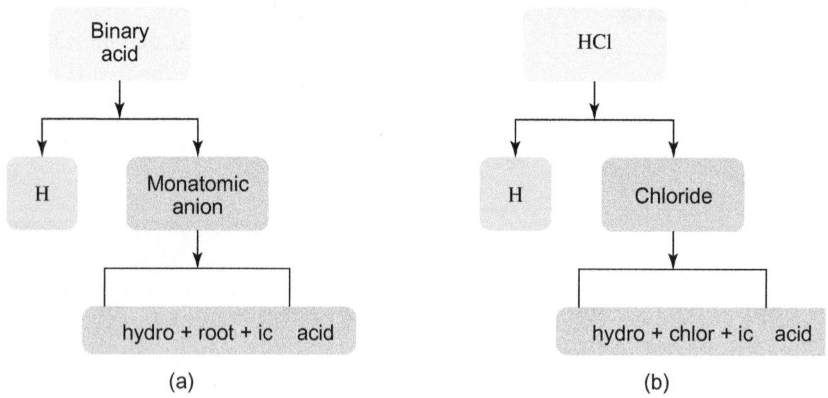

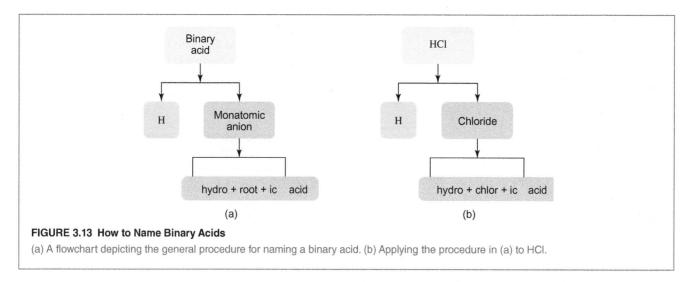

FIGURE 3.13 How to Name Binary Acids
(a) A flowchart depicting the general procedure for naming a binary acid. (b) Applying the procedure in (a) to HCl.

Solution

Since these compounds are all binary acids, the names will have the form *hydro-* + root + *-ic acid* (Figure 3.13).

a. *Hydro-* + fluor + *-ic acid* = hydrofluoric acid
b. *Hydro-* + sulfur + *-ic acid* = hydrosulfuric acid (When naming acids, *sulfur* rather than *sulf-* is used as the stem of sulfide.)
c. *Hydro-* + iod + *-ic acid* = hydroiodic acid

PRACTICE PROBLEM 3.18

Name the following binary acids.

a. HBr
b. H_2Se

Hint: Since these compounds are binary acids, the names will have the form *hydro-* + root + *-ic acid* (Figure 3.13).

The rules for naming acids apply only when the compound is dissolved in water. If a binary H compound, such as HF, HCl, HBr, HI, or H_2S is *not* dissolved in water, then it is named as if hydrogen were an alkali metal, using the naming rules for ionic compounds. For example, pure gaseous HCl is named hydrogen chloride with no prefixes for either element.

OXYACIDS

Oxyacids consist of hydrogen combined with oxyanions, such as those discussed in Section 3.5. The flowchart in Figure 3.14 shows how to name oxyacids—namely, begin with the name of the oxyanion in the acid, replace the *-ate* ending of the anion with *-ic*, or the *-ite* ending with *-ous*, and then add the word *acid*. If the oxyanion has a *hypo-* or *per-* prefix, then retain that prefix in the name of the acid.

With S and P, the stem of the oxyanion also changes slightly when naming the oxyacid from the oxyanion. For example, to name the oxyacid based on the sulfate ion, SO_4^{2-}, you would drop the *-ate* ending from *sulfate*

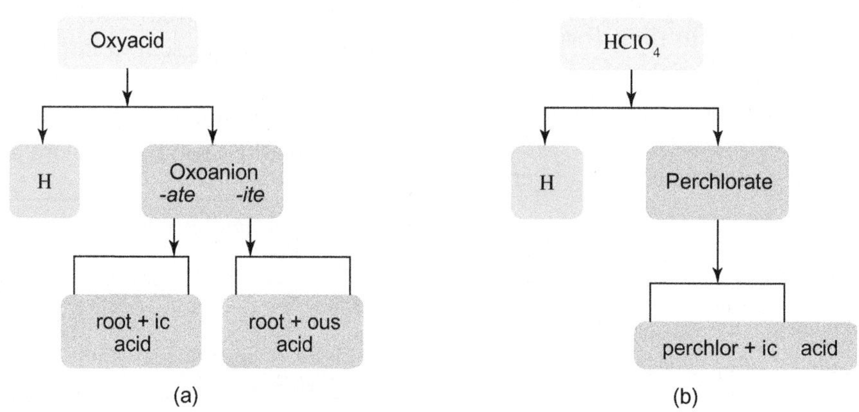

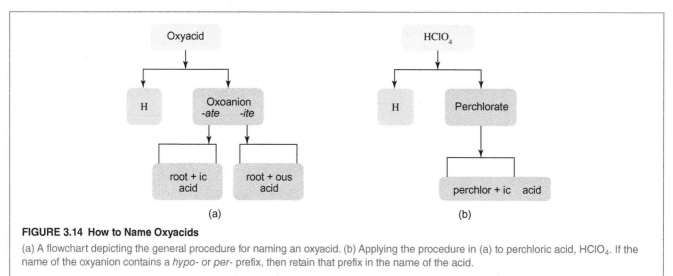

FIGURE 3.14 How to Name Oxyacids
(a) A flowchart depicting the general procedure for naming an oxyacid. (b) Applying the procedure in (a) to perchloric acid, $HClO_4$. If the name of the oxyanion contains a *hypo-* or *per-* prefix, then retain that prefix in the name of the acid.

and add *-ic*, resulting in *sulfic acid*. Instead, the stem changes from *sulf-* to *sulfur*, and the acid is known as sulfuric acid. Phosphate ion similarly changes its stem from *phosph-* to *phosphor* when the oxyacid is named.

SUMMARY OF ACID NOMENCLATURE

Table 3.5 summarizes the naming of an oxyacid from the name of its anion.

Example 3.19

Name the following acids.

a. H_3PO_3
b. H_2SO_3
c. HIO_3
d. HI

Solution

a. Phosphorous acid: The *-ite* suffix of the phosphite ion is changed to *-ous acid*. In this case, the stem is also changed from *phosph-* to *phosphor*.
b. Sulfurous acid: The *-ite* suffix of the sulfite ion is changed to *-ous acid*, and the stem is changed from *sulf-* to *sulfur*.
c. The anion is the iodate ion, IO_3^-. Iodate becomes iod + *-ic acid* = iodic acid.
d. Hydroiodic acid: The prefix *hydro-* distinguishes this binary acid from iodic acid, HIO_3.

PRACTICE PROBLEM 3.19

Name the following acids.

a. HBrO
b. HNO_3
c. HClO

Hint: First, name the anion. Then, change the *-ate* suffix to *-ic*, or the *-ite* suffix to *-ous* and add the word *acid* at the end. For additional information and examples, see Figure 3.14 or Table 3.4.

TABLE 3.5 Summary of Acid Nomenclature

Anion Suffix	Acid Name	Examples	
-ide	Hydro___ic acid	Cl^- = chloride HCl = hydrochloric acid	CN^- = cyanide HCN = hydrocyanic acid
-ate	___ic acid	ClO_4^- = perchlorate $HClO_4$ = perchloric acid	ClO_3^- = chlorate $HClO_3$ = chloric acid
-ite	___ous acid	ClO_2^- = chlorite $HClO_2$ = chlorous acid	ClO^- = hypochlorite HClO = hypochlorous acid

Example 3.20

What is the formula for each of the following acids?

a. Phosphoric acid
b. Chloric acid
c. Perbromic acid

Solution

a. H_3PO_4: The *-ic acid* suffix means the anion has an *-ate ion* suffix. That is, phosphor-ic acid → *phosph* + *-ate ion* = phosphate ion, PO_4^{3-}. PO_4^{3-} forms phosphoric acid by adding 3 H^+.
b. $HClO_3$: The *-ic acid* suffix means the anion has an *-ate ion* suffix. That is, chlor-ic acid → *chlor* + *-ate ion* = chlorate ion, ClO_3^-. ClO_3^- forms chloric acid by adding one H^+.
c. $HBrO_4$: Perbrom-ic acid → *perbrom* + *-ate ion* = perbromate ion, BrO_4^-. BrO_4^- forms perbromic acid by adding 1 H^+.

PRACTICE PROBLEM 3.20

Write the formulas for the following acids.

a. Nitrous acid
b. Sulfuric acid

Hint: Work backward from the acid name to the anion name by changing *-ous* to *-ite* and *-ic* to *-ate*, and then add the appropriate number of H^+ ions needed to balance the charge on the anion. (For sulfuric acid, there is also a slight difference between the name of the anion in the acid form and in the anion form.)

SECTION REVIEW

- Acids are a group of hydrogen-containing compounds that, when dissolved in water, can react with water molecules and release one or more H^+ ions.
- An acid will have one ionizable H atom for each negative charge on its anion, and for every H ion removed from the formula of an acid, one negative charge is added in the resulting anion.
- Most acids have H written first in their chemical formulas.
- The names of acids are derived from the names of the anions they contain:
  - The *-ate* suffix on an anion is replaced with *-ic acid.*
  - The *-ite* suffix on an anion is replaced with *-ous acid.*
  - The *-ide* suffix on an anion is replaced with *-ic acid*, and the prefix *hydro-* is added.

3.6 Nomenclature Review

GOAL

- Identify the appropriate naming system for a given compound.

The flowchart in Figure 3.15 outlines a systematic procedure for naming many compounds and ions. The flowchart can serve as a helpful guide, but you will still need to have some knowledge from earlier sections in this chapter to name the compounds properly.

Begin by identifying whether the compound is covalent or ionic. Within the covalent compounds (in the nonshaded regions of Figure 3.15), acids are distinguished from nonacids because acids follow a different naming procedure from other covalent compounds. For ionic compounds, the flowchart guides you first through naming the cation and then the anion in the shaded regions. The flowchart does not cover all compounds, and the names of polyatomic ions must still be memorized or looked up to name compounds that include them. If a compound is a hydrate, use the flowchart to name the ionic compound, then modify that name to include the number of water molecules per formula unit, as described in Section 3.4.

Example 3.21

Name the first three compounds listed in the Everyday Connection.

a. $NaClO$ in bleach
b. $HC_2H_3O_2$ in vinegar
c. $NaOH$ in drain cleaner

Solution

a. $NaClO$ contains a metal, so it is ionic. Sodium is a constant-charge cation and ClO^- is an oxyanion named hypochlorite (Table 3.2), so $NaClO$ is sodium hypochlorite.
b. $HC_2H_3O_2$ begins with H and is an acid. The anion is the acetate ion, $C_2H_3O_2^-$, so $HC_2H_3O_2$ is acetic acid.
c. $NaOH$ contains a metal, so it is ionic. Sodium is a constant-charge cation and OH^- is the hydroxide ion, so $NaOH$ is sodium hydroxide.

PRACTICE PROBLEM 3.21

Name the last three compounds listed in the Everyday Connection.

a. Battery acid, H_2SO_4
b. Blackboard chalk, $CaSO_4 \cdot 2\,H_2O$
c. $KClO_3$ in the head of a match

Hint: Name each compound according to the applicable naming system.

a. H_2SO_4 is an oxyacid (see Figure 3.14 or Table 3.5),
b. $CaSO_4 \cdot 2\,H_2O$ is a hydrate (see Section 3.4), and
c. $KClO_3$ is an ionic compound (see Section 3.4).

EVERYDAY CONNECTION

Here in Chapter 3, you have learned to name a variety of ionic compounds that contain polyatomic anions. Many compounds of this type are commonly found around the house. For example, the active ingredient in chlorine bleach is $NaClO$, and the main ingredient in vinegar is $HC_2H_3O_2$. Household drain cleaner contains $NaOH$, and the acid in a car battery is H_2SO_4. The white chalky material found in drywall is $CaSO_4 \cdot 2\,H_2O$, and it is sometimes used in blackboard chalk. The head of a match contains $KClO_3$.

Science History Images/Alamy Stock photo

Ingram Publishing/Alamy

Stockbyte/Getty Images

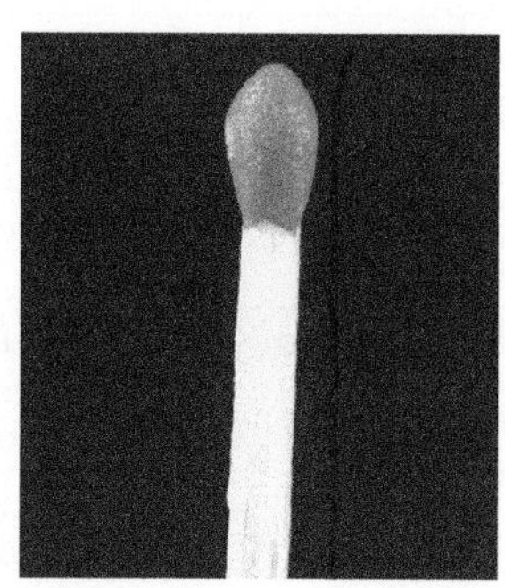

Stuart Monk/Shutterstock

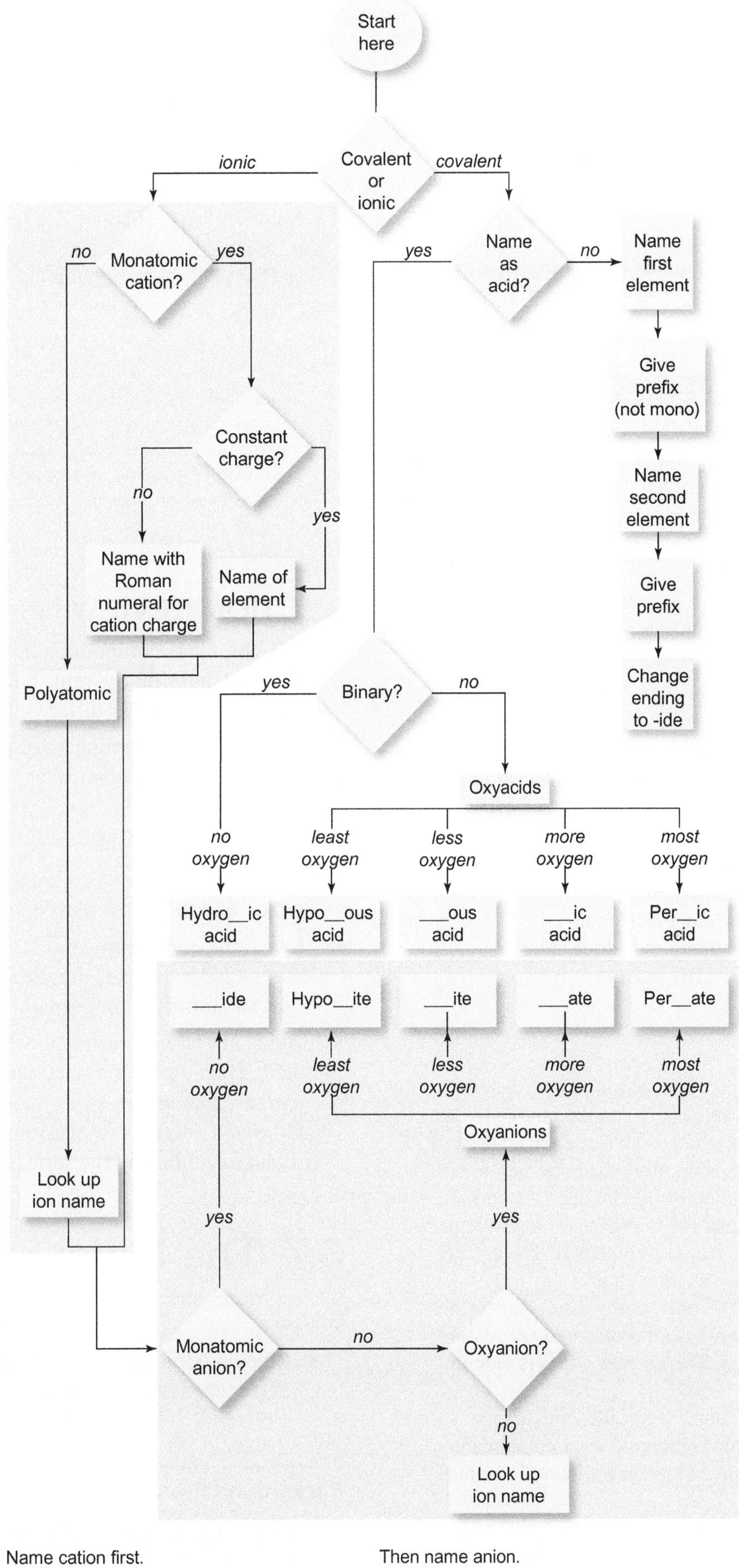

FIGURE 3.15 Nomenclature Summary

A flowchart that summarizes how to name compounds and ions.

Example 3.22

Water, H_2O, is a binary covalent compound. What would water be called if it were named according to the rules for naming binary covalent compounds?

Solution

A water molecule contains two hydrogen atoms and one oxygen, so its name would be dihydrogen monoxide.

PRACTICE PROBLEM 3.22

A H_2O molecule can also be considered a binary acid, HOH, made up of H^+ and the hydroxide ion, OH^-. What would water be called if its name were determined using the naming system for binary acids?

Hint: Follow the binary acid naming system, using *hydroxide* as the anion name. In a binary acid, the *-ide* ending of the anion is replaced with *-ic acid*, and the prefix *hydro-* is added.

Example 3.23

Each of the following compounds is named incorrectly. Determine what is wrong with each one, and provide the correct names.

a. NaCl	sodium(I) chloride
b. MnO	manganese(I) oxide
c. $Ca(ClO_3)_2$	calcium dichlorate
d. NH_4Cl	nitrogen trihydride chloride
e. $ZnBr_2$	zinc(II) bromite

Solution

a. Na^+ is a constant-charge ion and ". . . always has a +1 charge, so. . . " so the charge is not specified. The correct name is sodium chloride.

b. Manganese can form more than one cation, but the Roman numeral in this name is incorrect. Oxide is O^{2-}, so the manganese ion must be Mn^{2+}—that is, Mn(II), not Mn(I). The correct name is manganese(II) oxide.

c. $Ca(ClO_3)_2$ is an ionic compound, and ionic compounds do not need prefixes to specify the number of ions. The correct name is calcium chlorate.

d. NH_4^+ is a polyatomic ion called ammonium, so even though this compound does not contain a metal, it is ionic. The correct name is ammonium chloride.

e. Br^- is a monatomic anion, so its name ends in *-ide*. Only oxyanion names end in *-ite* or *-ate*. The correct name is zinc(II) bromide.

PRACTICE PROBLEM 3.23

Each of the following compounds is named incorrectly. Determine what is wrong with each one and provide the correct names.

a. $Cr(OH)_3$	chromium hydroxide
b. $SrCl_2$	strontium dichloride
c. KCN	potassium(I) cyanide
d. PCl_3	phosphorus chloride
e. CaS	calcium sulfate

Hint: Constant-charge cations are named using just their element name followed by *ion*. Variable-charge cations include their charge in Roman numerals. Polyatomic ions have special names (Table 3.4), and monatomic anions use the element name as a root, with an *-ide* ending. If a compound contains only nonmetals, is not an acid, and lacks the ammonium ion, it is covalent.

SECTION REVIEW

- All chemical compounds are named using some form of naming system, but there are different naming systems for different types of compounds.
- The first step in naming any compound is to identify whether it is ionic or covalent.
- Ionic compounds are named by naming the cation first and then the anion, with no prefixes.
- To name an ionic compound correctly, both the cation and the anion must be named correctly.
- Covalent compounds are named using a system that includes prefixes to indicate how many of each type of atom is in the formula for the compound.
- Acids are named based on the anion present in the acid. The names of binary acids include the prefix *hydro-*. The names of oxyacids use different prefixes and suffixes to distinguish between the different oxyanions in the series.

3.7 The Mole

GOAL

- Calculate the number of moles from the number of particles and vice versa.

Background Review

Chapter 1 Science and Measurement:
Section 1.7—Dimensional Analysis

Now that you know how to name compounds, it is time to learn how to quantify them. Chemists often need to know how much of a sample is present or how much of a compound can be made.

Some items, such as eggs, roses, and doughnuts, are sold by the dozen. Any time you buy something by the dozen, you get exactly 12 of them because one dozen always means 12 of whatever it is you are talking about. You can count things by the dozen—five dozen eggs means you have 60 individual eggs, 10 dozen eggs is 120 eggs, and 17 dozen eggs is

$$17 \text{ dozen eggs} \times \frac{12 \text{ eggs}}{1 \text{ dozen eggs}} = 204 \text{ eggs}$$

You can also calculate how many dozens you have if you know how many objects you have. For example, 12 eggs is one dozen, 24 eggs is two dozen, and 84 eggs is

$$84 \text{ eggs} \times \frac{1 \text{ dozen eggs}}{12 \text{ eggs}} = 7 \text{ dozen eggs}$$

Example 3.24

Three hundred children are expected to attend a party for a children's charity. If party hats are sold in packages of one dozen, how many packages do you need to have one hat for each child?

Solution

To calculate the number of packages from the number of hats, use the conversion factor 1 dozen = 12 hats. Since you are calculating dozens, dozens goes in the numerator of the conversion factor:

$$300 \text{ party hats} \times \frac{1 \text{ dozen party hats}}{12 \text{ party hats}} = 25 \text{ dozen}$$

Since 1 dozen hats = 1 package and you need 25 dozen hats, you will need 25 packages.

PRACTICE PROBLEM 3.24

If you bring eight dozen doughnuts to a meeting, and the company has 92 employees, will there be enough doughnuts for each employee to have one?

Hint: Determine how many doughnuts there are in 8 dozen and compare that with the number of employees.

CONVERTING BETWEEN MOLES AND FORMULA UNITS

One dozen may be a convenient way of counting eggs and doughnuts, but it is much too small a unit to count atoms and molecules. Atoms and molecules are so tiny that 12 of them is still an extremely small amount of mass and would be very difficult to measure. Instead, scientists use a much larger unit, called the mole, to count atoms, molecules, and formula units. In the same way that a dozen is 12, one **mole**, abbreviated mol, is 6.022×10^{23} of whatever it is you are talking about.

> 1 mole = 602,200,000,000,000,000,000,000
> $= 6.022 \times 10^{23}$

This value is named **Avogadro's number, N_A,** in honor of the Italian scientist Amedeo Avogadro (1776–1856). For any type of formula unit, such as a molecule, there is an Avogadro's number of that molecule in 1 mol. Similarly, if you have 1 mol of some type of molecule, you have an Avogadro's number of those molecules. Calculating the number of moles of something is done in the same way as calculating the number of dozens of something, except that, instead of multiplying by a conversion factor that converts between 12 of an item and 1 dozen, you multiply by a conversion factor that converts between 6.022×10^{23} of an item and 1 mole.

> Avogadro's number is the conversion factor for converting between the number of formula units and the number of moles.

Example 3.25

How many moles of helium are in a party balloon that contains 2.74×10^{23} helium atoms?

Solution

To calculate the number of moles from the number of atoms, use the conversion factor 1 mol = 6.022×10^{23} atoms. Since you are calculating the number of moles, moles go in the numerator of the conversion factor:

$$2.74 \times 10^{23} \text{ He atoms} \times \frac{1 \text{ mol of He}}{6.022 \times 10^{23} \text{ He atoms}}$$
$$= 0.455 \text{ mol He}$$

PRACTICE PROBLEM 3.25

A solid copper penny from before 1982 contains about 0.0490 mol of copper. How many copper atoms are in a solid copper penny?

Hint: Use Avogadro's number (1 mol = 6.022×10^{23} atoms) as a conversion factor between moles and atoms.

Mole conversions involving compounds use Avogadro's number as the conversion factor in exactly the same way as mole conversions involving atoms.

Example 3.26

How many moles of H_2O are in a drop of water that contains 1.67×10^{21} H_2O molecules?

Solution

To calculate the number of moles from the number of molecules, use the conversion factor 1 mol = 6.022×10^{23} molecules. Since you are calculating the number of moles, moles go in the numerator of the conversion factor:

$$1.67 \times 10^{21}\ \text{H}_2\text{O molecules} \times \frac{1\ \text{mol H}_2\text{O}}{6.022 \times 10^{23}\ \text{H}_2\text{O molecules}}$$

$$= 2.77 \times 10^{-3}\ \text{mol H}_2\text{O}$$

PRACTICE PROBLEM 3.26

A teaspoon of sugar is about 0.0123 mol of sucrose, $C_{12}H_{22}O_{11}$. How many $C_{12}H_{22}O_{11}$ molecules are in a teaspoon of sugar?

Hint: Use Avogadro's number (1 mol = 6.022 $\times 10^{23}$ molecules) as a conversion factor between moles and molecules.

MOLES OF ATOMS IN A COMPOUND

How many moles of carbon are in 1 mol of sucrose, $C_{12}H_{22}O_{11}$? Since you are already working in moles, you do not need Avogadro's number for this. Avogadro's number is only used for converting between the number of particles (i.e., the number of atoms, molecules, or formula units) and the number of moles.

To calculate the moles of one type of atom from the moles of a compound, simply multiply the number of moles of the compound by the number of atoms of that type in the chemical formula for the compound.

Moles of compound → Chemical formula → Moles of atoms

In the same way that one *molecule* of $C_{12}H_{22}O_{11}$ contains 12 C atoms, 22 H atoms, and 11 O atoms, one *mole* of $C_{12}H_{22}O_{11}$ contains 12 mol C, 22 mol H, and 11 mol O. *Five* moles of $C_{12}H_{22}O_{11}$, therefore, contain 60 mol C, 110 mol H, and 55 mol O.

Example 3.27

How many moles of each element are in each of the following samples?

a. 4.0 mol CCl_4
b. 0.50 mol $Fe_3(PO_4)_2$

Solution

In each case, multiply the number of moles of the compound by the subscript on the atom in the chemical formula to determine how many moles of that element are in the sample.

a. In 1 mol of CCl_4, there is 1 mol of C and 4 mol of Cl.

$$4.0\ \text{mol CCl}_4\left(\frac{1\ \text{mol C}}{1\ \text{mol CCl}_4}\right) = 4.0\ \text{mol C}$$

$$4.0\ \text{mol CCl}_4\left(\frac{4\ \text{mol Cl}}{1\ \text{mol CCl}_4}\right) = 16\ \text{mol Cl}$$

b. Remember to apply the subscript outside of the parentheses to each element inside the parentheses:

$$0.50\ \text{mol Fe}_3(\text{PO}_4)_2\left(\frac{3\ \text{mol Fe}}{1\ \text{mol Fe}_3(\text{PO}_4)_2}\right) = 1.5\ \text{mol Fe}$$

$$0.50\ \text{mol Fe}_3(\text{PO}_4)_2\left(\frac{2\ \text{mol P}}{1\ \text{mol Fe}_3(\text{PO}_4)_2}\right) = 1.0\ \text{mol P}$$

$$0.50\ \text{mol Fe}_3(\text{PO}_4)_2\left(\frac{8\ \text{mol O}}{1\ \text{mol Fe}_3(\text{PO}_4)_2}\right) = 4.0\ \text{mol O}$$

PRACTICE PROBLEM 3.27

How many moles of each element are in each of the following samples?

a. 2 mol Li_3PO_4
b. 0.2 mol $Ba(NO_3)_2$

Hint: Multiply the given number of moles of compound by the number of moles of each element in one mole of compound. Use the subscripts within the formula to determine the number of moles of each element in one mole of compound.

INDIVIDUAL ATOMS IN A COMPOUND

Once you know how many moles of each element are present in a sample, you can just multiply that value by Avogadro's number to determine the number of atoms of each element present.

Moles of compound → Chemical formula → Moles of atoms → Avogadro's number → Number of atoms

Example 3.28

The mineral pyrite, FeS_2, is more commonly known as fool's gold. If a desperate prospector finds a nugget of fool's gold containing 0.25 mol of FeS_2, (a) how many iron and sulfur atoms are in the nugget, and (b) if the nugget consists entirely of FeS_2, how many atoms make up the nugget?

Solution

a. For each element, first calculate the number of moles of that element, and then multiply that by Avogadro's number to get the number of atoms:

$$0.25 \text{ mol FeS}_2\left(\frac{1 \text{ mol Fe}}{1 \text{ mol FeS}_2}\right)\left(\frac{6.022 \times 10^{23} \text{ Fe atoms}}{1 \text{ mol Fe}}\right)$$
$$= 1.5 \times 10^{23} \text{ Fe atoms}$$

$$0.25 \text{ mol FeS}_2\left(\frac{2 \text{ mol S}}{1 \text{ mol FeS}_2}\right)\left(\frac{6.022 \times 10^{23} \text{ S atoms}}{1 \text{ mol S}}\right)$$
$$= 3.0 \times 10^{23} \text{ S atoms}$$

b. Add the numbers of each type of atom to get the total number of atoms in the nugget:

$$1.5 \times 10^{23} \text{ Fe atoms} + 3.0 \times 10^{23} \text{ S atoms}$$
$$= 4.5 \times 10^{23} \text{ atoms total}$$

PRACTICE PROBLEM 3.28

Limestone has the chemical name calcium carbonate, $CaCO_3$.

a. How many calcium, carbon, and oxygen atoms are in 1.00 mol of limestone?

b. What is the total number of atoms in 1.00 mol of limestone?

Hint: Convert the mass of limestone to moles of limestone, and then multiply by the subscripts in the chemical formula for each element in calcium carbonate to calculate how many moles of each element are present. Convert the number of moles of each element to atoms of each element, and then add them up.

Example 3.29

According to a 2016 estimate by the Environmental Protection Agency, the average passenger car in the United States emits 9.34 mol of CO_2 gas per mile driven. Based on this value, how many carbon atoms and how many oxygen atoms are in the CO_2 emissions of a car making a 1 mi drive?

Solution

Each mole of CO_2 contains 1 mol C and 2 mol O, so the CO_2 emissions from a 1 mi drive will contain 9.34 mol C and $2 \times 9.34 = 18.68$ mol O.

$$9.34 \text{ mol C} \times \frac{6.022 \times 10^{23} \text{ C atoms}}{1 \text{ mol C}}$$
$$= 5.62 \times 10^{24} \text{ C atoms}$$

$$18.68 \text{ mol O} \times \frac{6.022 \times 10^{23} \text{ O atoms}}{1 \text{ mol O}}$$
$$= 1.12 \times 10^{25} \text{ O atoms}$$

PRACTICE PROBLEM 3.29

The active ingredient in aspirin is acetylsalicylic acid, $HC_9H_7O_4$. A regular-strength aspirin tablet contains 1.80×10^{-3} mol $HC_9H_7O_4$ (along with some inactive ingredients). How many carbon, hydrogen, and oxygen atoms are in the active ingredient of a regular-strength aspirin tablet?

Hint: Calculate the number of moles of each element from the number of moles of the compound, and then calculate how many atoms that is for each element. (Note that the chemical formula for acetylsalicylic acid contains a total of eight H atoms.)

SECTION REVIEW

- In the same way that a dozen always means 12 of something, a mole always means 6.022×10^{23} of something.
- 6.022×10^{23} is known as Avogadro's number.
- Avogadro's number is used to convert between a number of particles and the corresponding number of moles, whether those particles are atoms, molecules, or formula units in an ionic compound.
- The number of moles of any element in a sample of a compound can be calculated by multiplying the number of moles of the compound by the subscript of that element in the chemical formula for the compound.

3.8 Molar Mass

GOAL

- Calculate the mass of 1 mol of a substance based on its chemical formula and atomic masses from the periodic table.

Background Review

Chapter 1 Science and Measurement:
Section 1.7—Dimensional Analysis

Chapter 2 Atoms and the Periodic Table:
Section 2.5—Atomic Masses

Avogadro's number is useful for converting between moles and the number of particles present in a sample, but chemists typically determine how much material is present by weighing it rather than by counting particles. To convert between mass and moles, the molar mass of the substance is used. The **molar mass** of any substance is the mass in grams of one mole of that substance. The molar mass for any element or compound is calculated using the atomic masses of the elements from the periodic table and the chemical formula for the substance.

MOLAR MASSES OF ATOMS

The **atomic mass** (or **atomic weight**) listed for each element in the periodic table is the average mass of a single atom of that element, expressed in atomic mass units, u (Section 2.7). For example, the average mass of one C atom is 12.011 u, and the average mass of one O atom is 15.999 u. One **atomic mass unit, u,** is equal to 1 g divided by Avogadro's number.

$$1\ \text{u} = \frac{1\ \text{g}}{6.022 \times 10^{23}} = 1.661 \times 10^{-24}\ \text{g}$$

If the mass of an element is given in units of u, it is the mass of one atom, and if the same number is given in units of grams, it is the mass of one *mole* of atoms. Thus, the atomic mass of C is 12.011 u, and the molar mass of C is 12.011 g/mol.

Since the molar mass has the same numerical value as the atomic mass, the atomic masses listed in the periodic table are the molar masses of the elements, too, expressed in grams per mole. Molar mass provides a conversion factor between mass and moles. For example, the molar mass of C is 12.011 g/mol, giving the conversion factor of 12.011 g C = 1 mol C.

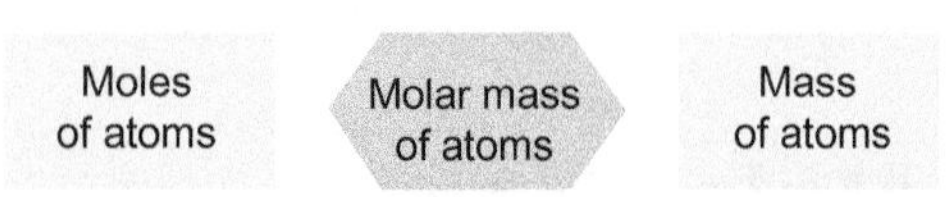

Example 3.30

A gold medal from the 2016 Olympics weighs 500 g and contains 0.0305 mol of gold. How many grams of pure gold were used to make each of these medals?

Solution

The molar mass of Au from the periodic table is 196.97 g/mol. Since you are calculating grams, put grams in the numerator of the conversion factor.

$$0.0305\ \text{mol Au} \times \frac{196.97\ \text{g Au}}{1\ \text{mol Au}} = 6.01\ \text{g Au}$$

PRACTICE PROBLEM 3.30

A silver medal from the 2016 Olympics weighs 500 g and contains 4.29 mol of silver. How many grams of pure silver were used to make each of these medals?

Hint: Find the molar mass of silver in the periodic table and use it as a conversion factor between grams of silver and moles of silver. The total mass of the Olympic medal is not used in this calculation.

Example 3.31

The "lead" in a pencil is actually graphite, an allotrope of carbon (Section 3.1). If the graphite in a pencil weighs 1.09 g, how many moles of carbon is that?

Solution

Use the molar mass of carbon, 12.011 g/mol, as a conversion factor between mass and moles. Since you are calculating moles, moles go in the numerator of the conversion factor:

$$1.09\ \text{g C} \times \frac{1\ \text{mol C}}{12.011\ \text{g C}} = 9.08 \times 10^{-2}\ \text{mol C}$$

PRACTICE PROBLEM 3.31

Diamond is another allotrope of carbon. If a 1-carat diamond has a mass of 0.200 g, how many moles of carbon is that?

Hint: Find the molar mass of carbon in the periodic table and use it as a conversion factor between grams and moles.

Example 3.32

If the mass of aluminum in an empty soda can is 13.9 g, how many moles of aluminum is that?

Solution

The molar mass of Al is 26.982 g/mol:

$$13.9\ \text{g Al} \times \frac{1\ \text{mol Al}}{26.982\ \text{g Al}} = 0.515\ \text{mol Al}$$

PRACTICE PROBLEM 3.32

An average Iron Age sword weighed about 1.3 kg. How many moles of iron, Fe, are in an Iron Age sword that contains 1.3 kg of iron?

Hint: Find the molar mass of iron in the periodic table and use it as a conversion factor between grams and moles. Don't forget to convert kilograms to grams (1 kg = 1000 g) before calculating moles.

MOLAR MASSES OF COMPOUNDS

Just as individual atoms have an atomic mass expressed in atomic mass units and a molar mass expressed in grams, individual molecules have a molecular mass, also expressed in atomic mass units, and a molar mass expressed in grams. The **molecular mass**, or **molecular weight**, of a molecule is the sum of the atomic masses of all of the atoms that make up that molecule. For example, C has a molar mass of 12.011 g/mol and O has a molar mass of 15.999 g/mol, so the molar mass of carbon monoxide, CO, is $12.011\ \text{g/mol} + 15.999\ \text{g/mol} = 28.010\ \text{g/mol}$. If a molecule has more than one of a given atom in its formula, such as the two O atoms in carbon dioxide, CO_2, the molar mass of that element is multiplied by the subscript when calculating the molar mass of the compound. As a result, the molar mass of CO_2 is $12.011\ \text{g/mol} + 2(15.999\ \text{g/mol}) = 44.009\ \text{g/mol}$.

Any time you are doing a mass-to-moles or moles-to-mass conversion problem that involves a compound, the first step is always to calculate the molar mass of the compound. Remember that some elements are diatomic, which means that, when these elements appear in their elemental form, there are always two atoms of that type bonded together. This must be taken into account when calculating the molar mass. For example, the molar mass of N in compounds is 14.007 g/mol, but the molar mass of N in its elemental state, N_2, is 28.014 g/mol because each N_2 molecule contains two N atoms.

Example 3.33

What is the molar mass of acetic acid, $HC_2H_3O_2$, the acid found in vinegar?

Solution

The molar mass for acetic acid can be calculated by adding the molar masses of all the atoms in one molecule of $HC_2H_3O_2$:

$$4 \times H = 4 \times 1.008\ \text{g/mol} = 4.032\ \text{g/mol}$$
$$2 \times C = 2 \times 12.011\ \text{g/mol} = 24.022\ \text{g/mol}$$
$$2 \times O = 2 \times 15.999\ \text{g/mol} = 31.998\ \text{g/mol}$$

The mass of 1 mol acetic acid is therefore $(4.032 + 24.022 + 31.998)\text{g/mol} = 60.052\ \text{g/mol}$.

PRACTICE PROBLEM 3.33

What is the molar mass of caffeine, $C_8H_{10}N_4O_2$?

Hint: Multiply the molar mass of each element in the compound by its subscript in the chemical formula and sum the results to get the molar mass of the compound.

In general, when calculating molar masses for compounds, keep as many significant digits as allowed based on the atomic masses provided in the periodic table. The rules for how many digits you can retain are different for multiplication and division than they are for addition and subtraction (Section 1.6), and you can gain or lose significant digits when adding and subtracting.

Molar masses for ionic compounds are calculated in the same way they are for molecules. Electrons have a negligible mass compared to the mass of an atom, so the atomic masses from the periodic table are also used as the masses of monatomic ions. For example, Sn atoms, Sn^{2+} ions, and Sn^{4+} ions all have the same atomic mass, 118.71 u, and the same molar mass, 118.71 g/mol. Since ionic compounds exist as extended ionic lattice structures, rather than as individual molecules, ionic compounds are said to have a **formula mass** or **formula weight**, rather than a molecular mass. *Formula mass* and *formula weight* are general terms that can refer to an atom, a molecule, or an ionic compound, but the terms *atomic mass* or *atomic weight* are normally used for the formula mass of an atom, and *molecular mass* or *molecular weight* are commonly used in place of formula mass for a molecule. The term *molar mass* can be used for the mass of one mole of any substance, whether it is one mole of atoms, one mole of molecules, or one mole of formula units of an ionic compound.

Example 3.34

Sodium fluoride, NaF, is the active ingredient in most toothpaste that makes tooth enamel harder and more resistant to decay. What is the molar mass of NaF?

Solution

Using the molar masses of Na and F from the periodic table, the molar mass of NaF is $22.99\ \text{g/mol} + 18.998\ \text{g/mol} = 41.99\ \text{g/mol}$.

PRACTICE PROBLEM 3.34

What is the molar mass of iron(III) oxide, a compound better known as rust?

Hint: First, determine the chemical formula for iron(III) oxide (Section 3.4), and then multiply the molar mass of each element by its subscript in the chemical formula and add the results.

Example 3.35

Calculate the molar mass of calcium sulfate dihydrate, which is used for blackboard chalk.

Solution

The ions in calcium sulfate are Ca^{2+} and SO_4^{2-}, which form a neutral compound in a 1:1 ratio, and *dihydrate* means there are two waters of hydration, so calcium sulfate dihydrate has the chemical formula $CaSO_4 \cdot 2\,H_2O$. The molar mass is determined by adding the molar masses of each of the atoms in the formula for the compound, multiplied by their subscripts in the formula for the compound. One mole of $CaSO_4 \cdot 2\,H_2O$ contains 1 mol Ca, 1 mol S, 6 mol O, and 4 mol H:

$$1 \times \text{Ca} = 1 \times 40.078\ \text{g/mol} = 40.078\ \text{g/mol}$$
$$1 \times \text{S} = 1 \times 32.06\ \text{g/mol} = 32.06\ \text{g/mol}$$
$$6 \times \text{O} = 6 \times 15.999\ \text{g/mol} = 95.994\ \text{g/mol}$$
$$4 \times \text{H} = 4 \times 1.008\ \text{g/mol} = 4.032\ \text{g/mol}$$

The molar mass is the sum of the molar masses of all the atoms in the chemical formula:

$$40.078\ \text{g/mol} + 32.06\ \text{g/mol} + 95.994\ \text{g/mol} + 4.032\ \text{g/mol} = 172.16\ \text{g/mol}$$

PRACTICE PROBLEM 3.35

Sodium thiosulfate pentahydrate, $Na_2S_2O_3 \cdot 5\,H_2O$, has a number of medicinal uses and is also used for dechlorinating tap water for aquariums. Calculate the molar mass of $Na_2S_2O_3 \cdot 5\,H_2O$.

Hint: Multiply the molar mass of each element by the number of atoms in one formula unit. For H and O, the number of atoms in the hydrate portion of the chemical formula is equal to the coefficient times the subscript.

CONVERTING BETWEEN GRAMS AND MOLES OF A COMPOUND

The molar mass of a compound can be used as a conversion factor between the mass of a compound and the number of moles in the sample.

Moles of compound → Molar mass of compound → Mass of compound

Example 3.36

A typical grain of table salt, NaCl, weighs about 0.30 mg. How many moles of NaCl is this?

Solution

The molar mass of NaCl is 22.99 g/mol + 35.45 g/mol = 58.44 g/mol. In this case, the mass of the sample is given in milligrams instead of grams, so it must be converted to grams before calculating moles:

$$0.30\ \text{mg NaCl} \times \frac{1\ \text{g}}{1000\ \text{mg}} \times \frac{1\ \text{mol NaCl}}{58.44\ \text{g NaCl}} = 5.1 \times 10^{-6}\ \text{mol NaCl}$$

PRACTICE PROBLEM 3.36

An average grain of beach sand weighs about 2.8 mg. If this average grain of sand is made up entirely of silica (silicon dioxide, SiO_2), how many moles of SiO_2 is this?

Hint: To calculate moles from mass, use the molar mass as a conversion factor.

Once you know how many moles of a compound are in a sample, you can use the chemical formula of the compound to determine how many moles of atoms are in the sample. You can then use Avogadro's number to calculate how many atoms are in the sample. The video in Figure 3.16 shows you how to do these kinds of calculations.

Example 3.37

How many atoms are in the typical 0.30 mg grain of salt from Example 3.36?

Solution

The 0.30 mg grain of salt consisted of 5.1×10^{-6} mol NaCl. First use the chemical formula to determine how many moles of Na and Cl this is, and then calculate how many individual atoms of each element you have based on the number of moles:

Moles of compound → Chemical formula → Moles of atoms → Avogadro's number → Number of atoms

Steven Lemon, Macmillan Learning

FIGURE 3.16 Video Tutorial: Molar Mass and Avogadro's Number

NOTE: You need to be online to access this video.
This video shows how to calculate the number of atoms of a particular element in a given mass of a compound.

One mole of NaCl contains 1 mol Na and 1 mol Cl, so 5.1×10^{-6} mol NaCl contains 5.1×10^{-6} mol Na and 5.1×10^{-6} mol Cl. To convert from moles of Na to the number of Na atoms, use Avogadro's number as a conversion factor:

$$5.1 \times 10^{-6} \text{ mol Na} \times \frac{6.022 \times 10^{23} \text{ Na atoms}}{1 \text{ mol Na}}$$
$$= 3.1 \times 10^{18} \text{ Na atoms}$$

There are equal numbers of Na and Cl atoms in the chemical formula for NaCl, so there must also be 3.1×10^{18} Cl atoms in the grain of salt, and the total number of atoms is 6.2×10^{18} atoms.

PRACTICE PROBLEM 3.37

How many atoms are in the 2.8 mg grain of sand from Practice Problem 3.36?

Hint: In Practice Problem 3.36 you calculated the number of moles of SiO_2 in the grain of sand. To convert from moles to number of formula units of SiO_2, multiply by Avogadro's number. Then use the subscripts in the chemical formula to determine how many moles of atoms are present.

At this point, you have learned enough to be able to calculate the total number of atoms in a sample of any element or compound if you know the mass and chemical formula of the substance. You also know how to calculate the mass of any number of individual atoms or formula units of a compound if you know the chemical formula for the compound. The next few examples show you how to determine the total number of atoms in a sample of known mass and to determine the total mass of a sample from the number of atoms it contains.

Example 3.38

Carbon dioxide in the solid phase is called *dry ice* because, when it is warmed up, it goes directly from solid to gas, with no liquid state in between (the solid-to-gas phase change is called *sublimation*; see Section 12.3). If a 750 g sample of dry ice sublimates to CO_2 gas, how many CO_2 molecules are released into the air?

Solution

To solve this, you need to convert mass to moles using the molar mass of CO_2 as a conversion factor, and then convert moles to molecules using Avogadro's number:

Mass of CO_2 → Molar mass of CO_2 → Moles of CO_2 → Avogadro's number → Number of CO_2 molecules

Since this problem involves a compound, the first step is to calculate the molar mass of the compound:

$$\text{Molar mass of } CO_2 = 12.011 \text{ g/mol} + 2(15.999 \text{ g/mol})$$
$$= 44.009 \text{ g/mol}$$

$$750 \text{ g } CO_2 \times \frac{1 \text{ mol } CO_2}{44.009 \text{ g } CO_2} = 17 \text{ mol } CO_2$$

$$17 \text{ mol } CO_2 \times \frac{6.022 \times 10^{23} \text{ } CO_2 \text{ molecules}}{1 \text{ mol } CO_2}$$
$$= 1.0 \times 10^{25} \text{ } CO_2 \text{ molecules}$$

PRACTICE PROBLEM 3.38

A standard 250-square-foot roll of household kitchen aluminum foil weighs 102 g. How many aluminum atoms is that?

Hint: Convert mass of Al to moles of Al, and then convert moles of Al to atoms of Al.

Example 3.39

What is the total mass of the helium in the party balloon from Example 3.25, which contained 2.74×10^{23} helium atoms?

Solution

First convert the number of He atoms to moles of He using Avogadro's number as a conversion factor, and then convert moles to grams using the molar mass of helium.

Number of He atoms → Avogadro's number → Moles of He → Molar mass of He → Mass of He

$$2.74 \times 10^{23} \text{ He atoms} \times \frac{1 \text{ mol of He}}{6.022 \times 10^{23} \text{ He atoms}}$$
$$= 0.455 \text{ mol He}$$

$$0.455 \text{ mol He} \times \frac{4.0026 \text{ g He}}{1 \text{ mol He}} = 1.82 \text{ g He}$$

PRACTICE PROBLEM 3.39

Suppose that the party balloon from Example 3.39 was filled with the same number of nitrogen gas molecules instead of helium atoms. What would be the mass of the nitrogen gas inside the balloon?

Hint: The balloon contains 2.74×10^{23} N_2 molecules. Convert molecules to moles and then moles to grams.

SECTION REVIEW

- The molar mass of any substance is the mass in grams of one mole of that substance.
- The atomic masses in the periodic table are also molar masses of the elements in units of grams per mole.
- The molar masses of individual elements can be added to calculate the molar masses of compounds.
- The molar mass of any substance can be used as a conversion factor to convert between mass and moles of that substance.

3.9 Percent Composition

GOAL

- Calculate the percent composition by mass of a compound based on its chemical formula and atomic mass from the periodic table.

Background Review

Chapter 0 Math Review: Section 0.6—Percentage

If you know the mass of each element in the formula unit for a compound and the overall mass of the entire formula unit, you can calculate the **percent composition** of the compound. The percent composition of a compound tells you what percentage of the compound (by mass) is made up by each of its component atoms.

Sodium chloride, NaCl, is made up of equal numbers of sodium, Na, and chloride, Cl, ions, but Cl ions are heavier than the Na ions, so NaCl contains more Cl by mass than it does Na by mass. To calculate the percent composition of a compound, divide the total mass of each element by the total mass of the formula unit, then multiply the result by 100% to convert it to a percentage:

$$\%\text{ Composition} = \frac{\text{Total mass of that element in the compound}}{\text{Total mass of the compound}} \times 100\% \qquad (3.2)$$

Together, the percent compositions for all the elements in a compound should add up to 100% (within rounding error).

Percent composition calculations can be done using either formula masses (in units of atomic mass units) or molar masses (in units of grams per mole). The calculations and the results are the same in either case. In this textbook the calculations will be shown using molar masses.

Example 3.40

Calculate the percent composition of each element in sodium chloride, NaCl.

Solution

For NaCl, the molar mass of sodium is 22.99 g/mol, and the molar mass of chlorine is 35.45 g/mol. The overall molar mass of NaCl is therefore 22.99 g/mol + 35.45 g/mol = 58.44 g/mol. This value should be rounded to four significant figures, but carrying an extra digit in the molar mass will eliminate rounding errors in the mass percent calculations.

The percentage by mass of sodium in NaCl is the mass of sodium in 1 mol NaCl divided by the molar mass of NaCl, times 100%:

$$\text{Mass percent Na} = \frac{\text{Molar mass of Na}}{\text{Molar mass of NaCl}} \times 100\%$$

$$\text{Mass percent Na} = \frac{22.99\text{ g/mol}}{58.44\text{ g/mol}} \times 100\% = 39.34\%$$

The final answer is rounded to four significant digits because the molar masses of Na and Cl have only four significant digits.

The percentage of chlorine in NaCl can be calculated the same way:

$$\text{Mass percent Cl} = \frac{\text{Molar mass of Cl}}{\text{Molar mass of NaCl}} \times 100\%$$

$$\text{Mass percent Cl} = \frac{35.45\text{ g/mol}}{58.44\text{ g/mol}} \times 100\% = 60.66\%$$

So, while a NaCl crystal is made up of equal numbers of sodium ions and chloride ions, the percent composition of NaCl shows that slightly more than 60% of its mass is made up of chlorine, and less than 40% of the mass is sodium.

The percentages of the elements making up any compound must total 100%. If the percentages of all but one element are known, the percentage of the remaining element can be calculated by the difference from 100%. Thus, the percentage of chlorine in NaCl could also have been calculated as follows:

$$100\% = \text{percentage of Cl in NaCl} + \text{percentage of Na in NaCl}$$

Percentage of Cl in NaCl = 100% − percentage of Na in NaCl = 100.00% − 39.34% = 60.66%

PRACTICE PROBLEM 3.40

Calculate the percent composition of magnesium chloride, $MgCl_2$.

Hint: Assume you have 1 mol $MgCl_2$ and use Equation 3.2 to calculate the percent composition for Mg and for Cl.

Example 3.41

Calculate the percent composition of iron(II) nitrate, $Fe(NO_3)_2$.

Solution

One mole of $Fe(NO_3)_2$ contains 1 mol Fe (55.845 g), 2 mol N (14.007 g each), and 6 mol O atoms (15.999 g each), for a total molar mass of (55.845 g/mol) + 2(14.007 g/mol) + 6(15.999 g/mol) = 179.853 g/mol.

For each element in the compound, the percent composition is equal to the total mass of that element divided by the molar mass of the compound, multiplied by 100%.

$$\text{Percent Fe} = \frac{\text{Molar mass of Fe}}{\text{Molar mass of Fe(NO}_3)_2} \times 100\%$$

$$\text{Percent Fe} = \frac{55.845\ \text{g/mol}}{179.853\ \text{g/mol}} \times 100\% = 31.05\%\ \text{Fe}$$

The percentages of N and O in the compound are calculated in the same way:

$$\text{Percent N} = \frac{2(14.007\ \text{g/mol})}{179.853\ \text{g/mol}} \times 100\% = 15.58\%\ \text{N}$$

$$\text{Percent O} = \frac{6(15.999\ \text{g/mol})}{179.853\ \text{g/mol}} \times 100\% = 53.37\%\ \text{O}$$

Because there are multiple atoms of nitrogen and oxygen present in a formula unit of $Fe(NO_3)_2$, the molar masses of nitrogen and oxygen were multiplied by their subscripts in the formula for the compound to calculate the total mass of each of these elements in 1 mol of the compound. The sum of all the percentages of elements in any compound should be 100%:

$$31.05\% + 15.58\% + 53.37\% = 100.00\%$$

The sum may not be exactly 100% because of prior rounding to the proper number of significant digits. You may find that your answer differs from 100% in the tenths place (totaling 100.3%, for example, or 99.8%, instead of 100.0%), and that's fine. If you get a total closer to 98% or 102%, however, then you should look for an error in your numbers or your calculations.

Getting 100% does not guarantee that your percentages are correct, but getting a sum that is significantly different from 100% guarantees that something is incorrect.

PRACTICE PROBLEM 3.41

Calculate the percent composition of $(NH_4)_3PO_4$.

Hint: Start by calculating the molar mass for $(NH_4)_3PO_4$, and the total mass of each element in 1 mol $(NH_4)_3PO_4$, and then use Equation 3.2 to calculate the percent composition for each element.

If you know the percent composition of a compound, it can be used to determine how much of any given element is contained in the sample. For example, if you know a compound is 15.3% carbon, C, by mass, then you know that there are 15.3 g C in every 100.0 g of compound, so the conversion factor is 15.3 g C = 100.0 g compound. You could then use that conversion factor to calculate the number of grams of C in a 234.8 g sample of the compound:

$$234.8\ \text{g compound} \times \frac{15.3\ \text{g C}}{100.0\ \text{g compound}} = 35.9\ \text{g C}$$

Example 3.42

How many grams of copper are in 20.0 g of copper sulfate pentahydrate, $CuSO_4 \cdot 5\,H_2O$?

Solution

The molar mass of $CuSO_4 \cdot 5\,H_2O$ is

$$1 \times \text{Cu} = 63.546\ \text{g/mol}$$
$$1 \times \text{S} = 32.06\ \text{g/mol}$$
$$9 \times \text{O} = 9 \times 15.999\ \text{g} = 143.99\ \text{g/mol}$$
$$10 \times \text{H} = 10 \times 1.008\ \text{g} = 10.08\ \text{g/mol}$$
$$63.546\ \text{g/mol} + 32.06\ \text{g/mol} + 143.99\ \text{g/mol} + 10.08\ \text{g/mol} = 249.68\ \text{g/mol}$$

$$\text{Percent Cu} = \frac{\text{Molar mass of Cu}}{\text{Molar mass of CuSO}_4 \cdot 5\,\text{H}_2\text{O}} \times 100\%$$

$$\text{Percent Cu} = \frac{63.546\ \text{g/mol Cu}}{249.68\ \text{g/mol CuSO}_4 \cdot 5\,\text{H}_2\text{O}} \times 100\% = 25.451\%\ \text{Cu}$$

The mass percent Cu in the compound can now be used as a conversion factor, knowing that

25.451% Cu means that 25.451 g Cu = 100.0 g $CuSO_4 \cdot 5\,H_2O$.

Mass of Cu in 20.0 g of $CuSO_4 \cdot 5\,H_2O$:

$$20.0\text{ g } CuSO_4 \cdot 5\,H_2O \times \frac{25.451\text{ g Cu}}{100.0\text{ g } CuSO_4 \cdot 5\,H_2O}$$
$$= 5.09\text{ g Cu}$$

PRACTICE PROBLEM 3.42

How many grams of copper, Cu, are in 20.0 g of anhydrous copper sulfate, $CuSO_4$?

Hint: There are two different ways you could approach this problem:

1. Calculate how many moles of anhydrous $CuSO_4$ are in 20.0 g. Since there is one Cu in the chemical formula, the moles of Cu will be equal to the number of moles of $CuSO_4$. Then calculate the mass of Cu using the molar mass of Cu.
2. Calculate the percent Cu, and multiply 20.0 g $CuSO_4$ by the percent Cu to determine how much of that mass is due to copper.

Example 3.43

How many pounds of carbon, hydrogen, and oxygen are in a 5.00 lb bag of sugar, $C_{12}H_{22}O_{11}$?

Solution

First, calculate the percent composition of sugar because the percent of each element can be used as a conversion factor to calculate the mass of the element from the mass of the compound. The percent for each element is the total mass of each element in 1 mol of sugar divided by the molar mass of the compound and multiplied by 100%:

$$12 \times C = 12 \times 12.011\text{ g/mol} = 144.13\text{ g/mol}$$
$$22 \times H = 22 \times 1.008\text{ g/mol} = 22.18\text{ g/mol}$$
$$11 \times O = 11 \times 15.999\text{ g/mol} = 175.99\text{ g/mol}$$

The molar mass of sucrose is the sum of these individual masses:

$$144.13\text{ g/mol} + 22.18\text{ g/mol} + 175.99\text{ g/mol} = 342.30\text{ g/mol}$$

Now that you know the molar mass of sugar and the mass of each element in 1 mol of sugar, you can calculate the percent composition of sugar:

$$\text{Percent C} = \frac{\text{Mass of C}}{\text{Molar mass}} \times 100\%$$
$$= \frac{144.13\text{ g/mol}}{342.30\text{ g/mol}} \times 100\% = 42.107\%\text{ C}$$

The percents by mass of hydrogen and oxygen are calculated in the same way, using the masses of each of those elements and the molar mass for sucrose:

$$\text{Percent H} = \frac{22.18\text{ g/mol H}}{342.30\text{ g/mol formula}} \times 100\%$$
$$= 6.479\%\text{ H}$$

$$\text{Percent O} = \frac{175.99\text{ g/mol O}}{342.30\text{ g/mol formula}} \times 100\%$$
$$= 51.414\%\text{ O}$$

As a quick check, the sum of the percentages should equal 100%:

$$42.107\% + 6.479\% + 51.414\% = 100.000\%$$

The mass of each element can now be calculated from the mass of the sample. Mass percents can be used with any unit of mass, as long as the masses of the element and the compound are in the same units. For example, 42.107 g C = 100.0 g sugar, 42.107 tons C = 100.0 tons sugar, and 42.107 lb C = 100.0 lb sugar.

$$\text{Carbon: } 5.0\text{ lb sugar} \times \frac{42.11\text{ lbs C}}{100\text{ lb sugar}} = 2.1\text{ lb C}$$

$$\text{Hydrogen: } 5.0\text{ lb sugar} \times \frac{6.479\text{ lbs H}}{100\text{ lb sugar}} = 0.32\text{ lb H}$$

$$\text{Oxygen: } 5.0\text{ lb sugar} \times \frac{51.414\text{ lbs O}}{100\text{ lb sugar}} = 2.6\text{ lb O}$$

A 5.0 lb bag of sugar contains 2.1 lb of carbon atoms, 0.32 lb of hydrogen atoms, and 2.6 lb of oxygen atoms.

PRACTICE PROBLEM 3.43

Rubies and sapphires are both forms of the mineral corundum, Al_2O_3. Corundum is a colorless mineral, but trace impurities of other metals give it a variety of colors. The world's most valuable ruby is the Sunrise Ruby, weighing 5.1 g. Assuming that the mass of the trace impurities in the Sunrise Ruby is negligible, use the percent composition of Al_2O_3 to calculate the mass of aluminum, Al, and oxygen, O, in the Sunrise Ruby.

Hint: Calculate the percent composition of each element using Equation 3.2, and then multiply the percent composition of each element by the mass of the ruby to determine how much of that mass is due to each element.

These examples have shown how percent composition can be used to calculate the mass of a given element in a sample of known mass. Percent composition can also be used to calculate the total mass of the sample if you know the percent composition and the mass of one element in the compound.

Example 3.44

If 100.0 g of carbon is converted to methane gas, CH_4, how many grams of methane would be formed?

Solution

The percent of carbon in methane is

$$\frac{\text{Molar mass of C}}{\text{Molar mass of CH}_4} \times 100\%$$
$$= \frac{12.011\ \text{g/mol C}}{12.011\ \text{g/mol C} + 4(1.008\ \text{g/mol H})} \times 100\%$$
$$= 74.85\%\ \text{C}$$

74.85% C means there are 74.85 g C in every 100 g CH_4. The conversion factor is therefore 74.85 g C = 100.0 g CH_4. To calculate the mass of CH_4, place 100.0 g CH_4 in the numerator of the conversion factor:

$$100.0\ \text{g C} \times \frac{100.0\ \text{g CH}_4}{74.85\ \text{g C}} = 133.6\ \text{g CH}_4$$

PRACTICE PROBLEM 3.44

If 100.0 g of carbon is converted to carbon dioxide gas, CO_2, how many grams of CO_2 would be formed?

Hint: First, calculate the percent by mass of carbon in CO_2, and then use this as a conversion factor to determine the mass of CO_2 formed from the given mass of carbon.

SECTION REVIEW

- The percent composition of a compound is a breakdown of the percentages by mass of all the elements in the compound.
- The percentage by mass of an element in a compound is 100% times the ratio of the total mass of the element divided by the formula mass.
- Percent composition can be calculated using either the molar masses (in grams) or the formula masses (in atomic mass units) for the elements and the compound.
- The percent composition calculation is done in the same way whether the compound is covalent or ionic.
- Percent composition values can be used as conversion factors to calculate how many grams of an element are in a given sample of a compound or how many grams of a compound can be formed from a given mass of an element.

3.10 Empirical Formulas

GOAL

- Determine the empirical formula of a compound from percent composition or other mass-ratio data.

Background Review

Chapter 2 Atoms and the Periodic Table:
Section 2.2—The Laws of Chemical Combination

Suppose that a chemical analysis of a 20.0 g sample of an unknown compound indicated that it contained 1.34 g H, 8.00 g C, and 10.7 g O. You could calculate the number of moles of each of these elements in the sample from these masses by using the molar mass of each element as a conversion factor:

$$1.34\ \text{g H} \times \frac{1\ \text{mol H}}{1.008\ \text{g H}} = 1.33\ \text{mol H}$$
$$8.00\ \text{g C} \times \frac{1\ \text{mol C}}{12.011\ \text{g C}} = 0.666\ \text{mol C}$$
$$10.7\ \text{g O} \times \frac{1\ \text{mol O}}{15.999\ \text{g O}} = 0.669\ \text{mol O}$$

These mole ratios correspond to the subscripts in the chemical formula of the compound $C_{0.666}H_{1.33}O_{0.669}$. These subscripts can be converted to whole numbers by dividing each of them by the lowest value of the three. Since they are all being divided by the same number, the ratio between them remains unchanged:

$$C_{\frac{0.666}{0.666}}H_{\frac{1.33}{0.666}}O_{\frac{0.669}{0.666}} = C_{1.00}H_{2.00}O_{1.00}$$

The ratio of elements in the compound is therefore 1 C to 2 H to 1 O. You cannot say for sure that this is the actual formula for the compound because there are any number of compounds that all have this same ratio—$C_2H_4O_2$, $C_6H_{12}O_6$, and $C_{42}H_{84}O_{42}$ (if there is such a compound) are just a few with the same 1:2:1 ratio. Although you do not know what the actual chemical formula of the compound is, you do know that the *ratio* of the atoms in the actual formula, whatever that formula is, will be 1 C to 2 H to 1 O.

This chemical formula for the compound that uses the smallest whole-number ratio of the atoms in the compound is called the **empirical formula**. The empirical formula for the compound described above is

CH_2O. The actual chemical formula for the compound will either be the same as the empirical formula or will be a whole-number multiple of the empirical formula.

Example 3.45

Indicate whether each of the following chemical formulas is a valid empirical formula. If not, determine the correct empirical formula for that compound.

a. $BO_{1.5}$
b. C_6H_6
c. $Na_{0.5}P_{0.25}O$
d. $C_3H_{2.67}O_{1.33}$

Solution

They are all invalid empirical formulas.

a. The subscript of 1.5 on O must be converted to an integer. Multiplying all of the subscripts by 2 (to keep the ratio between B and O the same) gives the correct empirical formula: B_2O_3.
b. The empirical formula must have the lowest whole-number ratio of the atoms that make up the compound. The subscripts in C_6H_6 can both be divided by 6 to yield CH.
c. To convert these subscripts to whole numbers, figure out first what must be done to make the smallest one a whole number, and then do that to all of them. The 0.25 subscript on P must be multiplied by 4 to make it equal to 1, so multiply all of the subscripts by 4: Na_2PO_4.
d. To convert these subscripts to whole numbers, figure out first what must be done to make the smallest subscript a whole number, and then do that to all of them. The 1.33 subscript on O must be multiplied by 3 to turn it into a whole number, so multiply all of the subscripts by 3: $C_9H_8O_4$.

PRACTICE PROBLEM 3.45

Indicate whether each of the chemical formulas written below is a valid empirical formula. If not, determine the correct empirical formula for that compound.

a. $C_5H_{10}N_0O_2$
b. $C_{11}H_{12}N_2O_2$
c. Fe_1O_1
d. C_8H_{18}

Hint: A valid empirical formula consists of the smallest whole-number ratio of the atoms in the compound.

If a value in the mole ratio is *very close* to a whole number, such as 1.98 or 3.02, then it can be rounded to the nearest whole number. Do not round, however, if it is much farther from a whole number.

TABLE 3.6 Converting Decimal Subscripts to Whole Numbers

Decimal Ending	Fractional Equivalent	To Convert to a Whole Number, Multiply All Subscripts by
.20	1/5	5
.25	1/4	4
.33	1/3	3
.40	2/5	5
.50	1/2	2
.67	2/3	3
.75	3/4	4

Table 3.6 lists common decimal endings (e.g., .20), their fractional equivalents (e.g., 1/5), and what number you need to multiply by to turn the decimals into whole numbers (e.g., 5). When multiplying, make sure you multiply *all* of the subscripts in the formula by the same number to maintain the correct mole ratio among the atoms in the formula.

Example 3.46

Write the empirical formulas for the compounds containing carbon, C, and hydrogen, H, in the following ratios.

a. 2 mol carbon to 3 mol hydrogen
b. 1.0 mol carbon to 1.5 mol hydrogen
c. 0.1712 mol carbon to 0.2568 mol hydrogen

Solution

a. The mole ratio given for carbon to hydrogen is 2:3, so the empirical formula is C_2H_3.
b. The mole ratio given is not an integer, but each value can be multiplied by 2 to get an integer ratio of 2:3. The empirical formula is again C_2H_3.
c. When the ratios are not integers and it is not clear what you should multiply them by to turn them into whole numbers, divide both values by the smaller one. This will generate values that are closer to whole-number ratios:

$$\frac{0.1712 \text{ mol C}}{0.1712} = 1.000 \text{ mol C}$$

$$\frac{0.2568 \text{ mol H}}{0.1712} = 1.500 \text{ mol H}$$

This gives you a ratio of $C_{1.0}H_{1.50}$. Multiplying both subscripts by 2 turns the subscript of 1.50 into a whole number. The empirical formula is again C_2H_3.

PRACTICE PROBLEM 3.46

Write the empirical formulas for the compounds containing nitrogen and oxygen in the following ratios.

a. 2 mol nitrogen to 1 mol oxygen
b. 1.0 mol nitrogen to 2.5 mol oxygen
c. 0.3325 mol nitrogen to 0.3325 mol oxygen

Hint: If none of the mole ratios is an integer, divide them all by the smallest one to turn one of them into an integer. If one is an integer and another is not, multiply them all by the same factor (see Table 3.5) that turns the decimal into an integer. If all the values are integers, make sure they are the lowest whole-number ratio and do not have a common factor.

Example 3.47

Use each of the following ratios of element A to element B to write an empirical formula for a compound consisting of A and B only.

a. 1:1
b. 1:1.5
c. 1:1.33
d. 1:1.20

Solution

a. A ratio of 1:1 is already reduced to the smallest whole numbers, so the empirical formula is AB.
b. According to Table 3.6, the 1.5 value can be converted to a whole number by multiplying it by 2. Multiplying both subscripts by 2 gives $(1 \times 2){:}(1.5 \times 2) = 2{:}3$. The empirical formula is A_2B_3.
c. According to Table 3.6, 1.33 can be converted to a whole number by multiplying it by 3. Multiplying both subscripts by 3 gives $(1 \times 3){:}(1.33 \times 3) = 3{:}4$. The empirical formula is A_3B_4.
d. According to Table 3.6, 1.20 can be converted to a whole number by multiplying it by 5. Multiplying both subscripts by 5 gives $(1 \times 5){:}(1.20 \times 5) = 5{:}6$. The empirical formula is A_5B_6.

PRACTICE PROBLEM 3.47

Given the following ratios of element A to element B, determine the empirical formula for the compound, assuming it consists of A and B only.

a. 1:1.25
b. 1:1.75
c. 1:1.67
d. 1:1.40

Hint: If none of the mole ratios is an integer, divide them all by the smallest one to turn one of them into an integer. If one is an integer and another is not, multiply them all by the same factor (see Table 3.6) that turns the decimal into an integer. If all the values are integers, make sure they are the lowest whole-number ratio and do not have a common factor.

Determining the empirical formula for a compound from its percent composition is a three-step—or sometimes a four-step—process.

1. Convert the percent of each element to a number of grams of each element by assuming you have a 100.0 g sample size. For example, if a compound is 39.2% phosphorus and 60.8% sulfur by mass, then a 100.0 g sample will contain 39.2 g of phosphorus and 60.8 g of sulfur.
2. Use the molar mass of each element to convert the number of grams from step 1 into moles. For example:

$$39.2 \text{ g P} \times \frac{1 \text{ mol P}}{30.974 \text{ g P}} = 1.266 \text{ mol P}$$

$$60.8 \text{ g S} \times \frac{1 \text{ mol S}}{32.06 \text{ g S}} = 1.896 \text{ mol S}$$

This gives you the mole ratio between the atoms of the compound. The mole ratio will be mathematically correct, but these are not valid subscripts in the chemical formula for the compound because they are not whole numbers: $P_{1.266}S_{1.896}$.

3. Convert the mole ratios to whole numbers by dividing all of the mole ratios by the smallest one. This will give you at least one integer subscript:

$$P_{\frac{1.266}{1.266}}S_{\frac{1.896}{1.266}} = P_{1.00}S_{1.50}$$

4. If the subscripts are not whole numbers at this point, they can be converted to whole numbers by multiplying all of the subscripts by the same small whole number—usually 2, 3, or 4 (see Table 3.6). In this case, the subscript of 1.50 on S will become a 3 if it is multiplied by 2, so multiply all of the subscripts in the formula by 2. The resulting formula, P_2S_3, is the empirical formula for the compound.

Example 3.48

Determine the empirical formula of a compound that has a percent composition of 43.7% P and 56.3% O.

Solution

Step 1: Assume that you have 100.0 g of the substance. The number of grams of each element in a 100.0 g sample is equal to the percentage of each element: 43.7 g P and 56.3 g O.

Step 2: Convert the numbers of grams of each element to moles using the molar mass of each element:

Mass of P → Molar mass of P → Moles of P

$$43.7 \text{ g P} \times \frac{1 \text{ mol P}}{30.974 \text{ g P}} = 1.411 \text{ mol P}$$

$$56.3 \text{ g O} \times \frac{1 \text{ mol O}}{15.999 \text{ g O}} = 3.519 \text{ mol O}$$

That gives a mole ratio of 1.411 mol P to 3.519 mol O, and a preliminary chemical formula of $P_{1.411}O_{3.519}$.

Step 3: Divide all of the subscripts by the lowest one in an attempt to convert them all to whole numbers:

$$P_{\frac{1.411}{1.411}}S_{\frac{3.519}{1.411}} = P_{1.000}S_{2.494}$$

Step 4: The subscript on O is still not a whole number, but it is very close to 2.5, so multiplying by 2 will convert it to 5. Multiplying both the subscripts in the formula by 2 gives P_2O_5 as the empirical formula for the compound.

PRACTICE PROBLEM 3.48

Determine the empirical formula of manganese(II) pyrophosphate, a compound containing 38.71% Mn, 21.82% P, and 39.46% oxygen.

Hint: Assume you have 100.0 g of manganese(II) pyrophosphate. Use the resulting masses (38.71 g Mn, 21.82 g P, and 39.46 g O) to determine the number of moles of each element, and then determine the mole ratios from there.

An empirical formula can also be calculated from mass data instead of from the percent composition. The initial calculation of the empirical formula CH_2O at the beginning of this section is an example of using mass data instead of percent compositions to determine an empirical formula.

Example 3.49

Determine the empirical formula of a compound if a sample of the compound contains 3.524 g of iron, 3.034 g of sulfur, and 4.542 g of oxygen.

Solution

Because the data are given in grams rather than percentages, you do not have to do the first step of changing percentages to grams. You can go directly to step 2 and convert the mass of each element in grams to moles using the molar masses of each element:

$$3.524 \text{ g Fe} \times \frac{1 \text{ mol Fe}}{55.845 \text{ g Fe}} = 0.06310 \text{ mol Fe}$$

$$3.034 \text{ g S} \times \frac{1 \text{ mol S}}{32.06 \text{ g S}} = 0.09464 \text{ mol S}$$

$$4.542 \text{ g O} \times \frac{1 \text{ mol O}}{15.999 \text{ g O}} = 0.2839 \text{ mol O}$$

Step 3: Divide each of these mole ratios by the smallest of the three, 0.06310 mol Fe:

$$Fe_{\frac{0.06310}{0.06310}}S_{\frac{0.09464}{0.06310}}O_{\frac{0.2839}{0.06310}} = Fe_{1.000}S_{1.500}O_{4.499}$$

Multiplying each of these by 2 yields the empirical formula for the compound, $Fe_2S_3O_9$.

This empirical formula corresponds to $Fe_2(SO_3)_3$, which is the correct formula for the ionic compound iron(III) sulfite.

PRACTICE PROBLEM 3.49

Determine the empirical formula of "hypo," a compound once popularly used in photographic film development, if a sample contains 2.453 g of sodium, 3.422 g of sulfur, and 2.561 g of oxygen.

Hint: Convert grams to moles for each element, then divide by the lowest value of the three to convert at least one to an integer, then multiply them by the same factor to convert them all to integers.

Most ionic compounds, such as NaCl, $MgBr_2$, Al_2S_3, and NH_4NO_3, are identified by their empirical formulas because ionic compounds are repeating patterns of ions, not discrete entities like the molecules formed by covalent compounds. For most ionic compounds, therefore, the empirical formulas are used for calculations. Some ionic compounds, such as K_2O_2, Hg_2Cl_2, $K_2C_2O_4$, and $Na_2S_2O_8$, include polyatomic ions that contain even numbers of atoms (namely, O_2^{2-}, Hg_2^{2+}, $C_2O_4^{2-}$, and $S_2O_8^{2-}$, respectively). The chemical formulas for these compounds cannot be reduced to the simplest whole-number ratio because that would mean breaking the polyatomic ion. These ionic compounds are therefore correctly written without having their formulas reduced to the simplest whole-number ratios. For molecular substances, empirical formulas are used to determine molecular formulas, as described next in Section 3.11.

SECTION REVIEW

- The empirical formula for a compound expresses the lowest whole-number ratio of the atoms in a compound. If the actual chemical formula is *not* the same as the empirical formula, then it is a multiple of the empirical formula. The formulas for most ionic compounds are empirical formulas.
- To determine an empirical formula, calculate the number of moles of each element in a sample (choose 100 g if percentages are given), divide each of them by the smallest number of moles, and then multiply by some small integer (if necessary) to obtain whole-number subscripts for each element in the formula.

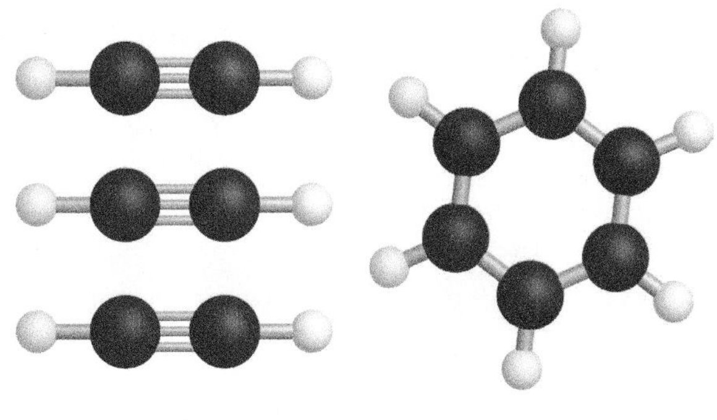

FIGURE 3.17 Acetylene and Benzene

NOTE: You need to be online to access the 3D view. Click each molecule to access a 3D version, then click and drag to rotate the 3D molecule. (a) Acetylene has the molecular formula C_2H_2 and the empirical formula CH. (b) Benzene has the molecular formula C_6H_6 and the empirical formula CH.

3.11 Molecular Formulas

GOALS

- Determine the molecular formula of a compound from its percent composition and molar mass data.
- Determine the molecular formula of a compound from its empirical formula and molar mass data.

The **molecular formula** gives the actual number of atoms of each element in one molecule of a covalent compound. Thus, a molecule of glucose, $C_6H_{12}O_6$, contains 6 C atoms, 12 H atoms, and 6 O atoms, whereas a molecule of benzene, C_6H_6, contains 6 C atoms and 6 H atoms.

The molecular formula is always an integer multiple (1, 2, 3, . . .) of the empirical formula. In the case of glucose and benzene, the integer multiple is 6, so their empirical formulas are CH_2O and CH, respectively. In the case of glycerol, $C_3H_8O_3$, the integer multiple is 1, so the molecular and empirical formulas are the same.

The molecular formula gives the number of atoms of each element in one *molecule*. Do not use the term *molecule* or *molecular mass* when discussing ionic compounds because they do not exist as molecules. Instead, refer to ionic compounds using the terms *formula unit* and *formula mass*.

Both acetylene, C_2H_2, and benzene, C_6H_6 (Figure 3.17) have the same percent composition of carbon and hydrogen because both have the same empirical formula—CH. As a result, you cannot distinguish acetylene from benzene based on percent composition data alone. If you also know their molar masses, however, you could combine that information with the percent composition data to determine not only the empirical formula but also the molecular formula. The molar mass of acetylene will be twice as large as the molar mass of its empirical formula, while the molar mass of benzene will be six times the molar mass of its empirical formula.

A sample containing three molecules of C_2H_2 and another sample containing one molecule of C_6H_6 have the same number of C atoms (six) and the same number of H atoms (six). As a result, both have the same percent composition. Because percent composition is an intensive property (Section 1.2), the two compounds have the same percent composition, no matter how many molecules are present.

Since the molecular formula is always a multiple of the empirical formula, determining the molecular formula of a compound involves first determining the empirical formula and then determining how many empirical formula units are in a molecule of the compound, using the molar mass of the compound. The video in Figure 3.18 shows that dividing the molar mass of the compound by the molar mass of the empirical formula calculates how many empirical formula units are in the molecule:

$$\frac{\text{Molar mass of the compound}}{\text{Molar mass of the empirical formula}} = \text{Multiplying factor} \tag{3.3}$$

Steven Lemon, Macmillan Learning

FIGURE 3.18 Video Tutorial: Empirical and Molecular Formulas

NOTE: You need to be online to access this video.
This video shows how to determine the empirical and molecular formulas of a compound from percent composition data and molar mass.

All of the subscripts in the empirical formula can then be multiplied by that factor to obtain the actual molecular formula.

Example 3.50

Styrene is used commercially to prepare the plastic wrapping material polystyrene. It is a molecular compound made up of carbon and hydrogen only. It contains 92.26% carbon and has a molar mass of 104 g/mol. What is the molecular formula of styrene?

Solution

The mass percentages must total 100.00%, so the percentage of hydrogen in the compound is 100.00% − 92.26% C = 7.74% H. Assuming 100.00 g of styrene, the masses of C and H are then equal to 92.26 g C and 7.74 g H.

These masses of the elements can be converted to moles by using their molar masses as conversion factors:

$$92.26 \text{ g C} \times \frac{1 \text{ mol C}}{12.011 \text{ g C}} = 7.681 \text{ mol C}$$

$$7.74 \text{ g H} \times \frac{1 \text{ mol H}}{1.008 \text{ g H}} = 7.68 \text{ mol H}$$

The ratio of carbon to hydrogen is 7.681:7.68, or 1 mol C:1 mol H, so the empirical formula is CH. The molar mass of the empirical formula CH is the sum of the molar masses of all the atoms in the empirical formula:

$$12.011 \text{ g/mol} + 1.008 \text{ g/mol} = 13.019 \text{ g/mol}$$

Dividing the molar mass of the compound (104 g/mol) by the molar mass of the empirical formula (13.019 g/mol) gives the number of empirical formula units per molecule (Equation 3.3):

$$\frac{\text{Molar mass of compound}}{\text{Molar mass of empirical formula}} = \frac{104 \text{ g/mol}}{13.019 \text{ g/mol}} = 7.99 \approx 8$$

The empirical formula CH is multiplied by 8 to get the molecular formula, so the molecular formula is C_8H_8.

PRACTICE PROBLEM 3.50

Determine the molecular formula of a hydrocarbon, a compound made up of only carbon and hydrogen, which contains 89.94% carbon and has a molar mass of 80.2 g/mol.

Hint: First, determine the empirical formula for the compound as described in Section 3.10, and then divide the molar mass of the compound by the empirical molar mass to determine the number of empirical formula units per molecule.

Example 3.51

A 72.33 g sample of a compound contains 28.90 g of carbon, 4.86 g of hydrogen, and 38.57 g oxygen. If the molar mass of the compound is 60.05 g/mol, what is its molecular formula?

Solution

Because you are given the masses of each of the elements in the compound, instead of their percent compositions, you do not need to calculate grams from the percent composition. The first step, then, is to convert the mass of each element to moles, using the molar mass of each element as a conversion factor.

$$28.90 \text{ g C} \times \frac{1 \text{ mol C}}{12.011 \text{ g C}} = 2.406 \text{ mol C}$$

$$4.86 \text{ g H} \times \frac{1 \text{ mol H}}{1.008 \text{ g H}} = 4.82 \text{ mol H}$$

$$38.57 \text{ g O} \times \frac{1 \text{ mol O}}{15.999 \text{ g O}} = 2.411 \text{ mol O}$$

This yields a preliminary chemical formula of $C_{2.406}H_{4.82}O_{2.411}$. Dividing each of these by the lowest of the three, 2.406, results in

$$C_{\frac{2.406}{2.406}}H_{\frac{4.82}{2.406}}O_{\frac{2.411}{2.406}} = C_{1.00}H_{2.00}O_{1.0} = CH_2O$$

The molar mass of this empirical formula is 12.011 g + 2(1.008 g) + 15.999 g = 30.026 g/mol. Dividing the molar mass of the compound by the molar mass of the empirical formula gives the number of empirical formula units in the actual molecular formula.

$$\frac{60.05\ \text{g/mol}}{30.026\ \text{g/mol}} = 2.000$$

Because there are two empirical formula units in the actual molecular formula, the molecular formula is $C_2H_4O_2$.

When you already have the masses of each element, the total mass of the sample (in this case, 72.33 g) is not needed for the calculation, but knowing the mass of the sample is still useful because you can compare it with the masses of the elements to make sure all elements in the compound are accounted for. In this case, 28.90 g + 4.86 g + 38.57 g = 72.33 g, so all of the mass of the sample is accounted for in those three elements.

PRACTICE PROBLEM 3.51

A 360.0 g sample of a compound contains 12.78 g of nitrogen and 347.2 g of iodine. The molar mass of the compound is 394.7 g/mol. What is the molecular formula for the compound?

Hint: Calculate the number of moles of each element in the compound from the masses given, and then determine the mole ratio between them and determine the empirical formula. Next, divide the molar mass of the compound by the molar mass of the empirical formula to determine how many empirical formula units are in the compound (Equation 3.3). Multiply the empirical formula by that factor to obtain the molecular formula.

SECTION REVIEW

- Empirical formulas can be determined from percent composition data for a compound or from the masses of each component of the compound. If you know the overall molecular mass as well, then the actual molecular formula for the compound can also be determined.
- Molecular formulas are always a whole-number multiple of the empirical formula.
- The number of empirical formula units in a molecule can be determined by dividing the molecular mass by the empirical formula mass.

3.12 Combustion Analysis

GOAL

- Determine the empirical formula for a compound based on data from a combustion analysis, in which the carbon in the compound is converted to carbon dioxide and the hydrogen is converted to water.

Combustion analysis is a laboratory technique designed to help determine the empirical formula of a chemical compound. Combustion analysis is used most often on compounds that contain only C and H, or on compounds that contain C, H, and one other element, usually O. In combustion analysis (Figure 3.19), a sample is combusted (reacted with O_2) to convert all of the C to CO_2 and all of the H to H_2O. The masses of the CO_2 and H_2O produced in the combustion are

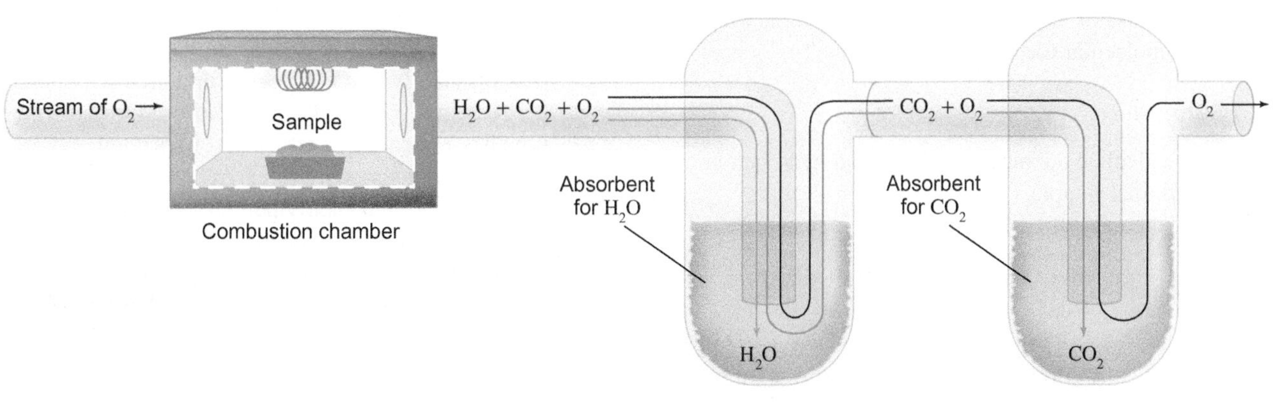

FIGURE 3.19 Combustion Analysis Apparatus

To measure the ratio of C to H (or C to H to O) in a compound, and thus determine its empirical formula, a sample of the compound is reacted with oxygen in a combustion chamber, and the products (carbon dioxide, CO_2, and water, H_2O) are collected and their masses measured.

measured, and from these masses, the masses of C and H in the original sample can then be calculated.

To determine the mass of C in the original sample from the mass of CO_2 produced, first convert the mass of CO_2 to moles. Each mole of CO_2 contains 1 mol C. The number of moles of C is then multiplied by the atomic mass of C to get the mass of C in the original sample:

$$\text{Mass of } CO_2 \times \frac{1 \text{ mol } CO_2}{44.009 \text{ g } CO_2} \times \frac{1 \text{ mol C}}{1 \text{ mol } CO_2} \times \frac{12.011 \text{ g C}}{1 \text{ mol C}} = \text{Mass of C} \quad (3.4)$$

A similar calculation is carried out to determine the mass of H from the mass of H_2O produced, but since each mole of H_2O contains 2 mol H, the number of moles of H is double the number of moles of H_2O. The mass of H is then calculated by multiplying the moles of H by its atomic mass:

$$\text{Mass of } H_2O \times \frac{1 \text{ mol } H_2O}{18.015 \text{ g } H_2O} \times \frac{2 \text{ mol H}}{1 \text{ mol } H_2O} \times \frac{1.008 \text{ g H}}{1 \text{ mol H}} = \text{Mass of H} \quad (3.5)$$

Once the masses of carbon and hydrogen are known, the empirical formula for the compound can be determined as described in Section 3.10. And, if the mass of the compound is also known, the molecular formula of the compound can be determined as described in Section 3.11.

Example 3.52

Naphthalene is a white solid that consists only of carbon and hydrogen. It was once used as the active ingredient in mothballs. When combustion analysis was carried out on a 5.00 g sample of naphthalene, 17.17 g CO_2 and 2.81 g H_2O were produced. If the molar mass of naphthalene is 128.17 g/mol, what is the molecular formula of naphthalene?

Solution

First, calculate the mass of carbon and hydrogen in the original sample.

The mass of carbon in the original sample is calculated by inserting the mass of CO_2, 17.17 g, into Equation 3.4:

$$17.17 \text{ g } CO_2 \times \frac{1 \text{ mol } CO_2}{44.009 \text{ g } CO_2} \times \frac{1 \text{ mol C}}{1 \text{ mol } CO_2} \times \frac{12.011 \text{ g C}}{1 \text{ mol C}} = 4.69 \text{ g C}$$

The mass of hydrogen in the original sample is calculated by inserting the mass of H_2O, 2.81 g, into Equation 3.5:

$$2.81 \text{ g } H_2O \times \frac{1 \text{ mol } H_2O}{18.015 \text{ g } H_2O} \times \frac{2 \text{ mol H}}{1 \text{ mol } H_2O} \times \frac{1.008 \text{ g H}}{1 \text{ mol H}} = 0.314 \text{ g H}$$

Determine the number of moles of each element in the sample to determine an elemental ratio for the compound:

$$\text{C: } 4.69 \text{ g} \times \frac{1 \text{ mol}}{12.011 \text{ g}} = 0.391 \text{ mol}$$

$$\text{H: } 0.314 \text{ g} \times \frac{1 \text{ mol}}{1.008 \text{ g}} = 0.312 \text{ mol}$$

This leads to an initial chemical formula of $C_{0.391}H_{0.312}$. Dividing each of these by the lowest mole value leads to

$$C_{\frac{0.391}{0.312}}H_{\frac{0.312}{0.312}} = C_{1.25}H_{1.00}$$

To convert the 1.25 subscript to an integer, multiply both subscripts by 4. This results in an empirical formula of C_5H_4.

The molecular formula can be determined by dividing the molar mass of the compound by the molar mass for the empirical formula to determine how many empirical units are in the actual molecule.

The molar mass of the empirical formula, C_5H_4, is $(5 \times 12.011) + (4 \times 1.008) = 64.087$ g/mol. The molar mass of the molecule, given in the problem statement, is 128.17 g/mol:

$$\frac{\text{Molar mass of the molecule}}{\text{Molar mass of the empirical formula}} = \frac{128.17 \text{ g/mol}}{64.087 \text{ g/mol}} = 2.00$$

The molecular formula for naphthalene is therefore twice the empirical formula, or $C_{10}H_8$.

PRACTICE PROBLEM 3.52

The octane rating on a gas pump is a measure of how efficiently that fuel burns compared with pure 2,2,4-trimethylpentane, a liquid compound that consists entirely of carbon and hydrogen. When combustion analysis was carried out on a 1.75 g sample of 2,2,4-trimethylpentane, 5.39 g CO_2 and 2.48 g H_2O were produced. If the molar mass of 2,2,4-trimethylpentane is 114.23 g/mol, what is the molecular formula of 2,2,4-trimethylpentane?

Hint: Determine the mass of carbon and the mass of hydrogen from the masses of CO_2 and H_2O (see Equation 3.4 and Equation 3.5). Once you have the masses of each element in the compound, determine the empirical formula (Section 3.10) and the molecular formula (Section 3.11).

If a sample contains a third element in addition to carbon and hydrogen, the mass of the third element is equal to the difference between the original sample mass and the combined mass of the carbon and hydrogen in the sample. Figure 3.20 is a flowchart showing this process for a compound of C, H, and O.

Example 3.53

Butyl butyrate, which contains C, H, and O only, is a naturally occurring compound found in many different kinds of fruit, including apples, bananas, melons, cherries, and strawberries. It is added as an artificial flavoring to some foods and drinks to create sweet, fruity flavors. When combustion analysis was carried out on a 2.50 g sample of butyl butyrate, 6.10 g CO_2 and 2.50 g H_2O were produced. If the molar mass of butyl butyrate is 144.21 g/mol, what is the molecular formula of butyl butyrate?

Solution

First, calculate the mass of carbon and hydrogen in the original sample.

The mass of carbon in the original sample is calculated by inserting the mass of CO_2, 6.10 g, into Equation 3.4:

$$6.10\text{ g }CO_2 \times \frac{1\text{ mol }CO_2}{44.009\text{ g }CO_2} \times \frac{1\text{ mol C}}{1\text{ mol }CO_2} \times \frac{12.011\text{ g C}}{1\text{ mol C}} = 1.66\text{ g C}$$

The mass of hydrogen in the original sample is calculated by inserting the mass of H_2O, 2.50 g, into Equation 3.5:

$$2.50\text{ g }H_2O \times \frac{1\text{ mol }H_2O}{18.015\text{ g }H_2O} \times \frac{2\text{ mol H}}{1\text{ mol }H_2O} \times \frac{1.008\text{ g H}}{1\text{ mol H}} = 0.280\text{ g H}$$

Together, the carbon and hydrogen amount to 1.66 g + 0.280 g = 1.94 g of the sample weight. Since the compound contains C, H, and O only, the remaining 0.56 g must be oxygen.

Determine the number of moles of each element in the sample to determine an elemental ratio for the compound:

$$\text{C: } 1.66\text{ g} \times \frac{1\text{ mol}}{12.011\text{ g}} = 0.138\text{ mol}$$

$$\text{H: } 0.280\text{ g} \times \frac{1\text{ mol}}{1.008\text{ g}} = 0.278\text{ mol}$$

$$\text{O: } 0.56\text{ g} \times \frac{1\text{ mol}}{15.999\text{ g}} = 0.035\text{ mol}$$

This leads to an initial chemical formula of $C_{0.138}H_{0.278}O_{0.035}$. Dividing each of these by the lowest mole value leads to

$$C_{\frac{0.138}{0.035}}H_{\frac{0.278}{0.035}}O_{\frac{0.035}{0.035}} = C_{3.94}H_{7.94}O_{1.0}$$

This suggests an empirical formula of C_4H_8O.

The molecular formula can be determined by dividing the molar mass of the compound by the molar mass for the empirical formula to determine how many empirical units are in the actual molecule.

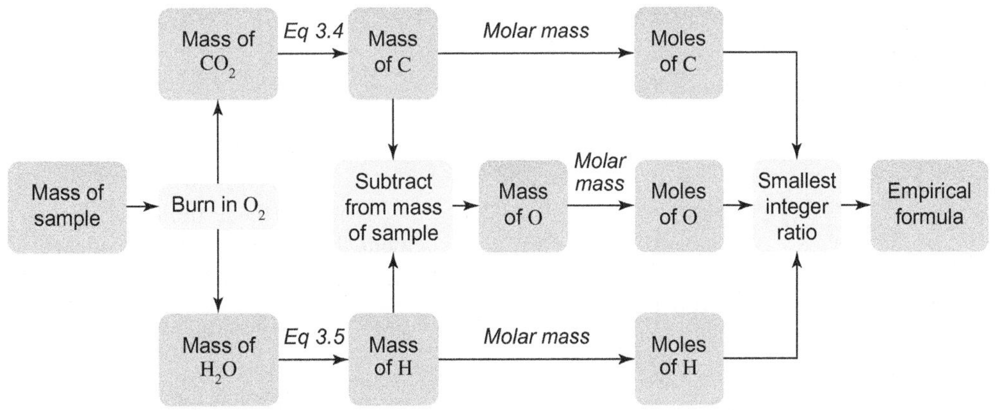

FIGURE 3.20 Combustion Analysis Calculation Flowchart

This flowchart shows the process of finding the empirical formula of a compound of C, H, and O from combustion analysis data.

The molar mass of C_4H_8O is $(4 \times 12.011) + (8 \times 1.008) + (15.999) = 72.106$ g/mol. The molar mass of the molecule is 144.21 g/mol.

$$\frac{\text{Molar mass of the molecule}}{\text{Molar mass of the empirical formula}} = \frac{144.21\ \text{g/mol}}{72.106\ \text{g/mol}} = 2.00$$

The molecular formula for butyl butyrate is therefore twice the empirical formula, or $C_8H_{16}O_2$.

PRACTICE PROBLEM 3.53

Rotting animal tissue such as road kill produces a foul-smelling compound commonly known as cadaverine. Cadaverine contains C, H, and N only. When combustion analysis was carried out on a 3.75 g sample of cadaverine, 8.08 g CO_2 and 4.63 g H_2O were produced. If the molar mass of cadaverine is 102.18 g/mol, what is the molecular formula of cadaverine?

Hint: Determine the mass of carbon and the mass of hydrogen from the masses of CO_2 and H_2O, using the equations given earlier in this section. The mass of nitrogen is the difference between the sample mass and the combined mass of carbon and hydrogen. Once you have the masses of each element in the compound, determine the empirical formula (Section 3.10) and the molecular formula (Section 3.11).

SECTION REVIEW

- Combustion analysis is a lab technique used for determining the empirical formula of compounds that contain C and H.
- In combustion analysis the C and H in the compound are converted to CO_2 and H_2O. The masses of CO_2 and H_2O are then used to determine the masses of C and H in the original sample.
- If there is a third element in the compound, its mass can be calculated by the difference in mass between the sample mass and the combined mass of C and H in the sample.

Putting It Together

The example problems in earlier sections of this chapter focus on just the new skills acquired in that section, but homework and exam questions in chemistry often require more than just one skill at a time. In fact, you will likely be expected to apply knowledge from across the entire chapter, or even multiple chapters, in a single problem. This final example problem is meant to help you prepare for these types of multiconcept questions. Additional examples can be found in the end-of-chapter exercises.

Example 3.54

Analysis of an ionic compound revealed that it had a molar mass of 504 g/mol and the following percent composition by mass:

Iridium 38.14%
Bromine 47.56%
Oxygen 12.70%
Hydrogen 1.60%

What is the name and chemical formula of the compound? *Hint:* If the formula for an ionic compound contains H and O in a 2:1 mole ratio, that might indicate that the compound is a hydrate (Section 3.4).

Solution

To determine the chemical formula, you must first determine the empirical formula. The empirical formula will most likely be the actual chemical formula, as it is with most ionic compounds.

To calculate the empirical formula for the compound, you need to know how many moles of each element are in a given sample of the compound. If you assume a 100 g sample of the compound, then the percent composition values are equivalent to the masses of each element:

Iridium 38.14 g
Bromine 47.56 g
Oxygen 12.70 g
Hydrogen 1.60 g

The number of moles of each element in a 100 g sample of the compound can now be calculated using the masses of each element and their molar masses:

$$\text{Moles of Ir} = 38.14\ \text{g} \times \frac{1\ \text{mol}}{192.22\ \text{g}} = 0.1984\ \text{mol Ir}$$

$$\text{Moles of Br} = 47.56\ \text{g} \times \frac{1\ \text{mol}}{79.904\ \text{g}} = 0.5952\ \text{mol Br}$$

$$\text{Moles of O} = 12.70\ \text{g} \times \frac{1\ \text{mol}}{15.999\ \text{g}} = 0.7938\ \text{mol O}$$

$$\text{Moles of H} = 1.60\ \text{g} \times \frac{1\ \text{mol}}{1.008\ \text{g}} = 1.59\ \text{mol H}$$

None of these mole values are integers, so divide them all by the lowest one to convert at least one of them to an integer.

$$\frac{0.1984\ \text{mol Ir}}{0.1984} = 1.00\ \text{mol Ir}$$

$$\frac{0.5952\ \text{mol Br}}{0.1984} = 3.00\ \text{mol Br}$$

$$\frac{0.7938\ \text{mol O}}{0.1984} = 4.00\ \text{mol O}$$

$$\frac{1.59\ \text{mol H}}{0.1984} = 8.00\ \text{mol H}$$

This would indicate a preliminary chemical formula of $Ir_1Br_3O_4H_8$. However, you know that ionic compounds are made up of a metal bonded to a nonmetal, and that many ionic compounds form as hydrates, with waters of hydration included in their crystals. The metal cation is written first in the formula for an ionic compound, followed by the nonmetal anion and then the waters of hydration. Hydrogen and oxygen are present in a 2:1 ratio, with eight hydrogen atoms and four oxygen atoms. This suggests four waters of hydration.

The revised chemical formula is $IrBr_3 \cdot 4\,H_2O$. You can check this by calculating the molar mass of this formula:

$$(1 \times 192.22\text{ g/mol}) + (3 \times 79.904\text{ g/mol}) + (8 \times 1.008\text{ g/mol}) + (4 \times 15.999\text{ g/mol}) = 504.0\text{ g/mol}$$

Iridium is not one of the constant-type ions in the periodic table in Figure 3.9, so the charge on the iridium ion can be determined from the total negative charge of the bromide anions: $3 \times -1 = -3$ total negative charge, so the iridium cation must be $+3$.

The ionic compound is therefore iridium(III) bromide, and the four waters of hydration add the suffix tetrahydrate.

Chemical formula: $IrBr_3 \cdot 4\,H_2O$

Name: Iridium(III) bromide tetrahydrate

PRACTICE PROBLEM 3.54

A sample of white powder is brought to a drug lab for analysis and is found to consist of 49.48% carbon, 28.85% nitrogen, 16.47% oxygen, and 5.19% hydrogen. The molar mass of the compound is 194.19 g/mol.

What is the molecular formula for the compound?

Hint: Determine the empirical formula (Section 3.10), and then determine the molecular formula (Section 3.11). Example 3.54 demonstrates how to solve a similar problem.

Key Terms, Symbols, and Equations

KEY TERMS

acid (3.5): A compound that produces H^+ ions in solution.

allotrope (3.1): One of two or more forms of an uncombined element; for example, diamond and graphite are allotropes of carbon.

ammonia (3.2): The binary covalent compound NH_3.

anhydrous (3.4): Without water; for example, anhydrous $CuSO_4$ results from the loss of water from $CuSO_4 \cdot 5\,H_2O$.

anion (3.3): A negatively charged ion.

atomic mass (3.8): The mass of an individual atom, expressed in units of atomic mass units, u.

atomic mass units, u (3.8): A unit of mass used for expressing the masses of individual atoms or molecules. One atomic mass unit, 1 u, $= 1.66 \times 10^{-24}$ g.

atomic weight (3.8): Another term for atomic mass.

Avogadro's number, N_A (3.7): 6.022×10^{23}—the number of atomic mass units in exactly 1 g.

binary compound (3.2): A compound composed of exactly two elements.

cation (3.3): A positively charged ion.

chemical formula (3.1): A combination of symbols, subscripts, and possibly superscripts that identifies the composition of an element, compound, or ion.

chemical nomenclature (3.1): The systematic naming of chemical substances.

combustion analysis (3.12): A laboratory technique which allows masses of carbon and hydrogen in a compound to be calculated by first converting the carbon and hydrogen to CO_2 and H_2O and then measuring the masses of the CO_2 and H_2O.

covalent compound (3.1): A compound that contains only nonmetals and/or metalloids bonded together; also called a molecular compound.

diatomic molecule (3.1): A molecule containing two atoms.

empirical formula (3.10): The simplest chemical formula for a compound that shows the ratio of elements in the compound but does not necessarily show the actual number of each type of atom in the compound.

formula mass (3.8): The mass of one formula unit of an atom, molecule, or ionic compound, expressed in units of u. The formula mass of an atom is also called the atomic mass, and the formula mass of a molecule is also called the molecular mass.

formula unit (3.1): The collection of atoms described by a chemical formula—an atom or molecule of an uncombined element, a molecule of a molecular compound, or the set of ions in the formula of an ionic compound.

formula weight (3.8): Another term for formula mass.

hydrate (3.4): An ionic compound that has water molecules bonded to it.

ion (3.3): An atom or group of atoms that has gained or lost electrons and therefore has a net negative or positive charge.

ionic compound (3.1): A compound made up of metal atoms bonded to nonmetal atoms.

ionizable hydrogen atom (3.5): Any of the hydrogen atoms in an acid that are capable of reacting with water to form H^+ ions.

lattice structure (3.1): A three-dimensional framework containing alternating positive and negative ions, in which the ions are bonded to multiple different ions of the opposite charge in all directions.

molar mass (3.8): The mass in grams of 1 mol of a substance.

mole, mol (3.7): The chemical unit of quantity for any substance; equal to 6.02×10^{23} individual atoms, molecules, or formula units of the substance.

molecular compound (3.1): A compound made up of only nonmetals bonded together; also called a covalent compound.

molecular formula (3.11): The formula of a molecular substance that gives the ratio of atoms of each element to the substance's molecules.

molecular mass (3.8): The mass of a molecule of a substance expressed in atomic mass units.

molecular weight (3.8): Another term for molecular mass.

molecule (3.1): An uncharged, covalently bonded group of atoms.

monatomic ion (3.3): An ion consisting of a single atom that has gained or lost one or more electrons.

monoprotic acid (3.5): An acid that has only one ionizable hydrogen atom per formula unit.

oxyacid (3.5): An acid of a nonmetal covalently bonded to one or more oxygen atoms, such as $HClO_3$.

oxyanion (3.4): An anion containing oxygen covalently bonded to another element, such as ClO_3^-.

ozone (3.1): O_3, an allotrope of oxygen.

percent composition (3.9): The percentage by mass of each element in a compound.

polyatomic ion (3.3): An ion composed of two or more atoms bonded together.

polyprotic acid (3.5): An acid that has two or more ionizable hydrogen atoms per formula unit.

Stock system (3.4): The nomenclature system for inorganic compounds in which the oxidation state (or charge for a monatomic cation) is represented as a Roman numeral in the name of the compound.

subscript (3.1): A number following the symbol of an element (or a closing parenthesis) that denotes the number of atoms of the element (or the number of groups) in the formula unit.

waters of hydration (3.4): Water molecules incorporated into the crystal lattice structure of some ionic compounds, indicated in the chemical formula by a centered dot after the ionic formula, followed by the number of waters of hydration per formula unit; for example, $CuSO_4 \cdot 5\,H_2O$.

SYMBOLS AND ABBREVIATIONS

N_A (Avogadro's number) (3.7)

· (centered dot in hydrate formulas) (3.4)

mol (mole) (3.7)

u (atomic mass unit) (3.8)

EQUATIONS

Total positive charge = Total negative charge (3.1)

$$\%\text{ Composition} = \frac{\text{Total mass of that element in the compound}}{\text{Total mass of the compound}} \times 100\% \quad (3.2)$$

$$\frac{\text{Molar mass of the compound}}{\text{Molar mass of the empirical formula}} = \text{Multiplying factor} \quad (3.3)$$

$$\text{Mass of } CO_2 \times \frac{1 \text{ mol } CO_2}{44.009 \text{ g } CO_2} \times \frac{1 \text{ mol C}}{1 \text{ mol } CO_2} \times \frac{12.011 \text{ g C}}{1 \text{ mol C}} = \text{Mass of C} \quad (3.4)$$

$$\text{Mass of } H_2O \times \frac{1 \text{ mol } H_2O}{18.015 \text{ g } H_2O} \times \frac{2 \text{ mol H}}{1 \text{ mol } H_2O} \times \frac{1.008 \text{ g H}}{1 \text{ mol H}} = \text{Mass of H} \quad (3.5)$$

PREFIXES AND SUFFIXES

-ate (3.4)
deca- (3.2)
di- (3.2)
hepta- (3.2)
hexa- (3.2)
hydro- (3.5)
hypo- (3.4)
-ic (3.5)
-ic acid (3.5)
-ide (3.2)
-ite (3.4)
mono- (3.2)
nona- (3.2)
octa- (3.2)
-ous (3.5)
-ous acid (3.5)
penta- (3.2)
per- (3.4)
tetra- (3.2)
tri- (3.2)

Chapter Summary

Chemical formulas identify elements, compounds, ions, or molecules. The formula implies that the atoms are held together by some kind of chemical bond. Seven elements (hydrogen, H; nitrogen, N; oxygen, O; fluorine, F; chlorine, Cl; bromine, Br; and iodine, I) exist as diatomic molecules when they are not attached to atoms of other elements (Figure 3.3). A formula unit represents the collection of atoms in the formula. For covalent compounds this represents one molecule, and for ionic compounds it represents the simplest repeating unit in a larger extended lattice. Subscripts in a formula indicate the numbers of atoms of the elements in each formula unit. For example, the formula unit H_2O has two H atoms and one O atom. Polyatomic ions are enclosed in parentheses in a chemical formula when more than one of the polyatomic ion appears in one formula unit. A subscript following the closing parenthesis multiplies everything within the parentheses. For example, a formula unit of $Ba(ClO_4)_2$ contains one Ba atom, two Cl atoms, and eight O atoms (Section 3.1).

Atoms of two nonmetal elements can combine in different ratios to form different binary covalent compounds. The names for binary covalent compounds therefore include prefixes to indicate how many atoms of each type are present in the compound. For binary covalent compounds, you typically name the element that is farther to the left or lower in the periodic table first, and then name the other element. Change the ending of the second element to *-ide*, and indicate the number of atoms of that element in the molecule by a prefix (Table 3.1). If more than one atom of the first element is present per molecule, use a prefix for that element, too (Section 3.2).

Formulas for ionic compounds can be deduced from the charges on the ions because all compounds have zero net charge. Most transition metals can form ions of different charges. If you are given specific positive and negative ions, you should be able to write a formula for an ionic compound made up of those ions. Conversely, if you are given the formula of an ionic compound, you should be able to deduce the charges on the ions (Section 3.3).

There are three different ways to name cations, depending on their type.

- Polyatomic cations have special names, such as the ammonium ion, NH_4^+.
- If the cation is a metal that forms only one type of ion, use the name of the element for the cation.

- If the cation is a metal that can form more than one type of cation, indicate the charge on the cation by a Roman numeral in parentheses after the name of the element (Section 3.4).

There are three different ways to name anions, depending on their type.

- The names of monatomic anions have the ending of the element's name changed to *-ide*.
- Oxyanions are negative ions that are made up of one or more O atoms bonded to another kind of atom (Table 3.3).
- Names of other polyatomic anions can be memorized or found in a reference table, such as Table 3.4 (Section 3.4).
  - The names of most familiar oxyanions end in *-ate* or *-ite*, depending on the relative number of oxygen atoms per ion.
  - Ions with more O atoms than have those whose names end in *-ate* have the prefix *per-* added to the name.
  - Ions with fewer oxygen atoms than have those whose names end in *-ite* have the prefix *hypo-* added to the name.

To name an ionic compound, you first name the cation and then the anion. Unlike binary covalent compounds, in which the two elements can combine in many different ratios to form a neutral compound, a given cation and anion can only combine in one lowest whole-number ratio to form a neutral compound. For this reason, there is no need to specify in the name how many of each type of ion is present, and the prefixes used for covalent compounds are not used for ionic compounds.

A Roman numeral in parentheses in the *name* of the compound designates the charge on a cation, and an Arabic numeral as a subscript in the *formula* designates the number of atoms or ions. The charges enable you to deduce the numbers of ions, and vice versa, but the Roman numerals and the Arabic numerals do not represent the same quantities.

Formulas for hydrates have a centered dot preceding a number and the formula for water, such as $CuSO_4 \cdot 5\ H_2O$. The number multiplies everything following it to the end of the formula. Name hydrates with a prefix (Table 3.1) before the word *hydrate* to indicate the number of water molecules. For example, $CuSO_4 \cdot 5\ H_2O$ is named copper(II) sulfate pentahydrate (Section 3.4).

The ionizable H atoms are written first in the formulas of acids. The word *hydrogen* does not appear in their names; instead, the word *acid* implies the presence of the hydrogen. Name oxyacids like the corresponding oxyanions with the *-ate* ending changed to *-ic acid* or the *-ite* ending changed to *-ous acid*. Names of binary acids have the *-ide* ending of the corresponding anion changed to *-ic acid* and the prefix *hydro-* added (Section 3.5).

The flowchart in Section 3.6 shows how these different naming rules are all used together to arrive at the correct name of any covalent or ionic compound, including acids and acid salts. If the compound is a hydrate, the waters of hydration are added after the compound name is determined.

The following outline summarizes the types of compounds and ions you have learned to name in this chapter.

- Binary covalent compounds
- Ionic compounds
  - Cations
    - Monatomic cations
      - Variable charge
      - Constant charge
    - Polyatomic cations

  - Anions
    - Monatomic anions
    - Polyatomic anions
    - Oxyanions
  - Hydrates
- Acids (except organic acids, which are covered in Chapter 21)

In the same way that a dozen is a quantity commonly used to count eggs and doughnuts, a mole (mol) is a quantity used for counting atoms and molecules. One mol is equal to Avogadro's number, which is 6.022×10^{23}. The conversion factor, 1 mol = 6.022×10^{23} particles, is used for converting between moles and the number of individual atoms, molecules, or formula units of a substance (Section 3.7).

The molar mass of a substance is the mass in grams of one mole of that substance. For atoms, the molar mass is the same value as the atomic mass taken from the periodic table, but expressed in grams, rather than atomic mass units. For compounds, the molar mass is determined by adding the molar masses of all the atoms in one formula unit of the compound. For example, 1 mol NH_3 contains 1 mol N atoms (14.007 g/mol) and 3 mol H atoms (1.008 g/mol), so the molar mass of NH_3 is $14.007\ g/mol + 3(1.008\ g/mol) = 17.03\ g/mol$ (Section 3.8).

The percent composition of a compound is the percentage by mass of each element in the compound. The percentage by mass of an element in a compound is calculated by finding the ratio of the total mass of that element in the compound to the formula mass and multiplying that ratio by 100%. The percentages of all the elements in a compound should total 100% (Section 3.9).

An empirical formula gives the lowest whole-number mole ratio of atoms of all the elements in a compound. An empirical formula may be determined from a percent composition by changing the percentages to numbers of grams (by assuming a 100 g sample) and then dividing the number of grams of each element by its molar mass. The noninteger mole ratio that results is converted to an integer mole ratio by dividing each of the numbers of moles by the magnitude of the smallest number of moles, and then, if necessary, multiplying every one of the quotients by the same small whole number (Section 3.10).

Molecular formulas provide the actual mole ratios of the atoms present in a molecule, rather than just the simplest whole-number ratio. A molecular formula will always be either the same as the empirical formula for that compound, or a whole-number multiple of the empirical formula. Molecular formulas are used only for molecular substances, not ionic substances. A molecular formula can be determined from the empirical formula of the compound and its molar mass. First, divide the molar mass of the compound by the molar mass of the empirical formula. Then, multiply each subscript of the empirical formula by the resulting integer to obtain the molecular formula (Section 3.11).

Combustion analysis is a laboratory technique in which the carbon and hydrogen in a sample of a compound are converted to CO_2 and H_2O, respectively. The masses of these compounds are then measured, making it possible to calculate the masses of carbon and hydrogen in the original sample. The empirical formula can then be determined for compounds that consist only of C and H, or C, H, and one other element. If the molar mass of the compound is known, the molecular formula can also be determined (Section 3.12).

END OF CHAPTER QUESTIONS

3.1 Chemical Formulas

1. What is the difference between the following?
   a. 2 N and N_2
   b. N_2O_4 and 2 NO_2
2. What is implied about bonding in the mercury(I) ion, Hg_2^{2+}?
3. How many atoms of each element are present in one formula unit of each of the following?
   a. $(NH_4)_3PO_4$
   b. Li_3N
   c. $Al(C_2H_3O_2)_3$
4. How many atoms of each element are present in one formula unit of each of the following?
   a. $UO_2(ClO_4)_2$
   b. $CaCr_2O_7$
   c. $(NH_4)_2CrO_4$
   d. $KHCO_3 \cdot MgCO_3 \cdot 4H_2O$
5. What information does the formula $Zn_3(PO_4)_2$ convey about the number of atoms in the compound and how they are bonded together?

3.2 Naming Binary Covalent Compounds

6. Name each of the following compounds:
   a. N_2O_5
   b. CF_4
   c. P_2S_3
   d. SF_4
   e. BrF_3
7. Write the formula for each of the following compounds:
   a. carbon dioxide
   b. hydrogen bromide
   c. silicon tetrafluoride
   d. iodine pentafluoride
   e. bromine dioxide
   f. dihydrogen sulfide
   g. dinitrogen trioxide
8. Name the following substances:
   a. HCl (pure)
   b. H_2Se
   c. HI (pure)
9. Write the formula for each of the following compounds:
   a. chlorine monofluoride
   b. ammonia
   c. arsenic trifluoride
   d. sulfur trioxide
   e. phosphorus pentachloride
   f. water
10. Name each of the following compounds:
    a. SO_2
    b. SiF_4
    c. AsF_3
    d. S_2Cl_2
    e. XeF_6
11. Write the formula for each of the following compounds:
    a. sulfur hexafluoride
    b. sulfur tetrafluoride
    c. sulfur difluoride
12. Write the formula for each of the following compounds:
    a. iodine dioxide
    b. diiodine trioxide
    c. diiodine monoxide
    d. diiodine heptoxide
13. Name each of the following compounds:
    a. NH_3
    b. P_4S_{10}
    c. CO_2
    d. P_2O_5
    e. CO
14. Write the formula for each of the following compounds:
    a. tetraarsenic hexoxide
    b. bromine monochloride
    c. tetrasulfur tetranitride
    d. diphosphorus pentasulfide

3.3 Formulas for Ionic Compounds

15. Write the formula for the ion formed by each of the following metals in all of its compounds.
    a. lithium
    b. calcium
    c. zinc
    d. aluminum
    e. silver
16. Chromium forms ions of +2 and +3 charges. Write formulas for the following:
    a. two different chlorides of chromium
    b. two different oxides of chromium

17. Write the formula for the compound formed between each of the following pairs of ions:
a. Al^{3+} and S^{2-}
b. Ag^{+} and O^{2-}
c. N^{3-} and Mg^{2+}

18. Complete the following table by writing the formula of the compound formed by the cation on the left and the anion at the top.

	O^{2-}	Br^{-}	N^{3-}
K^{+}			
Ca^{2+}			
Al^{3+}			

19. Complete the following table by writing the formula of the compound formed by the cation at the top and the anion on the left.

	Zn^{2+}	Cr^{3+}	NH_4^{+}
ClO_3^{-}		–	–
SO_4^{2-}			
PO_4^{3-}			
$Cr_2O_7^{2-}$			

20. For each of the following compounds, identify the individual ions and indicate how many of each are present per formula unit.
a. $Zn(C_2H_3O_2)_2$
b. $Al_2(CO_3)_3$
c. K_2SO_4
d. NH_4HCO_3

21. Write the formula for the compound formed by each of the following pairs of elements:
a. Mg and N
b. Mg and P
c. Ca and S
d. Al and N
e. Na and I
f. Al and P
g. Li and S
h. Mg and Br
i. Zn and Cl

22. What individual ions are present in the following?
a. Cu_2O
b. CuO

23. Identify the anion and *both* cations in each of the following pairs of compounds:
a. PtO and PtO_2
b. Fe_2O_3 and FeO
c. $CrSO_4$ and $Cr_2(SO_4)_3$

24. Complete the following table by writing the formula of the compound formed by each cation on the left with each anion at the top.

	NO_3^{-}	SO_4^{2-}	$Cr_2O_7^{2-}$	PO_4^{3-}
Na^{+}				
Mg^{2+}				
Zn^{2+}				
Fe^{3+}				

25. Complete the following table by writing the formula of the compound formed by each cation on the left with each anion at the top.

	ClO_2^{-}	SO_4^{2-}	PO_4^{3-}	$P_2O_7^{4-}$
NH_4^{+}				
Fe^{2+}				
Al^{3+}				

26. Write the formula for the compound of each of the following pairs of ions:
a. PO_4^{3-} and Fe^{3+}
b. SO_3^{2-} and NH_4^{+}
c. CO_3^{2-} and Ag^{+}

27. For each of the following compounds, identify the individual ions and indicate how many of each are present per formula unit.
a. $AlCl_3$
b. Al_2O_3
c. $Mg(HCO_3)_2$
d. $Sr_3(PO_4)_2$
e. $(NH_4)_2SeO_4$
f. $(NH_4)_2SO_4$
g. PbO_2

3.4 Naming Ionic Compounds

28. Write the formula for each of the following ions:
a. copper(I) ion
b. nickel(II) ion
c. lithium ion
d. ammonium ion
e. gold(I) ion

29. Name each of the following cations:
a. V^{2+}
b. Fe^{3+}
c. Mn^{2+}

30. Name each of the following anions:
    a. Cl^-
    b. P^{3-}
    c. O^{2-}
    d. N^{3-}

31. Write the formula for each of the following ions:
    a. nitrite ion
    b. perchlorate ion
    c. cyanide ion
    d. dichromate ion
    e. hypoiodite ion

32. Name each of the following anions:
    a. PO_4^{3-}
    b. SO_4^{2-}
    c. CO_3^{2-}

33. Name each of the following anions:
    a. $C_2H_3O_2^-$
    b. CrO_4^{2-}
    c. MnO_4^-
    d. $Cr_2O_7^{2-}$
    e. CN^-
    f. IO_3^-

34. Name each of the following compounds:
    a. $Co_2(SO_4)_3$
    b. $Ca_3(PO_4)_2$
    c. $(NH_4)_2SO_3$

35. Write the formula for each of the following compounds:
    a. cobalt(III) oxide
    b. nickel(II) sulfate
    c. lithium hydroxide
    d. copper(II) carbonate
    e. magnesium cyanide
    f. ammonium chlorate

36. Name each of the following compounds:
    a. Cu_2O
    b. CuS

37. Name each of the following compounds:
    a. $FePO_4$
    b. $MnSO_4$
    c. $(NH_4)_2SO_3$

38. Write the formula for each of the following compounds:
    a. potassium peroxide
    b. gold(III) chromate
    c. nickel(II) hydroxide
    d. copper(I) cyanide
    e. aluminum acetate
    f. ammonium dichromate

39. Complete the following table by writing the formula for each ionic compound whose cation is given on the left and whose anion is given at the top.

	Nitrate	Sulfate	Acetate	Phosphate
Ammonium				
Calcium				
Vanadium(III)				
Lead(IV)				

40. Complete the following table by writing the formula for each ionic compound whose cation is given on the left and whose anion is given at the top.

	Chloride	Hypochlorite	Phosphate
Lithium			
Mercury(II)			
Copper(II)			
Cobalt(III)			

41. Name each of the following hydrates:
    a. $Ba(ClO)_2 \cdot 2H_2O$
    b. $Na_2CO_3 \cdot 7H_2O$
    c. $FeBr_3 \cdot 6H_2O$

42. Write the formula for:
    a. iron(II) sulfate monohydrate
    b. barium bromide dihydrate

3.5 Naming Acids

43. Write the formula for each of the following acids:
    a. phosphoric acid
    b. hydrobromic acid
    c. chloric acid
    d. hydrosulfuric acid

44. Name each of the following acids:
    a. H_2SO_4
    b. $HClO_4$
    c. H_3PO_3

45. What is the difference between iodous acid and hypoiodous acid?

46. What is the difference between hypobromous acid and hydrobromic acid?

47. What is the difference between hydroiodic acid and periodic acid?

48. Name each of the following compounds as an acid and also as a pure compound:
   a. HBr
   b. H_2S
   c. HCl

49. Complete the following table by writing the formula for each ionic compound whose cation is given on the left and whose anion is given at the top.

	Hydrogen phosphate	Hydrogen sulfate	Dihydrogen phosphate
Magnesium			
Chromium(III)			
Ammonium			
Copper(II)			

50. What is the difference between the names "phosphorus" and "phosphorous"?

3.6 Nomenclature Review

51. Name each of the following:
   a. SO_3
   b. SO_3^{2-}
   c. Na_2SO_3
   d. H_2SO_3
   e. K_2SO_3

52. Name each compound:
   a. Na_2HPO_4
   b. NaH_2PO_4
   c. H_3PO_4
   d. Na_3PO_4

53. Complete the following table by writing the formula and name of each compound formed from an anion at the top and a cation on the left.

	NO_3^-	SO_4^{2-}	PO_4^{3-}
Potassium			
Iron(II)			
Titanium(III)			

54. Write formulas for:
   a. platinum(II) monohydrogen phosphate
   b. platinum(II) dihydrogen phosphate

55. Name each compound:
   a. XeF_2
   b. FeF_2
   c. CaF_2

56. Write formulas for the following substances:
   a. vanadium(V) oxide
   b. chlorous acid
   c. sodium dichromate
   d. hypoiodous acid
   e. platinum(II) oxide

57. Name each of the following compounds:
   a. Al_2O_3
   b. Cr_2O_3
   c. N_2O_3

58. Write the formula for sodium bisulfide.

59. Name each of the following substances:
   a. Cu_2O
   b. $Mn(OH)_2$
   c. BrF_5
   d. HNO_3
   e. AgBr
   f. BF_3
   g. H_3PO_3
   h. MnO_2
   i. CoF_2
   j. Ag_2O

60. Write the formulas for:
   a. magnesium nitride
   b. aluminum sulfate
   c. lead(IV) oxide

61. Name each of the following compounds:
   a. H_2SO_3
   b. N_2O
   c. XeF_6
   d. CrF_3
   e. NH_3

62. Name and write formulas for both ions in:
   a. $CaCl_2$
   b. Na_2S

63. Identify the type of substance, using the following categories, then name each. Ionic compounds containing variable-charge cations; Ionic compounds containing constant-charge cations; Acids (if dissolved in water); Binary covalent compounds; Elements
   a. FeF_3
   b. NiO
   c. ICl_3
   d. Au_2S
   e. $Mg(OH)_2$
   f. HNO_3

g. $(NH_4)_2SO_4$
h. $MgSO_3$
i. HCl
j. K_2CO_3
k. $(NH_4)_2Cr_2O_7$

64. Identify the type of substance using the categories of problem 3.63, and write the formula for each.
a. cobalt(II) carbonate
b. phosphorus triiodide
c. sulfurous acid
d. ammonium bromate
e. manganese(IV) oxide
f. sulfur hexafluoride
g. barium phosphate
h. nitrous acid
i. carbon tetrachloride
j. iron(II) chloride
k. diphosphorus pentasulfide

65. Identify the type of substance using the categories of problem 3.63, and name each.
a. PbO_2
b. $HBrO_2$
c. $Ca(OH)_2$
d. $HC_2H_3O_2$
e. CS_2
f. MnO_2
g. N_2O_3

66. Write formulas for the following substances:
a. iron(II) bromide
b. iron(III) chloride
c. ammonium sulfite
d. xenon tetrafluoride
e. iodine trichloride
f. ammonia
g. manganese(II) fluoride
h. lithium nitrate
i. barium peroxide

67. Name the following substances:
a. N_2O
b. CaS
c. HNO_3
d. $Ca(NO_2)_2$
e. $Fe(NO_3)_3$
f. $Ni(ClO_3)_2$
g. $HClO_3$
h. KNO_3
i. PI_3
j. $(NH_4)_3PO_4$
k. Li_3PO_4

68. Write formulas for the following substances:
a. silicon tetrafluoride
b. gold(I) chloride
c. phosphoric acid
d. silver sulfide
e. lead(IV) sulfate
f. copper(II) permanganate
g. tricarbon dioxide
h. potassium carbonate
i. chloric acid
j. nickel(II) cyanide

69. From Figure 3.15, identify the path by which you would name.
a. $Al(ClO_3)_3$
b. BrF_5
c. $(NH_4)_2Cr_2O_7$

70. If oxalate ion is $C_2O_4^{2-}$, what is the formula and name of its corresponding acid?

71. Azide ion has the formula N_3^-. Write the formula for the corresponding acid.

72. Name the following substances:
a. $CaSO_4$
b. $HC_2H_3O_2$
c. PCl_5
d. $BrCl_3$
e. CuO
f. $HClO_4$
g. $KHSO_4$
h. $HBrO_2$
i. HNO_2
j. $Pb(HPO_4)_2$

3.7 The Mole

73. How many atoms of chlorine are present in 1.00 mol of:
a. $MgCl_2$
b. CCl_4

74. How many moles of chlorine atoms are present in 1.00 mol of $Al(ClO_3)_3$?

75. How many moles of $(NH_4)_2SO_4$ contain 1.00 mol of hydrogen atoms?

76. How many moles of atoms of each element are present in 1.00 mol of each of the following compounds?
a. $CH_3CH_2NH_2$
b. $In(C_2H_3O_2)_3$
c. Na_3CoF_6
d. $Co(NH_3)_6PO_4$

77. How many moles of atoms of each element are present in 1.00 mol of each of the following compounds?
   a. $MgCO_3 \cdot 4H_2O$
   b. $(NH_4)_2C_2O_4$
   c. $C_6H_{12}O_6$
   d. $Co_2(CO)_8$

78. Calculate the number of molecules in 6.50 mol of CH_4.

79. Calculate the number of moles that contain 9.25×10^{20} formula units of $(NH_4)_2SO_4$.

80. Calculate the number of molecules in 1.67 mol of trinitrotoluene, TNT, $C_7H_5N_3O_6$.

81. Calculate the number of carbon atoms in 1.77 mol of butene, C_4H_8.

82. Calculate the number of hydrogen atoms in 1.11 mol of acetaldehyde, C_2H_4O.

83. Calculate the number of moles of H_3PO_4 that contains 6.78×10^{24} oxygen atoms.

84. Calculate the number of molecules of C_5H_{12} containing 1.44×10^{25} C atoms.

3.8 Molar Mass

85. What is the smallest molar mass known for:
   a. any atom
   b. any molecule

86. Calculate the molar mass of each of the following compounds to one decimal place:
   a. $NaHCO_3$
   b. $Ca(CNS)_2$
   c. $(NH_4)_2SO_3$
   d. Na_3PO_4
   e. C_8H_{18}
   f. $AsCl_3$

87. Calculate the molar mass of each of the following substances:
   a. $Ba(CN)_2$
   b. $(NH_4)_2Cr_2O_7$
   c. $Co(ClO_3)_3$
   d. UF_6
   e. $BaCO_3$
   f. P_4

88. Calculate the molar mass of:
   a. $CuSO_4 \cdot 5H_2O$
   b. $PbSiF_6 \cdot 4H_2O$

89. Calculate the number of grams of acetic acid, $HC_2H_3O_2$, in 1.76 mol of acetic acid.

90. Calculate the number of moles of butane, C_4H_{10}, in 151 g of butane.

91. Calculate the number of grams of acetaldehyde, C_2H_4O, in 0.848 mol of acetaldehyde.

92. Calculate the number of moles of methane (natural gas), CH_4, in 175 g of methane.

93. Calculate the number of moles in 12.9 g of a compound with a molar mass of 62.0 g/mol.

94. Calculate the number of moles in 1.93 g of a compound with a molar mass of 98.0 g/mol.

95. Calculate the mass in grams of:
   a. one oxygen atom
   b. one oxygen molecule

96. Calculate the mass of 6.68×10^{23} molecules of PCl_3.

97. Calculate the number of moles of C_2H_4 in 44.7 g of C_2H_4.

98. Calculate the number of moles of carbon atoms in 44.7 g of C_2H_4.

99. Calculate the number of individual carbon atoms in 44.7 g of C_2H_4.

100. Calculate the mass of hydrogen in 6.92 g of CH_4, methane (natural gas).

101. Calculate the number of hydrogen atoms in 41.4 g of ethyl alcohol, C_2H_6O.

102. Calculate the mass of aluminum chloride that contains 2.22×10^{23} chlorine atoms.

103. Calculate the mass of $Cr(ClO_2)_2$ that contains 5.57×10^{22} chlorine atoms.

104. Calculate the mass of N in 4.75×10^{23} formula units of Mg_3N_2.

105. Calculate the number of chlorine atoms in:
   a. 1.77 g of SCl_2
   b. 1.77 g of $SOCl_2$

3.9 Percent Composition

106. Calculate the percent composition of thiamine (a vitamin of the B complex family), $C_{12}H_{17}N_4OSCl$.

107. Calculate the percent composition of cholesterol, $C_{27}H_{45}OH$.

108. Calculate the percent composition of aspirin, $C_9H_8O_4$.

109. Calculate the percent composition of vitamin B12, $C_{63}H_{90}CoN_{14}P$.

110. Calculate the percent composition of ammonium monohydrogen phosphate.

111. Calculate the percent composition of:
a. sodium dichromate
b. potassium permanganate

112. Calculate the percent composition of ethylene glycol, $C_2H_6O_2$, commonly used as antifreeze in cars.

113. Calculate the percent chlorine in DDT, $C_{14}H_9Cl_5$, an insecticide that has been discontinued because it does not biodegrade.

114. Calculate the percent composition of niacin, a B-complex vitamin, $C_6H_5NO_2$.

115. Calculate the percent composition of vitamin E, $C_{29}H_{50}O_2$.

3.10 Empirical Formulas

116. Decide whether each of the following is an empirical formula:
a. $C_2H_8N_2$
b. $Na_2S_2O_8$
c. $K_2Cr_2O_7$
d. S_4N_4
e. $C_{12}H_{21}$

117. Decide whether each of the following is an empirical formula:
a. $K_4P_2O_7$
b. C_3F_6
c. $C_6H_{10}O_3$
d. Hg_2Br_2
e. $H_2C_2O_4$

118. Polyethylene, a plastic that is commonly used for plastic bags and bottles, is composed of 85.63% carbon and 14.37% hydrogen.
a. How many grams of each element are in 100.0 g of polyethylene?
b. How many moles of each element are in 100.0 g of polyethylene?
c. What is the mole ratio in integers?
d. What is the empirical formula?

119. Testosterone, a hormone, is composed of 79.12% carbon, 9.79% hydrogen, and 11.10% oxygen. What is its empirical formula?

120. Polypropylene, a durable and heat-resistant plastic, is composed of 85.63% carbon and 14.37% hydrogen. Determine its empirical formula.

121. Styrene, used in manufacturing Styrofoam™ and polystyrene packaging, is composed of 92.26% carbon and 7.74% hydrogen. Determine its empirical formula.

122. Determine an empirical formula from each of the following sets of percent composition data:
a. 82.66% C, 17.34% H
b. 72.03% Mn, 27.97% O
c. 43.64% P, 56.36% O
d. 37.82% C, 6.35% H, 55.83% Cl
e. 54.53% C, 9.15% H, 36.32% O

123. Determine an empirical formula from each of the following sets of percent composition data:
a. 47.05% K, 14.45% C, 38.50% O
b. 77.26% Hg, 9.25% C, 1.17% H, 12.32% O
c. 66.42% C, 5.57% H, 28.01% Cl
d. 74.98% C, 5.24% H, 19.77% F

124. Calculate the empirical formula of each of the substances from the following analyses:
a. 5.52 g C, 0.464 g H, 13.1 g F
b. 75.95 g C, 9.57 g H, 224.2 g Cl

125. Calculate the empirical formula of each of the following substances. Name each.
a. 9.07 g H, 288 g O, 144 g S
b. 76.8 g Na, 80.1 g O, 53.4 g S

126. Calculate the empirical formula mass of each of the following:
a. Hg_2Br_2
b. $Na_2S_2O_3$

3.11 Molecular Formulas

127. Calculate the molar mass of each compound and the molar mass of its empirical formula.
a. C_6H_6
b. C_3H_6
c. C_2H_6

128. Calculate the molar mass of each compound and the molar mass of its empirical formula.
a. C_6H_{12}
b. C_4H_6
c. C_6H_{10}

129. Determine the molecular formula of a substance if its empirical formula is NO_2 and its molar mass is:
a. 46.0 g/mol
b. 92.0 g/mol

130. Find the molecular formula of a substance with an empirical formula CH_2 and a molar mass of:
   a. 56.0 g/mol
   b. 126 g/mol
   c. 210 g/mol
   d. 98.0 g/mol

131. Find the molecular formula of a substance if the empirical formula is CH and its molar mass is:
   a. 52.0 g/mol
   b. 104 g/mol
   c. 156 g/mol
   d. 78.0 g/mol

132. Determine the molecular formula of a sugar from its percent composition of 40.0% C, 6.67% H, 53.3% O, and its molar mass of 180 g/mol.

133. Find the molecular formula of a compound composed of 87.73% carbon and 12.27% and has a molar mass of 82.1 g/mol.

134. The most widely used antifreeze, ethylene glycol, is composed of 38.70% carbon, 9.74% hydrogen, and 51.56% oxygen. Its molar mass is 62.07 g/mol. Find its molecular formula.

135. Calculate the molecular formula of a compound if a sample contains 135 g of phosphorus and 175 g of oxygen and its molar mass is 284 g/mol.

136. Octane and heptane are two ingredients of gasoline. Octane has 84.12% carbon and 15.88% hydrogen, and heptane has 83.90% carbon and 16.10% hydrogen. Their molecular masses are 114 u and 100 u, respectively. What are their molecular formulas?

3.12 Combustion Analysis

137. A 6.09 mg sample of a hydrocarbon was burned in air. The products were 17.9 mg of CO_2 and 11.0 mg of H_2O. What is the empirical formula of the sample?

138. A 17.1 mg sample of a hydrocarbon was burned in air. The products were 47.0 mg of CO_2 and 38.4 mg of water. What is the empirical formula of the hydrocarbon?

139. An 18.0 mg sample of a compound containing C, H, and O was burned in air. The products were 26.4 mg of CO_2 and 10.8 mg of H_2O. What is the empirical formula of the sample?

Putting It Together

140. A certain carbohydrate (a compound containing carbon plus hydrogen and oxygen in a 2:1 atom ratio) is 40.0% carbon. Calculate its empirical formula.

141. Calculate the percent composition of ammonium cyanide.

142. Calculate the number of hydrogen atoms in 42.7 g of a compound that contains 91.25% carbon and 8.75% hydrogen.

143. Calculate the number of molecules in 2.79 g of a compound that has a molar mass of 92.13 g/mol and contains 91.25% carbon and 8.75% hydrogen.

144. Calculate the number of hydrogen atoms in 12.8 g of a compound whose percent composition is 15.88% H and 84.12% C.

145. Calculate the number of hydrogen atoms in 41.8 g of a compound that contains 4.14% hydrogen.

146. Calculate the number of carbon atoms in 1.000 gallon of octane, C_8H_{18}, (1 gallon = 3.785 L; density = 0.7025 g/mL).

147. Vitamin B_{12} has one cobalt atom per formula unit. The compound is 4.348% Co. Calculate its molar mass.

148. Vitamin D_1 has two oxygen atoms per formula unit. The compound is 4.03% O. Calculate its molar mass.

149. A sample is 39.2% KCl by mass, and the rest is water. Calculate the number of molecules of water in 14.4 g of the sample.

150. A 6.055 g sample of a hydrate of copper(II) sulfate, $CuSO_4 \cdot xH_2O$, is heated until all the water is driven off. After the anhydrous salt cools, its mass is 3.870 g. Calculate the value of x. (Hint: Treat this problem as an empirical formula problem with one of the "elements" H_2O and the other as $CuSO_4$).

PRACTICE PROBLEM SOLUTIONS

Practice Problem 3.1 Solution

a. 2 Hg and 2 Cl

b. 1 N, 4H + 2H = 6 H, 1 P, and 4 O

Practice Problem 3.2 Solution

a. Na is a metal and Br is a nonmetal, so NaBr is an ionic compound.

b. N and H are both nonmetals, so NH_3 is a covalent (molecular) compound.

c. Al is a metal and Cl is a nonmetal, so $AlCl_3$ is an ionic compound.

d. C and O are both nonmetals, so CO_2 is a covalent (molecular) compound.

Practice Problem 3.3 Solution

The first element will always use its elemental name, along with a prefix from Table 3.1 if there is more than one atom of that type in the molecule. The second element will have the suffix *-ide*, along with a prefix from Table 3.1 to indicate how many atoms of that type are present.

a. Dichlorine trioxide

b. Tetrasulfur tetranitride

c. Diphosphorus pentasulfide

d. Sulfur difluoride

Practice Problem 3.4 Solution

a. Tetraphosphorus hexoxide

b. Diboron trioxide

c. Dinitrogen monoxide

d. Iodine pentachloride

e. Iodine heptafluoride

f. Phosphorus trichloride

For binary covalent compounds, the first element is named using its elemental name. If there is more than one atom of that type in the formula, then a prefix from Table 3.1 is used. The second element is named using the root of its elemental name with the suffix *-ide* and with a prefix from Table 3.1 to indicate how many atoms of that type are present.

Practice Problem 3.5 Solution

a. S_2F_{10}: *di-* = 2 sulfur atoms, followed by *deca-* = 10 fluorine atoms

b. IO_3: no prefix = 1 iodine atom, followed by *tri-* = 3 oxygen atoms

c. As_4O_6: *tetra-* = 4 arsenic atoms, followed by *hex-* = 3 oxygen atoms

Practice Problem 3.6 Solution

a. $AlCl_3$: Each aluminum cation has a charge of +3, whereas each chlorine anion has a −1 charge. It will take three Cl^- ions to balance the charge on each Al^{3+} ion.

b. Ca_3P_2: Each calcium cation has a charge of +2, whereas each phosphorus anion has a −3 charge. It will take three Ca^{2+} ions (+6 total charge) to balance the charge on two P^{3-} ions (−6 total charge).

c. BaO: Each barium cation has a charge of +2, and each oxygen anion has a −2 charge, so a simple 1:1 ratio will balance the charges and result in an electrically neutral compound.

d. Fe_2O_3: Each iron cation has a charge of +3, whereas each oxygen, O, anion has a charge of −2. It will require two Fe^{3+} ions (+6 total charge) to balance the charge on three O^{2-} ions (−6 total charge).

Practice Problem 3.7 Solution

According to Figure 3.7, a strontium cation has a +2 charge, whereas a nitrogen anion has a −3 charge. To balance the charges, three Sr^{2+} cations (+6 overall) must combine with two N^{3-} anions (−6 overall) to form Sr_3N_2.

Practice Problem 3.8 Solution

a. Each Cl anion is −1, so the total negative charge is −3. The total positive charge must be +3 for $FeCl_3$ to be neutral and there is only one Fe per formula unit, so the iron cation is Fe^{3+}.

b. Each O anion is −2, so the total negative charge is −4. The charge on the Sn cation must be +4.

Practice Problem 3.9 Solution

a. One Cu^{2+} ion can balance the charge on two OH^- ions, so the ions combine in a 1:2 ratio to form $Cu(OH)_2$.

b. It takes three Cr^{2+} ions [$3 \times (+2) = +6$] to balance the charge on two PO_4^{3-} ions [$2 \times (-3) = -6$], so the formula is $Cr_3(PO_4)_2$.

Practice Problem 3.10 Solution

Sr^{2+}, Al^{3+}, and Zn^{2+} are constant-charge cations, whereas the charge on cations of tin, Sn, can vary. Use the Stock system for the two Sn cations.

a. Strontium ion

b. Tin(II) ion

c. Tin(IV) ion

d. Aluminum ion

e. Zinc ion

Practice Problem 3.11 Solution

The cation is manganese(II) because the charge on the Mn cation is +2. It takes one Mn cation to balance the charge on one O^{2-} anion, so the Mn cation must have a +2 charge.

Practice Problem 3.12 Solution

a. There is only one Fe ion to balance the −2 charge on the oxygen ion, so the Fe ion must be +2. The name of this cation is iron(II).

b. There are three oxygen ions, each with a −2 charge, for a total negative charge of −6. There are only two Fe ions, so each must have a +3, for a total positive charge of +6. The name of this cation is iron(III).

Practice Problem 3.13 Solution

In naming oxyanions, an ion with the *-ate* suffix has one more oxygen atom than an ion with the *-ite* suffix. The carbon*ate* ion is CO_3^{2-}, so the carbon*ite* ion would have one fewer oxygen atom but have the same charge: CO_2^{2-}.

Practice Problem 3.14 Solution

a. The cation is Ba^{2+}, barium ion, and the anion is SO_4^{2-}, sulfate. The name of the compound is barium sulfate.

b. The cation is Al^{3+}, aluminum ion, and the anion is $C_2H_3O_2^-$, acetate ion (Table 3.4). The name of the compound is aluminum acetate.

c. Cobalt is a variable-charge cation (Figure 3.7 and Figure 3.9), so the charge on the cation has to be determined from the overall negative charge of the anions. There are three chlorate ions, ClO_3^-, in each formula unit for a total negative charge of −3, so the cobalt ion must be +3. The name of the compound is cobalt(III) chlorate.

Practice Problem 3.15 Solution

a. Pb^{4+} and SO_4^{2-} combine in a 1:2 ratio to form $Pb(SO_4)_2$.

b. Al^{3+} and S^{2-} combine in a 2:3 ratio to form Al_2S_3.

Practice Problem 3.16 Solution

a. Mg forms only a +2 ion, so $MgCl_2$ is magnesium chloride. If it was necessary to distinguish this compound from its hydrate, it could be referred to as anhydrous magnesium chloride.

b. The prefix for 6 is *hexa-* (Table 3.1), so this compound is named magnesium chloride hexahydrate. The waters of hydration, if they are present, must always be included in the name.

Practice Problem 3.17 Solution

$H_2C_8H_4O_4$ has two ionizable hydrogen atoms—namely, the two at the beginning of the formula. The four H atoms in $C_8H_4O_4^{2-}$ are *not* ionizable.

Practice Problem 3.18 Solution

a. *Hydro-* + brom + *-ic acid* = hydrobromic acid

b. *Hydro-* + selen + *-ic acid* = hydroselenic acid

Practice Problem 3.19 Solution

a. Hypobromous acid: The *-ite* suffix of the hypobromite ion is changed to *-ous acid*. The *hypo-* prefix for the anion is retained in the name of the acid.

b. Nitric acid: The *-ate* suffix of the nitrate ion is changed to *-ic acid*.

c. Chlorous acid: The *-ite* suffix of the chlorite ion is changed to *-ous acid*.

Practice Problem 3.20 Solution

a. HNO_2: Nitr*ite* ion, NO_2^-, forms nitr*ous* acid by adding one H^+.

b. H_2SO_4: Sulfate ion, SO_4^{2-}, forms sulfur*ic* acid by adding two H^+.

Practice Problem 3.21 Solution

a. H_2SO_4 begins with an H and is an acid. The anion is sulfate, SO_4^{2-} (Table 3.4). The *-ate* suffix becomes *-ic acid*, so the name of the acid is sulfuric acid.

b. Calcium is a constant-charge cation (Figure 3.9) and SO_4^{2-} is the sulfate ion, so $CaSO_4$ is calcium sulfate. Since $CaSO_4 \cdot 2\,H_2O$ has two waters of hydration (Section 3.4), the term *dihydrate* is added to the name, resulting in calcium sulfate dihydrate.

c. Potassium is a constant-charge cation (Figure 3.9) and ClO_3^- is the chlorate ion (Table 3.4), so $KClO_3$ is potassium chlorate.

Practice Problem 3.22 Solution

Hydro- + *hydrox* + *-ic acid* = hydrohydroxic acid.

Practice Problem 3.23 Solution

a. Chromium forms variable-charge ions, so its name must specify the charge with a Roman numeral.

The correct name for this ion is chromium(III) hydroxide.

b. $SrCl_2$ is an ionic compound, and ionic compounds do not use prefixes to specify the numbers of ions in the formula unit. The correct name is the strontium chloride.

c. K^+ is a constant-charge cation, so it does not need a Roman numeral. The correct name is potassium cyanide.

d. P and Cl are both nonmetals, so PCl_3 should be named according to the covalent naming system, which uses prefixes to specify the number atoms. The correct name is phosphorus trichloride.

e. Monoatomic anion names end in *-ide*, not *-ate*. The correct name is calcium sulfide.

Practice Problem 3.24 Solution

To calculate the number of doughnuts from the number of dozens, use the conversion factor 1 dozen = 12 doughnuts. Since you are calculating the number of doughnuts, doughnuts goes in the numerator of the conversion factor:

$$8 \text{ dozen doughnuts} \times \frac{12 \text{ doughnuts}}{1 \text{ dozen doughnuts}}$$
$$= 96 \text{ doughnuts}$$

Yes, eight dozen is enough doughnuts for each employee to have one. There will be four left over.

Practice Problem 3.25 Solution

To calculate the number of atoms from the number of moles, use the conversion factor 1 mol = 6.022×10^{23} atoms. Since you are calculating the number of atoms, atoms goes in the numerator of the conversion factor:

$$0.0490 \text{ mol Cu} \times \frac{6.022 \times 10^{23} \text{ Cu atoms}}{1 \text{ mol Cu}}$$
$$= 2.95 \times 10^{22} \text{ Cu atoms}$$

Practice Problem 3.26 Solution

To calculate the number of molecules from the number of moles, use the conversion factor 1 mol = 6.022×10^{23} molecules. Since you are calculating the number of molecules, molecules goes in the numerator of the conversion factor:

$$0.0123 \text{ mol } C_{12}H_{22}O_{11} \times \frac{6.022 \times 10^{23} \text{ molecules}}{1 \text{ mol}}$$
$$= 7.41 \times 10^{21}\ C_{12}H_{22}O_{11} \text{ molecules}$$

Practice Problem 3.27 Solution

a. Just as there are three Li atoms per Li_3PO_4 formula unit, there are 3 mol Li per mole of Li_3PO_4. Use a similar conversion factor for each element in the compound:

$$2 \text{ mol } Li_3PO_4\left(\frac{3 \text{ mol Li}}{1 \text{ mol } Li_3PO_4}\right) = 6 \text{ mol Li}$$
$$2 \text{ mol } Li_3PO_4\left(\frac{1 \text{ mol P}}{1 \text{ mol } Li_3PO_4}\right) = 2 \text{ mol P}$$
$$2 \text{ mol } Li_3PO_4\left(\frac{4 \text{ mol O}}{1 \text{ mol } Li_3PO_4}\right) = 8 \text{ mol O}$$

b. The subscript outside of the parentheses applies to each element inside the parentheses:

$$0.2 \text{ mol } Ba(NO_3)_2\left(\frac{1 \text{ mol Ba}}{1 \text{ mol } Ba(NO_3)_2}\right) = 0.2 \text{ mol Ba}$$
$$0.2 \text{ mol } Ba(NO_3)_2\left(\frac{2 \text{ mol N}}{1 \text{ mol } Ba(NO_3)_2}\right) = 0.4 \text{ mol N}$$
$$0.2 \text{ mol } Ba(NO_3)_2\left(\frac{6 \text{ mol O}}{1 \text{ mol } Ba(NO_3)_2}\right) = 1.2 \text{ mol O}$$

Practice Problem 3.28 Solution

a. One mol $CaCO_3$ contains 1 mol Ca, 1 mol C, and 3 mol O. Since there is 1 mol Ca, there is an Avogadro's number of Ca atoms: 6.022×10^{23} Ca atoms. Since there is 1 mol C, there is also an Avogadro's number of carbon atoms: 6.022×10^{23} C atoms. Since there are 3 mol O, there are $3(6.022 \times 10^{23}) = 1.807 \times 10^{24}$ O atoms.

b. The total number of atoms is the sum of these three, 3.011×10^{24} atoms.

Practice Problem 3.29 Solution

Use the subscripts in the chemical formula, $HC_9H_7O_4$, to convert the moles of the compound to moles of each element. Then convert moles to atoms using Avogadro's number:

$$1.80 \times 10^{-3} \text{ mol } HC_9H_7O_4\left(\frac{9 \text{ mol C}}{1 \text{ mol } HC_9H_7O_4}\right)\left(\frac{6.022 \times 10^{23} \text{ atoms}}{1 \text{ mol}}\right) = 9.76 \times 10^{21} \text{ C atoms}$$

$$1.80 \times 10^{-3} \text{ mol } HC_9H_7O_4\left(\frac{8 \text{ mol H}}{1 \text{ mol } HC_9H_7O_4}\right)\left(\frac{6.022 \times 10^{23} \text{ atoms}}{1 \text{ mol}}\right) = 8.67 \times 10^{21} \text{ H atoms}$$

$$1.80 \times 10^{-3} \text{ mol } HC_9H_7O_4 \left(\frac{4 \text{ mol O}}{1 \text{ mol } HC_9H_7O_4}\right)$$
$$\left(\frac{6.022 \times 10^{23} \text{ C atoms}}{1 \text{ mol O}}\right) = 4.34 \times 10^{21} \text{ O atoms}$$

Practice Problem 3.30 Solution

The molar mass of Ag from the periodic table is 107.87 g/mol. Since you are calculating grams, put grams in the numerator of the conversion factor:

$$4.29 \text{ mol Ag} \times \frac{107.87 \text{ g Ag}}{1 \text{ mol Ag}} = 463 \text{ g Ag}$$

Molar mass is also used as a conversion factor when you are calculating the number of moles in a sample from the mass of the sample.

Practice Problem 3.31 Solution

Use the molar mass of carbon, 12.011 g/mol, as a conversion factor between mass and moles. Since you are calculating moles, moles goes in the numerator of the conversion factor:

$$0.200 \text{ g C} \times \frac{1 \text{ mol C}}{12.011 \text{ g C}} = 1.67 \times 10^{-2} \text{ mol C}$$

Practice Problem 3.32 Solution

First, convert the mass from kilograms to grams (Section 1.7), given that 1 kg = 1000 g. Then convert the mass to moles using the molar mass. The molar mass of Fe is 55.845 g/mol:

$$1.3 \text{ kg Fe} \times \frac{1000 \text{ g}}{1 \text{ kg}} \times \frac{1 \text{ mol Fe}}{55.845 \text{ g Fe}} = 23 \text{ mol Fe}$$

Practice Problem 3.33 Solution

The molar mass of a compound is the total of the molar masses of each of its constituent elements, multiplied by their respective subscripts:

$$8 \times C = 8 \times 12.011 \text{ g/mol} = 96.088 \text{ g/mol}$$
$$10 \times H = 10 \times 1.008 \text{ g/mol} = 10.08 \text{ g/mol}$$
$$4 \times N = 4 \times 14.007 \text{ g/mol} = 56.028 \text{ g/mol}$$
$$2 \times O = 2 \times 15.999 \text{ g/mol} = 31.998 \text{ g/mol}$$

The mass of 1 mol caffeine is the sum of these, 194.19 g/mol.

Practice Problem 3.34 Solution

Iron(III) is the Fe^{3+} ion, and the oxide ion is O^{2-}. To balance the positive and negative charges on these two ions, there must be two Fe^{3+} ions for every three O^{2-} ions: Fe_2O_3.

Using the molar masses of Fe and O from the periodic table, the molar mass of Fe_2O_3 is 2(55.845 g/mol) + 3(15.999 g/mol) = 159.69 g/mol.

Practice Problem 3.35 Solution

The molar mass of a compound is calculated by adding up the molar masses of all of the atoms that make up the compound, multiplied by their subscripts in the chemical formula for the compound. One mole of $Na_2S_2O_3 \cdot 5\,H_2O$ consists of 2 mol Na, 2 mol S, 8 mol O, and 10 mol H:

$$2 \times Na = 2 \text{ mol} \times 22.99 \text{ g/mol} = 45.98 \text{ g/mol}$$
$$2 \times S = 2 \text{ mol} \times 32.06 \text{ g/mol} = 64.12 \text{ g/mol}$$
$$8 \times O = 8 \text{ mol} \times 15.999 \text{ g/mol} = 127.99 \text{ g/mol}$$
$$10 \times H = 10 \text{ mol} \times 1.008 \text{ g/mol} = 10.08 \text{ g/mol}$$

The molar mass is the sum of the masses of all the atoms in the chemical formula:

$$45.98 \text{ g/mol} + 64.12 \text{ g/mol} + 127.99 \text{ g/mol} + 10.08 \text{ g/mol} = 248.17 \text{ g/mol}$$

Practice Problem 3.36 Solution

The molar mass of SiO_2 is 28.086 g/mol + 2(15.999) g/mol = 60.084 g/mol. In this case, the mass of the sample is given in milligrams instead of grams, so it must be converted to grams before calculating moles:

$$2.8 \text{ mg } SiO_2 \times \frac{1 \text{ g}}{1000 \text{ mg}} \times \frac{1 \text{ mol } SiO_2}{60.084 \text{ g } SiO_2} = 4.7 \times 10^{-5} \text{ mol } SiO_2$$

Practice Problem 3.37 Solution

The 2.8 mg grain of sand contains 4.7×10^{-5} mol SiO_2 (Practice Problem 3.36). One mole of SiO_2 contains 1 mol Si and 2 mol O, so 4.7×10^{-5} mol SiO_2 contains 4.7×10^{-5} mol Si and $2(4.7 \times 10^{-5}) = 9.4 \times 10^{-5}$ mol O. To convert from moles of Si to the number of Si atoms, use Avogadro's number:

$$4.7 \times 10^{-5} \text{ mol Si} \times \frac{6.022 \times 10^{23} \text{ Si atoms}}{1 \text{ mol Si}} = 2.8 \times 10^{19} \text{ Si atoms}$$

$$9.4 \times 10^{-5} \text{ mol Si} \times \frac{6.022 \times 10^{23} \text{ Si atoms}}{1 \text{ mol Si}} = 5.7 \times 10^{19} \text{ Si atoms}$$

$$(2.8 \times 10^{19} \text{ Si atoms}) + (5.7 \times 10^{19} \text{ O atoms}) = 8.5 \times 10^{19} \text{ atoms total}$$

Practice Problem 3.38 Solution

First, convert mass to moles using the molar mass of Al as a conversion factor, then convert moles to atoms using Avogadro's number:

Mass of Al → Molar mass of Al → Moles of Al → Avogadro's number → Number of Al atoms

$$102 \text{ g Al} \times \frac{1 \text{ mol Al}}{26.982 \text{ g Al}} = 3.78 \text{ mol Al}$$

$$3.78 \text{ mol Al} \times \frac{6.022 \times 10^{23} \text{ Al atoms}}{1 \text{ mol Al}}$$
$$= 2.28 \times 10^{24} \text{ Al atoms}$$

Practice Problem 3.39 Solution

Nitrogen gas is a diatomic element, with the chemical formula N_2. The molar mass of N_2 is $2(14.007 \text{ g/mol}) = 28.014 \text{ g/mol}$.

To solve the problem, first convert the number of N_2 molecules to moles of N_2 using Avogadro's number as a conversion factor, then convert moles of N_2 to grams of N_2 using the molar mass of N_2 gas.

$$2.74 \times 10^{23} \text{ N}_2 \text{ molecules} \times \frac{1 \text{ mol of N}_2}{6.022 \times 10^{23} \text{ N}_2 \text{ molecules}}$$
$$= 0.455 \text{ mol N}_2$$

$$0.455 \text{ mol N}_2 \times \frac{28.014 \text{ g N}_2}{1 \text{ mol N}_2} = 12.7 \text{ g N}_2$$

Practice Problem 3.40 Solution

Each mole of $MgCl_2$ contains one mole Mg and *two* moles of Cl:

Molar mass of $MgCl_2$ = 24.305 g/mol
+ 2(35.45 g/mol) = 95.21 g/mol

The percent by mass of Mg in $MgCl_2$ is the mass of Mg in 1 mol $MgCl_2$ divided by the molar mass of $MgCl_2$, times 100%:

$$\text{Mass percent Mg} = \frac{24.305 \text{ g/mol}}{95.21 \text{ g/mol}} \times 100\% = 25.53\%$$

The percent by mass of Cl in $MgCl_2$ is the mass of Cl in one mole $MgCl_2$ divided by the molar mass of $MgCl_2$. Since there are *two* moles of Cl in each mole of $MgCl_2$, the mass of Cl in one mole of $MgCl_2$ is *twice* the molar mass of Cl.

$$\text{Mass percent Cl} = \frac{2 \times 35.45 \text{ g/mol}}{95.21 \text{ g/mol}} \times 100\%$$
$$= 74.47\%$$

Practice Problem 3.41 Solution

Molar mass of $(NH_4)_3PO_4$:

$$3 \times \text{N} = 3 \times 14.007 \text{ g/mol} = 42.021 \text{ g}$$
$$12 \times \text{H} = 12 \times 1.008 \text{ g/mol} = 12.096 \text{ g/mol}$$
$$1 \times \text{P} = 1 \times 30.974 \text{ g/mol} = 30.974 \text{ g/mol}$$
$$4 \times \text{O} = 4 \times 15.999 \text{ g/mol} = 63.996 \text{ g/mol}$$
$$\text{Total} = 149.087 \text{ g/mol}$$

$$\%\text{N} = \left(\frac{42.021 \text{ g/mol}}{149.087 \text{ g/mol}}\right) \times 100\% = 28.186\% \text{ N}$$

$$\%\text{H} = \left(\frac{12.096 \text{ g/mol}}{149.087 \text{ g/mol}}\right) \times 100\% = 8.113\% \text{ H}$$

$$\%\text{P} = \left(\frac{30.974 \text{ g/mol}}{149.087 \text{ g/mol}}\right) \times 100\% = 20.776\% \text{ P}$$

$$\%\text{O} = \left(\frac{63.996 \text{ g/mol}}{149.087 \text{ g/mol}}\right) \times 100\% = 42.925\% \text{ O}$$

$$\text{Total} = 100\%$$

Practice Problem 3.42 Solution

There are two ways to solve this problem, but both require the molar mass of $CuSO_4$:

$$1 \times \text{Cu} = 63.546 \text{ g/mol}$$
$$1 \times \text{S} = 32.06 \text{ g/mol}$$
$$4 \times \text{O} = 4 \times 15.999 = 63.996 \text{ g/mol}$$

Molar mass of $CuSO_4$ = 63.546 g/mol + 32.06 g/mol + 63.996 g/mol = 159.60 g/mol

Solution 1:

$$20.0 \text{ g CuSO}_4 \times \frac{1 \text{ mol Cu}}{159.60 \text{ g CuSO}_4} = 0.1253 \text{ mol CuSO}_4$$
$$= 0.1253 \text{ mol Cu}$$

$$0.1253 \text{ mol Cu} \times \frac{63.546 \text{ g Cu}}{1 \text{ mol Cu}} = 7.96 \text{ g Cu}$$

Solution 2:

$$\text{Percent Cu} = \frac{\text{Molar mass of Cu}}{\text{Molar mass of CuSO}_4} \times 100\%$$

$$\text{Percent Cu} = \frac{63.546 \text{ g/mol Cu}}{159.60 \text{ g/mol CuSO}_4} \times 100\%$$
$$= 39.815\% \text{ Cu}$$

The mass percent of Cu in the compound can now be used as a conversion factor because 39.815% Cu means that 39.815 g Cu = 100.0 g $CuSO_4$.

Mass of Cu in 20.0 g of anhydrous $CuSO_4$:

$$20.0 \text{ g CuSO}_4 \times \frac{39.815 \text{ g Cu}}{100.0 \text{ g CuSO}_4} = 7.96 \text{ g Cu}$$

These same calculations can be repeated for S and O to determine the mass of S and O in 20.0 g of anhydrous $CuSO_4$.

Practice Problem 3.43 Solution

First, calculate the percent composition of Al_2O_3. The percent for each element is the total mass of each element in 1 mol Al_2O_3 divided by the molar mass of Al_2O_3 and multiplied by 100%.

$$2 \times \text{Al} = 2 \times 26.982\ \text{g/mol} = 53.964\ \text{g/mol}$$
$$3 \times \text{O} = 3 \times 15.999\ \text{g/mol} = 47.997\ \text{g/mol}$$

The molar mass of Al_2O_3 is 53.964 g/mol + 47.997 g/mol = 101.96 g/mol.

Now use Equation 3.2 to calculate the percent composition of Al_2O_3.

$$\text{Percent Al} = \frac{\text{Mass of Al}}{\text{Molar mass of Al}_2\text{O}_3} \times 100\%$$
$$= \frac{53.964\ \text{g/mol Al}}{101.961\ \text{g/mol Al}_2\text{O}_3} \times 100\% = 52.926\%\ \text{Al}$$
$$\text{Percent O} = \frac{47.997\ \text{g/mol O}}{101.961\ \text{g/mol Al}_2\text{O}_3} \times 100\%$$
$$= 47.074\%\ \text{O}$$

Alternatively, the mass percent of O could have been calculated as the difference from 100%:

$$100\%\ \text{Al}_2\text{O}_3 - 52.926\%\ \text{Al} = 47.074\%\ \text{O}$$

The mass of each element can now be calculated from the mass of the sample.

$$\text{Al: } 5.1\ \text{g Al}_2\text{O}_3 \times \frac{52.926\ \text{g Al}}{100.0\ \text{g Al}_2\text{O}_3} = 2.7\ \text{g Al}$$
$$\text{O: } 5.1\ \text{g Al}_2\text{O}_3 \times \frac{47.074\ \text{g O}}{100.0\ \text{g Al}_2\text{O}_3} = 2.4\ \text{g O}$$

The Sunrise Ruby contains 2.7 g of aluminum and 2.4 g of oxygen.

Practice Problem 3.44 Solution

The percent of carbon in CO_2 is

$$\frac{\text{Molar mass of C}}{\text{Molar mass of CO}_2} \times 100\%$$
$$= \frac{12.011\ \text{g/mol C}}{12.011\ \text{g/mol C} + 2(15.999\ \text{g/mol O})} \times 100\%$$
$$= 27.292\%\ \text{C}$$

A mass percent of 27.292% means there are 27.292 g C in every 100 g CO_2. The conversion factor is therefore 27.292 g C = 100.0 g CO_2. To calculate the mass of CO_2, place 100.0 g CO_2 in the numerator of the conversion factor:

$$100.0\ \text{g C} \times \frac{100.0\ \text{g CO}_2}{27.292\ \text{g C}} = 366.4\ \text{g CO}_2$$

Practice Problem 3.45 Solution

a. The subscript on N indicates that there are no nitrogen atoms in the compound. Once N is excluded from the formula, what's left is a valid empirical formula: $C_5H_{10}O_2$.

b. This is the lowest whole-number ratio between the atoms of this compound, so $C_{11}H_{12}N_2O_2$ is a valid empirical formula.

c. These are the lowest whole-number ratios between Fe and O, but subscripts of 1 are not written in chemical formulas. This empirical formula should be rewritten as FeO.

d. Both subscripts in C_8H_{18} can be divided by 2 to yield the smaller ratio of C_4H_9.

Practice Problem 3.46 Solution

a. The mole ratio is 2:1, so the empirical formula is N_2O.

b. Multiplying both mole ratios by 2 turns the 2.5 value for oxygen into a whole number while maintaining the correct mole ratio between N and O: The empirical formula is N_2O_5.

c. These decimals are *not* among the common values listed in Table 3.5, so it's unclear what number they should be multiplied by to obtain whole numbers. Both values are the same, though, so dividing them both by 0.3325 converts them both to 1. A nitrogen-to-oxygen mole ratio of 1:1 means the empirical formula is NO.

Practice Problem 3.47 Solution

a. 1.25 can be converted to a whole number by multiplying it by 4, so multiply both subscripts by 4: (1×4):(1.25×4) = 4:5. The empirical formula is A_4B_5.

b. 1.75 can be converted to a whole number by multiplying it by 4, so multiply both subscripts by 4: (1×4):(1.75×4) = 4:7. The empirical formula is A_4B_7.

c. 1.67 can be converted to a whole number by multiplying it by 3, so multiply both subscripts by 3: (1×3):(1.67×3) = 3:5. The empirical formula is A_3B_5.

d. 1.40 can be converted to a whole number by multiplying it by 5, so multiply both subscripts by 5: (1 × 5):(1.40 × 5) = 5:7. The empirical formula is A_5B_7.

Practice Problem 3.48 Solution

Calculate the number of moles of Mn, P, and O in a 100 g sample:

$$38.71 \text{ g Mn} \times \left(\frac{1 \text{ mol Mn}}{54.94 \text{ g Mn}}\right) = 0.7046 \text{ mol Mn}$$

$$21.82 \text{ g P} \times \left(\frac{1 \text{ mol P}}{30.97 \text{ g P}}\right) = 0.7046 \text{ mol P}$$

$$39.46 \text{ g O} \times \left(\frac{1 \text{ mol O}}{16.00 \text{ g O}}\right) = 2.466 \text{ mol O}$$

None of these values is an integer, so divide them all by the smallest value to turn at least one of them into an integer.

$$\frac{0.7046 \text{ mol Mn}}{0.7046} = 1.000 \text{ mol Mn}$$

$$\frac{0.7046 \text{ mol P}}{0.7046} = 1.000 \text{ mol P}$$

$$\frac{2.466 \text{ mol O}}{0.7046} = 3.500 \text{ mol O}$$

Multiplying each of these numbers of moles by 2 yields an empirical formula of $Mn_2P_2O_7$.

Practice Problem 3.49 Solution

$$2.453 \text{ g Na} \times \left(\frac{1 \text{ mol Na}}{22.99 \text{ g Na}}\right) = 0.1067 \text{ mol Na}$$

$$3.422 \text{ g S} \times \left(\frac{1 \text{ mol S}}{32.06 \text{ g S}}\right) = 0.1067 \text{ mol S}$$

$$2.561 \text{ g O} \times \left(\frac{1 \text{ mol O}}{15.999 \text{ g O}}\right) = 0.1601 \text{ mol O}$$

None of these is an integer, so divide them all by the smallest value (0.1067) to turn at least one of them into an integer.

$$\frac{0.1067 \text{ mol Na}}{0.1067} = 1.000 \text{ mol Na}$$

$$\frac{0.1067 \text{ mol S}}{0.1067} = 1.000 \text{ mol S}$$

$$\frac{0.1601 \text{ mol O}}{0.1067} = 1.500 \text{ mol O}$$

Multiplying each of these values by 2 yields the empirical formula $Na_2S_2O_3$.

Practice Problem 3.50 Solution

The compound contains only carbon and hydrogen and it is 89.94% by mass carbon, so the remaining 10.06% must be hydrogen. One hundred grams of the compound therefore contains 89.94 g carbon and 10.06 g hydrogen. These masses can be converted to moles as follows:

$$89.94 \text{ g C} \times \left(\frac{1 \text{ mol C}}{12.011 \text{ g C}}\right) = 7.489 \text{ mol C}$$

$$10.06 \text{ g H} \times \left(\frac{1 \text{ mol H}}{1.008 \text{ g H}}\right) = 9.980 \text{ mol H}$$

Dividing them both by the smallest value turns the carbon value into an integer.

$$\frac{7.489 \text{ mol C}}{7.489} = 1.000 \text{ mol C}$$

$$\frac{9.980 \text{ mol H}}{7.489} = 1.333 \text{ mol H}$$

Multiplying each of these numbers of moles by 3 yields 3.000 mol C and 3.999 mol H. The empirical formula is therefore C_3H_4. The empirical formula has a molar mass of (3 × 12.011) + (4 × 1.008) = 40.065 g/mol.

The number of empirical formula units in the molecule is found by dividing the molar mass of the compound by the molar mass of the empirical formula (Equation 3.3):

$$\frac{80.2 \text{ g/mol}}{40.065 \text{ g/mol}} = 2.00$$

The molecular formula is therefore twice the empirical formula, or C_6H_8.

Practice Problem 3.51 Solution

You are given the masses of each of the elements in the compound instead of the percent composition, so the first step is to convert each one to moles, using their molar masses as a conversion factor. The total mass of the sample is not needed for the calculation.

$$12.78 \text{ g N} \times \frac{1 \text{ mol N}}{14.007 \text{ g N}} = 0.9124 \text{ mol N}$$

$$347.2 \text{ g I} \times \frac{1 \text{ mol I}}{126.9 \text{ g I}} = 2.736 \text{ mol I}$$

The preliminary chemical formula is $N_{0.9124}I_{2.736}$. Dividing each of these by the lowest value, 0.9124, yields

$$N_{\frac{0.9124}{0.9124}}I_{\frac{2.736}{0.9124}} = N_{1.00}I_{3.00} = NI_3$$

The molar mass of this empirical formula is $14.007\text{ g} + 3(126.9\text{ g}) = 394.7$ grams per mole. This is the same as the molar mass for the compound, so in this case the molecular formula is the same as the empirical formula.

Practice Problem 3.52 Solution

First calculate the mass of carbon and hydrogen in the original sample.

The mass of carbon in the original sample is calculated by inserting the mass of CO_2, 5.39 g, into Equation 3.4:

$$5.39\text{ g }CO_2 \times \frac{1\text{ mol }CO_2}{44.009\text{ g }CO_2} \times \frac{1\text{ mol C}}{1\text{ mol }CO_2} \times \frac{12.011\text{ g C}}{1\text{ mol C}} = 1.47\text{ g C}$$

The mass of hydrogen in the original sample is calculated by inserting the mass of H_2O, 2.48 g, into Equation 3.5:

$$2.48\text{ g }H_2O \times \frac{1\text{ mol }H_2O}{18.015\text{ g }H_2O} \times \frac{2\text{ mol H}}{1\text{ mol }H_2O} \times \frac{1.008\text{ g H}}{1\text{ mole H}} = 0.278\text{ g H}$$

Determine the number of moles of each element in the sample to determine an elemental ratio for the compound:

$$\text{C: } 1.47\text{ g} \times \frac{1\text{ mol}}{12.011\text{ g}} = 0.122\text{ mol}$$

$$\text{H: } 0.278\text{ g} \times \frac{1\text{ mol}}{1.008\text{ g}} = 0.275\text{ mol}$$

This leads to an initial chemical formula of $C_{0.122}H_{0.276}$. Dividing each of these by the lowest mole value leads to

$$C_{\frac{0.122}{0.122}}H_{\frac{0.275}{0.122}} = C_{1.00}H_{2.25}$$

To convert the 2.25 subscript to an integer, multiply both subscripts by 4. This results in an empirical formula of C_4H_9.

The molecular formula can be determined by dividing the molar mass of the compound by the molar mass for the empirical formula to determine how many empirical units are in the actual molecule.

The molar mass of the empirical formula, C_4H_9, is $(4 \times 12.011) + (9 \times 1.008) = 57.116\text{ g/mol}$. The molar mass of the molecule, given in the problem statement, is 114.23 g/mol.

$$\frac{\text{Molar mass of the molecule}}{\text{Molar mass of the empirical formula}} = \frac{114.23\text{ g/mol}}{57.116\text{ g/mol}} = 2.00$$

The molecular formula for 2,2,4-trimethylpentane is therefore twice the empirical formula, or C_8H_{18}.

Practice Problem 3.53 Solution

First, calculate the mass of carbon and hydrogen in the original sample.

The mass of carbon in the original sample is calculated by inserting the mass of CO_2, 8.08 g, into Equation 3.4:

$$8.08\text{ g }CO_2 \times \frac{1\text{ mol }CO_2}{44.009\text{ g }CO_2} \times \frac{1\text{ mol C}}{1\text{ mol }CO_2} \times \frac{12.011\text{ g C}}{1\text{ mol C}} = 2.21\text{ g C}$$

The mass of hydrogen in the original sample is calculated by inserting the mass of H_2O, 4.63 g, into Equation 3.5:

$$4.63\text{ g }H_2O \times \frac{1\text{ mol }H_2O}{18.015\text{ g }H_2O} \times \frac{2\text{ mol H}}{1\text{ mol }H_2O} \times \frac{1.008\text{ g H}}{1\text{ mole H}} = 0.518\text{ g H}$$

Together, the carbon and hydrogen amount to $2.21\text{ g} + 0.518\text{ g} = 2.73\text{ g}$ of the sample weight. Since the compound contains C, H, and N only, the remaining 1.02 g must be nitrogen.

Determine the number of moles of each element in the sample to determine an elemental ratio for the compound:

$$\text{C: } 2.21\text{ g} \times \frac{1\text{ mol}}{12.011\text{ g}} = 0.184\text{ mol}$$

$$\text{H: } 0.518\text{ g} \times \frac{1\text{ mol}}{1.008\text{ g}} = 0.514\text{ mol}$$

$$\text{N: } 1.02\text{ g} \times \frac{1\text{ mol}}{14.007\text{ g}} = 0.0728\text{ mol}$$

This leads to an initial chemical formula of $C_{0.184}H_{0.514}N_{0.0728}$. Dividing each of these by the lowest mole value leads to

$$C_{\frac{0.184}{0.0728}}H_{\frac{0.514}{0.0728}}O_{\frac{0.0728}{0.0728}} = C_{2.53}H_{7.06}O_{1.00}$$

The subscripts are close to $C_{2.5}H_{7.0}N_{1.0}$, so double all the subscripts to make them all integers. This results in an empirical formula of $C_5H_{14}N_2$.

The molar mass for $C_5H_{14}N_2$ is $(5 \times 12.011) + (14 \times 1.008) + (2 \times 14.007) = 102.181\text{ g/mol}$, which is equal to the molar mass of the compound, so the empirical formula is also the molecular formula for cadaverine.

Practice Problem 3.54 Solution

By assuming a 100.0 gram sample of the compound, the percentage composition values become equivalent to the masses in grams of each element:

Carbon: 49.48 g
Nitrogen: 28.85 g
Oxygen: 16.47 g
Hydrogen: 5.19 g

These masses can be converted to moles of each element by dividing by the molar mass of each element.

$$\text{Moles of C} = 49.48\ \text{g} \times \frac{1\ \text{mol}}{12.011\ \text{g}} = 4.120\ \text{mol C}$$

$$\text{Moles of N} = 28.85\ \text{g} \times \frac{1\ \text{mol}}{14.007\ \text{g}} = 2.060\ \text{mol N}$$

$$\text{Moles of O} = 16.47\ \text{g} \times \frac{1\ \text{mol}}{15.999\ \text{g}} = 1.029\ \text{mol O}$$

$$\text{Moles of H} = 5.19\ \text{g} \times \frac{1\ \text{mol}}{1.008\ \text{g}} = 5.15\ \text{mol H}$$

Although the value of 1.029 mol for oxygen seems close enough to 1 that it might be safe to round it to an integer value, the values for the other elements are too far from integer values to treat it as a rounding error. When none of the mole values are integers, divide all of them by the smallest value:

$$\frac{4.120\ \text{mol C}}{1.029} = 4.00\ \text{mol C}$$

$$\frac{2.060\ \text{mol N}}{1.029} = 2.00\ \text{mol N}$$

$$\frac{1.029\ \text{mol O}}{1.029} = 1.00\ \text{mol O}$$

$$\frac{5.15\ \text{mol H}}{1.029} = 5.00\ \text{mol H}$$

In this case, you would have gotten the correct answer if you had rounded the original mole values to the nearest integer, but that is not always the case and the recommended approach is to do the calculation when in doubt and be certain.

The chemical formulas for compounds containing these four elements are typically written in the order of C H N O. The empirical formula is therefore $C_4H_5N_2O$.

To determine the actual molecular formula, divide the molar mass of the compound by the molar mass of the empirical formula, and then multiply each subscript in the empirical formula by the result.

The molar mass of the compound is given as 194.19 g/mol, and the molar mass of the empirical formula is $(4 \times 12.011\ \text{g/mol}) + (5 \times 1.008\ \text{g/mol}) + (2 \times 14.007\ \text{g/mol}) + (1 \times 15.999\ \text{g/mol}) = 97.097\ \text{g/mol}$:

$$\frac{194.19\ \text{g/mol}}{97.097\ \text{g/mol}} = 2.0000$$

The molecular formula therefore includes two formula units of the empirical formula and is $C_8H_{10}N_4O_2$. (This is the molecular formula for caffeine.)

CHAPTER 4

Chemical Reactions and Aqueous Solutions

Tamisclao/Shutterstock

Burning (also known as combustion) is a chemical reaction between a fuel (in this case, the carbon-containing compounds in wood) and oxygen, O_2. In safety matches, a chemical reaction between potassium chlorate, $KClO_3$, in the match head and phosphorus, P, in the striking surface creates a spark to ignite the wood.

Chapter Outline

GOALS

- Identify the parts of a balanced chemical equation, including phases.
- Write complete and balanced chemical equations, based on either chemical symbols or word descriptions.
- Recognize and describe the five basic types of chemical reactions.
- List and describe the driving forces for reactions in aqueous solution.
- Describe and write equations representing the dissociation of ionic compounds upon dissolution in water.
- Define and apply the terms *strong electrolyte, weak electrolyte,* and *nonelectrolyte*.
- Identify compounds as being strong electrolytes, weak electrolytes, or nonelectrolytes from chemical formulas.
- Apply solubility guidelines to predict the formation of a precipitate in reactions of ionic compounds in aqueous solution.
- Write and interpret ionic and net ionic equations for precipitation reactions.
- Predict the products of acid–base reactions in aqueous solution.
- Write and interpret ionic and net ionic equations for acid–base reactions.
- Assign oxidation states to elements within compounds and polyatomic ions.
- Identify redox reactions using oxidation states.
- Define and apply the terms *oxidizing agent* and *reducing agent*.
- Write balanced equations for synthesis and decomposition reactions.
- Apply the activity series to predict the product of single-replacement reactions.

4.1 Chemical Equations

GOALS

- Identify the parts of a balanced chemical equation, including phases.
- Write complete and balanced chemical equations, based on either chemical symbols or word descriptions.

Background Review

Chapter 1 Science and Measurement: Section 1.2—Properties of Matter; Section 1.3—Matter and Energy

Chapter 2 Atoms and the Periodic Table: Section 2.2—The Laws of Chemical Combination

Chapter 3 Compounds and the Mole: Section 3.1—Chemical Formulas

INFORMATION IN A CHEMICAL EQUATION

The substances present at the beginning of a chemical reaction are called **reactants**. Reactants undergo a chemical change, rearranging their bonding to form the **products**. For example, two molecules of hydrogen, H_2, can react with a molecule of oxygen, O_2, to form two molecules of water, H_2O (Figure 4.1). In this reaction, the H atoms start out bonded to other H atoms, and the oxygen, O, atoms start out bonded to other O atoms. In the product, though, all the H atoms are bonded to O atoms, and all the O atoms are bonded to H atoms. Despite this rearrangement, all the same atoms are present before and after the reaction, in accordance with the law of conservation of mass (Section 2.2).

The reaction of H with O to form water can be represented symbolically as the following equation:

$$2\,H_2 + O_2 \rightarrow 2\,H_2O$$

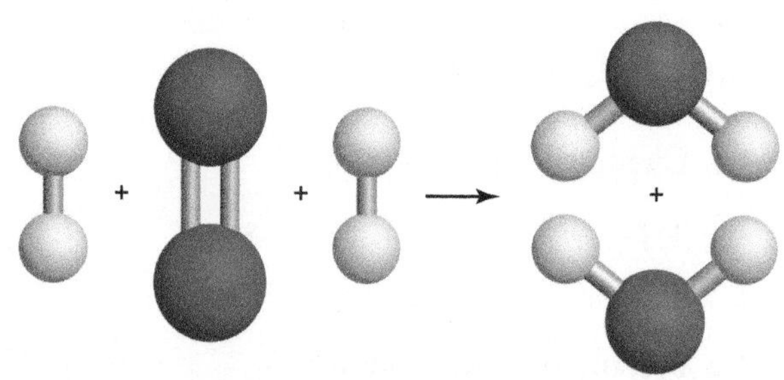

FIGURE 4.1 Reaction of Hydrogen and Oxygen to Form Water

The bonds in the diatomic molecules H_2 and O_2 are broken, and new bonds are formed between H and O atoms.

In a **chemical equation**, the chemical formulas for the reactants are written on the left side of an arrow, and those for the products are written on the right side. Either substance may be written first on each side of an equation. Thus, the equation $O_2 + 2\,H_2 \rightarrow 2\,H_2O$ means the same thing as $2\,H_2 + O_2 \rightarrow 2\,H_2O$.

Chemical equations can tell you *what happens* in the reaction, and, when balanced, they can tell you *in what proportions* the reaction occurs. In the case of $2\,H_2 + O_2 \rightarrow 2\,H_2O$, *what happens* is that hydrogen and oxygen combine to form water. The *proportions* are indicated by **coefficients**.

These *coefficients*—the numbers that are written before the chemical formulas in a chemical equation—tell the relative numbers of formula units, molecules, or moles of reactants and products involved in a reaction. In $2\,H_2 + O_2 \rightarrow 2\,H_2O$, the coefficient 2 indicates that two molecules (or two moles) of H react and two molecules (or two moles) of water are produced.

> In a balanced equation, the absence of a coefficient before a chemical formula implies a coefficient of 1.

Information about the physical **state** of a reactant or product, whether it is present as a solid, liquid, or gas, or in water solution, is provided by placing an abbreviation in parentheses after each reactant and product in the chemical equation. The following abbreviations are used: solid (s), liquid (l), gas (g), and aqueous solution (aq). An **aqueous solution** is a homogeneous mixture of a reactant or product dissolved in water.

The reaction between aqueous magnesium iodide, $MgI_2(aq)$, and aqueous silver nitrate, $AgNO_3(aq)$, is depicted in Figure 4.2 and in the equation

$$MgI_2(aq) + 2\,AgNO_3(aq) \rightarrow 2\,AgI(s) + Mg(NO_3)_2(aq)$$

This balanced equation tells us not only what happens and in what proportions, but also the physical state of each species (reactant or product). That is, 1 mol $MgI_2(aq)$ reacts with 2 mol $AgNO_3(aq)$ to produce 2 mol solid silver iodide, $AgI(s)$, and 1 mol of aqueous magnesium nitrate, $Mg(NO_3)_2(aq)$.

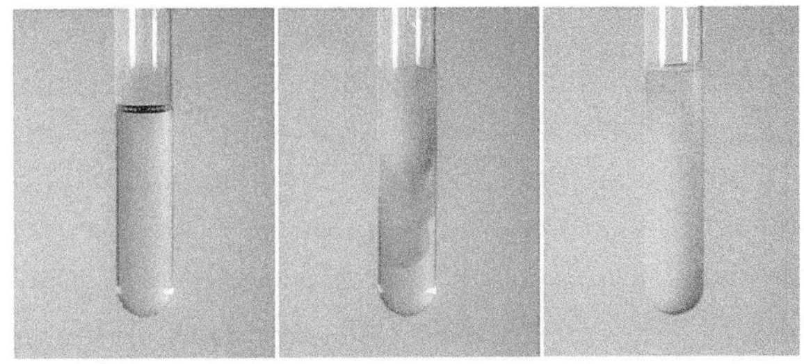

Sara Egner, Macmillan Learning

FIGURE 4.2 The Reaction of Dissolved Magnesium Iodide with Dissolved Silver Nitrate

NOTE: You need to be online to access this video.

Both of the reactants are dissolved in water, but when they are mixed, a chemical reaction occurs that produces $AgI(s)$ and $Mg(NO_3)_2(aq)$.

Reaction conditions are sometimes written above or below the arrow, as in the reaction

$$MgCO_3(s) \xrightarrow{\text{Heat}} MgO(s) + CO_2(g)$$

In this example, applying heat to solid magnesium carbonate, $MgCO_3(s)$, causes it to decompose into solid magnesium oxide, $MgO(s)$, and carbon dioxide gas, $CO_2(g)$. Without the application of heat, the reaction does not occur.

Table 4.1 summarizes some of the information that can be conveyed by a balanced chemical equation.

BALANCING EQUATIONS

Chemical reactions obey the law of conservation of mass, which says that all the atoms present at the beginning of a reaction must be present at the end of the reaction. Writing the reaction for forming water from H_2 and O_2 without coefficients, $H_2 + O_2 \rightarrow H_2O$, violates the law of conservation of mass because there are two O atoms present as reactants at the beginning of the reaction and only one O atom at the end of the reaction. When the coefficients are added, $2\,H_2 + O_2 \rightarrow 2\,H_2O$, however, the number and type of atoms are equal on both sides of the reaction (Figure 4.1).

The word *equation* is related to the word *equal*; an equation must have equal numbers of atoms of each element on each side. A **balanced equation** shows

TABLE 4.1 Information from Chemical Equations

Information	Notation	Example
What happens?	Identity (names and/or formulas) of the reactants and products	Hydrogen, H_2, and oxygen, O_2, react to produce water, H_2O.
In what proportions?	Coefficients placed before the formulas	$2\,H_2 + O_2 \rightarrow 2\,H_2O$
In what physical states?	Abbreviations (s), (l), (g), (aq) included after the formulas	$2\,H_2(g) + O_2(g) \rightarrow 2\,H_2O(l)$
Under what conditions?	Special conditions are written above or below the arrow	$\xrightarrow{\text{Heat}}$

the relative numbers of atoms of each of the elements involved. For each element involved in the reaction, the number of atoms on the left side of the balanced equation is equal to the number of atoms on the right.

The first step in writing a complete and balanced equation for a chemical reaction is to write *correct chemical formulas* (Chapter 3) for all the reactants and products. Next, use *coefficients* to change the numbers of formula units or molecules to get the same number of atoms of each element on the two sides of the equation.

For example, the unbalanced equation for the reaction of sulfur dioxide, SO_2, with O_2 to give sulfur trioxide, SO_3, is

$$SO_2 + O_2 \rightarrow SO_3 \qquad \text{(unbalanced, Figure 4.3a)}$$

With one molecule of each substance, the number of O atoms on the two sides of the equation is unequal, so the equation is unbalanced. The equation can be balanced by inserting the proper coefficients:

$$2\ SO_2 + O_2 \rightarrow 2\ SO_3 \qquad \text{(balanced, Figure 4.3b)}$$

Always check to make sure that the number of atoms of each element on each side of the arrow is equal after you balance the equation. In this case, there are two S atoms and six O atoms on both sides of the equation. You should also check to make sure that the coefficients are in the simplest form and do not contain a common factor. For example, if all the coefficients are even numbers, divide by 2 to obtain the simplest ratios for the proportions.

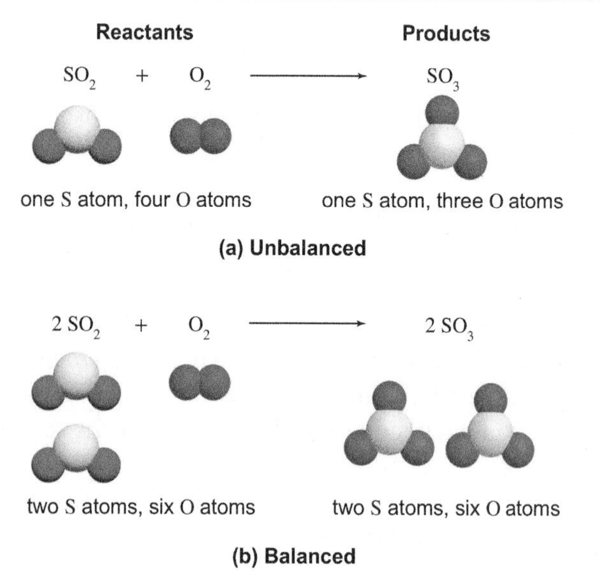

FIGURE 4.3 Reaction of Sulfur Dioxide and Oxygen

SO_2 reacts with diatomic O_2 to form SO_3. In (a), the process is not balanced, resulting in one atom of O not accounted for; (b) shows the balanced process and the correct proportions in which SO_2 and O_2 react to form SO_3.

> When balancing chemical equations, change the coefficients, not the subscripts of the chemical formulas!

Changing the coefficients changes the *amounts* of the compounds involved in the reaction, whereas changing the subscripts changes the *identities* of the compounds involved in the reaction—it changes the chemistry.

There are many different approaches to balancing chemical equations, but all have the same end goal of ensuring that equal numbers of each type of atom appear on both sides of the reaction arrow. The following strategy, which assumes that you already have the correct formulas for the reactants and products, works for most chemical equations, and is demonstrated in Figure 4.4.

1. If polyatomic ions are present as both reactants and products, balance them as a unit and not as separate elements. That is, if sulfate, SO_4^{2-}, is present on both sides of the arrow, balance it as units of SO_4^{2-} and not as separate S and O atoms.
2. Balance elements that appear in only one reactant and one product, reserving any that appear in more than one reactant or more than one product until last. Start by balancing the first element that appears and continue from left to right.
3. Balance any remaining elements. This may require changing previously determined coefficients.
4. Verify the balanced equation.
   - Verify that the number of each type of atom is the same in the reactants and products.

FIGURE 4.4 Video Tutorial: Balancing Chemical Equations

NOTE: You need to be online to access this video.
This video shows how to balance various chemical equations.

- Verify that the coefficients are in the smallest whole-number ratio. That is, if the coefficients have a common factor, divide all the coefficients by this common factor to reduce the ratio. If there is a fractional coefficient, multiply all the coefficients by the denominator of the fraction to get whole numbers.

Example 4.1

Balance the equation for the reaction of barium hydroxide and hydrobromic acid to give barium bromide and water:

$$Ba(OH)_2 + HBr \rightarrow BaBr_2 + H_2O$$

Solution

Step	Result
1. Balance polyatomic ions if present on both sides	Not applicable—hydroxide appears on only one side.
2. Balance elements that appear in only one reactant and product	$1\,Ba(OH)_2 + \_\_HBr \rightarrow 1\,BaBr_2 + \_\_H_2O$ Ba is balanced $1\,Ba(OH)_2 + \_\_HBr \rightarrow 1\,BaBr_2 + 2\,H_2O$ O is balanced $1\,Ba(OH)_2 + 2\,HBr \rightarrow 1\,BaBr_2 + 2\,H_2O$ Br is balanced
3. Balance remaining elements	$1\,Ba(OH)_2 + 2\,HBr \rightarrow 1\,BaBr_2 + 2\,H_2O$ H is balanced
4. Verify balanced equation	$Ba(OH)_2 + 2\,HBr \rightarrow BaBr_2 + 2\,H_2O$ 1 Ba, 2 O, 4 H, and 2 Br on each side Coefficients are in the smallest whole-number ratios.

PRACTICE PROBLEM 4.1

Balance the equation for the reaction of ammonium iodide with lead(II) nitrate to yield ammonium nitrate and lead(II) iodide:

$$NH_4I + Pb(NO_3)_2 \rightarrow NH_4NO_3 + PbI_2$$

Hint: The reactants and products include the same polyatomic ions (ammonium and nitrate). Balance these as units rather than as individual atoms.

When balancing, you may face a situation where an element has an odd number of atoms on one side but an even number on the other. In this case, you could use a fractional coefficient, but it is typically easier to double all existing coefficients.

Example 4.2

Balance this equation.

$$CoCl_2 + Cl_2 \rightarrow CoCl_3$$

Solution

Steps	Result
1. Balance polyatomic ions if present on both sides	Not applicable
2. Balance elements that appear in only one reactant and product	$1\,CoCl_2 + \_\_Cl_2 \rightarrow 1\,CoCl_3$ Co is balanced
3. Balance remaining elements	$2\,CoCl_2 + \_\_Cl_2 \rightarrow 2\,CoCl_3$ Double coefficients (even/odd issue) $2\,CoCl_2 + 1\,Cl_2 \rightarrow 2\,CoCl_3$ Cl is balanced
4. Verify balanced equation	$2\,CoCl_2 + Cl_2 \rightarrow 2\,CoCl_3$ 2 Co and 6 Cl on each side Coefficients are in the smallest whole-number ratios.

PRACTICE PROBLEM 4.2

Balance this equation.

$$C_8H_{18} + O_2 \rightarrow CO_2 + H_2O$$

Hint: Try doubling the existing coefficients if you encounter an odd/even situation during the balancing process.

As step (2) of the strategy used above indicates, if an element appears in more than one substance on the same side of the equation, balance that element last. This often occurs for O and H, though it can occur for other elements as well, as shown in Example 4.3. In Chapter 19, a more systematic approach to balancing this type of chemical equation is presented.

Example 4.3

Balance this equation.

$$KIO_3 + KI + HCl \rightarrow I_2 + H_2O + KCl$$

Solution

Step	Result
1. Balance polyatomic ions if present on both sides	Not applicable
2. Balance elements that appear in only one reactant and product	$1\ KIO_3 + \_KI + \_HCl \rightarrow \_I_2 + 3\ H_2O + \_KCl$ O is balanced $1\ KIO_3 + \_KI + 6\ HCl \rightarrow \_I_2 + 3\ H_2O + \_KCl$ H is balanced $1\ KIO_3 + \_KI + 6\ HCl \rightarrow \_I_2 + 3\ H_2O + 6\ KCl$ Cl is balanced
3. Balance remaining elements	$1\ KIO_3 + 5\ KI + 6\ HCl \rightarrow \_I_2 + 3\ H_2O + 6\ KCl$ K is balanced $1\ KIO_3 + 5\ KI + 6\ HCl \rightarrow 3\ I_2 + 3\ H_2O + 6\ KCl$ I is balanced
4. Verify balanced equation	$KIO_3 + 5\ KI + 6\ HCl \rightarrow 3\ I_2 + 3\ H_2O + 6\ KCl$ 6 K, 6 I, 3 O, 6 H, and 6 Cl on each side Coefficients are in the smallest whole-number ratios.

PRACTICE PROBLEM 4.3

Balance this equation.

$$H_2O + N_2O_5 \rightarrow HNO_3$$

Hint: Save balancing any elements that appear in more than one compound on the same side of the reaction until last.

The interactive activity in Figure 4.5 allows you to visually balance chemical equations. In each case, you must determine the correct coefficients to balance the equation for the reactants and products given.

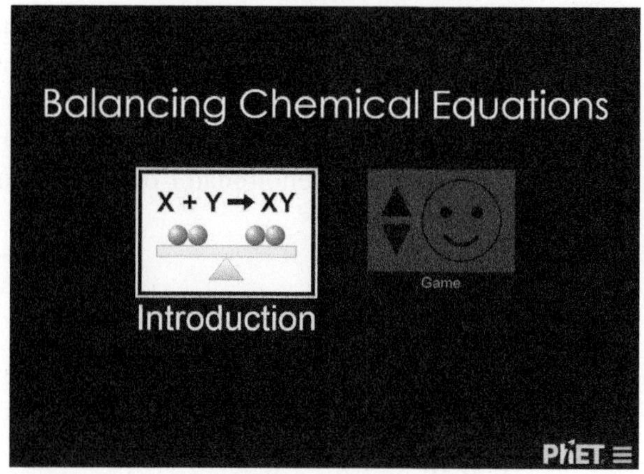

FIGURE 4.5 Balancing Chemical Equations

NOTE: You need to be online to access this activity.

In introduction mode, add the appropriate number of molecules to each reactant and product to balance the chemical equation. After trying the introduction, move on to the game mode. Start at any level of difficulty at which you feel comfortable, but keep trying until you can complete Level 3 successfully.

WORD EQUATIONS

Sometimes you will be asked to write and balance an equation given a description in words, rather than chemical symbols. In these cases, you will need to determine the correct formula for each reactant and product using the naming rules introduced in Chapter 3.

Example 4.4

Write the balanced equation for the reaction of sodium hydroxide with phosphoric acid to produce sodium hydrogen phosphate, Na_2HPO_4, and water.

Solution

The first step is to write the unbalanced equation with the correct formulas for each reactant and product. The sodium ion is Na^+ and hydroxide is OH^-, so the neutral formula is NaOH. The suffix *-ic* in an acid name indicates an *-ate* ion, so phosphoric acid contains the phosphate ion, PO_4^{3-}. To balance a −3 charge, there must be three H^+ ions, so the formula for phosphoric acid is H_3PO_4. The formula for water is H_2O. The unbalanced equation is

$$NaOH + H_3PO_4 \rightarrow Na_2HPO_4 + H_2O$$

Step	Result
1. Balance polyatomic ions if present on both sides	$\_NaOH + 1\ H_3PO_4 \rightarrow 1\ Na_2HPO_4 + \_H_2O$ PO_4^{3-} is balanced
2. Balance elements that appear in only one reactant and product	$2\ NaOH + 1\ H_3PO_4 \rightarrow 1\ Na_2HPO_4 + \_H_2O$ Na is balanced
3. Balance remaining elements	$2\ NaOH + 1\ H_3PO_4 \rightarrow 1\ Na_2HPO_4 + 2\ H_2O$ H, O are balanced
4. Verify balanced equation	$2\ NaOH + H_3PO_4 \rightarrow Na_2HPO_4 + 2\ H_2O$ 2 Na, 6 O, 5 H, and 1 P on each side Coefficients are in the smallest whole-number ratios.

PRACTICE PROBLEM 4.4

Write the balanced equation for the reaction of ammonium sulfide with copper(II) chloride to yield copper(II) sulfide and ammonium chloride.

Hint: Balance polyatomic ions as units and not as individual elements.

SECTION REVIEW

- Chemical equations are symbolic representations of what happens during a chemical reaction.
- Chemical equations must follow the law of conservation of matter and are balanced by placing coefficients in front of the formulas.
- The coefficients in a balanced equation indicate the proportions (ratios) of any one of the reactants or products to any of the other reactants or products in the chemical reaction in terms of the individual atoms, molecules, formula units, or ions, or in terms of the moles of these same individual units.
- The coefficients in a balanced equation multiply each element in the chemical formula.
- The coefficients in a balanced equation are assumed to be 1 if no coefficient is given.
- The physical states of reactants and products are generally included in the balanced equation by specifying solid (s), liquid (l), gas (g), or aqueous solution (aq) in parentheses after each chemical formula in the equation.
- One approach to balancing chemical equations is the following four-step strategy:
    1. Balance polyatomic ions as units if they are present as both reactants and products.
    2. Balance elements that appear in only one reactant and one product.
    3. Balance any remaining elements; resolve odd/even issues by doubling previously determined coefficients.
    4. Verify that the number of each type of atom is the same in the reactants and products and that the coefficients are in the simplest form.

4.2 Types of Chemical Reactions

GOALS

- Recognize and describe the five basic types of chemical reactions.
- List and describe the driving forces for reactions in aqueous solution.

Most of the many thousands of known chemical reactions can be grouped into five different categories, based on patterns observed in the chemical equations. The five categories are synthesis (or combination), decomposition, single-replacement (or single-displacement), double-replacement (or double-displacement), and combustion reactions.

Synthesis or **combination** reactions start with simple reactants that combine to form a single, more complex product. A common example of a synthesis reaction is the rusting of iron metal (Figure 4.6). The iron metal, Fe, reacts with O_2 in the air to form reddish brown iron(III) oxide, Fe_2O_3:

$$4\,Fe(s) + 3\,O_2(g) \rightarrow 2\,Fe_2O_3(s)$$

Decomposition reactions occur when a single reactant breaks down into less complex products. Figure 4.7 shows the decomposition of water, by

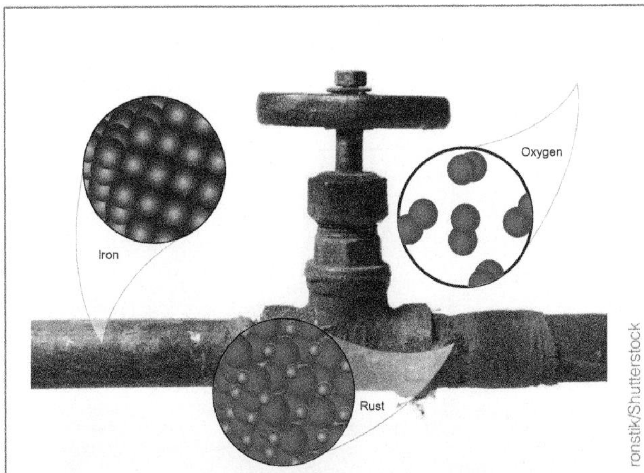

FIGURE 4.6 A Synthesis Reaction: Rust on Iron
Fe metal reacts with O_2 gas to form rust, Fe_2O_3, in a synthesis reaction: $4\,Fe(s) + 3\,O_2(g) \rightarrow 2\,Fe_2O_3(s)$.

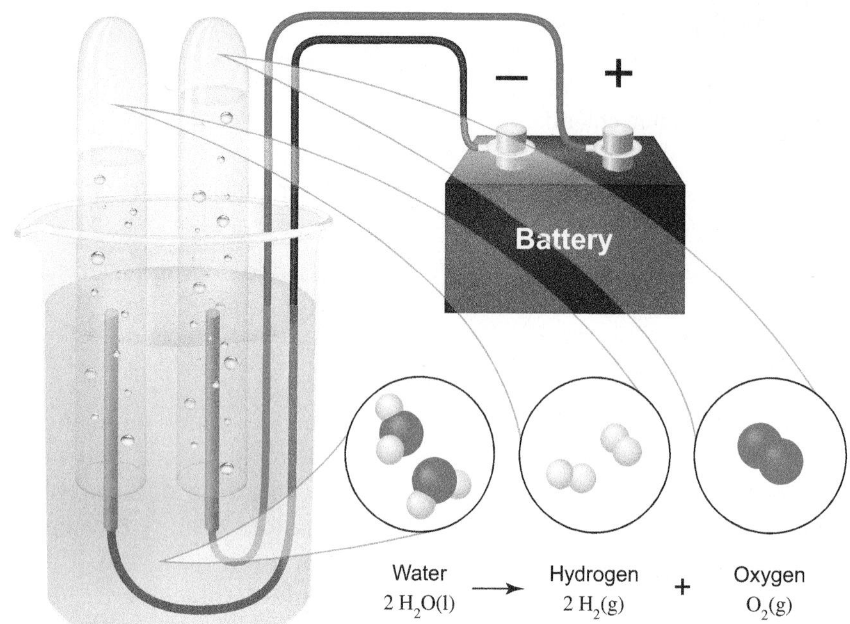

FIGURE 4.7 A Decomposition Reaction: Electrolysis of Water

As electrical current is passed through water, H_2 gas and O_2 gas are formed at the two electrodes. Since H_2O contains twice as many H atoms as O atoms, the decomposition of water generates twice as many moles of H_2 as O_2.

means of electrical energy, into H_2 gas and O_2 gas, as shown in the reaction

$$2\,H_2O(l) \rightarrow 2\,H_2(g) + O_2(g)$$

The video in Figure 4.8 shows the thermal decomposition of potassium chlorate, $KClO_3$, into potassium chloride, KCl, and O_2, as shown in the reaction below.

$$2\,KClO_3(s) \rightarrow 2\,KCl(s) + 3\,O_2(g)$$

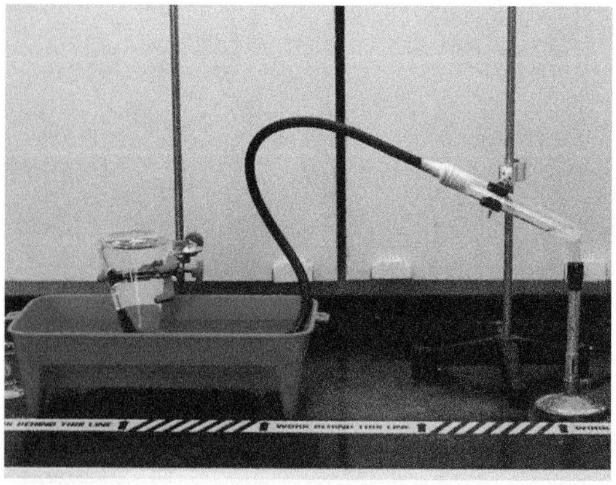

FIGURE 4.8 The Decomposition of Potassium Chlorate

NOTE: You need to be online to access this video.

When heated, $KClO_3$ decomposes into KCl and O_2.

A **single-replacement** reaction (also known as a **single-displacement** or a **displacement** reaction) occurs when an element reacts with a compound and displaces one of the elements in that compound, producing a new compound and a new element. In the reaction of zinc metal, Zn, with hydrochloric acid, HCl (Figure 4.9 and Figure 4.10), Zn replaces H in the compound:

$$Zn(s) + 2\,HCl(aq) \rightarrow ZnCl_2(aq) + H_2(g)$$

In a **double-replacement** reaction (also known as a **double-displacement** or **metathesis** reaction), two ionic compounds exchange ions to form two new compounds. An example is the reaction of lead(II)

FIGURE 4.9 Video: Reaction of Zn Metal with HCl

NOTE: You need to be online to access this video.

The reaction of a metal with an acid is a single-replacement reaction.

FIGURE 4.10 Molecular View of the Reaction of Zinc with Hydrochloric Acid

This image shows the molecular view of the video in Figure 4.9.

nitrate, $Pb(NO_3)_2$, with potassium iodide, KI (as shown in the reaction below), which is demonstrated in Figure 4.11. The molecular view of the reaction is shown in Figure 4.12.

$$2\ KI(aq) + Pb(NO_3)_2(aq) \rightarrow PbI_2(s) + 2\ KNO_3(aq)$$

An **acid** is a type of compound usually written with H at the beginning of its formula (Chapter 3). Similarly, a **base** is a type of compound often written with OH at the end of its formula because many bases are hydroxide compounds. The reaction of an acid and a base to form a salt and water is a type of double-replacement reaction:

$$HCl(aq) + NaOH(aq) \rightarrow NaCl(aq) + H_2O(l)$$
$$H_2SO_4(aq) + 2\ KOH(aq) \rightarrow K_2SO_4(aq) + 2\ H_2O(l)$$

In these examples, notice that the ions swap partners, and the H^+ ion from the acid combines with

FIGURE 4.11 A Double-Replacement Reaction

NOTE: You need to be online to access this video.

In this video demonstration, KI(aq) is mixed with $Pb(NO_3)_2(aq)$, forming aqueous potassium nitrate, $KNO_3(aq)$, and solid lead(II) iodide, $PbI_2(s)$.

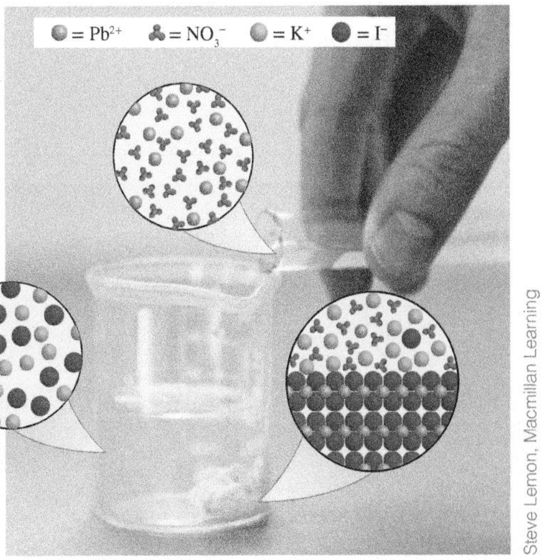

FIGURE 4.12 Molecular View of the Reaction of KI with $Pb(NO_3)_2$

This image gives a molecular view of the double-replacement reaction from Figure 4.11. Notice the exchange of ions.

the OH^- ion from the base to form water, H_2O. The remaining two ions combine to form a salt. Chemists use the term *salt* to refer to ionic compounds other than just sodium chloride, NaCl (e.g., in the second equation on the previous page, K_2SO_4 is the salt). A **salt** is any ionic compound that does not contain H^+ or OH^-. Since most ionic compounds are salts, they are sometimes treated as synonyms. In this text, however, salts are treated as a subset of ionic compounds.

The final reaction type, **combustion**, is the rapid combination of a substance with oxygen. A particularly important subset of combustion reactions involves the reaction of oxygen with **hydrocarbon** fuels. Hydrocarbons are compounds composed of carbon and hydrogen and react with excess oxygen to produce carbon dioxide and water.

$$C_3H_8(g) + 5\,O_2(g) \rightarrow 3\,CO_2(g) + 4\,H_2O(l)$$

Figure 4.13 shows that oxygen is needed to sustain the combustion reaction of candle wax. Paraffin, a human-made wax, is a mixture of various hydrocarbons, whereas natural waxes contain small amounts of oxygen as well. The reactant shown in this reaction is a typical molecule found in paraffin:

$$2\,C_{24}H_{50}(s) + 73\,O_2 \rightarrow 48\,CO_2(g) + 50\,H_2O(l)$$

The five reaction types are summarized here and in Table 4.2.

- In a *synthesis* reaction, simple substances combine to form more complex substances.
- In a *decomposition* reaction, more complex substances break down into simpler ones.
- In a *single-replacement* reaction, an element displaces another element within a compound.

FIGURE 4.13 A Combustion Reaction

NOTE: You need to be online to access this video.
When oxygen is unavailable to sustain a combustion reaction, the reaction stops.

TABLE 4.2 Summary of Reaction Types

Reaction Type	Generic Formula	Examples
Synthesis	$A + B \rightarrow AB$	$4\,Fe(s) + 3\,O_2(g) \rightarrow 2\,Fe_2O_3(s)$
Decomposition	$AB \rightarrow A + B$	$2\,H_2O(l) \rightarrow 2\,H_2(g) + O_2(g)$ $2\,KClO_3(s) \rightarrow 2\,KCl(s) + 3\,O_2(g)$
Single-replacement	$A + BC \rightarrow AC + B$	$Zn(s) + 2\,HCl(aq) \rightarrow ZnCl_2(aq) + H_2(g)$
Double-replacement	$AB + CD \rightarrow AD + CB$	$2\,KI(aq) + Pb(NO_3)_2(aq) \rightarrow PbI_2(s) + 2\,KNO_3(aq)$ $HBr(aq) + KOH(aq) \rightarrow KBr(aq) + H_2O(l)$
Combustion	$C_xH_y + O_2 \rightarrow CO_2 + H_2O$	$C_3H_8(g) + 5\,O_2(g) \rightarrow 3\,CO_2(g) + 4\,H_2O(l)$

- In a *double-replacement* reaction, ionic compounds exchange anions.
- In a *combustion* reaction, a substance, often referred to as a fuel, rapidly combines with oxygen, generally producing carbon dioxide and water.

Example 4.5

Identify the reaction type for each of the following equations.

a. $2\,H_2(g) + O_2(g) \rightarrow 2\,H_2O(l)$

b. $MgI_2(aq) + 2\,AgNO_3(aq) \rightarrow 2\,AgI(s) + Mg(NO_3)_2(aq)$

c. $CaCO_3(s) \rightarrow CaO(s) + CO_2(g)$

d. $2\,C_8H_{18}(l) + 25\,O_2(g) \rightarrow 16\,CO_2(g) + 18\,H_2O(l)$

Solution

Refer to Table 4.2 to match the patterns in the reactions to the generic formulas.

a. Two reactants form a single, more complex product, so this is a *synthesis* reaction.

b. Two ionic compounds exchange anions, so this is a *double-replacement* reaction.

c. A single substance breaks down into two simpler substances, so this a *decomposition* reaction.

d. A hydrocarbon reacts with oxygen to produce carbon dioxide and water, so this is a *combustion* reaction.

PRACTICE PROBLEM 4.5

Identify the reaction type for each of the following equations.

a. $2\,HBr(aq) + Ba(OH)_2(aq) \rightarrow BaBr_2(aq) + 2\,H_2O(l)$

b. $2\,CoCl_2(aq) + Cl_2(g) \rightarrow 2\,CoCl_3(aq)$

c. $2\,NH_4I(aq) + Pb(NO_3)_2(aq) \rightarrow 2\,NH_4NO_3(aq) + PbI_2(s)$

d. $(NH_4)_2S(aq) + CuCl_2(aq) \rightarrow CuS(s) + 2\,NH_4Cl(aq)$

e. $2\,NaOH(aq) + H_3PO_4(aq) \rightarrow Na_2HPO_4(aq) + 2\,H_2O(l)$

f. $H_2O(l) + N_2O_5(g) \rightarrow 2\,HNO_3(aq)$

g. $CuSO_4(aq) + Zn(s) \rightarrow ZnSO_4(aq) + Cu(s)$

h. $NH_4NO_3(s) \rightarrow N_2O(g) + 2\,H_2O(l)$

Hint: Compare the number of reactants on each side of the arrow with the pattern in Table 4.2 to rule out some of the reaction types and rule in others.

DRIVING FORCES FOR REACTIONS IN AQUEOUS SOLUTIONS

Reactions occur spontaneously due to a combination of changes in heat energy (enthalpy) and randomness (entropy), which you will learn about in Chapter 18. Certain patterns of reactants and products tend to be associated with spontaneous reactions and can be classified by their **driving force**. Driving forces are associated with the formation of stable, lower-energy products. Here in Chapter 4, three driving forces that are important for reactions in aqueous solutions are investigated—namely, precipitation, neutralization, and oxidation–reduction. Recognizing the driving forces helps chemists predict when a reaction will occur.

1. Double-replacement reactions that result in the formation of a lower-energy solid ionic compound are called **precipitation** reactions. The solid product is called a **precipitate**, and its formation is the driving force of the reaction.
2. The reaction of an acid and a base is called an **acid–base** reaction. **Neutralization** is the driving force in these reactions, where the products are a salt and often water.
3. Single-replacement, synthesis, and decomposition reactions involve the transfer of electrons to form lower-energy products. This driving force is known as **oxidation–reduction** or **redox**. Oxidation–reduction is discussed in more detail in Section 4.6.

Example 4.6

Identify the driving force for each of the following reactions.

a. $2\,H_2(g) + O_2(g) \rightarrow 2\,H_2O(l)$

b. $MgI_2(aq) + 2\,AgNO_3(aq) \rightarrow 2\,AgI(s) + Mg(NO_3)_2(aq)$

c. $CaCO_3(s) \rightarrow CaO(s) + CO_2(g)$

Solution

First, identify the reaction type and then refer to the descriptions of the three driving forces to determine which is the best fit.

a. Water is a product, but this is *not* a double-replacement reaction. It is a *synthesis* reaction (simple reactants combine to form a single, more complex product). The driving force, therefore, is the transfer of electrons, or *oxidation–reduction*.

b. This is a *double-replacement* reaction (two ionic compounds exchange ions to form two new compounds) that produces a solid product. Thus, *precipitation* is the driving force.

c. This *decomposition* reaction (a single substance breaks down into two simpler substances) is also an *oxidation–reduction* reaction.

PRACTICE PROBLEM 4.6

Identify the driving force for each of the following reactions.

a. $2\,HBr(aq) + Ba(OH)_2(aq) \rightarrow BaBr_2(aq) + 2\,H_2O(l)$

b. $2\,CoCl_2(aq) + Cl_2(g) \rightarrow 2\,CoCl_3(aq)$

c. $2\,NH_4I(aq) + Pb(NO_3)_2(aq) \rightarrow 2\,NH_4NO_3(aq) + PbI_2(s)$

d. $(NH_4)_2S(aq) + CuCl_2(aq) \rightarrow CuS(s) + 2\,NH_4Cl(aq)$

e. $2\,NaOH(aq) + H_3PO_4(aq) \rightarrow Na_2HPO_4(aq) + 2\,H_2O(l)$

f. $H_2O(l) + N_2O_5(g) \rightarrow 2\,HNO_3(aq)$

g. $CuSO_4(aq) + Zn(s) \rightarrow ZnSO_4(aq) + Cu(s)$

h. $NH_4NO_3(s) \rightarrow N_2O(g) + 2\,H_2O(l)$

Hint: First identify the reaction type and then refer to the descriptions of the three driving forces to determine which is the best fit.

SECTION REVIEW

- Typical reaction types can be determined from patterns observed in chemical equations.
- Synthesis reactions follow this pattern: $A + B \rightarrow AB$.
- Decomposition reactions follow this pattern: $AB \rightarrow A + B$.
- Single-replacement reactions follow this pattern: $A + BC \rightarrow AC + B$.
- Double-replacement reactions follow this pattern: $AB + CD \rightarrow AD + CB$.
- Combustion reactions follow this pattern: $C_xH_y + O_2 \rightarrow CO_2 + H_2O$.

- A reaction can also be classified by its driving force.
- The driving force for a double-replacement reaction with a solid product is precipitation.
- The driving force for a double-replacement reaction between an acid and a base is neutralization.
- The driving force for synthesis, decomposition, and single-replacement reactions is oxidation–reduction.

4.3 Compounds in Aqueous Solution

GOALS

- Describe and write equations representing the dissociation of ionic compounds upon dissolution in water.
- Identify compounds as being strong electrolytes, weak electrolytes, or nonelectrolytes from chemical formulas.

Background Review

Chapter 3 Compounds and the Mole:
Section 3.2—Naming Binary Covalent Compounds;
Section 3.3—Formulas for Ionic Compounds;
Section 3.4—Naming Ionic Compounds;
Section 3.5—Naming Acids.

A solid compound that readily dissolves in water is **soluble** in water, whereas a compound that remains solid when mixed with water is said to be **insoluble** in water. For reactions that occur in aqueous solution, the physical state gives you information about the solubility of the compound. That is, the notation NaCl(aq) tells you not only that sodium chloride has been mixed with water, but that it has dissolved. In contrast, an insoluble compound, such as silver chloride, will remain solid and undissolved, even after being mixed with water, as indicated by the notation AgCl(s).

IONIC COMPOUNDS IN WATER

Many reactions occur when compounds are together in aqueous solution that would not occur if you were to simply mix the dry reactants together. For example, if solid magnesium iodide, $MgI_2(s)$, and solid silver nitrate, $AgNO_3(s)$, were mixed together, there would be no reaction. However, mixing aqueous solutions of magnesium iodide, $MgI_2(aq)$, and silver nitrate, $AgNO_3(aq)$, produces solid silver iodide, AgI(s), and aqueous magnesium nitrate, $Mg(NO_3)_2(aq)$:

$$MgI_2(aq) + 2\,AgNO_3(aq) \rightarrow 2\,AgI(s) + Mg(NO_3)_2(aq)$$

One reason that reactions occur more readily in solution is that dissolved reactant particles are more likely to bump into each other. The particles in solids are held in fixed position and cannot move past one another, whereas particles in liquids (and solutions) are able to move and potentially bump into each other. A second, and more important, reason relates to how ionic compounds and molecules behave when they dissolve in water.

Ionic compounds (Section 3.3 and Section 3.4) are composed of cations and anions organized in a three-dimensional lattice. When ionic compounds dissolve in water, the ions **dissociate** into individual ions and disperse among the water molecules (Section 13.1). NaCl, when dissolved in water, forms separate Na^+ and Cl^- ions surrounded by water molecules. Ions that are surrounded by water molecules are referred to as **hydrated ions** (Figure 4.14). In fact, the notation (aq) in the formula NaCl(aq) implies the presence of $Na^+(aq)$ and $Cl^-(aq)$ ions dissolved in water:

$$NaCl(s) \xrightarrow{H_2O} NaCl(aq) \rightarrow Na^+(aq) + Cl^-(aq)$$

This is true for aqueous solutions of any ionic compound. The dissolved form of the compound is present as dissociated ions.

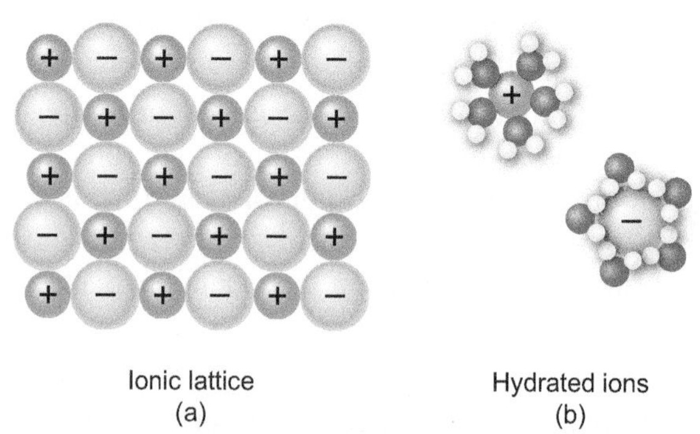

FIGURE 4.14 Hydrated Ions

(a) The ions in a solid ionic compound are arranged in a lattice. (b) When dissolved in water, the individual ions become hydrated (surrounded by water molecules).

Example 4.7

Write chemical equations showing the dissociation of $MgSO_4(aq)$ and $Pb(NO_3)_2(aq)$.

Solution

These ionic compounds dissociate in water to produce separate, hydrated ions:

$$MgSO_4(aq) \rightarrow Mg^{2+}(aq) + SO_4^{2-}(aq)$$
$$Pb(NO_3)_2(aq) \rightarrow Pb^{2+}(aq) + 2\ NO_3^-(aq)$$

Note the use of the coefficient to indicate that two units of nitrate ion are present per unit of lead(II) ion in the balanced equation.

PRACTICE PROBLEM 4.7

Write chemical equations showing the dissociation of the following aqueous ionic compounds.

a. $KOH(aq)$
b. $CaCl_2(aq)$
c. $Na_3PO_4(aq)$

Hint: Refer to Section 3.3 for the charges on monatomic and polyatomic ions. Use coefficients to indicate the number of each ion in the compound.

Solutions formed from ionic compounds can conduct electricity due to the presence of the dissociated ions, which are charged and mobile. Any substance that dissolves in water to produce a solution that conducts electricity is called an **electrolyte**. Ionic compounds are known as **strong electrolytes** because they dissociate 100% to produce solutions that conduct electricity readily. Figure 4.15 compares the mobile ions in an aqueous solution of an ionic compound with the fixed ions in a solid ionic compound in the presence of charged electrodes.

> Aqueous ionic compounds are strong electrolytes.

Not all ionic compounds are soluble in water. For insoluble ionic compounds, the attractive forces between the ions (the ionic bonds) are stronger than the potential interactions between the ions and water molecules. Section 4.4 presents guidelines that allow you to predict the solubility of ionic compounds.

MOLECULAR COMPOUNDS IN WATER

Compounds that dissolve to form solutions that do not conduct electricity are known as **nonelectrolytes**. Nonelectrolytes include molecular compounds like sugars (sucrose, glucose, fructose), which dissolve as molecules, as shown in Figure 4.16. The solution process is discussed more thoroughly in Section 13.1.

Acids, by contrast, are a type of molecular compound that **ionize** in water when dissolved. The ionization of HCl is as follows:

$$HCl(aq) \rightarrow H^+(aq) + Cl^-(aq)$$

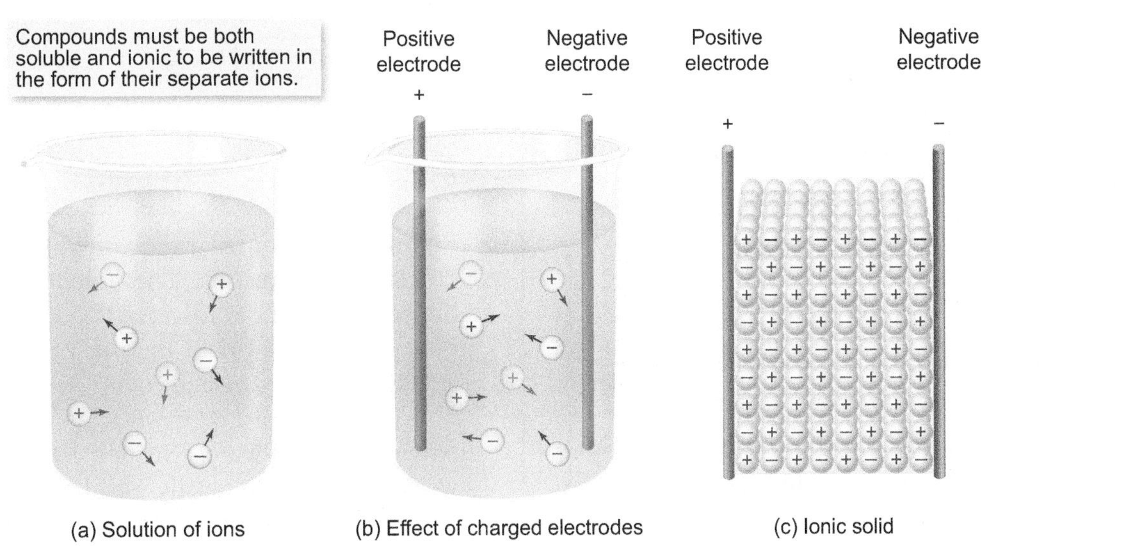

FIGURE 4.15 Mobility of Ions

(a) Ions in dilute solutions are free to move independently of other ions. In the absence of electrodes, they move in random directions. (b) Under the influence of the charges on electrodes, the ions move toward the electrode of opposite charge—that is, cations move toward the negative electrode and anions move toward the positive electrode. (c) In contrast, ions in solids cannot move, even if charged electrodes are present. In the lattice, each cation is surrounded by anions and each anion is surrounded by cations, so the only motion possible is vibration.

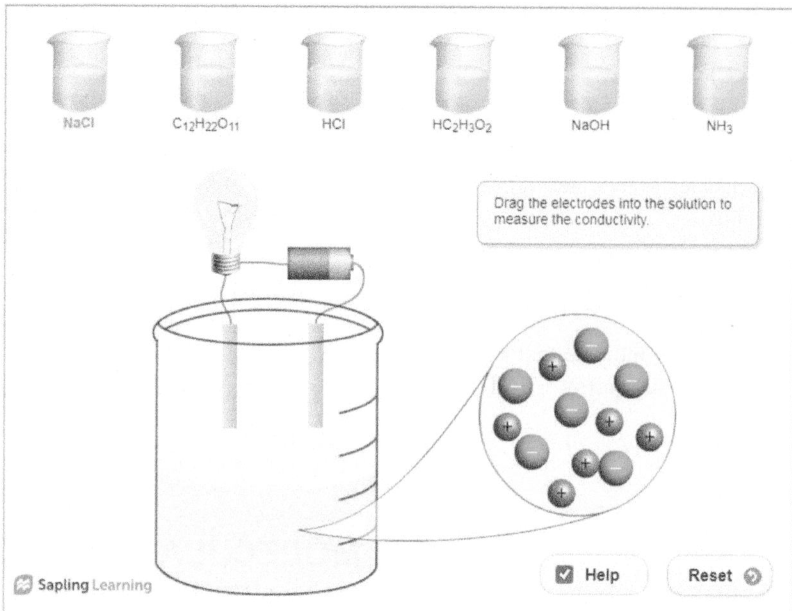

FIGURE 4.16 Conductivity Lab Simulation Activity

NOTE: You need to be online to access this activity.

Use the chemical formulas to predict if each compound is a strong electrolyte, a weak electrolyte, or a nonelectrolyte. Test your predictions by running the simulation, which tests the electrical properties of the aqueous solutions of the compounds.

EVERYDAY CONNECTION

You have probably heard that water conducts electricity, which is why you should *never* swim during a thunderstorm or use a hairdryer in the bathtub.

But how can this be true when H_2O is a molecular compound? The answer is that pool water and tap water are not pure H_2O. Even bottled and filtered water typically contains enough dissolved minerals to result in a weak electrolyte solution. In contrast, laboratory-grade purified water, prepared by distillation and/or deionization, is typically 100 to 1000 times less conductive than tap water.

TABLE 4.3 Strong Acids

Name	Formula	Ions
Hydrochloric acid	HCl	$H^+(aq) + Cl^-(aq)$
Hydrobromic acid	HBr	$H^+(aq) + Br^-(aq)$
Hydroiodic acid	HI	$H^+(aq) + I^-(aq)$
Nitric acid	HNO_3	$H^+(aq) + NO_3^-(aq)$
Perchloric acid	$HClO_4$	$H^+(aq) + ClO_4^-(aq)$
Chloric acid*	$HClO_3$	$H^+(aq) + ClO_3^-(aq)$
Sulfuric acid	H_2SO_4	$H^+(aq) + HSO_4^-(aq)$

*Chloric acid, $HClO_3$, is considered a weak acid in some sources.

Strong acids ionize 100% in water to form strong electrolyte solutions. The names and formulas of the seven strong acids are listed in Table 4.3. You may find it helpful to memorize the seven strong acids.

All other acids are *weak* acids. **Weak acids** ionize only partially in water (Section 19.2), so solutions of weak acids contain mostly intact molecules and only a few ions. As a result, solutions of weak acids conduct electricity only slightly, and they are known as **weak electrolytes**. The terms *strong* and *weak* refer to the behavior of the compound in water and not to the concentration of the solution. That is, it is possible to have a concentrated solution of a weak acid and a dilute solution of a strong acid.

TABLE 4.4 Electrolytic Properties of Various Types of Compounds

Solution Type	Compound Type	Examples
Strong electrolyte	Ionic (salts)	$NaCl(aq)$, $K_2SO_4(aq)$
	Ionic (strong bases)	$NaOH(aq)$, $KOH(aq)$
	Strong acid	$HCl(aq)$, $HNO_3(aq)$
Weak electrolyte	Weak acid	$HNO_2(aq)$, $H_3PO_4(aq)$
	Weak base	$NH_3(aq)$, $CH_3NH_2(aq)$
Nonelectrolyte	Molecular (most)	$C_6H_{12}O_6(aq)$ and other sugars

> Strong acids ionize 100% in water, regardless of their concentrations. Weak acids ionize to a small extent, typically less than 1%, again, regardless of the concentration of the weak acid.

Strong bases are *ionic* compounds—specifically, soluble hydroxides—that dissociate 100%. There are also *molecular* compounds that are **weak bases**, such as ammonia, NH_3. Weak bases react with water to a small extent to produce hydroxide ions in solution and are another example of weak electrolytes.

> Strong acids and strong bases are strong electrolytes; weak acids and weak bases are weak electrolytes, regardless of their concentrations.

The ability of various types of compounds to form electrolyte solutions is summarized in Table 4.4.

Figure 4.16 gives you an opportunity to explore different compounds to determine if they are strong electrolytes, weak electrolytes, or nonelectrolytes.

Example 4.8

Classify the following water-soluble substances as strong electrolytes, weak electrolytes, or nonelectrolytes in aqueous solution.

a. $CaCl_2$
b. $C_6H_{12}O_6$
c. HNO_2
d. NH_3 (weak base)
e. KOH
f. HBr

Solution

Soluble ionic compounds dissociate 100% to form hydrated ions and are strong electrolytes. Molecular compounds dissolve as molecules and are nonelectrolytes, unless they are acids or weak bases. Strong acids ionize 100% and are strong electrolytes, whereas weak acids ionize to a very small extent and are weak electrolytes. Weak bases are also weak electrolytes.

a. $CaCl_2$ consists of a metal and a nonmetal, so it is an ionic compound and a strong electrolyte.
b. $C_6H_{12}O_6$ does not contain any metal elements or the ammonium ion, so it is a molecular compound. Additionally, it is neither an acid nor a base, so it is a nonelectrolyte.
c. HNO_2 is an acid. It is not one of the seven strong acids listed in Table 4.3, so it must be a weak acid. Weak acids are weak electrolytes.
d. NH_3 is a weak base. Weak bases are weak electrolytes.
e. KOH contains a metal with a polyatomic ion, so it an ionic compound and a strong electrolyte. It is also a strong base.
f. HBr is a strong acid. Strong acids are strong electrolytes.

PRACTICE PROBLEM 4.8

Classify the following water-soluble substances as strong electrolytes, weak electrolytes, or nonelectrolytes.

a. Na_2SO_4
b. NaOH
c. C_2H_6O
d. $Pb(NO_3)_2$
e. HNO_3
f. H_3PO_4

Hint: Start by determining if the compound is ionic or molecular (recall that ionic compounds usually contain a metal). Also, consider which compounds are acids and whether those acids are strong or weak (Table 4.3). Finally, refer to the summary of electrolyte types in Table 4.4.

SECTION REVIEW

- Ionic compounds dissociate 100% when dissolved in water to produce hydrated ions.
- Strong bases are ionic compounds containing the hydroxide ion and dissociate 100%.
- Soluble molecular compounds may or may not ionize in solution.
  - Strong acids ionize in water 100%.
  - Weak acids and weak bases dissolve mainly as molecules but ionize to a very small extent.
  - Other molecular compounds (e.g., sugars) do not ionize.

- Solutions containing dissociated ions can conduct electricity and are called electrolyte solutions.
  - Ionic compounds and strong acids are strong electrolytes.
  - Weak acids and weak bases are weak electrolytes.
  - Molecular compounds that are neither acids nor bases are nonelectrolytes.

4.4 Precipitation Reactions

GOALS

- Apply solubility guidelines to predict the formation of a precipitate in reactions of ionic compounds in aqueous solution.
- Write and interpret ionic and net ionic equations for precipitation reactions.

PREDICTING THE SOLUBILITY OF IONIC COMPOUNDS

Ionic compounds that readily dissolve in water are said to be soluble, whereas ionic compounds that do *not* readily dissolve in water are said to be insoluble. Even *insoluble* ionic compounds dissolve to some degree, as is discussed in detail in Section 17.3, but the amount they dissolve is so small that it can be ignored for the purposes of this chapter.

You can look up the solubility of common ionic compounds in Table 4.5. To use the table, find the cation in the first column and the anion in the first row, then find the cell where they intersect. For example, sodium sulfide, Na_2S, is soluble because the cell where the Na^+ row meets the S^{2-} column contains the letter s.

The solubilities depicted in Table 4.5 can be summarized in the following **solubility guidelines**.

Solubility Guidelines

1. Compounds of group 1 elements (Li^+, Na^+, K^+, Rb^+, Cs^+, and Fr^+) or ammonium (NH_4^+) are soluble.
2. Nitrates (NO_3^-), chlorates (ClO_3^-), perchlorates (ClO_4^-), and acetates ($C_2H_3O_2^-$) are soluble.
3. Chlorides (Cl^-), bromides (Br^-), and iodides (I^-) are soluble, except for those of Ag^+, Pb^{2+}, and Hg_2^{2+}.
4. Except for compounds of the cations in guideline 1, carbonates (CO_3^{2-}), sulfites (SO_3^{2-}), phosphates (PO_4^{3-}), and chromates (CrO_4^{2-}) are *in*soluble.
5. With the exception of the ions in guideline 1 and the barium ion (Ba^{2+}), hydroxides (OH^-) and sulfides (S^{2-}) are *in*soluble.
6. With the exception of the ions in guideline 2, silver (Ag^+), mercury (Hg_2^{2+}), and lead (Pb^{2+}) salts are *in*soluble.
7. With the exception of compounds of calcium (Ca^{2+}), strontium (Sr^{2+}), barium (Ba^{2+}), and the ions listed in guideline 6, all sulfates are soluble.

You do not necessarily need to memorize all of these solubility guidelines, but remembering the first two may save you time when working problems involving precipitation.

TABLE 4.5 Solubility Chart

	NO_3^- ClO_3^- ClO_4^- $C_2H_3O_2^-$	Cl^- Br^- I^-	SO_4^{2-}	CO_3^{2-} SO_3^{2-} PO_4^{3-} CrO_4^{2-}	S^{2-}	OH^-
Li^+, Na^+, K^+, NH_4^+	s	s	s	s	s	s
Mg^{2+}	s	s	s	i	d	i
Ca^{2+}, Sr^{2+}	s	s	i	i	s	ss
Ba^{2+}	s	s	i	i	s	s
Ni^{2+}, Fe^{2+}, Zn^{2+}, Cu^{2+}	s	s	s	i	i	i
Ag^+	s	i	ss	i	i	i
Hg_2^{2+}	s	i	i	i	i	i
Pb^{2+}	s	ss-i	i	i	i	i

s = soluble (greater than about 1 g solute/100 g of water)
ss = slightly soluble (approximately 0.1 – 1 g solute/100 g of water)
i = insoluble (less than about 0.1 g solute/100 g of water)
d = decomposes in water

Example 4.9

Are the following salts soluble or insoluble in water?

a. Na_3PO_4
b. $MgSO_4$
c. Ag_2S

Solution

Start by identifying the ions present in the compound and then find those ions in Table 4.5 or the solubility guidelines.

a. Soluble. According to guideline 1, ionic compounds containing Na^+ ions are soluble.
b. Soluble. According to guideline 7, sulfates are soluble. There are exceptions (Ca^{2+}, Sr^{2+}, Ba^{2+}, Ag^+, $Hg_2{}^{2+}$, and Pb^{2+}), but Mg^{2+} is not one of them.
c. Insoluble. According to guideline 5, salts containing the sulfide ion are insoluble, unless the cation is Ba^{2+} or one of those listed in guideline 1.

PRACTICE PROBLEM 4.9

Are the following salts soluble or insoluble in water?

a. $BaCl_2$
b. $MgCO_3$
c. $Pb(NO_3)_2$

Hint: Start by identifying the ions present in the compound and then find those ions in Table 4.5 or the solubility guidelines.

Example 4.10

Predict the solubility of the following ionic compounds.

a. $AgNO_3$
b. $PbSO_4$
c. KOH
d. $PbCl_2$

Solution

Start by identifying the ions present in the compound and then find those ions in Table 4.5 or the solubility guidelines.

a. Soluble. All ionic compounds containing the nitrate ion are soluble (guideline 2).
b. Soluble. Although most ionic compounds containing Pb^{2+} are *in*soluble, most ionic compounds containing the sulfate ion are soluble (guidelines 3, 6, and 7).
c. Soluble. All ionic compounds containing alkali metal ions such as K^+ are soluble (guideline 1).
d. Insoluble. Although most chloride salts are soluble, Pb^{2+} is an exception (guideline 3).

PRACTICE PROBLEM 4.10

Predict the solubility of the following salts.

a. $Ba(ClO_4)_2$
b. $CaSO_4$
c. $Mg(OH)_2$
d. $CaCrO_4$

Hint: Start by identifying the ions present in the compound and then find those ions in Table 4.5 or the solubility guidelines.

PREDICTING THE FORMATION OF A PRECIPITATE

Precipitation reactions are double-replacement reactions that occur when solutions of two ionic compounds are mixed, thus allowing a new, insoluble ionic compound to form. Examples include the reaction of magnesium iodide, MgI_2, and silver nitrate, $AgNO_3$ (Figure 4.2), and the reaction of potassium iodide, KI, and lead(II) nitrate, $Pb(NO_3)_2$ (Figure 4.11 and Figure 4.12). Figure 4.17 shows the results of mixing various ionic compounds. In some cases, you will notice a cloudy substance forms, which is the precipitate. In other cases, no reaction occurs.

$$AgNO_3(aq) + NaCl(aq) \rightarrow AgCl(s) + NaNO_3(aq)$$

EVERYDAY CONNECTION

Stalactites and stalagmites in caves, such as those shown below, form as the result of a chemical reaction that produces insoluble calcium carbonate, $CaCO_3(s)$. $CaCO_3(s)$ is also the primary ingredient in some types of chalk.

Beautiful landscape/Shutterstock

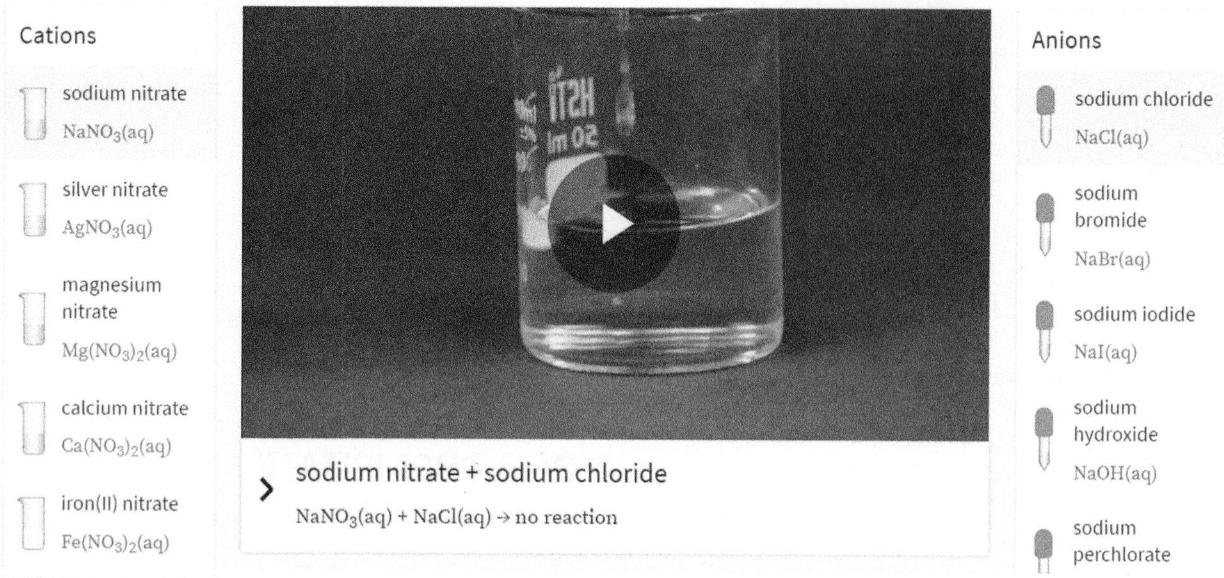

FIGURE 4.17 Precipitation Activity

NOTE: You need to be online to access this activity.

Choose two reactants to mix, one from the left side and one from the right, and then play the video to see the result. In some cases, a precipitate will form, as indicated by a cloudy substance in the video and a solid product in the chemical equation.

You can predict if a precipitation reaction will occur upon mixing of solutions of ionic compounds by considering all of the ions involved. Both ionic compounds dissolve in water as dissociated ions. The cations could form new ionic compounds by exchanging anions, but this will only happen if an insoluble compound is produced. Otherwise, all the ions will remain in solution as dissociated ions. For example, if solution 1 is made of an ionic compound consisting of cation A^+ and anion B^-, and the compound in solution 2 contains cation C^+ and anion D^-, then two new compounds are possible. One contains A^+ and D^-, and the other contains C^+ and B^-. If either of these possible new compounds is insoluble, a reaction will occur, forming the precipitate. If both possible compounds are soluble in water, no reaction will occur (Figure 4.18).

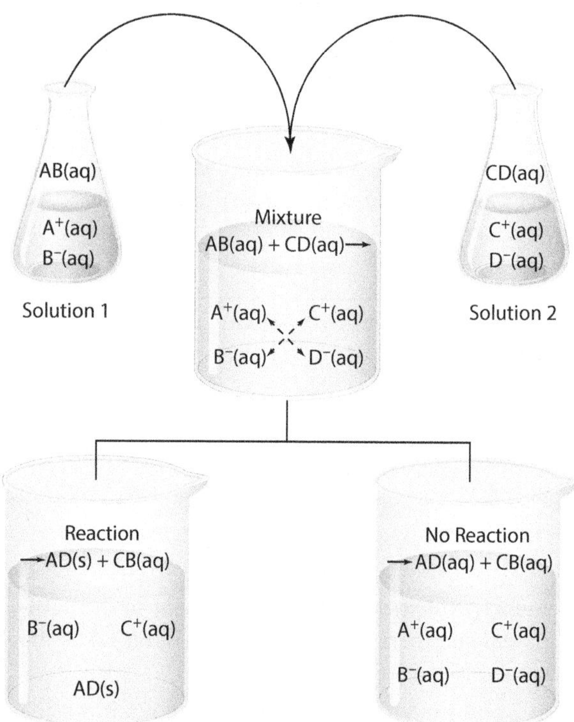

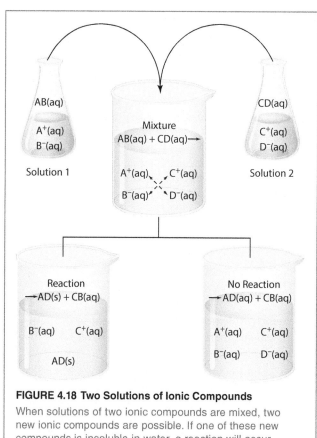

FIGURE 4.18 Two Solutions of Ionic Compounds

When solutions of two ionic compounds are mixed, two new ionic compounds are possible. If one of these new compounds is insoluble in water, a reaction will occur to form this new solid, referred to as a precipitate. If all cation–anion combinations are soluble, no reaction occurs.

When an aqueous solution of NaCl is mixed with an aqueous solution of $AgNO_3$ (the reaction from Figure 4.17), the resulting solution contains dissociated Ag^+ ions, NO_3^- ions, Na^+ ions, and Cl^- ions. Several combinations of cation and anion are possible—namely, Na^+/Cl^-, Ag^+/NO_3^-, Na^+/NO_3^-, and Ag^+/Cl^-—but only Na^+/NO_3^- and Ag^+/Cl^- are new. Of those two, only Ag^+ and Cl^- form an insoluble salt (in which case a precipitation reaction occurs), according to this reaction equation

$$AgNO_3(aq) + NaCl(aq) \rightarrow Ag^+(aq) + NO_3^-(aq) + Na^+(aq) + Cl^-(aq) \rightarrow AgCl(s) + NaNO_3(aq)$$

FIGURE 4.19 Video Tutorial: Predicting Precipitates

NOTE: You need to be online to access this video.
This video shows how to predict the products of precipitation reactions.

The following steps can be used to determine if combining solutions of two ionic compounds will result in a precipitation reaction:

1. Determine the two new ionic compounds that could form. Write their formulas based on the charges of the ions, as presented in Section 3.3.
2. Use the solubility guidelines or Table 4.5 to determine if either possible product is insoluble.
   - If both possible products are soluble, no reaction will occur.
   - If one product is insoluble, a precipitation reaction will occur.

The video in Figure 4.19 demonstrates how to predict the products of a precipitation reaction and how to write a balanced equation for the reaction.

Example 4.11

Determine whether the following reactions will occur. If they will, identify the formula of any insoluble product.

a. $Na_3PO_4(aq) + CaCl_2(aq)$
b. $Ba(ClO_3)_2(aq) + Pb(C_2H_3O_2)_2$

Solution

First, determine the two possible products by having the ions swap partners. Check Table 4.5 or the solubility guidelines to determine if either product is insoluble.

a. The ions are Na^+, PO_4^{3-}, Ca^{2+}, and Cl^-, and the two possible products are NaCl and $Ca_3(PO_4)_2$. Sodium chloride is soluble in water, but calcium phosphate is not. A precipitation reaction will occur, producing $Ca_3(PO_4)_2(s)$.

b. The ions are $Ba^{2+}, ClO_3^-, Pb^{2+}$, and $C_2H_3O_2^-$, and the two possible products are $Ba(C_2H_3O_2)_2$ and $Pb(ClO_3)_2$. Both barium acetate and lead(II) chlorate are soluble in water. No reaction will occur.

PRACTICE PROBLEM 4.11

Determine whether a reaction will occur and identify the formula of the insoluble product, if any.

a. $Na_2SO_4(aq) + BaCl_2(aq)$
b. $Ca(NO_3)_2(aq) + KOH(aq)$

Hint: First determine the two possible products by having the ions swap partners. Check Table 4.5 or the solubility guidelines to determine if either product is insoluble.

Precipitation reactions can be used to identify an unknown component in a solution. This is done by mixing the unknown solution with solutions of other known ionic compounds and observing (and recording) the results—namely, either the formation of a precipitate or no reaction. These results are then compared with the results of known compounds. Try the Precipitation Lab Activity (Figure 4.20) and learn how to use precipitation reactions to identify an unknown compound.

Ionic and Net Ionic Equations

The types of chemical equations you have been writing thus far are called overall or **total equations** because they show the complete formulas of the reactants and products, as described in Section 4.1. The behavior of electrolytes in the solution, though, is best depicted using an **ionic equation**.

An ionic equation shows all the aqueous strong electrolytes as separate ions.

For the reaction of $AgNO_3$ with NaCl, the total equation is

$$AgNO_3(aq) + NaCl(aq) \rightarrow AgCl(s) + NaNO_3(aq)$$

and the ionic equation is

$$Ag^+(aq) + NO_3^-(aq) + Na^+(aq) + Cl^-(aq) \rightarrow AgCl(s) + Na^+(aq) + NO_3^-(aq)$$

Notice in the ionic equation that the $NO_3^-(aq)$ and $Na^+(aq)$ ions are unchanged during the reaction—that is, they have the same formula and phase on both sides of the reaction arrow. These ions are called **spectator ions** because they do not participate in the reaction. Removing the spectator ions leaves a clearer picture

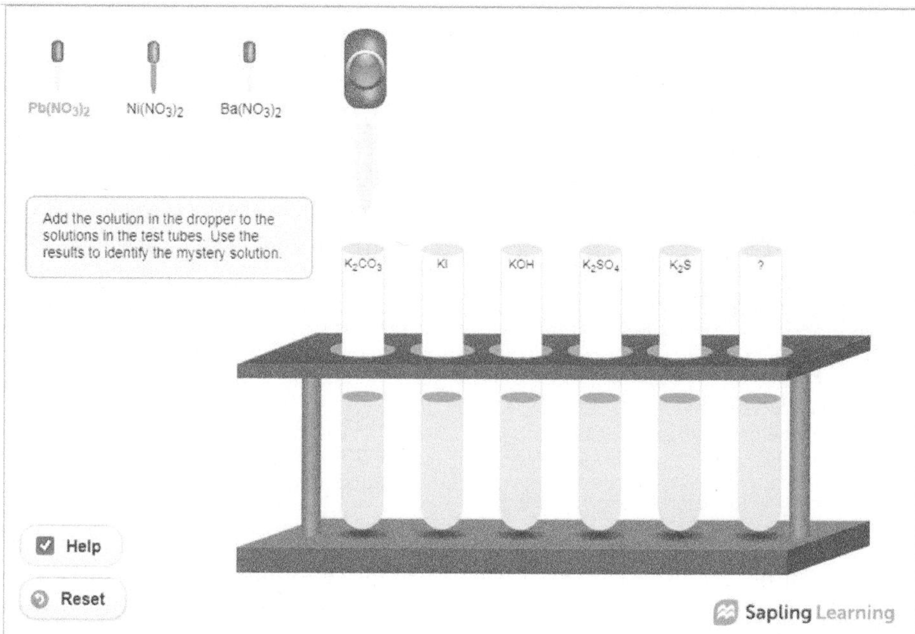

FIGURE 4.20 Precipitation Lab Activity

NOTE: You need to be online to access this activity.

Carry out the double-replacement reactions in the simulated experiment. Use the results to identify the unknown solution.

of what really happened, and the result is called a **net ionic equation**:

$$Ag^{+}(aq) + Cl^{-}(aq) \rightarrow AgCl(s)$$

> A net ionic equation is the ionic equation with the spectator ions removed.

The video in Figure 4.21 demonstrates how to write net ionic equations for three different chemical reactions.

FIGURE 4.21 Video Tutorial: Net Ionic Equations for Precipitation Reactions

NOTE: You need to be online to access this video.

This video shows how to write net ionic equations for precipitation and acid–base reactions.

Example 4.12

Write the net ionic equation for the following ionic equation.

$$Ca^{2+}(aq) + 2\,NO_3^{-}(aq) + 2\,K^{+}(aq) + SO_4^{2-}(aq) \rightarrow CaSO_4(s) + 2\,K^{+}(aq) + 2\,NO_3^{-}(aq)$$

Solution

The calcium and sulfate ions form the solid calcium sulfate. The potassium and nitrate ions are spectator ions.

$$Ca^{2+}(aq) + \cancel{2\,NO_3^{-}(aq)} + \cancel{2\,K^{+}(aq)} + SO_4^{2-}(aq) \rightarrow CaSO_4(s) + \cancel{2\,K^{+}(aq)} + \cancel{2\,NO_3^{-}(aq)}$$

Net ionic equation: $Ca^{2+}(aq) + SO_4^{2-}(aq) \rightarrow CaSO_4(s)$

PRACTICE PROBLEM 4.12

Write the net ionic equation for the following ionic equation.

$$3\,Sr^{2+}(aq) + 6\,NO_3^{-}(aq) + 6\,K^{+}(aq) + 2\,PO_4^{3-}(aq) \rightarrow Sr_3(PO_4)_2(s) + 6\,K^{+}(aq) + 6\,NO_3^{-}(aq)$$

Hint: Identify the spectator ions—the ions that have not changed during the reaction. Eliminating the spectator ions should leave only the net ionic equation.

Example 4.13

Write the ionic and net ionic equations for the following total equation.

$$2\,NaOH(aq) + Pb(NO_3)_2(aq) \rightarrow Pb(OH)_2(s) + 2\,NaNO_3(aq)$$

Solution

For the ionic equation, rewrite the aqueous strong electrolytes as dissociated, aqueous ions.

$$2\,Na^+(aq) + 2\,OH^-(aq) + Pb^{2+}(aq) + 2\,NO_3^-(aq) \rightarrow Pb(OH)_2(s) + 2\,Na^+(aq) + 2\,NO_3^-(aq)$$

For the net ionic equation, remove any spectator ions from the ionic equation.

$$Pb^{2+}(aq) + 2\,OH^-(aq) \rightarrow Pb(OH)_2(s)$$

PRACTICE PROBLEM 4.13

Write the ionic and net ionic equations for the following total equations.

a. $Hg_2(NO_3)_2(aq) + 2\,KBr(aq) \rightarrow Hg_2Br_2(s) + 2\,KNO_3(aq)$

b. $MgSO_4(aq) + Na_2CO_3(aq) \rightarrow MgCO_3(s) + Na_2SO_4(aq)$

Hint: For the ionic equation, rewrite the aqueous strong electrolytes as dissociated, aqueous ions. If you have trouble remembering the charges on certain ions, see Table 4.5. For the net ionic equation, remove any spectator ions from the ionic equation.

You have learned how to predict if a precipitation reaction will occur and how to give the formula of the precipitate based on the reactants and solubility guidelines. You have also learned how to write ionic and net ionic equations from total equations. Now you will combine these skills not just to predict precipitation reactions, but to write total, ionic, and net ionic equations for any that occur.

Example 4.14

Complete the following reactions by writing balanced total, ionic, and net ionic equations.

a. $Na_3PO_4(aq) + CaCl_2(aq) \rightarrow$

b. $BaCl_2(aq) + Pb(C_2H_3O_2)_2 \rightarrow$

Solution

a. $Na_3PO_4(aq) + CaCl_2(aq) \rightarrow$

The ions are Na^+, PO_4^{3-}, Ca^{2+}, and Cl^-, and the two possible products are $Ca_3(PO_4)_2$ and NaCl. Recall from Example 4.11 that this combination of reactants produces $Ca_3(PO_4)_2$ as an insoluble product. The unbalanced equation is

$$Na_3PO_4(aq) + CaCl_2(aq) \rightarrow Ca_3(PO_4)_2(s) + NaCl(aq)$$

The balanced, total equation is

$$2\,Na_3PO_4(aq) + 3\,CaCl_2(aq) \rightarrow Ca_3(PO_4)_2(s) + 6\,NaCl(aq)$$

To obtain the ionic equation, rewrite the total equation with each soluble strong electrolyte depicted as a dissociated ion:

$$6\,Na^+(aq) + 2\,PO_4^{3-}(aq) + 3\,Ca^{2+}(aq) + 6\,Cl^-(aq) \rightarrow Ca_3(PO_4)_2(s) + 6\,Na^+(aq) + 6\,Cl^-(aq)$$

Eliminating the spectator ions $[6\,Na^+(aq) + 6\,Cl^-(aq)]$ from the ionic equation gives the net ionic equation:

$$3\,Ca^{2+}(aq) + 2\,PO_4^{3-}(aq) \rightarrow Ca_3(PO_4)_2(s)$$

b. $BaCl_2(aq) + Pb(C_2H_3O_2)_2 \rightarrow$

The ions are Ba^{2+}, Cl^-, Pb^{2+}, and $C_2H_3O_2^-$, and the two possible products are $Ba(C_2H_3O_2)_2$ and $PbCl_2$. Barium acetate is soluble, but lead(II) chloride is insoluble in water, so a precipitation reaction will occur. The balanced total equation is

$$BaCl_2(aq) + Pb(C_2H_3O_2)_2(aq) \rightarrow PbCl_2(s) + Ba(C_2H_3O_2)_2(aq)$$

To obtain the ionic equation, rewrite the soluble strong electrolytes as their hydrated ions:

$$Ba^{2+}(aq) + 2\,Cl^-(aq) + Pb^{2+}(aq) + 2\,C_2H_3O_2^-(aq) \rightarrow PbCl_2(s) + Ba^{2+}(aq) + 2\,C_2H_3O_2^-(aq)$$

Eliminating the spectator ions $[Ba^{2+}(aq) + 2\,C_2H_3O_2^-(aq)]$ from the ionic equation gives the net ionic equation:

$$Pb^{2+}(aq) + 2\,Cl^-(aq) \rightarrow PbCl_2(s)$$

PRACTICE PROBLEM 4.14

Predict the products and write balanced total, ionic, and net ionic equations for the following reactions:

a. $Na_2SO_4(aq) + BaCl_2(aq) \rightarrow$

b. $Ca(NO_3)_2(aq) + KOH(aq) \rightarrow$

Hint: Start by writing the formulas for the two possible products, and then use Table 4.5 to determine their solubilities. If a reaction occurs, be sure to balance it. Recall that soluble strong electrolytes are written as ions in the ionic equation and that eliminating spectator ions from the ionic equation gives the net ionic equation.

SECTION REVIEW

- Ionic compounds range from soluble to insoluble in water.
- Solubility guidelines can be used to predict if a specific ionic compound is soluble or insoluble.

- Precipitation reactions occur when solutions of two ionic compounds are mixed and the ions form a new, insoluble ionic compound. The resulting solid is called a precipitate and the reactions are called precipitation reactions.
- Solubility guidelines can be used to predict whether a precipitation reaction will occur upon mixing solutions of ionic compounds.
- Three types of chemical equations are used to describe aqueous ionic reactions:
  - The total equation (Section 4.1)
  - The ionic equation, which shows all the aqueous strong electrolytes as separate ions
  - The net ionic equation, which excludes spectator ions and shows only those components that have changed

4.5 Acid–Base Reactions

GOALS

- Predict the products of acid–base reactions in aqueous solution.
- Write and interpret ionic and net ionic equations for acid–base reactions.

COMPLETING AND BALANCING ACID–BASE REACTIONS

The driving force for an acid–base reaction is neutralization. Hydrogen from the acid combines with hydroxide from the base to form liquid water, and the remaining ions form a salt:

$$HCl(aq) + KOH(aq) \rightarrow KCl(aq) + H_2O(l)$$
$$2\ HCl(aq) + Ba(OH)_2(aq) \rightarrow BaCl_2(aq) + 2\ H_2O(l)$$

These reactions are a type of double-replacement reaction (Section 4.2), and they occur in a very similar manner to the precipitation reactions discussed in Section 4.4. Unlike precipitation, however, there is usually no visible change in the reaction mixture. Neutralization often produces enough heat, though, that the container (if made of glass or other non-insulating material) will feel warm to the touch.

Example 4.15

Write the total balanced chemical equations for the following acid–base reactions:

a. $HClO_4(aq) + Ba(OH)_2(aq) \rightarrow$
b. $HC_2H_3O_2(aq) + NaOH(aq) \rightarrow$

Solution

The products are a salt and H_2O. Use ion charges to determine the formula of the salt produced. Be sure to balance the equation.

a. The formula for the salt composed of Ba^{2+} and ClO_4^- is $Ba(ClO_4)_2$. The balanced equation is

$$2\ HClO_4(aq) + Ba(OH)_2(aq) \rightarrow Ba(ClO_4)_2(aq) + 2\ H_2O(l)$$

b. The formula for the salt composed of Na^+ and $C_2H_3O_2^-$ is $NaC_2H_3O_2$. The balanced equation is

$$HC_2H_3O_2(aq) + NaOH(aq) \rightarrow NaC_2H_3O_2(aq) + H_2O(l)$$

PRACTICE PROBLEM 4.15

Write the total chemical equations for the following acid–base reactions.

a. $HNO_3(aq) + KOH(aq) \rightarrow$
b. $H_3PO_4(aq) + NaOH(aq) \rightarrow$

Hint: The products will be a salt and H_2O. Determine the formula of the salt by combining the cation from the base with the anion from the acid in the correct ratio to make a neutral compound. Be sure to balance the equation.

WRITING IONIC AND NET IONIC EQUATIONS FOR ACID–BASE REACTIONS

Ionic and net ionic equations are written for acid–base reactions in much the same way as for precipitation reactions. For the ionic equation, all the aqueous strong electrolytes are written as separate ions and the net ionic equation shows only the components of the ionic equation that changed during the reaction. The three equations (total, ionic, and net ionic) for the reaction of hydrochloric acid, HCl, and potassium hydroxide, KOH, are as follows:

Total equation: $HCl(aq) + KOH(aq) \rightarrow KCl(aq) + H_2O(l)$

Ionic equation:
$H^+(aq) + Cl^-(aq) + K^+(aq) + OH^-(aq) \rightarrow K^+(aq) + Cl^-(aq) + H_2O(l)$

Net ionic equation: $H^+(aq) + OH^-(aq) \rightarrow H_2O(l)$

The reaction of HCl with barium hydroxide, $Ba(OH)_2$, requires coefficients to balance the total and ionic equations, which are factored out in the net ionic equation.

Total equation: $2\ HCl(aq) + Ba(OH)_2(aq) \rightarrow BaCl_2(aq) + 2\ H_2O(l)$

FIGURE 4.22 Video Tutorial: Net Ionic Equations for Acid–Base Reactions

This video shows how to write net ionic equations for acid–base reactions

Ionic equation:

$$2\,H^+(aq) + 2\,Cl^-(aq) + Ba^{2+}(aq) + 2\,OH^-(aq) \rightarrow Ba^{2+}(aq) + 2\,Cl^-(aq) + 2\,H_2O(l)$$

Net ionic equation: $H^+(aq) + OH^-(aq) \rightarrow H_2O(l)$

Note that the net ionic equation is the same for both preceding examples. This is always true for the reaction of a strong acid with a strong base. The following is an example of a weak acid (hydrogen fluoride, HF) reacting with a strong base (KOH).

Total equation: $HF(aq) + KOH(aq) \rightarrow KF(aq) + H_2O(l)$

Ionic equation: $HF(aq) + K^+(aq) + OH^-(aq) \rightarrow K^+(aq) + F^-(aq) + H_2O(l)$

Net ionic equation: $HF(aq) + OH^-(aq) \rightarrow F^-(aq) + H_2O(l)$

Because a weak acid is a weak electrolyte, its molecular formula remains intact in the ionic equation, resulting in a unique net ionic equation. The video in Figure 4.22 shows how to write net ionic equations for acid–base reactions, including those with weak acids.

Example 4.16

Write the ionic and net ionic equations for the following acid–base reactions.

a. $2\,HClO_4(aq) + Ba(OH)_2(aq) \rightarrow Ba(ClO_4)_2(aq) + 2\,H_2O(l)$

b. $HC_2H_3O_2(aq) + NaOH(aq) \rightarrow NaC_2H_3O_2(aq) + H_2O(l)$

Solution

a. To obtain the ionic equation, write the aqueous strong electrolytes as separate ions:

$$2\,H^+(aq) + 2\,ClO_4^-(aq) + Ba^{2+}(aq) + 2\,OH^-(aq) \rightarrow Ba^{2+}(aq) + ClO_4^-(aq) + 2\,H_2O(l)$$

$HClO_4$ is on the list of strong acids (Table 4.3), so it is a strong electrolyte. As soluble ionic compounds, $Ba(OH)_2$ and $Ba(ClO_4)_2$ are also strong electrolytes. Water is not a strong electrolyte, so it remains intact.

To obtain the net ionic equation, cancel the spectator ions in the ionic equation:

$$H^+(aq) + OH^-(aq) \rightarrow H_2O(l)$$

b. To obtain the ionic equation, write the aqueous strong electrolytes as separate ions:

$$HC_2H_3O_2(aq) + Na^+(aq) + OH^-(aq) \rightarrow Na^+(aq) + C_2H_3O_2^-(aq) + H_2O(l)$$

$HC_2H_3O_2$ is a weak acid, so it is a weak electrolyte. As soluble ionic compounds, NaOH and $NaC_2H_3O_2$ are also strong electrolytes. Water is not a strong electrolyte.

To obtain the net ionic equation, cancel the spectator ions in the ionic equation:

$$HC_2H_3O_2(aq) + OH^-(aq) \rightarrow C_2H_3O_2^-(aq) + H_2O(l)$$

PRACTICE PROBLEM 4.16

Write ionic and net ionic equations for the following acid–base reactions.

a. $HNO_3(aq) + KOH(aq) \rightarrow KNO_3(aq) + H_2O(l)$

b. $H_3PO_4(aq) + 3\,NaOH(aq) \rightarrow Na_3PO_4(aq) + 3\,H_2O(l)$

Hint: Use Table 4.3 to determine whether the acid is strong or weak. Strong acids should be written as individual ions, whereas weak acids should be written as intact molecules.

SECTION REVIEW

- In an acid–base reaction, an acid and a strong base react to form a salt and water. This is a type of double-replacement reaction, where the driving force is neutralization (the formation of water from H^+ and OH^-).
- The salt produced in an acid–base reaction contains the cation from the base and the anion from the acid.
- Any reaction of a strong acid with a strong base has the net ionic equation

  $$H^+(aq) + OH^-(aq) \rightarrow H_2O(l)$$

- Weak acids are weak electrolytes, so the net ionic equation for the reaction of a weak acid with a strong base is different from that for the reaction of a strong acid with a strong base.

4.6 Oxidation States and Redox Reactions

GOALS

- Assign oxidation states to elements within compounds and polyatomic ions.
- Identify redox reactions using oxidation states.
- Define and apply the terms *oxidizing agent* and *reducing agent*.

Background Review

Chapter 3 Compounds and the Mole:
Section 3.3—Formulas for Ionic Compounds

ASSIGNING OXIDATION STATES

Oxidation–reduction (redox) reactions involve the transfer of electrons. **Oxidation states**, also known as **oxidation numbers**, are a type of electron bookkeeping used to keep track of the electrons transferred in redox reactions. The basic rules for assigning oxidation states are as follows:

1. A neutral element that is not part of a compound has an oxidation state of zero.
2. Monoatomic ions have oxidation states equal to their ionic charges.
3. The sum of the oxidation states in any formula is equal to the overall charge on that formula.
4. Oxygen tends to have an oxidation state of -2 in compounds.
5. Hydrogen tends to have an oxidation state of $+1$ in compounds.

Additional rules exist, but are beyond the scope of this chapter. The five rules just outlined cover all the compounds you will encounter here in Chapter 4 and nearly every compound you might encounter in redox problems in this course.

EVERYDAY CONNECTION

Many elements can exist in different oxidation states and have different properties in those different states. Redox reactions have an enormous impact on society because much of the damage to metal in automobiles and bridges is due to the oxidation of iron metal, Fe, to iron(III) oxide (rust), Fe_2O_3. The two photos shown below compare the oxidation of copper, Cu, and iron. (a) Cu oxidizes to form a green protective coating—a *desirable* reaction. (b) When Fe oxidizes to rust, however, the rust flakes off, which exposes new layers of Fe to oxidation and causes the metal to become pitted. Over time, the loss of Fe metal can be significant enough to greatly weaken the structure—a very *undesirable* consequence.

trappy76/Shutterstock

(a)

cmfotoworks/Deposit Photos

(b)

Example 4.17

Determine the oxidation state of each of the following species.

a. Mg
b. P^{3-}
c. Fe in $FeCl_3$

Solution

a. Mg is elemental (uncombined) magnesium. Its oxidation state is 0 (rule 1).
b. P^{3-} is a monoatomic ion. Its oxidation state is -3 (rule 2).
c. $FeCl_3$ is an ionic compound made up of two monoatomic ions. Although iron can have variable charge as an ion, the chloride ion is always -1 (see Section 3.3). Thus, the charge on iron is $+3$, which means its oxidation state is $+3$ (rule 2).

PRACTICE PROBLEM 4.17

Determine the oxidation state of each of the following species.

a. S^{2-}
b. N_2
c. Cr in $CrCl_2$

Hint: Monoatomic ions have oxidation states equal to their ionic charges (rule 2) and neutral elements have oxidation states of 0 (rule 1).

Example 4.18

What is the oxidation state of nitrogen in the nitrite ion, NO_2^-?

Solution

Oxygen tends to have an oxidation state of -2 in a compound (rule 4). Moreover, the sum of the oxidation states in any formula is equal to the overall charge on that formula (rule 3). As a result, the oxidation states of the two oxygen atoms plus that of the nitrogen atom must total -1, the overall charge on the ion:

$$x + 2(-2) = -1$$

x	2	(-2)	-1
Oxidation state of nitrogen	Number of oxygen atoms	Oxidation state of each oxygen atom	Overall charge on nitrate ion

Now solve for x, the oxidation state of nitrogen:

$$x + 2(-2) = -1$$
$$x - 4 = -1$$
$$x = -1 + 4 = 3$$

The oxidation state of the nitrogen atom is $+3$.

PRACTICE PROBLEM 4.18

Determine the oxidation state of the following elements.

a. Sulfur in the thiosulfate ion, $S_2O_3^{2-}$
b. Sulfur in the sulfite ion, SO_3^{2-}
c. Chromium in the dichromate ion, $Cr_2O_7^{2-}$

Hint: Start by assuming that oxygen has an oxidation state of -2 (rule 4). Then apply rule 3, which states that the sum of the oxidation states in any formula is equal to the overall charge.

Example 4.19

Determine the oxidation state of phosphorus in K_3PO_4.

Solution

Potassium always forms $+1$ ions (see Section 3.3), and the oxidation state of a monoatomic ion is equal to its charge (rule 2). Assign oxygen an oxidation state of -2 (rule 4) and use the fact that the oxidation states of the elements in the formula must sum to the overall charge of the ion or neutral compound (rule 3). In the following equation for the overall charge, x is the oxidation state of P:

$$3(+1) + x + 4(-2) = 0$$

Solve for x.

$$3 + x - 8 = 0$$
$$3 + x = 8$$
$$x = 8 - 3 = 5$$

The oxidation state of phosphorus in K_3PO_4 is $+5$.

PRACTICE PROBLEM 4.19

Determine the oxidation state of the indicated atoms.

a. Cl in $NaClO_2$
b. Cl in $HClO_4$

Hint: Write an equation for the overall charge in which x is the oxidation state of Cl. Both of these compounds are neutral overall, so the sum of the oxidation states must be zero (rule 3). Na has an oxidation state of $+1$ (rule 2), O has an oxidation state of -2 (rule 4), and H has an oxidation state of $+1$ (rule 5).

USING OXIDATION STATES TO IDENTIFY REDOX REACTIONS

Redox reactions involve the transfer of electrons. One reactant loses electrons (oxidation), while another gains electrons (reduction). Thus, oxidation occurs when the oxidation state of an element increases, while reduction occurs when the oxidation state decreases.

In the following equation for the synthesis of aluminum chloride, $AlCl_3$, from aluminum, Al, and chlorine, Cl, the oxidation states are written above and/or below the elements:

Reduction

0 → −1

$$2\ Al(s) + 3\ Cl_2(g) \longrightarrow 2\ AlCl_3(s)$$

0 → +3

Oxidation

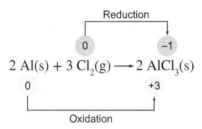

The oxidation state of Al increases from 0 to +3 during the reaction (Al is oxidized), while the oxidation state of Cl decreases from 0 to −1 (Cl is reduced). Electrons are transferred from Al to Cl, forming an Al ion and three Cl ions. Chlorine gas, Cl_2, is the **oxidizing agent**, the reactant that accepted the electrons from aluminum, causing it to be oxidized. Al metal is the **reducing agent**, the reactant that gave electrons to the Cl atoms, causing Cl_2 to be reduced. These terms are summarized in Table 4.6.

TABLE 4.6 Summary of Redox Terminology

Oxidation	Reduction
Increase in oxidation state	Decrease (reduction) in oxidation state
Loss of electrons	Gain of electrons
Reducing agent	Oxidizing agent

Oxidizing agents take electrons from the substance that gets oxidized; therefore, oxidizing agents get reduced. Reducing agents provide the electrons that are gained by the substance that gets reduced; therefore, reducing agents get oxidized.

Example 4.20

Determine whether the following reaction is a redox reaction. If it is, identify the reactant that is oxidized, the reactant that is reduced, the oxidizing agent, and the reducing agent.

$$3\ Ca(s) + 2\ N_2(g) \rightarrow Ca_3N_2(s)$$

Solution

Follow the oxidation state rules to assign oxidation numbers to each element in the reactants and products. An increase in oxidation number indicates that the element has been oxidized during the reaction, whereas a decrease in oxidation number indicates that the element has been reduced.

Reduction

0 → −3

$$3\ Ca(s) + N_2(g) \longrightarrow Ca_3N_2(s)$$

0 → +2

Oxidation

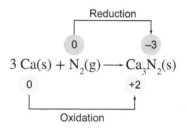

The reactants both are uncombined elements and have an oxidation state of 0 (rule 1). In the product, calcium has an oxidation state of +2 (rule 2), so N has an oxidation state of −3 (rule 3). Calcium's oxidation state increases from 0 to +2, indicating that calcium is oxidized during this reaction. Nitrogen's oxidation state decreases from 0 to −3, indicating that nitrogen is reduced during this reaction. Calcium is the reducing agent because it is oxidized, providing the electrons. Nitrogen is the oxidizing agent because it is reduced, accepting the electrons.

PRACTICE PROBLEM 4.20

Determine whether this reaction is a redox reaction. If it is, identify the reactant that is oxidized, the reactant that is reduced, the oxidizing agent, and the reducing agent.

$$2\ HgO(s) \rightarrow 2\ Hg(l) + O_2(g)$$

Hint: Follow the oxidation state guidelines to assign oxidation numbers to each element in the reactants and products. An increase in oxidation number indicates that the element has been oxidized during the reaction, whereas a decrease in oxidation number indicates that the element has been reduced.

Example 4.21

Which of the following are redox reactions?

a. $2\ H_2(g) + O_2(g) \rightarrow 2\ H_2O(g)$

b. $MgI_2(aq) + 2\ AgNO_3(aq) \rightarrow 2\ AgI(s) + Mg(NO_3)_2(aq)$

c. $CaCO_3(s) \rightarrow CaO(s) + CO_2(g)$

d. $2\ C_8H_{18}(g) + 25\ O_2(g) \rightarrow 16\ CO_2(g) + 18\ H_2O(l)$

e. $Zn(s) + 2\ HCl(aq) \rightarrow ZnCl_2(aq) + H_2(g)$

Solution

Assign oxidation states to the elements in the reactants and products and look for changes in oxidation numbers.

a. The oxidation numbers of hydrogen and oxygen change during this reaction. This is a redox reaction. Hydrogen is oxidized, and oxygen is reduced.

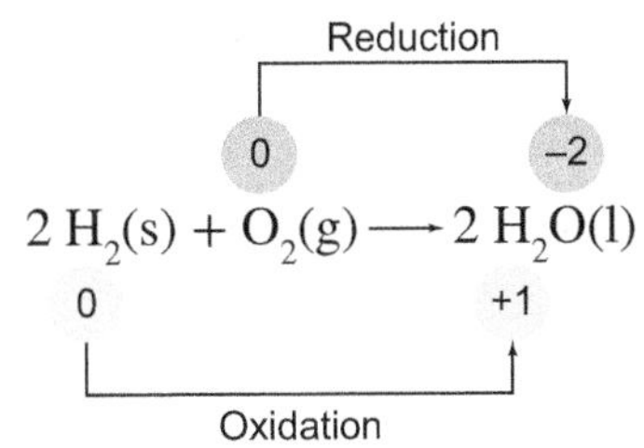

b. There are no changes in any of the oxidation states. This is *not* a redox reaction.

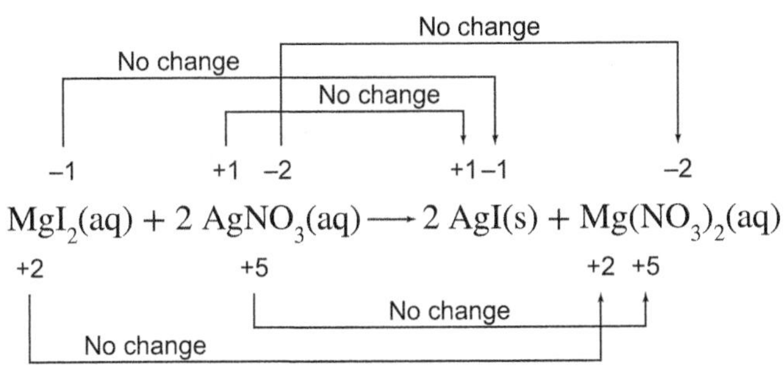

c. There is no change in oxidation state to indicate a transfer of electrons. This is *not* a redox reaction.

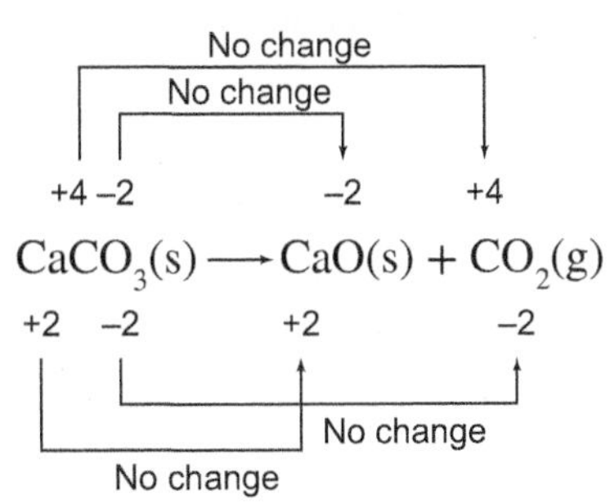

d. The oxidation states of carbon and oxygen change during this reaction. This is a redox reaction. Carbon is oxidized, and oxygen is reduced.

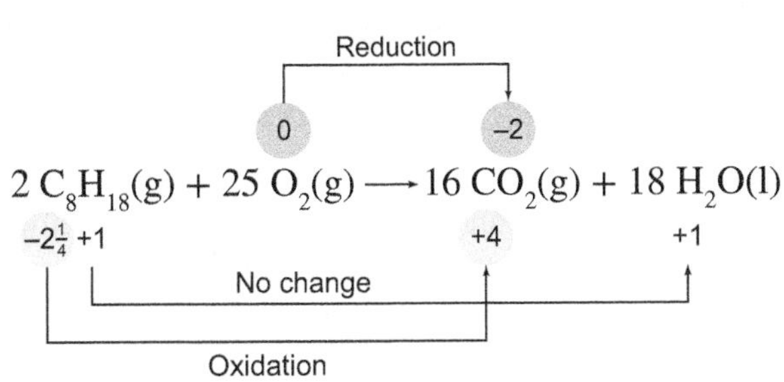

e. The oxidation states of zinc and hydrogen change during this reaction. This is a redox reaction. Zinc is oxidized, and hydrogen is reduced.

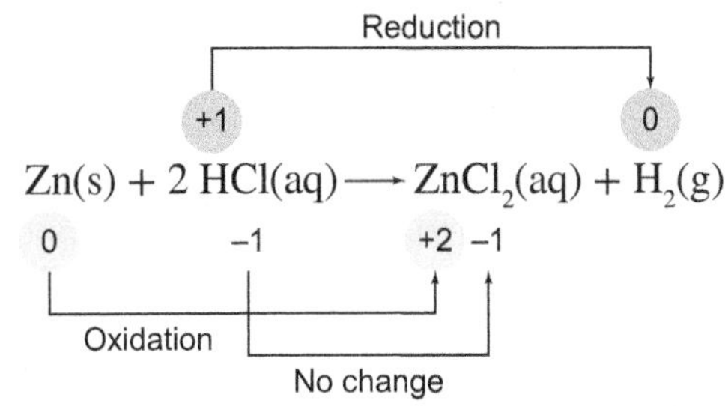

PRACTICE PROBLEM 4.21

Determine which of the following are redox reactions.

a. $2\ HBr(aq) + Ba(OH)_2(aq) \rightarrow BaBr_2(aq) + 2\ H_2O(l)$

b. $2\ CoCl_2(aq) + Cl_2(g) \rightarrow 2\ CoCl_3(aq)$

c. $2\ NH_4I(aq) + Pb(NO_3)_2(aq) \rightarrow 2\ NH_4NO_3(aq) + PbI_2(s)$

d. $(NH_4)_2S(aq) + CuCl_2(aq) \rightarrow CuS(s) + 2\ NH_4Cl(aq)$

e. $2\ NaOH(aq) + H_3PO_4(aq) \rightarrow Na_2HPO_4(aq) + 2\ H_2O(l)$

f. $H_2O(l) + N_2O_5(g) \rightarrow 2\ HNO_3(aq)$

g. $CuSO_4(aq) + Zn(s) \rightarrow ZnSO_4(aq) + Cu(s)$

h. $NH_4NO_3(s) \rightarrow N_2O(g) + 2\ H_2O(l)$

Hint: Follow the oxidation state guidelines to assign oxidation numbers to each element in the reactants and products. An increase in oxidation number indicates that the element has been oxidized during the reaction, whereas a decrease in oxidation number indicates that the element has been reduced.

SECTION REVIEW

- Oxidation states can be used to keep track of the transfer of electrons between atoms and are assigned according to a set of rules.
- Oxidation–reduction (redox) reactions can be identified by assigning oxidation states to all components and looking for changes in the oxidation states of the elements.
  - Oxidation = an increase in oxidation state
  - Reduction = a decrease in oxidation state
- Oxidizing agents accept electrons from the component that is being oxidized. Oxidizing agents get reduced.
- Reducing agents provide the electrons to the component that is being reduced. Reducing agents get oxidized.

4.7 Predicting the Products of Redox Reactions

GOALS

- Write balanced equations for synthesis and decomposition reactions.
- Apply the activity series to predict the product of single-replacement reactions.

SYNTHESIS AND DECOMPOSITION REACTIONS

Many synthesis and decomposition reactions involve electron transfer and are, therefore, redox reactions (see Section 4.6). One example is the synthesis of aluminum chloride, $AlCl_3$, from its elements:

$$\underset{0}{2\,Al(s)} + \underset{0}{3\,Cl_2(g)} \rightarrow \underset{+3\,-1}{2\,AlCl_3(s)}$$

Another is the decomposition of mercury(II) oxide, HgO, into its elements:

$$\underset{+2\,-2}{2\,HgO(s)} + \underset{0}{Hg(l)} \rightarrow \underset{0}{O_2(g)}$$

The products of reactions between nonmetals from groups 16 and 17 and metals from groups 1 and 2 plus aluminum, Al, can be predicted using their ionic charges or oxidation states. These metals will lose a characteristic number of electrons to form cations, and the nonmetals will gain a characteristic number of electrons to form anions. Example 4.22 shows how the charges of the ions can be used to determine the formula of the neutral compound.

Example 4.22

Complete and balance the following synthesis reactions.

a. $Rb(s) + F_2(g) \rightarrow$
b. $Ca(s) + N_2(g) \rightarrow$

Solution

Because this is a synthesis reaction, there will be only one product, a binary ionic compound. You can use the location of the elements in the periodic table to predict the charge of the ions that each element will form upon oxidation or reduction. Then use those charges to determine the formula of the product.

a. $Rb(s) + F_2(g) \rightarrow$

Rubidium is a group 1 metal and will oxidize to form a +1 cation, Rb^+; fluorine is a group 17 nonmetal and will reduce to form a −1 anion, F^-. These ions form RbF, rubidium fluoride. Finally, coefficients are needed to balance this equation:

$$2\,Rb(s) + F_2(g) \rightarrow 2\,RbF(s)$$

b. $Ca(s) + N_2(g) \rightarrow$

Calcium, a group 2 element, forms a +2 cation, while nitrogen, a group 15 element, forms a −3 anion. Together, they form calcium nitride, Ca_3N_2. Inserting the necessary coefficients balances the equation:

$$3\,Ca(s) + N_2(g) \rightarrow Ca_3N_2(s)$$

PRACTICE PROBLEM 4.22

Complete and balance the following synthesis reactions.

a. $Na(s) + S(s) \rightarrow$
b. $Al(s) + N_2(g) \rightarrow$

Hint: Because this is a synthesis reaction, there will be only one product, a binary ionic compound. Use the location of the elements in the periodic table to predict the charge of the ions that each element will form upon oxidation or reduction. Then use those charges to determine the formula of the product and then insert any coefficients needed to balance the equation.

SINGLE-REPLACEMENT REACTIONS

Single-replacement reactions, such as the reaction of zinc, Zn, with hydrogen chloride, HCl (Figure 4.9 and Figure 4.10), are redox reactions (Section 4.6). Based on the following oxidation states, Zn atoms are oxidized, and H atoms are reduced:

$$\underset{0}{Zn(s)} + \underset{+1\,-1}{2\,HCl(aq)} \rightarrow \underset{+2\,-1}{ZnCl_2(aq)} + \underset{0}{H_2(g)}$$

The change is also apparent in the net ionic equation:

$$Zn(s) + 2\,H^+(aq) \rightarrow Zn^{2+}(aq) + H_2(g)$$

Oxidation–reduction is the driving force for this reaction (Section 4.2). That is, the reaction occurs because the oxidized and reduced products are more stable than are the reactants. To put it another way, the reactants are more reactive than are the products. Metal atoms that oxidize readily are called **active metals**. Metals that do not oxidize readily are commonly used in coins and jewelry.

EVERYDAY CONNECTION

Gold, silver, and copper are not easily oxidized. Silver, which is more reactive than gold, tarnishes slowly in air to form silver sulfide, Ag_2S. Copper is more reactive than the other coinage metals and oxidizes more quickly than silver or gold.

I. Pilon/Shutterstock
Silver Spiral Arts/Shutterstock
I. Pilon/Shutterstock

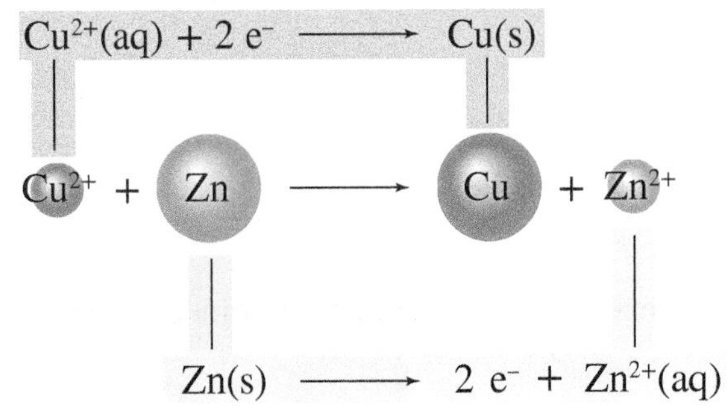

FIGURE 4.23 A Redox Reaction Between Zn Metal and Dissolved Cu^{2+} Ions

Copper(II) gains two electrons and is reduced to neutral copper, while neutral zinc loses two electrons and is oxidized to zinc(II). Since electrons are being transferred from Zn metal to Cu^{2+} ions, the oxidation process takes place simultaneously with the reduction process. The number of electrons given up by the Zn metal is equal to the number of electrons received by Cu^{2+} ions, so the electrons cancel out, and there are no electrons in the overall equation for the reaction.

Another common single-replacement reaction is the reaction of copper(II) sulfate, $CuSO_4$, with Zn metal. Zinc metal is more active than is copper metal and electrons move readily from zinc atoms to copper(II) ions (Figure 4.23).

$$\underset{+2}{CuSO_4(aq)} + \underset{0}{Zn(s)} \rightarrow \underset{0}{Cu(s)} + \underset{+2}{ZnSO_4(aq)}$$

The common active metals are listed in Table 4.7 in order of reactivity, forming an **activity series**. The metals at the top of the list are more active and are most readily oxidized. The metals at the bottom of the list are very stable, so their ions are very reactive and are most readily reduced. Metal *atoms* in the activity series can transfer electrons to *ions* of any metal that is lower on the activity series.

Table 4.7 can be used to predict if a single-replacement reaction will occur. In the activity series, an element is a potential reducing agent and can reduce the ions of any element that is lower on the list. In other words, elements at the top of the list are better reducing agents than those at the bottom of the list, and ions at the bottom of the list are better oxidizing agents than are those at the top of the list. Explore the activity series using Figure 4.24.

TABLE 4.7 Activity Series

Reducing Agent	Activity as Element	Oxidizing Agent	Activity as Ion
Group 1–2 metals Li, K, Ba, Ca, Na, Mg	Most active (best reducing agent)	Ions of group 1–2 metals Li^+, K^+, Ba^{2+}, Ca^{2+}, Na^+, Mg^{2+}	Least active (worst oxidizing agent)
Al		Al^{3+}	
Mn		Mn^{2+}	
Zn		Zn^{2+}	
Cr		Cr^{3+}	
Fe	↑ Ease of oxidation	Fe^{2+}	↓ Ease of reduction
Ni		Ni^{2+}	
Sn		Sn^{2+}	
Pb		Pb^{2+}	
H		H^+	
Cu		Cu^{2+}	
Ag		Ag^+	
Au	Least active (worst reducing agent)	Au^{3+}	Most active (best oxidizing agent)

FIGURE 4.24 Activity Series

NOTE: You need to be online to access this activity.

Select a metal and a solution, then play the video to see the result when they are combined. In some cases, there will be bubbles, sediment, and/or discoloration as evidence that a reaction has occurred. See if you can use Table 4.7 to predict whether a given combination will react *before* watching the video.

Example 4.23

Given Fe(s), Ag^+, Sn(s), Mg^{2+}, Li(s), and Ca^{2+}, identify

a. the most active metal.
b. the most reactive metal ion.
c. the strongest reducing agent.
d. the best oxidizing agent.

Solution

The most active metals are at the top of the activity series (Table 4.7) and are the most likely to give up electrons, which makes them the strongest reducing agents. The most reactive *ions* are the ions of the elements at the bottom of the activity series and are the most likely to accept electrons, making them the strongest oxidizing agents.

a. The three metal *atoms* are Fe, Sn, and Li. Of these three, Li is highest in the activity series, so Li is the most active metal.
b. The three metal *ions* are Ag^+, Mg^{2+}, and Ca^{2+}. Of these three, silver is lowest in the activity series, so Ag^+ is the most reactive metal ion.
c. Reducing agents donate electrons. Active metal *atoms* act as reducing agents when they give up valence electrons to form ions. Therefore, the most active metal, Li, is the strongest reducing agent of the metals listed.
d. Oxidizing agents accept electrons. Reactive metal *ions* act as oxidizing agents when they accept electrons to form atoms. Therefore, the most reactive metal ion, Ag^+, is the strongest oxidizing agent listed.

PRACTICE PROBLEM 4.23

Given Ba(s), Pb^{2+}, Cr(s), Mn^{2+}, Ni(s), and Al^{3+}, identify

a. the most active metal.
b. the most reactive metal ion.
c. the strongest reducing agent.
d. the best oxidizing agent.

Hint: The most active metals are at the top of the activity series (Table 4.7) and are the most likely to give up electrons, which makes them the strongest reducing agents. The most reactive ions are those ions at the bottom of the activity series and are the most likely to accept electrons, making them the strongest oxidizing agents.

Example 4.24

Determine whether the following pairs of reactants will react.

a. $Cu(s) + Li^+(aq) \rightarrow$
b. $Li(s) + Cu^{2+}(aq) \rightarrow$
c. $Zn^{2+}(aq) + Mg^{2+}(aq) \rightarrow$
d. $Al(s) + SnCl_2(aq) \rightarrow$
e. $Li(s) + Cr(s) \rightarrow$

Solution

Active metal atoms can donate electrons to less active metal ions. Use the activity series (Table 4.7) to identify the more active metal.

a. Metals donate electrons to ions. The metal, copper, is lower in the activity series than is lithium, so copper is less active than is lithium, and it is unable to donate electrons to the lithium ion:

$$Cu(s) + Li^+(aq) \rightarrow \text{no reaction}$$

b. Lithium is higher in the activity series than is copper, so lithium atoms can transfer electrons to copper ions:

$$Li(s) + Cu^{2+}(aq) \rightarrow \text{products}$$

c. Both reactants are ions; neither can donate electrons:

$$Zn^{2+}(aq) + Mg^{2+}(aq) \rightarrow \text{no reaction}$$

d. Chlorine is a spectator ion, so it can be ignored. Aluminum is higher in the activity series than is tin, so aluminum atoms can transfer electrons to tin ions:

$$Al(s) + Sn^{2+}(aq) \rightarrow \text{products}$$

e. Both reactants are metal atoms; neither can accept electrons:

$$Li(s) + Cr(s) \rightarrow \text{no reaction}$$

PRACTICE PROBLEM 4.24

Determine whether the following pairs of reactants will react.

a. $Ni(s) + Pb^{2+}(aq) \rightarrow$
b. $Na(s) + Ag(s) \rightarrow$
c. $Zn^{2+}(aq) + Mg(s) \rightarrow$
d. $CaCl_2(aq) + Cu(s) \rightarrow$
e. $Au(NO_3)_3(aq) + Ag(s) \rightarrow$
f. $Li^+(aq) + Mn^{2+}(aq) \rightarrow$

Hint: Active metal atoms can donate electrons to less active metal ions. Use the activity series (Table 4.7) to identify the more active metal.

Example 4.25

Write balanced chemical equations for the following single-replacement reactions.

a. $Li(s) + CuCl_2(aq) \rightarrow$
b. $Al(s) + Sn(NO_3)_2(aq) \rightarrow$

Solution

In both cases, the neutral metal is more active than the metal ion (as shown in Example 4.24), so the reactions occur. In a single-replacement reaction, the neutral metal displaces the metal ion as part of the compound. Determine the formula for the new compound based on the ion charges, and then balance the reaction.

a. A compound of lithium ion, Li^+, and chloride, Cl^-, has the formula LiCl:

$$2\,Li(s) + CuCl_2(aq) \rightarrow Cu(s) + 2\,LiCl(aq)$$

b. A compound of aluminum ion, Al^{3+}, and nitrate, NO_3^-, has the formula $Al(NO_3)_3$:

$$2\,Al(s) + 3\,Sn(NO_3)_2(aq) \rightarrow 3\,Sn(s) + 2\,Al(NO_3)_3(aq)$$

PRACTICE PROBLEM 4.25

Write balanced chemical equations for the following single-replacement reactions.

a. $Ni(s) + Pb(ClO_4)_2(aq) \rightarrow$
b. $ZnCl_2(aq) + Mg(s) \rightarrow$
c. $Au(NO_3)_3(aq) + Ag(s) \rightarrow$

Hint: First, use the activity series to determine whether the reaction occurs. In a single-replacement reaction, the neutral metal displaces the metal ion as part of the compound. Determine the formula for the new compound based on the ion charges, and then balance the reaction.

Some metals react with acids, which produce H^+ ions in aqueous solution; other metals do not. Neutral metals that appear *above* H in the activity series can transfer electrons to H^+ to form diatomic hydrogen gas, $H_2(g)$.

Example 4.26

Determine whether the following reactants will react with aqueous hydrochloric acid, HCl(aq), and write balanced equations for any reactions that occur.

a. Zn(s)
b. $Ca^{2+}(aq)$
c. Cu(s)

Solution

Active metal atoms can donate electrons to less active metal ions and to hydrogen ions. Locate the metal in the activity series (Table 4.7). If it is higher than is hydrogen, then the metal can react with hydrogen ions.

a. Zinc is higher than is hydrogen in the activity series, so it will react with acids. The formula for a compound of zinc ion, Zn^{2+}, with chloride, Cl^-, is $ZnCl_2$:

$$Zn(s) + 2\,HCl(aq) \rightarrow ZnCl_2(aq) + H_2(g)$$

b. Neutral calcium is higher in the activity series than is hydrogen, but this is a calcium ion, which has no valence electrons to lose. No reaction will occur.

c. Copper is lower in the activity series than is hydrogen, so it does *not* react with acid.

PRACTICE PROBLEM 4.26

Determine whether the following reactants will react with aqueous hydrochloric acid, HCl(aq), and write balanced equations for any reactions that will occur.

a. Mg(s)
b. Au(s)
c. $Ba^{2+}(aq)$

Hint: Active metal *atoms* can donate electrons to less active metal ions and to hydrogen ions. Locate the metal in the activity series (Table 4.7). If it is higher than is hydrogen, then the *neutral* metal can react with hydrogen ions to produce hydrogen gas, $H_2(g)$.

SECTION REVIEW

- The transfer of electrons in redox reactions consists of two simultaneous processes, the loss of electrons (oxidation) and the gain of electrons (reduction).
- Products of many synthesis and decomposition reactions can be predicted based on the location of the elements in the periodic table.
- The activity series can be used to predict the likelihood of a redox reaction occurring between a metal atom and the ion of another metal or between metal atoms and acid.

Putting It Together

The example problems in earlier sections of this chapter focus on the new skills acquired in that section, but homework and exam questions in chemistry often require more than just one skill at a time. In fact, you will likely be expected to apply knowledge from across the entire chapter, or even multiple chapters, in a single problem. This final problem is meant to help you prepare for these types of multiconcept questions. Additional examples can be found in the end-of-chapter exercises.

Example 4.27

Suppose that you have three colorless solutions—$Sn(NO_3)_2$, Na_2SO_4, and HCl—in unlabeled test tubes, so you do not know which is which. Fortunately, you also have some pieces of magnesium metal and labeled solutions of $Ca(NO_3)_2$ and KOH with which to work.

Predict the results of mixing each unknown solution with the known substances and indicate them in the chart. Write balanced chemical equations for the reactions that occur. Finally, describe how you will know which unknown is which.

	Mg	$Ca(NO_3)_2$	KOH
If $Sn(NO_3)_2$			
If Na_2SO_4			
If HCl			

Solution

	Mg	$Ca(NO_3)_2$	KOH
If $Sn(NO_3)_2$	Mg dissolves; new solid appears	No change	Precipitate forms
If Na_2SO_4	No change	Precipitate forms	No change
If HCl	Mg dissolves; gas bubbles form	No change	No visible change, but reaction gives off heat

Reactions with magnesium:

- According to the activity series, magnesium is more active than is tin and should reduce the tin ions in a single-replacement reaction:

$$Mg(s) + Sn(NO_3)_2(aq) \rightarrow Mg(NO_3)_2(aq) + Sn(s)$$

- According to the activity series, magnesium is less reactive than is sodium, so there will be no reaction with Na_2SO_4.

- According to the activity series, magnesium will react with H^+ from strong acids such as HCl:

$$Mg(s) + 2\,HCl(aq) \rightarrow MgCl_2(aq) + H_2(g)$$

Reactions with calcium nitrate:

- $Sn(NO_3)_2$ contains the same anion, so there can be no double-replacement reaction.
- According to the solubility guidelines, calcium sulfate is insoluble. Therefore, Na_2SO_4 and $Ca(NO_3)_2$ will react in a double-replacement reaction to form $CaSO_4$:

$$Na_2SO_4(aq) + Ca(NO_3)_2(aq) \rightarrow CaSO_4(s) + 2\,NaNO_3(aq).$$

- According to the solubility guidelines, $CaCl_2$ is soluble, so no double-replacement reaction occurs when $Ca(NO_3)_2$ and HCl are combined.

Reactions with potassium hydroxide:

- According to the solubility guidelines, tin(II) hydroxide is insoluble. Therefore, $Sn(NO_3)_2$ and KOH will react in a double-replacement reaction to form $Sn(OH)_2$:

$$Sn(NO_3)_2(aq) + 2\,KOH(aq) \rightarrow Sn(OH)_2(s) + 2\,KNO_3(aq).$$

- According to the solubility guidelines, NaOH and K_2SO_4 are both soluble, so no reaction is expected.
- HCl is a strong acid and KOH is a strong base. These two compounds will react to neutralize each other and produce KCl and water, which will remain colorless (see reaction below). However, this reaction will release heat, so the tube should feel quite warm.

$$HCl(aq) + KOH(aq) \rightarrow KCl(aq) + H_2O(l)$$

Conclusion: The $Sn(NO_3)_2$ solution formed precipitates in two tests. The solution that formed a precipitate in one test and gave no sign of a reaction in the other two tests must be Na_2SO_4. The solution that formed bubbles in one test and gave no visible sign of a reaction but generated heat in another test must be the HCl.

PRACTICE PROBLEM 4.27

You have been given some tiny pieces of silvery gray metal to identify. The metal could be barium, silver, or zinc. You also have labeled solutions of sodium sulfate and copper(II) nitrate. Describe how you would identify the metals.

Hint: Use the activity series to determine which metals are most likely to react with either of the labeled solutions. Then consider using solubility guidelines to distinguish between any active metals.

Key Terms, Symbols, and Equations

KEY TERMS

acid (4.2): A compound that ionizes in solution to produce H^+ ions.

acid–base reaction (4.2): The reaction of an acid and a base to produce a salt and usually water; also called a neutralization reaction.

active metal (4.7): A metal that is easily oxidized.

activity series (4.7): A list of metals showing the relative level of activity, with most active (most readily oxidized) at the top and the least active (least readily oxidized) at the bottom.

aqueous solution (4.1): A homogeneous mixture of a pure substance dissolved in water.

balanced equation (4.1): A chemical equation in which the number and type of atoms in the reactants are equal to the number and type of atoms in the products.

base (4.2): A compound that ionizes in solution to produce OH^- ions.

chemical equation (4.1): A symbolic description of a chemical reaction using chemical formulas for reactants and products and using coefficients to indicate the proportions of reactants and products.

coefficient (4.1): A number, usually an integer, placed before a chemical formula in a chemical equation to indicate the ratio or proportion of reactant and product in a chemical change.

combination (4.2): A chemical reaction in which simple reactants combine to form a more complex product; also called synthesis.

combustion (4.2): A chemical reaction involving the rapid combination of a substance with oxygen; also called burning.

decomposition (4.2): A chemical reaction in which a reactant breaks down into less complex products.

displacement (4.2): A chemical reaction in which an element reacts with a compound, replacing one of the elements in the compound to produce a new compound and a new element; also called single-replacement and single-displacement reactions.

dissociate (4.3): To separate into ions; applies to ionic compounds dissolved in water.

double-displacement (4.2): A chemical reaction in which two ionic compounds exchange ions to form two new ionic compounds; also called double-replacement or metathesis.

double-replacement (4.2): A chemical reaction in which two ionic compounds exchange ions to form two new ionic compounds; also called metathesis or double-displacement.

driving force (4.2): The reason that a reaction happens; what causes a reaction to occur.

electrolyte (4.3): A substance that dissolves in water to produce hydrated ions and a solution capable of conducting electricity; typically, an ionic compound, acid, or base.

hydrated ion (4.3): An ion surrounded by water molecules; formed when electrolytes dissolve in water.

hydrocarbon (4.2): A category of chemical compounds containing only carbon and hydrogen; commonly used as fuels, they produce carbon dioxide and water if excess oxygen is present.

ionic equation (4.4): A chemical equation in which any strong electrolytes in aqueous solution are written as hydrated ions.

ionize (4.3): To become an ion or ions; applies to acids and weak bases dissolved in water.

insoluble (4.3): Unable to dissolve.

metathesis (4.2): Another name for a double-replacement reaction.

net ionic equation (4.4): A chemical equation in which only the ions that undergo change during the reaction are present.

neutralization (4.2): A subcategory of double-replacement reactions in which an acid reacts with a base to form an ionic compound and water; also called an acid–base reaction.

nonelectrolyte (4.3): A substance that dissolves in water as molecules, not as hydrated ions.

oxidation number (4.6): A type of electron bookkeeping used to keep track of the electrons transferred in redox reactions; assigned according to a set of rules or guidelines; also called oxidation state.

oxidation–reduction (4.2): A reaction involving a transfer of electrons from a higher energy state to a lower energy state; a driving force in many types of reactions; also called redox.

oxidation state (4.6): A type of electron bookkeeping used to keep track of the electrons transferred in redox reactions; assigned according to a set of rules or guidelines; also called oxidation number.

oxidizing agent (4.6): A substance that accepts electrons (is reduced) in a redox reaction.

precipitate (4.2): The insoluble product of a double-replacement reaction.

precipitation (4.2): The formation of a new solid; a driving force in certain double-replacement reactions.

product (4.1): The substance present at the end of a chemical change; the result of the reaction.

reactant (4.1): The substance present at the beginning of a chemical reaction that undergoes a chemical change.

redox (4.2): A reaction involving electron transfer; also called oxidation–reduction.

reducing agent (4.6): A substance that donates electrons (is oxidized) in a redox reaction.

salt (4.2): An ionic compound that does not contain H^+ or OH^-.

single-displacement (4.2): A chemical reaction in which an element reacts with a compound, replacing one of the elements in the compound to produce a new compound and a new element; also called single-replacement or displacement.

single-replacement (4.2): A chemical reaction in which an element reacts with a compound, replacing one of the elements in the compound to produce a new compound and a new element; also called single-displacement or displacement.

solubility guidelines (4.4): A series of rules or guidelines used to help predict the solubility of an ionic compound.

soluble (4.3): Able to dissolve.

spectator ion (4.4): An ion that does not change during a chemical reaction; the ion is omitted from a net ionic equation.

state (4.1): The physical state of matter, shown as an abbreviation in parentheses after a chemical formula in a chemical equation: solid (s), liquid (l), gas (g), or aqueous solution (aq).

strong acid (4.3): A molecular compound that ionizes 100% in water to produce H^+ and an aqueous anion.

strong base (4.3): An ionic compound containing hydroxide ion, OH^-, that dissolves and dissociates 100% in water.

strong electrolyte (4.3)**:** A substance that produces ions when dissolved in water.

synthesis (4.2)**:** A chemical reaction in which simple reactants combine to form a more complex product; also called combination.

total equation (4.4)**:** The overall, balanced chemical equation that shows the formulas of the reactants and products and their states of matter.

weak acid (4.3)**:** A molecular compound that dissolves in water primarily as a molecule but ionizes to a small degree, thus producing aqueous H^+ and an aqueous anion.

weak base (4.3)**:** A molecular compound that dissolves in water primarily as a molecule but ionizes to a small degree, thus producing aqueous OH^- and an aqueous cation.

weak electrolyte (4.3)**:** A substance that dissolves in water primarily as a molecule but ionizes to a small degree, thus producing small percentages of hydrated ions.

SYMBOLS AND ABBREVIATIONS

(aq) (aqueous solution) (4.1)

(g) (gas) (4.1)

(l) (liquid) (4.1)

(s) (solid) (4.1)

$\rightarrow$ (yields or produces) (4.1)

Chapter Summary

Chemical equations, which are symbolic descriptions of what happens during a chemical reaction, must follow the law of conservation of matter and are balanced by placing coefficients in front of the formulas of the reactants and products. The coefficients in a balanced equation indicate the proportions (ratios) of any one of the reactants or products to any of the other reactants or products in a chemical reaction in terms of individual units (atoms, molecules, formula units, ions) or in terms of the moles of these same individual units. These coefficients also multiply each element in the chemical formula and are assumed to be 1 if there is no coefficient present. The physical states of reactants and products are generally included in the balanced equation by specifying solid (s), liquid (l), gas (g), or aqueous solution (aq) in parentheses after each chemical formula in the equation.

Chemical equations can be balanced by adding coefficients in a systematic way that still involves a certain amount of trial and error. Balancing polyatomic ions as units and saving elements that appear in multiple reactants or products for last can be helpful. Most importantly, verify that the number of each type of atom is the same in the reactants and products and that the coefficients are in the smallest whole-number ratios (Section 4.1).

Five reaction types were introduced and described in Chapter 4:

- Synthesis or combination reactions combine simpler reactants to form more complex products: $A + B \rightarrow AB$. The driving force is oxidation–reduction.
- Decomposition reactions start with more complex reactants and form simpler products: $AB \rightarrow A + B$. The driving force is oxidation–reduction.
- Single-replacement (single-displacement or displacement) reactions involve an element reacting with a compound to form a new compound and a new element: $A + BC \rightarrow AC + B$. The driving force is oxidation–reduction.
- Double-replacement (double-displacement or metathesis) reactions involve two ionic compounds that swap ions to form two new products: $AB + CD \rightarrow AD + CB$. Acid–base reactions that involve a strong base are a type of double-replacement reaction in which the products are water and a salt: $HA + BOH \rightarrow BA + H_2O$. When an insoluble product is produced, the driving

force is precipitation. When water is produced from an acid and a base, the driving force is neutralization.

- Combustion reactions generally involve hydrocarbon fuels reacting rapidly with oxygen to produce carbon dioxide and water: $C_xH_y + O_2 \rightarrow CO_2 + H_2O$ (Section 4.2).

Ionic compounds dissociate 100% when dissolved in water to produce hydrated ions. This includes strong bases, which are soluble ionic compounds containing the hydroxide ion. Most covalent compounds do not dissolve in water. Those that do dissolve as molecules—exceptions include strong acids, weak acids, and weak bases. Strong acids are covalent compounds that ionize in water 100%, whereas weak acids and weak bases mainly dissolve as molecules but ionize to a very small extent. Solutions containing hydrated ions can conduct electricity and are called electrolyte solutions. Ionic compounds and strong acids are strong electrolytes. Weak acids and weak bases are weak electrolytes. Soluble molecular compounds that are neither acids nor bases (e.g., sugars) are nonelectrolytes (Section 4.3).

Many ionic compounds are only sparingly soluble in water and are generally referred to as insoluble. Solubility guidelines can be used to predict whether an ionic compound is soluble or insoluble in water. Double-replacement reactions occur when solutions of two ionic compounds are mixed and the ions can form a new, insoluble, ionic compound. The resulting solid is called a precipitate and the reactions are also called precipitation reactions. Solubility guidelines can be used to predict whether precipitation reactions will occur upon mixing solutions of ionic compounds. Three types of chemical equations are used to describe precipitation reactions: a total chemical equation, such as those described in Section 4.1 and balanced in Section 4.2; an ionic equation, in which all aqueous strong electrolytes are written as separate ions; and a net ionic equation, in which all spectator ions have been removed so that only those components of the reaction that have changed are retained (Section 4.4).

The formulas of strong acids generally start with H, and strong bases are ionic compounds containing hydroxide ions. Acid–base reactions or neutralization reactions are the reaction of a strong acid and a strong base to form a salt and water. The salt is formed from a cation from the base and an anion from the acid. Any reaction of a strong acid with a strong base has the following net ionic equation: $H^+(aq) + OH^-(aq) \rightarrow H_2O(l)$ (Section 4.5).

The transfer of electrons in redox reactions consists of two simultaneous processes—the loss of electrons (oxidation) and the gain of electrons (reduction). Oxidation numbers can be used to keep track of the transfer of electrons between atoms and are assigned according to a series of general rules. Oxidation–reduction (redox) reactions can be identified by assigning oxidation numbers to all components and looking for changes in the oxidation numbers of the elements. Oxidation is defined as an increase in oxidation number and reduction is defined as a decrease in oxidation number. Oxidizing agents accept electrons from the component that is being oxidized. Oxidizing agents are reduced during redox reactions. Reducing agents provide the electrons to the component that is being reduced. Reducing agents are oxidized during redox reactions (Section 4.6).

The activity series lists metals from more active (more readily oxidized) to less active (less readily oxidized) and can be used to predict whether a single-replacement reaction will occur. The ionic products of synthesis and single-replacement reactions can be predicted using ion charges (Section 4.7).

END OF CHAPTER QUESTIONS

4.1 Chemical Equations

1. Write a balanced chemical equation for the reaction of aqueous potassium hydroxide with phosphoric acid to yield potassium phosphate plus water.
2. Write a balanced equation for the reaction of oxygen gas with nitrogen monoxide gas to form gaseous N_2O_3.
3. Balance the chemical equation for each of the following reactions:
   a. $Cu_2S(s) + O_2(g) \rightarrow Cu(s) + SO_2(g)$
   b. $CO_2(g) + H_2(g) \rightarrow CO(g) + H_2O(g)$
   c. $ZnS(s) + O_2(g) \rightarrow ZnO(s) + SO_2(g)$
   d. $H_2O(l) + SCl_4(s) \rightarrow HCl(aq) + H_2SO_3(aq)$
   e. $O_2(g) + MnO(s) \rightarrow Mn_3O_4(s)$
4. Write a balanced chemical equation for the reaction of water with sodium metal to produce aqueous sodium hydroxide and hydrogen gas.
5. Write a balanced chemical equation for the reaction of aqueous sodium sulfate and barium bromate to yield barium sulfate plus sodium bromate.
6. Balance the equation for each of the following reactions:
   a. $AlCl_3(aq) + NaOH(aq) \rightarrow NaAl(OH)_4(aq) + NaCl(aq)$
   b. $H_3PO_4(aq) + NaOH(aq) \rightarrow Na_3PO_4(aq) + H_2O(l)$
   c. $C_2H_6(g) + O_2(g) \rightarrow CO_2(g) + H_2O(l)$
   d. $MnO_2(s) + H_2C_2O_4(aq) \rightarrow CO_2(g) + MnO(s) + H_2O(l)$
   e. $As_2S_3(s) + O_2(g) \rightarrow As_2O_3(s) + SO_2(g)$
7. Write a balanced chemical equation for the reaction of 1-pentene gas (C_5H_{10}), which burns in excess oxygen to produce carbon dioxide and water.
8. Write a balanced chemical equation for the reaction of aqueous calcium hydrogen carbonate with hydrochloric acid to yield calcium chloride plus carbon dioxide plus water.
9. Balance the chemical equation for each of the following reactions:
   a. $CuSO_4 \cdot 5\,H_2O(s) + NH_3(aq) \rightarrow CuSO_4 \cdot 4\,NH_3(aq) + H_2O(l)$
   b. $Na_2SO_3(aq) + S(s) \rightarrow Na_2S_2O_3(aq)$
   c. $C_2H_4O(l) + O_2(g) \rightarrow CO_2(g) + H_2O(g)$
   d. $Zn(s) + NaOH(aq) + H_2O(l) \rightarrow Na_2Zn(OH)_4(aq) + H_2(g)$
10. Write a balanced chemical equation for the reaction of solid calcium sulfite, which decomposes on heating to produce solid calcium oxide and sulfur dioxide gas.
11. Balance the equation for each of the following reactions:
    a. $NaAl(OH)_4(aq) + HCl(aq) \rightarrow AlCl_3(aq) + H_2O(l) + NaCl(aq)$
    b. $C_6H_{12}(l) + O_2(g) \rightarrow CO(g) + H_2O(g)$
    c. $BiCl_3(aq) + H_2O(l) \rightarrow BiOCl(s) + HCl(aq)$
    d. $Mn_3O_4(s) + O_2(g) \rightarrow Mn_2O_3(s)$
    e. $C_7H_{14}O(l) + O_2(g) \rightarrow CO_2(g) + H_2O(g)$
12. Write a balanced equation for the reaction of aqueous copper(II) nitrate with aqueous sodium iodide to produce solid copper(I) iodide plus aqueous iodine plus aqueous sodium nitrate.
13. Write a balanced chemical equation for the reaction of solid sulfur with fluorine gas to yield liquid sulfur hexafluoride.
14. Balance the equation for each of the following reactions:
    a. $Al_2O_3(\text{in solution}) + C(s) \rightarrow Al(l) + CO(g)$
    b. $N_2(g) + O_2(g) \rightarrow NO(g)$
    c. $C_3O_2(s) + O_2(g) \rightarrow CO_2(g)$
    d. $B_2H_6(g) + O_2(g) \rightarrow B_2O_3(s) + H_2O(l)$
    e. $C(s) + O_2(g) \rightarrow CO_2(g)$
15. Write a balanced chemical equation for the reaction of potassium metal and chlorine gas to produce solid potassium chloride.
16. Balance the chemical equation for each of the following reactions:
    a. $NO_2(g) \rightarrow N_2O_4(l)$
    b. $Ba(s) + O_2(g) \rightarrow BaO(s)$
    c. $Na(s) + Cl_2(g) \rightarrow NaCl(s)$
    d. $P(s) + O_2(g) \rightarrow P_2O_5(s)$
17. Write a balanced chemical equation for the reaction of aqueous lithium hydroxide with gaseous carbon dioxide to produce aqueous lithium hydrogen carbonate.

4.2 Types of Chemical Reactions

18. Identify the type of reaction and its driving force in each of the following:
    a. In aqueous solution, sodium sulfate plus barium bromate yields solid barium sulfate plus sodium bromate.
    b. Solid sulfur plus fluorine gas yields gaseous sulfur hexafluoride.
    c. Aqueous copper(II) nitrate reacts with aqueous sodium iodide to produce solid copper(I) iodide plus aqueous iodine plus aqueous sodium nitrate.
    d. Oxygen gas and nitrogen monoxide gas react to form gaseous N_2O_3.

19. Identify the type of reaction for each of the following:
    a. $Cu_2S(s) + O_2(g) \rightarrow 2\,Cu(s) + SO_2(g)$
    b. $C_7H_{14}O(l) + 10\,O_2(g) \rightarrow 7\,CO_2(g) + 7\,H_2O(g)$
    c. $2\,Ba(s) + O_2\,(g) \rightarrow 2\,BaO(s)$
    d. $CaSO_3(s) \rightarrow CaO(s) + SO_2(g)$

20. Identify the type of reaction for each of the following:
    a. $As_2S_3(s) + {}^9\!/_2\,O_2(g) \rightarrow As_2O_3(s) + 3\,SO_2(g)$
    b. $C_2H_4O(l) + {}^5\!/_2\,O_2(g) \rightarrow 2\,CO_2(g) + 2\,H_2O(g)$
    c. $2\,Na(s) + Cl_2(g) \rightarrow 2\,NaCl(s)$
    d. $2\,Mn_3O_4(s) + {}^1\!/_2\,O_2(g) \rightarrow 3\,Mn_2O_3(s)$

21. Identify the type of reaction for each of the following:
    a. $N_2(g) + O_2(g) \rightarrow 2\,NO(g)$
    b. $Mg(s) + 2\,HCl(aq) \rightarrow MgCl_2(aq) + H_2(g)$
    c. $C_2H_6(g) + {}^7\!/_2\,O_2(g) \rightarrow 2\,CO_2(g) + 3\,H_2O(l)$
    d. $2\,P(s) + {}^5\!/_2\,O_2(g) \rightarrow P_2O_5(s)$

22. Identify the type of reaction for each of the following:
    a. Aqueous lithium hydroxide reacts with gaseous carbon dioxide to produce aqueous lithium hydrogen carbonate.
    b. Solid calcium sulfite, on heating, produces solid calcium oxide and sulfur dioxide gas.
    c. Pentene gas (C_5H_{10}) burns in excess oxygen to produce carbon dioxide and water.
    d. Lithium metal when heated with nitrogen gas reacts to produce solid lithium nitride.

23. Complete and balance the equations for the following combustion reactions:
    a. $C_5H_{10}O_2(l) + O_2(g) \rightarrow$
    b. $C_3H_8(g) + O_2(g) \rightarrow$
    c. $C_{12}H_{26}(l) + O_2(g) \rightarrow$
    d. $C_7H_{16}O(l) + O_2(g) \rightarrow$

4.3 Compounds in Aqueous Solution

24. Identify these compounds as containing covalent bonds or ionic bonds.
    a. PCl_3
    b. $FeCl_3$
    c. Cl_2

25. Write formulas for the ions that constitute each of the following compounds:
    a. $Mg(NO_2)_2$
    b. CrF_2
    c. $(NH_4)_3PO_4$
    d. K_2SO_4
    e. $KMnO_4$

26. Classify the following water-soluble substances as being strong electrolytes, weak electrolytes, or nonelectrolytes:
    a. $CuSO_4$
    b. H_2S
    c. HNO_2
    d. $UO_2(NO_3)_2$
    e. $(NH_4)_2Cr_2O_7$

27. Classify the following water-soluble substances as being strong electrolytes, weak electrolytes, or nonelectrolytes:
    a. ClO_4
    b. $CuCl_2$
    c. $HClO_2$
    d. $(NH_4)_2SO_3$
    e. CsOH

28. Classify the following water-soluble substances as being strong electrolytes, weak electrolytes, or nonelectrolytes:
    a. $ZnCl_2$
    b. $(NH_4)_2S_2O_3$
    c. Li_2SO_4
    d. H_3PO_4
    e. CCl_4

29. Classify the following water-soluble substances as being strong electrolytes, weak electrolytes, or nonelectrolytes:
    a. KCl
    b. C_3H_8O
    c. Na_2SO_4
    d. H_2SO_3
    e. $Mg(ClO_4)_2$

30. Suppose you need to prepare a solution containing fluoride ions. Why is NaF a better choice than HF as the source of fluoride ions in solution?

4.4 Precipitation Reactions

31. Predict the solubility of the following salts:
    a. $Ba(SO_4)$
    b. K_3PO_4
    c. $Mg(OH)_2$
    d. $Mg(ClO_4)_2$
32. Predict the solubility of the following salts:
    a. $Ba(NO_3)_2$
    b. Ag_2SO_4
    c. $PbCl_2$
    d. ZnS
33. Complete and balance the following double-replacement reactions. Include the phases for the products.
    a. $NaCl(aq) + AgC_2H_3O_2(aq) \rightarrow$
    b. $K_3PO_4(aq) + FeCl_2(aq) \rightarrow$
    c. $Sn(NO_3)_2(aq) + Na_2CO_3(aq) \rightarrow$
    d. $KOH(aq) + Mn(NO_3)_2(aq) \rightarrow$
    e. $MgSO_4(aq) + Ca(ClO_4)_2(aq) \rightarrow$
34. Predict if a precipitation reaction will occur.
    a. $Na_3PO_4(aq) + MgCl_2(aq) \rightarrow$
    b. $Na_2SO_4(aq) + KOH(aq) \rightarrow$
    c. $MgSO_4(aq) + CaCl_2(aq) \rightarrow$
35. Write a balanced total equation for any precipitation reaction from the previous question.
36. Write complete ionic and net ionic equations for the reactions in the previous question.
37. Predict if a precipitation reaction will occur:
    a. $KClO_4(aq) + BaBr_2(aq) \rightarrow$
    b. $NaOH(aq) + Fe(NO_3)_3(aq) \rightarrow$
    c. $Pb(C_2H_3O_2)_2(aq) + ZnCl_2(aq) \rightarrow$
38. Write a balanced total equation for any precipitation reaction from the previous question.
39. Write complete ionic and net ionic equations for the reactions in the previous question.
40. Predict if a precipitation reaction will occur:
    a. $K_2SO_4(aq) + BaCl_2(aq) \rightarrow$
    b. $Pb(ClO_4)_2(aq) + CaS(aq) \rightarrow$
    c. $CuSO_4(aq) + PbCl_2(aq) \rightarrow$
41. Write a balanced total equation for any precipitation reaction from the previous question.
42. Write complete ionic and net ionic equations for the reactions in the previous question.
43. Predict if a precipitation reaction will occur:
    a. $Hg_2(NO_3)_2(aq) + BaBr_2(aq) \rightarrow$
    b. $Ca(OH)_2(aq) + Ba(NO_3)_2(aq) \rightarrow$
    c. $Fe(C_2H_3O_2)_2(aq) + Li_2S(aq) \rightarrow$
44. Write a balanced total equation for any precipitation reaction from the previous question.
45. Write complete ionic and net ionic equations for the reactions in the previous question.

4.5 Acid–Base Reactions

46. Classify the following as strong or weak acids:
    a. HCl
    b. HNO_2
    c. H_2SO_4
    d. H_3PO_4
    e. H_2SO_3
    f. $HClO_4$
    g. HI
47. Which of these will ionize 100% in water?
    a. HBr
    b. H_3PO_4
    c. H_2S
    d. HNO_3
    e. $HClO_2$
    f. HNO_2
    g. HCO_2H
48. Complete and balance the following reaction. Then write a complete ionic equation and a net ionic equation for the reaction.
    $H_3PO_4(aq) + KOH(aq) \rightarrow$
49. Complete and balance the following reaction. Then write a complete ionic equation and a net ionic equation for the reaction.
    $Ba(OH)_2(aq) + HNO_3(aq) \rightarrow$
50. Complete and balance the following reaction. Then write a complete ionic equation and a net ionic equation for the reaction.
    $Na_2HPO_4(aq) + NaOH(aq) \rightarrow$
51. Write the indicated equations for the aqueous reaction of sulfuric acid with barium hydroxide.
    a. a balanced total equation
    b. a complete ionic equation
    c. a net ionic equation
52. Write the indicated equations for the aqueous reaction of nitrous acid with sodium hydroxide.
    a. a balanced total equation
    b. a complete ionic equation
    c. a net ionic equation

53. Write the indicated equations for the aqueous reaction of carbonic acid with sodium hydroxide:
    a. a balanced total equation
    b. a complete ionic equation
    c. a net ionic equation

54. Write the indicated equations for the aqueous reaction of formic acid (HCO_2H) with potassium hydroxide.
    a. a balanced total equation
    b. a complete ionic equation
    c. a net ionic equation

55. Write the indicated equations for the aqueous reaction of sulfurous acid with lithium hydroxide.
    a. a balanced total equation
    b. a complete ionic equation
    c. a net ionic equation

4.6 Oxidation States and Redox Reactions

56. Determine the oxidation state of nitrogen in each of these substances:
    a. HNO_3
    b. $Ba(NO_3)_2$
    c. $(NH_4)_2SO_3$
    d. NO_2
    e. N_2
    f. N^{3-}
    g. N_2O_4
    h. NH_3

57. Determine the oxidation state of manganese in each of these substances:
    a. MnO_2
    b. Mn
    c. Mn^{2+}
    d. MnO_4^-
    e. $MnCl_2$
    f. Mn_2O_7
    g. MnS_2
    h. Mn_3O_4

58. Determine the oxidation state of sulfur in each of these substances:
    a. H_2S
    b. S_8
    c. SF_6
    d. CaS
    e. S_3Cl_2
    f. SO_2^{2-}
    g. H_2SO_4
    h. S_2O

59. Identify any redox reactions in the following reactions.
    a. $Zn(s) + S(s) \rightarrow ZnS(s)$
    b. $Ba(OH)_2(aq) + 2\ HNO_3(aq) \rightarrow Ba(NO_3)_2(aq) + 2\ H_2O(l)$
    c. $2\ KClO_3(s) \rightarrow 2\ KCl(s) + 3\ O_2(g)$
    d. $2\ Na_3PO_4(aq) + 3\ MgCl_2(aq) \rightarrow Mg_3(PO_4)_2(s) + 6\ NaCl(aq)$
    e. $Co(s) + 2\ HBr(aq) \rightarrow CoBr_2(aq) + H_2(g)$
    f. $H_2O(l) + N_2O_5(g) \rightarrow 2\ HNO_3(aq)$
    g. $2\ FeI_2(aq) + I_2(g) \rightarrow 2\ FeI_3(aq)$
    h. $NiSO_4(aq) + Mg(s) \rightarrow MgSO_4(aq) + Ni(s)$
    i. $2\ SO_2(g) + O_2(g) \rightarrow 2\ SO_3(g)$

60. Given the equation below, identify: a) the reactant that is reduced, b) the reactant that is oxidized, c) the reducing agent, and d) the oxidizing agent.

$$Zn(s) + S(s) \rightarrow ZnS(s)$$

61. Given the equation below, identify: a) the reactant that is reduced, b) the reactant that is oxidized, c) the reducing agent, and d) the oxidizing agent.

$$2\ KClO_3(s) \rightarrow 2\ KCl(s) + 3\ O_2(g)$$

62. Given the equation below, identify: a) the reactant that is reduced, b) the reactant that is oxidized, c) the reducing agent, and d) the oxidizing agent.

$$Co(s) + 2\ HBr(aq) \rightarrow CoBr_2(aq) + H_2(g)$$

63. Given the equation below, identify: a) the reactant that is reduced, b) the reactant that is oxidized, c) the reducing agent, and d) the oxidizing agent.

$$2\ FeI_2(aq) + I_2(g) \rightarrow 2\ FeI_3(aq)$$

64. Given the equation below, identify: a) the reactant that is reduced, b) the reactant that is oxidized, c) the reducing agent, and d) the oxidizing agent.

$$NiSO_4(aq) + Mg(s) \rightarrow MgSO_4(aq) + Ni(s)$$

65. Given the equation below, identify: a) the reactant that is reduced, b) the reactant that is oxidized, c) the reducing agent, and d) the oxidizing agent.

$$2\ SO_2(g) + O_2(g) \rightarrow 2\ SO_3(g)$$

4.7 Predicting the Products of Redox Reactions

66. Write balanced combination equations for the production of these compounds from their elements.
    a. copper(I) bromide
    b. copper(I) sulfide
    c. sodium bromide
    d. sodium sulfide

e. aluminum bromide
f. aluminum sulfide

67. Write balanced equations for the decomposition of these compounds into their elements.
a. magnesium iodide
b. iron(III) chloride
c. zinc oxide
d. manganese(II) sulfide
e. lithium phosphide

68. Complete and balance the following single-replacement reactions:
a. $Zn(s) + CoCl_2(aq) \rightarrow$
b. $Sn(NO_3)_2(aq) + Al(s) \rightarrow$
c. $AgC_2H_3O_2(aq) + Cr(s) \rightarrow$
d. $Mg(s) + FeSO_4(aq) \rightarrow$
e. $Ca(s) + HClO_4(aq) \rightarrow$

69. Complete and balance the equation for each of the following reactions, which can be synthesis, decomposition, or single-replacement reactions. You do not need to include phases for the products.
a. $Ca(s) + I_2(s) \rightarrow$
b. $KCl(s) \rightarrow$
c. $Ba(s) + HNO_3(aq) \rightarrow$
d. $Ca(s) + Cl_2(g) \rightarrow$

70. Complete and balance the equation for each of the following reactions, which can be synthesis, decomposition, or single-replacement reactions. You do not need to include phases for the products.
a. $Al_2S_3(s) \rightarrow$
b. $Ga(s) + O_2(g) \rightarrow$
c. $Na_2O(s) \rightarrow$
d. $Cr(s) + SnSO_4(aq) \rightarrow$

71. Complete and balance the equation for each of the following reactions, which can be synthesis, decomposition, or single-replacement reactions. You do not need to include phases for the products.
a. $Mg(s) + N_2(g) \rightarrow$
b. $Ca(s) + Pb(C_2H_3O_2)_2 \rightarrow$
c. $Li_3P(s) \rightarrow$
d. $Al(s) + HBr(aq) \rightarrow$

72. Complete and balance the equation for each of the following reactions, which can be synthesis, decomposition, or single-replacement reactions. You do not need to include phases for the products.
a. $Li(s) + Br_2(l) \rightarrow$
b. $Cl_2(g) + NaBr(s) \rightarrow$
c. $Ba_3N_2(s) \rightarrow$
d. $Rb(s) + S(s) \rightarrow$

73. Determine if these pairs of reactants will react.
a. $Cu(s) + Cr(s)$
b. $Cu^{2+}(aq) + Cr(s)$
c. $Cu^{2+}(aq) + Cr^{2+}(aq)$
d. $Cu(s) + Cr^{2+}(aq)$

74. Write balanced equations for any of the reactant combinations from the previous question that will react.

75. Determine if these pairs of reactants will react.
a. $Mg(s) + Fe(NO_3)_2(aq)$
b. $Mg^{2+}(aq) + ZnSO_4(aq)$
c. $Zn(s) + CuCl_2(aq)$
d. $Cr(s) + CaSO_4(aq)$

76. Write balanced equations for any of the reactant combinations from the previous question that will react.

77. Determine if these pairs of reactants will react.
a. $Ag(s) + HNO_3(aq)$
b. $Fe(s) + AgNO_3(aq)$
c. $Cu^{2+}(aq) + Ni(ClO_3)_2(aq)$
d. $Al(s) + CuSO_4(aq)$

78. Write balanced equations for any of the reactant combinations from the previous question that will react.

Putting It Together

79. Complete and balance the following net ionic equations. There is a reaction in each case.
a. $Pb^{2+}(aq) + SO_4^{2-}(aq) \rightarrow$
b. $Ag^+(aq) + CN^-(aq) \rightarrow$
c. $H^+(aq) + OH^-(aq) \rightarrow$

80. Identify a pair of soluble salts that, when mixed, would produce the precipitate $NiS(s)$.

81. Write a balanced total equation and a balanced net ionic equation for each of the following reactions (there is a reaction in each case):
a. $BaS(s) + HCl(aq) \rightarrow$
b. $KC_2H_3O_2(aq) + HClO_3(aq) \rightarrow$
c. $NaH_2PO_4(aq) + HClO_4(aq) \rightarrow$

82. Write a balanced net ionic equation for each of the following reactions (there is a reaction in each case):
a. $Ba(NO_3)_2(aq) + K_3PO_4(aq) \rightarrow$
b. $Hg_2(NO_3)_2(aq) + NaCl(aq) \rightarrow$
c. $CuCl_2(aq) + (NH_4)_2S(aq) \rightarrow$

83. Write a balanced net ionic equation for each of the following reactions (there is a reaction in each case):
a. $ZnCl_2(aq) + (NH_4)_2S(aq) \rightarrow$
b. $Hg(C_2H_3O_2)_2(aq) + K_3PO_4(aq) \rightarrow$
c. $CaCl_2(aq) + K_2CO_3(aq) \rightarrow$

84. Identify an unknown metal based on the following observations. You may find it helpful to consult Table 4.7 and Table 1.9.
a. It is a very shiny, silver metal with a density of 7.3 g/cm^3.
b. It produces bubbles when placed in HCl(aq).
c. It reacts with $Zn(NO_3)_2(aq)$ but not with $Mg(NO_3)_2(aq)$.

85. Identify an unknown metal based on the following observations. You may find it helpful to consult Table 4.7 and Table 1.9.
a. It has density of 8.9 g/cm^3.
b. It has no reaction when placed in HCl(aq).
c. It reacts with $AgNO_3(aq)$.

86. Suppose you have a solution that could be either $MgCl_2$, $BaCl_2$, or $Pb(NO_3)_2$, which are all colorless solutions. Determine which of these is correct based on the following observations. You may find it helpful to consult Table 4.5.
a. no reaction with NaOH and NaCl
b. forms precipitate with Na_2SO_4 and $AgNO_3$

87. Suppose you have a solution that could be either $MgCl_2$, $BaCl_2$, or $Pb(NO_3)_2$, which are all colorless solutions. Determine which of these is correct based on the following observations. You may find it helpful to consult Table 4.5.
a. no reaction with Na_2SO_4 and NaCl
b. forms precipitate with NaOH and $AgNO_3$

88. Suppose you have a solution that could be either $MgCl_2$, $BaCl_2$, or $Pb(NO_3)_2$, which are all colorless solutions. Determine which of these is correct based on the following observations. You may find it helpful to consult Table 4.5.
a. no reaction with $AgNO_3$
b. forms precipitate with NaOH, NaCl, and Na_2SO_4

89. Suppose you must identify a sample of metal that could be nickel, iron, or zinc. Your sample consists of small, irregularly shaped pieces. You notice that the pieces tend to trap air bubbles when submerged in water, making it very difficult to obtain an accurate volume. Use the following observations to identify the metal.
a. produces bubbles when placed in HCl solution
b. reacts with $CuSO_4(aq)$
c. reacts (slowly) with $Cr(NO_3)_3$

PRACTICE PROBLEM SOLUTIONS

Practice Problem 4.1 Solution

Step	Result
1. Balance polyatomic ions if present on both sides	$\_NH_4I + 1\ Pb(NO_3)_2 \rightarrow 2\ NH_4NO_3 + \_PbI_2$ NO_3^- is balanced $2\ NH_4I + 1\ Pb(NO_3)_2 \rightarrow 2\ NH_4NO_3 + PbI_2$ NH_4^+ is balanced
2. Balance elements that appear in only one reactant and product, in any order	$2\ NH_4I + 1\ Pb(NO_3)_2 \rightarrow 2\ NH_4NO_3 + 1\ PbI_2$ I, Pb are balanced
3. Balance remaining elements	No elements left
4. Verify balanced equation	$2\ NH_4I + Pb(NO_3)_2 \rightarrow 2\ NH_4NO_3 + PbI_2$ 4 N, 8 H, 2 I, 1 Pb, and 6 O on each side Coefficients are in the smallest whole-number ratios.

Practice Problem 4.2 Solution

Steps	Example
1. Balance polyatomic ions if present on both sides	Not applicable
2. Balance elements that appear in only one reactant and product	$1\ C_8H_{18} + \_O_2 \rightarrow 8\ CO_2 + \_H_2O$ C is balanced $1\ C_8H_{18} + \_O_2 \rightarrow 8\ CO_2 + 9\ H_2O$ H is balanced
3. Balance remaining elements	$2\ C_8H_{18} + \_O_2 \rightarrow 16\ CO_2 + 18\ H_2O$ Double coefficients $2\ C_8H_{18} + 25\ O_2 \rightarrow 16\ CO_2 + 18\ H_2O$ O is balanced
4. Verify balanced equation	$2\ C_8H_{18} + 25\ O_2 \rightarrow 16\ CO_2 + 18\ H_2O$ 16 C, 36 H, and 50 O on each side Coefficients are in the smallest whole-number ratios.

Practice Problem 4.3 Solution

Step	Result
1. Balance any polyatomic ions present on both sides	Not applicable
2. Balance elements that appear in only one reactant and product	$1\ H_2O + \_N_2O_5 \rightarrow 2\ HNO_3$ H is balanced $1\ H_2O + 1\ N_2O_5 \rightarrow 2\ HNO_3$ N is balanced
3. Balance remaining elements	$1\ H_2O + 1\ N_2O_5 \rightarrow 2\ HNO_3$ O is already balanced
4. Verify balanced equation	$H_2O + N_2O_5 \rightarrow 2\ HNO_3$ 2 H, 6 O, and 2 N on each side Coefficients are in the smallest whole-number ratios.

Practice Problem 4.4 Solution

First, write the unbalanced equation based on the reaction described in the problem statement, recognizing that NH_4^+, the ammonium ion, will form a compound with the chloride ion in a 1:1 ratio and that Cu^{2+} forms a compound with the sulfide ion, S^{2-}, also in a 1:1 ratio:

$$(NH_4)_2S + CuCl_2 \rightarrow CuS + NH_4Cl$$

Steps	Example
1. Balance any polyatomic ions present on both sides	$1\ (NH_4)_2S + \_CuCl_2 \rightarrow CuS + 2\ NH_4Cl$ NH_4^+ is balanced
2. Balance elements that appear in only one reactant and product	$1\ (NH_4)_2S + 1\ CuCl_2 \rightarrow 1\ CuS + 2\ NH_4Cl$ S, Cu, Cl are balanced
3. Balance remaining elements	Not applicable
4. Verify balanced equation	$(NH_4)_2S + CuCl_2 \rightarrow CuS + 2\ NH_4Cl$ 2 N, 8 H, 1 S, and 2 Cl on each side Coefficients are in the smallest whole-number ratios.

Practice Problem 4.5 Solution

a. Double-replacement reaction: An acid reacts with a base to form a salt and water.

b. Synthesis reaction: Two reactants combine to form a single, more complex product.

c. Double-replacement reaction: Two ionic compounds exchange anions.

d. Double-replacement reaction: Two ionic compounds exchange anions.

e. Double-replacement reaction: An acid reacts with a base to form a salt and water.

f. Synthesis reaction: Two reactants combine to form a single, more complex product.

g. Single-replacement reaction: An element displaces another element within a compound.

h. Decomposition reaction: A single substance breaks down into two simpler substances.

Practice Problem 4.6 Solution

a. This is an acid–base reaction. Its driving force is neutralization.

b. This is a synthesis reaction. Its driving force is oxidation–reduction.

c. This is a double-replacement reaction with a solid product. Its driving force is precipitation.

d. This is a double-replacement reaction with a solid product. Its driving force is precipitation.

e. This is an acid–base reaction. Its driving force is neutralization.

f. This is a synthesis reaction. Its driving force is oxidation–reduction.

g. This is a single-replacement reaction. Its driving force is oxidation–reduction.

h. This is a decomposition reaction. Its driving force is oxidation–reduction.

Practice Problem 4.7 Solution

These ionic compounds dissociate in water to produce separate, hydrated ions.

a. $KOH(aq) \rightarrow K^+(aq) + OH^-\ (aq)$

b. $CaCl_2(aq) \rightarrow Ca^{2+}(aq) + 2\ Cl^-\ (aq)$

c. $Na_3PO_4(aq) \rightarrow 3\ Na^+ + PO_4^{3-}(aq)$

Practice Problem 4.8 Solution

a. Na_2SO_4 contains a metal and a polyatomic ion, so it is an ionic compound and a strong electrolyte.

b. NaOH contains a metal and a polyatomic ion, so it is an ionic compound and a strong electrolyte. It is also a strong base.

c. C_2H_6O contains only nonmetal elements, so it a molecular compound. It is also neither an acid nor a base, so it is a nonelectrolyte.

d. $Pb(NO_3)_2$ contains a metal and a polyatomic ion, so it is an ionic compound and a strong electrolyte.

e. HNO_3 is a strong acid. Strong acids are strong electrolytes.

f. H_3PO_4 is an acid. It is not one of the seven strong acids listed in Table 4.3, so it is a weak acid. Weak acids are weak electrolytes.

Practice Problem 4.9 Solution

a. Soluble. Most ionic compounds containing the chloride ion are soluble (guideline 3). There are exceptions, but Ba^{2+} is not one of them.

b. Insoluble. Most salts containing the carbonate ion are insoluble (guideline 4). Only the cations in guideline 1 are exceptions, and the magnesium ion is not one of them.

c. Soluble. Many ionic compounds containing Pb^{2+} as the cation are insoluble (guidelines 3 and 6), but *all* nitrate compounds are soluble (guideline 1).

Practice Problem 4.10 Solution

a. Soluble. All ionic compounds containing the perchlorate ion are soluble (guideline 2).

b. Insoluble. Most ionic compounds containing the sulfate ion are soluble, but Ca^{2+} is an exception (guideline 7).

c. Insoluble. Most compounds containing the hydroxide ion are insoluble (guideline 5).

d. Insoluble. Most compounds containing chromate ions are insoluble (guideline 4).

Practice Problem 4.11 Solution

a. The ions are Na^+, SO_4^{2-}, Ba^{2+}, and Cl^-. The two possible products are NaCl and $BaSO_4$. Sodium chloride is soluble in water, but barium sulfate is not. A precipitation reaction will occur, producing $BaSO_4(s)$.

b. The ions are Ca^{2+}, NO_3^-, K^+, and OH^-. The two possible products are $Ca(OH)_2$ and KNO_3. Potassium nitrate is soluble in water, but calcium hydroxide is insoluble. A precipitation reaction will occur, producing $Ca(OH)_2(s)$.

Practice Problem 4.12 Solution

The strontium and phosphate ions form the solid strontium phosphate and are highlighted in the equation. The potassium and nitrate ions are spectator ions.

$$3\,Sr^{2+}(aq) + \cancel{6\,NO_3^-(aq)} + \cancel{6\,K^+(aq)} + 2\,PO_4^{3-}(aq) \rightarrow Sr_3(PO_4)_2(s) + \cancel{6\,K^+(aq)} + \cancel{6\,NO_3^-(aq)}$$

Net ionic equation: $3\,Sr^{2+}(aq) + 2\,PO_4^{3-}(aq) \rightarrow Sr_3(PO_4)_2(s)$

Practice Problem 4.13 Solution

a. $Hg_2(NO_3)_2(aq) + 2\,KBr(aq) \rightarrow Hg_2Br_2(s) + 2\,KNO_3(aq)$

Rewriting the aqueous strong electrolytes as dissociated, aqueous ions yields the ionic equation

$$Hg_2^{2+}(aq) + 2\,NO_3^-(aq) + 2\,K^+(aq) + 2\,Br^-(aq) \rightarrow Hg_2Br_2(s) + 2\,K^+(aq) + 2\,NO_3^-(aq)$$

Eliminating the spectator ions from the ionic equation yields the net ionic equation

$$Hg_2^{2+}(aq) + 2\,Br^-(aq) \rightarrow Hg_2Br_2(s)$$

b. $MgSO_4(aq) + Na_2CO_3(aq) \rightarrow MgCO_3(s) + Na_2SO_4(aq)$

Ionic equation:

$$Mg^{2+}(aq) + SO_4^{2-}(aq) + 2\,Na^+(aq) + CO_3^{2-}(aq) \rightarrow MgCO_3(s) + 2\,Na^+(aq) + SO_4^{2-}(aq)$$

Net ionic equation:

$$Mg^{2+}(aq) + CO_3^{2-}(aq) \rightarrow MgCO_3(s)$$

Practice Problem 4.14 Solution

a. $Na_2SO_4(aq) + BaCl_2(aq) \rightarrow$

The ions are Na^+, SO_4^{2-}, Ba^{2+}, and Cl^-, and the two possible products are $BaSO_4$ and NaCl. Recall from Practice Problem 4.11 that this combination of reactants produces $BaSO_4$ as an insoluble product. The unbalanced equation is

$$Na_2SO_4(aq) + BaCl_2(aq) \rightarrow BaSO_4(s) + NaCl(aq)$$

The balanced total equation is

$$Na_2SO_4(aq) + BaCl_2(aq) \rightarrow BaSO_4(s) + 2\,NaCl(aq)$$

To write the ionic equation, show each of the soluble strong electrolytes as its dissociated ion:

$$2\,Na^+(aq) + SO_4^{2-}(aq) + Ba^{2+}(aq) + 2\,Cl^-(aq) \rightarrow BaSO_4(s) + 2\,Na^+(aq) + 2\,Cl^-(aq)$$

Eliminating any spectator ions gives the net ionic equation

$$Ba^{2+}(aq) + SO_4^{2-}(aq) \rightarrow BaSO_4(s)$$

b. $Ca(NO_3)_2(aq) + KOH(aq) \rightarrow$

Write the formulas for the ions Ca^{2+}, NO_3^-, K^+, and OH^-. The two possible products are $Ca(OH)_2$ and KNO_3. KNO_3 is soluble in water, but $Ca(OH)_2$ is insoluble. This reaction will produce $Ca(OH)_2$ as a solid product. The total, unbalanced equation is

$$Ca(NO_3)_2(aq) + KOH(aq) \rightarrow Ca(OH)_2(s) + KNO_3(aq)$$

The balanced total equation is

$$Ca(NO_3)_2(aq) + 2\,KOH(aq) \rightarrow Ca(OH)_2(s) + 2\,KNO_3(aq)$$

To write the ionic equation, show each of the soluble strong electrolytes as its hydrated ions:

$$Ca^{2+}(aq) + 2\,NO_3^-(aq) + 2\,K^+(aq) + 2\,OH^-(aq) \rightarrow Ca(OH)_2(s) + 2\,K^+(aq) + 2\,NO_3^-(aq)$$

Eliminating any spectator ions gives the net ionic equation

$$Ca^{2+}(aq) + 2\,OH^-(aq) \rightarrow Ca(OH)_2(s)$$

Practice Problem 4.15 Solution

a. The formula for the salt is KNO_3. The balanced equation is

$$HNO_3(aq) + KOH(aq) \rightarrow KNO_3(aq) + H_2O(l)$$

b. The formula for the salt is Na_3PO_4. The balanced equation is

$$H_3PO_4(aq) + 3\,NaOH(aq) \rightarrow Na_3PO_4(aq) + 3\,H_2O(l)$$

Practice Problem 4.16 Solution

a. To obtain the ionic equation, write the aqueous strong electrolytes as separate ions:

$$H^+(aq) + NO_3^-(aq) + K^+(aq) + OH^-(aq) \rightarrow K^+(aq) + NO_3^-(aq) + H_2O(l)$$

HNO_3 is one of the strong acids, so it is a strong electrolyte. As soluble ionic compounds, KOH and KNO_3 are also strong electrolytes. Water is not a strong electrolyte, so it remains an intact molecule.

To obtain the net ionic equation, cancel the spectator ions in the ionic equation:

$$H^+(aq) + OH^-(aq) \rightarrow H_2O(l)$$

b. To obtain the ionic equation, write the aqueous strong electrolytes as separate ions:

$$3\,H_3PO_4(aq) + 3\,Na^+(aq) + 3\,OH^-(aq) \rightarrow 3\,Na^+(aq) + PO_4^{3-}(aq) + 3\,H_2O(l)$$

H_3PO_4 is a weak acid, so it is a weak electrolyte. NaOH and Na_3PO_4 are strong electrolytes, and water is not a strong electrolyte.

To obtain the net ionic equation, cancel the spectator ions in the ionic equation:

$$3\,H_3PO_4(aq) + 3\,OH^-(aq) \rightarrow PO_4^{3-}(aq) + 3\,H_2O(l)$$

Practice Problem 4.17 Solution

a. S^{2-} is a monoatomic ion. Its oxidation state is -2 (rule 2).

b. N_2 is elemental nitrogen. Each nitrogen atom in N_2 has an oxidation state of 0 (rule 1).

c. $CrCl_2$ is an ionic compound made up of two monoatomic ions. Although chromium can have variable charge as an ion, the chloride ion is always -1 (see Section 3.3). Thus, the charge on chromium is $+2$, which means its oxidation state is $+2$ (rule 2).

Practice Problem 4.18 Solution

Oxygen has an oxidation state of -2, and the oxidation states of the elements in the formula must sum to the overall charge of the ion or neutral compound. In each case, set up an equation for the overall charge that uses x to denote the unknown oxidation state.

a. For $S_2O_3^{2-}$, x is the oxidation state of sulfur:

The oxidation state of S in $S_2O_3^{2-}$ is $+2$.

b. For SO_3^{2-}, x is the oxidation state of sulfur:

The oxidation state of S in SO_3^{2-} is $+4$.

c. For $Cr_2O_7^{2-}$, x is the oxidation state of chromium:

The oxidation state of Cr in $Cr_2O_7^{2-}$ is $+6$.

Practice Problem 4.19 Solution

The oxidation states in these two compounds must sum to zero because both are neutral overall.

a. The oxidation state of Cl in $NaClO_2$ is $+3$.

$$(+1) + x + 2(-2) = 0$$
$$x = 3$$

b. The oxidation state of Cl in $HClO_4$ is $+7$:

$$(+1) + x + 4(-2) = 0$$
$$x = 7$$

Practice Problem 4.20 Solution

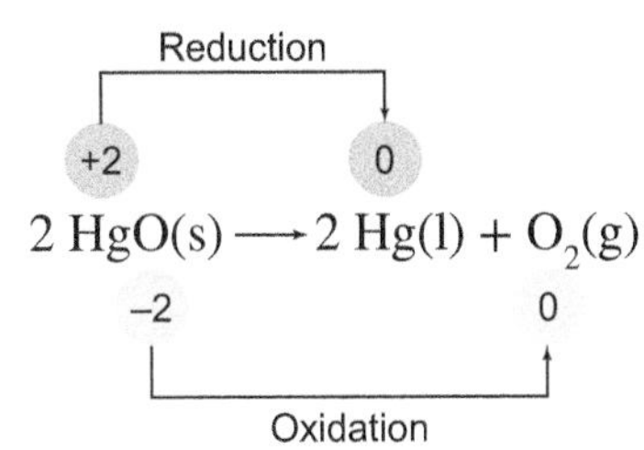

For mercury(II) oxide, mercury is a transition metal and can have more than one charge. Oxygen has an oxidation state of −2 (rule 4), so the oxidation state of mercury must be +2 (rule 3).

In the products, mercury and oxygen are uncombined elements, in which case each has an oxidation state of 0 (rule 1).

During the reaction, the oxidation state of mercury decreases from +2 to 0, indicating that mercury is reduced and is the oxidizing agent. The oxidation state of oxygen increases from −2 to 0, indicating that it is oxidized during the reaction and is the reducing agent.

Practice Problem 4.21 Solution

a. There is no change in oxidation states. This is *not* a redox reaction.

$$2\ HBr(aq) + Ba(OH)_2(aq) \rightarrow BaBr_2(aq) + 2\ H_2O(l)$$

+1 −1 | +2 −2 +1 | +2 −1 | +1 −2

b. Cobalt is oxidized and chlorine in chlorine gas is reduced. This is a redox reaction.

Reduction: 0 → −1

$$2\ CoCl_2(aq) + Cl_2(g) \longrightarrow 2\ CoCl_3(s)$$

+2 −1 | +3

Oxidation: +2 → +3

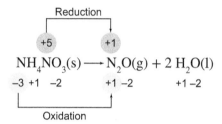

c. There is no change in oxidation states. This is *not* a redox reaction.

$$2\ NH_4I(aq) + Pb(NO_3)_2(aq) \rightarrow 2\ NH_4NO_3(aq) + PbI_2(s)$$

−3 +1 −1 | +2 +5 −2 | −3 +1 +5 −2 | +2 −1

d. There is no change in oxidation states. This is *not* a redox reaction.

$$(NH_4)_2S(aq) + CuCl_2(aq) \rightarrow CuS(s) + 2\ NH_4Cl(aq)$$

−3 +1 −2 | +2 −1 | +2 −2 | −3 +1 −1

e. There is no change in oxidation states. This is *not* a redox reaction.

$$2\ NaOH(aq) + H_3PO_4(aq) \rightarrow Na_2HPO_4(aq) + 2\ H_2O(l)$$

+1 −2 +1 | +1 +5 −2 | +1 +1 +5 −2 | +1 −2

f. There is no change in oxidation states. This is *not* a redox reaction.

$$H_2O(l) + N_2O_5(g) \rightarrow 2\ HNO_3(aq)$$

+1 −2 | +5 −2 | +1 +5 −2

g. Copper is reduced, and zinc is oxidized. This is a redox reaction.

Reduction: +2 → 0

$$CuSO_4(aq) + Zn(s) \longrightarrow ZnSO_4(aq) + Cu(s)$$

+6 −2 | 0 | +2 +6 −2

Oxidation: 0 → +2

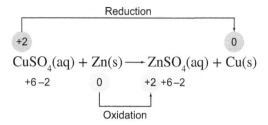

h. One nitrogen atom is oxidized, and the other nitrogen atom is reduced. This is a redox reaction.

Reduction: +5 → +1

$$NH_4NO_3(s) \longrightarrow N_2O(g) + 2\ H_2O(l)$$

−3 +1 −2 | +1 −2 | +1 −2

Oxidation: −3 → +1

Double-replacement and acid–base reactions generally do not involve electron transfer, so they are typically *not* redox reactions. In contrast, most synthesis, decomposition, single-replacement, and combustion reactions do involve electron transfer, so they tend to be redox reactions.

Practice Problem 4.22 Solution

a. $Na(s) + S(s) \rightarrow$
Sodium atoms oxidize to form +1 cations, Na^+, and sulfur atoms reduce to form −2 anions, S^{2-}. These ions form sodium sulfide, Na_2S:

$$2\ Na(s) + S(s) \rightarrow Na_2S(s)$$

b. $Al(s) + N_2(g) \rightarrow$
Aluminum atoms oxidize to form +3 ions, while nitrogen atoms reduce to form −3 ions. These ions combine to form aluminum nitride, AlN:

$$2\ Al(s) + N_2(g) \rightarrow 2\ AlN(s)$$

Practice Problem 4.23 Solution

a. The three metal *atoms* are Ba, Cr, and Ni. Of these three, Ba is highest in the activity series, so Ba is the most active metal.

b. The three metal *ions* are Pb^{2+}, Mn^{2+}, and Al^{3+}. Of these three, Pb^{2+} is lowest in the activity series, so Pb^{2+} is the most reactive metal ion.

c. Reducing agents donate electrons. Metal *atoms* can act as reducing agents and the most active metal, Ba, is the strongest reducing agent of the metals given.

d. Oxidizing agents accept electrons. Metal *ions* can act as oxidizing agents, and the most reactive metal ion, Pb^{2+}, is the strongest reducing agent of the ions given.

Practice Problem 4.24 Solution

a. Nickel is higher in the activity series than is lead, so nickel is more active and is able to donate electrons to the lead ion.

$$Ni(s) + Pb^{2+}(aq) \rightarrow \text{products}$$

b. Both reactants are metal atoms; neither can accept electrons.

$$Na(s) + Ag(s) \rightarrow \text{no reaction}$$

c. Magnesium is higher in the activity series than is zinc, so magnesium is more active and is able to donate electrons to the zinc ion.

$$Zn^{2+}(aq) + Mg(s) \rightarrow \text{products}$$

d. Chlorine is a spectator ion, so it can be ignored. Copper is lower in the activity series than is calcium, so copper is less active and is unable to donate electrons to the calcium ion.

$$CaCl_2(aq) + Cu(s) \rightarrow \text{no reaction}$$

e. Nitrate is a spectator ion. Silver is higher in the activity series than is gold, so silver is more active and is able to donate electrons to the gold ion.

$$Au(NO_3)_3(aq) + Ag(s) \rightarrow \text{products}$$

f. Both reactants are metal ions; neither can donate electrons.

$$Li^+(aq) + Mn^{2+}(aq) \rightarrow \text{no reaction}$$

Practice Problem 4.25 Solution

In all three cases, the neutral metal is more active than is the metal ion (as shown in Practice Problem 4.24), so the reactions occur.

a. The formula for a compound of nickel ion, Ni^{2+}, with perchlorate, ClO_4^-, is $Ni(ClO_4)_2$:

$$Ni(s) + Pb(ClO_4)_2(aq) \rightarrow Pb(s) + Ni(ClO_4)_2(aq)$$

b. The formula for a compound of magnesium ion, Mg^{2+}, with chloride, Cl^-, is $MgCl_2$:

$$ZnCl_2(aq) + Mg(s) \rightarrow Zn(s) + MgCl_2(aq)$$

c. The formula for a compound of silver ion, Ag^+, with nitrate, NO_3^-, is $AgNO_3$:

$$Au(NO_3)_3(aq) + 3\ Ag(s) \rightarrow Au(s) + 3\ AgNO_3(aq)$$

Practice Problem 4.26 Solution

a. Magnesium is higher than is hydrogen in the activity series, so it will react with acids. The formula for a compound of magnesium ion, Mg^{2+}, with chloride, Cl^-, is $MgCl_2$.

$$Mg(s) + 2\ HCl(aq) \rightarrow MgCl_2(aq) + H_2(g)$$

b. Gold is lower in the activity series than is hydrogen, so it does *not* react with acid.

c. Neutral barium is higher than is hydrogen in the activity series and will react with acids, but this is a barium ion, which has no valence electrons to lose. No reaction will occur.

Practice Problem 4.27 Solution

Step 1: Place a piece of the metal in a small amount of the copper nitrate solution.

- If there is no reaction, then the metal is likely to be silver. Silver is very low in the activity series and will not react with copper ions:

$$Ag(s) + Cu(NO_3)_2(aq) \rightarrow \text{no reaction}$$

- Both barium and zinc are higher in the activity series and will react with copper ions:

$$Ba(s) + Cu(NO_3)_2(aq) \rightarrow Cu(s) + Ba(NO_3)_2(aq)$$
$$Zn(s) + Cu(NO_3)_2(aq) \rightarrow Cu(s) + Zn(NO_3)_2(aq)$$

Step 2: If a reaction occurred in step 1, then the resulting solution contains either barium nitrate or zinc nitrate. Add a small amount of that solution to the sodium sulfate solution:

$$Ba(NO_3)_2(aq) + Na_2SO_4(aq) \rightarrow BaSO_4(s) + 2\ NaNO_3(aq)$$
$$Zn(NO_3)_2(aq) + Na_2SO_4(aq) \rightarrow \text{no reaction}$$

Zinc sulfate is soluble, but barium sulfate is insoluble. So, if a precipitate forms, then the solution from step 1 contains barium ions, and the metal is barium. If no precipitate forms, then the metal is zinc.

CHAPTER 5

Stoichiometry

NASA/Bill Ingalls

Just as a chemical formula for a compound indicates the ratio of atoms that make up that compound, a balanced chemical equation indicates the ratios of moles of reactants and products. For example, launching a rocket requires a precise ratio of fuel to oxygen. To calculate the necessary relative amounts, you must use the coefficients from the balanced chemical equation for the combustion reaction.

Chapter Outline

GOALS

- Calculate the number of moles of any substance involved in a chemical reaction from the number of moles of any other substance in the reaction.
- Use the mass of one substance to determine the masses of other substances involved in a chemical reaction.
- Calculate the quantities of substances produced in a reaction when quantities of more than one reactant are specified.
- Express the quantity of product obtained from a reaction as a percentage of what the reaction is theoretically capable of producing.
- Solve problems using molarity.
- Extend the concept of molarity to the individual ions in solutions of ionic substances.
- Determine how much of any substance is involved in a chemical reaction, given any quantity of another substance, no matter what units are involved.
- Calculate the numbers of moles involved in net ionic equations.
- Calculate the masses of complete compounds involved in net ionic equations.
- Discuss the limitations of net ionic equations in calculating masses of individual ions.
- Determine the concentration, or the number of moles present, of a substance by an experimental technique called *titration*.

5.1 Mole Calculations for Chemical Reactions

GOAL

- Calculate the number of moles of any substance involved in a chemical reaction from the number of moles of any other substance in the reaction.

Background Review

Chapter 3 Compounds and the Mole: Section 3.7—The Mole

Chapter 4 Chemical Reactions and Aqueous Solutions: Section 4.1—Chemical Equations

Stoichiometry is the calculation of quantities of any substances involved in a chemical reaction from the quantities of the other substances. Any time you see the word *stoichiometry*, it refers to the ratios of substances in the reaction, so you know you are dealing with the balanced equation for the reaction because the balanced equation gives the ratios of formula units of all the substances in a chemical reaction. The balanced equation also gives the corresponding ratios of moles of the substances. These relationships are shown in Figure 5.1. For example, one reaction of phosphorus, P, with chlorine gas, Cl_2, is governed by the equation

$$2\,P(s) + 3\,Cl_2(g) \rightarrow 2\,PCl_3(l)$$

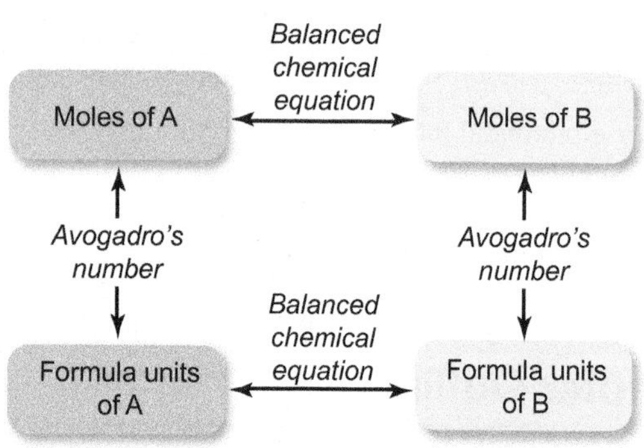

FIGURE 5.1 Flowchart of Mole Conversions for Stoichiometry Problems

A and B in this diagram can be any reactant or product in a reaction. The coefficients in the balanced equation relate the amount of any reactant or product to the amount of any other reactant or product. This amount can be expressed either in moles or in formula units but *not* in grams. Avogadro's number (Section 3.7) can be used to convert moles to formula units (Section 3.1) for any reactant or product. The double-headed arrows indicate that the conversions can be made in either direction.

This equation can be interpreted, as shown in Chapter 4, in two ways:

1. Two *atoms* of phosphorus react with three *molecules* of Cl_2 to produce two *molecules* of PCl_3.
2. Two *moles* of phosphorus react with three *moles* of Cl_2 to produce two *moles* of PCl_3.

USING REACTING RATIOS TO SOLVE MOLE-MOLE PROBLEMS

Consider the reaction of phosphorus, P, with chlorine, Cl, as shown in the previous equation. A chemist is not required to place exactly 2 mol P and 3 mol Cl_2 in a reaction flask. Instead, the equation gives the **reacting ratio**. Ratios of coefficients from balanced chemical equations can be used as conversion factors for solving problems.

Example 5.1

Write all of the possible reacting ratios (in moles) from the coefficients in the following combination reaction:

$$2\,P(s) + 3\,Cl_2(g) \rightarrow 2\,PCl_3(l)$$

Solution

If the equation had been *un*balanced, the first step would have been to balance it. Based on the balanced equation, though, the possible reacting ratios are

$$\frac{3\text{ mol }Cl_2}{2\text{ mol P}} \quad \frac{3\text{ mol }Cl_2}{2\text{ mol }PCl_3} \quad \frac{2\text{ mol P}}{2\text{ mol }PCl_3} \quad \frac{2\text{ mol P}}{3\text{ mol }Cl_2}$$

$$\frac{2\text{ mol }PCl_3}{3\text{ mol }Cl_2} \quad \frac{2\text{ mol }PCl_3}{2\text{ mol P}}$$

PRACTICE PROBLEM 5.1

The following reaction was used to make smokescreens in World War I:

$$TiCl_4(l) + H_2O(l) \rightarrow TiO_2(s) + HCl(g)$$

Write all of the possible reacting ratios from the coefficients in the equation.

Hint: One example of a reacting ratio is $\frac{1\text{ mol }TiCl_4}{2\text{ mol }H_2O}$. Before setting up the reacting ratios, be sure that the equation is balanced.

Reacting ratios can be used to determine the relationship between the number of moles of reactants and the number of moles of products in chemical reactions. For example, consider the formation of aluminum, Al, from the decomposition of aluminum oxide, Al_2O_3:

$$2\,Al_2O_3(s) \rightarrow 4\,Al(s) + 3\,O_2(g)$$

You can use dimensional analysis (Section 1.7) to calculate the number of moles of Al formed by the reaction of 1.10 mol Al_2O_3. Remember to set up the calculation so that number of moles of Al_2O_3 cancels. For example,

$$1.10\,\cancel{\text{mol }Al_2O_3}\left(\frac{4\text{ mol Al}}{2\,\cancel{\text{mol }Al_2O_3}}\right) = 2.20\text{ mol Al}$$

Example 5.2

Calculate the number of moles of aluminum that will react with 3.18 mol oxygen to form aluminum oxide.

$$4\,Al(s) + 3\,O_2(g) \rightarrow 2\,Al_2O_3(s)$$

Solution

If the equation had been *un*balanced, the first step would have been to balance it. Based on the preceding balanced equation, you can use the reacting ratio and dimensional analysis to determine the number of moles of Al that will react with O_2.

$$3.18\text{ mol }O_2\left(\frac{4\text{ mol Al}}{3\text{ mol }O_2}\right) = 4.24\text{ mol Al}$$

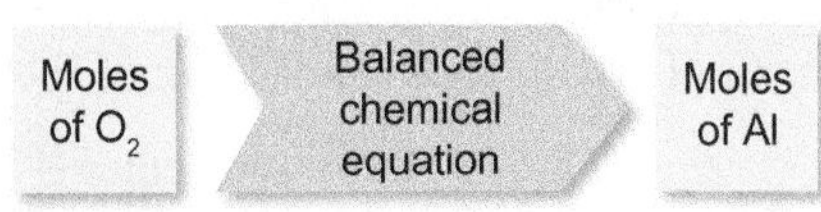

PRACTICE PROBLEM 5.2

Calculate the number of moles of Al_2O_3 that can be produced by the combination reaction of 3.18 mol O_2 with sufficient Al.

$$4\,Al(s) + 3\,O_2(g) \rightarrow 2\,Al_2O_3(s)$$

Hint: Use the reacting ratio between Al_2O_3 and O_2 that is provided by the balanced equation.

It is helpful to include the formulas of the substances involved with the units when using dimensional analysis to solve stoichiometry problems. For example, write "mol NaCl" rather than just "mol." Including these formulas can help you identify and correct mistakes.

Additionally, when molecules are involved, it is helpful to write the entire word "molecules" in the unit, as abbreviating it could lead to confusion with moles.

Example 5.3

Hydrochloric acid, HCl, reacts with metallic calcium to form gaseous H_2 and aqueous $CaCl_2$.

$$HCl(aq) + Ca(s) \rightarrow H_2(g) + CaCl_2(aq)$$

Calculate the number of H_2 molecules produced from the reaction of 0.750 mol HCl with sufficient calcium.

Solution

First, write the balanced chemical equation.

$$2\,HCl(aq) + Ca(s) \rightarrow H_2(g) + CaCl_2(aq)$$

As the flowchart in Figure 5.1 suggests, first use the coefficients from the balanced chemical equation as a conversion factor to convert moles of HCl to moles of H_2.

$$0.750 \text{ mol HCl}\left(\frac{1 \text{ mol } H_2}{2 \text{ mol HCl}}\right) = 0.375 \text{ mol } H_2$$

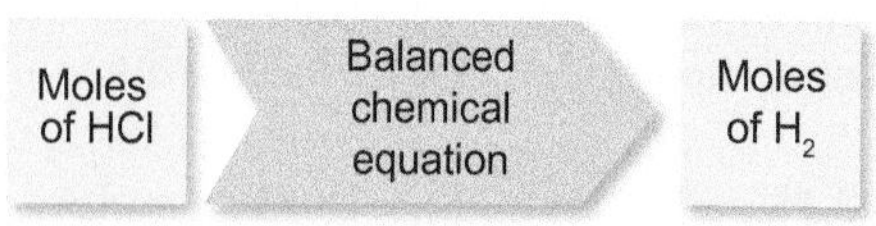

Finally, use Avogadro's number to calculate the number of H_2 molecules in 0.375 mol H_2.

$$0.375 \text{ mol } H_2\left(\frac{6.022 \times 10^{23} \text{ molecules } H_2}{1 \text{ mol } H_2}\right)$$
$$= 2.26 \times 10^{23}\ H_2 \text{ molecules}$$

PRACTICE PROBLEM 5.3

Aqueous NaOH reacts with aqueous H_2SO_4 to give aqueous Na_2SO_4 and water.

$$2\,NaOH(aq) + H_2SO_4(aq) \rightarrow Na_2SO_4(aq) + 2\,H_2O(l)$$

Calculate the number of formula units of NaOH that must react completely with H_2SO_4 to produce 1.24×10^{15} formula units of Na_2SO_4.

Hint: According to the flowchart in Figure 5.1, you can use the coefficients from the balanced chemical equation to go directly from formula units of Na_2SO_4 to formula units of NaOH. The reacting ratios work for either moles or formula units.

In stoichiometry problems, be sure that the chemical equations are balanced (Section 4.1). Otherwise, the reacting ratio may be incorrect.

Example 5.4

Potassium chlorate, $KClO_3$, is often used as an inexpensive source of oxygen gas. A sample of 0.1712 mol solid $KClO_3$ is heated gently for a time, and 0.1146 mol of the compound decomposes into KCl and O_2 gas. Calculate the number of moles of oxygen gas produced.

Solution

First, write the balanced equation for the reaction.

$$2\,KClO_3(s) \rightarrow 3\,O_2(g) + 2\,KCl(s)$$

Even though 0.1712 mol $KClO_3$ is present, only 0.1146 mol reacts. The number of moles of oxygen gas produced depends on the number of moles of $KClO_3$ that *reacts.*

$$0.1146 \text{ mol } KClO_3\left(\frac{3 \text{ mol } O_2}{2 \text{ mol } KClO_3}\right) = 0.1719 \text{ mol } O_2$$

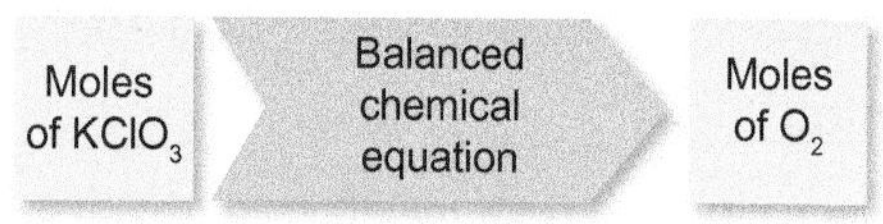

PRACTICE PROBLEM 5.4

In a certain reaction, 0.225 mol H_2 gas reacts partially with N_2 gas to yield gaseous NH_3. If 0.033 mol H_2 remains after the reaction is stopped, how many moles of N_2 react with H_2?

Hint: First, write the balanced equation. Then determine the number of moles of H_2 that reacts. This is the number of moles of H_2 originally present (0.225 mol) minus the number of moles of H_2 remaining (0.033 mol). Finally, use the reacting ratio between H_2 and N_2 to determine the number of moles of N_2 that react.

SECTION REVIEW

- The coefficients in the balanced chemical equation are the ratios of the number of moles or formula units of all the substances in the reaction.
- Reacting ratios can be used as conversion factors (from mole to mole or formula unit to formula unit) in calculations involving any two reactants and/or products in the reaction.

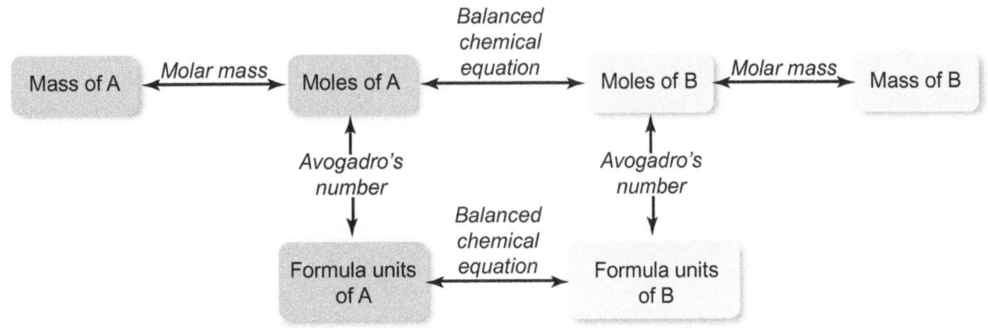

FIGURE 5.2 Flowchart of Mass and Mole Conversions for Stoichiometry Problems

A and B can be any reactant or product in the chemical equation. The coefficients in the balanced equation are mole ratios, not mass ratios. So, when given a mass, first convert it to moles using the molar mass for that substance. The double-headed arrows indicate that the conversions can be made in either direction.

5.2 Mass Calculations for Chemical Reactions

GOAL

- Use the mass of one substance to determine the masses of other substances involved in a chemical reaction.

Background Review

Chapter 3 Compounds and the Mole:
Section 3.8—Molar Mass

In Section 5.1, you learned to calculate the number of moles of any substances involved in a chemical reaction from the number of moles of any other substance using the reacting ratios. You can solve problems that include mass calculations by simply changing the masses to moles or the moles to masses, as discussed in Chapter 3. In Figure 5.2, these conversions have been added to those shown in Figure 5.1. Notice that it is not possible to directly convert from mass of one substance to mass of another substance without an intermediate mole conversion. Reacting ratios are mole ratios, not mass ratios.

The video in Figure 5.3 shows how reaction stoichiometry is used to convert from mass of reactant to expected mass of product.

Steve Lemon, Macmillan Learning

FIGURE 5.3 Video Tutorial: Stoichiometry

NOTE: You need to be online to access this video.

This video shows how to calculate the mass of product formed from a given mass of reactant.

Example 5.5

Calculate the mass of chlorine gas that will react with 2.80 g of phosphorus to form solid phosphorus pentachloride.

Solution

First, write the balanced chemical reaction.

$$5\ Cl_2(g) + 2\ P(s) \rightarrow 2\ PCl_5(s)$$

Next, convert the mass of phosphorus to moles of phosphorus. Then you can convert the number of moles of P reacted to the number of moles of Cl_2 reacted, as you did in Section 5.1.

$$2.80\ \text{g P}\left(\frac{1\ \text{mol P}}{30.974\ \text{g P}}\right) = 0.0904\ \text{mol P}$$

$$0.0904\ \text{mol P}\left(\frac{5\ \text{mol Cl}_2}{2\ \text{mol P}}\right) = 0.226\ \text{mol Cl}_2$$

Now, use the molar mass of Cl_2 to determine the mass of Cl_2 that will react.

$$0.226\ \text{mol Cl}_2\left(\frac{70.90\ \text{g Cl}_2}{1\ \text{mol Cl}_2}\right) = 16.0\ \text{g Cl}_2$$

Alternatively, the preceding steps can be combined into a single calculation.

$$2.80\text{ g P}\left(\frac{1\text{ mol P}}{30.974\text{ g P}}\right)\left(\frac{5\text{ mol Cl}_2}{2\text{ mol P}}\right)\left(\frac{70.90\text{ g Cl}_2}{1\text{ mol Cl}_2}\right)$$
$$= 16.0\text{ g Cl}_2$$

Grams of P → Molar mass → Moles of P → Balanced chemical equation → Moles of Cl_2 → Molar mass → Grams of Cl_2

PRACTICE PROBLEM 5.5

Calculate the mass of phosphorus pentachloride that will be produced by the reaction in Example 5.5.

Hint: Use the reacting ratio to determine the mass of PCl_5 that will be formed from 2.80 g P. Assume there is sufficient Cl_2.

Example 5.6

Electrolysis of concentrated aqueous sodium chloride solution (called brine) yields aqueous sodium hydroxide, hydrogen gas, and chlorine gas—three important industrial chemicals. Calculate the mass of chlorine in grams that can be produced by the electrolysis of 50.0 kg of sodium chloride in concentrated aqueous solution:

$$2\text{ NaCl(aq)} + 2\text{ H}_2\text{O(l)} \xrightarrow{\text{electricity}} 2\text{ NaOH(aq)} + \text{Cl}_2\text{(g)} + \text{H}_2\text{(g)}$$

Solution

$$50.0\text{ kg NaCl}\left(\frac{1000\text{ g NaCl}}{1\text{ kg NaCl}}\right)\left(\frac{1\text{ mol NaCl}}{58.44\text{ g NaCl}}\right)\left(\frac{1\text{ mol Cl}_2}{2\text{ mol NaCl}}\right)\left(\frac{70.903\text{ g Cl}_2}{1\text{ mol Cl}_2}\right)$$
$$= 3.03 \times 10^4\text{ g Cl}_2$$

Kilograms of NaCl → Definition of kilo → Grams of NaCl → Molar mass → Moles of NaCl → Balanced chemical equation → Moles of Cl_2 → Molar mass → Grams of Cl_2

PRACTICE PROBLEM 5.6

The industrial process for the production of sodium metal and chlorine gas involves the electrolysis of molten (melted) sodium chloride in the absence of water. Calculate the mass of sodium in grams that can be prepared by the electrolysis of 207 kg of sodium chloride. The balanced equation is

$$2\text{ NaCl(l)} + \xrightarrow{\text{electricity}} 2\text{ Na(l)} + \text{Cl}_2\text{(g)}$$

Hint: This problem can be solved in a similar manner to the one in Example 5.6. Be sure to convert the mass of sodium chloride to units of grams.

Example 5.7

Sulfuric acid, H_2SO_4, is the chemical produced in the greatest amount worldwide. The balanced equation for the overall reaction, which is actually carried out in several steps, is

$$2\text{ SO}_2\text{(g)} + \text{O}_2\text{(g)} + 2\text{ H}_2\text{O(l)} \rightarrow 2\text{ H}_2\text{SO}_4\text{(l)}$$

Calculate the number of moles of SO_2 gas required to prepare 50.0 metric tons of liquid H_2SO_4 (1 metric ton = 1×10^6 g).

Solution

Use the balanced equation to convert moles of product to moles of reactant. But first, convert metric tons to grams, and grams to moles.

$$50.0\text{ tons H}_2\text{SO}_4\left(\frac{1 \times 10^6\text{ g}}{1\text{ ton}}\right)\left(\frac{1\text{ mol H}_2\text{SO}_4}{98.07\text{ g H}_2\text{SO}_4}\right)\left(\frac{2\text{ mol SO}_2}{2\text{ mol H}_2\text{SO}_4}\right)$$
$$= 5.10 \times 10^5\text{ mol SO}_2$$

Tons of H_2SO_4 → Definition of ton → Grams of H_2SO_4 → Molar mass → Moles of H_2SO_4 → Balanced chemical equation → Moles of SO_2

PRACTICE PROBLEM 5.7

Hydrochloric acid was added to an aqueous solution of calcium hydrogen carbonate, $Ca(HCO_3)_2$, until the reaction was complete. Evaporating the resulting solution to dryness yielded 2.29 g solid $CaCl_2$ product. The chemical equation is

$$\text{Ca(HCO}_3)_2\text{(aq)} + \text{HCl(aq)} \rightarrow \text{CaCl}_2\text{(aq)} + \text{CO}_2\text{(g)} + \text{H}_2\text{O(l)}$$

Calculate the mass of calcium hydrogen carbonate in the original solution.

Hint: First, be sure that the chemical equation is balanced. Then, convert grams of $CaCl_2$ to moles of $CaCl_2$, using the molar mass of $CaCl_2$. Convert moles of $CaCl_2$ to moles of $Ca(HCO_3)_2$, using the coefficients from the balanced chemical equation. Finally, convert moles of $Ca(HCO_3)_2$ to grams of $Ca(HCO_3)_2$, using the molar mass of $Ca(HCO_3)_2$.

SECTION REVIEW

- When calculating the moles of one substance in a chemical reaction from the moles of another (Section 5.1), only the ratio of coefficients from the balanced equation is necessary. When calculating the mass of one substance from the mass of another, you also need the molar masses of each of the compounds in the calculation.

- Calculating the mass of one substance, B, from the mass of another, A, is a three-step process:
  1. Convert the mass of compound A to moles of A using the molar mass of A.
  2. Convert moles of A to moles of B using the ratio of coefficients in the balanced chemical equation.
  3. Convert moles of B to the mass of B using the molar mass of B.

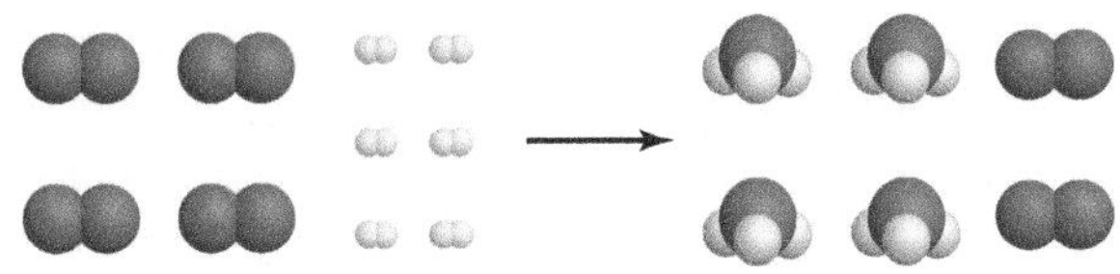

FIGURE 5.4 Limiting Reactant in $N_2(g) + 3\ H_2(g) \rightarrow 2\ NH_3(g)$

The larger spheres represent N and the smaller spheres represent H. When four N_2 molecules react with six H_2 molecules, four NH_3 molecules are formed and two N_2 molecules do not react. In this case, hydrogen is the limiting reactant, and nitrogen is in excess. You can try this and other ratios of reactants in the activity presented in Figure 5.5.

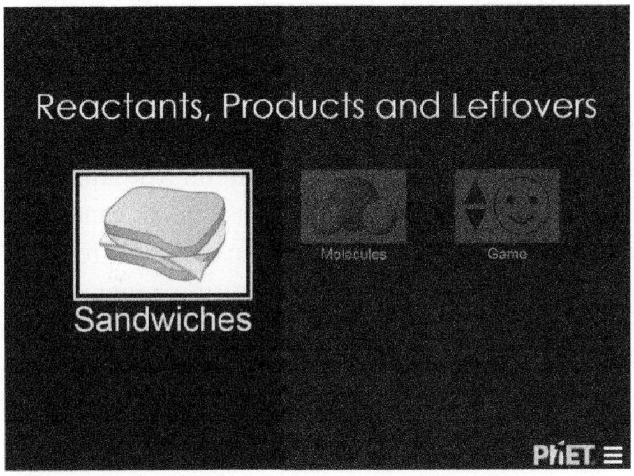

FIGURE 5.5 Reactants, Products, and Leftovers Activity

NOTE: You need to be online to access this activity.

To learn about the concept of limiting reactants, start with the sandwiches analogy. When you're ready, move on to the molecules section. Once you are comfortable with the concepts, test yourself with the game.

5.3 Problems Involving Limiting Quantities

GOAL

- Calculate the quantities of substances produced in a reaction when quantities of more than one reactant are specified.

Up to now, when the amount of one reactant was given, it was assumed that sufficient amounts of any other reactants were present. Similarly, when an amount of product was given, it was assumed that enough of every reactant was present. In Example 5.3, for instance, 0.750 mol HCl reacted with calcium. If no calcium were present, however, the reaction would not be possible—no matter how many moles of HCl were available. To solve that problem, you assumed that sufficient calcium was present to react with the entire 0.750 mol HCl, because nothing explicit was stated about the quantity of calcium used. You'll have to treat the problem differently when the amounts of more than one reactant are given because there may or may not be enough for all of the reactants to be used up. It is more likely that one of the reactants will be in a small enough quantity that it limits how much of the other will react. And, once any one of the reactants has been used up, the reaction stops. The reactant that is used up is called the **limiting reactant** and is referred to as being present in **limiting quantity**.

> The reactant that is present in limiting quantity determines the extent of reaction that can take place.

Any other reactant that is left over after the limiting reactant has been used up is said to be in **excess**. The reaction is said to have gone to **completion** when the limiting quantity has been used up. This concept is illustrated in Figure 5.4 and Figure 5.5.

Example 5.8 illustrates the limiting reactant principle using an analogy from everyday life.

Example 5.8

a. If coffee beans cost \$8.00 per pound, how many pounds of coffee beans can be purchased with \$108.00?

b. How many pounds of coffee beans can be purchased with \$108.00 if the store has 12.5 lb in stock?

Solution

a. Assuming that the store has a sufficient amount of coffee beans in stock,

$$108.00 \text{ dollars}\left(\frac{1 \text{ lb}}{8.00 \text{ dollars}}\right) = 13.5 \text{ lb}$$

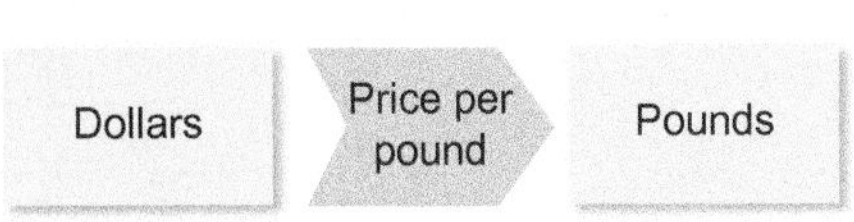

b. From part (a), you know that \$108.00 is enough to purchase 13.5 lb of coffee beans. The store has only 12.5 lb in stock, however, so only 12.5 lb of coffee beans can be purchased. Even with an excess of available money, the quantity of coffee beans in stock limits the purchase.

PRACTICE PROBLEM 5.8

How many pounds of coffee beans at \$8.00 per pound can be purchased with \$150.00 if the store has 20.0 lb of coffee beans in stock?

Hint: First, determine the number of pounds of beans that can be purchased for \$150.00. Then, determine what limits the purchase—this value or the store's 20.0 lb of beans in stock.

Figure 5.5 allows you to explore the concept of limiting quantities further and to transition from thinking in terms of tangible examples, such as nuts or sandwiches, to examples involving molecules in chemical reactions.

The first step in doing a limiting reactant problem is to recognize when you have been presented with one. You can identify a limiting reactant problem because the quantities of at least two different reactants are given.

> Limiting reactant problems have the quantities of two or more reactants given.

One way to identify which reactant is limiting is to calculate the amount of product that could be made from each reactant, assuming excess of the other one. With this strategy, the reactant that produces the least amount of product is the limiting reactant. One benefit of this method is that you now have the amount of one product, which may be one of the things you are asked for in the question. For example, suppose you are asked to determine the limiting reactant for the combustion reaction between 1.500 mol CH_3OH and 0.500 mol O_2. The balanced equation is

$$2\,CH_3OH(g) + 3\,O_2(g) \rightarrow 2\,CO_2(g) + 4\,H_2O(g)$$

In this case, determine the amount of either product (this example uses CO_2) that will be formed from the amounts of each reactant, assuming the other reactant is present in excess.

$$\text{From } CH_3OH\text{: } 1.500 \text{ mol } CH_3OH\left(\frac{2 \text{ mol } CO_2}{2 \text{ mol } CH_3OH}\right) = 1.500 \text{ mol } CO_2$$

$$\text{From } O_2\text{: } 0.500 \text{ mol } O_2\left(\frac{2 \text{ mol } CO_2}{3 \text{ mol } O_2}\right) = 0.333 \text{ mol } CO_2$$

In this case, O_2 produces less CO_2 than CH_3OH does, so O_2 is the limiting reactant and 0.500 mol O_2 reacts to form 0.333 mol CO_2. Some CH_3OH will react, but not all of it, so base all calculations involving reacting ratios off the given amount of O_2, not CH_3OH.

Another way to identify the limiting reactant is to divide the moles of each reactant by its coefficient in the balanced chemical equation; the smaller quotient is the limiting reactant.

$$\frac{1.500 \text{ mol } CH_3OH}{2 \text{ mol } CH_3OH} = 0.7500$$

$$\frac{0.500 \text{ mol } O_2}{3 \text{ mol } O_2} = 0.167$$

There is no physical meaning to these quotients—they are not useful for anything else. But as a method to quickly identify the limiting reactant, it is very efficient.

> Once you have identified the limiting reactant, base all subsequent calculations involving reacting ratios on the amount of limiting reactant, not the excess reactant.

The video in Figure 5.6 shows how to determine which reactant is limiting using the second method, as well as how many moles of product form.

Steve Lemon, Macmillan Learning

FIGURE 5.6 Video Tutorial: Limiting Reactant

NOTE: You need to be online to access this video.
This video shows how to calculate the number of moles of product formed and the number of moles of excess reactant left over given the initial number of moles of both reactants.

Example 5.9

Use the following balanced chemical equation

$$2\,CH_3OH(g) + 3\,O_2(g) \rightarrow 2\,CO_2(g) + 4\,H_2O(g)$$

to calculate the number of moles of reactants and products that are present after the reaction of 1.500 mol CH_3OH with 0.500 mol O_2 is complete.

Solution

It has already been shown that O_2 is the limiting reactant when starting with 1.500 mol CH_3OH and 0.500 mol O_2, because O_2 would form fewer moles of CO_2 (0.333 mol) than CH_3OH would. Thus, all 0.500 mol O_2 reacts with some of the 1.500 mol CH_3OH to form 0.333 mol CO_2. Find the amount of CH_3OH that reacted and the amount of H_2O produced based on the reaction of 0.500 mol O_2.

$$0.500\text{ mol }O_2\left(\frac{2\text{ mol }CH_3OH}{3\text{ mol }O_2}\right) = 0.333\text{ mol }CH_3OH\text{ reacted}$$

$$0.500\text{ mol }O_2\left(\frac{4\text{ mol }H_2O}{3\text{ mol }O_2}\right) = 0.667\text{ mol }H_2O\text{ formed}$$

It can be helpful to summarize the initial amounts, the change due to reaction, and the final amounts of reactants and products in a table such as

	$2\,CH_3OH$ +	$3\,O_2$ →	$2\,CO_2$ +	$4\,H_2O$
Initial amounts	1.500 mol	0.500 mol	0 mol	0 mol
Change due to reaction	−0.333 mol	−0.500 mol	+0.333 mol	+0.667 mol
Final amounts	1.167 mol	0 mol	0.333 mol	0.667 mol

The initial amounts go into the first row, and the amounts that you calculated based on the mole ratios go in the second row, where a negative sign is given to the reactants and a positive sign is given to the products. The last row is the sum of the first two rows.

PRACTICE PROBLEM 5.9

Use the following balanced chemical equation

$$2\,CH_3OH(g) + 3\,O_2(g) \rightarrow 2\,CO_2(g) + 4\,H_2O(g)$$

to calculate the number of moles of reactants and products that are present after the reaction of 0.500 mol CH_3OH with 1.000 mol O_2 is complete.

Hint: First, identify whether CH_3OH or O_2 is the limiting reactant. One way to do that is to determine how much product (arbitrarily choose one of them) forms when all of the CH_3OH reacts and compare it to the amount of that product that forms when all of the O_2 reacts. The reactant that produces the *smaller* amount of product is limiting.

Then, use the amount of the limiting reactant and the coefficients in the balanced equation to find the amounts of the other reactant used and the products formed. Finally, make a table summarizing the initial and final amounts.

A third strategy for identifying the limiting reactant compares the actual amounts of reactants to the amounts needed to completely react. All three methods can be summarized as follows:

1. Find the amounts of any product—one calculation for each reactant—assuming that each reactant is completely used up. The reactant that produces the smaller amount of product is limiting.
2. Divide the given number of moles of each reactant by its coefficient in the balanced equation. The reactant with the smallest quotient is the limiting reactant.
3. Find the amount of each reactant needed to completely use up the other reactant. Disregard the scenario that requires more of a reactant than is actually present.

The examples in this text focus on the first method.

Example 5.10

Calculate the number of moles of reactants and products present after the reaction of 0.250 mol PCl_5 with 1.50 mol H_2O is complete.

$$PCl_5 + 4\,H_2O \rightarrow H_3PO_4 + 5\,HCl$$

Solution

The first step is to determine whether or not the equation is balanced. (In this case, it is.) Next, identify the limiting reactant.

$$0.250\text{ mol }PCl_5\left(\frac{1\text{ mol }H_3PO_4}{1\text{ mol }PCl_5}\right) = 0.250\text{ mol }H_3PO_4$$

$$1.50\text{ mol }H_2O\left(\frac{1\text{ mol }H_3PO_4}{4\text{ mol }H_2O}\right) = 0.375\text{ mol }H_3PO_4$$

PCl_5 produces the least amount of product, so it is the limiting reactant in this case, and 0.250 mol H_3PO_4 is formed.

Now determine the amount of water that reacts with 0.250 mol PCl_5 and how many moles of HCl are formed.

$$0.250 \text{ mol } PCl_5\left(\frac{4 \text{ mol } H_2O}{1 \text{ mol } PCl_5}\right) = 1.00 \text{ mol } H_2O \text{ reacted}$$

$$0.250 \text{ mol } PCl_5\left(\frac{5 \text{ mol HCl}}{1 \text{ mol } PCl_5}\right) = 1.25 \text{ mol HCl formed}$$

Now set up a table to determine the number of moles of each species after the reaction.

	PCl_5 +	$4\,H_2O$ →	H_3PO_4 +	$5\,HCl$
Initial amounts	0.250 mol	1.50 mol	0 mol	0 mol
Change due to reaction	−0.250 mol	−1.00 mol	+0.250 mol	+1.25 mol
Final amounts	0 mol	0.50 mol	0.250 mol	1.25 mol

PRACTICE PROBLEM 5.10

Calculate the number of moles of reactants and products present after the double-replacement reaction of 0.100 mol $AgNO_3$(aq) with 0.0250 mol $BaCl_2$(aq) is complete.

$$AgNO_3(aq) + BaCl_2(aq) \rightarrow Ba(NO_3)_2(aq) + AgCl(s)$$

Hint: First, balance the chemical equation. Then identify the limiting reactant. One way to do that is to find how much product (arbitrarily choose one of them) forms when all of the $AgNO_3$ reacts and compare it to the amount of that product that forms when all of the $BaCl_2$ reacts. The reactant that produces the smaller amount of product is limiting.

Then, use the amount of the limiting reactant and the coefficients in the balanced equation to find the amounts of the other reactant used and product formed. Finally, make a table that summarizes the initial and final amounts of each species in the reaction.

The creation of a table to summarize the amounts of *all* products and reactants can be helpful, especially if you are asked to find the final amounts of multiple reactants and/or products. If you are asked about a specific reactant or product (as opposed to all of them), however, then it is not strictly necessary to complete the entire table.

Example 5.11

After the reaction of 0.750 mol HF with 0.250 mol NaOH is complete, how much excess reactant remains?

$$HF(aq) + NaOH(aq) \rightarrow NaF(aq) + H_2O(l)$$

Solution

First, determine whether or not the given chemical equation is balanced. (In this case, it is.) Then determine the limiting reactant.

$$0.750 \text{ mol HF}\left(\frac{1 \text{ mol NaF}}{1 \text{ mol HF}}\right) = 0.750 \text{ mol NaF}$$

$$0.250 \text{ mol NaOH}\left(\frac{1 \text{ mol NaF}}{1 \text{ mol NaOH}}\right) = 0.250 \text{ mol NaF}$$

NaOH is the limiting reactant. Now determine the amount of HF that reacts with 0.250 mol NaOH.

$$0.250 \text{ mol NaOH}\left(\frac{1 \text{ mol HF}}{1 \text{ mol NaOH}}\right) = 0.250 \text{ mol HF reacted}$$

Subtract this from the initial amount of HF to find the amount that remains.

	HF
Initial amount	0.750 mol HF
Change due to reaction	−0.250 mol HF
Final amount	0.500 mol HF

PRACTICE PROBLEM 5.11

How many moles of Na_2SO_4 are produced by the reaction of 0.550 mol H_2SO_4 with 0.375 mol NaOH?

$$H_2SO_4(aq) + 2\,NaOH(aq) \rightarrow Na_2SO_4(aq) + 2\,H_2O(l)$$

Hint: First, confirm that the given equation is balanced. Then identify the limiting reactant. Calculate how much Na_2SO_4 forms when all of the NaOH reacts and compare it to the amount of Na_2SO_4 that forms when all of the H_2SO_4 reacts. The reactant that produces the smaller amount of product is limiting, and that smaller amount of product is the answer to the question.

Problems involving limiting quantities may be stated in terms of masses, rather than moles, and a calculation of the mass of a product might be required. To solve problems that are given in mass instead of moles, follow the same procedure you have used up to now, but first convert the masses of reactants to moles (using the appropriate molar mass as the conversion factor). Then, convert the final number of moles of product to a mass, if required. Figure 5.7 summarizes the conversions and procedure.

Example 5.12

What mass of Na_2SO_4 will be formed by addition of 14.4 g $NaHCO_3$ in aqueous solution to an aqueous solution containing 4.90 g H_2SO_4?

$$H_2SO_4(aq) + 2\,NaHCO_3(aq) \rightarrow Na_2SO_4(aq) + 2\,H_2O(l) + 2\,CO_2(g)$$

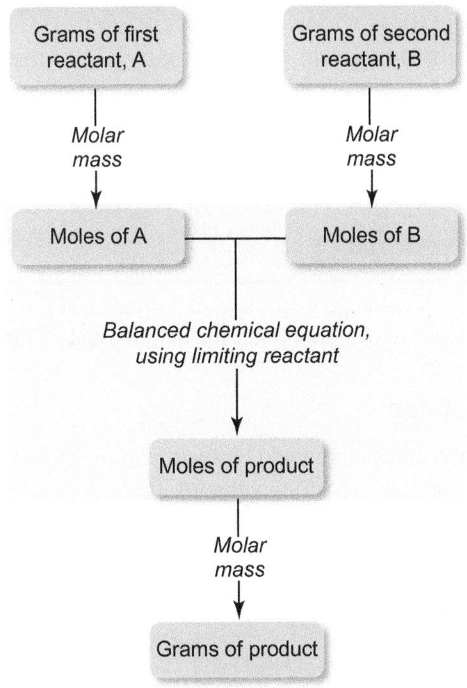

FIGURE 5.7 Procedure for Limiting-Reactant Problems Involving Masses

If the amounts of reactants are given in grams, the masses must first be converted to moles. Then calculate the moles of other reactants and products as needed from the number of moles and convert the final answer(s) to grams at the end. The shaded area in the center of this figure is done entirely in moles, and represents the types of limiting-reactant problems you've seen thus far.

Solution

The first step is to determine whether or not the given chemical equation is balanced. In this case, the equation is balanced. Next, determine the molar masses of the reactants.

The molar mass of H_2SO_4 is

$$2(1.008\text{ g/mol}) + 32.06\text{ g/mol} + 4(15.999\text{ g/mol}) = 98.07\text{ g/mol}$$

The molar mass of $NaHCO_3$ is

$$22.99\text{ g/mol} + 1.008\text{ g/mol} + 12.011\text{ g/mol} + 3(15.999\text{ g/mol}) = 84.01\text{ g/mol}$$

Convert the given masses to moles using the molar masses.

$$4.90\text{ g } H_2SO_4\left(\frac{1\text{ mol } H_2SO_4}{98.07\text{ g } H_2SO_4}\right) = 0.0500\text{ mol } H_2SO_4$$

$$14.4\text{ g } NaHCO_3\left(\frac{1\text{ mol } NaHCO_3}{84.01\text{ g } NaHCO_3}\right) = 0.171\text{ mol } NaHCO_3$$

Now, determine the limiting reactant.

$$0.0500\text{ mol } H_2SO_4\left(\frac{1\text{ mol } Na_2SO_4}{1\text{ mol } H_2SO_4}\right) = 0.0500\text{ mol } Na_2SO_4$$

$$0.171\text{ mol } NaHCO_3\left(\frac{1\text{ mol } Na_2SO_4}{2\text{ mol } NaHCO_3}\right) = 0.0856\text{ mol } Na_2SO_4$$

H_2SO_4 is the limiting reactant, so 0.0500 mol Na_2SO_4 is produced. The molar mass of Na_2SO_4 is

$$2(22.99\text{ g/mol}) + 32.06\text{ g/mol} + 4(15.999\text{ g/mol}) = 142.04\text{ g/mol}$$

Finally, convert the 0.04996 mol Na_2SO_4 to grams.

$$0.04996\text{ mol } Na_2SO_4\left(\frac{142.04\text{ g } Na_2SO_4}{1\text{ mol } Na_2SO_4}\right) = 7.10\text{ g } Na_2SO_4$$

PRACTICE PROBLEM 5.12

Aqueous HBr reacts with aqueous $NaHCO_3$ to produce aqueous NaBr, gaseous CO_2, and liquid water.

$$HBr(aq) + NaHCO_3(aq) \rightarrow NaBr(aq) + CO_2(g) + H_2O(l)$$

Determine the mass of NaBr produced when the reaction of 25.0 g HBr with 12.3 g $NaHCO_3$ is complete.

Hint: First, be sure that the reaction is balanced. Then, convert the reactant masses to moles using the molar masses of the reactants. Identify the limiting reactant. Determine the number of moles of NaBr produced based on the number of moles of limiting reactant, then convert moles to grams using the molar mass of NaBr.

SECTION REVIEW

- A chemical reaction proceeds until one of the reactants has been consumed, then the reaction stops.
- The reactant that runs out first is called the limiting reactant.
- When given the masses of multiple reactants, you need to identify which one is the limiting reactant. All calculations must be based on the amount of the limiting reactant, not the excess reactant(s).
- Three methods to determine which reactant is limiting were presented:
  - Separately calculate the amount of product formed from each reactant, assuming the reactant

is completely used up. The reactant that produces the smaller amount of product is limiting.
  - Divide the given number of moles of each reactant by its coefficients in the balanced equation. The reactant with the smallest quotient is the limiting reactant.
  - Find the amount of each reactant needed to completely use up the other reactant. Disregard the scenario that requires more of a reactant than is actually present.
- If a problem gives the amounts of reactants in grams instead of moles, the mass must first be converted to moles before proceeding with the rest of the problem.

5.4 Theoretical Yield and Percent Yield

GOAL

- Express the quantity of product obtained from a reaction as a percentage of what the reaction is theoretically capable of producing.

Background Review

Chapter 0 Math Review: Section 0.6—Percentages

The **theoretical yield** is the maximum amount of product that can be formed from a reaction, based on the amounts of reactants available. In Section 5.1, Section 5.2, and Section 5.3, all calculations of the amount of product formed have been calculations of the theoretical yield. It is almost impossible, however, to obtain the theoretical yield of a product. A competing reaction may form other products, or the reaction may not be allowed to proceed to completion. It is also nearly impossible to transfer all of the product from the reaction vessel to the balance when the mass of the product is determined. Regardless of the reason, all reactions produce less measured product than the theoretical yield predicts.

The **actual yield** is the amount of product that is actually obtained in an experiment. The actual yield may be very close to the theoretical yield, but the measured amount is always at least slightly less than the theoretical yield. It is impossible for the actual yield to exceed the theoretical yield. The actual yield may *appear* to be larger than the theoretical yield, but this just means the reaction product contains impurities, such as excess water. The **percent yield** is defined as 100% times the ratio of the actual yield to the theoretical yield.

$$\text{Percent yield} = \left(\frac{\text{Actual yield}}{\text{Theoretical yield}}\right) \times 100\% \qquad (5.1)$$

Example 5.13

Calculate the percent yield of a reaction if the theoretical yield is 7.44 g but the actual yield is 7.02 g.

Solution

Divide the actual yield by the theoretical yield, and multiply the resulting value by 100%.

$$\text{Percent yield} = \left(\frac{\text{Actual yield}}{\text{Theoretical yield}}\right) \times 100\%$$

$$\text{Percent yield} = \left(\frac{7.02\text{ g}}{7.44\text{ g}}\right) \times 100\% = 94.4\%$$

PRACTICE PROBLEM 5.13

The theoretical yield of a reaction product is 7.10 g. If the percent yield is 96%, what is the actual yield of the product?

Hint: Rearrange Equation 5.1 to calculate the actual yield.

Sometimes, you may need to determine both the limiting reactant and the percent yield in a chemical reaction.

Example 5.14

In photosynthesis, CO_2 and water react to form glucose ($C_6H_{12}O_6$) and O_2. The balanced chemical equation is

$$6\,CO_2(g) + 6\,H_2O(l) \rightarrow C_6H_{12}O_6(aq) + 6\,O_2(g)$$

Suppose that 12.0 g CO_2 reacts with 8.00 g H_2O to give 7.50 g $C_6H_{12}O_6$. Determine the percent yield of glucose from this reaction.

Solution

First, convert the masses of reactants to moles:

$$12.0\text{ g } CO_2\left(\frac{1\text{ mol } CO_2}{44.009\text{ g } CO_2}\right) = 0.273\text{ mol } CO_2$$

$$8.00\text{ g } H_2O\left(\frac{1\text{ mol } H_2O}{18.015\text{ g } H_2O}\right) = 0.444\text{ mol } H_2O$$

Now determine the limiting reactant.

$$0.273 \text{ mol } CO_2\left(\frac{1 \text{ mol } C_6H_{12}O_6}{6 \text{ mol } CO_2}\right) = 0.0454 \text{ mol } C_6H_{12}O_6$$

$$0.444 \text{ mol } H_2O\left(\frac{1 \text{ mol } C_6H_{12}O_6}{6 \text{ mol } H_2O}\right) = 0.0740 \text{ mol } C_6H_{12}O_6$$

[Note that because CO_2 and H_2O react in the same molar ratio to give each of the products (6 mol of each reactant gives 1 mol of glucose and 6 mol of oxygen), you could have determined that CO_2 is the limiting reactant without performing the standard calculation.]

Now determine the maximum number of grams of glucose that can form from 0.273 mol CO_2—that is, the theoretical yield of glucose:

$$0.273 \text{ mol } CO_2\left(\frac{1 \text{ mol glucose}}{6 \text{ mol } CO_2}\right)\left(\frac{180.16 \text{ g glucose}}{1 \text{ mol glucose}}\right) = 8.19 \text{ g glucose}$$

Finally, use Equation 5.1 to calculate the percent yield of glucose:

$$\text{Percent yield} = \left(\frac{\text{Actual yield}}{\text{Theoretical yield}}\right) \times 100\% = \left(\frac{7.50 \text{ g}}{8.19 \text{ g}}\right) \times 100\% = 91.6\%$$

PRACTICE PROBLEM 5.14

Ammonia, NH_3, can be formed by a reaction, known as the Haber process, of nitrogen and hydrogen gas under high temperature and pressure. The balanced chemical equation is

$$N_2(g) + 3\,H_2(g) \rightarrow 2\,NH_3(g)$$

Suppose that 4.80 g of ammonia is formed by the reaction of 5.50 g N_2 with 1.50 g H_2. Determine the percent yield of ammonia.

Hint: First, confirm that the reaction is balanced. Then determine the limiting reactant and then use the amount of the limiting reactant to determine the theoretical yield of NH_3. Finally, use Equation 5.1 to calculate the percent yield.

SECTION REVIEW

- The theoretical yield is the maximum amount of product that can be formed from a reaction, based on the amounts of reactants available.
- Many factors may reduce the actual yield of product. Competing reactions, product remaining in the reaction vessel, and reactions not going to completion all lead to forming less product than the theoretical amount.
- The percent yield is calculated using Equation 5.1.

$$\text{Percent yield} = \left(\frac{\text{Actual yield}}{\text{Theoretical yield}}\right) \times 100\%$$

5.5 Definition and Uses of Molarity

GOAL

- Solve problems using molarity.

Background Review

Chapter 0 Math Review: Section 0.2—Exponents and Scientific Notation

Chapter 1 Science and Measurement: Section 1.1—Classification of Matter

Chapter 3 Compounds and the Mole: Section 3.7—The Mole

A homogeneous mixture, which is a uniform mixture of two or more substances, is also called a solution (Section 1.1). The component of the solution that is present in the greatest amount is called the **solvent**, and the substance or substances dissolved in the solvent are the **solutes**. When water is a component of the solution, it is often regarded as the solvent even if another component is present in a greater amount. In an alcohol water solution, for example, the alcohol is regarded as the solute and the water as the solvent, no matter how much of each is present.

Concentration expresses the quantity of a solute in a given quantity of solvent or solution. For example, if you usually drink coffee with two teaspoons of sugar per cup, how much sugar would you use in half a cup of coffee to achieve the same sweetness? The sweetness depends on the concentration—the amount of sugar (the solute) *per given volume of coffee (the solution)*. You would use one teaspoon of sugar (half of the normal amount) in half a cup of coffee (half of the normal amount). Solutions that have a relatively large amount of solute per volume of solvent are typically referred to as **concentrated**. Solutions that have a relatively small amount of solute per volume of solvent are often described as **dilute** (Figure 5.8).

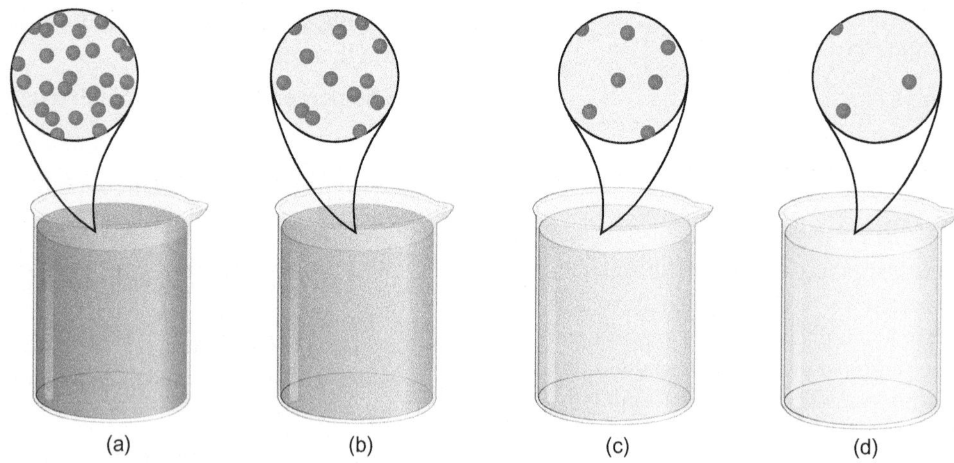

FIGURE 5.8 Concentrated and Dilute Solutions

The solution in beaker (a) has more solute per unit volume than the other solutions. As a result, the solution in beaker (a) is the most concentrated, whereas the solution in beaker (d) is the most dilute.

Example 5.15

Groggy from lack of sleep, you accidentally dissolve four teaspoons of sugar in your morning cup of coffee, instead of your usual two. How could you make your coffee less sweet?

Solution

Once the sugar (solute) has dissolved, it is difficult to remove it. If you add more fresh, unsweetened coffee (solvent) to the cup, though, you will decrease the amount of sugar *per unit volume of coffee.* The coffee will taste less sweet because the amount of solvent has increased whereas the amount of solute remains constant. In other words, the concentration decreases (the solute becomes more dilute) as the solvent volume increases. To attain your usual concentration of sugar (two teaspoons of sugar per cup), you will need to double the original volume of the coffee.

PRACTICE PROBLEM 5.15

Two sugar cubes are dissolved in some water, and then more water is added to fill a cup. A second cup of equal volume has one sugar cube dissolved in enough water to half fill the cup.

a. Which cup, if either, contains more sugar?
b. Which cup, if either, contains the sweeter-tasting solution?
c. What is the difference between quantity and concentration?

Hint: Consider the definition of concentration and the relative concentrations of sugar in the two cups in parts (a) and (b).

MOLARITY

Molarity, *M*, is a type of concentration, defined as the number of moles of solute per liter of solution:

$$\text{Molarity} = \frac{\text{Moles of solute}}{\text{Liter of solution}} \tag{5.2}$$

This definition is often shortened to "moles per liter," so keep in mind that this means the number of moles of *solute* per liter of *solution.* The unit of molarity is **molar, M.**

Example 5.16

Calculate the molarity of a solution containing 7.50 mol formaldehyde, CH_2O, in enough water to make 1.50 L of solution.

Solution

$$M = \frac{\text{Moles of solute}}{\text{Liter of solution}} = \frac{7.50\text{ mol}}{1.50\text{ L}} = 5.00\text{ M}$$

PRACTICE PROBLEM 5.16

A solution is prepared using 3.55 L of water and 2.10 mol solute. The total volume is 3.75 L. What is the molarity of the solute?

Hint: Use Equation 5.2 to determine the molarity of a solute. Pay close attention to the denominator of this equation.

Molarity (M) can also be defined as the number of *millimoles* of solute per *milliliter* of solution,

$$M = \frac{\text{Moles of solute}}{\text{Liter of solution}} = \frac{\text{Millimoles of solute}}{\text{Milliliter of solution}}$$

where 1 mol = 1000 millimoles, mmol, just as 1 L = 1000 mL (Section 1.5). If you are doing a molarity problem where the volume is given in milliliters, using the millimole version of the molarity formula can often save you the extra step of converting the volume to liters.

Example 5.17

Calculate the molarity of 60.0 mL of solution containing 1.25 mmol solute.

Solution

$$M = \frac{\text{mmol of solute}}{\text{mL of solution}} = \frac{1.25\text{ mmol}}{60.0\text{ mL}} = 0.0208\text{ M}$$

PRACTICE PROBLEM 5.17

Calculate the molarity of a solution containing 4.50 mmol NaCl in 3.80 mL of solution.

Hint: Equation 5.2 defines molarity as moles per liter, but dividing both the numerator and denominator by 1000 gives an analogous formula in units of millimoles and milliliters, respectively.

If quantities of solute and solution are given in units other than moles and liters or millimoles and milliliters, respectively, they can be converted to one of these sets of units to calculate the molarity.

Example 5.18

Calculate the molarity of 50.0 mL of solution containing 7.50 g of methanol, CH_4O.

Solution

The volume of solution must be converted to liters and the mass of the solute must be converted to moles before the molarity of the solution can be determined. The molar mass of CH_4O is

$$12.011\text{ g/mol} + 4(1.008\text{ g/mol}) + 15.999\text{ g/mol} = 32.033\text{ g/mol}$$

Convert the given quantities to moles and liters.

Mass of CH_3OH → Molar mass → Moles of CH_3OH

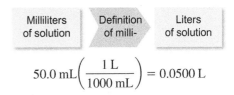

$$7.50\text{ g CH}_4\text{O}\left(\frac{1\text{ mol CH}_4\text{O}}{32.033\text{ g CH}_4\text{O}}\right) = 0.234\text{ mol CH}_4\text{O}$$

Milliliters of solution → Definition of milli- → Liters of solution

$$50.0\text{ mL}\left(\frac{1\text{ L}}{1000\text{ mL}}\right) = 0.0500\text{ L}$$

Now calculate the molarity, M, of methanol.

$$M = \frac{0.234\text{ mol CH}_4\text{O}}{0.0500\text{ L}} = 4.68\text{ M CH}_4\text{O}$$

Alternatively, you could convert the number of moles of CH_4O to millimoles and then divide it by the volume of the solution in milliliters.

$$0.234\text{ mol CH}_4\text{O}\left(\frac{1\text{ mmol}}{0.001\text{ mol}}\right) = 234\text{ mmol CH}_4\text{O}$$

$$M = \frac{234\text{ mmol CH}_4\text{O}}{50.0\text{ mL}} = 4.68\text{ M CH}_4\text{O}$$

PRACTICE PROBLEM 5.18

Calculate the molarity of 11.6 mL of a solution that contains 0.750 g $CaCl_2$.

Hint: First, convert the mass of $CaCl_2$ to moles. When calculating molarity, be sure to use the correct units of volume.

Molarity can also be used as a conversion factor between units of moles and liters. Consider the calculation to determine the number of moles of solute in 3.00 L of a 1.50 M solution.

$$3.00\text{ L}\left(\frac{1.50\text{ mol solute}}{1\text{ L}}\right) = 4.50\text{ mol solute}$$

Liters of solution → Molarity → Moles of solute

The concentration of the solution is 1.50 M, but the unit M is expanded to its mol/L form for the conversion. The total quantity of solute present in 3.00 L of solution is 4.50 mol. The relationship between quantity of solute and concentration of solute is shown in Figure 5.9.

The video in Figure 5.10 demonstrates calculations involving molarity.

Example 5.19

Calculate the number of millimoles of ethanol, C_2H_6O, in 29.21 mL of a 6.013 M solution.

Solution

One definition of molarity is the number of millimoles of solute per milliliter of solution, so the

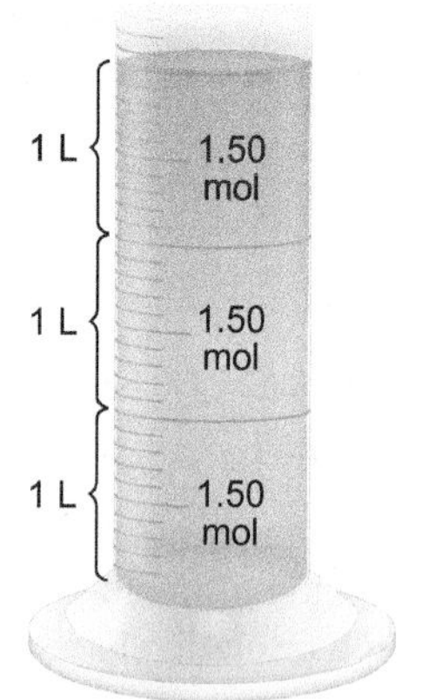

FIGURE 5.9 Moles and Concentration of Solute in a Solution

In a 1.50 M solution, each liter of solution contains 1.50 mol solute, so 3.00 L of solution contains a total of 4.50 mol of solute.

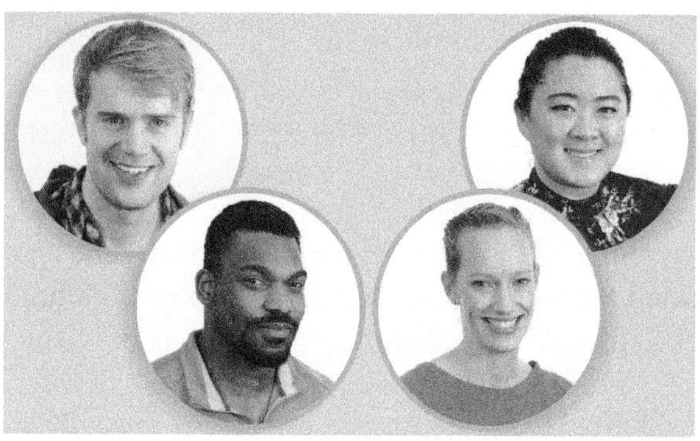

Steve Lemon, Macmillan Learning

FIGURE 5.10 Video Tutorial: Molarity

NOTE: You need to be online to access this video.

This video shows how to calculate molarity and use molarity as a conversion factor between moles and volume.

molarity of the ethanol solution can be expressed as 6.013 mmol/mL.

$$29.21 \text{ mL}\left(\frac{6.013 \text{ mmol}}{1 \text{ mL}}\right) = 175.6 \text{ mmol}$$

PRACTICE PROBLEM 5.19

How many liters of 0.415 M solution would contain 0.853 mol solute?

Hint: Note that 0.415 M means 0.415 mol/L. This value can be used as a conversion factor between moles and liters.

Example 5.20

In many jurisdictions, it is illegal to operate a motor vehicle with a blood alcohol content greater than 0.08 g of ethanol, C_2H_6O, per dL of blood. Convert this concentration of ethanol in blood to units of molarity.

Solution

To convert 0.08 g of ethanol per dL of blood to moles of ethanol per L of blood, the number of moles of ethanol must be known. First, calculate the molar mass of ethanol, C_2H_6O.

$$2(12.011 \text{ g/mol C}) + 6(1.008 \text{ g/mol H}) + 15.999 \text{ g/mol O} = 46.069 \text{ g/mol}$$

Now, convert the mass of ethanol to moles.

$$0.08 \text{ g ethanol}\left(\frac{1 \text{ mol ethanol}}{46.069 \text{ g ethanol}}\right) = 0.002 \text{ mol ethanol}$$

From Table 1.5, 1 dL = 0.1 L. Now the concentration of ethanol in molarity can be calculated:

$$\left(\frac{0.002 \text{ mol ethanol}}{0.1 \text{ L}}\right) = 0.02 \text{ M}$$

PRACTICE PROBLEM 5.20

The normal concentration range of glucose in healthy human adult blood is 79.2–110 mg/dL. Calculate this concentration range in units of molarity. The molar mass of glucose is 180.16 g/mol.

Hint: Molarity is in units of moles of solute (glucose) per liter of solution (blood). First, use the molar mass of glucose to convert both 79.2 mg and 110 mg of glucose to moles of glucose. Recall that there is 0.1 L in 1 dL. Then divide each value of moles of glucose by 0.1 L.

DILUTION

Dilution is the process of adding more solvent to decrease the concentration of solute in a solution (Figure 5.11). You can calculate the concentration of a solution that has been prepared by diluting a more **concentrated solution** using the basic definition of molarity.

For example, what concentration results when 0.750 L of 1.60 M NaCl is diluted with water to make 3.00 L of solution? When the solution is diluted with water, the *concentration* (molarity) of NaCl decreases, but the *quantity* (moles) of NaCl remains the same (Figure 5.11). First, calculate the original number of moles of NaCl in the solution, and then use that

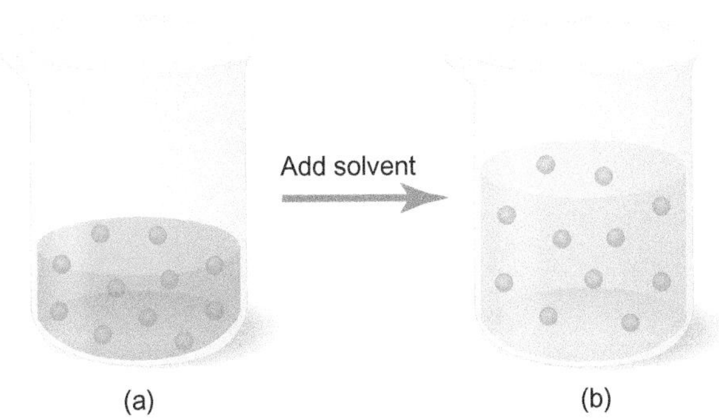

FIGURE 5.11 Dilution of a Solution

A solution is diluted via the addition of more solvent. Note that the number of solute molecules per unit volume in the original solution (a) is less than the number of solute molecules per unit volume in the diluted solution (b). However, the *total number* of solute molecules does not change after dilution.

amount, along with the final volume, to calculate the final concentration.

$$0.750\ \text{L}\left(\frac{1.60\ \text{mol NaCl}}{1\ \text{L}}\right) = 1.20\ \text{mol NaCl}$$

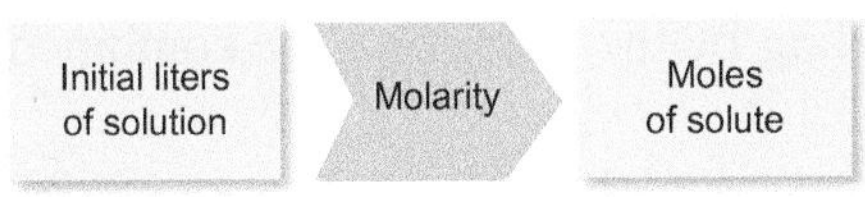

Because only solvent (water)—and no more solute—is added, the final solution still contains 1.20 mol solute. Thus, the concentration of the final solution is

$$M = \frac{1.20\ \text{mol NaCl}}{3.00\ \text{L}} = 0.400\ \text{M NaCl}$$

When the volume of the solution is quadrupled (from 0.750 L to 3.00 L), the concentration is diluted by a factor of 4 (from 1.60 M to 0.400 M).

When a solution is diluted with solvent, the number of moles of solute does not change during the dilution. Therefore, before the dilution, $M_1 \times V_1 = \text{mol}$, where M_1 and V_1 are the initial molarity and volume (in liters). After the dilution, $M_2 \times V_2 = \text{mol}$, where M_2 and V_2 are the final molarity and volume (in liters). Because the number of moles of solute has not changed, these two expressions are equal to one another:

$$M_1V_1 = M_2V_2 \qquad (5.3)$$

When a solution is diluted, the number of moles of solute remains constant. Only the concentration of solute changes.

EVERYDAY CONNECTION

Glucose is a sugar (Section 23.2) that functions as an energy source in most living organisms.

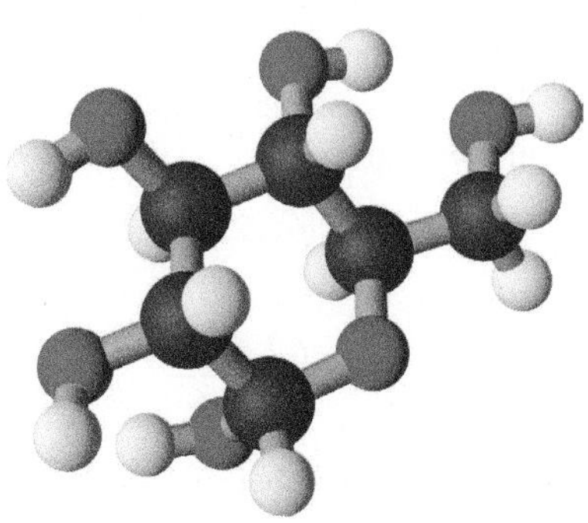

In humans, glucose provides the majority of the energy to the brain and is often formed in the body after an enzyme breaks apart a larger sugar named sucrose (table sugar) into glucose and fructose. It is important for the human body to maintain a specific concentration of glucose in the bloodstream. Too high of a glucose concentration in blood typically results in diabetes mellitus, commonly known as simply *diabetes*. Insulin, a peptide (Section 23.4) that promotes cellular uptake of glucose from the bloodstream, is most often used to treat diabetes. Left untreated, diabetes can result in stroke, kidney failure, heart disease, blindness, and foot ulcers. Too *low* of a glucose concentration in blood often results in a condition known as hypoglycemia. Symptoms of hypoglycemia include confusion, shaking, sweating, and clumsiness. Hypoglycemia can be treated by ingesting glucose pills or a fast-acting carbohydrate (Section 23.2) that will react in the body to produce glucose. Fast-acting carbohydrates include candy, fruit juices, and soft drinks.

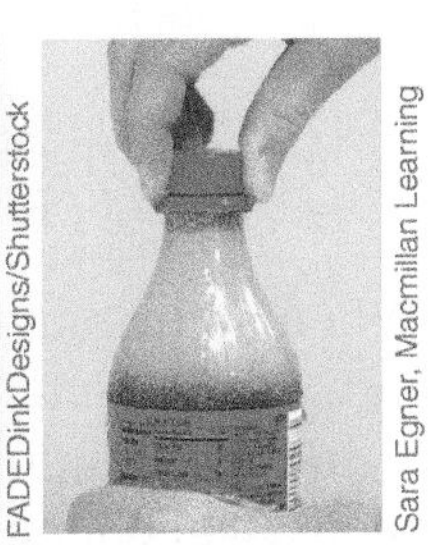

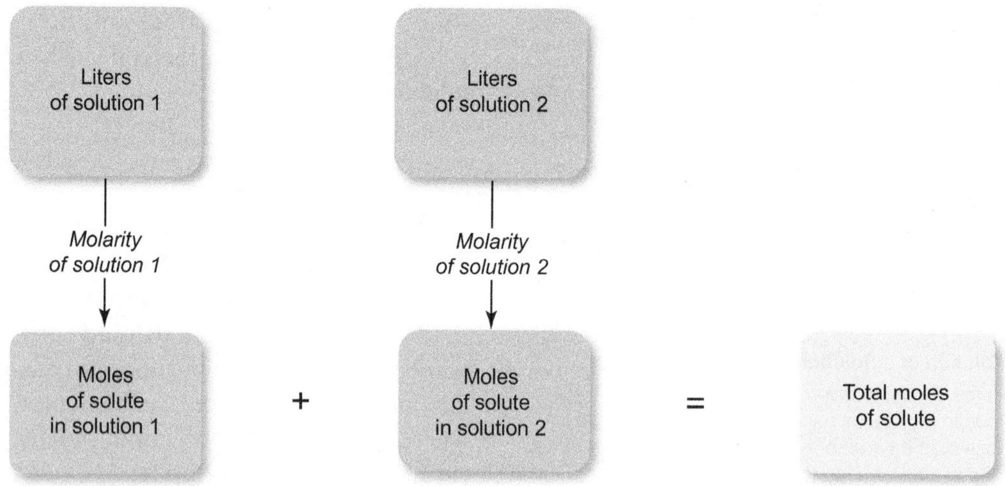

FIGURE 5.12 Combining Solutions of Unequal Concentration

After determining the number of moles of solute in each solution, the molarity of the combined solution is determined by adding the number of moles from each solution and dividing by the volume of the combined solution.

Example 5.21

Calculate the final concentration of NaCl after 1.25 L of 0.500 M NaCl is (a) diluted to 2.50 L with water and (b) diluted by the addition of 2.50 L of water.

Solution

a. Rearrange the $M_1V_1 = M_2V_2$ equation to solve for M_2.

$$M_2 = \frac{M_1V_1}{V_2} = \frac{(1.25\ \text{L})(0.500\ \text{M})}{2.50\ \text{L}} = 0.250\ \text{M}$$

b. When 2.50 L of water is added to 1.25 L, the total solution volume is 3.75 L.

$$M_2 = \frac{M_1V_1}{V_2} = \frac{(1.25\ \text{L})(0.500\ \text{M})}{3.75\ \text{L}} = 0.167\ \text{M}$$

PRACTICE PROBLEM 5.21

A nurse must prepare 4.00 L of 0.250 M saline (NaCl) solution. What volume of 6.00 M solution should the nurse dilute?

Hint: Use $M_1V_1 = M_2V_2$ (Equation 5.3), where M_1 = 6.00 M, M_2 = 0.250 M, and V_2 = 4.00 L. Solve for V_1.

When solutions of unequal solute concentration are mixed, determine the number of moles of solute in each solution separately. Then the concentration of the combined solution can be determined by adding the number of moles from each solution and dividing by the volume of the combined solution (Figure 5.12).

Example 5.22

Calculate the final concentration after 1.25 L of 2.25 M NaCl is added to 3.50 L of 2.45 M NaCl.

Solution

The molarity of the final solution is equal to the total number of moles of solute divided by the final volume. The number of moles of NaCl in the final solution is the sum of the numbers of moles in the two initial solutions.

$$\text{Solution 1: } 1.25\ \text{L}\left(\frac{2.25\ \text{mol}}{1\ \text{L}}\right) = 2.81\ \text{mol}$$

$$\text{Solution 2: } 3.50\ \text{L}\left(\frac{2.45\ \text{mol}}{1\ \text{L}}\right) = 8.58\ \text{mol}$$

The combined number of moles is

$$2.81 + 8.58 = 11.39\ \text{mol NaCl}$$

The combined solution volume is

$$1.25\ \text{L} + 3.50\ \text{L} = 4.75\ \text{L}$$

The molarity of the combined solution is the total number moles of NaCl divided by the combined volume of the two solutions:

$$M = \frac{11.39\ \text{mol NaCl}}{4.75\ \text{L}} = 2.40\ \text{M NaCl}$$

PRACTICE PROBLEM 5.22

Calculate the final concentration after 87.3 mL of 1.71 M sugar solution is combined with 71.7 mL of 3.11 M sugar solution and the resulting solution is diluted to 275 mL.

Hint: Separately determine the number of moles in each solution. Then add these and divide by the total final solution volume.

SOLUTION STOICHIOMETRY

As discussed in Section 5.4, masses should be converted to moles for the purposes of stoichiometry calculations based on chemical reactions. The same principle holds true when amounts of reactants and/or products are given as molarities. Molarities and volumes can be used to calculate the numbers of moles, which is the first step in any stoichiometry problem where molar concentrations are given. These conversions are summarized in Figure 5.13.

Example 5.23

Aqueous HCl reacts with aqueous NaOH to give aqueous NaCl and water.

$$HCl(aq) + NaOH(aq) \rightarrow NaCl(aq) + H_2O(l)$$

Find the volume (in milliliters) of 1.50 M HCl needed to react with 34.6 mL of 2.44 M NaOH.

Solution

First, confirm that the equation is balanced. Next, determine the number of moles of NaOH present.

$$34.6\text{ mL NaOH}\left(\frac{1\text{ L}}{1000\text{ mL}}\right)\left(\frac{2.44\text{ mol NaOH}}{1\text{ L NaOH}}\right)$$
$$= 0.0844\text{ mol NaOH}$$

According to the balanced chemical equation, HCl and NaOH react in a 1:1 molar ratio, so 0.0844 mol HCl is needed to react with NaOH.

$$0.0844\text{ mol NaOH}\left(\frac{1\text{ mol HCl}}{1\text{ mol NaOH}}\right) = 0.0844\text{ mol HCl}$$

Now determine the volume of 1.50 M HCl that contains 0.0844 mol.

$$0.0844\text{ mol HCl}\left(\frac{1\text{ L HCl}}{1.50\text{ mol HCl}}\right) = 0.0563\text{ L HCl}$$

$$0.0563\text{ L HCl}\left(\frac{1000\text{ mL}}{1\text{ L}}\right) = 56.3\text{ mL HCl}$$

Reacting ratios are millimole ratios as well as mole ratios, so you could have skipped the conversions to and from liters and gotten the same answer.

$$34.6\text{ mL NaOH}\left(\frac{2.44\text{ mmol NaOH}}{1\text{ mL NaOH}}\right) = 84.4\text{ mmol NaOH}$$

$$84.4\text{ mmol NaOH}\left(\frac{1\text{ mmol HCl}}{1\text{ mmol NaOH}}\right) = 84.4\text{ mmol HCl}$$

$$84.4\text{ mmol HCl}\left(\frac{1\text{ mL HCl}}{1.50\text{ mmol HCl}}\right) = 56.3\text{ mL HCl}$$

PRACTICE PROBLEM 5.23

Aqueous HNO_3 reacts with aqueous $Ba(OH)_2$ to give aqueous $Ba(NO_3)_2$ and water.

$$HNO_3(aq) + Ba(OH)_2(aq) \rightarrow Ba(NO_3)_2(aq) + H_2O(l)$$

Find the volume (in milliliters) of 0.5000 M HNO_3 needed to react with 41.77 mL of 0.1603 M $Ba(OH)_2$.

Hint: First, determine whether or not the equation needs to be balanced. Then, multiply the volume of $Ba(OH)_2$ by its molarity to give the number of moles of $Ba(OH)_2$ solution needed. Finally, use the stoichiometric relationship between $Ba(OH)_2$ and HNO_3 and the concentration of HNO_3 to obtain the volume of HNO_3 needed.

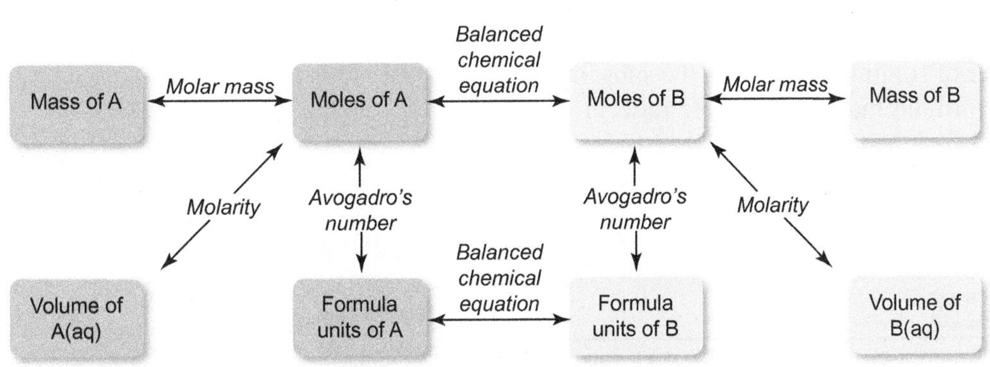

FIGURE 5.13 Stoichiometry Conversions Including Those Involving Molarity

The number of moles of any aqueous reactant or product can be calculated by multiplying the substance's molarity (moles/liter) by its volume (L). This is the first step in any stoichiometry problem involving aqueous solutions.

SECTION REVIEW

- Molarity, M, is the number of moles of solute per liter of solution.

$$M = \frac{\text{Moles of solute}}{\text{Liter of solution}}$$

  - Molarity can be used as a conversion factor between moles and volume for an aqueous solution.
  - Molarity can also be defined as the number of millimoles per milliliter of solution (but not the number of moles per milliliter of solution or the number of millimoles per liter of solution).
  - $M_1V_1 = M_2V_2$ can be used to calculate the volume or molarity of a solution that is diluted with additional solvent.
  - Since moles can be calculated from molarity and volume, the mole ratios expressed in a balanced chemical equation can be used to do stoichiometry calculations involving molarity.

5.6 Molarities of Ions

GOAL

- Extend the concept of molarity to the individual ions in solutions of ionic substances.

Background Review

Chapter 3 Compounds and the Mole: Section 3.1—Chemical Formulas

Chapter 4 Chemical Reactions and Aqueous Solutions: Section 4.3—Compounds in Aqueous Solution

Certain compounds (called strong electrolytes) dissociate into ions when dissolved in water (Chapter 4). The molarity of any ion is the number of moles of *that ion* per liter of solution. Moreover, the subscripts in a chemical formula indicate the mole ratio of the compound to its constituent elements (Chapter 3). For example, 1 mol $AlCl_3$ contains 1 mol Al^{3+} and 3 mol Cl^-, so the ion concentrations of a 1.0 M solution of $AlCl_3(aq)$ are 1.0 M Al^{3+} and 3.0 M Cl^-.

Example 5.24

a. Calculate the molarity of $AlCl_3$ if 0.220 mol $AlCl_3$ is dissolved in enough water to make 0.500 L of solution.
b. Calculate the concentration of each type of ion in the $AlCl_3$ solution.

Solution

a. Molarity is moles of solute per liter of solution.

$$M = \frac{0.220 \text{ mol AlCl}_3}{0.500 \text{ L}} = 0.440 \text{ M AlCl}_3$$

b. $AlCl_3$ consists of one Al^{3+} ion and three Cl^- ions. Use these relationships and the concentration of $AlCl_3$ from part (a) to determine the concentration of each ion.

$$0.220 \text{ mol AlCl}_3\left(\frac{1 \text{ mol Al}^{3+}}{1 \text{ mol AlCl}_3}\right) = 0.220 \text{ mol Al}^{3+}$$

$$0.220 \text{ mol AlCl}_3\left(\frac{3 \text{ mol Cl}^-}{1 \text{ mol AlCl}_3}\right) = 0.660 \text{ mol Cl}^-$$

Moles of salt → Formula → Moles of ions

Now calculate the concentrations of the ions.

$$\frac{0.220 \text{ mol Al}^{3+}}{0.500 \text{ L}} = 0.440 \text{ M Al}^{3+}$$

$$\frac{0.660 \text{ mol Cl}^-}{0.500 \text{ L}} = 1.32 \text{ M Cl}^-$$

PRACTICE PROBLEM 5.24

a. Calculate the molarity of $Al_2(SO_4)_3$ if 0.150 mol $Al_2(SO_4)_3$ is dissolved in enough water to make 2.70 L of solution.
b. Calculate the concentration of each type of ion in the $Al_2(SO_4)_3$ solution.

Hint: Use Equation 5.2 to determine the molarity of $Al_2(SO_4)_3$. When determining the molarities of the ions, use the number of moles of Al^{3+} and SO_4^{2-} produced per mole of dissolved $Al_2(SO_4)_3$.

Example 5.25

Calculate the concentration of each ion in a solution made by mixing 41.4 mL of 1.03 M NaCl with 66.2 mL of 0.818 M $CaCl_2$ and diluting to 150.0 mL. Assume that no reaction takes place.

Solution

First, calculate the number of moles of compound in each solution.

$$0.0414 \text{ L NaCl}\left(\frac{1.03 \text{ mol NaCl}}{1 \text{ L NaCl}}\right) = 0.0426 \text{ mol NaCl}$$

$$0.0662 \text{ L CaCl}_2\left(\frac{0.818 \text{ mol CaCl}_2}{1 \text{ L CaCl}_2}\right) = 0.0542 \text{ mol CaCl}_2$$

Now, determine the number of moles of each ion in each solution.

NaCl solution:

$$Na^+:\ 0.0426\ \text{mol NaCl}\left(\frac{1\ \text{mol}\ Na^+}{1\ \text{mol NaCl}}\right) = 0.0426\ \text{mol}\ Na^+$$

$$Cl^-:\ 0.0426\ \text{mol NaCl}\left(\frac{1\ \text{mol}\ Cl^-}{1\ \text{mol NaCl}}\right) = 0.0426\ \text{mol}\ Cl^-$$

$CaCl_2$ solution:

$$Ca^{2+}:\ 0.0542\ \text{mol}\ CaCl_2\left(\frac{1\ \text{mol}\ Ca^{2+}}{1\ \text{mol}\ CaCl_2}\right) = 0.0542\ \text{mol}\ Ca^{2+}$$

$$Cl^-:\ 0.0542\ \text{mol}\ CaCl_2\left(\frac{2\ \text{mol}\ Cl^-}{1\ \text{mol}\ CaCl_2}\right) = 0.108\ \text{mol}\ Cl^-$$

Now divide the concentration of each ion by the total solution volume (0.150 L). Cl^- is present in both of the original solutions, so the number of moles of Cl^- from both solutions must first be summed.

$$Na^+:\ \frac{0.0426\ \text{mol}}{0.150\ \text{L}} = 0.284\ \text{M}\ Na^+$$

$$Cl^-:\ \frac{(0.0426\ \text{mol} + 0.108\ \text{mol})}{0.150\ \text{L}} = 1.01\ \text{M}\ Cl^-$$

$$Ca^{2+}:\ \frac{0.0542\ \text{mol}\ Ca^{2+}}{0.150\ \text{L}} = 0.361\ \text{M}\ Ca^{2+}$$

PRACTICE PROBLEM 5.25

Calculate the concentration of each ion in a solution made by mixing 10.0 mL of 0.800 M $(NH_4)_3PO_4$ with 14.9 mL of 1.44 M NH_4Cl and diluting to 50.0 mL.

Hint: Multiply the volume of the original solutions by the molarity of each ionic compound to get the number of moles of each compound. When determining the molarity of each ion, be sure to use the final solution volume.

SECTION REVIEW

- In solutions of strong electrolytes, the molarities of individual ions can be determined from the molarity of the electrolyte and the number of each ion in the formula unit.
- The subscripts in the chemical formula express the mole ratio (and thus the molar ratio as well) of the ions to the formula unit. For example, a 1.0 M solution of $AlCl_3$ contains 1.0 M Al^{3+} and 3.0 M Cl^-.

5.7 Calculations Involving Other Quantities

GOAL

- Determine how much of any substance is involved in a chemical reaction, given any quantity of another substance, no matter what units are involved.

Background Review

Chapter 3 Compounds and the Mole:
Section 3.7—The Mole

As you have seen so far in Chapter 5, there are many ways of expressing the amounts of substances in a chemical reaction (e.g., grams and molarity) that must be converted to moles before performing stoichiometry calculations. When given the volume of an aqueous solution, use molarity as the conversion factor to moles. When given the volume of a pure substance (i.e., not a solution), on the other hand, use density to convert volume to mass, then use molar mass to convert mass to moles. These additional relationships are illustrated in the flowchart in Figure 5.14. This section explores the flowchart more fully, providing practice with variations on stoichiometry problems.

Example 5.26

Calculate the number of moles of solid mercury(I) oxide, Hg_2O, that can be produced by the combination reaction of excess oxygen gas with 25.0 mL of liquid mercury (density = 13.53 g/mL). Also, calculate the number of molecules of oxygen required.

Solution

First, write the balanced equation.

$$4\ Hg(l) + O_2(g) \rightarrow 2\ Hg_2O(s)$$

Calculate the number of moles of Hg_2O that can be formed based only on the amount of Hg present (O_2 is in excess).

$$25.0\ \text{mL Hg}\left(\frac{13.53\ \text{g Hg}}{1\ \text{mL Hg}}\right)\left(\frac{1\ \text{mol Hg}}{200.59\ \text{g Hg}}\right)\left(\frac{2\ \text{mol}\ Hg_2O}{4\ \text{mol Hg}}\right) = 0.843\ \text{mol}\ Hg_2O$$

Calculate the number of molecules of O_2 that are required to react with 25.0 mL Hg.

$$25.0\ \text{mL Hg}\left(\frac{13.53\ \text{g Hg}}{1\ \text{mL Hg}}\right)\left(\frac{1\ \text{mol Hg}}{200.59\ \text{g Hg}}\right)\left(\frac{1\ \text{mol}\ O_2}{4\ \text{mol Hg}}\right)\left(\frac{6.022 \times 10^{23}\ \text{molecules}\ O_2}{1\ \text{mol}\ O_2}\right)$$

$$= 2.54 \times 10^{23}\ \text{molecules}\ O_2$$

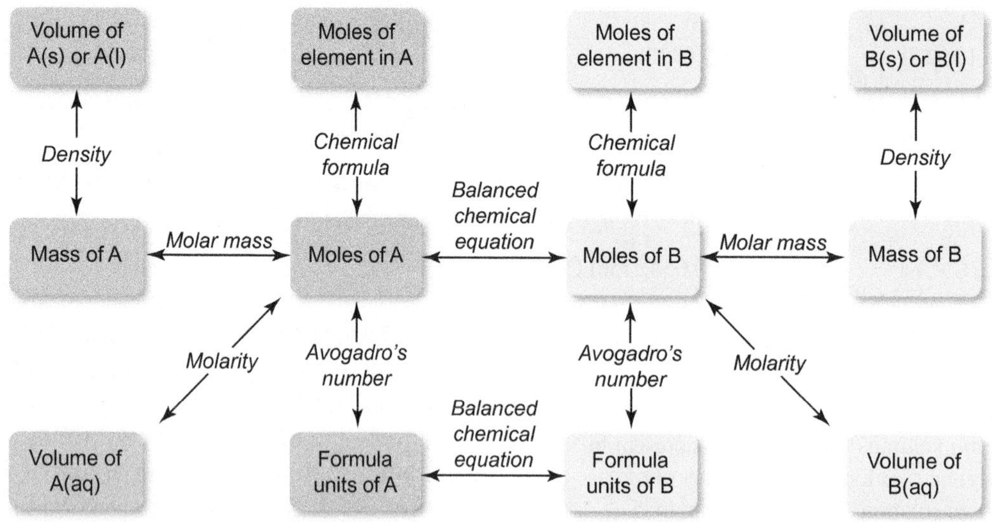

FIGURE 5.14 Mass, Mole, and Other Conversions

A and B can be any reactant or product in the reaction. Conversions from one quantity to another that involve only one substance can be based on that substance's chemical formula, its molar mass, its density, or on Avogadro's number. Conversions that relate one substance to another always use the balanced chemical equation as a conversion factor.

PRACTICE PROBLEM 5.26

The balanced equation for the combustion of propane, C_3H_8, is

$$C_3H_8(g) + 5\,O_2(g) \rightarrow 3\,CO_2(g) + 4\,H_2O(g)$$

Calculate the volume of liquid water (density = 1.00 g/mL) produced by burning 48.4 g of propane and condensing the gaseous water produced. Assume that O_2 is present in large excess.

Hint: After using the grams-to-moles and moles-to-grams conversions to get the mass of water formed, use the density of water to determine the volume of water formed.

PRACTICE PROBLEM 5.27

Barium and aluminum oxide can be heated to give aluminum and barium oxide via the single substitution reaction

$$3\,Ba(s) + Al_2O_3(s) \xrightarrow{\text{Heat}} 3\,BaO(s) + 2\,Al(s)$$

Calculate the number of individual atoms of barium metal that react when heated with excess aluminum oxide to form solid barium oxide and 7.33 g of aluminum.

Hint: After using the grams-to-moles and moles-to-moles conversions, use Avogadro's number to determine the number of barium atoms.

The number of moles of an element in a mole of a compound can also be used to calculate the number of moles of the compound involved in a reaction. The ratio of the number of moles of an element within a compound to the number of moles of the compound is determined by the compound's chemical formula. Thus, the subscripts of the formula may be used to form conversion factors.

Example 5.27

Sulfur dioxide reacts with oxygen to form sulfur trioxide. The balanced chemical equation is

$$2\,SO_2(g) + O_2(g) \rightarrow 2\,SO_3(g)$$

Determine the number of SO_2 molecules that are required to combine with excess O_2 to produce 0.751 mol SO_3.

Solution

Determine the number of moles of SO_2 that are needed to react to form 0.751 mol SO_3, and then use Avogadro's number to convert this value to the number of molecules of SO_2.

$$0.751 \text{ mol } SO_3\left(\frac{2 \text{ mol } SO_2}{2 \text{ mol } SO_3}\right)\left(\frac{6.022 \times 10^{23}\ SO_2 \text{ molecules}}{1 \text{ mol } SO_2}\right)$$
$$= 4.52 \times 10^{23}\ SO_2 \text{ molecules}$$

Example 5.28

Ammonia reacts with phosphoric acid, H_3PO_4, to give ammonium phosphate, $(NH_4)_3PO_4$.

$$3\,NH_3(aq) + H_3PO_4(aq) \rightarrow (NH_4)_3PO_4(aq)$$

The quantities of nitrogen, phosphorus, and potassium in a fertilizer are critical to the fertilizer's function in helping crops grow. Calculate the number of moles of nitrogen atoms in the ammonium phosphate, $(NH_4)_3PO_4$, produced by the reaction of excess aqueous ammonia with 227 mol phosphoric acid.

Solution

First, confirm that the chemical equation is balanced. Next, determine the number of moles of $(NH_4)_3PO_4$ that can be formed from 227 mol H_3PO_4, and then multiply this value by the number of moles of nitrogen per mole of $(NH_4)_3PO_4$.

$$227 \text{ mol } H_3PO_4\left(\frac{1 \text{ mol } (NH_4)_3PO_4}{1 \text{ mol } H_3PO_4}\right)\left(\frac{3 \text{ mol N}}{1 \text{ mol } (NH_4)_3PO_4}\right) = 681 \text{ mol N}$$

Moles of H_3PO_4 → Balanced chemical equation → Moles of $(NH_4)_3PO_4$ → Formula → Moles of N atoms

PRACTICE PROBLEM 5.28

Use the formation of ammonium phosphate, $(NH_4)_3PO_4$, in Example 5.28 to calculate the mass in grams of nitrogen in the ammonium phosphate prepared by treating 6.15×10^6 g of phosphoric acid with excess aqueous ammonia.

Hint: After using the grams-to-moles and moles-to-moles conversions, determine the number of nitrogen atoms per mole of $(NH_4)_3PO_4$ and use the atomic mass of nitrogen to calculate the mass of nitrogen formed.

SECTION REVIEW

- Converting moles of one reactant or product to another always uses the reacting ratio from the balanced chemical equation as a conversion factor.
- An additional unit conversion is required if the quantity of a substance is given in other units of one of the elements within the compound, such as mass, volume, or moles.

5.8 Calculations with Net Ionic Equations

GOALS

- Calculate the numbers of moles involved in net ionic equations.
- Calculate the masses of complete compounds involved in net ionic equations.
- Discuss the limitations of net ionic equations in calculating masses of individual ions.

Background Review

Chapter 4 Chemical Reactions and Aqueous Solutions: Section 4.3—Compounds in Aqueous Solution

Net ionic equations (Section 4.4), like all other balanced chemical equations, give the mole ratios of reactants and products. Therefore, any calculations that require mole ratios may be done with net ionic equations as well as with total equations. A net ionic equation does not yield mass data directly, however, because part of each soluble ionic compound (i.e., the spectator ion) is not included. For example, you can determine how many moles of silver ion are required to produce a certain number of moles of a product, but it is impossible to weigh out just the silver ions because all ionic compounds must contain some anions, too, and those anions have some mass. You cannot tell how much of the mass of the compound is composed of silver ions and how much is composed of anions if you do not specify which anions are present. Thus, net ionic equations have limited use when trying to directly compute masses.

Example 5.29

How many moles of barium ions are required to produce 175 g of solid barium sulfate?

Solution

The net ionic equation is

$$Ba^{2+}(aq) + SO_4^{2-}(aq) \rightarrow BaSO_4(s)$$

Use the molar mass of barium sulfate and the molar ratio between $BaSO_4$ and Ba^{2+} to determine the number of moles of Ba^{2+} needed to produce 175 g $BaSO_4$.

$$175 \text{ g } BaSO_4\left(\frac{1 \text{ mol } BaSO_4}{233.39 \text{ g } BaSO_4}\right)\left(\frac{1 \text{ mol } Ba^{2+}}{1 \text{ mol } BaSO_4}\right) = 0.750 \text{ mol } Ba^{2+}$$

Grams of $BaSO_4$ → Molar mass → Moles of $BaSO_4$ → Formula → Moles of Ba^{2+}

PRACTICE PROBLEM 5.29

How many moles of ammonium ions are required to produce 250 g of solid ammonium phosphate?

Hint: First convert the mass of ammonium phosphate to moles using its molar mass. Next, use stoichiometry to determine the number of NH_4^+ ions per mole of $(NH_4)_3PO_4$.

EVERYDAY CONNECTION

The masses of individual ions are important in food chemistry. For example, the mass of sodium is given on package labels, even though sodium is always consumed in ionic form with some anion present, such as NaCl. After a sodium salt dissolves in the bloodstream and in the fluid surrounding the cells, the dissociated $Na^{+}(aq)$ ions are what can trigger a response from the body. If the sodium ion concentration is high, the body will retain water as a way to dilute it. This increased volume of water in the bloodstream results in higher blood pressure, which can stiffen blood vessels and put extra strain on the heart. This can eventually cause a heart attack.

Nutrition Facts

Serving Size 2/3 cup (55g)
Servings Per Container About 8

Amount Per Serving	
Calories 230	Calories from Fat 40
	% Daily Value*
Total Fat 8g	**12%**
Saturated Fat 1g	**5%**
Trans Fat 0g	
Cholesterol 0mg	**0%**
Sodium 160mg	**7%**
Total Carbohydrate 37g	**12%**
Dietary Fiber 4g	**16%**
Sugars 1g	
Protein 3g	

U.S. Food and Drug Administration

In Example 5.29, you cannot weigh 0.750 mol Ba^{2+} if you do not know the identity of the anion that is bonded to Ba^{2+}. Even though the anion does not react, it still has mass and its identity is important in determining the correct mass of barium.

Example 5.30

a. Determine the mass of $Ba(NO_3)_2$ that is required to provide 0.750 mol Ba^{2+}.
b. Determine the mass of $Ba(ClO_3)_2$ that is required to provide 0.750 mol Ba^{2+}.

Solution

a. The molar mass of $Ba(NO_3)_2$ is
$137.33\ g/mol + 2\,(14.007\ g/mol) + 6(15.999\ g/mol) = 261.34\ g/mol.$

$$0.750\ \text{mol Ba}^{2+}\left(\frac{1\ \text{mol Ba(NO}_3)_2}{1\ \text{mol Ba}^{2+}}\right)\left(\frac{261.34\ \text{g Ba(NO}_3)_2}{1\ \text{mol Ba(NO}_3)_2}\right) = 196\ \text{g Ba(NO}_3)_2$$

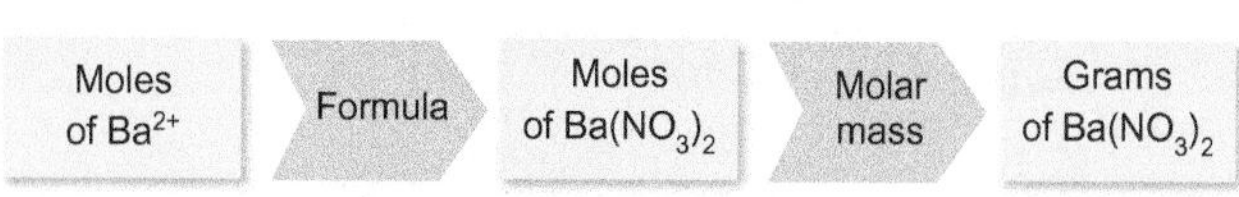

b. The molar mass of $Ba(ClO_3)_2$ is
$137.33\ g/mol + 2(35.45\ g/mol) + 6(15.999\ g/mol) = 304.22\ g/mol$

$$0.750\ \text{mol Ba}^{2+}\left(\frac{1\ \text{mol Ba(ClO}_3)_2}{1\ \text{mol Ba}^{2+}}\right)\left(\frac{304.22\ \text{g Ba(ClO}_3)_2}{1\ \text{mol Ba(ClO}_3)_2}\right) = 228\ \text{g Ba(ClO}_3)_2$$

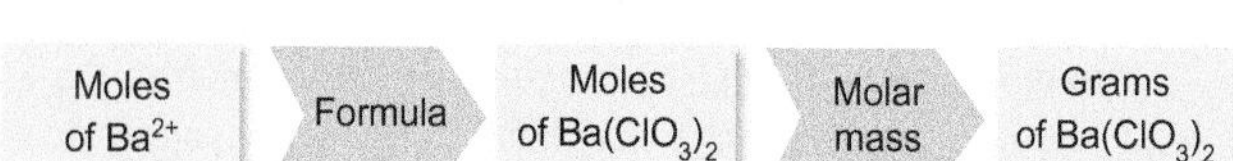

Note how the presence of different anions (NO_3^{2-} vs. ClO_3^{-}) changes the mass of the barium compound that is needed to supply the same number of moles of Ba^{2+}.

PRACTICE PROBLEM 5.30

How many moles of barium ions and how many grams of barium chloride would be required to produce 6.11 g of barium sulfate?

Hint: First, calculate the number of moles of Ba^{2+} ions that are contained in 6.11 g $BaSO_4$. Then determine the mass of $BaCl_2$ that is needed to supply that number of moles of Ba^{2+} ions.

SECTION REVIEW

- The masses of individual cations and anions cannot be measured on a balance. Instead, the mass of an ionic compound is measured on a balance, and you can use stoichiometry to find the masses of its constituent cations or anions.
- Stoichiometric calculations can be performed with net ionic equations to identify the number of moles of ions present in a reaction.

5.9 Titration

GOAL

- Determine the concentration, or the number of moles present, of a substance by an experimental technique called *titration.*

Background Review

Chapter 4 Chemical Reactions and Aqueous Solutions: Section 4.5—Acid–Base Reactions

Titration is a laboratory technique for determining the number of moles of a substance dissolved in an aqueous solution. In a titration, a reactant whose concentration is known precisely (called a **standard solution**) reacts with a sample whose concentration is unknown. An example of a titration setup is shown in Figure 5.15.

In a titration, one of the reactants (either the standard solution or the sample) is slowly added to the other. The solution that is slowly being added is called the **titrant**. In the reaction shown in Figure 5.15 and Figure 5.16, the titrant is sodium hydroxide, NaOH, and the solution being titrated is HCl. The HCl solution is in an **Erlenmeyer flask**. Erlenmeyer flasks are normally used for titrations instead of beakers because a solution in a flask can more easily be mixed by swirling without spilling any of the contents. The NaOH titrant is placed in a long glass tube called a **buret**. The buret has volume markings running along most of its length, with 0.00 mL near the top and 50.00 mL near the bottom. By taking an initial volume reading before the titration begins (Figure 5.15a) and a final volume reading when the titration is over (Figure 5.15c), the precise value of the volume of NaOH solution used in the reaction can be calculated. (Buret readings for a 50 mL buret are made to the nearest 0.01 mL.) The number of moles of standard used in the reaction can be calculated from the standard solution's known concentration and volume. From the moles of standard used and the balanced equation for the reaction, the number of moles of the reactant in the sample can be calculated.

FIGURE 5.16 Video: Titration

NOTE: You need to be online to access this video.
In this video, HCl is titrated with NaOH.

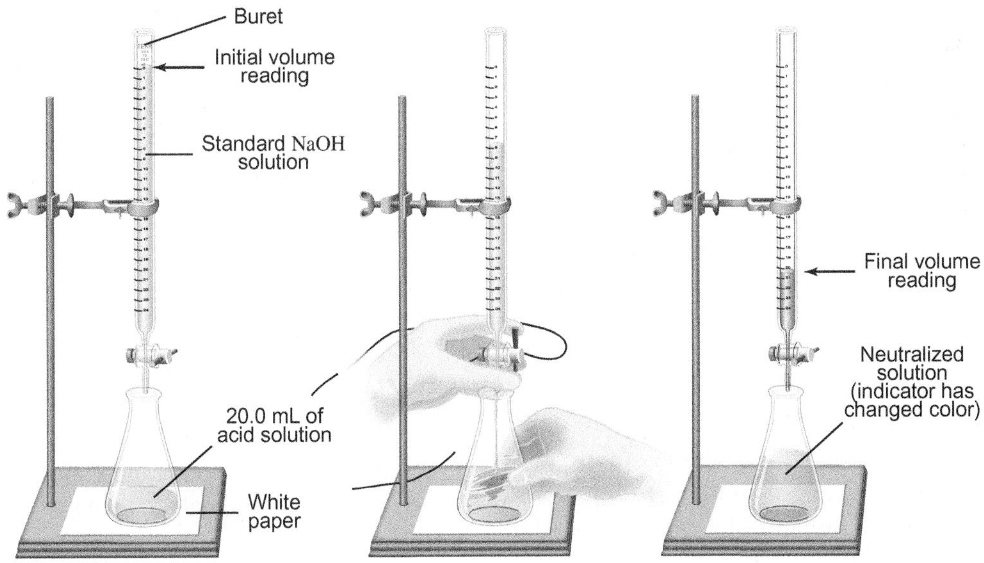

FIGURE 5.15 Titration Laboratory Setup

(a) Before the titration, no NaOH has been added from the buret. (b) Swirling the flask during the titration helps mix the solution.
(c) The change in color indicates when you should stop titrating. A piece of white paper below the reaction flask makes the color change easier to see.

The acid–base titrations shown in Figure 5.15 and Figure 5.16 are perhaps the most common titrations. Acid–base reactions produce a salt (consisting of the cation from the base and the anion from the acid) and often water (Section 4.5). The balanced equation for the reaction of HCl with NaOH is

$$HCl(aq) + NaOH(aq) \rightarrow NaCl(aq) + H_2O(l)$$

Before the titration begins, two drops of phenolphthalein **indicator** are added to the flask with the acid. Indicators are substances that change color based on the acidity of their solution. The titration begins when the valve at the bottom of the buret is opened, allowing the NaOH solution in the buret to drain into the flask, and the solution begins to turn pink where the NaOH enters the solution (Figure 5.15b). Eventually, all the acid in the flask will be reacted, and when one excess drop of base is added, the solution turns pink, and remains pink even after the flask is swirled. This color change signals the **end point** of the titration (Figure 5.15c). The end point of the titration is extremely close to the **equivalence point**, which is the point of the titration where all of the substance being titrated has reacted with the titrant. (The end point and the equivalence point are so close together that the difference between them contributes a negligible error to the final result.)

After the titration, the volume of NaOH that was used will be known, so it is possible at this point to calculate the concentration of the original HCl solution. Multiplying the NaOH concentration (in moles per liter) by the volume of NaOH used (in liters) provides the number of moles of NaOH used in the reaction. Because NaOH and HCl react in a 1:1 mole ratio, the number of moles of NaOH used is equal to the number of moles of HCl in the original sample, which can be expressed as a concentration by dividing by the volume of the original HCl solution.

For example, suppose that a chemist wants to determine the molarity of an HCl solution. The chemist adds 25.00 mL of HCl to a flask and titrates the HCl solution with 0.1500 M NaOH. The HCl solution is neutralized after 20.50 mL of NaOH solution is added. This point is the equivalence point, where the number of moles of H^+ is equal to the number of moles of OH^-. You can determine the number of moles of HCl in the flask from the number of moles of NaOH used to reach the equivalence point.

$$20.50 \text{ mL NaOH}\left(\frac{1 \text{ L}}{1000 \text{ mL}}\right)\left(\frac{0.1500 \text{ mol NaOH}}{1 \text{ L}}\right)$$
$$= 0.003075 \text{ mol NaOH}$$
$$= 0.003075 \text{ mol HCl}$$

The concentration of HCl is now obtained by dividing the number of moles of HCl by its volume (25.00 mL).

$$\frac{0.003075 \text{ mol HCl}}{0.02500 \text{ L}} = 0.1230 \text{ M HCl}$$

> The reaction is complete at the equivalence point, where the number of moles of H^+ is equal to the number of moles of OH^-.

Example 5.31

Suppose that 25.00 mL HCl is titrated with 2.000 M NaOH. Calculate the concentration of the HCl solution if the initial buret reading for the NaOH solution is 2.17 mL, and the final buret reading is 39.42 mL. (Lower numbers are toward the top of the buret.)

Solution

The volume of NaOH solution used is 39.42 mL − 2.17 mL = 37.25 mL. Find the number of moles of NaOH from the volume and molarity, then find the number of moles of HCl from the balanced chemical equation.

$$37.25 \text{ mL NaOH}\left(\frac{1 \text{ L}}{1000 \text{ mL}}\right)\left(\frac{2.000 \text{ mol NaOH}}{1 \text{ L NaOH}}\right)$$
$$\left(\frac{1 \text{ mol HCl}}{1 \text{ mol NaOH}}\right) = 0.07450 \text{ mol HCl}$$

The number of moles of HCl and NaOH are equal at the equivalence point because they react in a 1:1 mole ratio and because the titration was stopped at the equivalence point.

The HCl concentration can be calculated from the number of moles of HCl and the original volume of the HCl solution.

$$\frac{0.07450 \text{ mol HCl}}{0.02500 \text{ L HCl}} = 2.980 \text{ M HCl}$$

PRACTICE PROBLEM 5.31

A solution of 1.500 M NaOH is placed in a buret and is used to titrate 25.00 mL of a solution of sulfuric acid, H_2SO_4. If the initial buret reading is 1.28 mL and the buret reading at the equivalence point is 45.19 mL, calculate the concentration of the H_2SO_4.

Hint: First, write the balanced equation for this reaction. Note that H_2SO_4 has two ionizable hydrogens and so each mole of H_2SO_4 will react with *two* moles of NaOH. The rest of the problem is solved in a similar manner to Example 5.31.

Titrations can also be used to calculate the molar mass of an unknown solid acid or base. To do this, the mass of the sample must be known, along with the reaction stoichiometry of the titration. The titration provides the number of moles of the unknown acid or base.

Example 5.32

An unknown acid with only one ionizable hydrogen per formula unit, represented as HA, is prepared in the laboratory. The reaction can be represented by the following balanced chemical equation:

$$HA(aq) + NaOH(aq) \rightarrow NaA(aq) + H_2O(l)$$

Calculate the molar mass of the acid if it takes 33.48 mL of 0.5000 M NaOH to neutralize 25.00 mL of a solution of the unknown acid that is prepared by dissolving 3.172 g of the acid in water.

Solution

Calculate the number of moles of base used in the titration.

$$33.48 \text{ mL NaOH}\left(\frac{1 \text{ L}}{1000 \text{ mL}}\right)\left(\frac{0.5000 \text{ mol NaOH}}{1 \text{ L NaOH}}\right)$$
$$= 0.01674 \text{ mol NaOH}$$

According to the balanced equation, 0.01674 mol HA has reacted with 0.01674 mol NaOH at the equivalence point. Now that you know the number of moles of HA, you can use the mass of HA that was dissolved in solution to determine the molar mass of HA.

$$\text{Molar mass of HA} = \frac{\text{grams HA}}{\text{moles HA}} = \frac{3.172 \text{ g HA}}{0.01674 \text{ mol HA}}$$
$$= 189.5 \text{ g/mol}$$

Notice that the volume of the unknown acid was not used in this calculation.

PRACTICE PROBLEM 5.32

An unknown base, $M(OH)_2$, reacts with HCl in a 1:2 ratio.

$$M(OH)_2(aq) + 2\ HCl(aq) \rightarrow MCl_2(aq) + 2\ H_2O(l)$$

Calculate the molar mass of the base if it takes 26.28 mL of 1.000 M HCl to neutralize a solution of the unknown base that is prepared by dissolving 2.251 g of the base into 20.00 mL of water.

Hint: First, determine the number of moles of HCl that are needed to neutralize the solution of unknown base. Then use the reaction stoichiometry to find the moles of base. To determine the molar mass of the base, recall that molar mass has units of grams per mole, which can be achieved by dividing the given mass of base in grams by the number of moles of base you have calculated.

Acid–base titrations are discussed in greater detail in Section 17.3 and Section 17.4.

SECTION REVIEW

- A titration is a controlled reaction used for determining the number of moles of one substance by reacting it with a known number of moles of a second substance. Acid–base reactions are the most common type of reaction carried out by titration.
- The number of moles of the known substance used in the reaction is calculated by multiplying its volume by its known concentration. The number of moles of the unknown substance determined from the reacting ratios can be used to calculate the concentration of the unknown substance, its molar mass, or other quantities.

Putting It Together

The example problems in earlier sections of this chapter focus on just the new skills acquired in that section. But homework and exam questions in chemistry often require more than just one skill at a time. In fact, you will likely be expected to apply knowledge from across the entire chapter, or even multiple chapters in a single problem. This final example problem is meant to help you prepare for these types of multiconcept questions. Additional examples can be found in the end-of-chapter exercises.

Example 5.33

When 100.0 mL of 0.324 M aqueous silver nitrate reacts with 150.0 mL of 0.560 M aqueous sodium sulfate, 9.875 g of precipitate is formed. Determine the percent yield of the reaction.

Solution

First, identify the formulas of the compounds involved in this reaction. Silver nitrate consists of Ag^+ and NO_3^- ions for a neutral formula of $AgNO_3$. Sodium sulfate consists of Na^+ and SO_4^{2-} ions for a neutral formula of Na_2SO_4.

Now write the balanced equation. This is a double-replacement reaction, so the ions swap partners. Consult the solubility data in Table 4.5 to identify silver sulfate, Ag_2SO_4, as the insoluble precipitate.

$$2\,AgNO_3(aq) + Na_2SO_4(aq) \rightarrow Ag_2SO_4(s) + 2\,NaNO_3(aq)$$

Use the balanced equation to identify the limiting reactant.

$$100.0\text{ mL }AgNO_3\left(\frac{1\text{ L}}{1000\text{ mL}}\right)\left(\frac{0.324\text{ mol }AgNO_3}{1\text{ L }AgNO_3}\right)\left(\frac{1\text{ mol }Ag_2SO_4}{2\text{ mol }AgNO_3}\right) = 0.0162\text{ mol }Ag_2SO_4$$

$$150.0\text{ mL }Na_2SO_4\left(\frac{1\text{ L}}{1000\text{ mL}}\right)\left(\frac{0.560\text{ mol }Na_2SO_4}{1\text{ L }Na_2SO_4}\right)\left(\frac{1\text{ mol }Ag_2SO_4}{1\text{ mol }Na_2SO_4}\right) = 0.08400\text{ mol }Ag_2SO_4$$

$AgNO_3$ is the limiting reactant because it produces the smaller amount of product. The molar mass of Ag_2SO_4 is

$$2(107.87\text{ g/mol}) + 32.066\text{ g/mol} + 4(15.999\text{ g/mol}) = 311.80\text{ g/mol}.$$

Convert the theoretical yield of precipitate from moles to grams.

$$0.0162\text{ mol }Ag_2SO_4\left(\frac{311.80\text{ g }Ag_2SO_4}{1\text{ mol }Ag_2SO_4}\right) = 5.05\text{ g }Ag_2SO_4$$

Finally, use the theoretical yield (5.05 g) and the actual yield (4.94 g) to determine the percent yield.

$$\text{Percent yield} = \frac{4.94\text{ g }Ag_2SO_4}{5.05\text{ g }Ag_2SO_4} \times 100\% = 97.8\%$$

PRACTICE PROBLEM 5.33

Suppose that 5.832 g solid $Mg(OH)_2$ is dissolved in water and titrated with 35.54 mL of an HCl solution of unknown molarity.

a. Determine the concentration of the HCl solution.
b. Assuming a total solution volume of 36.15 mL at the equivalence point of the titration, calculate the molarity of Mg^{2+} in the titration solution at the equivalence point.

Hint: To begin, balance the equation for this reaction, and use the given mass of $Mg(OH)_2$, its molar mass, and the reaction stoichiometry to determine the number of moles of HCl that react with $Mg(OH)_2$. Then use the reaction stoichiometry to determine the number of moles of Mg^{2+} and the total solution volume to determine the molarity of Mg^{2+}.

Key Terms, Symbols, and Equations

KEY TERMS

actual yield (5.4): The amount of product that is actually obtained from a chemical reaction.

buret (5.9): A piece of laboratory glassware calibrated for measuring the volume of liquid delivered.

completion (5.3): The condition a reaction has reached when the limiting quantity of reactant has been consumed.

concentrated solution (5.5): A solution that has a relatively large amount of solute per volume of solvent.

concentration (5.5): The quantity of solute per unit volume of solution or per unit mass of solvent.

dilute solution (5.5): A solution that has a relatively low amount of solute per volume of solvent.

dilution (5.5): The process of adding more solvent to decrease the concentration of solute in a solution.

end point (5.9): The point in a titration at which the indicator signals that the reaction is complete.

equivalence point (5.9): The point in a titration at which the ratio of moles of reactants is the same as the ratio in the balanced equation.

Erlenmeyer flask (5.9): A flask designed to allow swirling of the liquid contents without spillage.

excess (5.3): The quantity of a reactant that exceeds that which can react with the limiting quantity of another reactant.

indicator (5.9): A compound that has different colors in solutions of different acidities and is used to signal the end of a titration.

limiting quantity (5.3): The quantity of the reactant that will be completely consumed first in a chemical reaction, limiting the quantity of product(s) that can be produced.

limiting reactant (5.3): The reactant that runs out first when a chemical reaction is carried out. The reaction stops at that point, and no more product is formed.

molar, M (5.5): The unit of molarity.

molarity, *M* (5.5): A measure of concentration defined as the number of moles of solute per liter of solution.

percent yield (5.4): The ratio of actual yield to theoretical yield, expressed as a percentage.

reacting ratio (5.1): A ratio of coefficients from a balanced equation, which represents the ratio of moles of any reactant or product to any other reactant or product in the reaction.

solute (5.5): The component of a solution that is dissolved in another component (the solvent).

solvent (5.5): The component of a solution that does the dissolving.

standard solution (5.9): An aqueous solution whose concentration is known precisely.

stoichiometry (5.1): The determination of how much product a reactant can produce or how much of a product can be produced from a given quantity of another substance in a reaction.

theoretical yield (5.4): The calculated quantity of product that would result from a chemical reaction based on the stoichiometry of the reaction.

titrant (5.9): The solution that is dispensed from the buret in a titration.

titration (5.9): An experimental technique used to determine the concentration of a solution of unknown concentration or the number of moles in an unknown sample of a substance.

SYMBOLS

M (molar) (5.5)

M (molarity) (5.5)

mmol (millimoles) (5.5)

EQUATIONS

$$\text{Percent yield} = \left(\frac{\text{Actual yield}}{\text{Theoretical yield}}\right) \times 100\% \quad (5.1)$$

$$M = \frac{\text{Moles of solute}}{\text{Liter of solution}} \quad (5.2)$$

$$M_1V_1 = M_2V_2 \quad (5.3)$$

Chapter Summary

The ratios of the numbers of moles of reactants and products involved in any chemical reaction are given by the coefficients in the balanced equation for the reaction. Each ratio of moles may be used as a reacting ratio to convert the number of moles of one reactant or product to the number of moles of any other reactant or product (Section 5.1).

If the quantity of any substance is given in terms of mass instead of moles, the mass must be converted to moles before calculating the number of moles of another substance in the reaction. If the mass of a substance is required as an answer to a problem, its number of moles must be converted to a mass (Section 5.2).

For problems in which the quantities of two or more reactants are given, you must determine if one of the reactants is present in a quantity less than, equal to, or greater than that required to react with all the other reactant(s). Determine which reactant is in limiting quantity, and use that quantity to calculate the quantities of the substances that will be consumed and produced. Tables of reactant and product quantities are useful. If masses are given, rather than moles, the masses must be converted to moles first (Section 5.3).

The theoretical yield is the quantity of product calculated from the quantity of reactant used, or the limiting quantity if more than one reactant quantity is given. In some reactions, not all of the calculated product can be collected. The percent yield is the ratio of the actual yield to the theoretical yield, converted to a percentage (Section 5.4).

$$\text{Percent yield} = \left(\frac{\text{Actual yield}}{\text{Theoretical yield}}\right) \times 100\%$$

Molarity, a unit of concentration, is defined as the number of moles of solute per liter of solution. Molarity is calculated by dividing the number of moles of solute by the volume of the solution in liters. Because molarity is a ratio, it can be used as a conversion factor to calculate the volume of solution from the number of moles of solute, or vice versa. The moles of solute can then be used in stoichiometric calculations with reacting ratios.

$$\text{Molarity}(M) = \frac{\text{Moles of solute}}{\text{Liter of solution}}$$

If a solution is diluted with solvent, the number of moles of solute does not change, but the molarity does. The final concentration of such a solution is calculated by dividing the number of moles of solute by the final volume.

$$M_1V_1 = M_2V_2$$

If two solutions of the same solute are mixed, the total number of moles present in the final solution is the sum of the numbers of moles in the two original solutions. The *molarities* are *not* added (Section 5.5).

The individual ions of a soluble ionic compound can be regarded as separate, independent solutes. The number of moles of each ion can be calculated from the number of moles of the compound and the formula of the compound. If solutions of two compounds containing one ion in common are mixed, the total number of moles of that ion is determined by adding the numbers of moles of the ion in both of the original solutions (Section 5.6).

Converting moles of one reactant or product to another always uses the reacting ratio from the balanced chemical equation as a conversion factor. If some other measure of the quantity of a substance is given or required—for example, the number of molecules of a substance—an appropriate conversion factor is needed to convert to or from moles (Section 5.7). Net ionic equations can be used to calculate moles from reacting ratios, but they often cannot be used directly with masses because they do not include spectator ions. Although spectator ions do not react, they do have mass, and the molar mass of the compound cannot be determined if not all the ions are specified (Section 5.8).

Titration is often used to determine the number of moles of a reactant in a given sample of an unknown, using a measured volume of a (standard) solution of known concentration. The color change of an indicator shows when the reaction is complete. The concentration and volume of the standard solution give the number of moles of solute in the standard solution, and then the number of moles of the unknown substance can be calculated from the reacting ratios in the balanced chemical equation. If an unknown substance is dissolved in a measured volume of solution, its molarity can be calculated from its volume and the calculated number of moles (Section 5.9).

END OF CHAPTER QUESTIONS

5.1 Mole Calculations for Chemical Reactions

1. Write all the possible conversion factors using the coefficients from the following equation:

$$2\,Al(s) + 3\,Cl_2\,(g) \rightarrow 2\,AlCl_3(s)$$

2. Write all the possible conversion factors using the coefficients from each of the following equations:
   a. $P_2O_5(s) + 3\,H_2O(l) \rightarrow 2\,H_3PO_4(l)$
   b. $2\,NO(g) + Cl_2(g) \rightarrow 2\,NOCl(g)$

3. Consider the following reaction:

$$2\,Al(s) + 6\,HCl(aq) \rightarrow 3\,H_2(g) + 2\,AlCl_3(aq)$$

Because two Al atoms react with six molecules of HCl, how many HCl molecules will react with each of the following?
a. 12 atoms of Al
b. 24 atoms of Al
c. 100 atoms of Al
d. 1 dozen atoms of Al
e. 1 mol of Al
f. 3 mol of Al

4. Consider the following reaction:

$$4\ NH_3(g) + 5\ O_2(g) \rightarrow 4\ NO(g) + 6\ H_2O(l)$$

Because four NH_3 molecules react with 5 O_2 molecules, how many O_2 molecules will react with each of the following quantities of NH_3?
a. 12 NH_3 molecules
b. 1 dozen NH_3 molecules
c. 4 dozen NH_3 molecules
d. 4 mol NH_3
e. 1 mol NH_3

5. Consider this reaction:

$$2\ KClO_3(s) + \text{heat} \rightarrow 2\ KCl(s) + 3\ O_2(g)$$

One student places 2.00 mol of $KClO_3$ in a flask, a second student places 0.750 mol of $KClO_3$ in a flask, and a third student places 0.250 mol of $KClO_3$ in a flask. Which student(s) could carry out the reaction specified in the equation?

6. Consider this reaction:

$$Sn(s) + 2\ HCl(aq) \rightarrow H_2(g) + SnCl_2(aq)$$

One student placed 1.00 mol of tin plus excess HCl in a flask, a second student placed 2.50 mol of tin plus excess HCl in a flask, and a third student placed 5.00 mol of tin plus excess HCl in a flask. Which student(s) could carry out the reaction specified in the equation?

7. What is the ratio of moles of HCl to moles of $CrCl_3$ in the following balanced equation?

$$14\ HCl(aq) + K_2Cr_2O_7(aq) + 6\ FeCl_2(aq) \rightarrow 2\ KCl(aq) + 2\ CrCl_3(aq) + 6\ FeCl_3(aq) + 7\ H_2O\ (l)$$

8. Calculate the number of moles of H_3PO_4 that will react with 1.29 mol of NaOH in aqueous solution to form Na_3PO_4.

$$H_3PO_4(aq) + 3\ NaOH(aq) \rightarrow Na_3PO_4(aq) + 3\ H_2O(l)$$

9. How many moles of C_6H_{14} can be produced by the reaction of 4.86 mol of H_2 and sufficient C_6H_{10}? The balanced equation is

$$C_6H_{10}(l) + 2\ H_2(g) \rightarrow C_6H_{14}(l)$$

10. How many moles of oxygen gas are required for the combustion of 7.04 mol of octane, C_8H_{18}, to yield CO_2 and water?

$$2\ C_8H_{18}(l) + 25\ O_2(g) \rightarrow 16\ CO_2(g) + 18\ H_2O(g)$$

11. How many moles of $AlCl_3$ are also produced along with 2.46 mol of H_2O from the reaction of $Al(OH)_3$ and HCl?

$$Al(OH)_3(s) + 3\ HCl(aq) \rightarrow AlCl_3(aq) + 3\ H_2O(l)$$

12. How many moles of $MgCl_2$ are produced along with 0.750 mol of CO_2 from the reaction of $Mg(HCO_3)_2$ and HCl?

$$Mg(HCO_3)_2(aq) + HCl(aq) \rightarrow MgCl_2(aq) + CO_2(g) + H_2O(l)$$

13. Consider the following reaction.

$$3\ Co^{2+}(aq) + CrO_4^{2-}(aq) + 8\ H^+(aq) \rightarrow 3\ Co^{3+}(aq) + Cr^{3+}(aq) + 4\ H_2O(l)$$

a. Calculate the number of millimoles of CrO_4^{2-} that reacts with 7.00 mmol of Co^{2+}.
b. How many millimoles of water are produced?

5.2 Mass Calculations for Chemical Reactions

14. In an internal combustion engine, octane, C_8H_{18}, burns in limited oxygen supply to produce carbon monoxide and water.
a. Write a balanced equation for the reaction.
b. Calculate the number of moles of carbon monoxide in 75.7 g of carbon monoxide.
c. Calculate the number of moles of octane required to produce that number of moles of carbon monoxide.
d. Calculate the mass of octane in that number of moles.
e. Combine the calculations for parts (b)–(d) into one dimensional analysis solution.

15. Aluminum is produced commercially by high-temperature electrolysis of aluminum oxide dissolved in a nonaqueous melt. The electrodes are carbon.

$$Al_2O_3(\text{solution}) + 3\ C(s) \rightarrow 2\ Al(l) + 3\ CO(g)$$

Calculate the mass of Al_2O_3 used to produce 10.0 metric tons (10.0×10^6 g) of aluminum by this process.

16. How many moles of KOH are required to completely neutralize 71.3 g of $H_2C_2O_4$?

17. When heat is applied to $NaHCO_3(s)$, the following reaction occurs:

$$2\ NaHCO_3(s) \rightarrow Na_2CO_3(s) + CO_2(g) + H_2O(g).$$

Heating 12.2 g of $NaHCO_3$ until no further reaction takes place can produce
a. what mass of Na_2CO_3?
b. what mass of solid product(s)?
c. What is the difference, if any, between parts (a) and (b)?

18. What mass of $CaCO_3$ can react with 82.3 g of $HClO_3$ according to the following reaction?

$$CaCO_3(s) + 2\ HClO_3(aq) \rightarrow Ca(ClO_3)_2(aq) + H_2O(l) + CO_2(g)$$

19. Compare two methods of preparing NaCl.
a. Calculate the mass of NaCl that can be prepared with 7.11 g of Cl_2 and sufficient Na.
b. Calculate the mass of NaCl that can be prepared with 7.11 g of HCl and sufficient NaOH.

20. The compound $(NH_4)_3PO_4$ is used as a fertilizer. Calculate the mass of $(NH_4)_3PO_4$ that can be produced by the reaction of 2.00 metric tons (2.00×10^6 g) of NH_3 with sufficient H_3PO_4.

$$3\ NH_3(aq) + H_3PO_4(aq) \rightarrow (NH_4)_3PO_4(aq)$$

21. The recharge of a lead storage cell in an automobile battery can be represented by the following equation:

$$2\ PbSO_4(s) + 2\ H_2O(l) \rightarrow Pb(s) + PbO_2(s) + 2\ H_2SO_4(aq)$$

Calculate the mass of elemental lead produced when 49.7 g of lead(II) sulfate reacts.

22. Calculate the mass of gaseous SO_2 that will be produced along with 1.500 kg of copper from the roasting of copper(II) sulfide.

$$CuS(s) + O_2(g) \rightarrow Cu(s) + SO_2(g)$$

23. Calculate the mass of NO that can be produced by the reaction of 14.0 g of Cu according to the following balanced equation:

$$8\ HNO_3(aq) + 3\ Cu(s) \rightarrow 2\ NO(g) + 3\ Cu(NO_3)_2(aq) + 4\ H_2O(l)$$

24. Excess $Ba(NO_3)_2(aq)$ was added to a sample of $NaHCO_3(aq)$, and 7.27 g of $BaCO_3(s)$ was produced (along with CO_2, H_2O, and $NaNO_3$). What mass of $NaHCO_3$ was present initially?

25. Silver bromide can react with aqueous $Na_2S_2O_3$ (called "hypo") in a process that is the basis for the development of black-and-white film.

$$AgBr(s) + 2\ Na_2S_2O_3(aq) \rightarrow Na_3Ag(S_2O_3)_2(aq) + NaBr(aq)$$

Calculate the mass of hypo necessary to react with 2.66 g of AgBr.

26. How many grams of stearic acid, $C_{17}H_{35}COOH$, a fatty acid, can be produced by the reaction of 1110 g of H_2 and sufficient $C_{17}H_{31}COOH$, a component of an oil? The balanced equation is

$$C_{17}H_{31}COOH(l) + 2\ H_2(g) \rightarrow C_{17}H_{35}COOH(s)$$

27. What mass of HNO_3 does it take to react with 14.4 g of aluminum?

$$8\ Al(s) + 30\ HNO_3(aq) \rightarrow 3\ NH_4NO_3(aq) + 8\ Al(NO_3)_3(aq) + 9\ H_2O(l)$$

28. Powdered aluminum metal can be used to reduce iron(II) oxide to molten iron, usable for spot welding. Calculate the mass of iron that can be produced by the reaction of 775 g of aluminum.

$$2\ Al(s) + 3\ FeO(s) + heat \rightarrow 3\ Fe(l) + Al_2O_3(s)$$

29. HBF_4 is a useful reagent, especially in organic chemistry. Calculate the mass of HF required to make 125 g of HBF_4 by the following reaction:

$$H_3BO_3(aq) + 4\ HF(aq) \rightarrow HBF_4(aq) + 3\ H_2O(l)$$

30. Iron ore is reduced to iron with coke (impure carbon). Calculate the mass of Fe that can be produced from Fe_2O_3 with 15.00 kg of carbon. The reaction may be represented as follows:

$$Fe_2O_3(s) + 3\ C(s) + heat \rightarrow 2\ Fe(l) + 3\ CO(g)$$

31. Calculate the mass of NH_3 that can be prepared by heating 122 g of solid $(NH_4)_2CO_3$. The balanced equation is

$$(NH_4)_2CO_3(s) + heat \rightarrow 2\ NH_3(g) + CO_2(g) + H_2O(g)$$

32. Calculate the number of moles of NH_3 that can be prepared by heating 122 g of solid $(NH_4)_2SO_3$. The balanced equation is

$$(NH_4)_2SO_3(s) + heat \rightarrow 2\ NH_3(g) + SO_2(g) + H_2O(g)$$

33. Calculate the total mass of the HCl and H_3PO_4 produced by the reaction of excess H_2O with 20.83 g of PCl_5:

$$PCl_5 + 4\ H_2O \rightarrow 5\ HCl + H_3PO_4$$

34. Calculate the total mass of the acids produced by the reaction of excess water with 20.83 g of phosphorus pentachloride:

$$PCl_5 + 4\,H_2O \rightarrow 5\,HCl + H_3PO_4$$

5.3 Problems Involving Limiting Quantities

35. Consider sandwich making in terms of limiting quantities.
   a. How many two-slice sandwiches can you make with 24 slices of bread?
   b. How many sandwiches can you make with 24 slices of bread and 14 hamburger patties?
   c. How many sandwiches can you make with 24 slices of bread and 11 hamburger patties?
   d. How can you recognize when a problem involves a limiting quantity?

36. How many moles of NaBr will be produced by the following reaction in each case?
   a. $2\,Na(s) + Br_2(l) \rightarrow NaBr(s)$
   b. 1 mol Na and 0 mol Br_2
   c. 2 mol Na and 1 mol Br_2
   d. 3 mol Na and 1 mol Br_2

37. Consider the following reaction:

$$Ba(OH)_2(aq) + 2\,HNO_3(aq) \rightarrow Ba(NO_3)_2(aq) + 2\,H_2O(l)$$

   a. How many moles of $Ba(NO_3)_2$ can be made with 2.50 mol of HNO_3?
   b. How many moles of $Ba(NO_3)_2$ can be made with 2.50 mol of HNO_3 and 1.10 mol of $Ba(OH)_2$?
   c. How many moles of $Ba(NO_3)_2$ can be made with 2.50 mol of HNO_3 and 2.00 mol of $Ba(OH)_2$?

38. Complete the "Change due to reaction" line for each of the following reactions:

	A +	2 B →	C +	3 D
a) Change due to reaction	−1.00 mol			
b) Change due to reaction		−2.00 mol		

39. Complete the "Change due to reaction" line for each of the following reactions:

	A +	3 B →	C +	2 D
a) Change due to reaction			+2.50 mol	
b) Change due to reaction		−4.50 mol		

40. Complete each table below:

a)	A +	B →	2 C +	2 D
Present initially	1.00 mol	1.10 mol	0.00 mol	0.00 mol
Change due to reaction				
Present finally				

b)	A +	2 B →	C +	2 D
Present initially	3.00 mol	4.00 mol	0.00 mol	0.00 mol
Change due to reaction				
Present finally				

c)	2 A +	3 B →	C +	2 D
Present initially	1.50 mol	4.00 mol	0.00 mol	0.00 mol
Change due to reaction				
Present finally				

d)	A +	2 B →	C +	2 D
Present initially	0.750 mol	1.25 mol	0.00 mol	0.00 mol
Change due to reaction				
Present finally				

41. For the following reaction:

$$Zn + 2\ AgNO_3 \rightarrow Zn(NO_3)_2 + 2\ Ag$$

calculate the number of moles of products as well as the number of moles of excess reagent after the following pairs of reagents are combined:
   a. 0.400 mol Zn + 0.400 mol $AgNO_3$
   b. 0.400 mol Zn + 1.000 mol $AgNO_3$
   c. 0.800 mol Zn + 2.000 mol $AgNO_3$
   d. 0.900 mol Zn + 1.800 mol $AgNO_3$

42. Explain why limiting reactant problems do not usually involve decomposition reactions.

43. Consider three different experiments involving the reaction of nitrogen and hydrogen:

$$N_2 + 3\ H_2 \rightarrow 2\ NH_3$$

   a. If 6.00 mol of H_2 reacts, how much N_2 reacts?
   b. If 6.00 mol of H_2 is placed in a vessel with N_2, can you tell how much N_2 reacts?
   c. If 3.00 mol of NH_3 is produced, can you tell how much H_2 reacts?

44. Consider the following reaction:

$$La(OH)_3(s) + 3\ HCl(aq) \rightarrow LaCl_3(aq) + 3\ H_2O(l)$$

   a. How many moles of $LaCl_3$ can be made with 9 mol of HCl?
   b. How many moles of $LaCl_3$ can be made with 9 mol of HCl and 5 mol of $La(OH)_3$?
   c. How many moles of $LaCl_3$ can be made with 9 mol of HCl and 2 mol of $La(OH)_3$?

45. The director of a summer baseball camp has five home plates and 12 bases. One home plate and three bases are needed for each baseball field.
   a. How many baseball fields can the director equip?
   b. How many extra pieces of equipment will there be?

46. Write the balanced chemical equation for the double replacement reaction of magnesium chloride with silver nitrate.
   a. Calculate the number of moles of $MgCl_2$ that will react with 5.00 mol of $AgNO_3$.
   b. Calculate the number of moles of $MgCl_2$ that will react if 2.00 mol of $MgCl_2$ is treated with 5.00 mol of $AgNO_3$.
   c. Calculate the number of moles of $MgCl_2$ that will react if 4.00 mol of $MgCl_2$ is treated with 5.00 mol of $AgNO_3$.
   d. Calculate the number of moles of AgCl that is produced in parts (a)–(c).

47. Consider the following equation:

$$C_4H_6(g) + 2\ Cl_2(g) \rightarrow C_4H_6Cl_4(l)$$

Calculate the mass of $C_4H_6Cl_4$ that can be prepared from 35.0 g of C_4H_6 and 105.0 g of Cl_2.

48. For the following reaction:

$$Cu(s) + 2\ AgNO_3(aq) \rightarrow Cu(NO_3)_2(aq) + 2\ Ag(s)$$

calculate the number of moles of each product as well as the number of moles of excess reagent after 0.272 mol of Cu and 0.576 mol of $AgNO_3$ are combined.

49. How many molecules of NO can be produced by the reaction of 65.00 g of NH_3 with 150.0 g of O_2 according to the following balanced equation?

$$4\ NH_3(g) + 5\ O_2(g) \rightarrow 4\ NO(g) + 6\ H_2O(g)$$

5.4 Theoretical Yield and Percent Yield

50. For 0.151 mol of liquid SO_2Cl_2 obtained from the reaction of 0.160 mol of gaseous SO_2 and excess gaseous Cl_2, calculate:
   a. the theoretical yield
   b. the percent yield

51. For 12.4 g of liquid SO_2Cl_2 obtained from the reaction of 6.11 g of gaseous SO_2 and excess gaseous Cl_2, calculate:
   a. the theoretical yield
   b. the percent yield

52. Calculate the percent yield for an experiment in which 29.8 g of PCl_5 was obtained by treatment of 4.50 g of P with sufficient Cl_2.

53. Calculate the percent yield of a reaction which produced 36.0 g of $C_4H_8Br_2$ from 10.0 g of C_4H_8 and excess Br_2 given this equation:

$$C_4H_8(g) + Br_2(l) \rightarrow C_4H_8Br_2(l)$$

54. Calculate the percent yield for an experiment in which 46.9 g of SO_3 was obtained by treatment of 51.2 g of SO_2 with 25.0 g of O_2.

5.5 Definition and Uses of Molarity

55. Calculate the molarity of each of the following solutes:
   a. 0.365 mol solute in 0.4000 L of solution
   b. 365 mmol solute in 0.4000 L of solution
   c. 0.365 mol solute in 400.0 mL of solution
   d. 365 mmol solute in 400.0 mL of solution

56. If 3.13 mL of a solution is poured from 100.0 mL of a 0.693 M sample, what is the concentration of the 3.13 mL portion?

57. Calculate the molarity of a solution containing
a. 0.123 mol of solute in 0.7000 L of solution.
b. 123 mmol of solute in 700.0 mL of solution.

58. What is the final volume (in liters) of solution if 2.2 L of solution is diluted
a. with 3.3 L of solvent?
b. to 3.3 L with solvent?

59. Calculate the molarity of a solution containing 1.17 mol of solute in 943 mL of solution.

60. Calculate the molarity of a solution containing 79.4 mmol of solute in 122.5 mL of solution.

61. Calculate the molarity of a solution containing 0.5050 mol of solute in 400.0 mL of solution.

62. Calculate the molarity of 29.7 mL of a solution that contains 6.11 g of methyl alcohol, CH_3OH.

63. Calculate the volume (in liters) of a 0.881 M solution that contains 0.175 mol of solute.

64. Calculate the number of milliliters of 1.38 M NaCl solution that contains 122 mg of NaCl.

65. Calculate the number of grams of $NaNO_3$ in 0.0112 L of 3.09 M $NaNO_3$ solution.

66. Calculate the molarity of 886 mL of a solution that contains 149 g of ethyl alcohol, C_2H_5OH.

67. Calculate the number of moles of solute in 0.8122 L of 2.163 M solution.

68. Calculate the number of millimoles of solute in 41.0 mL of 2.611 M solution.

69. Calculate the number of grams of $AlCl_3$ in 1255 mL of 0.909 M $AlCl_3$ solution.

70. What is the final concentration if 225 mL of 0.500 M solution is diluted
a. with 1.100 L of solvent?
b. to 1.100 L with solvent?

71. Calculate the volume (in liters) of 3.171 M solution that contains 25.5 mmol of solute.

72. Calculate the number of milliliters of 3.83 M NaCl solution that contains 14.7 g of NaCl.

73. Calculate the molarity of a solution that is prepared by diluting 20.8 mL of 2.11 M solution to 50.0 mL.

74. Calculate the final volume (in milliliters) of a solution that is prepared by diluting 69.7 mL of 2.13 M solution to 1.51 M.

75. Calculate the volume (in liters) of 2.50 M solution required to make 6.00 L of 0.450 M solution by dilution with water.

76. Calculate the molarity of a solution that is prepared by diluting 75.00 mL of 2.132 M solution to 125.0 mL.

77. Calculate the final volume (in milliliters) of solution that is prepared by diluting 6.929 mL of 3.555 M solution to 0.8229 M.

5.6 Molarities of Ions

78. What is the molarity of each ion in the following solutions?
a. 1.0 M NaCl
b. 1.0 M $MgCl_2$
c. 1.0 M $CrCl_3$
d. 1.0 M $LiNO_3$
e. 1.0 M $Co(NO_3)_2$
f. 1.0 M $Al(NO_3)_3$
g. 0.10 M $Al_2(SO_4)_3$
h. 1.0 M $(NH_4)_2SO_4$

79. Calculate the molarity of each ion in each of the following solutions:
a. 0.344 M $Al_2(SO_4)_3$
b. 1.61 M $(NH_4)_3PO_4$
c. 0.0808 M $Ba(OH)_2$
d. 3.75 M KBr
e. 3.09 M $NaClO_3$

80. Calculate the molarity of each ion in each of the following solutions:
a. 2.50 M HNO_3
b. 3.00 M $Co(ClO_3)_3$
c. 2.10 M $CuSO_4$
d. 0.136 M $Ca_3(PO_4)_2$
e. 3.11 M $(NH_4)_2SO_3$

81. Calculate the molarity of each ion in 0.0715 M $Al_2(SO_4)_3$ solution.

82. Calculate the *total* concentration (in molarity) of all the ions in each of the following solutions:
a. 3.25 M NaCl
b. 1.75 M $Ca(ClO_3)_2$
c. 12.1 g of $(NH_4)_2SO_3$ in 615 mL of solution

83. If 0.217 mol of Li_2SO_4 and 0.217 mol of K_2SO_4 are dissolved in enough water to make 650.0 mL

of solution, what is the molarity of each ion in the solution?

84. Calculate the molarity of each ion in solution after 35.3 mL of 2.17 M $MgCl_2$ is mixed with 21.4 mL of 0.500 M $AlBr_3$ and the resulting solution is diluted to 100.0 mL.

85. If 0.0500 mol of $Al_2(SO_4)_3$ and 0.0500 mol of Na_2SO_3 are dissolved in enough water to make 250.0 mL of solution, what is the concentration of each ion in the solution?

86. Assuming that the final volume is the sum of the initial volumes, calculate the concentration of each ion in solution after
    a. 30.00 mL of 4.000 M NaOH is added to 60.00 mL of 1.250 M HCl.
    b. 30.00 mL of 4.000 M NaCl is added to 60.00 mL of 1.250 M HCl.

87. Calculate the concentration of each type of ion in solution after 30.0 mL of 3.35 M NaCl and 70.0 mL of 1.35 M Na_2SO_4 are mixed. Assume that the final volume is 100.0 mL.

88. What is the concentration of each type of ion in solution after 23.69 mL of 3.611 M NaOH is added to 29.10 mL of 0.8921 M H_2SO_4? Assume that the final volume is the sum of the original volumes.

89. Calculate the concentration of each type of ion in solution after 50.0 mL of 4.00 M NaCl and 50.0 mL of 2.50 M NaBr are mixed. Assume that the final volume is 100.0 mL.

90. What is the molarity of each type of ion in solution after 42.00 mL of 3.000 M NaOH is added to 50.00 mL of 2.535 M $HClO_3$? Assume that the final volume is the sum of the original volumes.

91. Find the molarity of each type of ion in solution after 25.0 mL of 0.919 M $CoCl_2$ is diluted to 100.0 mL.

92. Find the molarity of each type of ion in solution after 10.0 mL of 0.650 M $(NH_4)_3PO_4$ is diluted to 50.0 mL.

5.7 Calculations Involving Other Quantities

93. Calculate the number of moles of H_2O produced and the number of moles of excess reactant when 0.444 mol of $Mg(OH)_2$ is treated with 6.66×10^{23} molecules of HNO_3.

94. Calculate the mass of solid Cu produced when 4.33×10^6 g of Cu_2S is treated with 2.00×10^6 g of O_2. SO_2 is the other product.

95. Calculate the number of moles of fluorine atoms in 61.7 mL of $CHClF_2$ (density = 1.49 g/mL).

96. What mass of $SOCl_2$ can be prepared by heating SO_2 gas with the quantity of PCl_5 that contains 3.01×10^{23} Cl atoms? The balanced equation for the reaction is

$$SO_2(g) + PCl_5(s) \rightarrow POCl_3(l) + SOCl_2(l)$$

97. How many nitrogen atoms are contained in the $N_2H_6(NO_3)_2$ prepared by treatment of 4.14 g of aqueous hydrazine, N_2H_4, with excess dilute nitric acid?

$$N_2H_4(aq) + 2\ HNO_3(aq) \rightarrow N_2H_6(NO_3)_2(aq)$$

98. What mass of nitrogen is contained in the ammonium nitrate prepared by treatment of 6.69 g of aqueous ammonia with excess dilute nitric acid?

$$NH_3(aq) + HNO_3(aq) \rightarrow NH_4NO_3(aq)$$

99. Calculate the number of moles of hydrogen atoms in 45.3 mL of pure H_2O_2 (density = 1.44 g/mL).

100. A solid combustible material can sometimes be changed into a more useful fuel if it is converted to a gas before burning. The following reaction, known as the water gas reaction, can be used to provide gaseous fuels from coal, which is mostly carbon.

$$H_2O(g) + C(s) \rightarrow CO(g) + H_2(g)$$

    a. Calculate the number of moles of water required to convert 1.00×10^{26} carbon atoms to carbon monoxide and hydrogen, a mixture known as water gas.
    b. What are the products of the complete combustion of water gas?

101. Calculate the number of fluorine atoms in the sulfur hexafluoride prepared by treating sulfur difluoride with 6.11 g of fluorine gas.

102. The hydrogen used for about 90% of the industrial synthesis of ammonia comes from the following reaction at high temperature in the presence of a nickel catalyst. Calculate the number of molecules of CH_4 required to produce 1.25 metric tons (1.25×10^6 g) of H_2.

$$CH_4(g) + H_2O(g) \rightarrow CO(g) + 3\ H_2(g)$$

5.8 Calculations with Net Ionic Equations

103. Calculate the following:
    a. the number of moles of Na^+ present in 0.750 mol of NaOH
    b. the number of moles of NaCl produced by the reaction of that quantity of NaOH (from part a) with 0.600 mol of HCl
    c. the number of moles of NaOH present after the reaction
    d. the number of moles of Na^+ present in the final solution
    e. Does your answer to part (d) confirm that Na^+ is a spectator ion?

104. How many moles of carbonate ion can be converted to carbon dioxide and water with 4.42 mol H^+?

$$2\,H^+(aq) + CO_3^{2-}(aq) \rightarrow H_2O(l) + CO_2(g)$$

105. Calculate the mass of solid Ag_2S that can be produced by the reaction of 0.300 mol of S^{2-} with excess Ag^+.

106. Calculate the number of moles of each ion in the final solution after 1.75 mol of aqueous $BaCl_2$ and 2.70 mol of aqueous $AgNO_3$ are mixed.

107. Calculate the number of moles of CO_2 that will be produced by the reaction of 2.20 mol of HCO_3^- with 1.80 mol of H^+.

$$H^+(aq) + HCO_3^-(aq) \rightarrow H_2O(l) + CO_2(g)$$

108. Calculate the mass of CO_2 that will be produced by the reaction of 0.550 mol of CO_3^{2-} with 1.25 mol of H^+.

$$2\,H^+(aq) + CO_3^{2-}(aq) \rightarrow H_2O(l) + CO_2(g)$$

109. Calculate the mass of $BaSO_4$ that can be produced by the reaction of 0.234 mol of SO_4^{2-} with 0.125 mol of Ba^{2+}.

110. Calculate the mass of PbI_2 that can be produced by the reaction of 0.105 mol of Pb^{2+} with 0.400 mol of I^-.

5.9 Titration

111. Calculate the concentration of an H_2SO_4 solution if 25.00 mL is completely neutralized by 21.73 mL of 4.000 M NaOH solution.

112. Calculate the concentration of a phosphoric acid solution if 25.00 mL is completely neutralized by 31.17 mL of 4.000 M sodium hydroxide solution.

113. Calculate the concentration of an H_3PO_4 solution if 25.00 mL is converted to Na_2HPO_4 by 39.13 mL of 2.000 M NaOH solution.

114. Calculate the concentration of a sulfuric acid solution if 25.00 mL is converted to sodium sulfate by 17.42 mL of 3.150 M sodium hydroxide solution.

115. When 2.818 g of potassium hydrogen phthalate (symbolized here as KHPh; molar mass = 204.2 g/mol) is titrated with KOH solution, it takes 31.74 mL of the base to achieve the end point. Calculate the concentration of the KOH solution.

$$KHPh(aq) + KOH(aq) \rightarrow K_2Ph(aq) + H_2O(l)$$

116. How many millimoles of H_2SO_4 will react completely with 12.88 mL of 1.500 M NaOH?

117. How many millimoles of $Ca(OH)_2(s)$ will react with 29.17 mL of 4.000 M $HClO_3$?

118. An antacid tablet contains $NaHCO_3$. What mass of this compound is required to neutralize 178 mL of 2.91 M stomach acid (HCl)?

119. An antacid tablet contains 31.3 g of $NaHCO_3$. What volume (in liters) of 2.84 M stomach acid, HCl, can this tablet neutralize?

Putting It Together

120. In each case, calculate the mass of the product other than water:
    a. 75.0 g of sulfuric acid is treated with sufficient aqueous potassium hydroxide so that the acid is completely neutralized
    b. 75.0 g of aqueous sodium hydroxide is treated with excess chloric acid

121. What mass of barium carbonate can be produced by treatment in aqueous solution of 31.2 g of sodium hydrogen carbonate with 30.0 g of barium nitrate? (CO_2 is also produced.)

122. Heating of solid sodium hydrogen carbonate is one step in the industrial process for production of washing soda—sodium carbonate. Carbon dioxide and water are also produced. Calculate the mass of solid produced when a 2.11 kg sample of sodium hydrogen carbonate is heated.

123. After 2.06 g of solid $KClO_3$ is heated for a brief time, 1.18 g of KCl has been produced.
    a. What mass of O_2 has been produced?
    b. What mass of $KClO_3$ remained undecomposed?

124. What mass of nitrogen is contained in the ammonium nitrate that can be prepared by treatment of 20.2 g of aqueous ammonia with 41.6 g of nitric acid?

125. What mass of barium sulfate can be produced by treatment in aqueous solution of 11.6 g of ammonium sulfate with 25.5 g of barium fluoride?

126. Calculate the number of moles of each substance in solution after 0.150 mol of $Ba(C_2H_3O_2)_2(aq)$ is added to 0.500 mol of HCl(aq). The balanced equation is

$$Ba(C_2H_3O_2)_2(aq) + 2\,HCl(aq) \rightarrow BaCl_2(aq) + 2\,HC_2H_3O_2(aq)$$

127. For a store's going-out-of business sale, a set consisting of a card table and four chairs is advertised at \$233. The store has 31 tables and 98 chairs. An outlet manager arrives with \$5000. What is the maximum number of sets the outlet manager can buy?

128. Determine the number of moles of $MnCl_2$ that can be prepared by the reaction of 0.300 mol $KMnO_4$, 1.08 mol of $FeCl_2$, and 3.10 mol of HCl, according to the following balanced equation:

$$KMnO_4(aq) + 5\,FeCl_2(aq) + 8\,HCl(aq) \rightarrow MnCl_2(aq) + KCl(aq) + 5\,FeCl_3(aq) + 4\,H_2O(l)$$

129. Calculate the concentration of each type of ion in solution after 37.22 mL of 1.000 M HCl is added to 19.29 mL of 4.107 M NaOH. Use a net ionic equation in solving this problem. Assume that the final volume is equal to the sum of the volumes of the two original solutions.

130. Calculate the number of milligrams of Na_2CO_3 in 725 mL of 715 mM solution. Note that mM is millimolar, where 1000 mM = 1 M, just as 1000 mg = 1 g, and 1000 mL = 1 L.

131. Calculate the concentration of H^+ ion produced when H_2S is bubbled into 0.300 M Cu^{2+} solution, causing precipitation of all the copper(II) ion as CuS. Assume no change in the volume of the solution.

$$Cu^{2+}(aq) + H_2S(g) \rightarrow CuS(s) + 2\,H^+(aq)$$

132. If 5.033 g of potassium hydrogen phthalate, an acid salt having one ionizable hydrogen atom and a molar mass of 204.2 g/mol, is used to neutralize 39.17 mL of NaOH solution, calculate the concentration of the base.

133. Calculate the sodium ion concentration after 20.0 mL of 3.00 M NaOH is mixed with 30.0 mL of 1.00 M HCl and diluted to 100.0 mL.

134. Calculate the final sugar concentration after 2.25 L of 3.00 M sugar solution is diluted to 5.00 L with (a) water and (b) 1.00 M NaCl solution.

135. The label has fallen off a bottle of a solid organic acid. If 26.2 mL of 2.00 M NaOH is needed to completely neutralize 2.36 g of the acid, determine if the acid is oxalic acid ($H_2C_2O_4$), benzoic acid ($HC_7H_5O_2$), or bromobenzoic acid ($HC_7H_4O_2Br$).

136. Calculate the hydrogen ion concentration and the chloride ion concentration:
  a. after 0.150 mol of hydrochloric acid and 0.100 mol of sodium chloride are dissolved in enough water to make 1.00 L of solution
  b. after 0.250 mol of hydrochloric acid and 0.100 mol of sodium hydroxide are dissolved in enough water to make 1.00 L of solution

137. Lithium nitride, Li_3N, reacts with water to form hydroxide ions and ammonia. What concentration of hydroxide ions is present after 0.110 mol of solid Li_3N is reacted with water and then diluted to 100.0 mL?

138. After a 10.00 g sample containing Na_2CO_3 and inert substances was treated with 41.04 mL of 3.000 M HCl, it took 4.22 mL of 1.000 M NaOH to neutralize the excess HCl. Calculate the percent of Na_2CO_3 in the original sample.

139. When an alkali metal oxide is treated with water, it reacts with the water to form hydroxide ions. What concentration of hydroxide ions is present if 0.250 mol of solid Li_2O is treated with water and the final volume is 500.0 mL?

140. Calculate the concentration of each ion in the following solutions.
  a. 58.99 mL of a solution containing 9.404 mmol of Na_2SO_4 and 29.11 mmol of NaOH
  b. 47.92 mL of 1.000 M NaOH is added to 11.07 mL of 0.8495 M Na_2SO_4. Assume that the volume of the final solution is the sum of the volumes of the two original solutions.
  c. Explain how parts (a) and (b) are related.

141. Calculate the concentrations of acetate ion and acetic acid in solution after 10.0 mL of 1.50 M $HC_2H_3O_2$ and 10.0 mL of 0.850 M NaOH are

mixed. Assume that the final volume is 20.0 mL and that the excess acetic acid yields no acetate ions to the final solution (because it is a *weak* acid).

$$OH^-(aq) + HC_2H_3O_2(aq) \rightarrow C_2H_3O_2^-(aq) + H_2O(l)$$

142. Calculate the concentrations of ammonium ion and ammonia in solution after 30.0 mL of 1.35 M NH_3 and 30.0 mL of 0.750 M HCl are mixed. Assume that the final volume is 60.0 mL and that the excess ammonia yields no ammonium ions to the final solution (because it is a *weak* base).

$$H^+(aq) + NH_3(aq) \rightarrow NH_4^+(aq)$$

143. Calculate the concentration of each type of ion in these solutions:
    a. 111.23 mL of a solution containing 49.68 mmol of NaCl plus 28.43 mmol of NaOH.
    b. 78.11 mL of 1.000 M NaOH is added to 33.12 mL of 1.500 M HCl. Assume that the volume of the final solution is the sum of the volumes of the two original solutions.

144. Calculate the concentration of each ion in solution after 27.3 mL of 3.08 M NaCl is mixed with 19.1 mL of 0.877 M $CaCl_2$ and then diluted to 100.0 mL.

145. Calculate the molar mass of an unknown acid, HA, if a 12.11 g sample of the acid takes 38.38 mL of 5.000 M NaOH to neutralize it.

146. Calculate the molar mass of an unknown acid, H_2A, if a 12.11 g sample of the acid takes 38.38 mL of 5.000 M NaOH to neutralize it.

PRACTICE PROBLEM SOLUTIONS

Practice Problem 5.1 Solution

The given equation is *not* balanced. The balanced equation is

$$TiCl_4(l) + 2\ H_2O(l) \rightarrow TiO_2(s) + 4\ HCl(g)$$

The possible reacting ratios are

$$\frac{1\text{ mol }TiCl_4}{2\text{ mol }H_2O}\quad \frac{1\text{ mol }TiCl_4}{1\text{ mol }TiO_2}\quad \frac{1\text{ mol }TiCl_4}{4\text{ mol }HCl}$$

$$\frac{2\text{ mol }H_2O}{1\text{ mol }TiCl_4}\quad \frac{1\text{ mol }TiO_2}{1\text{ mol }TiCl_4}\quad \frac{4\text{ mol }HCl}{1\text{ mol }TiCl_4}$$

$$\frac{2\text{ mol }H_2O}{1\text{ mol }TiO_2}\quad \frac{2\text{ mol }H_2O}{4\text{ mol }HCl}\quad \frac{1\text{ mol }TiO_2}{4\text{ mol }HCl}$$

$$\frac{1\text{ mol }TiO_2}{2\text{ mol }H_2O}\quad \frac{4\text{ mol }HCl}{2\text{ mol }H_2O}\quad \frac{4\text{ mol }HCl}{1\text{ mol }TiO_2}$$

Practice Problem 5.2 Solution

Follow the same procedure as shown in Example 5.2, except use the reacting ratio of moles of Al_2O_3 formed to the moles of O_2 reacted.

$$3.18\text{ mol }O_2\left(\frac{2\text{ mol }Al_2O_3}{3\text{ mol }O_2}\right) = 2.12\text{ mol }Al_2O_3$$

Practice Problem 5.3 Solution

Use the reacting ratio for formula units of NaOH reacted per formula units of Na_2SO_4 formed.

$$1.24 \times 10^{15}\text{ formula units }Na_2SO_4\left(\frac{2\text{ units NaOH}}{1\text{ unit }Na_2SO_4}\right)$$
$$= 2.48 \times 10^{15}\text{ formula units NaOH}$$

Practice Problem 5.4 Solution

First, write the balanced equation:

$$3\ H_2(g) + N_2(g) \rightarrow 2\ NH_3(g)$$

Next, determine the number of moles of H_2 that reacted. This is the number of moles of H_2 originally present minus the number of moles of H_2 remaining.

$$0.225\text{ mol }H_2\text{ originally present} - 0.033\text{ mol }H_2\text{ remaining} = 0.192\text{ mol }H_2\text{ reacted}$$

Now use the reacting ratio between H_2 and N_2 to determine the number of moles of N_2 that react.

$$0.192\text{ mol }H_2\left(\frac{1\text{ mol }N_2}{3\text{ mol }H_2}\right) = 0.0640\text{ mol }N_2\text{ reacted}$$

Practice Problem 5.5 Solution

Convert the mass of phosphorus to moles of phosphorus. Use the reacting ratio for the moles of PCl_5 formed per moles of phosphorus reacted. Then use the molar mass of PCl_5 to convert moles of PCl_5 to mass of PCl_5.

$$2.80\text{ g P}\left(\frac{1\text{ mol P}}{30.974\text{ g P}}\right)\left(\frac{2\text{ mol }PCl_5}{2\text{ mol P}}\right)\left(\frac{208.22\text{ g }PCl_5}{1\text{ mol }PCl_5}\right) = 19.4\text{ g }PCl_5$$

Practice Problem 5.6 Solution

First, convert the mass units of sodium chloride from kg to g. Then use the formula weight of NaCl, the reacting ratio of NaCl to Na, and the molar mass of Na to determine the mass of Na formed.

$$207\ \text{kg}\left(\frac{1000\ \text{g}}{1\ \text{kg}}\right)\left(\frac{1\ \text{mol NaCl}}{58.44\ \text{g NaCl}}\right)\left(\frac{2\ \text{mol Na}}{2\ \text{mol NaCl}}\right)\left(\frac{22.99\ \text{g Na}}{1\ \text{mol Na}}\right) = 8.14 \times 10^4\ \text{g Na}$$

Practice Problem 5.7 Solution

After evaporation to dryness, the only solid remaining is calcium chloride. The water and excess HCl evaporated and the gaseous carbon dioxide was lost to the atmosphere. Thus, all 2.29 g of product remaining is solid calcium chloride.

Balance the chemical equation.

$$Ca(HCO_3)_2(aq) + 2\ HCl(aq) \rightarrow CaCl_2(aq) + 2\ CO_2(g) + 2\ H_2O(l)$$

Use the molar masses of $Ca(HCO_3)_2$ and $CaCl_2$, as well as their reacting ratios, to calculate the mass of $Ca(HCO_3)_2$ initially present.

$$2.29\ \text{g}\ CaCl_2\left(\frac{1\ \text{mol}\ CaCl_2}{110.98\ \text{g}\ CaCl_2}\right)\left(\frac{1\ \text{mol}\ Ca(HCO_3)_2}{1\ \text{mol}\ CaCl_2}\right)\left(\frac{162.12\ \text{g}\ Ca(HCO_3)_2}{1\ \text{mol}\ Ca(HCO_3)_2}\right) = 3.35\ \text{g}\ Ca(HCO_3)_2$$

Practice Problem 5.8 Solution

Use dimensional analysis to calculate the amount of coffee beans that can be purchased with $150.00:

$$150.00\ \text{dollars}\left(\frac{1\ \text{lb beans}}{8.00\ \text{dollars}}\right) = 18.8\ \text{lb beans}$$

The store has 20.0 lb of coffee beans, but only 18.8 lb can be purchased with the $150.00. This time the amount of money limits the purchase.

Practice Problem 5.9 Solution

First, calculate the amount of one of the products formed if each reactant were allowed to completely react.

$$0.500\ \text{mol}\ CH_3OH\left(\frac{2\ \text{mol}\ CO_2}{2\ \text{mol}\ CH_3OH}\right) = 0.500\ \text{mol}\ CO_2$$

$$1.000\ \text{mol}\ O_2\left(\frac{2\ \text{mol}\ CO_2}{3\ \text{mol}\ O_2}\right) = 0.6667\ \text{mol}\ CO_2$$

This time, CH_3OH is the limiting reactant, so all 0.500 mol CH_3OH reacts to produce 0.500 mol CO_2. Now use the amount of CH_3OH to calculate the amount of O_2 remaining and the amount of H_2O formed.

$$0.500\ \text{mol}\ CH_3OH\left(\frac{3\ \text{mol}\ O_2}{2\ \text{mol}\ CH_3OH}\right) = 0.750\ \text{mol}\ O_2\ \text{reacted}$$

$$0.500\ \text{mol}\ CH_3OH\left(\frac{4\ \text{mol}\ H_2O}{2\ \text{mol}\ CH_3OH}\right) = 1.00\ \text{mol}\ H_2O\ \text{formed}$$

Finally, set up a table to determine the number of moles of each species after the reaction.

	$2\ CH_3OH$	+	$3\ O_2$	→	$2\ CO_2$	+	$4\ H_2O$
Initial amounts	0.500 mol		1.000 mol		0 mol		0 mol
Change due to reaction	−0.500 mol		−0.750 mol		+0.500 mol		+1.00 mol
Final amounts	0 mol		0.250 mol		0.500 mol		1.00 mol

Practice Problem 5.10 Solution

The given chemical equation is not balanced. The balanced equation is

$$2\ AgNO_3(aq) + BaCl_2(aq) \rightarrow Ba(NO_3)_2(aq) + 2\ AgCl(s)$$

Now determine the limiting reactant.

$$0.100\ \text{mol}\ AgNO_3\left(\frac{1\ \text{mol}\ Ba(NO_3)_2}{2\ \text{mol}\ AgNO_3}\right) = 0.0500\ \text{mol}\ Ba(NO_3)_2$$

$$0.0250\ \text{mol}\ BaCl_2\left(\frac{1\ \text{mol}\ Ba(NO_3)_2}{1\ \text{mol}\ BaCl_2}\right) = 0.0250\ \text{mol}\ Ba(NO_3)_2$$

$BaCl_2$ is the limiting reactant, so all 0.250 mol $BaCl_2$ is used up and 0.0250 mol $Ba(NO_3)_2$ forms. Now determine the amount of $AgNO_3$ that reacts with 0.0250 mol $BaCl_2$ and the amount of AgCl that forms.

$$0.0250 \text{ mol BaCl}_2\left(\frac{2 \text{ mol AgNO}_3}{1 \text{ mol BaCl}_2}\right) = 0.0500 \text{ mol AgNO}_3 \text{ reacted}$$

$$0.0250 \text{ mol BaCl}_2\left(\frac{2 \text{ mol AgCl}}{1 \text{ mol BaCl}_2}\right) = 0.0500 \text{ mol AgCl formed}$$

Finally set up a table that summarizes the initial and final numbers of moles of each reactant and product.

	$2\ AgNO_3(aq)$	+	$BaCl_2(aq)$	→	$Ba(NO_3)_2(aq)$	+	$2\ AgCl(s)$
Initial amounts	0.100 mol		0.0250 mol		0 mol		0 mol
Change due to reaction	−0.0500 mol		−0.0250 mol		+0.0250 mol		+0.0500 mol
Final amounts	0.0500 mol		0 mol		0.0250 mol		0.0500 mol

Practice Problem 5.11 Solution

The given equation is balanced. Determine the limiting reactant.

$$0.550 \text{ mol H}_2\text{SO}_4\left(\frac{1 \text{ mol Na}_2\text{SO}_4}{1 \text{ mol H}_2\text{SO}_4}\right) = 0.550 \text{ mol Na}_2\text{SO}_4$$

$$0.375 \text{ mol NaOH}\left(\frac{1 \text{ mol Na}_2\text{SO}_4}{2 \text{ mol NaOH}}\right) = 0.188 \text{ mol Na}_2\text{SO}_4$$

NaOH is the limiting reagent, so 0.188 mol Na_2SO_4 is produced.

Practice Problem 5.12 Solution

The first step is to determine whether or not the given reaction is balanced. In this case, the reaction is balanced. Next, calculate the molar masses of each reactant.

The molar mass of HBr is

$$1.008 \text{ g/mol} + 79.908 \text{ g/mol} = 80.916 \text{ g/mol}$$

The molar mass of $NaHCO_3$ is

$$22.99 \text{ g/mol} + 1.008 \text{ g/mol} + 12.001 \text{ g/mol} + 3(15.999 \text{ g/mol}) = 84.01 \text{ g/mol}$$

Determine the initial number of moles of HBr and $NaHCO_3$.

$$25.0 \text{ g HBr}\left(\frac{1 \text{ mol HBr}}{80.916 \text{ g HBr}}\right) = 0.309 \text{ mol HBr}$$

$$12.3 \text{ g NaHCO}_3\left(\frac{1 \text{ mol NaHCO}_3}{84.01 \text{ g NaHCO}_3}\right) = 0.146 \text{ mol NaHCO}_3$$

Now determine the limiting reactant.

$$0.309 \text{ mol HBr}\left(\frac{1 \text{ mol NaBr}}{1 \text{ mol HBr}}\right) = 0.309 \text{ mol NaBr}$$

$$0.146 \text{ mol NaHCO}_3\left(\frac{1 \text{ mol NaBr}}{1 \text{ mol NaHCO}_3}\right) = 0.146 \text{ mol NaBr}$$

$NaHCO_3$ is the limiting reactant, so 0.146 mol NaBr is produced. The molar mass of NaBr is

$$22.99 \text{ g/mol} + 79.908 \text{ g/mol} = 102.9 \text{ g/mol}$$

Finally, convert the moles of NaBr to grams using its molar mass.

$$0.146 \text{ mol NaBr}\left(\frac{102.9 \text{ g NaBr}}{1 \text{ mol NaBr}}\right) = 15.1 \text{ g NaBr}$$

Practice Problem 5.13 Solution

Rearrange the percent yield equation (Equation 5.1) to solve for actual yield.

$$\text{Actual yield} = \frac{(\text{Percent yield})(\text{Theoretical yield})}{100\%}$$

$$\text{Actual yield} = \frac{(96\%)(7.10 \text{ g})}{100\%} = 6.8 \text{ g}$$

Practice Problem 5.14 Solution

First, confirm that the reaction is balanced. Next, convert the masses of the reactants to moles.

$$5.50 \text{ g N}_2\left(\frac{1 \text{ mol N}_2}{28.014 \text{ g N}_2}\right) = 0.196 \text{ mol N}_2$$

$$1.50 \text{ g H}_2\left(\frac{1 \text{ mol H}_2}{2.016 \text{ g H}_2}\right) = 0.744 \text{ mol H}_2$$

Now determine the limiting reactant.

$$0.196 \text{ mol N}_2\left(\frac{2 \text{ mol NH}_3}{1 \text{ mol N}_2}\right) = 0.0393 \text{ mol NH}_3$$

$$0.744 \text{ mol H}_2\left(\frac{2 \text{ mol NH}_3}{3 \text{ mol H}_2}\right) = 0.496 \text{ mol NH}_3$$

N_2 is the limiting reactant. Determine the theoretical yield of NH_3 based on 0.196 mol N_2 reacting.

$$0.196 \text{ mol } N_2\left(\frac{2 \text{ mol } NH_3}{1 \text{ mol } N_2}\right)\left(\frac{17.031 \text{ g } NH_3}{1 \text{ mol } NH_3}\right)$$
$$= 6.69 \text{ g } NH_3$$

Finally, determine the percent yield from Equation 5.1.

$$\text{Percent yield} = \left(\frac{\text{Actual yield}}{\text{Theoretical yield}}\right) \times 100\%$$
$$= \left(\frac{4.80 \text{ g } NH_3}{6.69 \text{ g } NH_3}\right) \times 100\% = 71.7\%$$

Practice Problem 5.15 Solution

a. The first cup contains more sugar (two cubes) than the second cup (one cube).

b. The contents of the two cups taste equally sweet because the concentration of sugar is equal in each. The first cup contains two sugar cubes and enough water to fill the cup. The second cup contains half of the number of sugar cubes but also half of the volume of water.

c. *Quantity* describes the amount of a substance. *Concentration* describes the amount of a substance per unit volume.

Practice Problem 5.16 Solution

$$\text{Molarity} = \frac{\text{Moles of solute}}{\text{Liter of solution}} = \frac{2.10 \text{ mol}}{3.75 \text{ L}} = 0.560 \text{ M}$$

The total volume of solution (3.75 L) is used in the calculation rather than the volume of solvent (water) used to make the solution (3.55 L). This is because the denominator is liter of *solution*, not liter of *solvent*.

Practice Problem 5.17 Solution

$$M = \frac{\text{mmol of solute}}{\text{mL of solution}} = \frac{4.50 \text{ mmol NaCl}}{3.80 \text{ mL}}$$
$$= 1.18 \text{ M NaCl}$$

Practice Problem 5.18 Solution

The molar mass of $CaCl_2$ is 40.078 g/mol + 2(35.45 g/mol) = 110.98 g/mol.

Convert the mass of $CaCl_2$ to moles.

$$0.750 \text{ g } CaCl_2\left(\frac{1 \text{ mol } CaCl_2}{110.98 \text{ g } CaCl_2}\right) = 0.00676 \text{ mol } CaCl_2$$

Convert the solution volume to L, then divide the number of moles of $CaCl_2$ by the solution volume.

$$M = \frac{0.00676 \text{ mol } CaCl_2}{0.0116 \text{ L}} = 0.583 \text{ M}$$

Practice Problem 5.19 Solution

The two potential conversion factors are $\frac{0.415 \text{ mol}}{1 \text{ L}}$ and its inverse, $\frac{1 \text{ L}}{0.415 \text{ mol}}$. Use the inverted version of the conversion factor so that moles cancel out.

$$0.853 \text{ mol}\left(\frac{1 \text{ L}}{0.415 \text{ mol}}\right) = 2.06 \text{ L}$$

Practice Problem 5.20 Solution

Using the molar mass of glucose, convert 79.2 mg and 110 mg of glucose into moles of glucose.

$$79.2 \text{ mg glucose}\left(\frac{1 \text{ g}}{1000 \text{ mg}}\right)\left(\frac{1 \text{ mol}}{180.16 \text{ g}}\right)$$
$$= 4.40 \times 10^{-4} \text{ mol glucose}$$
$$110 \text{ mg glucose}\left(\frac{1 \text{ g}}{1000 \text{ mg}}\right)\left(\frac{1 \text{ mol}}{180.16 \text{ g}}\right)$$
$$= 6.11 \times 10^{-4} \text{ mol glucose}$$

From Table 1.5, 1 dL = 0.1 L. To obtain the concentrations in molarity, divide each of the number of moles of glucose by 0.1 L.

$$\frac{4.40 \times 10^{-4} \text{ mol glucose}}{0.1 \text{ L}} = 0.00440 \text{ M glucose}$$
$$\frac{6.11 \times 10^{-4} \text{ mol glucose}}{0.1 \text{ L}} = 0.00611 \text{ M glucose}$$

The glucose concentration range in the bloodstream of a healthy human is 0.00440 M–0.00611 M.

Practice Problem 5.21 Solution

Rearrange the $M_1V_1 = M_2V_2$ equation to solve for V_1. The final concentration (M_2) is 0.250 M, the final volume (V_2) is 4.00 L, and the initial concentration (M_1) is 6.00 M.

$$V_1 = \frac{M_2V_2}{M_1} = \frac{(0.250 \text{ M})(4.00 \text{ L})}{6.00 \text{ M}} = 0.167 \text{ L}$$

Practice Problem 5.22 Solution

One way to solve this problem is to convert the volumes from milliliters to liters before using molarity to convert volume to moles. Thus, 87.3 mL is 0.0873 L, 71.7 mL is 0.0717 L, and 275 mL is 0.275 L.

$$0.0873\ \text{L}\left(\frac{1.71\ \text{mol}}{1\ \text{L}}\right) = 0.149\ \text{mol}$$

$$0.0717\ \text{L}\left(\frac{3.11\ \text{mol}}{1\ \text{L}}\right) = 0.223\ \text{mol}$$

Total moles of sugar = 0.1493 + 0.2230 = 0.372 mol.

The solution was diluted to 275 mL, so the total volume is 0.275 L.

$$M = \frac{0.372\ \text{mol}}{0.275\ \text{L}} = 1.35\ \text{M}$$

Practice Problem 5.23 Solution

First, balance the equation.

$$2\ HNO_3(aq) + Ba(OH)_2(aq) \rightarrow Ba(NO_3)_2(aq) + 2\ H_2O(l)$$

Next, determine the number of moles of $Ba(OH)_2$ present.

$$0.04177\ \text{L}\ Ba(OH)_2\left(\frac{0.1603\ \text{mol}\ Ba(OH)_2}{1\ \text{L}\ Ba(OH)_2}\right)$$
$$= 0.0066957\ \text{mol}\ Ba(OH)_2$$

Use the stoichiometric ratio from the balanced chemical equation to determine the number of moles of HNO_3 that react with $Ba(OH)_2$ and then the volume of HNO_3 solution that contains that number of moles.

$$0.0066957\ \text{mol}\ Ba(OH)_2\left(\frac{2\ \text{mol}\ HNO_3}{1\ \text{mol}\ Ba(OH)_2}\right)$$
$$\left(\frac{1\ \text{L}\ HNO_3}{0.5000\ \text{mol}\ HNO_3}\right) = 0.02678\ \text{L}\ HNO_3$$

$$0.02678\ \text{L}\ HNO_3\left(\frac{1000\ \text{mL}}{1\ \text{L}}\right) = 26.78\ \text{mL}\ HNO_3$$

Practice Problem 5.24 Solution

a. Use the definition of molarity.

$$M = \frac{0.150\ \text{mol}\ Al_2(SO_4)_3}{2.70\ \text{L}} = 0.556\ \text{M}\ Al_2(SO_4)_3$$

b. $Al_2(SO_4)_3$ dissociates into 2 Al^{3+} ions and 3 SO_4^{2-} ions. Calculate the number of moles of each ion.

$$0.150\ \text{mol}\ Al_2SO_4\left(\frac{2\ \text{mol}\ Al^{3+}}{1\ \text{mol}\ Al_2SO_4}\right) = 0.300\ \text{mol}\ Al^{3+}$$

$$0.150\ \text{mol}\ Al_2SO_4\left(\frac{3\ \text{mol}\ SO_4^{2-}}{1\ \text{mol}\ Al_2SO_4}\right) = 0.450\ \text{mol}\ SO_4^{2-}$$

Calculate the concentrations of the ions.

$$\frac{0.300\ \text{mol}\ Al^{3+}}{2.70\ \text{L}} = 0.111\ \text{M}\ Al^{3+}$$

$$\frac{0.450\ \text{mol}\ SO_4^{2-}}{2.70\ \text{L}} = 0.167\ \text{M}\ SO_4^{2-}$$

Practice Problem 5.25 Solution

Calculate the number of moles of ionic compound in each solution.

$$0.0100\ \text{L}\ (NH_4)_3PO_4\left(\frac{0.800\ \text{mol}\ (NH_4)_3PO_4}{1\ \text{L}\ (NH_4)_3PO_4}\right)$$
$$= 0.00800\ \text{mol}\ (NH_4)_3PO_4$$

$$0.0149\ \text{L}\ NH_4Cl\left(\frac{1.44\ \text{mol}\ NH_4Cl}{1\ \text{L}\ NH_4Cl}\right)$$
$$= 0.0215\ \text{mol}\ NH_4Cl$$

Determine the number of moles of each ion in each solution. First, determine the number for the $(NH_4)_3PO_4$ solution.

$$NH_4^+:\quad 0.00800\ \text{mol}\ (NH_4)_3PO_4\left(\frac{3\ \text{mol}\ NH_4^+}{1\ \text{mol}\ (NH_4)_3PO_4}\right)$$
$$= 0.0240\ \text{mol}\ NH_4^+$$

$$PO_4^{3-}:\quad 0.00800\ \text{mol}\ (NH_4)_3PO_4\left(\frac{1\ \text{mol}\ PO_4^{3-}}{1\ \text{mol}\ (NH_4)_3PO_4}\right)$$
$$= 0.00800\ \text{mol}\ PO_4^{3-}$$

Then, determine the number for the NH_4Cl solution.

$$NH_4^+:\quad 0.0215\ \text{mol}\ NH_4Cl\left(\frac{1\ \text{mol}\ NH_4^+}{1\ \text{mol}\ NH_4Cl}\right)$$
$$= 0.0215\ \text{mol}\ NH_4^+$$

$$Cl^-:\quad 0.0215\ \text{mol}\ NH_4Cl\left(\frac{1\ \text{mol}\ Cl^-}{1\ \text{mol}\ NH_4Cl}\right)$$
$$= 0.0215\ \text{mol}\ Cl^-$$

Finally, use these values and the final solution volume to calculate the concentrations of each ion.

$$NH_4^+:\quad \frac{(0.0240\ \text{mol} + 0.0215\ \text{mol})}{0.050\ \text{L}} = 0.910\ \text{M}\ NH_4^+$$

$$PO_4^{3-}:\quad \frac{0.00800\ \text{mol}}{0.050\ \text{L}} = 0.160\ \text{M}\ PO_4^{3-}$$

$$Cl^-:\quad \frac{0.0215\ \text{mol}\ Cl^-}{0.050\ \text{L}} = 0.430\ \text{M}\ Cl^-$$

Practice Problem 5.26 Solution

Use the mass of propane to determine the number of moles of gaseous H_2O formed, which is the number of moles of liquid H_2O formed after condensation. Then, use the density of water to calculate the volume of liquid water.

$$48.4\text{ g }C_3H_8\left(\frac{1\text{ mol }C_3H_8}{44.097\text{ g }C_3H_8}\right)\left(\frac{4\text{ mol }H_2O}{1\text{ mol }C_3H_8}\right)\left(\frac{18.015\text{ g }H_2O}{1\text{ mol }H_2O}\right)\left(\frac{1\text{ mL }H_2O}{1.00\text{ g }H_2O}\right) = 79.1\text{ mL }H_2O$$

Practice Problem 5.27 Solution

Determine the number of moles of Ba that are needed to react to form 7.33 g Al, and then use Avogadro's number to convert this value to the number of atoms of Ba.

$$7.33\text{ g Al}\left(\frac{1\text{ mol Al}}{26.98\text{ g Al}}\right)\left(\frac{3\text{ mol Ba}}{2\text{ mol Al}}\right)\left(\frac{6.022\times 10^{23}\text{ Ba atoms}}{1\text{ mol Ba atoms}}\right) = 2.45\times 10^{23}\text{ Ba atoms}$$

Practice Problem 5.28 Solution

The balanced equation in Example 5.28 is

$$3\,NH_3(aq) + H_3PO_4(aq) \rightarrow (NH_4)_3PO_4(aq)$$

Use this equation to determine the number of moles of ammonium phosphate formed based on the reaction of 6.15×10^6 g of phosphoric acid. Then use the number of moles of nitrogen formed per mole of $(NH_4)_3PO_4$ and the molar mass of nitrogen to calculate the mass of nitrogen atoms.

$$6.15\times 10^6\text{ g }H_3PO_4\left(\frac{1\text{ mol }H_3PO_4}{97.994\text{ g }H_3PO_4}\right)\left(\frac{1\text{ mol }(NH_4)_3PO_4}{1\text{ }H_3PO_4}\right)\left(\frac{3\text{ mol N}}{1\text{ mol }(NH_4)_3PO_4}\right)\left(\frac{14.007\text{ g N}}{1\text{ mol N}}\right) = 2.64\times 10^6\text{ g N}$$

Practice Problem 5.29 Solution

The net ionic equation is

$$3\,NH_4^+(aq) + PO_4^{2-}(aq) \rightarrow (NH_4)_3PO_4(s)$$

Use the molar mass of ammonium phosphate and the molar ratio between $(NH_4)_3PO_4$ and NH_4^+ to determine the number of moles of NH_4^+ needed to produce 250 g $(NH_4)_3PO_4$.

$$250\text{ g }(NH_4)_3PO_4\left(\frac{1\text{ mol }(NH_4)_3PO_4}{149.10\text{ g }(NH_4)_3PO_4}\right)\left(\frac{3\text{ mol }NH_4^+}{1\text{ mol }(NH_4)_3PO_4}\right) = 5.0\text{ mol }NH_4^+$$

Practice Problem 5.30 Solution

From Example 5.29, the balanced equation for the formation of barium sulfate is

$$Ba^{2+}(aq) + SO_4^{2-}(aq) \rightarrow BaSO_4(s)$$

Determine the number of moles of Ba^{2+} ions needed to produce 6.11 g $BaSO_4$ and the mass of $BaCl_2$ needed to supply this number of moles.

$$6.11\text{ g }BaSO_4\left(\frac{1\text{ mol }BaSO_4}{233.39\text{ g }BaSO_4}\right)\left(\frac{1\text{ mol }Ba^{2+}}{1\text{ mol }BaSO_4}\right) = 0.0262\text{ mol }Ba^{2+}$$

$$0.0262\text{ mol }Ba^{2+}\left(\frac{1\text{ mol }BaCl_2}{1\text{ mol }Ba^{2+}}\right)\left(\frac{208.23\text{ g }BaCl_2}{1\text{ mol }BaCl_2}\right) = 5.45\text{ g }BaCl_2$$

Practice Problem 5.31 Solution

The balanced equation is

$$H_2SO_4(aq) + 2\,NaOH(aq) \rightarrow Na_2SO_4(aq) + 2\,H_2O(l)$$

The volume of NaOH used to reach the equivalence point is 45.19 mL − 1.28 mL = 43.91 mL.

Combining this value with the known concentration of the NaOH solution, you can calculate the number of moles of NaOH needed to reach the equivalence point.

$$43.91\text{ mL}\left(\frac{1\text{ L}}{1000\text{ mL}}\right)\left(\frac{1.500\text{ mol NaOH}}{1\text{ L NaOH}}\right) = 0.065865\text{ mol NaOH}$$

According to the balanced equation, 2 mol NaOH react with 1 mol H_2SO_4. The number of moles of H_2SO_4 that react is

$$0.065865\text{ mol NaOH}\left(\frac{1\text{ mol }H_2SO_4}{2\text{ mol NaOH}}\right) = 0.032933\text{ mol }H_2SO_4$$

Dividing this value by the original volume of the H_2SO_4 solution gives the concentration of H_2SO_4.

$$\frac{0.032933\text{ mol }H_2SO_4}{0.02500\text{ L}} = 1.317\text{ M }H_2SO_4$$

Practice Problem 5.32 Solution

Calculate the number of moles of acid used in the titration.

$$26.28\text{ mL HCl}\left(\frac{1\text{ L}}{1000\text{ mL}}\right)\left(\frac{1.000\text{ mol HCl}}{1\text{ L HCl}}\right) = 0.02628\text{ mol HCl}$$

According to the balanced equation, 2 mol HCl react with 1 mol $M(OH)_2$, so the number of moles of $M(OH)_2$ that reacted is

$$0.02628 \text{ mol HCl}\left(\frac{1 \text{ mol M(OH)}_2}{2 \text{ mol HCl}}\right) = 0.01314 \text{ mol M(OH)}_2$$

Knowing the number of moles of $M(OH)_2$, you can use the given mass of $M(OH)_2$ that was dissolved in solution to determine the molar mass of $M(OH)_2$.

$$\text{Molar mass of M(OH)}_2 = \frac{\text{g M(OH)}_2}{\text{moles M(OH)}_2} = \frac{2.251 \text{ g M(OH)}_2}{0.01314 \text{ mol M(OH)}_2} = 171.3 \text{ g/mol}$$

Note that the volume of water in which the unknown base is dissolved is not used to solve the problem.

Practice Problem 5.33 Solution

a. Start by writing the balanced chemical equation. This is a double-replacement reaction, so the ions swap partners. More specifically, this is an acid–base reaction that produces water and a salt.

$$\text{Mg(OH)}_2\text{(aq)} + 2 \text{ HCl(aq)} \rightarrow \text{MgCl}_2\text{(aq)} + 2 \text{ H}_2\text{O(l)}$$

Use the molar mass of $Mg(OH)_2$ and the reaction stoichiometry to convert the given mass of $Mg(OH)_2$ in grams to moles of HCl.

$$5.832 \text{ g Mg(OH)}_2\left(\frac{1 \text{ mol Mg(OH)}_2}{58.319 \text{ g Mg(OH)}_2}\right)\left(\frac{2 \text{ mol HCl}}{1 \text{ mol Mg(OH)}_2}\right) = 0.20000 \text{ mol HCl}$$

Calculate the molarity from the moles of HCl and the volume of the solution.

$$M = \frac{0.20000 \text{ mol HCl}}{0.03554 \text{ L}} = 5.628 \text{ M HCl}$$

b. The 0.2000 mol HCl added to reach the equivalence point corresponds to the following number of moles of Mg^{2+}.

$$0.2000 \text{ mol HCl}\left(\frac{1 \text{ mol Mg(OH)}_2}{2 \text{ mol HCl}}\right)\left(\frac{1 \text{ mol Mg}^{2+}}{1 \text{ mol Mg(OH)}_2}\right) = 0.10000 \text{ mol Mg}^{2+}$$

The total solution volume at the equivalence point is 36.15 mL. Therefore, the concentration of Mg^{2+} is

$$M = \frac{0.10000 \text{ mol Mg}^{2+}}{0.03615 \text{ L}} = 2.766 \text{ M Mg}^{2+}$$

CHAPTER 6

Thermochemistry

anyaivanova/Shutterstock

Human survival depends on energy, and it all begins with the Sun. The Sun provides energy that plants store in the bonds of chemical compounds, and this stored energy is released when organisms eat those plants. When you consume plants or animals that have eaten plants, the chemical bonds of proteins, fatty acids, sugars, and other molecules are broken, which releases energy that nourishes you and allows you to function. Over the past several thousand years, humans have learned to harness energy for other purposes. For example, the energy stored in the chemical bonds of wood has long been used to heat our homes. Other sources of energy, such as the chemical energy in the bonds of fossil fuels and the kinetic energy of a river, are now used to provide electricity to our homes. Combustion engines, driven by fossil fuels, power our vehicles. Chemical energy stored in batteries powers many of our devices, such as flashlights, smartphones, and even cars.

Chapter Outline

GOALS

- Describe kinetic energy and potential energy.
- Recognize the SI units for kinetic energy and potential energy.
- Define work and heat.
- Summarize the concept of conservation of energy.
- Discuss state function.
- Apply the concept of state function to predict the energy changes involved in reactions.
- Summarize the roles of enthalpy and heat flow in chemical reactions.
- Calculate pressure–volume work.
- Calculate the heat required to change the temperature of a substance.
- Calculate changes in enthalpy and internal energy in chemical reactions.
- Apply Hess's law to calculate the enthalpies of different reactions.
- Determine the enthalpy of formation of a chemical compound from its constituent elements in their standard states.

6.1 Energy and Energy Units

GOALS

- Describe kinetic energy and potential energy.
- Recognize and convert between units of energy.

Background Review

Chapter 1 Classification of Matter: Section 1.3—Matter and Energy; Section 1.5—The International System of Units

INTRODUCTION TO ENERGY

Energy is the capacity to do work or transfer heat. Work and heat are related to force and temperature, respectively, and will be defined in Section 6.2. Several types of energy, such as chemical energy, heat (thermal) energy, electrical energy, and electromagnetic energy, are summarized in Section 1.3. **Thermochemistry** is the study of heat and energy in chemical reactions, and you will explore these concepts later in the chapter. This section will focus on the two forms of mechanical energy: kinetic energy and potential energy. **Mechanical energy** is energy that is due to an object's motion, position, or both.

Kinetic energy, KE, is energy of motion. When a pitcher throws a baseball, for example, the baseball possesses kinetic energy. Similarly, a rock that is dropped off a bridge has kinetic energy as it falls into the water below. The kinetic energy of an object is mathematically related to its mass, m, and velocity, v, as shown in the following equation.

$$KE = \frac{1}{2}mv^2 \tag{6.1}$$

Potential energy is energy related to position. The rock you hold in your hand as you stand on the bridge has potential energy. When the rock is dropped, its potential energy is converted to kinetic energy as it falls into the water. Another example of potential energy is a skateboarder at the top of a half-pipe (Figure 6.1).

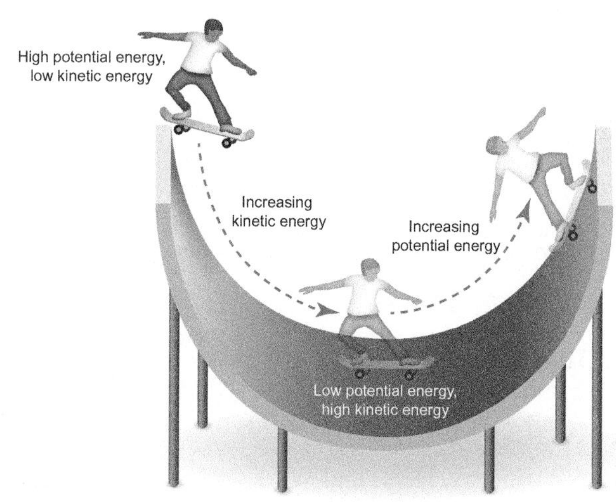

FIGURE 6.1 The Relationship Between Kinetic and Potential Energy

When the skateboarder first begins his descent from the top of the half-pipe, he has low kinetic energy but high potential energy. As the skateboarder moves down the half-pipe, his potential energy is converted to kinetic energy, and then back again to potential energy as he moves up the other side.

Example 6.1

A pitcher throws a baseball with a mass of 5.13 oz (0.145 kg) at a velocity of 95.0 mph (42.5 m/s). Using the correct SI units, calculate the kinetic energy of the baseball.

Solution

Section 1.7 explains that the SI unit of mass is kilogram and the SI unit of distance is meter. Therefore, the mass of 0.145 kg and the velocity of 42.5 m/s are substituted into the formula to calculate the kinetic energy of the baseball.

$$\begin{aligned} KE &= \frac{1}{2}mv^2 = \frac{1}{2}(0.145\ \text{kg})(42.5\ \text{m/s})^2 \\ &= 131\ \text{kg} \cdot \text{m}^2/\text{s}^2 \end{aligned}$$

As will be discussed later, $\text{kg} \cdot \text{m}^2/\text{s}^2$ is a unit of energy that is more commonly known as a joule, J.

PRACTICE PROBLEM 6.1

Calculate the kinetic energy of a 1.95×10^5 kg locomotive that is traveling at 22.4 m/s.

Hint: Substitute the given values into the equation $KE = \frac{1}{2}mv^2$, where m is the mass in kilograms and v is the velocity in meters per second.

ENERGY UNITS

As discussed earlier, **joule, J**, is the SI unit of energy.

$$1\ \text{J} = 1\ \text{kg} \cdot \frac{\text{m}^2}{\text{s}^2}$$

The **calorie, cal**, is another commonly used unit of energy. A calorie is defined as the amount of energy needed to raise the temperature of exactly 1 g of water by exactly 1°C. There is exactly 4.184 J in 1 cal. In the field of nutrition, the **Calorie, Cal**, distinguished from the calorie with an uppercase letter "C," is equal to 1000 calories. The units of "calories" that are displayed on food items are Calories. These units are summarized in Table 6.1.

TABLE 6.1 Common Units of Energy

Unit	Equivalent Value
joule (J)	$1\ \text{kg} \cdot \text{m}^2/\text{s}^2$
calorie (cal)	4.184 J
Calorie (Cal)	1000 cal = 1 kcal = 4184 J = 4.184 kJ

SECTION REVIEW

- Energy is the ability to do work or transfer heat.
- Kinetic energy, the energy of motion, is mathematically expressed as $KE = \frac{1}{2}mv^2$.
- Potential energy is energy related to an object's position.
- Energy can be converted from one form to another.
- The commonly used units of energy are the joule, J, and the calorie, cal.

$$1\ \text{cal} = 4.184\ \text{J}$$

6.2 Energy, Heat, and Work

GOALS

- Define work and heat.
- Identify appropriate signs for w and q for a given scenario.
- Summarize the concept of conservation of energy.
- Calculate the change in internal energy of a system given values for work and heat.

Background Review

Chapter 1 Science and Measurement:
Section 1.9—Temperature Scales

THE SYSTEM AND THE SURROUNDINGS

Given that energy can be transferred from one form to another, it is important to be able to define where this energy is coming from and where it is going. One convenient way to do this is to define the source of the energy, such as a container with chemical reactants and products, as the **system**, and to define the rest of the universe as the **surroundings**. That is,

$$\text{Universe} = \text{system} + \text{surroundings}$$

The system is typically the part of the universe that a scientist studies. However, you should note that scientists have great flexibility in defining the boundary of the system. For example, if a scientist is studying a chemical reaction that takes place inside a beaker,

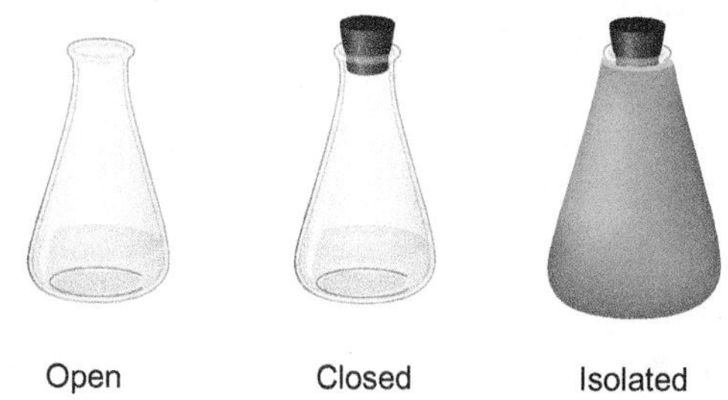

FIGURE 6.2 Open, Closed, and Isolated Systems
Heat and matter can both enter and escape an open system. In a closed system, heat can be transferred between the system and surroundings, but matter is trapped inside the system. In an isolated system, both heat and matter are trapped inside the system.

the scientist can choose to define both the beaker and the chemical species involved in the reaction as the system, or the scientist can choose to define only the chemical species as the system. Therefore, it is important to clearly define the system and the surroundings when discussing transfers of energy.

Systems can be open, closed, or isolated (Figure 6.2). In an open system, both matter and energy can move between the system and the surroundings. An example of an open system is a fireplace with burning wood, where heat and gaseous products are allowed to escape into the atmosphere, while cooler atmospheric air is allowed to enter the fireplace. In a closed system, energy but not matter can move between the system and the surroundings. An example of a closed system is a pressure cooker, where heat can escape the system but the water and steam remain trapped inside. In an isolated system, neither matter nor energy can leave or enter the system. A thermos approximates an isolated system, but you typically need high-grade laboratory equipment for a truly isolated system.

WORK AND HEAT FLOW

Work, *w*, is the energy resulting from a force acting on an object over a distance. For example, a person pushing a stalled car down a road does work on the car. Similarly, a person throwing a ball does work on the ball. But recall that energy is the capacity to do work *or* transfer heat. The flow of energy that causes a temperature change in an object or its surroundings is known as **heat, *q*.**

An ice cube melting in a person's hand is an example of heat transfer. In this case, heat is transferred from the person's hand to the ice cube.

Given that work and heat can be exchanged between the system and surroundings, it is important to mathematically define the flow of energy in a consistent manner. In the example of work above, the car is defined as the system and everything around the car, including the person, is the surroundings. When the person pushes the car, work is being done on the system by the surroundings. If a moving car were to hit the person instead, the system would be doing work on the surroundings. When work is done *on* the system, w has a positive value (Figure 6.3a). When work is done *by* the system, w has a negative value (Figure 6.3b).

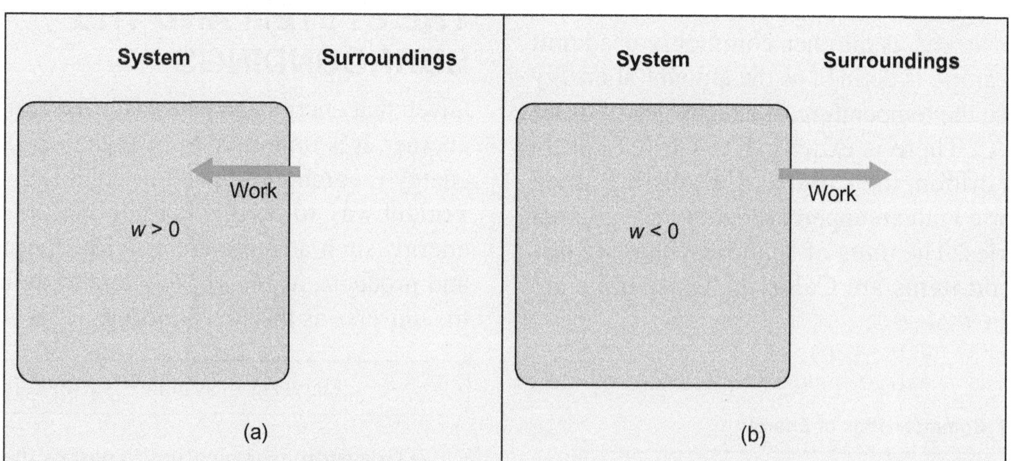

FIGURE 6.3 Work Flow Between the System and Surroundings
The sign of w is from the perspective of the system. (a) The sign of w is positive ($w > 0$) when work is done on the system by the surroundings. (b) The sign of w is negative ($w < 0$) when work is done by the system on the surroundings.

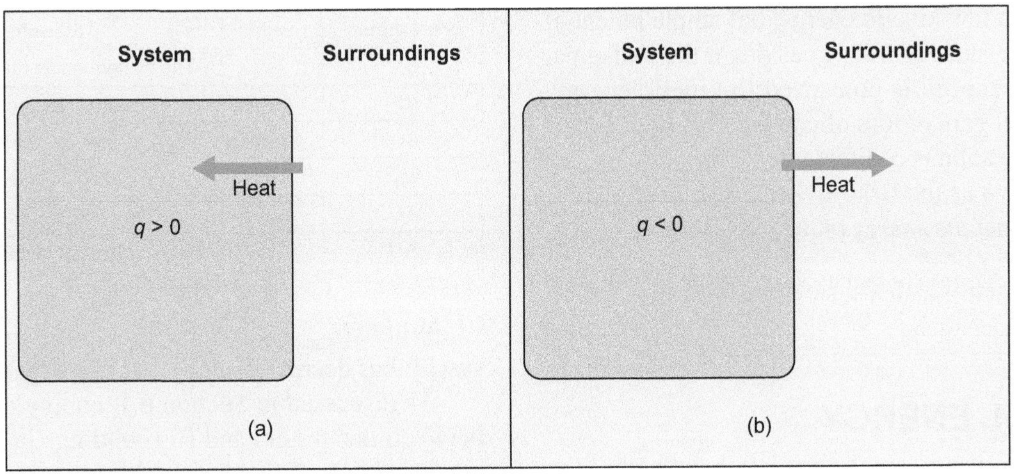

FIGURE 6.4 Heat Transfer Between the System and Surroundings
The sign of q is from the perspective of the system. (a) The sign of q is positive ($q > 0$) when heat is transferred to the system from the surroundings. (b) The sign of q is negative ($q < 0$) when heat is transferred from the system to the surroundings.

Similarly, if the ice cube in the person's hand is defined as the system, then the heat transferred from the person's hand (the surroundings) to the ice cube (the system) results in a positive value of q (Figure 6.4a) If a bowl of room-temperature water is left outside on a cold winter night and the water freezes, then the transfer of heat from the system (the bowl of water) to the surroundings results in a negative value of q (Figure 6.4b).

Example 6.2

Determine whether the value of w or q is positive or negative in each of the following scenarios.

a. A person rolls a bowling ball across the floor, where the bowling ball is defined as the system.
b. A person rolls a bowling ball across the floor, where the person is defined as the system.
c. An ice pack is placed on a person's sore back, where the ice pack is defined as the system.

Solution

a. Work is being done on the system (the bowling ball) by the surroundings. The value of w is positive.
b. Work is being done by the system (the person) on the surroundings. The value of w is negative.
c. Heat is being transferred from the surroundings (the person's back) to the system (the ice pack). The value of q is positive.

PRACTICE PROBLEM 6.2

Identify the type of energy transfer (work or heat) in each scenario, then determine whether the sign of w or q is positive or negative.

a. A crane lifts a steel beam, where the steel beam is defined as the system.
b. Steam condenses on a cool mirror, where the mirror is defined as the system.

Hint: To identify when w changes, look for an object being moved. To determine its sign, look at whether the system is receiving the work (+) or doing the work (−). To identify when q changes, look for references to the relative temperature or phase of a substance. To determine its sign, look at whether the system is absorbing heat (+) or releasing heat (−).

THE FIRST LAW OF THERMODYNAMICS

As explained in Section 6.1, energy can move between a system and its surroundings, and some types of energy can be converted from one form to the other. When you hold an ice cube in your hand, heat is released from your body through your hand but the heat does not disappear. Instead, the heat travels to, and eventually melts, the ice cube. Similarly, the potential energy of a raindrop in a cloud is not lost as it falls to the ground, but is instead converted to kinetic energy. The **law of conservation of energy** states that energy cannot be created or destroyed, just transferred from one form to another. The skateboarder at the top of the half-pipe in Figure 6.1 has low kinetic energy, but ample potential energy. As the skateboarder goes down the half-pipe, his potential energy is converted to kinetic energy. There is no net gain or loss of energy. This principle of energy conservation is codified into an important scientific law known as the **first law of thermodynamics**, which states that *the energy of the universe is constant.*

The first law of thermodynamics states that the energy of the universe is constant.

INTERNAL ENERGY

The **internal energy,** U, of a system is defined as the sum of all kinetic and potential energies of the particles within a system. The kinetic energy includes not only the motions of the molecules inside the system but also the motions of the atoms and subatomic particles within those atoms. Internal energy describes energy at the molecular, atomic, and subatomic scale but does *not* include the macroscopic kinetic and potential energies of the system as a whole. The absolute internal energies of systems are generally difficult to determine, so scientists measure *changes* in internal energy, ΔU, instead, where the Greek letter Delta, Δ, means "change in." The change in internal energy of a system is defined as

$$\Delta U = U_{\text{final}} - U_{\text{initial}}$$

where U_{initial} refers to the internal energy of the system in its initial state and U_{final} refers to the internal energy of the system in its final state.

When $U_{\text{final}} > U_{\text{initial}}$, the internal energy of the system has increased and ΔU has a positive value.

TABLE 6.2 Expressions and Meanings of q, w, and ΔU

Parameter	Sign	Meaning
q	+	The system gains heat.
q	−	The system loses heat.
w	+	Work is done *on* the system.
w	−	Work is done *by* the system.
ΔU	+	The system gains internal energy.
ΔU	−	The system loses internal energy.

When $U_{\text{final}} < U_{\text{initial}}$, the internal energy of the system has decreased and ΔU has a negative value.

As discussed in Section 6.1, energy can exchange between the system and surroundings in the forms of work and heat. This idea can be expressed in terms of the first law of thermodynamics as

$$\Delta U = q + w \tag{6.2}$$

When work is done on the system (w is positive) and heat is added to the system (q is positive), then the internal energy of the system increases (ΔU is positive). If work is done by the system (w is negative) and heat is released by the system (q is negative), then ΔU is negative. If q is positive and w is negative, or if q is negative and w is positive, then their relative magnitudes will determine whether ΔU is positive or negative. The signs of q, w, and ΔU and their physical meanings are summarized in Table 6.2.

It is very important to use the correct signs when expressing q, w, and ΔU.

Figure 6.5 shows how work and heat done on or by a system affects the internal energy of the system.

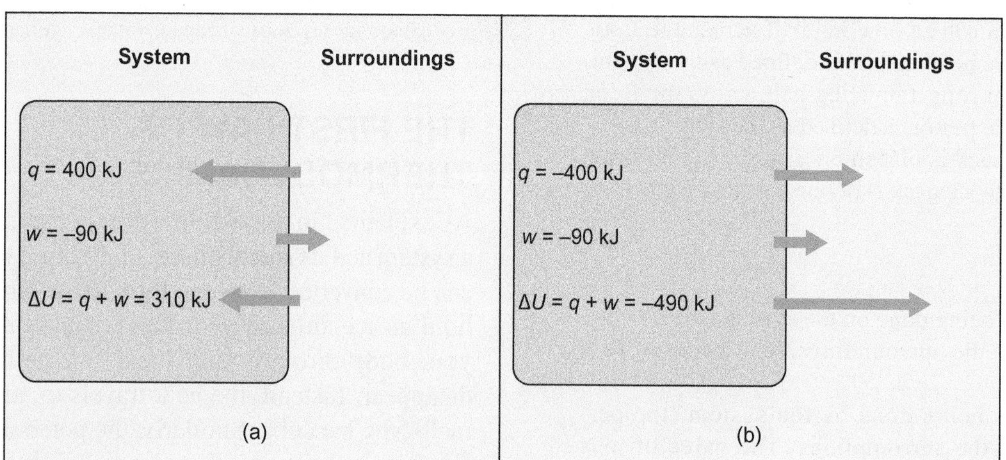

FIGURE 6.5 Internal Energy
Adjust the values of q (heat) and w (work) to see the result on ΔU (internal energy).

Example 6.3

A chemical reaction is performed in a flask that is connected to a piston. Heat is allowed to enter or escape this system, but matter cannot. (Does this make the system open, closed, or isolated?) The reaction releases 890 J of heat to the surroundings and the gas produced performs 450 J of work on the surroundings by pushing the piston upward.

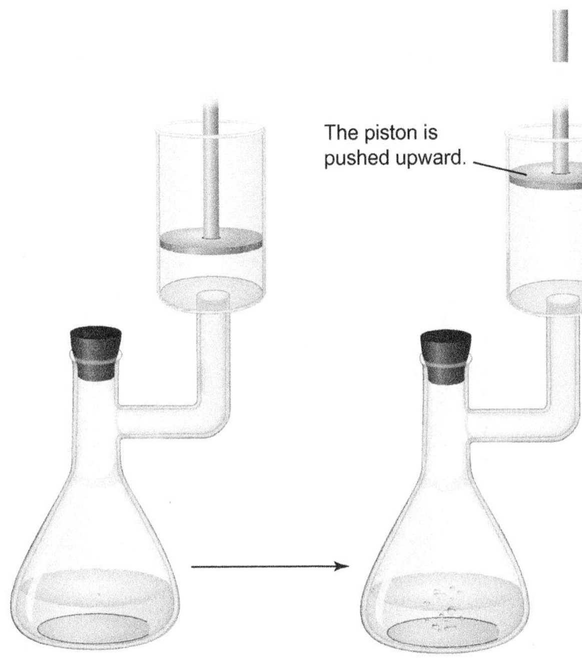
The piston is pushed upward.

a. Determine the signs of q and w in this reaction.
b. Determine ΔU for this reaction.

Solution

a. The reaction produces heat and releases it to the surroundings, so q is negative: $q = -890$ J. The reaction produces a gas that does work on the surroundings, so w is negative, too: $w = -450$ J.
b. Negative values of q and w are used to calculate the change in internal energy:

$$\Delta U = q + w = (-890\text{ J}) + (-450\text{ J}) = -1340\text{ J}$$

PRACTICE PROBLEM 6.3

A chemical reaction is performed in the same flask connected to a piston that was used in Example 6.3. It is a closed system because heat can enter or escape this system but matter cannot. The reaction of two gases to form a solid consumes 550 J of heat from the surroundings, and the surroundings do 210 J of work on the system as the gases are consumed during the reaction.

a. Determine the signs of q and w in this reaction.
b. Determine ΔU for this reaction.

Hint: First, identify the signs of q and w based on the scenario description. Then, substitute the values, with their appropriate signs, into the formula $\Delta U = q + w$.

SECTION REVIEW

- Energy, in the form of work or heat, can be transferred between a system and the surroundings.
- Work, w, is the energy resulting from a force acting on an object over a distance.
- Heat, q, is the flow of energy that causes a temperature change in an object or its surroundings.
- Work done *on* the system is mathematically defined as positive in value, whereas work done *by* the system is defined as negative in value.
- Heat transferred to the system is mathematically defined as positive in value, whereas heat transferred from the system to the surroundings is defined as negative in value.
- The internal energy, U, of a system is defined as the sum of all kinetic and potential energies of a system.
- The first law of thermodynamics states that the energy of the universe is constant.
- The relationship between a system's internal energy change, work, and heat is expressed in terms of the first law of thermodynamics as $\Delta U = q + w$.

6.3 Energy as a State Function

GOALS

- Define state function.
- Apply the concept of a state function to predict the energy changes involved in reactions.

Background Review

Chapter 1 Science and Measurement: Section 1.9—Temperature Scales

Two people need to get from the ground floor in a building to the 6th floor, as shown in Figure 6.6. One person takes the elevator directly from the ground floor to the 6th floor. The other person takes the elevator from the ground floor to the 10th floor, and then takes the elevator down to the 6th floor. The two people took different paths, traveled different overall distances, and took different amounts of time to reach their destination, but both began their journey at the ground floor and arrived at the 6th floor. The end result for both people was the same—it was independent of the pathway taken to achieve it. A **state function** describes the current state of a system and is *independent of the path taken to achieve its value*.

The internal energy, U, of a system is independent of the pathway taken to achieve it, too. Consider a known mass of solid ethanol, C_2H_6O, at $-115°C$, first melting and then evaporating to form gaseous ethanol at 79°C. The change in internal energy of this process is $\Delta U_{\text{initial}}$. Suppose that the same mass of solid ethanol at $-115°C$ sublimes directly to gaseous ethanol at 79°C, with an internal energy change of ΔU_{final}. Despite the fact that solid ethanol was transformed to gaseous ethanol in each case, the change in internal energy of each process is the same ($\Delta U_{\text{initial}} = \Delta U_{\text{final}}$).

$$C_2H_6O(s, -115°C) \rightarrow C_2H_6O(l) \rightarrow C_2H_6O(g, 79°C) \qquad \Delta U_{\text{initial}}$$

$$C_2H_6O(s, -115°C) \rightarrow C_2H_6O(g, 79°C) \qquad \Delta U_{\text{final}}$$

$$\Delta U_{\text{initial}} = \Delta U_{\text{final}}$$

The internal energies of the gaseous ethanol products at 79°C in each case are also equal because the masses and temperatures of the gaseous ethanol are identical.

Since the internal energy of a system is independent of the pathway taken to achieve it, a system with a particular internal energy can also be achieved from two different starting points. For example, suppose that a known mass of C_2H_6O melts to form liquid ethanol at 25°C, and that the liquid ethanol has an internal energy given by U_{liquid}. If the same mass of gaseous ethanol condenses to form liquid ethanol at 25°C, then it, too, has an internal energy given by U_{liquid}.

$$C_2H_6O(s) \rightarrow C_2H_6O(l) \; U_{\text{liquid}}$$

$$C_2H_6O(g) \rightarrow C_2H_6O(l) \; U_{\text{liquid}}$$

As shown in Figure 6.7, the internal energy of liquid ethanol at 25°C (U_{liquid}) in both examples is the same, regardless of whether it was formed from solid ethanol or gaseous ethanol.

FIGURE 6.6 Height of an Elevator as a State Function
The change in height depends on the initial and final states, not the path taken.

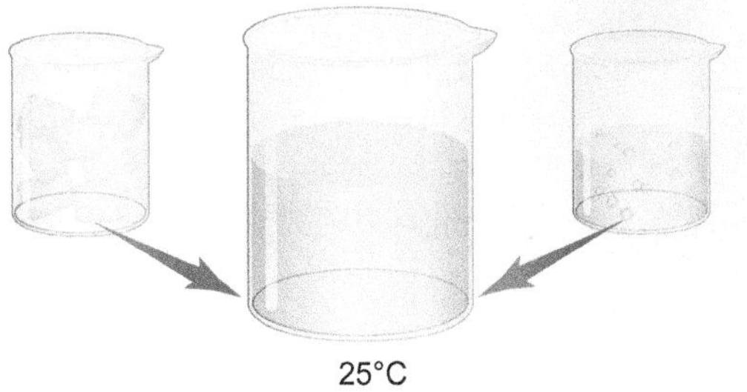

FIGURE 6.7 Internal Energy as a State Function
Liquid ethanol at 25°C that is formed by melting solid ethanol has the same internal energy, U_{liquid}, as liquid ethanol formed by condensing gaseous ethanol.

Internal energy, therefore, is a state function. Work and heat are *not* state functions—their values depend on the path taken. Work and heat are examples of **path functions**, since their values depend on the sequence of steps that move the system from its initial state to its final state. Path functions do not describe the current state of a system. For example, systems are not said to possess a specific value of heat or work. That said, two systems with unequal values of q and w can have the same net ΔU value (Section 6.2).

Example 6.4

Determine whether temperature is a state function or a path function and explain your reasoning.

Solution

Temperature is a state function. Recall that state functions describe the current state of a system and not the path taken to achieve that state. For example, the sample of ethanol in Figure 6.7 is at 25°C, whether it was originally a solid at −115°C or a gas at 79°C. The amount of energy that the liquid ethanol at 25°C possesses is described as a temperature (a state function) and not as heat (a path function).

PRACTICE PROBLEM 6.4

Determine whether pressure is a state function or a path function and explain your reasoning.

Hint: Consider two identical bicycle tires, each filled to 70 pounds per square inch (psi). Can you say they are at the same tire pressure, even if one of them started at a higher pressure and deflated down to 50 psi, whereas the other one started out flat and got inflated to 70 psi?

SECTION REVIEW

- A state function is a property of a system that only depends on the state of the system. A state function is independent of the path taken to achieve that state. In contrast, the values of path functions depend on the sequence of steps to achieve a particular state.
- State functions allow scientists to predict energy changes involved in reactions.
- Internal energy is a state function, whereas heat and work are not.

6.4 Energy and Enthalpy

GOALS

- Summarize the roles of enthalpy and heat flow in chemical reactions.
- Calculate pressure–volume work.

Background Review

Chapter 1 Science and Measurement:
Section 1.7—Dimensional Analysis

PRESSURE–VOLUME WORK

The experimental apparatus shown in Figure 6.8, which was used previously in Example 6.3, consists of a flask attached to a piston of negligible mass. The system (the flask, the piston, and the tubing connecting the two) is closed to the atmosphere, but the piston may move up or down in response to an increase or decrease in pressure in the flask. This allows the pressure in the flask to remain constant and equal to atmospheric pressure.

When solid sodium carbonate, Na_2CO_3, is mixed with an aqueous solution of acetic acid, $C_2H_4O_2$, in the flask, gaseous carbon dioxide, CO_2, and aqueous sodium acetate, $NaC_2H_3O_2$, form according to the following balanced chemical equation:

$$Na_2CO_3(s) + 2\,C_2H_4O_2(aq) \rightarrow CO_2(g) + 2\,NaC_2H_3O_2(aq) + H_2O(l)$$

Because gaseous CO_2 forms in this reaction, pressure builds inside the flask, which moves the piston upward.

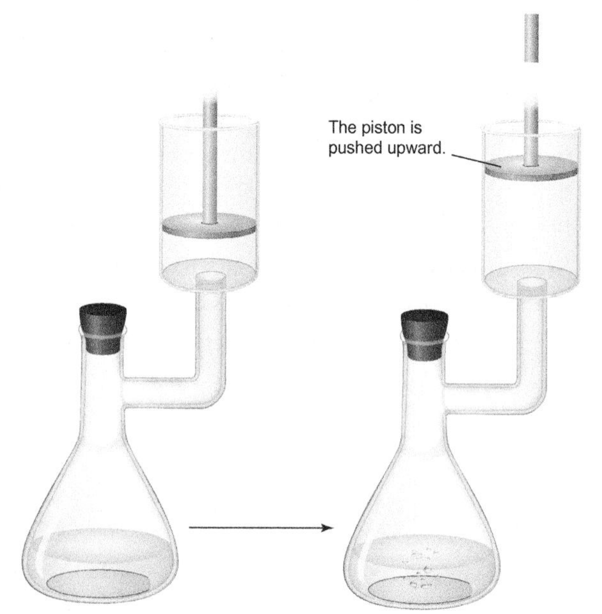
The piston is
pushed upward.

FIGURE 6.8 A Constant-Pressure Reaction System That Does Work on the Surroundings

When gas is formed inside the reaction apparatus, the piston is moved upward. The system does pressure–volume work on the surroundings.

As a result, the system does work on the surroundings. This type of work is known as pressure–volume work. **Pressure–volume work** is work done on or by a system when there is a volume change as measured against an external pressure. Work and pressure, P, are related to the change in volume, ΔV, according to the following equation:

$$w = -P\Delta V \tag{6.3}$$

The change in volume, ΔV, is the difference between the final volume and the initial volume:

$$\Delta V = V_{final} - V_{inital}$$

When the gas inside the flask *increases* in volume, the piston moves upward and ΔV is a positive value. The value of w in this case is negative, however, because the system is doing work on the surroundings. If the volume of gas inside the flask *decreases* rather than increases, then the piston moves downward and ΔV has a negative value. The value of w in this case is positive, because now the surroundings are doing work on the system.

It may not be immediately obvious how multiplying a unit of volume by a unit of pressure results in a unit of energy, but L · atm is indeed a unit of energy, equal to 101.325 J.

$$1 \text{ L} \cdot \text{atm} = 101.325 \text{ J}$$

Example 6.5

A chemical reaction is performed in a flask that is sealed with a piston, similar to the experimental setup shown in Figure 6.8. The initial volume of the system is 0.550 L and the final volume is 0.375 L. The pressure remains constant at 1.00 atm.

a. Given that 1 L · atm = 101.325 J, calculate the amount of work performed (in joules) during this reaction.
b. Determine whether the piston moves upward or downward over the course of this reaction.

Solution

a. The change in volume, ΔV, is calculated as follows:

$$\Delta V = V_{final} - V_{initial} = (0.375 \text{ L}) - (0.550 \text{ L}) = -0.175 \text{ L}$$

Next, multiply the change in volume by the pressure to calculate the work performed.

$$w = -P\Delta V = -(1.00 \text{ atm})(-0.175 \text{ L}) = 0.175 \text{ L} \cdot \text{atm}$$

The work value in units of L · atm is converted to units of J.

$$w = 0.175 \text{ L} \cdot \text{atm}\left(\frac{101.325 \text{ J}}{1 \text{ L} \cdot \text{atm}}\right) = 17.7 \text{ J}$$

b. The sign of the work is positive, so the surroundings do work on the system, as further evidenced by the volume decrease. A decrease in volume means that the piston moves downward.

PRACTICE PROBLEM 6.5

A chemical reaction is performed in a flask that is connected to a piston, similar to the experimental setup shown in Figure 6.8. The initial volume of the system is 0.350 L and the final volume is 0.885 L. The pressure remains constant at 1.00 atm.

a. Determine whether the piston moves upward or downward over the course of this reaction.
b. Given that 1 L · atm = 101.325 J, calculate the amount of work performed (in joules) during this reaction.

Hint: (a) Start by finding the change in volume, $\Delta V = V_{final} - V_{initial}$, paying attention to the sign. If the volume increases, the piston moves up. If the volume decreases, the piston moves down.
(b) Then insert the given pressure and the change in volume into the formula $w = -P\Delta V$. Again, pay attention to negative signs. Finally, convert the work to joules using 1 L · atm = 101.325 J.

ENTHALPY

Most chemical reactions are performed in open systems, such as in a beaker on a lab bench, where both heat and work can be exchanged between the system and surroundings. However, the work exchanged is often of little interest to chemists. Therefore, it is useful to describe the flow of heat in systems where the pressure remains constant and equal to atmospheric pressure. The property of **enthalpy, *H***, is a state function that relates the state functions of internal energy, *U*, pressure, *P*, and volume, *V*, as

$$H = U + PV \qquad (6.4)$$

At constant pressure, the change in enthalpy (ΔH) is equal to the change in internal energy plus the product of the pressure and change in volume.

$$\Delta H = \Delta U + P\Delta V \qquad (6.5)$$

Recalling that $\Delta U = q + w$, the following substitution can be made, where q_p represents the heat flow at constant pressure.

$$\Delta H = (q_p + w) + P\Delta V \qquad (6.6)$$

Given that $w = -P\Delta V$, the equation above can be further simplified as

$$\Delta H = (q_p + w) - w = q_p$$

or

$$\Delta H = q_p \qquad (6.7)$$

Thus, a change in enthalpy is simply equal to the flow of heat at constant pressure.

ENDOTHERMIC AND EXOTHERMIC PROCESSES

In the same manner as *q*, ΔH is positive when heat is transferred from the surroundings to the system. Reactions that absorb heat from the surroundings are known as **endothermic processes**. Conversely, ΔH is negative when heat is transferred from the system to the surroundings, and these reactions are known as **exothermic processes**.

Example 6.6

Wood is burned in an open fireplace. The reaction releases 250 kJ of heat and does 15.0 kJ of work on the surroundings.

a. Determine whether this reaction is endothermic or exothermic.
b. Calculate ΔH for this reaction.
c. Calculate ΔU for this reaction.

EVERYDAY CONNECTION

Instant hand and toe warmers contain iron powder, Fe(s), in a breathable pouch wrapped in air-tight plastic packaging. When opened and exposed to air, the iron reacts with oxygen to form iron oxide, $Fe_2O_3(s)$. The reaction is exothermic ($\Delta H < 0$), releasing heat to the surroundings.

$$4\,Fe(s) + 3\,O_2(g) \rightarrow 2\,Fe_2O_3(s) \qquad \Delta H < 0$$

Instant cold packs contain solid ammonium nitrate, $NH_4NO_3(s)$, and an inner bag of water that is broken upon squeezing. The dissolving process is endothermic ($\Delta H > 0$), absorbing heat from the surroundings.

$$NH_4NO_3(s) \xrightarrow{H_2O} NH_4NO_3(aq) \qquad \Delta H > 0$$

Solution

a. Heat is transferred from the system to the surroundings, so the reaction is exothermic (i.e., $\Delta H < 0$).

b. Since this is an open system, the pressure is constant. Therefore, ΔH is equal to the amount of heat transferred and it has a negative value because the heat is transferred from the system to the surroundings: $\Delta H = q = -250$ kJ.

c. ΔH depends only on q, but ΔU depends on q and w. In this case, the work (15.0 kJ) is done on the surroundings, so it also has a negative value.

$$\Delta U = q + w = (-250\text{ kJ}) + (-15.0\text{ kJ}) = -265\text{ kJ}$$

PRACTICE PROBLEM 6.6

Water inside of a bowl evaporates after it is left outside on a hot summer day. This phase change absorbs 1150 kJ of heat from the surroundings.

a. Determine whether this reaction is endothermic or exothermic.

b. Determine the value of ΔH for this reaction.

Hint: Endothermic means the system absorbs heat from the surroundings. Exothermic means the system releases heat to the surroundings.

For an endothermic reaction, both ΔH and q_p have positive values. For an exothermic reaction, ΔH and q_p have negative values.

SECTION REVIEW

- Pressure–volume work is work caused by a volume change against an external pressure. The relationship between work, pressure, and a change in volume is expressed as

$$w = -P\Delta V$$

- Enthalpy, H, is a state property that is related to internal energy, pressure, and volume by the following equations:

$$H = U + PV$$
$$\Delta H = \Delta U + P\Delta V$$

- The change in enthalpy of a system, ΔH, is equal to the flow of heat at constant pressure, q_p, expressed as

$$\Delta H = q_p$$

- Endothermic reactions absorb heat from the surroundings and have positive ΔH values, whereas exothermic reactions release heat to the surroundings and have negative ΔH values.

6.5 Specific Heat

GOAL

- Calculate the heat required to change the temperature of a substance.

Background Review

Chapter 0 Math Review: 0.4—Algebra

When you add energy to a sample of matter, you generally expect the sample to warm up. The sample does warm up, unless the sample happens to be a pure substance at its melting, sublimation, or boiling point (Section 12.3). Thus, when calculating how much the temperature of a substance will rise when a certain amount of heat energy is put into it, there are two different types of calculations that you might encounter: one in which a substance simply increases its temperature as heat is added and another one in which the added heat causes a transition from one physical state to another. In this section, heat flow in the absence of a phase change is discussed.

SPECIFIC HEAT CALCULATIONS

When there is no phase change involved, the amount of heat required to change the temperature of a substance is given by the equation

$$q = mc\Delta T \qquad (6.8)$$

where m is the mass of the substance, c is the specific heat of the substance, and ΔT is the *change* in temperature in either degrees Celsius or kelvins. The **specific heat, c** (J/g·°C), of a substance is the number of calories required to raise exactly 1 g of the substance by exactly 1°C. The specific heats of selected substances are listed in Table 6.3.

Substances with higher specific heat values resist temperature changes more than substances with lower specific heat values. In Table 6.3, note that liquid water has a higher specific heat than most of the other elements and compounds in the table. Due to its high specific heat of 4.184 J/g·°C, water can absorb a significant amount of heat without experiencing

EVERYDAY CONNECTION

Minneapolis, Minnesota (left), and Portland, Oregon (right), are located at nearly the same latitude, but have very different overnight low temperatures in the winter. Minneapolis experiences an average overnight low of 8°F (−13°C) in January. Portland, located approximately 50 miles east of the Pacific Ocean, has an average overnight low temperature of 36°F (2°C) in January. The vast size of the Pacific Ocean and the high specific heat of water result in the ocean absorbing an incredible amount of the Sun's heat. The ocean retains much of this heat at night, preventing temperatures in Portland from dropping below 20°F (−7°C) for the vast majority of the winter. In contrast, cities that are located more than 1000 miles from an ocean, such as Minneapolis, lose more heat to the atmosphere at night and tend to have much lower overnight temperatures in the winter.

MarynaG/Shutterstock

tusharkoley/Shutterstock

TABLE 6.3 Specific Heats of Selected Substances

Substance, Formula	Specific Heat, c (J/g · °C)
Covalent molecules	
Carbon dioxide, CO_2	0.852
Carbon monoxide, CO	1.04
Hydrogen, H_2	14.4
Nitrogen, N_2	1.04
Oxygen, O_2	0.922
Water, gaseous, $H_2O(g)$	2.042
Water, liquid, $H_2O(l)$	4.184
Water, solid, $H_2O(s)$	2.089
Metals	
Aluminum, Al	0.892
Chromium, Cr	0.45
Cobalt, Co	0.46
Copper, Cu	0.385
Gold, Au	0.129
Iron, Fe	0.442
Lead, Pb	0.13
Magnesium, Mg	1.0
Silver, Ag	0.24
Sodium, Na	0.293
Tin, Sn	0.22
Zinc, Zn	0.388

an increase in temperature. This is why dry sand on a beach can be uncomfortably hot to walk on barefoot during a summer afternoon. However, the adjacent water is far cooler and much more comfortable to the skin. The major component of sand, silicon dioxide, has a specific heat of 1.0 J/g · °C, which is significantly lower than the specific heat of water. Therefore, water requires more thermal energy from the Sun to experience the same temperature increase that sand does.

Because the equation used for specific heat calculations includes the *change* in temperature, ΔT, but not the actual temperature itself, you can use temperature values in either degrees Celsius or kelvins. The difference between the final and initial temperatures will be the same numerical value, no matter which scale is used.

Example 6.7

Calculate the specific heat of water if 83.68 J is required to raise the temperature of 4.000 g of water by 5.000°C.

Solution

The heat flow of a reaction is given by the equation

$$q = mc\Delta T$$

After substituting the mass of water and the temperature increase, you can solve for the specific heat, *c*.

$$83.68\ \text{J} = (4.000\ \text{g})(c)(5.000^\circ\text{C})$$

$$c = \frac{(83.68\ \text{J})}{(4.000\ \text{g})(5.000^\circ\text{C})} = 4.184\ \text{J/g}\cdot{}^\circ\text{C}$$

Note that the unit for specific heat has two different units in its denominator (g and °C).

PRACTICE PROBLEM 6.7

Calculate the specific heat of ice if 128 J is required to raise the temperature of 4.00 g of ice by 15.3°C.

Hint: Insert the given values into the formula $q = mc\Delta T$. Solve for *c*.

Example 6.8

Calculate the number of joules of heat required to raise the temperature of 123 g of water from 14.7°C to 31.1°C.

Solution

The equation to use is

$$q = mc\Delta T$$

The mass of the water is given in the problem. The *change* in temperature is the final temperature minus the initial temperature:

$$\Delta T = T_{\text{final}} - T_{\text{initial}} = 31.1^\circ\text{C} - 14.7^\circ\text{C} = 16.4^\circ\text{C}$$

The specific heat of the water, as calculated in Example 6.7 and as listed in Table 6.3, is $4.184\ \text{J/g}\cdot{}^\circ\text{C}$. Thus, the heat required is

$$q = (123\ \text{g})(4.184\ \text{J/g}\cdot{}^\circ\text{C})(16.4^\circ\text{C}) = 8440\ \text{J} = 8.44\ \text{kJ}$$

PRACTICE PROBLEM 6.8

Calculate the number of joules of heat required to raise the temperature of 123 g of iron from 14.7°C to 31.1°C. Does heating the iron take more energy or less energy than heating the same mass of water?

Hint: First, find the change in temperature. Then look up the specific heat, *c*, of iron in Table 6.3 and use $q = mc\Delta T$ to calculate *q*. Finally, compare the *q* value in this problem to the answer from the previous example.

Example 6.9

Calculate the final temperature after 1485 J of energy is added to 16.7 g of water at 23.4°C.

Solution

The equation to use is

$$q = mc\Delta T$$

Rearrange the equation to solve for the temperature change.

$$\Delta T = \frac{q}{mc} = \frac{1485\ \text{J}}{(16.7\ \text{g})(4.184\ \text{J/g}\cdot{}^\circ\text{C})} = 21.3^\circ\text{C}$$

Since ΔT is 21.3°C, a positive quantity, the final temperature is 21.3°C greater than the initial temperature. Also, the problem statement said that heat was *added* to the mass of water, so the temperature must increase. Therefore, the final temperature is equal to the initial temperature plus 21.3°C.

$$T_{\text{final}} = T_{\text{initial}} + \Delta T = 23.4^\circ\text{C} + 21.3^\circ\text{C} = 44.7^\circ\text{C}$$

PRACTICE PROBLEM 6.9

Calculate the final temperature after 987 J of energy is *removed* from 14.9 g of water at 22.0°C.

Hint: First, look up the specific heat, *c*, of water in Table 6.3 and use $q = mc\Delta T$ to solve for ΔT. Then use $\Delta T = T_{\text{final}} - T_{\text{initial}}$ to solve for T_{final}.

The process of dissolving a solute in water can be either endothermic or exothermic, depending on the solute. The amount of heat absorbed or given off in the process is called the *enthalpy of solution*, and depends on how much solute is dissolved. The extent of the temperature change of the solution depends both on how much solute is dissolved and the mass of water used. Figure 6.9 is a simulated experiment in which six different ionic solutes can be dissolved in water. Open the activity and observe the temperature changes as each solute is dissolved. Vary the amount of solute used and the amount of water used. Which combination of solute, amount of solute, and amount of water results in the greatest temperature change? Which combination results in the smallest temperature change?

SECTION REVIEW

- When there is no phase change involved, the energy necessary to change the temperature of a substance is expressed as $q = mc\Delta T$.

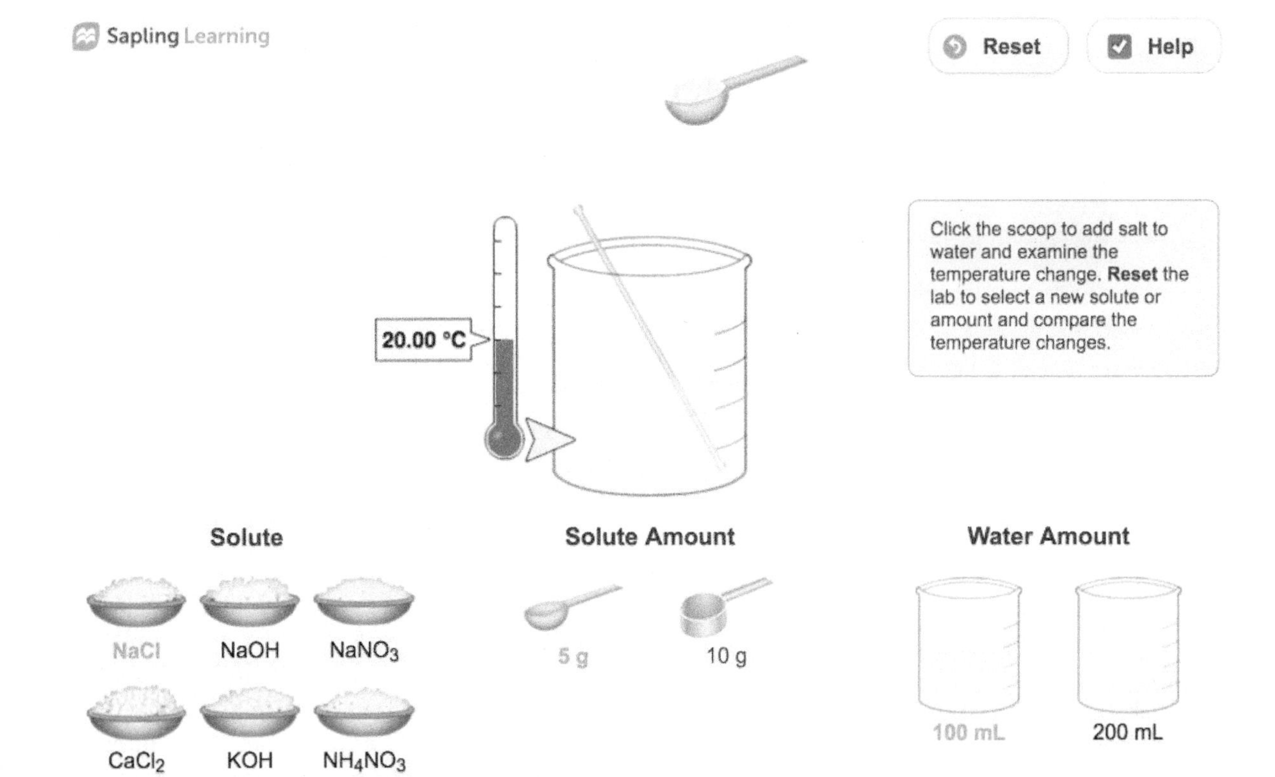

FIGURE 6.9 Endothermic and Exothermic Reactions Lab Activity
NOTE: You need to be online to access this activity.
This activity shows the heat of solution for six ionic solutes. Vary the amount of solute and the amount of water to determine the minimum and maximum temperature changes attainable in this simulation.

- The specific heat, c, is the number of calories required to raise exactly 1 g of the substance by exactly 1°C.
- Substances with higher specific heat values resist temperature changes more readily than substances with lower specific heat values.

6.6 Calorimetry: Measuring Energy Changes

GOAL

- Calculate changes in enthalpy and internal energy in chemical reactions.

Background Review

Chapter 0 Math Review: Section 0.2—Exponents and Scientific Notation; Section 0.4—Algebra

When heat is transferred from one object to another, with no energy gained from or lost to the surroundings, the total change in energy is the sum of the changes in energy of the two objects. For example, if a piece of hot metal is placed in cold water, the water is warmed and the metal is cooled. Both the metal and the water eventually will reach the same temperature. **Calorimetry** is the study of heat transfers by measuring the temperature changes in the substances involved.

In the example of a hot metal placed in cold water, the amount of heat lost by the metal is equal to the amount of heat gained by the water, and the amount of heat transferred to or from the surroundings is zero. Thus,

$$q = 0 = (m_{\text{water}})(c_{\text{water}})(\Delta T_{\text{water}}) + (m_{\text{metal}})(c_{\text{metal}})(\Delta T_{\text{metal}}) \quad (6.9)$$

This relationship can be used in a controlled experiment to find the specific heat of a metal (Figure 6.10).

When heat is transferred from one object to another in a controlled experiment, and no heat is transferred to or from the surroundings, the heat gained or lost by the system is equal to zero.

Steven Lemon, Macmillan Learning

FIGURE 6.10 Video Tutorial: Calorimetry

NOTE: You need to be online to access this video.

This video shows how to determine the specific heat of a metal based on heat transfer to water.

Example 6.10

A 25.0-g sample of a metal at 87.7°C is placed in 37.4 g of water at 10.3°C, and the final temperature of the system is 15.4°C. Calculate the specific heat of the metal. Which of the metals in Table 6.3 is it most likely to be?

Solution

The amount of heat lost by the metal is equal to the amount of heat gained by the water. Therefore, the equation to use is

$$q = 0 = (m_{\text{water}})(c_{\text{water}})(\Delta T_{\text{water}}) + (m_{\text{metal}})(c_{\text{metal}})(\Delta T_{\text{metal}})$$

The change in the temperature of the water is

$$\Delta T_{\text{water}} = 15.4°\text{C} - 10.3°\text{C} = 5.1°\text{C}$$

The change in the temperature of the metal is

$$\Delta T_{\text{metal}} = 15.4°\text{C} - 87.7°\text{C} = -72.3°\text{C}$$

Note that both the water and the metal end up at the same temperature, 15.4°C. Note also that the change in temperature of the metal is negative because it lost heat energy to the water. Substituting into the equation yields

$$q = 0 = (37.4\text{ g})(4.184\text{ J/g}\cdot°\text{C})(5.1°\text{C}) + (25.0\text{ g})(c_{\text{metal}})(-72.3°\text{C})$$

$$0 = 798.1\text{ J} + (-1800\text{ g}\cdot°\text{C})(c_{\text{metal}})$$

$$c_{\text{metal}} = \frac{798.1\text{ J}}{1800\text{ g}\cdot°\text{C}}$$

$$c_{\text{metal}} = 0.44\text{ J/g}\cdot°\text{C}$$

This value most closely matches iron (0.442 J/g · °C) in Table 6.3, but chromium (0.45 J/g · °C) and cobalt (0.46 J/g · °C) are quite close, too.

PRACTICE PROBLEM 6.10

A 186-g sample of a metal at 74.0°C is placed in 251 g of water at 18.0°C, and the final temperature of the system is 26.4°C. Calculate the specific heat of the metal. Which of the metals in Table 6.3 could it be?

Hint: Hot metal is being placed into cool water. The heat lost by the metal is equal to the heat gained by the water, so $0 = (m_{\text{metal}})(c_{\text{metal}})(\Delta T_{\text{metal}}) + (m_{\text{water}})(c_{\text{water}})(\Delta T_{\text{water}})$. Solve for c_{metal}. Finally, refer to Table 6.3 to identify the metal based on its specific heat.

Figure 6.11 is an activity that simulates a calorimetry experiment. Use this activity to carry out the experiment, and then compare your results to the specific heats listed for various metals in Table 6.3 to identify the metal. In this simulation the metal is heated with a Bunsen burner, and its temperature is measured with a thermometer, but in practice, the metal is usually heated in water, and the temperature of the hot water is measured.

To carry out the experiment, you will need to collect data to use in the calorimetry equation:

$$q = 0 = (m_{\text{water}})(c_{\text{water}})(T_{\text{final}} - T_{\text{water}}) + (m_{\text{metal}})(c_{\text{metal}})(T_{\text{final}} - T_{\text{metal}})$$

When measuring the mass of the water, m_{water}, do not forget to measure the mass of the container before adding water. Also be sure to measure the temperature of the heated metal, T_{metal}, before adding it to the water.

Example 6.11

Calculate the final temperature after 6.80 g of aluminum ($c = 0.892$ J/g · °C) at 67.4°C is placed in 195 g of water at 19.6°C.

Solution

The amount of heat lost by the metal is equal to the amount of heat gained by the water. Therefore, the equation to use is

$$q = 0 = (m_{\text{water}})(c_{\text{water}})(\Delta T_{\text{water}}) + (m_{\text{metal}})(c_{\text{metal}})(\Delta T_{\text{metal}})$$

Let T_{final} represent the final temperature of *both* the metal and the water:

$$0 = (m_{\text{water}})(c_{\text{water}})(T_{\text{final}} - T_{\text{water}}) + (m_{\text{metal}})(c_{\text{metal}})(T_{\text{final}} - T_{\text{metal}})$$

Substituting the known quantities gives

$$0 = (195\text{ g})(4.184\text{ J/g}\cdot°\text{C})(T_{\text{final}} - 19.6°\text{C}) + (6.80\text{ g})(0.892\text{ J/g}\cdot°\text{C})(T_{\text{final}} - 67.4°\text{C})$$

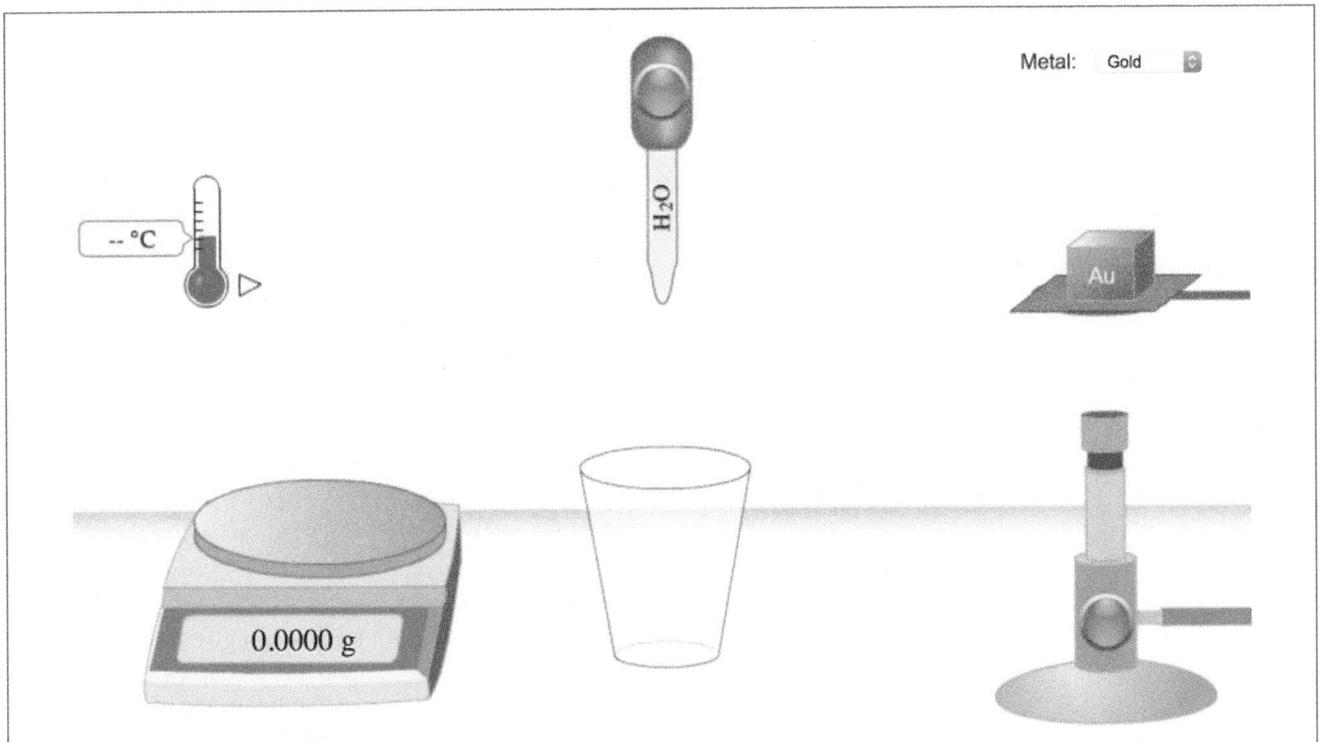

FIGURE 6.11 Calorimetry Lab Activity

NOTE: You need to be online to access this activity.

Select the mystery metal from the drop-down menu and carry out the experiment. Then use your calculated specific heat and Table 6.3 to identify the metal. Feel free to experiment with the other metals included in the simulation as well.

$$0 = (195)(4.184)(T_{final} - 19.6°C) + (6.80)(0.892)(T_{final} - 67.4°C)$$

$$0 = 815.9T_{final} - 15991°C + 6.066T_{final} - 408.8°C$$

$$822T_{final} = 16400°C$$

$$T_{final} = 20.0°C$$

PRACTICE PROBLEM 6.11

Calculate the final temperature after 11.3 g of iron ($c = 0.44$ J/g · °C) at 60.0°C is placed in 97.2 g of water at 19.0°C.

Hint: The heat lost by the iron is equal to the heat gained by the water, and their final temperatures, T_{final}, will be the same. $0 = (m_{metal})(c_{metal})(\Delta T_{final} - T_{iron}) + (m_{water})(c_{water})(\Delta T_{final} - T_{water})$. Solve for T_{final}.

CONSTANT-PRESSURE CALORIMETRY

Constant-pressure calorimetry is the technique that is most commonly used to measure heat transfer between substances in undergraduate laboratories. The most common setup includes one or two coffee cups, a plastic lid, a thermometer, and a stir bar (Figure 6.12). The system is not sealed, so the pressure inside the calorimeter is essentially atmospheric pressure. Constant-pressure calorimetry offers the advantages of low-cost equipment and the ability to directly measure the change in enthalpy of the reaction because the change in heat of the reaction, q_p, is equal to the change in enthalpy of the reaction, ΔH. See Equation 6.7.

$$q_p = \Delta H$$

The Styrofoam® cups help to prevent heat from escaping to the surroundings. The walls of the cups do absorb some heat from the reaction, and the calorimeter is sometimes calibrated to account for this. (For the sake of simplicity, the constant-pressure calorimetry example and practice problems in this text do not account for absorption of heat by the calorimeter walls.) In constant-pressure calorimetry, the heat absorbed or released by the solution, q_{soln}, has the opposite sign of the heat absorbed or released by the reaction, q_p.

$$q_{soln} = -q_p \quad (6.10)$$

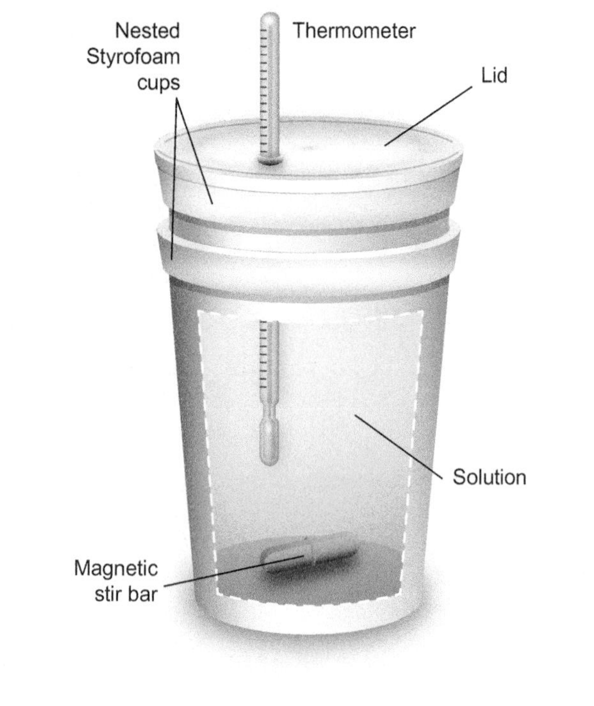

FIGURE 6.12 A Coffee Cup Calorimeter

The coffee cups are used to minimize the amount of heat that can escape to the surroundings. The thermometer indicates the temperature of the system.

Example 6.12

A small mass of solid potassium chloride, KCl, is dissolved in 100 mL of water inside a constant-pressure calorimeter. As the reaction solution is mixed, temperature of the solution drops from 20.1°C to 17.4°C.

a. Determine the signs of q_{soln} and q_p in the reaction.
b. Determine whether the reaction is endothermic or exothermic.

Solution

a. In this reaction, the temperature of the water inside the calorimeter decreases, indicating that heat is transferred from the water to the reaction. Therefore, q_{soln} is negative (heat is lost) and q_p is positive (heat is gained).
b. Heat is transferred from the solution to the reaction, so the reaction is endothermic.

PRACTICE PROBLEM 6.12

A small mass of solid calcium chloride, $CaCl_2$, dissolves exothermically in 100 mL of water, originally at 21°C, inside a constant-pressure calorimeter.

a. Determine the signs of q_{soln} and q_p in the reaction.
b. Determine whether the final temperature of the solution is above or below 21°C after the calcium chloride is completely dissolved.

Hint: An exothermic reaction means that heat is transferred to the surroundings. Use that understanding to determine the signs of q for the system and surroundings and the sign of the temperature change for the surroundings.

The release or absorption of heat that occurs when a solid compound, such as KCl or $CaCl_2$, dissolves in a solvent at constant pressure to infinite dilution is known as the enthalpy of solution, ΔH_{sol}.

Heat of Solution

Example 6.13

A student adds 25 mL of a strong acid to 25 mL of a strong base inside a coffee cup calorimeter and immediately places the lid on top. The solution temperature rises from 20.5°C to 25.0°C. The specific heat of water is 4.184 J/mol·°C and the density of water is 1.00 g/mL in this temperature range. Assume that the densities of the acid and base solutions are also 1.00 g/mL.

a. Calculate the enthalpy change of this reaction.
b. Assuming that the strong acid has a concentration of 1.5 M, calculate the enthalpy change per mole of acid.

Solution

First, calculate the total volume of water:

$$25\text{ mL} + 25\text{ mL} = 50\text{ mL}$$

Next, calculate the total mass of the solution. The acid and base solutions are almost all water and have a density of 1.00 g/mL. Therefore, the mass of solution is essentially the mass of water.

$$\text{Mass of water} = 50\text{ mL}\left(\frac{1.00\text{ g}}{\text{mL}}\right) = 50\text{ g}$$

$$\Delta T_{water} = 4.5°\text{C}$$

a. $q_{soln} = (m_{water})(c_{water})(\Delta T_{water})$

The temperature of the system rises, so the reaction gives off heat (it is exothermic), in which case, ΔH is negative. Recall that $\Delta H = q_p = -q_{soln}$.

$$\Delta H = -q_{soln} = -(50\text{ g})(4.184\text{ J/g}\cdot°\text{C})(4.5°\text{C}) = -940\text{ J}$$

b. First, calculate the number of moles of acid:

$$0.025\text{ L acid}\left(\frac{1.5\text{ mol}}{\text{L}}\right) = 0.0375\text{ moles of acid}$$

Next, divide the enthalpy change by the number of moles of acid.

$$\Delta H = \frac{-940\ \text{J}}{0.0375\ \text{mol}} = -25{,}000\ \text{J/mol} = -25\ \text{kJ/mol}$$

PRACTICE PROBLEM 6.13

Ammonium nitrate, NH_4NO_3, is an ionic compound that is soluble in water. The dissolution of ammonium nitrate is endothermic.

$$NH_4NO_3(s) \rightarrow NH_4^+(aq) + NO_3^-(aq) \qquad \Delta H < 0$$

Suppose that 3.1 g of solid ammonium nitrate is added to enough water to make a solution of 60.0 mL, and the resulting temperature of the mixture drops from 20.1°C to 16.7°C as the ammonium nitrate is dissolved.

a. Calculate the enthalpy change of this reaction. Assume that the density of the resulting solution is 1.00 g/mL.
b. Calculate the enthalpy change per mole of ammonium nitrate (molar mass = 80.04 g/mol).

Hint: (a) First, use the density to convert milliliters of solution to grams of solution. Then, calculate q for the solution via $q = mc\Delta T$ using the specific heat of water (since this solution is mostly water). The solution is the surroundings, so change the sign of your answer to get q for the system (the reaction), which is equal to ΔH.
(b) Convert the mass of ammonium nitrate to moles using the molar mass. Finally, divide ΔH by the moles of ammonium nitrate to get the enthalpy per mole.

CONSTANT-VOLUME CALORIMETRY

The other major method of measuring the transfer of heat in chemical reactions is **constant-volume calorimetry**. These measurements are typically carried out in a **bomb calorimeter**, as shown in Figure 6.13. These instruments can withstand high temperature and pressure changes and are better sealed from the surroundings than coffee cup calorimeters. Therefore, bomb calorimeters deliver more accurate results. They also measure heat flow, q_v, in a fundamentally different manner. Because the system inside a bomb calorimeter has a constant volume with

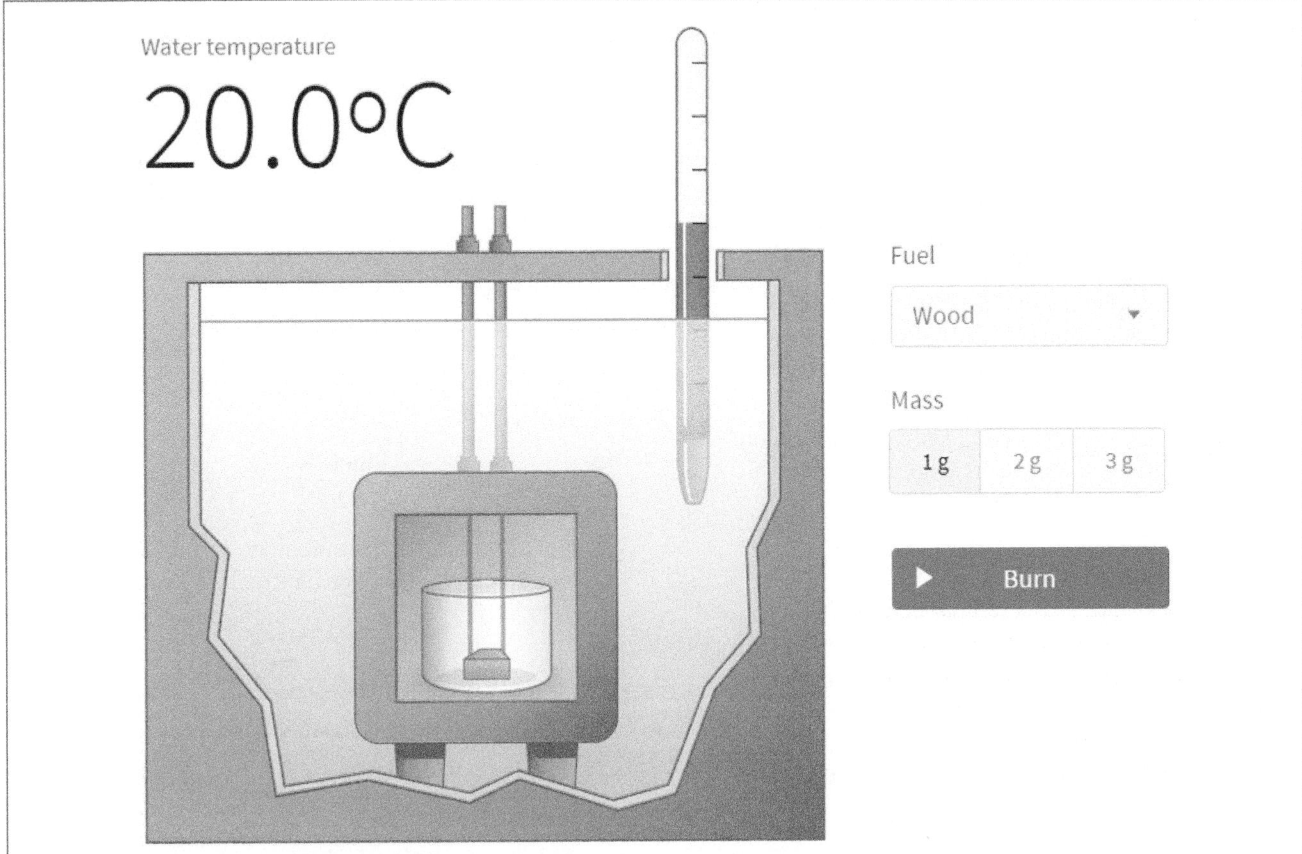

FIGURE 6.13 Bomb Calorimeter Activity
NOTE: You must be online to access this activity.
A sample of known mass is placed inside a rigid steel container that is surrounded by water. An outer container holds the water and thermally insulates the water from the atmosphere. The sample is ignited via an electrical current, typically in the presence of excess oxygen, and the temperature change inside the calorimeter is measured.

variable pressure, the heat transferred corresponds to the change in internal energy, ΔU. Recall that $\Delta U = q + w$ and that the work term, w, is zero inside a rigid container with a constant volume.

In bomb calorimetry, it is standard to use the total heat capacity of the calorimeter components *and* the water inside the calorimeter, rather than just the specific heat of the water. This combined heat capacity is known as C_{cal}, and is measured with a known mass of a substance (typically benzoic acid) and an accurately measured volume of water inside the calorimeter. Once C_{cal} is known, it can be used in all reactions for that particular calorimeter with that particular volume of water. The product of C_{cal} and ΔT is equal to the heat flow of the solution and calorimeter, q_{soln}, which is opposite in sign of the heat flow of the reaction, q_v.

$$q_{soln} = C_{cal}\Delta T \qquad (6.11)$$

$$q_{soln} = -q_v \qquad (6.12)$$

Therefore, q_v is related to C_{cal} and ΔT by

$$q_v = -C_{cal}\Delta T$$

The heat flow of the reaction, q_v, is equal to the change in internal energy of the reaction, ΔU_{rxn}.

$$\Delta U_{rxn} = q_v = -C_{cal}\Delta T \qquad (6.13)$$

Example 6.14

Lactose reacts with O_2 to form CO_2 and H_2O.

$$C_{12}H_{22}O_{11}(s) + 12\,O_2(g) \rightarrow 12\,CO_2(g) + 11\,H_2O(l)$$

A small mass of lactose reacts with excess O_2 inside a bomb calorimeter and the temperature of the water inside the calorimeter increases from 19.4°C to 28.6°C.

a. Determine the signs of q_{soln} and q_v in the reaction.
b. Determine whether the reaction is endothermic or exothermic.

Solution

a. In this reaction, the temperature of the water inside the calorimeter increases, indicating the heat is transferred from the reaction to the water. Therefore, q_{soln} is positive (heat is gained) and q_v is negative (heat is lost).
b. Heat is transferred from the reaction to the solution, so the reaction is exothermic.

PRACTICE PROBLEM 6.14

Elemental boron reacts with oxygen gas to form diboron trioxide, B_2O_3,

$$4\,B(s) + 3\,O_2(g) \rightarrow 2\,B_2O_3(s) \qquad \Delta H < 0$$

A sample of elemental boron reacts with excess O_2 inside a bomb calorimeter.

a. Determine whether the reaction is endothermic or exothermic.
b. Determine the signs of q_{soln} and q_v in the reaction.

Hint:
a. Use the sign of ΔH to classify the reaction as endothermic or exothermic.
b. The reaction is the system, and its heat transfer is symbolized as q_v. The solution is the surroundings, and its heat transfer is symbolized as q_{soln}. The signs of q for the system and surroundings are opposite.

Example 6.15

A 1.000 g sample of decane, $C_{10}H_{22}$ is ignited inside a bomb calorimeter. The temperature rises from 20.0°C to 78.8°C. Given that the heat capacity of the calorimeter is 810.1 J/°C, determine ΔU_{rxn} for the combustion of decane in units of kJ/mol of decane.

Solution

$$\Delta T = 78.8°C - 20.0°C = 58.8°C$$
$$C_{cal} = 810.1\ J/°C$$

This reaction is exothermic, so the heat transfer in this reaction, q_v, has a negative value.

$$q_v = -C_{cal}\Delta T = -(810.1\ J/°C)(58.8°C) = -47{,}634\ J = -47.634\ kJ$$

Convert the mass of decane into the number of moles of decane. The molar mass of decane, $C_{10}H_{22}$, is 142.32 g/mol.

$$1.000\ g\ decane\left(\frac{1\ mol}{142.32\ g}\right) = 0.007026\ mol\ decane$$

Now divide q_v by the number of moles of decane. Recall that, in constant-volume calorimetry, $q_v = U_{rxn}$.

$$\Delta U_{rxn} = q_v = \left(\frac{-47.634\ kJ}{0.007026\ mol\ decane}\right) = -6.78 \times 10^3\ kJ/mol\ decane$$

PRACTICE PROBLEM 6.15

A 3.50 g sample of glucose is ignited inside a bomb calorimeter in the presence of excess oxygen gas. The temperature rises from 20.0°C to 85.9°C. Given that the heat capacity of the calorimeter is 810.1 J/°C, determine ΔU_{rxn} for the combustion of glucose in units of kJ/mol of glucose.

Hint: First, find the change in temperature. Then use $q_v = -C_{cal}\Delta T$ to find q_v. With constant-volume calorimetry, work is zero and $\Delta U_{rxn} = q_v$. To express ΔU_{rxn} per mole of glucose, first convert the mass of glucose to moles, then divide ΔU_{rxn} by the moles of glucose.

SECTION REVIEW

- Calorimetry is the study of heat transfer by measuring the temperature changes in the substances involved.
- Calorimetry can be used to measure the heat absorbed or released by a reaction at constant pressure, q_p, or constant volume, q_v.
- In calorimetry, the heat absorbed or released by the solution, q_{soln}, has the opposite sign of the heat absorbed or released by the reaction (q_p or q_v).

$$q_{soln} = -q_p$$
$$q_{soln} = -q_v$$

- In bomb calorimetry, the total heat capacity of the calorimeter components and water are combined into a calorimeter constant, C_{cal}. The relationship between C_{cal} and q_v is

$$q_v = -C_{cal}\Delta T$$

- In constant-pressure calorimetry, $q_p = \Delta H$. In constant-volume calorimetry, $q_v = \Delta U$.

6.7 Enthalpy in Chemical Reactions

GOAL

- Apply Hess's law to calculate the enthalpies of different reactions.

Background Review

Chapter 5 Stoichiometry: Section 5.1—Mole Relationship for Chemical Reactions

All chemical reactions either absorb energy from their surroundings or release energy to their surroundings. This energy is usually in the form of heat, although you are probably familiar with chemical reactions that give off energy in other forms as well. For example, an exploding firecracker gives off energy in the form of heat, light, sound, and kinetic energy; and the chemical reaction in a battery gives off energy in the form of electricity. This section applies the concepts of enthalpy (Section 6.4) and calorimetry (Section 6.6) to chemical reactions. This section and Section 6.8 show how enthalpy values obtained from the measurements of chemical reactions can be used to predict the enthalpy values of other reactions.

EVERYDAY CONNECTION

Energy is stored in chemical bonds. Fuels, such as gasoline and butane, can be burned to release heat and do work.

Sara Egner, Macmillan Learning

Exevia/Shutterstock

Because the heat produced by a chemical reaction cannot be measured directly, it is calculated by determining its effect on another substance, as discussed in Section 6.6. In calorimetry, the heat produced by burning 1.00 mol of methane (natural gas) is calculated by measuring the increase in temperature it causes to a certain mass of water and by using the equation $q = mc\Delta T$.

Example 6.16

Burning 1.00 mol of CH_4 in a calorimeter warms 10.0 kg of water by 21.3°C. Calculate the heat produced in this combustion process:

$$CH_4(g) + 2\,O_2(g) \rightarrow CO_2(g) + 2\,H_2O(l)$$

Solution

The heat transferred to the water, q_{soln}, is

$$q_{soln} = mc\Delta T = (10{,}000\ g)(4.184\ J/g \cdot {}^\circ C)(21.3^\circ C)$$
$$= 8.91 \times 10^5\ J = 891\ kJ$$

The amount of heat gained by the water is equal to the amount of heat released by the reaction. In other words, the magnitude of q is the same for each, but their signs are opposite. The reaction *produced* the heat, so the system lost 891 kJ to its surroundings.

PRACTICE PROBLEM 6.16

Burning 1.00 mol of diborane, B_2H_6, in excess oxygen in a constant-volume calorimeter warms 20.0 kg of water by 25.7°C. Calculate the heat produced in this combustion process:

$$B_2H_6(g) + 3\,O_2(g) \rightarrow B_2O_3(s) + 3\,H_2O(l)$$

Hint: The heat produced by the reaction is equal to the heat gained by the water. Use $q = mc\Delta T$ to find the heat gained by the water.

Example 6.17

Water can be formed via the reaction of gaseous hydrogen and oxygen.

$$2\,H_2(g) + O_2(g) \rightarrow 2\,H_2O(l) \qquad \Delta H = -572\ kJ$$

a. Write the balanced equation that shows 1 mol water produced.
b. Determine the enthalpy of the reaction in units of kJ/mol of water produced.

Solution

a. To show 1 mol water produced, divide the coefficients of the equation by 2:

$$H_2(g) + \frac{1}{2}O_2(g) \rightarrow H_2O(l)$$

b. The reaction that produces 2 mol of H_2 has an enthalpy of −572 kJ. Therefore, the enthalpy of the reaction per mole of water produced is:

$$\frac{-572\ kJ}{2\ mol\ water} = -286\frac{kJ}{mol}\ \text{water produced}$$

PRACTICE PROBLEM 6.17

Nitrogen fixation is the process by which atmospheric nitrogen gas reacts to form ammonia, NH_3. The enthalpy value is given in units of kJ/mol of NH_3 formed.

$$\frac{1}{2}N_2(g) + \frac{3}{2}H_2(g) \rightarrow NH_3(g) \qquad \Delta H = -42\ kJ/mol$$

a. Write the balanced equation that shows 1 mol of N_2 consumed.
b. Determine the enthalpy of the reaction per mole of N_2 consumed.

Hint:
a. Double the equation coefficients for all species.
b. The equation coefficients have been multiplied by 2, so the enthalpy must also be multiplied by 2.

Example 6.18

The equation and enthalpy for the combustion of methane, CH_4, is as follows.

$$CH_4(g) + 2\,O_2(g) \rightarrow CO_2(g) + 2\,H_2O(l)$$
$$\Delta H = -891\ kJ$$

a. Determine the amount of heat produced by the combustion of 3.30 mol of methane.
b. Determine the enthalpy for the equation

$$2\,CH_4(g) + 4\,O_2(g) \rightarrow 2\,CO_2(g) + 4\,H_2O(l)$$

Solution

a. The coefficient of CH_4 in the equation is 1, so 891 kJ of heat is produced per 1 mol of CH_4.

$$3.30\ mol\ CH_4\left(\frac{891\ kJ}{1\ mol\ CH_4}\right) = 2940\ kJ$$

b. The equation coefficients have been multiplied by 2, so the enthalpy value must also be multiplied by 2. $\Delta H = 2(-891\ kJ) = -1780\ kJ$.

PRACTICE PROBLEM 6.18

Hydrazine, N_2H_4, can react with oxygen, O_2, to form dinitrogen pentoxide, N_2O_5, and water, H_2O.

$$2\,N_2H_4(l) + 7\,O_2(g) \rightarrow 2\,N_2O_5(s) + 4\,H_2O(g)$$
$$\Delta H = -1154\ kJ$$

a. Determine the amount of heat produced when 4.6 mol of N_2H_4 reacts with O_2.

b. Determine the enthalpy for the equation:

$$N_2H_4(l) + \frac{7}{2}O_2(g) \rightarrow N_2O_5(s) + 2\,H_2O(g)$$

Hint:

a. The coefficient of N_2H_4 is 2, so 1154 kJ of heat is produced per 2 mol of N_2H_4. Use this as a conversion factor.

b. The equation coefficients have been divided by 2, so the enthalpy of reaction must also be divided by 2.

ENTHALPY CHANGE

Recall from Section 6.4 that enthalpy change, ΔH, is equal to the heat transfer for a process carried out at constant pressure. Most laboratory procedures, where chemical reactions occur in open beakers or test tubes, are done under constant pressure, so ΔH is equal to the heat absorbed or given off by a process. As discussed in Section 6.4, enthalpy is a state function, where the value of ΔH for a reaction is independent of the path taken from the initial state to the final state. As a result, ΔH depends only on what the reactants and products are and not on the particular chemical reactions that were carried out to get from one state to the other.

For example, nitrogen, N_2, and oxygen, O_2, can react to form nitrogen dioxide, $NO_2(g)$, and a certain amount of heat is generated by the reaction. Under different reaction conditions, N_2 and O_2 can react to form NO gas. This NO gas can then further react with more O_2 to produce NO_2. Whether the reaction is carried out in one step or in two, the total change in heat, ΔH, for the overall process will be the same because even though the reaction conditions are different, both cases begin with the same reactants and end with the same product.

The ΔH value of any given process is typically referred to as the enthalpy of that process. In Section 6.5, you were introduced to the enthalpy of solution, ΔH_{sol}, which is the enthalpy change when a solid dissolves in a solvent. The enthalpy change of the vaporization process is called the enthalpy of vaporization, ΔH_{vap}, whereas the enthalpy change for the fusion (melting) process is ΔH_{fus}. The enthalpy of combustion of a substance is, by definition, the enthalpy change accompanying the burning of the substance in excess oxygen. (These specialized changes in enthalpy are discussed in greater detail in Chapter 12.) Essentially, enthalpy change is a single function that can be applied to many different processes, and the name used as a subscript to ΔH is the name of the particular process.

HESS'S LAW

One way to calculate values of ΔH for reactions involves manipulating equations for other reactions with known ΔH values. When chemical equations are added together to yield a different chemical equation, the corresponding ΔH values are added to get the ΔH for the desired equation. This principle is called **Hess's law**. There are three rules associated with manipulating chemical equations.

(1) When an equation is reversed, the sign of its enthalpy changes.

$$N_2(g) + O_2(g) \rightarrow 2\,NO(g) \qquad \Delta H = 180.6\text{ kJ}$$
$$2\,NO(g) \rightarrow N_2(g) + O_2(g) \qquad \Delta H = -180.6\text{ kJ}$$

(2) As mentioned earlier in this section, when the coefficients in an equation are multiplied or divided by a factor, the enthalpy value is multiplied or divided by that same factor.

$$Ca(s) + \frac{1}{2}O_2(g) \rightarrow CaO(s) \qquad \Delta H = -635.1\text{ kJ}$$
$$2\,Ca(s) + O_2(g) \rightarrow 2\,CaO(s)$$
$$\Delta H = 2(-635.1\text{ kJ}) = -1270\text{ kJ}$$

(3) When reactions are summed, the enthalpy of the overall reaction is the sum of the enthalpies of the component reactions.

$$C(\text{diamond}) + O_2(g) \rightarrow CO_2(g)$$
$$\Delta H = -395.4\text{ kJ}\ CO_2(g) \rightarrow C(\text{graphite}) + O_2(g)$$
$$\Delta H = 393.5\text{ kJ} \text{———} C(\text{diamond}) \rightarrow C(\text{graphite})$$
$$\Delta H = 395.4\text{ kJ} + 393.5\text{ kJ} = -1.9\text{ kJ}$$

Consider the example of calculating ΔH for the partial combustion of carbon with oxygen gas to yield carbon monoxide (Figure 6.14):

$$C(s) + \frac{1}{2}O_2(g) \rightarrow CO(g) \qquad \Delta H = ?$$

This value can be obtained from the ΔH values for the following reactions by manipulating them algebraically until they add up to the reaction of interest:

$$C(s) + O_2(g) \rightarrow CO_2(g) \qquad \Delta H = -393\text{ kJ}$$
$$CO(g) + \frac{1}{2}O_2(g) \rightarrow CO_2(g) \qquad \Delta H = -283\text{ kJ}$$

The first chemical equation given includes C as a reactant but produces CO_2 as a product, and the desired reaction does not have CO_2. The second equation also

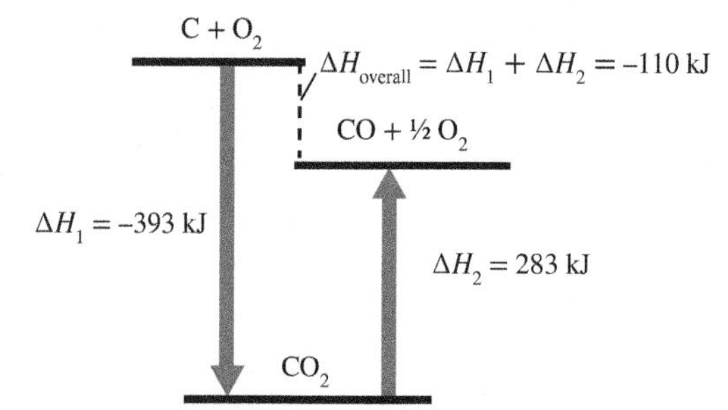

FIGURE 6.14 An Enthalpy Diagram for the Oxidation of Carbon to Carbon Monoxide

The enthalpy change of the one-step reaction of C to CO is related to the enthalpy changes of C to CO_2 and CO_2 to CO.

Steven Lemon, Macmillan Learning

FIGURE 6.15 Video Tutorial: Hess's Law

NOTE: You need to be online to access this video.

This video shows how to determine enthalpy by manipulating reaction equations.

contains CO_2 as a product, but if the second reaction is reversed, the CO_2 appears on the reactant side of the equation and will cancel the CO_2 product from the first equation when the equations are added. The second equation, once reversed, also provides CO as a product, which the desired equation requires.

Reversing the second equation gives

$$CO_2(g) \rightarrow CO(g) + \frac{1}{2}O_2(g) \qquad \Delta H = +283 \text{ kJ}$$

Adding this to the first equation yields:

$$C(s) + O_2(g) \rightarrow CO_2(g) \qquad \Delta H = -393 \text{ kJ}$$

$$CO_2(g) \rightarrow CO(g) + \frac{1}{2}O_2(g)$$

$$\Delta H = 283 \text{ kJ} \text{———} C(s) + O_2(g) + CO_2(g) \rightarrow$$

$$CO_2(g) + CO(g) + \frac{1}{2}O_2(g)$$

Note that the sign of the enthalpy value for the second reaction has changed. When a reaction is reversed, the sign of the enthalpy changes.

The CO_2 terms on both sides of the equation cancel and the O_2 terms simplify to the desired equation:

$$C(s) + \frac{1}{2}O_2(g) \rightarrow CO(g)$$

Therefore, adding the ΔH values for the two reactions that were added together will give us ΔH for the desired reaction:

$$\Delta H = (-393 \text{ kJ}) + (283 \text{ kJ}) = -110 \text{ kJ}$$

The combustion of C(s) and the combustion of CO(g) are both easy reactions to carry out and measure the amount of generated heat, but the partial combustion of C(s) to CO(g) is far more difficult to carry out without also producing some CO_2 gas. Hess's law (Figure 6.15) makes it possible to calculate the ΔH of reactions that are difficult to perform.

Example 6.19

Use the ΔH values for equations I and II to calculate ΔH for the vaporization of ethanol, C_2H_6O.

$$C_2H_6O(l) \rightarrow C_2H_6O(g)$$

I $\quad 2\,C(s) + 3\,H_2(g) + \frac{1}{2}O_2(g) \rightarrow C_2H_6O(g)$

$$\Delta H = -235.1 \text{ kJ}$$

II $\quad 2\,C(s) + 3\,H_2(g) + \frac{1}{2}O_2(g) \rightarrow C_2H_6O(l)$

$$\Delta H = -277.7 \text{ kJ}$$

Solution

Reversing equation II puts liquid ethanol on the reactant side of the equation and reverses the sign of ΔH for the reaction. Doing so also makes it possible to cancel the carbon, H_2, and O_2 from the overall reaction, giving the desired equation.

$$2\,C(s) + 3\,H_2(g) + \frac{1}{2}O_2(g) \rightarrow C_2H_6O(g) \;\; \Delta H = -235.1 \text{ kJ}$$

$$C_2H_6O(l) \rightarrow 2\,C(s) + 3\,H_2(g) + \frac{1}{2}O_2(g)$$

$$\Delta H = +277.7 \text{ kJ} \text{———} C_2H_6O(l) \rightarrow C_2H_6O(g)$$

Adding the enthalpies from these two reactions gives ΔH for the vaporization of ethanol.

$$\Delta H = (-235.1 \text{ kJ}) + (+277.7 \text{ kJ}) = +42.6 \text{ kJ}$$

As discussed in Chapter 12, the change in enthalpy for the vaporization of a liquid is commonly known as the enthalpy of vaporization, ΔH_{vap}.

PRACTICE PROBLEM 6.19

Use the ΔH values for equations I, II, and III to calculate the enthalpy change of the general reaction

$$\mathrm{Z + Q \rightarrow X + 2R}$$

I	$\mathrm{E + 2\,D \rightarrow Z + Q}$	$\Delta H = 41.7\ \mathrm{kJ}$
II	$\mathrm{J + A \rightarrow E + 2\,D}$	$\Delta H = -17.1\ \mathrm{kJ}$
III	$\mathrm{J + A \rightarrow X + 2\,R}$	$\Delta H = 10.6\ \mathrm{kJ}$

Hint: First, determine how equations I–III must be manipulated to add up to $\mathrm{Z + Q \rightarrow X + 2\,R}$. Next, adjust their enthalpy values accordingly. That is, if you reverse an equation, change the sign of ΔH, and/or if you multiply the equation coefficients by a factor, multiply ΔH by the same factor. Finally, sum the adjusted enthalpy values.

Using Hess's law is relatively straightforward if the equations given are in a form in which simply adding them yields the desired equation. More often, however, obtaining the desired equation requires multiplying or dividing a given equation by a small integer. In that case, you must also multiply or divide the corresponding ΔH value by that same integer. As mentioned earlier, if the given equation must be reversed, the sign of the corresponding ΔH value must be reversed, too. Sometimes, both of these processes are necessary. Whatever algebraic manipulations you must do to a chemical equation to obtain the desired equation, those same manipulations must be applied to the corresponding ΔH value.

> Be especially careful to include the correct signs when performing these calculations.

Example 6.20

Use the ΔH values for equations I, II, and III to calculate ΔH for the following reaction:

$$C_2H_2 + 2H_2(g) \rightarrow C_2H_6$$

I	$2\,C_2H_2 + 5\,O_2 \rightarrow 4\,CO_2 + 2\,H_2O$	$\Delta H = -2320\ \mathrm{kJ}$
II	$2\,C_2H_6 + 7\,O_2 \rightarrow 4\,CO_2 + 6\,H_2O$	$\Delta H = -3040\ \mathrm{kJ}$
III	$2\,H_2 + O_2 \rightarrow 2\,H_2O$	$\Delta H = -572\ \mathrm{kJ}$

Solution

Because you need 1 mol of C_2H_2 on the left of the required equation, and you have 2 mol of C_2H_2 in equation I, you need to divide equation I by 2, including its ΔH value:

$$C_2H_2 + \frac{5}{2}O_2 \rightarrow 2\,CO_2 + H_2O$$

$$\Delta H = (-2320\ \mathrm{kJ})/2 = -1160\ \mathrm{kJ}$$

You also need 2 mol of H_2 on the left, so you must add equation III unchanged.

Reversing equation II and dividing it by 2 will give 1 mol of C_2H_6 on the right. Reversing the equation requires that you change the sign of ΔH, and you must also divide ΔH for that reaction by 2:

$$2\,CO_2 + 3\,H_2O \rightarrow C_2H_6 + \frac{7}{2}O_2$$

$$\Delta H = -(-3040\ \mathrm{kJ})/2 = +1520\ \mathrm{kJ}$$

Adding the equations and their corresponding ΔH values results in the desired equation:

$C_2H_2 + \frac{5}{2}O_2 \rightarrow 2\,CO_2 + H_2O$	$\Delta H = -1160\ \mathrm{kJ}$
$2\,H_2 + O_2 \rightarrow 2\,H_2O$	$\Delta H = -572$
$2\,CO_2 + 3\,H_2O \rightarrow C_2H_6 + \frac{7}{2}O_2$	$\Delta H = +1520\ \mathrm{KJ}$

The undesired substances cancel out, leaving

$$C_2H_2 + 2\,H_2(g) \rightarrow C_2H_6$$

$$\Delta H = (-1160\ \mathrm{kJ}) + (-572\ \mathrm{kJ}) + (+1520\ \mathrm{kJ}) = -212\ \mathrm{kJ}$$

PRACTICE PROBLEM 6.20

Use the ΔH values for equations I, II, and III to calculate the enthalpy change of the oxidation of metallic copper to copper(II) oxide:

$$Cu(s) + \frac{1}{2}O_2(g) \rightarrow CuO(s)$$

I	$2\,Cu + S(s) \rightarrow Cu_2S(s)$	$\Delta H = -75.9\ \mathrm{kJ}$
II	$S(s) + O_2(g) \rightarrow SO_2(g)$	$\Delta H = -297\ \mathrm{kJ}$
III	$Cu_2S(s) + 2\,O_2(g) \rightarrow 2\,CuO(s) + SO_2(g)$	$\Delta H = -528\ \mathrm{kJ}$

Hint: First, determine how equations I–III must be manipulated to add up to $Cu(s) + \frac{1}{2}O_2(g) \rightarrow CuO(s)$. Next, adjust their enthalpy values accordingly. That is, if you reverse an equation, change the sign of ΔH, and/or if you multiply the equation coefficients by a factor, multiply ΔH by the same factor. Finally, sum the adjusted enthalpy values.

SECTION REVIEW

- The enthalpy of a reaction can be calculated by combining enthalpies of any reactions, using Hess's law.
- If a process is reversed, its ΔH value must be multiplied by -1. If a process must be multiplied or divided by an integer, the ΔH value must also be multiplied or divided by that integer, too. If two or more reactions must be added together, their ΔH values must be added together, too.

6.8 Standard Enthalpies of Formation

GOAL

- Determine the enthalpy of formation of a chemical compound from its constituent elements in their standard states.

Background Review

Chapter 0 Math Review: Section 0.2—Exponents and Scientific Notation

Steven Lemon, Macmillan Learning

FIGURE 6.16 Video Tutorial: Enthalpy of Formation

NOTE: You need to be online to access this video.
This video shows how to use a table of ΔH_f° values to calculate the enthalpy of reaction.

One particularly useful type of process to consider is the formation of 1 mol of a substance in its standard state from its elements in their standard states. The **standard state** is the state in which the substance is most stable at 25°C (298 K) and 1 atm pressure. For example, the standard state of elemental oxygen is $O_2(g)$, not $O_2(l)$, $O(g)$, or $O_3(g)$. Thus, the equation for the formation reaction of water is

$$2\,H_2(g) + O_2(g) \rightarrow 2\,H_2O(l)$$

The enthalpy change for this reaction can be called the enthalpy of formation of water, $\Delta H_f(H_2O)$. The **standard enthalpy of formation, ΔH_f°**, is the enthalpy of formation of 1 mol of a compound from its constituent elements in their standard states (25°C and 1 atm). Table 6.4 is a list of some standard enthalpies of formation. This table and the longer table in Appendix A.2 will be useful for doing energy calculations for a myriad of chemical reactions, including those in this section of the chapter (Figure 6.16).

TABLE 6.4 Some Standard Enthalpies of Formation at 298 K

Compound	Formula	State	ΔH_f° (kJ/mol)
Methane	CH_4	g	−74.6
Ethane	C_2H_6	g	−84.0
Ethanol	C_2H_6O	g	−234.8
Ethanol	C_2H_6O	l	−277.6
Propane	C_3H_8	g	−103.8
Butane (n-butane)	C_4H_{10}	g	−125.5
Carbon monoxide	CO	g	−110.5
Carbon dioxide	CO_2	g	−393.5
Water	H_2O	l	−285.8
Water	H_2O	g	−241.8
Mercury(II) sulfide	HgS	s	−58.2
Sulfur dioxide	SO_2	g	−296.8

See Appendix A.2 for additional values.

Values of ΔH for many reactions can be determined experimentally; for other reactions, measuring ΔH may be impossible because the process is too slow or too difficult to carry out cleanly. Values of ΔH_f° are useful because you can calculate the standard enthalpy change for any reaction, ΔH_{rxn}°, by subtracting the sum of the ΔH_f° values of the reactants of the reaction from the sum of the ΔH_f° values of the products of the reaction:

$$\Delta H_{rxn}^\circ = [\text{sum of } \Delta H_f^\circ \text{ (products)}] - [\text{sum of } \Delta H_f^\circ \text{(reactants)}]$$

The ΔH_f° of an element in its standard state is zero because converting an element in its standard state to the element in its standard state does not involve any change. That "reaction" would have a ΔH of zero.

In cases where there are multiple moles of reactants and products,

$$\Delta H_{rxn}^\circ = \Sigma m[\Delta H_f^\circ(\text{products})] - \Sigma n[\Delta H_f^\circ(\text{reactants})] \tag{6.14}$$

where m is the number of moles of each product and n is the number of moles of each reactant from the balanced chemical equation. When performing such a calculation, the ΔH_f° value of each species must be multiplied by its number of moles (i.e., its stoichiometric coefficient from the balanced chemical equation for the reaction).

Example 6.21

Calculate ΔH_{rxn}° for the complete combustion of 1.00 mol of propane, C_3H_8, at 25°C and 1 atm.

$$C_3H_8(g) + 5\,O_2(g) \rightarrow 3\,CO_2(g) + 4\,H_2O(l)$$

Solution

Values of ΔH_f° are obtained from Table 6.4. For the products,

$$\Delta H_f^\circ = 3\text{ mol CO}_2\left(\frac{-393.5\text{ kJ}}{1\text{ mol CO}_2}\right) + 4\text{ mol H}_2\text{O}\left(\frac{-285.8\text{ kJ}}{1\text{ mol H}_2\text{O}}\right)$$
$$= -2324\text{ kJ}$$

For the reactants,

$$\Delta H_f^\circ = 1\text{ mol C}_3\text{H}_8\left(\frac{-103.8\text{ kJ}}{1\text{ mol C}_3\text{H}_8}\right) + 5\text{ mol O}_2\left(\frac{0\text{ kJ}}{1\text{ mol O}_2}\right)$$
$$= -103.8\text{ kJ}$$

$$\Delta H_{rxn}^\circ = \Sigma m[\Delta H_f^\circ(\text{products})] - \Sigma n[\Delta H_f^\circ(\text{reactants})]$$

$$\Delta H_{rxn}^\circ = (-2324\text{ kJ}) - (-103.8\text{ kJ}) = -2.220 \times 10^3\text{ kJ}$$

Note that the value of ΔH_f° of O_2 is not in Table 6.4 because ΔH_f° of every uncombined element in its standard state is zero.

ΔH_f° of an element in its standard state is zero by definition.

PRACTICE PROBLEM 6.21

Calculate ΔH_{rxn}° for the complete combustion of 1.00 mol of ethane, C_2H_6.

$$C_2H_6(l) + \frac{5}{2}O_2(g) \rightarrow 2\,CO_2(g) + 3\,H_2O(l)$$

Hint: Refer to Table 6.4. Add up the ΔH_f° values for the products, taking into account their coefficients. Then add up the ΔH_f° values for the reactants, also taking into account the coefficients. Finally, subtract the two results. The coefficient for ethane is 1, and you are asked to find the enthalpy for the combustion of 1.00 mol of ethane, so no further calculation is needed.

You can multiply the number of kilojoules per mole by the number of moles undergoing reaction to get the number of kilojoules for any given quantity of reactant or product involved. For example, if 2.50 mol of C_3H_8 had been involved, the enthalpy change would have been

$$2.50\text{ mol}\left(\frac{-2220\text{ kJ}}{1\text{ mol}}\right) = -5.55 \times 10^3\text{ kJ}$$

Example 6.22

Calculate the enthalpy change for the combustion of 1.00 mol of butane (bottled gas), C_4H_{10}, to give carbon monoxide, CO, and water, H_2O. Use the following equation:

$$2\,C_4H_{10}(g) + 9\,O_2(g) \rightarrow 8\,CO(g) + 10\,H_2O(l)$$

Solution

For the products,

$$\Delta H_f^\circ = 8\text{ mol CO}\left(\frac{-110.5\text{ kJ}}{1\text{ mol CO}}\right) + 10\text{ mol H}_2\text{O}\left(\frac{-285.8\text{ kJ}}{1\text{ mol H}_2\text{O}}\right)$$
$$= -3742\text{ kJ}$$

For the reactants,

$$\Delta H_f^\circ = 2\text{ mol C}_4\text{H}_{10}\left(\frac{-125.5\text{ kJ}}{1\text{ mol C}_4\text{H}_{10}}\right) + 9\text{ mol O}_2\left(\frac{0\text{ kJ}}{1\text{ mol H}_2\text{O}}\right)$$
$$= -251.0\text{ kJ}$$

For this equation,

$$\Delta H_{rxn}^\circ = \Sigma n[\Delta H_f^\circ(\text{products})] - \Sigma n[\Delta H_f^\circ(\text{reactants})]$$
$$\Delta H_{rxn}^\circ = (-3742\text{ kJ}) - (-251.0\text{ kJ}) = -3491\text{ kJ}$$

Notice, however, that the balanced equation you used for this calculation involves 2 mol C_4H_{10}, whereas the problem asked for the enthalpy change for only 1.00 mol. You can use the value of ΔH_{rxn}° that you calculated for 2 mol C_4H_{10} to obtain ΔH_{rxn}° for 1 mol C_4H_{10} as follows:

$$1.00\text{ mol C}_4\text{H}_{10}\left(\frac{-3491\text{ kJ}}{-2\text{ mol C}_4\text{H}_{10}}\right) = 1.75 \times 10^3\text{ kJ}$$

An enthalpy diagram for the combustion of 2.00 mol of butane is shown on page 298, where $\Delta H_{rxn}^\circ = -3490$ kJ.

PRACTICE PROBLEM 6.22

Calculate the enthalpy change for the combustion of 1.00 mol of butane using the following equation, and compare the results to Example 6.22.

Repeat Example 6.22 using the following equation, and compare the results:

$$C_4H_{10}(g) + \frac{9}{2}O_2(g) \rightarrow 4\,CO(g) + 5\,H_2O(l)$$

Hint: Refer to Table 6.4. Add up the ΔH_f° values for the products, taking into account their coefficients. Then add up the ΔH_f° values for the reactants, also taking into account the coefficients. Finally, subtract the two results. The coefficient for butane is 1, and you are asked to find the enthalpy for 1.00 mol of butane, so no further calculation is needed.

Example 6.23

Metallic mercury, Hg, can be obtained by heating the mineral cinnabar, HgS, in the presence of oxygen, O_2. Use the following equation:

$$HgS(s) + O_2(g) \rightarrow Hg(l) + SO_2(g)$$

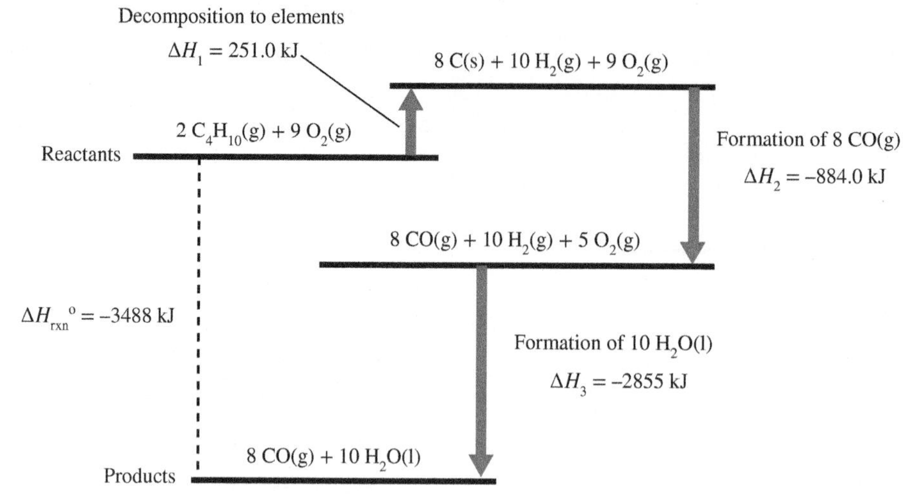

Determine the amount of heat released when 5.50 g of HgS is heated in the presence of excess oxygen.

Solution

For the products,

$$\Delta H_f^\circ = 1\ \text{mol Hg}\left(\frac{0\ \text{kJ}}{1\ \text{mol Hg}}\right) + 1\ \text{mol SO}_2\left(\frac{-296.8\ \text{kJ}}{1\ \text{mol SO}_2}\right)$$
$$= -296.8\ \text{kJ}$$

For the reactants,

$$\Delta H_f^\circ = 1\ \text{mol HgS}\left(\frac{-58.2\ \text{kJ}}{1\ \text{mol HgS}}\right) + 1\ \text{mol O}_2\left(\frac{0\ \text{kJ}}{1\ \text{mol H}_2\text{O}}\right)$$
$$= -58.2\ \text{kJ}$$

For this equation,

$$\Delta H_{rxn}^\circ = \Sigma n[\Delta H_f^\circ(\text{products})] - \Sigma n[\Delta H_f^\circ(\text{reactants})]$$
$$\Delta H_{rxn}^\circ = (-296.8\ \text{kJ}) - (-58.2\ \text{kJ}) = -238.6\ \text{kJ}$$

As shown by the balanced equation at the beginning of this problem, the calculated enthalpy of reaction, −238.7 kJ, is per 1 mol of HgS. However, only 5.50 g of HgS reacted. Therefore, you need to use the molar mass of HgS to convert 5.50 g to moles of HgS. The resulting value is multiplied by −238.7 kJ/mol to determine the amount of heat released in this particular reaction.

$$5.50\ \text{g HgS}\left(\frac{\text{mol HgS}}{232.66\ \text{g HgS}}\right)\left(\frac{-238.6\ \text{kJ}}{\text{mol HgS}}\right) = -5.64\ \text{kJ}$$

This reaction releases 5.64 kJ of heat.

PRACTICE PROBLEM 6.23

Methane, CH_4, can be synthesized by the following reaction of carbon dioxide, CO_2, with hydrogen gas, H_2:

$$CO_2(g) + 4\,H_2(g) \rightarrow CH_4(g) + 2\,H_2O(g)$$

Determine the amount of heat released when 25 kg of H_2 is heated in the presence of excess CO_2.

Hint: Refer to Table 6.4. Add up the ΔH_f° values for the products, taking into account their coefficients. Then add up the ΔH_f° values for the reactants, also taking into account the coefficients. Finally, subtract the two results. The coefficient for H_2 is 4, so the enthalpy value is the heat produced per 4 mol of H_2. Convert 25 kg of H_2 to moles, and scale the enthalpy up to that number of moles.

Referring back to the example of ethanol vaporization in Section 6.7, notice that the calculation of the standard enthalpy of a reaction is actually an application of Hess's law.

$$C_2H_6O(l) \rightarrow C_2H_6O(g)$$

$$\text{I}\quad C_2H_6O(l) \rightarrow 2\,C(s) + 3\,H_2(g) + \frac{1}{2}O_2(g) \qquad \Delta H^\circ = +277.7\ \text{kJ}$$

$$\text{II}\quad 2\,C(s) + 3\,H_2(g) + \frac{1}{2}O_2(g) \rightarrow C_2H_6O(g) \qquad \Delta H^\circ = -235.1\ \text{kJ}$$

In Step I, the reactant is *decomposed* into its constituent elements in their standard states. In Step II, the reaction product is *formed* from its constituent elements. The constituent elements cancel when Steps I and II are added together, as was done previously with Hess's law. The remaining species constitute the reaction of interest. An enthalpy diagram of the vaporization of ethanol is shown in Figure 6.17.

$$C_2H_6O(l) \rightarrow C_2H_6O(g) \qquad \Delta H_{rxn}^\circ = +42.6\ \text{kJ}$$

The two equations above can also be expressed in terms of the enthalpy of formation of gaseous ethanol and the enthalpy of formation of liquid ethanol. The same enthalpy change can be determined by

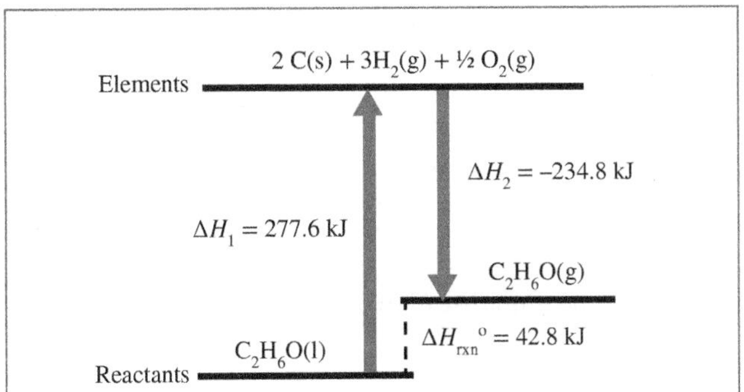

FIGURE 6.17 Enthalpy Diagram of the Formation of Gaseous Ethanol

Enthalpy diagram for the formation of both liquid and gaseous ethanol from their respective elements in their standard states. The energy difference between liquid and gaseous ethanol is the enthalpy of vaporization of ethanol, ΔH_{vap}.

calculating ΔH°_{rxn} using the equation given here. Note that adding the reactant decomposition ΔH° value to the product formation ΔH° is the same as subtracting the ΔH°_f of the reactants from the ΔH°_f of the products. Both give the result of 43 kJ.

$$2\,C(s) + 3\,H_2(g) + \frac{1}{2}O_2(g) \rightarrow C_2H_6O(g)$$
$$\Delta H^\circ_f = -234.8\text{ kJ}$$
$$2\,C(s) + 3\,H_2(g) + \frac{1}{2}O_2(g) \rightarrow C_2H_6O(l)$$
$$\Delta H^\circ_f = -277.7\text{ kJ}$$
$$\Delta H^\circ_{rxn} = (\Delta H^\circ_f\text{ gaseous } C_2H_6O) - (\Delta H^\circ_f\text{ liquid } C_2H_6O)$$
$$\Delta H^\circ_{rxn} = (-235.1\text{ kJ}) - (-277.7\text{ kJ}) = +42.8\text{ kJ}$$

> The enthalpy change of a chemical reaction can be calculated based on the ΔH°_f values of the reactants and products or based on the ΔH values of other chemical equations, via Hess's law.

SECTION REVIEW

- The enthalpy of a reaction can be calculated from the enthalpies of formation of the products and reactants.
- When calculating the enthalpy of a reaction from enthalpies of formation, $\Delta H^\circ_{rxn} = \Sigma m[\Delta H^\circ_f(\text{products})] - \Sigma n[\Delta H^\circ_f(\text{reactants})]$.

Putting It Together

The example problems in earlier sections of this chapter focus on just the new skills acquired in that section. But homework and exam questions in chemistry often require more than just one skill at a time. In fact, you will likely be expected to apply knowledge from across the entire chapter, or even multiple chapters, in a single problem. This final example problem is meant to help you prepare for these types of multi-concept questions. Additional examples can be found in the end-of-chapter exercises.

Example 6.24

When 1 mol of liquid ethanol, C_2H_6O, was combusted in a bomb calorimeter with a heat capacity of 22.1 kJ/°C, the temperature of the water rose by 56.1°C.

$$C_2H_6O(l) + 3\,O_2(g) \rightarrow 2\,CO_3(g) + 2\,H_2O(g)$$

What would the change in volume have been if this reaction had been done at a constant pressure of 1 atm?

Solution

Since ΔU is a state function, the combustion of 1 mol of ethanol has the same change in internal energy whether it was done at constant volume or constant pressure.

$$\Delta U = q_v = q_p + w$$

And since $q_p = \Delta H$ and $w = P\Delta V$, the equation becomes

$$q_v = \Delta H - P\Delta V$$

Calculate q_v using the calorimetry data.

$$q_v = -C_{cal}\Delta T = -\left(22.1\frac{\text{J}}{^\circ\text{C}}\right)(56.1^\circ\text{C})$$
$$= -1240\text{ kJ} = -1.24 \times 10^6\text{ J}$$

Calculate ΔH from enthalpy of formation values.

$$\Delta H = 2\text{ mol}\left(-393.5\frac{\text{kJ}}{\text{mol}}\right) + 3\text{ mol}\left(-241.8\frac{\text{kJ}}{\text{mol}}\right)$$
$$-1\text{ mol}\left(-277.6\frac{\text{kJ}}{\text{mol}}\right) = -1235\text{ kJ}$$
$$-1235\text{ kJ}\left(\frac{1000\text{ J}}{1\text{ kJ}}\right) = -1.235 \times 10^6\text{ J}$$

Finally, solve for ΔV, keeping in mind that $1\text{ L}\cdot\text{atm} = 101.325\text{ J}$.

$$q_v = \Delta H - P\Delta V$$
$$P\Delta V = \Delta H - q_v$$
$$P\Delta V = -1.235 \times 10^6\text{ J} - (-1.24 \times 10^6\text{ J}) = 5000\text{ J}$$
$$P\Delta V = 5000\text{ J}\left(\frac{1\text{ L}\cdot\text{atm}}{101.325\text{ J}}\right) = 50\text{ L}\cdot\text{atm}$$
$$\Delta V = \frac{50\text{ L}\cdot\text{atm}}{P} = \frac{50\text{ L}\cdot\text{atm}}{1\text{ atm}} = 50\text{ L}$$

PRACTICE PROBLEM 6.24

When 1.0 mol of boron, B, reacted with oxygen, O_2, in a bomb calorimeter with a heat capacity of 16.50 kJ/°C, the temperature of the water rose by 38.48°C.

$$4\,B(s) + 3\,O_2(g) \rightarrow 2\,B_2O_3(s)$$

What would the change in volume have been if this reaction had been done at a constant pressure of 1.0 atm?

Hint: As in the previous example, use $q_v = \Delta H - P\Delta V$. Calculate q_v using the calorimetry data and calculate ΔH from enthalpy of formation values.

Key Terms, Symbols, and Equations

KEY TERMS

bomb calorimeter (6.6): Instrument used to measure the heat of combustion of a reaction.

calorie, cal (6.1): A unit of energy that is equal to 4.184 J; the amount of energy required to raise the temperature of 1 g of water 1°C.

Calorie, Cal (6.1): A unit of energy used in the field of nutrition that is equal to exactly 1000 cal, 1 kcal, 4184 J, or 4.184 kJ.

calorimetry (6.6): The study of heat transfer between substances by measuring the temperature changes of the substances involved.

constant-volume calorimetry (6.6): Science of measuring changes in heat transfer between substances by measuring the temperature changes of the substances involved.

endothermic process (6.4): A process in which heat is absorbed from outside the system and ΔH is positive.

energy (6.1): The capacity to do work or transfer heat.

enthalpy, *H* (6.4): The sum of internal energy of a system and the product of its pressure and volume change.

exothermic process (6.4): A process in which heat is transferred from the system to the surroundings and the change in enthalpy is negative.

first law of thermodynamics (6.2): The energy of the universe is constant.

heat, *q* (6.2): The flow of energy that causes a temperature change in an object or its surroundings.

Hess's law (6.7): When two or more processes combine to give a resulting process, their enthalpy changes add to give the enthalpy change for the resulting process.

internal energy, *U* (6.2): The sum of all kinetic and potential energies of a system.

joule, J (6.1): The SI unit of energy; it takes 4.184 J to raise the temperature of 1 g of water 1°C.

kinetic energy, KE (6.1): The energy of motion.

law of conservation of energy (6.2): Energy cannot be created or destroyed.

mechanical energy (6.1): Energy in an object that is attributable to its motion, position, or both.

path function (6.3): A function that is dependent on the sequence of steps that move the system from its initial state to its final state.

potential energy (6.1): The energy of an object that is related to its position.

pressure–volume work (6.4): The work done on or by a system when there is a volume change against an external pressure.

specific heat, c (6.5): The quantity of heat required to raise the temperature of 1 g of a substance by 1°C.

standard enthalpy of formation, ΔH_f° (6.8): The enthalpy change in the formation of 1 mol of a compound from its elements in their standard states.

standard state (6.8): The state in which the substance is most stable at 25°C (298 K) and 1 atm pressure.

state function (6.3): A function that is independent of the path taken to achieve its value.

surroundings (6.2): The part of the universe that is separate from a system of study.

system (6.2): A specified portion of the universe that is studied.

thermochemistry (6.1): The study of heat and energy in chemical reactions.

work, *w* (6.2): The energy resulting from a force acting on an object over a distance.

SYMBOLS/ABBREVIATIONS

cal, calorie (6.1)

Cal, Calorie (6.1)

C_{cal} (combined heat capacity) (6.6)

Δ (change in) (6.2)

ΔH (enthalpy change) (6.4)

ΔH°_f (standard enthalpy of formation) (6.8)

ΔH°_{rxn} (standard enthalpy of reaction) (6.8)

ΔU (change in internal energy) (6.2)

ΔV (change in volume) (6.4)

J (joule) (6.1)

P (pressure) (6.4)

q (heat) (6.2)

q_p (heat absorbed or released by the reaction at constant pressure) (6.6)

q_{soln} (heat absorbed or released by the solution) (6.6)

q_v (heat absorbed or released by the reaction at constant volume) (6.6)

V (volume) (6.4)

w (work) (6.2)

EQUATIONS

$\mathrm{KE} = \frac{1}{2}mv^2$ (6.1)

$\Delta U = q + w$ (6.2)

$w = -P\Delta V$ (6.3)

$H = U + PV$ (6.4)

$\Delta H = \Delta U + P\Delta V$ (6.5)

$\Delta H = (q_p + w) + P\Delta V$ (6.6)

$\Delta H = (q_p + w) - w = q_p$ (6.7)

$q = mc\Delta T$ (6.8)

$q = 0 = (m_{water})(c_{water})(\Delta T_{water}) + (m_{metal})(c_{metal})(\Delta T_{metal})$ (6.9)

$q_{soln} = -q_p$ (6.10)

$q_{soln} = C_{cal}\Delta T$ (6.11)

$q_{soln} = -q_v$ (6.12)

$\Delta U_{rxn} = q_v = -C_{cal}\Delta T$ (6.13)

$\Delta H^\circ_{rxn} = \Sigma m[\Delta H^\circ_f(\text{products})] - \Sigma n[\Delta H^\circ_f(\text{reactants})]$ (6.14)

Chapter Summary

Energy is typically defined as the capacity to do work or transfer heat. Two forms of mechanical energy are kinetic energy (energy of motion) and potential energy (energy of position). Kinetic energy, KE, is equal to one-half the product of the mass of an object and the square of its velocity.

$$\mathrm{KE} = \frac{1}{2}mv^2$$

Energy is most often expressed in units of joules or calories (Section 6.1).

Energy can be transferred from a system, such as a chemical reaction, to the surroundings in the form of either work, w, or heat, q. Work performed *on* a system or heat added *to* a system is positive in value, whereas work performed *by* a system or heat released *from* a system has a negative value.

According to the first law of thermodynamics, the energy of the universe is constant. This idea is expressed mathematically by the following equation, which states that the change in internal energy of a system, ΔU, is the sum of the heat and work of the system (Section 6.2).

$$\Delta U = q + w$$

ΔU is a state function, which means that its value depends only on the initial and final states of the system and is independent of the path taken to achieve that value (Figure 6.3).

Pressure–volume work is equal to the work done by a volume change against an external pressure.

$$w = -P\Delta V$$

The change in enthalpy of a system, ΔH, is equal to the change in heat at constant pressure, q_p. Reactions that absorb heat from their surroundings have positive ΔH values and are endothermic. Reactions that release heat to their surroundings have negative ΔH values and are exothermic (Section 6.4).

The quantity of energy, q, required to raise the temperature of a substance is given by the equation

$$q = mc\Delta T$$

where m is the mass, c is the specific heat capacity, and ΔT is the change in temperature. Any one of these four quantities may be calculated if the other three are known. Note that the change in temperature involves an initial temperature and a final temperature, either of which may be unknown. The specific heat capacity, c, also known as specific heat, is the number of calories required to raise exactly 1 g of the substance by exactly 1°C. The specific heat of each substance is different, and substances with higher specific heat values resist temperature changes more than substances with lower specific heat values (Section 6.5).

Calorimetry is the study of heat transfers by measuring the temperature changes in the substances involved. In constant-pressure calorimetry, $q_p = \Delta H$. In constant-volume calorimetry, $q_v = \Delta U$ (Section 6.6).

Values of ΔH can also be obtained from ΔH values of other reactions using Hess's law, which involves adding their chemical equations and the corresponding ΔH values (Section 6.7). Alternatively, the standard enthalpy change ($\Delta H°$) for any reaction is equal to the sum of the standard enthalpies of formation of the products minus the sum of the standard enthalpies of formation of the reactants (Section 6.8).

$$\Delta H^\circ_{rxn} = \Sigma m[\Delta H^\circ_f(\text{products})] - \Sigma n[\Delta H^\circ_f(\text{reactants})]$$

END OF CHAPTER QUESTIONS

6.1 Energy and Energy Units

1. Identify the primary type of energy exhibited by each of the following.
   a. a train traveling at 80 mph
   b. a leaf falling from a tree
   c. a roller coaster at the top of a hill
   d. a slingshot pulled taut

2. Which of these represents potential energy?
   a. a stretched rubber band
   b. a skier moving down the slope
   c. a snowboarder at the top of a half-pipe
   d. a motorcycle traveling at 35 mph

3. Which of these represents kinetic energy?
   a. water behind a dam
   b. an orange falling from a tree
   c. a rock rolling down a hill
   d. a penny held at the top of the Empire State Building

4. Calculate the kinetic energy in joules of a 5.65 kg bald eagle diving at 41.5 m/s.

5. A rider and her bicycle weigh 60.24 kg. What is the kinetic energy in kJ of the bike and rider while traveling at a speed of 25.1 km/h?

6.2 Energy, Heat, and Work

6. Identify the following systems as open, closed, or isolated.
   a. a BBQ pit burning charcoal
   b. hot chocolate in a high-quality insulated bottle
   c. a bomb calorimeter burning naphthalene, $C_{10}H_8$
   d. a pressure cooker in which asparagus is being cooked
   e. water boiling in an open saucepan

7. At constant pressure, which of these systems do work on the surroundings?
   a. $2\,A(g) + B(g) \rightarrow 4\,C(g)$
   b. $A(g) + B(g) \rightarrow C(g)$
   c. $2\,A(g) + 2\,B(g) \rightarrow 3\,C(g)$
   d. $2\,A(g) + B(s) \rightarrow 3\,C(g)$

8. Determine whether w is positive or negative in each scenario. The system is underlined.
   a. A person is pedaling a bicycle down the street.
   b. A person is pedaling a bicycle down the street.
   c. An elevator takes a person from the first floor of a building to the seventh floor.

9. A system does 467 kJ of work and loses 157 kJ of heat to the surroundings. What is the change in internal energy of the system?

10. What is the change in internal energy of a system that has 275 kcal of work done to it and it releases 526 kJ of heat to its surroundings?

6.3 Energy as a State Function

11. What is a state function?

12. What is a path function?

13. Classify the following as either state or path functions.
   a. heat
   b. work
   c. energy

14. What pattern do you notice in the capitalization of the symbols for state functions versus path functions?

6.4 Energy and Enthalpy

15. A sample of gas occupies a volume of 55.2 mL. As the gas expands, it does 110.5 J of work on its surroundings at a constant pressure of 1.05 atm. What is the final volume of the gas?

16. How much work is done on a system to decrease its volume from 14.5 mL to 7.8 mL when exerting a constant pressure of 3.65 atm?

17. A sample of Ne(g) occupying 1.40 L is confined in a flask by a piston. The gas is allowed to expand to 2.50 L against a constant pressure of 1.05 atm. How much work is performed? What is the sign of w?

18. A chemical reaction takes place in a closed system confined by a piston. The pressure remains constant at 1.00 atm. If 55.6 J of work is performed by the system, calculate the change in volume.

19. Classify each process as endothermic or exothermic and give the sign of ΔH.
   a. boiling water
   b. freezing water
   c. burning a candle
   d. making popcorn in a microwave

20. Classify each reaction as endothermic or exothermic
   a. $NH_3(g) + HCl(g) \rightarrow NH_4Cl(s)$ $\quad \Delta H = -176\ \text{kJ/mol}$
   b. $C_3H_8(g) + 5\,O_2(g) \rightarrow 3\,CO_2(g) + 4\,H_2O(g)$ $\quad \Delta H = -2044\ \text{kJ/mol}$
   c. $AgCl(s) \rightarrow Ag^+(aq) + Cl^-(aq)$ $\quad \Delta H = 127\ \text{kJ/mol}$

21. An evaporating dish containing solid iodine is left uncovered on a lab bench. The iodine sublimes, absorbing 884 kJ of heat from the surroundings.
   a. Is this reaction endothermic or exothermic?
   b. Calculate ΔH for this reaction.

22. A chemical reaction takes place in an open flask. The reaction releases 355 kJ of heat and does 25 kJ of work on the surroundings.
   a. Is the reaction endothermic or exothermic?
   b. Calculate ΔH for the reaction.
   c. Calculate ΔU for the reaction.

6.5 Specific Heat

23. A 42.25 g sample of a substance is initially at 22.4°C. After absorbing 1567 J of heat, the temperature of the substance is 122.6°C. Calculate the specific heat, c, of the substance.

24. An unknown substance has a mass of 23.5 g. The temperature of the substance increases by 17.1°C when 154.7 J of heat is added to the substance. What is the most likely identity of the substance?

25. The temperature of a 33.7 g sample of metal increases by 27.2°C after absorbing 201.7 J of heat. What is the most likely identity of the metal?

26. Calculate the heat required
   a. to warm 35.0 g of water from 10.5°C to 41.6°C.
   b. to cool 35.0 g of water from 41.6°C to 10.5°C.

27. Calculate the heat required
   a. to warm 23.1 g of water from −20.0°C to −10.0°C.
   b. to cool 35.0 g of water from −10.0°C to −20.0°C.

28. Calculate the final temperature after 127 J of heat is added to 51.5 g of iron at 23.0°C.

29. How much energy is required to raise the temperature of iron by 41.7°C?

30. Calculate the final temperature after 415 J of heat is added to 123.0 g of magnesium at 22.2°C.

31. How much energy is required to raise the temperature of 40.9 g of zinc by 38.1°C?

32. How much energy is required to raise the temperature of 37.8 g of silver from 19.2°C to 63.5°C?

33. Calculate the energy required to raise the temperature of 10.0 g of chromium from 41.3°C to 104.0°C.

6.6 Calorimetry: Measuring Energy Changes

34. A 122 mL sample of water at 97°C is added to a beaker containing 255 mL of water at 23.0°C. Calculate the final temperature of the water. The density of water is 1.00 g/mL.

35. Calculate the final temperature after 17.0 g of water at 20.0°C is mixed with
    a. 17.0 g of water at 50.0°C.
    b. 34.0 g of water at 50.0°C.

36. A 102.8 g sample of a metal initially at 183.0°C is placed in 35.0 mL of water initially at 25.0°C. After reaching thermal equilibrium, the final temperature of the system is 58.8°C. What is the identity of the metal? Assume no heat is lost to the surroundings.

37. Calculate the specific heat of a metal if 46.0 g of the metal at 78.0°C warms 32.0 g of water at 23.1°C to 36.1°C. Which metal in Table 6.3 is it likely to be?

38. A 90.6 g sample of a metal initially at 75.0°C warms 224 g of water at 15.0°C to 17.5°C. Calculate the specific heat of the metal. Which metal in Table 6.3 is it likely to be?

39. Calculate the final temperature after 25.0 g of chromium at 54.5°C is placed in 215 g of water at 14.6°C. Assume no heat is lost to the surroundings.

40. A 10.7 g sample of aluminum at 85.3°C is added to 117 mL of water initially at 14.6°C. Assuming no heat is lost to the surroundings, calculate the final temperature of the system.

41. Calculate the final temperature of the water after 2.47 g of zinc at 60.1°C is added to 29.4 g of water at 16.4°C. Assume no heat is lost to the surroundings.

42. A beaker contains 94.3 mL of water at 61.4°C. Calculate the final temperature after 29.4 g of cobalt at 15.9°C is added. Assume no heat is lost to the surroundings.

43. Calculate the final temperature after 14.9 g of a metal alloy, $c = 0.650\ \text{J/g}\cdot{}^{\circ}\text{C}$, at 81.6°C is placed in 88.8 g of water at 15.5°C. Assume no heat is lost to the surroundings.

44. A certain reaction emits 3.95 kJ of heat. What temperature change will 250.0 g of water at 16.0°C undergo if the heat from the reaction is added to it?

45. A 10.5 g sample of an ionic compound with a molar mass of 163 g/mol was added to water to form 65.2 mL of solution. The temperature of the water was initially 25.6°C. After the ionic compound dissolved, the temperature of the solution was 23.7°C. Assume the specific heat, *c*, and the density of the resulting solution are the same as those of water, $4.184\ \text{J/g}\cdot{}^{\circ}\text{C}$, and 1.00 g/mL, respectively. Calculate the enthalpy of solution, ΔH_{sol}, for one mole of ionic compound.

46. A coffee cup calorimeter contains 100.0 mL of water at 23.8°C.
    a. Calculate the energy change in joules when the temperature of the water increases to 27.4°C.
    b. Calculate the mass of LiOH needed to release this amount of energy when dissolved in water. $\Delta H_{\text{sol}}(\text{LiOH}) = -23.56\ \text{kJ/mol}$.

47. A sample of 17.1 g of a solid with the molar mass 71.9 g/mol is dissolved in 331 g of water initially at 22.5°C in a constant-pressure calorimeter. Upon dissolution, the temperature rises to 26.8°C. The specific heat of the solution is $4.184\ \text{J/g}\cdot{}^{\circ}\text{C}$. What is the enthalpy of the reaction, ΔH_{rxn}?

48. When a 3.013 g sample of compound A was combusted in a constant-volume calorimeter, the temperature rose from 23.89°C to 27.18°C. The heat capacity of the calorimeter is 8.218 kJ/°C. What is the heat of combustion per gram of compound A?

49. When a 1.621 g sample of an organic compound was combusted in a bomb calorimeter, the temperature of the calorimeter and its contents rose from 24.75°C to 30.10°C. The heat capacity of the calorimeter is 32.31 kJ/°C. What is the heat of combustion per gram of the organic compound?

50. The combustion of 1.839 g of glucose, $C_6H_{12}O_6(s)$, in a bomb calorimeter results in an increase in

the temperature of the calorimeter and its contents from 22.07°C to 28.30°C. The heat capacity of the calorimeter is 4.60 kJ/mol.

a. Determine the enthalpy of combustion, ΔH_c, for glucose in kJ/mol.

b. Calculate the change in internal energy, ΔU, for the combustion of 1.839 g of glucose in the calorimeter.

51. The combustion of 1.904 g of ethanol, $C_2H_5OH(l)$, in a constant-volume calorimeter results in an increase in the temperature of the calorimeter and its contents from 22.46°C to 35.0°C. The heat capacity of the calorimeter is 4.70 kJ/mol.

a. Determine the enthalpy of combustion, ΔH_c, for ethanol in kJ/mol.

b. Calculate the change in internal energy, ΔU, for the combustion of 1.904 g of ethanol in the calorimeter.

6.7 Enthalpy in Chemical Reactions

52. An 11.6 g sample of an ionic compound with a molar mass of 157 g/mol was added to water to form 55.3 mL of solution. The temperature of the water was initially 23.6°C. After the ionic compound dissolved, the temperature of the solution was 21.5°C. Assume the specific heat, c, and the density of the resulting solution are the same as those of water, 4.184 J/g · °C, and 1.00 g/mL, respectively.

a. Calculate the heat change experienced by the calorimeter contents.

b. Calculate the heat change produced by the solution process.

53. A constant-pressure calorimeter is used to measure the heat change when an ionic compound dissolves in water. The mass of the contents of the calorimeter is 49.8 g. The change in temperature is 2.82°C.

a. The specific heat, c, of the solution is 4.12 J/g · °C. Calculate the heat change of the calorimeter contents.

b. The heat capacity of the calorimeter is 8.2 J/°C. Calculate the heat change of the calorimeter.

c. Calculate the heat change for the solution process.

54. Given the thermochemical equations

$A(g) \rightarrow B(g) \quad \Delta H = 78\ kJ$

$B(g) \rightarrow C(g) \quad \Delta H = -137\ kJ$

determine the enthalpy change, ΔH, for each reaction.

a. $2\ A(g) \rightarrow 2\ B(g)$

b. $B(g) \rightarrow A(g)$

c. $A(g) \rightarrow C(g)$

55. Given the information

$R + X \rightarrow Q + Z \quad \Delta H = 165\ kJ$

$Q + Z \rightarrow T \quad \Delta H = 165\ kJ$

calculate ΔH for each of the following reactions.

a. $R + X \rightarrow T$

b. $Q + Z \rightarrow R + X$

c. $2\ Q + 2\ Z \rightarrow 2\ R + 2\ X$

56. Given the thermochemical equation

$2\ A + B \rightarrow 3\ C + D \quad \Delta H = 165\ kJ$

determine the enthalpy change, ΔH, for each reaction.

a. $3\ C + D \rightarrow 2\ A + B$

b. $A + \frac{1}{2}B \rightarrow \frac{3}{2}C + \frac{1}{2}D$

c. $9\ C + 3\ D \rightarrow 6\ A + 3\ B$

57. The value of ΔH for the reaction $X + Q \rightarrow Z$ is 13.3 kJ. What is the value of ΔH for each of the following reactions?

a. $2\ X + 2\ Q \rightarrow 2\ Z$

b. $Z \rightarrow Q + Y$

58. Calculate the enthalpy of reaction, ΔH_{rxn}, for $2\ SO_2(g) + O_2(g) \rightarrow 2\ SO_3(g)$ given

$S(s) + O_2(g) \rightarrow SO_2(g) \quad \Delta H = -299\ kJ$

$S(s) + \frac{3}{2}O_2(g) \rightarrow SO_3(g) \quad \Delta H_{sol} = -395\ kJ$

59. Calculate the ΔH_{rxn} for the reaction

$7\ C(s) + 8\ H_2(g) \rightarrow C_7H_{16}(g)$

given the following reactions and ΔH values.

$C_7H_{16}(g) + 11\ O_2 \rightarrow 7\ CO_2(g) + 8\ H_2O(g)$

$\Delta H = -4817\ kJ$

$C(s) + O_2(g) \rightarrow CO_2(g) \quad \Delta H = -393.5\ kJ$

$2\ H_2(g) + O_2(g) \rightarrow 2\ H_2O(g) \quad \Delta H = -483.6\ kJ$

60. Calculate the enthalpy of hydrogenation of C_2H_2 to $C_2H_6C_2H_2(g) + 2H_2(g) \rightarrow C_2H_6(g)$ given the following reactions and enthalpy data.

$2\ C_2H_2(g) + 5\ O_2(g) \rightarrow 4\ CO_2(g) + 2\ H_2O(g)$

$\Delta H = -2602.2\ kJ$

$2\ C_2H_6(g) + 7\ O_2(g) \rightarrow 4\ CO_2(g) + 6\ H_2O(g)$

$\Delta H = -3121.4\ kJ$

$2\ H_2(g) + O_2(g) \rightarrow 2\ H_2O(g) \quad \Delta H = -483.6\ kJ$

61. Calculate the enthalpy of dehydrogenation of C_2H_4 to $C_2H_2C_2H_4(g) \rightarrow C_2H_2(g) + H_2(g)$ given the following reactions and enthalpy data.

$$C_2H_2(g) + \frac{5}{2}O_2(g) \rightarrow 2\,CO_2(g) + H_2O(g) \qquad \Delta H = -1301.1\text{ kJ}$$

$$C_2H_4(g) + 3\,O_2(g) \rightarrow 2\,CO_2(g) + 2\,H_2O(g) \qquad \Delta H = -1560.7\text{ kJ}$$

$$H_2(g) + \frac{1}{2}O_2(g) \rightarrow H_2O(g) \qquad \Delta H = -241.8\text{ kJ}$$

6.8 Standard Enthalpies of Formation

62. Use standard enthalpies of formation, ΔH_f°, to calculate ΔH_{rxn}° for
   a. $2\,H_2S(g) + 3\,O_2(g) \rightarrow 2\,H_2O(l) + 2\,SO_2(g)$
   b. $Cl_2(g) + CHCl_3(g) \rightarrow HCl(g) + CCl_4(g)$
   c. $N_2O(g) + NO(g) \rightarrow N_2(g) + NO_2(g)$

63. Use standard enthalpies of formation, ΔH_f°, to calculate ΔH_{rxn}° for
   a. $2\,NO(g) + 2\,H_2(g) \rightarrow N_2(g) + 2\,H_2O(g)$
   b. $H_2(g) + I_2(g) \rightarrow 2\,HI(g)$
   c. $NO_2(g) + CO(g) \rightarrow NO(g) + CO_2(g)$

64. Hexane, $C_6H_{14}(l)$, burns according to the balanced reaction

$$C_6H_{14}(g) + \frac{19}{2}O_2(g) \rightarrow 6\,CO_2(g) + 7\,H_2O(g)$$

Calculate ΔH_{rxn}° for the combustion of hexane using standard enthalpies of formation. The enthalpy of formation for hexane is -166.9 kJ/mol.

65. Aniline, $C_6H_7N(l)$, burns in the presence of oxygen to form carbon dioxide, water, and nitrogen.

$$C_6H_7N(l) + \frac{31}{4}O_2(g) \rightarrow 6\,CO_2(g) + \frac{7}{2}H_2O(g) + \frac{1}{2}N_2(g)$$

Calculate ΔH_{rxn}° for the combustion of aniline using standard enthalpies of formation. The enthalpy of formation for aniline is 31.6 kJ/mol.

66. Determine the enthalpy change for the combustion of 125 g CO at 25°C.

67. The value of $\Delta H_{combustion}(C_6H_6)$ is -3266 kJ. Calculate ΔH_f of C_6H_6.

68. Calculate ΔH for the reaction of 4.000 mol of octane, C_8H_{18}, with excess O_2 to form CO_2 and H_2O.

69. Determine ΔH for the reaction of 50.0 g SO_3 with MgO at 25°C. Values of ΔH_f are -602 kJ/mol for MgO, -395 kJ/mol for SO_3, and -1280 kJ/mol for $MgSO_4$.

Putting It Together

70. In a coffee cup calorimeter, 60.0 mL of 0.340 M $Ba(OH)_2$ was added to 60.0 mL of 0.680 M $HClO_4$. The temperature of the solution rose from 23.96°C to 28.59°C. What is ΔH per mole of H_2O produced for this reaction? Assume that the solution has the same density and specific heat as those of water, 1.00 g/mL and 4.184 J/g·°C, respectively.

71. An 8.9 g sample of an ionic compound was added to 65.8 mL of water initially at 23.4°C. After dissolving, the temperature of the solution was 21.6°C. The specific heat of the resulting solution is 4.07 J/g·°C. Calculate the enthalpy of solution, ΔH_{sol}, per mole of ionic compound dissolved.

72. Calcium metal reacts with water to form hydrogen gas according to the reaction

$$Ca(s) + 2\,H^+(aq) \rightarrow Ca^{2+}(aq) + H_2(g)$$

A sample of 0.339 g of calcium metal is added to 125 mL of 2.08 M HCl in a coffee cup calorimeter. The temperature of the solution increases by 11.4°C. Assume the final volume of the solution is 125 mL, the density of the solution is 1.00 g/mL, and the specific heat, c, is 4.148 J/g·°C. Calculate the heat of reaction, ΔH_{rxn}.

73. A generic compound, X, has a molar mass of 100.51 g/mol. The heat of combustion of compound X is -3566.0 kJ/mol at constant volume. When 1.265 g of compound X was burned in a bomb calorimeter, the temperature of the calorimeter and its contents rose by 7.455°C. Calculate the heat capacity of the calorimeter. When 3.611 g of a different compound, compound Y, was combusted in the same calorimeter, the temperature rose from 24.25°C to 27.28°C. Calculate the heat of combustion per gram of compound Y.

74. A sample of 16.7 g of a solid with a molar mass 82.6 g/mol is dissolved in 346 g of water initially at 23.5°C in a constant-pressure calorimeter. Upon dissolution, the temperature rises to 28.9°C. The specific heat of the solution is 4.184 J/g·°C.
   a. How much heat was absorbed by the solution?
   b. What is the enthalpy of the reaction, ΔH_{rxn}?

75. Calculate the enthalpy of formation, ΔH_f, of $CH_2O(g)$ given the following reactions and ΔH values.

$$CH_2O(g) + O_2(g) \rightarrow CO_2(g) + H_2O(g) \qquad \Delta H = -561\text{ kJ}$$

$$H_2O(g) \rightarrow H_2(g) + \frac{1}{2}O_2(g) \qquad \Delta H = -242\text{ kJ}$$

$$C(s) + O_2(g) \rightarrow CO_2(g) \qquad \Delta H = -394\text{ kJ}$$

76. Calculate the ΔH values for
   a. $C_4H_6(g) + H_2(g) \rightarrow C_4H_8(g)$
   b. $C_4H_6(g) + 2\,H_2(g) \rightarrow C_4H_{10}(g)$

   given the following reactions and ΔH values.

$$C_4H_6(g) + \frac{1}{2}O_2(g) \rightarrow 4\,CO_2(g) + 3\,H_2O(g) \qquad \Delta H = -2600\text{ kJ}$$

$$H_2O(g) \rightarrow H_2(g) + \frac{1}{2}O_2(g) \qquad \Delta H = -242\text{ kJ}$$

$$2\,C_4H_{10}(g) + 13\,O_2(g) \rightarrow 8\,CO_2(g) + 10\,H_2O(g) \qquad \Delta H = -5755\text{ kJ}$$

$$C_4H_8(g) + 6\,O_2(g) \rightarrow 4\,CO_2(g) + 4\,H_2O(g) \qquad \Delta H = -2710\text{ kJ}$$

PRACTICE PROBLEM SOLUTIONS

Practice Problem 6.1 Solution

The equation that relates mass and velocity to kinetic energy is $KE = \frac{1}{2}mv^2$.

$$m = 1.95 \times 10^5\text{ kg};\ v = 22.4\text{ m/s}$$

$$KE = \frac{1}{2}(1.95 \times 10^5\text{ kg})(22.4\text{ m/s})^2$$

$$= 4.89 \times 10^7\ \frac{\text{kg} \cdot \text{m}^2}{\text{s}^2} = 4.89 \times 10^7\text{ J}$$

Practice Problem 6.2 Solution

a. Work is being done on the system (the steel beam) by lifting it against gravity. The value of w is positive.

b. Steam cools and loses thermal energy when it goes from the gas phase to the liquid phase on the surface of the mirror. The transfer of heat from the steam (part of the surroundings) to the mirror (the system) results in a positive value of q.

Practice Problem 6.3 Solution

a. The reaction consumes heat from the surroundings, so q is positive. The piston does work on the system, so w is positive, too.

b. Positive values of q and w are used to calculate the change in internal energy:

$$\Delta U = q + w = 550\text{ J} + 210\text{ J} = 760\text{ J}$$

Practice Problem 6.4 Solution

Pressure is a state function because it describes the current state of a system and is independent of the path taken to achieve that state. For example, suppose that a bicycle tire has a pressure of 70 psi. If the tire originally had a pressure of 20 psi, more work would have been needed to inflate it to 70 psi than if the tire had an original pressure of 50 psi. However, the pressure value of 70 psi merely describes the current state of the tire and is independent of the amount of work needed to achieve that pressure.

Practice Problem 6.5 Solution

a. The change in volume (ΔV) is

$$\Delta V = V_{\text{final}} - V_{\text{initial}} = (0.885\text{ L}) - (0.350\text{ L}) = 0.535\text{ L}$$

An increase in volume means that the piston moves upward.

b. The change in volume is now multiplied by the pressure to calculate the work performed.

$$w = -P\Delta V = -(1.00\text{ atm})(0.535\text{ L}) = -0.535\text{ L} \cdot \text{atm}$$

Convert units of L · atm to units of J.

$$w = -0.535\text{ L} \cdot \text{atm}\left(\frac{101.325\text{ J}}{1\text{ L} \cdot \text{atm}}\right) = -54.2\text{ J}$$

The sign of the work is negative, so work is done by the system on the surroundings, as further evidenced by the volume increase that pushes up on the piston.

According to the equation that relates work to pressure and volume, there must be a volume change for work to be performed. Therefore, if a reaction occurs in a system with a fixed volume, such as a sealed, rigid container, the only energy that can be exchanged with the system is heat.

Practice Problem 6.6 Solution

a. Energy must be added to the system (the water) to cause it to evaporate. Therefore, heat is transferred from the surroundings to the system and the reaction is endothermic (i.e., $\Delta H > 0$).

b. This is an open system, so the pressure is constant. Therefore, ΔH is equal to the amount of heat transferred and it has a positive value because the heat is transferred from the surroundings to the system. $\Delta H = 1150$ kJ.

Practice Problem 6.7 Solution

The heat flow of a reaction is given by the equation $q = mc\Delta T$.

Substitute the mass of water and the temperature increase, and then solve for the specific heat, c.

$$128\ \text{J} = (4.00\ \text{g})(c)(15.3°\text{C})$$

$$c = \frac{128\ \text{J}}{(4.00\ \text{g})(15.3°\text{C})} = 2.09\ \text{J/g}\cdot°\text{C}$$

Practice Problem 6.8 Solution

The equation to use is $q = mc\Delta T$

where $m = 123$ g

$c = 0.442\ \text{J/g}\cdot°\text{C}$ (see Table 6.3)

$$\Delta T = T_{\text{final}} - T_{\text{initial}} = 31.1°\text{C} - 14.7°\text{C} = 16.4°\text{C}$$

Thus,

$$q = (123\ \text{g})(0.442\ \text{J/g}\cdot°\text{C})(16.4°\text{C}) = 892\ \text{J} = 0.892\ \text{kJ}$$

Heating iron takes much *less* energy (0.892 kJ) than heating the same mass of water (8.44 kJ) because the specific heat of iron ($0.442\ \text{J/g}\cdot°\text{C}$) is so much lower than the specific heat of water ($4.184\ \text{J/g}\cdot°\text{C}$).

Practice Problem 6.9 Solution

This problem is solved the same way as Example 6.9, but in this case, energy is removed from the system, so $q = -987$ J in the equation for the temperature change:

$$\Delta T = \frac{q}{mc} = \frac{-987\ \text{J}}{(14.9\ \text{g})(4.184\ \text{J/g}\cdot°\text{C})} = -15.8°\text{C}$$

The final temperature is

$$T_2 = T_1 + \Delta T = -15.8°\text{C} + 22.0°\text{C} = 6.2°\text{C}$$

Energy was removed from the system, so the temperature decreased.

Practice Problem 6.10 Solution

The amount of heat lost by the metal is equal to the amount of heat gained by the metal. The equation to use is

$$q = 0 = (m_{\text{metal}})(c_{\text{metal}})(\Delta T_{\text{metal}}) + (m_{\text{water}})(c_{\text{water}})(\Delta T_{\text{water}})$$

In this case, you will want to solve for c_{metal}. Substituting the values into the equation gives

$$(186\ \text{g})(c_{\text{metal}})(26.4°\text{C} - 74.0°\text{C}) = -(251\ \text{g})(4.184\ \text{J/g}\cdot°\text{C})(26.4°\text{C} - 18.0°\text{C})$$

$$(c_{\text{metal}})(186\ \text{g})(-47.6°\text{C}) = -8.82 \times 10^3\ \text{J}$$

$$c_{\text{metal}} = (-8.82 \times 10^3\ \text{J})/(186\ \text{g})(-47.6°\text{C}) = 1.00\ \text{J/g}\cdot°\text{C}$$

From Table 6.3, the metal is magnesium.

Practice Problem 6.11 Solution

$$0 = (m_{\text{iron}})(c_{\text{iron}})(\Delta T_{\text{iron}}) + (m_{\text{water}})(c_{\text{water}})(\Delta T_{\text{water}})$$

$$0 = (11.3\ \text{g})(0.44\ \text{J/g}\cdot°\text{C})(T_{\text{final}} - 60.0°\text{C}) + (97.2\ \text{g})(4.184\ \text{J/g}\cdot°\text{C})(T_{\text{final}} - 19.0°\text{C})$$

$$(4.97T_{\text{final}}) - (298°\text{C}) + (406.7T_{\text{final}}) - (7727°\text{C}) = 0$$

$$411.7T_{\text{final}} = 8025°\text{C}$$

$$T_{\text{final}} = 20°\text{C}$$

Practice Problem 6.12 Solution

a. The reaction is exothermic, so the heat is transferred from the reaction to the water. Therefore, q_{soln} is positive (heat is gained) and q_{p} is negative (heat is lost).

b. Heat is transferred from the reaction to the solution, so final temperature of the water will be above 21°C.

Practice Problem 6.13 Solution

Calculate the total mass of the solution. The vast majority of the solution is water and the solution density is 1.00 g/mL, so the mass of solution is essentially the mass of water.

$$\text{Mass of water} = 60.0\ \text{mL}\left(\frac{1.00\ \text{g}}{\text{mL}}\right) = 60.0\ \text{g}$$

$$\Delta T_{\text{water}} = -3.4°\text{C}$$

$$q_{\text{soln}} = (m_{\text{water}})(c_{\text{water}})(\Delta T_{\text{water}})$$

a. The temperature of the system decreases, so the reaction absorbs heat (it is endothermic), in which case, ΔH is positive. Recall that $\Delta H = q_{\text{p}} = -q_{\text{soln}}$.

$$\Delta H = -q_{\text{soln}} = -(60.0\ \text{g})(4.184\ \text{J/g}\cdot°\text{C})(-3.4°\text{C}) = 850\ \text{J}$$

b. First, calculate the number of moles ammonium nitrate:

$$3.1\ \text{g}\ NH_4NO_3\left(\frac{\text{mol}}{80.04\ \text{g}}\right) = 0.0387\ \text{moles of}$$

ammonium nitrate

Next, divide the enthalpy change by the number of moles of ammonium nitrate.

$$\Delta H = \frac{850\ \text{J}}{0.0387\ \text{mol}} = 22{,}000\ \text{J/mol} = 22\ \text{kJ/mol}$$

Practice Problem 6.14 Solution

a. If $\Delta H < 0$, the reaction is exothermic.

b. In an exothermic reaction inside a calorimeter, the temperature of the water inside the calorimeter increases, indicating the heat is transferred from the reaction to the water. Therefore, q_{soln} is positive (heat is gained) and q_v is negative (heat is lost). Despite the fact that ΔH is not mathematically equivalent to q_v, you can still qualitatively state that the reaction releases heat to the water and calorimeter.

Practice Problem 6.15 Solution

$$\Delta T = 85.9°C - 20.0°C = 65.9°C$$
$$C_{cal} = 810.1\ J/°C$$
$$q_v = -C_{cal}\Delta T = -(810.1\ J/°C)(65.9°C) = -53{,}390\ J = -53.390\ kJ$$

This reaction is exothermic.

Use molar mass of glucose (180.156 g/mol) to calculate the number of moles of glucose in the 3.50 g sample.

$$3.50\ g\ glucose\left(\frac{1\ mol}{180.156\ g}\right) = 0.01943\ mol\ glucose$$

Divide q_v by the number of moles of glucose. Recall that, $q_v = \Delta U_{rxn}$.

$$\Delta U_{rxn} = q_v = \frac{-53.390\ kJ}{0.01943\ mol\ glucose} = -2.75 \times 10^3\ kJ/mol\ glucose$$

Practice Problem 6.16 Solution

The heat added to the water is

$$q = mc\Delta T = (20{,}000\ g)(4.184\ J/g \cdot °C)(25.7°C) = 2.15 \times 10^6\ J$$
$$2.15 \times 10^6\ J = 2.15 \times 10^3\ kJ$$

The amount of heat gained by the water is equal to the amount of heat released by the reaction. The magnitude of q is the same for each, but their signs are opposite. The reaction *produced* the heat, so it lost 2150 kJ to its surroundings and its q value is -2150 kJ.

Practice Problem 6.17 Solution

a. To show 1 mol of N_2 consumed, multiply the equation coefficients by 2:

$$N_2(g) + 3\,H_2(g) \rightarrow 2\,NH_3(g)$$

b. The enthalpy change to produce one mole of NH_3 is -42 kJ. If twice as much NH_3 is produced, the enthalpy value is multiplied by 2.

$$2\ (mol\ NH_3)\left(\frac{-42\ kJ}{mol\ NH_3}\right) = -84\ kJ$$

Practice Problem 6.18 Solution

a. The coefficient of N_2H_4 is 2, so 1154 kJ of heat is produced per 2 mol of N_2H_4.

$$4.6\ mol\ N_2H_4\left(\frac{1154\ kJ}{2\ mol\ N_2H_4}\right) = 5300\ kJ$$

b. The equation coefficients have been divided by 2, so the enthalpy of reaction (1154 kJ) must also be divided by 2. The enthalpy value is $\Delta H = (-1154\ kJ)/2 = -577$ kJ.

Practice Problem 6.19 Solution

Equation I must be reversed because Z and Q are reactants in the desired reaction. Equation II is also reversed to cancel E, D, J, and A, none of which appears in the desired reaction.

−I	$Z + Q \rightarrow E + 2\,D$	−41.7
−II	$E + 2\,D \rightarrow J + A$	17.1
III	$J + A \rightarrow X + 2\,R$	10.6

Adding the reverse of equations I and II to equation III cancels the highlighted substances, yielding the desired reaction:

$$Z + Q \rightarrow X + 2\,R$$

Doing the same with the enthalpy values for these equations gives the enthalpy change for the overall reaction:

$$\Delta H = (-41.7\ kJ) + (17.1\ kJ) + (+10.6\ kJ) = -14.0\ kJ$$

Practice Problem 6.20 Solution

Cu(s) is a reactant, so the first equation does not need to be altered. The third equation shows the formation of CuO, which is also desired. Reversing the second equation will cause S(s) and $SO_2(g)$ to cancel when it is added to the other two equations.

$$2\,Cu(s) + S(s) \rightarrow Cu_2S(s) \qquad \Delta H = -75.9\ kJ$$
$$SO_2(g) \rightarrow S(s) + O_2(g) \qquad \Delta H = +297\ kJ$$
$$Cu_2S(s) + 2\,O_2(g) \rightarrow 2\,CuO(s) + SO_2(g) \qquad \Delta H = -528\ kJ$$

Addition of these three equations yields an equation that is similar to the desired reaction:

$$2\,Cu(s) + O_2(g) \rightarrow 2\,CuO(s)$$
$$\Delta H = (-75.9\ kJ) + (297\ kJ) + (-528\ kJ) = -306.9\ kJ$$

The enthalpy of formation for the desired reaction is $\frac{1}{2}$ of the ΔH value listed above.

$$\text{For } Cu(s) + \frac{1}{2}O_2(g) \rightarrow CuO(s)$$
$$\Delta H = (-306.9/2) = -153\ kJ$$

Practice Problem 6.21 Solution

The sum of the enthalpies of formation of the reactants is subtracted from the sum of the enthalpies of formation of the products:

$$\Delta H^\circ_{rxn} = \Sigma m[\Delta H^\circ_f(\text{products})] - \Sigma n[\Delta H^\circ_f(\text{reactants})]$$

$$\begin{aligned}\Delta H^\circ_{rxn} &= 2[\Delta H^\circ_f(CO_2)] + 3[\Delta H^\circ_f(H_2O)] \\ &\quad - [\Delta H^\circ_f(C_2H_6)] - \frac{5}{2}[\Delta H^\circ_f(O_2)] \\ &= 2(-393.5\text{ kJ}) + 3(-285.8\text{ kJ}) \\ &\quad - (-84.0\text{ kJ}) - \frac{5}{2}(0\text{ kJ}) \\ &= -1560.4\text{ kJ}\end{aligned}$$

Practice Problem 6.22 Solution

For the products,

$$\Delta H^\circ_f = 4\text{ mol CO}\left(\frac{-110.5\text{ kJ}}{1\text{ mol CO}}\right)$$

$$+ 5\text{ mol }H_2O\left(\frac{-285.8\text{ kJ}}{1\text{ mol }H_2O}\right) = -1871\text{ kJ}$$

For the reactants,

$$\Delta H^\circ_f = 1\text{ mol }C_4H_{10}\left(\frac{-125.5\text{ kJ}}{1\text{ mol }C_4H_{10}}\right) = -125.5\text{ kJ}$$

$$\Delta H^\circ_{rxn} = (-1871\text{ kJ}) - (-125.5\text{ kJ}) = -1.746 \times 10^3\text{ kJ}$$

For 1.00 mol, the answer is the same within the limits of significant digits.

Practice Problem 6.23 Solution

For the products,

$$\Delta H^\circ_f = 1\text{ mol }CH_4\left(\frac{-74.6\text{ kJ}}{1\text{ mol }CH_4}\right) + 2\text{ mol }H_2O$$

$$\left(\frac{-241.8\text{ kJ}}{1\text{ mol }H_2O}\right) = -558.2\text{ kJ}$$

For the reactants,

$$\Delta H^\circ_f = 1\text{ mol }CO_2\left(\frac{-393.5\text{ kJ}}{1\text{ mol }CO_2}\right) = -393.5\text{ kJ}$$

$$\Delta H^\circ_{rxn} = (-558.2\text{ kJ}) - (-393.5\text{ kJ}) = -164.7\text{ kJ}$$

The calculated enthalpy of reaction is per 4 mol of H_2 (-164.7 kJ/4 mol H_2). However, 25 kg of H_2 reacted. Use the molar mass of H_2 (2.016 g/mol) to convert 25 kg of H_2 to moles of H_2 and scale the enthalpy up to match the actual number of moles of H_2.

$$\begin{aligned}&25{,}000\text{ g }H_2\left(\frac{1\text{ mol }H_2}{2.016\text{ g }H_2}\right)\left(\frac{-164.7\text{ kJ}}{4\text{ mol }H_2}\right) \\ &= -5.1 \times 10^5\text{ kJ}\end{aligned}$$

This reaction releases 5.1×10^5 kJ of heat.

Practice Problem 6.24 Solution

Since ΔU is a state function, the combustion of a mole of ethanol has the same change in internal energy whether it was done at constant volume or constant pressure.

$$\Delta U = q_v = q_p + w$$

And since $q_p = \Delta H$ and $w = P\Delta V$, the equation becomes

$$q_v = \Delta H - P\Delta V$$

Calculate q_v using the calorimetry data.

$$\begin{aligned}q_v &= -C_{cal}\Delta T = -\left(16.50\frac{\text{J}}{^\circ\text{C}}\right)(38.48^\circ\text{C}) \\ &= -634.92\text{ kJ} = -634{,}920\text{ J}\end{aligned}$$

Calculate ΔH from enthalpy of formation values.

$$\Delta H = 2\text{ mol}\left(-1275.5\frac{\text{kJ}}{\text{mol}}\right) - (0 + 0) = -2547.0\text{ kJ}$$

This ΔH value is per 4 mol of B. Scale it down for 1.0 mol of B.

$$1.0\text{ mol B}\left(\frac{-2547.0\text{ kJ}}{4\text{ mol B}}\right)\left(\frac{1000\text{ J}}{1\text{ kJ}}\right) = -636{,}750\text{ J}$$

Finally, solve for ΔV, keeping in mind that $1\text{ L}\cdot\text{atm} = 101.325\text{ J}$.

$$q_v = \Delta H - P\Delta V$$

$$P\Delta V = \Delta H - q_v$$

$$P\Delta V = -636{,}750\text{ J} - (-634{,}920\text{ J}) = -1830\text{ J}$$

$$P\Delta V = -1830\text{ J}\left(\frac{1\text{ L}\cdot\text{atm}}{101.325\text{ J}}\right) = -18\text{ L}\cdot\text{atm}$$

$$\Delta V = \frac{-18\text{ L}\cdot\text{atm}}{P} = \frac{-18\text{ L}\cdot\text{atm}}{1.0\text{ atm}} = -18\text{ L}$$

CHAPTER 7

Gases

Vishwanath Bhat/Getty Images

There's a common misconception that hot-air balloons use helium to make them rise, but that's not the case. The gas inside a hot-air balloon is literally just hot air; the same air as found all around you, but heated with a torch at the base of the balloon. Heating a gas causes it to expand, so the air inside the balloon is less dense than the cooler air around it. This allows the balloon to rise.

Chapter Outline

GOALS

- Define gas pressure and its units.
- Measure gas pressures.
- Calculate the volume or the pressure of a sample of gas at a constant temperature.
- Calculate the volume or the temperature of a sample of gas at a constant pressure.
- Using volume, pressure, and temperature data, calculate the volume, pressure, or temperature of a sample of gas.
- Using pressure, volume, and temperature, calculate the number of moles or the volume of a sample of gas that is at a constant temperature and pressure.
- Calculate the number of moles, pressure, volume, or temperature in a sample of gas using the quantities of the other three.
- Calculate the properties of each gas in a mixture of gases.
- Use the number of moles in a chemical reaction along with a balanced equation to determine the number of moles and the mass of any other reactant or product in the reaction.
- Predict how the pressure in a fixed-volume container will change after a complete reaction.
- Use the kinetic molecular theory to explain the behavior of gases.
- Describe the relationship between molecular mass and speed.
- Calculate the relative speeds and molecular masses of gases using root-mean-square speed and Graham's law of effusion.
- Discuss the circumstances that lead to deviations from ideal gas behavior.
- Use the van der Waals equation to calculate volumes and pressures for gases that display nonideal behavior.

7.1 Gas Pressure

GOALS

- Define gas pressure and its units.
- Measure gas pressure.

Background Review

Chapter 1 Science and Measurement:
Section 1.8—Density; Section 1.7— Dimensional Analysis

Matter occurs in three states, or phases: **solid**, **liquid**, and **gas** (Section 1.2). Unlike a solid or a liquid, a gas does not have a definite volume; instead, a gas expands to fill the entire volume of the container it occupies. Since the particles of a gas are much farther apart than they are in a solid or liquid state, the density of a gas is generally very much lower than the density of the same substance in the solid or liquid state (Figure 7.1), so much so that the density of a gas is typically expressed in grams per liter, g/L, rather than grams per milliliter, g/mL. The particles of a gas are in constant motion and collide with each other and any surfaces that the sample contacts (Section 7.9).

FIGURE 7.1 States of Matter Video

NOTE: You need to be online to access this video.

A solid has a fixed volume and shape. A liquid has a fixed volume but no fixed shaped. A gas has neither a fixed volume nor a shape. Since the molecules of a gas expand to fill their container, the molecules are much more spread out in a gas than in the other phases.

When a gas molecule strikes a surface of any kind, such as the walls of its container, it exerts a tiny **force**, a push or a pull, against the surface. **Pressure** is defined as force per unit area (Section 6.2 and Section 6.4). The gas pressure is the sum of all the tiny forces exerted by gas molecules impacting the surface, divided by the area of the surface.

A common method of measuring gas pressure is with a simple **barometer**, as shown in Figure 7.2. Historically, barometers were constructed by filling a meter-long tube with mercury, Hg, holding a finger over the open end, and inverting the tube into a dish of Hg. When the finger was removed, the Hg level would fall until the force of gravity pulling the mercury down was equal to the force of the air pressure on the open surface of the mercury in the dish, which pushed the mercury up into the tube. The greater the air pressure, the higher the level of mercury in the tube. The vertical height of the mercury column, corresponding to h in Figure 7.2, is a measure of pressure given as millimeters of Hg, mmHg. This unit is also called the **torr**, named for Evangelista Torricelli (1608–1647), an Italian physicist who discovered the principle of the barometer.

At sea level at 0°C on a clear, non-stormy day, the atmosphere can push the Hg into the tube to a height of 760 mm; its pressure is 760 torr, which is equal to another unit of gas pressure, the **atmosphere, atm**.

$$1 \text{ atm} = 760 \text{ torr} = 760 \text{ mmHg}$$

Atmospheric pressure, also known as **barometric pressure**, can vary depending on the weather, but 1 atm of pressure is a constant. The International System of Units (SI) unit of pressure, the pascal, Pa, is a very small unit; atmospheric pressure is generally reported in kilopascals, kPa.

$$1 \text{ atm} = 1.01325 \times 10^5 \text{ Pa} = 101.325 \text{ kPa}$$

Units of pressure you may hear if you listen to weather forecasts are the bar and millibar.

$$1 \text{ bar} = 100 \text{ kPa} = 1000 \text{ mbar}$$

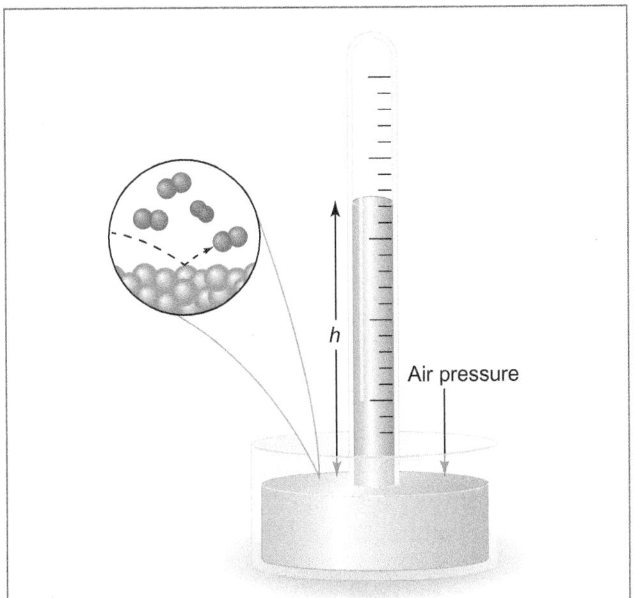

FIGURE 7.2 Simple Barometer

A simple barometer is made with a long tube closed at one end that is filled with Hg. When the open end of the filled tube is inverted under the surface of Hg in a dish, the Hg in the tube falls to a height, h, that is determined by the pressure of the air on the surface of the Hg in the dish. There is essentially no gas (and thus nearly zero pressure) in the tube above the Hg. Note that the image is not drawn to scale.

Example 7.1

a. Convert a pressure of 648 torr to atm.
b. Convert 105 kPa to atm.

Solution

Use dimensional analysis (Section 1.5) and the conversion factors provided in this section.

a. 648 torr to atm:

$$648 \text{ torr}\left(\frac{1 \text{ atm}}{760 \text{ torr}}\right) = 0.853 \text{ atm}$$

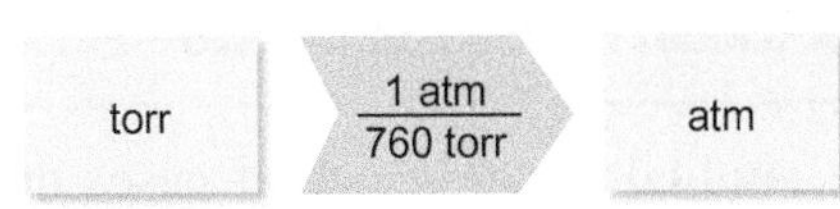

b. 105 kPa to atm:

$$105 \text{ kPa}\left(\frac{1 \text{ atm}}{101.325 \text{ kPa}}\right) = 1.04 \text{ atm}$$

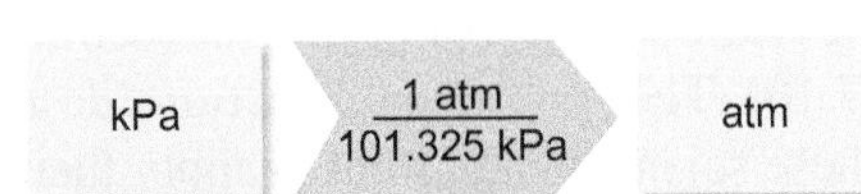

PRACTICE PROBLEM 7.1

a. Convert a pressure of 1.23 atm to torr.
b. Convert 0.911 atm to kPa.

Hint: The relevant conversion factors are 1 atm = 760 mmHg = 760 torr = 101.325 kPa.

For many years, **standard temperature and pressure (STP)** was defined as 0°C and 1 atm pressure. However, other standards were used at the same time in various industries. In 1982, the International Union of Pure and Applied Chemistry (IUPAC) redefined STP to be 0°C and 100 kPa pressure. A pressure of 100 kPa is equal to 0.98692 atm, and it is also equal to 1 bar. Because both definitions of STP are currently in use, temperature and pressure values are specified for problems in this text rather than using the abbreviation.

FIGURE 7.3 Boyle's Law Video

NOTE: You need to be online to access this video.
Boyle's law states that the pressure and volume of a sample of gas are inversely proportional, so increasing (or decreasing) one decreases (or increases) the other by the same ratio.

SECTION REVIEW

- Pressure is defined as the force per unit area.
- Gases exert a pressure at any point within them, acting in all directions.
- The pressure of a gas can be measured using a barometer.
- The most frequently used units of pressure are the atmosphere (atm), the torr (1 atm = 760 torr), the kilopascal (1 atm = 101.325 kPa), and the bar (1 bar = 100 kPa).

7.2 Boyle's Law

GOAL

- Calculate the volume or the pressure of a given sample of gas at a constant temperature.

Background Review

Chapter 0 Math Review: Section 0.8—Proportionality

Scientists studied the behavior of gases during the 17th and 18th centuries and developed a series of mathematical statements describing this behavior, called scientific laws. The work of these scientists contributed to the development of both Dalton's atomic theory (Section 2.3) and kinetic molecular theory (Section 7.10). The next several sections describe the work of these scientists and how to apply their laws to solve problems involving gases.

Robert Boyle (1627–1691), an Irish physical scientist, discovered that the volume of a given sample of a gas at a constant temperature is *inversely proportional* (Section 0.8) to its pressure.

$$V \propto \frac{1}{P}$$

This generalization, known as **Boyle's law**, applies approximately to any gas, no matter what its composition. According to Boyle's law, if you double the volume of a given sample of gas at a given temperature (increased by a factor of 2), its pressure is halved (decreased by a factor of 2). Figure 7.3 and Figure 7.4 demonstrate that the volume of a container of gas is reduced as the pressure is proportionately increased.

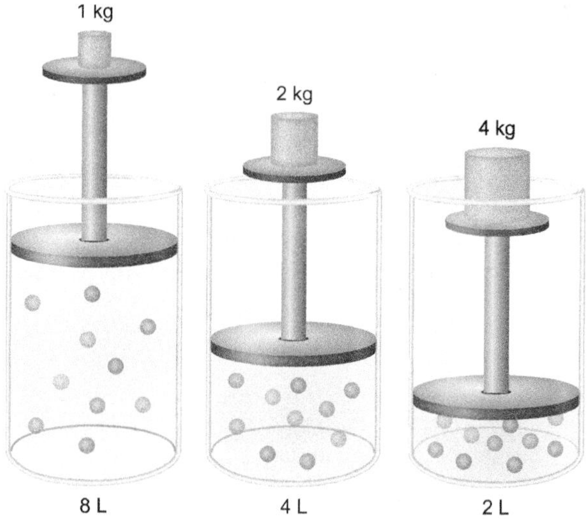

FIGURE 7.4 Boyle's Law

At the same temperature and the same number of particles, doubling the pressure reduces the volume by half. (Assume a weightless piston.)

Table 7.1 lists four different sets of pressure and volume conditions for a specific sample of gas at a constant temperature.

TABLE 7.1 Volume and Pressure Data for a Given Gas Sample at Constant Temperature

Trial Number	Volume (L)	Pressure (atm)	Volume × Pressure (L · atm)	1/V (1/L)
1	4.00	1.00	4.00	0.250
2	2.00	2.00	4.00	0.500
3	1.00	4.00	4.00	1.00
4	0.500	8.00	4.00	2.00

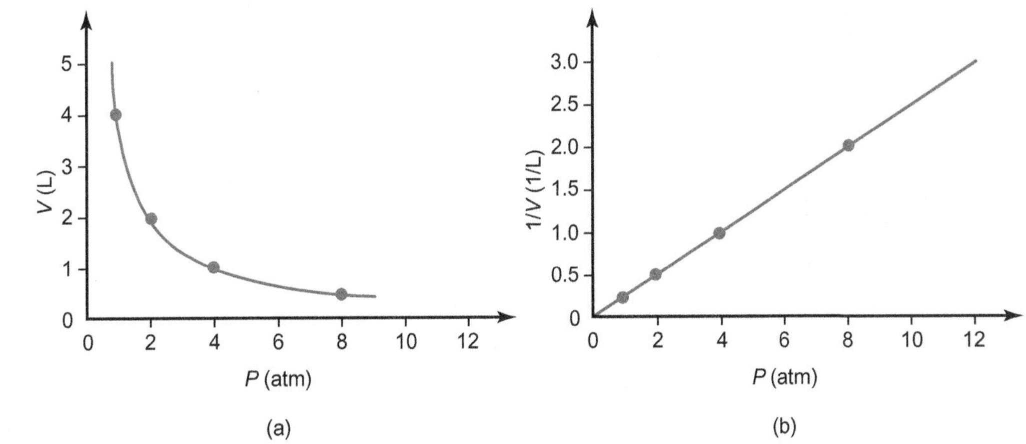

FIGURE 7.5 Graphs of Volume and Pressure Data

(a) Volume plotted against pressure results in a curved line. (b) When the reciprocal of volume is plotted against pressure, a straight line through the origin results. This indicates that $1/V$ is directly proportional to P, which is just another way of saying that V is *inversely* proportional to P.

The values in the column on the far right show that the product of the volume, V, and the pressure, P, is a constant, k. This relationship,

$$PV = k$$

is another way to express the inverse proportionality that is Boyle's law.

Boyle's law can also be represented graphically. A plot of V versus P results in the *curve* shown in Figure 7.5a, while a plot of $1/V$ versus P (data shown in Table 7.1) results in the *linear* plot shown in Figure 7.5b.

Example 7.2

The following P and V data were obtained in a laboratory experiment:

P (atm)	*V* (L)
0.700	0.707
1.102	0.450
1.524	0.325
1.902	0.261
2.420	0.205

a. Plot these data, and determine what pressure would result in a volume of 0.600 L and what pressure would result in a volume of 0.150 L.
b. Plot P versus $1/V$, and determine the two pressures again.

Solution

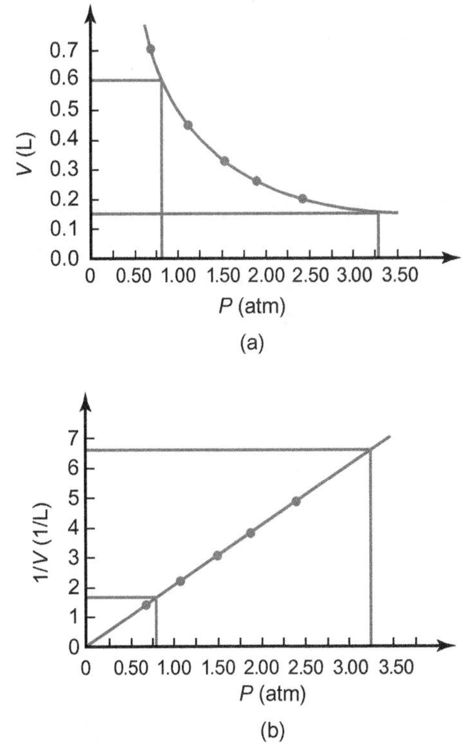

a. For $V = 0.600$ L, the pressure is 0.82 atm. The pressure is estimated to be 3.3 atm when $V = 0.150$ L.
b. When $V = 0.600$ L, $1/V = 1.67$/L, and the pressure is 0.82 atm. When $V = 0.150$ L, $1/V = 6.67$/L, and the pressure is 3.26 atm. It is easier to estimate data beyond the experimental points in the linear plot than it is in the curved plot.

PRACTICE PROBLEM 7.2

The following P and V data were obtained in a laboratory experiment:

P (atm)	V (L)	$1/V$ (L^{-1})
0.303	1.62	
0.595	0.829	
0.910	0.545	
1.202	0.412	
1.601	0.309	

a. Calculate $1/V$ and plot $1/V$ versus P.
b. Determine the pressure required to obtain a volume of 0.675 L.
c. Determine the volume that would be present at a pressure of 1.4 atm.

Hint: Start by completing the table and plotting $1/V$ versus P

For any given sample of gas, multiplying the pressure by the volume gives you a constant value, $PV = k$. If you change that sample of gas from one pressure (P_1) to another (P_2) at constant temperature, the volume will change from V_1 to V_2. Here, the subscripts represent the different times at which the measurements were made; that is, subscript 1 stands for the initial conditions, whereas subscript 2 denotes the final conditions. Both products of P and V must equal the same constant, k.

$$P_1V_1 = k = P_2V_2$$

Because both products are equal to the same constant, they must also equal each other.

$$P_1V_1 = P_2V_2 \qquad (7.1)$$

You can use this expression of Boyle's law to solve for any one of these variables when the other three are known. The units must be the same on each side of the equation in all gas law calculations.

Example 7.3

A 3.50 L sample of hydrogen gas has a pressure of 0.750 atm. What is its volume if its pressure is increased to 1.50 atm at constant temperature?

Solution

You are given the initial pressure, the initial volume, and the final pressure, and you are asked to calculate the final volume. Use Boyle's law (Equation 7.1):

$$P_1V_1 = P_2V_2$$

The data for the initial and final conditions can be tabulated as follows:

Initial Conditions	Final Conditions
$P_1 = 0.750$ atm	$P_2 = 1.50$ atm
$V_1 = 3.50$ L	$V_2 = ?$

The pressure increases (i.e., $P_2 > P_1$), so the volume should decrease (i.e., $V_2 < V_1$).

Rearrange Equation 7.1 to solve for V_2, and plug in the values from the table.

$$V_2 = \frac{P_1V_1}{P_2}$$

$$V_2 = \frac{(0.750 \text{ atm})(3.50 \text{ L})}{1.50 \text{ atm}}$$

$$V_2 = 1.75 \text{ L}$$

Once the values have been placed into the equation, the pressure units cancel and the remaining unit, L, is appropriate for what was asked in the problem, the volume. Once you complete the math, you can see that the final volume, V_2, is less than the initial volume, V_1, as predicted. Doubling the pressure caused the volume to decrease to one-half of its initial value.

PRACTICE PROBLEM 7.3

A sample of helium gas initially occupies 35.0 mL at 1.50 atm. What pressure is needed to reduce its volume to 20.5 mL at constant temperature?

Hint: Start with the relationship between pressure and volume, Boyle's law.

The units of pressure and volume must be the same on each side of the equation, $P_1V_1 = P_2V_2$. If the units are not the same, one or more of the units must be converted.

Example 7.4

A 1.45 L sample of argon gas has a pressure of 0.950 atm. What is its volume after its pressure is increased to 787 torr at constant temperature?

Solution

Use Boyle's law (Equation 7.1) when the variables in the problem involve pressure and volume:

$$P_1V_1 = P_2V_2$$

Tabulating the data gives

Initial Conditions	Final Conditions
$P_1 = 0.950$ atm	$P_2 = 787$ torr
$V_1 = 1.45$ L	$V_2 = ?$

Because the pressures are given in two different units, one of them must be converted to the units of the other. In this case, convert P_2 from torr to atm:

$$P_2 = 787 \text{ torr}\left(\frac{1 \text{ atm}}{760 \text{ torr}}\right) = 1.036 \text{ atm}$$

$$V_2 = \frac{P_1V_1}{P_2}$$

$$V_2 = \frac{(0.950 \text{ atm})(1.45 \text{ L})}{1.036 \text{ atm}} = 1.33 \text{ L}$$

Alternatively, you could have converted P_1 from atm to torr:

$$P_1 = 0.950 \text{ atm}\left(\frac{760 \text{ torr}}{1 \text{ atm}}\right) = 722 \text{ torr}$$

$$V_2 = \frac{P_1V_1}{P_2}$$

$$V_2 = \frac{(722 \text{ torr})(1.45 \text{ L})}{787 \text{ torr}} = 1.33 \text{ L}$$

Since the pressure of the gas increased, it makes sense that the volume of the gas decreased.

PRACTICE PROBLEM 7.4

The pressure of a nitrogen gas sample of unknown volume was changed from 1.20 atm to 744 torr at constant temperature, resulting in a volume of 70.4 mL. What was its initial volume?

Hint: Start with the relationship between pressure and volume, Boyle's law, and rearrange the equation to solve for V_1. Make sure the pressure units are consistent.

Example 7.5

Calculate the pressure required to change a 3.38 L sample of neon gas initially at 1.15 atm to 925 mL, at constant temperature.

Solution

Start by tabulating the data:

Initial Conditions	Final Conditions
$P_1 = 1.15$ atm	$P_2 = ?$
$V_1 = 3.38$ L	$V_2 = 925 \text{ mL}\left(\frac{1 \text{ L}}{1000 \text{ mL}}\right) = 0.925 \text{ L}$

The two volume measurements were in different units, so one of them has been changed (V_2, in this case). Once the volumes are in consistent units, you can see that the volume decreases. As a result, the pressure must increase, which means $P_2 > P_1$.

Now, rearrange Boyle's law (Equation 7.1) to isolate P_2 and plug in the appropriate values:

$$P_1V_1 = P_2V_2$$

$$P_2 = \frac{P_1V_1}{V_2}$$

$$P_2 = \frac{(1.15 \text{ atm})(3.38 \text{ L})}{0.925 \text{ L}} = 4.20 \text{ atm}$$

The final pressure is, in fact, greater than the initial pressure.

PRACTICE PROBLEM 7.5

Calculate the initial pressure of a 485 mL sample of helium gas that has been changed at constant temperature to 1.16 L and 1.18 atm.

Hint: Use Boyle's law, and make sure measurements of the same property are expressed in the same units.

SECTION REVIEW

- Boyle's law states that the pressure and volume of a sample of gas are inversely proportional.

EVERYDAY CONNECTION

You apply Boyle's law with every breath that you take. As you prepare to breathe in, you contract your diaphragm, which pulls down on your lungs and expands their internal volume. This increased volume lowers the internal pressure of your lungs and allows air to rush in until the internal pressure matches the atmospheric (external) pressure. This completes an inhalation. To exhale, you relax your diaphragm, which pushes your lungs back up and decreases their volume. This increases the internal pressure of your lungs and forces air out. Try the Lung Volume and Pressure tab in the Respiratory System Activity in Figure 7.6.

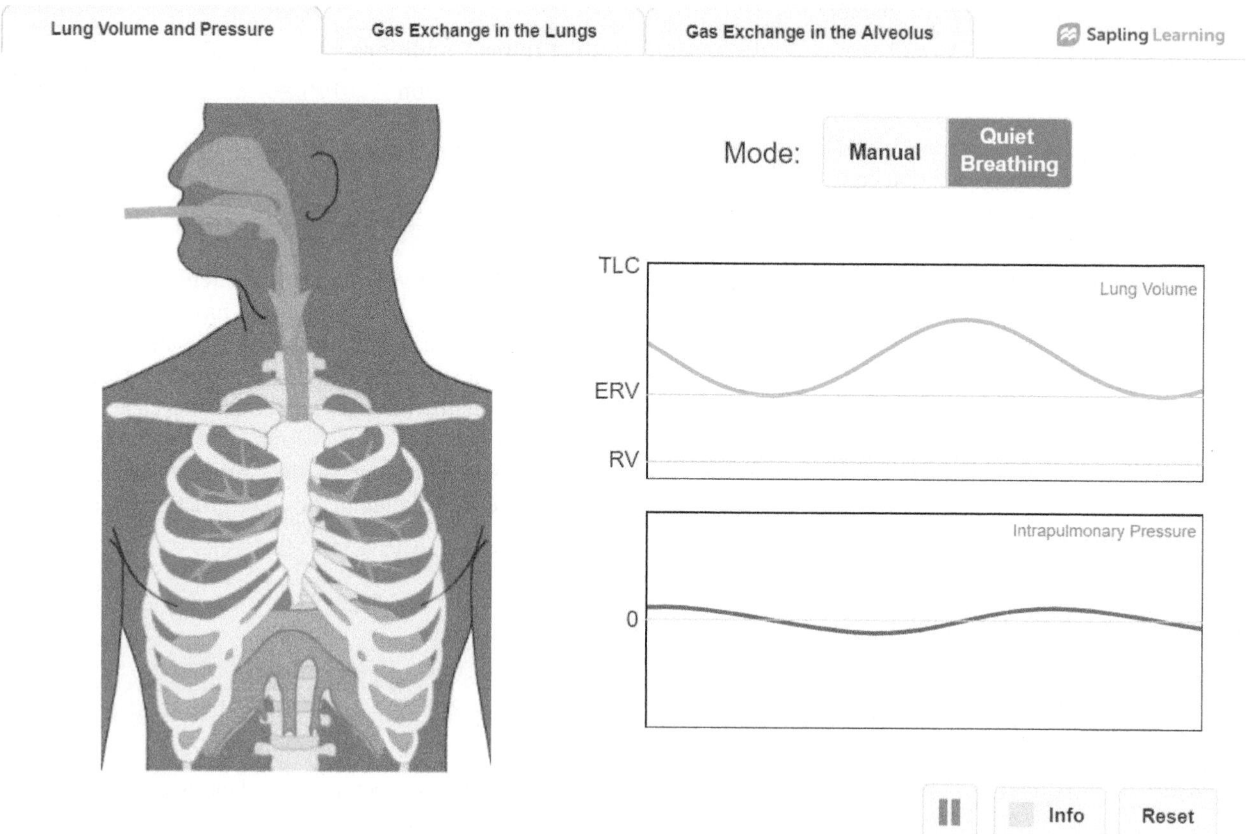

FIGURE 7.6 Respiratory System Activity

NOTE: You need to be online to access this activity.

Start by clicking the **Quiet Breathing** button and watch how the graphs of volume and pressure are related to each other. Next, click the **Manual** button. In manual mode, you can change the lung volume by dragging the circled areas within the chest diagram, then see how both graphs respond. Note that the acronyms TLC, ERV, and RV stand for total lung capacity, expiratory reserve volume, and residual volume, respectively, which are terms you might encounter in the medical professions. Also note that only the first tab of the activity is relevant to this section.

- Boyle's law applies to a given sample of gas at constant temperature. That means that no gas particles may enter or leave the container, and the temperature remains the same.
- The form of Boyle's law most often used in calculations, $P_1V_1 = P_2V_2$, allows for the use of any units of pressure and volume, provided the units are consistent within the calculation.

7.3 Charles's Law

GOAL

- Calculate the volume or the temperature of a given sample of gas at a constant pressure.

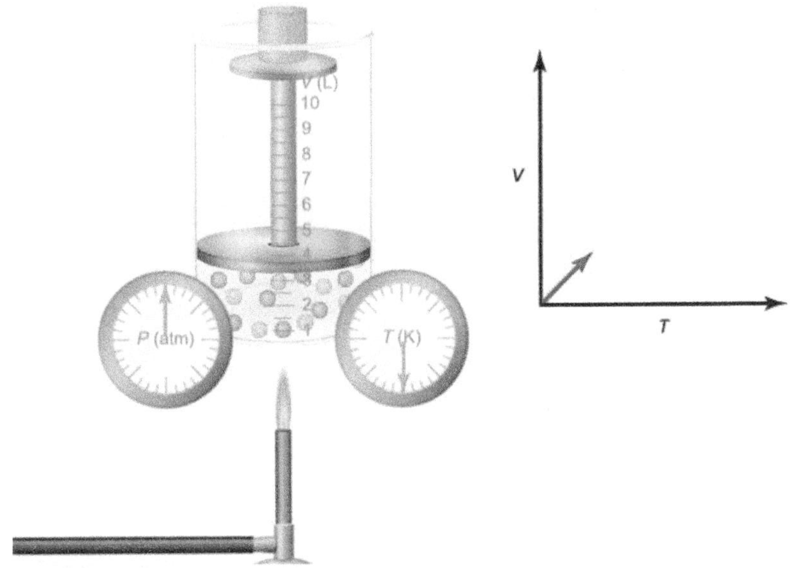

FIGURE 7.7 Charles's Law Video I

NOTE: You need to be online to access this video.

A gas is held at a constant pressure of 1.50 atm. As the temperature increases from 250 K to 450 K, the molecules move faster and spread out, pushing the movable piston upward and increasing the volume of the container. The plot of volume, *V*, versus absolute temperature, *T*, shows that these quantities are directly proportional.

Background Review

Chapter 0 Math Review: Section 0.8—Proportionality

Chapter 1 Science and Measurement
Section 1.9—Temperature Scales

In 1787, J. A. C. Charles (1746–1823) discovered that when the pressure is constant, the volume of a sample of gas varies directly (Section 0.8) with the absolute or Kelvin temperature,

$$V \propto T$$

Demonstrations of this relationship, referred to as **Charles's law**, are available in the videos in Figure 7.7 and Figure 7.8.

Temperature and volume data for a specific gas sample are given in Table 7.2 and plotted in Figure 7.9.

The column on the far right of Table 7.2 gives the results of dividing the volume by the corresponding *absolute* temperature, which yields the same ratio for all the experiments.

$$\frac{V}{T} = k \quad \text{or} \quad V = kT$$

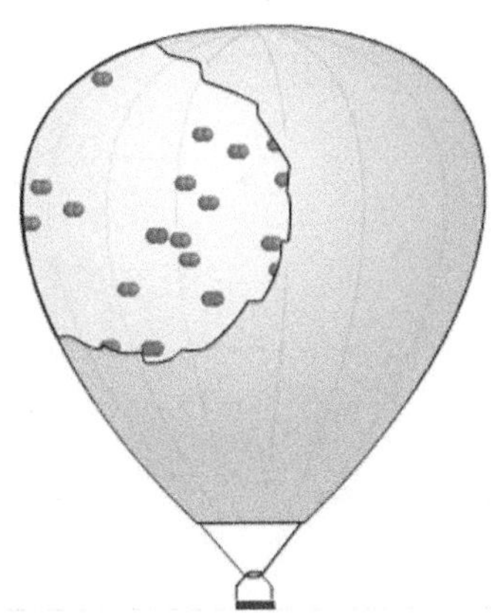

FIGURE 7.8 Charles's Law Video II

NOTE: You need to be online to access this video.

When a sample of gas is heated at constant pressure, its volume expands.

TABLE 7.2 Temperature and Volume Data for a Given Sample of Gas at Constant Pressure

	Temperature (K)	Volume (L)	*V/T* (L/K)
1	273	0.400	0.00147
2	373	0.548	0.00147
3	473	0.692	0.00146
4	573	0.840	0.00147

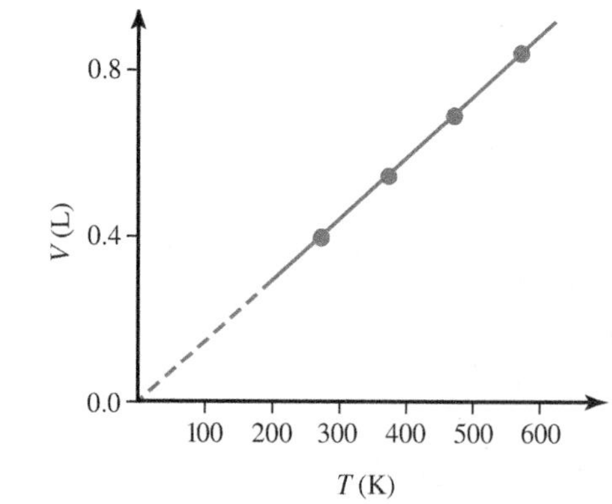

FIGURE 7.9 Dependence of Volume on Temperature at Constant Pressure

Plot of the data given in Table 7.2, showing the directly proportional relationship between the volume of a gas and the Kelvin temperature.

The Charles's law equation can also be written in terms of two sets of conditions for a given sample of gas at constant pressure.

$$\frac{V_1}{T_1} = \frac{V_2}{T_2} \tag{7.2}$$

This relationship can be visualized in Figure 7.10, where doubling the absolute temperature doubles the volume of the gas, while the pressure (exerted by the 2 kg mass) remains constant.

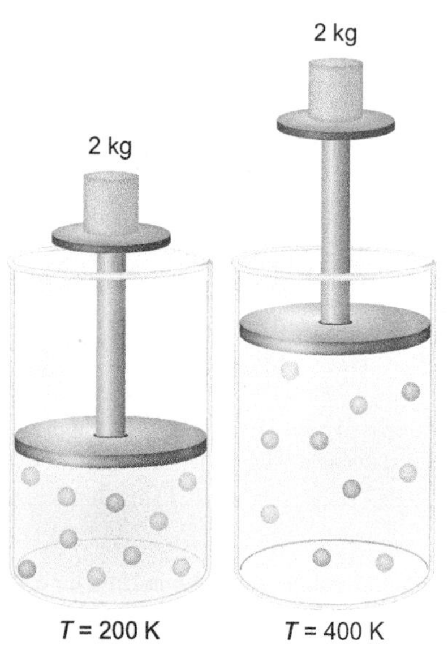

FIGURE 7.10 Charles's Law

At the same pressure with the same number of particles, doubling the absolute temperature of a gas, will double the volume.

The Kelvin (absolute) scale must be used in all gas law problems involving temperature.

Equation 1.4 allows you to convert temperatures between the Celsius and Kelvin scales.

Example 7.6

A 678 mL sample of helium gas, initially at 0°C, is heated at constant pressure. If the final volume of the gas is 0.896 L, what is its final temperature in °C?

Solution

You are given the initial temperature, the initial volume, and the final volume, and you are asked to calculate the final temperature. Use Charles's law (Equation 7.2):

$$\frac{V_1}{T_1} = \frac{V_2}{T_2}$$

The data for the initial and final conditions, after converting to consistent and appropriate units, can be tabulated as follows:

Initial Conditions	Final Conditions
$T_1 = 0°\text{C} + 273.15 = 273\ \text{K}$	$T_2 = ?$
$V_1 = 678\ \text{mL}\left(\frac{1\ \text{L}}{1000\ \text{mL}}\right) = 0.678\ \text{L}$	$V_2 = 0.896\ \text{L}$

You can see in the problem that the sample is heated, so the final temperature will be larger than the initial temperature (i.e., $T_2 > T_1$).

Rearrange Equation 7.2 to solve for T_2 and substitute the values from the table:

$$T_2 = \frac{T_1 V_2}{V_1}$$

$$T_2 = \frac{(273\ \text{K})(0.896\ \text{L})}{0.678\ \text{L}} = 361\ \text{K}$$

Finally, convert the absolute temperature to °C:

$$361\ \text{K} - 273.15 = 88°\text{C}$$

Because the volume of the sample increased when there was no change in pressure or number of gas particles, the temperature must have increased as well.

PRACTICE PROBLEM 7.6

A 456 mL sample of argon gas is expanded at constant pressure to 1.75 L at 55°C. What was the original temperature of the gas in °C?

Hint: Use the gas law that relates temperature and volume and verify that the units are appropriate.

Steve Lemon, Macmillan Learning

FIGURE 7.14 Video Tutorial: Gas Laws

NOTE: You need to be online to access this video.

This video shows how to identify the correct formula and units to use for gas law calculations.

the second condition is labeled with a subscript 2, then the equation for the first condition is divided by the equation for the second.

$$\frac{P_1V_1}{P_2V_2} = \frac{n_1RT_1}{n_2RT_2}$$

The gas law constant R is the same for all conditions and always cancels out.

$$\frac{P_1V_1}{P_2V_2} = \frac{n_1T_1}{n_2T_2}$$

When solving problems by using $PV = nRT$ in a ratio for two different conditions, any variable that does not change can be canceled out of the equation. In Example 7.10, the number of moles is constant, so the equation reduces to the combined gas law. If only pressure and volume change, the equation reduces to Boyle's law. If only volume and temperature change, the equation reduces to Charles's law. If only volume and moles change, the equation reduces to Avogadro's law. The video in Figure 7.14 demonstrates how to identify which gas law to use and how to quickly derive other formulas from the ideal gas law, so that you only need to memorize one gas law.

Example 7.10

Calculate the final volume of a sample of hydrogen gas that has an initial volume of 7.10 L at 0°C and 760 torr pressure, if the temperature and pressure are changed to 33°C and 696 torr, respectively.

Solution

Start by tabulating the variables and making any necessary adjustments to the units.

Initial Conditions	Final Conditions
$V_1 = 7.10\ \text{L}$	$V_2 = ?$
$P_1 = 760\ \text{torr}$	$P_2 = 696\ \text{torr}$
$T_1 = 0°\text{C} + 273.15 = 273\ \text{K}$	$T_2 = 33°\text{C} + 273.15 = 306\ \text{K}$

Because the temperature increases and the pressure decreases between the initial and final conditions, the volume will increase (i.e., $V_2 > V_1$). R is constant, and no change has been indicated for the number of moles of gas, so assume that $n_1 = n_2$, which simplifies the equation to

$$\frac{P_1V_1}{P_2V_2} = \frac{\cancel{n_1}\cancel{R}T_1}{\cancel{n_2}\cancel{R}T_2}$$

$$\frac{P_1V_1}{P_2V_2} = \frac{T_1}{T_2}$$

Rearrange to isolate V_2.

$$V_2 = \frac{T_2P_1V_1}{T_1P_2}$$

Substitute the data and calculate.

$$V_2 = \frac{(306\ \text{K})(760\ \text{torr})(7.10\ \text{L})}{(273\ \text{K})(696\ \text{torr})} = 8.7\ \text{L}$$

PRACTICE PROBLEM 7.10

Calculate the final pressure of a sample of helium gas that has an initial volume of 8.35 L at 10°C and 1.13 atm pressure if the number of moles doubles and the volume is changed to 5.25 L with no change in temperature.

Hint: Start with

$$\frac{P_1V_1}{P_2V_2} = \frac{n_1RT_1}{n_2RT_2}$$

Then, cancel any variables that do not change from the initial conditions to the final conditions and solve for P_2.

Example 7.11

Calculate the volume of 1.63 mol carbon dioxide gas at 295 K and 1.14 atm.

Solution

Begin with the ideal gas law (Equation 7.5).

$$PV = nRT$$

Rearrange the ideal gas law to solve for V, and substitute the values from the problem for the variables, taking care that like units cancel as shown in the second equation.

$$V = \frac{nRT}{P}$$

$$V = \frac{(1.63\ \cancel{\text{mol}})\left(0.08206\ \frac{\text{L}\cdot\cancel{\text{atm}}}{\cancel{\text{mol}}\cdot\cancel{\text{K}}}\right)(295\ \cancel{\text{K}})}{1.14\ \cancel{\text{atm}}}$$

$$= 34.6\ \text{L}$$

PRACTICE PROBLEM 7.11

Calculate the volume of 0.898 mol methane gas (CH_4) at 292 K and 1.06 atm.

Hint: The number of moles of gas, the temperature, and the pressure are known. Using the ideal gas law, solve for the volume.

Example 7.12

Calculate the volume of 42.6 g of oxygen gas at 35°C and 792 torr.

Solution

Use the ideal gas law (Equation 7.5), but first convert the data in the problem to the units that are compatible with the given value of R.

For n: $42.6\ \text{g O}_2\left(\frac{1\ \text{mol O}_2}{32.00\ \text{g O}_2}\right) = 1.33\ \text{mol O}_2$

For T: $35°\text{C} + 273 = 308\ \text{K}$

For P: $792\ \text{torr}\left(\frac{1\ \text{atm}}{760\ \text{torr}}\right) = 1.04\ \text{atm}$

Now, rearrange the ideal gas law to solve for V.

$$PV = nRT$$

$$V = \frac{nRT}{P}$$

$$V = \frac{(1.33\ \text{mol})\left(0.08206\ \frac{\text{L}\cdot\text{atm}}{\text{mol}\cdot\text{K}}\right)(308\ \text{K})}{1.04\ \text{atm}}$$

$$= 32.3\ \text{L}$$

PRACTICE PROBLEM 7.12

Calculate the volume of 7.11 g of nitrogen gas at 16°C and 799 torr.

Hint: Adjust the units given in the problem to match the units of R, and then use the ideal gas law to solve for the volume of the gas.

Example 7.13

Calculate the pressure of 0.0789 mol of chlorine gas that occupies 891 mL at −15°C.

Solution

You must convert the data in the problem into the appropriate units and then rearrange the ideal gas law to solve for P:

For T: $-15°\text{C} + 273.15 = 258\ \text{K}$

For V: $891\ \text{mL}\left(\frac{1\ \text{L}}{1000\ \text{mL}}\right) = 0.891\ \text{L}$

Rearrange the ideal gas law to solve for P:

$$PV = nRT$$

$$P = nRT/V$$

$$P = \frac{(0.0789\ \text{mol})\left(0.08206\ \frac{\text{L}\cdot\text{atm}}{\text{mol}\cdot\text{K}}\right)(258\ \text{K})}{0.891\ \text{L}}$$

$$= 1.88\ \text{atm}$$

PRACTICE PROBLEM 7.13

Calculate the pressure of 0.0855 mol neon gas if it occupies 66.1 mL at 25°C.

Hint: Values for n, V, and T are given. Use the ideal gas law to solve for P. Be sure to convert the volume to liters and the temperature to kelvins.

Example 7.14

Calculate the number of moles of oxygen gas in a 2.60 L container at 19°C and 755 torr.

Solution

First, convert the data in the problem into the appropriate units.

For P: $755\ \text{torr}\left(\frac{1\ \text{atm}}{760\ \text{torr}}\right) = 0.993\ \text{atm}$

For T: $19°\text{C} + 273 = 292\ \text{K}$

Next, rearrange the ideal gas law and solve for n.

$$PV = nRT$$

$$n = \frac{PV}{RT}$$

$$n = \frac{(0.993\ \text{atm})(2.60\ \text{L})}{\left(0.08206\ \frac{\text{L}\cdot\text{atm}}{\text{mol}\cdot\text{K}}\right)(291\ \text{K})}$$

$$= 0.108\ \text{mol}$$

PRACTICE PROBLEM 7.14

Calculate the number of moles of carbon dioxide gas in a 375 mL container at 15°C and 655 torr.

Hint: Values for P, V, and T are given. Use the ideal gas law to solve for n. Be sure to convert the pressure to atmospheres, the temperature to kelvins, and the volume to liters.

SECTION REVIEW

- The ideal gas law (Equation 7.5), $PV = nRT$, makes it possible to calculate any one of the four variables (P, V, n, and T) when the other three are known.
- The gas law constant R is equal to $0.08206 \frac{\text{L} \cdot \text{atm}}{\text{mol} \cdot \text{K}}$ and is the same for all samples of gas.
- The ideal gas law is exact for a hypothetical *ideal gas*, and it approximates the behavior of real gases.

7.7 Dalton's Law of Partial Pressures

GOAL

- Calculate the properties of each gas in a mixture of gases.

Background Review

Chapter 3 Compounds and the Mole: Section 3.7—The Mole; Section 3.1—Chemical Formulas

In a mixture of gases, all the components occupy the entire volume of the container at the same temperature. However, the pressures of the individual gases depend on the number of individual particles of each gas and will vary as the number of moles varies.

A mixture of gases follows the same laws as a pure gas that is composed of only one substance. **Dalton's law of partial pressures** enables you to consider the properties of each component of a gas mixture individually. The law states that the total pressure of the mixture is equal to the sum of the individual pressures of the components of a gaseous mixture.

$$P_{\text{total}} = P_1 + P_2 + \cdots + P_n \tag{7.6}$$

The individual pressure, P_i, of each component of a mixture is referred to as a **partial pressure**. If the mixture is in a container with a pressure equal to that of the atmosphere, the total pressure is equal to the barometric pressure.

Example 7.15

A mixture of oxygen and neon contains oxygen at a pressure of 726 torr and neon at a pressure of 44 torr. What is the total pressure of the mixture?

Solution

$$P_{\text{total}} = P_{O_2} + P_{\text{Ne}}$$

$$P_{\text{total}} = 726 \text{ torr} + 44 \text{ torr} = 770 \text{ torr}$$

P_{total}, therefore, is just slightly greater than 1 atm (760 torr).

PRACTICE PROBLEM 7.15

A mixture of oxygen and neon has a pressure of 1.031 atm. If the pressure of the oxygen is 0.922 atm, what is the pressure of the neon?

Hint: Rearrange Dalton's law (Equation 7.6) to solve for the pressure of neon.

Thus, the partial pressure of any gas in a mixture can be calculated if the total pressure and the partial pressures of the other gases in the mixture are known. Figure 7.15 is an animation that demonstrates how each gas contributes to the overall pressure when two gases, A and B, are mixed together.

The video in Figure 7.16 shows how to use Dalton's law to solve a problem.

The ideal gas law applies to the total pressure of a mixture of gases, P_{total}, and to each of the components of the mixture, separately, P_i. That is,

$$P_{\text{total}} = \frac{n_{\text{total}}RT}{V}$$

and

$$P_i = \frac{n_iRT}{V}$$

where i represents any component of the mixture. Combining these two equations gives you a relationship between the partial pressure of a component of a gas mixture and its **mole fraction**, X_i (Equation 7.7). Mole fraction is the number of moles of a component divided by the total moles in the mixture, $X_i = n_i/n_{\text{total}}$.

$$\frac{P_i}{P_{\text{total}}} = \frac{\left(\frac{n_iRT}{V}\right)}{\left(\frac{n_{\text{total}}RT}{V}\right)}$$

$$\frac{P_i}{P_{\text{total}}} = \frac{n_i}{n_{\text{total}}} \tag{7.7}$$

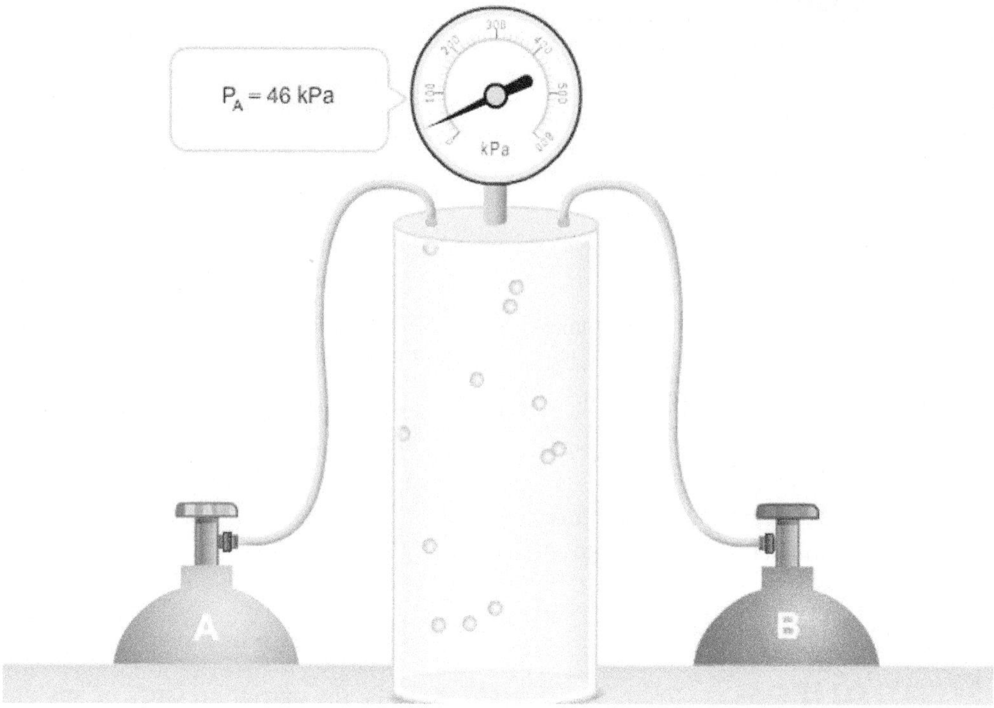

FIGURE 7.15 Dalton's Law of Partial Pressures Video

NOTE: You need to be online to access this video.

Gas B is pumped into a container that already contains gas A, and the partial pressure of gas B is calculated.

Steve Lemon, Macmillan Learning

FIGURE 7.16 Video Tutorial: Partial Pressure

NOTE: You need to be online to access this video.

This video shows how to calculate pressures in a mixture of gases.

Example 7.16

A 10.5 L sample of gas at 292 K contains O_2 at 0.622 atm and N_2 at 0.517 atm. Calculate (a) the total number of moles of gas in the sample and (b) the number of moles of O_2 present.

Solution

a. Use Dalton's law (Equation 7.6) to calculate the total pressure of the gas mixture, then use the ideal gas law (Equation 7.5) to calculate the total number of moles of gas in the sample.

First, determine the total pressure of the mixture.

$$P_{\text{total}} = P_{O_2} + P_{N_2}$$
$$P_{\text{total}} = 0.622 \text{ atm} + 0.517 \text{ atm} = 1.139 \text{ atm}$$

Next, rearrange the ideal gas law to calculate the total number of moles of gas in the mixture:

$$n_{\text{total}} = \frac{P_{\text{total}}V}{RT}$$
$$n_{\text{total}} = \frac{(1.139 \text{ atm})(10.5 \text{ L})}{\left(0.08206 \dfrac{\text{L}\cdot\text{atm}}{\text{mol}\cdot\text{K}}\right)(292 \text{ K})}$$
$$= 0.499 \text{ mol}$$

b. To calculate the number of moles of O_2, use the ideal gas law again, but this time use the partial pressure of O_2:

$$n_{O_2} = \frac{P_{O_2}V}{RT}$$
$$n_{O_2} = \frac{(0.622 \text{ atm})(10.5 \text{ L})}{\left(0.08206 \dfrac{\text{L}\cdot\text{atm}}{\text{mol}\cdot\text{K}}\right)(292 \text{ K})}$$
$$= 0.273 \text{ mol}$$

Alternative solution for Example 7.16 part (b): Use the total number of moles in the mixture from part (a) and Equation 7.7 to calculate the number of moles of oxygen.

$$\frac{P_i}{P_{total}} = \frac{n_i}{n_{total}}$$

$$\frac{P_{O_2}}{P_{total}} = \frac{n_{O_2}}{n_{total}}$$

Now, rearrange this equation to solve for the number of moles of oxygen.

$$n_{O_2} = \frac{P_{O_2}(n_{total})}{P_{total}}$$

$$n_{O_2} = \frac{(0.622 \text{ atm})(0.499 \text{ mol})}{1.139 \text{ atm}}$$

$$= 0.273 \text{ mol}$$

PRACTICE PROBLEM 7.16

A 2.48 L sample of gas at 272 K and 0.934 atm contains 2.95 g O_2 and an unknown amount of N_2. Calculate (a) the partial pressures of O_2 and N_2 and (b) the mass of N_2 present.

Hint: Determine the number of moles of O_2 and then the partial pressure of O_2 using the ideal gas law. Then use Dalton's law to determine the partial pressure of N_2, which can be used in the ideal gas law to determine the number of moles of N_2.

Gases that are only slightly soluble in water are often collected over water (Figure 7.17).

However, any gases in contact with liquid water will contain water vapor. The pressure of the water vapor in such a system does not vary in the same way that the pressure of an ordinary gas varies, because it is in contact with liquid water and the temperature determines how much water vapor is present in the gas above the water. At a given temperature, the pressure of water vapor in contact with liquid water is a constant, called the **vapor pressure** of water at that temperature. The vapor pressure of water increases as the temperature increases (Figure 7.18), but the relationship is *not* a direct proportionality (Section 0.8). Some water vapor values at various temperatures are listed in Table 7.3.

Vapor pressure is independent of the volume of the liquid and the volume of the gas mixture; vapor

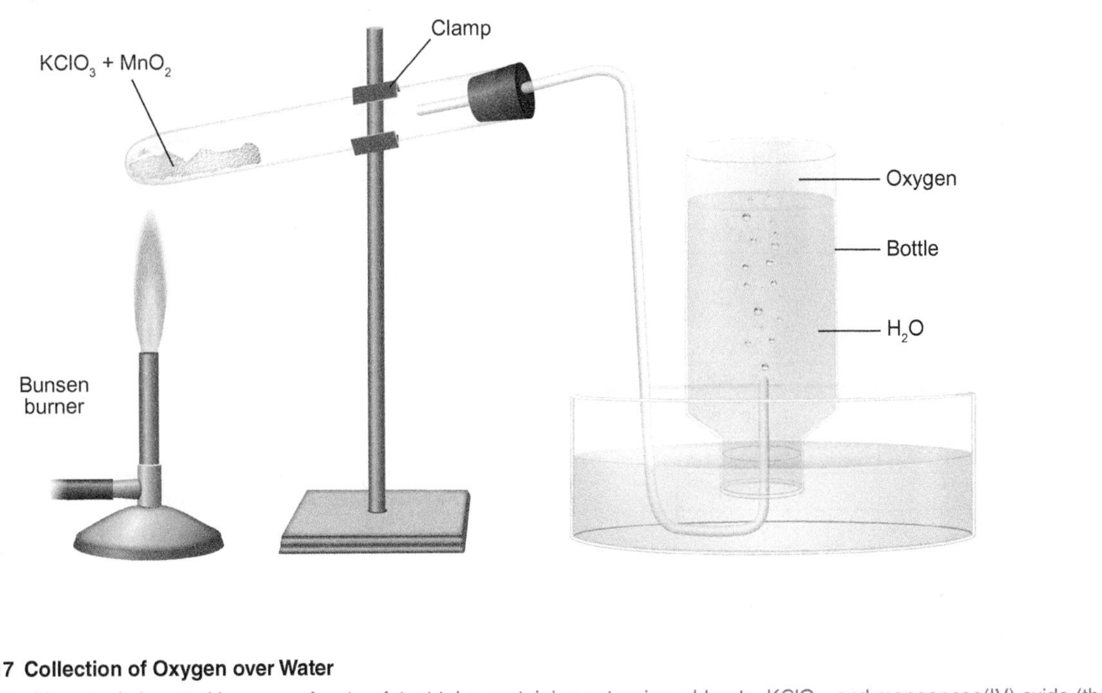

FIGURE 7.17 Collection of Oxygen over Water

A bottle filled with water is inverted in a pan of water. A test tube containing potassium chlorate, $KClO_3$, and manganese(IV) oxide (the catalyst) is arranged so that the oxygen produced when the tube is heated displaces the water in the bottle. When the $KClO_3$ in the test tube is heated, the following decomposition reaction occurs.

$2\,KClO_3 \rightarrow 2\,KCl + 3\,O_2$

The mass lost from the test tube corresponds to the mass of oxygen produced. The oxygen gas that is trapped in the bottle will have water vapor mixed with it.

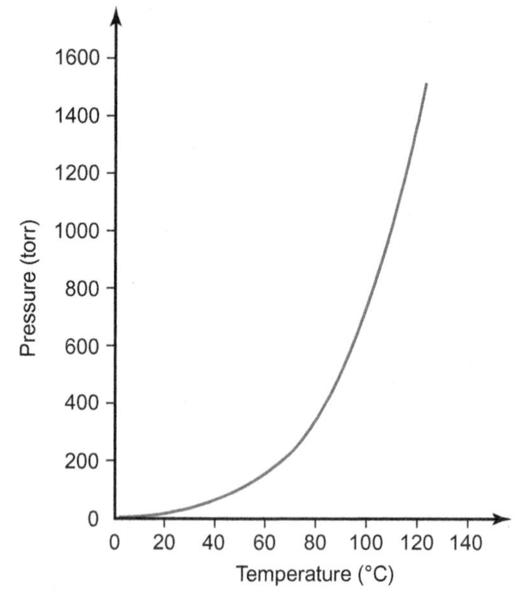

FIGURE 7.18 Variation of the Vapor Pressure of Water with Temperature

The vapor pressure of water increases exponentially as the temperature increases.

TABLE 7.3 Vapor Pressure Values for Water

Temperature (°C)	Vapor Pressure (torr)
0	4.579
5	6.543
10	9.209
15	12.788
20	17.535
25	23.756
30	31.824
35	42.175
40	55.324
45	71.88
50	92.51
55	118.04
60	149.38
65	187.54
70	233.7
75	289.1
80	355.1
85	433.6
90	525.76
95	633.90
100	760.00

pressure is also independent of the shape of the container and the surface area of the liquid. The *only* factor that determines the vapor pressure of pure water is *temperature*. For example, if you expand the volume of a gas collected over water, you would expect, using Boyle's law (Equation 7.1), that the pressure of the sample would decrease, which is true for every component *except* water vapor. The pressure of the water vapor does decrease initially as the volume expands, but more liquid water will evaporate into the gas phase, and the pressure of the water vapor will eventually climb back to its original value, as long as liquid water is present. If the gas mixture is compressed instead, the pressure of the water vapor will initially increase, but then some of the water vapor will condense back into the liquid phase and the vapor pressure will return to its original value.

The law of partial pressures applies to mixtures containing water vapor, as well as to other gas mixtures. Problems involving water vapor in contact with liquid water are solved using the water vapor pressure values found in Table 7.3.

Example 7.17

Oxygen gas is collected over water in an apparatus such as that shown in Figure 7.18 at a barometric pressure of 759 torr at 25°C.

a. What is the pressure of the water vapor?
b. What is the pressure of the oxygen gas?

Solution

a. According to Table 7.3, the water vapor pressure (P_{H_2O}) at 25°C is 23.756 torr.
b. Use Dalton's law to calculate the pressure of the oxygen gas (P_{O_2}) from P_{H_2O} and the given P_{total},

$$P_{O_2} = P_{total} - P_{H_2O} = 759 \text{ torr} - 23.756 \text{ torr}$$
$$= 783 \text{ torr}$$

PRACTICE PROBLEM 7.17

What volume of oxygen, collected over water, will be obtained at 25°C and 762 torr barometric pressure from the thermal decomposition of 0.0600 mol $KClO_3$ to form KCl and O_2?

Hint: Find the water vapor pressure at the specified temperature and subtract that from the total pressure to determine the volume due to oxygen alone based on the partial pressure of oxygen.

SECTION REVIEW

- Dalton's law of partial pressures (Equation 7.6) states that the total pressure of a mixture of gases is the sum of the individual, or partial pressures, of each component gas in the mixture; that is, $P_{\text{total}} = P_1 + P_2 + \cdots + P_n$.
- Because the pressure of each component depends on the amount of each component, Dalton's law is often used with the ideal gas law to determine the number of moles or the pressure due to individual component gases of a mixture.
- A gas sample in contact with liquid water contains water vapor at a partial pressure determined by the temperature. The values for water's vapor pressure at various temperatures are listed in Table 7.3.

7.8 Molar Mass and Density in Gas Law Calculations

GOAL

- Use the number of moles in a chemical reaction along with a balanced equation to determine the number of moles and the mass of any other reactant or product in the reaction.

Background Review

Chapter 5 Stoichiometry: Section 5.1—Mole Calculations for Chemical Reactions; Section 5.7—Calculations Involving Other Quantities

The ideal gas law relates the number of moles of the gas to the volume, pressure, and absolute temperature. Examples of some of the many applications of the ideal gas law are introduced in this section. One application involves starting with the mass of a known gas rather than the number of moles. The ideal gas law can also be used to calculate the number of moles of an unknown sample, and given the mass of gas in the sample, its molar mass, $\mathcal{M}$, can then be determined.

Example 7.18

Calculate the volume that 48.3 g of sulfur dioxide gas occupies at 0°C and 1.00 atm pressure.

Solution

Use the molar mass of SO_2 to calculate the number of moles of SO_2 present.

$$n_{SO_2} = 48.3 \text{ g } SO_2\left(\frac{1 \text{ mol } SO_2}{64.064 \text{ g } SO_2}\right) = 0.754 \text{ mol } SO_2$$

Now use the ideal gas law (Equation 7.5) to calculate the volume under the stated conditions of T and P. Do not forget to convert the temperature to kelvins ($T = 0°\text{C} + 273.15 = 273 \text{ K}$).

$$PV = nRT$$

$$V = \frac{nRT}{P}$$

$$V = \frac{(0.754 \text{ mol})\left(0.08206 \frac{\text{L} \cdot \text{atm}}{\text{mol} \cdot \text{K}}\right)(273 \text{ K})}{1.00 \text{ atm}} = 16.9 \text{ L}$$

PRACTICE PROBLEM 7.18

Calculate the volume that 48.3 g CO_2 occupies at 0°C and 1.00 atm pressure. Compare the answer with that of Example 7.18, and explain any difference.

Hint: First determine the number of moles of CO_2 present, and then use the ideal gas law.

Example 7.19 shows you how to use the ideal gas law to determine the molar mass of a gaseous substance. For this, you need the mass of the given sample and the number of moles in that sample.

Example 7.19

A 93 g sample of a pure gaseous substance occupies 29.5 L at 27°C and 1.25 atm. What is the molar mass of the gas?

Solution

Given the volume, temperature, and pressure of a gaseous substance, you can use the ideal gas law (Equation 7.5) to calculate the number of moles. Be sure to first convert the temperature to kelvins.

$$(T = 27°\text{C} + 273.15 = 300 \text{ K})$$

$$PV = nRT$$

$$n = \frac{PV}{RT}$$

$$n = \frac{(1.25 \text{ atm})(29.5 \text{ L})}{\left(0.08206 \frac{\text{L} \cdot \text{atm}}{\text{mol} \cdot \text{K}}\right)(300 \text{ K})} = 1.50 \text{ mol}$$

The molar mass, $\mathcal{M}$, can now be calculated from the given mass of the gas sample and the number of moles just calculated from the ideal gas law.

$$\mathcal{M} = \frac{93\text{ g}}{1.50\text{ mol}} = 62\text{ g/mol}$$

PRACTICE PROBLEM 7.19

Calculate the molar mass of a gas if a 3.38 g sample occupies 2.76 L at 22°C and 793 torr.

Hint: First, use the ideal gas law to determine the number of moles present. Then, use the given mass of gas to determine the number of grams per mole (i.e., the molar mass).

You can also use the ideal gas law to calculate the density of a gas, which is typically given in grams/liter. For these calculations, you will also need to use the molar mass.

Example 7.20

Determine the density of nitrogen gas at 0°C and 1.00 atm pressure.

Solution

There are at least two ways to approach this problem. Remember that density is mass per volume ($d = m/V$).

In the first method, begin by choosing an arbitrary amount of gas, such as 1 mol, and determining both its mass and volume:

$$m = 1\text{ mol N}_2\left(\frac{28.014\text{ g}}{1\text{ mol N}_2}\right) = 28.014\text{ g}$$

$$V = \frac{nRT}{P} = \frac{(1.00\text{ mol})\left(0.08206\,\frac{\text{L}\cdot\text{atm}}{\text{mol}\cdot\text{K}}\right)(273\text{ K})}{1.00\text{ atm}}$$
$$= 22.4\text{ L}$$

Now divide the mass of 1 mol of the gas (its molar mass) by the volume of 1 mol of the gas:

$$d = \frac{m_{(1\text{ mol})}}{V_{(1\text{ mol})}} = \frac{28.014\text{ g}}{22.4\text{ L}} = 1.25\text{ g/L}$$

In the second method, the mass (m) of the gas is equal to the number of moles (n) times the molar mass ($\mathcal{M}$):

$$m = n \times \mathcal{M}$$

As a result, density (d) can be expressed as

$$d = \frac{m}{V} = \frac{n}{V} \times \mathcal{M}$$

The ideal gas equation ($PV = nRT$) can then be rearranged to isolate n/V:

$$\frac{n}{V} = \frac{P}{RT}$$

Substituting $\frac{P}{RT}$ for $\frac{n}{V}$ in the density formula then gives

$$d = \frac{P}{RT} \times \mathcal{M}$$

$$d = \frac{(1.00\text{ atm})}{\left(0.08206\,\frac{\text{L}\cdot\text{atm}}{\text{mol}\cdot\text{K}}\right)(273\text{ K})}\left(\frac{28.014\text{ g}}{1\text{ mol N}_2}\right)$$
$$= 1.25\text{ g/L}$$

PRACTICE PROBLEM 7.20

Determine the density of SO_3 at 25°C and 789 torr.

Hint: Calculate the volume of 1 mol of the gas, and then divide the molar mass by that volume.

Example 7.21

Calculate the pressure at which oxygen has a density of 1.44 g/L at 22°C.

Solution

You need to use the ideal gas law, so first convert the temperature to kelvins and the density from g/L to mol/L.

For T: $22°\text{C} + 273.15 = 295\text{ K}$

For d: $$\left(\frac{1.44\text{ g O}_2}{1\text{ L}}\right)\left(\frac{1\text{ mol O}_2}{31.998\text{ g O}_2}\right) = \frac{0.0450\text{ mol O}_2}{1\text{ L}}$$

The density expressed in mol/L can be used for n/V in the ideal gas law:

$$P = \frac{nRT}{V}$$

$$P = \left(\frac{0.0450\text{ mol}}{1\text{ L}}\right)\left(0.08206\,\frac{\text{L}\cdot\text{atm}}{\text{mol}\cdot\text{K}}\right)295\text{ K}$$
$$= 1.09\text{ atm}$$

PRACTICE PROBLEM 7.21

Calculate the temperature at which oxygen has a density of 3.00 g/L at 1.50 atm.

Hint: Use the molar mass of O_2 to convert the density from g/L to mol/L, and then use this value for n/V in the ideal gas law.

SECTION REVIEW

- If the pressure, temperature, and volume of a gas are known, the number of moles can be calculated using the ideal gas law. If the mass is also known, the molar mass can be determined by dividing the mass by the number of moles.
- The ideal gas law, along with molar mass data, can be used to determine the density of a gas at various temperatures and pressures.
- The ideal gas law can be used to determine specific temperatures or pressures that would result in a specific gas density.

7.9 Gases in Chemical Reactions

GOAL

- Predict how the pressure in a fixed-volume container will change after a complete reaction.

Background Review

Chapter 5 Stoichiometry: Section 5.1—Mole Calculations for Chemical Reactions; Section 5.7—Calculations Involving Other Quantities

STOICHIOMETRY AND GAS LAWS

Gases that are involved in chemical reactions obey the same laws of stoichiometry that apply to substances in any other state, as described in Chapter 5. Therefore, the ideal gas law can be used to calculate the quantities of gaseous substances involved in a reaction, and then those results can be used to find the quantities of other substances. The flowchart in Figure 7.19 is similar to the one in Figure 5.14, but it now includes the conversions allowed by the ideal gas law.

Example 7.22

How many liters of oxygen gas at 21°C and 1.13 atm can be prepared by the thermal decomposition of 0.950 g $KClO_3$?

$$2\ KClO_3(s) \xrightarrow{\text{heat}} 2\ KCl(s) + 3\ O_2(g)$$

Solution

First, convert the mass of $KClO_3$ to moles of $KClO_3$, then use reaction stoichiometry to convert moles of $KClO_3$ to moles of O_2.

$$0.950\text{ g }KClO_3\left(\frac{1\text{ mol }KClO_3}{122.55\text{ g }KClO_3}\right)\left(\frac{3\text{ mol }O_2}{2\text{ mol }KClO_3}\right)$$
$$= 0.01163\text{ mol }O_2$$

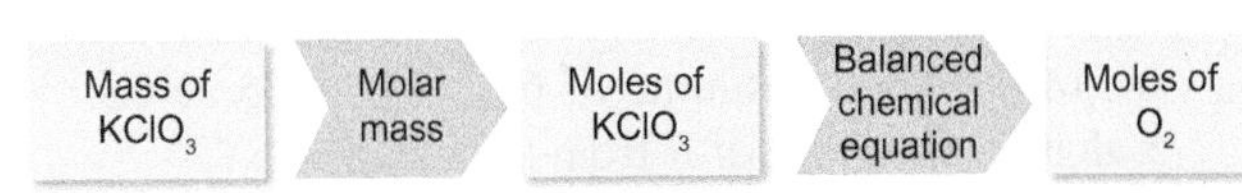

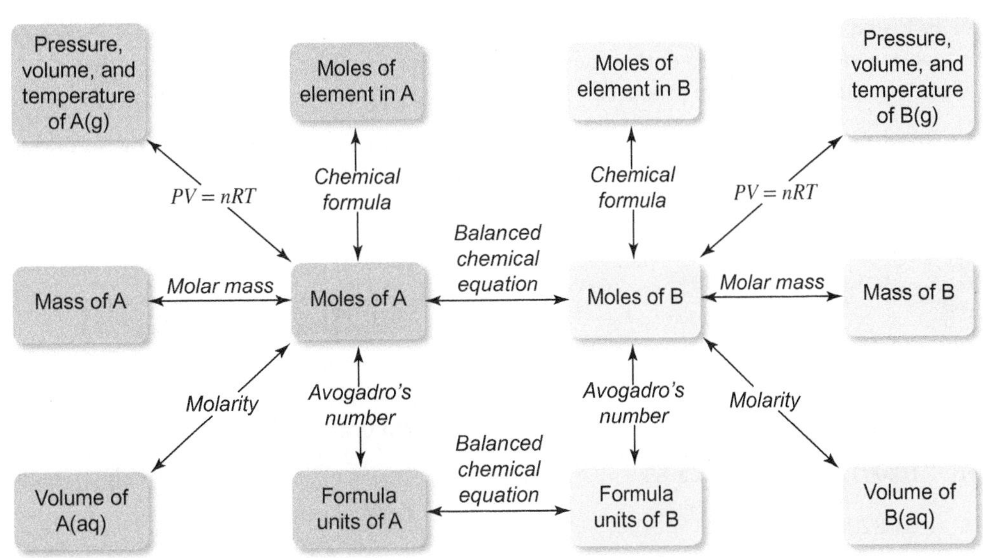

FIGURE 7.19 Stoichiometry Flowchart Including Gases

This flowchart details the connections between moles and mass, number of particles, and, by way of the ideal gas law, pressure, volume, and temperature.

Now use the ideal gas law (Equation 7.5) to find the volume of O_2 from the number of moles, the pressure, and the temperature of O_2. Be sure to convert the temperature to kelvins ($T = 21°C + 273.15 = 294$ K).

$$V = \frac{nRT}{P}$$

$$V = \frac{(0.01163 \text{ mol})\left(0.08206 \frac{\text{L} \cdot \text{atm}}{\text{mol} \cdot \text{K}}\right)(294 \text{ K})}{1.13 \text{ atm}}$$

$$= 0.248 \text{ L } O_2$$

PRACTICE PROBLEM 7.22

What mass of $KClO_3$ must undergo thermal decomposition to produce 0.555 L of oxygen gas at 742 mmHg and 22°C?

$$2\ KClO_3(s) \xrightarrow{\text{heat}} 2\ KCl(s) + 3\ O_2(g)$$

Hint: Use the ideal gas law to determine the number of moles of oxygen produced by the reaction. Then use reaction stoichiometry to convert moles of O_2 to moles and mass of $KClO_3$.

Example 7.23

When 1.06 g Hg_2O is decomposed in a sealed system, the oxygen produced has a pressure of 0.514 atm and a volume of 62.5 mL at 35.25°C. Calculate the value of R from these data.

$$2\ Hg_2O(s) \xrightarrow{\text{heat}} 4\ Hg(l) + O_2(g)$$

Solution

The values for P, V, and T are provided, so the first step is to use reaction stoichiometry to determine the number of moles of oxygen that are produced.

$$n = 1.06 \text{ g } Hg_2O\left(\frac{1 \text{ mol } Hg_2O}{417.18 \text{ g } Hg_2O}\right)\left(\frac{1 \text{ mol } O_2}{2 \text{ mol } Hg_2O}\right)$$

$$= 0.001270 \text{ mol } O_2$$

Mass of Hg_2O → Molar mass → Moles of Hg_2O → Balanced chemical equation → Moles of O_2

Then, solve for R in the ideal gas law.

$$R = \frac{PV}{nT} = \frac{(0.514 \text{ atm})(0.0625 \text{ L})}{(0.001270 \text{ mol})(308.25 \text{ K})}$$

$$= 0.08206 \frac{\text{L} \cdot \text{atm}}{\text{mol} \cdot \text{K}}$$

As expected, the value of R is the same as it has been throughout the chapter because R is a constant.

EVERYDAY CONNECTION

Airbags became mandatory equipment in automobiles in the United States in 1998 and have been credited with saving as many as 28,000 lives since they first became available in the 1980s. Airbags consist of a crash detector, which triggers an inflator that rapidly deploys and expands the airbag, after which the bag quickly deflates to allow the occupant to leave the vehicle.

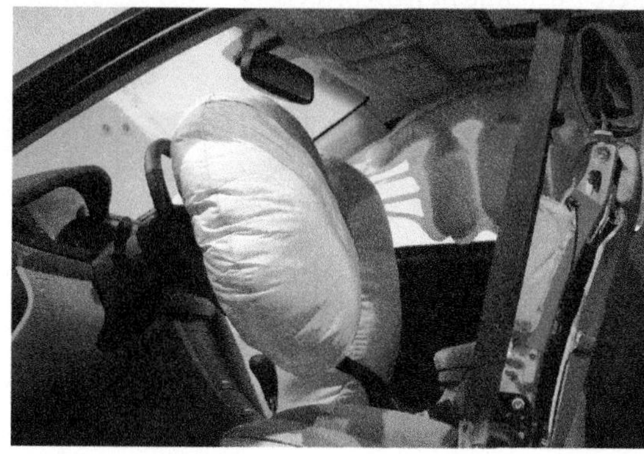

Sony Ho/Shutterstock

Some inflator models contain sodium azide, NaN_3, which undergoes thermal decomposition to form sodium metal and nitrogen gas, with heat provided by an electrical pulse (igniter) sent from the crash detector. The nitrogen gas fills the bag while the highly reactive sodium metal undergoes a series of reactions to form a stable solid.

$$2\ NaN_3(s) \rightarrow 2\ Na(s) + 3\ N_2(g)$$

$$10\ Na(s) + 2\ KNO_3(s) \rightarrow K_2O(s) + 5\ Na_2O(s) + N_2(g)$$

$$K_2O(s) + Na_2O(s) + SiO_2(s) \rightarrow Na_2K_2SiO_4(s)$$

PRACTICE PROBLEM 7.23

How many grams of Hg_2O are needed to produce a sample of oxygen that occupies 0.375 L at 22°C and 0.95 atm?

$$2\ Hg_2O(s) \xrightarrow{\text{heat}} 4\ Hg(l) + O_2(g)$$

Hint: Start by using the ideal gas law to find the number of moles of O_2; then use stoichiometry to find the number of moles and the mass of Hg_2O.

EVERYDAY CONNECTION

It is not always easy to tell if a reaction has occurred when all the components of the reaction—the reactants and products—are colorless gases in a sealed container. However, a change in pressure of the gases in the container signals a change in the number of moles of gases present. The first reported reaction of a noble gas (group 18 element) was observed in 1962, by Neil Bartlett, then a chemistry professor at the University of British Columbia in Vancouver, B.C., Canada, when he reacted xenon gas with fluorine gas. The reaction shown here is one of three possible reactions between xenon and fluorine:

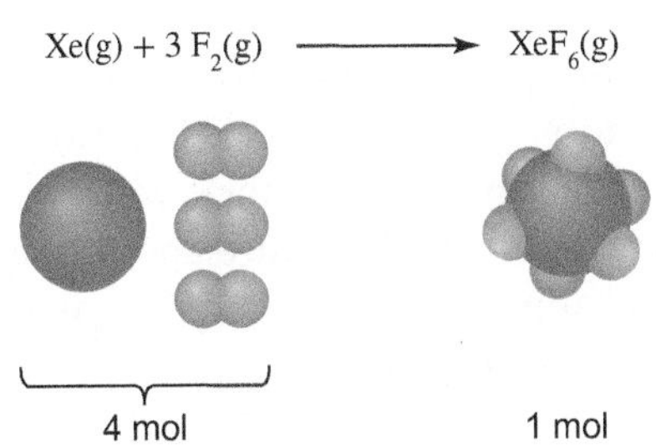

The total number of moles of gas drops from 4 mol on the reactant side to 1 mol on the product side. As the reaction occurs, the drop in the number of moles of gases causes a drop in the pressure—eventually to one-fourth of the original pressure if the reaction goes to completion. Monitoring the pressure of the reaction allowed Bartlett to demonstrate that a reaction had occurred while keeping the highly reactive fluorine gas and the highly reactive product safely contained.

Example 7.24

As N_2 and H_2 react to form NH_3 in a large cylinder at 500°C, what happens to

a. the total number of atoms?
b. the total number of molecules?
c. the total pressure?

Solution

Start by writing the balanced chemical equation,

$$N_2(g) + 3\,H_2(g) \rightarrow 2\,NH_3(g).$$

a. The number of *atoms* stays the same, as it does for *all* reactions. That is the basis for the balanced chemical equation.
b. The total number of *moles* of gas decreases from 4 to 2 as the reaction proceeds, so the number of molecules also decreases by a ratio of 4 to 2.
c. The *total pressure* decreases as the total number of moles of gas decreases. Since there are only half as many moles of gaseous product as there are of gaseous reactants, the total pressure would decrease to one-half of its original value if the reaction goes to completion.

PRACTICE PROBLEM 7.24

As Cl_2 and H_2 react to form HCl in a large cylinder at 650°C, what happens to

a. the total number of atoms?
b. the total number of molecules?
c. the total pressure?

Hint: Start by writing a balanced chemical equation.

VOLUME RATIOS IN CHEMICAL REACTIONS

When more than one gas is involved in a chemical reaction, the **volume ratio** of the gases is equal to the mole ratio in the balanced equation if all the gases are at the same temperature and pressure. This statement is known as **Gay-Lussac's law of combining volumes.** In the following reaction, for example, where all gases are at the same temperature and pressure,

$$1\,A(g) + 1\,B(g) \rightarrow 3\,C(g) + 1\,D(g)$$

1 mol of A produces 3 mol of C, so 1.00 L of A would produce 3.00 L of C. Similarly, the total number of moles of products is twice the total number of moles of reactants, so the total volume of the products would be twice the total volume of the reactants. The law of combining volumes holds only for gases and only when the temperatures and pressures of the gases are equal. In *exothermic* combustion reactions (Section 4.1 and Section 6.7), for example, where the products are at higher temperatures than the reactants, the law of combining volumes would not apply.

Gay-Lussac's law is true only for separate gases and only when their temperatures and their pressures are equal.

Example 7.25

Ammonium carbonate decomposes when heated to yield carbon dioxide, ammonia, and water vapor.

$$(NH_4)_2CO_3(s) \xrightarrow{\text{heat}} 2\ NH_3(g) + CO_2(g) + H_2O(g)$$

If the products are separated after the reaction is complete, calculate the ratio of the volume of ammonia to the volume of water vapor, each at 450°C and 1.00 atm.

Solution

The mole ratio of the gases, given in the balanced equation, is

$$2\text{ mol } NH_3 : 1\text{ mol } CO_2 : 1\text{ mol } H_2O$$

According to Gay-Lussac's law, the ratio of the volume of ammonia and the volume of water is equal to the mole ratio from the balanced chemical equation, or 2:1.

You can verify this using the ideal gas law as

$$\frac{(V_{NH_3})}{(V_{H_2O})} = \frac{\left(\frac{n_{NH_3}RT}{P}\right)}{\left(\frac{n_{H_2O}RT}{P}\right)}$$

Because R is a constant and both T and P are the same for the two gases, this equation reduces to

$$\frac{V_{NH_3}}{V_{H_2O}} = \frac{n_{NH_3}}{n_{H_2O}}$$

The right side of this equation is the ratio of the numbers of moles—the ratio given by the balanced chemical equation. The left side of the equation is the ratio of the volumes, so the ratio given by the balanced chemical equation is equal to the volume ratio *under these conditions.* The ratio is 2:1.

PRACTICE PROBLEM 7.25

If 2.00 L of H_2 and 1.00 L of O_2 are combined in a reaction vessel at 0°C and 1.00 atm pressure and then gases react to form water vapor at 250°C and 1.00 atm, will the water vapor occupy 2.00 L, as predicted from Gay-Lussac's law?

$$2\ H_2(g) + O_2(g) \rightarrow 2\ H_2O(g)$$

Hint: Consider the conditions necessary for Gay-Lussac's law to be valid.

> In problems involving chemical reactions, use the ideal gas law only for substances in the gas phase.

SECTION REVIEW

- The number of moles of gas involved in a chemical reaction, calculated from the ideal gas law, can be used with the balanced chemical equation to determine the number of moles and the mass of any other reactant or product in the reaction.
- The number of moles of any gas, calculated from the balanced chemical equation, can be used with other data in the ideal gas law to calculate the volume, temperature, or pressure of the gas.
- The balanced chemical equation can provide information about the relative number of moles of gases present before and after a reaction occurs, and this information can be used to predict how the pressure in a fixed-volume container will change after a complete reaction.
- Two or more gases in a chemical reaction have a volume ratio equal to their mole ratio as long as the gases are separated and their volumes are measured at the same temperature and the same pressure. This applies only to reactants and products that are in the gas phase.

7.10 Kinetic Molecular Theory of Gases

GOAL

- Use the kinetic molecular theory to explain the behavior of gases.

Background Review

Chapter 1 Science and Measurement:
Section 1.9—Temperature Scales

Several gas laws have been introduced in this chapter, but no explanation as to *why* those laws apply to all gases has yet been proposed. The **kinetic molecular theory** of gases, presented in this section, explains the gas laws, and when extended, it also explains some properties of liquids and solids. The five postulates of the kinetic molecular theory explain why ideal gases behave as they do:

1. Gases are composed of small molecules that are in constant, *random motion.*
2. The volume that is taken up by the molecules themselves is insignificant compared with the overall volume occupied by the gas.

3. Forces between the molecules are negligible, except when the molecules collide with one another.
4. Molecular collisions are *perfectly elastic*; that is, no energy is lost when the molecules collide.
5. The *average kinetic energy* of the gas molecules is directly proportional to the absolute temperature of the gas.

The **random motion** referred to in postulate 1 means that the molecules travel in straight lines in any arbitrary direction until they hit other molecules or the walls of the container. The short animation in Figure 7.20 follows the movement of a typical gas molecule in a sample. A **perfectly elastic collision**, referred to in postulate 4, means that the molecules bounce off one another without any loss of total energy. No friction or energy loss of any kind occurs.

The kinetic molecular theory of gases explains the behavior of gases described by the various gas laws. Consider the factors affecting the pressure of a gas sample.

- First, what causes gases to exhibit pressure? According to postulates 1 and 3 of the kinetic molecular theory, the particles of gases are in constant motion and are colliding with each other. The particles also must be colliding with the walls of their containers. The force of those collisions is the source of gas pressure, as discussed in Section 7.1.

FIGURE 7.20 Gas Motion Video

NOTE: You need to be online to access this video.

The path of the labeled molecule demonstrates the constant, random movement of molecules in the gas phase, as described by kinetic molecular theory. The gas particles are shown much larger than they would be in a real gas to make the interactions more evident.

Steve Lemon, Macmillan Learning

FIGURE 7.21 Video Tutorial: Kinetic Molecular Theory

NOTE: You need to be online to access this video.

This video shows how changes in volume and temperature affect gases at the particulate (molecular) level.

- When the volume of a gas sample decreases (Boyle's law, Section 7.2) without a change in the number of particles, the rate of collisions of those particles with the container walls must increase, causing pressure to increase.
- According to postulate 5 of the kinetic molecular theory, an increase in temperature causes gas particles to have more energy and move at higher speeds. When the temperature of a gas is increased, these faster-moving particles collide with the walls of the container more frequently and with greater force, thus increasing the pressure, as predicted by Charles's law (Section 7.3).
- When the number of moles of a gas are increased, the rate of collisions of those particles with the walls of the container increases, thus explaining Avogadro's law (Section 7.5).
- Kinetic molecular theory tells you to consider only the number of particles of the gas and not the identity of the gas, which explains why the partial pressure of a gas in a mixture is related to the number of moles of each component gas (Dalton's law, Section 7.7).

The video in Figure 7.21 explains the behavior of gas molecules and how that relates to measurable properties.

Example 7.26

Calculate the volume occupied by 1.00 mol H_2O at 100.00°C and 1.00 atm pressure when it is

a. in the vapor state and
b. in the liquid state (the density of liquid water at 100°C is 0.958 g/mL).

Solution

a. Convert the temperature to kelvins ($T = 100.00°C + 273.15 = 373.15$ K), then apply the ideal gas law (Section 7.6) and solve for volume:

$$V = \frac{nRT}{P} = \frac{(1.00 \text{ mol})\left(0.08206 \frac{\text{L} \cdot \text{atm}}{\text{mol} \cdot \text{K}}\right)(373.15 \text{ K})}{1.00 \text{ atm}}$$
$$= 30.6 \text{ L}$$

b. Calculate the volume of liquid water using density as a conversion factor (Section 1.9):

$$1.00 \text{ mol } H_2O\left(\frac{18.0 \text{ g } H_2O}{1 \text{ mol } H_2O}\right)\left(\frac{1 \text{ mL } H_2O}{0.958 \text{ g } H_2O}\right)$$
$$= 18.8 \text{ mL}$$

The same mole of H_2O occupies only 0.0188 L in the liquid state, but after it has been evaporated into the gas state, it occupies 30.6 L. When a sample goes from a liquid to a gas, the molecules themselves do not expand; only the space between the molecules gets larger. Because the molecules do not expand, they cannot occupy more than 0.0188 L of the 30.6 L of the gas. The volume occupied by the molecules is therefore negligible (less than one-tenth of 1% of the total volume). Thus, most of the volume of a sample of gas is empty space.

PRACTICE PROBLEM 7.26

The boiling point of ammonia (NH_3) is −2.2°C. Calculate the volume occupied by 1.00 mol NH_3 at −2.2°C and 1.00 atm pressure when it is

a. in the vapor state and
b. in the liquid state (the density of liquid ammonia at −2.2°C is 0.769 g/mL).

Hint: Use the ideal gas law to determine the volume of gaseous ammonia; then use the density of liquid ammonia to calculate its volume.

Go to the animation in Figure 7.20 and select a specific molecule to focus on. Watch how its velocity changes after each collision. The **average kinetic energy** of the molecules referred to in postulate 5 is the overall average of all the kinetic energies of all the individual molecules at any instant. Not all molecules have the same kinetic energy at any one time, and a particular molecule might not have a constant kinetic energy for any appreciable time. However, the average kinetic energy of a gas at a given temperature is constant.

The kinetic molecular theory also explains why real gases do not always follow the ideal gas law exactly. Recall that the theory assumes that the volume of the gas particles is insignificant, and that there are no attractive or repulsive forces between the gas molecules. The volume of the molecules in a real gas may be very, very small, but it is not zero. Very high pressures cause gas particles to be compressed into very small volumes. At these small volumes, the actual volume of the molecules may no longer be negligible. Very low temperatures result in low average kinetic energy, which may allow intermolecular forces (Section 12.1) to form between the gas molecules. Section 7.12 explores these deviations from ideal gas behavior more fully.

Real gases behave more like ideal gases at higher temperatures and at lower pressures. At higher temperatures, the molecules are moving too fast to interact, and at lower pressures, the gas molecules have a much smaller volume, proportionally, than the volume that the gas sample occupies.

SECTION REVIEW

- The kinetic molecular theory explains the behavior of gases based on the behavior of their molecules.
- In kinetic molecular theory,
  - gases consist of particles in random motion,
  - the molecules in a sample of gas are assumed to be much smaller than the empty spaces that surround them,
  - the particles move in constant straight-line motion unless they collide with other particles or the walls of the container,
  - the molecules do not interact with one another except when they collide, and no energy is lost in their collisions, and
  - the kelvin temperature of a gas (or of a liquid or solid as well) is a measure of the average kinetic energy of the particles that make up the sample.
- Very high pressures and very low temperatures are associated with deviations from the ideal gas law.

7.11 Movement of Gas Particles

GOALS

- Describe the relationship between molecular mass and speed.
- Calculate the relative speeds and molecular masses of gases using root-mean-square speed and Graham's law of effusion.

ROOT-MEAN-SQUARE SPEED

If gas particles are in constant motion, as stated in the kinetic molecular theory, then how fast are they moving? Is there a way to calculate or measure these speeds, and if so, what information can the measured speeds supply about the gas particles?

Postulate 5 of the kinetic molecular theory (Section 7.10) states that the average kinetic energy of gas molecules is proportional to the kelvin temperature of the gas sample. This tells you that all gas samples at the same temperature have the same *average* kinetic energy:

KE_{avg} of gas A at temperature $T = KE_{avg}$ of gas B at temperature T

The directly proportional relationship (Section 0.8) between average kinetic energy and temperature can be written as an equation by including a constant,

$$KE_{avg} = kT$$

The value of this constant has been determined experimentally and is generally written using the gas law constant, R,

$$k = \frac{3}{2}R$$

Thus,

$$KE_{avg} = \frac{3}{2}RT \tag{7.8}$$

For energy calculations, the units of R must be converted from L · atm to joules (J) (Section 6.4), giving a version of R with a value of 8.3145 $\frac{\text{J}}{\text{K} \cdot \text{mol}}$. Using these units of R, Equation 7.8 gives the average kinetic energy of a *mole* of gas particles at a particular temperature. Dividing the KE_{avg} of a mole of particles by Avogadro's number, N_A, gives the average kinetic energy per *particle* (atom or molecule).

$$KE_{\text{avg per particle}} = \frac{\frac{3}{2}RT}{N_A} \tag{7.9}$$

Recall from Section 6.1 that the kinetic energy is related to the mass and velocity of those particles as

$$KE = \frac{1}{2}mv^2$$

As shown in the video (Figure 7.20), all particles of gas A have the same mass but all do not move at the same speed. For this reason, velocity, v, in Equation 6.1 refers to the average velocity of all the particles in the sample of gas A. Since all gases have the same kinetic energy at a given temperature, the direct relationship between m and v in Equation 6.1 means that gas particles with smaller masses have faster average velocities than gas particles with larger masses. If the particles of gas A have smaller masses than those of gas B, you can predict that the particles of gas A move faster, on average, than those of gas B. The bar graph in Figure 7.22 compares the average speeds of gaseous H_2, He, H_2O, and O_2 at 25°C.

The average speeds of gas particles depend on the temperature and the mass of the gas particles. Gas particles with very low mass, such as hydrogen and helium, move at higher average speeds than gas particles of higher mass, such as water and oxygen.

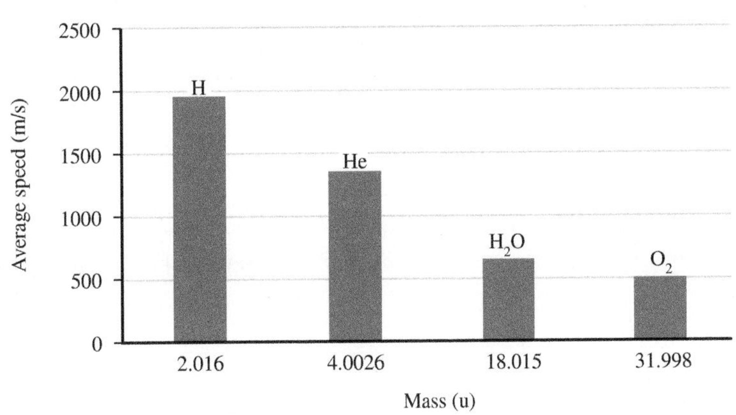

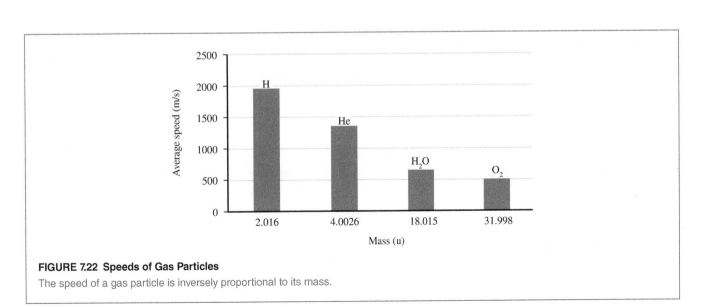

FIGURE 7.22 Speeds of Gas Particles
The speed of a gas particle is inversely proportional to its mass.

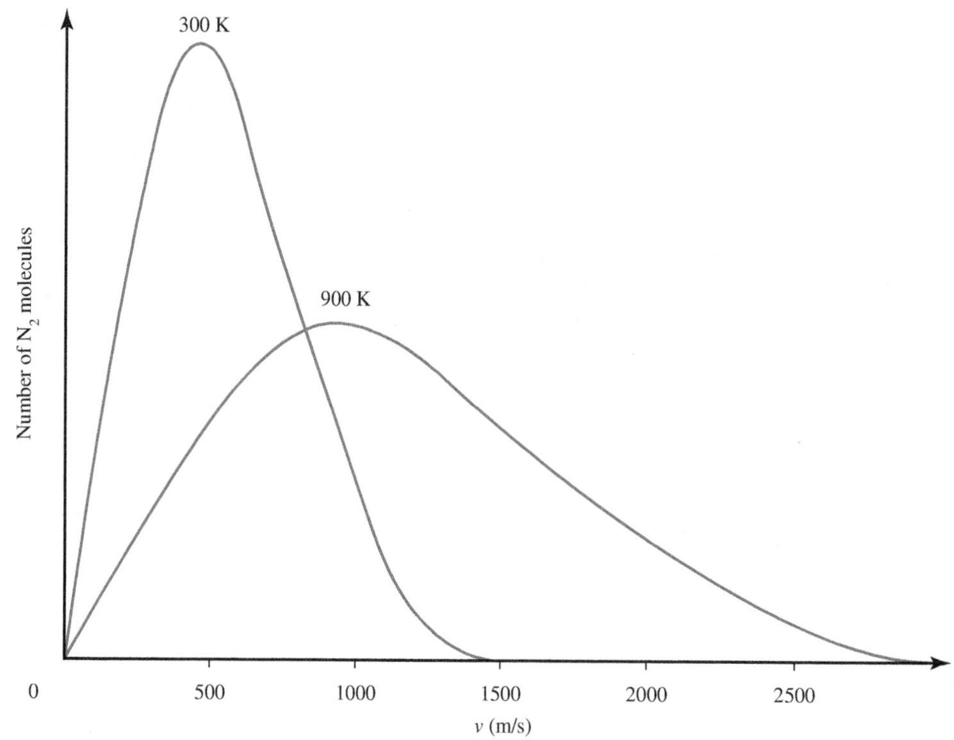

FIGURE 7.23 Temperature and the Range of Speeds of Gas Particles

At lower temperatures, the average speed of gas particles is low and the range of speeds is narrow. At higher temperatures, the average speed increases and the range of speeds broadens.

Temperature also affects the range of the speeds of gas particles, as shown in Figure 7.23 for N_2. At lower temperatures, the speeds of the different gas particles are close to the average speed, with only a small range of speeds above and below the average. At higher temperatures, not only is the average speed higher but also the range of speeds of the particles in the gas sample is much broader.

By combining the two equations for kinetic energy (Equation 7.7 and Equation 7.8), it is possible to calculate the velocity of the particles possessing the average kinetic energy in any gas sample of known molar mass. This velocity is known as the **root-mean-square speed, v_{rms}**. Remember that molar mass, $\mathcal{M}$, can be calculated by multiplying the mass of an individual particle, m, by Avogadro's number, N_A—that is, $\mathcal{M} = mN_A$. The equation used to calculate the root-mean-square speed of a gas sample can be derived as follows:

$$KE_{avg} = \frac{3RT}{2N_A} = \frac{1}{2}mv^2$$

$$v^2 = \frac{3(RT)}{mN_A} = \frac{3RT}{\mathcal{M}}$$

$$v_{rms} = \sqrt{\frac{3RT}{\mathcal{M}}} \quad (7.10)$$

You can use Equation 7.10 to calculate the root-mean-square speed of particles in any gas sample for which you know both the temperature and the identity of the gas.

Example 7.27

a. Predict the root-mean-square speed, v_{rms}, of nitrogen at 25°C, and then
b. calculate it.

Solution

a. Compare the molar mass of nitrogen, N_2, to the masses of the gas samples in Figure 7.22. Nitrogen has a molar mass of 28.0 g/mol, which is less than that of O_2 but greater than that of H_2O. Thus, the root-mean-square speed of nitrogen molecules at 25°C should be greater than that of oxygen (490 m/s) but less than that of water (650 m/s).
b. For the calculation, use Equation 7.10,

$$v_{rms} = \sqrt{\frac{3RT}{\mathcal{M}}}$$

where

$$R = 8.3145\frac{\text{J}}{\text{K}\cdot\text{mol}} = 8.3145\frac{\text{kg}\cdot\text{m}^2}{\text{s}^2\cdot\text{K}\cdot\text{mol}}$$

Because R now contains mass in units of kilogram, the molar mass of nitrogen must also be expressed in kilograms (1 kg = 1000 g).

$$28.0\ \text{g/mol} = 0.0280\ \text{kg/mol or } 2.80 \times 10^{-2}\ \text{kg/mol}$$

You can now plug values into the root-mean-square speed equation.

$$v_{\text{rms}} = \sqrt{\frac{3RT}{\mathcal{M}}} = \sqrt{\frac{3\left(8.3145\dfrac{\text{kg}\cdot\text{m}^2}{\text{s}^2\cdot\text{K}\cdot\text{mol}}\right)(298\ \text{K})}{2.8\times10^{-2}\dfrac{\text{kg}}{\text{mol}}}}$$

$$v_{\text{rms}} = \sqrt{265470\frac{\text{m}^2}{\text{s}^2}}$$

$$v_{\text{rms}} = 5.15 \times 10^2\ \text{m/s}$$

Nitrogen molecules travel at an average speed of 515 m/s at 25°C, which is consistent with the prediction made in part (a).

PRACTICE PROBLEM 7.27A

a. Predict whether the root-mean-square speed of carbon dioxide is likely to be higher or lower than that of nitrogen at the same temperature.
b. Calculate the root-mean-square speed of carbon dioxide at 25°C.

Hint:
a. Consider the relative molar masses of CO_2 and N_2 and the effect that molar mass has on velocity when particles of different masses are at the same temperature and, therefore, have the same kinetic energy.
b. Use Equation 7.10.

PRACTICE PROBLEM 7.27B

A sample of nitrogen gas is warmed from 25°C to 100°C.

a. How would this change in temperature affect the *average* speed of the nitrogen molecules?
b. How would this change in temperature affect the *range* of speeds of the individual molecules?
c. Finally, calculate the root-mean-square speed of N_2 at 100°C.

Hint: What effect does a higher temperature have on average kinetic energy and range of speeds of gas particles?

DIFFUSION AND EFFUSION

If someone opens a bottle of perfume (or a can of gasoline) on one side of a room, it will not take long before you smell it on the other side of the room. The process by which the evaporated perfume (or gasoline) molecules reach your nose is called diffusion. **Diffusion** occurs when a gas sample is introduced into a larger volume and the gas particles spread out to occupy the entire volume, mixing with the other gases present. The rate of diffusion depends on the temperature, the mass of the particle, and the collisions with other particles. You already know that temperature is proportional to kinetic energy and the average speed of the particles and that the mass of the particles also affects their speed. Collisions alter the direction of the particles, as shown in Figure 7.24.

The **mean free path** of a particle, which is the average distance traveled between collisions, is related to the pressure of the gas particles. At higher pressures, there are more particles per unit volume, which makes collisions more likely to occur and reduces the mean free path.

Effusion, the escape of gas molecules through a tiny hole into a vacuum, is simpler to quantify than diffusion because it does not depend on collisions. You can explore the effect of temperature and molecular mass on the rate of effusion by testing out the effusion activity in Figure 7.25.

Graham's law of effusion states that the ratio of rates of effusion of two gases, $\frac{r_1}{r_2}$, is equal to the square root of the inverse ratio of the molar masses, $\sqrt{\frac{\mathcal{M}_2}{\mathcal{M}_1}}$.

$$\frac{r_1}{r_2} = \sqrt{\frac{\mathcal{M}_2}{\mathcal{M}_1}} \qquad (7.11)$$

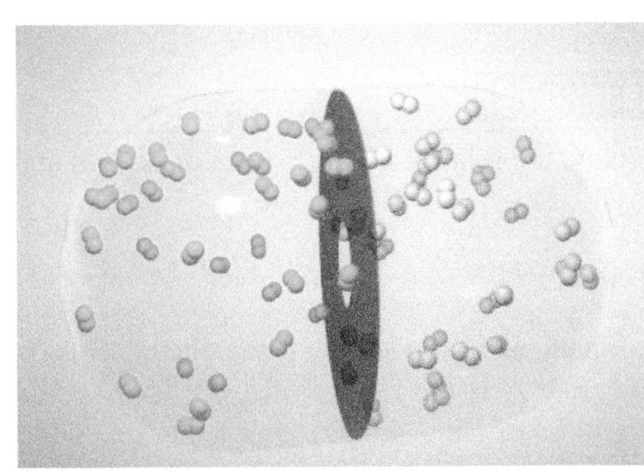

FIGURE 7.24 Diffusion Video

NOTE: You need to be online to access this video.

Gas particles diffuse by random motion and collisions with other particles.

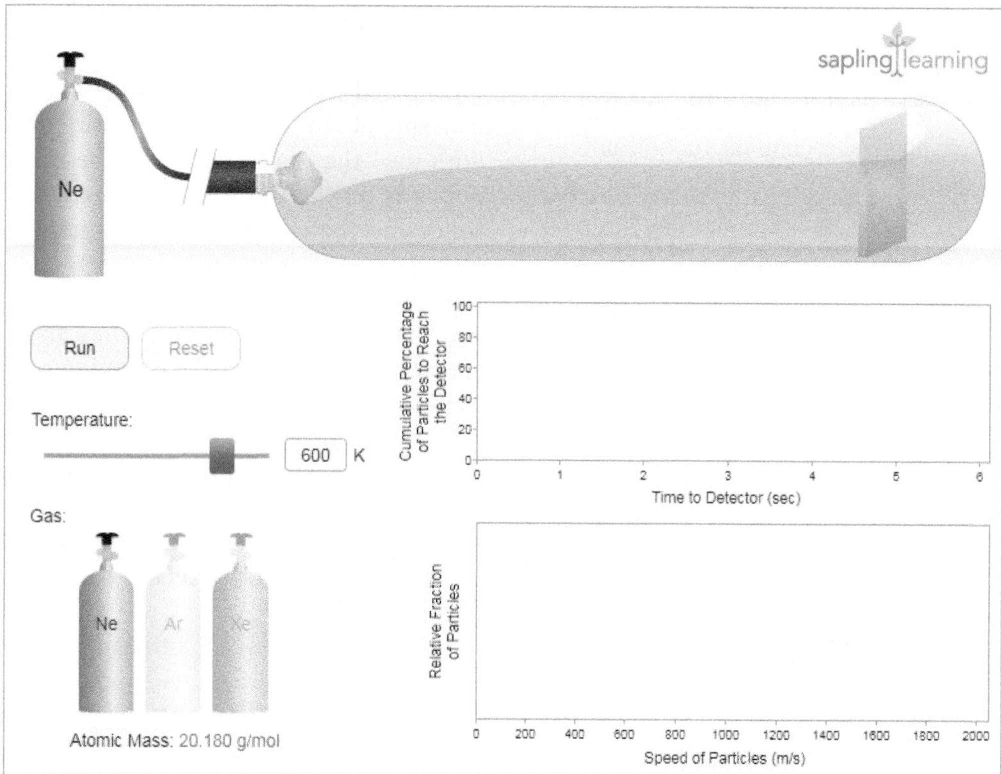

FIGURE 7.25 Effusion Activity

NOTE: You need to be online to access this activity.

Click **Run** to measure the effusion time and then click **Calculate** to see a distribution of particle speeds. Adjust the temperature slider and/or select a different gas (Ne, Ar, or Xe), then repeat the experiment to compare the results.

Graham's law of effusion is derived from the root-mean-square speed equation (Equation 7.10).

$$\frac{r_1}{r_2} = \frac{v_{rms_1}}{v_{rms_2}} = \frac{\sqrt{\frac{3RT}{\mathcal{M}_1}}}{\sqrt{\frac{3RT}{\mathcal{M}_2}}} = \sqrt{\frac{\mathcal{M}_2}{\mathcal{M}_1}}$$

Example 7.28

Calculate the relative effusion rates of helium and oxygen gases.

Solution

Use Equation 7.11, where r_1 is the rate of effusion for He and r_2 is the rate of effusion for O_2. The molar mass of He is 4.0026 g/mol, and the molar mass of O_2 is 31.9988 g/mol.

$$\frac{r_{He}}{r_{O_2}} = \sqrt{\frac{\mathcal{M}_{O_2}}{\mathcal{M}_{He}}} = \sqrt{\frac{31.9988}{4.0026}} = \frac{2.83}{1} = 2.83$$

Helium atoms effuse at a rate that is 2.83 times faster than the effusion rate of oxygen molecules.

This answer is reasonable because helium atoms are less massive than oxygen molecules.

PRACTICE PROBLEM 7.28

Calculate the relative effusion rates of hydrogen and carbon monoxide gases.

Hint: Use Graham's law of effusion (Equation 7.11), where gas 1 is H_2 and gas 2 is CO.

Example 7.29

A gas known to have a formula of NO_x was found to effuse at a rate that is 0.834 times the rate of effusion of oxygen. Determine (a) the molar mass of NO_x and (b) the value of x.

Solution

a. NO_x effuses more slowly than O_2, so NO_x must have a higher molar mass. Rearrange Graham's law to solve for the molar mass of NO_x.

$$\frac{r_{NO_x}}{r_{O_2}} = \sqrt{\frac{\mathcal{M}_{O_2}}{\mathcal{M}_{NO_x}}}$$

$$\sqrt{\mathcal{M}_{NO_x}} = \frac{\sqrt{\mathcal{M}_{O_2}}}{\frac{r_{NO_x}}{r_{O_2}}}$$

$$\mathcal{M}_{NO_x} = \left(\frac{\sqrt{\mathcal{M}_{O_2}}}{\frac{r_{NO_x}}{r_{O_2}}}\right)^2 = \left(\frac{\sqrt{31.998}}{\frac{0.834}{1}}\right)^2 = 46.0\ \text{g/mol}$$

b. Because the molar mass of NO_x is 46 g/mol, you can determine the value of x from the definition of molar mass.

$$1(\text{molar mass of N}) + x(\text{molar mass of O}) = 46.0\ \text{g/mol}$$

$$14.007\ \text{g/mol} + x(15.999\ \text{g/mol}) = 46.0\ \text{g/mol}$$

$$x = \frac{46.0 - 14.007}{15.9994} = 1.99 = 2$$

Thus, NO_x is NO_2.

PRACTICE PROBLEM 7.29

A homonuclear diatomic gas, X_2, effuses at a rate of 0.447 times the rate of effusion of oxygen. ("Homonuclear" means that both atoms of X_2 are the same.) Determine (a) the molecular mass of X_2 and (b) the identity of X.

Hint: Rearrange Graham's law to calculate the molar mass of X_2 and then compare it to the elements that are known to be diatomic.

SECTION REVIEW

- All gases have the same average kinetic energy at a given temperature, but they all move at different average speeds that depend on the mass of the particles.
- This average speed can be calculated as the root-mean-square speed, v_{rms}, using Equation 7.10.

$$v_{rms} = \sqrt{\frac{3RT}{\mathcal{M}}}$$

- The energy unit versions of R, the gas law constant, are used in these calculations:

$$R = 8.3145 \frac{\text{J}}{\text{K} \cdot \text{mol}} = 8.3145 \frac{\text{kg} \cdot \text{m}^2}{\text{s}^2 \cdot \text{K} \cdot \text{mol}}$$

- Root-mean-square speed is only one factor in understanding the diffusion rate of gases.
- Effusion is the movement of gas particles through a tiny opening without collisions.
- Effusion is directly related to root-mean-square speed (Graham's law of effusion, Equation 7.11) and can be used to determine the molar mass of an unknown gas.

$$\frac{r_1}{r_2} = \frac{v_{rms_1}}{v_{rms_2}} = \frac{\sqrt{\frac{3RT}{\mathcal{M}_1}}}{\sqrt{\frac{3RT}{\mathcal{M}_2}}} = \sqrt{\frac{\mathcal{M}_2}{\mathcal{M}_1}}$$

7.12 Behavior of Real Gases

GOALS

- Discuss the circumstances that lead to deviations from ideal gas behavior.
- Use the van der Waals equation to calculate volumes and pressures for gases that display nonideal behavior.

Ideal gas behavior, according to the kinetic molecular theory, is based on two assumptions about the particles of a gas. One assumption is that the volume of gas particles is negligible, and the other is that there are no interactions, attractive or repulsive, between gas particles. At high pressures and low temperatures, these assumptions are not always valid, and real gases may exhibit considerable deviations from ideal behavior. This section explores the reasons for this and explains how to use the **van der Waals equation** to make more accurate predictions regarding the pressures of real gases.

Real gas particles do have finite volumes, which, at typical pressures, are quite small compared with the volume occupied by the gas sample. When very high pressures compress the gas sample into correspondingly very small volumes, however, that finite volume of the particles is no longer negligible. You can see a model of this in Figure 7.4, although the size of the gas particles is greatly exaggerated in the images.

As the pressure increases and the volume decreases, the volume taken up by the particles becomes a higher percentage of the total volume of the sample. For this reason, the measured properties of real gases at these high temperatures deviate from what is predicted by the ideal gas law, as shown in the graphs in Figure 7.26.

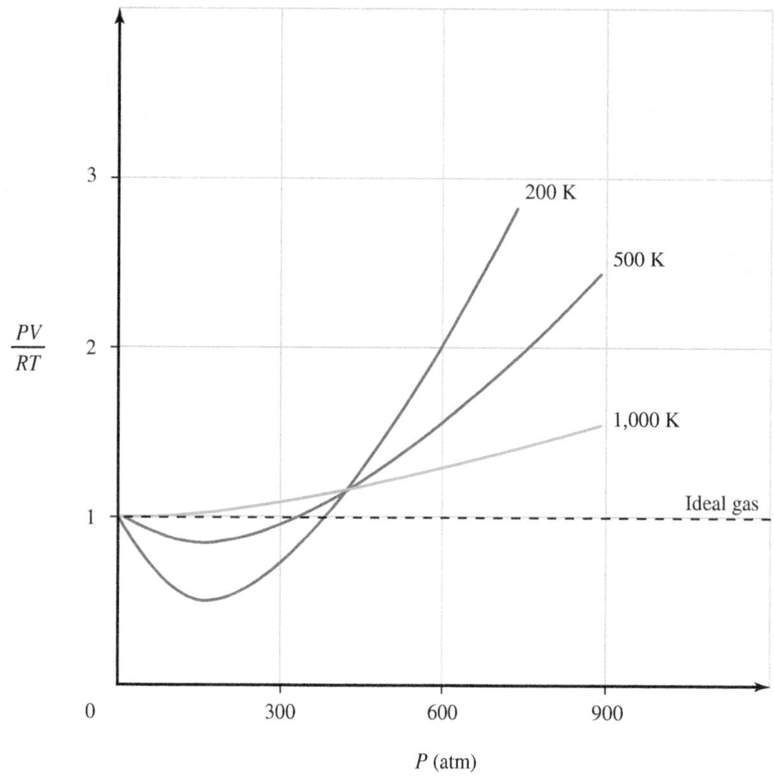

FIGURE 7.26 A Real Gas Versus an Ideal Gas

For a mole of ideal gas, $n = PV/RT = 1$ as shown by the dashed line. The other lines show the value of PV/RT for a mole of nitrogen at various temperatures. At typical atmospheric pressures (around 1 atm), real gases behave nearly ideally. At high pressures, however, the properties of real gases deviate from an ideal gas. At lower temperatures, these properties deviate even more.

Example 7.30

The radius of an atom increases as you move down a group in the periodic table (Section 9.2), so the radius of Br is greater than the radius of Cl and the radius of Cl is greater than the radius of F. If you have 1 mol each of gaseous F_2, Cl_2, and Br_2 at the same temperature and at a very high pressure, which do you expect to have the largest volume?

Solution

At high pressures, gases are compressed into smaller volumes, and the actual sizes of the gas particles contribute to that volume. If the radius of Br is greater than that of Cl or F, then Br_2 has a larger volume than Cl_2 or F_2, too. The larger volume of the bromine molecules causes a greater deviation from ideal behavior and a larger observed volume for the bromine gas.

PRACTICE PROBLEM 7.30

The radius of an atom increases as you move down a group in the periodic table (Section 9.2). If you have 1 mol each of gaseous Ar, Kr, Xe, and Ne at the same temperature and at a very high pressure, which do you expect to have the smallest volume?

Hint: Use periodic trends in atomic radius to predict which of the elements has the smallest volume.

Real gas particles can form attraction between the particles, but these *intermolecular forces* (Section 12.1) are weak. At higher temperatures, the particles are moving too quickly for these forces to have an effect. At lower temperatures, however, the kinetic energy of the particles is also lower, making the collisions less energetic. The particles are moving more slowly, allowing them to form weak attractions, which then decreases the number of collisions with the walls of the container, effectively lowering the pressure (Figure 7.26).

Johannes van der Waals (1837–1923) studied these deviations from ideal behavior and suggested ways to modify the ideal gas law (Equation 7.5) to account for them. Van der Waals suggested that the volume needed to be increased by a small factor related to the number of gas particles, n, and a constant specific to each gas, b, related to the volume of the gas particles.

$$V_{\text{ideal gas}} = \frac{nRT}{P}$$

$$V_{\text{real gas}} = \frac{nRT}{P} + nb$$

Rearranging the equation yields the general form

$$V - nb = \frac{nRT}{P}$$

Van der Waals also suggested a correction factor to account for the decrease in pressure due to the formation of attraction between particles. This factor, $a\left(\frac{n}{V}\right)^2$, which includes the number of moles, n, and the volume, V, as well as a constant specific to each gas, a, is subtracted from the pressure in the ideal gas law.

$$P_{\text{ideal gas}} = \frac{nRT}{V}$$

$$P_{\text{real gas}} = \frac{nRT}{V} - a\left(\frac{n}{V}\right)^2$$

This equation can also be rearranged to obtain the general form

$$P + a\left(\frac{n}{V}\right)^2 = \frac{nRT}{V}$$

The corrected volume equation and the corrected pressure equation are then combined to yield the van der Waals equation,

$$\left[P + a\left(\frac{n}{V}\right)^2\right](V - nb) = nRT \qquad (7.12)$$

which takes into account both the correction for the volume of the gas particles and any attractions between them, using the values listed in Table 7.4.

TABLE 7.4 Van der Waals Constants

Gas	a (atm · L^2/mol^2)	b (L/mol)
CH_4	2.273	0.0431
CO_2	3.610	0.0429
Cl_2	6.260	0.0542
NH_3	4.170	0.0371
H_2O	5.465	0.0305
Xe	4.137	0.0516
CCl_4	19.75	0.1281
O_2	1.363	0.0319
N_2	1.351	0.0387
Kr	5.121	0.0106
Ar	1.336	0.0320
CO	1.452	0.0395
H_2S	4.481	0.0434
NO	1.351	0.0387
N_2O	3.799	0.0444
NO_2	5.29	0.0443
SO_2	6.770	0.0568
HF	9.431	0.0739
HCl	3.648	0.0406
HBr	4.437	0.0442
HI	6.221	0.0530

Example 7.31

Calculate the pressure of 1.00 mol of argon gas at 7.50 L and 273 K using (a) the ideal gas equation and (b) the van der Waals equation. (c) Explain any difference between the results.

Solution

a. Solve the ideal gas law for pressure and substitute the values given in the problem:

$$PV = nRT$$

$$P = \frac{nRT}{V}$$

$$= \frac{1.00\ \text{mol}\left(\frac{0.08206\ \text{L} \cdot \text{atm}}{\text{mol} \cdot \text{K}}\right)(273\ \text{K})}{7.50\ \text{L}}$$

$$= 2.99\ \text{atm}$$

b. Solve the van der Waals equation for P, find the constants in Table 7.4, and substitute the values given in the problem:

$$\left[P + a\left(\frac{n}{V}\right)^2\right](V - nb) = nRT$$

$$P = \frac{nRT}{(V - nb)} - a\left(\frac{n}{V}\right)^2$$

$$P = \frac{1.00\text{ mol}\left(\frac{0.08206\text{ L}\cdot\text{atm}}{\text{mol}\cdot\text{K}}\right)(273\text{ K})}{7.50\text{ L} - (1.00\text{ mol})\left(0.0320\frac{\text{L}}{\text{mol}}\right)} - 1.336\frac{\text{atm}\cdot\text{L}^2}{\text{mol}^2}\left(\frac{1.00\text{ mol}}{7.50\text{ L}}\right)^2$$

$$P = 2.82\text{ atm}$$

c. The difference in pressure values is very small: 2.99 atm for the ideal gas law and 2.82 atm for the van der Waals equation. The intermolecular forces between argon atoms are just barely strong enough to reduce the pressure at that temperature and volume.

PRACTICE PROBLEM 7.31

Calculate the pressure of 34.06 g of ammonia, NH_3, gas at 11.2 L and 500.0 K using (a) the ideal gas equation and (b) the van der Waals equation. (c) Explain any differences between the results.

Hint:

a. Determine the number of moles of ammonia gas present.

b. Use the constants for NH_3 listed in Table 7.4.

SECTION REVIEW

- Real gases differ from ideal gases in two important ways: Real gas particles have finite volumes, and real gas particles form attractions, called intermolecular forces, at low temperatures and high pressures.
- These differences lead to deviations from ideal gas behavior.
- The van der Waals equation (Equation 7.12), which includes constants specific for each gas, is used for more accurate calculations of gas pressures.

$$\left[P + a\left(\frac{n}{V}\right)^2\right](V - nb) = nRT$$

Putting It Together

The example problems in earlier sections of this chapter focus on the new skills acquired in that section, but homework and exam questions in chemistry often require more than just one skill at a time. In fact, you will likely be expected to apply knowledge from throughout the chapter, or even multiple chapters in a single problem. This final example problem is meant to help you prepare for these types of multi-concept questions. Additional examples can be found in the end of chapter exercises.

Example 7.32

A gaseous compound is composed of 92.26% C and 7.74% H, and a 0.507 g sample of the compound occupies 478 mL at 23°C and 0.989 atm pressure. What is the molecular formula of the compound?

Solution

To determine the molecular formula, you need to have both the empirical formula and the molar mass. The empirical formula can be calculated from the percent composition (Section 3.10) as

$$92.26\text{ g C}\left(\frac{1\text{ mol C}}{12.01\text{ g C}}\right) = 7.682\text{ mol C}$$

$$7.74\text{ g H}\left(\frac{1\text{ mol H}}{1.008\text{ g H}}\right) = 7.679\text{ mol H}$$

The mole ratio of carbon to hydrogen is 1:1, so the empirical formula is CH.

The molar mass can be calculated from the mass given in the problem statement and the number of moles of gas present, which can be calculated from the pressure, volume, and temperature data, using the ideal gas law.

$$n = \frac{PV}{RT} = \frac{(0.989\text{ atm})(0.478\text{ L})}{\left(0.08206\frac{\text{L}\cdot\text{atm}}{\text{mol}\cdot\text{K}}\right)(296\text{ K})} = 0.01945\text{ mol}$$

The molar mass, $\mathcal{M}$, is the mass divided by the number of moles.

$$\mathcal{M} = \frac{0.507\text{ g}}{0.01945\text{ mol}} = 26.1\text{ g/mol}$$

The mass of 1 mol of an empirical formula unit, CH, is the mass of 1 mol of carbon atoms (12.01 g) and the mass of 1 mol of hydrogen atoms (1.01 g).

$$12.01\text{ g} + 1.01\text{ g} = 13.02\text{ g}$$

Dividing the molar mass by the empirical formula mass will determine the ratio of the molecular formula to the empirical formula.

$$\frac{26.1\text{ g}}{13.02\text{ g}} = 2.00$$

Thus, the molecular formula is twice the empirical formula, so the molecular formula is C_2H_2, which is the formula for acetylene.

PRACTICE PROBLEM 7.32

A 3.53 g sample of a gaseous hydrocarbon occupies 2.90 L at 24°C and 749 torr. The gas is composed of 79.89% C by mass, with the rest being hydrogen. What is the molecular formula of the gas?

Hint: First, determine the empirical formula using the percent mass data. Then, determine the number of moles using the ideal gas law. The number of moles, combined with the mass data given, leads to the molar mass. Finally, comparing the molar mass of the empirical formula to the calculated molar mass leads to the molecular formula.

Key Terms, Symbols, and Equations

KEY TERMS

atmosphere, atm (7.1): A unit of pressure equal to 760 torr that is the pressure of the atmosphere on a "normal" day at sea level; the envelope of air surrounding Earth.

atmospheric pressure (7.1): The pressure of the atmosphere.

average kinetic energy (7.10): The total kinetic energy of all the molecules of a sample, divided by the number of molecules; the average kinetic energy depends on temperature only.

Avogadro's law (7.5): Equal volumes of gas, at the same temperature and pressure, contain an equal number of gas particles (atoms or molecules): $\frac{V_1}{n_1} = \frac{V_2}{n_2}$.

barometer (7.1): An instrument for measuring the pressure of a gas, especially the atmosphere.

barometric pressure (7.1): The pressure of the atmosphere.

Boyle's law (7.2): At constant temperature, the volume of a given sample of gas is inversely proportional to its pressure: $P_1V_1 = P_2V_2$.

Charles's law (7.3): At constant pressure, the volume of a given sample of gas is directly proportional to its absolute temperature: $\frac{V_1}{T_1} = \frac{V_2}{T_2}$.

combined gas law (7.4): For a given sample of gas, the volume is directly proportional to the absolute temperature and inversely proportional to the pressure.

Dalton's law of partial pressures (7.7): The total pressure of a gas mixture is equal to the sum of the partial pressures of its components: $P_{\text{total}} = P_1 + P_2 + \cdots + P_n$.

diffusion (7.11): The spreading out of gas particles by random motion and collisions to occupy an entire volume.

effusion (7.11): The movement of gas particles through a tiny opening without collisions.

force (7.1): A push or a pull.

gas (7.1): A state of matter; a sample of matter that has its volume and shape determined by the volume and shape of its container.

Gay-Lussac's law of combining volumes (7.9): At equal temperatures and equal pressures, the volumes of separate gases involved in a chemical reaction are directly proportional to their coefficients in the balanced chemical equation.

Graham's law of effusion (7.11): The ratio of rates of effusion of two gases, $\frac{r_1}{r_2}$, is equal to the square root of the inverse ratio of their molar masses, $\sqrt{\frac{\mathcal{M}_2}{\mathcal{M}_1}}$.

ideal gas (7.6): Hypothetical gas whose behavior is predicted by the gas laws and explained by kinetic molecular theory.

ideal gas constant (7.6): $R = 0.08206\frac{\text{L}\cdot\text{atm}}{\text{mol}\cdot\text{K}}$ or $R = 8.3145\frac{\text{J}}{\text{K}\cdot\text{mol}}$. R is the same for all gases.

ideal gas law (7.6): The pressure, volume, number of moles, and temperature of a sample of gas are related by the equation $PV = nRT$, where $R = 0.08206\frac{\text{L}\cdot\text{atm}}{\text{mol}\cdot\text{K}}$.

kinetic molecular theory (7.10): The theory that explains the gas laws (and other phenomena) in terms of the motions and characteristics of the molecules of a gas.

liquid (7.1): A state of matter; a sample of matter that has a definite volume but assumes the shape of its container.

mean free path (7.11): The average distance traveled by a gas particle between collisions.

mole fraction (7.7): The number of moles of a component in a mixture divided by the total number of moles in the mixture, $X_i = n_i/n_t$.

partial pressure (7.7): The pressure of one gas in a mixture of gases.

perfectly elastic collision (7.10): A collision that occurs with no loss of kinetic energy.

pressure (7.1): Force divided by area.

random motion (7.10): Motion of molecules in arbitrary directions.

root-mean-square speed, v_{rms} (7.11): A measure of the average speed of a gas particle: $v_{rms} = \sqrt{\frac{3RT}{\mathcal{M}}}$.

solid (7.1): A state of matter; a sample of matter that has a definite shape and volume.

standard temperature and pressure, STP (7.1): Standard temperature and pressure, usually defined as 0°C and 100 kPa pressure (1 bar).

torr (7.1): A unit of pressure equal to 1 mmHg or $\frac{1}{760}$ atm.

van der Waals equation (7.12): A modification of the ideal gas law to account for the finite volumes of particles and intermolecular forces between particles:

$$\left[P + a\left(\frac{n}{V}\right)^2\right](V - nb) = nRT$$

vapor pressure (7.7): The pressure of the vapor in equilibrium with its liquid (or solid).

volume ratio (7.9): The ratio of volumes of separate gases involved in a chemical reaction.

SYMBOLS/ABBREVIATIONS

a (one of the van der Waals constants) (7.12)
atm (atmosphere) (7.1)
b (one of the van der Waals constants) (7.12)
d (density) (7.8)
KE (kinetic energy) (7.11)
kPa (kilopascal) (7.1)
$\mathcal{M}$ (molar mass) (7.8)
mmHg (millimeters of mercury) (7.1)
n (moles of gas) (7.5)
N_A (Avogadro's number) (7.11)
P (pressure) (7.2)
Pa (pascal) (7.1)
R (ideal gas law constant) (7.6)
STP (standard temperature and pressure) (7.1)
V (volume) (7.2)
v_{rms} (root-mean-square speed) (7.11)
X_i (mole fraction) (7.7)

EQUATIONS

$P_1V_1 = P_2V_2$ (Boyle's law) (7.1)

$\frac{V_1}{T_1} = \frac{V_2}{T_2}$ (Charles's law) (7.2)

$\frac{P_1V_1}{T_1} = \frac{P_2V_2}{T_2}$ (combined gas law) (7.3)

$\frac{V_1}{n_1} = \frac{V_2}{n_2}$ (Avogadro's law) (7.4)

$PV = nRT$ (ideal gas law) (7.5)

$P_{total} = P_1 + P_2 + \cdots + P_n$ (Dalton's law) (7.6)

$\frac{P_i}{P_{total}} = \frac{n_i}{n_{total}} = X_i$ (partial pressure and mole fraction) (7.7)

$KE_{\text{avg per mole}} = \frac{3}{2}RT$ (7.8)

$KE_{\text{avg per particle}} = \frac{\frac{3}{2}RT}{N_A}$ (7.9)

$v_{rms} = \sqrt{\frac{3RT}{\mathcal{M}}}$ (7.10)

$\frac{r_1}{r_2} = \sqrt{\frac{\mathcal{M}_2}{\mathcal{M}_1}}$ (Graham's law) (7.11)

$\left[P + a\left(\frac{n}{v}\right)^2\right](V - nb) = nRT$ (van der Waals equation) (7.12)

Chapter Summary

The physical properties of ideal gases do not depend on the composition of the gas because all gases obey the same set of gas laws. Pressure is defined as force per unit area and can be measured with a simple barometer. One torr is the amount of pressure required to hold 1 mm mercury (mmHg) vertically in a barometer, and one standard atmosphere (atm) is the pressure required to hold 760 mmHg. Standard temperature and pressure (STP) was once defined as 0°C and 1.00 atm, but it has been redefined as 0°C and 100 kPa pressure (0.98692 atm, 1 bar) (Section 7.1).

Boyle's law states that the volume of a sample of gas at *constant temperature* is inversely proportional to its pressure. The law is often expressed in equation form as $P_1V_1 = P_2V_2$ (Equation 7.1) (Section 7.2).

Charles's law states that the volume of a sample of gas at *constant pressure* is directly proportional to its *absolute* temperature. The Kelvin temperature scale is used with all gas laws in which temperature is involved. In equation form, Charles's law (Equation 7.2) can be written as $\frac{V_1}{T_1} = \frac{V_2}{T_2}$ (Section 7.3).

Boyle's and Charles's laws can be combined into one law related to a given sample of gas. This combined gas law (Equation 7.3) can be expressed as $\frac{P_1V_1}{T_1} = \frac{P_2V_2}{T_2}$ (Section 7.4).

Avogadro's law (Equation 7.4), $\frac{V_1}{n_1} = \frac{V_2}{n_2}$, states that volume and number of moles are proportional when temperature and pressure are held constant (Section 7.5). The ideal gas law (Equation 7.5) relates the pressure, volume, number of moles, and temperature of any sample of any gas under any conditions: $PV = nRT$, where R is the ideal gas constant. $R = 0.08206 \frac{\text{L} \cdot \text{atm}}{\text{mol} \cdot \text{K}}$, and these units determine the units that must be used for the pressure and volume, respectively (Section 7.6).

Dalton's law of partial pressures (Equation 7.6), $P_{\text{total}} = P_1 + P_2 + \cdots + P_n$, states that in a mixture of gases the total pressure is equal to the sum of the pressures of the individual gases—their partial pressures. The partial pressures are directly proportional to the number of moles of each individual gas in the mixture. Water vapor in a gas mixture, like any other gas in the mixture, obeys Dalton's law, with its vapor pressure being a constant at any given temperature (Section 7.7).

The ideal gas law can be used to determine the molar mass of a gas sample of known mass (Section 7.8). The ideal gas law also can be usefully combined with stoichiometric manipulations to calculate the quantity of any other reactant or product in a reaction.

Gay-Lussac's law of combining volumes relates the volumes of gases involved in a reaction, all measured separately at the same temperature and pressure, to the mole ratio and, therefore, to the ratio of coefficients in the balanced chemical equation (Section 7.9).

Kinetic molecular theory explains the behavior of gases in terms of characteristics of their molecules by postulating that ideal gases are made up of molecules that are in constant, random motion and those molecules have a total volume that is insignificant relative to the total volume of the gas. Forces of attraction between the molecules are negligible, and when the molecules collide, the collisions are perfectly elastic. The average kinetic energy of the gas molecules is directly proportional to the absolute temperature of the gas (Section 7.10).

All gas samples have the same average kinetic energy at the same temperature, and this average kinetic energy is also related to the mass and average speed of the molecules by the equation for root-mean-square speed, $v_{\text{rms}} = \sqrt{\frac{3RT}{\mathcal{M}}}$ (Equation 7.10). In this equation, the value of the gas constant is given in energy units, so $R = 8.3145 \frac{\text{J}}{\text{K} \cdot \text{mol}} = 8.3145 \frac{\text{kg} \cdot \text{m}^2}{\text{s}^2 \cdot \text{K} \cdot \text{mol}}$. Increasing the temperature not only increases the average speed of the gas particles, but it also expands the range of speeds of the gas particles.

Effusion, the movement of gas particles through a tiny opening without collisions, is directly related to root-mean-square speed and can be used to determine the molecular mass of an unknown gas using Graham's law of effusion, $\frac{r_1}{r_2} = \sqrt{\frac{\mathcal{M}_2}{\mathcal{M}_1}}$ (Equation 7.11). This relationship can be used to determine the relative rates of effusion of two gases of known molar mass or can be used to determine the molar mass of an unknown gas by comparing its rate of effusion to rates of known gases (Section 7.11).

Real gases differ from ideal gases in two important ways: Real gas particles have finite volumes, and real gas particles form attractions, called intermolecular forces, at low temperatures and high pressures, both of which lead to deviations from ideal gas behavior. The van der Waals equation (Equation 7.12), $\left[P + a\left(\frac{n}{V}\right)^2\right](V - nb) = nRT$, includes two constants, *a* and *b*. Constant *a* accounts for the finite volume of the gas particles, whereas *b* accounts for the effect of intermolecular forces. This equation is used to calculate more accurate gas pressures under extreme conditions (Section 7.12).

END OF CHAPTER QUESTIONS

7.1 Gas Pressure

1. In the diagram of a solid, liquid, and gas shown in Figure 7.1, there is space between the gas particles. What is in this space?
   a. air
   b. nothing
   c. gas vapors
   d. ether
   e. dust or other impurities

2. The simple barometer diagram in Figure 7.2 shows gas molecules in the air colliding against the surface of the Hg in the dish but does not show any gas molecules colliding against the Hg in the tube.
   a. Why are there no gas molecules shown colliding against the surface of the Hg in the tube?
   b. What would be the height of the Hg in the tube if the air pressure inside the tube were equal to the air pressure outside the tube?

3. Calculate the pressure in atmospheres corresponding to
   a. 1.000 kPa.
   b. 213.4 kPa.
   c. 3.09×10^3 Pa.
   d. 1.013×10^5 Pa.

4. Calculate the pressure in torr corresponding to
   a. 1.000 kPa.
   b. 213.4 kPa.
   c. 3.09×10^3 Pa.
   d. 1.013×10^5 Pa.

5. Calculate the pressure in atmospheres corresponding to
   a. 743.9 torr.
   b. 125 mmHg.
   c. 397 torr.
   d. 1224 mmHg.

6. In the United States, weather reports often provide the atmospheric pressure in units of inches of Hg (in Hg) rather than mmHg. What is normal atmospheric pressure in units of inches (confusing otherwise; reads as in an not the abbreviation in.) Hg?

7. If the atmospheric pressure in the eye of a hurricane is 26.63 in Hg, what is the atmospheric pressure of the eye in units of
   a. mmHg.
   b. atm.
   c. kPa.

8. Atmospheric pressure on the surface of Venus is 93.2 bar. Calculate the atmospheric pressure on Venus in units of
   a. kPa.
   b. atm.
   c. mmHg.

7.2 Boyle's Law

9. Calculate the final pressure of a sample of gas that is changed at constant temperature to 14.3 L from 7.55 L at 828 torr.

10. Calculate the final pressure of a sample of gas that is changed at constant temperature to 0.980 L from 2.112 L at 1.12 atm.

11. A sample of gas is compressed at constant temperature from 6.44 L at 1.75 atm to 548 mL.
    a. Change the number of milliliters to liters.
    b. Calculate the final pressure of the sample.

12. Calculate the final pressure when a sample of gas is expanded at constant temperature from 898 mL at 1.09 atm to 1.63 L.

13. Calculate the final pressure required to increase the volume of a 3.00-L sample of gas initially at 1.00 atm
    a. by 5.00 L.
    b. to 5.00 L.

14. Consider these two situations:
    a. Calculate the final pressure of a sample of gas that is expanded to 3.79 L at constant temperature from 992 mL at 1.13 atm.
    b. Calculate the initial pressure of a sample of gas compressed at constant temperature to 992 mL at 1.13 atm from 3.79 L.
    c. Compare the answers to (a) and (b).

15. Consider these two situations:
    a. Calculate the final pressure of a sample of gas that is expanded to 1.16 L at constant temperature from 457 mL at 812 torr.
    b. Calculate the initial pressure of a sample of gas compressed at constant temperature to 457 mL at 812 torr from 1.16 L.
    c. Compare the answers to (a) and (b).

16. Calculate the pressure required to change a 689-mL sample of gas at 712 torr and 25°C to 1.31 L at 25°C.

17. Calculate the pressure required to change a 2.26 L sample of gas at 1.61 atm and 30°C to 671 mL at 30°C.

18. Calculate the final volume of a 4.68 L sample of gas that has its pressure tripled.

7.3 Charles's Law

19. Calculate the final volume at 302 K of a 5.41 L sample of gas originally at 353 K if the pressure does not change.

20. Calculate the initial volume at 301 K of a sample of gas that is changed to 52.5 mL by cooling to 285 K at constant pressure.

21. A sample of gas is heated at constant pressure from 7°C to 21°C.
    a. Will the volume triple?
    b. If not, by what ratio will the volume increase?

22. A sample of gas is cooled at constant pressure from 50°C to 10°C.
    a. Will the volume decrease to one-fifth its original volume?
    b. If not, by what ratio will the volume decrease?

23. Calculate the final volume at 402 K of a 122 mL sample of gas originally at 55°C if the pressure does not change.

24. Calculate the final volume at 319°C of a 51.3 mL sample of gas originally at 171°C if the pressure does not change.

25. Calculate the final volume at 33°C of a 6.00 L sample of gas originally at −33°C, assuming that the pressure does not change.

26. Calculate the initial volume at 0°C of a sample of gas that is changed to 731 mL by cooling to −14°C at constant pressure.

27. Plot the following data and extrapolate to zero volume, then estimate the value of absolute zero on the Celsius scale.

V (L)	1.20	1.40	1.60	1.80	2.00
T (°C)	25	75	125	175	225

7.4 The Combined Gas Law

28. Describe how to use Boyle's law and Charles's law to form the combined gas law.

29. Calculate the final volume of a sample of gas initially occupying 6.40 L at 0°C and 1.00 atm pressure after its pressure is increased to 1.17 atm and its temperature is increased to 37°C.

30. Calculate the final pressure of a gas that is expanded from 769 mL at 24°C and 1.15 atm to 2.00 L at 33°C.

31. Calculate the final temperature of a sample of gas initially at 22.3°C that is expanding from 2.335 L to 4.117 L while its pressure has risen from 772 mmHg to 825 mmHg.

32. Calculate the final volume of a sample of gas initially occupying 3.46 L at 5°C and 1.12 atm pressure after its pressure is increased to 5.17 atm and its temperature is increased 57°C.

33. Calculate the final pressure of a gas that is expanded from 322 mL at 18°C and 0.815 atm to 1.75 L at 53°C.

34. Calculate the final temperature of a sample of gas initially at 72.3°C that has expanded from 1.305 L to 2.887 L while its pressure has risen from 372 mmHg to 1825 mmHg.

35. Calculate the final volume of a sample of gas initially occupying 2.23 L at 9°C and 1.72 atm pressure after its pressure is increased to 3.17 atm and its temperature is increased to 78°C.

36. Calculate the final pressure of a gas that is expanded from 275 mL at 22°C and 1.315 atm to 1.35 L at 65°C.

37. Calculate the final temperature of a sample of gas initially at 42.3°C that has expanded from 0.635 L to 1.862 L while its pressure has risen from 472 mmHg to 1935 mmHg.

7.5 Avogadro's Law

38. A sample of 0.425 mol of oxygen gas occupies a volume of 0.625 L. What will be the volume if the number of moles of $O_2(g)$ is increased to 0.994, with no change in temperature or pressure?

39. 0.853 mol of methane gas occupies a volume of 15.0 L at a certain temperature and pressure. What volume is occupied by 3.72 mol of methane at this same temperature and pressure?

40. A sample of 0.329 mol of oxygen gas occupies a volume of 0.944 L. More oxygen gas is added, with no change in temperature or pressure, to a final volume of 2.47 L. What is the final number of moles of $O_2(g)$ in the sample?

41. 0.283 mol of methane gas occupies a volume of 5.80 L at a certain temperature and pressure. How many moles of methane would be needed to expand that volume to 23.8 L at this same temperature and pressure?

42. A sample of 0.536 mol of NO gas occupies a volume of 0.514 L. What will be the volume if the number of moles of NO(g) is increased to 0.883, with no change in temperature or pressure?

43. 0.742 mol of SO_2 gas occupies a volume of 715 mL at a certain temperature and pressure. What volume is occupied by 4.83 mol of sulfur dioxide at this same temperature and pressure?

44. A sample of 0.218 mol of carbon dioxide gas occupies a volume of 1.252 L. More oxygen gas is added, with no change in temperature or pressure, to a final volume of 3.581 L. What is the final number of moles of $CO_2(g)$ in the sample?

45. 0.283 mol of methane gas occupies a volume 5.80 L at a certain temperature and pressure. How many moles of methane must be removed to decrease that volume to 2.38 L at this same temperature and pressure?

46. A 15.3 g sample of nitrogen gas occupies a volume of 2.64 L. Assuming no change in temperature or pressure, what will be the new volume upon addition of an additional 2.4 g of nitrogen gas?

47. A 24.6 g sample of chlorine gas occupies a volume of 1.37 L at a particular temperature and pressure. What mass of chlorine gas occupies 4.85 L at this same temperature and pressure?

7.6 Ideal Gas Law

48. 1.50 mol of an unknown gas occupies 14.0 L at 1.25 atm.
    a. Determine the temperature of the gas.
    b. Is the gas more likely to be H_2 or H_2O? Explain.

49. Determine the volume of 0.800 mol of $SO_2(g)$ at 55°C and 0.950 atm.

50. Determine the pressure of 0.515 mol of NH_3 gas occupying 8.05 L at 307 K.

51. Calculate the value of R in
    a. $L \cdot torr/mol \cdot K$.
    b. $mL \cdot atm/mol \cdot K$.

52. Determine the number of moles of O_2 in a volume of 14.3 mL at 292 K and 606 torr.

53. Determine the number of moles of gas in a volume of 152 mL at 419 K and 382 torr.

54. Determine the volume of 0.413 mol of F_2 at 31°C and 787 torr.

55. Determine the temperature of a gas if 0.813 mol occupies 10.1 L at 798 torr.

56. Determine the number of moles of gas in a volume of 14.0 L at 333 K and 1.73×10^{-3} torr.

57. Determine the pressure of 0.300 mol of CO gas in a volume of 14.7 L at 303 K.

58. Determine the number of moles of gas in a volume of 1.90×10^{-3} mL at 273 K and 1.00 atm.

59. Use the ideal gas law to derive
   a. Boyle's law.
   b. Charles's law.
   c. the combined gas law.

7.7 Dalton's Law of Partial Pressures

60. A gaseous mixture contains 2.00 mol of He, 2.00 mol of Ne, and 2.00 mol of Ar. The total pressure of the mixture is 6.69 atm. What is the partial pressure of each gas?

61. A gaseous mixture contains 0.170 mol of H_2, 0.230 mol of N_2, and 0.200 mol of Ne. The total pressure of the mixture is 1.45 atm. What is the partial pressure of each gas?

62. A gaseous mixture contains 1.50 mol of O_2, 2.50 mol of He, and 0.500 mol of N_2. The partial pressure of the oxygen is 0.300 atm. What are the partial pressures of the nitrogen and the helium?

63. A mixture of gases exists in which the numbers of moles of all the components are the same. What can be said about the partial pressures of the components?

64. A gaseous mixture contains 0.550 mol of H_2, 0.350 mol of N_2, and 0.950 mol of Ne. The partial pressure of the nitrogen is 0.517 atm.
   a. What are the partial pressures of the hydrogen and the neon?
   b. If the temperature is 325 K, what is the volume of the nitrogen?
   c. What is the volume of the mixture?

65. Oxygen gas is standing over water at a total pressure of 784 torr. The partial pressure of the oxygen is found to be 752 torr. Determine the temperature of the system.

66. Oxygen gas is standing over water at a total pressure of 781 torr at 35°C. Determine the partial pressure of the oxygen.

7.8 Molar Mass and Density in Gas Law Calculations

67. Determine the pressure of
   a. 0.901 g of N_2 in a 12.4 L vessel at 25°C.
   b. 0.901 g of Cl_2 in a 12.4 L vessel at 25°C.
   c. Explain the difference between (a) and (b)

68. A 3.50 L flask at STP is filled with propane, C_3H_8. Calculate the mass of propane in the tank.

69. What is the volume of 6.04 g of CO_2 at 1.00 atm and 27°C?

70. Determine the molar mass of a gaseous substance if 11.4 g occupies 5.52 L at 1.10 atm and 12°C.

71. Calculate the molar mass of a gas if 15.0 g occupies 11.8 L at 314 K and 1.06 atm.

72. Calculate the density of argon at 258°C and 1.11 atm.

73. Calculate the density of carbon monoxide at 25°C and 723 mmHg.

74. Calculate the density of helium at 215°C and 1275 mmHg.

75. Calculate the molar mass of a gas with density 6.53 g/L at 0°C and 1.00 atm pressure.

76. A 1.60 g sample of a gaseous hydrocarbon occupies 1.55 L at 25°C and 682 torr. The gas is composed of 85.63% C and 14.37% H. What is the molecular formula of the gas?

77. Calculate the molecular formula of a gaseous hydrocarbon of which 24.0 g occupies 19.9 L at 791 torr and 21°C. The hydrocarbon consists of 85.6% C and 14.4% H.

7.9 Gases in Chemical Reactions

78. Explain why it is important to write the correct formula for an elemental gas that exists as diatomic molecules.

79. What mass of H_2 is required to react with O_2 to produce 912 mL of $H_2O(g)$ at 112°C and 0.989 atm?

80. What volume of ammonia at 456 K and 1.00 atm can be produced by the reaction of 1.00 metric ton (1.00×10^6 g) of hydrogen gas with nitrogen gas?

81. How many moles of aluminum metal are required to produce 4.04 L of hydrogen gas at 1.11 atm and 27°C by reaction with HCl?

82. Calculate the volume of CO_2 (measured after cooling to 25°C at 1.00 atm) that will be liberated by heating 22.9 g of $Mg(HCO_3)_2$. $MgCO_3$ is also a product.

83. What mass of O_2 is required to react with H_2 to produce 4.19 L of $H_2O(g)$ at 172°C and 0.801 atm?

84. How many moles of mercury(II) oxide must be thermally decomposed to produce 2.26 L of oxygen gas at 1.00 atm and 23°C?

85. What volume of hydrogen at 282 K and 1.00 atm can be produced by the reaction of 6.59 g of aluminum with hydrochloric acid?

86. Determine the number of moles of aqueous sodium hydroxide required to react with 16.7 L of carbon dioxide gas at 298 K and 1.00 atm to form sodium carbonate.

87. Calculate the volume of CO_2 (measured after cooling to 25°C at 1.00 atm) that will be liberated by heating 14.2 g of $NaHCO_3$. (Na_2CO_3 is also a product).

88. What volume of ammonia at 555 K and 1.77 atm can be produced by the reaction of 1.50 kg of hydrogen gas with nitrogen gas?

89. How many moles of mercury(I) oxide must be thermally decomposed to produce 1.03 L of oxygen gas at 1.00 atm and 25°C?

90. When 5.00 mol of O_2 reacts with 4.00 mol of NH_3, 4.00 mol of NO and 6.00 mol of H_2O are formed.
   a. Write a balanced chemical equation for the reaction.
   b. Calculate the volumes of 5.00 mol of O_2, 4.00 mol of NH_3, and 4.00 mol of NO at 0°C and 1.00 atm pressure.
   c. Compare the ratio of the volumes of the gases to the coefficients in the balanced equation. What can be stated about the volumes of gases involved in a reaction when they are *in separate vessels at the same temperature and pressure*?

91. Repeat the previous problem at 25°C and 1.50 atm pressure. Are the volume ratios the same as the mole ratios in the balanced chemical equation?

92. Repeat the previous problem with any other given temperature and pressure. Are the volume ratios the same as the mole ratios in the balanced chemical equation?

93. What ratio of volumes (all at 25°C and 1.00 atm) would be involved in the reaction represented by the following equation?

$$2\,SO_2(g) + O_2(g) \rightarrow 2\,SO_3(g)$$

94. What ratio of volumes (all at 327°C and 1.00 atm) would be involved in the reaction represented by the following equation?

$$2\,C(s) + O_2(g) \rightarrow 2\,CO(g)$$

95. Using the ideal gas law, show that equal volumes of two gases under like conditions of temperature and pressure have equal numbers of moles of gas and thus equal numbers of molecules.

7.10 Kinetic Molecular Theory of Gases

96. Imagine a sheet of paper suspended by one edge and hanging vertically. What would happen if a rapid succession of peas was shot from a peashooter at the paper? Compare the impact of the peas to the impact of gas molecules bombarding a wall.

97. Use the kinetic molecular theory to explain why gases exhibit pressure.

98. Use the kinetic molecular theory to explain why the volume of a gas at a certain temperature is inversely proportional to the gas pressure.

99. Use the kinetic molecular theory to explain why the pressure of a gas enclosed in a certain container is directly proportional to the temperature.

100. Use the kinetic molecular theory to explain why the number of moles of gas enclosed in a certain container at a certain temperature is directly proportional to the volume of the gas sample.

101. Use the kinetic molecular theory to explain why the number of moles of gas enclosed in a certain container at a certain temperature is directly proportional to the gas pressure.

102. Use the kinetic molecular theory to explain why Dalton's law of partial pressure works.

103. Calculate the percentage of the 30.6 L occupied by the molecules of the 1.00 mol of water vapor at 1.00 atm and 100°C as found in Example 7.26. Assume that the molecules of liquid water actually occupy all the 18.8 mL volume.

104. Calculate the volume occupied by 1.00 mol of H_2O at 100.00°C and 5.00 atm pressure when it is
   a. in the vapor state.
   b. in the liquid state (the density of liquid water at 100°C is 0.958 g/mL).

105. Calculate the percentage of the volume of the gas samples occupied by the water molecules in the previous two questions and compare this answer to the percentage in question 103.

7.11 Movement of Gas Particles

106. Describe how an increase in temperature
   a. affects the average speed of gas particles in a sample.
   b. affects the range of speeds of gas particles in a sample.

107. Describe how the mass of a gas particle affects the average speed of particles in a gas sample.

108. Calculate the root-mean-square speed of carbon monoxide gas
   a. at 25°C.
   b. at 100°C.
   c. Compare the answers for (a) and (b).

109. Calculate the root-mean-square speed of sulfur dioxide gas
   a. at 25°C.
   b. at 100°C.
   c. Compare the answers for (a) and (b).

110. Consider two gases, fluorine, F_2, and chlorine, Cl_2.
   a. Predict their relative root-mean-square speeds at any given temperature.
   b. Calculate the root-mean-square speed of F_2 at 75°C.
   c. Calculate the root-mean-square speed of Cl_2 at 75°C.
   d. Compare the answers for (b) and (c) to (a).

111. A gas known to have a formula of NO_x was found to effuse at a rate that is 1.033 times the rate of effusion of oxygen. Determine
   a. the molar mass of NO_x.
   b. the value of x.

112. A gas known to have a formula of SO_x was found to effuse at a rate that is 0.707 times the rate of effusion of oxygen. Determine
   a. the molar mass of SO_x.
   b. the value of x.

113. A gas known to have a formula of SO_x was found to effuse at a rate that is 0.632 times the rate of effusion of oxygen. Determine
   a. the molar mass of SO_x.
   b. the value of x.

114. A homonuclear diatomic gas, X_2, effuses at a rate of 0.672 times the rate of effusion of oxygen. Determine
   a. the molar mass of X_2.
   b. the identity of X.

115. A homonuclear diatomic gas, X_2, effuses at a rate of 0.918 times the rate of effusion of oxygen. Determine
   a. the molar mass of X_2.
   b. the identity of X.

7.12 Behavior of Real Gases

116. Describe the circumstances under which gases are most likely to deviate from ideal behavior.

117. Determine if Cl_2 or HCl is more likely to deviate from ideal behavior, assuming that the gases are at the same temperature and pressure, and explain why.

118. Determine if CH_4 or CCl_4 is more likely to deviate from ideal behavior, assuming that the gases are at the same temperature and pressure, and explain why.

119. Determine if H_2S or H_2O is more likely to deviate from ideal behavior, assuming that the gases are at the same temperature and pressure, and explain why.

120. Determine if ethane, C_2H_6, or propane, C_3H_8, is more likely to deviate from ideal behavior, assuming that the gases are at the same temperature and pressure, and explain why.

121. What does the a constant in the van der Waals equation correct for in nonideal gas behavior?

122. What does the b constant in the van der Waals equation correct for in nonideal gas behavior?

123. Calculate the pressure of 1.00 mol of nitrogen gas at 7.50 L and 273 K using
   a. the ideal gas equation.
   b. the van der Waals equation. (See Table 7.4 for the values of the constants.)

124. Calculate the pressure of 95.00 g of NO_2 gas at 11.2 L and 400.0 K using
   a. the ideal gas equation.
   b. the van der Waals equation.

125. Calculate the pressure of 80.00 g of hydrogen fluoride, HF, gas at 11.2 L and 500.0 K using
   a. the ideal gas equation.
   b. the van der Waals equation.

Putting It Together

126. A 5.43 g sample of which elemental diatomic gas occupies 4.38 L at 25°C and 0.950 atm?

127. A 5.84 g sample of which noble gas occupies 1.00 L at 0°C and 1.00 atm pressure?

128. A 6.50 L steel vessel that holds a sample of oxygen gas at 25°C and 1.00 atm develops a leak, and 3.00 g of oxygen escapes before the leak is repaired.
    a. Calculate the initial number of moles of oxygen present.
    b. Calculate the number of moles that escape.
    c. Calculate the pressure of oxygen in the vessel, still at 25°C, after the leak is repaired.
    d. Calculate the final volume of a sample of gas initially occupying 355 mL after its pressure is increased to 25% of its original pressure and its absolute temperature is decreased to 10.0% of its original absolute temperature.

129. What, if anything, happens to the total pressure in the system as each of the following reactions occurs in a constant-volume reaction vessel at constant temperature?
    a. $2\ SO_2(g) + O_2(g) \rightarrow 2\ SO_3(g)$
    b. $Br_2(g) + H_2(g) \rightarrow 2\ HBr(g)$
    c. $2\ C(s) + O_2(g) \rightarrow 2\ CO(g)$

130. Fill in the blanks in the following table for a given sample of gas, assuming constant temperature.

	V_1	P_1	V_2	P_2
(a)	3.38 L	1.07 atm		2.11 atm
(b)		372 torr	909 mL	492 torr
(c)	3.18 L		702 mL	2.46 atm
(d)	3.19 mL	811 torr		1.35 atm

131. What are the volume and the pressure for neon, argon, and the mixture in the following experiments?
    a. Samples of 0.0110 mol of Ne and 0.0200 mol of Ar are placed in two identical 1.00-L containers at 25°C.
    b. Samples of 0.0110 mol of Ne and 0.0200 mol of Ar are placed in a single 1.00-L container at 25°C.

132. What volume of O_2 can be collected over water at 25°C and barometric pressure of 1.14 atm from thermal decomposition of 0.200 g of $KClO_3$?
$KClO_3(s) \rightarrow KCl(s) + O_2(g)$

133. What mass of $KClO_3$ must be decomposed to produce 207 mL of O_2, collected over water, at 25°C and a barometric pressure of 771 torr?
$KClO_3(s) \rightarrow KCl(s) + O_2(g)$

134. What volume will 0.500 g of hydrogen occupy when collected over water at 25°C and 0.877 atm barometric pressure?

135. Calculate the pressure ratio of He to N_2 at which helium would have the same density as nitrogen if their temperatures were the same.

136. Will the volume of sample (a) or sample (b) be increased more (at constant pressure) by the indicated changes in temperature?
    a. 10°C to 20°C
    b. 100°C to 200°C

137. Fill in the blanks in the following table for a given sample of gas, assuming constant pressure.

	V_1	T_1	V_2	T_2
(a)		312 K	1.55 L	393 K
(b)	104 mL		141 mL	27°C
(c)	1.72 L	77°C	972 mL	
(d)	0.171 m^3	22°C		88°C

138. Calculate the percentage by mass of oxygen in a mixture of oxygen and nitrogen that has a density of 1.41 g/L at 0°C and 1 atm pressure.

139. Use Equation 1.3 to fill in the missing values, then plot volume versus Fahrenheit temperature to determine the value of absolute zero on the Fahrenheit scale.

Temperature (°C)	Temperature (°F)	Volume (L)
0		0.400
100		0.548
200		0.692
300		0.840

140. Determine the formula of a gaseous substance if 1.40 g occupies 14.9 L at 1.08 atm and 9°C.

141. A 4.92 g sample of which hydrogen halide occupies 3.00 L at 25°C and 836 torr?

142. Fill in the blanks in the following table.

	V_1	P_1	T_1	V_2	P_2	T_2
(a)	829 mL	1.57 atm	30°C		982 torr	289 K
(b)	602 mL	717 torr	47°C		3.00 atm	47°C
(c)	6.12 L	1.33 atm	382 K	4.48 L	665 torr	
(d)	2.13 L	797 torr	31°C	9.11 L		351 K

143. Fill in the blanks in the following table.

	V_1	P_1	T_1	V_2	P_2	T_2
(a)	213 mL		273 K	0.822 L	2.04 atm	321 K
(b)	627 mL	4.89 atm		0.552 L	4.89 atm	49°C
(c)	1.71 L	6.86 atm	22°C	3.11 L	2.19 atm	
(d)	13.1 L		298 K	10.0 L	1.99 atm	27°C

144. Fill in the blanks in the following table.

	V_1	P_1	T_1	V_2	P_2	T_2
(a)	6.55 mL	2.27 atm	330 K	14.8 mL	2.11 atm	
(b)	1.13 L		303 K	909 mL	891 torr	281 K
(c)		0.995 atm	299 K	173 mL	2.03 atm	332 K
(d)	1.07 L	616 torr	72°C		1.25 atm	72°C

145. A 2.71 g sample of a substance occupies 6.87 L at 2.59 atm and 320 K. Determine the identity of the substance.

146. Calculate the volume of a 75.0 mL sample of gas after its pressure is halved and its absolute temperature is increased to 25.0% of its original value.

147. A gaseous mixture contains 2.75 L of helium, some argon at 1.10 atm, and some neon at 25°C. Calculate the number of moles present of one of the gases.

148. A 0.756 g sample of a substance occupies 4.32 L at 1.00 atm and 280 K. Determine the identity of the substance.

149. A 10.0 L steel vessel that holds a sample of oxygen gas at 25°C and 741 torr develops a leak, and 5.75 g of oxygen escapes before the leak is repaired. After the leak is repaired, what is the pressure of oxygen in the vessel, if the temperature is still 25°C?

150. Potassium chlorate, $KClO_3$, decomposes into KCl and O_2 gas when heated: $2\ KClO_3(s) \rightarrow 2\ KCl(s) + 3\ O_2(g)$. If the reaction is performed in a sealed 1.50 L container, determine the pressure resulting from the formation of O_2 when 50.0 g of $KClO_3$ decomposes at 20.0°C. Assume that the decomposition of $KClO_3$ goes to completion.

PRACTICE PROBLEM SOLUTIONS

Practice Problem 7.1 Solution

a. 1.23 atm to torr:

$$1.23\ \text{atm}\left(\frac{760\ \text{torr}}{1\ \text{atm}}\right) = 935\ \text{torr}$$

b. 0.911 atm to kPa:

$$0.911\ \text{atm}\left(\frac{101.325\ \text{kPa}}{1\ \text{atm}}\right) = 92.3\ \text{kPa}$$

Practice Problem 7.2 Solution

a. Calculate $1/V$ and plot $1/V$ versus P.

P (atm)	V (L)	$1/V$ (L^{-1})
0.303	1.62	0.617
0.595	0.829	1.21
0.910	0.545	1.83
1.202	0.412	2.43
1.601	0.309	3.24

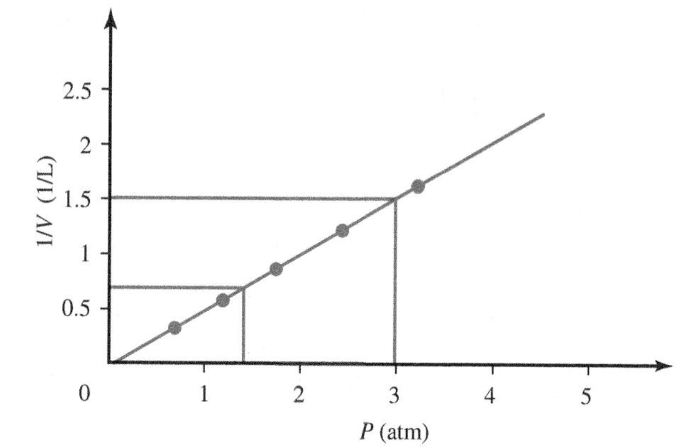

b. The pressure required to obtain a volume of 0.675 L (which corresponds to $1/V = 1.48\ L^{-1}$) is approximately 3 atm.

c. The volume present at 1.4 atm pressure is approximately 1.4 L (which corresponds to $1/V = 0.7\ L^{-1}$).

Practice Problem 7.3 Solution

Use Boyle's law (Equation 7.1) when the variables in the problem involve pressure and volume:

$$P_1V_1 = P_2V_2$$

The initial and final conditions can be tabulated as follows:

Initial Conditions	Final Conditions
$P_1 = 1.50$ atm	$P_2 = ?$
$V_1 = 35.0$ mL	$V_2 = 20.5$ mL

In this case, the volume decreases (i.e., $V_2 < V_1$), so the pressure should increase (i.e., $P_2 > P_1$).

Rearrange Equation 7.1 to solve for P_2, and plug in the values from the table:

$$P_1V_1 = P_2V_2$$

$$P_2 = \frac{P_1V_1}{V_2}$$

$$P_2 = \frac{(1.50\ \text{atm})(35.0\ \text{mL})}{20.5\ \text{mL}}$$

$$P_2 = 2.56\ \text{atm}$$

The pressure does, in fact, increase when the volume decreases.

Practice Problem 7.4 Solution

Start by tabulating the data:

Initial Conditions	Final Conditions
$P_1 = 1.20$ atm	$P_2 = 744\ \text{torr}\left(\frac{1\ \text{atm}}{760\ \text{torr}}\right) = 0.978\ \text{atm}$
$V_1 = ?$	$V_2 = 70.4$ mL

Because the pressures were given in two different units, one of them has been changed (P_2, in this case). Once the pressures are in consistent units, you can see that the pressure decreases. As a result, the volume must increase, which means $V_1 < V_2$.

Now, rearrange Boyle's law (Equation 7.1) to isolate V_1 and plug in the appropriate values:

$$P_1V_1 = P_2V_2$$

$$V_1 = \frac{P_2V_2}{P_1}$$

$$V_1 = \frac{(0.978\ \text{atm})(70.4\ \text{mL})}{1.20\ \text{atm}} = 57.4\ \text{mL}$$

The initial volume is, in fact, less than the final volume.

Practice Problem 7.5 Solution

Start by tabulating the data:

Initial Conditions	Final Conditions
$P_1 = ?$	$P_2 = 1.18$ atm
$V_1 = 485\ \text{mL}\left(\frac{1\ \text{L}}{1000\ \text{mL}}\right) = 0.485\ \text{L}$	$V_2 = 1.16$ L

The two volume measurements were in different units, so V_1 has been changed to match V_2. Once the volumes are in consistent units, you can see that the volume increases. As a result, the pressure must decrease, which means $P_1 > P_2$.

Now, rearrange Boyle's law (Equation 7.1) to isolate P_1 and plug in the appropriate values:

$$P_1V_1 = P_2V_2$$

$$P_1 = \frac{P_2V_2}{V_1}$$

$$P_1 = \frac{(1.18\ \text{atm})(1.16\ \text{L})}{0.485\ \text{L}} = 2.82\ \text{atm}$$

The initial pressure is, in fact, greater than the final pressure.

Practice Problem 7.6 Solution

Because the temperature and volume are changing and the pressure is constant, you can use Charles's law, Equation 7.2, to solve this problem. Start by organizing the data and making sure the units are consistent and appropriate.

Initial Conditions	Final Conditions
$T_1 = ?$	$T_2 = 55°C + 273.15 = 328\ K$
$V_1 = 456\ mL\left(\frac{1\ L}{1000\ mL}\right) = 0.456\ L$	$V_2 = 1.75\ L$

Charles's law is

$$\frac{V_1}{T_1} = \frac{V_2}{T_2}$$

Solve for T_1 and substitute the values from the table:

$$T_1 = \frac{T_2 V_1}{V_2}$$

$$T_1 = \frac{(328\ K)(0.456\ L)}{1.75\ L} = 85.5\ K$$

Finally, convert the absolute temperature to °C:

$$T_1 = 85.5\ K - 273.15 = -188\ °C$$

Practice Problem 7.7 Solution

First, tabulate the given data and convert to consistent, appropriate units:

Initial Conditions	Final Conditions
$T_1 = 22°C + 273 = 295\ K$	$T_2 = 85°C + 273 = 358\ K$
$V_1 = 575\ mL$	$V_2 = ?$
$P_1 = 737\ torr\left(\frac{1\ atm}{760\ torr}\right) = 0.970\ atm$	$P_2 = 1.55\ atm$

This is another example of opposing effects on the volume, because the increase in the temperature causes the volume to *increase*, while the increase in the pressure causes the volume to *decrease*. To find out which effect is greater, rearrange the combined gas law (Equation 7.3) to isolate V_2, then plug in the values from the table:

$$\frac{P_1 V_1}{T_1} = \frac{P_2 V_2}{T_2}$$

$$V_2 = \frac{P_1 V_1 T_2}{T_1 P_2}$$

$$V_2 = \frac{(0.970\ atm)(575\ mL)(358\ K)}{(295\ K)(1.55\ atm)} = 437\ mL$$

The value for V_2 tells you that, in this case, the change in pressure had a greater impact on the volume than the change in temperature.

Practice Problem 7.8 Solution

Organize the data, and make any needed conversions to the units.

Initial Conditions	Final Conditions
$T_1 = 52°C + 273.15 = 325\ K$	$T_2 = 0°C + 273.15 = 273\ K$
$V_1 = 49.7\ mL$	$V_2 = ?$
$P_1 = 811\ torr$	$P_2 = 760\ torr$

The decrease in temperature should *decrease* V_2, while the decrease in pressure should *increase* V_2. Therefore, you cannot predict the actual result without doing the calculation using the combined gas law (Equation 7.3):

$$\frac{P_1 V_1}{T_1} = \frac{P_2 V_2}{T_2}$$

$$V_2 = \frac{P_1 V_1 T_2}{T_1 P_2}$$

$$V_2 = \frac{(811\ torr)(49.7\ mL)(273\ K)}{(325\ K)(760\ torr)} = 44.5\ mL$$

Thus, the volume *decreased* slightly, so the decrease in temperature had a greater effect than the decrease in pressure.

Practice Problem 7.9 Solution

Start by tabulating the data and making any necessary changes to the units. You can predict from the increase in number of moles that the volume must increase.

Initial Conditions	Final Conditions
$n_1 = 0.225\ mol\ N_2$	$n_2 = 0.866\ mol\ N_2$
$V_1 = 0.325\ L$	$V_2 = ?$

The number of moles increases, so the volume must increase, too.

Write Avogadro's law, then rearrange it to isolate V_2.

$$\frac{V_1}{n_1} = \frac{V_2}{n_2}$$

$$V_2 = \frac{V_1 n_2}{n_1}$$

Substitute the values from the table and calculate:

$$V_2 = \frac{(0.325\ \text{L})(0.866\ \text{mol})}{0.225\ \text{mol}} = 1.25\ \text{L}$$

As expected, the increase in the number of moles of $N_2(g)$ resulted in an increase in the volume.

Practice Problem 7.10 Solution

The only constants in this scenario are T and R, so they cancel out.

$$\frac{P_1V_1}{P_2V_2} = \frac{n_1\cancel{RT_1}}{n_2\cancel{RT_2}}$$

Solve for P_2.

$$P_2 = \frac{P_1V_1n_2}{V_2n_1}$$

The initial and final values for n are not given, but the number of moles doubles, so $\frac{n_2}{n_1} = 2$.

$$P_2 = \frac{P_1V_1}{V_2} \times \frac{n_2}{n_1} = \frac{(1.13\ \text{atm})(8.35\ \text{L})}{(5.25\ \text{L})} \times 2 = 3.59\ \text{atm}$$

Practice Problem 7.11 Solution

$$PV = nRT$$

Isolate V by dividing both sides of the equation by P.

$$V = \frac{nRT}{P}$$

$$V = \frac{(0.898\ \text{mol})\left(0.08206\ \frac{\text{L} \cdot \text{atm}}{\text{mol} \cdot \text{K}}\right)(292\ \text{K})}{1.06\ \text{atm}} = 20.3\ \text{L}$$

Practice Problem 7.12 Solution

Convert the data in the problem to the appropriate units.

For n: $7.11\ \text{g}\ N_2\left(\frac{1\ \text{mol}\ N_2}{28.01\ \text{g}\ N_2}\right) = 0.254\ \text{mol}\ N_2$

For T: $16°\text{C} + 273.15 = 289\ \text{K}$

For P: $799\ \text{torr}\left(\frac{1\ \text{atm}}{760\ \text{torr}}\right) = 1.05\ \text{atm}$

Then rearrange the ideal gas law and plug in the data from above to solve for V:

$$PV = nRT$$

$$V = \frac{nRT}{P}$$

$$V = \frac{(0.254\ \text{mol})\left(0.08206\ \frac{\text{L} \cdot \text{atm}}{\text{mol} \cdot \text{K}}\right)(289\ \text{K})}{1.05\ \text{atm}} = 5.74\ \text{L}$$

Practice Problem 7.13 Solution

First, convert the data in the problem into the appropriate units, and then rearrange the ideal gas law to solve for P.

For T: $25°\text{C} + 273 = 298\ \text{K}$

For V: $66.1\ \text{mL}\left(\frac{1\ \text{L}}{1000\ \text{mL}}\right) = 0.0661\ \text{L}$

Rearrange the ideal gas law to solve for P.

$$PV = nRT$$

$$P = \frac{nRT}{V}$$

$$P = \frac{(0.0855\ \text{mol})\left(0.08206\ \frac{\text{L} \cdot \text{atm}}{\text{mol} \cdot \text{K}}\right)(298\ \text{K})}{0.0661\ \text{L}}$$

$$= 31.6\ \text{atm}$$

Practice Problem 7.14 Solution

First, convert the data in the problem into the appropriate units.

For P: $655\ \text{torr}\left(\frac{1\ \text{atm}}{760\ \text{torr}}\right) = 0.862\ \text{atm}$

For V: $375\ \text{mL}\left(\frac{1\ \text{L}}{1000\ \text{mL}}\right) = 0.375\ \text{L}$

For T: $15°\text{C} + 273 = 288\ \text{K}$

Next, rearrange the ideal gas law and solve for n.

$$PV = nRT$$

$$n = \frac{PV}{RT}$$

$$n = \frac{(0.862\ \text{atm})(0.375\ \text{L})}{\left(0.08206\ \frac{\text{L} \cdot \text{atm}}{\text{mol} \cdot \text{K}}\right)(288\ \text{K})} = 0.0137\ \text{mol}$$

Practice Problem 7.15 Solution

Begin with Dalton's law, then rearrange it to solve for the pressure of neon.

$$P_{\text{total}} = P_{O_2} + P_{\text{Ne}}$$

$$P_{\text{Ne}} = P_{\text{total}} - P_{O_2}$$

$$P_{\text{Ne}} = 1.031\ \text{atm} - 0.922\ \text{atm} = 0.109\ \text{atm}$$

Practice Problem 7.16 Solution

a. Use the molar mass of O_2 to convert the given mass of O_2 to moles.

$$n_{O_2} = 2.95\ \text{g}\ O_2\left(\frac{1\ \text{mol}\ O_2}{31.9988\ \text{g}\ O_2}\right) = 0.0922\ \text{mol}\ O_2$$

Now use n_{O_2} in the ideal gas law to determine P_{O_2}.

$$PV = nRT;$$

$$P = \frac{nRT}{V}$$

$$P_{O_2} = \frac{(0.0922 \text{ mol})\left(0.08206 \dfrac{\text{L} \cdot \text{atm}}{\text{mol} \cdot \text{K}}\right)(272 \text{ K})}{2.48 \text{ L}}$$

$$= 0.830 \text{ atm}$$

Finally, use Dalton's law to calculate P_{N_2} from P_{O_2} and the given P_{total}.

$$P_{total} = P_{N_2} + P_{O_2}$$

$$P_{N_2} = P_{total} - P_{O_2}$$

$$P_{N_2} = 0.934 \text{ atm} - 0.830 \text{ atm} = 0.104 \text{ atm}$$

b. Use P_{N_2} in the ideal gas equation to determine the number of moles of N_2.

$$PV = nRT; \qquad n = \frac{PV}{RT}$$

$$n_{N_2} = \frac{PV}{RT} = \frac{(0.104 \text{ atm})(2.48 \text{ L})}{\left(0.08206 \dfrac{\text{L} \cdot \text{atm}}{\text{mol} \cdot \text{K}}\right)(272 \text{ K})}$$

$$= 0.0116 \text{ mol } N_2$$

Next, use the molar mass of N_2 to convert n_{N_2} to mass of N_2.

$$0.0116 \text{ mol } N_2 \left(\frac{28.0134 \text{ g } N_2}{1 \text{ mol } N_2}\right) = 0.325 \text{ g } N_2$$

Practice Problem 7.17 Solution

$$2 \text{ KClO}_3 \text{ (S)} \xrightarrow{\text{Heat}} 2 \text{ KCl(s)} + 3 \text{ O}_2\text{(g)}$$

$$0.0600 \text{ mol KClO}_3 \left(\frac{3 \text{ mol O}_2}{2 \text{ mol KClO}_3}\right) = 0.0900 \text{ mol O}_2$$

The total pressure given in the problem includes the pressure of both the trapped O_2 and evaporated H_2O vapor. First, calculate the partial pressure of just the oxygen, then use that pressure in the ideal gas law to calculate the volume of the O_2. The partial pressure of the oxygen is the total barometric pressure minus the water vapor pressure at 25°C (Table 7.3).

$$P_{O_2} = P_{total} - P_{H_2O} = 762 \text{ torr} - 23.756 \text{ torr} = 738 \text{ torr}$$

$$V_{O_2} = \frac{nRT}{P_{O_2}}$$

$$V_{O_2} = \frac{(0.0900 \text{ mol})\left(0.08206 \dfrac{\text{L} \cdot \text{atm}}{\text{mol} \cdot \text{K}}\right)(298 \text{ K})}{(738 \text{ torr})\left(\dfrac{1 \text{ atm}}{760 \text{ torr}}\right)} = 2.27 \text{ L}$$

If you had not corrected the pressure to account for water vapor and had instead solved this problem using the total pressure that was given in the problem, the pressure used in the calculation would have been about 3% too high. Therefore, the calculated volume for O_2 would have been about 3% too low (Boyle's law, Equation 7.1).

Practice Problem 7.18 Solution

Use the molar mass of CO_2 to calculate the number of moles of CO_2 present.

$$n_{CO_2} = 48.3 \text{ g CO}_2 \left(\frac{1 \text{ mol CO}_2}{44.01 \text{ g CO}_2}\right) = 1.10 \text{ mol CO}_2$$

Now use the ideal gas law to calculate the volume under the stated conditions of T and P.

$$PV = nRT$$

$$V = \frac{nRT}{P}$$

$$V = \frac{(1.10 \text{ mol})\left(0.08206 \dfrac{\text{L} \cdot \text{atm}}{\text{mol} \cdot \text{K}}\right)(273 \text{ K})}{1.00 \text{ atm}}$$

$$= 24.6 \text{ L}$$

V_{CO_2} is considerably larger than V_{SO_2} in Example 7.18, because SO_2 has a larger molar mass than CO_2. Therefore, 48.3 g CO_2 represents more moles of gas than the same mass of SO_2, and according to Avogadro's law (Equation 7.4), the CO_2 must take up a greater volume than the SO_2 under the same conditions of temperature and pressure.

Practice Problem 7.19 Solution

Values are given for V, T, and P, so use the ideal gas law (Equation 7.5) to calculate n. First, though, convert both the temperature and the pressure to units compatible with the value of R.

For T: $22°\text{C} + 273.15 = 295 \text{ K}$

For P: $793 \text{ torr}\left(\dfrac{1 \text{ atm}}{760 \text{ torr}}\right) = 1.04 \text{ atm}$

$$PV = nRT$$

$$n = \frac{PV}{RT}$$

$$n = \frac{(1.04 \text{ atm})(2.76 \text{ L})}{\left(0.08206 \dfrac{\text{L} \cdot \text{atm}}{\text{mol} \cdot \text{K}}\right)(295 \text{ K})}$$

$$= 0.119 \text{ mol}$$

The molar mass can now be calculated from the mass of the gas sample given in the problem statement and the number of moles just calculated:

$$\mathcal{M} = \frac{3.38\ \text{g}}{0.119\ \text{mol}} = 28.4\ \text{g/mol}$$

Practice Problem 7.20 Solution

Use one of the two methods outlined in Example 7.20. Both use the ideal gas equation, so first convert the pressure to torr and the temperature to kelvins.

For P: $789\ \text{torr}\left(\frac{1\ \text{atm}}{760\ \text{torr}}\right) = 1.04\ \text{atm}$

For T: $25°\text{C} + 273.15 = 298\ \text{K}$

To use the first method from Example 7.20, first calculate the volume of 1 mol of SO_3 gas.

$$V = \frac{nRT}{P} = \frac{(1.00\ \text{mol})\left(0.08206\ \frac{\text{L}\cdot\text{atm}}{\text{mol}\cdot\text{K}}\right)(298\ \text{K})}{1.04\ \text{atm}}$$
$$= 23.6\ \text{L}$$

Next, divide the mass of 1 mol of SO_3 (its molar mass) by the volume of 1 mol of SO_3 gas that you just calculated.

$$d = \frac{m_{(1\ \text{mol})}}{V_{(1\ \text{mol})}} = \frac{(1\ \text{mol}\ SO_3)\left(\frac{80.063\ \text{g}}{1\ \text{mol}\ SO_3}\right)}{23.6\ \text{L}\ SO_3} = 3.40\ \text{g/L}$$

The answer is the same using the second method from Example 7.20.

$$d = \frac{P}{RT} \times \mathcal{M}$$

$$d = \frac{(1.04\ \text{atm})}{\left(0.08206\ \frac{\text{L}\cdot\text{atm}}{\text{mol}\cdot\text{K}}\right)(298\ \text{K})}\left(\frac{80.063\ \text{g}}{1\ \text{mol}\ SO_3}\right)$$
$$= 3.40\ \text{g/L}$$

Practice Problem 7.21 Solution

First, convert the density of O_2 from grams per liter to moles per liter.

$$\left(\frac{3.00\ \text{g}\ O_2}{1\ \text{L}}\right)\left(\frac{1\ \text{mol}\ O_2}{31.9988\ \text{g}\ O_2}\right) = \frac{0.0938\ \text{mol}\ O_2}{1\ \text{L}}$$

Use this result for n/V in the ideal gas law.

$$T = \frac{PV}{nR}$$

$$T = \frac{(1.50\ \text{atm})}{\left(\frac{0.0938\ \text{mol}}{1\ \text{L}}\right)\left(0.08206\ \frac{\text{L}\cdot\text{atm}}{\text{mol}\cdot\text{K}}\right)} = 195\ \text{K}$$

Practice Problem 7.22 Solution

Use the ideal gas law to determine the number of moles of oxygen gas present, but first convert P and T to appropriate units.

For P: $742\ \text{mmHg}\left(\frac{1\ \text{atm}}{760\ \text{mmHg}}\right) = 0.976\ \text{atm}$

For T: $22°\text{C} + 273.15 = 295\ \text{K}$

$$n = \frac{PV}{RT} = \frac{(0.976\ \text{atm})(0.555\ \text{L})}{\left(0.08206\ \frac{\text{L}\cdot\text{atm}}{\text{mol}\cdot\text{K}}\right)(295\ \text{K})}$$
$$= 0.0224\ \text{mol}\ O_2$$

Then use the balanced chemical equation and the molar mass of $KClO_3$ to determine the mass of potassium chlorate.

$$0.0224\ \text{mol}\ O_2\left(\frac{2\ \text{mol}\ KClO_3}{3\ \text{mol}\ O_2}\right)\left(\frac{122\ \text{g}\ KClO_3}{1\ \text{mol}\ KClO_3}\right)$$
$$= 1.82\ \text{g}\ KClO_3$$

Practice Problem 7.23 Solution

Convert the temperature to kelvins.

$$22°\text{C} + 273.15 = 295\ \text{K}$$

The values for P, V, and T are given, so use the ideal gas equation to determine the number of moles of oxygen produced.

$$n = \frac{PV}{RT} = \frac{(0.95\ \text{atm})(0.375\ \text{L})}{\left(0.08206\ \frac{\text{L}\cdot\text{atm}}{\text{mol}\cdot\text{K}}\right)(295\ \text{K})} = 0.015\ \text{mol}\ O_2$$

Then use reaction stoichiometry to determine the mass of the reactant, Hg_2O.

$$(0.015\ \text{mol}\ O_2)\left(\frac{2\ \text{mol}\ Hg_2O}{1\ \text{mol}\ O_2}\right)\left(\frac{417.179\ \text{g}\ Hg_2O}{1\ \text{mol}\ Hg_2O}\right)$$
$$= 12\ \text{g}\ Hg_2O$$

Practice Problem 7.24 Solution

$$Cl_2(g) + H_2(g) \rightarrow 2\ HCl(g)$$

a. The number of *atoms* stays the same, as it does for *all* reactions. That is the basis for the balanced chemical equation.

b. The total number of *moles* of gas does not change, so the number of molecules remains the same.

c. If the number of moles of gas does not change, then neither does the pressure.

Practice Problem 7.25 Solution

The coefficients given in the balanced equation can be used as the volume ratio for H_2 and O_2 *because the two gases have the same temperature and pressure.* The volume of water vapor formed is *not* in that ratio, however, because its temperature is different. The reactants were at 0°C, but the products are much hotter at 250°C. The volume of a sample of gas is proportional to its temperature in kelvins, so the volume of the water vapor will therefore be much greater than 2.00 L.

Practice Problem 7.26 Solution

a. Convert the temperature to kelvins ($T = -2.2°\text{C} + 273.15 = 271.0\text{ K}$); then use the ideal gas law (Section 7.6) to find the volume:

$$V = \frac{nRT}{P} = \frac{(1.00\text{ mol})\left(0.08206\dfrac{\text{L}\cdot\text{atm}}{\text{mol}\cdot\text{K}}\right)(271.0\text{ K})}{1.00\text{ atm}}$$
$$= 22.2\text{ L}$$

b. The volume of liquid ammonia is calculated using density as the conversion factor (Section 1.9):

$$1.00\text{ mol NH}_3\left(\frac{17.03\text{ g NH}_3}{1\text{ mol NH}_3}\right)\left(\frac{1\text{ mL NH}_3}{0.769\text{ g NH}_3}\right)$$
$$= 22.1\text{ mL}$$

The same mole of NH_3 occupies 0.0221 L in the liquid state, but after it has been evaporated into the gas state, it occupies 22.2 L. The molecules themselves do not expand, but the distances between them do, so the molecules take up only 0.0221 L of the entire 22.2 L that the gas occupies. Again, most of the volume of a sample of gas is empty space.

Practice Problem 7.27A Solution

a. The molar mass of carbon dioxide (44.0 g/mol) is greater than the molar mass of nitrogen (28.0 g/mol), so the root-mean-square speed of CO_2 molecules should be less than the root-mean-square speed of N_2 molecules at any given temperature.

b. Use Equation 7.10 to calculate the root-mean-square speed of carbon dioxide (after converting the molar mass of CO_2 from g/mol to kg/mol).

$$v_{\text{rms, CO}_2} = \sqrt{\frac{3RT}{\mathcal{M}}} = \sqrt{\frac{3\left(8.3145\dfrac{\text{kg}\cdot\text{m}^2}{\text{s}^2\cdot\text{K}\cdot\text{mol}}\right)(298\text{ K})}{4.40\times10^{-2}\dfrac{\text{kg}}{\text{mol}}}}$$

$$v_{\text{rms, CO}_2} = \sqrt{168935\frac{\text{m}^2}{\text{s}^2}} = 4.11\times10^2\text{ m/s}$$

The calculated root-mean-square speed for CO_2 at 25°C is 411 m/s, which *is* less than the 515 m/s calculated for N_2 at 25°C in Example 7.27.

Practice Problem 7.27B Solution

a. As the temperature increases, the average kinetic energy increases, so the root-mean-square speed will also increase.

b. The range of speeds will also increase (become broader) as the temperature increases, as shown in Figure 7.23.

c. Use Equation 7.10 to calculate the root-mean-square speed of nitrogen (after converting the molar mass of N_2 from g/mol to kg/mol).

$$v_{\text{rms, }N_2} = \sqrt{\frac{3RT}{M}} = \sqrt{\frac{3\left(8.3145\dfrac{\text{kg}\cdot\text{m}^2}{\text{s}^2\cdot\text{K}\cdot\text{mol}}\right)(373\text{ K})}{2.80\times10^{-2}\dfrac{\text{kg}}{\text{mol}}}}$$
$$= 5.76\times10^2\text{ m/s}$$

As expected, the average speed of nitrogen molecules at 100°C (576 m/s) is higher than the root-mean-square speed of nitrogen molecules at 25°C (515 m/s).

Practice Problem 7.28 Solution

Use the equation for Graham's law, where the molar mass of hydrogen is 2.0158 g/mol and the molar mass of carbon monoxide is 28.0101 g/mol.

$$\frac{r_{\text{H}_2}}{r_{\text{CO}}} = \sqrt{\frac{\mathcal{M}_{\text{CO}}}{\mathcal{M}_{\text{H}_2}}} = \sqrt{\frac{28.0101}{2.0158}} = \frac{3.73}{1} = 3.73$$

Hydrogen molecules effuse at a rate that is 3.73 times faster than the effusion rate of carbon monoxide molecules.

Practice Problem 7.29 Solution

a. You know from the given rate of effusion that this molecule has a larger molecular mass than oxygen. Rearrange Graham's law to solve for the molecular mass of X_2.

$$\frac{r_{\text{X}_2}}{r_{\text{O}_2}} = \sqrt{\frac{\mathcal{M}_{\text{O}_2}}{\mathcal{M}_{\text{X}_2}}}$$

$$\sqrt{\mathcal{M}_{\text{X}_2}} = \frac{\sqrt{\mathcal{M}_{\text{O}_2}}}{\dfrac{r_{\text{X}_2}}{r_{\text{O}_2}}}$$

$$\mathcal{M}_{\text{X}_2} = \left(\frac{\sqrt{\mathcal{M}_{\text{O}_2}}}{\dfrac{r_{\text{X}_2}}{r_{\text{O}_2}}}\right)^2 = \left(\frac{\sqrt{31.998}}{\dfrac{0.447}{1}}\right)^2 = 160.1\text{ g/mol}$$

b. X_2 is a homonuclear diatomic molecule, so it contains two identical atoms. Dividing the molar mass by 2 gives 80.07 g/mol, which is very close to the 79.904 g/mol molar mass of bromine. X_2 must be Br_2.

Practice Problem 7.30 Solution

At high pressures, gases are compressed into smaller volumes, and the actual sizes of the gas particles contribute to that volume. Based on periodic trends in atomic radius, the radii of these group 18 elements are Ne < Ar < Kr < Xe. If the radius of Ne is smaller than that of the other noble gases, then so is its volume. The smaller volume of the neon atoms means they experience less deviation from ideal behavior and an observed volume closer to that of an ideal gas.

Practice Problem 7.31 Solution

a. Solve the ideal gas law for pressure and substitute the values given in the problem, after first converting the 34.06 g of ammonia gas to moles of ammonia:

$$34.06\text{ g NH}_3\left(\frac{1\text{ mol NH}_3}{17.03\text{ g NH}_3}\right) = 2.00\text{ mol NH}_3$$

$$PV = nRT$$

$$P = \frac{nRT}{V} = \frac{2.00\text{ mol}\left(\frac{0.08206\text{ L}\cdot\text{atm}}{\text{mol}\cdot\text{K}}\right)(500.0\text{ K})}{11.2\text{ L}}$$

$$= 7.33\text{ atm}$$

b. Solve the van der Waals equation for P, find the constants in Table 7.4, and substitute the values given in the problem:

$$\left[P + a\left(\frac{n}{V}\right)^2\right](V - nb) = nRT$$

$$P = \frac{nRT}{(V - nb)} - a\left(\frac{n}{V}\right)^2$$

$$P = \frac{2.00\text{ mol}\left(\frac{0.08206\text{ L}\cdot\text{atm}}{\text{mol}\cdot\text{K}}\right)(500.0\text{ K})}{11.2\text{ L} - (2.00\text{ mol})\left(0.0371\frac{\text{L}}{\text{mol}}\right)}$$

$$- 4.170\frac{\text{atm}\cdot\text{L}^2}{\text{mol}^2}\left(\frac{2.00\text{ mol}}{11.2\text{ L}}\right)^2$$

$$P = 6.63\text{ atm}$$

c. The difference in pressure values is moderate: 7.33 atm for the ideal gas law and 6.63 atm for the van der Waals equation. The intermolecular forces between the ammonia molecules are sufficient to reduce the pressure at that temperature and volume.

Practice Problem 7.32 Solution

To determine the molecular formula, you need to have both the empirical formula and the molar mass. The empirical formula can be calculated from the percent composition (Section 3.10) as

$$79.89\text{ g C}\left(\frac{1\text{ mol C}}{12.01\text{ g C}}\right) = 6.652\text{ mol C}$$

$$20.11\text{ g H}\left(\frac{1\text{ mol H}}{1.008\text{ g H}}\right) = 19.950\text{ mol H}$$

The mole ratio of carbon to hydrogen is 1:3, so the empirical formula is CH_3.

The number of moles of gas present can be calculated from the pressure, volume, and temperature data, using the ideal gas law.

$$n = \frac{PV}{RT} = \frac{\left(\frac{749}{760}\text{ atm}\right)(2.90\text{ L})}{\left(0.08206\frac{\text{L}\cdot\text{atm}}{\text{mol}\cdot\text{K}}\right)(297\text{ K})} = 0.117\text{ mol}$$

The molar mass, $\mathcal{M}$, is the mass divided by the number of moles.

$$\mathcal{M} = \frac{3.53\text{ g}}{0.117\text{ mol}} = 30.1\text{ g/mol}$$

The mass of 1 mol of empirical formula units is

$$12.0\text{ g} + 3.0\text{ g} = 15.0\text{ g}$$

Dividing the molar mass by the empirical formula mass gives the ratio of the molecular formula to the empirical formula.

$$\frac{30.1\text{ g}}{15.0\text{ g}} = 2$$

Thus, the molecular formula is twice the empirical formula, so the molecular formula is C_2H_6. This is the formula for ethane.

CHAPTER 8

The Quantum Model of the Atom

PapaBear/iStock/Getty Images

When substances burn, they release energy in the form of heat, but they also emit electromagnetic radiation in the form of infrared rays and visible light, which is why a fire glows. When metal salts are burned, they emit characteristic colors of light. The varied colors seen in fireworks are a result of this phenomenon. For example, lithium salts burn with a red flame, whereas certain copper salts burn with a green flame.

Chapter Outline

GOALS

- Discuss the dual nature of light.
- Explain the relationships among light energy, frequency, and wavelength.
- Perform calculations involving energy, frequency, and wavelength of light.
- Use the Bohr model of energy levels in atoms to explain light emission and absorption by gaseous atoms.
- Calculate the energy or wavelength of a specific electronic transition in a hydrogen atom.
- Explain the spatial arrangement in which electrons are distributed around the nucleus of an atom.
- Sketch the electronic energy levels of an atom.
- Add electrons to energy-level diagrams.
- Devise electron configurations for the elements based on each element's position in the periodic table, using the concepts of shells, subshells, and orbitals.
- Use the concept of quantum numbers to describe the general location and energy of each electron in an atom.

8.1 A Brief Exploration of Light

GOALS

- Discuss the dual nature of light.
- Explain the relationships among light energy, frequency, and wavelength.
- Perform calculations involving energy, frequency, and wavelength of light.

Light is a form of energy that is usually thought of as a moving wave of magnetic and electrical potential, and **visible light** is light that can be perceived by the human eye. Light can be described as a wave because it travels through space, and it can be refracted (have its direction altered) by passing it through a prism (Figure 8.1).

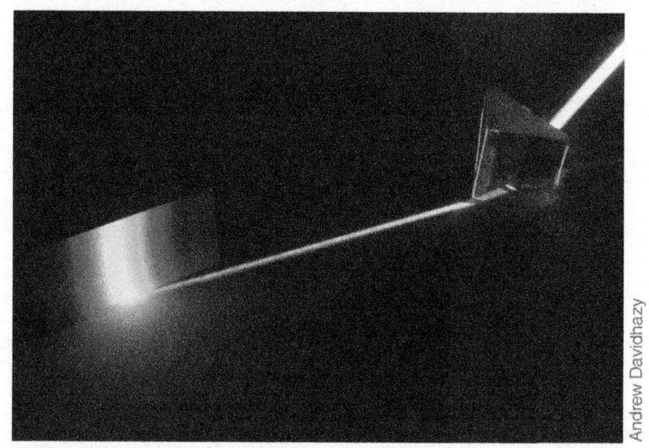

FIGURE 8.1 Components of White Light
Visible light is separated into the colors of the rainbow (red, orange, yellow, green, blue, and violet) by passing it through a prism. When these colors are combined, the result is white light. Although visible light is actually a continuum of millions of colors, these six colors of visible light are most easily differentiated and perceived as separate colors by the human eye.

The **wavelength, λ,** of light is the distance between two corresponding points on the wave—they could be successive peaks (crests), or they could be two successive troughs (as shown in Figure 8.2), or any other two matching points on the wave. In Figure 8.1, each color of visible light has a different wavelength, and each wavelength is refracted, or bent, by a different amount as the light passes through the prism, resulting in a spreading out of the different components of white light.

Waves are always moving in a constant forward direction. The **frequency, ν,** of light is the number of crests that pass a given point per second. The frequency of any wave is inversely proportional (Section 0.8) to its wavelength, which means that as the frequency increases, the wavelength decreases, and as the frequency decreases, the wavelength increases. Figure 8.3 is an activity in which you can change the wavelength of a wave and see the effect this has on the frequency. Choose any point, such as the center of the app screen, and notice how the number of wave crests that pass that point per second changes as you change the wavelength.

While frequency and wavelength are inversely proportional to one another, did you notice in Figure 8.3 that amplitude is independent of them both? Thus, the intensity of light is independent of its color. Since frequency and wavelength are inversely proportional, the product of frequency times wavelength is a

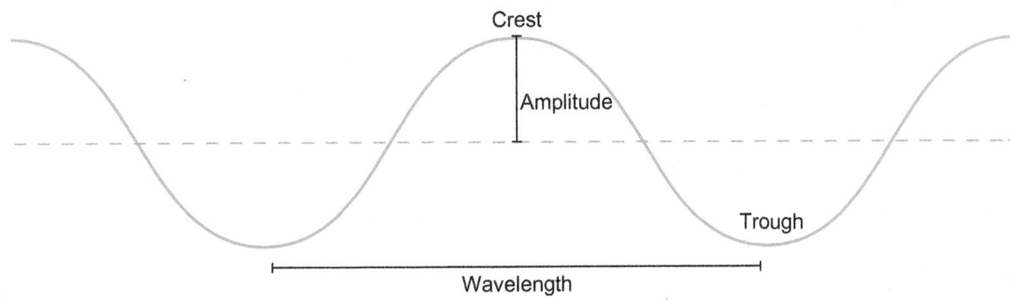

FIGURE 8.2 One Wavelength
One wavelength is the distance between two corresponding points on the wave (shown here as two successive troughs on the wave) and is symbolized using the Greek letter lambda, λ, and expressed in distance units, such as meters or nanometers. The amplitude (height) of a wave is the distance from the midpoint of the wave to its crest or trough and determines the intensity (brightness) of the light. Different colors of light have different wavelengths.

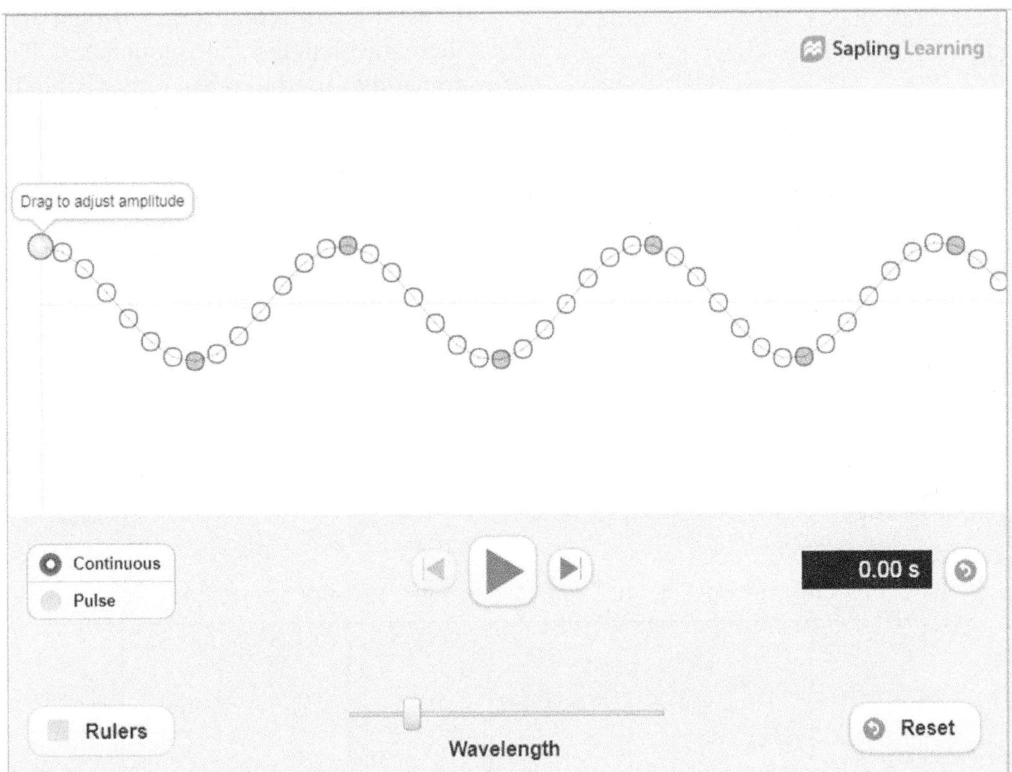

FIGURE 8.3 Properties of Wave Motion
NOTE: You need to be online to access this activity.
Open the wave activity and adjust the wavelength using the wavelength slider to see how that affects the frequency of the wave. A crest is the top point of each wave, and a trough is the lowest point. The wavelength is the distance from one crest to the next or from one trough to the next. The frequency is the number of wavelengths per second.

constant. In the case of light, that constant is the speed of light, c, which is 2.998×10^8 m/s (186,300 miles per second).

$$\nu\lambda = c \tag{8.1}$$

Since the typical units for speed of light are m/s, the wavelength of light used in Equation 8.1 must be converted from the units in which it is given (e.g., nanometers) to meters. Notice, too, that the units of frequency are 1/s (sometimes written as s^{-1}), which is spoken as "per second." The unit s^{-1} is also known as hertz, Hz.

Because the product of frequency times wavelength for light is always equal to the speed of light, you can use Equation 8.1 to calculate the frequency if you know the wavelength, or you can calculate the wavelength if you know the frequency.

$$\nu = c/\lambda \quad \text{or} \quad \lambda = c/\nu$$

Example 8.1

Calculate the wavelength of light that corresponds to a frequency of 7.30×10^{14} per second. Report your answer in units of nanometers ($1\text{ m} = 1 \times 10^9\text{ nm}$).

Solution

Rearrange Equation 8.1, $\nu\lambda = c$, to isolate wavelength.

$$\lambda = c/\nu$$

$$\lambda = c/\nu = \frac{2.998 \times 10^8\text{ m/s}}{7.30 \times 10^{14}\text{ s}^{-1}} = 4.11 \times 10^{-7}\text{ m}$$

Next, convert the wavelength in meters to the wavelength in nanometers as

$$4.11 \times 10^{-7}\text{ m} \times \frac{1 \times 10^9\text{ nm}}{1\text{ m}} = 411\text{ nm}$$

PRACTICE PROBLEM 8.1

Calculate the frequency of light that has a wavelength of 511 nm.

Hint: Rearrange Equation 8.1 to isolate frequency. Make sure the units of wavelength are compatible with the units used for the speed of light. The conversion factor between meters and nanometers is $1\text{ m} = 1 \times 10^9\text{ nm}$.

Visible light is a tiny fraction of the much broader **electromagnetic spectrum** (Figure 8.4), which includes radio waves, microwaves, infrared light, visible light, ultraviolet light, X-rays, and gamma rays. All of these are different forms of light and differ only in their wavelengths and frequencies. The word *light* is sometimes used to mean only visible light and sometimes refers to the entire electromagnetic spectrum. In this text, *light* refers to the entire electromagnetic spectrum, whereas *visible light* always refers to that

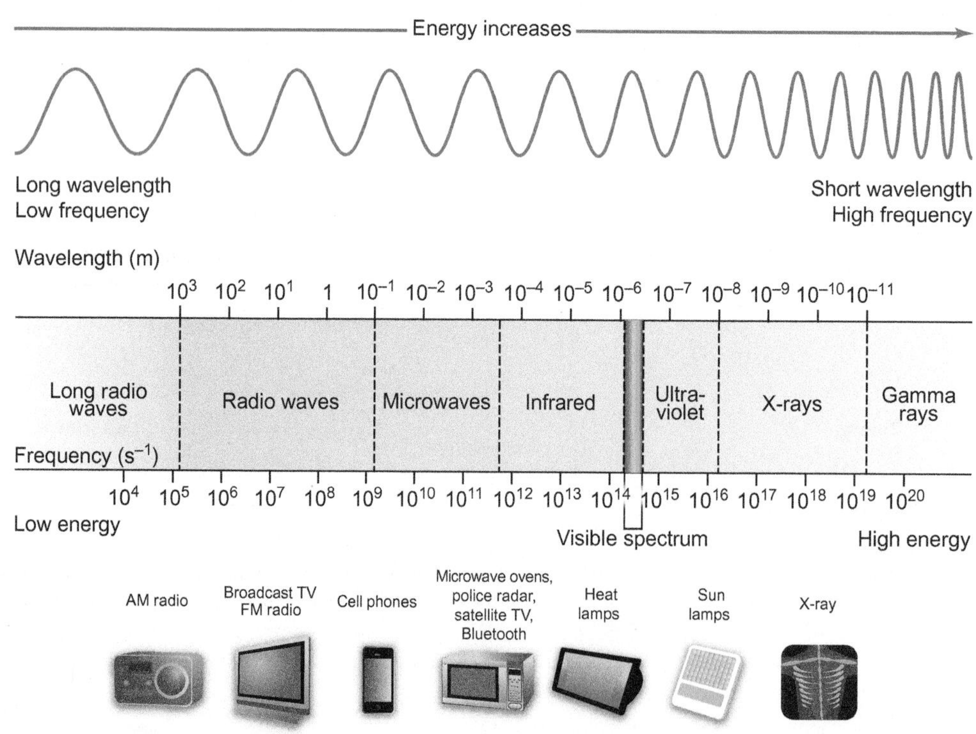

FIGURE 8.4 The Electromagnetic Spectrum

The electromagnetic spectrum is divided into different regions based on the frequency and wavelength of the electromagnetic radiation there. Long wavelengths correspond to low energies and low frequencies, whereas short wavelengths correspond to high energies and high frequencies. The visible region of the spectrum comprises red, orange, yellow, green, blue, and violet light.

TABLE 8.1 Approximate Wavelength and Frequency Values for Different Types of Electromagnetic Radiation

Electromagnetic Radiation Type	Wavelength (m)	Frequency (s^{-1})
Radio waves	10^3	3×10^5
Microwaves	10^{-2}	3×10^{10}
Infrared light	10^{-5}	3×10^{13}
Visible light	4.0×10^{-7} to 7.5×10^{-7}	4×10^{14} to 7.5×10^{14}
Ultraviolet light	10^{-8}	3×10^{16}
X-rays	10^{-10}	3×10^{18}
Gamma rays	10^{-12}	3×10^{20}

portion of the electromagnetic spectrum that is detectable by the human eye. Light of all types is collectively referred to as **electromagnetic radiation**.

The wavelength of electromagnetic radiation varies considerably over the spectrum, from approximately a kilometer, 10^3 m, for radio waves to a picometer, 10^{-12} m, for gamma rays. Table 8.1 lists approximate values for wavelengths and frequencies for each of the types of radiation shown in Figure 8.4.

Wavelengths for visible light are often given in nanometers, rather than meters, in which case visible light ranges from 400 nm (violet light) to 750 nm (red light).

Example 8.2

Using Figure 8.4 as a reference, arrange the following types of electromagnetic radiation in order from lowest energy to highest energy.

Gamma rays
Visible light
Microwaves
Radio waves
Infrared light
X-rays
Ultraviolet light

Solution

Figure 8.4 shows low energy (radio waves) on the left and high energy (gamma rays) on the right, so energy increases from left to right. The order from lowest energy to highest energy is radio waves < microwaves < infrared light < visible light < ultraviolet light < X-rays < gamma rays.

PRACTICE PROBLEM 8.2

All types of electromagnetic radiation exist over a range of wavelengths and frequencies (Figure 8.4). In Table 8.1, visible light is listed over a specific range of wavelengths, but for the other forms only one representative approximate wavelength and frequency are listed. For each type of light listed in Table 8.1, calculate $\nu \times \lambda$ (for visible light, remember that the *shortest* wavelength corresponds to the *highest* frequency).

Hint: When multiplying numbers in scientific notation, multiply the coefficients and add the exponents. If there is no coefficient, the coefficient is equal to 1. For example, $(10^{-3}) \times (3 \times 10^5) = (1 \times 3) \times 10^{(-3+5)} = 3 \times 10^2$.

Matter and energy are constantly interacting with each other. Matter can absorb energy from an outside source and can also give off excess stored energy, and that energy is often in the form of light. **Light absorption** occurs when an atom absorbs light energy from the surroundings and gains energy. **Light emission** occurs when an atom has excess energy and gives some energy off by emitting light. The bright colors given off by the fireworks in the opening image of this chapter, for example, are the result of energy being released by atoms in a chemical reaction. Atoms of different elements give off characteristically different colors of light in these reactions. For example, sodium atoms in fireworks give off yellow light, whereas barium atoms give off pale green light. The exact wavelengths of light that are given off by an atom of a particular element when it releases energy are also the same wavelengths that atoms of that element are able to absorb. Each element therefore absorbs or emits a unique pattern of wavelengths of light. Since different colors of light have different energies, the colors of light that are associated with each element provide a clue about how energy is stored and released in its atoms.

The precise wavelengths that are absorbed by an atom of an element are known as that element's **absorbance spectrum**. Each element's absorbance spectrum is unique, so this "spectral fingerprint" allows an element to be identified by the specific wavelengths of light that it absorbs. Helium, He, was first discovered in the Sun because the spectral lines in sunlight (Figure 8.5) included some absorption lines that did not match any element known at the time. The first positive discovery of He as an element on Earth came 27 years later.

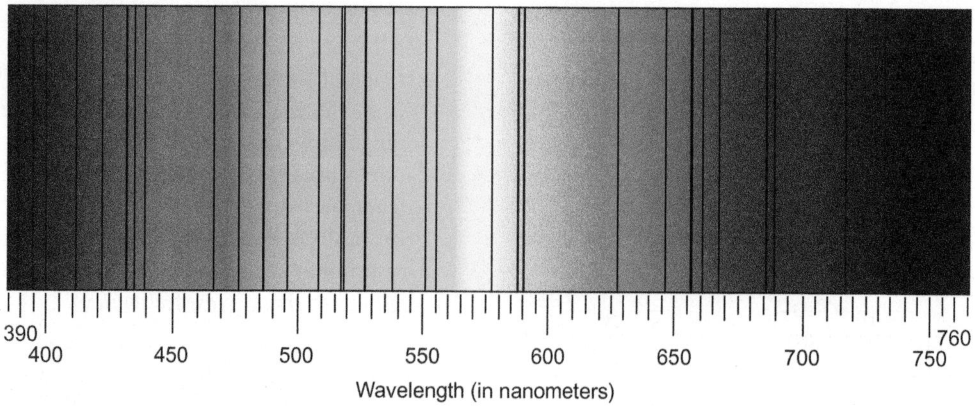

FIGURE 8.5 Spectral Lines in Sunlight

The dark lines on the visible spectrum of sunlight are due to precise wavelengths of light that are missing from the spectrum because they are absorbed by atoms of various elements in the outer layers of the Sun. Each wavelength of light absorbed corresponds to a specific energy. When gaseous samples of those elements are excited electrically and release the excess energy as light, they emit bright lines of the same colors that are missing here.

Example 8.3

Identify the colors of visible light that have (a) the longest wavelength, (b) the highest frequency, and (c) the highest energy.

Solution

a. Longest wavelength = red
b. Highest frequency = violet
c. Highest energy = violet

The colors of visible light, in order from longest wavelength to shortest wavelength, are red, orange, yellow, green, blue, and violet (Figure 8.5). Since a longer wavelength corresponds to a lower frequency, the highest frequency will be associated with the shortest wavelength, violet. Energy is directly proportional to frequency, so the color with the highest frequency, violet, is also the color with the highest energy.

PRACTICE PROBLEM 8.3

The black lines in Figure 8.5 are due to wavelengths of light from the Sun that are absorbed by other elements.

a. How does the line at 495 nm compare in frequency with the one at 590 nm?
b. Which line corresponds to a higher energy?

Hint: Wavelength and frequency are inversely proportional. Energy is directly proportional to frequency.

THE PHOTOELECTRIC EFFECT

In some experiments, such as passing light through a prism, light behaves like a wave, but in other experiments light behaves like a stream of tiny particles. The most famous example of this is a phenomenon called the **photoelectric effect** (Figure 8.6). In this experiment, a beam of light is shined onto a metal surface in a vacuum. If the light is of a certain minimum energy, electrons will be ejected from the metal surface. Shining a higher-energy (higher-frequency) light on the surface does not cause more electrons to be ejected, but the electrons that are ejected leave the surface with greater kinetic energy. Increasing the brightness of the light at the same frequency causes more electrons to be emitted, and dimming the light without changing

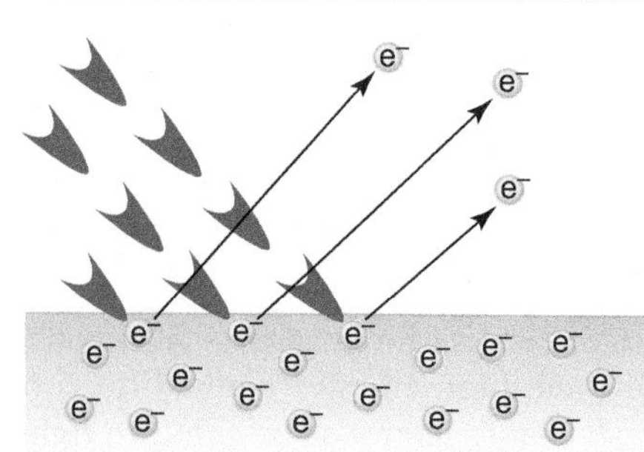

FIGURE 8.6 The Photoelectric Effect

When light hits the surface of the metal, electrons are ejected from the metal. In this context, light behaves as a stream of individual packets of energy, rather than as a wave.

its frequency causes fewer electrons to be emitted. An electron that is ejected from a surface as a result of an interaction between the surface and a photon is called a **photoelectron**.

Albert Einstein explained these results by proposing that light was behaving as tiny individual packets of energy, rather than as a wave. Each packet of light, if it contains enough energy, knocks an electron from the metal surface. Increasing the brightness of the light increases the number of light packets striking the metal and therefore results in ejecting more electrons. If the energy of the light packet is below the minimum threshold required to free an electron, it does not matter how bright the light is or how long it is shined on the surface—no electrons are emitted. Einstein was awarded the Nobel Prize in Physics in 1921 for his explanation of light as individual particles.

Light can therefore be considered to be both a wave and a stream of particles, although in any given experiment it will behave as one or the other. This is known as the *wave–particle duality of light*. When light behaves as a stream of tiny particles, the particles are called **photons**. Low-energy photons correspond to light with a long wavelength (and low frequency), and high-energy photons correspond to light with a short wavelength (and high frequency). These relationships are confirmed in Figure 8.4, where the energy of a wave increases as its frequency increases and its wavelength decreases. The direct relationship between energy and frequency is given by

$$E = h\nu \tag{8.2}$$

where E is the energy per photon and h is Planck's constant, which has a value of 6.626×10^{-34} J·s. Thus, a photon of blue light (high ν, short λ) has a higher energy than does a photon of red light (low ν, long λ), and a photon of gamma radiation (high ν, short λ) has a higher energy than does a photon of microwave radiation (low ν, long λ).

The energy, E, in Equation 8.2 is for a single photon. The total energy of a pulse of light scales proportionally with the number of photons.

Example 8.4

For violet light with a frequency of $7.50 \times 10^{14}\ \text{s}^{-1}$, calculate

a. the energy of a single photon in joules.
b. the energy of a mole of photons in joules per mole.

Solution

a. The energy of a photon is calculated from its frequency using Equation 8.2 as

$$E = h\nu = (6.626 \times 10^{-34}\ \text{J}\cdot\text{s})(7.50 \times 10^{14}\ \text{s}^{-1}) = 4.97 \times 10^{-19}\ \text{J}$$

b. The answer from part (a) is the number of joules *per photon*. To convert it to joules *per mole*, multiply by Avogadro's number.

$$\frac{4.97 \times 10^{-19}\ \text{J}}{1\ \text{photon}} \times \frac{6.022 \times 10^{23}\ \text{photons}}{1\ \text{mol}} = 2.99 \times 10^{5}\ \text{J/mol}$$

PRACTICE PROBLEM 8.4

A photon from the ultraviolet region of the electromagnetic spectrum has a frequency of $1.50 \times 10^{15}\ \text{s}^{-1}$, which is double the frequency of the photon in Example 8.4.

a. How does the energy of this photon of ultraviolet light compare with the energy of the photon in Example 8.4?
b. How many of these photons of ultraviolet light would you need for a total energy equal to that of a single photon from Example 8.4?

Hint: The relationship between the energy of a photon and the frequency of the light is $E = h\nu$ (Equation 8.2). If the frequency, ν, is doubled, how will that affect the energy? If the number of photons is doubled, what happens to the total energy?

Equation 8.1 and Equation 8.2 can be used together to relate the wavelength of a photon to its energy. The short video in Figure 8.7 demonstrates these calculations.

Steve Lemon, Macmillan Learning

FIGURE 8.7 Video Tutorial: Calculations Involving Light

NOTE: You need to be online to access this video.

This video shows how to calculate the energy of a photon of light given its wavelength.

Example 8.5

What color is a photon that has an energy of 3.28×10^{-19} J?

Solution

First, calculate ν from E using Equation 8.2.

$$E = h\nu$$

$$\nu = \frac{E}{h} = \frac{3.28 \times 10^{-19}\ \text{J}}{6.626 \times 10^{-34}\ \text{J} \cdot \text{s}} = 4.95 \times 10^{14}\ \text{s}^{-1}$$

Then, calculate λ from ν using Equation 8.1.

$$\nu\lambda = c$$

$$\lambda = \frac{c}{\nu} = \frac{2.998 \times 10^{8}\ \text{m/s}}{4.95 \times 10^{14}\ \text{s}^{-1}} = 6.06 \times 10^{-7}\ \text{m}$$

$$6.06 \times 10^{-7}\ \text{m} \times \frac{1 \times 10^{9}\ \text{nm}}{1\ \text{m}} = 606\ \text{nm}$$

Based on Figure 8.5, 606 nm is in the orange to red-orange portion of the visible spectrum.

PRACTICE PROBLEM 8.5

What color is a photon that has an energy of 4.01×10^{-19} J?

Hint: First, calculate ν from E using $E = h\nu$, and then calculate λ from ν using $\nu\lambda = c$. Once you know the wavelength, use Figure 8.5 to determine the color.

For an electron to be ejected from the surface of the metal in the photoelectric effect, the photon must have an energy equal to or greater than the work function of the metal. The **work function, Φ**, is the minimum energy necessary to remove an electron from the surface of the material in a vacuum. Different metals have different values for their work functions, so a photon that has sufficient energy to remove an electron from a magnesium surface, for example, might not have enough to eject an electron from gold. The work function is represented by the Greek letter phi, Φ, and has units of energy.

Since the energy of a photon is given by $E = h\nu$ (Equation 8.2) and the minimum energy required to remove an electron from a surface is equal to the work function, the minimum energy of a photon necessary to remove an electron from the surface is given by

$$h\nu = \Phi \qquad (8.3)$$

The frequency of the photon in Equation 8.3 is the minimum frequency necessary to eject a photoelectron and is called the **threshold frequency**. Wavelength can be determined from frequency using $\nu\lambda = c$ (Equation 8.1). Combining Equation 8.1 with Equation 8.3 results in the following equation, which relates the wavelength of the photon to the minimum energy for releasing an electron.

$$\frac{hc}{\lambda} = \Phi \qquad (8.4)$$

Example 8.6

Sodium metal has a work function equal to 3.78×10^{-19} J. What minimum frequency of light is necessary to remove a surface electron from sodium? To what wavelength of light (in nm) does this correspond?

Solution

The minimum energy of a photon required to remove an electron is given by Equation 8.3.

$$h\nu = \Phi$$

$$\nu = \frac{\Phi}{h} = \frac{3.78 \times 10^{-19}\ \text{J}}{6.626 \times 10^{-34}\ \text{J} \cdot \text{s}} = 5.70 \times 10^{14}\ \text{s}^{-1}$$

Wavelength can be calculated from frequency by rearranging Equation 8.1, $\lambda = c$, as

$$\lambda = \frac{c}{\nu} = \frac{2.998 \times 10^{8}\ \text{m/s}}{5.70 \times 10^{14}\ \text{s}^{-1}} = 5.26 \times 10^{-7}\text{m}$$

$$5.26 \times 10^{-7}\text{m} \times \frac{1 \times 10^{9}\ \text{nm}}{1\ \text{m}} = 526\ \text{nm}$$

From Figure 8.5, this is in the blue-green portion of the visible spectrum, so in a vacuum, light with a wavelength of 526 nm or shorter will have enough energy to remove an electron from the surface of sodium.

PRACTICE PROBLEM 8.6

Lithium has a work function equal to 4.65×10^{-19} J. If a violet photon with a wavelength of 405 nm impacts a lithium surface in a vacuum, will an electron be ejected?

Hint: Equation 8.1 and Equation 8.2 can be combined to give an equation that relates energy to wavelength, $E = \frac{hc}{\lambda}$. Calculate the energy of a photon with a wavelength of 405 nm, and then compare this value with the work function for lithium.

When the photon that impacts the surface of a metal has more than the minimum energy required to eject an electron from the surface, the excess energy of the photon is transferred to the electron in the form of kinetic energy. As shown in Equation 8.5, the kinetic energy, KE, of the ejected electron is equal to the energy of the photon minus the energy required to remove the electron from the surface.

$$KE = h\nu - \Phi \qquad (8.5)$$

Example 8.7

What is the kinetic energy of the photoelectron that is produced when a blue photon with a wavelength of 472 nm strikes a strontium surface in a vacuum? Strontium has a work function of $\Phi = 4.15 \times 10^{-19}$ J.

Solution

First, use Equation 8.1 and Equation 8.2 to calculate the energy of the photon from its wavelength, and then subtract the work function from the photon energy to determine the excess energy, which is equal to the kinetic energy of the electron (Equation 8.5).

Combining $E = h\nu$ and $\nu = \frac{c}{\lambda}$ yields $E = \frac{hc}{\lambda}$.

$$E = \frac{hc}{\lambda} = \frac{(6.626 \times 10^{-34}\ \text{J} \cdot \text{s})(2.998 \times 10^{8}\ \text{m/s})}{4.72 \times 10^{-7}\ \text{m}}$$
$$= 4.21 \times 10^{-19}\ \text{J}$$

This is equal to the energy of the photon, $h\nu$, which is then used to calculate the kinetic energy of the electron using Equation 8.5.

$$KE = h\nu - \Phi = 4.21 \times 10^{-19}\ \text{J} - 4.15 \times 10^{-19}\ \text{J}$$
$$= 6 \times 10^{-21}\ \text{J}$$

PRACTICE PROBLEM 8.7

What is the kinetic energy of the photoelectron that is produced when a blue photon with a wavelength of 472 nm strikes a potassium surface in a vacuum? Potassium has a work function of 3.67×10^{-19} J. Compare this kinetic energy with that of the photoelectron produced in Example 8.7, and explain the reason for the difference in kinetic energies between the two electrons.

Hint: First use Equation 8.1 and Equation 8.2 to calculate the energy of the photon from its wavelength, and then subtract the work function from the photon energy to determine the excess energy, which is equal to the kinetic energy of the electron (Equation 8.5). When comparing the kinetic energies of the two photoelectrons, consider Equation 8.5.

SECTION REVIEW

- Light can behave as both an energy wave and a stream of particles (photons).
- The wavelength, λ, of a light wave is inversely proportional to its frequency, ν, and the product of the frequency of a light wave and its wavelength is always equal to the speed of light, c: $\nu\lambda = c$ (Equation 8.1).
- The energy of a photon is proportional to its frequency: $E = h\nu$ (Equation 8.2).
- The entire range of energies of light is known as the electromagnetic spectrum.
- In the visible region, violet light has the highest energy (highest frequency, shortest wavelength), whereas red light has the lowest energy (lowest frequency, longest wavelength).
- In the photoelectric effect, photons that have sufficiently high energy can eject electrons from a metal surface in a vacuum.

8.2 The Bohr Model of the Atom

GOALS

- Use the Bohr model of energy levels in atoms to explain light emission and absorption by gaseous atoms.
- Calculate the energy or wavelength of a specific electronic transition in a hydrogen atom.

Background Review

Chapter 2 Atoms and the Periodic Table: Section 2.4—Subatomic Particles, Isotopes, and Ions

When gaseous atoms of a given element are heated, they emit light of only specific colors, which correspond to specific wavelengths and energies. Exploding fireworks, for example, are hot chemical reactions. The different colors in fireworks result from different compounds that contain specific elements (Figure 8.8).

When gaseous atoms of that same element absorb light, they absorb those same energies (see Figure 8.5). This finding was inconsistent with the Rutherford model of the atom (Section 2.4), in which electrons freely circled the atom's nucleus. If the electrons could be found at any distance from the nucleus within the atom, then the atom should be able to absorb and emit light over a continuous range of energies. Niels Bohr (Figure 8.9) hypothesized that since only certain energies of light could be absorbed and emitted, the electrons must be

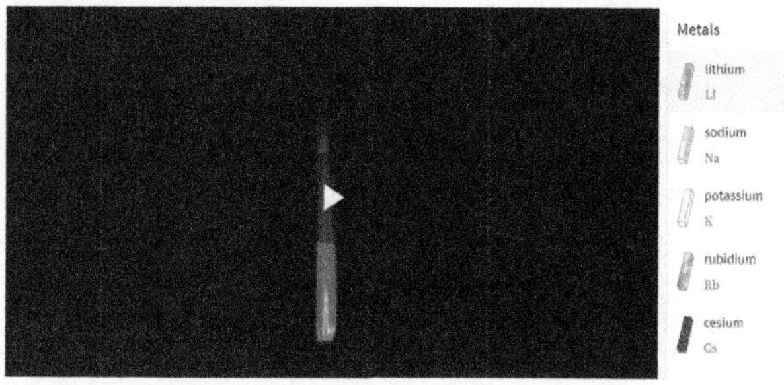

FIGURE 8.8 Flame Test Activity

NOTE: You need to be online to access this activity.
Select a metal to see the color of the flame when its ions are burned. Compare the colors shown here with their corresponding wavelengths in the visible spectrum of Figure 8.5.

FIGURE 8.9 Niels Bohr (1885–1962)

Danish physicist Niels Bohr was the first person to suggest that the electrons in an atom could have only certain specific energies. This revolutionized the development of atomic theory.

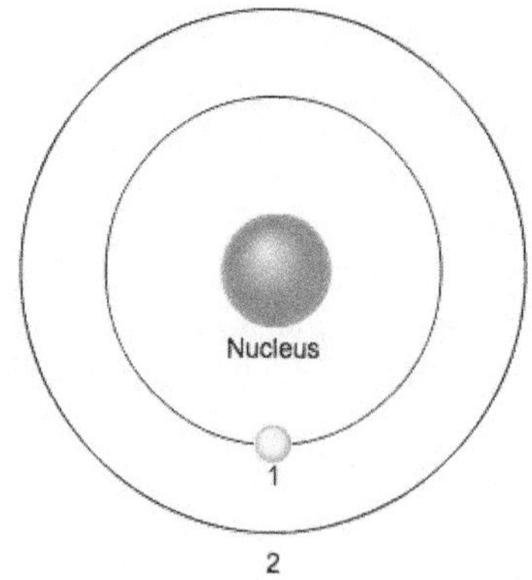

FIGURE 8.10 Bohr Model of an Atom and Light Absorption and Emission

NOTE: You need to be online to access this video.
This animation demonstrates how absorbing light promotes an electron to a higher energy level, and how an electron falling to a lower energy level releases energy as light in the Bohr model of the atom. The primary difference between this model and the modern model of the atom is that electrons do not orbit the nucleus, as is discussed in Section 8.3.

found at only certain specific distances from the nucleus. He called these allowed distances from the nucleus **orbits** after how the planets orbit the Sun at particular distances. In fact, Bohr hypothesized that electrons travel in circular paths around the nucleus, although this has since been shown to be untrue and is not part of the modern model of the atom. Despite its imperfections, the **Bohr model** was the first to place electrons in **discrete energy levels** in atoms, an idea that significantly changed the way other scientists thought about atomic structure.

Since each orbit in Bohr's model of the atom has a specific energy, the orbits are also called energy levels. The energy level closest to the nucleus is the lowest energy level and is called the **ground state**. When an atom absorbs light of a specific energy, an electron moves up from a lower energy level to a higher energy level, called an **excited state**. Each energy level has a particular energy value associated with it, so the *difference* in energy between the two energy levels can be determined and is equal to the energy of the light that was absorbed to cause the transition. In other words, a photon of light can be absorbed by an atom only if the energy of the photon *exactly* matches the energy difference between two electronic energy levels. An electron in an excited state is unstable, so it may return to a lower energy level. When it does, light of energy equal to the difference in energy between the levels is emitted from the atom. The animation in Figure 8.10 shows the absorption and emission of light energy between the first two Bohr energy levels in an atom.

Example 8.8

How many photons of light will be emitted (a) when an electron falls from the third energy level directly to the first energy level and (b) when an electron falls from the third energy level to the second energy level and then to the first energy level in a two-step process?

Solution

a. One photon; when an electron falls from a higher energy level to a lower one, it emits a photon of light.
b. Two photons; one photon is emitted for each transition (two transitions = two photons).

PRACTICE PROBLEM 8.8

How does the energy of the one photon emitted in part (a) of Example 8.8 compare with the sum of the energies of the two photons emitted in part (b)?

Hint: The energy of a photon depends on the difference in energy between the electron's final level and its initial level.

The spacing between the electronic energy levels is different for each type of atom. This means that each atom will absorb and emit characteristic wavelengths or colors of light that are unique to that element. Figure 8.11 shows how different colors of light can be produced by adding electrical energy to gaseous atoms of different elements. All atoms have many more energy levels than just the two shown in the animation in Figure 8.10. Transitions between some of the energy levels absorb and emit photons that are of higher energy than is visible light, so they appear in the ultraviolet and X-ray regions of the spectrum for that element. The emission spectra shown in Figure 8.11b for hydrogen, H, helium, He, and neon, Ne, are limited to transitions whose energies lie in the visible region of the spectrum.

Although at first glance the atomic emission lines shown in Figure 8.11b appear to be random, with no pattern, mathematicians in the late 1800s discovered a mathematical relationship between the wavelengths in the H emission spectrum. Johannes Balmer, a Swiss high school math teacher, was the first to develop a simple mathematical formula that related the wavelengths of the four visible emission lines. His formula was later amended to apply to all H emission lines, including those that lie outside of the visible region. The mathematical formula that predicts the wavelengths of all H emission lines is known as the **Rydberg equation**,

$$\frac{1}{\lambda} = (1.097 \times 10^7\ \text{m}^{-1})\left(\frac{1}{n_1^2} - \frac{1}{n_2^2}\right) \qquad (8.6)$$

where λ is the wavelength in meters and n_1 and n_2 are positive integers (the energy levels of the transition, where $n_2 > n_1$). The value $1.097 \times 10^7\ \text{m}^{-1}$ in Equation 8.6 is called the **Rydberg constant,** R_H. But there are other forms of the equation where the constant must be converted to other units. For example, in the form shown in Equation 8.7, $R_H = hc(1.097 \times 10^7\ \text{m}^{-1}) = 2.179 \times 10^{-18}\ \text{J}$.

$$E = (2.179 \times 10^{-18}\ \text{J})\left(\frac{1}{n_1^2} - \frac{1}{n_2^2}\right) \qquad (8.7)$$

Since n is unitless, the units of the Rydberg constant (m^{-1} or J) match the units of quantity for which you are solving ($1/\lambda$ or E) in both versions of the Rydberg equation.

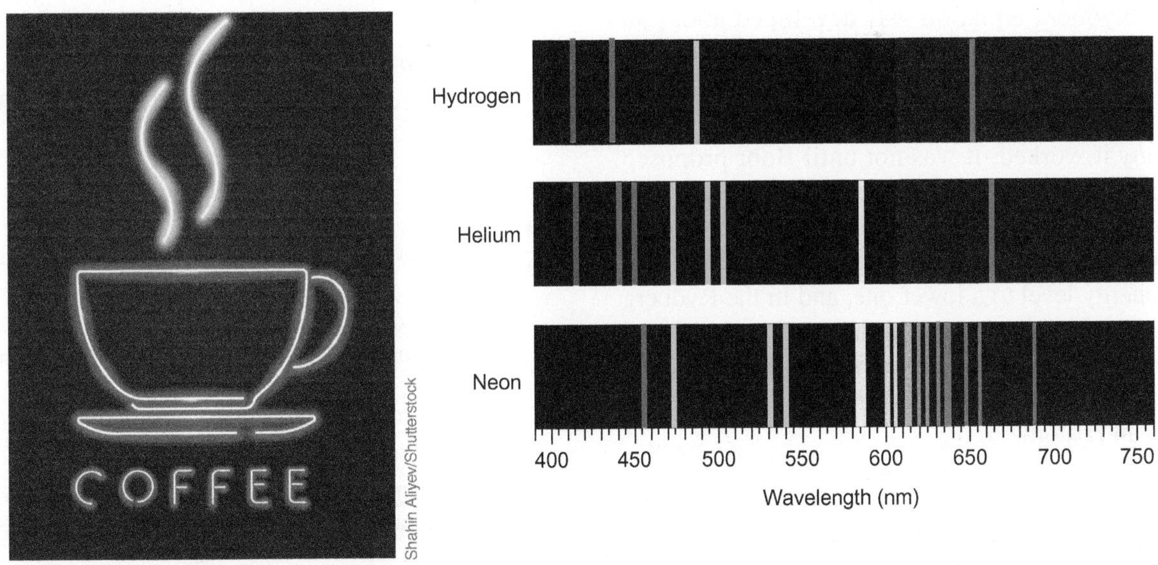

(a) (b)

FIGURE 8.11 Emission of Light by Gaseous Atoms

(a) When Ne atoms are excited by electrical energy, electronic transitions between their energy levels yield wavelengths of light that produce the familiar red color of a neon sign. Wavelengths corresponding to a large number of different transitions combine to yield that color. Other gases are used to produce other colors, although people refer to all such signs in everyday conversation as "neon" signs.
(b) When H and He, with fewer electrons than Ne, are similarly excited, fewer transitions occur. The emission spectra shown here are limited to the visible region of the electromagnetic spectrum.

EVERYDAY CONNECTION

The Doppler effect causes a sound wave, such as that emitted by a train whistle or the siren of an ambulance, to be perceived at a higher pitch (higher frequency) when the object emitting the sound is moving toward you and at a lower pitch (lower frequency) when it is moving away. A similar phenomenon occurs with light, which means that astronomers can use atomic emission spectra to determine the speed of distant objects in space. Light emitted by a distant galaxy consists of the emission spectra of the elements making up that galaxy (mostly H and He). If the galaxy is moving away from Earth, the wavelengths of that light will be shifted to longer wavelengths. This phenomenon is known as red-shifting, and the extent of red-shifting of a H spectrum, for example, indicates how fast the object is moving away from Earth. Many objects that give off visible light are moving away from Earth at such a high speed that their emission spectra are red-shifted all the way into the radio-wave region of the electromagnetic spectrum (Figure 8.4). These emissions are detected using radio telescopes. An object moving toward Earth will similarly have its emission spectra shifted to shorter wavelengths (called blue-shifting), and the speed of its approach can be calculated from the extent of the blue-shifting.

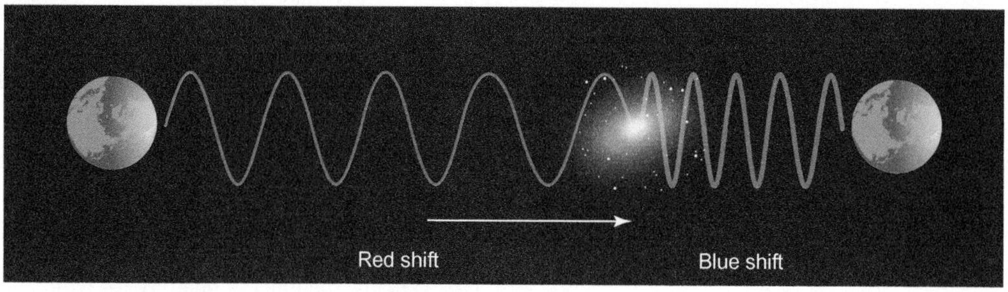

The Rydberg equation was developed about 30 years before the Bohr model of the atom, and although the Rydberg equation successfully predicted the wavelengths of the H emission lines, nobody understood *why* it worked. It was not until Bohr proposed his atomic model with quantized energy levels that the variables n_1 and n_2 took on physical meaning. Emission lines result when an electron drops from a higher energy level to a lower one, and in the Rydberg equation, n_2 represents the higher energy level and n_1 represents the lower one. Thus, the emission wavelength can be calculated for any electronic transition in an H atom.

Example 8.9

Calculate the emission wavelength of the photon that is emitted when an electron in a hydrogen atom drops from the fourth energy level to the third energy level. Is this photon in the visible region?

Solution

Use the Rydberg equation with $R_H = 1.097 \times 10^7\ \text{m}^{-1}$ (Equation 8.6) and with $n_2 = 4$ and $n_1 = 3$.

$$\frac{1}{\lambda} = R_H\left(\frac{1}{n_1^2} - \frac{1}{n_2^2}\right)$$

$$\frac{1}{\lambda} = (1.097 \times 10^7\ \text{m}^{-1})\left(\frac{1}{3^2} - \frac{1}{4^2}\right) = 5.333 \times 10^5\ \text{m}^{-1}$$

The equation gives inverse wavelength, so take the reciprocal of the answer to get wavelength.

$$\lambda = \frac{1}{5.333 \times 10^5\ \text{m}^{-1}} = 1.875 \times 10^{-6}\ \text{m}$$

To compare this wavelength with the visible spectrum range, convert it to nanometers.

$$1.875 \times 10^{-6}\ \text{m} \times \frac{1 \times 10^9\ \text{nm}}{1\ \text{m}} = 1875\ \text{nm}$$

This is longer than 750 nm, so this lower-energy emission line lies outside of the visible region, in the infrared region.

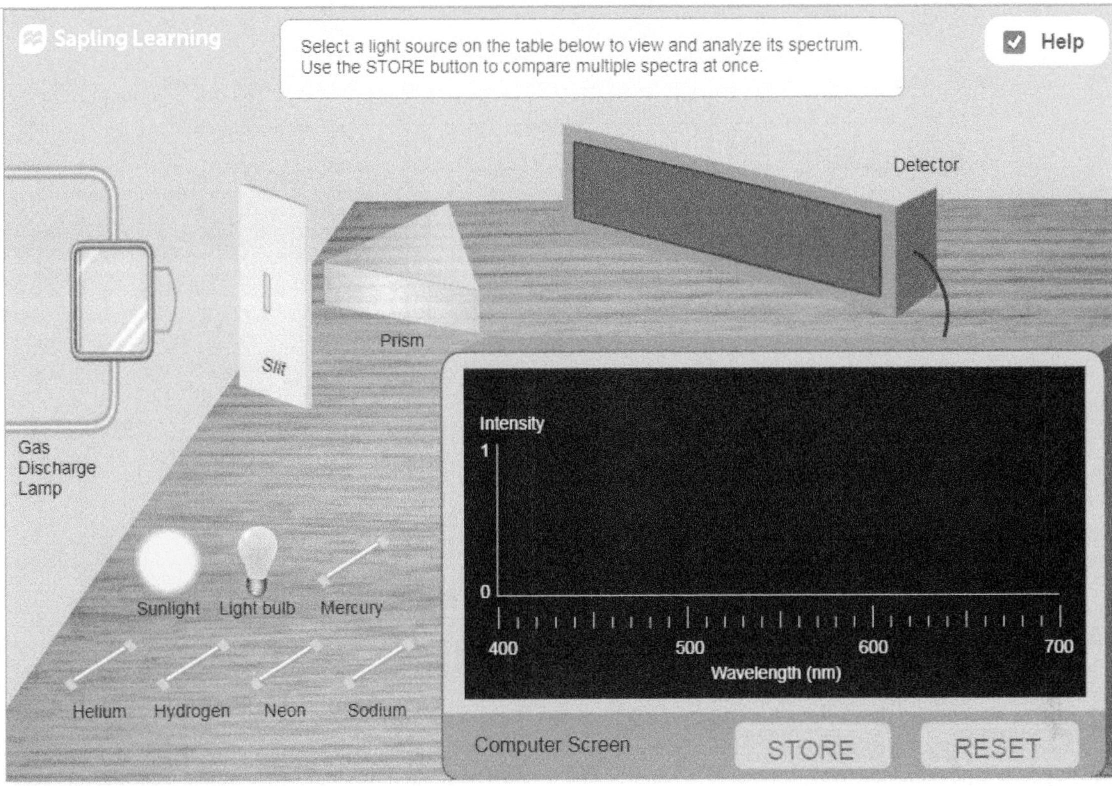

FIGURE 8.12 Spectroscopy Activity

NOTE: You need to be online to access this activity.

Use this activity to view and analyze the spectra of various light sources. Each element gives off a unique emission spectrum that can be used to identify that element.

PRACTICE PROBLEM 8.9

If an electron in a hydrogen atom falls from the fourth energy level to the second energy level, does the photon that is emitted lie in the visible region?

Hint: Use the Rydberg equation with $R_H = 1.097 \times 10^7\ \text{m}^{-1}$ (Equation 8.6) and with $n_2 = 4$ and $n_1 = 2$.

The Rydberg equation only works for H, which has a single electron. For any atom that has two or more electrons, the mathematics becomes significantly more complicated and the Rydberg equation does not apply.

When energy is absorbed by an atom and then released as light, an **emission spectrum** like those seen in Figure 8.11b for H, He, and Ne results. These characteristic emission spectra are unique for each element and can be used to identify the element. When the emission spectrum consists of individual lines such as those in Figure 8.11b, it is known as a **line spectrum**. Use the spectroscopy app in Figure 8.12 to compare the emission spectra of various light sources.

The energy levels in any atom get closer together the farther out you get from the nucleus. The energy difference between the first and second energy levels, for example, is always greater than that between the second and third energy levels, which is then greater than that between the third and fourth energy levels. An energy-level diagram for the first six energy levels in an H atom is shown in Figure 8.13. The corresponding energy for each level is also given, in units of joules. The energy level that is labeled infinity, ∞, indicates an electron that has been completely removed from the atom.

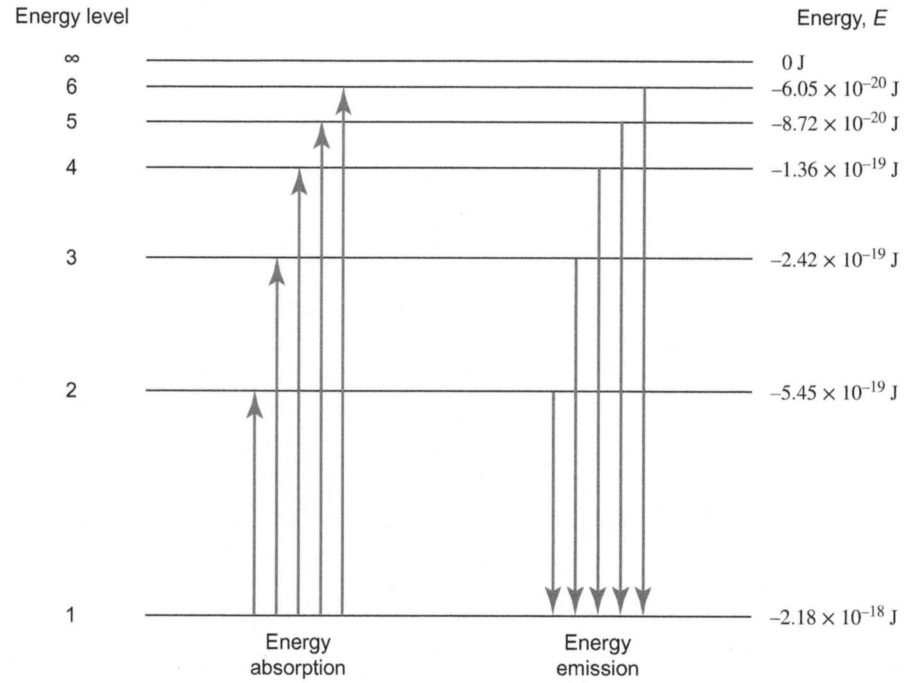

FIGURE 8.13 Energy Levels and Some Possible Electronic Transitions in the Hydrogen Atom

The upward arrows represent six electron transitions that can occur when an ordinary H atom absorbs energy and its electron moves up to a higher energy level. The downward arrows indicate the energy that is given off when the electron in a higher energy level returns to the lowest energy level (the ground state). There are many more energy levels between level 6 and infinity. When the electron reaches the energy level labeled ∞, it has escaped from the atom. Note that the diagram is not drawn to scale.

The energy levels in Figure 8.13 are labeled with negative energy values because a free electron that has been removed from its atom is assigned a potential energy of 0. To understand how that results in negative energy values, consider this analogy: Imagine that you have a staircase, and on each stair you place an identical wooden block. You place one extra block on the floor at the bottom of the stairs and one block at the very top. Gravitational potential energy increases with height, so you could say that the block resting on the floor at the bottom has a potential energy of 0, and each successive block going up the stairs has a greater potential energy than the one before. Electron energy levels in an atom work exactly the same way—electrons in the lower energy levels have less potential energy than do electrons in the higher energy levels—but now the block at the very top, which represents a free electron in energy level ∞, is the one that is assigned a potential energy of 0. The blocks on the lower levels still have less potential energy than does the one at the top, so if the one at the top has a value of 0, each successive block going down the stairs must have a lower potential energy than the one before. The potential energy values therefore get increasingly negative as you move down, just as they are shown in Figure 8.13.

Atoms *absorb* energy when electrons undergo transitions to *higher* energy levels; atoms *emit* energy when electrons undergo transitions to *lower* energy levels.

Bohr hypothesized that electrons travel about the nucleus in circular orbits, similar to the orbits of the planets about the Sun, except that, where planetary orbits grow increasingly farther apart as you move farther from the center, electron orbits get increasingly closer together. Bohr developed a mathematical model to calculate the energies of the electron orbits in an atom, as well as their distances from the atom's nucleus. His model worked very well for the H atom—in fact, it could be used to calculate the energy of the emitted and absorbed light, as well as the radius of the atom. Unfortunately, however, Bohr's model could *not* explain the spectra of any other elements, or why some emission lines were brighter than others. Although Bohr's model was a major step in the right direction, because it was the first to describe energy levels for electrons in atoms, it was clear to scientists that it was

EVERYDAY CONNECTION

Fireworks are not the only way that the emission spectra of different elements play a role in ordinary life. Many chemical compounds are also able to absorb and/or emit energy as light. Sunscreen, for example, is a mixture of compounds designed to absorb specific wavelengths of ultraviolet light that can be damaging to skin. The absorbed energy is radiated away as heat. The fluorescent Day-Glo colors seen on highlighter markers are due to compounds that absorb higher-energy ultraviolet light, release some of that energy as heat, and emit the rest of the energy as lower-energy visible light. These objects therefore give off more light of a given color than is ordinarily present in sunlight, making them appear brighter than the objects around them.

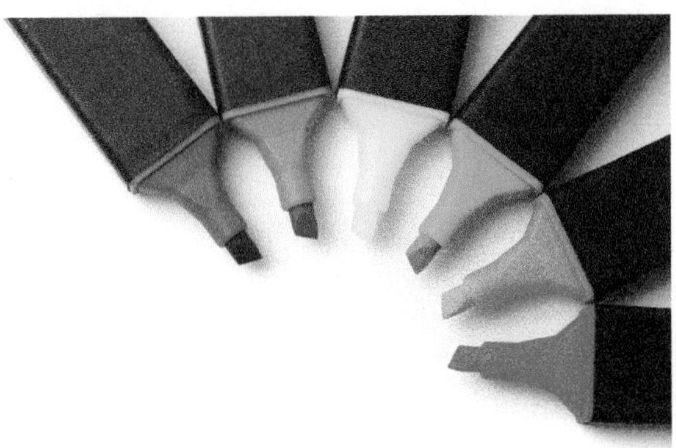

Dave Denby/Shutterstock

not entirely correct. A quantum mechanical model has since replaced Bohr's model.

SECTION REVIEW

- Bohr postulated that the electrons in an atom revolved about the nucleus in circular orbits and absorbed or emitted light only when they changed from one orbit to another.
- An electron can move from a lower energy level to a higher energy level if it absorbs an amount of energy that is exactly equal to the energy difference between the two energy levels.
- When an electron drops from a higher energy level to a lower energy level, it gives off energy equal to the difference in the energies of the two levels.
- The Rydberg equation allows you to calculate the wavelength or energy of the emission line that results from any electronic transition in an H atom.
- The electronic energy levels in atoms are unique for each element, so each element absorbs and emits light of particular wavelengths that can serve as a "fingerprint" to identify that element.
- Bohr's postulate that electrons have distinct energy levels in atoms was a milestone in the understanding of the nature of the atom.

8.3 Electron Shells, Subshells, and Orbitals

GOAL

- Explain the spatial arrangement in which electrons are distributed around the nucleus of an atom.

Background Review

Chapter 2 Atoms and the Periodic Table:
Section 2.6—The Periodic Table

As the photoelectric effect showed, light can behave as both a wave and as a particle. In 1924, French physicist Louis de Broglie (1892–1987) proposed that matter also exhibits a wave nature, and in 1927 he showed that the wavelength of a moving electron can be calculated from its mass and velocity. This wave–particle duality presented a puzzling paradox until German physicist Werner Heisenberg (1901–1976) presented his uncertainty principle in 1927. Since the velocity of an electron is related to its wave nature, whereas its position is related to its particle nature, the velocity and position of an electron cannot both be known simultaneously. Furthermore, the more accurately you know one, the less accurately you can know the other. In other words, electrons can be observed either as a wave or as a particle, but not both at once.

In 1926, Austrian physicist Erwin Schrödinger (1887–1961) proposed an equation that, along with the **Heisenberg uncertainty principle**, led to a new model for the atom. The **Schrödinger wave equation**, when solved, gives a three-dimensional distribution map for the probable position of an electron in an atom. The Bohr model had placed electrons in specific orbits around the nucleus, but this new model—the quantum mechanical model of the atom—was based on mathematical calculations designed to determine how *likely* it was to find an electron at any point in space around the nucleus.

Using this approach Schrödinger found that electrons were not confined to specific orbits as Bohr had suggested, but could be found nearly anywhere in a spherical space around the nucleus. However, the probability of finding an electron in some regions around the nucleus was much higher than was the probability of finding it in other places. This discovery led to the development of the concepts of electron shells, subshells, and orbitals.

An electron **orbital** is a region of space surrounding the nucleus where an electron is likely to be found. Orbitals come in different shapes and sizes (described later in this section), but no matter what its shape or size, each orbital can hold a maximum of only two electrons.

> Although the words *orbit* and *orbital* sound similar, the difference between an orbital and an orbit is significant. An electron orbit is a circular path, whereas an orbital is a three-dimensional region of space that can house up to two electrons anywhere within that region. An electron in an orbit is always the same distance from the nucleus, but electrons in orbitals can move closer to or farther from the nucleus.

A **subshell** is a group of orbitals (regions of space around the nucleus) that all have the same energy. There are four different types of subshells, designated by the letters *s*, *p*, *d*, and *f*. The orbitals that make up each type of subshell are given those same designations. An *s* subshell, for example, is made up of one *s* orbital, a *p* subshell is made up of three *p* orbitals, a *d* subshell is made up of five *d* orbitals, and an *f* subshell is made up of seven *f* orbitals. Since each orbital (no matter what type) can hold a maximum of two electrons, the different kinds of subshells each have a different maximum number of electrons.

An electron **shell**, sometimes referred to as a **principal energy level** and symbolized *n*, is a grouping of subshells. The first energy level is made up of one type of subshell, the second is made up of two types of subshells, the third is made up of three types, and so on. Like the energy levels of the Bohr atom, lower-energy electron shells are closer to the nucleus. They are made up of fewer subshells and can contain fewer electrons. Higher-energy electron shells extend farther away from the nucleus. They can be made up of more subshells and can therefore contain a larger maximum number of electrons. The shell within which a given subshell is located is indicated by adding the shell as a coefficient. For example, the *s* subshell in the first energy level is written 1*s*, and the *p* subshell in the third energy level is written 3*p*.

Example 8.10

Each orbital, regardless of type, can hold a maximum of two electrons. Using information given in the preceding paragraph about subshells, what is the maximum number of electrons that can be found in each *s* and *p* subshell?

Solution

An *s* subshell is made up of only one *s* orbital, so an *s* subshell can hold a maximum of two electrons.

Each *p* subshell is made up of three *p* orbitals, so a *p* subshell can hold a maximum of six electrons.

PRACTICE PROBLEM 8.10

What is the maximum number of electrons that can be found in each *d* and *f* subshell?

Hint: An orbital can hold up to two electrons each. A *d* subshell is made up of five orbitals and an *f* subshell is made up of seven orbitals.

Table 8.2 summarizes the number of orbitals that make up each type of subshell and the maximum number of electrons each type of subshell can hold.

TABLE 8.2 Subshells, Orbitals, and Electrons

Type of Subshell	Number of Orbitals	Maximum Number of Electrons per Orbital	Maximum Number of Electrons in This Type of Subshell
s	1	2	2
p	3	2	6
d	5	2	10
f	7	2	14

Example 8.11

Which of the following statements are true and which are false?

a. If a subshell contains two electrons, then it must be an *s* subshell.
b. Any orbital can contain zero, one, or two electrons, with two being the maximum.
c. A *d* subshell can hold more electrons than can a *p* subshell because the *d* subshell is made up of more orbitals than is the *p* subshell.

Solution

a. False: Although an *s* subshell can hold a maximum of 2 electrons, the *p*, *d*, and *f* subshells can hold *up to* 6, 10, and 14 electrons, respectively, so any of these can have 2 electrons in them, too.
b. True: An orbital of any subshell type can contain zero, one, or two electrons.
c. True: A *d* subshell is made up of five orbitals that can hold up to two electrons each, whereas a *p* subshell is made up of only three orbitals, which also hold up to two electrons each.

PRACTICE PROBLEM 8.11

Select the correct word or phrase from the choices in square brackets to complete each sentence.

a. An orbital is a [circular path/region in space] surrounding the nucleus where an electron is most likely to be found.
b. Shells, also called energy levels, are made up of a collection of [orbitals/subshells], which in turn are made up of a collection of [orbitals/subshells]. (Choose each word only once.)

Hint:

a. How do orbitals in the Schrödinger model of the atom differ from orbitals in the Bohr model?
b. What is the relationship between shells, subshells, and orbitals in the Schrödinger model?

Ever since Dmitri Mendeleev drew up his first periodic table, it was known that all the elements in a group shared similar properties. As you move from left to right across the rows of the periodic table (especially among the main group elements), the same pattern of properties seems to repeat, but it was many years before anyone could explain why. The concept of shells, subshells, and orbitals made it possible for the first time for scientists to understand the arrangement of electrons around each atom. As discussed in Section 8.5, the arrangement of the outermost electrons in atoms repeats in a predictable pattern, and this repeating pattern of outer electron arrangements explains why the chemical properties of the elements repeat in a periodic, predictable pattern.

SHAPES OF ORBITALS

The Schrödinger wave equation allows for the calculation of the probability of finding an electron at any given point in the space surrounding the nucleus. When the most likely places to find an electron are plotted out, they form regions in space around the nucleus known as orbitals. Although an orbital extends infinitely from the nucleus, it is commonly represented by drawing a boundary around a portion of the orbital that includes 90% of the electron density. These types of drawings are known as *contour representations* (Figure 8.14) and are the primary way that orbitals will be depicted throughout this text.

In an *s* orbital, there is an equal probability of finding the electron in any direction about the nucleus because an *s* orbital is spherically symmetrical. The *s* orbital, pictured in Figure 8.14a, is a spherical region centered on the nucleus. A *p* subshell is made up of three orbitals. Each *p* orbital, shown in Figure 8.14b, consists of two three-dimensional lobes centered on one of the Cartesian (*x*, *y*, or *z*) coordinate axes. A **lobe** is a region of an orbital that is distinct from other regions of the same orbital. The electrons in a *p* orbital can freely move between the two lobes, and at any given instant, the two electrons in a *p* orbital may both be found in one lobe, both in the other lobe, or one in each lobe.

Each *d* subshell consists of five orbitals, shown in Figure 8.14c. Four of them are four-lobed and roughly cloverleaf in appearance, and the fifth is a two-lobed region (similar to a *p* orbital) that lies along the *z*-axis, with a torus, or ring, horizontally around its center. The shapes of the seven *f* orbitals, which are not pictured in Figure 8.14, are even more complicated, having either four, six, or eight distinct regions in which the electron is likely to be found. The discussion of orbitals from this point forward focuses primarily on the *s*, *p*, and *d* orbitals.

Since all of the orbitals in an atom exist around the nucleus at the same time, the same point in space can be part of more than one orbital at the same time. For example, all *s* orbitals are spherical and centered on the nucleus. Figure 8.15 shows that the 3*s* orbital is larger than the 2*s* orbital, and the 2*s* orbital is larger than the 1*s* orbital. The general rule is that the size of a particular type of orbital (*s*, *p*, *d*) increases as the principal energy level increases. As a result, the 1*s*

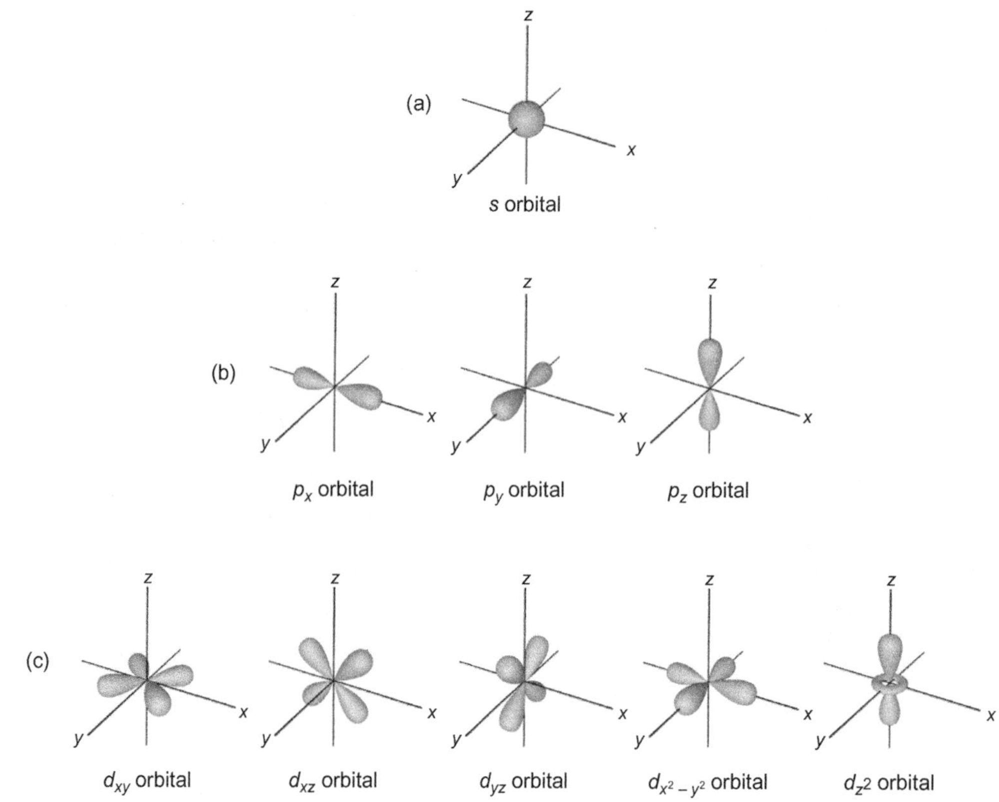

FIGURE 8.14 Shapes of Orbitals
(a) The *s* orbital, (b) the three *p* orbitals, and (c) the five *d* orbitals.

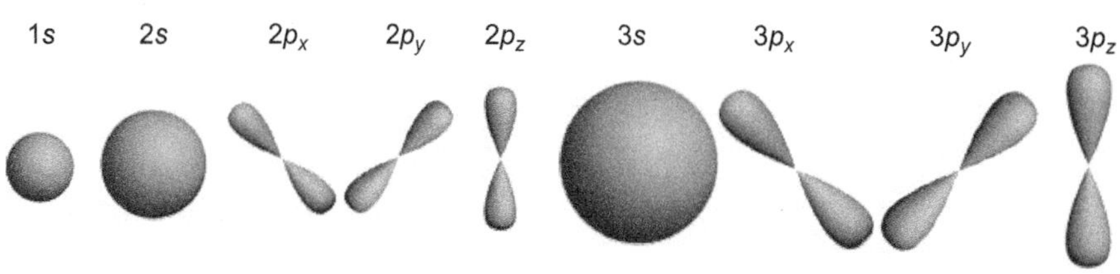

FIGURE 8.15 Relative Sizes of Orbitals
The size of the orbital increases as the principal energy level increases. Thus, the 2*s* orbital is the same shape as the 1*s* orbital, but it is bigger.

orbital is a region of space that is entirely within the 2*s* orbital, and the 2*s* orbital is a region of space that is entirely within the 3*s* orbital.

The 1*s*, 2*s*, and 3*s* orbitals are all the same shape, but increase in size as *n* increases. Similarly, the 3*p* orbitals in an atom are the same shape and orientation as are the 2*p* orbitals (Figure 8.15), but they encompass a larger region of space, which includes the 2*p* orbitals. Although this means that the 1*s* and 2*s* electrons are within the same region of space defined by the 3*s* orbital, it does not mean that the 3*s* orbital "holds" six electrons because the energies of the 1*s*, 2*s*, and 3*s* electrons are different from one another, and the electrons are assigned to orbitals on the basis of energy and location. Thus, no orbital ever has more than two electrons assigned to it.

Within the same principal energy level, the general order of subshells from lowest energy to highest energy is $s < p < d < f$. Individual electrons may have higher or lower energies, but the average energy of the electrons in the 3*d* orbitals, for example, is generally higher than the average energy of the electrons in the 3*p* orbitals. As you move across the periodic table, then, from one subshell to the next and from one

EVERYDAY CONNECTION

Russian nesting dolls, also called *matryoshka* dolls, are hollow wooden figures that fit one inside the next, so the volume of the smaller dolls is entirely within the volume of the larger dolls. This is similar to the way that smaller orbitals of the lower-energy levels are regions of space that lie entirely within the larger regions of the higher-energy orbitals (see Figure 8.21).

Brian Anderson

energy level to the next, each successive subshell is at a higher energy than the one before.

The orbital shapes shown in Figure 8.14 and Figure 8.15 are not "containers" that hold electrons. Instead, they are representations of the most likely places to find the electron in the space surrounding the nucleus. Electrons can and do stray outside of these boundaries, but at any given time, there is about a 95% chance of finding the electron within the boundaries of its orbital.

Example 8.12

Based on the subshells that make up each one, how many electrons can each of the first three principal energy levels hold?

a. $n = 1$, which consists only of the 1*s* subshell
b. $n = 2$, which consists of the 2*s* and 2*p* subshells
c. $n = 3$, which consists of the 3*s*, 3*p*, and 3*d* subshells

Solution

a. The 1*s* subshell can hold a maximum of two electrons, so the first principal energy level can hold a maximum of two electrons.
b. The 2*s* subshell can hold two electrons and the 2*p* can hold six, so the second principal energy level can hold a total of eight electrons.
c. The 3*s* subshell can hold 2 electrons, the 3*p* can hold 6, and the 3*d* can hold 10, so the third energy level can hold a total of 18 electrons.

PRACTICE PROBLEM 8.12

Based on the subshells that make up the fourth principal energy level, what is the maximum number of electrons the fourth principal energy level can hold?

Hint: See Table 8.2 for the maximum number of electrons each subshell can hold. The fourth energy level is made up of *s*, *p*, *d*, and *f* subshells. Add the maximum number of electrons possible in each subshell to get the maximum number of electrons possible in the overall energy level.

SECTION REVIEW

- Electrons occupy specific regions of space around the nucleus known as subshells.
- Each principal energy level in an atom is made up of one or more subshells. The first energy level is made up of one type of subshell (*s*), the second energy level is made up of two types of subshells (*s* and *p*), the third energy level is made up of three types (*s*, *p*, and *d*), and so on.
- Each subshell is made up of one or more orbitals. Orbitals are regions of space that can contain up to two electrons.
- The *s* orbitals are spherically symmetrical, whereas the *p* and *d* orbitals are oriented as shown in Figure 8.14.
- The *p*, *d*, and *f* orbitals have more than one lobe each. The lobes of these orbitals make up a single orbital, and electrons can move freely among the lobes of an orbital.
- In general, electrons in higher energy levels are farther from the nucleus than are electrons in lower energy levels.
- Within the same principal energy level, the energies of the subshells generally increase in the order $s < p < d < f$.

8.4 Energy-Level Diagrams

GOALS

- Sketch the electronic energy levels of an atom.
- Add electrons to energy-level diagrams.

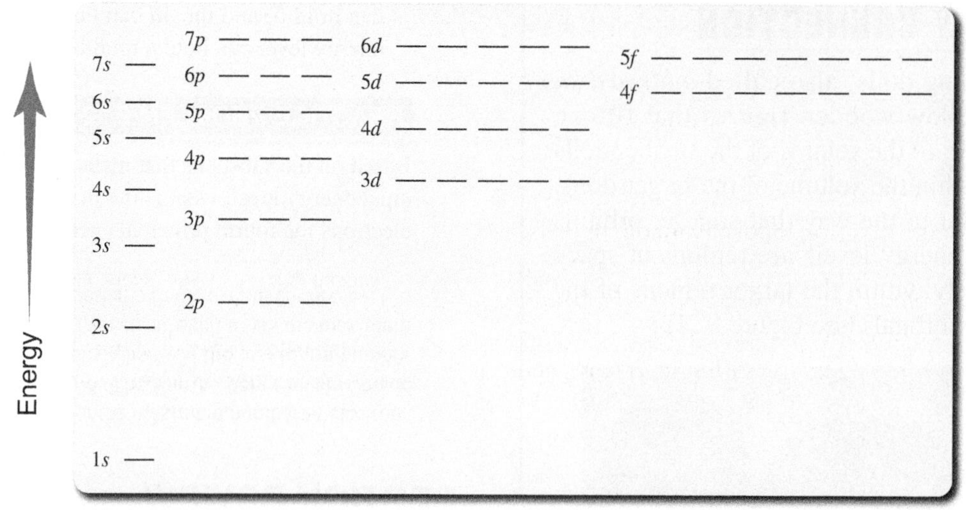

FIGURE 8.16 Energy-Level Diagram

The lowest energy level (1*s*) is at the bottom of the figure and represents the energy level closest to the nucleus in an atom. The spacing between electronic energy levels becomes increasingly smaller the farther out you get from the nucleus. The electrons in an atom fill the available orbitals from the lowest energy level upward. Note that the diagram is not drawn to scale.

How are the electrons distributed among the individual orbitals in an atom? The answer has important consequences for determining an atom's magnetic properties and chemical bonding properties. When determining the arrangement of electrons in orbitals, scientists often make use of energy-level diagrams like the one shown in Figure 8.16.

Energy-level diagrams are graphical representations of the subshells of an atom, in which each subshell is separated vertically from the others in order of increasing energy. In Figure 8.16, each individual orbital is represented by a short, horizontal line. Lines that are drawn higher up in the diagram represent higher-energy orbitals. All of the orbitals that make up a single subshell are at the same energy, so each *p* subshell, for example, is represented by three short lines that are all at the same height. Orbitals that are at the same energy are said to be **degenerate**. The lines are spaced out horizontally in this diagram only to prevent crowding so that the diagram is easier to read.

Each electron in an energy-level diagram is represented by an arrow pointing either up or down. The direction of the arrow represents something called the *spin* of the electron. Electron spin is a property related to the electron's angular momentum and is described further in Section 8.6, but it is important to the energy-level diagrams in two ways—when an orbital holds two electrons, they must have opposite spins, and when a subshell contains more than one unpaired electron, the unpaired electrons in a ground state atom will have the same spin.

Since each horizontal line represents one orbital and each orbital can hold a maximum of two electrons, each line may have a maximum of two arrows. If two arrows are present, they must point in opposite directions to represent opposite spins. The energy-level diagram representing a neon, Ne, atom is shown in Figure 8.17. It has 10 arrows because a Ne atom has 10 electrons.

When the electrons are all in the lowest-energy subshells available, the atom is in the ground state. If electrons are moved up to higher-energy subshells while there are spots for electrons available in lower-energy orbitals, the atom is said to be in an excited state. The ground state is the most stable electronic

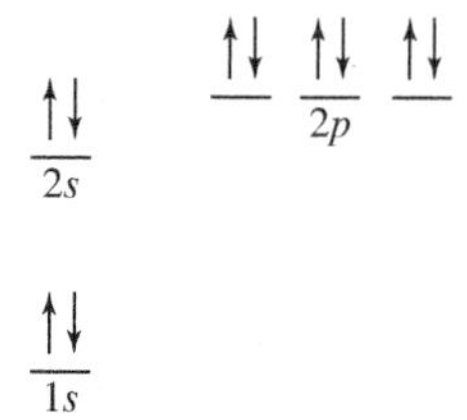

FIGURE 8.17 Electronic Occupancy of the Orbitals in a Neon Atom

All of the electron orbitals in the highest occupied energy level (n = 2) are completely filled with paired electrons.

state for the atom. Unless specified otherwise, electron configurations should always be written for ground-state atoms.

The process of filling the subshells from the lowest energy upward is known as the **aufbau principle**, or the **building-up principle**. According to the aufbau principle, the electrons in a ground-state atom always fill the lowest-energy position that is available to them.

Hund's rule states that the electrons *within a given subshell* remain as *unpaired as possible*. Moreover, if there are two or more unpaired electrons in a given subshell, they must occupy different orbitals and must have the same electronic spin; that is, in a subshell, all arrows representing unpaired electrons either all point up or all point down. The energy-level diagrams for the carbon, C, nitrogen, N, and oxygen, O, atoms that follow illustrate these rules.

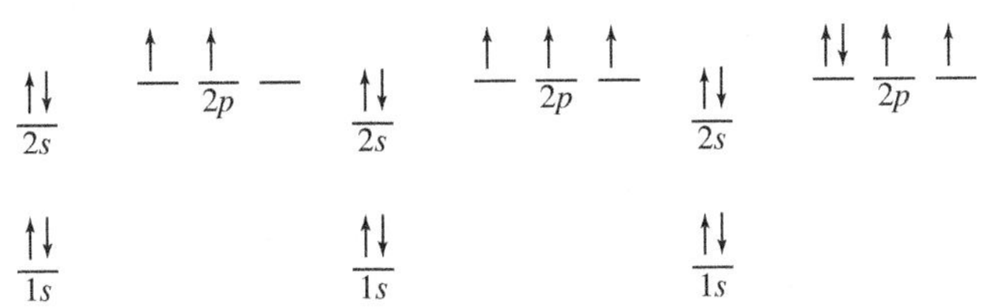

Carbon atom — Nitrogen atom — Oxygen atom

In the C atom (six electrons), the lowest two subshells (1*s* and 2*s*) are filled; all electrons are paired in filled subshells. The 2*p* subshell has only two electrons in the three orbitals, so each electron occupies a separate orbital. Moreover, both electrons have the same spin, where both arrows point upward or both point downward. They are said to have parallel spin. In the N atom (seven electrons), the 2*p* subshell is half-filled. Each electron occupies a different orbital, and all arrows point in the same direction. In the O atom (eight electrons), the 2*p* subshell is again partially filled. To place four electrons into the three orbitals requires the pairing of two electrons in one orbital. In the other two orbitals, the electrons are unpaired and have the same spin. Chapter 9 and Chapter 10 explain how the number of unpaired electrons in an atom's outermost subshell contributes to the atom's ability to form chemical bonds with other atoms.

Example 8.13

Use electronic energy-level diagrams to determine the number of unpaired electrons in (a) a fluorine atom, (b) an oxygen atom, and (c) a boron atom.

Solution

Use the aufbau principle and Hund's rule to fill the energy-level diagrams that follow with the appropriate number of electrons for a fluorine atom, an oxygen atom, and a boron atom.

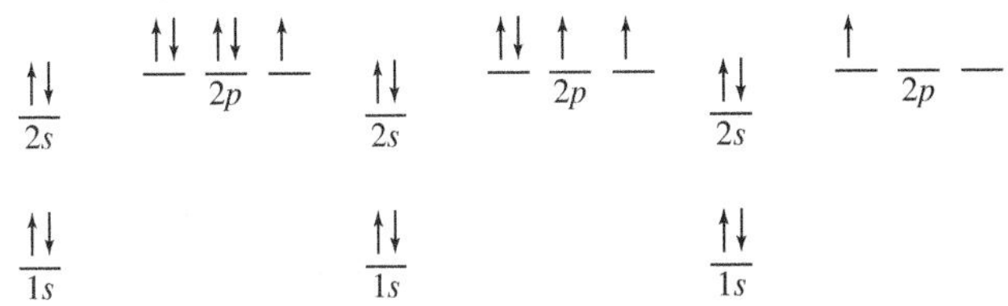

Fluorine atom (a) — Oxygen atom (b) — Boron atom (c)

The energy-level diagrams show one unpaired electron in a fluorine atom, two in an oxygen atom, and one in a boron atom.

PRACTICE PROBLEM 8.13

How many unpaired electrons are in (a) an aluminum atom and (b) an argon atom?

Hint: Draw energy-level diagrams for each of these atoms and place the electrons in the orbitals from the lowest energy up (aufbau principle). Electrons that are in the same subshell should be unpaired with parallel spins until it becomes necessary to pair them up (Hund's rule).

Filling energy-level diagrams according to the aufbau principle is not just a matter of filling the first principal shell (1*s*), followed by the second shell (2*s* then 2*p*), followed by the third shell (3*s* then 3*p* then 3*d*), followed by the fourth shell (4*s* then 4*p* then 4*d* then 4*f*), and so on. The third and fourth shells are already so close in energy that the energies of their subshells begin to overlap. Notice that in Figure 8.16 the energy of the 3*d* subshell is between that of the 4*s* and the 4*p*. Therefore, even though the 3*d* subshell is part of the third shell, it fills *after* the 4*s* subshell. Similarly, the energy (and thus the filling order) of the 4*f* subshell is between that of the 6*s* and 5*d* subshells.

Before you try to memorize Figure 8.16, though, make a chart that looks like the one that follows.

1*s*
2*s* 2*p*
3*s* 3*p* 3*d*
4*s* 4*p* 4*d* 4*f*
5*s* 5*p* 5*d* 5*f*
6*s* 6*p* 6*d* 6*f*
7*s* 7*p* 7*d* 7*f*

Then draw a series of parallel arrows pointing down and to the left, with each arrow going through the sublevels in the chart that lie in its path, as shown in Figure 8.18.

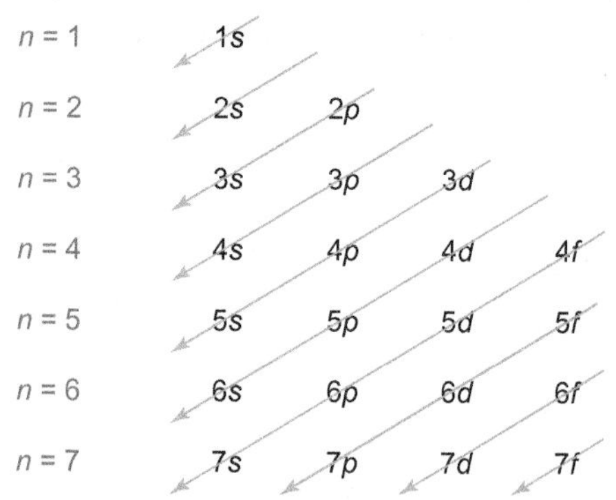

FIGURE 8.18 Orbital-Filling Diagram

Electrons fill subshells in the order found by following the diagonal arrows from the top of the diagram to the bottom. Thus, subshells fill in the order *1s 2s 2p 3s 3p 4s 3d 4p 5s 4d 5p 6s 4f 5d 6p 7s 5f 6d 7p*. Following this order fills out the populated orbitals found in ground-state atoms of all 118 elements in the current periodic table. If the arrow ending with *7p* was continued, it would strike the *8s* orbital next.

The order in which the arrows pass through the subshells in Figure 8.18 tells you the order in which the subshells are filled. When you are writing the electron configuration for an atom, you continue filling subshells in this order until you run out of electrons.

SECTION REVIEW

- An energy-level diagram depicts the individual orbitals as short horizontal lines with the lowest-energy level at the bottom. Each subshell is then placed in order of increasing energy as you move up the diagram.
- Each individual orbital in an energy-level diagram (each short horizontal line) can hold a maximum of two electrons.
- For atoms in the ground state, electrons fill an energy-level diagram from the lowest available level upward (aufbau principle).
- When there is more than one orbital at the same energy (such as in the *p* subshells), electrons will be distributed across the orbitals so that they remain unpaired, with their spins aligned, until there are enough electrons in the subshell that it becomes necessary to pair them up (Hund's rule).
- The electron configuration of the atom can be determined from the energy-level diagram by counting the number of electrons in each subshell in the diagram.

8.5 Electron Configurations

GOAL

- Devise electron configurations for the elements based on each element's position in the periodic table, using the concepts of shells, subshells, and orbitals.

The arrangement of electrons in the shells and subshells around the nucleus can also be represented using a notation known as an electron configuration. An **electron configuration** shows the arrangement of electrons in an atom by listing each subshell in order of increasing energy, with the lowest-energy subshell always written first, and adding a superscript to each subshell to indicate how many electrons it contains.

To write an electron configuration for neon, Ne, first look at its energy-level diagram. Ne has an atomic number, *Z*, of 10, so a neutral Ne atom has 10 electrons to balance the charge of its 10 protons.

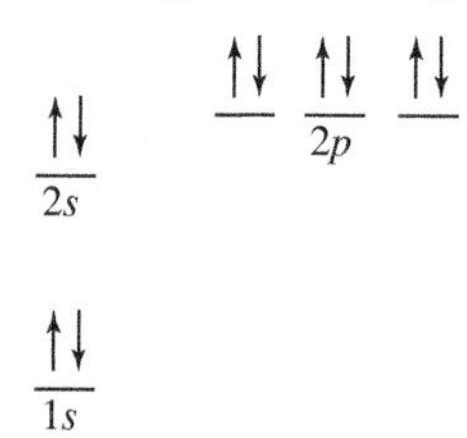

Now, write all of the occupied subshells in order from lowest energy to highest energy.

$$1s\ 2s\ 2p$$

Then, indicate the number of electrons in each subshell using a superscript as shown below.

Shell number or energy level — Subshell type — Number of electrons in each subshell

Neon $1s^2$ $1s^2$ $2p^6$

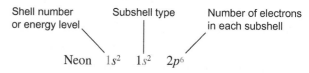

The superscripts are read as numbers, not as exponents, so the electron configuration for Ne is read as "one ess two, two ess two, two pee six." The sum of the superscripts (2 + 2 + 6) is the total number of electrons in the atom (10). In the case of a neutral atom, this is also the atomic number of the element.

The electron configuration indicates the shell and the subshell of each electron but typically does not make a distinction between individual orbitals. For example, the $2p^6$ in the electron configuration for Ne lumps all three $2p$ orbitals together. However, in some sources you may see electron configurations that do specify the orbitals with a subshell (e.g., $2p_x^2 2p_y^2 2p_z^2$ instead of $2p^6$).

Example 8.14

Write the electron configuration for oxygen from its energy-level diagram.

Solution

Oxygen is atomic number 8, so an oxygen atom has a total of eight electrons. Place eight electrons, up to two per orbital, using Figure 8.16, starting from the bottom.

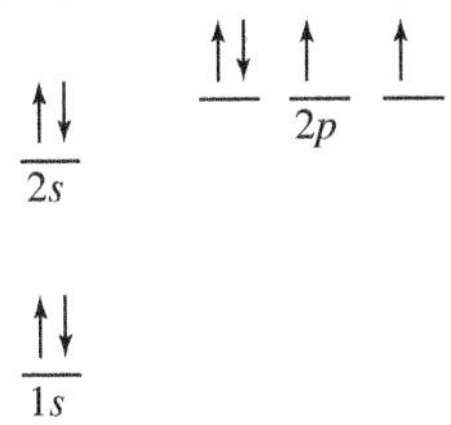

Now, write the occupied subshells with a superscript to indicate the number of electrons.

$$1s^2 2s^2 2p^4$$

The $2p$ subshell in oxygen is not filled. It still has room for two more electrons, but an oxygen atom does not have enough electrons to completely fill the subshell.

PRACTICE PROBLEM 8.14

Write the electron configuration for sulfur from its energy-level diagram.

Hint: The number of electrons in a neutral atom is equal to its atomic number.

ELECTRON CONFIGURATIONS AND THE PERIODIC TABLE

The elements in each group of the periodic table all have the same outermost electron configuration. For example, both oxygen, O, and sulfur, S, have configurations ending in np^4 as seen in Example 8.12 and Practice Problem 8.14. The alkali metals (group 1) all have a single electron in their outermost *s* subshell, ns^1; the alkaline earth metals (group 2) all have two electrons in their outermost *s* subshell, ns^2; and the halogens (group 17) all have seven electrons in their outermost *s* and *p* subshells, ns^2np^5. It is the arrangement of an atom's outermost electrons, called **valence electrons**, that gives an element its chemical properties. Moreover, the elements of each group have similar chemical properties because they have the same outermost (valence) electron configuration.

The periodic table is an extremely useful tool for writing electron configurations. The periodic table can be divided into blocks corresponding to the type of subshell occupied by the highest-energy electrons (Figure 8.19). The two groups at the left of the periodic table—the alkali metals and the alkaline earth metals—constitute the *s* block because the last electrons in their electron configurations occupy *s* subshells. Hydrogen, H, and helium, He, are in this block, too, so you must mentally shift He to a place beside H for this purpose. The six groups at the right side of the periodic table (groups 13–18) constitute

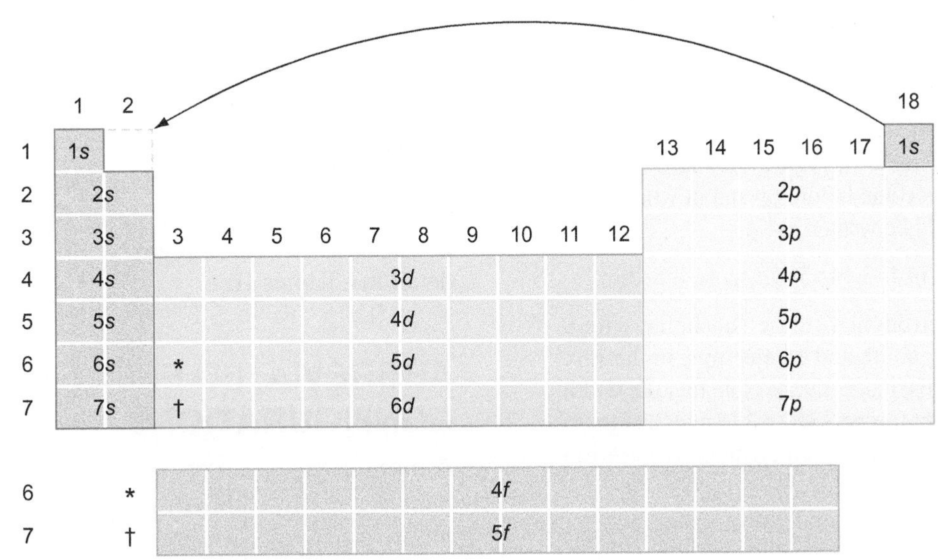

FIGURE 8.19 Subshell Blocks in the Periodic Table

Labeling the periodic table in this manner makes it easier to predict electron configurations. It also highlights the fact that the outermost electron configurations are the same for elements in the same group.

Steve Lemon, Macmillan Learning

FIGURE 8.20 Video Tutorial: Electron Configuration

NOTE: You need to be online to access this video.

This video shows how to determine electron configurations from the periodic table and from orbital diagrams.

the *p* block; the last electrons in their electron configurations go into *p* subshells. The transition metals (groups 3–12) belong to the *d* block, and the *f* block (the lanthanides and actinides) consists of the inner transition metals.

The video in Figure 8.20 demonstrates how to use the periodic table to write electron configurations.

Example 8.15

Write the complete electron configuration for lead, Pb.

Solution

Pb is in the sixth row of the *p* block, so its outermost electrons will be in the 6*p* subshell. Additionally, Pb is in the second column of the 6*p* block, so its configuration will end in $6p^2$. Use Figure 8.18 or the periodic table in Figure 8.19 to determine which subshells come before 6*p* and in what order. The order would be written as

$$1s\ 2s\ 2p\ 3s\ 3p\ 4s\ 3d\ 4p\ 5s\ 4d\ 5p\ 6s\ 4f\ 5d\ 6p^2$$

Place electrons into these subshells, with a maximum of 2, 6, 10, and 14 electrons in the *s*, *p*, *d*, and *f* subshells, respectively. Note that the width of each block in the periodic table matches these numbers. The complete electron configuration would be written as

$$1s^22s^22p^63s^23p^64s^23d^{10}4p^65s^24d^{10}5p^66s^24f^{14}5d^{10}6p^2$$

As a check, the total number of electrons (the sum of the superscripts) must equal 82, the atomic number of Pb.

PRACTICE PROBLEM 8.15

Write the complete electron configuration for nickel, Ni.

Hint: Consult the orbital-filling diagram in Figure 8.18 and/or the subshell blocks in the periodic table in Figure 8.19.

Example 8.16

Which neutral element has the ground-state electron configuration $1s^22s^22p^63s^23p^64s^2$?

Solution

You could sum the superscripts ($2 + 2 + 6 + 2 + 6 + 2 = 20$) and find the element with atomic number 20. However, you may find it faster to locate the element in the fourth row ($n = 4$) of the *s* block and in the second column (s^2), which is calcium.

PRACTICE PROBLEM 8.16

Which neutral element has the ground-state electron configuration $1s^22s^22p^63s^23p^64s^23d^{10}4p^5$?

Hint: Locate the element in the fifth column of the 4*p* block of the periodic table.

The activity in Figure 8.21 lets you place electrons in orbitals surrounding an atom's nucleus to construct a neutral atom in its lowest-energy state. As you select the orbitals and fill them with electrons, the corresponding electron orbital diagram will populate with up arrows and down arrows representing each electron in the atom, and the electron configuration will be shown. Additionally, the app shows a *Lewis dot structure* for the atom, which depicts the valence electrons as dots around the chemical symbol and is covered in detail in Chapter 10.

ABBREVIATED ELECTRON CONFIGURATIONS

A more compact notation can sometimes be used to reduce the effort of writing long electron configurations while retaining almost as much information. The detailed electron configurations you have seen so far include all of the filled inner shells of the atom along with the electrons in the outer shell. For example, the

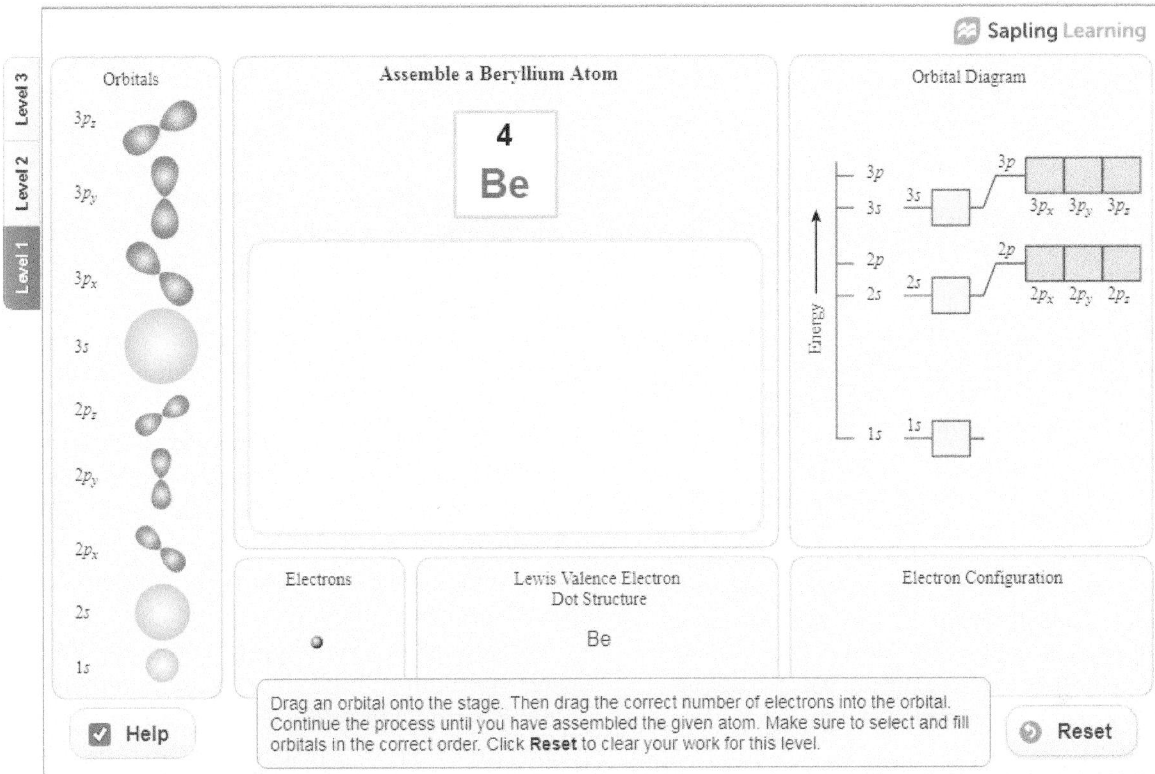

FIGURE 8.21 Electron Arrangement Lab Activity

NOTE: You need to be online to access this activity.

Open the Electron Arrangement Lab activity and test your understanding of the material covered in the previous sections by constructing at least one atom from each challenge level—Level 1, Level 2, and Level 3. To change the level, use the tabs on the upper left.

electron configuration for lead, Pb, in Example 8.15 includes a detailed accounting of every single electron in the atom, even though most of those electrons, often referred to as inner *core electrons*, are effectively "buried" by the outer-shell electrons and play no role in reactions with other atoms. **Core electrons** are the electrons in an atom that are in lower energy levels than are the outer valence electrons. All of the electrons in an atom that are not valence electrons are core electrons.

In an abbreviated electron configuration, the inner core electrons are not explicitly written out. Instead, the symbol for the noble gas that has the same electron configuration as the inner core electrons is written in square brackets, and then the electron configuration for the atom's outer-shell electrons is added to that. For example, the noble gas with the highest atomic number that is less than that of Pb is xenon, Xe. Following are the electron configurations for Pb and Xe and the abbreviated electron configuration for Pb.

Electron configuration for Pb:

$$1s^2 2s^2 2p^6 3s^2 3p^6 4s^2 3d^{10} 4p^6 5s^2 4d^{10} 5p^6 6s^2 4f^{14} 5d^{10} 6p^2$$

Electron configuration for Xe:

$$1s^2 2s^2 2p^6 3s^2 3p^6 4s^2 3d^{10} 4p^6 5s^2 4d^{10} 5p^6$$

Abbreviated configuration for Pb:

$$[\text{Xe}]\ 6s^2 4f^{14} 5d^{10} 6p^2$$

Abbreviated electron configurations are written using the symbols for noble gases to represent the core electrons because noble gases always have a completed outer electron shell. Thus, the detailed portion of the abbreviated electron configuration always begins with the outermost electron shell in the atom (and always begins with an *s* subshell). For all elements except the noble gases, the outermost electron shell is incomplete.

Example 8.17

Write the abbreviated electron configuration for astatine, At (element 85).

Solution

$$\text{At: [Xe]}6s^2 4f^{14} 5d^{10} 6p^5$$

The symbol for the noble gas that precedes astatine, Xe, is written in square brackets. Then, starting at the beginning of the next row, you fill in one electron for each spot in the periodic table: $6s^2$ for Cs and Ba, $4f^{14}$ for the lanthanides (elements 58–71), $5d^{10}$ for the elements from La to Hg, and $6p^5$ to get across the *p* block to At. Because the lanthanide and actinide elements are placed underneath the rest of the periodic table, it is easy to go straight across the 5*d* block and forget to include the 4*f* electrons when writing electron configurations for elements late in the sixth row. Note that the superscripts in the abbreviated electron configuration plus the atomic number of Xe (54) add up to 85, the atomic number of At.

PRACTICE PROBLEM 8.17

Write the abbreviated electron configuration for uranium.

Hint: What noble gas precedes uranium in the periodic table? After that noble gas, how many additional electrons must be included in the electron configuration for uranium?

ANOMALOUS ELECTRON CONFIGURATIONS

Most of the time, you can determine the electron configuration of an element from its place in the periodic table, but sometimes an atom can reach a lower-energy state by shifting some electrons from one subshell to another, resulting in an electron configuration that differs from the one that would be expected. Electrons shift sometimes because atoms gain stability when their subshells are either completely empty, completely full, or exactly half-filled. Compare, for example, the expected and actual electron configurations of chromium, Cr ($Z = 24$), and copper, Cu ($Z = 29$):

Element	Chromium, Cr	Copper, Cu
Expected Configuration	$1s^2 2s^2 2p^6 3s^2$ $3p^6 4s^2 3d^4$	$1s^2 2s^2 2p^6 3s^2$ $3p^6 4s^2 3d^9$
Actual Configuration	$1s^2 2s^2 2p^6 3s^2$ $3p^6 4s^1 3d^5$	$1s^2 2s^2 2p^6 3s^2$ $3p^6 4s^1 3d^{10}$

In the case of Cr, shifting one electron from the filled 4*s* subshell to the 3*d* subshell makes both subshells exactly half-filled, and that creates an overall lower-energy state for the atom. In the case of Cu, moving an electron from the filled 4*s* subshell to the nearly filled 3*d* fills the 3*d* and leaves the 4*s* exactly half-filled, so this again creates an overall lower-energy state for the atom.

This effect is seen in the transition metals due to the closeness in energy of the *ns* and $(n - 1)d$ orbitals. This is even more common in the elements near the bottom of the periodic table, such as the lanthanides and actinides, because the atoms of these elements have electrons in some of the highest-energy subshells, including the 6*d* and 5*f* subshells. The energy level differences between these higher-energy *nd* and $(n - 1)f$ subshells are small, so moving electrons between the different subshells is relatively easy and can result in a lower overall energy for the atom. For example, the electron configurations of europium, Eu ($Z = 63$), and ytterbium, Yb ($Z = 70$), based on their positions in the periodic table are expected to be $[\text{Xe}]6s^2 5d^1 4f^6$ and $[\text{Xe}]6s^2 5d^1 4f^{13}$, respectively, but one 5*d* electron moves to the 4*f* subshell to create a half-filled or completely filled 4*f* subshell. The observed electron configurations for Eu and Yb are $[\text{Xe}]6s^2 4f^7$ and $[\text{Xe}]6s^2 4f^{14}$.

ELECTRON CONFIGURATIONS OF IONS

Electron configurations for monoatomic ions are written the same way they are for neutral atoms, except that the number of electrons is no longer equal to the atomic number of the element. For example, the fluoride ion, F^-, has 9 protons and 10 electrons, so its electron configuration must have a total of 10 electrons. Similarly, a sodium ion, Na^+, has 11 protons and 10 electrons, so its electron configuration must have 10 electrons.

Example 8.18

Write the electron configuration for the fluoride ion, F^-, and the sodium ion, Na^+.

Solution

A fluorine atom has 9 protons and 9 electrons, so F^- will have 1 extra electron, or 10 electrons total. The electron configuration for F^- is $1s^2 2s^2 2p^6$, which is the same as the electron configuration for neon, Ne.

A sodium atom has 11 protons and 11 electrons, so Na^+ will have 1 fewer electron, or 10 electrons total. The electron configuration for Na^+ is $1s^22s^22p^6$, which is also the same as the electron configuration for Ne.

Atoms or ions that have the same electron configuration are said to be **isoelectronic**. F^-, Na^+, and Ne are isoelectronic because the electron configuration for all three of them is $1s^22s^22p^6$.

PRACTICE PROBLEM 8.18

What is the electron configuration for Ca^{2+} and for S^{2-}? Are these two ions isoelectronic? If they are, with which element are they also isoelectronic?

Hint: Use the atomic number for each element and the charge on each ion to determine how many electrons need to be placed in the electron configurations. Atoms or ions are isoelectronic if they have the same electron configuration.

When transition metal atoms lose electrons to become positive ions, the first electrons lost come from the outermost *s* subshell, rather than from the *d* subshell (which in most cases is only partially occupied). For example, the electron configuration of zinc, Zn, is $[Ar]4s^23d^{10}$, and the electron configuration of the Zn^{2+} ion is $[Ar]3d^{10}$, not $[Ar]4s^23d^8$. The empty 4*s* subshell in Zn^{2+} is omitted from the electron configuration.

Example 8.19

Write the electron configuration for the iron(II) and iron(III) ions.

Solution

Iron(II) is Fe^{2+}, and iron(III) is Fe^{3+}. The electron configuration for neutral iron is $[Ar]4s^23d^6$. Fe^{2+} has two fewer electrons, so its electron configuration is $[Ar]3d^6$. Fe^{3+} has three fewer electrons, so after losing the two 4*s* electrons, it loses one 3*d* electron, giving an energetically favorable half-filled subshell: $[Ar]3d^5$. The empty 4*s* subshell is omitted from the electron configurations of the ions.

PRACTICE PROBLEM 8.19

Write the electron configuration for the copper(I) and copper(II) ions.

Hint: Both copper ions will lose their outermost *s* electrons before losing any *d* electrons, but remember that copper was one of the elements with an anomalous electron configuration.

SECTION REVIEW

- Knowing the order in which subshells fill with electrons allows you to write an electron configuration for an atom of any element.
- The shape of the periodic table results from the electron configurations of the atoms, so an element's place in the periodic table can be used to help determine its electron configuration.
- Atoms in a given periodic group have similar outermost electron configurations. This is why their chemical properties are similar.
- Some elements in the *d* block and *f* block have anomalous electron configurations because shifting electrons from one subshell to another creates completely empty, completely filled, or exactly half-filled subshells that are more stable.
- Electron configurations for monoatomic ions are determined the same way they are for atoms, except that the number of electrons has to be adjusted (more for anions, less for cations) to account for the charge on the ion. Ions and atoms that have the same electron configurations are isoelectronic.

8.6 Quantum Numbers

GOAL

- Use the concept of quantum numbers to describe the general location and energy of each electron in an atom.

The electron configurations described in Section 8.5 identify which of an atom's shells and subshells have electrons and exactly how many electrons there are in each subshell. The energy-level diagrams introduced in Section 8.4 break the electron distribution down even further by showing how many electrons are in each individual orbital. Section 8.4 and Section 8.5 describe the arrangement of electrons in the atom, but the focus here in Section 8.6 turns from the arrangement of the electrons as a group to identifying any given electron within the arrangement.

Each of the electrons in an atom has four **quantum numbers** associated with it, which essentially provide an "address" for the electron. Given the four quantum numbers for an electron, you can tell exactly which shell, subshell, and orbital that electron is in (they give an acceptable solution to the Schrödinger wave equation and thus describe the region with the greatest probability of finding the electron), and in an orbital that contains two electrons, you can tell which of the two electrons it is. In the same way that a home mailing address includes a state or province, a city, a street name, and a house number, the four quantum numbers work together to identify one precise individual electron in the entire atom.

The first quantum number is called the **principal quantum number, n**. This represents the electron shell, just like the coefficients in the electron configuration, so the values of n are positive integers that start at 1. Although n can be any positive integer, the highest value of n is 7 in ground-state atoms of the 118 elements in the current periodic table. An electron with a principal quantum number $n = 1$ is in the 1*s* orbital of its atom; if $n = 2$, the electron is in the second energy level, so it is in a 2*s* or 2*p* subshell; if $n = 3$, the electron is in the 3*s*, 3*p*, or 3*d* subshell, and so on.

The type of subshell that the electron occupies is identified by the second quantum number, known as the **angular momentum quantum number, ℓ**. The value of ℓ ranges from 0 to $(n - 1)$, and each ℓ value corresponds to a particular subshell.

Value of ℓ	Subshell
0	*s*
1	*p*
2	*d*
3	*f*

Example 8.20

If the first two quantum numbers for an electron are $n = 3$ and $\ell = 2$, which energy level and subshell does that electron occupy?

Solution

The principal quantum number n is the energy level, and $\ell = 2$ corresponds to a *d* orbital, so $n = 3$ and $\ell = 2$ identifies an electron that is in the 3*d* subshell.

PRACTICE PROBLEM 8.20

Which quantum numbers, n and ℓ, are valid for the third energy level?

Hint: The energy level is indicated by the principal quantum number, n, and the subshell is indicated by ℓ. The ℓ values are integers that range from 0 to $(n - 1)$.

The allowed values of ℓ depend on the value of n. For example, the pair of quantum numbers $n = 2$ and $\ell = 3$ are invalid because $\ell = 3$ is outside the allowed range of 0 to $(n - 1)$ when $n = 2$. If it did exist, this combination would correspond to a 2*f* subshell, but there is no 2*f* subshell. The allowed values of ℓ for $n = 2$ are 0 and 1, which correspond to the 2*s* and 2*p* subshells, respectively.

The first two quantum numbers identify the energy level and subshell that the electron occupies, and the third quantum number, known as the **magnetic quantum number, m_ℓ**, identifies an individual orbital within the subshell where the electron is found. Each subshell is made up of a number of orbitals that are all of equal energy (Section 8.3). The *s* subshell is made up of a single *s* orbital, the *p* subshell is made up of three *p* orbitals, the *d* subshell is made up of five *d* orbitals, and the *f* subshell is made up of seven *f* orbitals. The magnetic quantum number can be any integer from $-\ell$ to $+\ell$, including 0. For example, if $\ell = 1$, indicating an electron in a *p* subshell, the allowed values for m_ℓ are -1, 0, and $+1$ (Figure 8.13(b)).

Example 8.21

Which subshell is indicated by $\ell = 2$, and what are the allowed m_ℓ values?

Solution

An angular momentum quantum number of $\ell = 2$ indicates that the electron is in a *d* subshell. The allowed m_ℓ values range from $-\ell$ to $+\ell$, or in this case, $-2, -1, 0, +1$, and $+2$, corresponding to the five *d* orbitals (Figure 8.12(c)).

PRACTICE PROBLEM 8.21

How many m_ℓ values are allowed for $\ell = 0$?

Hint: The m_ℓ values are integers that range from $-\ell$ to $+\ell$.

Example 8.22

If the first two quantum numbers for an electron are $n = 3$ and $\ell = 1$, which values for m_ℓ are possible, and which orbital does the electron occupy?

Solution

$n = 3$ means that the electron is in the third energy level. $\ell = 1$ means that the electron is in a *p* subshell.

EVERYDAY CONNECTION

Tickets to a concert or sporting event provide an everyday analogy to the Pauli exclusion principle. Each ticket has four variables that describe a precise date and seat location. No two tickets can have the exact same date, section number, row number, and seat number or there will be chaos and hurt feelings.

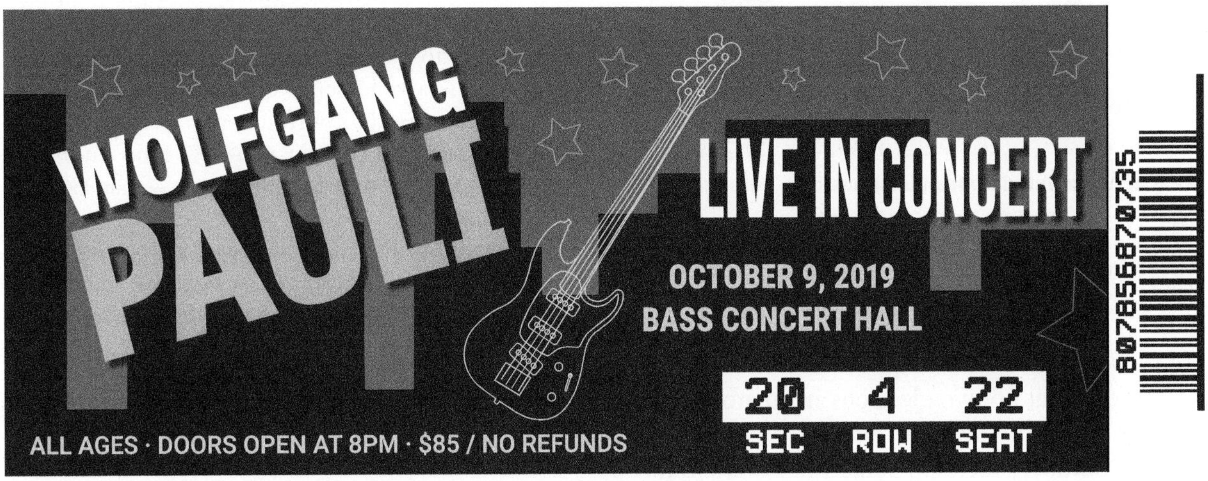

m_ℓ is an integer ranging from $-\ell$ to $+\ell$, so the allowed values are -1, 0, and $+1$.

The electron is in one of the three $3p$ orbitals.

PRACTICE PROBLEM 8.22

How many electrons in one atom can have the quantum numbers $n = 6$ and $\ell = 2$?

Hint: Quantum number n identifies the energy level; ℓ identifies the subshell.

Each orbital can hold a maximum of two electrons, and the fourth quantum number, called the **spin quantum number, m_s**, distinguishes between those two electrons based on something called quantum spin. The allowed values for m_s are $+\frac{1}{2}$ and $-\frac{1}{2}$ only, and these values do not depend on any other quantum numbers.

Electrons do not actually spin in the same sense that Earth rotates on its axis, but electrons exhibit magnetic properties related to their angular momentum that in some ways are analogous to those of a spinning electrical charge. The magnetic properties of two electrons that share the same orbital are always equal but opposite, so this is represented by assigning them m_s values of $+\frac{1}{2}$ and $-\frac{1}{2}$. (Fractional values, instead of integer values such as $+1$ and -1, are required to satisfy some advanced quantum mechanical mathematics that are beyond the scope of this course.)

The names of the quantum numbers, along with their symbols, allowed values, and what each quantum number represents, are summarized in Table 8.3.

The allowed values listed in Table 8.3 are not the only limitations placed on the quantum numbers of electrons in atoms. There is the **Pauli exclusion principle,**

TABLE 8.3 The Four Quantum Numbers

Name	Symbol	Allowed Values	Examples	Corresponds to
Principal quantum number	n	Any positive integer	1, 2, 3, ...	The energy level the electron occupies
Angular momentum quantum number	ℓ	Any integer from 0 to $(n-1)$	0, 1, ..., $(n-1)$	The type of subshell the electron occupies
Magnetic quantum number	m_ℓ	Any integer from $-\ell$ to $+\ell$	$-\ell$, ..., 0, ..., $+\ell$ For $\ell = 1$, $m_\ell = -1$, 0, or $+1$	The orbital the electron occupies
Spin quantum number	m_s	$-\frac{1}{2}$ or $+\frac{1}{2}$	$-\frac{1}{2}, +\frac{1}{2}$	The particular electron in a filled orbital

Steve Lemon, Macmillan Learning

FIGURE 8.22 Video Tutorial: Quantum Numbers

NOTE: You need to be online to access this video.

This video shows how to write sets of quantum numbers for each electron in a particular shell.

too, which states that no two electrons in an atom can have the same set of four quantum numbers.

Quantum numbers are also sometimes compared with a street address, where each U.S. state has only certain valid city names, and each city has only certain valid street names, and each street has only certain valid house numbers. All four of these bits of information must fall within the allowed values in order for an address to be valid.

The video in Figure 8.22 demonstrates how to write valid sets of quantum numbers for a given value of n.

Example 8.23

Determine whether each of the following sets of quantum numbers is valid or invalid. If the set of quantum numbers is valid, indicate which energy level and subshell the electron occupies. If it is invalid, explain why it is invalid.

	Quantum Numbers			
	n	ℓ	m_ℓ	m_s
(a)	1	0	0	0
(b)	2	0	0	$-\frac{1}{2}$
(c)	3	1	1	$+\frac{1}{2}$
(d)	4	3	-3	$+\frac{1}{2}$
(e)	3	-1	-1	$+\frac{1}{2}$

Solution

a. Invalid. The first three values are allowed for an electron in a 1*s* orbital, but $m_s = 0$ is invalid. The only values allowed for m_s are $+\frac{1}{2}$ and $-\frac{1}{2}$.

b. This is a valid set of quantum numbers for an electron in the second energy level ($n = 2$), in an *s* subshell ($\ell = 0$). $m_\ell = 0$ falls within the range of $-\ell$ to $+\ell$, and $m_s = -\frac{1}{2}$ is an allowed value.

c. This is a valid set of quantum numbers for an electron in the third energy level ($n = 3$), in a *p* subshell ($\ell = 1$). $m_\ell = 1$ falls within the range of $-\ell$ to $+\ell$, and $m_s = +\frac{1}{2}$ is an allowed value.

d. This is a valid set of quantum numbers for an electron in the fourth energy level ($n = 4$), in an *f* subshell ($\ell = 3$). $m_\ell = -3$ falls within the range of $-\ell$ to $+\ell$, and $m_s = +\frac{1}{2}$ is an allowed value.

e. Invalid. Allowed values for ℓ are positive integers from 0 to $(n - 1)$. A negative value of ℓ does not correspond to a specific subshell type.

PRACTICE PROBLEM 8.23

In each of the following sets of quantum numbers, one number is invalid. Indicate which one is invalid, and suggest an allowed replacement value for it.

	Quantum Numbers			
	n	ℓ	m_ℓ	m_s
(a)	3	-2	-2	$-\frac{1}{2}$
(b)	2	2	2	$-\frac{1}{2}$
(c)	1	0	-1	$+\frac{1}{2}$
(d)	0	0	0	$+\frac{1}{2}$
(e)	3	1	1	1

Hint: The allowed values for each quantum number are listed in Table 8.3. Start with n because allowed values for ℓ depend on n, and allowed values for m_ℓ depend on ℓ. The spin quantum number m_s can only be $+\frac{1}{2}$ or $-\frac{1}{2}$, regardless of the values of the other quantum numbers.

SECTION REVIEW

- Each electron in an atom can be identified by four quantum numbers, which describe its location in the atom.
- The principal quantum number n corresponds to which energy level the electron occupies.
- The angular momentum quantum number ℓ corresponds to which type of subshell the electron occupies.
- The magnetic quantum number m_ℓ corresponds to which orbital within the subshell the electron occupies.

- The magnetic spin quantum number m_s distinguishes between the two electrons in a filled orbital.
- According to the Pauli exclusion principle, no two electrons in an atom can have same four quantum numbers.

Putting It Together

The example problems in earlier sections of this chapter focus on just the new skills acquired in that section, but homework and exam questions in chemistry often require more than just one skill at a time. In fact, you will likely be expected to apply knowledge from across the entire chapter or even multiple chapters in a single problem. This final example problem is meant to help you prepare for these types of multiconcept questions. Additional examples can be found in the end-of-chapter exercises.

Example 8.24

a. Write the electron configuration for phosphorus, and then draw the corresponding energy-level diagram. What are the first two quantum numbers for the last electron that was added to the energy-level diagram?
b. An excited electron in a phosphorus atom falls back to the ground state, and a photon with an energy of 3.06×10^{-19} J is emitted. Calculate the frequency and wavelength of the photon. What color is the photon?

Solution

a. Phosphorus is atomic number 15, so a neutral phosphorus atom has 15 electrons. The order of the electron orbitals from lowest energy to highest energy is 1*s* 2*s* 2*p* 3*s* 3*p*. This can be determined using the periodic table or by following the arrows in Figure 8.18. Placing a maximum of two electrons in each *s* subshell and a maximum of six in each *p* subshell until you run out of electrons yields an electron configuration of $1s^22s^22p^63s^23p^3$. As a check, the total number of electrons is 15, and the last part of the electron configuration should indicate where phosphorus is located in the periodic table. Phosphorus is in the third energy level of the periodic table and is the third element in the *p* block.

The *s* subshells are each made up of a single *s* orbital, and the *p* subshells are made up of three degenerate *p* orbitals (Figure 8.13). Placing the electrons in these orbitals beginning at the bottom and working up (in accordance with the aufbau principle) and filling degenerate subshells with unpaired electrons that all have the same spin before pairing any of them up (in accordance with Hund's rule) yields the energy-level diagram that follows.

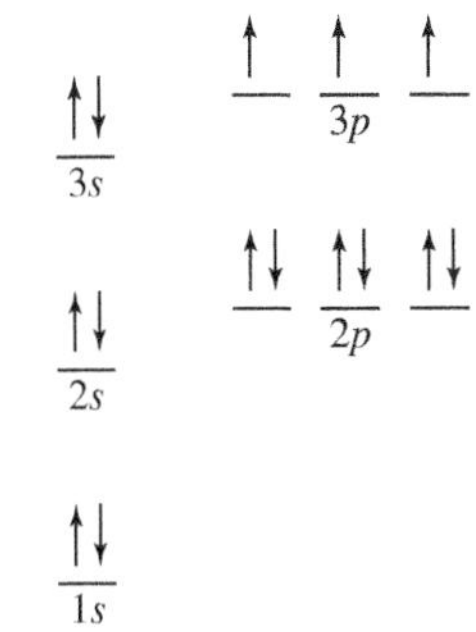

(The three unpaired electrons in the 3*p* subshell could all be spin up or all spin down. Both arrangements are correct. The electrons in the unfilled subshell must be unpaired as much as possible, however, and the unpaired electrons must all have the same spin.)

The last electron added is one of the 3*p* electrons. Since the 3*p* orbitals are all at the same energy, no distinction is made between them, and any one of them could have been the first, second, or third electron added to the 3*p* subshell. This electron is in the third energy level, in a *p* orbital. The first two quantum numbers for this electron are therefore $n = 3$ and $\ell = 1$.

b. The frequency of the electron can be calculated from its energy using $E = h\nu$ (Equation 8.2), and then the wavelength can be calculated from the frequency using $\nu\lambda = c$ (Equation 8.1). Review Figure 8.7 for a video demonstration of this calculation. The frequency and wavelength are calculated as

$$E = h\nu$$

$$\nu = \frac{E}{h} = \frac{3.06 \times 10^{-19}\ \text{J}}{6.626 \times 10^{-34}\ \text{J} \cdot \text{s}} = 4.62 \times 10^{14}\ \text{s}^{-1}$$

$$\nu\lambda = c$$

$$\lambda = \frac{c}{\nu} = \frac{2.998 \times 10^{8}\ \text{m/s}}{4.62 \times 10^{14}\ \text{s}^{-1}} = 6.49 \times 10^{-7}\ \text{m}$$

$$6.49 \times 10^{-7}\ \text{m} \times \frac{1 \times 10^{9}\ \text{nm}}{1\ \text{m}} = 649\ \text{nm}$$

Based on Figure 8.5, 649 nm is in the red portion of the visible spectrum, so this is a red photon.

PRACTICE PROBLEM 8.24

a. Write the electron configuration for iron, and then draw the corresponding energy-level diagram. What are the first two quantum numbers for the last electron that was added to the energy-level diagram?

b. An excited electron in an iron atom falls back to the ground state, and a photon with an energy of 4.54×10^{-19} J is emitted. Calculate the frequency and wavelength of the photon. What color is the photon?

Hint: The number of electrons in a neutral iron atom is equal to its atomic number. Use the periodic table as a guide or follow the arrows in Figure 8.18 to determine the order in which the subshells fill with electrons. The energy-level diagram starts with 1*s* on the bottom, and each subshell is drawn higher than the one before. Add the electrons to the energy-level diagram one at a time following the aufbau principle and Hund's rule.

The frequency of the electron can be calculated from its energy using $E = h\nu$ (Equation 8.2), and then the wavelength can be calculated using $\nu\lambda = c$ (Equation 8.1). The video in Figure 8.7 demonstrates these calculations. The color of the photon can be determined by converting the wavelength from meters to nanometers and consulting Figure 8.5.

Key Terms, Symbols, and Equations

KEY TERMS

absorbance spectrum (8.1): The specific wavelengths of light that are absorbed by an atom when it gains energy.

angular momentum quantum number, ℓ (8.6): The number that corresponds to a particular subshell within the atom.

aufbau principle (8.4): When filling the subshells of an atom with electrons, the electrons always fill the lowest-energy subshell available before any electrons are added to higher-energy subshells.

Bohr model (8.2): The first model of the atom to propose that electrons in atoms were in definite energy levels.

building-up principle (8.4): Another name for the aufbau principle.

core electron (8.5): An electron in an atom that is in a lower energy level than is a valence electron; any electron in an atom that is not a valence electron.

degenerate (8.4): Having the same energy.

discrete energy level (8.2): An atomic energy level that has specific energy.

electromagnetic radiation (8.1): A collective term for light of all wavelengths in the electromagnetic spectrum.

electromagnetic spectrum (8.1): The complete collection of electromagnetic waves, including visible light, infrared, ultraviolet, X-rays, gamma rays, and microwaves.

electron configuration (8.5): The arrangement of the electrons in the shells and subshells of an atom, or the shorthand notation used to represent this arrangement.

emission spectrum (8.2): The specific wavelengths of light that are emitted by an atom when it releases stored energy.

energy-level diagram (8.4): A diagram in which horizontal lines represent the orbitals of an atom, those with higher energies toward the top, in which arrows may be used to represent electrons.

excited state (8.2): The state of an atom that has more energy than does its lowest energy state.

frequency, ν (8.1): The number of times a wave crest passes a certain point per second.

ground state (8.2): The lowest energy state of the set of electrons in an atom.

Heisenberg uncertainty principle (8.2): The accuracies with which the position and the velocity of an electron can be measured are inversely related.

Hund's rule (8.4): The electrons in a partially filled subshell in an atom spread out to occupy the orbitals singly as much as possible.

isoelectronic (8.5): Having the same electron configuration.

light (8.1): In general, any electromagnetic radiation; specifically, visible light—the wave motion that is visible to the human eye.

light absorption (8.1): The process in which the energy of certain wavelengths of light increases the energy of electrons in atoms.

light emission (8.1): The process in which light of specific wavelengths is produced when electrons in atoms fall to lower energy levels.

line spectrum (8.2): The emission spectrum of an element when it appears as a series of discrete lines.

lobe (8.3): One portion of an atomic orbital.

magnetic quantum number, m_ℓ (8.6): The number that represents an individual orbital within a subshell.

orbit (8.2): As described by Bohr and later revised, the circular path for electrons in an atom, the most important characteristic of which is its energy.

orbital (8.3): A region of space in an atom that makes up part or all of a subshell and can hold a maximum of two electrons.

Pauli exclusion principle (8.6): No two electrons in the same atom can have the same four quantum numbers.

photoelectric effect (8.1): An experiment that demonstrates the particle nature of light.

photoelectron (8.1): An electron that is emitted from a surface as a result of an interaction between the surface and a photon.

photon (8.1): A particle of light.

principal energy level (8.3): Another term for an electron shell.

principal quantum number, n (8.6): The number that identifies the principal energy level in which the electron can be found.

quantum number (8.6): One of four numbers that is assigned to each electron in an atom that identifies the electron based on its location and energy.

Rydberg constant, R_H (8.2): A mathematical constant in the Rydberg equation.

Rydberg equation (8.2): An equation that predicts the wavelengths of all hydrogen atomic emission lines.

Schrödinger wave equation (8.3): A mathematical formula that produces a distribution map for the probable position of an electron in an atom.

shell (8.3): A set of energy levels for electrons in an atom, made up of one or more subshells.

spin quantum number, m_s (8.6): The number that represents the two allowed spin angular momentum states of an electron, commonly referred to as "spin up" or "spin down" and assigned values of either $+\frac{1}{2}$ or $-\frac{1}{2}$, respectively.

subshell (8.3): The portion of a shell characterized by the same energy level and the same orbital type (*s*, *p*, *d*, or *f*).

threshold frequency (8.1): The minimum frequency of light required to eject an electron from the surface of a metal in the photoelectric effect.

valence electron (8.5): An electron in the highest occupied shell (principal quantum number *n*) of an atom or ion. A valence electron is an electron that takes part in chemical reactions and chemical bonding.

visible light (8.1): The narrow range of the electromagnetic spectrum that can be detected by the human eye. Visible light corresponds to a wavelength range of approximately 400 nm to 750 nm.

wavelength, λ (8.1): The length of a single wave, measured from one crest to the next or one trough to the next or any point to the next corresponding point.

work function, Φ (8.1): The minimum amount of energy required to eject an electron from the surface of a material in a vacuum.

SYMBOLS AND ABBREVIATIONS

c (speed of light) (8.1)

d (a type of subshell) (8.3)

E (energy) (8.1)

f (a type of subshell) (8.3)

h (Planck's constant) (8.1)

λ (*lambda*, wavelength) (8.1)

ν (*nu*, frequency) (8.1)

p (a type of subshell) (8.3)

R_H (Rydberg constant, $1.097 \times 10^7\ m^{-1}$ or 2.179×10^{-18} J) (8.2)

s (a type of subshell) (8.3)

EQUATIONS

$\nu\lambda = c$ (8.1)

$E = h\nu$ (8.2)

$h\nu = \Phi$ (8.3)

$\frac{hc}{\lambda} = \Phi$ (8.4)

$KE = h\nu - \Phi$ (8.5)

$\frac{1}{\lambda} = (1.097 \times 10^7\ m^{-1})\left(\frac{1}{n_1^2} - \frac{1}{n_2^2}\right)$ (8.6)

$E = (2.179 \times 10^{-18}\ J)\left(\frac{1}{n_1^2} - \frac{1}{n_2^2}\right)$ (8.7)

Chapter Summary

The chemical properties of elements, and many of their physical properties as well, depend on the arrangement of electrons around the nucleus. The number of electrons in a neutral atom is equal to the number of protons in the nucleus and, therefore, is equal to the atomic number of the element.

Light, also called electromagnetic radiation, is a form of energy that has properties of both wave motion and a stream of particles. Particles of light are called photons. Light energy can be absorbed by atoms, and energy can also be released by atoms in the form of light. Atoms absorb or emit light only at specific wavelengths that are characteristic of that element. The wavelength of light (as a wave) is inversely proportional to the energy of its photons, or particles. Wavelength is also inversely proportional to frequency. All electromagnetic radiation travels at the speed of light. If a photon's energy, frequency, or wavelength is known, the other two can be calculated. In the photoelectric effect, photons with sufficient energy are able to eject electrons from a metal surface (Section 8.1).

Bohr first proposed the concept that electrons orbit the nucleus in discrete energy levels in the atom, which explained the emission of specific energies of light when gaseous atoms are heated. Although Bohr's theory could not explain many other details of the behavior of atoms, it was a milestone in relating electronic structure and the properties of atoms. Bohr's energy level model also helped explain why the Rydberg equation was able to successfully predict the wavelengths of the lines in the hydrogen emission spectrum (Section 8.2).

Schrödinger proposed a new model of the atom that replaced the orbits of the Bohr model with three-dimensional regions in space called orbitals. There are four different types of orbitals, designated *s*, *p*, *d*, and *f*. Orbitals of any kind can hold a maximum of two electrons. Electrons can be found anywhere within the three-dimensional region of the orbital. Together, a group of degenerate (same-energy) orbitals makes up a subshell, and one or more subshells make up an electron shell. This model of shells, subshells, and orbitals makes it possible to determine the arrangement of electrons in an atom, known as its electron configuration. The arrangement of the outermost electrons (the valence electrons) in an atom in particular is what gives each element its characteristic properties. The electron configuration of an element can usually be determined from its location in the periodic table, although there are exceptions for some transition elements, some lanthanides, and some actinides. Each type of orbital type has a distinct shape. Orbitals in the lower-energy electron shells are smaller, and the same type of orbital in a higher-energy electron shell has the same shape but includes a larger area of space within the atom. The region of space included in an orbital can overlap with the region of space included in another orbital (Section 8.3).

Energy-level diagrams portray how individual electrons occupy the orbitals in an atom. These diagrams are useful for visually representing the distribution of electrons within the orbitals of an atom, and this can help in understanding chemical properties of the elements. In an energy-level diagram, each orbital is represented by a short horizontal line. Higher-energy orbitals are written higher up than are lower-energy orbitals, and all orbitals that make up a single subshell have the same energy and are written at the same level. Electrons are represented in energy-level diagrams as short vertical arrows pointing either up or down. Since each orbital can hold zero, one, or two electrons, each horizontal line can have zero, one, or two vertical arrows on it. If a line representing an orbital has two arrows, they must point in opposite directions to reflect the opposite spins of paired electrons. Hund's rule states that, in partially filled subshells, the electrons occupy orbitals singly as much as possible, and all of the unpaired electrons in the same subshell have the same spin (Section 8.4).

The distribution of an atom's electrons in its shells and subshells is represented using a notation called an electron configuration. In an electron configuration, shells are written as coefficients in front of the subshell type, and the number of electrons in that subshell is written as a superscript on the subshell. For example, the element sulfur ($Z = 16$) has 16 electrons, and the arrangement of these electrons is represented by the electron configuration $1s^22s^22p^63s^23p^4$. The final part of the electron configuration indicates where the element is located in the periodic table. That is, sulfur is the fourth element in the $3p$ block of the periodic table. The individual orbitals that make up a subshell are not explicitly represented in an electron configuration (Section 8.5).

Individual electrons within an atom can be distinguished by their quantum numbers, which are a set of four numbers that serves as a unique "address" for each electron. The principal quantum number, n, is the energy level that the electron occupies. For ground-state elements in the current periodic table, n is an integer from 1 to 7. The angular momentum quantum number, ℓ, indicates which type of subshell the electron occupies, and it has integer values ranging from 0 to $(n - 1)$. The magnetic quantum number, m_ℓ, indicates which orbital the electron occupies within that subshell, and it has integer values ranging from $-\ell$ to $+\ell$, including 0. The spin quantum number, m_s, is either $+\frac{1}{2}$ or $-\frac{1}{2}$, indicating either a spin "up" or spin "down" orientation, respectively, in the energy-level diagram. According to the Pauli exclusion principle, no two electrons in an atom can have the same set of four quantum numbers (Section 8.6).

END OF CHAPTER QUESTIONS

8.1 A Brief Exploration of Light

1. What is the frequency of an athlete running around a track 12 times in an hour?

2. What difference in meaning is there, if any, when the instructor states, "The first line in the visible spectrum of hydrogen has a definite
   a. wavelength."
   b. frequency."
   c. energy of its photons."

3. Calculate the frequency of a photon of light with a wavelength 6.563×10^{-7} m, corresponding to a line in the visible spectrum of hydrogen.

4. Use the equation $E = hc/\lambda$ with the units E in joules, c in meters per second, and λ in meters, to determine the units of h.

5. Calculate the wavelength of a photon of light with energy 4.09×10^{-19} J, corresponding to a line in the visible spectrum of hydrogen.

6. Consult Figure 8.4 and answer the following questions:
   a. Which type of electromagnetic radiation has the highest energy?
   b. Which type of electromagnetic radiation has the lowest energy?
   c. Which color of visible light has the highest energy?

7. Calculate the frequency and wavelength of a 4.85×10^{-19} J photon, corresponding to a line in the visible spectrum of hydrogen.

8. Calculate the energy of a photon of light with a wavelength 4.340×10^{-7} m, corresponding to a line in the visible spectrum of hydrogen.

9. The frequency of a certain beam of light is 7.00×10^{11}/s. Calculate the wavelength and the energy of its photons.

10. The frequency of a certain beam of light is 4.95×10^{16}/s. Calculate the energy of one mole of its photons.

11. Describe how these observed phenomena of light support the wave–particle duality of light.
    a. line spectra of elements
    b. photoelectric effect

8.2 The Bohr Model of the Atom

12. Describe qualitatively the relationship between energy and the electron transitions occurring in the neon gas in a neon sign.

13. List the possible series of electron transitions for an electron descending from the sixth shell to the third in a hydrogen atom.

14. How many different wavelengths of light would be emitted if many identical atoms underwent the changes described in the prior problem?

15. List the possible series of electron transitions for an electron descending from the fourth shell to the first in a hydrogen atom.

16. How many photons of light are emitted when an electron falls from
 a. the fourth energy level to the first in a hydrogen atom?
 b. the fourth energy level to the third and then to the first energy level?
 c. Compare the total energy released in parts (a) and (b).

17. Use the Rydberg equation to determine the
 a. energy difference between the fourth and first energy levels of the hydrogen atom.
 b. wavelength of the photon released by the transition of an electron from the fourth to the first energy level.
 c. section of the electromagnetic spectrum that this photon represents (see Figure 8.4).

18. Use the Rydberg equation to determine the
 a. energy difference between the fourth and second energy levels of the hydrogen atom.
 b. wavelength of the photon released by the transition of an electron from the fourth to the second energy level.
 c. section of the electromagnetic spectrum that this photon represents (see Figure 8.4).

19. Use the Rydberg equation to determine the
 a. energy difference between the first and third energy levels.
 b. wavelength of the photon absorbed by the transition of an electron from the first to the third energy level.
 c. section of the electromagnetic spectrum that this photon represents (see Figure 8.4).

20. Use the Rydberg equation to determine the
 a. energy difference between the second and fifth energy levels.
 b. wavelength of the photon absorbed by the transition of an electron from the second to the fifth energy level.
 c. section of the electromagnetic spectrum that this photon represents (see Figure 8.4).

21. Sodium metal has a work function of 3.78×10^{-19} J. Does light of 585 nm have sufficient energy to trigger the photoelectric effect of sodium?

22. Lithium metal has a work function of 4.65×10^{-19} s^{-1}.
 a. Does light of 585 nm have sufficient energy to trigger the photoelectric effect of lithium?
 b. Calculate the maximum possible kinetic energy of electrons emitted from lithium irradiated with 585 nm light.

23. Molybdenum metal undergoes the photoelectric effect when irradiated with light with a minimum frequency of 1.09×10^{15} s^{-1}.
 a. Calculate the minimum energy of a photon needed to eject an electron from the surface of molybdenum.
 b. What wavelength of light does this correspond to?

24. Molybdenum metal is irradiated with light of 120 nm wavelength. What is the maximum possible kinetic energy of the emitted electrons? (Refer to the previous problem.)

25. Describe the Bohr model in terms of its
 a. historical importance.
 b. limitations.

8.3 Electron Shells, Subshells, and Orbitals

26. Give definitions for the terms *shell*, *subshell*, and *orbital*.

27. Describe how the terms *shell* and *subshell* relate to energy levels.

28. How does the term *orbital* relate to the terms *subshell*, *shell*, and *energy level*?

29. Describe the shape and orientation of
 a. *s* orbitals.
 b. *p* orbitals.
 c. *d* orbitals.

30. How many electrons are permitted
 a. in a *d* orbital?
 b. in a *d* subshell?

31. How many orbitals are there in the
 a. 2*p* subshell?
 b. 3*p* subshell?
 c. 4*p* subshell?

32. Identify the orbital:
    a. 2 lobes aligned along the coordinate axes, 3 per subshell
    b. spherical, only 1 per subshell
    c. multiple lobes, 5 per subshell

33. What is the maximum number of electrons permitted in a 5*p* subshell?

34. How many 2*p* orbitals are present in any atom?

35. What is the maximum number of electrons in the 3*d* subshell?

36. According to Figure 8.14, which two 3*d* orbitals cannot have an electron in the *xz*-plane?

37. According to Figure 8.14, which 2*p* orbital cannot have an electron in the *xz*-plane?

38. How many *d* orbitals are pictured in Figure 8.14?

39. How many of the *p* orbitals pictured in Figure 8.14 are oriented along an axis?

40. How many of the *d* orbitals pictured in Figure 8.14 are oriented along axes?

8.4 Energy-Level Diagrams

41. Give definitions for these terms and explain how these relate to drawing energy-level diagrams:
    a. ground state
    b. excited state
    c. aufbau principle
    d. Hund's rule

42. Explain why there are no electrons present in *p* orbitals in a ground-state atom of beryllium.

43. How many electrons are present in the 2*p* subshell of a fluorine atom?

44. Explain why the 2*p* subshell is not full in the fluorine atom.

45. What is the maximum number of *unpaired* electrons in the following?
    a. an *s* subshell
    b. a *p* subshell
    c. a *d* subshell
    d. an *f* subshell

46. How many unpaired electrons are present in the ground state of an atom if six electrons are present in each of the following subshells? There are no other unpaired electrons.
    a. 4*p* subshell
    b. *d* subshell
    c. 5*f* subshell

47. Draw an energy-level diagram, and determine the number of unpaired electrons in an atom of each of the following.
    a. B
    b. O

48. Draw an energy-level diagram, and determine the number of unpaired electrons in an atom of each of the following.
    a. Ne
    b. Si

49. How many unpaired electrons are in an atom in the ground state, assuming that all other subshells are either completely full or empty, if its outermost *p* subshell contains the following?
    a. three electrons
    b. five electrons
    c. four electrons

50. Draw an energy-level diagram for the cobalt atom.

51. How many unpaired electrons are in an atom in the ground state, assuming that all other subshells are either completely full or empty, if its outermost *d* subshell contains the following?
    a. four electrons
    b. six electrons
    c. seven electrons

8.5 Electron Configurations

52. How many electrons are present in each of the following atoms? Assuming that each is a neutral atom, identify the element.
    a. $1s^2\ 2s^2\ 2p^6\ 3s^2\ 3p^1$
    b. $1s^2\ 2s^2\ 2p^6\ 3s^2\ 3p^6\ 4s^2\ 3d^1$
    c. $1s^2\ 2s^2\ 2p^6\ 3s^2\ 3p^6\ 4s^2\ 3d^{10}\ 4p^6$

53. Use the periodic table to determine how many electrons can fit into any of the following.
    a. *s* subshell
    b. *p* subshell
    c. *d* subshell
    d. *f* subshell

54. Answer the following questions.
    a. How many electrons can be added to an atom before the start of the second shell?
    b. How many elements are in the periodic table before the start of the second period?

55. Answer the following questions.
    a. How many electrons can be added to an atom before the start of the third shell?
    b. How many elements are in the periodic table before the start of the third period?

56. Answer the following questions.
  a. How many electrons can be added to an atom before the start of the fourth shell?
  b. How many elements are in the periodic table before the start of the fourth period?

57. Locate the following in the periodic table.
  a. the element that has the first 3*d* electron
  b. the element that is the first to complete its 2*s* subshell

58. Write detailed electron configurations for the following.
  a. Li
  b. C
  c. Mg

59. Write detailed electron configurations for the following.
  a. Be
  b. Mg
  c. Ca
  d. Sr

60. Write detailed electron configurations for the following.
  a. As
  b. Ar
  c. Al
  d. V
  e. Ni

61. Write detailed electron configurations of the following.
  a. Ge
  b. Mn
  c. N
  d. Br
  e. Fe

62. Write detailed electron configurations for the following.
  a. O
  b. S
  c. Se
  d. Te

63. Determine the abbreviated configuration for Po.

64. Use the periodic table to write abbreviated electron configurations for each of the following elements.
  a. Tl
  b. La
  c. Gd

65. Use the periodic table to write abbreviated electron configurations for the following elements.
  a. Pb
  b. Fr
  c. Lu
  d. Pt

66. Use the periodic table to write abbreviated electron configurations for the following elements.
  a. Hf (element 72)
  b. U
  c. Ba

67. Write abbreviated electron configurations for the following.
  a. Os
  b. Hf
  c. Ce

68. Complete the following table.

	Symbol	Atomic Number	No. of Protons	No. of Electrons	Net Charge
(a)	Cl^-				
(b)		16		18	
(c)			19	18	
(d)		26			+3
(e)			78		+2

69. Complete the following table.

	Symbol	Atomic Number	No. of Protons	No. of Electrons	Net Charge
(a)	Zn^{2+}				
(b)		13			+3
(c)			9	10	
(d)			34		−2
(e)			39	36	

70. Write a detailed electron configuration for each of the following ions.
  a. Na^+
  b. Al^{3+}
  c. Zn^{2+}

71. Write a detailed electron configuration for each of the following ions.
  a. N^{3-}
  b. S^{2-}
  c. Cl^-

72. Write a detailed electron configuration for each of the following ions.
   a. Co^{2+}
   b. Cr^{3+}
   c. Cu^{2+}

8.6 Quantum Numbers

73. What values of ℓ are permitted for an electron with $n = 4$?

74. What values of m_ℓ are permitted for an electron with $\ell = 3$?

75. What values of m_s are permitted for an electron with $n = 5$, $\ell = 3$, and $m_\ell = +2$?

76. Which of the following sets of quantum numbers is (are) *not* permitted?
   a. $n = 3, \ell = 0, m_\ell = +1, m_s = -\frac{1}{2}$
   b. $n = 3, \ell = 2, m_\ell = -1, m_s = -1$
   c. $n = 3, \ell = -2, m_\ell = 0, m_s = -\frac{1}{2}$
   d. $N = 3, \ell = 3, m_\ell = -2, m_s = +\frac{1}{2}$

77. Make a chart showing all possible values of ℓ, m_ℓ, and m_s for an electron with
   a. $n = 2$.
   b. $n = 3$.

78. What values of m_ℓ are permitted for an electron with $\ell = 4$?

79. How many different values of m_ℓ are permitted for an electron with $\ell = 5$?

80. Arrange the following electrons, identified only by their n and ℓ quantum numbers, in order of increasing energy from lowest to highest. Hint: See Figure 8.16.
   a. $n = 6, \ell = 3$
   b. $n = 6, \ell = 2$
   c. $n = 5, \ell = 3$
   d. $n = 5, \ell = 2$

81. Arrange the following electrons in order of increasing energy. Hint: See Figure 8.16.
   a. $n = 5, \ell = 1$
   b. $n = 4, \ell = 2$
   c. $n = 4, \ell = 3$
   d. $n = 6, \ell = 0$

82. Write a set of four quantum numbers for each electron in the 4*p* subshell.

83. Identify a set of four quantum numbers for each of the valence electrons in a calcium, Ca, atom.

84. Arrange the following four electrons in order of increasing energy. Hint: See Figure 8.16.
   a. $n = 4, \ell = 0, m_\ell = 0, m_s = -\frac{1}{2}$
   b. $n = 3, \ell = 1, m_\ell = -1, m_s = +\frac{1}{2}$
   c. $n = 3, \ell = 2, m_\ell = 0, m_s = -\frac{1}{2}$
   d. $n = 4, \ell = 1, m_\ell = +1, m_s = -\frac{1}{2}$

85. In a given atom, what is the maximum number of electrons that can have the following quantum numbers?
   a. $n = 5, \ell = 2$
   b. $n = 4, \ell = 3$
   c. $n = 3, \ell = 0$
   d. $n = 4, \ell = 1, m_\ell = -1$

86. Consider the quantum number $\ell = 3$.
   a. What is the letter designation for $\ell = 3$?
   b. How many different m_ℓ values are possible for an electron in a subshell for which $\ell = 3$?
   c. How many different orbitals are in an $\ell = 3$ subshell?
   d. What is the maximum number of electrons in an $\ell = 3$ subshell?

Putting It Together

87. What does the number of ℓ values permitted for a given n value have to do with the number of subshells in a shell?

88. What does the number of m_ℓ values permitted for a given ℓ value have to do with the number of orbitals in a subshell?

89. Explain why the helium atom is totally unreactive with only two electrons in its outermost shell, but beryllium is not.

90. Using the periodic table, the $n + \ell$ rule, or other rules or memory devices for determining the electron configurations of atoms, the electron configuration of copper would seem to be $1s^2\,2s^2\,2p^6\,3s^2\,3p^6\,4s^2\,3d^9$. But the actual electron configuration is $1s^2\,2s^2\,2p^6\,3s^2\,3p^6\,4s^1\,3d^{10}$. Starting with *each* of these configurations, deduce the electron configuration of Cu^{2+} and compare the results.

91. Write the abbreviated electron configuration of lead.

92. In this chapter you learned that the Bohr model, while useful, has been replaced. Explain why *any* hypothesis might be rejected.

93. Identify the element from each of the following *partial* configurations of neutral atoms.
   a. $4s^2\,3d^5$
   b. $5s^2\,4d^{10}\,5p^4$
   c. $6p^3$
   d. $5s^1$
   e. $3d^{10}\,4p^5$

94. Consider all the possible transitions when electrons in hydrogen atoms descend from the fifth shell to the second shell.
   a. List the possible transitions.
   b. Use the Rydberg equation to calculate the energies of these transitions.

95. Work function values are commonly given in units of eV, electron volts. $1\text{eV} = 1.602 \times 10^{-19}$ J. Convert the following work function values to J.
   a. Cs: 2.14 eV
   b. Ag: 4.26 eV
   c. Cu: 4.65 eV

96. Using the work function values from the previous problem, calculate the minimum energy required to eject an electron from
   a. cesium metal.
   b. silver metal.
   c. copper metal.

97. Calculate the minimum kinetic energy of an electron emitted upon irradiation of ultraviolet light of 275 nm of
   a. cesium metal.
   b. silver metal.
   c. copper metal.

98. In which type of orbital (*s, p, d,* or *f*) would you find the outermost electron in each of the following types of elements?
   a. a nonmetal
   b. a transition element
   c. an inner transition element
   d. a main group metal (two answers)

99. The orange line in the hydrogen spectrum (Figure 8.10) is the change of the electron from the third orbit to the second; the green line is the change from the fourth orbit to the second; the two violet lines are the changes from the fifth and sixth orbits to the second, respectively. Use the information given in this problem to deduce which color represents the most energy, and which represents the least. Is wavelength directly proportional to energy?

100. Can you identify the following element from its *inner* electron configuration? $1s^2\,2s^2$ ... Explain.

101. In answering the question, "What is the maximum value for ℓ for any electron in the ground state of Lr, element 103?," several students gave the following answers and reasoning. Which one is correct?
   a. The maximum $\ell = 6$ because the outermost shell has $n = 7$ and ℓ cannot be more than $n - 1$.
   b. The maximum $\ell = 3$ because the *f* subshell has an ℓ value of 3, and there is no subshell with a bigger ℓ value in Lr.
   c. The maximum $\ell = 1$ because the outermost shell cannot have more than 8 electrons, and $\ell = 1$ is the maximum ℓ for a filled octet.

102. Does an electron gain or lose energy in each of the following transitions?
   a. from a 5*f* subshell to a 4*d* subshell
   b. from a 5*s* subshell to a 4*p* subshell
   c. from a 6*p* subshell to a 5*d* subshell

103. What is the maximum number of *unpaired* electrons in the following?
   a. the 3*d* subshell of an atom
   b. the 4*f* subshell of an atom

104. What is wrong with each of the following ground-state configurations?
   a. $1s^2\,1p^6\,2s^2\,2p^3$
   b. $1s^1\,2s^2\,2p^4$
   c. $1s^2\,2p^6\,3d^{10}\,4f^{14}$
   d. $1s^2\,2s^2\,2p^4\,3s^2\,3p^6$
   e. $[\text{Xe}]\,6s^2\,4f^{15}\,5d^{10}$

105. What is wrong with each of the following ground-state configurations?
   a. $1s^2\,2s^2\,2p^6\,3s^2\,3p^6\,4s^2\,3d^{14}$
   b. $1s^2\,2s^4\,2p^6\,3s^2$
   c. $1s^2\,2s^2\,2p^6\,2d^{10}$
   d. $1s^2\,2s^2\,2p^6\,3s^2\,3p^6\,4s^2\,4d^{10}\,4p^3$

106. Which of the following configurations are *not* permitted for an atom in its ground state?
   a. $1s^2\,2s^2\,2p^2$
   b. $1s^2\,2s^2$
   c. $1s^6\,2s^6\,2p^6$
   d. $1s^1\,2s^1$

107. How many unpaired electrons are present in the ground state of an atom if there are five electrons in each of the following subshells? There are no other unpaired electrons.
   a. 3*p* subshell
   b. 3*d* subshell
   c. 4*f* subshell

108. Give the symbols for following atoms or ions that all share the electron configuration $1s^22s^22p^63s^23p^6$.
   a. a 2^- ion
   b. a neutral atom
   c. a 2^+ ion

109. Write the expected electron configuration for each of the following.
   a. Cr
   b. Cu

110. Calculate the energy of the first line of the hydrogen spectrum. Its wavelength (λ) is 410 nm.

111. Figure 8.19 shows that the organization of the periodic table is based on the electron configurations of the atoms. Explain how Mendeleev was able to create the periodic table without knowing about the electron at all.

112. What is the maximum number of unpaired electrons in the ground state of an atom in which only the 1*s*, 2*s*, 2*p*, 3*s*, and 3*p* subshells have any electrons?

113. Which one(s) of the following sets of quantum numbers is (are) *not* permitted?
   a. $n = 4, \ell = 3, m_\ell = 2, m_s = -\frac{1}{2}$
   b. $n = 4, \ell = 2, m_\ell = -3, m_s = +\frac{1}{2}$
   c. $n = 2, \ell = 1, m_\ell = 1, m_s = -\frac{1}{2}$
   d. $n = 2, \ell = 2, m_\ell = 1, m_s = +\frac{1}{2}$
   e. $n = 3, \ell = 1, m_\ell = 1, m_s = -1$

114. Which metal in each of the following sets has the most unpaired electrons and would therefore be drawn most strongly into a magnetic field?
   a. Zn Mn V
   b. Ca Cu Cd
   c. Sc Cu V
   d. Ti Tl Ga

115. Draw an energy-level diagram for iodine.
   a. Can you use this same diagram for sodium simply by removing some electrons?
   b. Explain why one large energy-level diagram is sufficient for all the elements.

116. Based on the electron configuration shown in the table below, would an atom with the actual configuration of the chromium atom or the expected configuration be drawn more strongly into a magnetic field?

Element	Expected Configuration	Actual Configuration
Chromium, Cr	$1s^2\,2s^2\,2p^e\,3s^2\,3p^6\,4s^2\,3d^4$	$1s^2\,2s^2\,2p^e\,3s^2\,3p^6\,4s^1\,3d^5$
Copper, Cu	$1s^2\,2s^2\,2p^e\,3s^2\,3p^6\,4s^2\,3d^9$	$1s^2\,2s^2\,2p^e\,3s^2\,3p^6\,4s^1\,3d^{10}$

PRACTICE PROBLEM SOLUTIONS

Practice Problem 8.1 Solution

First, convert the wavelength from nanometers to meters.

$$511\text{ nm} \times \frac{1\text{ m}}{1 \times 10^9\text{ nm}} = 5.11 \times 10^{-7}\text{ m}$$

Then use Equation 8.1.

$$\nu\lambda = c$$

$$\nu = \frac{c}{\lambda} = \frac{2.998 \times 10^8\text{ m/s}}{5.11 \times 10^{-7}\text{ m}} = 5.87 \times 10^{14}\text{ s}^{-1}$$

Practice Problem 8.2 Solution

In each case the product of frequency, ν, times wavelength, λ, is the speed of light, *c*, 3×10^8 m/s.

Electromagnetic Radiation Type	Wavelength (m)	Frequency (s^{-1})	$\nu \times \lambda$ (m/s)
Radio waves	10^3	3×10^5	3×10^8
Microwaves	10^{-2}	3×10^{10}	3×10^8
Infrared light	10^{-5}	3×10^{13}	3×10^8
Visible light (lower)	4.0×10^{-7}	7.5×10^{14}	3.0×10^8
Visible light (upper)	7.5×10^{-7}	4.0×10^{14}	3.0×10^8
Ultraviolet light	10^{-8}	3×10^{16}	3×10^8
X-rays	10^{-10}	3×10^{18}	3×10^8
Gamma rays	10^{-12}	3×10^{20}	3×10^8

For visible light, the shortest wavelength (4.0×10^{-7} m) corresponds to the highest frequency ($7.5 \times 10^{14}\ s^{-1}$), whereas the longest wavelength (7.5×10^{-7} m) corresponds to the lowest frequency ($4.0 \times 10^{14}\ s^{-1}$). Both products come out to 3.0×10^8 m/s.

Practice Problem 8.3 Solution

a. Since wavelength and frequency are inversely proportional, a shorter wavelength corresponds to a higher frequency. Therefore, the line at 495 nm represents light that has a higher frequency than does the line at 590 nm.

b. Energy is directly proportional to frequency, so the line that represents a higher frequency correlates to a higher energy. The 495 nm line has a higher frequency than does the 590 nm line, so it correlates to higher energy light.

Practice Problem 8.4 Solution

a. According to Equation 8.2, $E = h\nu$, the energy and the frequency of a photon are directly related. Thus, doubling the frequency of this photon should double its energy, too. You can verify this by calculating the energy of this photon and comparing it with the one in Example 8.4.

$$E = h\nu = (6.626 \times 10^{-34}\ \text{J} \cdot \text{s})(1.50 \times 10^{15}\ \text{s}^{-1}) = 9.94 \times 10^{-19}\ \text{J}$$

$$\frac{\text{Energy of this photon}}{\text{Energy of Example 8.4 photon}} = \frac{9.94 \times 10^{-19}\ \text{J}}{4.97 \times 10^{-19}\ \text{J}} = 2.00$$

b. Since the energy of one photon is double the energy of the other, the total energy of two of the lower-energy photons will equal the energy of one of the higher-energy photons.

Practice Problem 8.5 Solution

First, calculate ν from E using Equation 8.2.

$$E = h\nu$$

$$\nu = \frac{E}{h} = \frac{4.01 \times 10^{-19}\ \text{J}}{6.626 \times 10^{-34}\ \text{J} \cdot \text{s}} = 6.05 \times 10^{14}\ \text{s}^{-1}$$

Then calculate λ from ν using Equation 8.1.

$$\nu\lambda = c$$

$$\lambda = \frac{c}{\nu} = \frac{2.998 \times 10^8\ \text{m/s}}{6.05 \times 10^{14}\ \text{s}^{-1}} = 4.96 \times 10^{-7}\ \text{m}$$

$$4.96 \times 10^{-7}\ \text{m} \times \frac{1 \times 10^9\ \text{nm}}{1\ \text{m}} = 496\ \text{nm}$$

Based on Figure 8.5, 496 nm is in the green to blue-green portion of the visible spectrum.

Practice Problem 8.6 Solution

The energy of the photon can be calculated from its wavelength by combining Equation 8.1, $\nu = \frac{c}{\lambda}$, and Equation 8.2, $E = h\nu$, as $E = \frac{hc}{\lambda}$, which yields

$$E = \frac{hc}{\lambda} = \frac{(6.626 \times 10^{-34}\ \text{J} \cdot \text{s})(2.998 \times 10^8\ \text{m/s})}{4.05 \times 10^{-7}\ \text{m}} = 4.91 \times 10^{-19}\ \text{J}$$

The energy of this photon is greater than the work function of lithium, so an electron will be ejected.

Practice Problem 8.7 Solution

Combining Equation 8.1, $\nu = \frac{c}{\lambda}$, with Equation 8.2, $E = h\nu$, yields $E = \frac{hc}{\lambda}$.

$$E = \frac{hc}{\lambda} = \frac{(6.626 \times 10^{-34}\ \text{J} \cdot \text{s})(2.998 \times 10^8\ \text{m/s})}{4.72 \times 10^{-7}\ \text{m}} = 4.21 \times 10^{-19}\ \text{J}$$

This is the same wavelength of photon used in Example 8.5, so the calculation produces the same resulting energy as that in the example problem. Again, this energy is equal to the energy of the photon, $h\nu$, which is then used to calculate the kinetic energy of the electron using Equation 8.5 and the work function for potassium.

$$KE = h\nu - \Phi = 4.21 \times 10^{-19}\ \text{J} - 3.67 \times 10^{-19}\ \text{J} = 5.4 \times 10^{-20}\ \text{J}$$

When identical photons are impacted onto surfaces of strontium and potassium in a vacuum, the kinetic energy of the photoelectron from potassium is almost nine times greater than that of the photoelectron from strontium. This is because strontium has a higher work function, so a greater portion of the photon's energy goes into freeing the electron from the surface, leaving less excess energy to become kinetic energy in the ejected photoelectron.

Practice Problem 8.8 Solution

The difference in energy between the third energy level and the first one is the same whether the electron falls in one step or in two. Therefore, the energy of the photon given off when the transition is made in one step is equal to the sum of the energies of the two photons given off when the transition is done in two steps.

Practice Problem 8.9 Solution

Use the Rydberg equation with $R_H = 1.097 \times 10^7\ \text{m}^{-1}$ (Equation 8.6) and with $n_2 = 4$ and $n_1 = 2$.

$$\frac{1}{\lambda} = R_H\left(\frac{1}{n_1^2} - \frac{1}{n_2^2}\right)$$

$$\frac{1}{\lambda} = (1.097 \times 10^7\text{m}^{-1})\left(\frac{1}{2^2} - \frac{1}{4^2}\right) = 2.057 \times 10^6\ \text{m}^{-1}$$

$$\lambda = \frac{1}{2.057 \times 10^6\ \text{m}^{-1}} = 4.861 \times 10^{-7}\ \text{m}$$

To compare this wavelength with the visible spectrum range, convert it to nanometers.

$$4.861 \times 10^{-7}\ \text{m} \times \frac{1 \times 10^9\ \text{nm}}{1\ \text{m}} = 486.1\ \text{nm}$$

The visible region of the spectrum corresponds to wavelengths from about 400 nm to about 750 nm, so this wavelength lies within that range. This emission line corresponds to the blue-green line in the hydrogen emission spectrum (Figure 8.11b).

Practice Problem 8.10 Solution

Each *d* subshell is made up of five *d* orbitals, so a *d* subshell can hold a maximum of 10 electrons.

Each *f* subshell is made up of seven *f* orbitals, so a *f* subshell can hold a maximum of 14 electrons.

Practice Problem 8.11 Solution

a. An orbital is a [region in space] surrounding the nucleus where an electron is most likely to be found. (A circular path is an orbit, not an orbital.)

b. Shells, also called energy levels, are made up of a collection of [subshells], which in turn are made up of a collection of [orbitals]. (Electron shells are made up of subshells, designated *s*, *p*, *d*, and *f*, which are made up of one, three, five, and seven orbitals, respectively.)

Practice Problem 8.12 Solution

The fourth energy level can hold a maximum of 2 (*s*) + 6 (*p*) + 10 (*d*) + 14 (*f*) = 32 electrons.

Practice Problem 8.13 Solution

a. Aluminum (atomic number 13) has 13 electrons, which are placed in orbitals going from the lowest energy upward as follows: 1*s*, 1*s*, 2*s*, 2*s*, 2*p*, 2*p*, 2*p*, 2*p*, 2*p*, 2*p*, 3*s*, 3*s*, 3*p*. The last electron is placed in a 3*p* orbital. Since all of the 3*p* orbitals are at the same energy, it does not matter in which 3*p* orbital the last electron is placed. And, since there are no other electrons in that orbital, it also does not matter in which direction the arrow points. An aluminum atom has one unpaired electron in the 3*p* subshell.

b. Argon has 18 electrons, which completely fill all of the subshells from 1*s* through 3*p*, so there are no unpaired electrons in an argon atom.

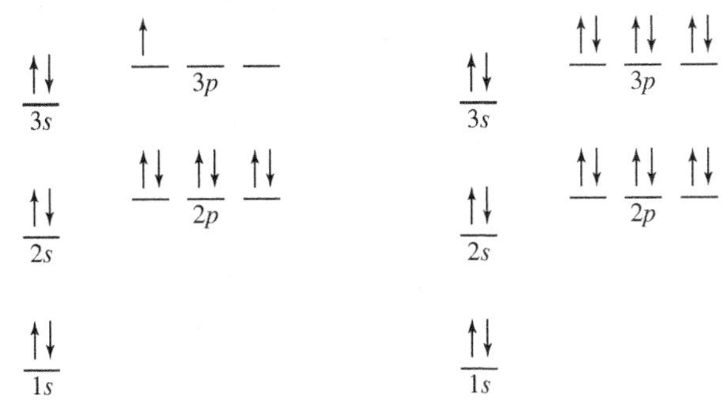

Aluminum atom (a) Argon atom (b)

Practice Problem 8.14 Solution

Sulfur is atomic number 16, so a sulfur atom has a total of 16 electrons. Place 16 electrons, up to 2 per orbital, into Figure 8.16, starting from the bottom. Then write the occupied subshells with a superscript to indicate the number of electrons.

$$1s^22s^22p^63s^23p^4$$

Practice Problem 8.15 Solution

Ni is in the fourth row of the periodic table, but that's the top row of the *d* block, which is the 3*d* block (see Figure 8.19). Remember that the *d* block is moved down one row from its principal energy level, so nickel is in the 3*d* subshell, not the 4*d*.

Additionally, Ni is in the eighth column of the 3*d* block, so its configuration will end in $3d^8$. Use the orbital-filling diagram in Figure 8.18 and/or the subshell blocks in the periodic table in Figure 8.19 to determine which subshells come before 3*d*, in what order, and how many electrons each should have. The complete electron configuration would be written as

$$1s^22s^22p^63s^23p^64s^23d^8$$

As a check, the total number of electrons (the sum of the superscripts) must equal 28, the atomic number of Ni.

Practice Problem 8.16 Solution

You could sum of the superscripts (2 + 2 + 6 + 2 + 6 + 2 + 10 + 5 = 35) and find the element with atomic number 35. However, you may find it faster to locate the element in the fifth column of the 4*p* block of the periodic table, which is bromine.

Practice Problem 8.17 Solution

The noble gas that precedes uranium ($Z = 92$) in the periodic table is radon ($Z = 86$), so $92 - 86 = 6$ electrons must be accounted for. The last orbitals filled in radon are in the 6*p* subshell. Based on the periodic table, the first two electrons go in the 7*s* orbital, the next one goes in the 6*d* orbital (actinium, element 89), and the last three go into the 5*f* orbital. The resulting electron configuration is $[Rn]7s^26d^15f^3$.

If you use the arrow diagram in Figure 8.18, the 5*f* orbital follows directly after the 7*s* orbital, resulting in $[Rn]7s^25f^4$.

In this case, $[Rn]7s^26d^15f^3$ is correct, but because the energy difference between the 6*d* and 5*f* orbitals is so small, electrons often redistribute themselves among the two orbitals to achieve a lower-energy configuration. This is a fairly common phenomenon and is described further in the next subsection.

Practice Problem 8.18 Solution

A calcium atom ($Z = 20$) has 20 protons and 20 electrons, so Ca^{2+} has 18 electrons total. The electron configuration for Ca^{2+} is $1s^22s^22p^63s^23p^6$.

A sulfur atom ($Z = 16$) has 16 protons and 16 electrons, so S^{2-} has 18 electrons total. The electron configuration for S^{2-} is $1s^22s^22p^63s^23p^6$, which is the same as that of Ca^{2+}. Ca^{2+} and S^{2-} are isoelectronic.

The atom with the electron configuration $1s^22s^22p^63s^23p^6$ has a completely filled 3*p* subshell, which places it in the third row of the periodic table and in the last column of the *p* block (group 18). This is argon ($Z = 18$). (You could get the same answer by counting the electrons in the electron configuration because the number of electrons in a neutral atom is equal to the number of protons in the nucleus.)

Practice Problem 8.19 Solution

The electron configuration for copper ($Z = 29$) is $1s^22s^22p^63s^23p^64s^13d^{10}$. The Cu^+ ion will lose one electron from the 4*s* subshell, resulting in $1s^22s^22p^63s^23p^63d^{10}$. The Cu^{2+} ion will lose one more electron, from the outer 3*d* subshell, resulting in $1s^22s^22p^63s^23p^63d^9$.

Practice Problem 8.20 Solution

The principal quantum number *n* is the energy level, so the third energy level has $n = 3$. This is the only allowed value for *n* for the third energy level. Since ℓ values are integers that range from 0 to $(n - 1)$, allowable ℓ values for $n = 3$ are 0, 1, and 2. These values correspond to the 3*s* subshell, the 3*p* subshell, and the 3*d* subshell.

Practice Problem 8.21 Solution

If $\ell = 0$, the electron occupies an *s* subshell. The allowed m_ℓ values range from $-\ell$ to $+\ell$, so in this case the only allowed value is $m_\ell = 0$, corresponding to the lone *s* orbital.

Practice Problem 8.22 Solution

When $n = 6$, the electron is in the sixth energy level.

When $\ell = 2$, the electron is in a *d* subshell.

A *d* subshell is made up of five orbitals, each of which can hold 2 electrons, so a total of 10 electrons can have $n = 6$ and $\ell = 2$.

Practice Problem 8.23 Solution

a. $\ell = -2$ is invalid. ℓ ranges in value from 0 to $(n - 1)$ and corresponds to a specific subshell type ($0 = s$, $1 = p$, $2 = d$, $3 = f$). There is no subshell that corresponds to a negative ℓ value. Allowed values for ℓ when $n = 3$ are 0, 1, and 2, which correspond to the 3*s*, 3*p*, and 3*d* subshells. In this case, since $m_\ell = 2$, only $\ell = 2$ is allowed.

b. $\ell = 2$ is invalid. ℓ ranges in value from 0 to $(n - 1)$ and corresponds to a specific subshell type ($0 = s$, $1 = p$, $2 = d$, $3 = f$). The quantum numbers $n = 2$ and $\ell = 2$ would correspond to the 2*d* subshell, which does not exist. Allowed values for ℓ when $n = 2$ are 0 and 1, which correspond to the 2*s* and 2*p* subshells. In this case, since $\ell = 2$, allowed values for *n* are integers greater than or equal to 3.

c. $m_\ell = -1$ is invalid. m_ℓ ranges in value from $-\ell$ to $+\ell$ and corresponds to the orbitals within a subshell. $\ell = 0$ corresponds to the *s* subshell, which has only one orbital, so the only allowed value of m_ℓ is 0 when $\ell = 0$. The first two quantum numbers in this set correspond to an electron in a 1*s* subshell.

d. $n = 0$ is invalid. It corresponds to a nonexistent row of the periodic table that precedes the first row. Allowed values for *n* are positive integers (1, 2, 3, ...).

e. $m_s = 1$ is invalid. The first three quantum numbers in this set are valid for an electron in a 3*p* subshell, but m_s must be $+\frac{1}{2}$ or $-\frac{1}{2}$. m_s values are independent of all of the other quantum numbers, so either $+\frac{1}{2}$ or $-\frac{1}{2}$ would be correct in this case.

Practice Problem 8.24 Solution

a. Iron is atomic number 26, so a neutral iron atom has 26 electrons. The order of the electron orbitals from lowest energy to highest energy is 1*s* 2*s* 2*p* 3*s* 3*p* 4*s* 3*d*. It can be determined from the periodic table or by following the arrows in Figure 8.18. Placing a maximum of 2 electrons in each *s* subshell, 6 in each *p* subshell, and up to 10 in the *d* subshell until you run out of electrons yields an electron configuration of $1s^22s^22p^63s^23p^64s^23d^6$. As a check, the total number of electrons is 26, and the last part of the electron configuration should indicate where iron is located in the periodic table. Iron is in the fourth row, which is the top row of the *d* block. Since this is the first *d* subshell, it must be the 3*d* subshell. Iron is the sixth element along in this row of the *d* block.

The *s* subshells are each made up of a single *s* orbital, the *p* subshells are made up of three degenerate *p* orbitals, and the *d* subshell is made up of five degenerate *d* orbitals (Figure 8.13). Placing the electrons in these orbitals beginning at the bottom and working up (in accordance with the aufbau principle) and filling degenerate subshells with unpaired electrons that all have the same spin before pairing any of them up (in accordance with Hund's rule) yields the following energy-level diagram.

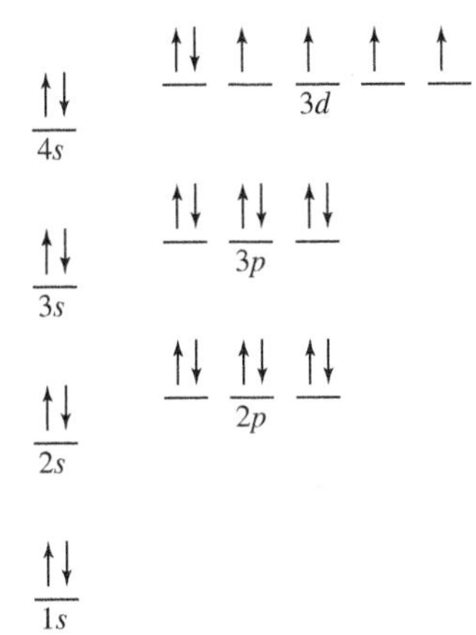

(The unpaired electrons in the 3*d* subshell could all be spin up or all spin down. Both arrangements are correct. The electrons in the unfilled subshell must be unpaired as much as possible, however, and the unpaired electrons must all have the same spin. It does not matter which of the five *d* orbitals contains the paired electrons because all of the *d* orbitals have the same energy.)

The last electron added is the paired electron in the 3*d* subshell. This electron is in the third energy level, in a *d* orbital, so the first two quantum numbers are $n = 3$ and $\ell = 2$.

b. The frequency of the electron can be calculated from its energy using $E = h\nu$ (Equation 8.2), and then the wavelength can be calculated from the frequency using $\nu\lambda = c$ (Equation 8.1). The frequency and wavelength are calculated as

$$E = h\nu$$

$$\nu = \frac{E}{h} = \frac{4.54 \times 10^{-19}\ \text{J}}{6.626 \times 10^{-34}\ \text{J} \cdot \text{s}} = 6.85 \times 10^{14}\ \text{s}^{-1}$$

$$\nu\lambda = c$$

$$\lambda = \frac{c}{\nu} = \frac{2.998 \times 10^{8}\ \text{m/s}}{6.85 \times 10^{14}\ \text{s}^{-1}} = 4.38 \times 10^{-7}\ \text{m}$$

$$4.38 \times 10^{-7}\ \text{m} \times \frac{1 \times 10^{9}\ \text{nm}}{1\ \text{m}} = 438\ \text{nm}$$

Based on Figure 8.5, 438 nm is in the violet portion of the visible spectrum, so this is a violet photon.

CHAPTER 9 Periodicity and Ionic Bonding

Sara Egner, Macmillan Learning

The periodic table is a powerful tool for predicting properties of elements. For example, you can predict the metallic properties of an element (Section 2.6) or the charge of its ion (Section 3.3) based on its position in the periodic table. But there are many more periodic trends, some of which will be introduced in this chapter. For example, the size of the Na^+ ion compared to the Cl^- ion follows a predictable trend and influences the properties of table salt, NaCl.

Chapter Outline

GOALS

- Relate each element's electron configuration and position in the periodic table to its number of valence electrons.
- Discuss the periodic trends of atomic and ionic radius based on the concept of effective nuclear charge.
- Calculate the relative ionization energies of different elements from their positions in the periodic table.
- Calculate the relative electron affinities of different elements from their positions in the periodic table.
- Determine the charges of common ions based on their electron configurations.
- Describe how electrostatic attractive forces allow ionic compounds to exist as very large, three-dimensional lattices.
- Use the Born–Haber cycle and Hess's law to determine the lattice energy of ionic compounds.
- Discuss the periodic trends in lattice energy.

9.1 Valence Electrons

GOAL

- Relate each element's electron configuration and position in the periodic table to its number of valence electrons.

Background Review

Chapter 2 Atoms and the Periodic Table:
Section 2.1—Chemical Symbols;
Section 2.6—The Periodic Table

Chapter 8 The Quantum Model of the Atom

The elements display a periodicity of electron configuration. For example, the electron configurations of the group 1 (1A) metals all contain one electron in their outer *s* orbital. The group 2 (2A) metals have two electrons in their outer *s* orbitals. The elements within every other group of the periodic table have similar outermost electron configurations. These outermost electrons are known as **valence electrons**. All electrons that are not valence electrons are known as **core electrons**. For main group elements (groups 1, 2, and 13–18), valence electrons are those in the highest occupied shell (or principal quantum number *n*) and are the electrons involved in bonding. Elements with the same valence electron configurations (such as lithium, Li, and sodium, Na) tend to have similar chemical properties.

Example 9.1

Write electron configurations and determine the number of valence electrons for O, S, Se, and Te. What feature makes them have similar chemical properties?

Solution

Use the methods described in Section 8.5 to determine the electron configurations.

O: $1s^2\mathbf{2s^22p^4}$

S: $1s^22s^22p^6\mathbf{3s^23p^4}$

Se: $1s^22s^22p^63s^23p^6\mathbf{4s^2}3d^{10}\mathbf{4p^4}$

Te: $1s^22s^22p^63s^23p^64s^23d^{10}4p^6\mathbf{5s^2}4d^{10}\mathbf{5p^4}$

Each of these elements has six valence electrons (two *s* electrons and four *p* electrons in the outermost shell). These electrons are boldfaced in the electron configurations. The ns^2np^4 configuration of the outermost (n^{th}) shell is common to all group 16 (6A) elements and is different from the outermost configuration of the other elements. This is why their chemical properties are similar.

PRACTICE PROBLEM 9.1

Write the electron configurations and determine the number of valence electrons for nitrogen and phosphorus. Name the period 4 element that has similar chemical properties to these two elements, and write its electron configuration.

Hint: N and P are in group 15, which is the third column of the *p* block, so their configurations will end in p^3. When counting valence electrons, count only those in the subshells with the highest *n* value.

A summary of the trends in the valence electrons of the main group elements is shown in Figure 9.1. With the exception of helium, the number of valence electrons is equal to the "A" group number.

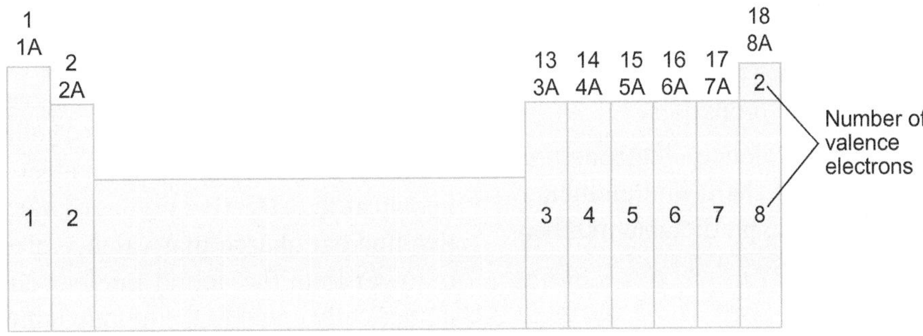

FIGURE 9.1 Periodicity of Valence Electrons

The number of valence electrons in a main group element can be predicted from its group number in the periodic table. Helium, with only two valence electrons, is an exception in that it differs from the other members of group 18 (8A).

Example 9.2

Determine the number of valence electrons in Na and Cl.

Solution

As a group 1 (1A) element, Na has one valence electron. As a group 17 (7A) element, Cl has seven valence electrons.

PRACTICE PROBLEM 9.2

Determine the number of valence electrons in Be and B.

Hint: Locate the position of each element in the periodic table, and refer to Figure 9.1.

Example 9.3

Identify the main group element that (a) is in row 3 and has two valence electrons and (b) is in row 5 and has six valence electrons.

Solution

a. From Figure 9.1, the main group elements that have two valence electrons will be in group 2 (2A). The group 2 element in row 3 is Mg.
b. From Figure 9.1, the main group elements that have six valence electrons will be in group 16 (6A). The group 16 element that is in row 5 is Te.

PRACTICE PROBLEM 9.3

Identify the main group element that (a) has an electron configuration of $1s^22s^22p^63s^23p^2$ and (b) has an electron configuration of $1s^22s^22p^63s^23p^64s^23d^{10}4p^5$.

Hint: Determine the number of valence electrons of each element (the sum of the electrons in the outer *s* and *p* subshells), and refer to Figure 9.1.

EVERYDAY CONNECTION

Solar panels are made of two types of semiconductors. One type is mostly silicon, Si, with some atoms of a group 13 element such as boron, B. Since silicon atoms have four valence electrons and boron atoms have only three valence electrons, the boron impurities within the silicon create electron "holes." The other type of semiconductor is also mostly silicon but with some atoms of a group 15 element such as phosphorus, P. Since phosphorus atoms have five valence electrons, the phosphorus impurities create an excess of electrons within the silicon. When the two types of semiconductors are layered and sunlight strikes the surface, electrons will begin to flow, from excess to hole, creating electricity.

U.S. Air Force photo/Airman 1st Class Nadine Y. Barclay

SECTION REVIEW

- Elements in a given group of the periodic table have similar outermost electron configurations and tend to have similar chemical properties.
- For main group elements, valence electrons are those in the outermost (*n*th) shell, and elements within a group have the same, predictable number of valence electrons.

9.2 Atomic and Ionic Sizes

GOAL

- Discuss the periodic trends of atomic and ionic radii based on the concept of effective nuclear charge.

Background Review

Chapter 2 Atoms and the Periodic Table: Section 2.4—Subatomic Particles, Isotopes, and Ions; Section 2.6—The Periodic Table

Chapter 3 Compounds and the Mole: Section 3.3—Formulas for Ionic Compounds

Chapter 8 The Quantum Model of the Atom

The sizes of atoms and ions are determined by the electronic structure of the atom or ion and by interactions between the nucleus and the electrons. Atomic size depends on interactions between the positively charged nucleus and the negatively charged electrons. These interactions follow electrostatic principles:

1. Oppositely charged particles attract each other.
2. Like-charged particles repel each other.
3. As the charges increase, so does the attraction or repulsion.
4. As the two charged bodies get closer to each other, the force of attraction or repulsion gets stronger.

Electrons have a -1 charge and lie outside the nucleus, whereas protons have a $+1$ charge and lie within the nucleus. The sizes of atoms and ions are strongly governed by how strongly their outer electrons are attracted to the nucleus.

EFFECTIVE NUCLEAR CHARGE

In an atom or ion with multiple electrons, there are both repulsions between the negatively charged electrons and attractive forces between the electrons and the positively charged protons in the nucleus. It is difficult to measure the many electron–electron repulsions, but the average attractive force between the nucleus and outer electrons is easier to quantify and is the focus of this discussion. The net positive charge from the nucleus that such an electron experiences is known as the **effective nuclear charge**, Z_{eff}. The effective nuclear charge that valence electrons experience is lower than the actual nuclear charge, Z, which is numerically equal to the atomic number of the element (Section 2.4). In other words, for valence electrons, $Z_{eff} < Z$. The difference between these two values is the nuclear charge that is *shielded* or *screened*, S, by the inner electrons. This relationship is summarized in Equation 9.1.

$$Z_{eff} = Z - S \qquad (9.1)$$

To understand how valence electrons are shielded by the inner (core) electrons, consider the valence electrons in the 3*s* orbitals of sodium, Na, and magnesium, Mg (Figure 9.2). In Na, the one 3*s* valence electron is shielded by 10 core electrons from the nuclear charge of $+11$. In Mg, there are two 3*s* valence electrons. Each of these valence electrons is shielded from the nuclear charge of $+12$ by the other valence electron and the 10 core electrons. Core electrons shield the valence electrons from nuclear charge more effectively than other valence electrons. Since Mg has a higher nuclear charge than Na but the same number of core electrons, Mg's valence electrons experience a higher Z_{eff} value than Na's valence electrons. The amount that each type of electron shields nuclear charge was quantified by American physicist John Slater (1900–1976). **Slater's rules** state that for a given valence electron, electrons in the same principal quantum number n orbital each contribute a value of 0.35 toward the value of the shielding constant S in Equation 9.1. Electrons in shells with lower n values each contribute a value of 0.85 toward the value of S.

> Core electrons shield valence electrons more effectively than other valence electrons.

Applying Slater's rules, you can now use Equation 9.1 to calculate Z_{eff} for Na and Mg. For Na ($Z = 11$), the electron configuration is $1s^2 2s^2 2p^6 3s^1$. There are 10 core electrons and one valence electron, so for the one valence electron there are 10 core electrons: $S = 10(0.85) = 8.5$.

$$Z_{eff} = Z - S = 11 - 8.5 = +2.5$$

For Mg ($Z = 12$), the electron configuration is $1s^2 2s^2 2p^6 3s^2$. There are 10 core electrons and two

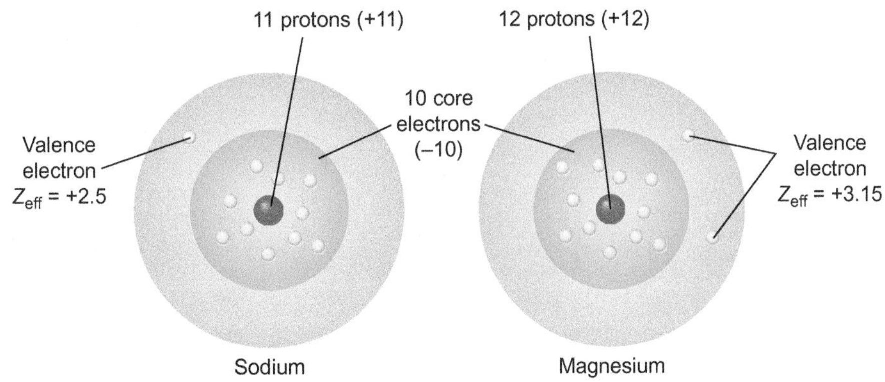

FIGURE 9.2 Effective Nuclear Charges of Sodium and Magnesium

A valence electron in Mg experiences a higher effective nuclear charge, Z_{eff}, than a valence electron in Na. In Na, there are 10 core electrons to shield the valence electrons from the nuclear charge of +11. In Mg, there are also 10 core electrons, but a nuclear charge of +12.

valence electrons, so for each valence electron there are 10 core electrons and one other valence electron: $S = 10(0.85) + 1(0.35) = 8.85$. Note that when calculating the effective nuclear charge experienced by an electron, *that particular electron is not included in the calculation of the shielding constant.* For Mg, only the first 11 electrons are used to calculate S, not the 12th $3s$ electron.

$$Z_{eff} = Z - S = 12 - 8.85 = +3.15$$

Z_{eff} increases across a row of the periodic table. This is because Z increases by one for each element, and S increases by less than one because the number of core electrons does not change and each additional valence electron only contributes 0.35 toward Z_{eff}. Therefore, the $Z - S$ term in Equation 9.1 increases across a row. Z_{eff} decreases slightly going down a group because while Z and S both increase, the addition of a new shell of core electrons causes S to increase at a slightly higher rate than Z.

Example 9.4

Calculate the effective nuclear charges experienced by the valence electrons of K and Ca.

Solution

Use Equation 9.1 and Slater's rules to calculate Z_{eff} for potassium ($Z = 19$) and calcium ($Z = 20$).

For potassium, there are 18 core electrons and zero other valence electrons. So, $S = 18(0.85) = 15.3$.

$$Z_{eff} = Z - S$$
$$Z_{eff} = 19 - 15.3 = +3.7$$

For each valence electron in calcium, there are 18 core electrons and one other valence electron. So, $S = (18)(0.85) + (1)(0.35) = 15.65$.

$$Z_{eff} = Z - S$$
$$Z_{eff} = 20 - 15.65 = +4.35$$

The two valence electrons of calcium ($Z_{eff} = +4.35$) experience a stronger effective nuclear charge than the valence electron of potassium ($Z_{eff} = +3.7$).

PRACTICE PROBLEM 9.4

Calculate the effective nuclear charges experienced by the valence electrons of Be and B^+.

Hint: Use Equation 9.1 and Slater's rules to calculate Z_{eff} for each element. Recall that each core electron contributes 0.85 to the value of S and that each valence electron contributes 0.35 to the value of S.

ATOMIC RADIUS

Atomic radius generally decreases while moving from left to right across a period (Figure 9.3). This is due to the increasing effective nuclear charge (Z_{eff}) that the valence electrons of an atom experience across a period. Going from left to right across a period, the addition of protons increases the charge of the nucleus, but the corresponding increase in the number of valence electrons shields the other valence electrons poorly from the nuclear charge. The resulting increase in valence electron Z_{eff} across a period (as shown in Example 9.4) results in a decrease in atomic radius. The trend is more complex for transition metals and the reasons behind this are discussed in greater detail in Section 22.2.

Atoms and ions get larger as you move down the groups of the periodic table (Figure 9.3 and Figure 9.4). As discussed in Section 8.3, orbitals with larger

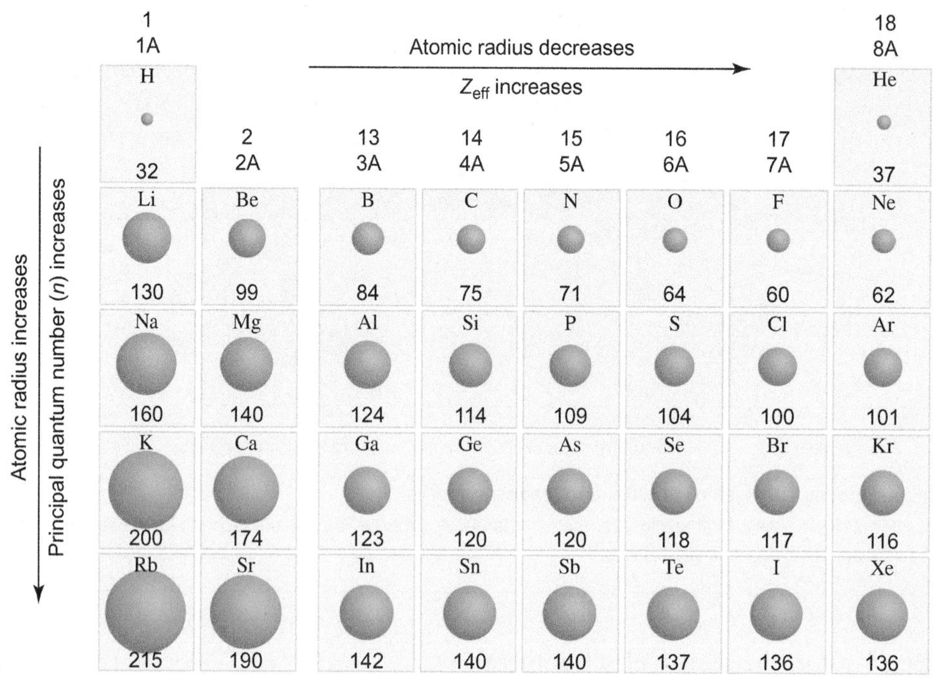

FIGURE 9.3 Atomic Radii of the Main Group Elements in Picometers, pm

Atomic radius increases down a group and generally decreases from left to right across a period.

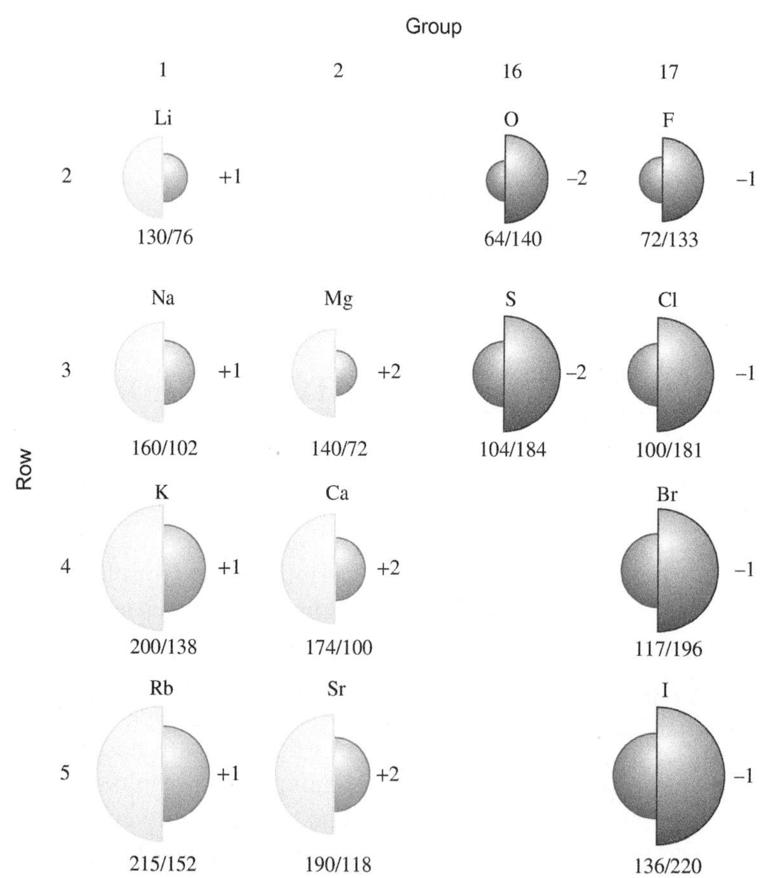

FIGURE 9.4 Relative Sizes of Ions and Atoms in Picometers, pm

Radii of atoms and ions in groups 1, 2, 16, and 17 are shown below each set. Cations are smaller than their corresponding neutral atoms, whereas anions are larger than their corresponding neutral atoms.

principal quantum numbers are larger than the same types of orbitals with smaller principal quantum numbers. Consequently, the outer electrons of elements that are located farther down a group occupy higher energy orbitals and electron density is likely to be farther from the nucleus.

> In the periodic table, the atomic radius of the elements increases down a group and generally decreases from left to right across a period.

Example 9.5

Without consulting Figure 9.3, compare the relative sizes of oxygen and sulfur.

Solution

Oxygen and sulfur are both in group 16 (6A). Since sulfur is farther down this group than oxygen, a sulfur atom should be larger than an oxygen atom.

PRACTICE PROBLEM 9.5

Without consulting Figure 9.3, determine whether an atom of aluminum or an atom of argon would have a larger radius.

Hint: Aluminum and argon are both in period 3. Consider the relative Z_{eff} values of their valence electrons.

IONIC RADIUS

How does removing an electron from K to form K^+ change potassium's size? Elemental potassium has 19 protons and 19 electrons, with one of those being a 4*s* valence electron that is shielded from potassium's nuclear charge by 18 core electrons. In K^+, the 4*s* electron has been removed, but 19 protons still remain. The 18 core electrons are not enough to offset the +19 nuclear charge, so the core electrons contract significantly. The result is that K^+ has a far smaller radius than K (138 pm vs. 200 pm, respectively). Recall from Section 1.6 that the SI prefix *pico-* means 10^{-12}, so $1\ pm = 1 \times 10^{-12}$ m. All cations have smaller radii than their corresponding neutral atoms (Figure 9.4).

Now consider the case of anions. If an electron is added to F to produce F^-, there are now 10 electrons but still just nine protons. Because there is an extra valence electron and the ion has a net negative charge, the electron–electron repulsions in the valence shell are increased. The result is that F^- has a larger radius than F (133 pm vs. 72 pm). All anions have larger radii than their corresponding neutral atoms (Figure 9.4).

> All cations are smaller than their corresponding neutral atoms, whereas all anions are larger than their corresponding neutral atoms.

Example 9.6

Compare the relative sizes of Cl and Cl^-.

Solution

Cl^- is significantly larger than Cl because it has an extra electron, but the same nuclear charge of +17. The net negative charge of Cl^- allows for greater electron–electron repulsion and results in an increase in size. According to Figure 9.4, Cl has a radius of 100 pm, whereas Cl^- has a radius of 181 pm.

PRACTICE PROBLEM 9.6

Compare the relative sizes of Co, Co^{2+}, and Co^{3+}.

Hint: These three species all have the same number of protons (27), so all three have a nuclear charge of +27. Determine how the removal of electrons from an atom affects the strength of the attraction between the nucleus and the electrons and how the strength of this attraction determines the size of the resulting ion.

When comparing cations to other cations or anions to other anions, the trends in size that hold true for neutral atoms still apply. That is, the radii of cations or anions increase moving down a group in the periodic table, and they generally decrease moving left to right across a period (Figure 9.5).

Example 9.7

Without consulting Figure 9.5, compare the sizes of Cl^-, K^+, and Ca^{2+}.

Solution

The three species each have 18 electrons and are isoelectronic (Section 8.5). The Ca^{2+} nucleus has 20 protons and a nuclear charge of +20, however, resulting in a stronger attractive force on the electrons than in K^+ (19 protons) and Cl^- (17 protons). Therefore, Ca^{2+} is the smallest of the three species. Additionally, Ca^{2+} and K^+ are both in the fourth row of the periodic table, but Ca is to the right of K, so Ca^{2+} should be smaller than K^+.

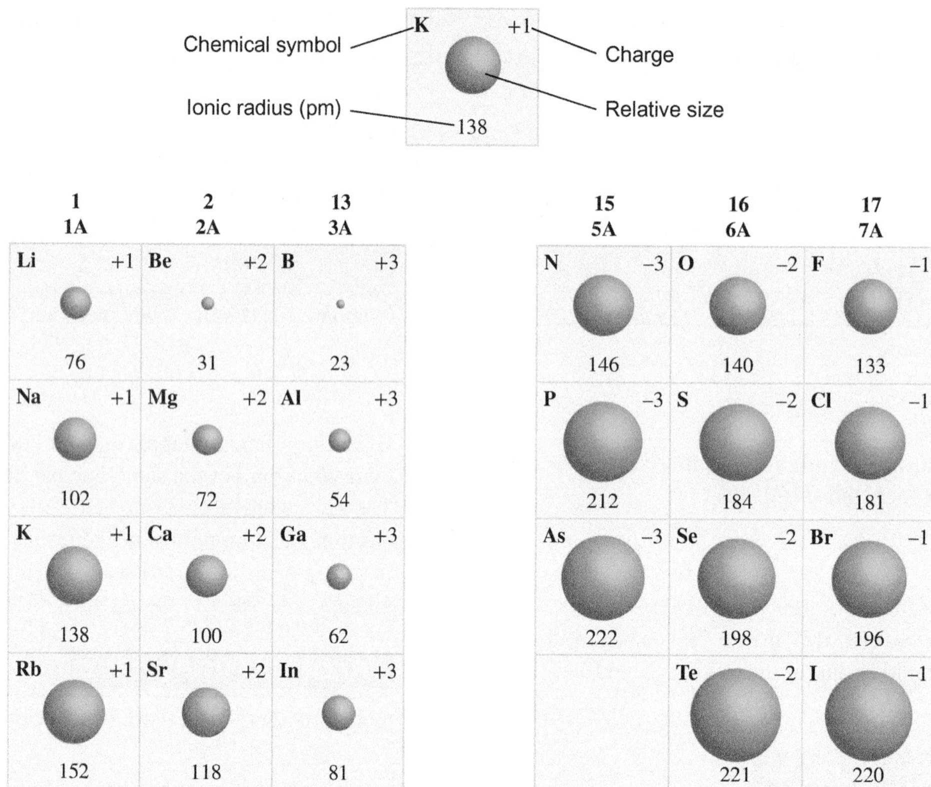

FIGURE 9.5 Trends in Ionic Radii of the Main Group Elements in Picometers, pm

When comparing cations to cations or anions to anions, ionic radius increases down a group and generally decreases from left to right across a period.

Cl^- is the largest of the three species because it has more electrons than protons (i.e., it is an anion) and the resulting electron–electron repulsions allow the valence electrons to occupy a position farther from the nucleus.

The relative order of these ions is confirmed in Figure 9.5: Ca^{2+} (100 pm) < K^+ (138 pm) < Cl^- (181 pm).

PRACTICE PROBLEM 9.7

Without consulting Figure 9.5, compare the sizes of O^{2-}, F^-, and Na^+.

Hint: These three species are isoelectronic (10 electrons), but they have a different number of protons in their nuclei. Determine the number of protons in each, and calculate the relative attractive forces between these protons and the 10 electrons in each species.

SECTION REVIEW

- The atomic radius of the elements generally decreases going from left to right across the periodic table. This is because the increasing numbers of valence electrons across the periodic table do a relatively poor job of shielding each other from the corresponding increase in nuclear charge.
- The atomic radius of the elements increases going down a group in the periodic table. This is because heavier elements have additional electrons in orbitals farther from the nucleus.
- All cations have smaller ionic radii than their corresponding elements because there are not enough electrons to offset the positive charge of the nucleus. The electrons are positioned closer to the nucleus in a cation than in the corresponding element.
- All anions have larger ionic radii than their corresponding elements. Due to the extra valence electron(s) and the net negative charge of the anion, the electron–electron repulsions in the valence shell are increased and the electrons are positioned farther from the nucleus.

9.3 Ionization Energy and Electron Affinity

GOALS

- Calculate the relative ionization energies of different elements from their positions in the periodic table.
- Calculate the relative electron affinities of different elements from their positions in the periodic table.

Background Review

Chapter 3 Compounds and the Mole: Section 3.3—Formulas for Ionic Compounds

IONIZATION ENERGY

The **ionization energy, IE**, of an element is the energy required to *remove* an electron from a *gaseous* atom to produce a gaseous cation. For example,

$$Na(g) \rightarrow Na^{+}(g) + e^{-}$$

This example represents the *first* ionization of Na. Subsequent ionizations, such as the ionization of Na^{+} to Na^{2+} are also possible and are discussed later in this section.

The ionization energy of an element is a measure of the nucleus–electron attraction. The measurements are acquired in the gaseous state due to the limited interactions between atoms (Section 7.10). If the same process occurs in the liquid or solid state, interactions with neighboring atoms or ions are unavoidable, and the measured energy will reflect not only the ionization process but the other interactions as well.

The ionization energy of the elements in their gas phase varies periodically (Figure 9.6) with peaks and troughs occurring at regular intervals corresponding to specific groups in the periodic table. The same factors that influence atomic radius—namely, effective nuclear charge (Section 9.2)—also influence ionization energy. In general, as effective nuclear charge decreases, an atom gets larger and the outermost electron gets farther away from the nucleus, so less energy is needed to remove that electron. The elements closest to the bottom of the graph, which are those from which the *least* amount of energy is required to remove an electron, are the alkali metals in group 1 of the periodic table. Also, the elements nearest the top of the graph, which are those from which it is *most difficult* to remove an electron, are the noble gases. Between the alkali metals and the noble gases, the trend is a general increase in ionization energy as you move from left to right in the periodic table. The trend for elements in the same group is less dramatic but shows a general decrease in ionization energy moving from the lighter elements to the heavier elements.

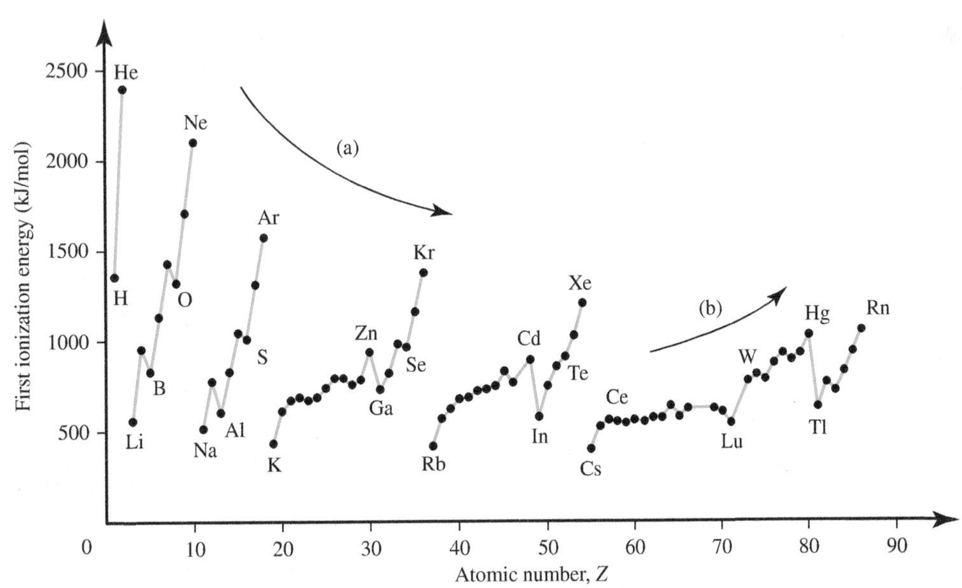

FIGURE 9.6 First Ionization Energy as a Function of Atomic Number

(a) Ionization energy generally decreases going down a group. (b) Ionization energy generally increases going from left to right across a period. The elements that have the lowest ionization energies are the group 1 alkali metals. The elements that are most difficult to ionize are the group 18 noble gases.

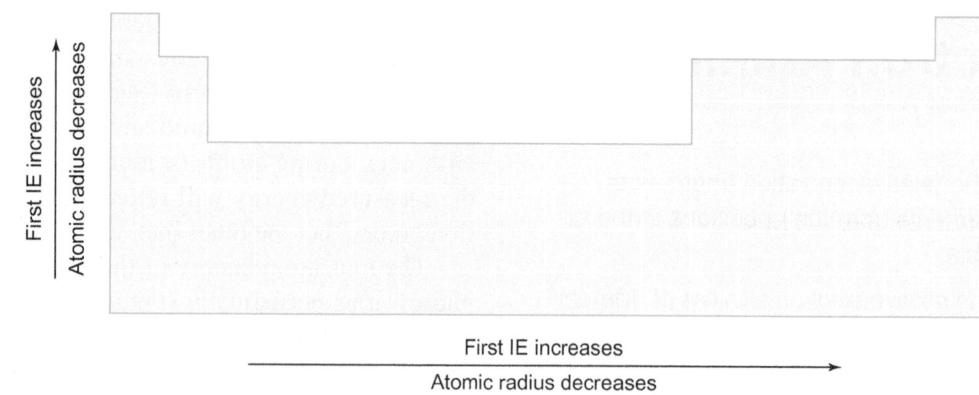

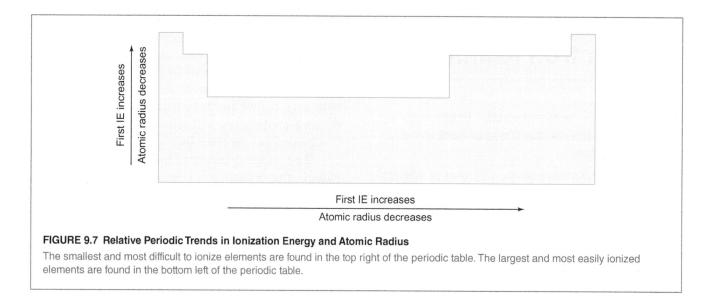

FIGURE 9.7 Relative Periodic Trends in Ionization Energy and Atomic Radius

The smallest and most difficult to ionize elements are found in the top right of the periodic table. The largest and most easily ionized elements are found in the bottom left of the periodic table.

> The ionization energy of the elements tends to increase across a row of the periodic table and tends to decrease down a group on the periodic table. Ionization energy generally increases as effective nuclear charge increases and as atomic radius decreases, because it is more difficult to remove an electron that is closer and more strongly attracted to the nucleus.

Figure 9.7 illustrates the inverse relationship between ionization energy and atomic radius.

Example 9.8

In each of the following sets, identify the element with the highest first ionization energy:

a. K, Ga, Se
b. O, S, Se
c. In, As, Cl

Solution

a. K, Ga, and Se are all in period 4. Because Se is the farthest right in the periodic table, it will have the smallest radius and, therefore, the highest first ionization energy.
b. O, S, and Se are all in group 16 (6A). Because O is located at the top of the group, it will have the smallest radius and, therefore, the highest first ionization energy.
c. Indium is in period 5, group 13 (3A); As is in period 4, group 15 (5A); and Cl is in period 3, group 17 (7A). Of the three elements, Cl is closest to the upper right side of the periodic table, so it has the smallest radius and, therefore, the highest first ionization energy.

PRACTICE PROBLEM 9.8

In each of the following sets, identify the element with the highest first ionization energy.

a. Be, C, N
b. Mg, Ca, Sr
c. Sn, Se, F

Hint: Recall that ionization energy increases going from left to right across the periodic table and going up a group (Figure 9.7).

Although the general trend is for ionization energies to increase toward the right of the periodic table, some exceptions exist (see Figure 9.6). For example, beryllium has a higher first ionization energy (899 kJ/mol) than boron (801 kJ/mol). This is opposite of the general trend shown in Figure 9.7. Boron has an electron configuration of $1s^2 2s^2 2p^1$, whereas beryllium has an electron configuration of $1s^2 2s^2$. The $2s$ subshell is lower in energy than the $2p$ subshell, making it harder to remove an electron from the $2s$ of beryllium than from the $2p$ of boron. This exception to the general trend holds true each time a new subshell begins, as also seen in the relative first ionization energies of magnesium (738 kJ/mol) and aluminum (578 kJ/mol).

Also, nitrogen (1402 kJ/mol) has a higher first ionization energy than oxygen (1314 kJ/mol). The electron configuration of nitrogen ($1s^2 2s^2 2p^3$; Figure 9.8) has three electrons each occupying individual $2p$ orbitals. However, the electron configuration of oxygen ($1s^2 2s^2 2p^4$; Figure 9.8) has four electrons occupying three $2p$ orbitals, so one orbital contains a pair of electrons. When two electrons occupy a single orbital, they

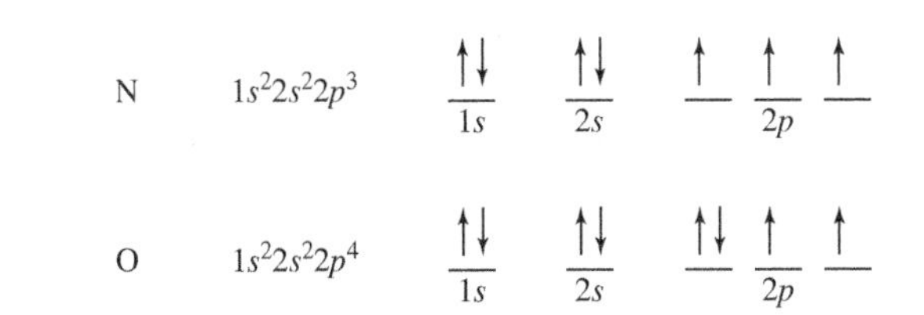

FIGURE 9.8 Electron Configurations of Nitrogen and Oxygen
The first ionization energy of oxygen is lower than that of nitrogen because it is more energetically favorable to remove one of the paired electrons in the 2*p* orbital of oxygen. This is because the paired electrons in one of the 2*p* orbitals electrostatically repel one another, and the removal of one of these electrons eliminates this repulsion.

electrostatically repel one another. It takes less energy to remove one electron from oxygen than from nitrogen because removing one of the paired 2*p* electrons eliminates the electron–electron repulsions. In other words, half-filled subshells are particularly stable.

As mentioned at the beginning of this section, subsequent ionization energies are also possible. The **second ionization energy** of an atom is the energy required to remove the second electron from the +1 gaseous ion. For Na, the second ionization energy is

$$Na^+(g) \rightarrow Na^{2+}(g) + e^-$$

Similarly, the **third ionization energy** is the energy required to remove the third electron from the +2 ion.

$$Na^{2+}(g) \rightarrow Na^{3+}(g) + e^-$$

For every element, the second ionization energy is higher than the first because it is more difficult to remove a negatively charged electron from a positively charged species than from the corresponding neutral atom. In Table 9.1, note that the second ionization energy of Na (4562 kJ/mol) is much higher than the first ionization energy (495 kJ/mol). This is because Na^+ has the same very stable electron configuration as Ne, and the second ionization of Na^+ to give Na^{2+} disrupts this. Similarly, the third ionization energy of Mg (7733 kJ/mol) is much higher than the first two (738 kJ/mol and 1451 kJ/mol).

TABLE 9.1 Successive Ionization Energies for Some Main Group Elements (kJ/mol)

Element	First IE	Second IE	Third IE
Na	495	4562	6910
Mg	738	1451	7733
Al	578	1817	2745
Si	787	1578	3231
P	1012	1908	2914
S	1000	2252	3357
Cl	1251	2297	3822
Ar	1521	2666	3931

> Ionization energy increases dramatically when a noble gas configuration of electrons will be disrupted.

Example 9.9

Does the largest increase in ionization energy for potassium occur between removing the first and second electrons or the second and third electrons?

Solution

Like sodium, the second ionization energy of potassium is much greater than the first because K^+ (electron configuration = [Ar]) has an octet of electrons that is disrupted during its ionization to K^{2+}. The actual values for the first three ionization energies are 418 kJ/mol, 3050 kJ/mol, and 4400 kJ/mol, respectively.

PRACTICE PROBLEM 9.9

Which of the first three ionizations of calcium has the greatest increase in ionization energy?

Hint: The ion of calcium that is most difficult to ionize has the same electron configuration as argon. Which of the first three ionizations is this?

ELECTRON AFFINITY

The **electron affinity, EA,** of an element is the energy change when an electron is added to a gaseous atom to form a gaseous anion. For example,

$$Cl(g) + e^- \rightarrow Cl^-(g) \qquad \Delta H = -348.6\ \text{kJ/mol}$$

Like ionization energy, electron affinity is based on gaseous atoms and ions because they have limited interactions with other chemical species that might interfere with the nucleus–electron attraction.

Figure 9.9 shows the electron affinities of a number of elements. Negative electron affinities represent a *decrease* in energy when an electron is added to a gas-phase atom (i.e., an energetically favorable process). In other words, a negative electron affinity is reflective of an *exothermic* process (Section 6.4). Conversely, positive electron affinities reflect an *endothermic* process: energy is required to add an electron to the gaseous atoms. Main group elements that have common anions, such as chlorine and oxygen, often

≥0 kJ/mol — −348.6 kJ/mol

	1	2	3	4	5	6	7	8	9	10	11	12	13	14	15	16	17	18
1	H −72.8																	He ≥0
2	Li −59.6	Be ≥0											B −27.0	C −121.8	N ≥0	O −141.0	F −328.2	Ne ≥0
3	Na −52.9	Mg ≥0											Al −41.8	Si −134.1	P −72.0	S −200.4	Cl −348.6	Ar ≥0
4	K −48.4	Ca −2.4	Sc −18	Ti −8	V −51	Cr −65.2	Mn ≥0	Fe −15	Co −64.0	Ni −111.7	Cu −119.2	Zn ≥0	Ga −40	Ge −118.9	As −78	Se −195.0	Br −324.5	Kr ≥0
5	Rb −46.9	Sr −5.0	Y −30	Zr −41	Nb −86	Mo −72.1	Tc −60	Ru −101.0	Rh −110.3	Pd −54.2	Ag −125.9	Cd ≥0	In −39	Sn −107.3	Sb −101.1	Te −190.2	I −295.2	Xe ≥0
6	Cs −45.5	Ba −14.0	La −45	Hf ≥0	Ta −31	W −79	Re −20	Os −104.0	Ir −150.9	Pt −205.0	Au −222.7	Hg ≥0	Tl −37	Pb −35	Bi −90.9	Po −180	At −270	Rn ≥0

FIGURE 9.9 Electron Affinities of Some Elements (kJ/mol)

A negative electron affinity signifies a more favorable, lower energy process, whereas a positive electron affinity indicates that energy is needed to add the electron to a gas-phase atom. The periodic trend in electron affinity is not very clear, though the electron affinity of the main group elements generally becomes more negative (more favorable) from left to right across the periodic table.

have negative electron affinities. Noble gases and some other elements have positive electron affinities. Electron affinities are more difficult to measure than ionization energies, so there is greater uncertainty in EA values. For some elements, reliable EA values have not been determined. The periodic trend in electron affinity is also more difficult to rationalize than is the trend in ionization energy. For main group elements, though, electron affinity tends to become more negative (more exothermic, more energetically favorable) going from left to right across the periodic table. The halogens (group 17) have the most negative electron affinities of all the elements because the addition of an electron to a halogen gives it a noble gas configuration.

> Negative electron affinity values indicate that energy is released (an exothermic process) when an electron is added to a gas-phase atom. Positive electron affinity values indicate that energy must be added (an endothermic process) when an electron is added to a gas-phase atom.

Example 9.10

Using Figure 9.9, determine which four elements release the greatest amount of energy when forming an anion in the gas phase.

Solution

Elements that release energy when forming an anion in the gas phase have negative electron affinity values. The halogens (group 17) have the greatest negative electron affinities of all the elements and, therefore, give off the most energy when forming a gas-phase anion. According to Figure 9.9, the values for F, Cl, Br, and I are −328.2 kJ/mol, −348.6 kJ/mol, −324.5 kJ/mol, and −295.2 kJ/mol, respectively.

PRACTICE PROBLEM 9.10

Why does potassium have a much less negative electron affinity than bromine?

Hint: Compare the electron configurations of the two elements. How would adding an electron affect the stability of the resulting anion?

SECTION REVIEW

- Ionization energy is a measure of the energy required to remove an electron from a gas-phase atom of that element, creating a positive ion. Ionization energy increases from left to right across the periodic table and from the bottom to the top of the periodic table.
- Ionization energies are particularly large in cases where a stable electron configuration (e.g., a filled octet) will be disrupted.
- Electron affinity is the energy *released* when a neutral gas-phase atom gains an electron to become a negative ion. A negative electron affinity value reflects the release of energy (adding the electron is an exothermic process), while a positive electron affinity value indicates that energy must be added (adding the electron is an endothermic process).
- The periodic trend of electron affinity is not particularly clear, though the electron affinities of main group elements generally become more negative from left to right across the periodic table. The halogens have the most negative electron affinities.

9.4 Ionic Bonding

GOALS

- Determine the charges of common ions based on their electron configurations.
- Describe how electrostatic attractive forces allow ionic compounds to exist as very large, three-dimensional lattices.

Background Review

Chapter 2 Atoms and the Periodic Table: Section 2.4—Subatomic Particles, Isotopes, and Ions; Section 2.6—The Periodic Table

Chapter 3 Compounds and the Mole: Section 3.3—Formulas for Ionic Compounds

Chapter 8 The Quantum Model of the Atom

Atoms from metallic and nonmetallic elements can combine to form compounds by transferring electrons from the metal atoms to the nonmetal atoms (Section 3.3). The ions that are formed from this transfer attract each other because of their opposite charges, and these attractions are called ionic bonds. The animation in Figure 9.10 shows a neutral Na atom with one valence electron and a neutral chlorine, Cl, atom with seven valence electrons. The Na atom gives up an electron to become a Na^+ ion, and the Cl atom accepts an electron to become a Cl^- ion. The resulting opposite electrical charges on the two ions cause them to attract one another, and that attraction is an ionic bond.

The transfer of an electron from Na to Cl to give Na^+ and Cl^- is particularly favorable because it results in the formation of a noble gas electron configuration for both elements (Section 3.3):

$$\underset{(1s^2 2s^2 2p^6 3s^1)}{\mathrm{Na}} \rightarrow \underset{(1s^2 2s^2 2p^6)}{\mathrm{Na}^+} + \mathrm{e}^-$$

$$\underset{(1s^2 2s^2 2p^6 3s^2 3p^5)}{\mathrm{Cl}} + \mathrm{e}^- \rightarrow \underset{(1s^2 2s^2 2p^6 3s^2 3p^6)}{\mathrm{Cl}^-}$$

For main group elements, noble gas configurations are achieved when the element has eight valence electrons. For example, elemental Na has one valence electron (in the 3*s* orbital) and loses this valence electron to form Na^+. Na^+ has eight valence electrons (two in the 2*s* orbital and six in the 2*p* orbitals). Elemental chlorine has seven valence electrons (two in the 2*s* orbital and five in the 2*p* orbitals). When an electron is added to chlorine to form Cl^-, it has eight valence electrons. The periodic table can be used to determine the charge of an ion (Section 3.3), and this information can be used to determine the number of electrons transferred from the metal to the nonmetal during the formation of an ionic compound.

When forming ionic compounds, atoms tend to accept or donate electrons to achieve the electronic structure of the nearest noble gas.

FIGURE 9.10 Ionic Bonding in Sodium Chloride

NOTE: You need to be online to access this video.

When a Na atom gives up its outer valence electron to a Cl atom, the Na becomes a +1 ion, and the Cl atom becomes a −1 ion. The opposite electrical charges on the two ions cause them to be attracted to one another. Chemists call this attraction an ionic bond.

In an ionic compound, a single pair of ions does not bond together; instead, an almost inconceivably huge number of both types of ions form a lattice (Section 3.1) that extends in three dimensions. The three-dimensional nature of the sodium chloride, NaCl, structure (Figure 9.11) is typical of ionic solids. It is impossible to accurately write the actual chemical formula for the extensive array of ions that makes up an ionic compound—even a tiny salt crystal has a million trillion sodium ions and an equal number of chloride ions in it. So, instead, the chemical formula of the simplest ratio of ions in the ionic compound is written. The formula unit (Section 3.1) is the lowest whole-number ratio of ions present. In the case of sodium chloride, there is one sodium ion for each chloride ion, so the chemical formula for sodium chloride is written as NaCl. The structure in Figure 9.11 is held together by the attractive forces of the oppositely charged Na^+ and Cl^- ions. This kind of attraction is called an **electrostatic attraction**. In general, the transfer of electrons from one atom to another produces oppositely charged ions, which attract each other.

The bonding in ionic compounds is different than the bonding in molecules (Section 3.1). The bonds between atoms in molecules (known as *covalent bonds*; Section 10.1) result in discrete molecules, such as F_2 in Figure 9.12. In contrast, the formula unit of an ionic compound such as NaCl is the most basic unit of a more complex structure.

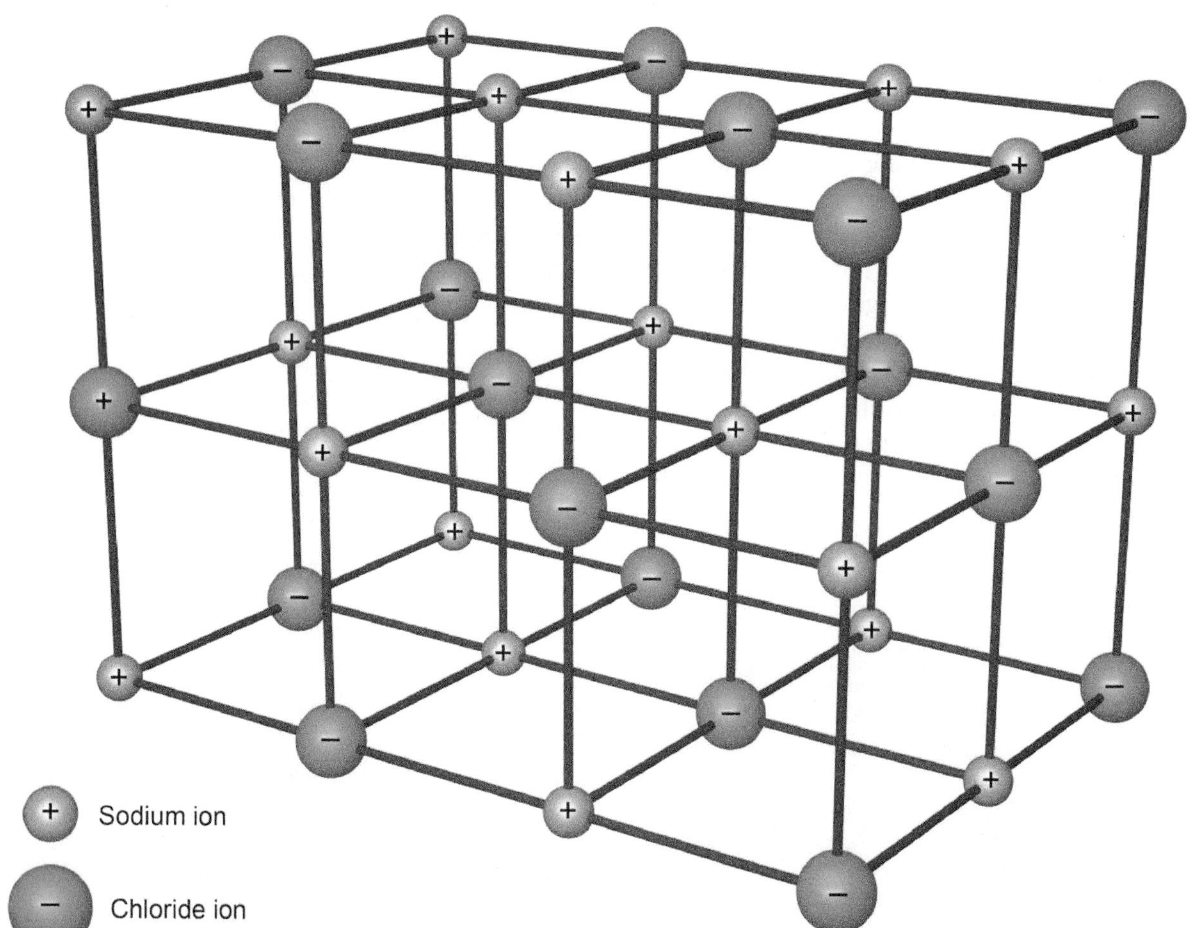

FIGURE 9.11 Sodium Chloride Structure

NOTE: You need to be online to access this 3D structure.

Each sodium ion is surrounded by six chloride ions, and each chloride ion is surrounded by six sodium ions. The ratio of sodium ions to chloride ions is 1:1, and the formula for sodium chloride is written NaCl. This figure shows only a small portion of the structure, which extends thousands of ions or more in each direction. Because this sample is so small, only the middle two ions are seen to have six surrounding ions each.

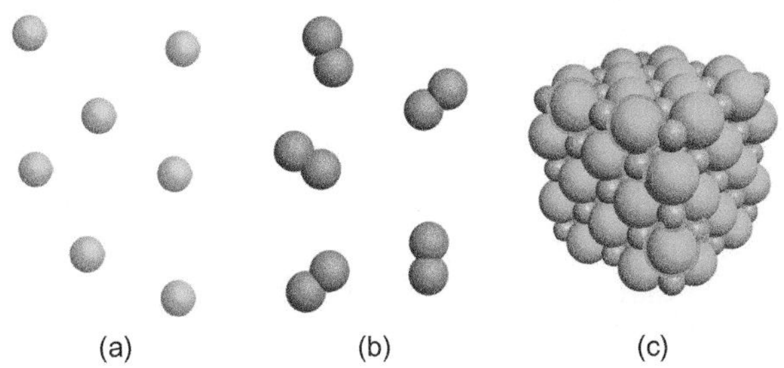

FIGURE 9.12 Formula Units of Atoms and Compounds

(a) The formula units of argon, Ar, are single atoms. (b) The formula units of bromine, Br_2, are diatomic molecules. In a Br_2 molecule, one bromine atom is covalently bonded to a specific other bromine atom. (c) In the ionic compound NaCl, on the other hand, one Na^+ ion is electrostatically attracted to six Cl^- ions that are adjacent to it. Similarly, each of the Cl^- ions is electrostatically attracted to six Na^+ ions that are adjacent to it. The ratio of Na^+ ions to Cl^- ions is, therefore, 1:1. Any pair of Na^+ and Cl^- ions, such as those highlighted, is a formula unit.

Example 9.11

Write the electron configurations of both the neutral atoms and stable ions of calcium and bromine. Then identify the formula unit of the ionic compound that forms between calcium and bromine.

Solution

The most stable ions of calcium and bromine that form this ionic compound are those that have noble gas configurations. Calcium loses two electrons to obtain the same electron configuration as argon.

$$\underset{(1s^2 2s^2 2p^6 3s^2 3p^6 4s^2)}{\text{Ca}} \rightarrow \underset{(1s^2 2s^2 2p^6 3s^2 3p^6)}{\text{Ca}^{2+}} + 2e^-$$

Br^- has the same electron configuration as krypton:

$$\underset{(1s^2 2s^2 2p^6 3s^2 \; 3p^6 4s^2 3d^{10} 4p^5)}{\text{Br}} + e^- \rightarrow \underset{(1s^2 2s^2 2p^6 3s^2 \; 3p^6 4s^2 3d^{10} 4p^6)}{\text{Br}^-}$$

The combination of one Ca^{2+} ion and two Br^- ions gives a neutral $CaBr_2$ compound. The formula unit, which is the lowest ratio of ions, is $CaBr_2$.

PRACTICE PROBLEM 9.11

Write the electron configurations of both the neutral atoms and stable ions of magnesium and nitrogen. Then identify the formula unit of the ionic compound that forms between magnesium and nitrogen.

Hint: To begin, identify the ions of magnesium and nitrogen that have noble gas configurations.

SECTION REVIEW

- Ionic compounds are formed by ions that each have noble gas electron configurations.
- Ionic compounds are *not* individual pairs of bonded cations and anions. Instead, they are arranged in an extremely large three-dimensional lattice that consists of both types of ions in a ratio that is neutral overall. The ions are held together by electrostatic attractive forces.
- The formula unit of an ionic compound is the lowest whole-number ratio of the ions present.

9.5 Lattice Energy

GOALS

- Use the Born–Haber cycle and Hess's law to determine the lattice energy of ionic compounds.
- Discuss the periodic trends in lattice energy.

Background Review

Chapter 3 Compounds and the Mole:
Section 3.3—Formulas for Ionic Compounds

INTRODUCTION TO LATTICE ENERGY

The enthalpy (Section 6.4) of formation of solid potassium chloride, KCl, from solid potassium, K, and gaseous chlorine, Cl_2, is highly exothermic (energy is released):

$$\text{K(s)} + \frac{1}{2}\text{Cl}_2\text{(g)} \rightarrow \text{KCl(s)} \qquad \Delta H_f^\circ = -437\ \text{kJ/mol}$$

The enthalpy value for this reaction, however, is not simply related to the ionization energy of K (+419 kJ/mol) or the electron affinity of atomic Cl (−349 kJ/mol). The difference between these two values (+70 kJ/mol) reflects an endothermic process (energy is absorbed). As a result, the enthalpy of formation of solid KCl depends on more than just the ionization energy and electron affinity of the reactants. This is because ionization energies and electron affinities are determined in the gas phase, where the species do not strongly interact with one another. The energetically favorable exothermic formation of KCl is driven by these interactive forces.

TABLE 9.2 Lattice Energies of Some Ionic Compounds

Compound	Lattice Energy (kJ/mol)	Compound	Lattice Energy (kJ/mol)
LiF	−1030	KF	−808
LiCl	−834	KCl	−717
LiBr	−818	KBr	−671
NaF	−910	$MgCl_2$	−2524
NaCl	−788	$CaCl_2$	−2260
NaBr	−732	$SrCl_2$	−2127

The stability of ionic compounds is mainly attributed to the electrostatic attraction between ions of opposite charge. Energy is released when ions assemble into a lattice structure (Figure 9.11). This energy is known as the **lattice energy, ΔH_L°**, of the ionic compound. The lattice energy is the energy *released* when gas-phase ions are converted into a solid ionic compound. For KCl,

$$K^+(g) + Cl^-(g) \rightarrow KCl(s) \qquad \Delta H_L^\circ = -717\ \text{kJ/mol}$$

Some texts define lattice energy as the energy *absorbed* when a solid ionic compound is converted into gas-phase ions. This is simply the reverse process of the previous equation [e.g., $KCl(s) \rightarrow K^+(g) + Cl^-(g)$]. The sign of the lattice energy is reversed, reflecting the fact that this is an endothermic process.

Table 9.2 lists the lattice energies of some ionic compounds.

THE BORN–HABER CYCLE

Lattice energies cannot be directly determined in the laboratory. Instead, they can be calculated via Hess's law (Section 6.6) based on the ionization energies and electron affinities of the respective ions and the energies of related processes. These processes include the reverse enthalpy of formation of a compound (Section 6.8), the **bond energy, BE**, of a compound (the energy required to break a chemical bond), and the enthalpy of **sublimation** of an element (the energy required to convert the element directly from the solid phase to the gas phase). These processes can be used to construct a diagram known as the **Born–Haber cycle**. The Born–Haber cycle for KCl is shown in Figure 9.13.

The lattice energy, ΔH_L°, of KCl can be determined from the following steps (shown in Figure 9.13):

- Step 1: The reverse of the enthalpy of formation, ΔH_f°, of KCl:

$$KCl(s) \rightarrow K(s) + \frac{1}{2}Cl_2(g)$$

$$\Delta H_1^\circ = -\Delta H_f^\circ = +437\ \text{kJ/mol}$$

- Step 2: The conversion of K(s) to K(g) (enthalpy of *sublimation*):

$$K(s) \rightarrow K(g) \qquad \Delta H_2^\circ = \Delta H_{sub}^\circ = +89\ \text{kJ/mol}$$

- Step 3: The ionization of K(g) to $K^+(g)$:

$$K(g) \rightarrow K^+(g) + e^- \qquad \Delta H_3^\circ = \text{IE} = +122\ \text{kJ/mol}$$

(This is the first ionization energy, IE, of potassium.)

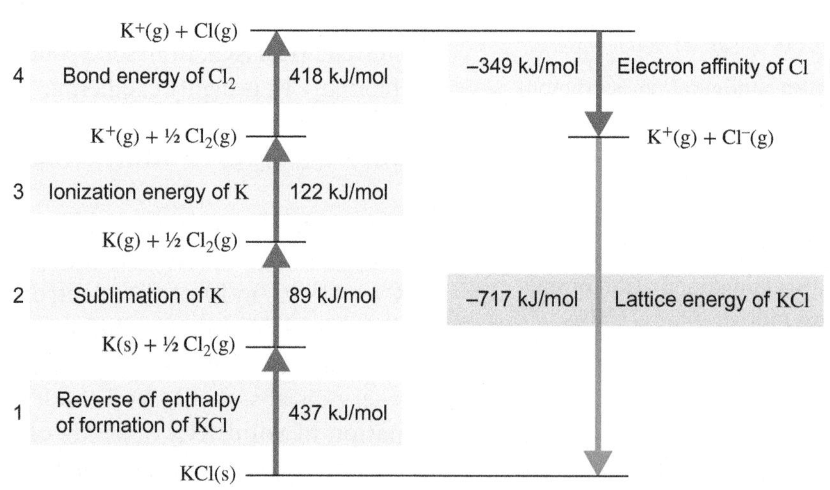

FIGURE 9.13 Born–Haber Cycle for Potassium Chloride

The experimentally measured enthalpy values for each these processes are used to calculate ΔH_L° via Hess's law. The enthalpy values are in units of kJ/mol.

- Step 4: The formation of Cl(g) from $Cl_2(g)$ (*bond energy*, BE, of Cl_2):

$$\frac{1}{2}Cl_2(g) \rightarrow Cl(g) \qquad \Delta H_4^\circ = BE = +418\ kJ/mol$$

- Step 5: The addition of an electron to Cl(g) to form $Cl^-(g)$, the electron affinity, EA, of chlorine:

$$Cl(g) + e^- \rightarrow Cl^-(g) \quad \Delta H_5^\circ = EA = -349\ kJ/mol$$

According to Hess's law, the sum of steps 1–5 is equal to the overall reaction, $KCl(s) \rightarrow K^+(g) + Cl^-(g)$, which is the reverse of the lattice enthalpy of KCl.

$$\Delta H_L^\circ = -(\Delta H_1^\circ + \Delta H_2^\circ + \Delta H_3^\circ + \Delta H_4^\circ + \Delta H_5^\circ)$$

$$\Delta H_L^\circ = -\left[437\frac{kJ}{mol} + 89\frac{kJ}{mol} + 122\frac{kJ}{mol} + 418\frac{kJ}{mol} + \left(-349\frac{kJ}{mol}\right)\right]$$

$$\Delta H_L^\circ = -717\ kJ/mol$$

In fact, for any compound of a +1 metal cation with a halogen anion, the general formula for lattice energy is

$$\Delta H_L^\circ = -(-\Delta H_f^\circ + \Delta H_{sub}^\circ + BE + IE + EA)$$

Example 9.12

Write the chemical equation that corresponds to the lattice energy of $CaCl_2$.

Solution

The lattice energy is the energy released when gas-phase ions are converted into a solid ionic compound. The only stable ion of calcium is Ca^{2+}, and the only stable ion of chlorine is Cl^-. So, for $CaCl_2$, this is the combination of one gaseous Ca^{2+} ion and two gaseous Cl^- ions:

$$Ca^{2+}(g) + 2\ Cl^-(g) \rightarrow CaCl_2(s)$$

PRACTICE PROBLEM 9.12

Write the chemical equation that corresponds to the lattice energy of strontium nitride, Sr_3N_2.

Hint: The lattice energy is the energy released when gas-phase ions are converted into a solid ionic compound. Sr_3N_2 consists of the Sr^{2+} ion and the N^{3-} ion. The chemical formula of Sr_3N_2 tells you the number of each gas-phase ion that combines to form strontium nitride.

Example 9.13

The thermodynamic values listed here are for the compound MX, where M is an alkali metal and X is a halogen.

Enthalpy of sublimation (ΔH_{sub}°) of M: $M(s) \rightarrow M(g)$	(+108 kJ/mol)
Breaking of X_2 to form X (BE): $\frac{1}{2}X_2(g) \rightarrow X(g)$	(+122 kJ/mol)
The ionization of M (IE): $M(g) \rightarrow M^+(g) + e^-$	(+496 kJ/mol)
Adding an electron to X (EA): $X(g) + e^- \rightarrow X^-(g)$	(−349 kJ/mol)
The reverse of the enthalpy of formation of MX ($-\Delta H_f^\circ$)	(+411 kJ/mol)

Use these values to solve for the lattice energy, ΔH_L°, of MX and identify this compound using the information in Table 9.2.

Solution

Begin by drawing a Born–Haber cycle diagram:

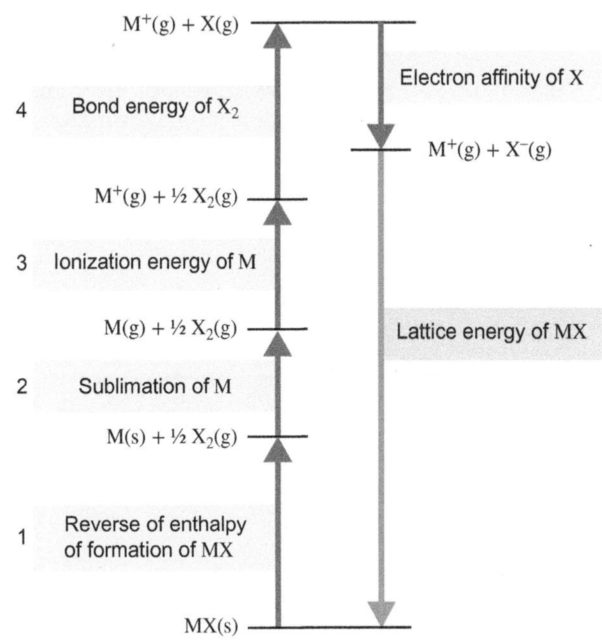

Now use Hess's law to solve for ΔH_L°:

$$\Delta H_L^\circ = -(-\Delta H_f^\circ + \Delta H_{sub}^\circ + BE + IE + EA)$$

$$\Delta H_L^\circ = -\left[411\frac{kJ}{mol} + 108\frac{kJ}{mol} + 122\frac{kJ}{mol} + 496\frac{kJ}{mol} + \left(-349\frac{kJ}{mol}\right)\right]$$

$$\Delta H_L^\circ = -788\ kJ/mol$$

Based on the lattice energy values given in Table 9.2, this compound is NaCl.

PRACTICE PROBLEM 9.13

The thermodynamic values that follow are for the compound MX_2, where M is an alkaline earth metal and X is a halogen:

Enthalpy of sublimation (ΔH°_{sub}) of M: $M(s) \rightarrow M(g)$	(+148 kJ/mol)
Breaking of X_2 to form X (BE): $X_2(g) \rightarrow 2X(g)$	(+244 kJ/mol)
The ionization of M to M^+ (IE_1): $M(g) \rightarrow M^+(g) + e^-$	(+738 kJ/mol)
The ionization of M^+ to M^{2+}: (IE_2): $M^+(g) + e^- \rightarrow M^{2+}(g)$	(+1,451 kJ/mol)
Adding an electron to X (EA): $X(g) + e^- \rightarrow X^-(g)$	(−349 kJ/mol)
The reverse of the enthalpy of formation of MX_2 ($-\Delta H^\circ_f$)	(+641 kJ/mol)

Use these values to solve for the lattice energy, ΔH°_L, of MX_2 and identify this compound using the information in Table 9.2.

Hint: This problem is solved just like Example 9.13, but you will need to account for the fact that there are two X^- ions. (In other words, the electron affinity is twice the given value.) Also, the ionization energy to form M^{2+} from M is the sum of the first two ionization energies.

PERIODIC TRENDS IN LATTICE ENERGY

Ionic radius increases moving down a group in the periodic table (Section 9.2). You can see in Table 9.2 and Figure 9.14 that there is a corresponding *decrease* in the magnitude of the lattice energy of ionic compounds as the sizes of the cations and anions increase. In other words, the formation of ionic compounds becomes less exothermic as the size of the ions increase. This is because ionic compounds that consist of larger ions have longer ionic bond lengths (Figure 9.15), and the electrostatic attraction gets weaker as the nuclei move farther apart (Section 9.2). As Equation 9.2 shows, the potential energy of two interacting charged particles, E_{el}, is inversely proportional to the distance between the center of the two particles, d.

$$E_{el} = k\frac{q_1 q_2}{d} \tag{9.2}$$

In Equation 9.2, q_1 and q_2 are the charges of the particles and K is the constant $8.99 \times 10^9\ J \cdot m/C^2$. (The coulomb, C, is the derived SI unit for electrical charge.) As the distance between the center of two ions increases due to increasing ionic radius, the potential energy between the two particles decreases.

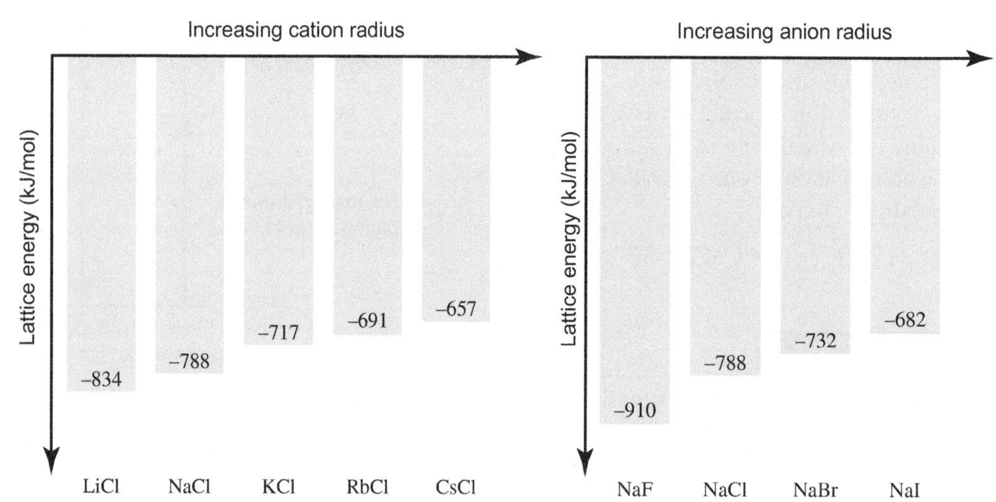

FIGURE 9.14 Lattice Energy as a Function of Ionic Radius

Lattice energy decreases in magnitude as the size of one or both ions of an ionic compound increases. This is because the electrostatic forces that hold ionic compounds together become weaker as the distance between the cations and anions increases. In the graph on the left, the cation radius increases as you go down group 1 of the periodic table and the anion is kept constant. In the graph on the right, the anion radius increases as you go down group 17 and the cation is kept constant.

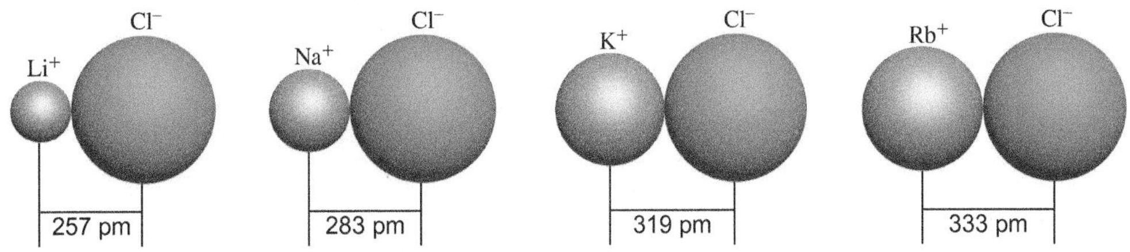

FIGURE 9.15 Bond Lengths of Alkali Metal Chlorides

Bond lengths of ionic compounds increase as the size of one or both of the ions increases.

TABLE 9.3 Ionic Bond Lengths and Lattice Energies for Lithium Fluoride and Magnesium Oxide

Compound	Bond Length (pm)	Lattice Energy (kJ/mol)
LiF	209	−1030
MgO	212	−3850

The bond length of an ionic compound increases as the radii of its constituent ions increase. Consequently, the lattice energy of an ionic compound decreases in magnitude (becomes less exothermic) as the size of one or more of the ions increases.

Lattice energy depends highly on the charges on the ions, too. Compare lithium fluoride, LiF, for example, to magnesium oxide, MgO. The bond length of LiF is determined by summing the ionic radii of its ions (see Figure 9.4): 76 pm for Li^+ + 133 pm for F^- = 209 pm for LiF. This is nearly the same as the bond length for MgO (72 + 140 = 212 pm), but the lattice energy of MgO (−3,850 kJ/mol; Table 9.3) is almost *four* times more negative than that of LiF (−1,030 kJ/mol; Table 9.3). This is because of the difference in charges on the ions. For LiF, the values of q_1 and q_2 in Equation 9.2 are +1 and −1, resulting in a product of −1. For MgO, however, q_1 and q_2 are +2 and −2, resulting in a product of −4.

Lattice energies tend to be larger in magnitude (more negative) for ionic compounds consisting of ions with large charges.

Example 9.14

Arrange the lattice energies for the following compounds in order from least negative to most negative: $MgCl_2$, NaF, CsF, and ScN.

Solution

The charges on the cations and anions in both NaF and CsF are +1 and −1, so any difference in their lattice energies will be due to differences in ionic bond distances, not differences in the magnitudes of the charges. Cs^+ has a larger ionic radius than Na^+ (Figure 9.4), so CsF has a longer ionic bond length than NaF, and you would expect CsF to have a lower (less negative) lattice energy than NaF.

The +2 charge on the Mg^{2+} ion in $MgCl_2$ should give $MgCl_2$ a larger (more negative) lattice energy than either NaF or CsF. In ScN, the anion is nitride, N^{3-}, which has a charge of −3. Therefore, scandium has a charge of +3. Since ScN consists of more highly charged constituent ions than the other three compounds, it should have the most negative lattice energy. The expected order, from least negative to most negative, is $CsF < NaF < MgCl_2 < ScN$.

The expected order is confirmed by the actual values:

$$CsF = -744\ kJ/mol$$
$$NaF = -910\ kJ/mol$$
$$MgCl_2 = -2{,}524\ kJ/mol$$
$$ScN = -7{,}547\ kJ/mol$$

PRACTICE PROBLEM 9.14

Arrange the lattice energies of the following compounds in order from least negative to most negative: MgO, NaCl, CaO, and Al_2O_3.

Hint: Ionic compounds whose constituent ions have the highest charges are expected to have the highest (most negative) lattice energies. When compounds consist of ions with the same charge, the magnitude of the lattice energy decreases (becomes less negative) as the size of the ions increases.

SECTION REVIEW

- The lattice energy is the energy required to separate an ionic compound into its constituent gaseous ions. Lattice energies can be determined from experimentally obtained values via the Born–Haber cycle and Hess's law.
- The bond length of an ionic compound increases as the radii of its constituent ions increase. Consequently, the lattice energy of an ionic compound decreases as the size of one or more of the ions increases.
- Ionic compounds whose constituent ions have high charges have higher (more negative) lattice energies than ionic compounds whose ions have low charges.

Putting It Together

The example problems in earlier sections of this chapter focus on the new skills acquired in that section, but homework and exam questions in chemistry often require more than just one skill at a time. In fact, you will likely be expected to apply knowledge from across the chapter, or even multiple chapters in a single problem. This final example problem is meant to help you prepare for these types of multi-concept questions. Additional examples can be found in the end of chapter exercises.

Example 9.15

Provide the following information about the radii of nitrogen and fluorine.

a. Predict whether N or F has the larger atomic radius.
b. Use Slater's rules to calculate the effective nuclear charges of N and F, and use these values to justify your answer to part (a).
c. Determine the formula units of the ionic compounds that are formed between Mg and N and Mg and F.
d. Arrange the following compounds in order of increasing (more negative) lattice energy: NaF, CsF, CaF_2, and ScN.

Solution

a. Both N (group 15) and F (group 17) are in the second row of the periodic table. Atomic radius tends to decrease from left to right across a row (Figure 9.3), so nitrogen should have a larger atomic radius than fluorine.
b. Use Equation 9.1 and Slater's rules to calculate Z_{eff} for N and for F.

For N ($Z = 7$), the electron configuration is $1s^22s^22p^3$. There are two core electrons and five valence electrons, so for each valence electron there are two core electrons and four other valence electrons: $S = 2(0.85) + 4(0.35) = 3.10$.

$$Z_{\text{eff}} = 7 - 3.10 = +3.90$$

For F ($Z = 9$), the electron configuration is $1s^22s^22p^5$. There are two core electrons and seven valence electrons, so for each valence electron there are two core electrons and six other valence electrons: $S = 2(0.85) + 6(0.35) = 3.80$.

$$Z_{\text{eff}} = 9 - 3.80 = 5.20$$

The Z_{eff} for a valence electron of N (3.90) is less than the Z_{eff} for a valence electron of F (5.20). Because the valence electrons of N experience less effective nuclear charge than those of F, it makes sense that nitrogen has a larger atomic radius than fluorine.

c. The formulas of the ionic compounds are found by determining the most stable charges of the ions. The most stable charges are those that give the ions a noble gas electron configuration. For magnesium, the loss of two electrons gives Mg^{2+}, which has the same noble gas configuration as neon. The F^- and N^{3-} ions are also isoelectronic with neon. The ionic compounds must be charge neutral overall, so their formula units are MgF_2 and Mg_3N_2.
d. More highly charged ions form compounds with more highly negative lattice energies (Equation 9.2 and Table 9.3). Of NaF, CsF, CaF_2, and ScN, ScN will have the most negative lattice energy because it is composed of trivalent ions, Sc^{3+} and N^{3-}, whereas the other compounds consist of divalent and monovalent ions.

Of NaF, CsF, and CaF_2, CaF_2 will have the next most negative lattice energy because the charge of Ca^{2+} is greater than the charges of Na^+ and Cs^+.

Compounds with shorter bond lengths also have more negative lattice energies. The ionic radii (Figure 9.5) of Ca^{2+} and Na^+ are very similar (100 pm vs. 102 pm, respectively), so the bond length differences between CaF_2 and NaF are not going to strongly impact their relative lattice energies. However, the ionic radii of Na^+ and Rb^+ (102 pm vs. 167 pm, respectively) are different enough that the longer bond length of CsF gives it a lattice energy that is lower in magnitude (less negative) than that of NaF.

Thus, the predicted order, from least negative to most negative, is $\text{CsF} < \text{NaF} < CaF_2 < \text{ScN}$, and the measured lattice energies of these compounds confirm the predicted trend: CsF ($\Delta H^\circ_L = -744$ kJ/mol) < NaF ($\Delta H^\circ_L = -910$ kJ/mol) < CaF_2 ($\Delta H^\circ_L = -2{,}640$ kJ/mol) < ScN ($\Delta H^\circ_L = -7{,}547$ kJ/mol).

PRACTICE PROBLEM 9.15

Using the thermodynamic values given, (a) determine the lattice energies of LiI and MgI_2 and explain why they differ. (b) Predict what the relative lattice energies of LiI and MgI_2 would be if Li and Mg had the same ionic radii.

For LiI

Enthalpy of sublimation (ΔH°_{sub}) of Li: $Li(s) \rightarrow Li(g)$	(+161 kJ/mol)
Breaking of I_2 to form I (BE): $\frac{1}{2}I_2(g) \rightarrow I(g)$	(+122 kJ/mol)
The ionization of Li to Li^+ (IE_1): $Li(g) \rightarrow Li^+(g)$	(+513 kJ/mol)
Adding an electron to I (EA): $I(g) \rightarrow I^-(g)$	(−295 kJ/mol)
Reverse of the enthalpy of formation of LiI ($-\Delta H^\circ_f$)	(+270 kJ/mol)

For MgI_2

Enthalpy of sublimation (ΔH°_{sub}) of Mg: $Mg(s) \rightarrow Mg(g)$	(+146 kJ/mol)
Breaking of I_2 to form I (BE): $I_2(g) \rightarrow 2I(g)$	(+122 kJ/mol)
The ionization of Mg to Mg^+ (IE_1): $Mg(g) \rightarrow Mg^+(g)$	(+738 kJ/mol)
The ionization of Mg^+ to Mg^{2+} (IE_2): $Mg^+(g) \rightarrow Mg^{2+}(g)$	(+1,451 kJ/mol)
Adding an electron to I (EA): $I(g) \rightarrow I^-(g)$	(−295 kJ/mol)
Reverse of the enthalpy of formation of MgI_2 ($-\Delta H^\circ_f$)	(+367 kJ/mol)

Hint:

a. Use Hess's law to solve for ΔH°_L.

b. Use Equation 9.2 to determine how the charges of the constituent ions of LiI and MgI_2 will affect their respective lattice energies.

Key Terms, Symbols, and Equations

KEY TERMS

bond energy, BE (9.5): The energy needed to break a mole of a specific type of bond; also called bond enthalpy.

Born–Haber cycle (9.5): A thermodynamic cycle that uses Hess's law, ionization energy, electron affinity, and the energies of other processes to calculate the lattice energy of an ionic compound.

core electrons (9.1): The electrons in the shells of an atom or ion that are lower in energy (principal quantum number $n - 1$ or lower) than the highest occupied shell (n); all electrons that are not valence electrons.

effective nuclear charge (9.2): The net positive charge from the nucleus that a valence electron experiences.

electron affinity, EA (9.3): The energy liberated when an electron is added to a gaseous atom to form a gaseous anion.

electrostatic attraction (9.4): The forces of attraction between oppositely charged species.

ionization energy, IE (9.3): The energy required to remove an electron from a gaseous atom to produce a gaseous cation.

lattice energy (9.5): The energy released when gas-phase ions combine to form a solid ionic compound.

second ionization energy (9.3): The energy required to remove an electron from the +1 gaseous ion.

Slater's rules (9.2): A set of rules that provides a numerical value for the shielding constant S when calculating effective nuclear charge.

sublimation (9.5): The phase change from solid to gas.

third ionization energy (9.3): The energy required to remove an electron from the +2 gaseous ion.

valence electrons (9.1): The electrons in the highest occupied shell (principal quantum number n) of an atom or ion.

SYMBOLS AND ABBREVIATIONS

BE (bond energy) (9.5)

d (distance between two particles) (9.5)

ΔH°_f (enthalpy of formation) (9.5)

ΔH°_L (lattice energy) (9.5)

ΔH°_{sub} (enthalpy of sublimation) (9.5)

EA (electron affinity) (9.3)

E_{el} (potential energy of two interacting charged particles) (9.5)

IE (ionization energy) (9.3)

k (constant equaling $8.99 \times 10^9\ J \cdot m/C^2$) (9.5)

q_1 and q_2 (charges of particles) (9.5)

S (shielding constant) (9.2)

Z (nuclear charge) (9.2)

Z_{eff} (effective nuclear charge) (9.2)

EQUATIONS

$Z_{eff} = Z - S$ (9.1)

$E_{el} = k\frac{q_1 q_2}{d}$ (9.2)

Chapter Summary

Compounds with the same valence, or outer, electron configurations tend to have similar chemical properties. For example, group 1 (1A) elements such as sodium, potassium, and cesium all have one electron in their outer *s* subshells and react violently with water. The periodic table is based on the electron configurations of the atoms and, as shown in Figure 9.2, it can be used to deduce these configurations (Section 9.1).

In an atom or ion with multiple electrons, the core, or inner, electrons partially shield the valence electrons from the charge of the nucleus, *Z*. The charge that the valence electrons experience is known as the effective nuclear charge, Z_{eff}. Slater's rules can be used to determine the shielding constant, *S*, that is used to calculate Z_{eff}:

$$Z_{\text{eff}} = Z - S$$

Effective nuclear charge affects the radius of an atom or an ion. Valence electrons shield each other relatively poorly, so atomic radii generally decrease going from left to right across the periodic table due to the increased number of protons in the nucleus that can attract the electrons. Atomic radii increase going down a group because their electrons are located in higher energy orbitals. The radii of cations and anions also decrease going from left to right across the periodic table and increase going down a group. All cations are smaller than their corresponding elements, while all anions are larger than their corresponding elements (Section 9.2).

Ionization energy, IE, is a measure of the energy *required* to remove an electron from a gas-phase atom of that element, creating a positive ion. Ionization energy increases from left to right across the periodic table and from the bottom to the top of the periodic table. The trend for ionization energy is opposite the trend for atomic radius because it is more difficult to remove electrons from smaller atoms where electrons are more strongly attracted to the nucleus.

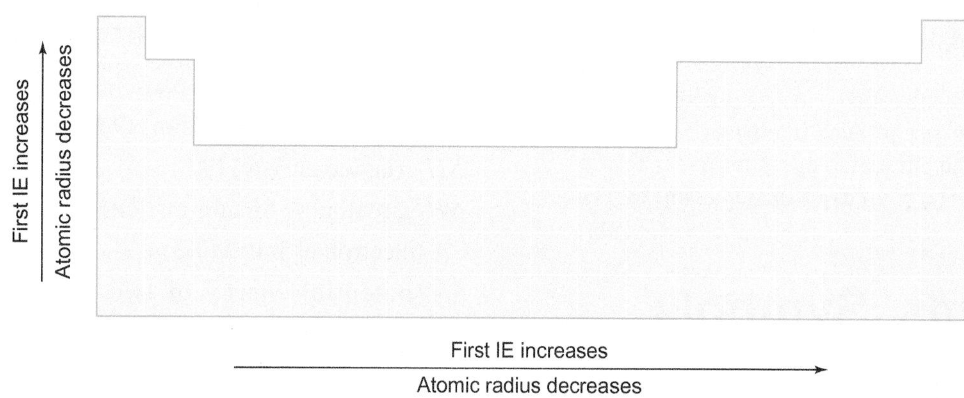

Subsequent ionization energies can also be measured, such as the second ionization energy to form a +2 ion or the third ionization energy to form a +3 ion, but they tend to be larger than the first ionization energy because it becomes more and more difficult to remove an electron from a positively charged ion. Ionization energies are particularly large in cases where an electron configuration consisting of a stable noble gas configuration must be disrupted.

Electron affinity is the energy *released* when a neutral gas-phase atom gains an electron to become a negative ion. An electron affinity with a negative value reflects the favorable release of energy (an exothermic process), while an electron affinity with a positive value indicates that energy must be added to add the electron to the gas-phase atom (an endothermic process). Electron affinity does not have a clear periodic trend, though the electron affinity of the main group elements generally increases from left to right across the periodic table, with the halogens having the highest (most negative) electron affinity values (Section 9.3).

Ionic compounds are formed by ions that each have noble gas configurations. Ionic compounds are not individual pairs of bonded cations and anions but instead are arranged in an extremely large three-dimensional lattice that consists of both types of ions. The ions are held together by electrostatic attractive forces. The formula unit of an ionic compound is the lowest whole-number ratio of ions present (Section 9.4).

Lattice energy is the energy required to separate an ionic compound into its constituent gaseous ions. Lattice energies can be determined from experimentally obtained values via the Born–Haber cycle and Hess's law. The magnitude of a compound's lattice energy is due mainly to the bond length of the ionic compound (shorter bond lengths correlate with higher—more negative—lattice energies) and the magnitude of the charge of the constituent ions (more highly charged ions increase electrostatic attraction and lattice energy) (Section 9.5).

END OF CHAPTER QUESTIONS

9.1 Valence Electrons

1. Write electron configurations for the following elements, and identify what feature makes these elements have similar chemical properties:
   a. Mg
   b. Ca
   c. Sr
2. Sodium and potassium both react violently with water. Suggest another element that would be expected to react similarly with water.
3. When heated, potassium reacts with atmospheric oxygen to give K_2O. Give the formula of the product that is formed when lithium reacts with oxygen in the presence of heat.
4. Cl_2 reacts with and destroys bacteria and, consequently, is often used as a disinfectant. Use the periodic table to identify another diatomic element that would be expected to kill bacteria in a similar manner.
5. Give the number of valence electrons in the following:
   a. Be
   b. Te
   c. Ge
6. Give the number of valence electrons in a main group element that is located in the following:
   a. Group 14 (4A)
   b. Group 17 (7A)
   c. Group 13 (3A)
7. Determine the number of valence electrons in an element that is located in each of the following groups:
   a. Group 2 (2A)
   b. Group 14 (4A)
   c. Group 17 (7A)
8. Determine the valence electron configuration of the element in each of the following groups, and whether that element would be a metal or a nonmetal:
   a. Group 1 (1A)
   b. Group 2 (2A)
   c. Group 18 (8A)

9. Select the expected valence electron configuration of a noble gas.
   a. ns^1
   b. ns^2
   c. ns^2np^3
   d. ns^2np^6

10. Select the expected valence electron configuration of a main group nonmetal or metalloid.
   a. ns^1
   b. ns^2
   c. ns^2np^3
   d. ns^2np^6

9.2 Atomic and Ionic Sizes

11. Compare the effective nuclear charge of an electron in a 1*s* orbital to that of an electron in a 2*s* orbital of the same atom. Explain your reasoning.

12. Explain why the valence electrons of chlorine are shielded less effectively than the valence electrons of aluminum.

13. Calculate the effective nuclear charges experienced by the valence electrons of chlorine and aluminum. Describe how the difference in Z_{eff} between these two elements predicts their relative atomic radii.

14. Calculate the effective nuclear charges experienced by the valence electrons in Mg and Mg^{2+}. Describe how the difference in Z_{eff} between these two species predicts their relative atomic radii.

15. Arrange Mg and Sr in order of increasing atomic radius and explain the reason why their radii increase in that order.

16. Determine the larger species in each of the following pairs of atoms and/or ions:
   a. F or F^-
   b. Ne or O
   c. Ne or O^{2-}
   d. Na or Na^+
   e. N or Li
   f. N^{3-} or Li^+

17. Determine the largest species in each of the following sets of atoms and/or ions:
   a. Na^+, Na
   b. Rb^+, Na^+, K^+
   c. Br^-, Cl^-, F^-
   d. S, S^{2-}
   e. Sr^{2+}, Rb^+, Br^-
   f. O, S^{2-}

18. Which species in each of the following groups is largest?
   a. Co, Co^{2+}
   b. Fe, Fe^{2+}, Fe^{3+}
   c. S^{2-}, SO_4^{2-}

19. Which species in each of the following groups is largest?
   a. O^{2-}, F^-, Ne, Na^+, Mg^{2+}
   b. Na^+, Al^{3+}, F^-

20. Which second-period anion is the smallest?

21. Referring to the periodic table only, identify the element, excluding hydrogen, that has
   a. the largest atoms.
   b. the smallest atoms.

22. Select the largest atom in each of the following parts:
   a. F, Cl, Br, I
   b. P, N, O
   c. K, Fe, Zn
   d. K, Li, Na
   e. Cs, Si, F
   f. Ge, Si, N

9.3 Ionization Energy and Electron Affinity

23. Referring to the periodic table only, deduce which element has the
   a. highest ionization energy.
   b. lowest ionization energy.

24. What periodic group of elements, on average, has
   a. the highest ionization energies?
   b. the lowest ionization energies?

25. Is hydrogen an alkali metal,
   a. as reflected by ionization energy?
   b. as reflected by size?

26. Identify the
   a. periodic group of elements that has the lowest ionization energy.
   b. the main group elements with the next lowest ionization energy.

27. Select the atom with the highest ionization energy in each of the following sets:
   a. O, S, Se
   b. Li, K, Rb
   c. Ca, Se, Kr
   d. Na, O, S
   e. C, O, P
   f. Cs, Ga, F

28. Atoms of elements belonging to which periodic group(s) do not release energy as they gain electrons?

29. Ionization energy and electron affinity processes are usually associated with the absorption or release of energy. Classify each process as endothermic, exothermic, or variable.

30. Use the ionization energy values provided in Table 9.1 and the electron affinity values provided in Figure 9.9 to calculate the total energy change for this hypothetical reaction:

$$Na(g) + Cl(g) \rightarrow Na^+(g) + Cl^-(g)$$

31. Place all the period 2 elements in order of increasing first ionization energy, taking into account the exceptions to the general trend.

32. Place all the period 3 elements in order of increasing first ionization energy, taking into account the exceptions to the general trend.

9.4 Ionic Bonding

33. Explain the difference between molecular formula and formula unit.

34. Why are formula units used to describe ionic compounds?

35. Write the electron configurations of both the neutral atoms and stable ions of cesium and oxygen. Then identify the formula unit of the ionic compound that forms between cesium and oxygen.

36. Describe how the three-dimensional structure of cesium oxide (previous question) differs from the structure for NaCl shown in Figure 9.11.

37. Write the electron configurations of both the neutral atoms and stable ions of Fe^{2+} and N^{3-}. Then identify the formula unit of the ionic compound that forms between Fe^{2+} and N^{3-}.

38. Describe how the three-dimensional structure of iron(II) nitride (previous question) differs from the structure for NaCl shown in Figure 9.11.

39. Write the electron configurations of both the neutral atoms and stable ions of aluminum and bromine. Then identify the formula unit of the ionic compound that forms between aluminum and bromine.

40. Describe how the 3D structure of aluminum bromide (previous question) differs from the structure for NaCl shown in Figure 9.11.

41. Describe how the formula units of BCl_3 and $CoCl_3$ differ.

42. Beryllium forms molecular compounds with halogens, while iron forms ionic compounds with halogens. Describe how the formula units of $BeBr_3$ and $FeBr_3$ differ.

9.5 Lattice Energy

43. The lattice energy of an ionic compound, ΔH°_L, is defined as the energy released when gas-phase ions are converted into a solid ionic compound. Is the ΔH°_L of an ionic compound endothermic or exothermic? Explain.

44. Write the equation that corresponds to the lattice energy of MgI_2.

45. Write the equation that corresponds to the lattice energy of K_2O.

46. Calculate the lattice energy, ΔH°_L, of LiCl, given the following values:

$$Li(s) \rightarrow Li(g) \qquad \Delta H^\circ_{sub} = +161\ kJ/mol$$
$$\frac{1}{2}Cl_2(g) \rightarrow Cl(g) \qquad BE = +122\ kJ/mol$$
$$Li(g) \rightarrow Li^+(g) + e^- \qquad IE = +513\ kJ/mol$$
$$Cl(g) + e^- \rightarrow Cl^-(g) \qquad EA = -349\ kJ/mol$$
$$Li(s) + \frac{1}{2}Cl_2(g) \rightarrow LiCl(s) \qquad \Delta H^\circ_f = -445.6\ kJ/mol$$

47. Calculate the lattice energy, ΔH°_L, of $MgCl_2$, given the following values:

$$Mg(s) \rightarrow Mg(g) \qquad \Delta H^\circ_{sub} = +178\ kJ/mol$$
$$Cl_2(g) \rightarrow 2\ Cl(g) \qquad BE = +244\ kJ/mol$$
$$Mg(g) \rightarrow Mg^+(g) + e^- \qquad IE_1 = +590\ kJ/mol$$
$$Mg^+(g) \rightarrow Mg^{2+}(g) + e^- \qquad IE_2 = +1145\ kJ/mol$$
$$Cl(g) + e^- \rightarrow Cl^-(g) \qquad EA = -349\ kJ/mol$$
$$Mg(s) + Cl_2(g) \rightarrow MgCl_2(s) \qquad \Delta H^\circ_f = -877\ kJ/mol$$

48. Arrange KCl, KF, and KI in order of increasing lattice energy and explain the reason why.

49. Arrange NaCl, Na_2O, and MgO in order of decreasing lattice energy and explain the reason why.

50. Arrange LiF, KCl, CaO, and FeN in order of increasing lattice energy and explain the reason why.

51. Alkali metals form ionic compounds with carbonate ions, CO_3^{2-}, with varying lattice energies. The lattice energy values for these compounds are provided in the table below, but are unidentified. Write the formula of the group 1 carbonate compound in the row that most likely matches the corresponding lattice energy value.

Group 1 Carbonate Compound	Lattice Energy, kJ/mol
	2301
	2523
	1920
	2084
	2000

Putting It Together

52. Refer to the ionization energy data in the table to answer these questions.

	First Ionization Energy, kJ/mol	Second Ionization Energy, kJ/mol	Third Ionization Energy, kJ/mol
Na	495.8	4562	6912
Mg	737.7	1451	7733
Al	577.6	1817	2745

a. Calculate the sum of the first *two* ionization energies of sodium.
b. Calculate the sum of the first *three* ionization energies of aluminum.
c. Would Na^{2+} or Al^{3+} be easier to obtain in the gas state?
d. Which is a familiar ion in the solid state?

53. The force of attraction between oppositely charged ions varies inversely as the square of the distance between them.

$$f = k/d^2$$

a. Ions in a solid might be at a distance of about 2.0×10^{-10} m apart. If a pair of ions is separated to twice the distance in the solid, what percentage of the force of attraction remains?
b. If they are separated to the average distance between gas molecules (3×10^{-9} m), how much force is expected to remain?
c. If two ions are separated to a distance 10 times their normal separation, what happens to their normal force of attraction?

54. Which anion in Figure 9.9, when compared with its parent atom, has had the greatest percentage increase in radius in acquiring the extra electron(s)?

55. A photon of what wavelength would have the same energy as is absorbed in each the following processes? Use the ionization energy values provided in Table 9.1.
a. a sodium atom forms a Na^+ ion
b. a Mg^+ ion forms an Mg^{2+} ion

56. A photon of what wavelength would have the same energy as is released in each the following processes? Refer to Figure 9.9 for electron affinity values.
a. a chlorine atom gains an electron to form a chloride ion
b. an oxygen atom gains an electron to form an O^- ion

57. Atomic number, *Z*, is sometimes called nuclear charge. Explain how these are the same value for a given atom.

58. Select the largest ion of the following:
a. ClO^-
b. ClO_3^-
c. IO_3^-

59. The ionization energy of lithium is 520.2 kJ/mol, and the electron affinity of bromine is −324.5 kJ/mol. Deduce whether the transfer of an electron from Li to Br in the gas phase is endothermic or exothermic.

60. Sum the first two ionization energies of magnesium and the first two electron affinities of oxygen. Deduce whether the transfer of two electrons from Mg to O in the gas phase is endothermic or exothermic. (The second electron affinity of oxygen is −816 kJ/mol.)

61. The ionization energy of Li(g) is +520.6 kJ/mol and the electron affinity of Cl(g) is −348.6 kJ/mol. However, the lattice energy for the formation of LiCl(s) from these gaseous ions is −834 kJ/mol. Explain why this lattice energy is exothermic, while the sum of the ionization energy of Li(g) and the electron affinity of Cl(g), +164 kJ/mol, is endothermic.

62. The lattice energy of KCl is −717 kJ/mol. Estimate the lattice energy for the formation of the theoretical compound K_2Z(s) from its constituent ions K^+(g) and Z^{2-}(g). Assume that Z^{2-} has the same ionic radius as Cl^-.

63. A certain metalloid has the following ionization energies: first IE = 800.6 kJ/mol, second IE = 2427.1 kJ/mol, third IE = 3659.7 kJ/mol, fourth IE = 25,025.8 kJ/mol, fifth IE = 32,836.7 kJ/mol. Identify the element.

64. A certain metal that forms a soluble hydroxide compound has the following ionization energies: first IE = 502.9 kJ/mol, second IE = 965.2 kJ/mol, third IE = 3600 kJ/mol. Identify the element.

65. A certain nonmetal has a higher first ionization energy than the nonmetals on either side of it in the periodic table. Identify the element.

66. A cation with the same electron configuration as argon, Ar, and two anions with the same electron configuration as neon, Ne, combine to form one formula unit of a neutral ionic compound. Give a possible identity for this compound.

67. Two cations and one anion, each with the same electron configuration as Ar, combine to form one formula unit of a neutral ionic compound. Give a possible identity for this compound.

68. Using Figure 2.19, describe the periodic trend in metallic character by completing this sentence. The metallic character of an element increases as you move toward the _______ corner of the periodic table.
   a. top right
   b. top left
   c. bottom right
   d. bottom left

69. A certain metal with a positive electron affinity was found to react with manganese ions in a single-replacement reaction. Identify the element.

70. For NaCl:
   a. Write the chemical equation associated with its lattice energy.
   b. Write the chemical equation associated with its heat of solution.
   c. Use your answers to parts a-b to describe why lattice energy is not simply the opposite reaction as heat of solution.
   d. Use Figure 6.10 to determine the value of the heat of solution for NaCl (in kilojoules per mole of NaCl), and compare it to the lattice energy of NaCl from Figure 9.14.

PRACTICE PROBLEM SOLUTIONS

Practice Problem 9.1 Solution

N: $1s^2\mathbf{2s^22p^3}$

P: $1s^22s^22p^6\mathbf{3s^23p^3}$

Nitrogen and phosphorus are both in group 15 (5A) and have five valence electrons (two *s* electrons and three *p* electrons in the outermost shell—boldfaced in the electron configurations). The element in the fourth row of group 15 is arsenic.

$$\text{As: } 1s^22s^22p^63s^23p^6\mathbf{4s^2}3d^{10}\mathbf{4p^3}$$

Because As is in the same group as N and P, it has the same number of valence electrons, and its chemical properties are predicted to be similar. All three elements have the same ns^2np^3 outer electron configuration and five valence electrons.

Practice Problem 9.2 Solution

As a group 2 (2A) element, Be has two valence electrons. As a group 13 (3A) element, B has three valence electrons.

Practice Problem 9.3 Solution

a. This main group element has four valence electrons (two 3*s* electrons and two 3*p* electrons) and is in row 3. From Figure 9.1, the element is Si.

b. This main group element has seven valence electrons (two 4*s* electrons and five 4*p* electrons) and is in row 4. From Figure 9.1, the element is Br.

Practice Problem 9.4 Solution

For Be ($Z = 4$), the electron configuration is $1s^22s^2$. There are two core electrons and two valence electrons, so for each valence electron there are two core electrons and one other valence electron $S = 2(0.85) + 1(0.35) = 2.05$.

$$Z_{\text{eff}} = 4 - 2.05 = +1.95$$

For B^+ ($Z = 5$), the electron configuration is the same as Be: $1s^22s^2$. There are two core electrons and two valence electrons, so for each valence electron there are two core electrons and one other valence electron: $S = 2(0.85) + 1(0.35) = 2.05$.

$$Z_{\text{eff}} = 5 - 2.05 = +2.95$$

Despite B^+ and Be being isoelectronic (Section 8.5), the effective nuclear charge experienced by a valence electron of B^+ is much higher than that experienced by a valence electron of Be, because B^+ has one more proton than Be.

Practice Problem 9.5 Solution

The effective nuclear charge experienced by an element's valence electrons increases from left to right across a period. This increase in effective nuclear charge results in a decrease in atomic radius. As a result, an aluminum atom should have a larger radius than an argon atom.

Practice Problem 9.6 Solution

In each case, the nucleus has 27 protons and, therefore, a charge of +27. Co has 27 electrons, Co^{2+} has 25 electrons, and Co^{3+} has 24 electrons. Co^{3+} has the fewest number of electrons to offset the positive charge of the nucleus, so the electrons in Co^{3+} are held closest to the nucleus. Co has the greatest number of electrons to offset the positive charge of the nucleus, so its electrons are held least closely to the nucleus. Therefore, Co is the largest of the three species: $Co > Co^{2+} > Co^{3+}$.

Practice Problem 9.7 Solution

Each of these three ions has 10 electrons, but Na^+ has 11 protons, F^- has 9 protons, and O^{2-} has 8 protons. The larger number of protons in the Na^+ nucleus results in a stronger attractive force on its electrons than in F^- and O^{2-}. Therefore, Na^+ is the smallest of the three species. O^{2-} is the largest of the three species because it has more electrons than protons (i.e., it is an anion) and the resulting electron–electron repulsions allow the valence electrons to occupy a position farther from the nucleus. Also, based on the trend that ionic radius decreases from left to right across a row of the periodic table, you should expect F^- to be smaller than O^{2-}.

Finally, the relative order of these ions can be confirmed in Figure 9.5: Na^+ (102 pm) < F^- (133 pm) < O^{2-} (140 pm).

Practice Problem 9.8 Solution

a. Be, C, and N are all in period 2. Because N is the farthest right in the periodic table, it has the smallest radius and, therefore, the highest first ionization energy.

b. Mg, Ca, and Sr are all in group 2 (2A). Because Mg is located closest to the top of the group, it has the smallest radius and, therefore, the highest first ionization energy.

c. Sn is in period 5, group 14 (4A); Se is in period 4, group 16 (6A); and F is in period 2, group 17 (7A). Of the three elements, F is closest to the upper right side of the periodic table, so it has the smallest radius and, therefore, the highest first ionization energy.

Practice Problem 9.9 Solution

Like magnesium, the third ionization energy of calcium is much greater than the first two because Ca^{2+} (electron configuration = [Ar]) has an octet of electrons that is disrupted during its ionization to Ca^{3+}. The actual values for the first three ionization energies are 590 kJ/mol, 1145 kJ/mol, and 6490 kJ/mol, respectively.

Practice Problem 9.10 Solution

The electron configuration of bromine is $[Ar]4s^2 3d^{10} 4p^5$. The addition of one electron would give Br^- with the very stable noble gas configuration of krypton. The electron configuration of potassium is $[Ar]4s^1$ and adding an electron would give K^- with a configuration of $[Ar]4s^2$. The electron configuration of K^- is not nearly as stable as that of Br^-, so the electron affinity of K (−48.4 kJ/mol) is much less negative than that of Br (−324.5 kJ/mol). Or, put another way, adding an electron to Br is much more energetically favorable than adding an electron to K.

Practice Problem 9.11 Solution

The most stable ions of magnesium and nitrogen that form this ionic compound are those that have noble gas configurations. Mg loses two electrons to obtain the same electron configuration as neon.

$$\underset{(1s^2 2s^2 2p^6 3s^2)}{Mg} \rightarrow \underset{(1s^2 2s^2 2p^6)}{Mg^{2+}} + 2e^-$$

N^{3-} has the same electron configuration as neon.

$$\underset{(1s^2 2s^2 2p^3)}{N} + 3e^- \rightarrow \underset{(1s^2 2s^2 2p^6)}{N^{3-}}$$

The combination of three Mg^{2+} ions and two N^{3-} ions gives a neutral Mg_3N_2 compound. The formula unit, which is the lowest ratio of ions, is Mg_3N_2.

Practice Problem 9.12 Solution

The lattice energy is the energy released when gas-phase ions are converted into a solid ionic compound. The only stable ion of strontium is Sr^{2+} and the only stable ion of nitrogen is N^{3-}. So, for Sr_3N_2, this is the combination of three gaseous Sr^{2+} ions and two gaseous N^{3-} ions:

$$3\ Sr^{2+}(g) + 2\ N^{3-}(g) \rightarrow Sr_3N_2(s)$$

Practice Problem 9.13 Solution

Begin by drawing a Born–Haber cycle diagram:

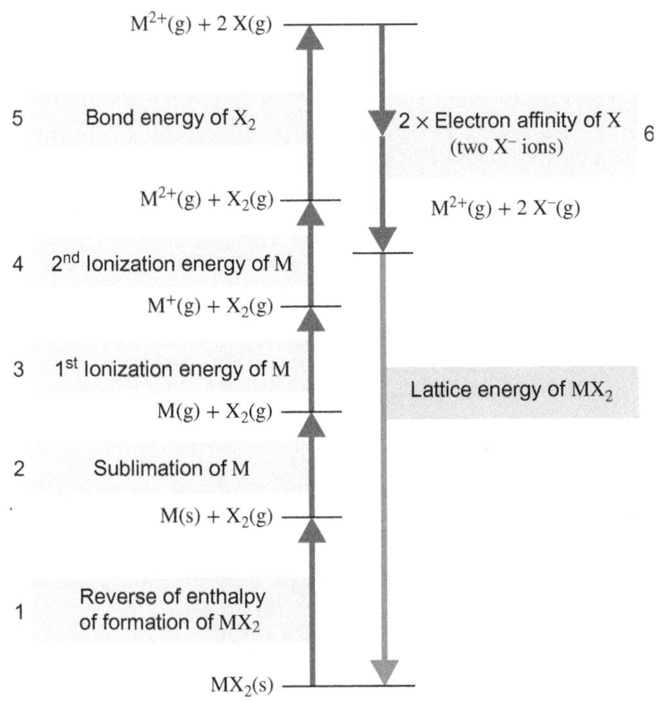

$$\Delta H^\circ_L = -(-\Delta H^\circ_f + \Delta H^\circ_{sub} + BE + IE_1 + IE_2 + 2EA)$$

$$\Delta H^\circ_L = -\left[641\,\frac{kJ}{mol} + 148\,\frac{kJ}{mol} + 244\,\frac{kJ}{mol} + 738\,\frac{kJ}{mol} + 1451\,\frac{kJ}{mol} + 2\left(-349\,\frac{kJ}{mol}\right)\right]$$

$$\Delta H^\circ_L = -2524\ kJ/mol$$

The compound in Table 9.2 whose lattice energy matches this value is $MgCl_2$.

Practice Problem 9.14 Solution

NaCl is the only compound of the four that consists of monovalent ions, so it should have the lowest (least negative) lattice energy. MgO and CaO both consist of divalent ions, while Al_2O_3 consists of trivalent Al^{3+} and divalent O^{2-} ions. Al_2O_3, therefore, should have the highest (most negative) lattice energy.

Ca and Mg are both in group 2 of the periodic table, but Ca is below Mg, so Ca^{2+} has a larger ionic radius than Mg^{2+}. CaO, then, should have a lower (less negative) lattice energy than MgO. The expected order, from least negative to most negative, is $NaCl < CaO < MgO < Al_2O_3$.

The actual values confirm the expected order: $NaCl\,(-788\ kJ/mol) < CaO\,(-3414\ kJ/mol) < MgO\,(-3850\ kJ/mol) < Al_2O_3\,(-15{,}916\ kJ/mol)$.

Practice Problem 9.15 Solution

a. For LiI:

$$\Delta H^\circ_L = -(-\Delta H^\circ_f + \Delta H^\circ_{sub} + BE + IE + EA)$$

$$\Delta H^\circ_L = -[(161\ kJ/mol) + (122\ kJ/mol) + (513\ kJ/mol) + (-295\ kJ/mol) + (270\ kJ/mol)]$$

$$\Delta H^\circ_L = -771\ kJ/mol$$

For MgI_2:

$$\Delta H^\circ_L = -(-\Delta H^\circ_f + \Delta H^\circ_{sub} + BE + IE_1 + IE_2 + 2EA)$$

$$\Delta H^\circ_L = -[(367\ kJ/mol) + (146\ kJ/mol) + 2(122\ kJ/mol) + (738\ kJ/mol) (1451\ kJ/mol) + 2(-295\ kJ/mol)]$$

$$\Delta H^\circ_L = -2356\ kJ/mol$$

The ionic bond distance of LiI is 76 pm + 220 pm = 296 pm, whereas the Mg–I ionic bond distance in MgI_2 is 72 pm + 220 pm = 292 pm. These bond distances are very close, so these two lattice energy values do *not* differ due to differences in bond distances. Instead, the lattice energy of MgI_2 is approximately three times greater in magnitude than that of LiI, and this is largely because the charge of Mg^{2+} is greater than the charge of Li^+.

b. In Equation 9.2,

$$E_{el} = k\frac{q_1 q_2}{d}$$

q_1 and q_2 represent the charges of the ionic compound's constituent ions. Because they are in the numerator of Equation 9.2, the electrostatic potential energy E_{el} increases as q_1 and/or q_2 increases; and as E_{el} increases, the magnitude of the lattice energy increases (becomes more negative).

Let q_2 represent I^- in both LiI and MgI_2, in which case q_2 will have a value of -1 for both compounds. The value of q_1, then, is $+1$ for Li^+ and $+2$ for Mg^{2+}. Based solely on Equation 9.2, you would expect the lattice energy of MgI_2 to be twice as large in magnitude as the lattice energy of LiI. As shown in part (a), however, the lattice energy of MgI_2 is approximately three times greater in magnitude than that of LiI. This underscores the dependence of lattice energies on the properties of the individual ions, rather than their charges alone.

CHAPTER 10

Covalent Bonding

Alexeysun/Shutterstock

Table salt and sugar are both white, crystalline solids. However, these two substances have many other properties that are very different from each other, such as melting point and conductivity in solution. One reason for these differences is that salt is held together by ionic bonds, whereas sugar molecules are held together by covalent bonds.

Chapter Outline

GOALS

- Predict the number of bonds an atom is likely to make in a molecule.
- Draw Lewis structures for molecules and polyatomic ions that follow the octet rule.
- Calculate formal charge.
- Use formal charges and electronegativity values to identify the Lewis structure that best represents the molecule.
- Apply the typical exceptions to the octet rule in drawing Lewis structures, including H, Be, B, radicals, and expanded octets.
- Determine bond polarity using electronegativity values.
- Describe the bonding continuum.
- Discuss how bond length relates to bond strength.

10.1 Formation of Covalent Bonds

GOAL

- Predict the number of bonds an atom is likely to make in a molecule.

Background Review

Chapter 2 Atoms and the Periodic Table

Chapter 3 Compounds and the Mole

Chapter 9 Periodicity and Ionic Bonding

Chapter 3 discusses the concept that valence electrons can be transferred between metal atoms and nonmetal atoms to form ions and ionic bonds and that valence electrons could also be shared to form covalent bonds between nonmetal atoms to form *molecules*.

As the atoms come together to form a molecule and share electrons, they become more stable. According to Lewis theory, atoms gain, lose, or share electrons to achieve a noble-gas electron configuration, which is particularly stable. It is the reason noble gases are so unreactive, as discussed in Chapter 3. For atoms of elements such as hydrogen, the nearest noble gas in the periodic table is helium, with two valence electrons. For most other atoms, the nearest stable valence electron configuration will be ns^2np^6, which consists of eight valence electrons and is why this phenomenon is referred to as the **octet rule** (Chapter 9). Hydrogen, H_2, however, follows the **duet rule** because the first shell can only hold two electrons and so its nearest stable configuration is $1s^2$.

As discussed previously, covalent bonds typically form between nonmetal atoms, which are found mainly in groups 14–18 of the periodic table, plus hydrogen and, although less common, beryllium and boron (Section 10.4). Two hydrogen atoms can share their single valence electrons with each other, forming a covalent bond and completing each hydrogen atom's valence shell ($n = 1$). Other elements can form more than one bond by sharing more than one electron with other atoms. With each bond, each atom gains access to another shared electron. For period 2 nonmetals, the number of electrons the atom needs to gain to have a full valence shell predicts how many bonds it is most likely to make in a molecule. You can also use this method as a starting point to predict bonding for elements from period 3 and beyond, but keep in mind that these larger elements also form molecules that are exceptions to the octet rule (Section 10.4).

Example 10.1

How many bonds is a carbon atom likely to make in a molecule?

Solution

Carbon is a group 14 element with four valence electrons. These valence electrons are shown as dots around the element symbol to yield a Lewis-dot diagram for carbon in which each dot represents a valence electron.

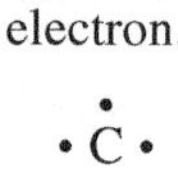

To satisfy the octet rule, carbon atoms must make four bonds to gain access to an additional four valence electrons.

PRACTICE PROBLEM 10.1

Use the octet rule to determine the number of bonds an atom of the following elements is likely to make in a molecule.

a. nitrogen, N
b. oxygen, O
c. fluorine, F
d. neon, Ne

Hint: First determine how many valence electrons each atom has. How many more electrons would each atom need to achieve a full valence shell (eight electrons)?

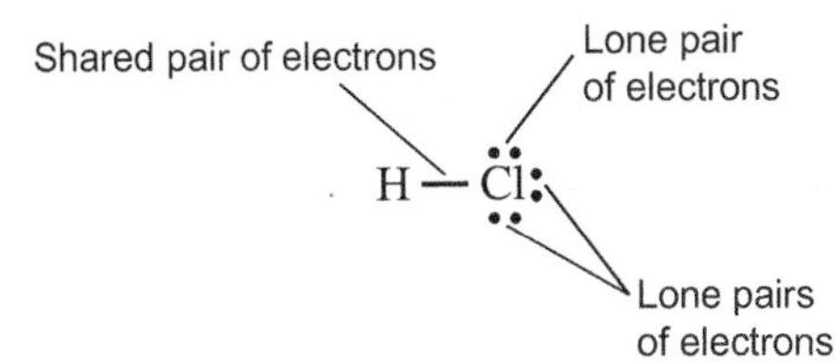

FIGURE 10.2 Lewis Structure of HCl

The line between H and Cl represents a shared pair of electrons, called a bond. Each dot represents an unshared electron. Unshared electrons are usually shown in pairs, called lone pairs.

The H_2 molecule, as mentioned earlier, forms when two H atoms share two electrons, forming a bond (Figure 10.1). Each individual hydrogen atom had an unfilled valence shell, but when electrons are shared between two atoms, the shared electrons are counted toward both atoms' electronic configurations, fulfilling the duet rule. When the two hydrogen atoms each share one electron, the hydrogen atom on the left has two electrons (i.e., a filled valence shell), and so does the hydrogen atom on the right. The resulting hydrogen molecule, H_2, has two valence electrons that occupy orbitals that overlap and include both atoms.

How is it possible for these electrons to count for both atoms involved in the bond? Electrons are extremely small particles and their properties are more wave-like than particle-like. This makes it impossible to depict an electron's location accurately. Chapter 8 discusses the concept that electrons occupy orbitals, which represent a three-dimensional distribution of the electron's probable location. It might be useful to think of electrons existing as charge clouds that occupy those specific three-dimensional orbital shapes. Shared electrons exist as overlapping charge clouds accessible to both atoms of the bond.

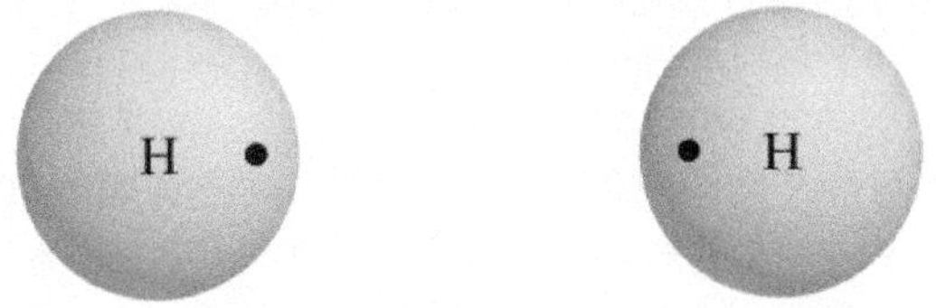

FIGURE 10.1 Formation of a Covalent Bond between Hydrogen Atoms

NOTE: You need to be online to access this animation.
Each individual H atom has one electron in a spherical 1*s* orbital. When the atoms are close enough to share the two electrons, a covalent bond has formed.

In the hydrochloric acid, HCl, molecule, hydrogen has one valence electron, while chlorine has seven. Both atoms need one additional electron to be most stable (a duet for H and an octet for Cl), and both atoms can achieve those electron configurations if they share a pair of electrons—that is, if they form a bond. Chemists indicate that bond using the notation shown below, where a shared pair of electrons is represented as a line. This representation is called a **Lewis structure**. In addition to the shared pair of bonding electrons, Cl will have three unshared pairs or **lone pairs** of electrons around it, as shown in the Lewis structure of HCl (Figure 10.2).

The Lewis structure for HCl showed one shared pair of electrons to form a **single bond**. Atoms can share two or even three electron pairs at once, forming **double bonds** and **triple bonds** (Figure 10.3). The oxygen atoms in O_2 share two pairs of electrons to form a double bond. The nitrogen atoms in N_2 share three pairs of electrons to form a triple bond.

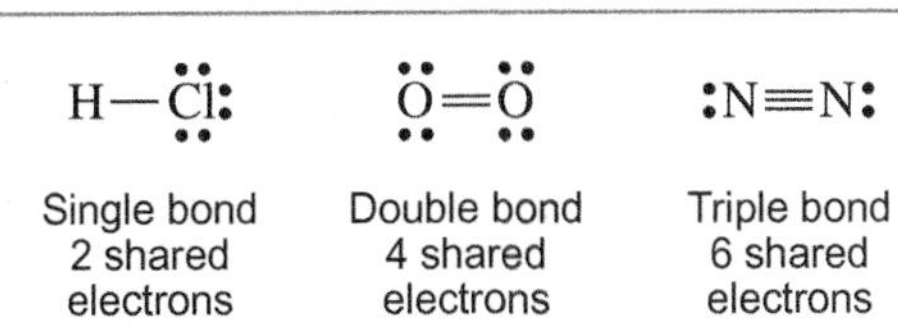

FIGURE 10.3 Single, Double, and Triple Bonds

Shared electrons result in covalent bonds. The number of electrons shared between two atoms determines the type of bond. Single, double, and triple bonds are made up of two, four, and six shared electrons, respectively.

Example 10.2

Identify the numbers of shared electrons and unshared electrons in the Lewis structures for (a) hydrazine, N_2H_4, and (b) hydrogen cyanide, HCN.

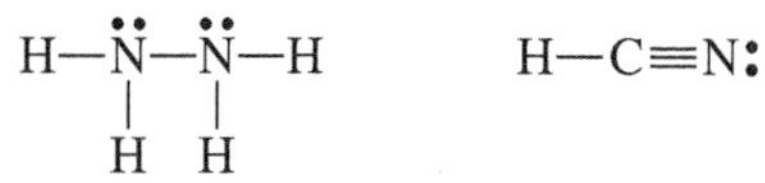

(a) (b)

Solution

a. N_2H_4 has five single bonds (10 shared electrons) and two lone pairs (4 unshared electrons).

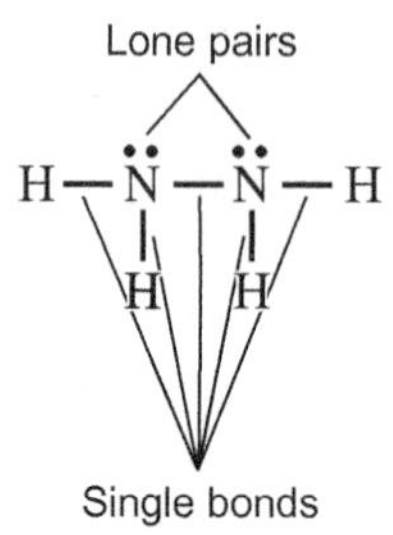

b. HCN has a single bond (two shared electrons) and a triple bond (six shared electrons), for a total of eight shared electrons, and one lone pair (two unshared electrons).

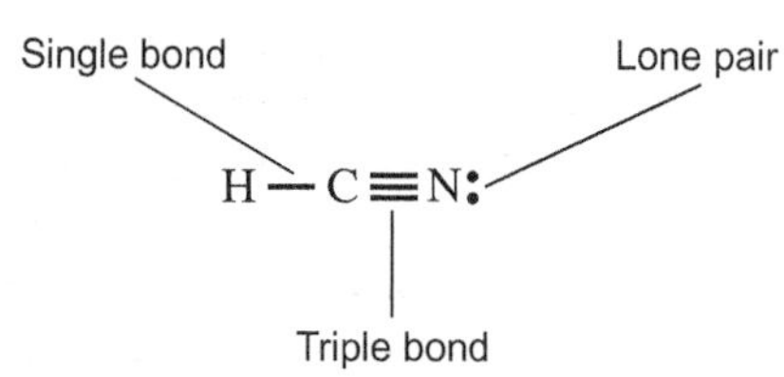

PRACTICE PROBLEM 10.2

Identify the numbers of shared electrons and unshared electrons in the Lewis structure for (a) chloroform, $CHCl_3$, and (b) acetamide, CH_3CONH_2.

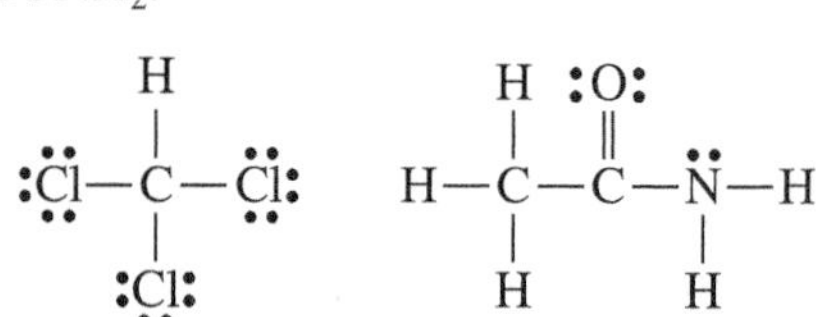

Hint: Each line in the structures represents two shared electrons. Each dot represents one unshared electron. The dots usually come in pairs, called lone pairs, which makes it convenient to count by twos when counting electrons in structures.

The terms *single bond*, *double bond*, and *triple bond* refer to covalent bonds only.

Section 10.2 discusses how to recognize the important features of a Lewis structure and how to use a set of step-by-step guidelines to draw Lewis structures for molecules and polyatomic ions.

SECTION REVIEW

- The shared electrons count toward the valence electrons of both atoms.
- The number of bonds an atom is likely to make in a molecule can be predicted using the octet/duet rule.
- Nonmetal atoms become more stable when they share electrons to form molecules.
- Atoms can share one, two, or three pairs of electrons to form single, double, or triple bonds, respectively.
- Unshared valence electron pairs are called lone pairs.

10.2 Lewis Structures

GOAL

- Draw Lewis structures for molecules and polyatomic ions that follow the octet rule.

Background Review

Chapter 2 Atoms and the Periodic Table: Section 2.4—Subatomic Particles, Isotopes, and Ions

Chapter 8 The Quantum Model: Section 8.3—Electron Shells, Subshells, and Orbitals

In this section you will learn how to draw basic Lewis structures. Later sections in this chapter will help you to fine-tune your Lewis structures to make good representations of real molecules. Later chapters discuss how to combine Lewis structures with other concepts to predict shapes of molecules and properties of compounds.

DRAWING LEWIS STRUCTURES TO REPRESENT MOLECULES

Recall that atoms share electrons to form molecules to become more stable and lower in energy. Each atom in a stable molecule must have access to an appropriate number of electrons—eight for elements that follow the octet rule and two for hydrogen, which follows the duet rule.

Throughout this text and throughout your studies in science, you will see molecular compounds represented by Lewis structures, which are two-dimensional drawings or models of three-dimensional molecules. It is very important to be able to draw them, but you must also be able to interpret them and know their limitations. Methane, CH_4, is the simplest organic compound and has the Lewis structure shown below.

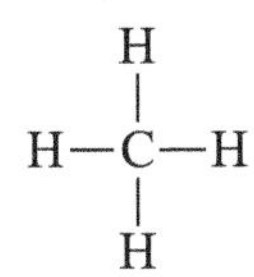

The Lewis structure of CH_4 shows eight electrons (two from each single bond). This matches the total valence contributed by the atoms (four valence electrons from C and one from each H). This may seem obvious, but it is very important. The number of electrons shown in a Lewis structure must always equal the total number of valence electrons in the atoms of the molecule. Another feature of a Lewis structure is that the atoms in the molecule obey the octet rule whenever possible. The carbon atom, with four single bonds, is surrounded by a total eight electrons, which satisfies the octet rule. Each hydrogen atom has one single bond and is sharing two electrons, which is appropriate for hydrogen as a first period element. Other exceptions to the octet rule are discussed in Section 10.4.

Consider the carbon dioxide molecule shown in Figure 10.4. The number of electrons shown in the structure is equal to the number of valence electrons in the atoms (4 from carbon and 6 from each of the oxygen atoms for a total of 16). Why are there double bonds between the C and O atoms? This is the simplest way to arrange 16 electrons among three atoms and provide each atom with an octet. Furthermore, their numbers of valence electrons indicate that carbon atoms are likely to make four bonds in a molecule and that oxygen atoms are likely to make two bonds.

(a) (b)

FIGURE 10.4 Octets in Carbon Dioxide

(a) Each oxygen atom has an octet, with a double bond (four shared electrons) and two lone pairs (four unshared electrons), for a total of eight electrons in its valence shell. (b) The carbon atom has an octet with two double bonds (two × four shared electrons), for a total of eight electrons in its valence shell.

Example 10.3

Verify that each of these Lewis structures is valid by checking octets (or duets for H) and the number of valence electrons.

a. ammonia, NH_3

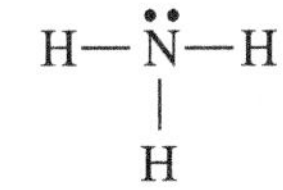

b. formaldehyde, H_2CO

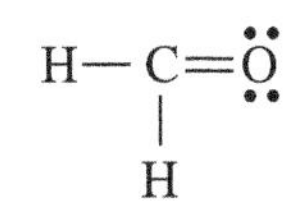

Solution

a. To verify octets (and duets) look at the lines and dots surrounding each atom. The nitrogen atom has three single bonds (six electrons) and a lone pair (two electrons), for a total of eight electrons. Each hydrogen has one bond (two electrons), which is appropriate for hydrogen.

To verify valence electrons, start by counting the electrons shown in the structure.

Three single bonds (six electrons) + one lone pair (two electrons) = eight electrons.

Next, count the available valence electrons from each atom. Nitrogen is a group 15 element with five valence electrons and hydrogen has only one electron: $5 + 3(1) = 8$. This matches the number of electrons shown in the structure.

b. To verify octets (and duets), look at the lines and dots surrounding each atom. The carbon atom shares eight electrons in the bonds (two single and one double); the oxygen atom shares four electrons in the double bond and has four additional electrons in the lone pairs. Each hydrogen atom shares two electrons in the single bond.

To verify valence electrons, start by counting the electrons shown in the structure.

One double bond (4 electrons) + two single bonds (4 electrons) + two lone pairs (4 electrons) = 12 electrons.

Next, count the available valence electrons from each atom. Carbon, a group 14 element, has 4 valence electrons; oxygen, a group 16 element, has 6 valence electrons; and each hydrogen atom has 1, for a total of 12 electrons. This matches the number of electrons shown in the structure.

PRACTICE PROBLEM 10.3

Verify that each of these Lewis structures is valid by (1) comparing the number of electrons shown in the structure to (2) the number of valence electrons available and (3) describing how the octet or duet rule is satisfied for each atom in the structure.

a. hydrazine, N_2H_4
b. hydrogen cyanide, HCN

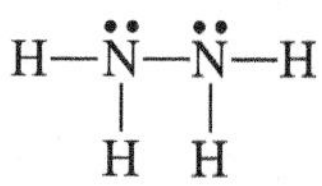

$H{-}C{\equiv}N{:}$

Hint: To verify octets (and duets), look at the lines and dots surrounding each atom. Hydrogen should be surrounded by two electrons (a duet) and all other atoms should be surrounded by eight electrons (an octet). To verify valence electrons, start by counting the total number of electrons shown in the structure. Recall that each dot is one electron and each line is two electrons. Next, sum the available valence of all the atoms and compare that sum to the number you counted in the structure.

Now that you have a basic idea of the characteristics of a valid Lewis structure, you are ready to learn how to draw basic Lewis structures by following the guidelines presented here.

GUIDELINES FOR DRAWING LEWIS STRUCTURES

1. Sum up the valence electrons for each atom present in the molecule.
2. Select a central atom and arrange the symbols for the other atoms around it. The central atom is generally the atom that needs to make the most bonds to become stable. It may also be the first atom written in the formula, unless that atom is hydrogen, which can never be a central atom. Section 10.3 discusses how to select a central atom based on electronegativity.
3. Connect the central atom to each of the outer atoms with a single bond.
4. Keeping in mind that each single bond counts as two electrons, distribute the remaining valence electrons from step 1 to the outer atoms as lone pairs to complete their octets. Hydrogen is an exception and is complete with a single bond only.
5. Assign any remaining electrons to the central atom.
6. If the central atom has less than an octet, move lone pairs from outer atoms into shared positions to form double or triple bonds as needed.
7. Verify that your final structure fulfills the duet rule for hydrogen and the octet rule for all other atoms (exceptions are discussed in Section 10.4). Verify, too, that the number of electrons shown in the structure matches the total calculated in step 1.

A reasonable Lewis structure for chloroform, $CHCl_3$, can be drawn using these steps.

Step	$CHCl_3$
1. Sum up the valence electrons.	Carbon contributes four, hydrogen contributes one, and each chlorine contributes seven. $1(4) + 1(1) + 3(7) = 26$ valence electrons
2. Select a central atom and arrange the other atoms around it.	Hydrogen is never the central atom; it is always a terminal atom. Chlorine has seven valence electrons, so it needs only one electron to have an octet. Thus, chlorine is usually a terminal atom, too. Carbon needs four more electrons to reach an octet, so it needs to make the most bonds to be stable. Thus, carbon is the central atom in $CHCl_3$. H Cl C Cl Cl
3. Draw single bonds between the central atom and each terminal atom.	This process utilizes 8 of the 26 valence electrons available (remember: each single bond represents a pair of electrons). 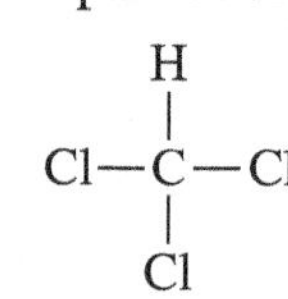
4. Distribute the remaining electrons to the outer atoms.	$26 - 8 = 18$ electrons remain. Place three lone pairs on each Cl atom. 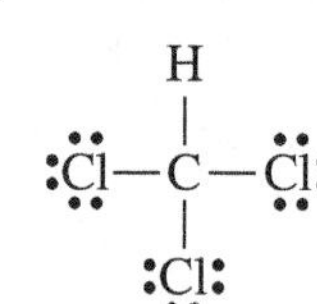
5. Assign any remaining electrons to the central atom.	There are no electrons remaining.
6. Move lone pairs to create multiple bonds if the central atom has less than an octet.	The central carbon atom has an octet, so no multiple bonds are needed.

Step	$CHCl_3$
7. Verify duets, octets, and the total number of valence electrons.	H has one shared pair = two electrons = a duet. C has four shared pairs (four single bonds) = eight electrons = an octet. Each Cl has one bond + three lone pairs = eight electrons = an octet. Total # of electrons = 8 shared + 18 unshared = 26

Example 10.4

Draw a Lewis structure for formaldehyde, CH_2O, in which the hydrogen and oxygen atoms are all bonded to the carbon atom.

Solution

Step	CH_2O
1. Sum up the valence electrons.	Carbon contributes four, each hydrogen contributes one, and oxygen contributes six: $1(4) + 2(1) + 1(6) = 12$ valence electrons
2. Select a central atom and arrange the other atoms around it.	The problem statement indicates that carbon is the central atom, but carbon is also the element in CH_2O that needs to make the most bonds (four). Oxygen (group 16) only needs to make two bonds, and hydrogen is always a terminal atom. H C O H
3. Draw single bonds between the central atom and each terminal atom.	This process utilizes 6 of the 12 valence electrons available. 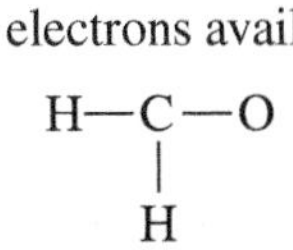
4. Distribute the remaining electrons to the outer atoms.	12 − 6 = 6 electrons remain. Place three lone pairs on the O atom. 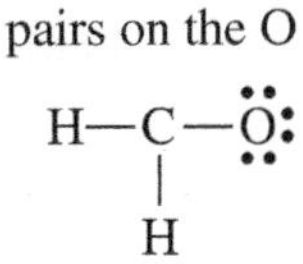
5. Assign any remaining electrons to the central atom.	There are no electrons remaining.
6. Move lone pairs to create multiple bonds if the central atom has less than an octet.	Both hydrogen atoms have a duet and the oxygen atom has an octet, but the central carbon atom has only six electrons around it. Moving one lone pair from oxygen to form a carbon–oxygen double bond gives carbon an octet while leaving oxygen's octet intact. 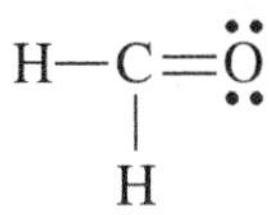
7. Verify duets, octets, and the total number of valence electrons.	Each H has one shared pair = two electrons = a duet. C has four shared pairs (two single bonds + one double bond) = eight electrons = an octet. O has four shared + four unshared = eight electrons = an octet. Total # of electrons = 8 shared + 4 unshared = 12

PRACTICE PROBLEM 10.4

Draw a Lewis structure for hydrogen peroxide, H_2O_2. The atoms are connected in a line, with H on each end.

Hint: The atoms are arranged H O O H.

Following the step-wise procedure can be helpful, or you may prefer a trial-and-error approach. The most important thing is to verify that each atom has an octet (or a duet in the case of H) and that the total number of electrons shown in your structure matches the expected total valence of the atoms.

Example 10.5

Draw a Lewis structure for carbon dioxide, CO_2.

Solution

Step	CO_2
1. Sum up the valence electrons.	Carbon contributes four and each oxygen contributes six: $1(4) + 2(6) = 16$ valence electrons
2. Select a central atom and arrange other atoms around it.	Carbon is written first in the formula and it needs to form more bonds (four) to be stable than oxygen, which needs to form two bonds. Carbon is the central atom. O C O

(*Continued*)

Step	CO_2
3. Draw single bonds between the central atom and each terminal atom.	This process utilizes 4 of the 16 available valence electrons. O—C—O
4. Distribute the remaining electrons to the outer atoms.	16 − 4 = 12 electrons remain. Place three lone pairs on each O atom. :Ö—C—Ö:
5. Assign any remaining electrons to the central atom.	There are no electrons remaining.
6. Move lone pairs to create multiple bonds if the central atom has less than an octet.	Both oxygen atoms have an octet, but the central carbon atom has only four electrons. It needs four more electrons or two more bonds. Moving a lone pair from each O atom to form double bonds with C maintains the octets on each O and gives C an octet. Ö=C=Ö
7. Verify duets, octets, and the total number of valence electrons.	C has four shared pairs (two double bonds) = eight electrons = an octet. Each O has one double bond + two lone pairs = eight electrons = an octet. Total # of electrons = 8 shared + 8 unshared = 16

PRACTICE PROBLEM 10.5

Draw Lewis structures for

a. oxygen dichloride, OCl_2
b. ammonia, NH_3
c. hydroxylamine, NH_2OH (there is an O—H bond in this molecule)

Hint: The arrangement of atoms in hydroxylamine is

H N O H
  H

Following the step-wise procedure can be helpful, or you may prefer a trial-and-error approach. The most important thing is to verify that each atom has an octet (or a duet in the case of H) and that the total number of electrons shown in your structure matches the expected total valence of the atoms.

Example 10.6

Draw a Lewis structure for ethene, C_2H_4, which has two connected carbon atoms in the center and two hydrogen atoms connected to each carbon atom.

Solution

Step	C_2H_4
1. Sum up the valence electrons.	Hydrogen contributes one and each carbon contributes four: 4(1) + 2(4) = 12 valence electrons
2. Select a central atom and arrange the other atoms around it.	In this case there are two central atoms. H C C H H H
3. Draw single bonds between appropriate atoms.	This process utilizes 10 of the 12 valence electrons available. H—C—C—H H H
4. Distribute the remaining electrons to the outer atoms. 5. Assign any remaining electrons to the central atom.	12 − 10 = 2 electrons remain. All of the outer atoms are H atoms and need lone pairs. Since both carbon atoms need an additional pair of electrons to gain an octet, it makes sense to use this pair of electrons to form a second bond between the carbon atoms. (Alternatively, place these last two electrons as a lone pair on one of the carbon atoms.) H—C=C—H (H H) or H—C—C̈—H (H H)
6. Move lone pairs to create multiple bonds if the central atom has less than an octet.	There are no lone pairs to move. (Alternatively, move the lone pair to form a double bond between the carbon atoms.) H—C=C—H H H
7. Verify duets, octets, and the total number of valence electrons.	All H atoms have a shared pair of electrons = two electrons = a duet. Each C atom has one double bond + two single bonds = four shared pairs electrons = an octet. Total # of electrons = four single bonds(8) + a double bond(4) = 12

PRACTICE PROBLEM 10.6

Draw a Lewis structure for the following molecules, in which the atoms are arranged in a line with hydrogen on each end.

a. acetylene, C_2H_2
b. diazine, N_2H_2

Hint: The arrangement of atoms will be
a. H C C H
b. H N N H

Following the step-wise procedure can be helpful, or you may prefer a trial-and-error approach. The most important thing is to verify that each atom has an octet (or a duet in the case of H) and that the total number of electrons shown in your structure matches the expected total valence of the atoms.

Formulas for more complex molecules sometimes give clues as to how the atoms are arranged in the molecule. For example, in Practice Problem 10.5c, which asked you to draw the Lewis structure of NH_2OH, the OH in the formula indicated that there was an O—H bond in the molecule. There are many, many compounds involving carbon, hydrogen, and atoms of other elements. In these compounds, it is common to see the symbols for the atoms that are bonded to each carbon atom placed immediately after that atom. In ethanol, CH_3CH_2OH, for example, the first carbon is bonded to three H atoms and is bonded to the second carbon, which is bonded to two H atoms and an O, which is bonded to the last H atom. Compounds such as ethanol, which consist primarily of carbon and hydrogen, and to a lesser degree oxygen, sulfur, the halogens, nitrogen, and/or phosphorus (and sometimes other elements) are classified as organic compounds. The carbon atoms in organic compounds are often bonded together in chains.

Example 10.7

Draw the complete Lewis structure for CH_3CH_2OH, the alcohol in alcoholic beverages.

Solution

Step	**CH_3CH_2OH**
1. Sum up the valence electrons.	Each C contributes four, each H contributes one, and O contributes six: $2(4) + 6(1) + 1(6) = 20$ valence electrons
2. Select a central atom and arrange the other atoms around it.	The two carbon atoms are bonded to each other in a short chain. Each C is a central atom. H H H C C O H H H
3. Draw single bonds between appropriate atoms.	This process utilizes 16 of the 20 valence electrons available. 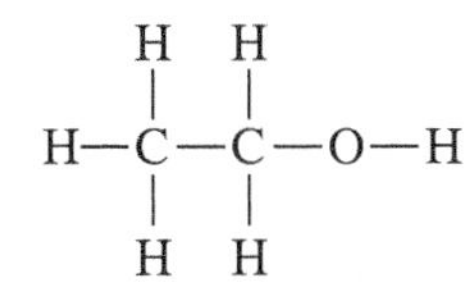
4. Distribute the remaining electrons to the outer atoms.	$20 - 16 = 4$ electrons remain. Place two lone pairs on the O, because the other outer atoms are all hydrogen. 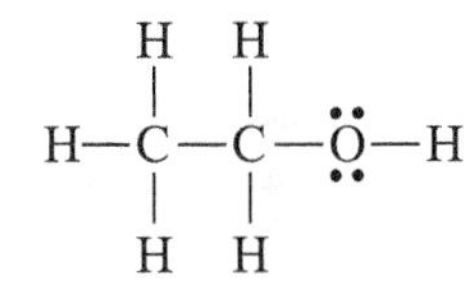
5. Assign any remaining electrons to the central atom.	There are no electrons remaining.
6. Move lone pairs to create multiple bonds if the central atom has less than an octet.	Both central C atoms have octets.
7. Verify duets, octets, and total number of valence electrons.	Each H atom has a shared pair of electrons = two electrons = a duet. Each C atom has four shared pairs (four single bonds) = eight electrons = an octet. The O has two shared pairs + two lone pairs = eight electrons = an octet Total # of electrons = 16 shared + 4 unshared = 20

PRACTICE PROBLEM 10.7

Draw a complete Lewis structure for diethyl ether, $CH_3CH_2OCH_2CH_3$.

Hint: Recall that carbon typically forms four bonds, hydrogen forms one bond, and oxygen typically has two bonds and two lone pairs.

POLYATOMIC IONS

Many compounds contain **polyatomic ions**, which consist of two or more atoms covalently bonded together and have a net positive or negative charge. Examples of common polyatomic ions are given in Table 3.4 and include nitrite, NO_2^-; ammonium, NH_4^+; and phosphate, PO_4^{3-}.

Lewis structures for polyatomic ions are drawn following the same guidelines as for neutral molecules, with a few minor additions. You *must consider the charge* when summing the valence electrons in step 1, so you must *add* a valence electron for each negative charge on an anion and *subtract* a valence electron for each positive charge on a cation. The final structure for a polyatomic ion always includes brackets around the structure, with the charge indicated outside the brackets.

Example 10.8

Draw a Lewis structure for the chlorite ion, ClO_2^-.

Solution

The single negative charge on the chlorite ion means that one extra valence electron must be included in the total in step 1.

Step	ClO_2^-
1. Sum up the valence electrons, adding valence electrons for each negative charge and subtracting electrons for each positive charge.	Chlorine contributes seven, each oxygen contributes six; add one electron for the −1 charge: $1(7) + 2(6) + 1 = 20$ valence electrons
2. Select a central atom and arrange the other atoms around it.	The central atom is Cl, even though group 17 elements are usually terminal atoms, not central atoms, because they usually need to form only one bond to be stable. In this case, though, it is listed first in the formula because it is the central atom. $[O\ \ Cl\ \ O]^-$
3. Draw single bonds between appropriate atoms.	This process utilizes 4 of the 20 valence electrons available. $[O-Cl-O]^-$
4. Distribute the remaining electrons to the outer atoms.	$20 - 4 = 16$ electrons remain. Place three lone pairs on each O atom. This uses 12 of the 16 remaining electrons. 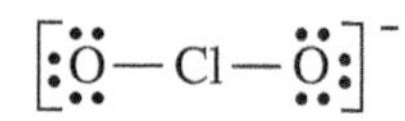
5. Assign any remaining electrons to the central atom.	Place two lone pairs on the central Cl atom. 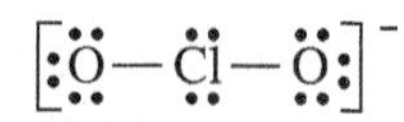
6. Move lone pairs to create multiple bonds if the central atom has less than an octet.	The central atom has an octet, so no multiple bonds are necessary.
7. Verify duets, octets, and the total number of valence electrons.	Both O atoms have three lone pairs + one bond = eight electrons = an octet. Cl has two bonds + two lone pairs = eight electrons = an octet. Total # of electrons = 4 shared + 16 unshared = 20.

Be sure to include the charge on polyatomic ions. The charge is an integral part of the formula. For example, chlorine dioxide, ClO_2, a covalent compound, is a green, noxious gas, whereas ClO_2^-, a polyatomic anion, is found in many ionic compounds.

The structure of the chlorite ion is the same regardless of whether you consider it alone or in an ionic compound. The additional electron that gives the chlorite ion its negative charge can be considered to come from a metal atom during the formation of chlorite. In general, ions do not exist in isolation, even though they are often written alone.

PRACTICE PROBLEM 10.8

Draw Lewis structures for these polyatomic ions: (a) ammonium ion, NH_4^+, and (b) cyanide ion, CN^-.

Hint: When adding up the total valence, subtract 1 for each positive charge and add 1 for each negative charge. Other than that, drawing these structures is done exactly the same way as in the earlier examples.

SECTION REVIEW

- Molecules contain all the valence electrons of their atoms, organized to provide an octet for most atoms in the molecule and a duet for hydrogen atoms.

- A systematic method for drawing Lewis structures produces consistent diagrams that can help you visualize the bonding in the molecule.
- Lewis structures of molecules show shared electrons as straight lines and unshared electrons as dots.
- Atoms can share one, two, or three pairs of electrons, thereby forming single, double, or triple bonds, respectively.
- Polyatomic ions consist of two or more atoms covalently bonded together that have a net positive or negative charge. Polyatomic ions form ionic bonds with other ions.

10.3 Resonance and Formal Charges

GOALS

- Calculate formal charge.
- Use formal charges and electronegativity values to identify the Lewis structure that best represents the molecule.

Background Review

Chapter 9 Periodicity and Ionic Bonding: Section 9.3—Ionization Energy and Electron Affinity

Atoms come together to form molecules by sharing electrons according to the octet rule (Section 10.1), and the models of these molecules are called Lewis structures (Section 10.2). Lewis structures can help you visualize the bonding in molecules, but they have limitations when it comes to accurately representing the locations of electrons.

RESONANCE

One limitation of the Lewis model is that a single Lewis structure cannot adequately depict many molecules and polyatomic ions. A molecule or ion with multiple possible Lewis structures that differ only in the placement of multiple bonds and lone pairs is said to exhibit **resonance** (i.e., have resonance structures). The carbonate ion, CO_3^{2-}, has three possible Lewis structures (Figure 10.5), which can be drawn by following these steps.

Step	CO_3^{2-}
1. Sum up the valence electrons, adding valence electrons for each negative charge and subtracting electrons for each positive charge.	C contributes four, each O contributes six; add two electrons for the −2 charge: $1(4) + 3(6) + 2 = 24$ valence electrons
2. Select a central atom and arrange the other atoms around it.	Carbon is the likely central atom. 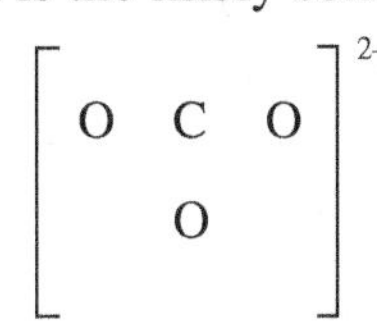
3. Draw single bonds between appropriate atoms.	This process accounts for 6 of the 24 valence electrons available. 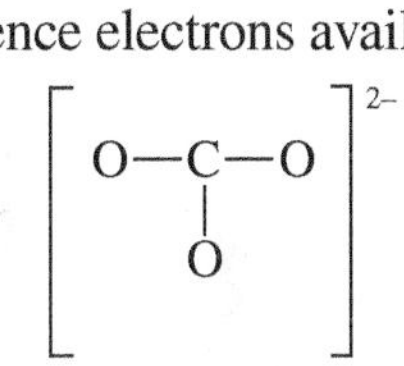
4. Distribute the remaining electrons to the outer atoms.	$24 - 6 = 18$ electrons remain. 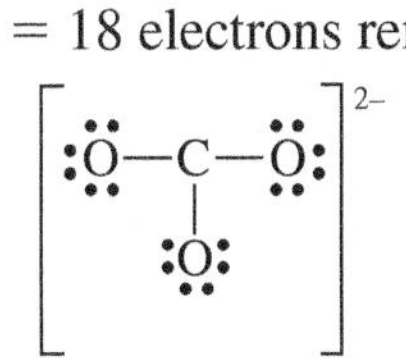
5. Assign any remaining electrons to the central atom.	There are no electrons remaining.

(Continued)

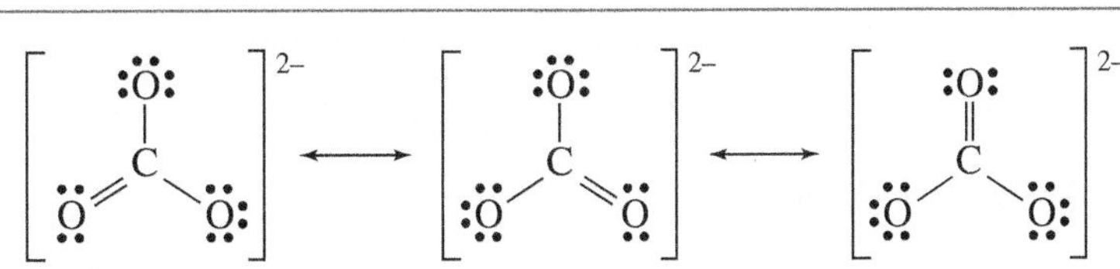

FIGURE 10.5 Resonance Structures of the Carbonate Ion

The placement of the double bond in the Lewis structure representing carbonate is arbitrary. These three resonance structures, separated by a double-headed arrow, show all possible placements of the double bond in otherwise equivalent structures.

Step	CO_3^{2-}
6. Move lone pairs to create multiple bonds if the central atom has less than an octet.	The central C atom has only six electrons around it, so a lone pair from one of the three terminal O atoms must be used to make a carbon–oxygen double bond: 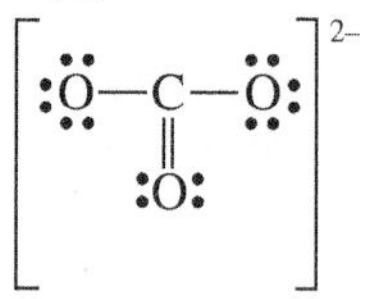
7. Verify duets, octets, and the total number of valence electrons.	C has two single bonds + one double bond = eight electrons = an octet. The single-bonded terminal O atoms have one bond + three lone pairs = eight electrons = an octet. The double-bonded terminal O has two bonds + two lone pairs = eight electrons = an octet. Total # of electrons = 8 shared + 16 unshared = 24

With its three equivalent Lewis structures, called **resonance structures**, the carbonate ion is an example of an ion that exhibits resonance. It is equally likely that the double bond is located between carbon and any of the three oxygen atoms. No single Lewis structure adequately describes the carbonate ion. Instead, the pair of electrons that is shown as a double bond is shared or *spread out* among all three locations and is said to be a **delocalized bond**. Since delocalized bonds are difficult to represent on paper, the accepted way to draw the structure is to show all possible resonance forms with double-headed arrows between them (Figure 10.5). The C—O bonds in the carbonate ion are equivalent with properties in between a single bond and a double bond.

Figure 10.6 is called a **resonance hybrid**; it shows the delocalized bond as dashed lines. It is an average of the three separate resonance structures and closer to the true structure of the carbonate ion.

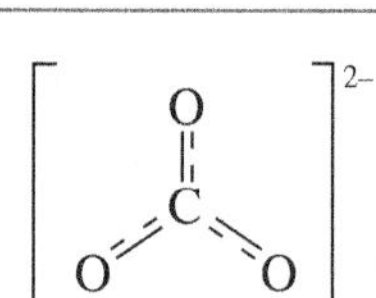

FIGURE 10.6 Resonance Hybrid: Delocalized View of the Carbonate Ion

The true structure of carbonate resembles a hybrid of the three resonance forms, where each bond is neither single nor double, but somewhere in between, which is represented in the artwork by the combination of a line and a broken line.

Example 10.9

Draw all resonance structures for the nitrite ion, NO_2^-.

Solution

Step	NO_2^-
1. Sum up the valence electrons, adding valence electrons for each negative charge and subtracting electrons for each positive charge.	N contributes five, each O atom contributes six; add one electron for the −1 charge: 1(5) + 2(6) + 1 = 18 valence electrons
2. Select a central atom and arrange other atoms around it.	Nitrogen is the likely central atom. 
3. Draw single bonds between appropriate atoms.	This accounts for 4 of the 18 valence electrons available. 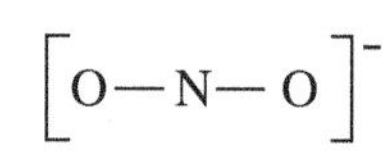
4. Distribute the remaining electrons to the outer atoms.	18 − 4 = 14 electrons remain, so place three lone pairs on each O atom. This utilizes 12 of the 14 electrons that remain. 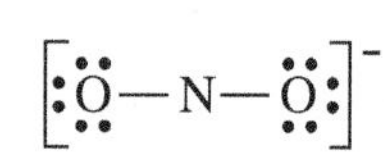
5. Assign any remaining electrons to the central atom.	Two electron remain, so they are placed on N. 
6. Move lone pairs to create multiple bonds if the central atom has less than an octet.	Both O atoms have octets, but N has only six electrons around it. Move a lone pair from either O atom to form a nitrogen–oxygen double bond. 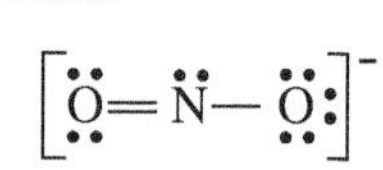
7. Verify duets, octets, and the total number of valence electrons.	N has one double bond + one single bond + one lone pair = eight electrons. One O atom has one double bond + two lone pairs = eight electrons. One O atom has one single bond + three lone pairs = eight electrons. Total # of electrons = 6 shared + 12 unshared = 18.

There are two resonance forms.

A better representation of the nitrite ion is an average of these two structures, with the double-bond electrons being shared among all three atoms of the molecule. Neither N—O bond is really a single bond or a double bond. Both bonds are equivalent, with the experimental evidence suggesting that they are somewhere between a single bond and a double bond in length and strength. These bonds are perhaps better described as 1.5 bonds.

PRACTICE PROBLEM 10.9

Draw all the resonance structures for

a. the nitrate ion, NO_3^-
b. the hydrogen carbonate ion, HCO_3^-

Hint: As you've seen before with polyatomic ions, you need to account for the charge when determining the total valence: add one valence electron for each negative charge and subtract one valence electron for each positive charge.

Once you have drawn a valid structure with octets for each atom and the proper total valence, look for other ways to draw the structure with a different arrangement of double or triple bonds. When you switch the position of a double or triple bond, be sure to adjust the number of lone pairs accordingly for the outer atoms.

Example 10.10

Draw all possible resonance structures for the acetate ion, $CH_3CO_2^-$.

Solution

Step	$CH_3CO_2^-$
1. Sum up the valence electrons, adding valence electrons for each negative charge and subtracting electrons for each positive charge.	Each C contributes four, each H contributes one, each O contributes six, plus one for the −1 charge: $2(4) + 3(1) + 2(6) + 1 = 24$ valence electrons
2. Select a central atom and arrange the other atoms around it.	The two C atoms are bonded in a chain with three H atoms around the first C and two O atoms bonded to the other C. 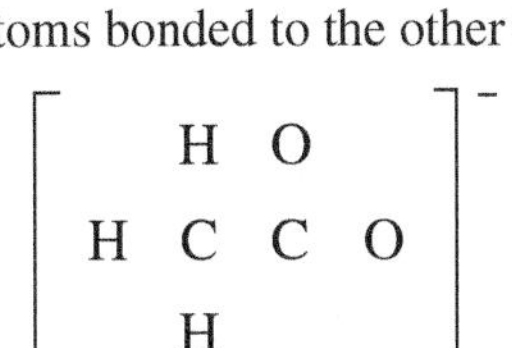
3. Draw single bonds between appropriate atoms.	This accounts for 12 of the 24 available valence electrons. 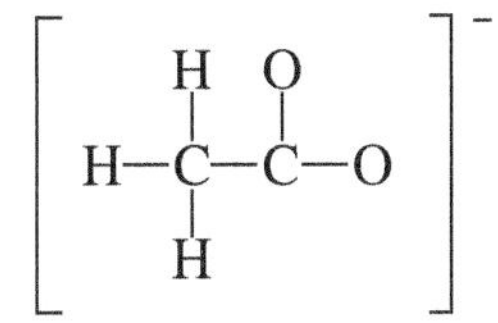
4. Distribute the remaining electrons to the outer atoms.	$24 - 12 = 12$ electrons remain. Place three lone pairs on both O atoms. 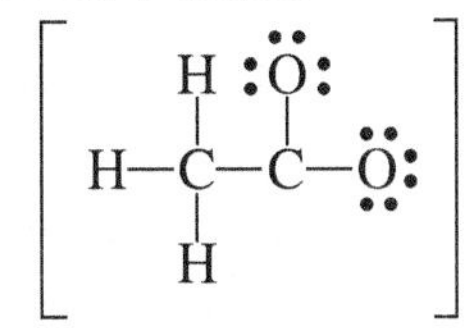
5. Assign any remaining electrons to the central atom.	There are no electrons remaining.
6. Move lone pairs to create multiple bonds if the central atom has less than an octet.	All atoms have their required duet or octet except the C bonded to the O atoms. Move a lone pair from either O to form a carbon–oxygen double bond. 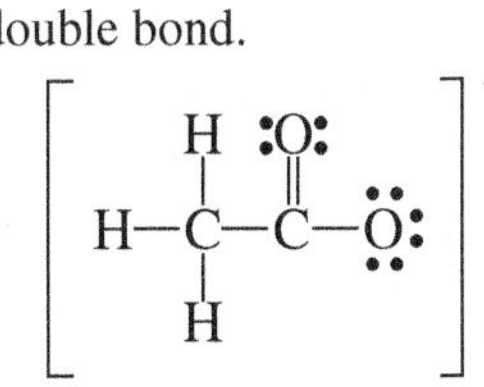
7. Verify duets, octets, and the total number of valence electrons.	Each H has one bond = two electrons. One C has four single bonds = eight electrons. One C has two single bonds + one double bond = eight electrons. One O atom has one double bond + two lone pairs = eight electrons. One O atom has one bond + three lone pairs = eight electrons. Total # of electrons = 14 shared + 10 unshared = 24.

The resonance structures for the acetate ion are these two equivalent structures:

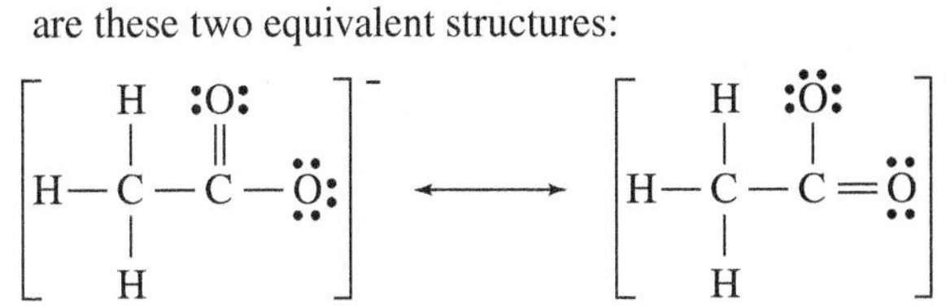

PRACTICE PROBLEM 10.10

Draw all resonance structures for ozone, O_3.

Hint: Once you have drawn a valid structure with octets for each atom and the proper total valence, look for other ways to draw the structure with a different arrangement of double or triple bonds. When you switch the position of a double or triple bond, be sure to adjust the number of lone pairs accordingly for the outer atoms.

ELECTRONEGATIVITY AND FORMAL CHARGE

Chapter 9 explains that there are periodic trends in ionization energy and electron affinity that relate to an atom's attraction to its outermost electrons. In this section, you will learn about two related concepts that help to explain why atoms of different elements have different attractions for electrons in molecules or polyatomic ions and how to draw Lewis structures that are better representations of the real molecules.

Electronegativity is a relative measure of the ability of a bonded atom to attract shared electrons. The greater the electronegativity of an atom, the more strongly the atom attracts bonding electrons to itself. In general, electronegativity increases as you proceed from left to right across a row of the periodic table and as you proceed from the bottom to the top of a column, just as ionization energy increases. The lighter noble gases do not have defined electronegativity values, however, because they form no bonds. Electronegativity values for the main group elements are shown in Figure 10.7.

Electronegativity values, which have no units, reflect how strongly a neutral atom of an element attracts electrons from bonded atoms. The higher the electronegativity value, the more strongly that element pulls shared electrons from other elements. Fluorine has the highest electronegativity of any element (4.0), and oxygen has the second highest value (3.5).

You can use electronegativity values to determine the central atom in a Lewis structure. Central atoms are in a position to make more bonds (share more electrons) than the outer atoms, which tend to have more lone pairs. Elements with higher electronegativity values are less likely to share electrons and, therefore, are more likely to be the outer atoms in a molecule. For example, when drawing the Lewis structure for selenium trioxide, SeO_3, all atoms have the same number of valence electrons and are predicted to make two bonds to complete their octets, so you cannot use that to determine which is the central atom. Selenium has

1 1A	2 2A	13 3A	14 4A	15 5A	16 6A	17 7A	18 8A
H 2.1							He
Li 1.0	Be 1.5	B 2.0	C 2.5	N 3.0	O 3.5	F 4.0	Ne
Na 0.9	Mg 1.2	Al 1.5	Si 1.8	P 2.1	S 2.5	Cl 3.0	Ar
K 0.8	Ca 1.0	Ga 1.6	Ge 1.8	As 2.0	Se 2.4	Br 2.8	Kr 3.0
Rb 0.8	Sr 1.0	In 1.7	Sn 1.8	Sb 1.9	Te 2.1	I 2.5	Xe 2.6
Cs 0.7	Ba 0.9	Tl 1.8	Pb 1.9	Bi 1.9	Po 2.0	At 2.2	Rn
Fr 0.7	Ra 0.9						

Electronegativity increases (→ across a row)

Electronegativity increases (↑ up a column)

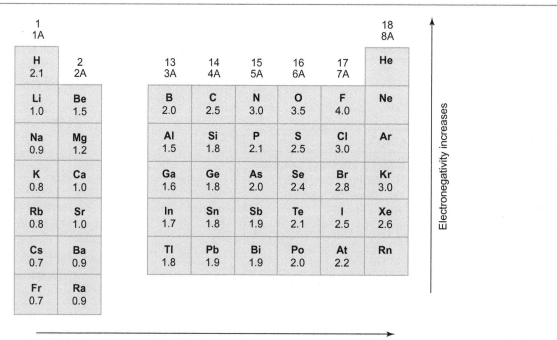

FIGURE 10.7 Electronegativity of the Main Group Elements

Electronegativity is a unitless number that reflects how strongly a neutral atom of each element attracts electrons when bonded to another atom or atoms.

an electronegativity value, 2.4, that is much lower than that of oxygen, 3.5. Thus, selenium is the likely central atom.

One possible Lewis structure for SeO_3 is shown here, which you can verify for yourself.

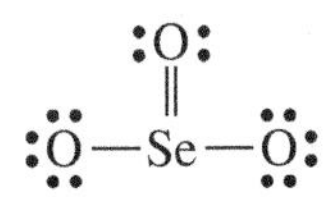

Two additional Lewis structures can also be drawn if you move the location of the double bond and one of the lone pairs. Section 10.4 discusses yet another way to draw the Lewis structure for this molecule.

Example 10.11

What is the central atom of $POBr_3$?

Solution

Use the electronegativity values of the three elements in the molecule to determine the central atom: O = 3.5, Br = 2.8, and P = 2.1. As the element with the lowest electronegativity, P will be the central atom.

PRACTICE PROBLEM 10.11

What is the central atom of cyanate, OCN^-?

Hint: You can use Figure 10.7 to find the electronegativity value of each atom, or rank the atoms by relative electronegativity using the general trend that electronegativity increases as you move up and to the right in the periodic table. The atom with the lowest electronegativity is typically the central atom.

FORMAL CHARGE

Sometimes it is possible to draw multiple *valid* Lewis structures that are not equivalent. The concept of formal charge can help you decide which structure (or structures) is the better representation of the real molecule. **Formal charge** is a type of electron bookkeeping in which you assign fictitious charges to atoms in a molecule by comparing the number of valence electrons it *appears* to have in the structure to the number of valence electrons it brought to the molecule. The process starts with a completed Lewis structure for a molecule. To assign a formal charge to an atom, subtract the sum of unshared electrons and half the number of shared electrons from the valence for that atom. Basically, you are comparing the number of electrons the free atom has in its valence shell to the number of electrons the atom *owns* in the molecule. The atom owns *all* its unshared electrons but owns *only half* of each shared pair or bond.

$$\text{Formal charge} = \#\text{ valence e}^- - \left(\frac{\#\text{ shared e}^-}{2} + \#\text{ unshared e}^-\right) \quad (10.1)$$

The formal charges of all the atoms in a Lewis structure should sum to zero for a molecule and to the net charge for a cation or anion.

> The most likely Lewis structures are those that have small formal charges, or no formal charges, especially for the central atom. They also have negative formal charges associated with atoms of higher electronegativity and positive formal charges assigned to the atoms of lower electronegativity.

If a positive formal charge appears on an atom of higher electronegativity or a negative formal charge appears on an atom of lower electronegativity, then the structure is highly unfavorable. Formal charge helps to determine which structure is more energetically favorable and more closely resembles the real molecule. (Figure 10.8).

The cyanate ion, OCN^-, has three possible Lewis structures, as shown here.

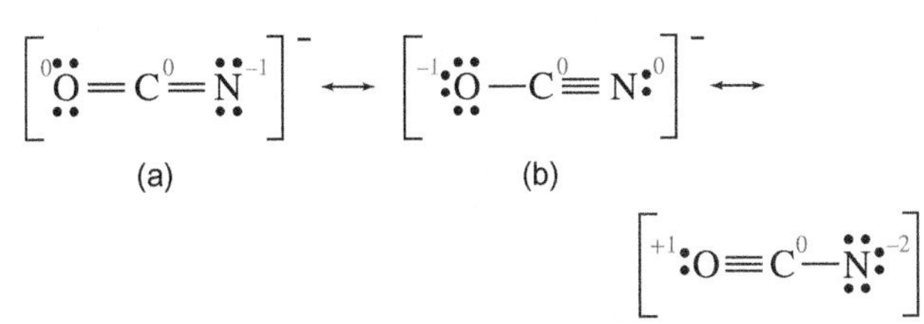

All three structures place a formal charge of zero on carbon, $4 - \left[\frac{1}{2}(8) + 0\right] = 0$. Here are the formal charge calculations for O and N for each structure.

Structure	(a)	(b)	(c)
Formal charge of O	$6 - \left[\frac{1}{2}(4) + 4\right] = 0$	$6 - \left[\frac{1}{2}(2) + 6\right] = -1$	$6 - \left[\frac{1}{2}(6) + 2\right] = +1$
Formal charge of N	$5 - \left[\frac{1}{2}(4) + 4\right] = -1$	$5 - \left[\frac{1}{2}(6) + 2\right] = 0$	$5 - \left[\frac{1}{2}(2) + 6\right] = -2$

FIGURE 10.8 Video Tutorial: Formal Charge

NOTE: You need to be online to access this video.

This video shows how to assign formal charge and how to use formal charge to identify the best Lewis structure for carbon dioxide, CO_2.

Structure (c) is the least likely contributor to the true structure of this ion because it has higher formal charge than the other two structures and places a positive charge on the atom of the highest electronegativity. While structures (a) and (b) both have a single formal charge of −1, structure (b) places that −1 formal charge on oxygen, the element with the higher electronegativity, while structure (a) places it on an atom of lower electronegativity, nitrogen. Therefore, you would predict that structure (b) most closely resembles the true structure of the cyanate ion.

Example 10.12

Draw the resonance structures of dinitrogen monoxide, N_2O, and use formal charge to determine which structure is more likely to resemble the real molecule.

Solution

Step	N_2O
1. Sum up the valence electrons.	Each N contributes five, each O contributes six: $2(5) + 1(6) = 16$ valence electrons
2. Select a central atom and arrange the other atoms around it.	One of the N atoms is the central atom because the electronegativity of N (3.0) is less than that of O (3.5). N N O
3. Draw single bonds between appropriate atoms.	This process uses 4 of the 16 valence electrons available. N—N—O
4. Distribute the remaining electrons to the outer atoms.	$16 - 4 = 12$ electrons remain. Place three lone pairs on each terminal atom. 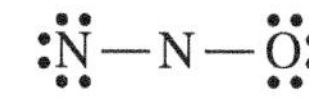
5. Assign any remaining electrons to the central atom.	There are no electrons remaining.
6. Move lone pairs to form multiple bonds if the central atom has less than an octet.	You could move one lone pair from each atom, or two from N, or two from O. 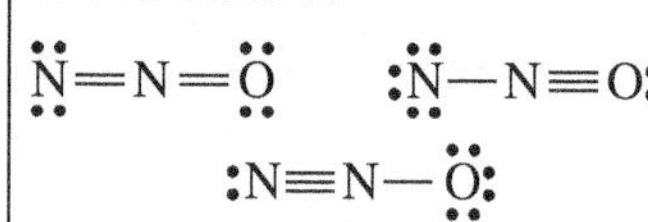
7. Verify octets and the total number of valence electrons.	All three are valid Lewis structures. The central N has four bonds = eight electrons. The O and terminal N have either two bonds + two lone pairs = eight electrons, or one bond + three lone pairs = eight electrons. Total # of electrons: 4 pairs + 4 bonds = 16 electrons.

Here are the three resonance structures, shown with their formal charges.

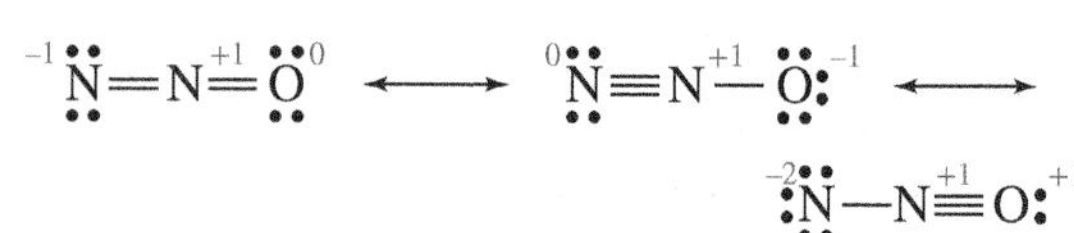

The structure on the left has low formal charges, but it places a formal charge of −1 on the terminal nitrogen, which is less electronegative than oxygen. The structure on the right does not minimize formal charge and places the most negative formal charge (−2) on nitrogen, not oxygen. It also places a positive formal charge on oxygen. The structure in the center has low formal charges overall and it places the negative charge on oxygen, the most electronegative atom, so it is most likely to resemble the real molecule.

PRACTICE PROBLEM 10.12

Draw the resonance structures of the following molecules and use formal charge to determine which structure is most likely to resemble the real molecule.

a. thiocyanate ion, SCN^-

b. nitrous acid, HNO_2 (H is bonded to O)

Hint: In thiocyanate, C is the central atom. In nitrous acid, the atoms are arranged H O N O.

In summary, properly drawn Lewis structures must

1. include all the valence electrons of the atoms in the molecule, adjusting for charge in the case of polyatomic ions;
2. distribute the available electrons such that hydrogen has a duet and all other atoms have an octet;
3. have small formal charges that, when added together, equal the charge of the molecule or ion; and
4. include all reasonable resonance structures.

SECTION REVIEW

- Molecules and polyatomic ions that can be depicted with multiple Lewis structures are said to display resonance and are best described by an average or hybrid of the various diagrams.
- Electronegativity is a measure of a bonded atom's ability to attract bonding electrons and is used to help determine the central atom in a molecule and the most likely Lewis structure when multiple structures are possible.
- Formal charge, a type of electron bookkeeping, assigns a charge to atoms in Lewis structures based on the valence electrons and electronic structure of the molecule. Formal charge, combined with electronegativity, is used to determine which Lewis structures are more energetically favorable when multiple structures are possible.
- The most likely Lewis structures are those that have small formal charges, or no formal charges, especially for the central atom. They also have negative formal charges associated with atoms of higher electronegativity and positive formal charges assigned to the atoms of lower electronegativity.

10.4 Exceptions to the Octet Rule

GOAL

- Apply the typical exceptions to the octet rule in drawing Lewis structures, including H, Be, B, radicals, and expanded octets.

LESS THAN AN OCTET

Not all atoms in molecules or polyatomic ions obey the octet rule. The most common of these exceptions is hydrogen, which always forms a duet rather than an octet.

H—H

(a) (b)

FIGURE 10.9 Beryllium and Boron with Less Than an Octet
Be and B do not follow the octet rule. (a) Beryllium tends to form two bonds in molecules, as seen here in beryllium hydride. (b) Boron tends to form three bonds, as seen in boron trichloride, BCl_3.

Beryllium, Be, and boron, B, are also unable to form octets of electrons. Beryllium, with two valence electrons, tends to share these with nonmetals to make two bonds in molecules such as beryllium hydride, BeH_2 (Figure 10.9), giving Be only four electrons in its valence shell in these molecules. When boron atoms form compounds, they usually have six rather than eight electrons in their valence shells, as in the case of BCl_3 (Figure 10.9). All the other guidelines for Lewis structures apply—that is, all the valence electrons must be included in the structure and each atom in the structure should have a formal charge of zero or close to zero. In the structures shown in Figure 10.9, all the atoms have formal charges of zero.

Some compounds, such as nitrogen monoxide, NO, and nitrogen dioxide, NO_2 (Figure 10.10), have an odd number of electrons, which makes it impossible to have an octet around each atom. Molecules that have single, unpaired electrons in their Lewis structures are referred to as **radicals**. In both cases, nitrogen, which has a lower electronegativity than oxygen, has seven valence electrons instead of eight. An analysis of the structures will show they include all valence electrons. In the NO structure, all the atoms have a formal charge of zero. The NO_2 structure contains one O atom with a formal charge of −1, one N atom with a formal charge

(a) (b)

FIGURE 10.10 Nitrogen Monoxide, NO, and Nitrogen Dioxide, NO_2
(a) NO and (b) NO_2 are common examples of radicals, which have an odd number of valence electrons. The unpaired electron is placed on an atom of lower electronegativity as seen in the structures here, which include all valence electrons and have a low formal charge. Radical substances are typically quite reactive due to their unpaired electrons.

of +1, and one oxygen atom with a formal charge of zero. Again, this follows the basic guidelines for Lewis structures in assigning negative formal charge to the atom of higher electronegativity and having the total formal charge equal to the overall charge on the molecule or ion.

Because these molecules have an odd number of valence electrons (11 electrons in NO and 17 electrons in NO_2), there is no way to arrange the atoms to have an (even-numbered) octet around each atom. The more electronegative atom—in this case, oxygen—attracts electrons more strongly, so it should be given an octet before a less electronegative atom. NO and NO_2, which have single, unpaired electrons in their Lewis structure, are radicals. Radicals are involved in the chemistry of photochemical smog production, ozone depletion in the stratosphere, and initiating polymerization reactions to make certain plastics.

Example 10.13

Draw the Lewis structure of chlorine monoxide, ClO.

Solution

Step	ClO
1. Sum up the valence electrons.	Cl contributes seven, and O contributes six: $1(7) + 1(6) = 13$
2. Select a central atom and arrange the other atoms around it.	Diatomic molecules do not have a central atom: Cl O
3. Draw single bonds between appropriate atoms.	This utilizes 2 of the 13 valence electrons available. Cl—O
4. Distribute the remaining electrons to the outer atoms.	$13 - 2 = 11$ electrons remain. Place three lone pairs on O (the more electronegative atom) and the rest on Cl. $:\underset{\cdot\cdot}{\dot{\mathrm{Cl}}}-\underset{\cdot\cdot}{\ddot{\mathrm{O}}}:$
5. Assign any remaining electrons to the central atom.	None remain.
6. Move lone pairs to form multiple bonds if the central atom has less than an octet.	The Cl does not have an octet, but sharing an additional pair with O would give the Cl atom nine electrons, which is not supported by the experimental evidence.
7. Verify duets, octets, formal charge, and the total number of valence electrons.	No H atoms in the structure. O has one bond + three lone pairs = eight electrons. Cl has one bond + two lone pairs + a single electron = seven electrons. Formal charges: O $6 - \left[\frac{1}{2}(2) + 6\right] = -1$ Cl $7 - \left[\frac{1}{2}(2) + 5\right] = +1$ Total # of electrons = 1 bond + 5 lone pairs + 1 unpaired electron = 13 electrons.

It is appropriate to leave chlorine's octet incomplete because Cl has a lower electronegativity (3.0) than oxygen (3.5). Because of the unpaired electron in its structure, ClO is a radical.

PRACTICE PROBLEM 10.13

Draw the Lewis structure of hydroxyl, OH. Note that this is *not* the polyatomic, hydrox*ide* ion, OH^-, but a neutral molecule.

Hint: There is an odd number of electrons in this molecule, so one of the atoms will have less than an octet. Typically, the electron-deficient atom would be the one with the lower electronegativity, but in this case it has to be oxygen that is electron-deficient because hydrogen can't bond without a duet.

EVERYDAY CONNECTION

Because they are highly reactive, radicals (sometimes called *free radicals*) can cause DNA mutations and cellular damage, contributing to aging and cancer. Radicals in the body are typically produced in oxidation reactions (Section 4.6). Molecules that can prevent oxidation, and thus deter the production of free radicals, are called antioxidants. Vitamin E and vitamin C are examples of antioxidants in food.

Gregor Schuster/Getty Images

A healthy diet including fruits and vegetables typically contains more than enough of these vitamins.

MORE THAN AN OCTET

If the central element in a molecule or polyatomic ion is in the third period or beyond, it can sometimes expand its valence shell beyond eight electrons. Only elements in the third row and higher of the periodic table can expand beyond an octet. This never happens with elements in the second row of the periodic table because their outer energy level ($n = 2$) can hold no more than eight electrons (Section 8.5). Elements with outer energy levels of $n = 3$ and beyond have the capacity to hold more than eight electrons. Two common examples of expanded octets are the sulfate ion, SO_4^{2-}, and the phosphate ion, PO_4^{3-}, shown in Figure 10.11.

> Elements in the third period and beyond can expand their valence shell and, therefore, have more than an octet of electrons around them when they are the central atom in a molecule or polyatomic ion. Central atoms with more than an octet have **expanded valence shells**, also known as expanded octets.

The sulfur atom in the center of the sulfate ion has two double bonds and two single bonds to the surrounding oxygen atoms, giving a total of six shared electron pairs (12 electrons) around the sulfur atom and a formal charge of zero. The phosphorus atom in the phosphate ion has 10 shared electrons around it and a formal charge of zero. It is possible to draw a Lewis structure for each of these polyatomic ions that obeys the octet rule. The one for SO_4^{2-} is shown in Figure 10.12a, but notice that it results in many atoms having a formal charge other than 0. You should draw the structure for PO_4^{3-} that obeys the octet rule and calculate the formal charges on each atom.

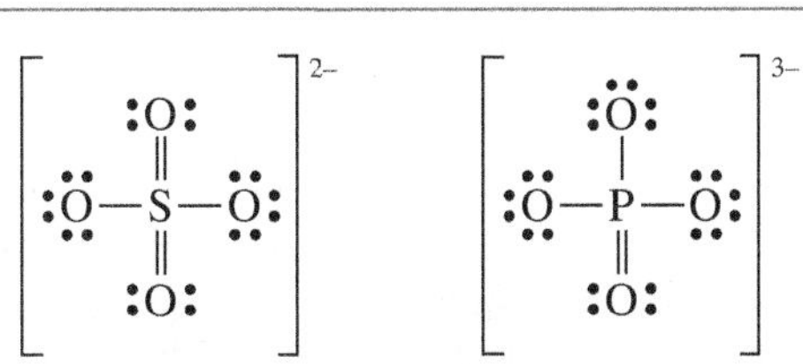

(a) (b)

FIGURE 10.11 Expanded Valence Shells in the Sulfate and Phosphate Ions

Both sulfur and phosphorus, as period 3 elements, can expand their valence shells to share more than four pairs of electrons. Expanded valence Lewis structures are shown here for the (a) sulfate, SO_4^{2-}, and (b) phosphate, PO_4^{3-}, ions.

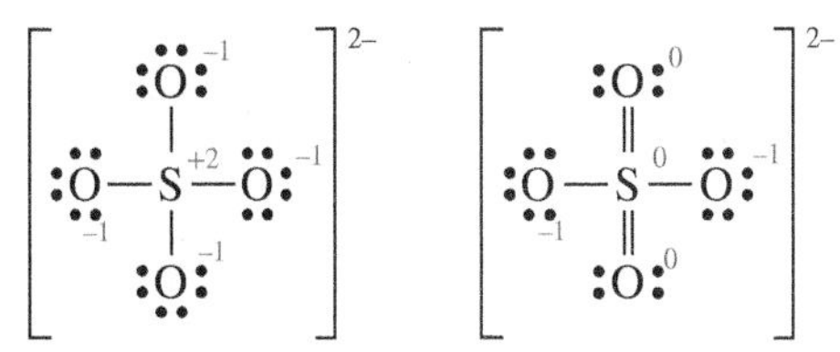

Octet (a) Expanded valence (b)

FIGURE 10.12 Octet versus Expanded Valence in Sulfate

In structure (a), the appropriate number of valence electrons are present and each atom has an octet. In doing so, though, each of the four O atoms must be assigned a formal charge of −1 and the sulfur a formal charge of +2. Structure (b) uses an expanded valence shell for the central atom, and it has much smaller formal charges. Which is correct? There is not always an easy answer to this question, and in fact there may not be a way to predict the true structure in every case.

Another example is selenium trioxide, SeO_3, which can be drawn by either following the octet rule or using expanded octets. The structure using expanded octets greatly minimizes the formal charge, suggesting that this is a better representation of the real molecule. However, the only way to know this for sure would be to use experimental evidence.

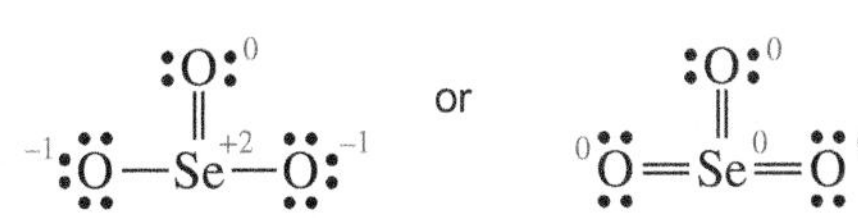

The octet rule is a good general guideline for determining bonding arrangements in molecular compounds, but it does not apply in all circumstances. There are many compounds involving period 3 and beyond elements as the central atom that have expanded valence shells. It is time to revisit the guidelines for drawing Lewis structures to add features that include electronegativity and formal charge to draw the most appropriate diagrams (Figure 10.13).

GUIDELINES FOR DRAWING LEWIS STRUCTURES, REVISITED

1. Sum the valence electrons for each atom in the formula, adding electrons (anions) or subtracting electrons (cations) to account for the charges on polyatomic ions.
2. Select as a central atom the one that (a) needs to make the most bonds to become stable and (b) has the lower electronegativity value. Arrange the symbols for the other atoms around the symbol for the central atom.

FIGURE 10.13 Video Tutorial: Exceptions to the Octet Rule

NOTE: You need to be online to access this video.
This video shows how to draw Lewis structures with exceptions to the octet rule.

3. Connect the central atom to each of the outer atoms with a single bond using two electrons for each bond.
4. Distribute the remaining valence electrons from step 1 to the outer atoms as lone pairs to complete their octets. Hydrogen is an exception and is complete with a single bond only.
5. Assign any remaining electrons to the central atom.
6. If the central atoms has less than an octet, move lone pairs from outer atoms into shared positions to form double or triple bonds as needed.
7. Verify that your final structure fulfills the duet rule for all hydrogen atoms and fulfills the octet rule for all period 2 atoms (unless the atom is Be or B or the molecule is a radical). Verify, too, that the number of electrons shown in the structure matches the total from step 1, that formal charges are small, and that atoms of greater electronegativity are assigned negative formal charges.

Example 10.14

Draw a Lewis structure for sulfur hexafluoride, SF_6.

Solution

Step	SF_6
1. Sum up the valence electrons.	S contributes six, and each F contributes seven: $1(6) + 6(7) = 48$ valence electrons
2. Select a central atom and arrange other atoms around it.	F F F S F F F
3. Draw single bonds between appropriate atoms.	This utilizes 12 of the 48 valence electrons available. 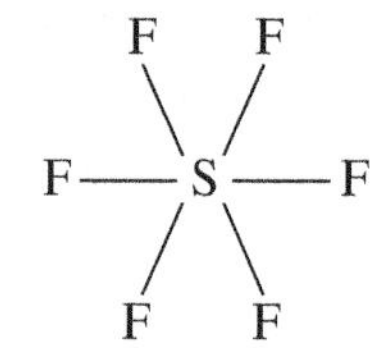
4. Distribute the remaining electrons as lone pairs to the outer atoms.	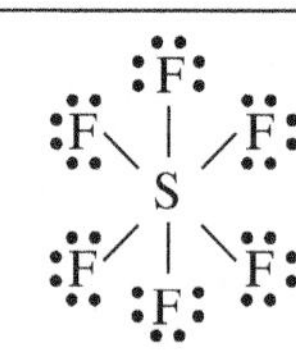
5. Assign any remaining electrons to the central atom.	No electrons remain.
6. If the central atom has less than an octet, move lone pairs to form multiple bonds.	The central atom has more than an octet, which is acceptable because S is a period 3 element.
7. Verify octets, formal charge assignments, and the total number of valence electrons.	S has 6 bonds = 12 electrons = expanded valence. Each F has one bond + three lone pairs = eight electrons. Formal charges: S $6 - \left[\frac{1}{2}(12) + 0\right] = 0$ F $7 - \left[\frac{1}{2}(2) + 6\right] = 0$ Total # of electrons = 6 bonds + 18 lone pairs = 12 shared + 36 unshared = 48 electrons.

PRACTICE PROBLEM 10.14

Draw the Lewis structure for phosphorus pentachloride, PCl_5.

Hint: Phosphorus is in period 3 of the periodic table, so it can have more than eight electrons as the central atom of a molecule. Once you've drawn the structure, verify the total number of valence electrons as usual. When verifying the octets, each outer atom must have exactly eight electrons, and the central P must have at least eight electrons.

Example 10.15

Draw the Lewis structure for chlorine pentafluoride, ClF_5.

Solution

Step	ClF_5
1. Sum up the valence electrons.	Cl contributes seven, and each F contributes seven: $1(7) + 5(7) = 42$ electrons
2. Select a central atom and arrange the other atoms around it.	Cl is the central atom because it has the lower electronegativity value. 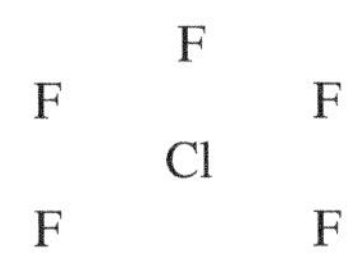
3. Draw single bonds between the central atom and each terminal atom.	This utilizes 10 of the 42 valence electrons available. 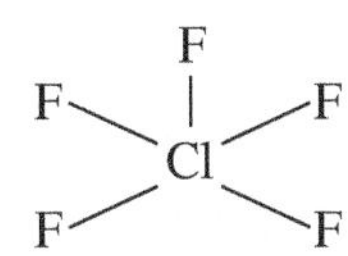
4. Distribute the remaining electrons as lone pairs to the outer atoms.	$42 - 10 = 32$ electrons remain. Placing three lone pairs on each F utilizes 30 of those 32 electrons. 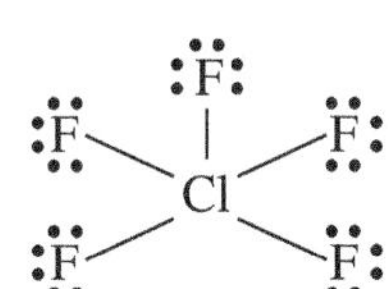
5. Assign any remaining electrons to the central atom.	Two electrons remain, so one lone pair is placed on Cl. 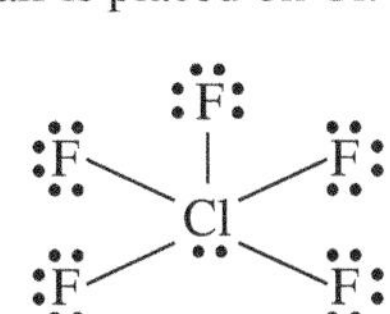
6. If the central atom has less than an octet, move lone pairs to create multiple bonds if the central atom has less than an octet.	The central atom has more than an octet (12 electrons, to be exact), which is acceptable because Cl is a period 3 element.
7. Verify octets, formal charge assignments, and the total number of valence electrons.	Cl has 5 bonds + 1 lone pair = 12 electrons. Each F has 1 bond + 3 lone pairs = 8 electrons. Formal charges: Cl: $7 - \left[\frac{1}{2}(10) + 2\right] = 0$ F: $7 - \left[\frac{1}{2}(2) + 6\right] = 0$ Total # of electrons = 5 bonds + 16 lone pairs = 42 electrons.

PRACTICE PROBLEM 10.15

Draw the Lewis structure for xenon difluoride, XeF_2.

Hint: Xenon is in period 5 of the periodic table, so it can have more than eight electrons as the central atom of a molecule. Once you've drawn the structure, verify the total number of valence electrons as usual. When verifying the octets, each outer atom must have exactly eight electrons, and the central Xe atom must have at least eight electrons.

Table 10.1 summarizes the criteria for when a structure or atom will obey or violate the octet rule.

SECTION REVIEW

- Exceptions to the octet rule occur for hydrogen, beryllium, and boron, which have only two,

TABLE 10.1 Summary of Octet Rule and Its Exceptions

Criterion	Description	Examples
H, Be, or B	Do not obey the octet rule; H, Be, and B have two, four, and six electrons, respectively, in structures.	H_2, BeH_2, BH_3
C, N, O, or F (period 2 nonmetals)	Obey the octet rule; must have exactly eight electrons in structures (unless there is an odd number of valence electrons).	CO_2, NF_3, CN^-
Unpaired, single electron (radical)	Odd number of valence electrons; the least electronegative atom has seven electrons.	NO, NO_2
Period 3 elements and beyond as the central atom	Must have at least eight electrons (with the exception of radicals) but can accommodate more than eight electrons.	PCl_5, I_3^- (central atom)
Period 3 elements and beyond as an outer atom	Obey the octet rule; tend to have exactly eight electrons in structures (unless there is an odd number of valence electrons).	PCl_5, I_3^- (outer atoms)

four, and six valence electrons, respectively, in compounds.

- When drawing Lewis structures for molecules and ions with odd numbers of valence electrons, give the odd electron to the atom of lower electronegativity.
- Elements in period 3 and beyond can expand their valence shells to accommodate more than eight electrons.
- Lewis structures for molecules and polyatomic ions in which the central atom is an element from the third period or beyond follow the same guidelines as for elements from the second period *except* that the central atom may have an expanded valence shell. This often results in multiple valid structures; the structure most like the real compound may be determined by comparing formal charges.
- Molecules that have single, unpaired electrons in their Lewis structures are referred to as radicals.

10.5 Polar Bonds and the Bonding Continuum

GOALS

- Determine bond polarity using electronegativity values.
- Describe the bonding continuum.

Background Review

Chapter 9 Periodicity and Ionic Bonding

ELECTRONEGATIVITY AND BOND POLARITY

Section 10.3 explains that electronegativity, the attraction of an atom for shared electrons, can be used to determine the central atom for a Lewis structure. In this section, you will use electronegativity values to predict the degree to which the electrons in a covalent bond are shared. Two identical atoms share electrons completely evenly, but two different atoms usually share electrons unevenly to form **polar covalent bonds**.

In hydrogen fluoride, HF, the fluorine atom has a higher electronegativity than the hydrogen atom, so the H–F bond is polar with the charge cloud of the bonding electrons having a greater density toward F than toward H (Figure 10.14a). This uneven distribution of the charge cloud causes fluorine to carry a partial negative charge, δ^-, and hydrogen to carry a partial positive charge, δ^+. These positive and negative poles indicate a charge separation, giving these polar covalent bonds some level of **ionic character**. In contrast, the bond in fluorine, F_2, is nonpolar and purely covalent in character because it forms between identical atoms with identical electronegativity values (Figure 10.14b).

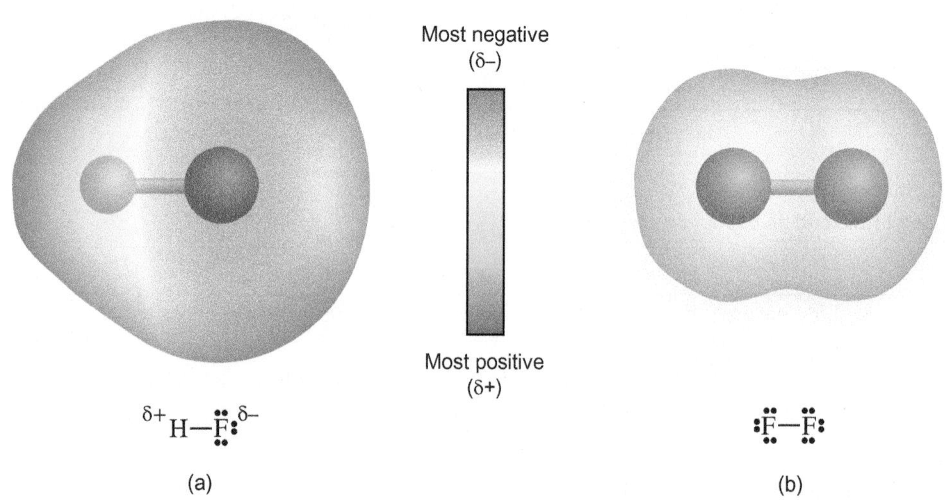

FIGURE 10.14 Electrostatic Potential Map for Polar and Nonpolar Bonds

Electrostatic potential maps (also known as electron density maps) show the electron density via a color gradient and the relative size of the electron cloud. (a) The bond between atoms of different electronegativities is polar. (b) The bond between atoms of the same electronegativity is nonpolar.

Large differences in electronegativity, ΔEN, between atoms indicate that these atoms do not share electrons evenly and perhaps even transfer electrons to form ionic bonds. The only truly nonpolar bond exists when the two atoms have exactly the same electronegativity. Very small differences in electronegativity are associated with slightly unevenly shared electrons and slightly polar covalent bonds. Moderate ΔEN values indicate less even sharing and polar covalent bonds, where the more electronegative element is the negative pole.

> ΔEN values are always positive and always refer to individual bonds.

Example 10.16

Use electronegativity values (see Figure 10.7) to indicate the location of the partial charges for a bond between the following pairs of atoms.

a. C and H
b. O and H

Solution

a. The electronegativity of C (2.5) is greater than that of H (2.1), so the C—H bond is slightly polar with the very weak negative pole at C and the very weak positive pole at H:

$$^{\delta+}H—C^{\delta-}$$

Often, bonds with such small electronegativity differences are referred to as nonpolar, but, strictly speaking, the bond is very slightly polar.

b. The electronegativity of O (3.5) is much greater than that of H (2.1), so the O—H bond is polar with the negative pole at O and the positive pole at H:

$$^{\delta+}H—O^{\delta-}$$

PRACTICE PROBLEM 10.16

Use electronegativity values to indicate the location of the partial charges for a bond between the following pairs of atoms.

a. N and H
b. Br and O

Hint: You can use Figure 10.7 to find the electronegativity value of each atom, or rank the atoms by relative electronegativity using the general trend that electronegativity increases as you move up and to the right in the periodic table. The atom with the higher electronegativity has a partial negative charge and the atom with the lower electronegativity has a partial positive charge.

Example 10.17

Complete the table below (see Figure 10.7) and use the data to describe the relative polarity of the bonds in the hydrogen halides. Which of these compounds has the most ionic character? Which has the most covalent character?

Compound	ΔEN
HCl	
HBr	
HF	
HI	

Solution

The electronegativity value of H is 2.1. The electronegativity values of F, Cl, Br, and I are 4.0, 3.0, 2.8, and 2.5, respectively. Subtract to find the difference.

Compound	ΔEN
HF	4.0 − 2.1 = **1.9**
HCl	3.0 − 2.1 = **0.9**
HBr	2.8 − 2.1 = **0.7**
HI	2.5 − 2.1 = **0.4**

HF has the largest ΔEN, so it is the most strongly polar of the four hydrogen halides and has the most ionic character. HCl and HBr have similar ΔEN values and are both polar, with HCl slightly more polar than HBr. HI, with the lowest ΔEN, has the least polar covalent bond and the most covalent character of these four compounds.

PRACTICE PROBLEM 10.17

Complete the table below and use the data to describe the relative polarity of the bonds in the Group 15 hydrides.

Compound	ΔEN
H_2O	
H_2S	
H_2Se	
H_2Te	

Hint: Use Figure 10.7 to find the electronegativity value of each element in the compound, then subtract them to find ΔEN. The polarity of the bond increases as ΔEN increases.

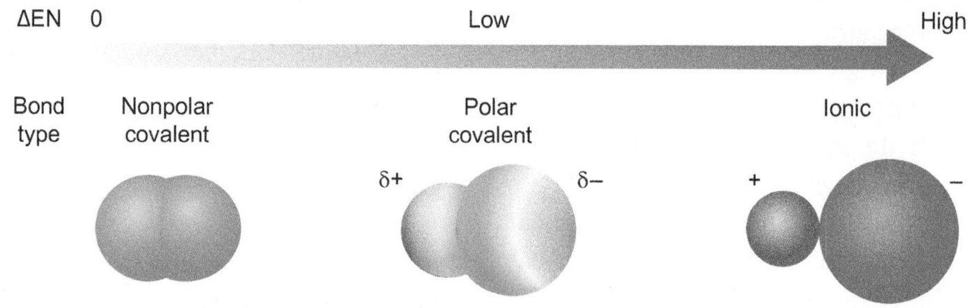

FIGURE 10.15 Bonding Continuum

When $\Delta EN = 0$, the electrons are shared equally between atoms and the bond is 100% covalent. When electrons are shared unequally, a covalent bond is polar and has some ionic character. When electrons are completely transferred, the bond is classified as ionic.

THE BONDING CONTINUUM

Bonds between atoms can range in type based on whether the electrons are evenly shared, unevenly shared, or completely transferred (Figure 10.15). The magnitude of ΔEN predicts the amount of charge separation for the bonds that share electrons unevenly. Some texts may use specific ranges of ΔEN values to designate nonpolar, polar, and ionic bonding. However, it is important to realize that there are no sharp cutoffs between nonpolar and polar bonds or between polar and ionic bonds. The types of bonds that form between atoms and/or ions truly represent a continuum of bonding between 100% electron sharing and 100% electron transfer.

DIPOLE MOMENT

Polar covalent bonds are **dipoles** because they exhibit separate areas of opposite charge of equal magnitude. The **dipole moment, μ,** is a *measurable* quantity related to the magnitude of the charge, q, and the distance between the charges, r, and is reported in ***units of debye, D***. The debye includes the charge unit, coulomb, and the distance unit, meter: $1\ \text{D} = 3.34 \times 10^{-30}\ \text{C} \cdot \text{m}$.

$$\mu = qr \tag{10.2}$$

These measured values for dipole moment are an indication of how much ionic character is present in a covalent bond. This can be quantified as percent ionic character by comparing the measured dipole moment (μ_{measured}) to a calculated dipole moment ($\mu_{\text{calculated}}$) for 100% electron transfer (indicating an ionic bond). For any bond, if you use the bond length and the charge of an electron (1.6×10^{-19} C) to determine $\mu_{\text{calculated}}$, you will have a value for the dipole moment as if the electron was completely transferred, indicating 100% ionic character. The percent ionic character of that bond is calculated by comparing the measured dipole moment, μ_{measured}, to this calculated, 100% value.

$$\%\text{ionic character} = \frac{\mu_{\text{measured}}}{\mu_{\text{calculated}}} \times 100\% \tag{10.3}$$

TABLE 10.2 Measured Dipole Moments and Bond Lengths for the Hydrogen Halides

Compound	Measured Dipole Moment, μ_{measured} (D)	Bond Length (pm)
HF	1.82	92
HCl	1.08	127
HBr	0.82	141
HI	0.44	161

Table 10.2 lists measured dipole moments (in debye units) and bond lengths (in picometers, pm) for the hydrogen halides. Notice that these observed data correspond well to the conclusions based on ΔEN in Example 10.21.

Example 10.18

Calculate the percent ionic character for the gaseous hydrogen chloride, HCl, molecule.

Solution

Step 1: Calculate $\mu_{\text{calculated}}$, the dipole moment for 100% charge separation. Use $\mu = qr$, but don't forget to convert pm to m and C · m to D. Recall that $1\ \text{pm} = 1 \times 10^{-12}\ \text{m}$.

$$\mu = qr$$

$$\mu_{\text{calculated}} = 1.6 \times 10^{-19}\ \text{C} \times \left(127\ \text{pm} \times \frac{1 \times 10^{-12}\ \text{m}}{1\ \text{pm}}\right) \times \frac{1\ \text{D}}{3.34 \times 10^{-30}\ \text{C} \cdot \text{m}}$$

$$\mu_{\text{calculated}} = 6.1\ \text{D}$$

Step 2: Determine the percent ionic character.

$$\% \text{ ionic character} = \frac{\mu_{\text{measured}}}{\mu_{\text{calculated}}} \times 100\%$$

The value of μ_{measured} for HCl is available in Table 10.2 and the value of $\mu_{\text{calculated}}$ was calculated in step 1.

$$\% \text{ ionic character} = \frac{1.08 \text{ D}}{6.1 \text{ D}} \times 100\% = 18\%$$

PRACTICE PROBLEM 10.18

Calculate the percent ionic character for the gaseous hydrogen fluoride, HF, molecule.

Hint:

Step 1: Find the calculated dipole in debye units.

Find the bond length of HF in Table 10.2 and convert it to meters ($1 \text{ pm} = 1 \times 10^{-12} \text{ m}$). Then use $\mu = qr$ to find the calculated dipole ($\mu_{\text{calculated}}$) where q is the charge on an electron (1.6×10^{-19} C) and r is the bond length in meters. Convert $\mu_{\text{calculated}}$ to debye units ($1 \text{ D} = 3.34 \times 10^{-30} \text{ C} \cdot \text{m}$).

Step 2: Find the percent ionic character.

Divide the measured dipole from Table 10.2 by the calculated dipole from step 1, and multiply the result by 100%.

SECTION REVIEW

- In covalent bonds, atoms with different electronegativity values share electrons unevenly, resulting in a polar bond with partially charged atoms of opposite polarities at each end.
- Differences in electronegativity values, ΔEN, can be used to predict the relative polarity of a bond: Nonpolar covalent bonds have small ΔEN, polar covalent bonds have moderate ΔEN, and ionic bonds have large ΔEN.
- The types of bonds that form between atoms or ions represent a continuum of bonding between 100% electron sharing and 100% electron transfer.
- The separation of charges in a polar covalent bond is called a dipole, which has an associated dipole moment, μ, that is related to the magnitude of the charge, q, and distance, r, by the formula $\mu = qr$. Dipole moment is measured in debye units, D, where $1 \text{ D} = 3.34 \times 10^{-30} \text{ C} \cdot \text{m}$.
- The percent ionic character of a polar covalent bond is calculated by comparing its measured dipole moment, μ_{measured}, to a calculated dipole moment, $\mu_{\text{calculated}}$, that is based on complete charge separation: $\% \text{ ionic character} = \left(\frac{\mu_{\text{measured}}}{\mu_{\text{calculated}}}\right) \times 100\ \%$.

10.6 Bond Enthalpy

GOAL

- Discuss how bond length relates to bond strength.

Background Review

Chapter 4 Chemical Reactions and Aqueous Solutions: Section 4.1—Chemical Equations

Chapter 6 Thermochemistry: Section 6.7—Enthalpy in Chemical Reactions

The strength of the bonds within a molecule determines the stability of that molecule. Bond strengths are generally measured as **bond enthalpies**, which are defined as the enthalpy change, ΔH (Section 6.4), associated with breaking a specific bond in 1 mol of gaseous molecules. The ΔH associated with the separation of a diatomic molecule, such as Br_2, into its component atoms is an example of a bond enthalpy.

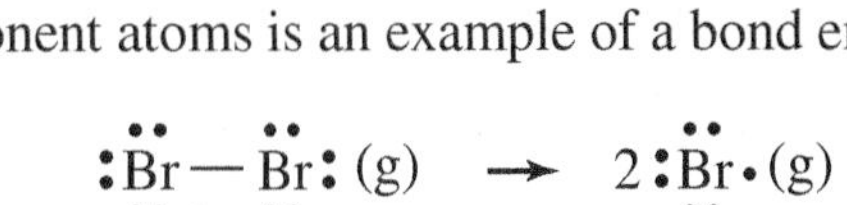

It is possible to measure exact bond enthalpy values for diatomic elements, but not for most other types of bonds. Some molecules may contain only one type of bond but have more than one of them, such as carbon tetrachloride, CCl_4. If you assume that all C—Cl bonds are equivalent, the bond enthalpy value of one C—Cl bond is equal to one-fourth of the ΔH of the following reaction,

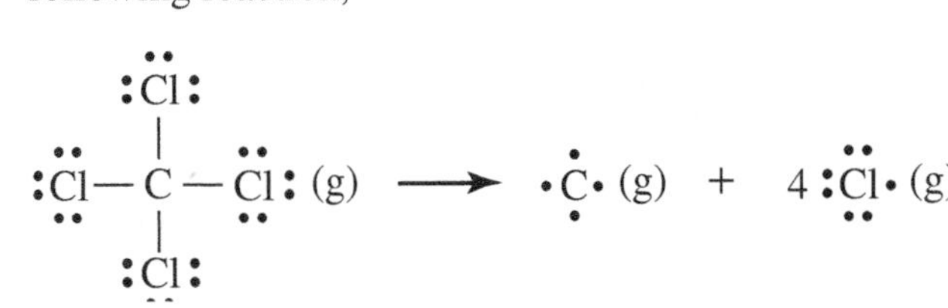

in which 1 mol of CCl_4 is decomposed into its component atoms. Other molecules contain C—Cl bonds, too, and they may have similar but not identical bond enthalpy values to those in CCl_4. For example, there are many different molecules that contain a bond between the same two elements, such as O—H in H_2O, H_2O_2, and NH_2OH, all of which will have similar but not identical bond enthalpies. Because of this, bond enthalpies are average values obtained from measurements from many different molecules that contain bonds between the same pairs of atoms. Table 10.3 lists average values

TABLE 10.3 Bond Enthalpy Values

Hydrogen		Carbon		Nitrogen		Oxygen		Sulfur		Halogens		Multiple Bonds	
Bond	ΔH (kJ/mol)	Bond	ΔH (kJ/mol)	Bond	ΔH (kJ/mol)	Bond	ΔH (kJ/mol)	Bond	ΔH (kJ/mol)	Bond	ΔH (kJ/mol)	Bond	ΔH (kJ/mol)
H—H	436	C—H	410*	N—H	390*	O—H	460*	S—H	340*	Br—F	234	O=O	498
H—O	460*	C—O	350*	N—O	200*	O—O	142*	S—O	265*	Br—Cl	219	C=C	611*
H—F	569	C—F	450*	N—F	270*	O—F	180*	S—F	310*	Br—Br	194	C≡C	835*
H—Cl	432	C—Cl	330*	N—Cl	200*	O—Cl	200*	S—Cl	250*	Br—I	179	C=O	745*
H—Br	366	C—Br	270*	N—Br	240*	O—Br	210*	S—Br	210*	Cl—F	251	C≡O	1077
H—I	298	C—I	240*	N—I	159*	O—I	220*	S—I	170*	Cl—Cl	243	N=O	607*
H—C	410*	C—C	350*	N—C	300*	O—C	350*	S—C	260*	F—F	157	N=N	418*
H—N	390*	C—N	300*	N—N	240*	O—N	200*	S—S	225*	I—F	280	N≡N	941
H—S	340*	C—S	260*			O—S	265*			I—I	153	C=N	615*
												C≡N	891*
												C=S	477*

*Indicates an energy that is an average for that type of bond in several different molecules.

for bond enthalpies in kilojoules per mole (kJ/mol) for many common pairs of atoms. Note that bond enthalpies shown for multiple bonds, such as O=O or C≡N, represent the ΔH associated with separating the two atoms completely.

> Energy must be added to break bonds; bond-breaking is endothermic.
>
> Energy is released when bonds are formed; bond-making is exothermic.

Example 10.19

Based on bond enthalpy values, which is more reactive: hydrogen chloride, HCl, or hydrogen bromide, HBr?

Solution

The bond enthalpy for the H—Cl bond is 431 kJ/mol, whereas the bond enthalpy for the H—Br bond is 366 kJ/mol. Thus, it takes less energy to break the H—Br bond, so it is reasonable to predict that HBr is more reactive than HCl.

PRACTICE PROBLEM 10.19

Based on bond enthalpy values, which is more reactive: methane, CH_4, or carbon tetrachloride, CCl_4?

Hint: Look up the enthalpy of a C—H bond and a C—Cl bond in Table 10.3. Molecules with lower bond enthalpy (weaker bonds) tend to be more reactive.

BOND ENTHALPY AND REACTION ENTHALPY

Bond enthalpy values are often used to estimate enthalpies for reactions involving molecular compounds. This is especially helpful because you can predict whether the reaction will be endothermic or exothermic and have a good idea of how large the energy change will be before carrying out the experiment. Using bond enthalpies to estimate reaction enthalpy is an example of Hess's law (Section 6.7). The process is as follows:

- Calculate the total energy that would be *added* to turn the reactant molecules into individual atoms (bond-breaking is endothermic).
- Calculate the total energy that would be *released* when these atoms combine to form the product molecules (bond-making is exothermic).
- Compare the two energy values.

$$\Delta H_{rxn} = \Sigma(\Delta H \text{ of bonds broken}) - \Sigma(\Delta H \text{ of bonds formed}) \quad (10.4)$$

If it takes more energy to break the bonds in the reactant molecules than is released when making the bonds in the product molecules, then the reaction must absorb energy and, therefore, is endothermic. If more energy is released in bond-making than was used in bond-breaking, then the reaction is exothermic (Figure 10.16).

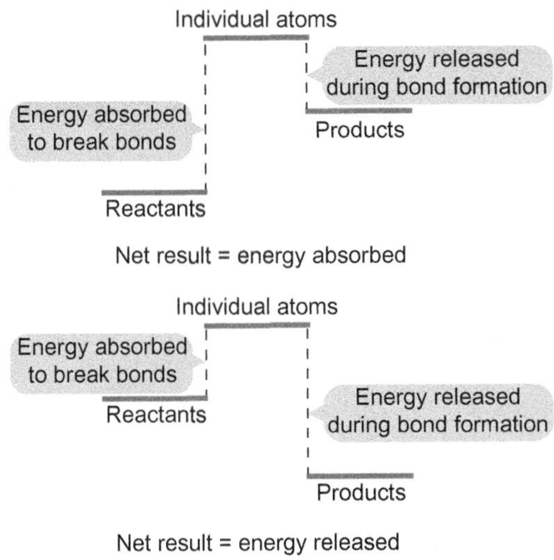

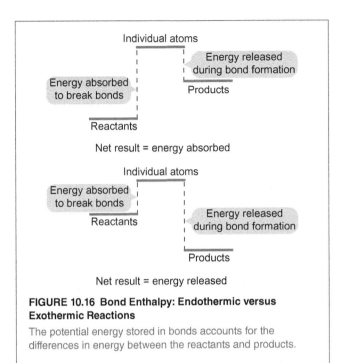

FIGURE 10.16 Bond Enthalpy: Endothermic versus Exothermic Reactions

The potential energy stored in bonds accounts for the differences in energy between the reactants and products.

FIGURE 10.18 Video Tutorial: Bond Enthalpy

NOTE: You need to be online to access this video.

This video shows how to estimate reaction enthalpy from bond enthalpies.

The calculation below and Figure 10.17 show the steps used to calculate the ΔH for the formation of H_2O from its elements, H_2 and O_2.

$$2\,H_2(g) + O_2(g) \rightarrow 2\,H_2O(l)$$

$$\Delta H_{rxn} = \Sigma(\Delta H \text{ of bonds broken}) - \Sigma(\Delta H \text{ of bonds formed})$$

$$\Delta H_{rxn} = [2\Delta H_{H-H} + \Delta H_{O=O}] - [4\Delta H_{O-H}]$$

$$\Delta H_{rxn} = [2(436\text{ kJ}) + 498\text{ kJ}] - 4(460\text{ kJ})$$

$$\Delta H_{rxn} = 1370\text{ kJ} - 1840\text{ kJ}$$

$$\Delta H_{rxn} = -470\text{ kJ}$$

According to the data from Table 10.3, breaking two moles of H—H bonds requires 2(436 kJ) = 872 kJ and breaking one mole of O=O bonds requires 498 kJ. Thus, for a total of 1370 kJ of energy is absorbed (spent) to break the reactant molecules into separate atoms. Making four moles of O—H bonds releases 4(460 kJ) = 1840 kJ. Overall, 1370 kJ absorbed and 1840 kJ released is a net energy release of 470 kJ. The estimated ΔH_{rxn} is −470 kJ.

Example 10.20

Use bond enthalpies to estimate ΔH_{rxn} for the combustion of methane, CH_4, the major component of natural gas.

$$CH_4(g) + 2\,O_2(g) \rightarrow CO_2(g) + 2\,H_2O(g)$$

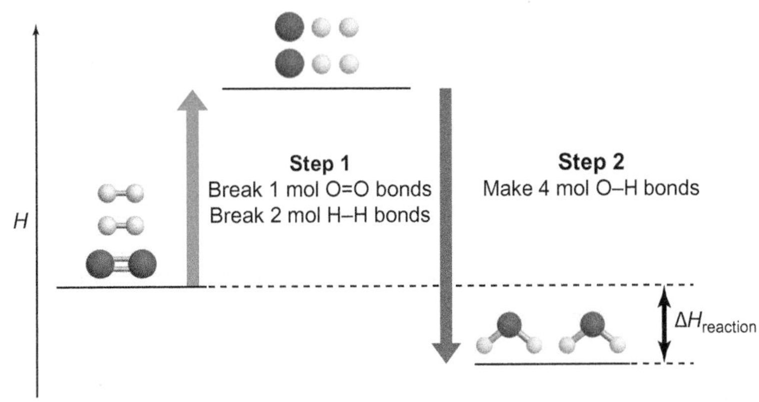

FIGURE 10.17 Using Bond Enthalpies to Estimate a Reaction Enthalpy

The enthalpy change for a reaction is approximately equal to the difference in energy between the reactant and product bonds.

TABLE 10.4 Bond Lengths

Hydrogen		Carbon		Nitrogen, Oxygen, Fluorine		Larger Elements		Multiple Bonds	
Bond	Length (pm)	Bond	Length (pm)	Bond	Length (pm)	Bond	Length (pm)	Bond	Length (pm)
H—H	74	C—C	154	N—N	158	Si—Si	235	C=C	133
H—C	109	C—Si	186	N—Cl	145	Si—Cl	203	P=O	150
H—Si	148	C—N	213	O—O	148	P—P	221	C≡C	120
H—Si	148	C—O	187	O—Si	163	P—Cl	203	C=N	138
H—N	104	C—P	143	O—P	157	S—S	205	S=O	143
H—P	142	C—S	147	O—S	190	S—Cl	207	C≡N	116
H—O	96	C—F	181	F—P	156	Cl—Cl	199	C=O	120
H—S	134	C—Cl	135	F—Xe	142	Br—Br	229	C≡O	113
H—F	92	C—Br	177	F—S	175	I—I	266	O=O	121
H—Cl	127	C—I	194	F—F	156			N≡N	110
H—Br	141			F—Si	166				

Solution

First, draw Lewis structures of each reactant and product to help identify the bonds that are broken and formed during this reaction.

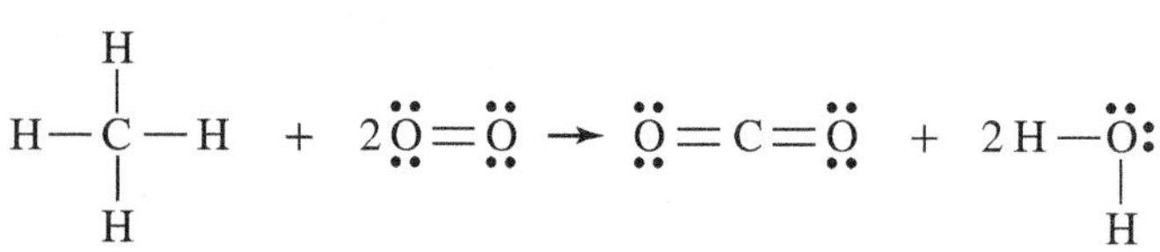

Note that each bond shown in the Lewis structures represents 1 mol of bonds. This makes it possible to use the bond enthalpy values directly from Table 10.3. Based on the Lewis structures, then, 4 mol of C—H bonds and 2 mol of O=O bonds are broken, whereas 2 mol of C=O bonds and 4 mol of O—H bonds are formed.

The general equation for estimating ΔH_{rxn} is

$$\Delta H_{rxn} = \Sigma(\Delta H \text{ of bonds broken}) - \Sigma(\Delta H \text{ of bonds formed})$$

The equation specific to the combustion of methane is

$$\Delta H_{rxn} = [4\Delta H_{C-H} + 2\Delta H_{O=O}] - [2\Delta H_{C=O} + 4\Delta H_{O-H}]$$

$$\Delta H_{rxn} = [4(413\text{ kJ}) + 2(495\text{ kJ})] - [2(799\text{ kJ}) + 4(463\text{ kJ})]$$

$$\Delta H_{rxn} = 2642\text{ kJ} - 3450\text{ kJ} = -810\text{ kJ}$$

The final answer, −810 kJ, indicates a highly exothermic reaction, which is why methane (natural gas) is used as a fuel.

PRACTICE PROBLEM 10.20

a. Use bond enthalpies to estimate ΔH_{rxn} of this reaction.

$$NH_3(g) + Cl_2(g) \rightarrow N_2H_4(g) + HCl(g)$$

b. Use bond enthalpies to estimate ΔH_{rxn} to produce acetylene, C_2H_2, from ethane, C_2H_6.

$$C_2H_6(g) \rightarrow C_2H_2(g) + 2\,H_2(g)$$

Hint: Start by drawing the Lewis structure of each species so you can more easily identify and count the bonds. Sum the enthalpies of all the bonds in the reactants, then subtract the sum of the enthalpies of the bonds in the products.

BOND ENTHALPY AND BOND LENGTH

Covalent bond length is the distance between the nuclei of two atoms that share electrons in a covalent bond. Published bond lengths, such as those in Table 10.4, are average values obtained from the measurements of many different molecules that contain bonds between the same pairs of atoms, just as bond enthalpies are.

Example 10.21

Describe the relationship between bond lengths and bond enthalpies for single, double, and triple bonds between carbon atoms.

Solution

Gather the appropriate data from Tables 10.3 and 10.4:

Bond	Enthalpy (kJ/mol)	Length (pm)
C—C	348	154
C=C	614	134
C≡C	839	120

In going from single bond to double bond to triple bond, bond length decreases while bond enthalpy increases. For similar atom pairs, there is an inverse relationship between bond length and bond enthalpy. That is, shorter bonds are stronger bonds.

PRACTICE PROBLEM 10.21

Describe the relationship between bond lengths and bond enthalpies for single, double, and triple bonds between carbon and nitrogen atoms.

Hint: It might help to set up a table to summarize the information in this problem.

Bond	Enthalpy (kJ/mol)	Length (pm)
C—N		
C=N		
C≡N		

Fill in the blank cells using data from Tables 10.3 and 10.4.

> In general, as bond length increases, the bond enthalpy decreases. That is, longer bonds tend to be weaker than shorter bonds.

However, comparing bond lengths and bond enthalpies for bonds in diatomic halogen molecules reveals that the pattern does not always hold.

Bond	Enthalpy (kJ/mol)	Length (pm)
F—F	155	143
Cl—Cl	242	199
Br—Br	193	228
I—I	151	266

The bond length between halogen atoms increases moving down the group. At first glance, the bond enthalpy data do not seem to follow a discernable pattern. However, second period elements are often exceptions in periodic trends, so perhaps a closer look at the data for chlorine, bromine, and iodine is in order. The data for the halogens other than fluorine show that as bond lengths increase, bond enthalpies decrease, which is consistent with the data in the previous examples.

SECTION REVIEW

- Bond enthalpy is the enthalpy change associated with separating bonded atoms. Bond enthalpies are average values measured from many different molecules that contain bonds between atom pairs of the same type.
- Reaction enthalpies can be estimated by applying Hess's law and using bond enthalpy values: $\Delta H_{rxn} = \Sigma(\Delta H \text{ of bonds broken}) - \Sigma(\Delta H \text{ of bonds formed})$.
- Bond lengths depend upon the nature of the atom pair and the type of bonding. They are average values measured from many different molecules that contain bonds between atom pairs of the same type.
- Bond enthalpies increase and bond lengths decrease when the same atom pairs share more than one pair of electrons. That is, triple bonds are strongest and shortest, whereas single bonds are weakest and longest.

Putting It Together

The example problems in earlier sections of this chapter focus on just the new skills acquired in that section. But homework and exam questions in chemistry often require more than just one skill at a time. In fact, you will likely be expected to apply knowledge from across the entire chapter or even multiple chapters in a single problem. This final example problem is meant to help you prepare for these types of multi-concept questions. Additional examples can be found in the end-of-chapter exercises.

Example 10.22

Draw a Lewis structure for sulfur trioxide, SO_3, in which all atoms obey the octet rule, and another Lewis structure in which all formal charges are zero. The experimentally determined bond length in SO_3 is 142 pm. Based on this information and the S—O and S=O bond lengths in Table 10.4, which structure is correct?

Solution

If all atoms follow the octet rule, the Lewis structure has two single bonds and one double bond.

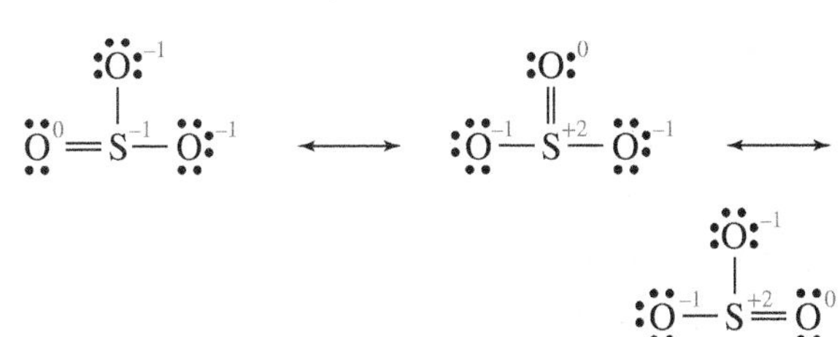

In the resonance hybrid, each sulfur–oxygen bond would be somewhere between single and double, and we would expect the bond length to be between the lengths of an S—O bond (158 pm) and a S═O double bond (143 pm).

If S expands beyond an octet, all atoms can have a formal charge of zero and the Lewis structure has three double bonds.

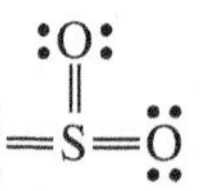

In this case, we'd expect the bond lengths to match that of a S═O double bond (143 pm).

The experimentally determined bond length is 142 pm, meaning the structure with only double bonds most closely resembles the true structure of SO_3.

PRACTICE PROBLEM 10.22

Draw a structure for sulfur dioxide, SO_2, in which all atoms obey the octet rule, and another structure in which all formal charges are zero. The experimentally determined bond length in SO_2 is 143.2 pm. Based on this information and the S—O and S═O bond lengths in Table 10.4, which structure is correct?

Hint: A valid Lewis structure for SO_2 must show exactly $6 \times 3 = 18$ electrons total, and the outer oxygen atoms must have octets (exactly 8 electrons each). The central S atom must have at least 8 electrons.

Key Terms, Symbols, and Equations

KEY TERMS

bond enthalpy (10.6): The enthalpy change, ΔH, associated with breaking a specific bond in one mole of gaseous molecules.

debye (D) (10.5): The unit of dipole moment measurement, where $1\ D = 3.34 \times 10^{-30}\ C \cdot m$.

delocalized bond (10.3): Multiple bonds in resonance structures that are spread out over more than one location.

dipole (10.5): A bond that exhibits separate areas of opposite charge of equal magnitude.

dipole moment, μ (10.5): Measurable quantity related to the magnitude of the charge, q, and the distance between the charges, r, and is reported in debye units, D: $\mu = qr$.

double bond (10.1): A bond consisting of two atoms sharing two pairs of electrons and shown as two short lines in Lewis structures.

duet rule (10.1): Hydrogen forms only one bond in covalent compounds, filling its 1s valence shell.

electronegativity (10.3): Measure of the electron-attracting ability of an atom in a covalent bond.

expanded valence shell (10.4): Elements from periods 3–7 can form more than four bonds when making compounds, expanding beyond the octet rule.

formal charge (10.3): Compares an atom's electron status within a molecule to the number of valence electrons of the atom.

$$\text{Formal charge} = \#\text{ valence e}^- - \left(\frac{\#\text{ shared e}^-}{2} + \#\text{ unshared e}^-\right)$$

ionic character (10.5): Measured as percent comparing the observed charge separation to 100% charge separation: % ionic character $= (\mu_{\text{measured}}/\mu_{\text{calculated}})(100\%)$.

Lewis structure (10.1): Diagram of a molecule or polyatomic ion showing shared pairs or bonds as straight lines and unshared or lone pairs as dots.

lone pair (10.1): Unshared pairs of electrons in molecules or polyatomic ions.

octet rule (10.1): Atoms gain, lose, or share electrons to achieve a stable noble-gas electron configuration, ns^2np^6 (8 electrons), for elements in periods 2 especially and, with expanded valence exceptions, for elements in periods 3–7.

polar covalent bond (10.5): A bond resulting from uneven sharing of electrons and characterized by a separation of partial charges.

polyatomic ion (10.2): Connected by covalent bonds that carry a charge, allowing them to form ionic compounds.

radical (10.4): A molecule or ion with an unpaired electron in its Lewis structure.

resonance (10.3): The property of having resonance structures.

resonance hybrid (10.3): A single structure with delocalized bonds that represents the average of the separate resonance structures.

resonance structures (10.3): Multiple, equivalent, or close-to-equivalent Lewis structures for a molecule or ion that differ only in the placement of multiple bonds and lone pairs.

single bond (10.1): A bond consisting of two atoms sharing one pair of electrons and shown as a short, straight line in Lewis structures.

triple bond (10.1): A bond consisting of two atoms sharing three pairs of electrons and shown as three short lines in Lewis structures.

SYMBOLS/ABBREVIATIONS

C (coulomb) (10.5)

D (debye) (10.5)

δ (partial charge) (10.5)

ΔEN (difference in electronegativity values) (10.5)

ΔH (enthalpy change) (10.6)

μ (dipole moment) (10.5)

q (charge) (10.5)

r (distance between charges) (10.5)

EQUATIONS

$$\text{Formal charge} = \#\text{ valence e}^- - \left(\frac{\#\text{ shared e}^-}{2} + \#\text{ unshared e}^-\right) \quad (10.1)$$

$$\mu = qr \quad (10.2)$$

$$\%\text{ ionic character} = \frac{\mu_{\text{measured}}}{\mu_{\text{calculated}}} \times 100\% \quad (10.3)$$

$$\Delta H_{\text{rxn}} = \Sigma(\Delta H \text{ of bonds broken}) - \Sigma(\Delta H \text{ of bonds formed}) \quad (10.4)$$

Chapter Summary

Molecular compounds form when electrons are shared between atoms of nonmetal elements, completing the valence shells of both atoms to form more stable species. Atoms tend to form a certain number of bonds in a molecule, which is equal to the number of electrons needed to complete their valence shell, following the octet rule for period 2–7 nonmetals and the duet rule for hydrogen (Section 10.1).

Molecules contain all the valence electrons of their atoms, organized to provide an octet for most atoms in the molecule and a duet for hydrogen atoms. Within molecules, atoms can share one, two, or three pairs of electrons to form single, double, or triple bonds, respectively. Lewis structures of molecules show these shared electrons as straight lines and display unshared electrons as dots. Polyatomic ions, which consist of atoms that are covalently bonded together but carry an overall net positive or negative charge, can form ionic bonds with other ions. The final Lewis structure for a polyatomic ion always includes brackets around the structure, with the charge indicated outside the brackets (Section 10.2).

Molecules and polyatomic ions with multiple Lewis structures are said to display resonance and are best described as an average or hybrid when more than one diagram is possible. The double and triple bonds that exist in different places in the different resonance structures are said to be delocalized (Section 10.3).

Electronegativity is a measure of a covalently bonded atom's ability to attract electrons. Electronegativity is used to determine the central atom in a molecule and to select the most likely Lewis structure when multiple structures are possible. Formal charge, a type of electron bookkeeping, assigns a charge to atoms in Lewis structures based on the valence electrons and electron structure of the molecule.

$$\text{Formal charge} = \#\text{ valence e}^- - \left(\frac{\#\text{ shared e}^-}{2} + \#\text{ unshared e}^-\right)$$

Formal charges, when combined with electronegativity values, are used to select Lewis structures that are more energetically favorable when multiple structures are possible.

A systematic method for drawing Lewis structures produces consistent diagrams of the more energetically favorable structures.

1. Sum the valence electrons for each atom in the formula, adding electrons (anions) or subtracting electrons (cations) to account for the charges on polyatomic ions.

2. Select a central atom as the one that (a) needs to make the most bonds to become stable and (b) has the lower electronegativity value. Arrange the symbols for the other atoms around the symbol for the central atom.
3. Connect the central atom to each of the outer atoms with a single bond using two electrons for each bond.
4. Distribute the remaining valence electrons from step 1 to the outer atoms as lone pairs to complete their octets. Hydrogen is an exception and is complete with a single bond only.
5. Assign any remaining electrons to the central atom.
6. If the central atom has less than an octet, move lone pairs from outer atoms into shared positions to form double or triple bonds as needed.
7. Verify that your final structure fulfills the duet rule for all hydrogen atoms and fulfills the octet rule for all period 2 atoms (unless the atom is Be or B or the molecule is a radical). Verify, too, that the number of electrons shown in the structure matches the total from step 1, that formal charges are small, and that atoms of greater electronegativity are assigned negative formal charges (Section 10.4).

In covalent bonds, atoms of different electronegativity share electrons unevenly, resulting in a polar bond with partially but oppositely charged atoms at each end. Differences in electronegativity values, ΔEN, can be used to predict the relative polarity of a bond. Nonpolar covalent bonds have small ΔEN values, polar covalent bonds have moderate ΔEN values, and ionic bonds have large ΔEN values. The types of bonds that form between atoms or ions represent a continuum of bonding between 100% electron sharing and 100% electron transfer.

The separation of charges in a polar covalent bond is called a dipole, which has an associated dipole moment, μ, that is related to the magnitude of the charge, q, and distance, r, by the formula $\mu = qr$. The dipole moment is measured in debye units, D, where $1\text{ D} = 3.34 \times 10^{-30}\text{ C} \cdot \text{m}$. The percent ionic character of a polar covalent bond is calculated by comparing its measured dipole moment to a calculated dipole moment based on complete charge separation:

$$\%\text{ ionic character} = \left(\frac{\mu_{\text{measured}}}{\mu_{\text{calculated}}}\right) \times 100\%$$

(Section 10.5)

Bond enthalpy is the enthalpy change associated with separating bonded atoms. It represents average values measured from many different molecules that contain bonds between atom pairs of the same type. Bond enthalpies can be used to estimate reaction enthalpies in an application of Hess's law:

$$\Delta H_{\text{rxn}} = \Sigma(\Delta H \text{ of bonds broken}) - \Sigma(\Delta H \text{ of bonds formed}).$$

Bond lengths depend upon the identity of the atoms in the pair and the type of bonding (single bond, double bond, or triple bond). Bond lengths represent average values measured from many different molecules that contain bonds between atom pairs of the same type. When comparing bonds between the same two atoms, bond enthalpies increase and bond lengths decrease as you go from single bonds to double bonds and from double bonds to triple bonds. Thus, triple bonds are strongest and shortest, while single bonds are weakest and longest (Section 10.6).

END OF CHAPTER QUESTIONS

10.1 Covalent Bonding

1. Write the Lewis dot symbol for each atom.
   a. C
   b. O
   c. F
   d. S

2. Write the Lewis dot symbol for the atom or ion.
   a. Na^+
   b. Cl^-
   c. Si
   d. P

3. Draw the Lewis dot symbol for each ion.
   a. O^{2-}
   b. Br^-
   c. N^{3-}
   d. Ca^{2+}

4. Draw the Lewis dot symbol for each ion.
   a. Al^{3+}
   b. Sn^{2+}
   c. Li^+
   d. F^-

5. Based on the octet rule, determine the number of bonds an atom of each of the following elements is likely to make in a molecule.
   a. Si
   b. P
   c. S
   d. Cl
   e. Ar

6. How many shared electrons and unshared electrons are there in the following Lewis structures?
   a. SiH_4
   b. C_2H_3Cl

7. How many shared electrons and unshared electrons are there in the following Lewis structures?
   a. COF_2
   b. SO_3

10.2 Lewis Structures

8. Determine what, if anything, is wrong with each Lewis structure and make corrections if necessary.
   a. HCl

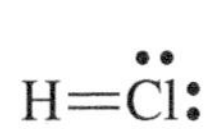

   b. CS_2

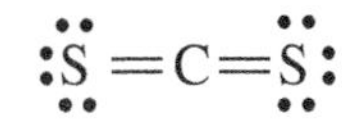

   c. CHF_3

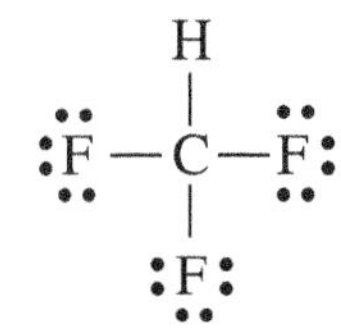

   d. I_2

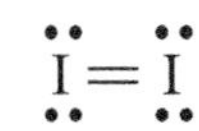

9. Determine what, if anything, is wrong with each Lewis structure and make corrections if necessary.
   a. SH_2

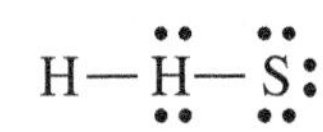

   b. PCl_3

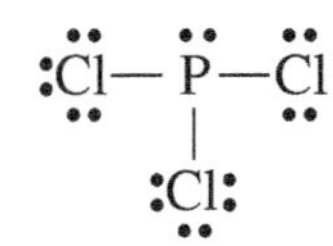

   c. SO_2

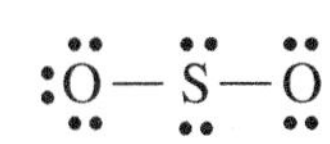

   d. NCl_3

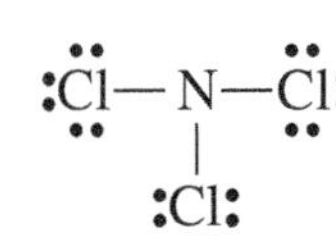

10. Draw the Lewis structure for each molecule.
    a. CO
    b. SF_2
    c. CCl_4
    d. SiO_2

11. Draw the Lewis structure for each molecule.
    a. PH_3
    b. HBr
    c. NF_3
    d. OCl_2

12. Draw the Lewis structure for each molecule.
    a. N_2H_4
    b. CH_2Br_2
    c. SeF_2
    d. H_2O

13. Draw the Lewis structure for each molecule.
    a. N_2H_2
    b. C_2Cl_4
    c. CH_3SH (C and S are central)
    d. C_2H_4

14. Draw the Lewis structure for each molecule.
    a. $CH_3CH_2CH_2OH$
    b. $CH_3CH_2NH_2$
    c. $HOCH_2CH_2OH$
    d. CH_3OCH_3

15. Draw the Lewis structure for each ion.
    a. NO_2^-
    b. OH^-
    c. NH_4^+

16. Draw the Lewis structure for each ion.
    a. CO_2H^-
    b. NO_3^-
    c. O_2^{2-}

10.3 Resonance and Formal Charges

17. Draw all possible resonance structures for SeO_2.

18. Draw all possible resonance structures for the bicarbonate ion, HCO_3^- (the H is attached to one of the O atoms).

19. Draw all possible resonance structures for the thiocyanate ion, SCN^- (C is the central atom).

20. Consider this Lewis structure for N_2O:

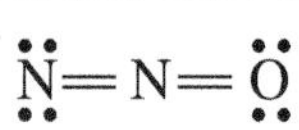

Which of these is *not* a resonance structure of the Lewis structure shown above?

a. 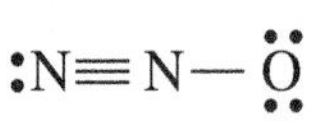

b. 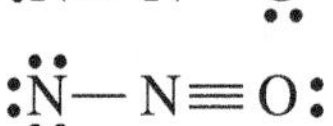

c. 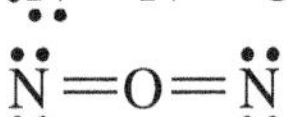

21. The formate ion has two resonance structures. The first one is shown. Draw the other resonance structure of formate.

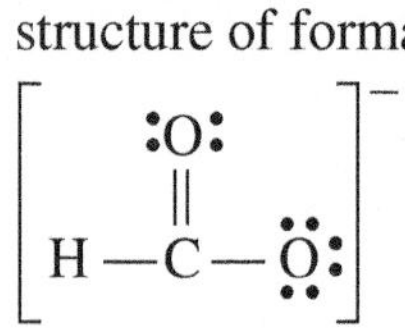

22. What is the central atom of $SOCl_2$?

23. What is the central atom of ONF?

24. Draw the resonance structures of CSO where C is the central atom, and use formal charge to determine which structure is more likely to resemble the real molecule.

25. Draw the resonance structures of the thioformate ion, $CHSO^-$, where C is the central atom. Use formal charge and electronegativity to determine which structure is more likely to resemble the real ion.

26. Draw the resonance structures for NOCl and use formal charge to determine which structure is more likely to resemble the real molecule.

27. Draw the resonance structures for $COCl_2$ and use formal charge to determine which structure is more likely to resemble the real molecule.

28. Draw two Lewis structures for CSF_2, one with C as the central atom and one with S as the central atom. Use formal charges to identify which structure is more likely to resemble the real molecule.

29. Which structure is more likely to represent the true structure of hydrogen cyanide? Why?

H—C≡N: H—N≡C:

10.4 Exceptions to the Octet Rule

30. Draw the Lewis structure for each molecule. These molecules *do not* follow the octet rule.
    a. BBr_3
    b. $BeCl_2$
    c. ClO_2

31. Draw the Lewis structure for each molecule. These molecules *do not* follow the octet rule.
    a. BF_3
    b. BeF_2
    c. BrO_2

32. Draw the Lewis structure for each molecule or ion, using expanded octets.
    a. SF_4
    b. IF_5
    c. $XeCl_4$
    d. I_3^-

33. Draw the Lewis structure for each molecule or ion, using expanded octets.
    a. KrF_2
    b. $TeCl_4$
    c. F_3PO
    d. IBr_4^-

34. Draw the Lewis structure for each molecule or ion, using expanded octets.
    a. $AsBr_5$
    b. IF_4^+
    c. ClF_3
    d. SO_3

35. Draw the Lewis structure for each ion, using expanded octets. Include resonance structures where necessary.
    a. PO_4^{3-}
    b. HSO_4^- (the H is attached to one of the O atoms)
    c. AsO_4^{3-}
    d. ClO_3^-

36. Draw the Lewis structure for each ion, using expanded octets as necessary. Include resonance structures where necessary.
    a. IO_3^-
    b. HPO_4^{2-} (the H is attached to one of the O atoms)
    c. SO_3^{2-}
    d. BrO_4^-

10.5 Polar Bonds and the Bonding Continuum

37. Rank these elements in order of decreasing electronegativity: Cs, Cl, Sr, Ge, P.

38. Rank these elements in order of increasing electronegativity: Se, Ba, F, As, In.

39. For each of the following pairs, determine if a bond between the atoms would be ionic, polar, covalent, or nonpolar covalent.
    a. H—H
    b. Ca—Br
    c. P—F
    d. Na—Cl

40. For each of the following pairs of atoms, classify the bond between them as ionic, polar covalent, or nonpolar covalent
    a. Si—F
    b. Cl—Cl
    c. O—N
    d. Mg—I

41. Rank these bonds from most polar to least polar: Si—Cl, F—F, C—P, N—Br.

42. Rank these bonds from least polar to most polar: C—O, H—F, P—S, Br—Br.

43. Rank these molecules in order of increasing bond polarity: ICl, O_2, CO, HF.

44. Rank these molecules in order of decreasing bond polarity: Cl_2, HBr, NO, HI.

45. Complete the table that follows and use the data to describe the relative polarity of the bonds in the group 15 hydrides. Which of these compounds has the most ionic character? Which has the most covalent character?

Compound	ΔEN
NH_3	
PH_3	
AsH_3	

46. Complete the table below and use the data to describe the relative polarity of the bonds in the group 14 hydrides. Which of these compounds has the most ionic character? Which has the most covalent character?

Compound	ΔEN
CH_4	
SiH_4	
GeH_4	

47. Indicate the location of the partial charges for a bond between each pair of atoms.
    a. Se and H
    b. Si and Cl
    c. N and O
    d. C and F

48. Indicate the location of the partial charges for a bond between each pair of atoms.
    a. S and O
    b. P and Br
    c. O and F
    d. C and H

49. Calculate the percent ionic character for the gaseous HBr molecule. Refer to Table 10.2 for the measured dipole moment and bond length.

50. Calculate the percent ionic character for the gaseous HI molecule. Refer to Table 10.2 for the measured dipole moment and bond length.

51. The measured dipole moment for gaseous ClF is 0.88 D. The Cl—F bond length is 163 pm. Calculate the percent ionic character for this molecule.

52. The measured dipole moment for gaseous CO is 0.112 D. The C≡O triple bond is 112.8 pm in length. Calculate the percent ionic character for this molecule.

10.6 Bond Enthalpy

53. Based on bond enthalpy values, which is more reactive, H_2S or H_2O?

54. Based on bond enthalpy values, which is more reactive, Br_2 or I_2?

55. Use bond enthalpies to calculate ΔH°_{rxn} for the hydrogenation of ethene.
$H_2C = CH_2(g) + H_2(g) \rightarrow H_3C - CH_3(g)$

56. Use bond enthalpies to calculate ΔH°_{rxn} for the reaction of methane with chlorine and fluorine to form CF_2Cl_2 (Freon–12).
$CH_4(g) + 2\,Cl_2(g) + 2\,F_2(g) \rightarrow CF_2Cl_2(g) + 2\,HF(g) + 2\,HCl(g)$

57. Use bond enthalpies to calculate ΔH_{rxn} for the following reaction.
$H_2S(g) + 3\,F_2(g) \rightarrow SF_4(g) + 2\,HF(g)$

58. Use bond enthalpies to calculate ΔH°_{rxn} for the following reaction.
$N_2(g) + 3\,Cl_2(g) \rightarrow 2\,NCl_3(g)$

59. Use bond enthalpies to calculate ΔH°_{rxn} for the following reaction.
$CH_4(g) + CCl_4(g) \rightarrow CHCl_3(g) + CH_3Cl(g)$

60. Use bond enthalpies to calculate ΔH°_{rxn} for the following reaction.
$2\,H_2S(g) + 3\,O_2(g) \rightarrow 2\,H_2O(g) + 2\,SO_2(g)$

61. Rank the following bonds from strongest to weakest and from longest to shortest. What relationship between bond strength and bond length, if any, can be observed from these rankings?
a. S—Br
b. S—I
c. S—Cl
d. S—F

62. Rank the following bonds from strongest to weakest and from longest to shortest. What relationship between bond strength and bond length, if any, can be observed from these rankings?
a. H—Te
b. H—O
c. H—S
d. H—Se

63. Rank the following bonds from strongest to weakest and from longest to shortest. What relationship between bond strength and bond length, if any, can be observed from these rankings?
a. C≡N
b. C—N
c. C═N

64. Rank the following bonds from strongest to weakest and from longest to shortest. What relationship between bond strength and bond length, if any, can be observed from these rankings?
a. C≡O
b. C—O
c. C═O

Putting It Together

65. Determine whether each compound is ionic or covalent. Draw the appropriate Lewis structure.
a. Na_2O
b. AsF_3
c. CH_2O
d. $CaBr_2$

66. Determine whether each compound is ionic or covalent. Draw the appropriate Lewis structure.
a. CH_2F_2
b. SrO
c. KF
d. CS_2

67. Each of these compounds is an ionic compound containing a metal ion and a polyatomic ion. Draw the Lewis structure for each ionic compound, including the covalent structure for the polyatomic ion. Include resonance structures where necessary.
a. NaSCN
b. $MgCO_3$
c. $Sr(OH)_2$
d. KH_2PO_4

68. Each of these compounds is an ionic compound containing a metal ion and a polyatomic ion. Draw the Lewis structure for each ionic compound, including the covalent structure for the polyatomic ion. Include resonance structures where necessary.
a. $KClO_4$
b. $LiHSO_3$
c. NH_4Cl
d. $Ca(NO_3)_2$

69. Draw the Lewis structure for each molecule or ion. Some of the molecules or ions may not follow the octet rule. Use expanded octets where necessary and include resonance structures where appropriate.
a. PCl_5
b. BH_3
c. SiO_3^{2-}
d. CBr_4

70. Draw the Lewis structure for each molecule or ion. Some of the molecules or ions may not follow the octet rule. Use expanded octets where necessary and include resonance structures where appropriate.
    a. NBr_3
    b. BO_3^{3-}
    c. SeF_4
    d. KrF_4

71. Draw Lewis structures for the reactants and products. Use bond enthalpies to calculate ΔH°_{rxn}.
    $HCN(g) + 2\,H_2(g) \rightarrow CH_3NH_2(g)$

72. Draw Lewis structures for the reactants and products. Use bond enthalpies to calculate ΔH°_{rxn}.
    $2\,C_2H_6(g) + 7\,O_2(g) \rightarrow 4\,CO_2(g) + 6\,H_2O(g)$

73. Draw Lewis structures for the reactants and products. Use bond enthalpies to calculate ΔH_{rxn}.
    $2\,H_2O_2(g) \rightarrow 2\,H_2O(g) + O_2(g)$

74. Thioformaldehyde has a molar mass of 46.086 g/mol and is 26.06% C, 69.57% S, and 4.37% H by mass. Determine the molecular formula of the compound and draw its possible Lewis structures. Use formal charge to determine which structure is more likely to resemble the real molecule.

75. Cyanic acid has a molar mass of 43.028 g/mol and is 27.91% C, 32.56% N, 37.19% O, and 2.34% H by mass. Determine the molecular formula of the compound and draw its possible Lewis structures. Use formal charge to determine which structure is more likely to resemble the real molecule.

PRACTICE PROBLEM SOLUTIONS

Practice Problem 10.1 Solution

a. Nitrogen is a group 15 element, so it has five valence electrons. To satisfy the octet rule, nitrogen atoms must make three bonds to gain access to an additional three valence electrons.

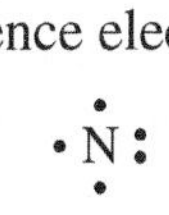

b. Oxygen is a group 16 element, so it has six valence electrons. To satisfy the octet rule, oxygen atoms must make two bonds to gain access to an additional two valence electrons.

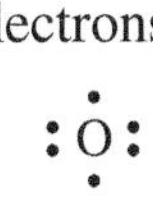

c. Fluorine is a group 17 element, so it has seven valence electrons. To satisfy the octet rule, fluorine atoms must make one bond to gain access to an additional valence electron.

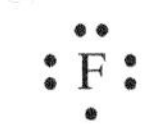

d. Neon is a group 18 element, so it has eight valence electrons. The octet rule is already satisfied, so it is unlikely to make any bonds.

Practice Problem 10.2 Solution

a. $CHCl_3$, has four single bonds (8 shared electrons) and nine lone pairs (18 unshared electrons).

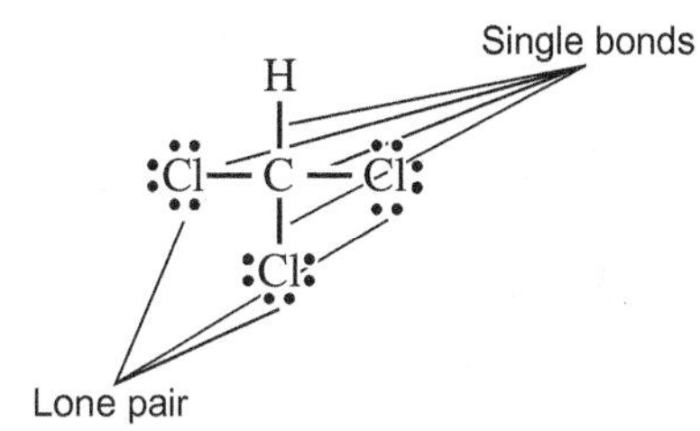

b. CH_3CONH_2, has seven single bonds (14 shared electrons) and one double bond (4 shared electrons), for a total of 18 shared electrons. It also has three lone pairs (6 unshared electrons).

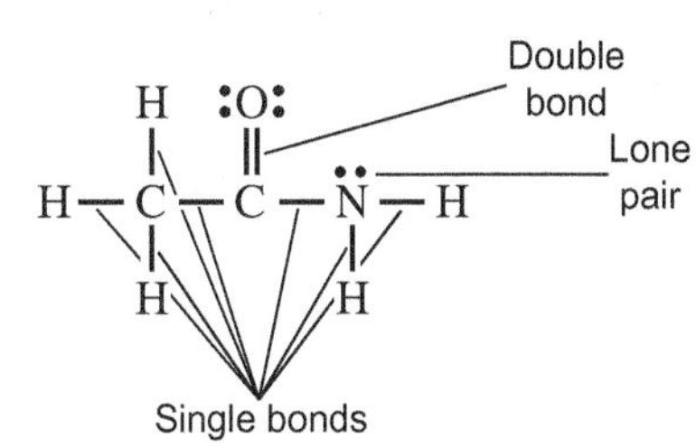

Practice Problem 10.3 Solution

a. The nitrogen atom shares six electrons in the bonds (three single bonds) and two in the lone pair to complete its octet. Each hydrogen shares two electrons in the single bond, a duet.

The hydrazine Lewis structure has five single bonds (10 electrons) and two lone pairs (4 electrons), for a total of 14 electrons shown in the structure.

Nitrogen, a group 15 element, has 5 valence electrons, and hydrogen, a group 1 element, has one valence electron: $2(5) + 4(1) = 14$ electrons. This matches the number of electrons shown in the structure.

b. The nitrogen atom has access to six electrons in the triple bond and two more with the lone pair, for a total of eight. Carbon has access to six electrons in the triple bond and two more with the single bond, for a total of eight. Hydrogen has access to two electrons. The octet/duet rule is satisfied.

The hydrogen cyanide Lewis structure has one single bond (2 electrons), a triple bond (6 electrons), and a lone pair (2 electrons), for a total of 10 electrons.

Nitrogen is a group 15 element with five valence electrons, carbon is a group 14 element with four valence electrons, and hydrogen has only one electron: 5 + 4 + 1 = 10. This matches the number of electrons shown in the structure.

Practice Problem 10.4 Solution

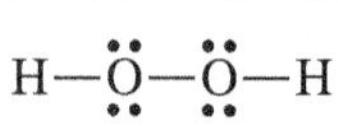

1. Sum up the valence electrons.	Each hydrogen contributes one, and each oxygen contributes six: 2(1) + 2(6) = 14 valence electrons
2. Verify duets, octets, and the total number of valence electrons.	Each H has one shared pair = two electrons = a duet. Each O has four shared + four unshared = eight electrons = an octet. Total # of electrons = 6 shared + 8 unshared = 14

Practice Problem 10.5 Solution

a. OCl_2

1. Sum up the valence electrons.	Oxygen contributes six electrons and each chlorine contributes seven: 1(6) + 2(7) = 20 valence electrons
2. Verify duets, octets, and the total number of valence electrons.	O has two single bonds + two lone pairs + eight electrons + an octet. Each Cl has one shared pair (single bond) and three lone pairs = eight electrons = an octet. Total # of electrons = 4 shared + 16 unshared = 20

b. NH_3

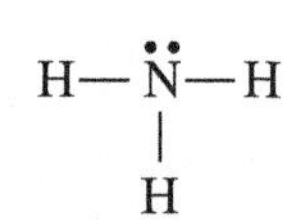

1. Sum up the valence electrons.	Nitrogen contributes five electrons and each hydrogen contributes one: 1(5) + 3(1) = 8 valence electrons
2. Verify duets, octets, and the total number of valence electrons.	Each H has one shared pair = two electrons = a duet. N has three single bonds + one lone pair = eight electrons = an octet. Total # of electrons = six shared + two unshared = eight

c. NH_2OH

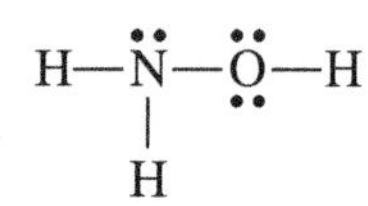

1. Sum up the valence electrons.	Nitrogen contributes five electrons, oxygen contributes six, and each hydrogen contributes one: 1(5) + 1(6) + 3(1) = 14 valence electrons
2. Verify duets, octets, and the total number of valence electrons.	Each H has one shared pair = two electrons = a duet. N has three single bonds + one lone pair = eight electrons = an octet. O has two single bonds + two lone pairs = eight electrons = an octet. Total # of electrons = 8 shared + 6 unshared = 14

Practice Problem 10.6 Solution

a. C_2H_2

H—C≡C—H

1. Sum up the valence electrons.	Hydrogen contributes one and each carbon contributes four: 2(1) + 2(4) = 10 valence electrons
2. Verify duets, octets, and the total number of valence electrons.	All H atoms have a shared pair of electrons = two electrons = a duet. Each C atom has a triple bond and a single bond = four shared pairs electrons = an octet. Total # of electrons = two single bonds (4) + a triple bond (6) = 10

b. N_2H_2

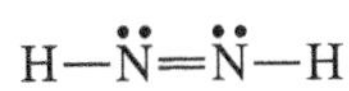

1. Sum up the valence electrons.	Hydrogen contributes one and each nitrogen contributes five: $2(1) + 2(5) = 12$ valence electrons
2. Verify duets, octets, and the total number of valence electrons.	All H atoms have a shared pair of electrons = two electrons = a duet. Both N atoms have one double bond + one single bond + one lone pair = an octet. Total # of electrons = 8 shared + 4 unshared = 12

Practice Problem 10.7 Solution

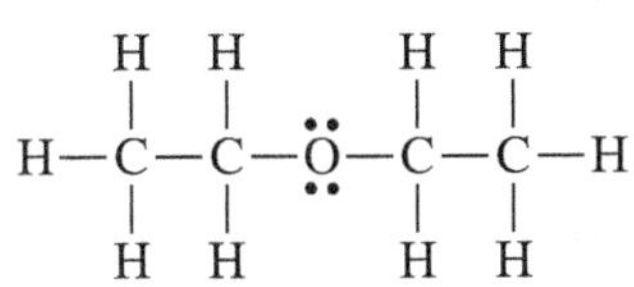

1. Sum up the valence electrons.	Each C contributes four, each H contributes one, and O contributes six: $4(4) + 10(1) + 1(6) = 32$ valence electrons
2. Verify duets, octets, and total number of valence electrons.	Each H atom has a shared pair of electrons = two electrons = a duet. Each C atom has four shared pairs (four single bonds) = eight electrons = an octet. The O has two shared pairs + two lone pairs = eight electrons = an octet. Total # of electrons = 28 shared + 4 unshared = 32

Practice Problem 10.8 Solution

a. ammonium ion, NH_{4+}

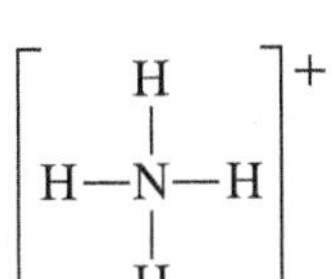

1. Sum up the valence electrons, adding valence electrons for each negative charge and subtracting electrons for each positive charge.	Nitrogen contributes five, each hydrogen contributes one; subtract one electron for the + 1 charge: $1(5) + 4(1) - 1 = 8$ valence electrons
2. Verify duets, octets, and the total number of valence electrons	Each H atom has a shared pair of electrons = two electrons = a duet. N has four bonds = eight electrons = an octet. Total # of electrons = four single bonds = eight.

b. cyanide ion, CN^-

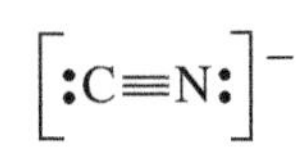

1. Sum up the valence electrons, adding valence electrons for each negative charge and subtracting electrons for each positive charge.	Carbon contributes four, nitrogen contributes five; add one electron for the −1 charge: $1(4) + 1(5) + 1 = 10$ valence electrons
2. Verify duets, octets, and the total number of valence electrons	C has one triple bond and one lone pair = eight electrons = an octet. N has one triple bond and one lone pair = eight electrons = an octet. Total # of electrons = 6 shared + 4 unshared = 10.

Practice Problem 10.9 Solution

a. The nitrate ion, NO_3^-, has three equivalent Lewis structures.

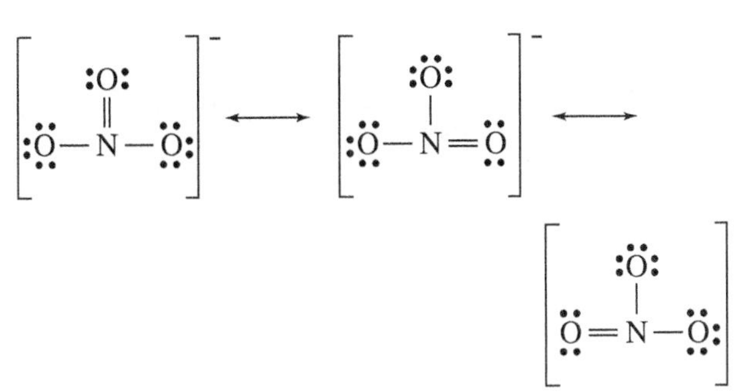

1. Sum up the valence electrons, accounting for the charge.	N contributes five, each O atom contributes six; add one electron for the −1 charge: $1(5) + 3(6) + 1 = 24$ valence electrons
2. Verify duets, octets, and the total number of valence electrons.	N has two single bonds + one double bond = eight electrons. Two O atoms have one bond + three lone pairs = eight electrons. One O atom has one double bond + two lone pairs = eight electrons. Total # of electrons = 8 shared + 16 unshared = 24

These three equivalent resonance structures for the nitrate ion indicate that the double bond is delocalized among all three positions. A structure that is the average of these three would be closer to the true structure of the nitrate ion, and is supported by the measured properties of the ion.

b. The hydrogen carbonate ion, HCO_3^-, has two equivalent Lewis structures.

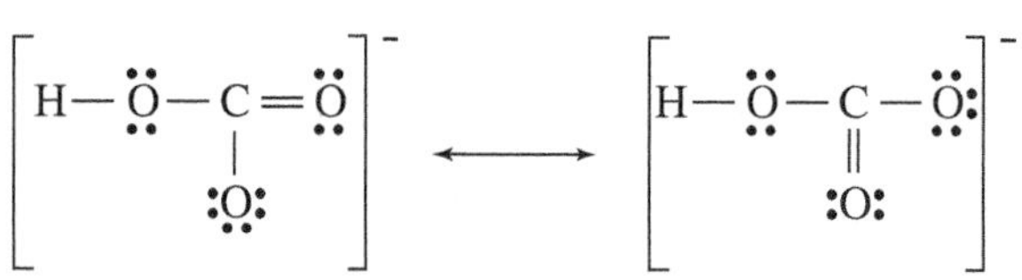

1. Sum up the valence electrons, accounting for the charge.	C contributes four, H contributes one, each O contributes six; add one electron for the −1 charge: $1(4) + 1(1) + 3(6) + 1 = 24$ valence electrons
2. Verify duets, octets, and the total number of valence electrons.	C has two single bonds + one double bond = eight electrons = an octet. The single-bonded terminal O atoms have one bond + three lone pairs = eight electrons = an octet. The double-bonded terminal O has two bonds + two lone pairs = eight electrons = an octet. Total # of electrons = 10 shared + 14 unshared = 24

Practice Problem 10.10 Solution

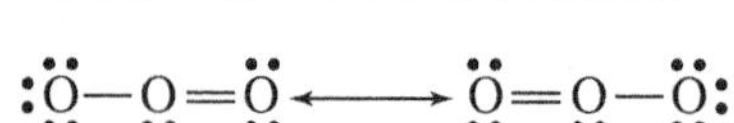

1. Sum up the valence electrons.	Each O contributes six: $3(6) = 18$ valence electrons
2. Verify octets and the total number of valence electrons.	The central O has one single bond + two double bonds + one lone pair = eight electrons. One O atom has one single bond + three lone pairs = eight electrons. One O atom has one double bond + two lone pairs = eight electrons. Total # of electrons = 6 shared + 12 unshared = 18

Note that the oxygen atom in the middle forms three bonds, which is more than is generally predicted for oxygen. This is the accepted Lewis structure for ozone because all three oxygen atoms achieve an octet in the resonance structures. Neither Lewis structure is a good representative of the actual ozone molecule. An average of these two structures, with the double-bonded electrons delocalized and shared among the three atoms of the molecule, is a better representation of the ozone molecule than either structure by itself. Experimental evidence indicates that the two bonds in ozone are equivalent and exhibit properties in between those of single and double bonds.

Practice Problem 10.11 Solution

Carbon is the central atom of OCN^- because it has the lowest electronegativity value of the elements carbon (2.5), oxygen (3.5), and nitrogen (3.0).

Practice Problem 10.12 Solution

a. thiocyanate ion, SCN^-

The resonance structures for SCN^-, including formal charge, are as follows:

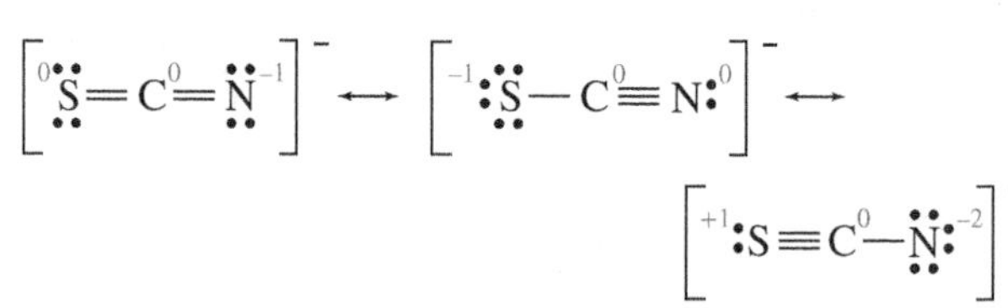

The structure on the left is the most likely structure because it assigns the negative formal charge to nitrogen, which is more electronegative (3.0) than sulfur (2.5).

b. nitrous acid, HNO_2 (Note that the H atom is bonded to a terminal O atom.)

Nitrous acid has two possible resonance structures with the indicated formal charges.

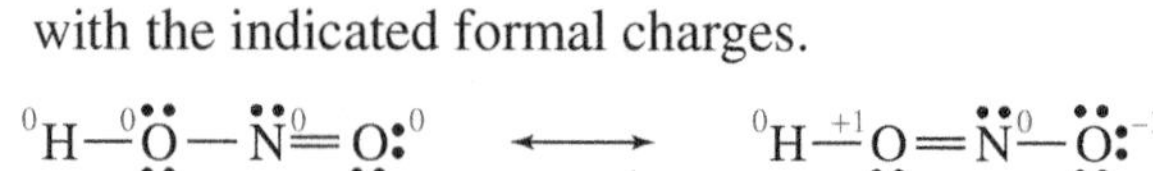

Practice Problem 10.13 Solution

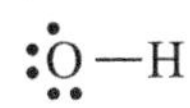

1. Sum up the valence electrons.	$1(6) + 1(1) = 7$ electrons
2. Verify duets, octets, formal charge, and the total number of valence electrons.	H has one bond = two electrons. O has one bond + two lone pairs + a single electron = seven electrons. Formal charges: O $6 - \left[\frac{1}{2}(2) + 5\right] = 0$ H $1 - \left[\frac{1}{2}(2) + 0\right] = 0$ Total # of electrons = 1 bond + 2 lone pairs + 1 unpaired electron = 7 electrons.

The only possible location for the single electron is on the oxygen, which has a formal charge of zero in the structure. This substance is often referred to as the hydroxyl radical, which emphasizes its unusual structure.

Practice Problem 10.14 Solution

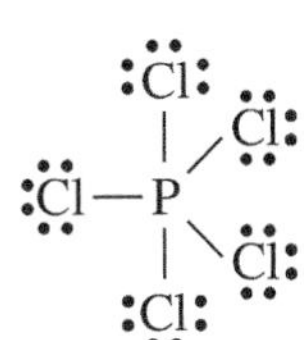

1. Sum up the valence electrons.	$1(5) + 5(7) = 40$ electrons
2. Verify octets, formal charge assignments, and the total number of valence electrons.	P has 5 bonds = 10 electrons for expanded valence. Each Cl has 1 bond + 3 lone pairs =8 electrons. Formal charges: P: $5 - \left[\frac{1}{2}(10) + 0\right] = 0$ Cl: $7 - \left[\frac{1}{2}(2) + 6\right] = 0$ Total # of electrons = 5 bonds + 16 lone pairs = 42 electrons.

Practice Problem 10.15 Solution

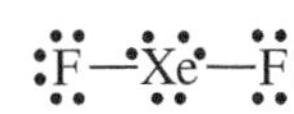

1. Sum up the valence electrons.	$1(8) + 2(7) = 22$ electrons
2. Verify octets, formal charge assignments, and the total number of valence electrons.	Xe has 2 bonds + 3 lone pairs = 10 electrons for expanded valence. Each F has one bond + three lone pairs = eight electrons. Formal charges: Xe: $8 - \left[\frac{1}{2}(4) + 6\right] = 0$ F: $7 - \left[\frac{1}{2}(2) + 6\right] = 0$ Total # of electrons = 5 bonds + 16 lone pairs = 42 electrons.

Practice Problem 10.16 Solution

a. N (3.0) is more electronegative than H (2.1).

$$^{\delta+}\text{H}-\text{N}^{\delta-}$$

b. (3.5) is more electronegative than Br (2.8).

$$^{\delta+}\text{Br}-\text{O}^{\delta-}$$

Practice Problem 10.17 Solution

Compound	ΔEN
H_2O	$3.5 - 2.1 = 1.4$
H_2S	$2.5 - 2.1 = 0.4$
H_2Se	$2.4 - 2.1 = 0.3$
H_2Te	$2.1 - 2.1 = 0$

Of these compounds, only the O—H bonds in water are strongly or even moderately polar. The S—H bonds in hydrogen sulfide are weakly polar, while the Se—H bonds in hydrogen selenide are just slightly polar and the Te—H bonds in hydrogen telluride are nonpolar.

Practice Problem 10.18 Solution

Step 1: Calculate the dipole moment for 100% charge separation.

$$\mu_{\text{calculated}} = (1.6 \times 10^{-19}\ \text{C})(92\ \text{pm})\left(\frac{1 \times 10^{-12}\ \text{m}}{\text{pm}}\right)\left(\frac{1\ \text{D}}{3.34 \times 10^{-30}\ \text{C} \cdot \text{m}}\right) = 4.4\ \text{D}$$

$$\text{Step 2: \% ionic character} = \left(\frac{\mu_{measured}}{\mu_{calculated}}\right) \times 100\ \%$$
$$= \frac{1.82\ D}{4.4\ D} = 41\%$$

Practice Problem 10.19 Solution

The average bond enthalpy for a C—H bond is 413 kJ/mol, whereas the average bond enthalpy of a C—Cl bond is 328 kJ/mol. Thus, it takes less energy to break the C—Cl bond, so it is reasonable to predict that CCl_4 is more reactive than CH_4.

Practice Problem 10.20 Solution

a. Draw Lewis structures to identify the bonds that are broken and formed during the reaction.

$$NH_3(g) + Cl_2(g) \rightarrow N_2H_4(g) + HCl(g)$$

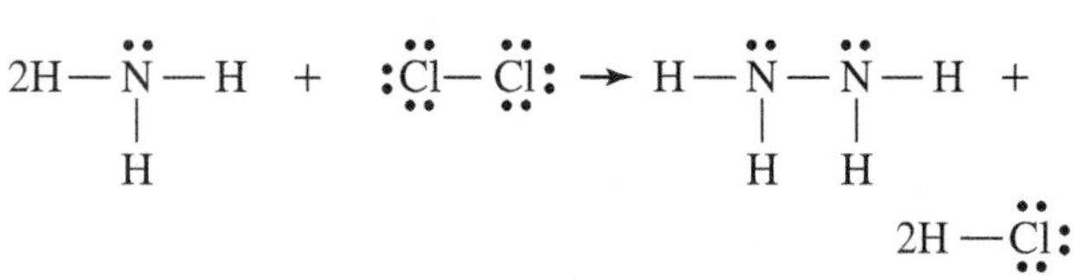

Thus, 6 mol of N—H bonds and 1 mol of Cl—Cl bonds are broken, whereas 4 mol of N—H bonds, 1 mol of N—N bonds, and 2 mol of H—Cl bonds are formed.

$$\Delta H_{rxn} = \Sigma(\Delta H \text{ of bonds broken}) - \Sigma(\Delta H \text{ of bonds formed})$$
$$\Delta H_{rxn} = [6\Delta H_{N-H} + \Delta H_{Cl-Cl}] - [4\Delta H_{N-H} + \Delta H_{N-N} + 2\Delta H_{H-Cl}]$$
$$\Delta H_{rxn} = [6(391\ kJ) + 242\ kJ] - [4(391\ kJ) + 167\ kJ + 2(431\ kJ)]$$
$$\Delta H_{rxn} = 2588\ kJ - 2593\ kJ$$
$$\Delta H_{rxn} = -5\ kJ$$

The results of the calculation tell you that this reaction is exothermic, with a small reaction enthalpy.

b. Draw Lewis structures to identify the bonds that are broken and formed during the reaction.

$$C_2H_6(g) \rightarrow C_2H_2(g) + 2\ H_2(g)$$

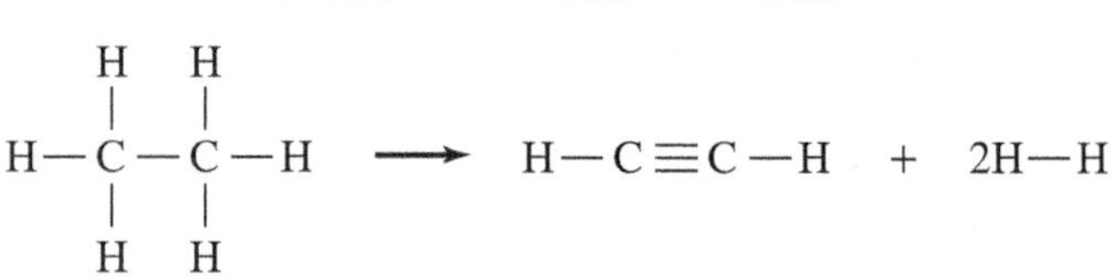

Thus, 6 mol of C—H bonds and 1 mol of C—C bonds are broken, whereas 2 mol of C—H bonds, 1 mol of C≡C bonds, and 2 mol of H—H bonds are formed.

$$\Delta H_{rxn} = \Sigma(\Delta H \text{ of bonds broken}) - \Sigma(\Delta H \text{ of bonds formed})$$
$$\Delta H_{rxn} = [6\Delta H_{C-H} + \Delta H_{C-C}] - [2\Delta H_{C-H} + \Delta H_{C\equiv C} + 2\Delta H_{H-H}]$$
$$\Delta H_{rxn} = [6(413\ kJ) + 348\ kJ] - [2(413\ kJ) + 839\ kJ + 2(436\ kJ)]$$
$$\Delta H_{rxn} = 2826\ kJ - 2537\ kJ$$
$$\Delta H_{rxn} = 290\ kJ$$

The results of the calculation tell you that the formation of acetylene from ethane is an endothermic reaction with a positive reaction enthalpy.

Practice Problem 10.21 Solution

Gather the appropriate data from Tables 10.3 and 10.4:

Bond	Enthalpy (kJ/mol)	Length (pm)
C—N	293	147
C═N	615	128
C≡N	891	116

In going from single bond to double bond to triple bond, the bond length decreases while bond enthalpy increases. This is the same inverse relationship between bond length and bond enthalpy that was found in Example 10.21 for carbon–carbon bonds.

Practice Problem 10.22 Solution

If all atoms follow the octet rule, the Lewis structure has one single bond and one double bond.

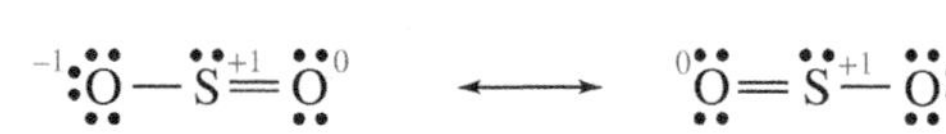

In the resonance hybrid, each sulfur–oxygen bond would be somewhere between single and double, and we'd expect the bond length to be between the lengths of an S—O bond (158 pm) and a S═O double bond (143 pm).

If S expands beyond an octet, all atoms can have a formal charge of zero and the Lewis structure has two double bonds.

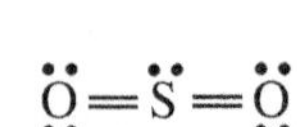

In this case, we'd expect the bond lengths to match that of a S═O double bond (143 pm).

The experimentally determined bond length is 143.2 pm, meaning the structure with only double bonds most closely resembles the true structure of SO_2 and that the other structures are not major contributors.

CHAPTER 11 Molecular Shape and Bonding Theories

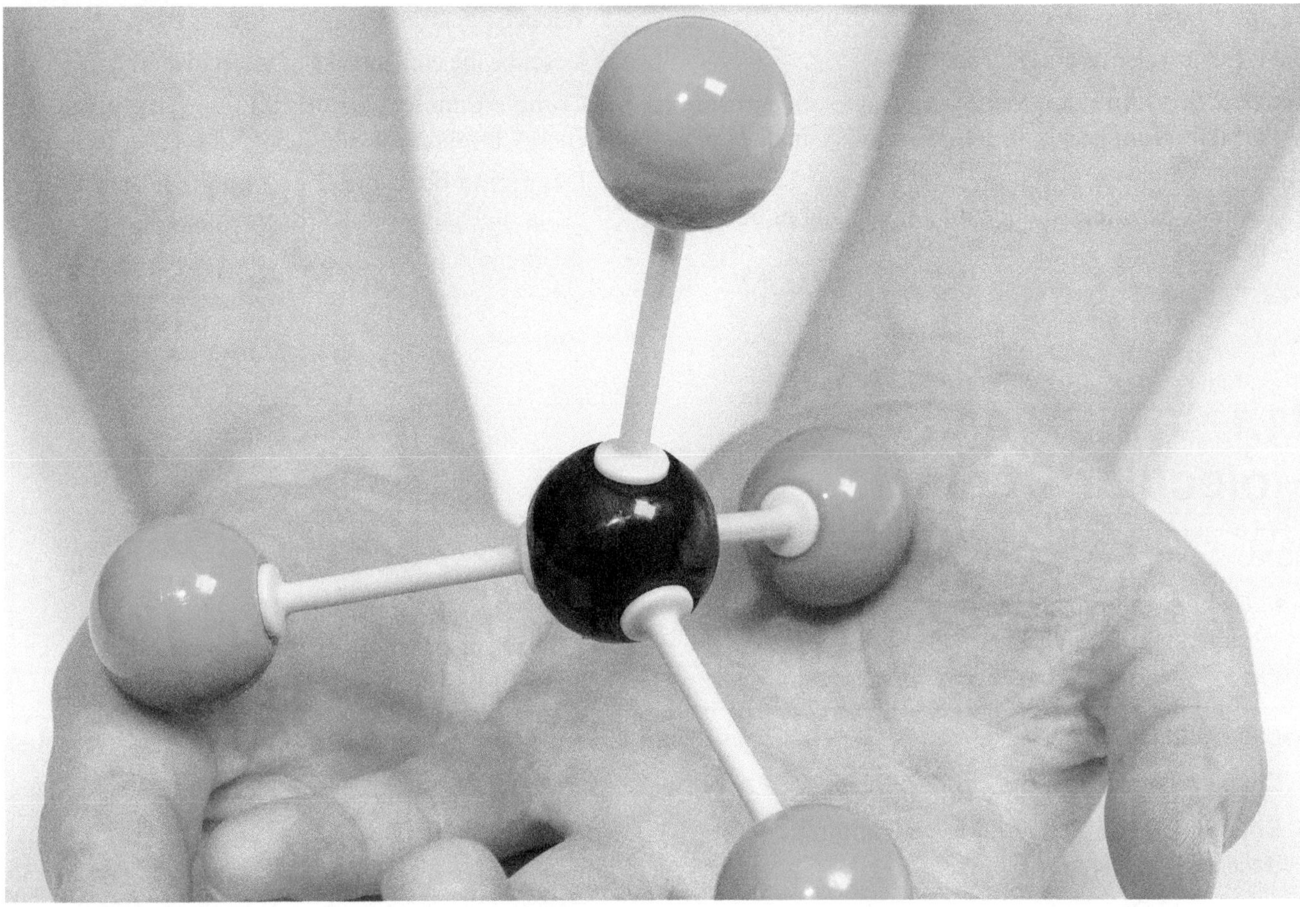

graphbottles/Shutterstock

Molecules have predictable three-dimensional shapes and bond angles. These shapes affect the properties of the substance. For example, the shape of carbon dioxide makes it a greenhouse gas. Artificial sweeteners taste sweet because their shape allows them to fit into certain receptor sites on our taste buds. The shape of carbon tetrachloride, shown here, makes it nonpolar and thus suitable as an additive to wax in lava lamps.

Chapter Outline

GOALS

- Use Lewis structures to predict molecular geometry using VSEPR.
- Identify polar and nonpolar molecules using electronegativity values and molecular shape.
- Explain valence bond theory.
- Describe and recognize *sp*, *sp*^{2}, and *sp*^{3} hybrid orbitals from Lewis structures or other images of molecules.
- Define, describe, and identify sigma and pi bonds in molecules.
- Apply valence bond theory to reactivity and bond rotation.
- List and describe some of the limitations of valence bond theory.
- Describe the components of molecular orbital theory.
- Complete molecular orbital diagrams given the energy levels.
- Determine bond order and magnetic properties using molecular orbital diagrams.
- Write molecular orbital electron configurations.

11.1 VSEPR and Molecular Geometry

GOAL

- Use Lewis structures to predict molecular geometry using VSEPR.

Background Review

Chapter 2 Atoms and the Periodic Table

Chapter 9 Periodicity and Ionic Bonding:
Section 9.1—Valence Electrons

Chapter 10 Covalent Bonding

Lewis structures are two-dimensional models of atoms and molecules. Atoms and molecules are three-dimensional, however, and the three-dimensional shapes of molecules affect their chemical properties, their physical properties, and their uses. Figure 11.1 compares the properties of 1-butanol and 2-butanol, two **isomers** with the formula $C_4H_{10}O$. Notice that the melting and boiling points of 2-butanol are much lower than for 1-butanol and that 2-butanol is much more soluble in water and is more reactive, as indicated by its lower **flash point**. (The flash point is the lowest temperature at which the vapor of a compound will ignite when provided with an ignition source.) In this section you will learn how to use Lewis structures to predict the shapes of molecules. In Section 11.2, you will learn how to use the shapes of molecules and electronegativity values to predict if a molecule is polar or nonpolar.

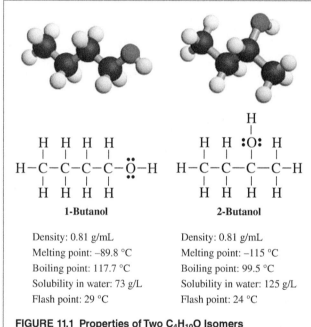

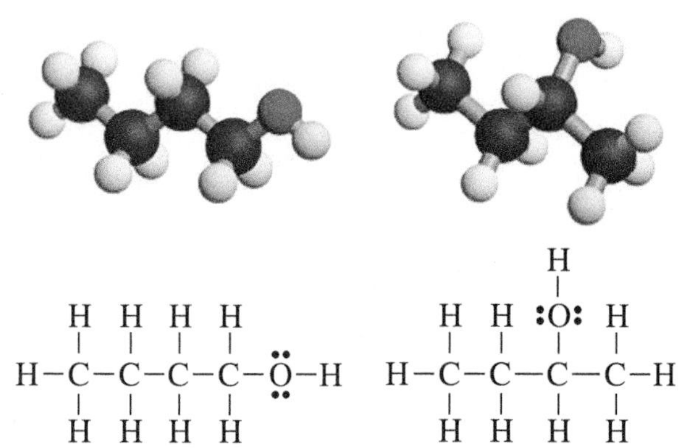

1-Butanol

Density: 0.81 g/mL
Melting point: –89.8 °C
Boiling point: 117.7 °C
Solubility in water: 73 g/L
Flash point: 29 °C

2-Butanol

Density: 0.81 g/mL
Melting point: –115 °C
Boiling point: 99.5 °C
Solubility in water: 125 g/L
Flash point: 24 °C

FIGURE 11.1 Properties of Two $C_4H_{10}O$ Isomers
The placement of the OH group along the chain of carbon atoms affects the melting point, boiling point, solubility in water, and flash point. 2-butanol melts and boils at a far lower temperature, is 71% more soluble in water, and is more highly combustible than 1-butanol.

VALENCE SHELL ELECTRON PAIR REPULSION

Although electrons have very little mass, they occupy the vast majority of the volume of an individual atom (Section 2.3) and likewise take up most of the volume of molecules. Molecules consist of atoms that share valence electrons and may also have lone pairs of electrons on the central atom. Repulsions between these groups of electrons determine the overall shapes of molecules.

The **valence shell electron pair repulsion, VSEPR, model** provides a way to predict the shape of a molecule based on the number of individual **electron domains** surrounding the central atom (the domain number). Each of these electron domains is a *charge cloud* made up of either *shared* or *lone-pair electrons*. The most stable arrangement of these charge clouds is the one in which there is the least repulsion, where they are as far apart as possible while maintaining their connection to the central atom. This most stable arrangement is known as the **electron geometry** or domain geometry. Electrons, whether they are shared or unshared, do not act like the rigid connectors you may use with a molecular model kit. Rather, electrons are charge clouds capable of shifting their locations with respect to each other. The *relative locations* of these domains around the central atom of a molecule affect the shape of that molecule. Table 11.1 summarizes the *five electron geometries* and gives examples of the **molecular geometries** or molecular shapes that can exist for each electron geometry. Molecular geometry refers to the shape occupied by the atoms in the molecule, which is affected by the total number of electron domains.

TABLE 11.1 Summary of Electron Geometries and Molecular Geometries

Electron Domains	Bonded Groups	Lone Pairs	Electron Geometry	Molecular Geometry	Bond Angles	Example	Model
2	2	0	Linear	Linear	180°	CO_2	
3	3	0	Trigonal planar	Trigonal planar	120°	NO_3^-	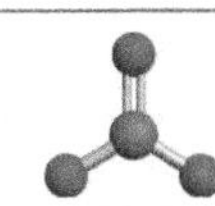
	2	1	Trigonal planar	Bent	<120°	NO_2^-	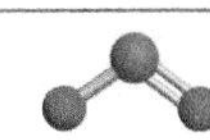
4	4	0	Tetrahedral	Tetrahedral	109.5°	CH_4	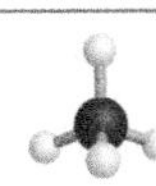
	3	1	Tetrahedral	Trigonal pyramidal	<109.5°	NH_3	
	2	2	Tetrahedral	Bent	<109.5°	H_2O	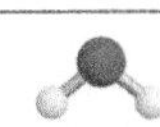
5	5	0	Trigonal bipyramidal	Trigonal bipyramidal	90°, 120°, 180°	PCl_5	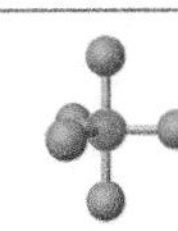
	4	1	Trigonal bipyramidal	Seesaw	<90°, <120°, <180°	SF_4	
	3	2	Trigonal bipyramidal	T-shaped	<90°, <180°	ClF_3	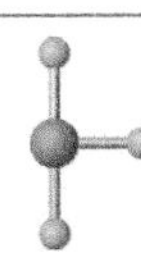
	2	3	Trigonal bipyramidal	Linear	180°	I_3^-	
6	6	0	Octahedral	Octahedral	90°, 180°	SF_6	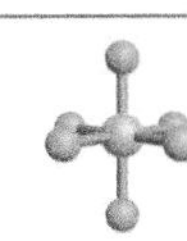
	5	1	Octahedral	Square pyramidal	<90°, <180°	ClF_5	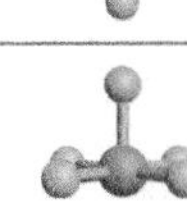
	4	2	Octahedral	Square planar	90°, 180°	XeF_4	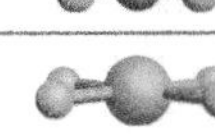

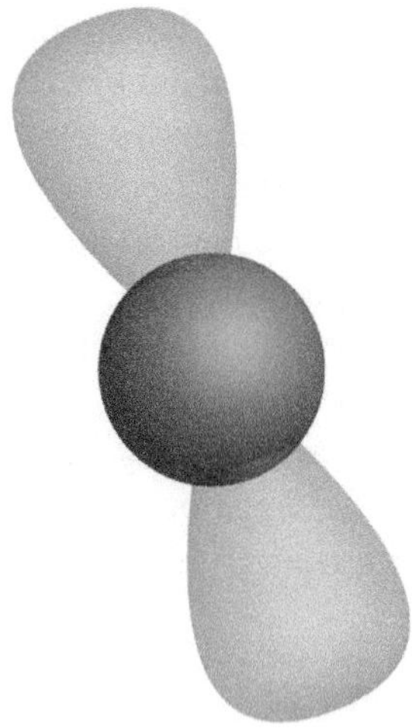

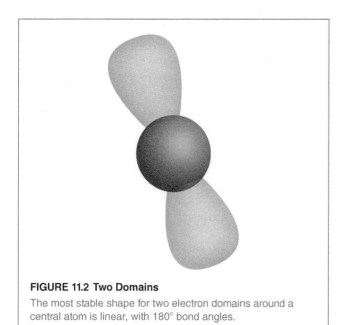

FIGURE 11.2 Two Domains
The most stable shape for two electron domains around a central atom is linear, with 180° bond angles.

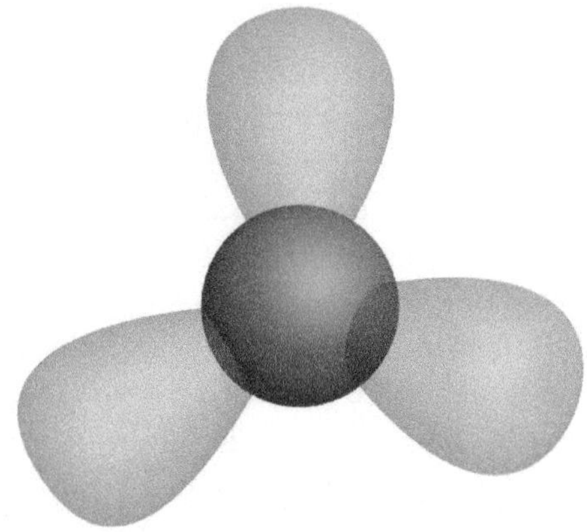

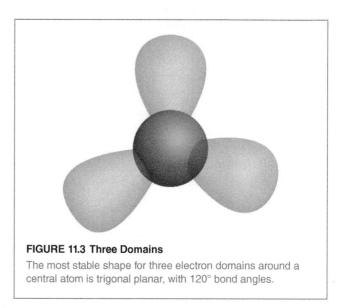

FIGURE 11.3 Three Domains
The most stable shape for three electron domains around a central atom is trigonal planar, with 120° bond angles.

In a Lewis structure, an individual electron domain can consist of any of the following: a lone pair of electrons, a single unshared electron, a single covalent bond, a double covalent bond, or a triple covalent bond.

Two Electron Domains

If a central atom has only two electron domains around it, the most stable arrangement—which places the two domains as far apart as possible while still attracted to the central atom—is the **linear** electron geometry shown in Figure 11.2. This shape results from the electron–electron repulsion between the electron domains.

The electron domains adopt a linear shape. Therefore, molecules and polyatomic ions with two electron domains around the central atom have a linear shape with a bond angle of 180°. Beryllium hydride, BeH_2, carbon dioxide, CO_2, and cyanate, OCN^-, are each linear with 180° bond angles. Notice how the two domains can be two single bonds, two double bonds, or a single bond and a triple bond.

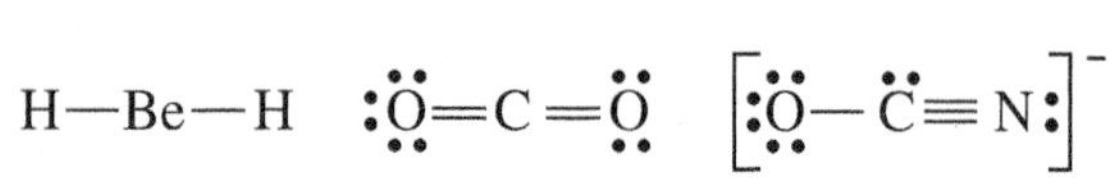

Three Electron Domains

Three electron domains connected to the same central atom repel each other to form an equilateral triangle. This shape places the three domains as far apart as possible from each other. This electron geometry is referred to as **trigonal planar** (Figure 11.3).

Nitrate, NO_3^-, has three electron domains around the central nitrogen atom, and all three domains are shared electron pairs. Molecules or ions with three identical electron domains have a perfect trigonal planar shape, with 120° bond angles. Molecules or ions with three electron domains that are not identical will have a shape very close to a trigonal planar shape, but may have slight variations in the bond angles.

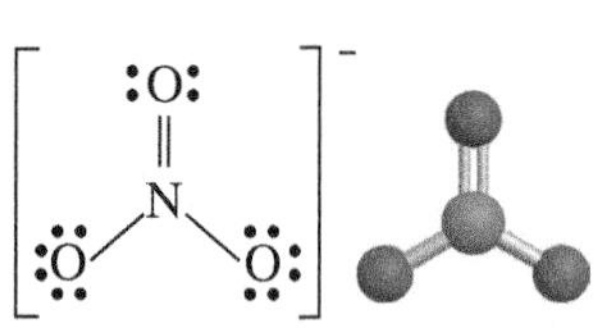

Lone pair electrons on the central atom play an important role in determining the electron geometry and have an additional impact on the molecular geometry. Because these electrons are only attracted to one nucleus, they are located more closely to that nucleus than a bonded pair is and, therefore, take up more volume around that nucleus. Lone pair electrons, because they are not shared, are also more strongly repelling than bonded (shared) electron pairs.

When one of the three electron domains is a lone pair of electrons instead of another atom or group of

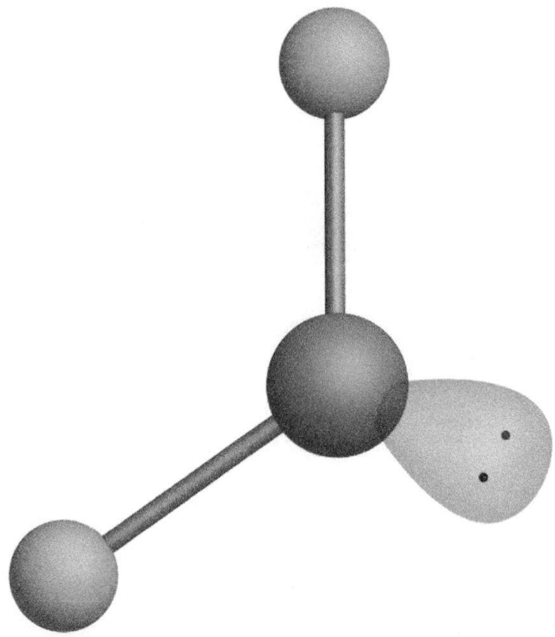

FIGURE 11.4 Three Domains, One of Which Is a Lone Pair

The presence of a lone pair in the three-domain electron geometry results in a bent molecular geometry with a bond angle slightly less than the predicted bond angle of 120°.

atoms, the electron geometry is still trigonal planar, but these molecules have the **bent** molecular geometry shown in Figure 11.4.

The bond angle in bent molecules is usually a little less than 120° because of the lone pair of electrons. Nitrite, NO_2^-, has three electron domains around the central atom, two of which are bonded groups and one of which is a lone pair. NO_2^- has a bent molecular geometry.

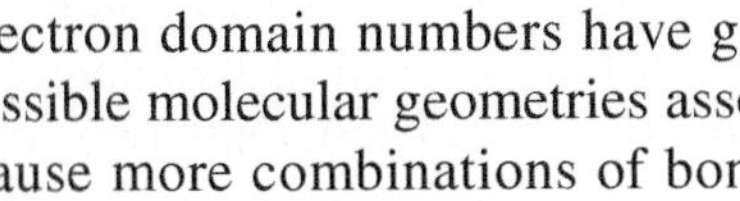

Each domain number has one characteristic electron geometry but may have additional molecular geometries associated with it, based on the number of bonded groups and lone pairs around the central atom. Higher electron domain numbers have greater numbers of possible molecular geometries associated with them because more combinations of bonded groups and lone pairs are possible.

Four Electron Domains

When four electron domains are associated with a central atom as in Figure 11.5, the largest possible bond angle in a planar arrangement is 90°. However, the repulsion among four charge clouds pushes the domains into a three-dimensional shape called a **tetrahedron**, which consists of four triangular faces. In a **tetrahedral** molecule or ion, the central atom occupies the three-dimensional center of the tetrahedron and the charge clouds point to the four corners (Figure 11.5).

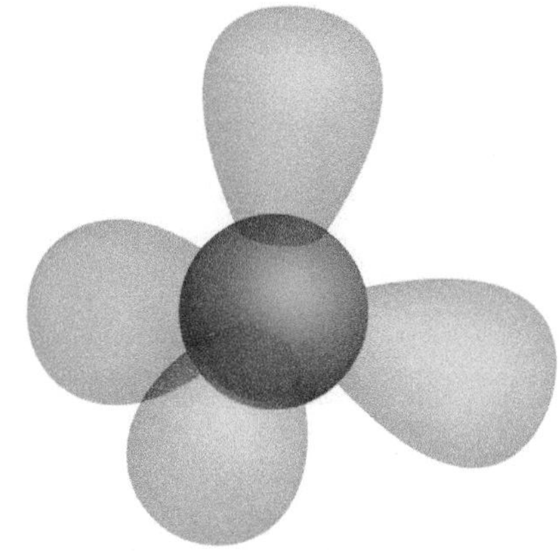

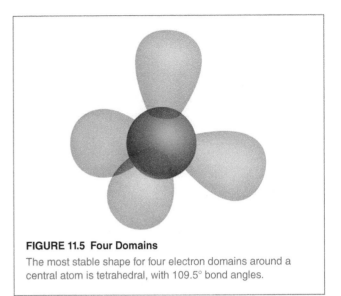

FIGURE 11.5 Four Domains

The most stable shape for four electron domains around a central atom is tetrahedral, with 109.5° bond angles.

Methane, CH_4, is a tetrahedral molecule. Notice in Figure 11.6 how the carbon atom is located at the center of the tetrahedron and each hydrogen atom is located at one of the four corners. Tetrahedral molecules with four identical bonded groups have bond angles of 109.5°. Molecules with four domains that include nonidentical bonded groups have bond angles that deviate slightly from the predicted tetrahedral angle.

In addition to the four single bonds in CH_4, there are two other ways for a molecule to have four electron domains, which are exemplified by ammonia, NH_3, and water, H_2O. The four electron domains in NH_3 consist of three bonded H atoms and one lone pair around the central N atom. The shape occupied by these four domains is tetrahedral, but no atom occupies the fourth corner of the tetrahedron (Figure 11.7a). Thus, the shape occupied by the atoms (the molecular geometry) is a three-sided pyramid called a trigonal pyramid. A **trigonal pyramidal** molecule has angles slightly less than the expected 109.5° (they are ≈106.6° in NH_3) due to greater repulsion from the lone pair electrons.

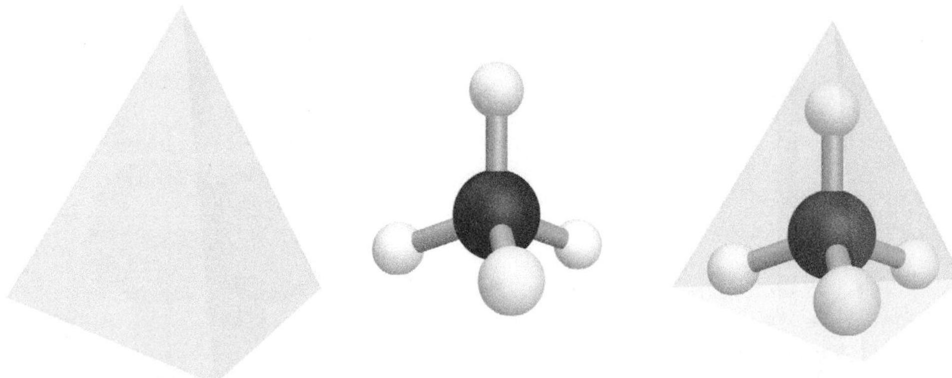

(a) (b) (c)

FIGURE 11.6 Three-Dimensional Images of Methane, CH_4

NOTE: You need to be online to access this 3D molecule.

These images show (a) a tetrahedron, (b) a methane molecule, and (c) a methane molecule with the four domains pointing to the four corners of the tetrahedron. *Click each image to open an interactive view.*

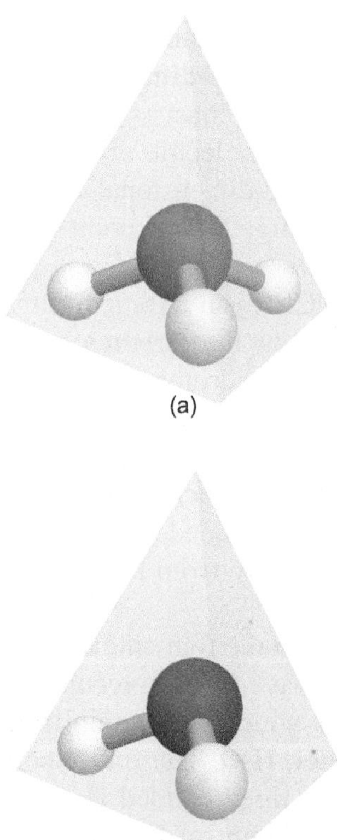

(a)

(b)

FIGURE 11.7 Three-Dimensional Images of Ammonia, NH_3, and Water, H_2O

(a) The presence of a lone pair in the four-domain electron geometry results in a trigonal pyramidal molecular geometry with a bond angle slightly less than the predicted bond angle of 109.5°. (b) The presence of two lone pairs in the four-domain electron geometry results in a bent molecular geometry with a bond angle slightly less than the predicted bond angle of 109.5°.

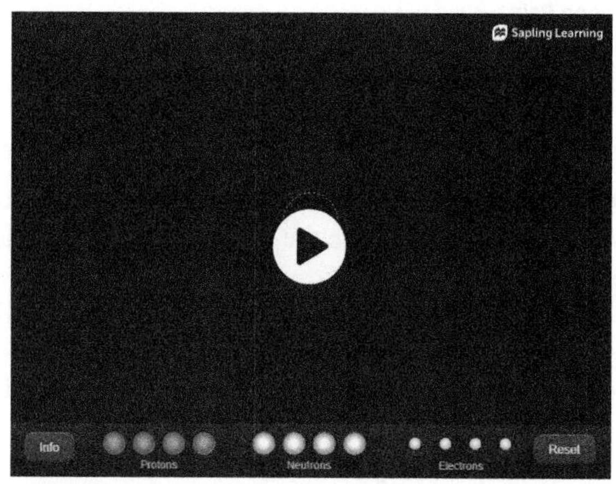

FIGURE 11.8 Molecular and Electron Geometry Activity

NOTE: You need to be online to access this activity.

Start in "Model" mode, dragging bonds and lone pairs to the central atom. Using the checkboxes, you can display or hide the resulting geometries and angles to test yourself. Then switch to "Real Molecule" mode, where you can load the molecule for a specific formula, such as H_2O. In this mode, you can toggle between "real" and "model" bond angles, such as 104.5° versus 109.5° in H_2O.

Similarly, the four electron domains around the central atom in H_2O consist of two single bonds and two lone pairs (Figure 11.7b). Only two corners of the tetrahedron are now unoccupied by atoms, leaving a bent molecular geometry with a bond angle of 104.5°. This is less than the perfect tetrahedral angle of 109.5°, again due to the stronger repulsion of the lone pairs.

The activity in Figure 11.8 allows you to build molecules of various electron geometries and molecular geometries.

Steven Lemon, Macmillan Learning

FIGURE 11.9 Video Tutorial: Molecular Geometry I

NOTE: You need to be online to access this video.

This video shows how to determine molecular geometry from Lewis structures.

It is important to be able to predict the geometry of a molecule based on its Lewis structure (Figure 11.9).

Example 11.1

Determine the molecular geometries and bond angles for (a) phosphorus trichloride, PCl_3, (b) oxygen difluoride, OF_2, and (c) dibromodichloromethane, CCl_2Br_2.

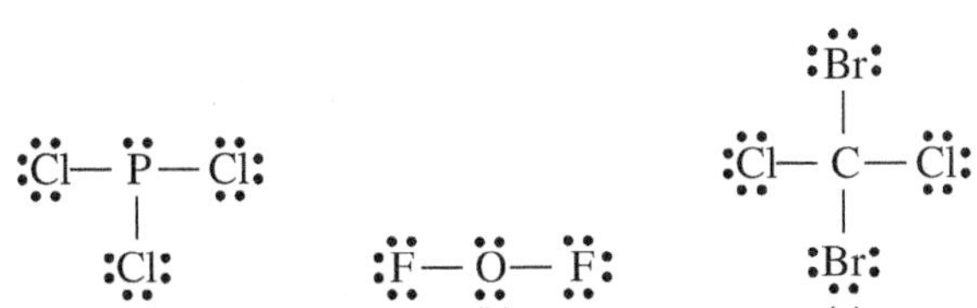

(a) (b) (c)

Solution

a. There are four electron domains around the central P atom in PCl_3, giving it a tetrahedral electron geometry. The molecular geometry, though, is trigonal pyramidal, because one of the four electron domains is a lone pair. As a result, the bond angles will be slightly less than the tetrahedral angle of 109.5°.

b. There are four electron domains around the central O atom in OF_2, giving it a tetrahedral electron geometry. The molecular geometry is bent, however, because two of the electron domains are lone pairs. As a result, the bond angles will be less than the tetrahedral angle of 109.5°.

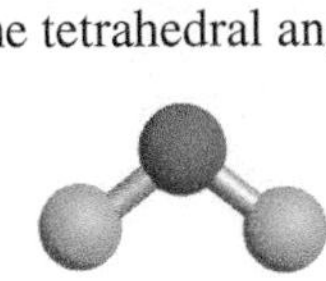

c. There are four electron domains around the central C atom in CCl_2Br_2, giving it a tetrahedral electron geometry. The molecular geometry is also tetrahedral, because all four electron domains are bonded groups. As a result, the bond angles are predicted to be equal to the tetrahedral angle of 109.5°. However, the bonded groups are not all the same (two are Cl atoms and two are Br atoms), so there are likely to be some minor deviations from the perfect tetrahedral angles.

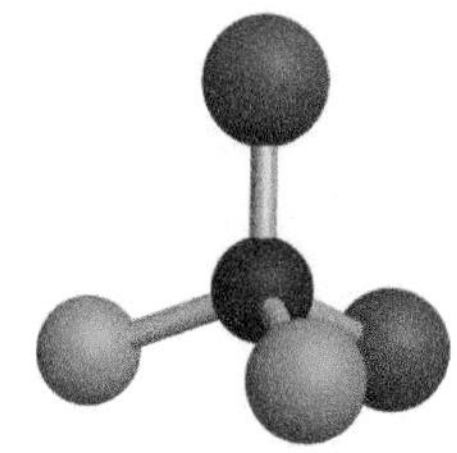

PRACTICE PROBLEM 11.1

Determine the molecular geometries and bond angles for (a) silicon tetrachloride, $SiCl_4$, (b) borane, BH_3, and (c) sulfur dioxide, SO_2.

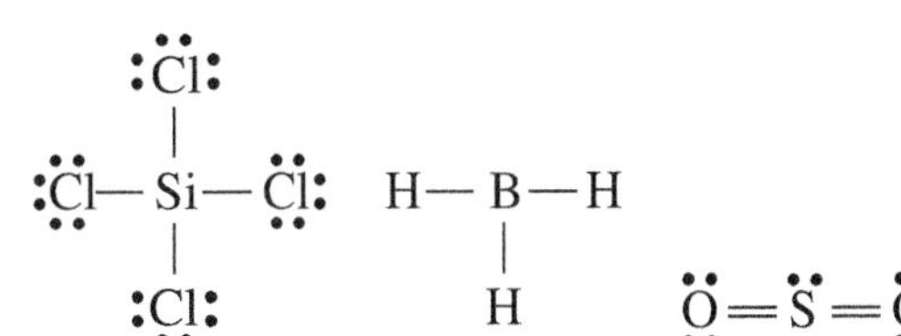

(a) (b) (c)

Hint: Count the number of bonded groups and lone pairs on the central atom. Refer to Table 11.1, Figure 11.8 (Molecular and Electron Geometry Activity) and Figure 11.9 (Video Tutorial) as needed.

LARGER MOLECULES

As molecules become larger and more structurally complex, it becomes hard to succinctly describe either their electron geometries or their overall molecular shapes succinctly. For this reason, molecules that have many atoms are described as a series of smaller geometries, one for each central (nonterminal) atom. This is particularly true of carbon compounds, which commonly consist of carbon atoms bonded to each other in chains. Section 10.2 (Example 10.7) explains how to draw the Lewis structure of ethanol, CH_3CH_2OH. From the structure repeated here in Figure 11.10, notice that each carbon is a central atom with four electron domains (four single bonds), and the oxygen is another central atom with four electron domains (two single bonds and two lone pairs). As a result, the two carbon atoms have

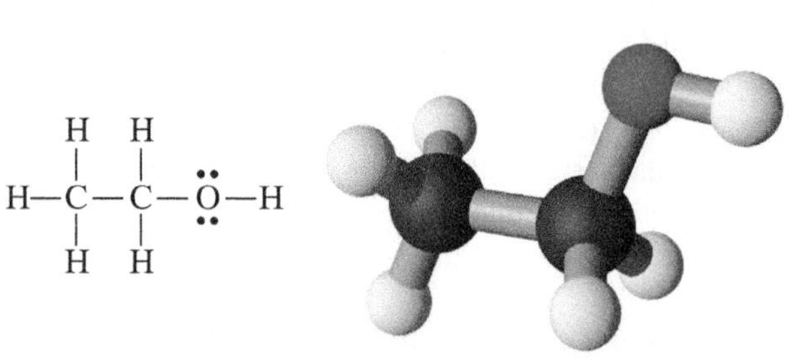

FIGURE 11.10 Lewis Structure and Ball-and-Stick Model of Ethanol, CH_3CH_2OH

The molecular geometry around each central atom (the two carbon atoms and the oxygen atom) helps describe the overall shape of the molecule.

tetrahedral molecular geometries, whereas the oxygen atom has a bent molecular geometry.

Example 11.2

Describe the geometry around each carbon atom in propanol, CH_3CH_2CHO, using the Lewis structure below:

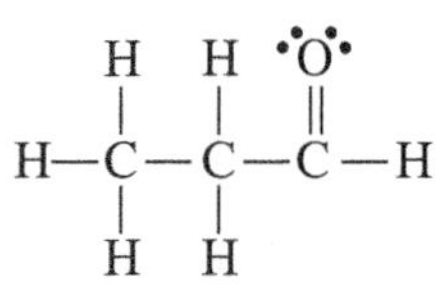

Solution

The CH_3 and CH_2 carbon atoms have four electron domains each, all bonded groups, so both are tetrahedral. The CHO carbon atom has three electron domains, all bonded groups, so it is trigonal planar.

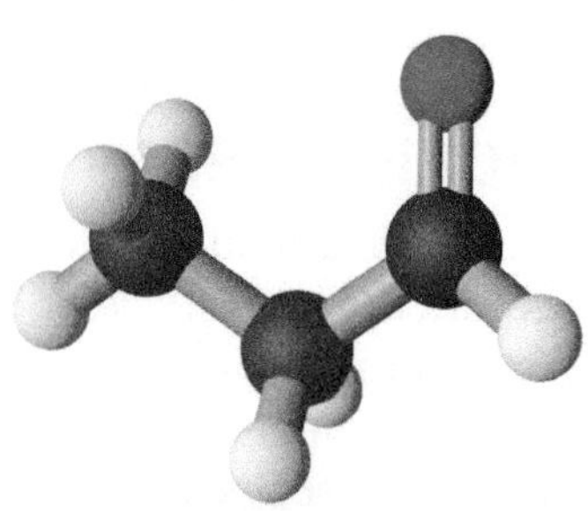

PRACTICE PROBLEM 11.2

Describe the geometry around each carbon atom in propene, CH_2CHCH_3, using the Lewis structure below:

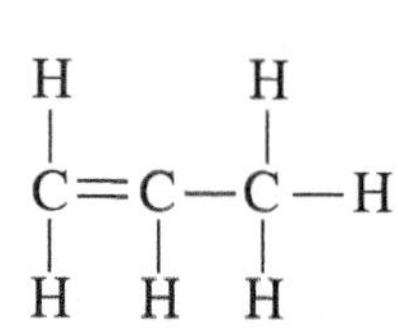

Hint: There are no lone pairs in this molecule, so the domains are all bonded groups, and the molecular geometry around each atom is the same as its electron geometry. The left-most carbon atom has three domains. The middle carbon atom has three domains. The right-most carbon atom has four domains.

MOLECULAR GEOMETRIES FOR CENTRAL ATOMS WITH EXPANDED VALENCE SHELLS

Five Electron Domains

You can use VSEPR to predict the shapes of molecules with expanded valence shells, but with more domains comes more possible molecular geometries, depending on the number of lone pairs on the central atom. The most stable electron geometry for five electron domains around a central atom is the **trigonal bipyramid** (Figure 11.11), which can be described as two three-sided pyramids sharing a base.

In the trigonal bipyramidal electron geometry, the bond angles are not all the same, leading to two subsets of domains—called axial when they are along the vertical axis, and equatorial when located within the equatorial plane. Bond angles are 180° between two axial domains, 120° between two equatorial domains, and 90° from an axial domain to an equatorial domain.

EVERYDAY CONNECTION

The axial and equatorial positions in a trigonal bipyramidal molecule are analogous to the axis and equator of Earth.

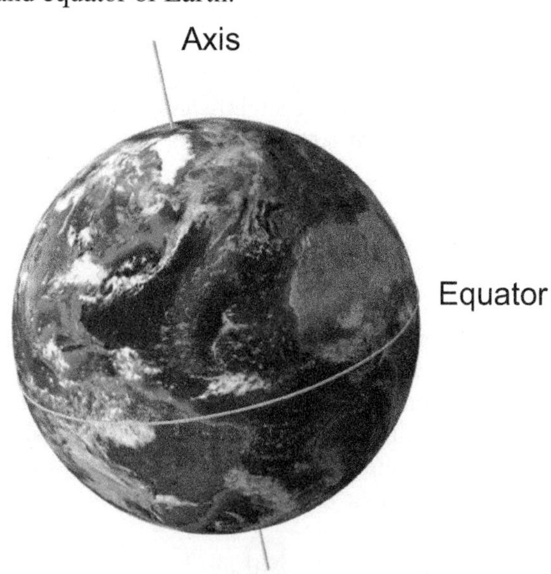

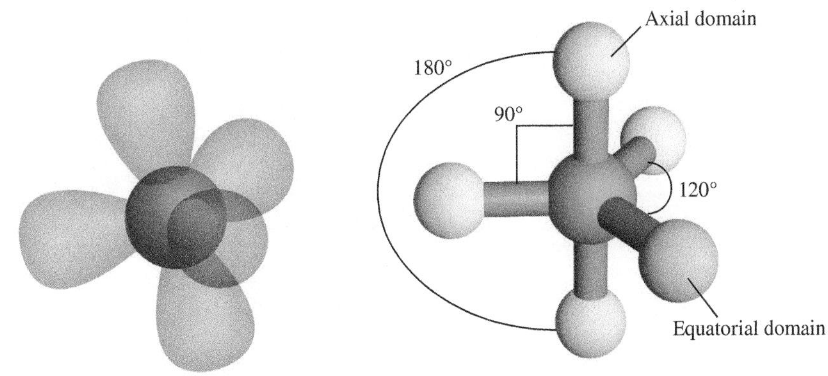

FIGURE 11.11 Five Domains

The most stable shape for five electron domains is trigonal bipyramidal, with two domains oriented along a vertical axis and three within an equatorial plane. Adjacent bond angles are 90° and 120°. The 180° bond angle between axial domains is not always mentioned since it is between nonadjacent domains, but it becomes more important in the molecular geometries derived from this electron geometry.

Any lone pairs of electrons will occupy positions with the most available space. In the case of the trigonal bipyramidal electron geometry, the positions with the larger bond angles are the equatorial positions, giving rise to the series of molecular geometries shown in Table 11.1 and briefly described here:

- A trigonal bipyramidal electron geometry with one lone pair has the lone pair in an equatorial position. The resulting molecules have a **see-saw** molecular geometry.

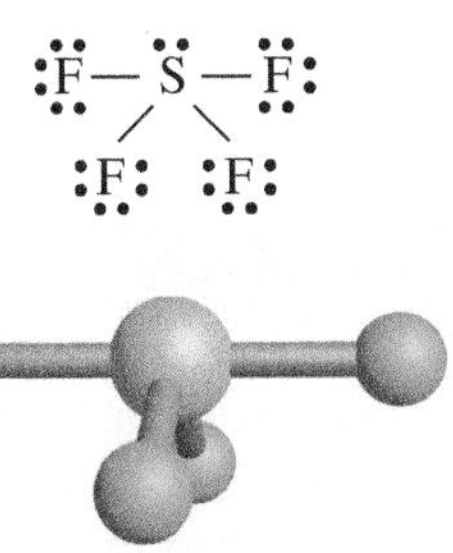

- Two lone pairs, both in equatorial positions, results in a **T-shaped** molecular geometry.

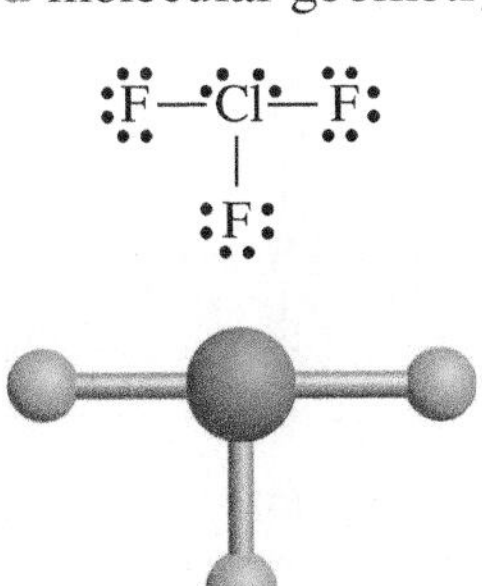

- Three lone pairs occupy all the equatorial positions, leaving the central atom and the two axial atoms in a linear geometry.

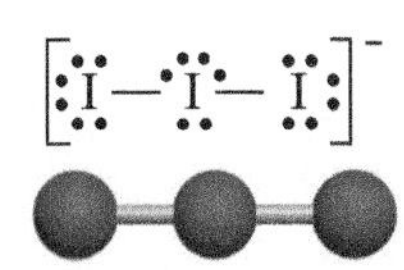

Six Electron Domains

The most stable arrangement for six electron domains around a central atom is the octahedron (Figure 11.12), demonstrating **octahedral** electron geometry, named for the eight triangular faces making up its surface. All the domain positions are equal, and bond angles are 90° and 180°.

Names for the molecular geometries when lone pairs are present on the central atoms are summarized in Table 11.1 and briefly described here and in Figure 11.13.

- An octahedral electron geometry with one lone pair results in a **square pyramidal** molecular geometry.

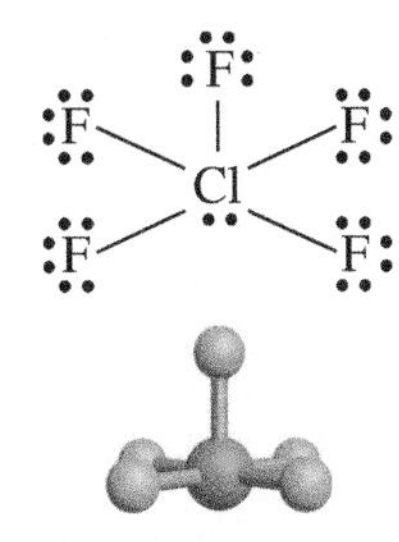

- When an octahedral electron geometry contains two lone pairs, they occupy positions opposite each other, resulting in a **square planar** molecule.

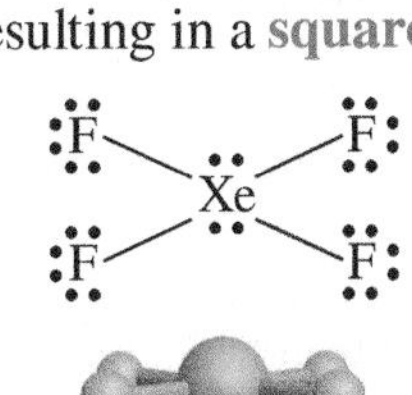

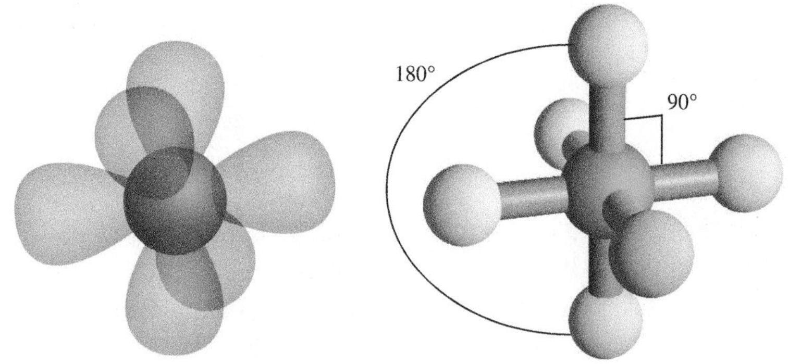

FIGURE 11.12 Six Domains

The most stable shape for six domains is an octahedral shape with 90° bond angles between adjacent domains.

Steven Lemon, Macmillan Learning

FIGURE 11.13 Video Tutorial: Molecular Geometry II

NOTE: You need to be online to access this video.

This video shows how to determine molecular geometry from Lewis structures with five or six electron domains around the central atom.

Example 11.3

Determine the electron domain and molecular geometries for (a) xenon difluoride, XeF_2, (b) bromine trifluoride, BrF_3, and (c) iodine pentafluoride, IF_5, using the Lewis structures below:

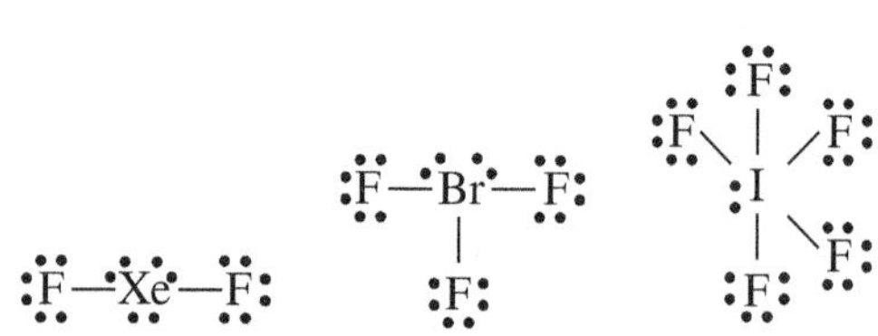

(a) (b) (c)

Solution

a. The Lewis structure for XeF_2 shows that the central Xe atom has five electron domains—two bonded groups and three lone pairs. Five electron domains indicate a trigonal bipyramid electron geometry. The three lone pairs will occupy the equatorial positions and the two bonded pairs the axial positions. The two bonded groups form a linear molecular geometry with the central atom.

b. The Lewis structure for BrF_3 has five electron domains—three bonded groups and two lone pairs, indicating a trigonal bipyramid electron geometry. The two lone pairs will occupy equatorial positions, so the three bonded groups will form a T-shaped molecular geometry with the central Br atom.

c. The Lewis structure for IF_5 has five bonded groups and a lone pair. Six electron domains indicate an octahedral electron geometry, while the one lone pair indicates a square pyramidal molecular geometry.

PRACTICE PROBLEM 11.3

Determine the molecular geometries and bond angles for (a) xenon tetrachloride, $XeCl_4$, (b) sulfur tetrachloride, SCl_4, and (c) iodine tetrachloride, ICl_4, using the Lewis structures below. Refer to the Molecular and Electron Geometry Activity as needed.

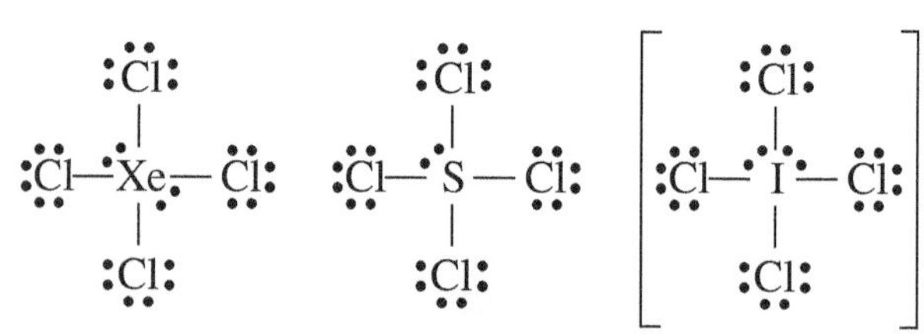

(a) (b) (c)

Hint: Count the number of bonded groups and lone pairs on the central atom. Refer to Table 11.1, Figure 11.8 (Molecular and Electron Geometry Activity) and Figure 11.13 (Video Tutorial) as needed.

SECTION REVIEW

- Electron domains around a central atom repel each other to adopt the most stable shape, which is related to the total number of electron domains on the central atom.
- Any of the following is an electron domain: single bond, double bond, triple bond, lone pair of electrons, unshared electron.
- The electron geometries associated with specific numbers of electron domains are linear (two electron domains), trigonal planar (three), tetrahedral (four), trigonal bipyramidal (five), and octahedral (six).
- The actual molecular geometry can be predicted from the electron geometry based on the number of lone pairs on the central atom.
- Larger molecules can be described as a series of the molecular geometries associated with each central atom found in the molecule.

11.2 Polar and Nonpolar Molecules

GOAL

- Identify polar and nonpolar molecules using electronegativity values and molecular shape.

Background Review

Chapter 10 Covalent Bonding: Section 10.3—Resonance and Formal Charge; Section 10.5—Polar Bonds and the Bonding Continuum

Section 10.3 explained that electronegativity (EN) is the ability of a bonded atom to draw electron density toward itself and that it can be used to determine the central atom when drawing a Lewis structure. Section 10.5 discussed how to use electronegativity to predict the polarity of individual bonds. In Section 11.2, you will combine what you know about bond dipoles with the molecular geometry to predict the polarity of molecules (Figure 11.14). Bond dipoles can add together to form a molecular dipole or may oppose each other and cancel out. **Molecular dipoles** have measurable dipole moments (Section 10.5), which cause intermolecular forces (Section 12.1).

If the polar bonds within a molecule are arranged symmetrically around the center atom, the bond dipoles cancel, resulting in a nonpolar molecule. If the polar bonds are arranged asymmetrically around a center atom, then the bond dipoles will combine to form a molecular dipole and a **polar molecule**.

Every molecule with only one polar bond is a polar molecule. In diatomic molecules, if the only bond is polar, the molecule has an asymmetrical electronic distribution. For example, hydrogen fluoride, HF, with $\Delta EN = 1.9$, has an unequally shared electron pair (a polar bond, as shown in Figure 11.15a). In contrast, the electrons in fluorine, F_2, are shared equally, so the F—F bond is nonpolar (Figure 11.15b). In all cases of molecules with only one bond, such as HF and F_2, the molecules can be described as polar or nonpolar based on the polarity of that one bond.

When there are two or more bonds—that is, more than two atoms in the molecule—polar bonds might cancel out each other's effects, resulting in a **nonpolar molecule**. In carbon dioxide (Figure 11.16a), for example, both carbon–oxygen double bonds are polar

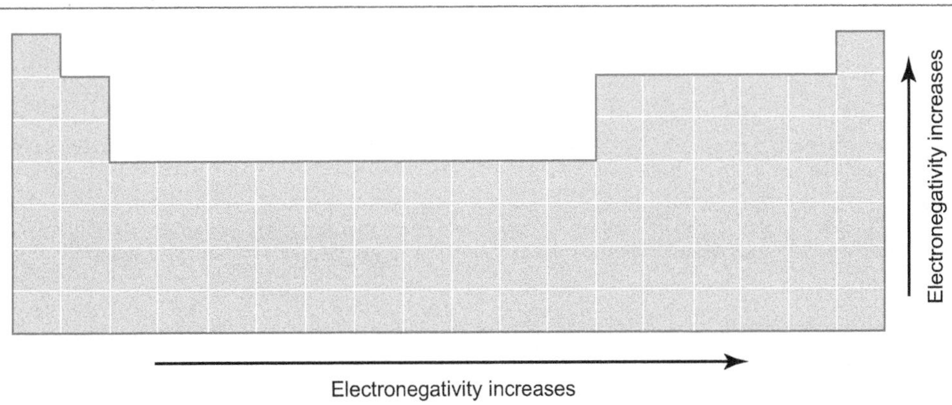

FIGURE 11.14 Electronegativity Trends

Electronegativity tends to increase as you move up and to the right in the periodic table.

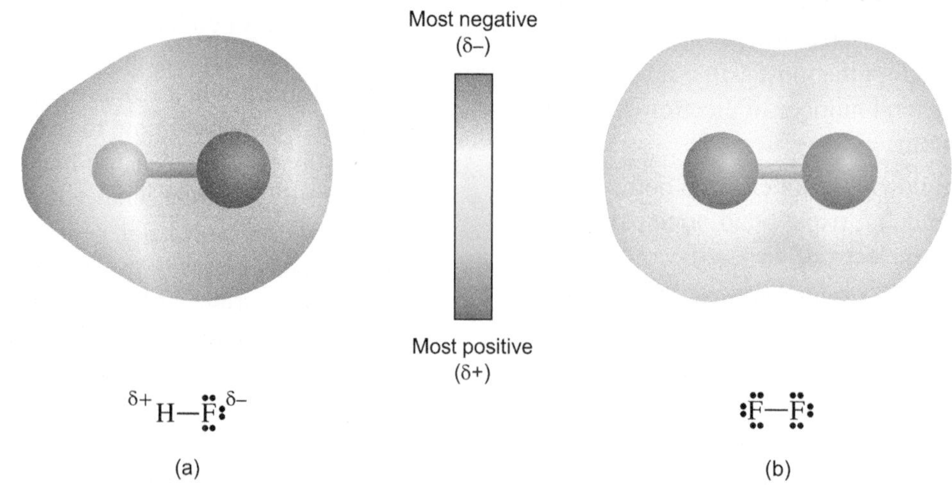

FIGURE 11.15 Electrostatic Potential Map of a Polar Molecule and a Nonpolar Molecule

Electrostatic potential maps show the electron density via a color gradient. (a) The bond between H and F is polar, making the HF molecule polar. (b) The bond between F and F is nonpolar, making the F_2 molecule nonpolar.

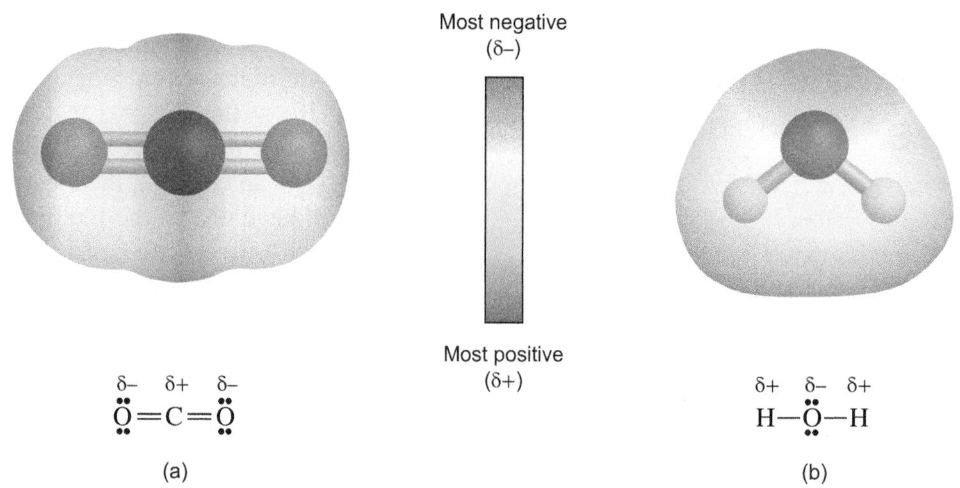

FIGURE 11.16 Symmetry and Polarity

Electrostatic potential maps show the electron density via a color gradient. (a) The CO_2 molecule has two polar C=O bonds in a linear geometry. This symmetric arrangement causes the bond dipoles to cancel, resulting in a nonpolar molecule. (b) Water contains two polar O—H bonds in a bent geometry. This asymmetric shape means that the bond dipoles do *not* cancel, thus resulting in a polar molecule.

($\Delta EN = 1.0$). The molecular geometry of CO_2 is linear, however, so the effect of one polar bond exactly cancels the effect of the other, resulting in a symmetric distribution of charge. As a result, the CO_2 molecule has no net dipole—it is nonpolar, even though it contains two polar bonds. Any molecule in which the central atom is bonded to identical groups and has no lone pairs is symmetrical. In symmetrical molecules, the bond dipoles will always cancel, resulting in a nonpolar molecule.

The water molecule (Figure 11.16b) also contains two polar bonds, but it has a different molecular geometry than CO_2. H_2O is bent, so the two bond dipoles combine to form a net molecular dipole, making H_2O a polar molecule.

Example 11.4

Determine whether the following molecules are polar or nonpolar using the Lewis structures below:

a. ammonia, NH_3

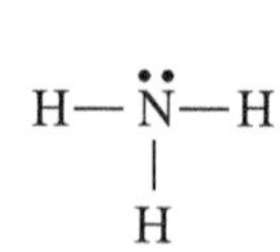

b. difluoromethane, CH_2F_2

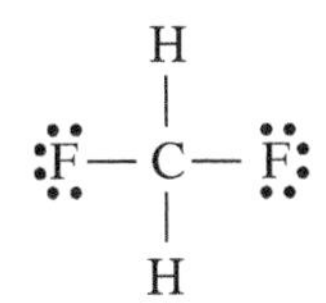

Solution

a. The Lewis structure of ammonia shows four electron domains—three single bonds and a lone pair. When a molecule with a tetrahedral electron geometry has one lone pair, the molecular geometry is trigonal pyramidal. The three N—H bonds are polar ($\Delta EN = 0.9$), and they do not cancel each other, so NH_3 is polar. In fact, the three bond dipoles combine to form a molecular dipole with the partial negative region centered on the lone pair of electrons on the N atom and the partial positive region located between the three H atoms.

b. The Lewis structure of CH_2F_2 shows four electron domains, all bonded groups, indicating a tetrahedral domain and molecular geometry. The small ΔEN for C and H (0.4) indicates that the C—H bonds are only very slightly polar, while the larger value (1.5) for C and F indicates that the C—F bonds are strongly polar. These four bond dipoles will combine to form a molecular dipole with a partially positive region located between the fluorine atoms and the partially positive region located between the hydrogen atoms.

PRACTICE PROBLEM 11.4

Determine whether the following molecules are polar or nonpolar:

a. chlorine, Cl_2,
b. nitrogen triflouride, NF_3,
c. bromine monofluoride, BrF,
d. boron trichloride, BCl_3, and
e. beryllium hydride, BeH_2, using the Lewis structures below:

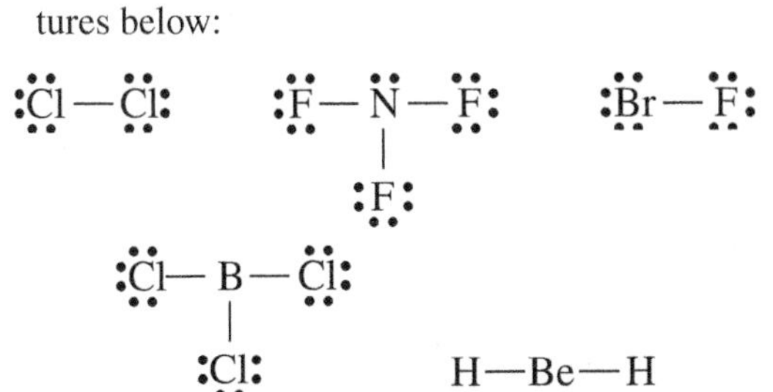

Hint: In general, you can assume that a bond between two different atoms is polar (so you don't need to look up electronegativity values). In this case, Cl_2 has a nonpolar bond, but the other molecules all have polar bonds.

Next, identify the molecular geometry of each molecule to determine whether it is symmetric. An asymmetric molecule with polar bonds is polar. A symmetric molecule is nonpolar, even with polar bonds, because they cancel.

Example 11.5

Determine the polarity of (a) sulfur hexafluoride, SF_6, and (b) bromine pentafluoride, BrF_5, using the Lewis structures below:

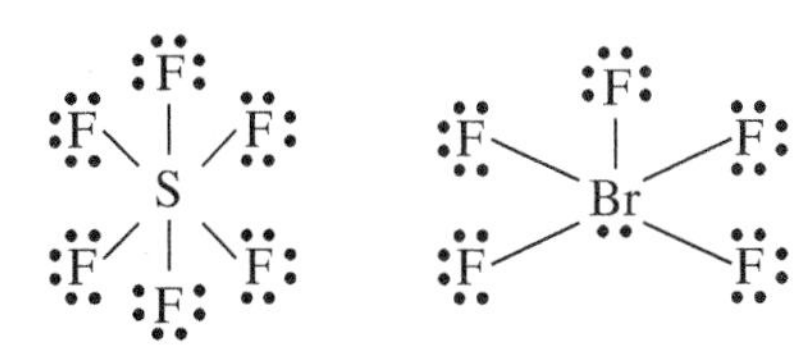

(a) (b)

Solution

a. The Lewis structure shows that SF_6 adopts a symmetric, octahedral molecular geometry (six bonds). The individual bonds are polar ($\Delta EN = 1.5$), but the bond dipoles cancel, resulting in a nonpolar molecule.

b. The Lewis structure shows that BrF_5 adopts a square pyramidal molecular geometry (five bonds and one lone pair). Each Br—F bond is polar ($\Delta EN = 1.2$). The individual dipoles of the four Br—F bonds in the base of the square pyramid cancel each other, but the dipole of the bond to the F atom at the top of the pyramid gives the molecule a net dipole overall, resulting in a polar molecule.

PRACTICE PROBLEM 11.5

Determine the polarity of (a) phosphorus pentachloride, PCl_5, and (b) sulfur tetrafluoride, SF_4, using the Lewis structures below:

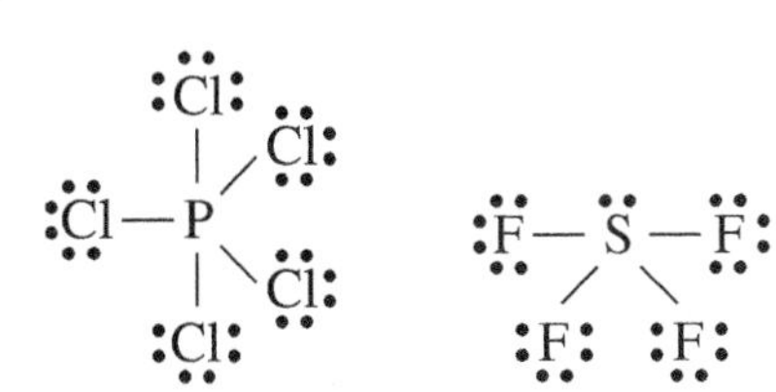

(a) (b)

Hint: In general, you can assume that a bond between two different atoms is polar (so you don't need to look up electronegativity values). In this case, all the bonds are polar.

Next, identify the molecular geometry of each molecule to determine whether it is symmetric. An asymmetric molecule with polar bonds is polar. A symmetric molecule is nonpolar, even with polar bonds, because they cancel each other out.

SECTION REVIEW

- Electronegativity and molecular geometry can be used to predict molecular polarity.

- Molecules with nonpolar bonds are almost always nonpolar (the exceptions are beyond the scope of this text).
- Molecules with a symmetrical arrangement of polar bonds are nonpolar.
- Molecules with an asymmetrical arrangement of polar bonds are polar.

11.3 Valence Bond Theory: Hybrid Orbitals and Bonding

GOALS

- Explain valence bond theory.
- Describe and recognize *sp*, *sp*^{2}, and *sp*^{3} hybrid orbitals from Lewis structures or other images of molecules.
- Define, describe, and identify sigma and pi bonds in molecules.

Background Review

Chapter 8 The Quantum Model of the Atom: Section 8.3—Electron Shells, Subshells, and Orbitals; Section 8.6 Quantum Numbers

Lewis structures help to visualize bonding within a molecule and, with the help of the VSEPR model, the three-dimensional shape of a molecule. The polarity of a molecule can be determined using electronegativity and bond dipoles. However, none of these concepts tells you what a covalent bond really is or allows you to explain why certain shapes are observed or why some molecules are more or less stable than others. For this you must learn about valence bond (VB) theory in Sections 11.3 and 11.4 and molecular orbital (MO) theory in Section 11.5. Both theories are based in quantum mechanics, and are only discussed from a conceptual viewpoint in this text. These theories explain how it is possible for atoms to share electrons and also explain the known properties of molecules such as molecular geometry and reactivity.

VB THEORY: THE BASICS

According to **valence bond, VB, theory**, a covalent bond forms from an overlap in the valence orbitals of the atoms involved. As two atoms approach closely enough for their valence orbitals to overlap, the potential energy decreases (Figure 11.17) until it reaches a minimum energy, which determines the bond length. These overlapping orbitals are typically each half-filled, with one electron each and initially with independent spins (Section 4.3). Once the bond forms, both electrons occupy the area of the overlap and must

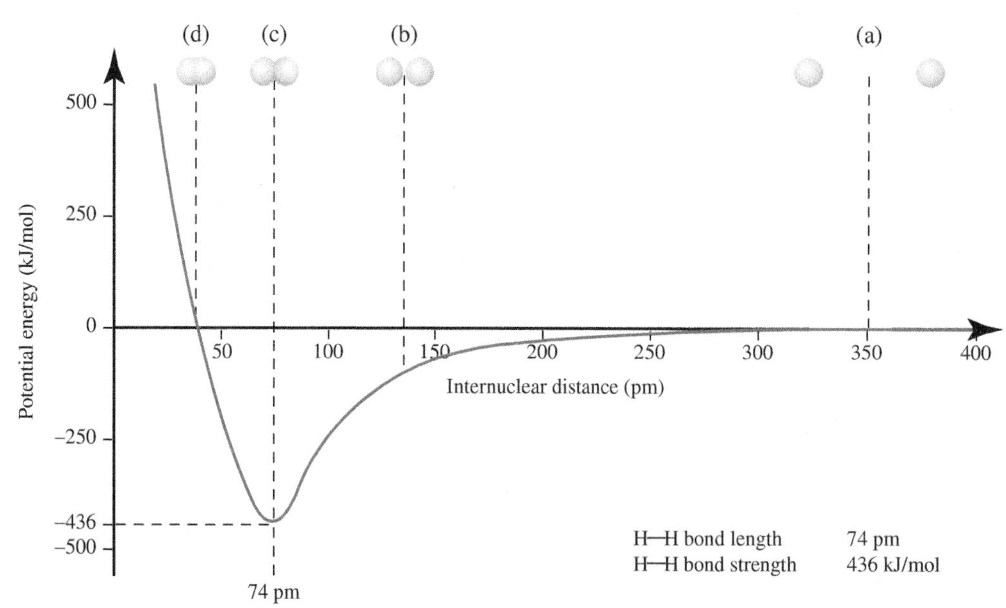

FIGURE 11.17 Covalent Bond Formation between H Atoms

(a) Two separate hydrogen atoms have equal potential energy. (b) As they approach each other, the attraction between the nuclei of each hydrogen atom and the electron of the other atom increases, causing the potential energy to decrease. (c) The potential energy reaches a minimum at a distance for which the nucleus–electron attraction is stronger than the repulsion between the two nuclei. (d) If the atoms got any closer, the potential energy would increase due to repulsion between the positively charged nuclei.

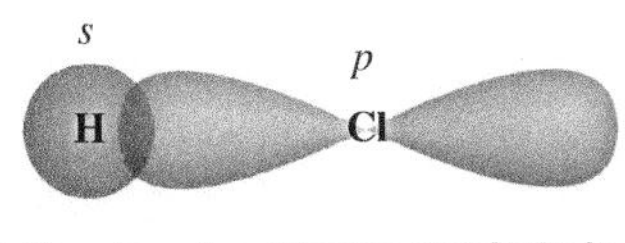

FIGURE 11.18 Overlapping Atomic Orbitals in HCl
According to VB theory, the 1*s* orbital of H overlaps with one of the 3*p* orbitals of Cl to form a bond.

be spin-paired, which means that one of the electrons may have to reverse its spin. Sometimes, filled orbitals on one atom overlap with empty orbitals on another to form **coordinate covalent bonds**, which are discussed in Chapter 21. According to VB theory, the shape of a molecule is determined by the geometry of the overlapping orbitals.

This simplest version of VB theory works quite well for many diatomic molecules. The hydrogen chloride, HCl, molecule forms from a hydrogen atom with a half-filled 1*s* orbital overlapping with a half-filled 3*p* orbital on the chlorine atom to form a linear molecule, as shown in Figure 11.18. Notice that this orbital overlap results in increased electron density between two nuclei (along the internuclear axis).

However, this basic VB theory does not work as well for slightly more complex examples, such as water, H_2O. Oxygen has two half-filled 2*p* orbitals available to overlap with a half-filled 1*s* orbital from each H. Section 8.6 explained that *p* orbitals are at 90° angles to each other, which would suggest that the bond angles are 90°. (Figure 11.19).

The observed bond angles for water are 105°, a bit less than the tetrahedral angle of 109.5° but quite a bit more than the 90° angle predicted by basic VB theory. This takes us to the next and very important aspect of VB theory, the mixing of atomic orbitals to produce hybrid orbitals.

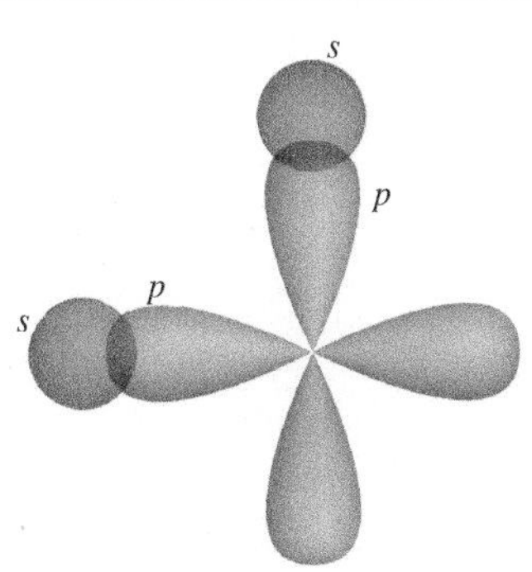

FIGURE 11.19 Hypothetical Atomic-Orbital Overlap in H_2O
With overlapping atomic orbitals, H_2O would have 90° bond angles, not 105°. This illustrates the need to expand VB theory to account for observed bond angles.

VB THEORY: HYBRIDIZATION OF ORBITALS AND BONDING

Hybrid orbitals are mathematical combinations of atomic orbitals that result in maximal overlap of orbitals in bonds. The orientations of these hybrid orbitals explain the observed molecular geometries. Central atoms are most likely to hybridize while outer atoms tend to use nonhybridized atomic orbitals for bonding. Some important features of VB theory regarding hybridization are as follows:

- The number of hybrid orbitals that result is always equal to the number of atomic orbitals being combined.
- The shapes and energies of the atomic orbitals being combined determine the shapes and energies of the hybrid orbitals formed.
- Several possible types of hybrid orbitals are possible. The type of hybrid orbital that forms for a specific molecule is the one that will result in a molecule with the lowest possible energy.

According to VB theory, atoms hybridize when bonding is imminent and when the energy cost of forming the hybrid orbitals is offset by the lower energy of the final molecule. For example, according to the VB model, an element such as carbon will always hybridize. Because of this, carbon features in many of the examples in this section.

sp^3 Hybridization

Carbon makes four single bonds with hydrogen to form the tetrahedral methane, CH_4, molecule. VB theory explains this shape by the hybridization of the 2*s* orbital with all three 2*p* orbitals of the carbon atom. Note that the energies of the four resulting **sp^3 hybrid orbitals** are between that of the 2*s* and 2*p* atomic orbitals, and each hybrid orbital contains one unpaired electron (Figure 11.20).

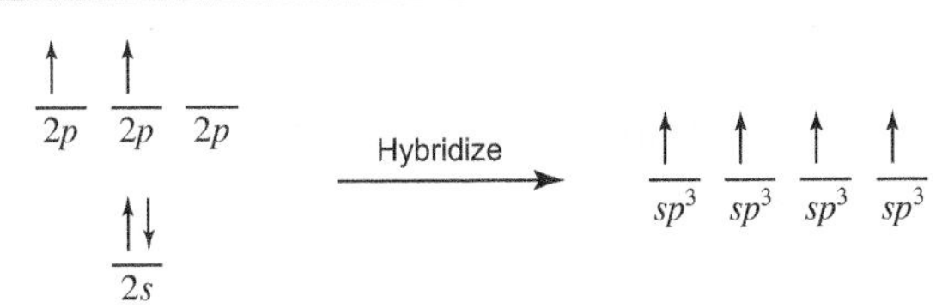

FIGURE 11.20 Formation of sp^3 Hybrid Orbitals in Carbon
One *s* orbital and three *p* orbitals combine to form four equivalent sp^3 hybrid orbitals at an intermediate energy. The total number of orbitals and the total number of electrons remains the same.

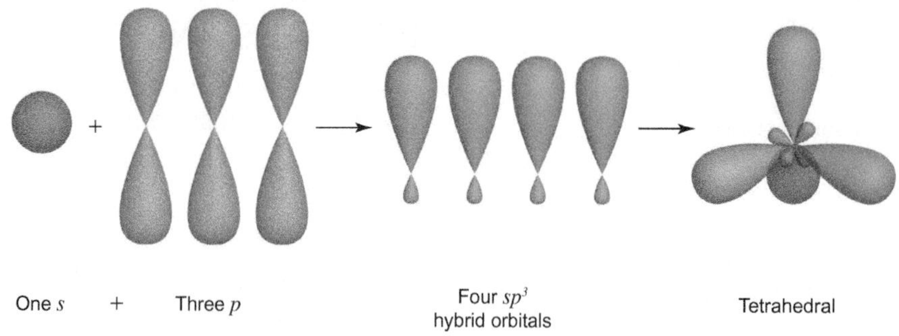

FIGURE 11.21 Formation of sp^3 Hybrid Orbitals

One s orbital and three p orbitals combine to form four equivalent sp^3 hybrid orbitals that are oriented in a tetrahedral shape.

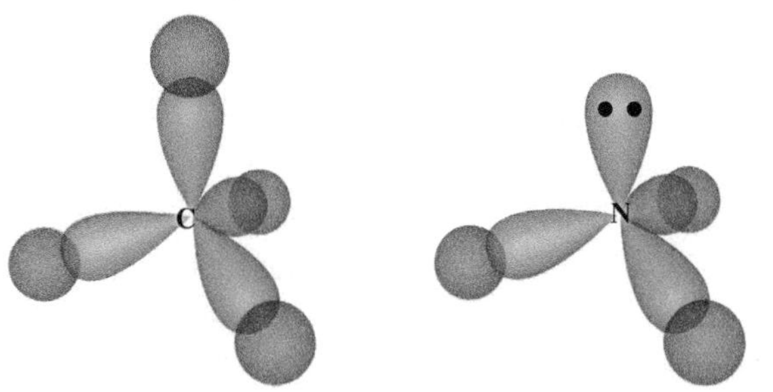

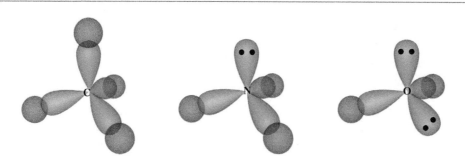

FIGURE 11.22 Molecules with sp^3 Hybridization of the Central Atom

The central atoms in methane, CH_4, ammonia, NH_3, and water, H_2O, use sp^3 hybrid orbitals in bonding. This hybridization is associated with four electron domains and tetrahedral electron geometry.

The orientations of the four new sp^3 hybrid orbitals are at 190.5° angles, forming a tetrahedral shape (Figure 11.21).

The sp^3 orbitals on carbon can then form four equivalent, overlapping bonds with the 1s orbitals of the four hydrogen atoms (Figure 11.22) in a tetrahedral geometry that matches the observed geometry of methane, CH_4, and the geometry predicted by VSEPR. Central atoms with four electron domains, especially those of second period elements, typically are sp^3 hybridized. In molecules like ammonia, NH_3, and water, H_2O, each lone pair of electrons on the central atom occupies a hybrid orbital.

Sigma Bonds

The orbital overlap in each of the bonds in the molecules discussed thus far—H_2, HCl, CH_4, NH_3, and H_2O—occurs around and along an axis between the nuclei of the two bonded atoms. The term **sigma (σ) bond** is used for the head-to-head overlap of any type of orbitals if the overlap occurs along the internuclear axis. Figure 11.23 shows σ bonds between two atomic orbitals (s with s, s with p, p with p), between an atomic orbital and a hybrid orbital (s with sp^3), and between two hybrid orbitals (sp^3 with sp^3).

sp^2 Hybridization

In ethene, C_2H_4, each carbon atom bonds with three other atoms—two hydrogen atoms and one carbon atom.

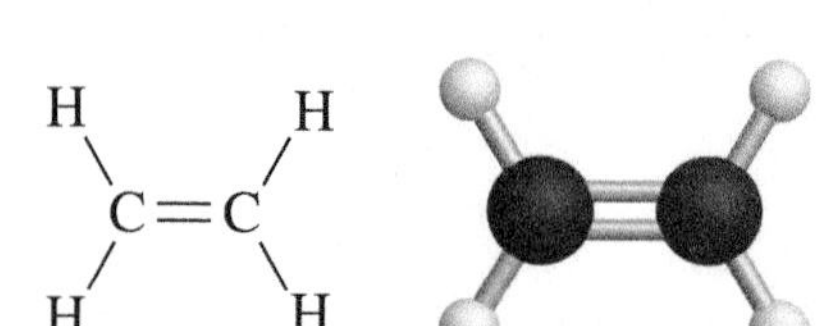

Each carbon atom hybridizes by combining the 2s orbital with two of the 2p orbitals to

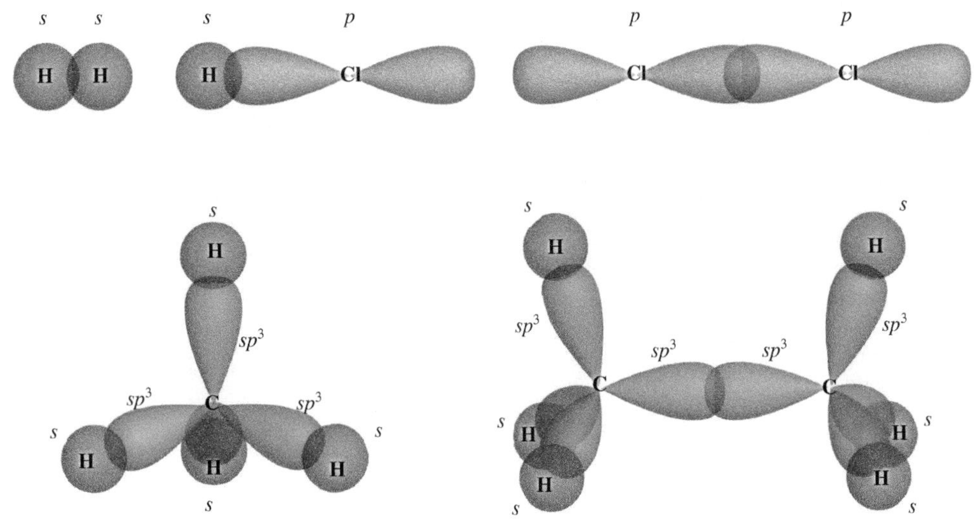

FIGURE 11.23 σ Bonds

Any overlap of orbitals that occurs along the internuclear axis (i.e., head-to-head overlap) is classified as a σ bond. σ bonds can form from the overlap of many types of orbitals: two *s* orbitals as in the H_2 molecule, *s* with *p* as in HCl, two *p* orbitals in Cl_2, *s* with sp^3 as in CH_4 and C_2H_6, and two sp^3 orbitals as in C_2H_6. All are examples of σ bonds.

form three equivalent, half-occupied, **sp^2 hybrid orbitals** (Figure 11.24). The unhybridized *p* orbital also plays an important role in bonding in this molecule.

The sp^2 orbitals occupy the plane determined by the orientation of the *p* orbitals involved in the hybridization, with the three sp^2 orbitals forming a trigonal planar shape. The unhybridized *p* orbital is oriented perpendicular to the plane occupied by the sp^2 hybrid orbitals, as shown in Figure 11.24.

Pi Bonds

As the two carbon atoms in ethene approach each other and the overlap between sp^2 hybrid orbitals forms a sigma bond, the unhybridized *p* orbitals also become close enough to overlap and form a second bond. In this bond, both lobes of the *p* orbitals overlap side-to-side, forming *one bond that exists in two separate areas of overlap*, above and below the internuclear axis (Figure 11.25). This type of bond is referred to as a **pi (π) bond**. Double bonds, therefore, as seen in the figure in ethene, are made up on one σ bond and one π bond.

sp Hybridization

In ethyne, C_2H_2 (commonly called acetylene), the carbon atoms form bonds with two atoms: one hydrogen atom and the other carbon atom.

$H{-}C{\equiv}C{-}H$ 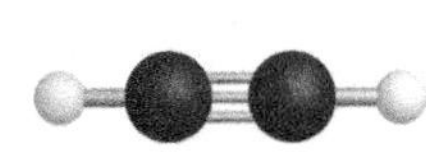

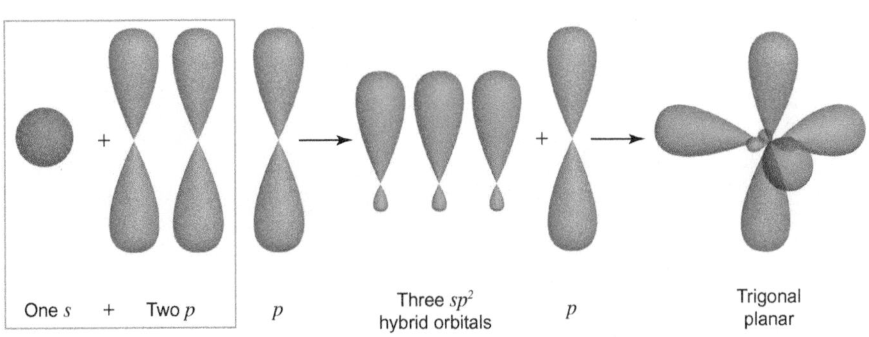

FIGURE 11.24 Formation of sp^2 Hybrid Orbitals

One *s* orbital and two *p* orbitals combine to form three equivalent sp^2 hybrid orbitals that are oriented in a trigonal planar shape. The unhybridized *p* orbital is at right angles to the plane occupied by the hybrid orbitals.

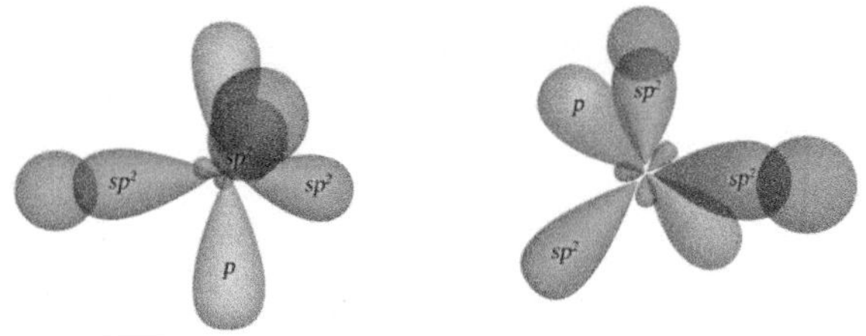

FIGURE 11.25 π Bond Animation: sp^2

The head-to-head overlap of sp^2 hybrid orbitals between the two carbon atoms forms a σ bond. The side-to-side overlap of the unhybridized *p* orbitals form a π bond. Four additional σ bonds are present between the 1*s* orbital of hydrogen and the remaining sp^2 hybrid orbitals of carbon.

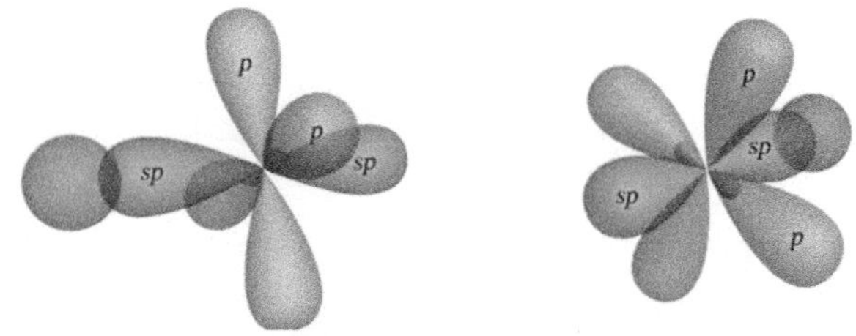

FIGURE 11.27 π Bond Animation: *sp*

The head-to-head overlap of *sp* hybrid orbitals between the two carbon atoms forms a σ bond. The side-to-side overlap of the unhybridized *p* orbitals (two from each carbon atom) form two π bonds. Two additional σ bonds are present between the 1*s* orbital of hydrogen and the remaining *sp* hybrid orbitals of carbon.

Each carbon atom hybridizes by combining the lower energy 2*s* orbital and one of the 2*p* orbitals to form two equivalent, half-occupied, ***sp* hybrid orbitals** (Figure 11.26). As with ethene, the unhybridized *p* orbitals (there are two of them) play an important role in bonding in this molecule.

The *sp* orbitals project along the line determined by the orientation of the *p* orbital involved in the hybridization, usually considered the *x* axis, and are associated with linear electron geometries. The two unhybridized *p* orbitals are oriented at right angles to that axis and to each other (Figure 11.26).

Pi Bonding and *sp* Hybridization

As the two carbon atoms in ethyne approach each other and the overlap between *sp* hybrid orbitals forms a σ bond along the internuclear, *x* axis, the unhybridized *p* orbitals also become close enough to overlap and form π bonds. The two sets of unhybridized *p* orbitals overlap to form two π bonds, one in the *xy* plane and the other in the *xz* plane. Triple bonds, therefore, as shown in Figure 11.27 for ethyne, are made up of one σ bond and two π bonds.

TABLE 11.2 Hybridizations and Electron Geometries

Hybrid Orbitals	Electron Geometries
sp	linear
sp^2	trigonal planar
sp^3	tetrahedral

Table 11.2 summarizes how VB theory uses hybrid orbitals to explain the electron geometries predicted by VSEPR, which lead to the observed molecular geometries.

The video in Figure 11.28 demonstrates how to solve problems related to valence bond theory.

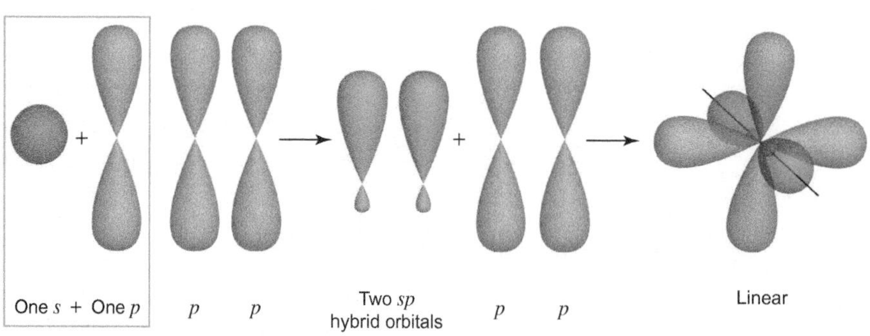

FIGURE 11.26 Formation of *sp* Hybrid Orbitals

One *s* orbital and a *p* orbital combine to form two equivalent *sp* hybrid orbitals that are oriented in a linear shape. The unhybridized *p* orbitals are at right angles to each other and to the hybrid orbitals.

FIGURE 11.28 Video Tutorial: VB Theory

NOTE: You need to be online to access this video.

This video shows how to determine hybridization and identify σ and π bonds.

Example 11.6

Determine the molecular geometry of formaldehyde, CH_2O, the hybridization of the central atom, and identify the σ and π bonds.

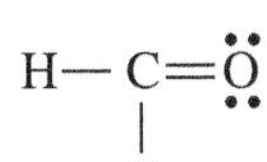

Solution

Carbon has three bonded groups and no lone pairs, so formaldehyde has a trigonal planar molecular geometry. The C—H bonds are σ bonds, formed by the overlap of the 1*s* orbitals on hydrogen with an sp^2 hybrid orbital on carbon, because the three sp^2 hybrid orbitals lie in a plane at angles of 120° to each other (i.e., they make the trigonal planar shape possible). The double bond between C and O consists of one σ bond and one π bond. The σ bond is formed by the overlap of one of the *p* orbitals on oxygen and an sp^2 hybrid orbital on carbon. The π bond results from the overlap of the unhybridized *p* orbital on carbon and another *p* orbital on oxygen.

PRACTICE PROBLEM 11.6

Determine the molecular geometry of hydrogen cyanide, HCN, the hybridization of the central atom, and identify the σ and π bonds.

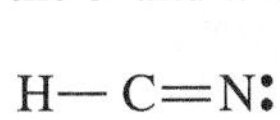

Hint: The Lewis structure shows that the central carbon atom has two bonded groups and no lone pairs. This tells you both the geometry (see Table 11.1) and the hybridization (see Table 11.2). Then, look at the type of bond (single, double, or triple) to identify the sigma and pi bonds.

Example 11.7

Determine the total number of σ bonds and π bonds in the following molecule, which is the pain reliever acetylsalicylic acid (aspirin), $C_9H_8O_4$.

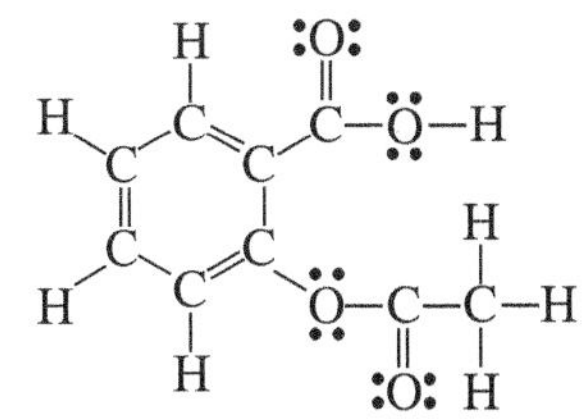

Solution

All of the single bonds are σ bonds, and all of the double bonds consist of one σ bond and one π bond. There are 21 σ bonds (remember to count the O—H bond and the three C—H bonds on the right side of the diagram) and 5 π bonds.

PRACTICE PROBLEM 11.7

Determine the total number of σ and π bonds in the following molecule.

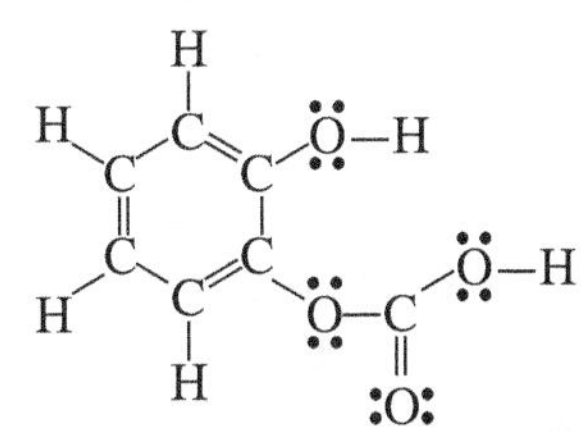

Hint: Each single bond is a sigma bond. Each double bond consists of one sigma bond and one pi bond.

HYBRID ORBITALS FOR EXPANDED VALENCES?

Molecules involving expanded octets always involve larger atoms as their central atoms, which are in the third period or beyond and have *d* orbitals in their valence shell. It was once thought, and it still appears in some general chemistry texts, that *s*, *p*, and *d* orbitals could combine to form hybrid orbitals such as sp^3d and sp^3d^2 for trigonal bipyramidal and octahedral geometries, respectively. Within a major energy level, however, the *d* sublevel energy is far higher than the *s* and *p* sublevel energies, making these combinations energetically unfavorable. VB theory does not provide an easy explanation for bonding in molecules with expanded valences.

SECTION REVIEW

- VB theory describes covalent bonds as the overlap between valence atomic orbitals of the bonded atoms with the degree of overlap determining the strength of the bond.
- The *s* and *p* orbitals on central atoms will combine to form equivalent hybrid orbitals for bonding.
- Hybridization depends on the number of electron domains (bonded groups + lone pairs).
  - Central atoms with four electron domains use sp^3 hybrid orbitals, resulting in tetrahedral electron geometries.
  - Central atoms with three electron domains use sp^2 hybrid orbitals, resulting in trigonal planar electron geometries.
  - Central atoms with two electron domains use *sp* hybrid orbitals, resulting in linear electron geometries.
- Bonds that form by the overlap of orbitals along the internuclear axis are σ bonds. All single bonds are σ bonds.
- In the case of sp^2 and *sp* hybrid orbitals, the unhybridized *p* orbitals can also overlap to form π bonds, which exist as two separate areas of overlap perpendicular to the internuclear axis. All multiple bonds contain one σ bond and one or two π bonds.
- VB theory does not currently support any hybridizations that can explain the expanded octet geometries.

11.4 Using Valence Bond Theory

GOALS

- Apply valence bond theory to reactivity and bond rotation.
- List and describe some of the limitations of valence bond theory.

Section 11.3 discussed the basic features of VB theory and how the hybridization of *s* and *p* orbitals can explain the shapes of molecules predicted from VSEPR. In Section 11.4, you will learn how VB theory can be used to explain observations concerning molecules and reactivity, such as:

- compounds with multiple bonds are more reactive than compounds with single bonds, and
- compounds with single bonds have free rotation around those bonds, but compounds with multiple bonds do not.

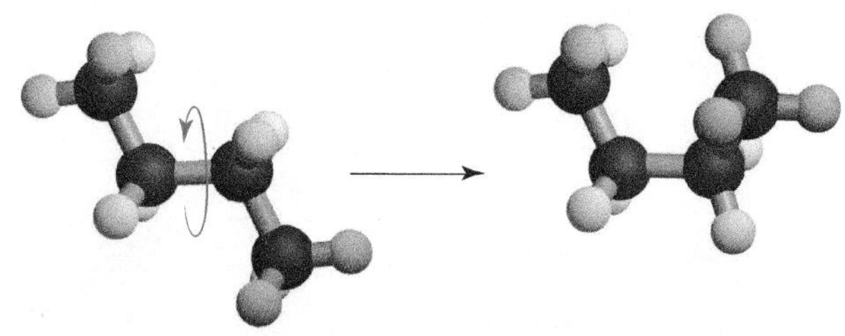

FIGURE 11.29 Free Rotation Around Single Bonds in Butane, C_4H_{10}

Butane, C_4H_{10}, contains only single bonds, which have free rotation around them. Notice in the first image that the last carbon atom is pointed downward. The second image shows the result of a rotation around the bond between the central carbon atoms, causing the last carbon atom to point in a different direction. Free rotation is possible around all of the bonds in butane, making these examples only two of the many possible conformations of butane.

Chemical reactions involve rearrangements of electrons. According to VB theory, σ bonds are created by the head-to-head overlap of atomic or hybrid orbitals along the internuclear axis and, therefore, exist between the two nuclei. Pi bonds are formed by the side-to-side overlap of *p* orbitals and exist above and below that internuclear axis. VB theory also tells us that the strength of a bond is related to the amount of overlap. Pi bonds have less extensive overlap than σ bonds, so pi bonds are easier to break than sigma bonds, making compounds with pi bonds more reactive.

Molecules can rotate around the bond axis of a single bond because this does not interfere with the orbital overlap creating the bond. Molecules exist in many different shapes or **conformations** due to free rotation about single bonds. In Figure 11.29, the two carbon atoms in the center of the butane molecule can rotate with respect to each other, creating many different possible conformations.

In Figure 11.30, however, no rotation is possible about the central carbons in ethene without breaking the π bond in the carbon–carbon double bond. The *p* orbitals on each carbon atom must be in the same plane to form the π bond.

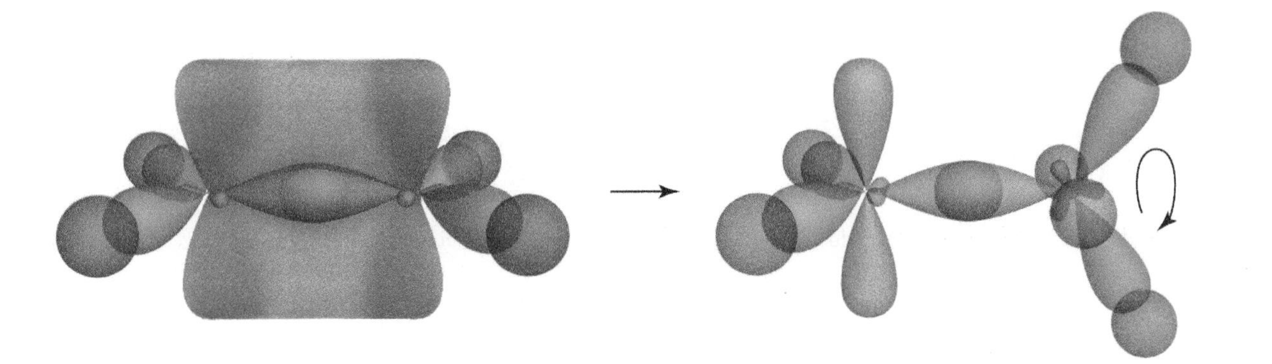

FIGURE 11.30 No Rotation in Ethene, C_2H_4

Ethene, C_2H_4, contains a double bond between the second and third carbon atoms, which consists of a σ bond and a π bond. Any rotation around that bond would interfere with the overlap of the unhybridized *p* orbitals that forms the π bond. In other words, the π bond would have to be broken to allow rotation around the bond. There is no free rotation around double bonds.

Example 11.8

Use VB theory to determine whether propane, $CH_3—CH_2—CH_3$, or propene, $CH_3—CH{=}CH_2$, is more reactive, and explain why.

Solution

Propane contains all σ bonds (10 of them), whereas propene contains 7 σ bonds and 1 π bond. Since π bonds have less extensive overlap than sigma bonds, they are easier to break, making propene more reactive than propane.

PRACTICE PROBLEM 11.8

Use VB theory to determine whether formaldehyde, CH_2O, or methanol, CH_3OH, is more reactive, and explain why.

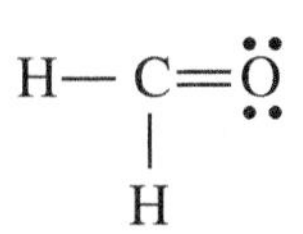

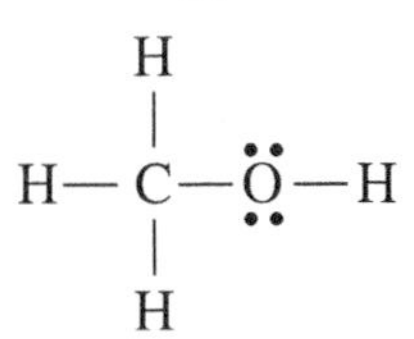

Hint: Pi bonds are easier to break than sigma bonds, so molecules with pi bonds tend to be more reactive.

VB theory views covalent bonds as the overlap between atomic orbitals and explains tetrahedral, trigonal planar, and linear geometries using hybrid orbitals. VB theory is consistent with Lewis theory and the VSEPR model and explains the lack of rotation around double bonds. However, VB theory is unable to explain some very important observations, such as why molecules have different electronic energy levels than their component atoms and why oxygen, O_2, is paramagnetic, which suggests that it has unpaired electrons. Molecular orbital theory (Section 11.5) offers another explanation of covalent bonding that helps chemists understand and predict these properties.

SECTION REVIEW

- VB theory provides a means for explaining why compounds with multiple bonds are more reactive than compounds with single bonds.
- VB theory explains why double bonds restrict the rotation of the atoms involved.
- VB theory does not explain all the important properties of molecules.

11.5 Molecular Orbital Theory

GOALS

- Describe the components of molecular orbital theory.
- Complete molecular orbital diagrams given the energy levels.
- Determine bond order and magnetic properties using molecular orbital diagrams.
- Write molecular orbital electron configurations.

Molecular orbital, MO, theory is based on quantum mechanical principles and is discussed only in

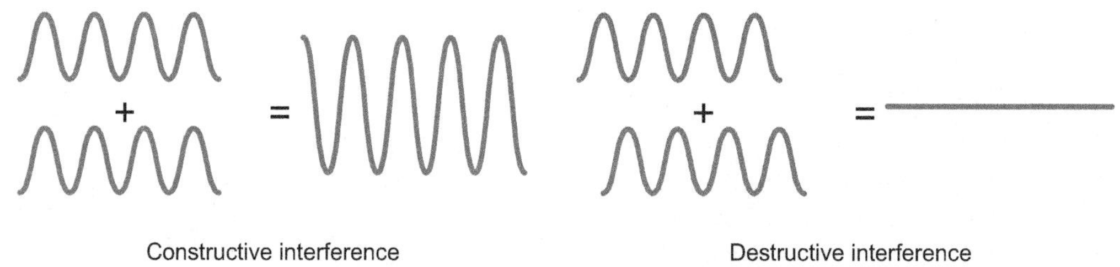

FIGURE 11.31 Constructive and Destructive Interference in a Sine Wave

Constructive interference occurs when waves that are in phase add together, enhancing the size of the peaks and valleys. Destructive interference occurs when waves that are precisely out of phase add together, canceling out all the peaks and valleys.

the most basic terms in this text. As mentioned in Section 11.4, VB theory is unable to explain several important properties of molecules, such as electronic energy levels specific to the molecule and the magnetic properties known as paramagnetism and diamagnetism. MO theory explains these properties and gives chemists the ability to imagine molecules that do not exist and predict the feasibility of their existence.

According to molecular orbital theory, when atoms combine to form molecules, *atomic* orbitals of *different* atoms combine to form *molecular* orbitals that are *delocalized* over the resulting molecule. This may remind you of VB theory, in which atomic orbitals *within* an atom combined to form hybrid orbitals. But hybrid orbitals are still technically *atomic* orbitals, because they belong to a single atom and merely overlap with the orbitals of other atoms. In MO theory, on the other hand, the new orbitals belong to the molecule and extend over the molecule in specific shapes. Chapter 8 explained that electron energies are described by wave functions, the square of which provides the shapes of the atomic orbitals. Molecular orbitals are also described by wave functions that predict their shapes.

Atomic orbitals from different atoms can combine to form **molecular orbitals** in two ways, **bonding orbitals** and **antibonding orbitals**, from the additive and subtractive combination of the wave functions. Additive combination results in constructive interference, in which wave peaks add together, whereas subtractive combination changes the phase of the second wave and results in destructive interference. **Constructive** and **destructive interference** of a simple sine wave are shown in Figure 11.31.

When two hydrogen atoms come together, the 1*s* orbitals from each atom undergo additive combination to form a σ_{1s} bonding orbital, with the highest probability of electron density along the axis between the nuclei and of lower energy than the 1*s* atomic orbitals (Figure 11.32). Electrons occupying this molecular orbital would form a sigma bond.

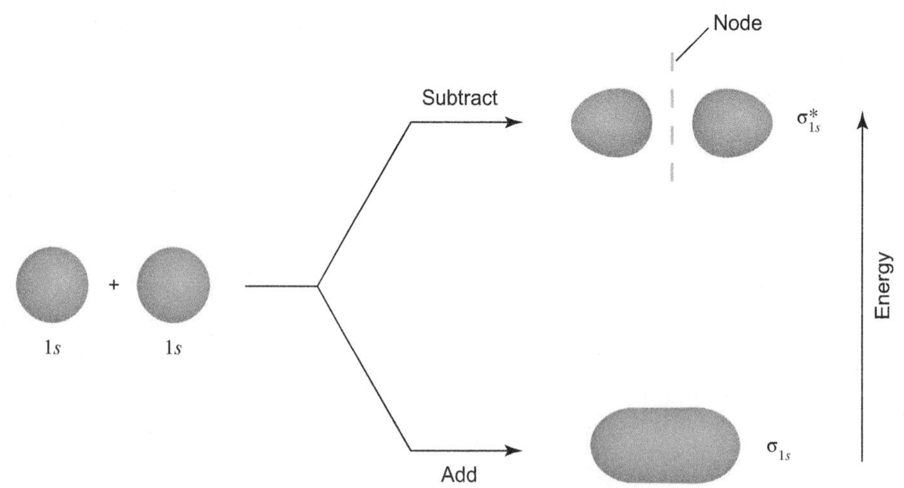

FIGURE 11.32 Constructive and Destructive Combination of 1*s* Orbitals in Hydrogen

The 1*s* orbitals in two hydrogen atoms undergo constructive (additive) combination to form the lower energy σ_{1s} bonding orbital and destructive (subtractive) combination to form the higher energy σ^*_{1s} antibonding orbital.

These same two atomic orbitals also undergo subtractive combination to form a σ_{1s}^{*} antibonding orbital with a node or region of zero probability of electron density between the nuclei. The energy level of this antibonding orbital is higher than the 1*s* atomic energy level. In general, *s* atomic orbitals combine to form bonding and antibonding molecular orbitals with the shapes and relative energies shown in Figure 11.32.

MOLECULAR ORBITAL DIAGRAMS

A **molecular orbital, MO, diagram** is another way of representing the molecule by showing how the molecular orbitals are populated with electrons. The MO diagram for H_2 (Figure 11.33) places the valence electrons in the lowest possible energy level, the σ_{1s}, suggesting that the energy of the H_2 molecule is lower than that of the individual H atoms.

It is possible to write a molecular electron configuration from an MO diagram. It is written like an atomic electron configuration, but it uses the symbols for the molecular orbitals. For H_2, the molecular electron configuration is $(\sigma_{1s})^2$.

It is also possible to use an MO diagram to determine a measure of the stability of a molecule by calculating the **bond order**. The bond order is calculated by comparing the number of electrons in bonding and antibonding orbitals according to the following equation:

$$\text{bond order} = \frac{1}{2}(\text{bonding e}^- - \text{antibonding e}^-)$$

H_2 has a bond order of $\frac{1}{2}(2 - 0) = 1$. The values of bond orders are somewhat analogous to the number of bonds in a Lewis structure, meaning that, according to molecular orbital theory, the atoms in H_2 are connected by a single bond.

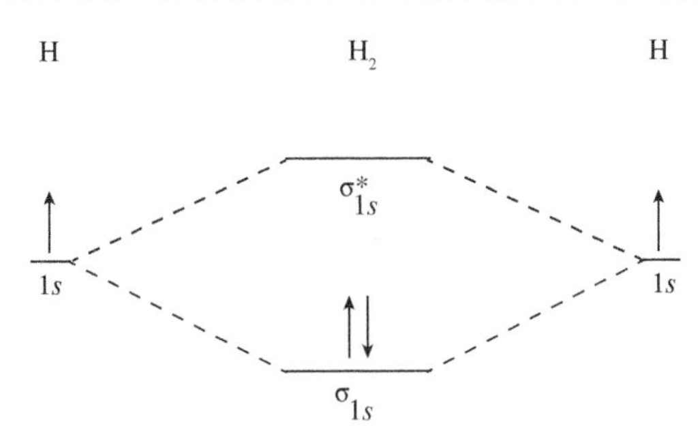

FIGURE 11.33 MO Diagram for the Hydrogen Molecule

The 1*s* electrons from each atom are placed in the lower energy, bonding orbital, σ_{1s}. There are no electrons to place in the higher energy, antibonding orbital, σ_{1s}^{*}.

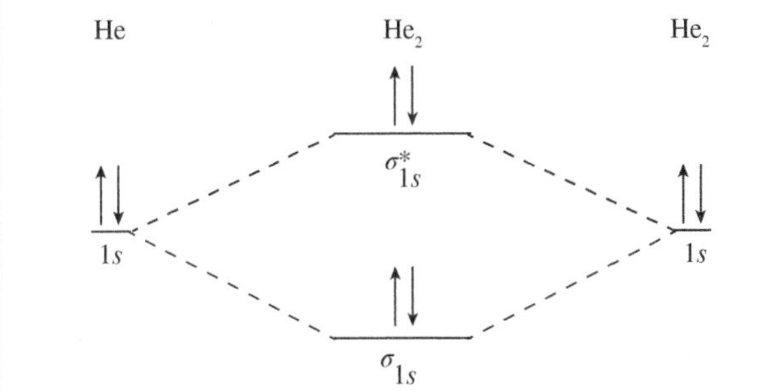

FIGURE 11.34 MO Diagram for the Hypothetical Dihelium Molecule

The two 1*s* electrons from each atom are placed in the lower energy, bonding orbital, σ_{1s}, and in the higher energy, antibonding orbital, σ_{1s}^{*}. There is no net decrease in energy for He_2 compared to separate He atoms and, therefore, He_2 does not form.

This finding agrees with what is known about hydrogen—that it is more stable as a diatomic molecule than as individual atoms and has a single bond. But what about helium, He? Can molecular orbital theory be used to explain why helium isn't diatomic? Helium is a first-period element just like hydrogen, so the hypothetical He_2 has the same basic MO diagram as H_2, but it has four valence electrons rather than two. The completed MO diagram for He_2 (Figure 11.34) shows two electrons in the bonding orbital and two electrons in the antibonding orbital for a molecular electron configuration of $(\sigma_{1s}^{*})^2$. Zero bond order means that the bond cannot form; it has no stability. This agrees with the observation that helium is found as separate, unreactive atoms.

Example 11.9

Give the molecular electron configuration and bond order for the H_2^- ion. Can it exist according to molecular orbital theory?

Solution

Start with the same blank MO diagram that was used for H_2, but the atomic orbitals on each side will be H and H^- instead of H and H. Populate the atomic orbitals with one and two electrons, respectively, then populate the molecular orbitals in the middle with the total of three electrons.

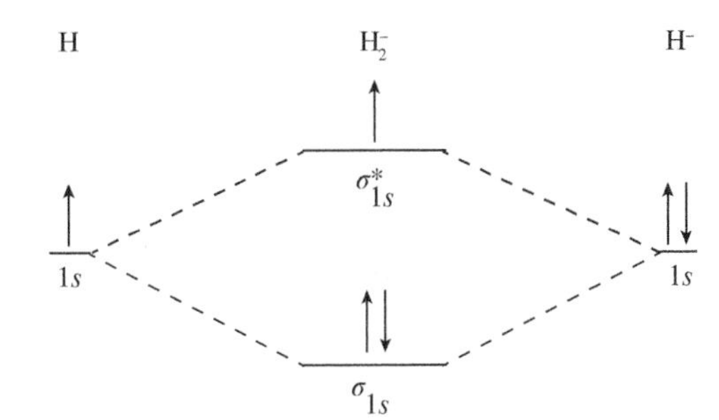

The MO electron configuration is $(\sigma_{1s})^2(\sigma^*_{1s})^1$. With two bonding electrons and one antibonding electron, the bond order is 0.5:

$$\text{bond order} = \frac{1}{2}(\text{bonding } e^- - \text{antibonding } e^-)$$
$$= \frac{1}{2}(2 - 1) = 0.5$$

A positive value for the bond order indicates that H_2^- is stable but less stable than H_2, which has a bond order of 1.

PRACTICE PROBLEM 11.9

Give the molecular electron configuration and bond order for the He_2^+ ion. Does MO theory support the existence of this ion?

Hint: Start with the same blank MO diagram that was used for H_2 and label the atomic orbitals as He and He^+.

MOLECULAR ORBITAL THEORY AND SECOND-PERIOD DIATOMIC MOLECULES

When atoms of second-period elements combine to form molecules, the valence orbitals of the two atoms will combine, forming multiple pairs of bonding and antibonding orbitals. First, consider the smaller second-period elements, such as beryllium, Be, and lithium, Li, with 2*s* valence electrons only. The 2*s* atomic orbitals combine to form shapes much like those of the 1*s* orbitals. MO diagrams for Li_2 and Be_2 are identical to that of H_2 and He_2, respectively, except 2*s* designations have replaced the ones with 1*s*. Based on these MO diagrams, you expect Li_2, with a bond order of 1 to form and be stable, but do not expect Be_2, with a bond order of 0, to be stable.

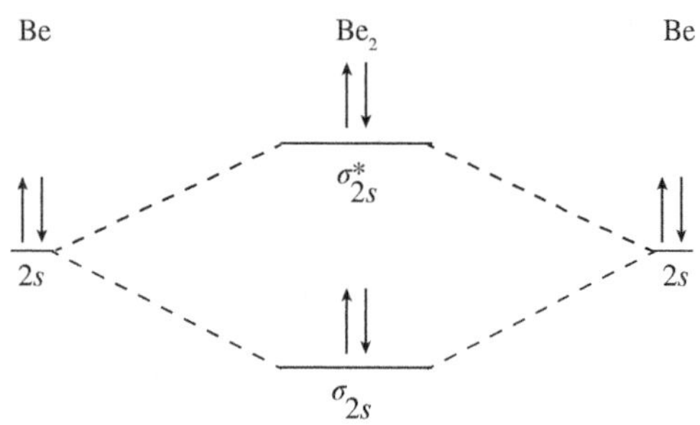

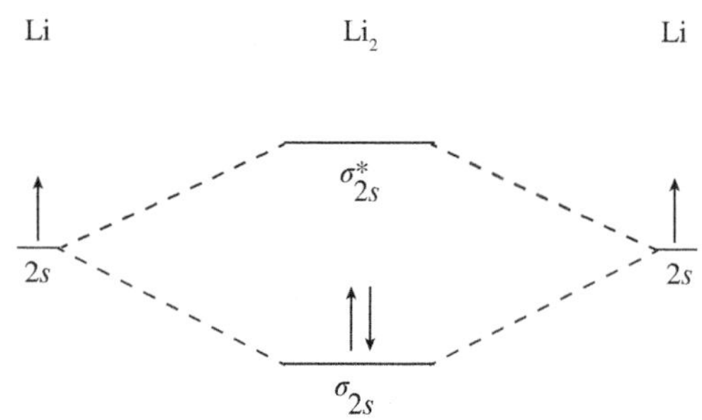

The remaining second-period elements also have valence electrons in the 2*p* subshell. Combining the *p* orbitals is somewhat more complex. With three 2*p* orbitals, each along a different axis, only one of them is oriented along the internuclear axis allowing for head-to-head overlap with the 2*p* orbital of another identical atom. The molecular orbitals resulting from additive and subtractive combination of these *p* orbitals are shown in Figure 11.35. Note that these combinations form sigma orbitals, located along the internuclear axis. One orbital, the σ_{2p}, is a bonding orbital while the other, the σ^*_{2p}, is an antibonding orbital.

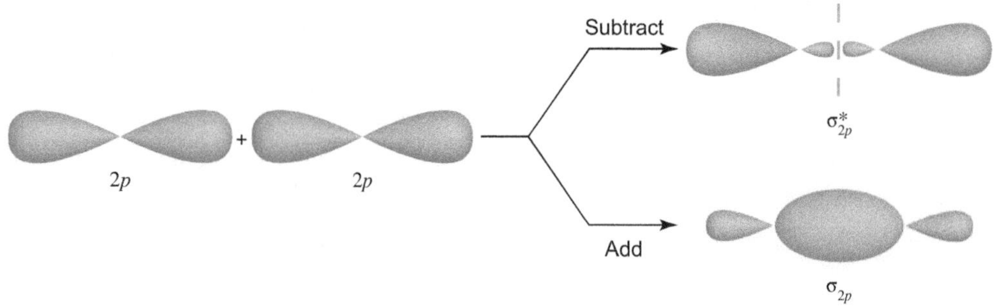

FIGURE 11.35 Head-On Combination of 2*p* Orbitals

In the head-to-head orientation, the combination of the 2*p* orbitals forms sigma-type orbitals along the internuclear axis. The additive combination forms a lower energy bonding orbital (σ_{2p}) with the majority of the electron density located between the nuclei. The subtractive combination forms a higher energy antibonding orbital (σ^*_{2p}) with the majority of the electron density located on the far sides of the nuclei rather than between the nuclei.

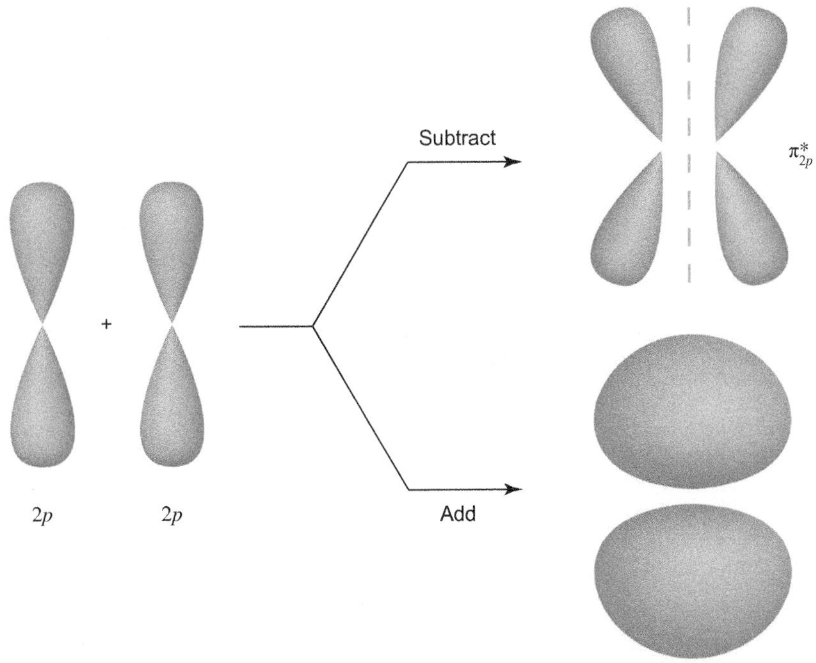

FIGURE 11.36 Sideways Combination of 2*p* Orbitals

In a side-to-side orientation, the combination of the 2*p* orbitals forms π-type orbitals above and below the internuclear axis. The additive combination forms a lower energy, bonding orbital (π_{2p}) with the majority of the electron density located between the nuclei. The subtractive combination forms a higher energy antibonding orbital (π_{2p}) and antibonding (π^*_{2p}) with the majority of the electron density located on the far sides of the nuclei rather than between the nuclei.

The other two 2*p* orbitals are oriented at right angles to the internuclear axis and will combine sideways to form two sets of bonding (π_{2p}) and antibonding (π^*_{2p}) orbitals, as shown in Figure 11.36. The resulting π orbitals are located above and below the internuclear axis and are oriented at right angles to each other and to the internuclear axis.

> Homonuclear diatomic molecules consist of two atoms of the same element. Heteronuclear diatomic molecules consist of two atoms of different elements.

The relative energy levels of the molecular orbitals derived from 2*p* atomic orbitals vary for reasons beyond the scope of this text. Figure 11.37 shows

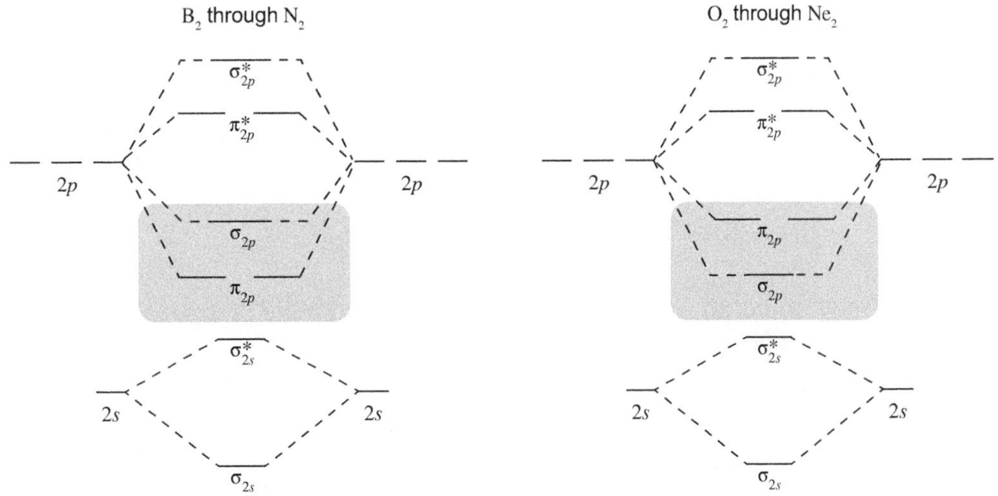

FIGURE 11.37 Blank MO Diagrams for the Second Period

The shaded area draws attention to the relative energies of the σ_{2p} and π_{2p} orbitals, the only difference between the two diagrams.

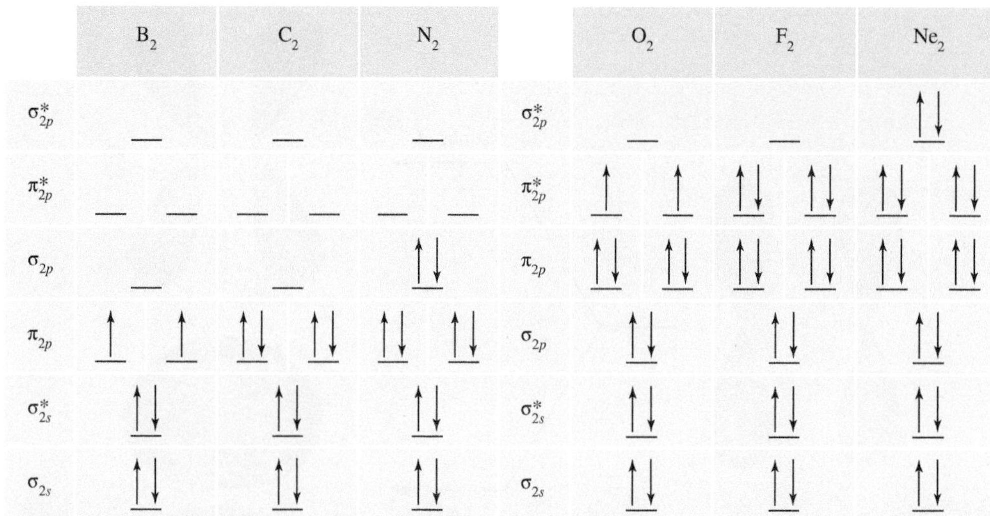

	B_2	C_2	N_2		O_2	F_2	Ne_2
Bond order	1	2	3	Bond order	2	1	0
Bond enthalpy (kJ/mol)	290	611	941	Bond enthalpy (kJ/mol)	498	157	–
Bond length (pm)	159	131	110	Bond length (pm)	121	142	–

FIGURE 11.38 Summary of Period 2 Homonuclear Diatomic Molecules

The MO diagrams for B_2, C_2, N_2, O_2, F_2, and Ne_2 are shown here. Note the change in the relative energy levels of the σ_{2p} and the π_{2p} between N_2 and O_2. Also notice the relationship of bond enthalpy and bond length to bond order; double bonds are stronger and shorter than single bonds, and triple bonds are stronger and shorter than double bonds.

the two MO energy level diagrams appropriate for homonuclear diatomic molecules of second-period elements; the one on the left pertains to B_2, C_2, and N_2, whereas the one on the right pertains to O_2, F_2, and Ne_2.

Valence electrons from both atoms are placed in the molecular orbitals starting with the lowest energy level and follow Hund's rule (Section 8.4) to half-fill all same-energy orbitals before filling any one orbital. Figure 11.38 shows the completed MO diagrams plus calculated bond orders and measured bond enthalpies and bond lengths. Notice that the lower bond orders have lower bond enthalpies and longer bond lengths. Higher bond orders have higher bond enthalpies and shorter lengths, indicating stronger bonds. Notice also that N_2 has a bond order of 3 and O_2 has a bond order of 2, which agrees with the Lewis theory view of triple-bonded N_2 and double-bonded O_2. However, the Lewis structure of O_2 shows all the electrons as paired, while there are two unpaired electrons in the MO diagram for oxygen.

One of the unusual properties of oxygen is that it is **paramagnetic**, that is, liquid oxygen is attracted to

FIGURE 11.39 Demonstration of the Magnetic Properties of Oxygen

NOTE: You need to be online to access this video.

Oxygen's unpaired electrons make it paramagnetic, so oxygen is attracted to a magnet.

a magnetic field and can be suspended between the poles of a magnet (Figure 11.39). Paramagnetic materials have unpaired electrons that align with an external magnetic field, creating the weak attraction. Materials with no unpaired electrons display no attraction to magnetic fields, are very slightly repelled by them, and

EVERYDAY CONNECTION

Nitrogen, N_2, is the major component of Earth's atmosphere but, since it is so unreactive, people are rarely aware of it. The atoms in a nitrogen molecule are connected with a triple bond. From VB theory, you would predict that N_2 would be reactive with the two sets of π-bond electrons available. In fact, you might predict that N_2 would be more reactive than oxygen, O_2, which contains only a double bond. However, you may know from experience that oxygen is quite reactive, especially in combustion reactions (burning). MO theory can help to explain this. The MO diagram for N_2 has all paired electrons, whereas the MO diagram for O_2 has two unpaired electrons, helping to explain its greater reactivity.

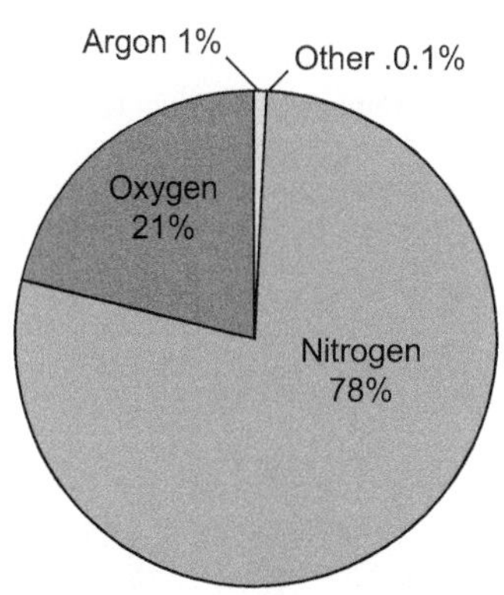

are referred to as **diamagnetic**. Molecular orbital theory explains the observed paramagnetism of oxygen and the observed diamagnetism of N_2.

Example 11.10

Draw an MO diagram for peroxide, O_2^{2-}, a polyatomic ion. Once drawn, use the diagram to answer the following questions:

a. What is the MO electron configuration for the peroxide ion?
b. Is the peroxide ion more stable than the O_2 molecule?
c. Is O_2^{2-} paramagnetic or diamagnetic?
d. Is the O—O bond in the peroxide ion shorter or longer than the one in O_2?

Solution

The peroxide ion has two more electrons than the oxygen molecule. Simply adding two electrons to the MO diagram for oxygen yields the MO diagram for peroxide ion.

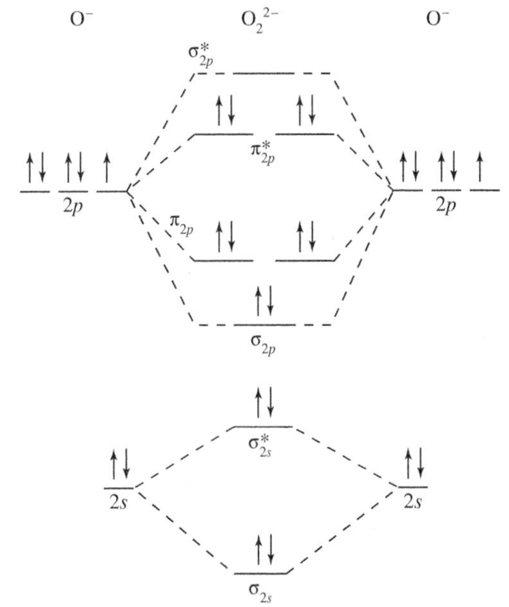

a. The MO electron configuration is $(\sigma_{2s})^2 (\sigma^*_{1s})^2(\sigma_{2p})^2(\pi_{2p})^4(\pi_{2p})$ and antibonding $(\pi^*_{2p})^4$.
b. The bond order for the peroxide ion is $\frac{1}{2}(8 - 6) = 1$, which is less than the bond order of 2 for oxygen. Peroxide is predicted to be stable but less stable than oxygen, making the expected bond enthalpy value for peroxide less than that of oxygen as well.
c. All the electrons in the peroxide ion are paired, so it is diamagnetic.
d. A bond order of 1 indicates a longer, weaker bond in the peroxide ion than in oxygen.

PRACTICE PROBLEM 11.10

Draw an MO diagram for the superoxide ion, O_2^-. Use the diagram to answer the following questions:

a. What is the MO electron configuration for the superoxide ion?
b. Is the superoxide ion more stable than the O_2 molecule?
c. Is superoxide paramagnetic or diamagnetic?
d. Is the O—O bond in superoxide shorter or longer than the one in O_2?

Hint: There are 13 valence electrons in O_2^-, so your diagram should show 13 arrows in the molecular orbitals (one more than neutral O_2, or one fewer than O_2^{2-} from the previous example). Use the diagram to determine the electron configuration, magnetism, and bond order. Use bond order to determine relative stability and bond length.

MO diagrams can also be written for heteronuclear diatomic molecules and ions, as shown in Figure 11.40. The relative energy levels must be determined computationally and cannot be readily predicted.

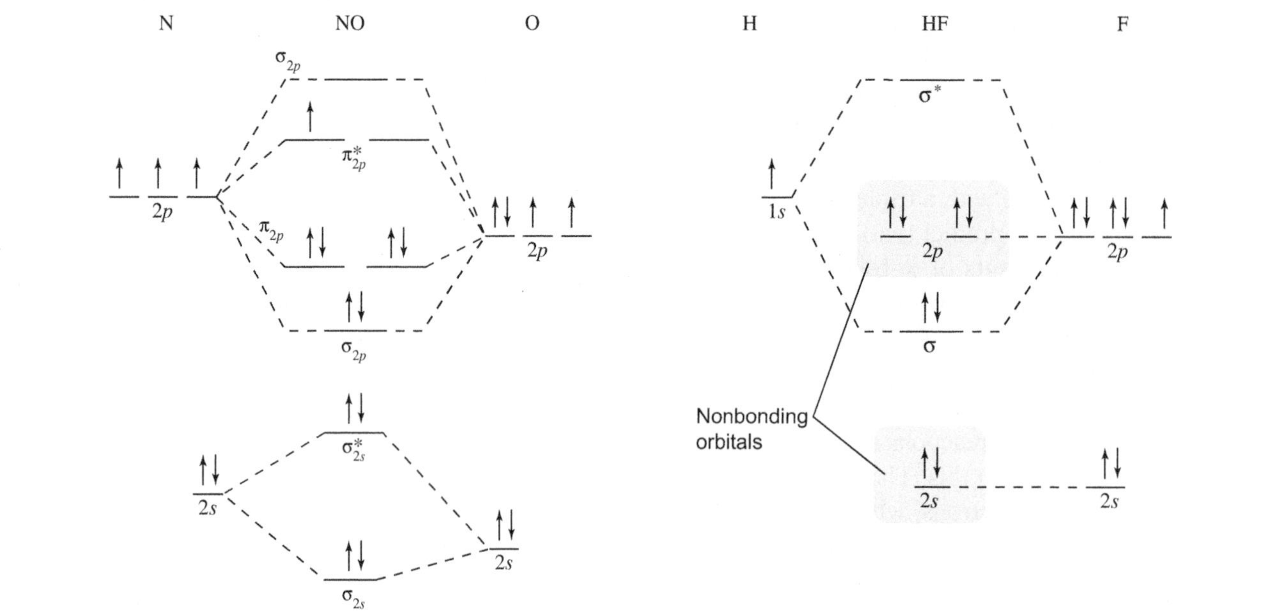

FIGURE 11.40 MO Diagrams of NO and HF

In NO, the greater electronegativity of the O atom means its atomic orbitals are slightly lower in energy than those of N, but the overall result is a diagram that looks very similar to that of a homonuclear molecule such as O_2^+. In HF, however, the electronegativity difference between atoms is so great that the 1*s* orbital of H combines with one of the 2*p* orbitals of F, creating σ and σ^* molecular orbitals and leaving the 2*s* and two of the 2*p* as nonbonding orbitals, which do not factor into bond order. Thus, the bond order of HF is calculated as $\frac{1}{2}(2 - 0) = 1$.

Any unshared valence electrons maintain their atomic orbital energy level and occupy **nonbonding orbitals** in the MO diagram. Electrons in nonbonding orbitals do not contribute to bonding and are not considered in bond order calculations.

MOLECULAR ORBITAL THEORY AND RESONANCE

Pi bonds can also help explain resonance. Resonance occurs when multiple, equivalent (or nearly equivalent) Lewis structures can be drawn for a molecule (Section 10.3) and differ only in the location of the multiple bonds and the lone pairs of electrons, as is seen in the resonance structures of ozone:

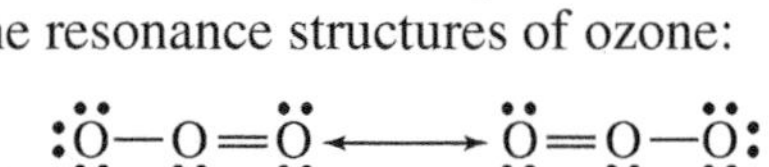

Compounds with resonance are generally much less reactive than would be expected from the number of multiple bonds. To explain this phenomenon, we can look at the molecular orbitals of ozone as shown in Figure 11.41.

All three oxygen atoms have adjacent *p* orbitals that can overlap to form a π bond that is not located between one pair of atoms or the other, but is spread over all three atoms. This spreading of a π bond is called delocalization. Compared to localized π electrons, which are shared between only two atoms, delocalized π electrons are less available for reactions.

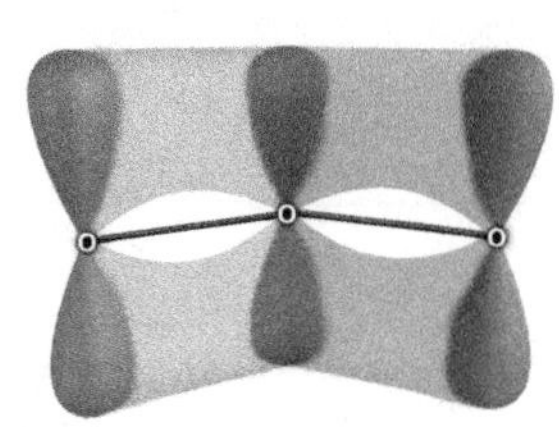

FIGURE 11.41 Pi Bonding in Ozone

The *p* orbitals from the three O atoms overlap to form a delocalized π bond sharing a pair of electrons among the three atoms.

The structure of benzene, C_6H_6, is generally drawn as a hexagon with three double bonds.

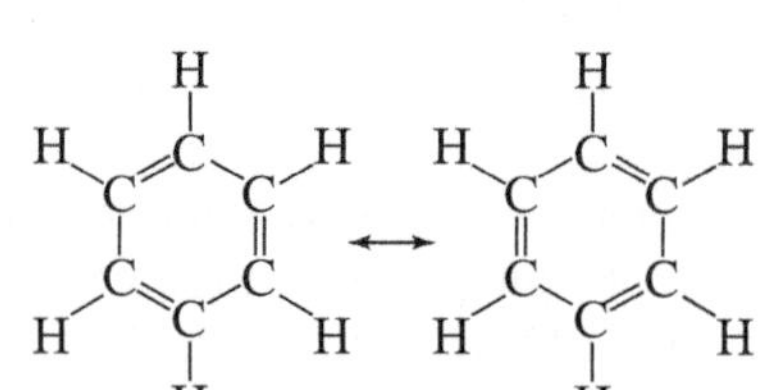

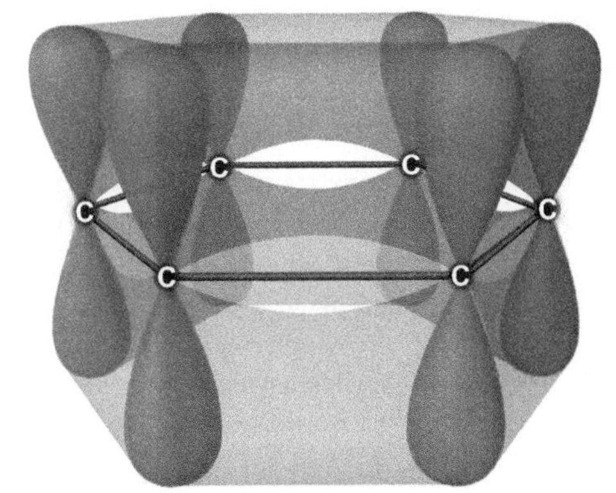

FIGURE 11.42 Pi Bonding in Benzene

The *p* orbitals from the six carbon atoms of benzene overlap to form a continuous, circular π bond above and below the plane of the benzene molecule. This π bond consists of three pairs of electrons shared among the six carbon atoms.

From the Lewis structure, you might predict that this molecule is quite reactive and that it has different C—C bond lengths—namely, longer for the single bonds and shorter for the double bonds. However, all of the C—C bond lengths are the same in benzene (part way between the typical length of a carbon–carbon single bond and the typical length of a carbon–carbon double bond), and benzene is not very reactive. The π bond in benzene is a combination of a $2p$ orbital from each of the six carbon atoms, forming a bonding MO that is delocalized over the whole molecule (Figure 11.42).

REVISITING THE BONDING THEORIES

Lewis theory, the valence shell electron pair repulsion model, valence bond theory, and molecular orbital theory are all important, and all are currently in use by chemists. Although MO theory provides greater explanation and is capable of more accurate predictions, it is also very complex. Chemists use the theory that best suits their needs at the time. If your goal is to determine whether a substance is likely to be polar, you do not need to draw its MO diagram. Instead, you can draw the Lewis structure, apply VSEPR, and use electronegativity values to make a prediction. If you need to determine whether a substance is likely to be paramagnetic or determine its bond order, then you need to draw its MO diagram. Table 11.3 summarizes and compares the various bonding theories.

SECTION REVIEW

- MO theory can explain many of the properties of molecules that VB theory cannot.
- In MO theory, atomic orbitals undergo additive and subtractive combination to produce bonding and antibonding molecular orbitals, respectively.
  - $1s$ and $2s$ orbitals of two atoms combine to form σ bonding and σ^* antibonding orbitals.
  - $2p_x$ orbitals of two atoms also combine to form σ bonding and σ^* antibonding orbitals.

TABLE 11.3 Summary and Comparison of Bonding Theories

Theory	Summary	Uses	Drawbacks
Lewis Theory	Atoms in molecules and polyatomic ions have completed valence shells following the octet/duet rule.	Molecular diagrams show relative bond strengths as single, double, and triple bonds.	Two-dimensional model of three-dimensional molecules; no distinction between bonds in different compounds. Does not explain how/why bonds form.
VSEPR	The number of electron domains around the central atom in Lewis structure determines the three-dimensional shape of the molecule or polyatomic ion.	Predicts shapes and can apply polar bonds to determine the polarity of the molecule.	Does not explain how/why bonds form.
Valence Bond Theory and Hybridization of Atomic Orbitals	Covalent bonds form by overlap of atomic orbitals in sigma and pi bonds. The degree of overlap determines the strength of the bond.	Description of pi bonds helps to explain greater reactivity of compounds with double bonds and lack of rotation around double bonds. Hybrid atomic orbitals explain some molecular geometries, but not all.	Does not explain certain properties such as paramagnetism. Not easily used to predict properties of hypothetical molecules or ions.
Molecular Orbital Theory	Atomic orbitals combine to form bonding and antibonding molecular orbitals that extend over the entire molecule.	Explains the electron energy levels of molecules, explains paramagnetism/diamagnetism, and makes it possible to predict the properties of hypothetical molecules and ions.	Easily used for diatomic molecules of the first- and second-period atoms; becomes more complex as the size of the molecule increases.

  - $2p_y$ and $2p_z$ orbitals of two atoms combine to form two sets of equivalent π bonding and π^* antibonding orbitals.
- MO diagrams place the valence electrons in the MOs starting with the lowest MO and following Hund's rule.
  - MO electron configurations are written in a manner similar to atomic electron configurations using MO labels.
  - Bond order $= \frac{1}{2}(\text{bonding e}^- - \text{antibonding e}^-)$.
  - Bond orders greater than 0 indicate a stable particle.
  - Paramagnetism is indicated by the presence of one or more unpaired electrons.
  - Diamagnetism results when all electrons are paired.
- Resonance is explained by the delocalization of π bonds over the entire molecule.
- All bonding theories presented have limitations but still remain useful to chemists.

Putting It Together

The example problems in earlier sections of this chapter focus on just the new skills acquired in that section. But homework and exam questions in chemistry often require more than just one skill at a time. In fact, you will likely be expected to apply knowledge from across the entire chapter, or even multiple chapters in a single problem. This final example problem is meant to help you prepare for these types of multi-concept questions. Additional examples can be found in the end of chapter exercises.

Example 11.11

a. Calculate the bond order of nitric oxide, NO, from its molecular orbital diagram. How does this compare to the bond order predicted by the Lewis structure of NO?
b. Based on the number of pi bonds predicted by the Lewis structure, what is the hybridization of each atom? How does this hybridization compare to the angle between domains as predicted by VSEPR?

Solution

a. From the MO diagram of NO shown in Figure 11.40, we see there are eight electrons in bonding orbitals and three electrons in antibonding orbitals for a bond order of $(8 - 3)/2 = 2.5$

In contrast, the Lewis structure of NO predicts a bond order of two.

$$\cdot\ddot{N}=\ddot{O}:$$

b. A double bond consists of one σ bond and one π bond. With one set of p orbitals overlapping to form the π bond, that leaves two p orbitals from each atom that were involved in hybridization with the s orbital for a hybridization of sp^2. This implies that the electron domains are at approximately 120° angles, which agrees with the VSEPR prediction for an atom with three domains.

PRACTICE PROBLEM 11.11

Draw a Lewis structure for chloryl fluoride, ClO_2F, that minimizes formal charges. Predict the electronic geometry, molecular geometry, and polarity of the molecule, and the hybridization of the central atom.

Hint: The Lewis structure should show a total of $2(7) + 2(6) = 26$ electrons. All outer atoms must have exactly an octet, and the central Cl atom must have at least an octet. Once you have the Lewis structure, count the number of bonded groups and lone pairs on the central atom to determine the geometries and hybridization. Use the molecular geometry to predict polarity.

Key Terms, Symbols, and Equations

KEY TERMS

antibonding orbital (11.5): A higher-energy molecular orbital resulting from the subtractive combination of atomic orbitals, designated by *.

bent (11.1): A molecular geometry associated with three electron domains with one lone pair, or four electron domains with two lone pairs.

bond order (11.5): Measure of the stability of the molecule, calculated from the MO diagram as: bond order $= \frac{1}{2}(\text{bonding } e^- - \text{antibonding } e^-)$.

bonding orbital (11.5): Lower energy molecular orbital resulting from the additive combination of atomic orbitals.

conformation (11.4): Various shapes possible for larger molecules due to rotation around single bonds.

constructive interference (11.5): Waves combine in phase to increase peaks and decrease troughs.

coordinate covalent bonds (11.3): Covalent bond in which both electrons in the shared pair is supplied by one of the atoms.

destructive interference (11.5): Waves combine out of phase to cancel peaks and troughs.

diamagnetism (11.5): Very slight repulsion for a magnetic field; property of molecules with all paired electrons.

electron domain (11.1): A charge cloud around a central atom that can be: lone pairs, single unshared electrons, single bond, double bond, or triple bond.

electron geometry (11.1): Shape determined by the number of electron domains.

flash point (11.1): Temperature at which vapors of a liquid fuel can be ignited.

hybrid orbitals (11.3): Mathematical combinations of the standard atomic orbitals that result in maximal overlap of orbitals in bonds.

isomers (11.1): Different compounds with the same molecular formula.

linear (11.1): An electron geometry associated with two electron domains. Also a molecular geometry resulting from two bonded groups at a 180° bond angle, which occurs with two electron domains with no lone pairs, and five electron domains with three lone pairs.

molecular dipole (11.2): Molecule with uneven electron distribution; polar molecule.

molecular geometry (11.1): Three-dimensional shape of molecule.

molecular orbital, MO (11.5): A type of orbital resulting from the combination of atomic orbitals in a molecule.

molecular orbital, MO, diagram (11.5): Similar to an atomic orbital diagram; shows the relative energy levels and electron population of the molecular orbital; used to predict properties.

molecular orbital, MO, theory (11.5): Theory that explains bonding by the combination of atomic orbitals to form bonding molecular orbitals and antibonding molecular orbitals.

nonbonding orbitals (11.5): Orbitals occupied by lone pairs in MO diagrams.

nonpolar molecule (11.2): Molecule with symmetric electron distribution; no dipole.

octahedral (11.1): An electron geometry associated with six electron domains. Also a molecular geometry if all six domains are bonded groups; symmetrical shape consisting of eight triangular faces and 90° and 180° bond angles.

paramagnetism (11.5): Weak attraction to a magnetic field; property of molecules with unpaired electrons.

pi, π, bond (11.3): Bond formed by side-on overlap of unhybridized *p* orbitals above and below the internuclear axis; found in double and triple bonds.

polar molecule (11.2): A molecule with asymmetric electron distribution; molecular dipole.

see-saw (11.1): A molecular geometry associated with five electron domains with one lone pair.

sigma, σ, bond (11.3): A type of bond formed by head-to-head overlap of orbitals along the internuclear axis; found in all covalent bonds.

***sp* hybrid orbitals** (11.3): Hybrid orbitals formed from one *s* orbital and one *p* orbital; associated with linear electron geometry.

sp^2 hybrid orbitals (11.3): Hybrid orbitals formed from one *s* orbital and two *p* orbitals; associated with trigonal planar electron geometry.

sp^3 hybrid orbitals (11.3): Hybrid orbitals formed from one *s* orbital and three *p* orbitals; associated with tetrahedral electron geometry.

square planar (11.1): A molecular geometry associated with six electron domains with two lone pairs.

square pyramidal (11.1): A molecular geometry associated with six electron domains with one lone pair.

tetrahedral (11.1): An electron geometry associated with four electron domains. Also a molecular geometry if all four electron domains are bonded groups; having the shape of a tetrahedron; 109.5° bond angles.

tetrahedron (11.1): Symmetric three-dimensional shape consisting of four equilateral triangular faces.

trigonal bipyramidal (11.1): An electron geometry associated with five electron domains consisting of two three-sided pyramids sharing a base. Also a molecular geometry if all five electron domains are bonded groups; 90°, 120°, and 180° bond angles.

trigonal planar (11.1): An electron geometry associated with three electron domains. Also a molecular geometry if all three electron domains are bonded groups; 120° bond angles.

trigonal pyramidal (11.1)**:** Molecular geometry associated with four electron domains with one lone pair; a three-sided pyramid.

T-shaped (11.1)**:** A molecular geometry associated with five electron domains with two lone pairs.

valence bond, VB, theory (11.3)**:** Theory that explains bonding by the overlap of atomic orbitals and hybridization of atomic orbitals.

valence shell electron pair repulsion, VSEPR, model (11.1)**:** Model that uses the number of electron domains around a central atom to predict the most stable shape occupied by the domain due to repulsion.

SYMBOLS AND ABBREVIATIONS

MO (molecular orbital) (11.5)

π (pi) (11.3)

π^* (pi star) (11.5)

σ (sigma) (11.3)

σ^* (sigma star) (11.5)

sp (11.3)

sp^2 (11.3)

sp^3 (11.3)

VB (valence bond) (11.3)

VSEPR (valence shell electron pair repulsion) (11.1)

Chapter Summary

The valence shell electron pair repulsion model uses the number of electron domains around a central atom to predict the shapes of molecules. These electron domains repel each other to adopt the most stable shape or geometry. Any of the following is an electron domain: single bond, double bond, triple bond, lone pair of electrons, unshared electron. The geometries associated with specific numbers of electron domains are: 2: linear, 3: trigonal planar, 4: tetrahedral, 5: trigonal bipyramidal, 6: octahedral. However, the actual molecular geometry is different from the electron shape when one or more of the electron domains are lone pairs. These molecular geometries are predicted from the electron geometry and the number of lone pairs on the central atom. Larger molecules can be described as a series of the molecular geometries associated with each central atom found in the molecule (Section 11.1).

Molecular geometry, combined with electronegativity, is used to predict if a molecule is polar or nonpolar. Molecules with nonpolar bonds are almost always nonpolar (the exceptions are beyond the scope of this text). Molecules with a symmetrical arrangement of the polar bonds are nonpolar. Only molecules with an asymmetrical arrangement of polar bonds are polar (Section 11.2).

Valence bond theory describes covalent bonds as the overlap between valence atomic orbitals of the bonded atoms, with the degree of overlap determining the strength of the bond. When energetically favorable, *s* and *p* orbitals on central atoms will combine to form equivalent hybrid orbitals for bonding.

- Central atoms with four electron domains use sp^3 hybrid orbitals, forming tetrahedral electron geometries.
- Central atoms with three electron domains use sp^2 hybrid orbitals, forming trigonal planar electron geometries.
- Central atoms with two electron domains use *sp* hybrid orbitals, forming linear electron geometries.

Bonds that form by overlap of orbitals along the internuclear axis are σ bonds. All single bonds are σ bonds. In the case of sp^2 and *sp* hybrid orbitals, the unhybridized *p* orbitals will also overlap to form π bonds, which exist as two separate areas of overlap above and below the internuclear axis. All multiple bonds contain one σ bond and one or two π bonds. Valence bond theory does not currently support any hybridizations that can explain the expanded octet geometries (Section 11.3).

Valence bond theory provides a means for explaining why compounds with multiple bonds are more reactive than compounds with single bonds and explains why double bonds restrict the rotation of the atoms involved. However, valence bond theory does not explain all the important properties of molecules (Section 11.4).

Molecular orbital theory can explain many of the properties of molecules that valence bond theory cannot. In MO theory, atomic orbitals undergo additive and subtractive combination to produce bonding and antibonding molecular orbitals, respectively.

- $1s$ and $2s$ orbitals of two atoms combine to form σ bonding and σ^* antibonding orbitals.
- $2p_x$ orbitals of two atoms also combine to form σ bonding and σ^* antibonding orbitals.
- $2p_y$ and $2p_z$ of two atoms orbitals combine to form two sets of equivalent π bonding and π^* antibonding orbitals.

MO diagrams place the valence electrons in the MOs starting with the lowest MO and following Hund's rule, and they can be used to interpret and predict molecular properties. MO electron configurations can be written from MO diagrams and bond order calculated.

$$\text{bond order} = \frac{1}{2}(\text{bonding } e^- - \text{antibonding } e^-)$$

MO theory explains/predicts:

- The stability and/or relative stability of molecules or ions by comparing bond orders.
- Paramagnetism by the presence of unpaired electrons.
- Resonance as the delocalization of π bonds over the entire molecule.

All bonding theories have limitations but remain useful to chemists. You must learn to use the most appropriate theory or model for the circumstances (Section 11.5).

END OF CHAPTER QUESTIONS

11.1 VSEPR and Molecular Geometry

1. Determine the electron geometry, molecular geometry, and bond angles for each molecule.

a. CF_4

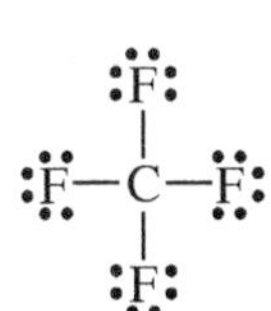

b. CS_2

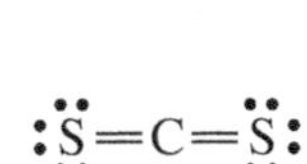

c. BCl_3

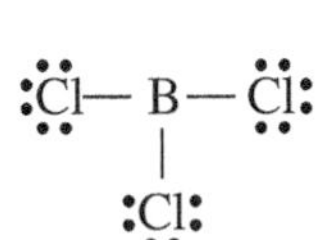

d. PCl_3

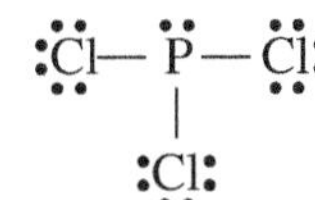

2. Determine the electron geometry, molecular geometry, and bond angles for each molecule or ion.

a. $AsBr_5$

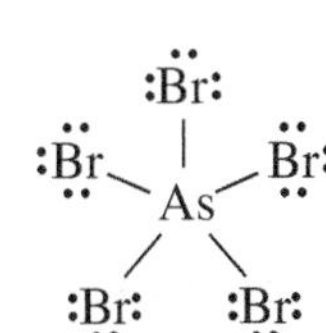

b. SO_4^{2-}

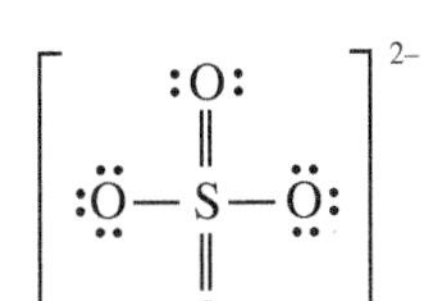

c. NF_3

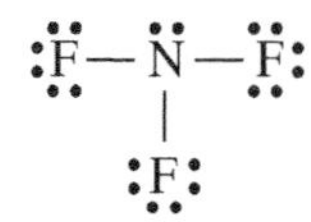

d. SBr_2

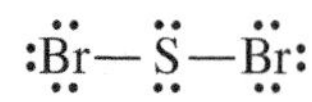

3. Determine the electron geometry, molecular geometry, and bond angles for each molecule or ion.
   a. SiO_2
   b. IF_2^-
   c. CHF_3
   d. $TeCl_4$

4. Determine the electron geometry, molecular geometry, and bond angles for each molecule or ion.
   a. N_2O
   b. ClF_3
   c. BrO_2^-
   d. H_2S

5. Determine the electron geometry, molecular geometry, and bond angles for each molecule or ion.
   a. BeF_2
   b. ClO_4^-
   c. CCl_4
   d. CO_3^{2-}

6. Determine the electron geometry, molecular geometry, and bond angles for each molecule or ion.
   a. SeF_6
   b. SiH_4
   c. SCl_2
   d. ClO_3^-

7. The symbol X represents the central atom, Y represents outer atoms, and Z represents lone pairs of electrons on the central atom. Determine the molecular geometry of each of the generic molecules.
   a. XY_4Z
   b. XY_2
   c. XY_3Z

8. The symbol X represents the central atom, Y represents outer atoms, and Z represents lone pairs of electrons on the central atom. Determine the molecular geometry of each of the generic molecules.
   a. XY_3
   b. XY_3Z_2
   c. XY_2Z_3

9. Identify the molecular geometry around each of the central atoms in the following structure

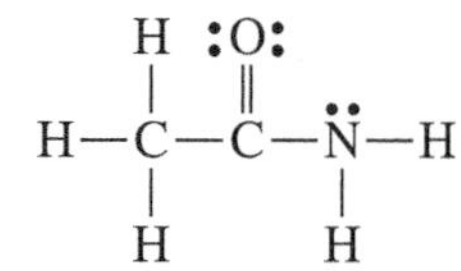

10. Identify the molecular geometry around each of the central atoms in 2-butyne.

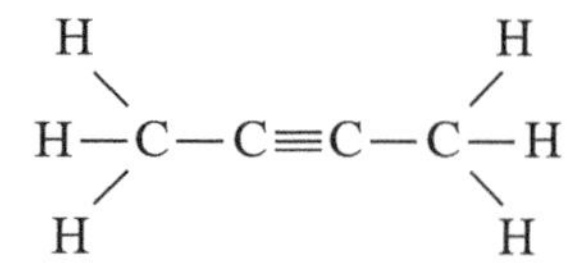

11.2 Polar and Nonpolar Molecules

11. Can a molecule have polar bonds and not have a dipole?

12. Can a molecule have only nonpolar bonds and have a dipole?

13. Can a molecule have a mix of polar and nonpolar bonds and have a dipole?

14. Give an example of a nonpolar molecule with
    a. two polar bonds.
    b. three polar bonds.
    c. four polar bonds.

15. Give an example of a polar molecule with
    a. two polar bonds.
    b. three polar bonds.
    c. four polar bonds.

16. Determine whether each diatomic molecule is polar or nonpolar.
    a. HBr
    b. Cl_2
    c. N_2

17. Determine whether each diatomic molecule is polar or nonpolar.
    a. O_2
    b. CO
    c. H_2

18. Determine the polarity of each bond and whether each molecule or ion is polar or nonpolar.
    a. $CHCl_3$

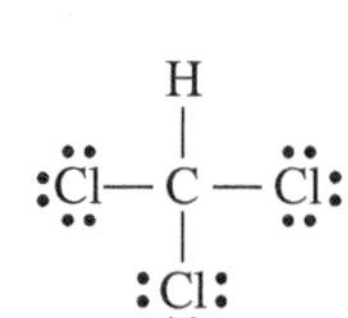

b. SO_2

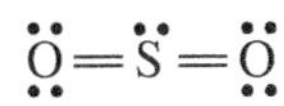

c. $SiCl_4$

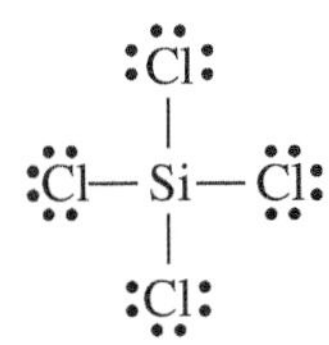

d. NO_2^-

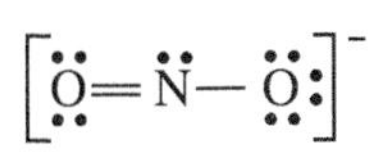

19. Determine the polarity of each bond and whether each molecule is polar or nonpolar.
    a. SF_6

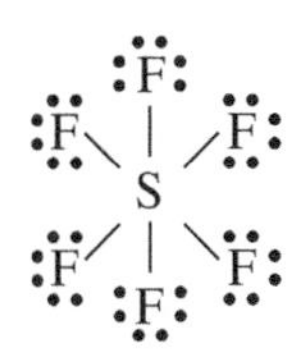

    b. BCl_3

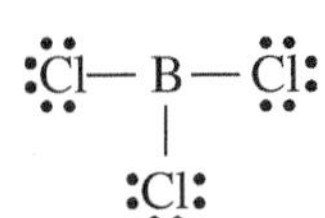

    c. SCl_2

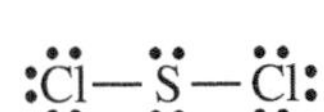

    d. IF_5

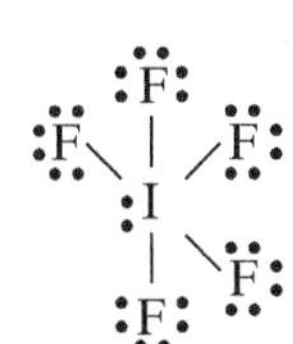

20. Determine the polarity of each bond and whether each molecule is polar or nonpolar.
    a. PF_3
    b. OCl_2
    c. KrF_2

21. Determine the polarity of each bond and whether each molecule is polar or nonpolar.
    a. ClF_3
    b. CF_2Cl_2
    c. GeF_4

11.3 Valence Bond Theory: Hybrid Orbitals and Bonding

22. Determine the hybridization of the central atom for a molecule with a
    a. linear electron geometry.
    b. trigonal planar electron geometry.
    c. tetrahedral electron geometry.

23. Determine the hybridization of carbon in each of the molecules.
    a. HCN
    b. $CHCl_3$
    c. H_2CO
    d. CO_2

24. Determine the hybridization of the central atom in each molecule and identify the sigma and pi bonds.
    a. SF_2

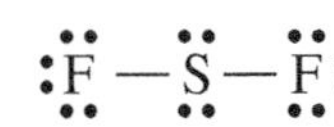

    b. N_2O

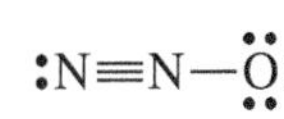

    c. NF_3

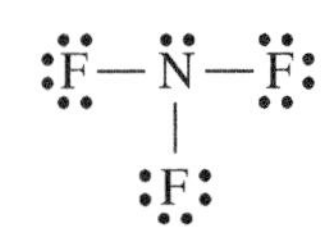

    d. CO_2

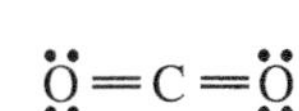

25. Determine the hybridization of the central atom in each molecule and identify the sigma and pi bonds.
    a. OF_2

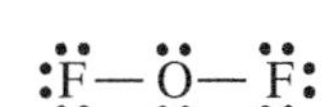

    b. BCl_3

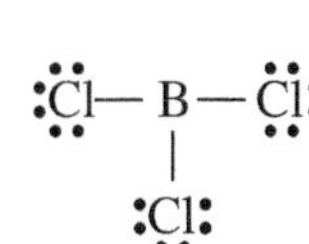

    c. CHF_3

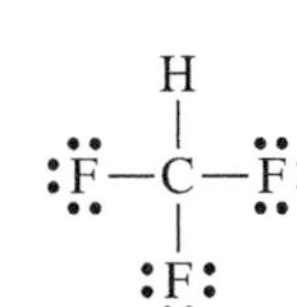

d. SiH_4

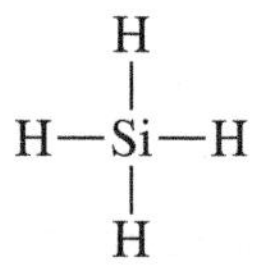

26. Determine the hybridization of the central atom in each molecule and identify the sigma and pi bonds.
   a. NO_2
   b. $COCl_2$
   c. PCl_3
   d. CS_2

27. Determine the hybridization of the central atom in each molecule and identify the sigma and pi bonds.
   a. O_3
   b. CH_2O
   c. SiO_2

28. The symbol X represents the central atom, Y represents outer atoms, and Z represents lone pairs of electrons on the central atom. Determine the hybridization of the central atom in each of the generic molecules.
   a. XY_2Z
   b. XY_2Z_2
   c. XY_2
   d. XY_2Z

29. Determine the hybridization of the highlighted atoms in the pain reliever acetaminophen.

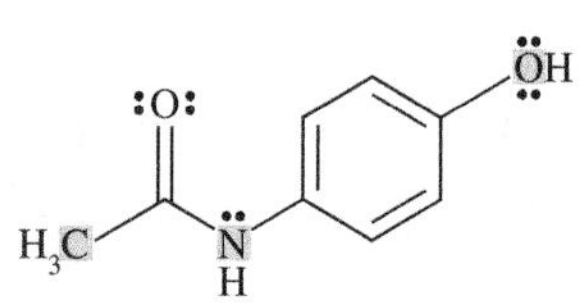

30. Determine the hybridization of the carbon atom in formic acid.

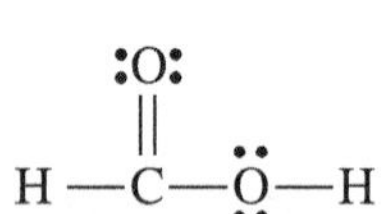

31. Determine the number of sigma and pi bonds in acetic acid.

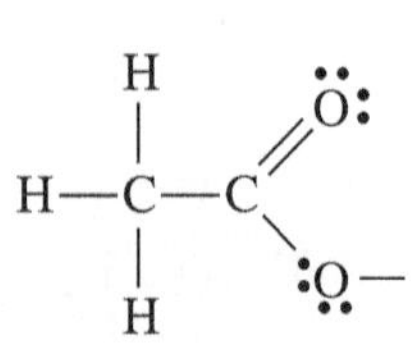

32. Determine the number of sigma and pi bonds in phthalic acid.

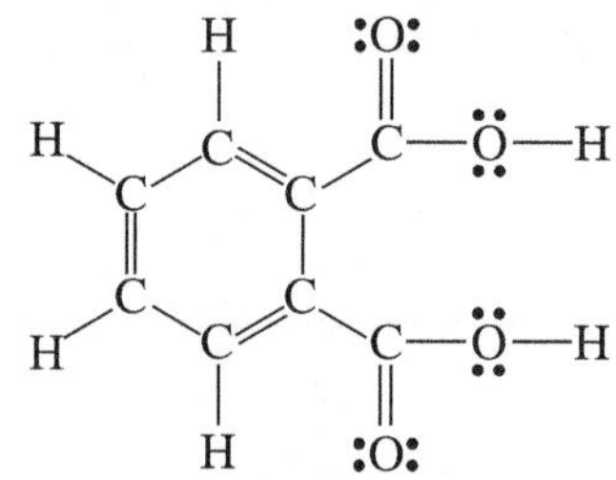

11.4 Using Valence Bond Theory

33. Use valence bond theory to determine whether ethane, $CH_3—CH_3$, or ethene, $CH_2=CH_2$, is more reactive and explain why.

34. Use valence bond theory to determine whether pentane, $CH_3—CH_2—CH_2—CH_2—CH_3$, or 2-pentene, $CH_3—CH=CH—CH_2—CH_3$, is more reactive and explain why.

35. Use valence bond theory to determine whether acetaldehyde or ethanol is more reactive and explain why.

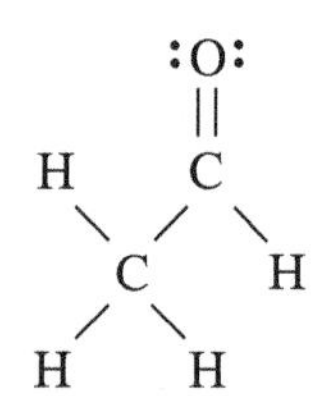

Acetaldehyde

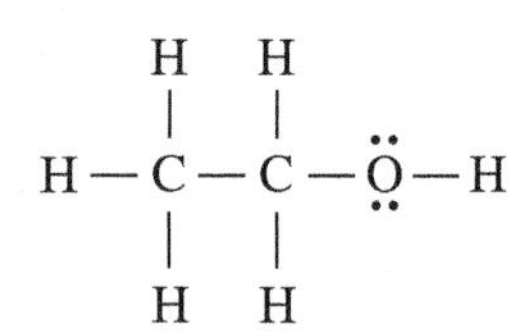

Ethanol

36. Use valence bond theory to determine whether propanal or 1-propanol is more reactive and explain why.

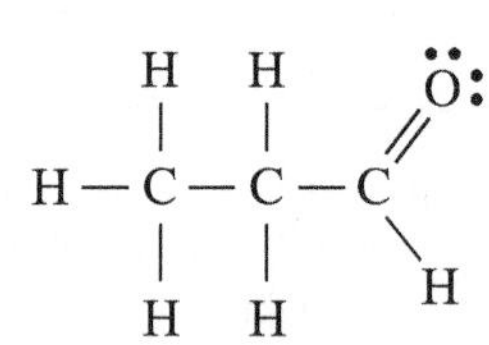

Propanol

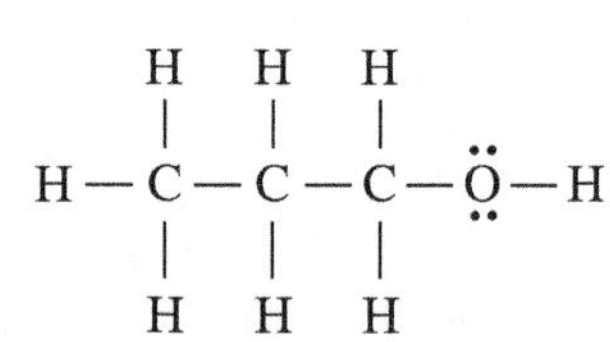

1-Propanol

37. Explain how the reaction of *cis*-1,2-dichloroethene to form *trans*-1,2-dichloroethene requires breaking a pi bond, but not a sigma bond.

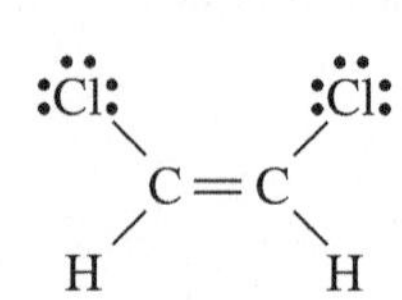

cis-1,2-Dichloroethene

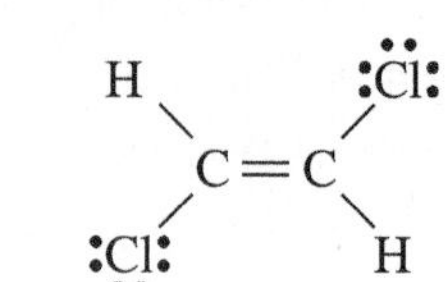

trans-1,2-Dichloroethene

38. Draw the Lewis structure of N_2H_2, then use valence bond theory to predict whether the orbitals in this molecule look more like that of C_2H_4 (Figure 11.25) or C_2H_2 (Figure 11.26).

11.5 Molecular Orbital Theory

39. Determine the molecular electron configuration and bond order for He_2^{2+}.

40. Determine the molecular electron configuration and bond order for H_2^{2-}.

41. Draw the molecular orbital diagram for N_2^{2-} and use it to answer the following questions.
   a. What is the molecular electron configuration for this ion?
   b. What is the bond order?
   c. Is this ion paramagnetic or diamagnetic?

42. Draw the molecular orbital diagram for C_2^{2-} and use it to answer the following questions.
   a. What is the molecular electron configuration for this ion?
   b. What is the bond order?
   c. Is this ion paramagnetic or diamagnetic?

43. Draw the molecular orbital diagram for Li_2^{2-} and use it to answer the following questions.
   a. What is the molecular electron configuration for this ion?
   b. What is the bond order?
   c. Is this ion paramagnetic or diamagnetic?

44. Draw the molecular orbital diagram for Be_2^{2+} and use it to answer the following questions.
   a. What is the molecular electron configuration for this ion?
   b. What is the bond order?
   c. Is this ion paramagnetic or diamagnetic?

45. Draw the molecular orbital diagrams for C_2^+ and C_2, and use them to answer the following questions.
   a. What is the molecular electron configuration for C_2^+ and C_2?
   b. Is the C_2^+ ion more stable than the C_2 molecule?
   c. Are C_2^+ and C_2 paramagnetic or diamagnetic?
   d. Is the C—C bond in C_2^+ shorter or longer than the one in C_2?

46. Draw the molecular orbital diagrams for F_2^- and F_2, and use them to answer the following questions.
   a. What is the molecular electron configuration for F_2^- and F_2?
   b. Is the F_2^- ion more stable than the F_2 molecule?
   c. Are F_2^- and F_2 paramagnetic or diamagnetic?
   d. Is the F—F bond in F_2^- shorter or longer than the one in F_2?

47. Use molecular orbital theory to arrange N_2^-, N_2, and N_2^+ in order of increasing bond length.

48. Use molecular orbital theory to arrange O_2^-, O_2, and O_2^+ in order of increasing bond length.

49. Complete the MO diagram for CO and determine the bond order. Is the molecule paramagnetic or diamagnetic?

50. Complete the MO diagram for CN^- and determine the bond order. Is the ion paramagnetic or diamagnetic?

Putting It Together

51. Classify each of the following as an atomic orbital, hybrid orbital, or molecular orbital.
   a. sp^3
   b. d
   c. σ_{1s}
   d. sp

52. Classify each of the following as an atomic orbital, hybrid orbital, or molecular orbital.
   a. p
   b. π_{2p}
   c. sp^2
   d. s

53. For each molecule, draw the Lewis structure, determine the electron and molecular geometry using VSEPR theory, determine the bond angles, and determine whether the molecule is polar or nonpolar.
   a. $XeCl_4$
   b. $BeCl_2$
   c. CH_2Br_2
   d. $CH_3CH_2NH_2$

54. For each molecule or ion, draw the Lewis structure, determine the electron and molecular geometry using VSEPR theory, determine the bond angles, and determine whether the molecule is polar or nonpolar.
   a. SO_3^{2-}
   b. F_3PO
   c. PF_3
   d. $CH_3CH_2CH_2OH$

55. For each molecule or ion, draw the Lewis structure, determine the electron and molecular geometry using VSEPR theory, determine the bond

angles, and determine whether the molecule is polar.
a. NF_3
b. KF_4
c. TeF_4
d. CH_3OCH_3

56. For each molecule or ion, draw the Lewis structure, determine the electron and molecular geometry using VSEPR theory, state whether the molecule is polar, and list the bond angles, the hybridization around the central atoms, and the number of sigma and pi bonds in the structure.
a. OCl_2
b. H_2Se
c. CH_3SH

57. For each molecule or ion, draw the Lewis structure, determine the electron and molecular geometry using VSEPR theory, state whether the molecule is polar, and list the bond angles, the hybridization around the central atoms, and the number of sigma and pi bonds in the structure.
a. BCl_3
b. COF_2
c. CH_2CHCl

58. Add lone pairs of electrons as necessary to complete the octet of each atom in this structure. Determine the hybridization for each central atom and the number of sigma and pi bonds.

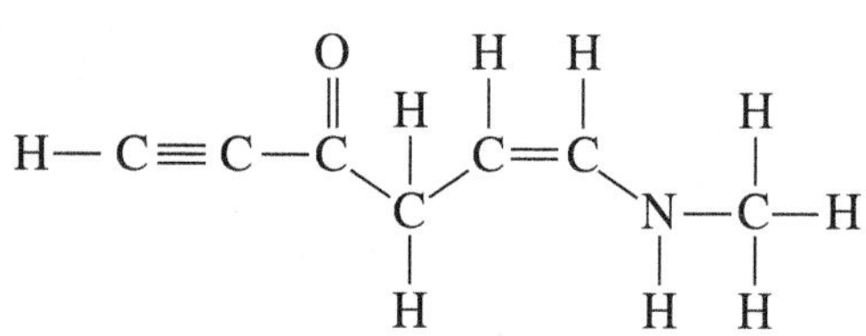

59. Add lone pairs of electrons as necessary to complete the octet of each atom in this structure. Determine the hybridization for each central atom and the number of sigma and pi bonds.

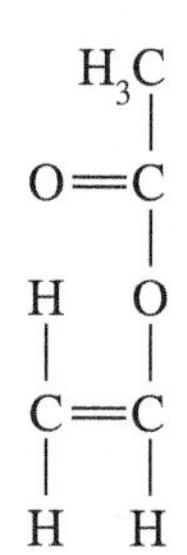

60. Add lone pairs of electrons as necessary to complete the octet of each atom in this structure. Determine the hybridization for each central atom and the number of sigma and pi bonds.

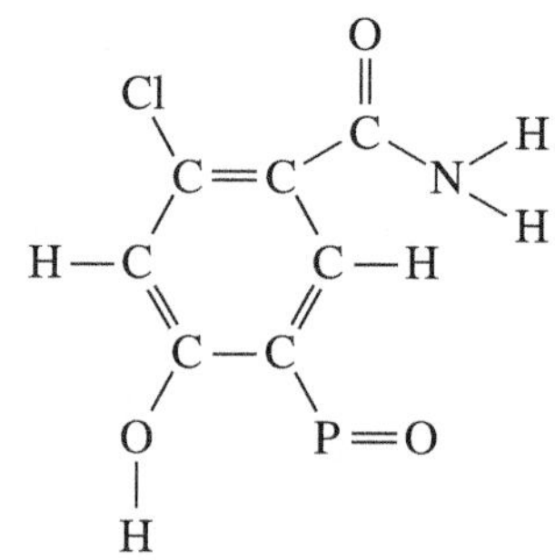

61. The symbol X represents the central atom, Y represents outer atoms, and Z represents lone pairs of electrons on the central atom. Determine the electron and molecular geometry of each of the generic molecules. Determine whether the molecule is polar, given that Y is more electronegative than X.
a. XY_5Z
b. XY_2
c. XY_2Z

62. The symbol X represents the central atom, Y represents outer atoms, and Z represents lone pairs of electrons on the central atom. Determine the electron and molecular geometry of each of the generic molecules. Determine whether the molecule is polar, given that Y is more electronegative than X.
a. XY_2Z_2
b. XY_4Z_2
c. XY_3

63. Draw the molecular orbital diagrams for NF^-, NF, and NF^+ (use the MO diagram for O_2), and use them to answer the following questions.
a. What is the molecular electron configuration for NF^-, NF, and NF^+?
b. Which ion or molecule is the most stable?
c. Are NF^-, NF, and NF^+ paramagnetic or diamagnetic?
d. Which ion or molecule has the longest bond? The shortest bond?

64. Draw the molecular orbital diagrams for CO, CO^+, and CO^{2+} (use the MO diagram for O_2), and use them to answer the following questions.
a. What is the molecular electron configuration for CO, CO^+, and CO^{2+}?
b. Which ion or molecule is the most stable?

c. Are CO, CO^+, and CO^{2+} paramagnetic or diamagnetic?
d. Which ion or molecule has the longest bond? The shortest bond?

65. The first excited state of N_2 has the electron configuration: $(\sigma_{2s})^2(\sigma^*_{2s})^2(\pi_{2p})^4(\sigma_{2p})^1(\pi^*_{2p})^1$
a. Determine the bond order of N_2 in the excited state and in the ground state.
b. Is N_2 diamagnetic or paramagnetic in the excited and ground state?
c. Is the bond in the excited state of N_2 weaker or stronger than the bond in the ground state of N_2?

66. Molecular orbital theory can be extended to the third row elements. The next orbitals, in order of increasing energy are: σ_{3s}, σ^*_{3s}, π_{3p}, σ_{3p}, π^*_{3p}, and σ^*_{3s}. Determine the bond order of a Na_2 molecule. Predict the stability of the molecule. Is the molecule paramagnetic or diamagnetic?

67. Molecular orbital theory can be extended to the third row elements. The next orbitals, in order of increasing energy are: σ_{3s}, σ^*_{3s}, π_{3p}, σ_{3p}, π^*_{3p}, and σ^*_{3s}. Determine the bond order of a Si_2 molecule. Predict the stability of the molecule. Is the molecule paramagnetic or diamagnetic?

68. A certain gaseous molecular compound is 22.0% S and 78.0% F and has an approximate molar mass of 146 g/mol. Are the molecules of this compound polar?

69. A certain gaseous molecular compound is 29.7% S and 70.3% F. A 50.0 g sample of this gas occupies 11.3 L at 1.00 atm and 298 K. Are the molecules of this compound polar?

70. Consider all the molecular geometries shown in Table 11.1.
a. Assuming all polar bonds, which molecular geometries are always polar?
b. Assuming all outer atoms are the same element, which molecular geometries are always nonpolar?
c. Which of the geometries from part (b) could still be nonpolar even if there were two different elements present in the outer atoms?

PRACTICE PROBLEM SOLUTIONS

Practice Problem 11.1 Solution

a. There are four bonded groups and no lone pairs around the central Si atom. The electron geometry and the molecular geometry are both tetrahedral. The bond angles are 109.5°.

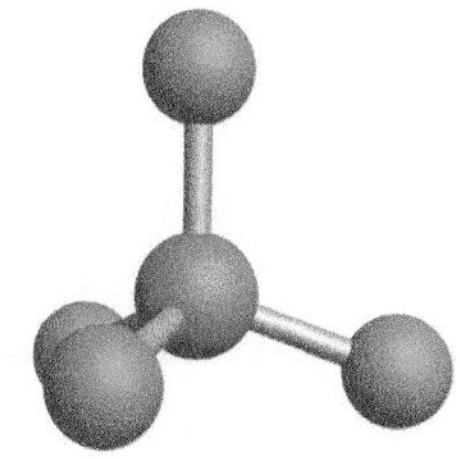

b. There are three bonded groups and no lone pairs around the central B atom. The electron geometry and the molecular geometry are both trigonal planar. The bond angles are 120°.

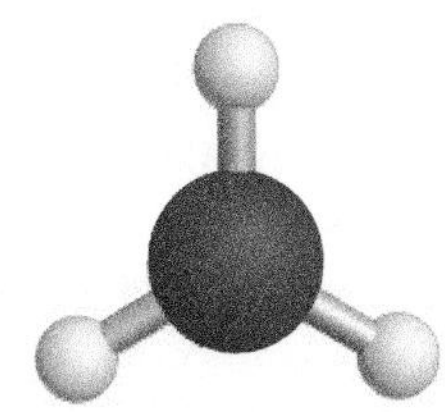

c. There are two bonded groups and a lone pair, for a total of three electron domains around the central S atom. The electron geometry is trigonal planar, and the molecular geometry is bent with bond angles that are slightly less than 120°.

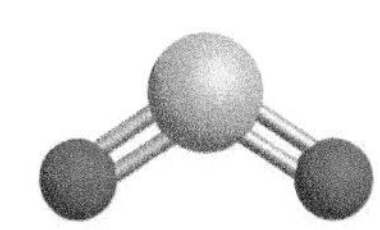

Practice Problem 11.2 Solution

The carbon atom on the right has four bonded groups and no lone pairs, making it tetrahedral. The other two carbon atoms have three electron domains each, all of which are bonded groups, so both are trigonal planar.

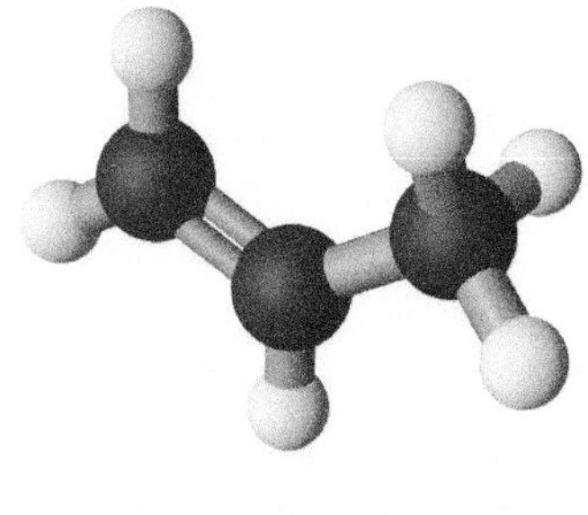

Practice Problem 11.3 Solution

a. The Lewis structure for $XeCl_4$ has four bonded groups and two lone pairs. Six electron domains indicate an octahedral electron geometry. The two lone pairs will occupy positions opposite each other, so the molecular geometry will be square planar.

b. The Lewis structure for SCl_4 has four bonded groups and one lone pair. Five electron domains indicate a trigonal bipyramidal electron geometry. The one lone pair will occupy an equatorial position, so the resulting molecular geometry is a see-saw.

c. The Lewis structure for ICl_4^- has four bonded groups and two lone pairs. Six electron domains indicate an octahedral electron geometry, and the two lone pair mean the molecular geometry will be square planar.

Practice Problem 11.4 Solution

a. Cl_2: A bond between two atoms of the same element is nonpolar ($\Delta EN = 0$), so this diatomic molecule is nonpolar.

b. NF_3: The molecule has trigonal pyramidal geometry, and the three N—F bonds are polar ($\Delta EN = 1.0$). The bond dipoles combine to form a molecular dipole. NF_3 is polar.

c. BrF: A bond between two atoms of different elements is usually polar ($\Delta EN = 1.2$ in this case), so this diatomic molecule is polar.

d. BCl_3: Each B—Cl bond is polar ($\Delta EN = 1.0$). BCl_3 has a trigonal planar molecular geometry, though, so the three bond dipoles cancel, forming a nonpolar molecule.

e. BeH_2: Both Be—H bonds are polar ($\Delta EN = 0.6$). BeH_2 is a linear molecule, however, so the two polar bonds cancel to form a nonpolar molecule.

Practice Problem 11.5 Solution

a. PCl_5 is a symmetrical molecule with a trigonal bipyramidal electron geometry. Although the P—Cl bonds are polar ($\Delta EN = 0.9$), the dipoles in the three equatorial bonds cancel each other (similar to the B—Cl bonds in BCl_3 in Practice Problem 11.4d), and the dipoles in the two axial bonds cancel each other (similar to the Be—H bonds in BeH_2 in Practice Problem 11.4e), so PCl_5 is nonpolar.

b. SF_4 is polar with a see-saw molecular geometry (four bonds and one lone pair). The positive end of the dipole is located on the S, whereas the negative end is located between the four F atoms.

Practice Problem 11.6 Solution

The Lewis structure shows that carbon has two bonded groups and no lone pairs. HCN, then, has a linear molecular geometry, and carbon must be *sp* hybridized, because *sp* hybrid orbitals are needed to make the linear shape possible. The C—H bond is a sigma bond, formed by the overlap of the 1*s* orbital on hydrogen with an *sp* hybrid orbital on carbon. The triple bond between C and N consists of one sigma bond and two pi bonds. The sigma bond is formed by the overlap of one of the *p* orbitals on nitrogen with the second *sp* hybrid orbital on carbon. Each pi bond results from the overlap of an unhybridized *p* orbital on carbon and another *p* orbital on nitrogen.

Practice Problem 11.7 Solution

All of the single bonds are sigma bonds, and all of the double bonds consist of one sigma bond and one pi bond. There are 17 sigma bonds and four pi bonds.

Practice Problem 11.8 Solution

Both molecules contain only C, H, and O. However, formaldehyde has a double bond, while methanol has only single bonds. The pi bond in formaldehyde most likely makes it more reactive than methanol.

Practice Problem 11.9 Solution

Populate the atomic orbitals with two and one electrons, respectively, and populate the molecular orbitals with the total of three electrons.

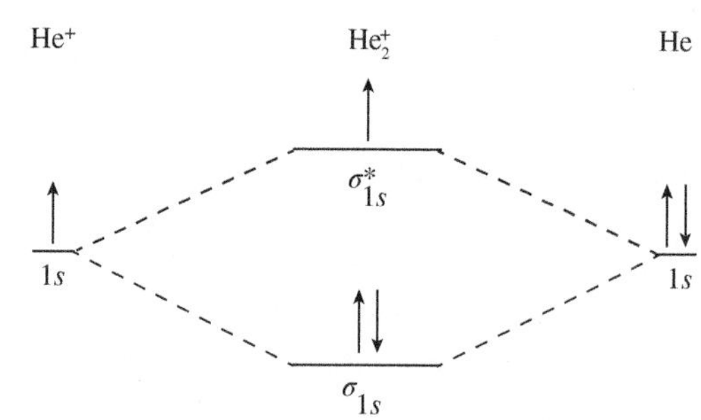

The MO electron configuration is $(\sigma_{1s})^2(\sigma_{1s}^*)^2$ and the bond order is $\frac{1}{2}(2 - 1) = 0.5$. Since this is a positive value for the bond order, He_2^+ should be more stable than He_2, which has a bond order of 0, but it is less stable than H_2, which has a bond order of 1.

Practice Problem 11.10 Solution

The superoxide ion has one more electron than the oxygen molecule. Simply adding an electron to the MO diagram for O_2 yields the MO diagram for O_2^-.

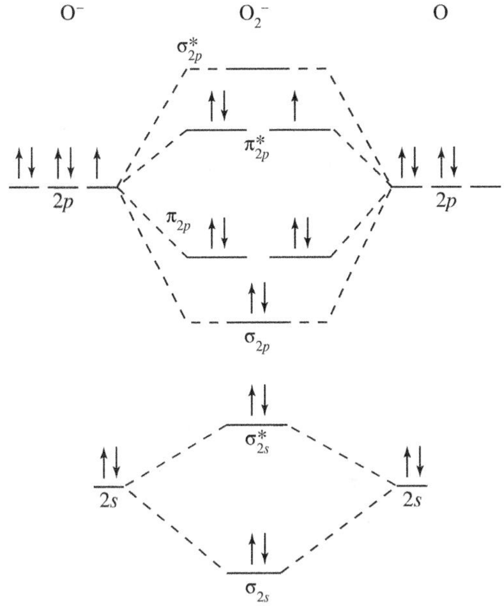

a. The MO electron configuration is $(\sigma_{2s})^2(\sigma_{1s}^*)^2$ $(\sigma_{2p})^2(\pi_{2p})^4(\pi_{2p})$ and antibonding $(\pi_{2p}^*)^3$.

b. The bond order for the superoxide ion is $\frac{1}{2}(8 - 5) = 1.5$, which is less than the bond order of 2 for oxygen and greater than the bond order of 1 for the peroxide ion. Superoxide is predicted to be stable but less stable than oxygen, making the expected bond enthalpy value for peroxide less than that of oxygen as well.

c. There is one unpaired electron in the superoxide ion, so it is paramagnetic.

d. A bond order of 1.5 indicates a longer, weaker bond in O_2^- than in O_2 but a shorter and stronger one than in O_2^{2-}.

Practice Problem 11.11 Solution

The Lewis structure should show a total of $2(7) + 2(6) = 26$ electrons. All outer atoms must have exactly an octet, and the central Cl atom must have at least an octet.

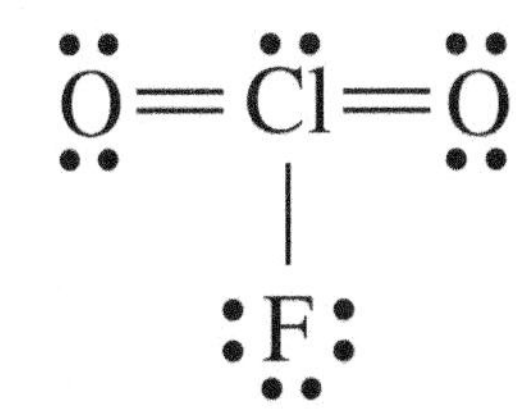

There are three bonded groups and one lone pair for a total of four domains and a tetrahedral electronic geometry. With one lone pair, the molecular geometry is trigonal pyramidal. With polar bonds and an asymmetric shape, the molecule is polar. Four electron domains means the central atom uses sp^3 hybrid orbitals.

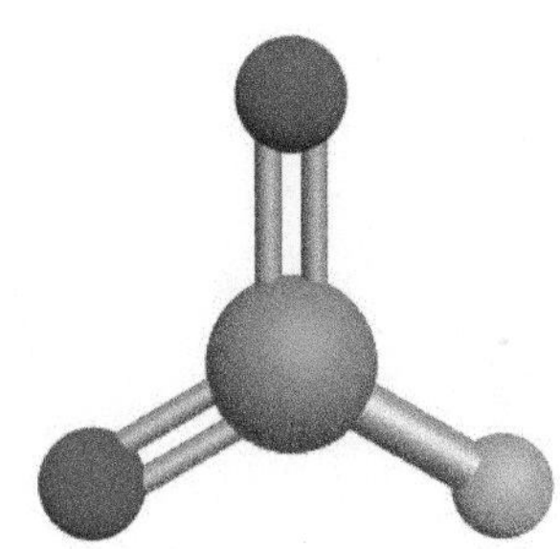

CHAPTER 12

Liquids and Solids

Dreef/Getty Images

The melting point of water occurs when the H_2O molecules in ice have enough kinetic energy to break from their hexagonal crystal structure, allowing them to flow as a liquid. When you can begin to visualize the world around you in terms of how the molecules are arranged and how they interact, you will be thinking like a chemist *and* you'll be able to make predictions about how substances behave under various conditions.

Chapter Outline

GOALS

- List and describe the four types of intermolecular forces.
- Distinguish intermolecular forces from chemical bonds.
- Identify the predominant intermolecular force for specific substances.
- Define and describe the basic properties of liquids (viscosity, surface tension, capillary action).
- Relate each of the basic properties of liquids to intermolecular forces.
- List and define terms related to phase changes.
- Identify the sign of the enthalpy change for each phase change.
- Calculate energy changes related to phase changes.
- Interpret heating curves.
- Describe and explain the relationship between temperature and vapor pressure.
- Predict relative vapor pressures based on intermolecular forces.
- Calculate the enthalpy of vaporization from vapor pressure and temperature data using the Clausius–Clapeyron equation.
- Calculate the vapor pressure at various temperatures using the Clausius–Clapeyron equation.
- Define, describe, and interpret phase diagrams.
- Predict phase changes from changes in temperature and/or pressure using phase diagrams.
- Define and describe the various types of solids.
- Classify solids based on their chemical formulas.
- Describe relative trends in physical properties based on the type of solid.
- Describe the structure of various cubic unit cells.
- Perform calculations involving the number of atoms per unit cell as a conversion factor.

12.1 Intermolecular Forces

GOALS

- List and describe the four types of intermolecular forces.
- Distinguish intermolecular forces from chemical bonds.
- Identify the predominant intermolecular force for specific substances.

Background Review

Chapter 7 Gases: Section 7.10—Kinetic Molecular Theory of Gases

Chapter 9 Periodicity and Ionic Bonding: Section 9.2—Atomic and Ionic Sizes

Chapter 11 Molecular Shape and Bonding Theories: Section 11.2—Polar and Nonpolar Molecules

One of the postulates of kinetic molecular theory (Section 7.10) is that the attractive forces between molecules in a gas are negligible. This explains why gases expand in every direction when their containers are opened: The particles are moving in random directions, and there is no force holding them together. The particles in solids and liquids, however, do *not* spread out in every direction. Solid and liquid samples have definite volumes, which means that there must be an attractive force of some kind holding the particles in a liquid or solid together. This section focuses on the temporary attractive forces that form between particles in the liquid and solid phases.

These temporary attractive forces are generally known as **intermolecular forces**, even though these forces can be applied to particles such as atoms and ions. Intermolecular forces are weak electrostatic interactions that are temporary in nature. Just as the ionic bonds and covalent bonds within a compound that hold the compound together internally are based on electrical charges, the intermolecular forces between particles are also based on electrical charges. However, intermolecular forces between molecules are *much weaker* than the covalent bonds that hold atoms together in molecules or the ionic bonds that hold ions together in ionic compounds.

Molecules of methanol CH_4O, shown in Figure 12.1, illustrate the difference between chemical bonds and intermolecular forces. Within each molecule, the atoms

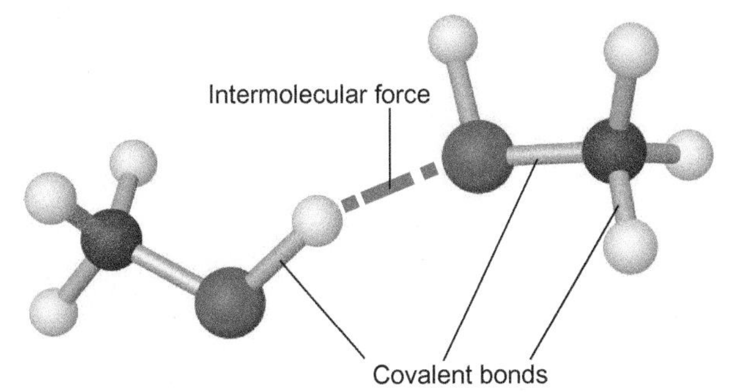

FIGURE 12.1 Covalent Bonds versus Intermolecular Forces

Covalent bonds hold atoms together within molecules, whereas intermolecular forces are weaker attractions between neighboring molecules.

are held together by covalent bonds. There is also a weak, temporary, intermolecular force (the dashed line) where areas of higher electron density are attracted to areas of lower electron density. Intermolecular forces are not permanent "bonds" in the same sense that covalent bonds are. The methanol molecules are still free to move about, continually breaking existing intermolecular attractions and forming new ones, but, nonetheless, the intermolecular forces influence their movements and their chemical and physical properties. For example, the boiling point of a liquid increases with the strength of its intermolecular forces because stronger intermolecular attractions make it more difficult (require more energy) for the molecules to escape into the vapor phase.

The different types of intermolecular forces described in this section are attractions between ions and polar molecules (called *ion–dipole attractions*), attractions between two polar molecules (called *dipole–dipole attractions*), a particularly strong type of dipole–dipole attraction involving hydrogen (called *hydrogen bonding*), and attractions between two nonpolar molecules (called *dispersion forces*). You will use intermolecular forces in this and later sections to help explain how some substances dissolve in water and why other substances are insoluble in water. In addition, you can use intermolecular forces to explain the periodic trends in melting points and boiling points, and many of the unique properties of water.

ION–DIPOLE ATTRACTIONS

Polar molecules have partial positive and partial negative charges at separate locations within the molecule (Section 10.5), and ionic compounds dissolve in water to form *hydrated ions* (Section 4.3). What is the relationship between these two facts? The cations and anions of the ionic compound form electrostatic attractions with the polar water molecules, as shown in Figure 12.2. These attractive forces are a type of intermolecular force known as **ion–dipole attractions**. Ion–dipole attractions are the strongest of the temporary attractions that form between particles.

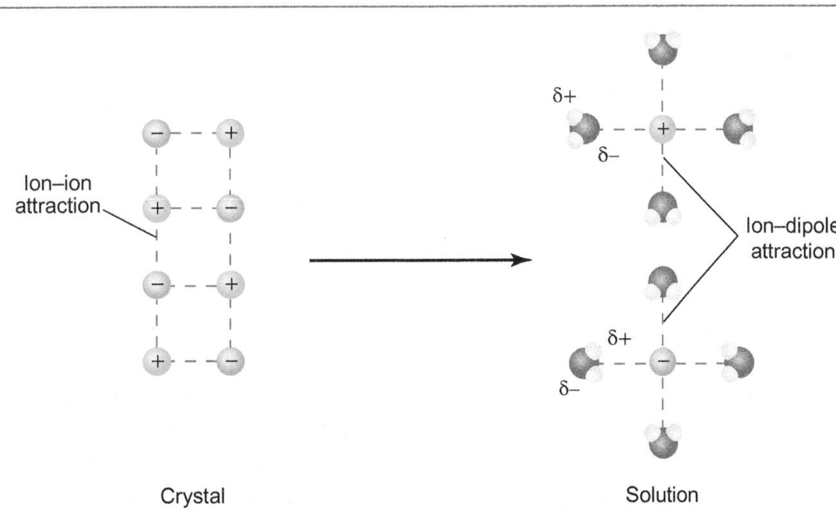

FIGURE 12.2 Ions Form Ion–Dipole Attractions on Dissolution

Ionic compounds like the crystal shown here dissociate into separate ions and dissolve into solutions when they form ion–dipole attractions with polar solvents. When the solvent is water, as in this example, the ions are said to be hydrated.

Example 12.1

Predict whether any of the following pairs of compounds can form ion–dipole attractions.

a. H_2O and CO_2
b. NaCl and H_2O
c. NaCl and CO_2

Solution

Ion–dipole attractions form between ions and polar molecules. A compound is ionic if it contains a metal and a nonmetal or a metal and a polyatomic ion. A molecule is polar if it has polar bonds that are arranged asymmetrically (Section 11.2).

a. H_2O and CO_2: Water is polar, but carbon dioxide is nonpolar. Without any ions present, ion–dipole attractions are not possible.
b. NaCl and H_2O: Sodium chloride is ionic, and water is polar, so ion–dipole attractions are possible.

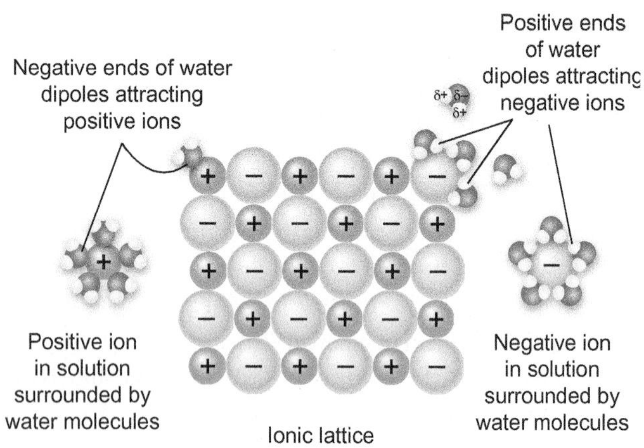

c. NaCl and CO_2: Sodium chloride is ionic, but carbon dioxide is nonpolar. Ion–dipole attractions are not possible without a polar compound.

PRACTICE PROBLEM 12.1

Predict whether any of the following pairs of compounds can form ion–dipole attractions.

a. KBr and NH_3
b. NH_3 and Cl_2
c. KBr and Cl_2

Hint: Ion–dipole attractions form between ions and polar molecules. A compound is ionic if it contains a metal and a nonmetal. A molecule is polar if it has polar bonds that are arranged asymmetrically (Section 11.2).

DIPOLE–DIPOLE ATTRACTIONS

Polar molecules interact with other polar molecules as shown in Figure 12.1 and in more detail in Figure 12.3. The negative pole of one polar molecule is attracted to the positive pole of another polar molecule. These attractions are a type of intermolecular force known as **dipole–dipole attractions**.

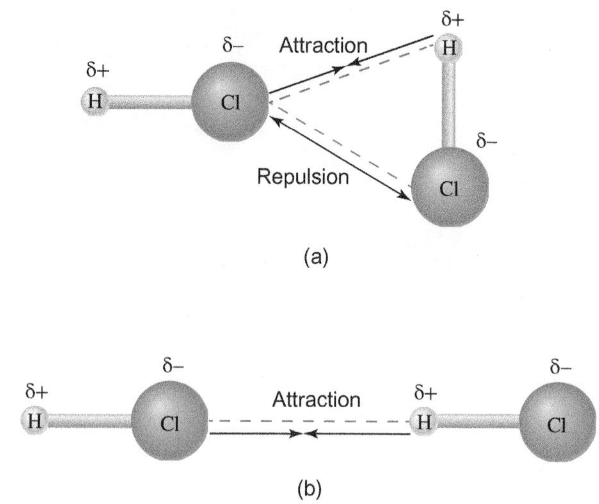

FIGURE 12.3 Orientation of Dipoles in Polar Molecules
The solid lines represent covalent bonds, whereas the dashed lines represent intermolecular forces. (a) The oppositely charged ends of polar molecules attract, whereas the like-charged ends repel. (b) The molecules in a polar substance are oriented to maximize the attractive interactions and minimize the repulsive interactions.

Example 12.2

Predict whether either of the following compounds can form dipole–dipole attractions between their molecules.

a. CH_2O
b. CCl_4

Solution

Dipole–dipole attractions form between polar molecules. You can identify a molecule as polar if it has polar bonds that are arranged asymmetrically (Section 11.2).

a. CH_2O: Formaldehyde has a trigonal planar shape and a polar C=O bond, making the overall molecule polar. CH_2O molecules can form dipole–dipole attractions with each other.
b. CCl_4: Carbon tetrachloride has a tetrahedral shape and polar C—Cl bonds. The symmetry of the molecule causes the bond dipoles to cancel, however, making CCl_4 nonpolar and incapable of forming dipole–dipole attractions.

PRACTICE PROBLEM 12.2

Predict whether either of the following compounds can form dipole–dipole attractions between their molecules.

a. CH_2Cl_2
b. Br_2

Hint: Dipole–dipole attractions form between polar molecules. A molecule is polar if it has polar bonds that are arranged asymmetrically (Section 11.2).

HYDROGEN BONDS

A **hydrogen bond** is a special case of dipole–dipole attraction and is stronger than other dipole–dipole attractions. The name *hydrogen bond* is somewhat misleading; like all other dipole–dipole attractions, hydrogen bonds are a type of intermolecular force between molecules, not a covalent bond between atoms within a molecule. Hydrogen bonds require specific conditions to exist—namely, hydrogen bonding occurs only when a hydrogen, H, atom that is bonded to nitrogen, N, oxygen, O, or fluorine, F, is attracted to the unshared electron pairs of an N, O, or F atom in an adjacent molecule. The molecule with the H—N, H—O, or H—F bond is called the **hydrogen bond donor**, and the molecule with the lone pair on N, O, or F is called the **hydrogen bond acceptor**.

Hydrogen fluoride, HF, exhibits very strong hydrogen bonding (Figure 12.4). The large electronegativity difference between H and F ($\Delta EN = 1.9$) indicates a strongly polar covalent bond. The partially positive H atom in one molecule is attracted to the unshared electron pair of the F atom on an adjacent HF molecule.

The conditions required for hydrogen bond formation are met in a wide variety of compounds, including water and ammonia (Figure 12.5), alcohols, organic acids, and biological molecules that contain O or N, such as amino acids and proteins.

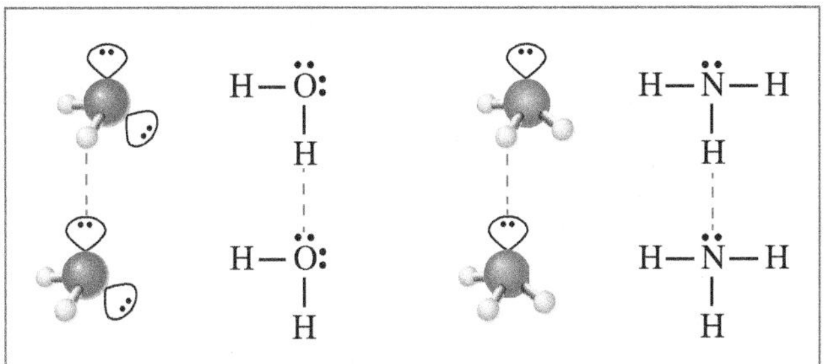

FIGURE 12.5 Hydrogen Bonding in Water and Ammonia

(a) Water and (b) ammonia can form hydrogen bonds (dashed lines) between molecules. Hydrogen bonds are especially strong dipole–dipole attractions between a partially positive H atom on one molecule and a lone pair of electrons on a partially negative O, N, or F of another molecule.

Example 12.3

Which of the following substances can form hydrogen bonds to other identical molecules?

a. HF
b. C_2H_4
c. HBr
d. NH_4^+
e. H_2

Solution

Hydrogen bonding occurs when one molecule contains an H atom bonded to N, O, or F (the hydrogen bond donor), and another molecule contains an N, O, or F atom with a lone pair of electrons (the hydrogen bond acceptor). Draw Lewis structures to determine if the molecules meet these requirements.

a. The Lewis structure of HF is

H—F:

HF is both a hydrogen bond donor (it has an H—F bond) and a hydrogen bond acceptor (the F atom has a lone pair of electrons). Therefore, HF molecules can form hydrogen bonds to other HF molecules.

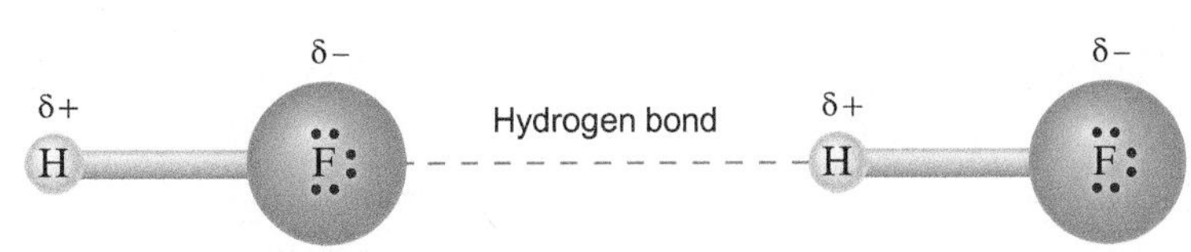

FIGURE 12.4 Hydrogen Bonding in Hydrogen Fluoride

The solids lines represent covalent bonds between H and F. The dashed line represents a hydrogen bond between the H atom of one molecule and a lone pair on the F atom of an adjacent molecule. Notice that the positive pole of one molecule is attracted to the negative pole of the next molecule, just as with dipole–dipole attractions.

b. C_2H_4 does not contain F, O, or N, so it is neither a hydrogen bond donor nor a hydrogen bond acceptor, and it is incapable of forming hydrogen bonds.
c. HBr does not contain F, O, or N, so it is neither a hydrogen bond donor nor a hydrogen bond acceptor, and it is incapable of forming hydrogen bonds. HBr is polar, however, so it will form lower-strength dipole–dipole attractions.
d. The Lewis structure of NH_4^+ is

$$\left[\begin{array}{c} \mathrm{H} \\ | \\ \mathrm{H{-}N{-}H} \\ | \\ \mathrm{H} \end{array}\right]^+$$

NH_4^+ contains H—N bonds and is therefore a hydrogen bond donor. The N has no lone-pair electrons, however, so it cannot accept hydrogen bonds. Therefore, NH_4^+ cannot form hydrogen bonds to other NH_4^+ particles, but it can form hydrogen bonds to a molecule that does have available lone pairs on F, O, or N, such as H_2O.
e. The Lewis structure of H_2 is

H—H

The covalent bond in H_2 is a nonpolar covalent bond. It is neither a hydrogen bond donor nor a hydrogen bond acceptor, so it is incapable of forming hydrogen bonds.

PRACTICE PROBLEM 12.3

Which of the following substances are expected to form hydrogen bonds?

a. H_2O
b. CH_2O
c. CH_3OH
d. NH_3

Hint: Hydrogen bond donors must contain an H atom bonded to F, O, or N. Hydrogen bond acceptors must contain an F, O, or N atom with available lone-pair electrons. Draw Lewis structures to determine if the molecules meet the requirements.

Example 12.4

In which of the following does the dashed line depict a hydrogen bond? Choose all that apply.

a. H—F:- - - - - - - - -H—Cl:
b. H—Cl:- - - - - - - - -H—F:
c. H—F:- - - - - - - - -H—H
d. H—F:- - - - - - - - -H—F:

Solution

Only choice (d) shows a hydrogen bond. One side of the bond must be an H atom that is covalently bonded to N, O, or F (choices (b) and (d) have this), and the other side of the bond must be an N, O, or F atom with a lone pair (choices (a), (c), and (d) have this). Choice (d) is the only one that meets both criteria.

PRACTICE PROBLEM 12.4

In which of the following does the dashed line depict a hydrogen bond? Choose all that apply.

a. H—C≡N:- - - - - - -H—F:
b. H—H- - - - - - - - -:NH_3
c. :F—H- - - - - - - - -:NH_3
d. H—H- - - - - - - - -H—H

Hint: One side of the bond must be an H atom that is covalently bonded to N, O, or F, and the other side of the bond must be an N, O, or F atom with a lone pair.

Hydrogen bonding is responsible for the low density of ice compared with liquid water (Figure 12.6). This difference is necessary for life. Because ice is less dense than water, it floats on top of water and acts as a blanket to protect the aquatic life below from the extremes of cold that occur above the ice. If it is pure, the water at the bottom never gets below 0°C (32°F), unless it freezes. Hydrogen bonding is also responsible for the helical structure of DNA and the shapes of certain proteins

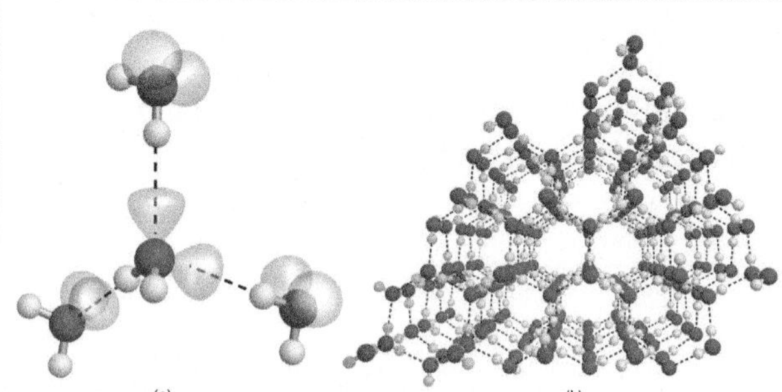

FIGURE 12.6 Hydrogen Bonding in Ice
Hydrogen bonding (a) forces a hexagonal orientation (b) of water molecules as they freeze, which pushes the water molecules apart slightly, making ice slightly less dense than liquid water.

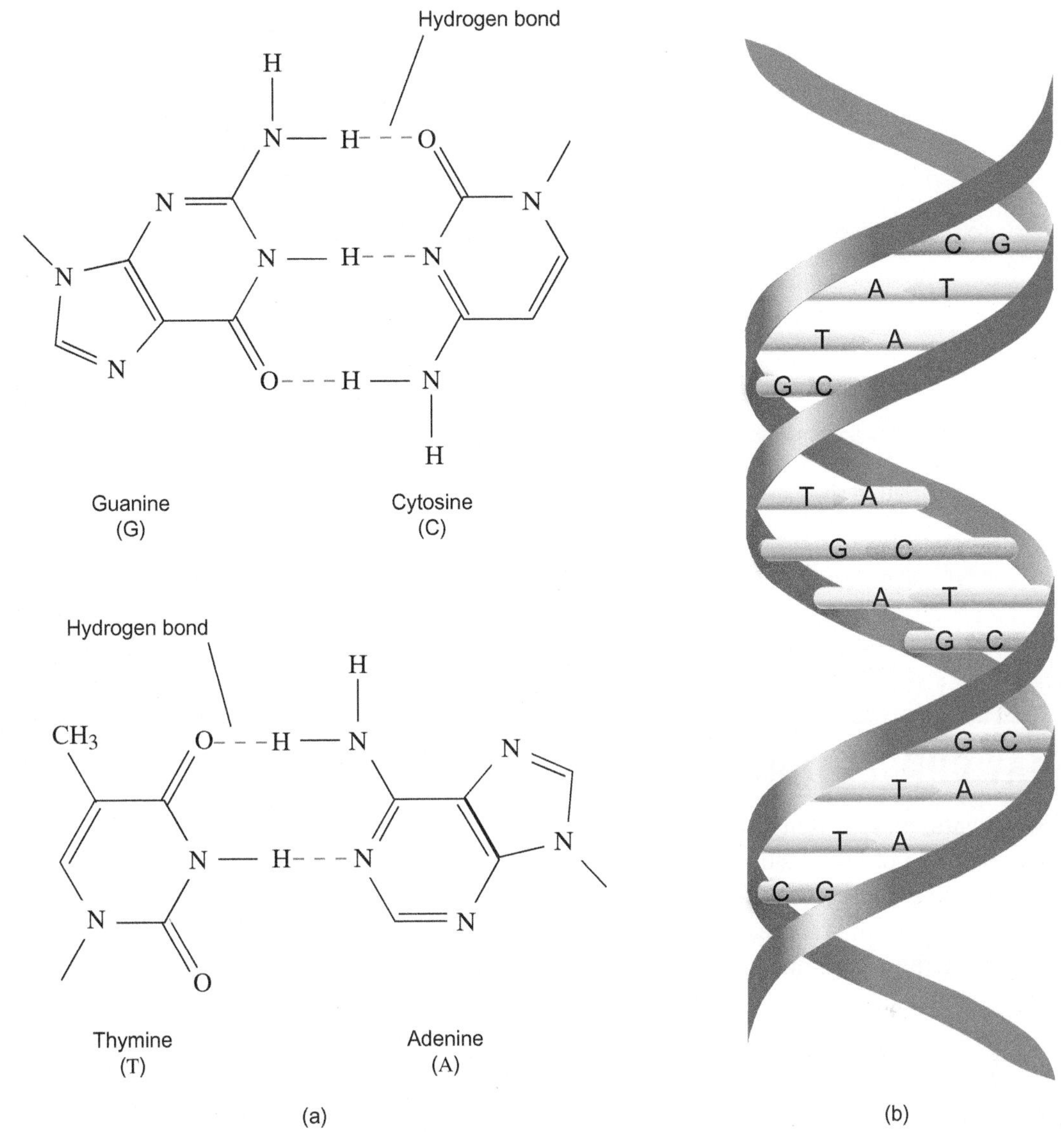

FIGURE 12.7 Hydrogen Bonding in the DNA Double Helix

Hydrogen bonding occurs in DNA. (a) You can interpret these structures as having a carbon, C, atom at each intersection or end of a line, unless a different element is indicated. (b) Thymine, T, adenine, A, guanine, G, and cytosine, C, are represented by their initials in the double helix.

and other large biomolecules in plants and animals (Figure 12.7).

DISPERSION FORCES

The electrons surrounding atoms are in constant random motion. Because of this, a molecule with no permanent dipole, or the electrons surrounding individual atoms, may have an asymmetric distribution of electrons for just an instant, forming an **instantaneous dipole**. In that instant, the asymmetric charge distribution tends to induce a similar charge asymmetry, or **induced dipole**, in an adjacent molecule. The resulting short-lived attractions between instantaneous dipoles and induced dipoles are referred to **dispersion forces** (Figure 12.8). Dispersion forces are also referred to as London forces or London dispersion forces. Because this instantaneous dipole–induced dipole attraction may last for only an instant, this type of intermolecular force is weaker than dipole–dipole

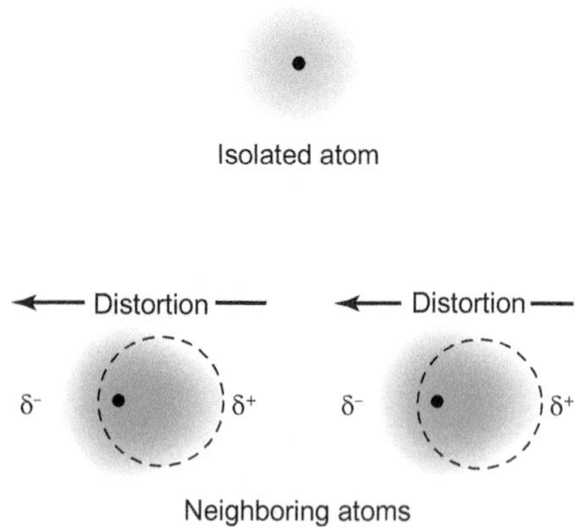

FIGURE 12.8 Dispersion Forces are Instantaneous Dipole–Induced Dipole Attractions

Fluctuations in electron density in an atom or molecule form instantaneous dipoles that can trigger the formation of an induced dipole in a nearby atom or molecule, leading to weak and very short-lived attractions known as dispersion forces.

EVERYDAY CONNECTION

Because solid water is less dense than liquid water, ice forms on top of lakes and ponds, insulating the water below and preventing lakes and ponds from freezing solid. As a result, aquatic wildlife can survive the winter and hardy people can catch fish year-round.

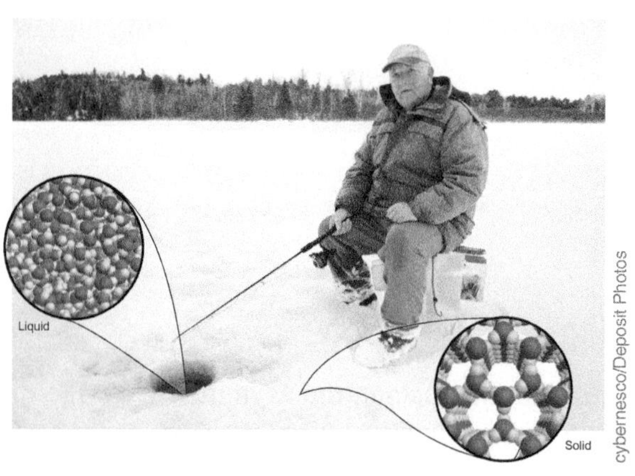

attractions. All atoms and molecules exhibit dispersion forces, so these forces are especially important for understanding the physical properties of *nonpolar* substances.

The strength of the dispersion force depends on several factors. One factor is how readily the electron cloud of the atom in question becomes asymmetric, or its **polarizability**. Larger atoms, whose outer electrons are more weakly attracted to the nucleus, polarize more readily than do smaller atoms, whose outer electrons are both closer to the nucleus and less shielded by core electrons (Section 9.2). The halogens, which as diatomic elements form nonpolar molecules, are good examples of this. Atomic radius increases as you move down a group of the periodic table (Section 9.2), so polarizability increases, too. The smaller halogens, fluorine, F, and chlorine, Cl, being less polarizable, form weaker dispersion forces and are gases at room temperature. Bromine, Br, is larger and more polarizable, so Br_2 is capable of forming stronger dispersion forces than are F_2 and Cl_2. Br_2 is a liquid at room temperature, although it vaporizes readily, indicating that its dispersion forces are just barely strong enough to hold the molecules together in a liquid. Iodine, I, is the largest of the halogen molecules, so it is quite polarizable, and I_2 forms dispersion forces strong enough to be a solid at room temperature. I_2 readily sublimes (i.e., goes directly from the solid state to the gaseous state), however, so its dispersion forces are just barely strong enough to hold the molecules together in a solid (Table 12.1).

A second factor that affects the strength of dispersion forces involves the number of electrons that can be polarized. Compounds that contain many atoms have a greater number of polarizable electrons and therefore have more opportunities to form instantaneous dipoles than do compounds with fewer atoms. Molecules that can form more instantaneous dipoles at one time are able to form stronger dispersion forces to one another. The unbranched alkanes, a family of compounds containing C and H atoms connected in long chains, are an example of this. Figure 12.9 shows the boiling points of several unbranched alkanes plotted versus their numbers of C atoms. Boiling point is a reasonable measure of the strength of the intermolecular forces because molecules must overcome their intermolecular forces to escape into the vapor phase.

A third factor is shape. Molecules that have shapes that allow them to interact with nearby molecules form stronger dispersion forces than do molecules whose shapes do not support this attraction. You can use Figure 12.10 to compare the boiling points of unbranched alkanes with branched alkanes containing

TABLE 12.1 Atomic Size and Polarizability

Halogen	Atomic Radius (pm)	Boiling Point (K)	Diagram
Fluorine, F_2	60	85	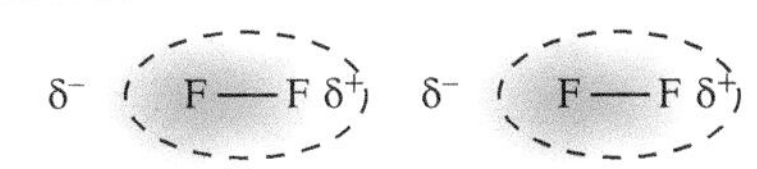
Chlorine, Cl_2	100	239	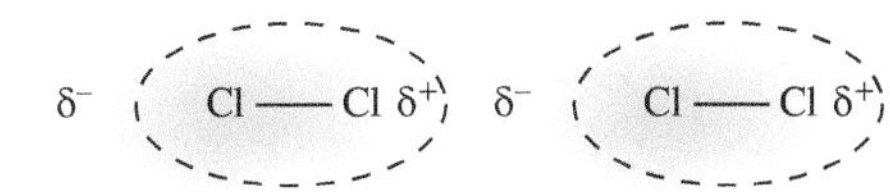
Bromine, Br_2	117	332	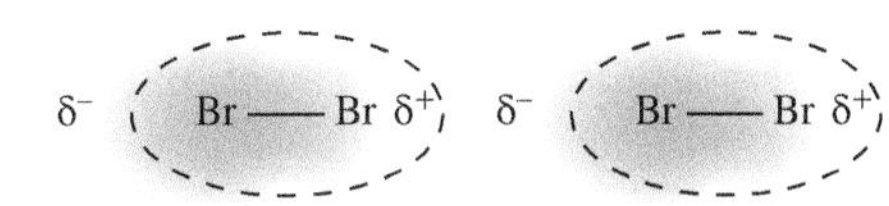
Iodine, I_2	136	457	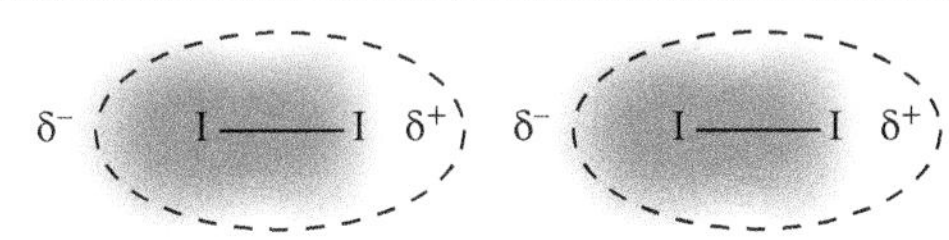

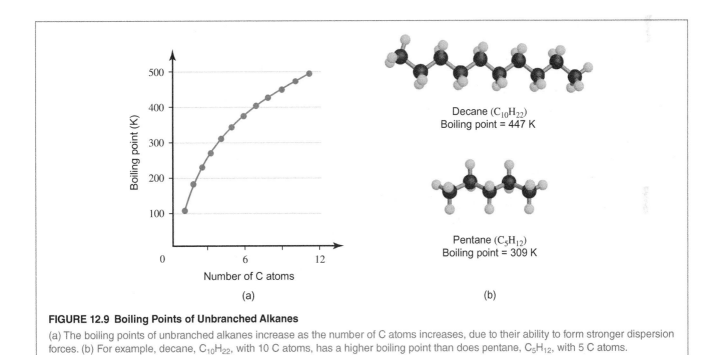

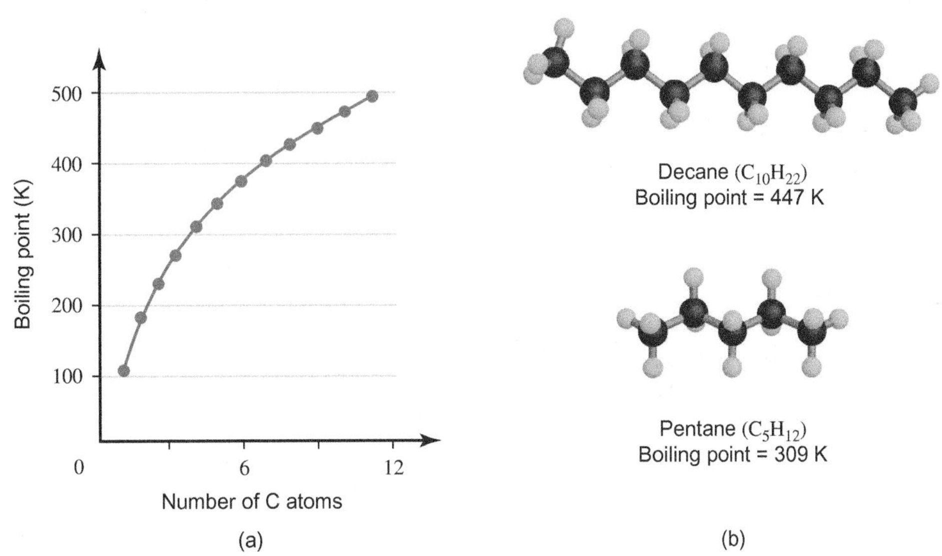

FIGURE 12.9 Boiling Points of Unbranched Alkanes

(a) The boiling points of unbranched alkanes increase as the number of C atoms increases, due to their ability to form stronger dispersion forces. (b) For example, decane, $C_{10}H_{22}$, with 10 C atoms, has a higher boiling point than does pentane, C_5H_{12}, with 5 C atoms.

the same number of C atoms. Compounds that have overall linear shapes tend to be able to form stronger dispersion forces than do those that have bulky shapes.

Boiling (or melting or sublimation) cannot occur without breaking intermolecular forces (not bonds). As an intermolecular force increases, therefore, so does the melting point, the boiling point, and the sublimation point of the substance, and more energy is required to melt, vaporize, and sublimate the substance.

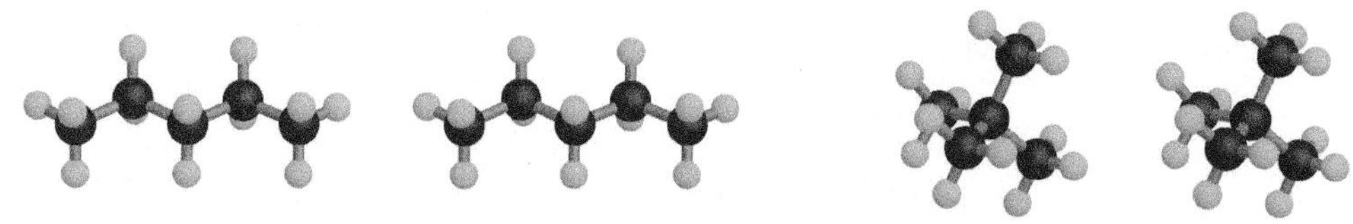

Pentane (C_5H_{12})
Boiling point = 36°C
Density = 0.626 g/mL

(a)

2,2-Dimethylpropane (C_5H_{12})
Boiling point = 10°C
Density = 0.585 g/mL

(b)

FIGURE 12.10 Comparing Shapes and Boiling Points of Three C_5H_{12} Compounds
(a) *n*-Pentane, in which all the C atoms are bonded in a chain, has a higher boiling point than does (b) 2,2-dimethylpropane, a more highly branched compound. This trend in boiling points indicates that the unbranched compounds have stronger dispersion forces than do branched compounds with a similar number of atoms.

Example 12.5

Which substance—C_2H_6 or C_8H_{18}—is expected to have the stronger dispersion forces?

Solution

The larger molecule, C_8H_{18}, has more bonds that can form instantaneous dipoles, so it should have stronger dispersion forces than does C_2H_6.

PRACTICE PROBLEM 12.5

Which substance—F_2, Cl_2, O_2, H_2, or N_2—would be expected to exhibit the weakest dispersion forces, and which would exhibit the strongest?

Hint: The three factors that affect the strength of dispersion forces are polarizability, the number of bonds, and molecular shape.

Example 12.6

Which substance—C_2H_6 or C_8H_{18}—will boil at the highest temperature at 1 atm pressure?

Solution

For a substance to boil, its intermolecular forces must be overcome. Thus, stronger intermolecular forces are associated with higher boiling points. In Example 12.5, you learned that the larger of the two compounds, C_8H_{18}, has stronger dispersion forces than does the smaller compound, C_4H_{10}. C_8H_{18}, therefore, has the higher boiling point.

PRACTICE PROBLEM 12.6

Which substance—Cl_2, F_2, O_2, N_2, or H_2—will boil at the highest temperature at 1 atm pressure?

Hint: Stronger intermolecular forces are associated with higher boiling points. Refer to Practice Problem 12.5 for information about the intermolecular forces of these substances.

All the forces of attraction discussed so far are summarized in Table 12.2. In other sources, you may encounter the term **van der Waals forces**, which is often used as a general term for any type of intermolecular force but is sometimes used as a synonym for dispersion forces.

For large molecules, dispersion forces can be extremely strong, making it tricky to rank their strength relative to other intermolecular forces. For small mol-

TABLE 12.2 Types of Intermolecular Forces from Strongest to Weakest

Intermolecular Force	Present in	Example(s)
Ion–dipole	Mixtures of ionic and polar covalent compounds	Salt water (NaCl dissolved in H_2O)
Hydrogen bonding	Substances containing both hydrogen bond donors (molecules with H bonded to N, O, or F) and hydrogen bond acceptors (molecules with a lone pair on N, O, or F)	H_2O
Dipole–dipole	Substances with polar molecules	H_2O, HCl
Dispersion	All molecular substances	H_2O, HCl, Cl_2

Steve Lemon, Macmillan Learning

FIGURE 12.11 Video Tutorial: Intermolecular Forces in Pure Substances

NOTE: You need to be online to access this video.
This video shows how to identify intermolecular forces based on molecular formula.

ecules, though, the relative strength of intermolecular forces follows the predictable order shown in Table 12.2, with ion–dipole being the strongest and dispersion being the weakest.

Ion–dipole forces can only occur in a mixture (i.e., an ionic substance mixed with a polar molecular substance). The other three types of intermolecular forces can occur in either a mixture or a pure substance.

The video in Figure 12.11 demonstrates how to identify all the intermolecular forces within a pure substance.

For a substance that exhibits multiple types of intermolecular forces, its predominant intermolecular force is the strongest one.

Example 12.7

Identify all of the intermolecular forces in (a) PCl_3 and (b) CH_3F, and specify which one predominates.

Solution

All substances can form dispersion forces, but they are only important for nonpolar substances. Determine if each substance is polar or nonpolar. If it is polar, determine whether it can form hydrogen bonds.

a. PCl_3: The Lewis structure is

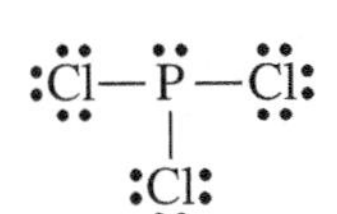

PCl_3 is a molecular substance, so it has dispersion forces. $\Delta EN = 1.0$ for the P—Cl bond, so each P—Cl bond is polar. Moreover, PCl_3 has a trigonal pyramidal shape, so the bond dipoles do not cancel. PCl_3 is a polar molecule, so it has dipole–dipole forces, but it does not meet the requirements for hydrogen bonding. Dipole–dipole forces are stronger than dispersion forces in small molecules, so the predominant intermolecular force in PCl_3 is the dipole–dipole force.

b. CH_3F: The Lewis structure is

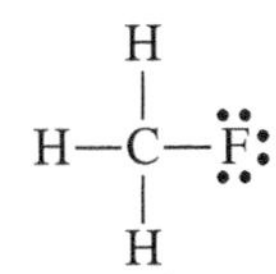

CH_3F is a molecular substance, so it has dispersion forces. The C—F bond is polar, and it is arranged asymmetrically with the marginally polar C—H bonds. CH_3F, then, is polar overall, so it has dipole–dipole forces. CH_3F has a lone pair on an F atom, making it a hydrogen bond acceptor, but it lacks an H—F bond, so it is *not* a hydrogen bond donor, in which case pure CH_3F does not form hydrogen bonds. CH_3F exhibits both dispersion and dipole–dipole forces, with the predominant intermolecular force being the dipole–dipole force.

PRACTICE PROBLEM 12.7

Identify all of the intermolecular forces in (a) CH_3OH and (b) CBr_4, and specify which one predominates.

Hint: All substances can form dispersion forces, but they are only important for nonpolar substances. Determine whether each substance is polar or nonpolar. If it is polar, determine whether it can form hydrogen bonds.

SECTION REVIEW

- Attractive forces—called intermolecular forces—exist between ions and molecules in the liquid and solid state. These attractive forces are weak and temporary, which distinguishes them from ionic and covalent bonds.
- Intermolecular forces are all based on weak, temporary electrical attractions between ions and molecules.
- When ionic compounds dissolve in water or other polar solvents, the ions and the polar molecules interact to form ion–dipole forces, the strongest of the intermolecular forces.
- Polar molecules contain partially positive and partially negative regions, forming dipoles. Oppositely charged ends of neighboring dipoles interact to form dipole–dipole attractions.

- Unusually strong dipole–dipole attractions, known as hydrogen bonds, form between hydrogen bond donors and hydrogen bond acceptors. Hydrogen bond donor molecules contain an H atom bonded to F, O, or N (which makes the H atom strongly partially positive), and hydrogen bond acceptor molecules have an available lone pair on a highly electronegative F, O, or N atom. The hydrogen bond forms between the H atom on the donor and the lone pair of electrons on the acceptor. Some molecules, such as water, can be both hydrogen bond donors and acceptors.
- In nonpolar molecules, momentary asymmetry in the distribution of electrons around the molecule causes weak dipoles to form briefly. These instantaneous dipoles can cause the formation of temporary dipoles in adjacent molecules, resulting in short-lived dipole-induced dipole attractions known as dispersion forces.
- For small molecules, the relative strength of the intermolecular forces are as follows: ion–dipole > hydrogen bonding > dipole–dipole > dispersion.
- Within a pure substance, the only possible types of intermolecular forces are hydrogen bonding, dipole–dipole, and dispersion.
- If a substance exhibits more than one type of intermolecular forces, the strongest one predominates.
- The strength of the intermolecular forces acting between molecules of a substance influences its melting point and boiling point. Both the melting point and the boiling point increase as the intermolecular forces increase.

12.2 Properties of Liquids

GOALS

- Define and describe the basic properties of liquids (viscosity, surface tension, capillary action).
- Relate each of the basic properties of liquids to intermolecular forces.

Background Review

Chapter 7 Gases: Section 7.1—Gas Pressure

The basic differences between the three states of matter are discussed in Section 7.1. To summarize, the molecules of a liquid are in contact with one another, but they are not as close together as are the particles in solids (with the exception of water). The particles of a liquid are in constant motion, but they do not move as quickly or as freely as the particles of a gas. Particles of a liquid interact via intermolecular forces, but those forces are weak and temporary, allowing the liquid particles to slip and slide past one another as fluids, and giving liquids properties such as viscosity, surface tension, and capillary action.

VISCOSITY

Although liquids flow, not all liquids flow with the same ease. Water flows more readily than does honey, for example, so honey has a higher **viscosity** than does water. Viscosity, the resistance to flow, is determined by the strength of the intermolecular attractions and, to a lesser extent, the length of the molecule. Substances with strong intermolecular forces are more viscous than are substances with weaker intermolecular forces. Gasoline, a nonpolar substance with only dispersion forces, flows more readily than does water, a polar substance that forms hydrogen bonds. Temperature also affects the viscosity of a given liquid. As temperature increases, the corresponding increase in kinetic energy overcomes some of the intermolecular attractions. This decreases the overall viscosity of the liquid and allows the liquid to flow more freely.

Example 12.8

Based on the Lewis structures of water and hydrogen peroxide, which do you think has a higher viscosity at room temperature?

Water Hydrogen peroxide

Solution

Viscosity depends on the strength of the intermolecular forces and the temperature. Temperature can be ignored in this case, however, because it is the same for both substances. The difference in the viscosities will depend on the relative strengths of the intermolecular forces.

Water is both a hydrogen bond donor and a hydrogen bond acceptor, so it can form hydrogen bonds with other water molecules. Hydrogen peroxide is also a hydrogen bond donor and a hydrogen bond acceptor, but with two oxygen atoms, each H_2O_2 molecule can accept more hydrogen bonds than can a water molecule, giving H_2O_2 a slightly higher viscosity than H_2O.

PRACTICE PROBLEM 12.8

Based on the structures of pentane and decane, which has a higher viscosity at room temperature?

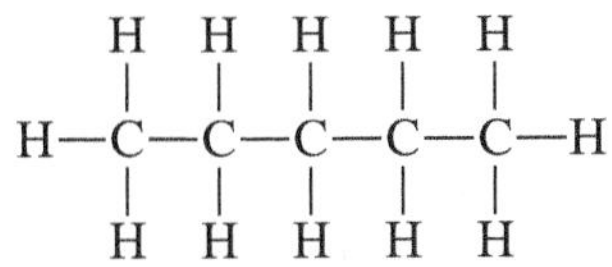

Pentane

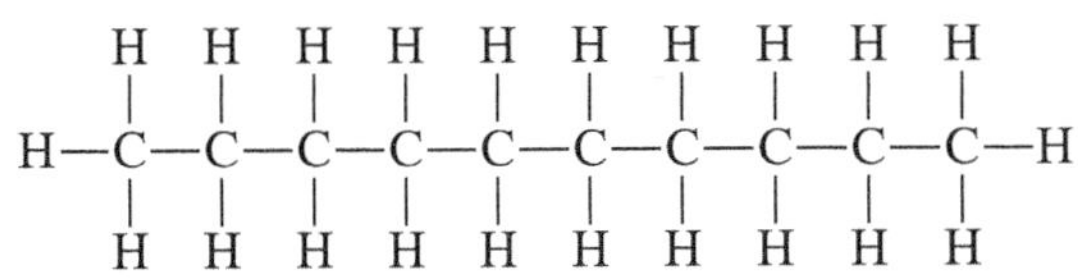

Decane

Hint: Viscosity depends on the strength of the intermolecular forces and the temperature.

SURFACE TENSION

Surface tension, the tendency of liquids to minimize their surface area, is also determined by the strength of the intermolecular forces. Molecules in the center of a liquid sample can interact via intermolecular forces with other molecules of the liquid in all directions (Figure 12.12), resulting in no net pull in any direction for any molecule. Molecules at the surface of the liquid, however, have no other liquid molecules above them with which to interact, so they experience a downward pull.

This downward pull causes all liquids to minimize their surface area. The three-dimensional shape with the smallest ratio of surface area to volume is the sphere. Water beads up on the freshly waxed surface of a car because the wax is nonpolar and will not form strong intermolecular forces with water. Mercury is another liquid with a very high surface tension that forms beads when it is spilled, while nonpolar solvents with low surface tension, such as hexane, spread out into a thin layer.

Cohesion is the attraction of atoms and molecules to like particles. Thus, water and mercury exhibit strong cohesion because they have strong intermolecular forces. **Adhesion**, the attraction to different particles, is also possible, provided the other particle can form similar intermolecular forces. Water exhibits adhesion to other hydrogen-bonding materials, for example, which is why paper towels work so well at cleaning up spilled water. Paper is composed of cellulose, which contains many, many O—H bonds capable of hydrogen bonding with water molecules.

CAPILLARY ACTION

Cohesion and adhesion help to explain **capillary action**, the ability of a liquid to flow against gravity up a narrow tube. Molecules of a liquid such as water can form intermolecular forces with the material on the inner surface of the tube, causing the water to move into the tube. Because the molecules of a liquid are interconnected via intermolecular forces, this loose network climbs up the tube as the lead molecules continue to form attractions to the inner surface of the tube.

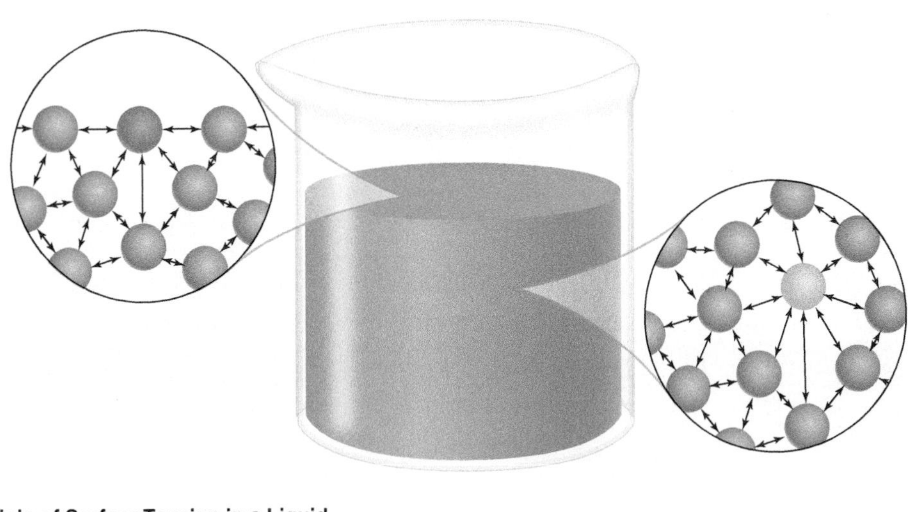

FIGURE 12.12 Origin of Surface Tension in a Liquid

Particles in the middle of a liquid experience intermolecular attractions in all directions, resulting in no net attraction in any direction. Particles at the surface experience a net downward or net inward attraction, causing liquids to minimize their surface area.

EVERYDAY CONNECTION

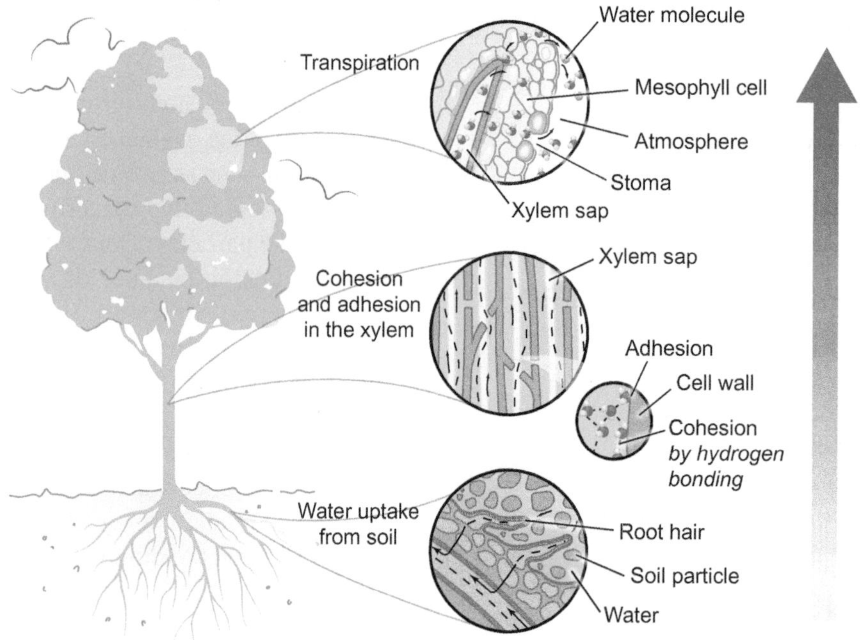

Adhesion and cohesion play important roles in living things. One example is the movement of water from the soil up to the leaves of plants, where it is lost to evaporation. This process, called transpiration, moves water from the roots up through the stems of the plants via a structure called the xylem, thus providing water for all parts of the plant. Movement of water through the xylem occurs by water molecules adhering to the surface of the xylem and cohering to other water molecules. During the process of transpiration, water moves against gravity from the roots up the stems of plants to their leaves via capillary action.

The forces of cohesion and adhesion explain the formation of a meniscus when liquid is poured into narrow-diameter containers such as graduated cylinders. Liquids such as water that are attracted to the glass or plastic of the cylinder and have a high surface tension exhibit a concave meniscus (Figure 12.13a), while

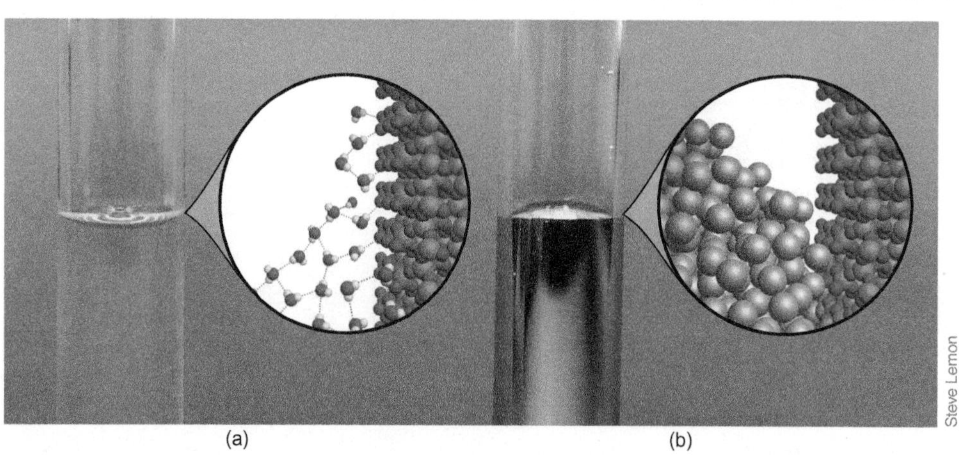

FIGURE 12.13 Adhesion, Cohesion, and the Shape the Meniscus

(a) Water in a glass cylinder has a concave meniscus because water has strong adhesive forces with the glass. (b) Mercury has strong cohesive forces but weak adhesive forces and thus forms a convex meniscus.

liquids such as mercury that have no cohesion to the cylinder but high surface tension exhibit a convex meniscus (Figure 12.13b). Liquids with low surface tension appear to have a flat surface in a graduated cylinder.

Example 12.9

N_2, HF, and HBr can be liquids under the right conditions of temperature and pressure. Rank their surface tensions from lowest to highest.

Solution

The strength of the intermolecular forces determines the surface tension. Start by determining the predominant intermolecular force for each molecule:

- N_2 is nonpolar and interacts with other N_2 molecules via dispersion forces.
- HF is a strongly polar molecule that forms hydrogen bonds.
- HBr is polar and will interact with other HBr molecules via dipole–dipole forces but not hydrogen bonds.

Since dispersion is the weakest intermolecular force, N_2 will have low surface tension as a liquid. Since hydrogen bonding is the strongest of the intermolecular forces in these examples, HF will have high surface tension as a liquid. The ranking is $N_2 < HBr < HF$.

PRACTICE PROBLEM 12.9

CBr_4, H_2O, and CH_2Cl_2 can be liquids under the right conditions of temperature and pressure. Rank their surface tensions from lowest to highest.

Hint: The strength of the intermolecular forces determines the surface tension. Start by determining the most important intermolecular force for each molecule.

SECTION REVIEW

- Particles in liquids interact via intermolecular forces, which give liquids specific properties such as viscosity, surface tension, cohesion, and adhesion.
- The viscosity of a liquid, which is the resistance to flow, depends on the strength of the intermolecular forces and the temperature.
- Surface tension is the tendency of a liquid to reduce its surface area. It, too, depends on the strength of the intermolecular forces.
- Capillary action, the ability of a liquid to move up a narrow tube, involves cohesion—the attraction between molecules of a liquid—and adhesion—the attraction between molecules of a liquid and the surface of the tube. Both cohesion and adhesion involve the formation of intermolecular forces.

12.3 Phase Changes and Heating Curves

GOALS

- List and define terms related to phase changes.
- Identify the sign of the enthalpy change for each phase change.
- Calculate energy changes related to phase changes.
- Interpret heating curves.

Background Review

Chapter 6 Thermochemistry: Section 6.4—Energy and Enthalpy; Section 6.7—Enthalpy in Chemical Reactions

PHASE CHANGES

Any process of changing phase (or state) for a sample of matter is called a phase change.

- The transition from the solid phase to the liquid phase, commonly called melting, is also referred to as **fusion** by chemists. The opposite process, of liquid to solid, is called **freezing**.
- The process of changing a liquid to a gas is called evaporation, or **vaporization**, which goes with the use of the term **vapor** for a gas in contact with its liquid phase. The opposite process, of gas to liquid, is called **condensation**.
- Solids that enter the gas state directly do so by **sublimation**. The opposite process, of gas directly to solid, is called **deposition**. A common example of deposition is the formation of frost on a cold morning.

The various terms used for the states or phases of matter and the transitions between them are summarized in Figure 12.14.

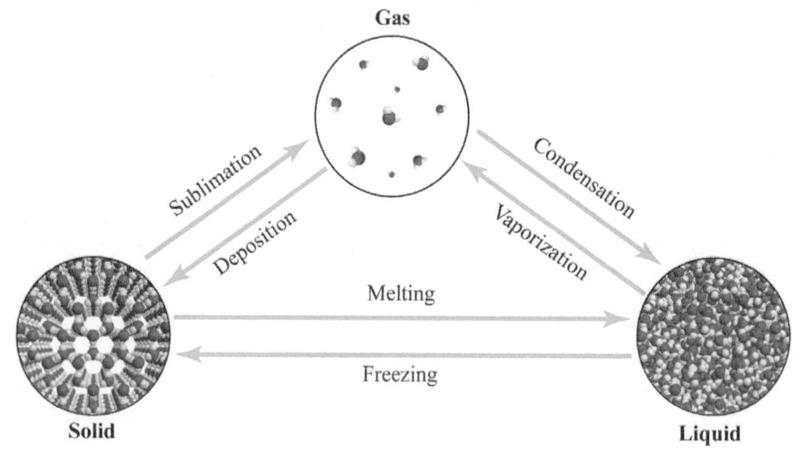

FIGURE 12.14 Terminology of Phase Changes

Each phase transition has a specific name. *Boiling* is not listed here because boiling is a special case of vaporization.

Example 12.10

Identify the phase change described by the following equations.

a. $C_{18}H_{38}(s) \rightarrow C_{18}H_{38}(l)$
b. $CO_2(g) \rightarrow CO_2(s)$
c. $NH_3(l) \rightarrow NH_3(g)$

Solution

a. The transition from a solid to a liquid is called *melting* or *fusion*.
b. The transition from a gas directly to a solid is called *deposition*.
c. The transition from a liquid to a gas is called *vaporization* to form gases.

PRACTICE PROBLEM 12.10

Identify the phase change described by the following equations.

a. $H_2O_2(l) \rightarrow H_2O_2(s)$
b. $H_2O(s) \rightarrow H_2O(g)$
c. $H_2CO(g) \rightarrow H_2CO(l)$

Hint: Use the states of matter provided in each equation to identify the transition.

ENTHALPY AND PHASE CHANGES

Vaporization, the conversion of a liquid to a gas, requires an input of energy, whereas condensation, the conversion of a gas to a liquid, releases energy. When you climb out of a swimming pool, your body cools as the water evaporates from your skin because heat is removed from your skin to provide the energy necessary to evaporate the water. If you place your bare arm in the steam from a boiling pot of water, you may get severely burned because an enormous amount of energy is released when the water vapor condenses to a liquid on your skin.

The energy change for the vaporization of 1 mole of a liquid is referred to as the **enthalpy of vaporization, ΔH_{vap}**. Similarly, the **enthalpy of fusion, ΔH_{fus}**, and **enthalpy of sublimation, ΔH_{sub}**, refer to the energy changes associated with the melting and sublimation, respectively, of one mole of a substance. These enthalpy changes (Section 6.7) are sometimes referred to as *heats* of vaporization, fusion, and sublimation.

The enthalpy of fusion of water is 6.01 kJ/mol and the enthalpy of vaporization of water is 40.7 kJ/mol. Much more energy is required to vaporize water than to melt ice. While the transition from solid to liquid provides enough kinetic energy for water molecules to overcome some intermolecular forces and begin to move freely past each other in the liquid phase, much more energy is needed to overcome the intermolecular forces present in liquid water to allow the water molecules to escape into the gas phase. Sublimation is a one-step process that starts and ends at the same states as the two-step process of fusion and vaporization. You can use the values for ΔH_{fus}, ΔH_{vap}, and Hess's law (Section 6.7) to calculate the enthalpy of sublimation of water. Figure 12.15 illustrates the relationship between the enthalpies of changes of state for several substances.

$$\Delta H_{sub} = \Delta H_{fus} + \Delta H_{vap}$$

$$\Delta H_{sub} = 6.01\frac{\text{kJ}}{\text{mol}} + 40.7\frac{\text{kJ}}{\text{mol}}$$

$$\Delta H_{sub} = 46.7\frac{\text{kJ}}{\text{mol}}$$

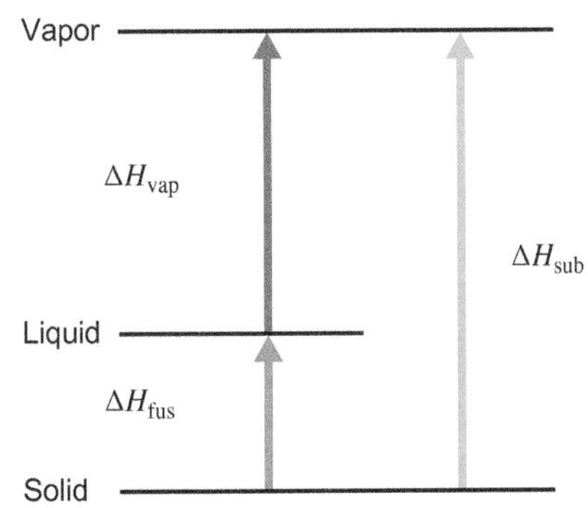

FIGURE 12.15 Enthalpies of Changes of State

The relationships among ΔH_{fus}, ΔH_{vap}, and ΔH_{sub} are shown in the diagram. Enthalpies of vaporization are always larger than enthalpies of fusion, and the enthalpy of sublimation for a substance is equal to the sum of the enthalpies of fusion and vaporization of that substance.

When the enthalpies of fusion, vaporization, and sublimation are given in kilojoules per mole, the product of the enthalpy, ΔH, and the amount of substance in moles, n, gives the heat change, q, in kilojoules:

$$q = n(\Delta H) \tag{12.1}$$

When the enthalpies of fusion, vaporization, and sublimation are given in joules per gram, the product of the enthalpy and the mass of the substance, m, gives the heat change in joules:

$$q = m(\Delta H) \tag{12.2}$$

As long as you pay attention to the enthalpy units (per mole versus per gram), you should be able to tell which formula to use.

Example 12.11

Calculate the energy required to melt 16.4 g of ice at 0°C. For water, $\Delta H_{fus} = 6.01\ \text{kJ/mol}$.

Solution

The heat of fusion of water is 6.01 kJ/mol, so first convert the mass of water to moles:

$$n = (16.4\ \text{g})\left(\frac{1\ \text{mol}}{18.02\ \text{g}}\right) = 0.910\ \text{mol}$$

Then, use Equation 12.1 to calculate q:

$$q = n(\Delta H_{fus})$$

$$q = 0.910\ \text{mol}\left(6.01\ \frac{\text{kJ}}{\text{mol}}\right)$$

$$q = 5.47\ \text{kJ}$$

PRACTICE PROBLEM 12.11

Calculate the heat required to vaporize 16.4 g of water at 100°C. For water, $\Delta H_{vap} = 40.7\ \text{kJ/mol}$ at 100°C. Compare your answer with the amount of heat needed to melt the same mass of ice (Example 12.11).

Hint: Convert the mass to moles before using the enthalpy of vaporization to determine q.

Specific amounts of heat energy must be added to a substance to change its temperature, as shown in Figure 12.16. These amounts of energy are called the *specific heat capacity*, c (Section 6.5). The specific heat capacity and the enthalpy for phase changes for water are listed in Table 12.3.

The **heating curve** for a pure substance is a graph that shows how the temperature changes as the pure substance is heated. The heating curve of water is shown in Figure 12.16. It begins with a sample of ice at some temperature below its melting point. When heat energy is steadily added to it, its temperature rises

EVERYDAY CONNECTION

Water and steam are very useful for heating buildings thanks to the properties of water. Water has a very high specific heat capacity (Section 6.5) and a high heat of vaporization, and it is a liquid over reasonable temperatures. To heat a building, water can be boiled to steam at a central location. Then the steam can be pumped through pipes to nearby buildings, where the steam condenses to water, giving off heat. The water is then pumped back to the boiler for reheating. As steam condenses, it releases 40.7 kJ/mol of heat energy. This corresponds to 2.26 kJ of heat released per gram of water, which is less than one-fourth of a teaspoon of water.

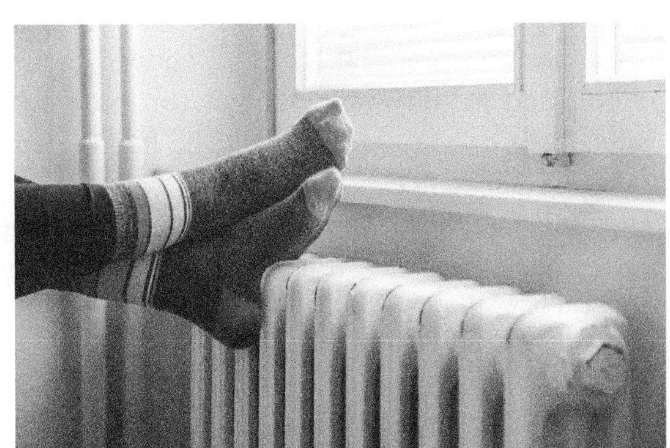

Miroslav Lukic/Shutterstock

TABLE 12.3 Enthalpy and Specific Heat Values for Water

Quantity	c, $H_2O(s)$	c, $H_2O(l)$	c, $H_2O(g)$	ΔH_{fus}	ΔH_{vap}
Value (per gram)	$2.087 \frac{J}{g \cdot °C}$	$4.184 \frac{J}{g \cdot °C}$	$2.042 \frac{J}{g \cdot °C}$	334 J/g	2,260 J/g
Value (per mole)	$37.60 \frac{J}{mol \cdot °C}$	$75.37 \frac{J}{mol \cdot °C}$	$36.03 \frac{J}{mol \cdot °C}$	6.01 kJ/mol	40.7 kJ/mol

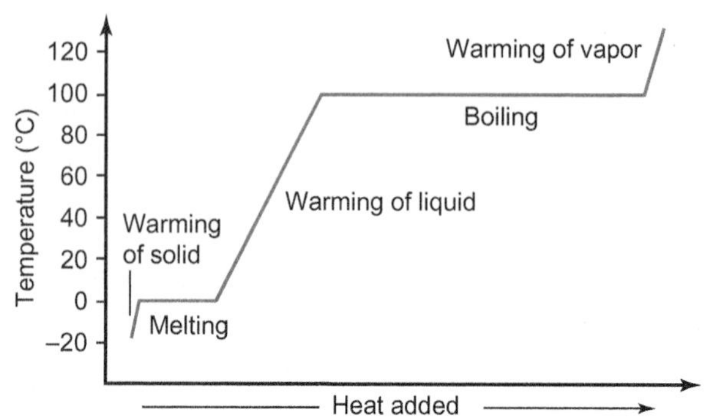

FIGURE 12.16 Heating Curve for Water

The slopes of the upward lines reflect the heat capacity of each phase of the water. A steeper slope indicates a lower heat capacity because the temperature increases more quickly as heat energy is added. The horizontal lines occur at the phase transitions—at the melting and boiling points. Here, the lengths of the lines reflect the enthalpy of the phase changes, so the length of the line for vaporization is proportionately longer than that for melting.

as the solid warms. When the melting point is reached (0°C for water), the temperature no longer changes because the heat energy is now being absorbed to transition the solid to the liquid at 0°C. Once the entire sample has melted, the continued addition of energy causes the temperature of the liquid water to rise. Once the liquid water reaches the boiling point (100°C for water), the temperature remains constant until all the liquid water has vaporized to produce steam at 100°C. If the process is carried out in a closed container, the continued addition of energy causes the temperature of the trapped steam to rise.

The animation in Figure 12.17 shows the heating curves and the physical changes for three different substances as they are heated. The heating curve for any pure substance is qualitatively similar to the one shown in Figure 12.17, but differences in the heat capacities and in the enthalpies of the phase changes result in lines with different lengths and slopes.

The video in Figure 12.18 shows how to calculate the total energy for a process that includes both raising the temperature and going through one or more phase changes. Separate energy calculations are done for each line segment on the graph, and then the energies of all the steps are added together.

Example 12.12

Calculate the energy required to change a 17.0 g sample of liquid water from 87.7°C to steam at 121.0°C and 1.00 atm.

Solution

Calculate each segment separately.

- Segment 1: The water in the liquid phase is heated from 87.7°C to its boiling point, 100°C.
- Segment 2: It then boils, producing water vapor at 100°C.
- Segment 3: The water vapor is then heated to 121.0°C.

Since the amount of water is given in grams, use the "per gram" values of enthalpy and specific heat from Table 12.3.

Segment 1: Heating the liquid water involves the use of the specific heat of liquid water and Equation 6.8.

$$q = mc(\Delta T)$$

$$q = (17.0 \text{ g})\left(\frac{4.184 \text{ J}}{\text{g} \cdot °\text{C}}\right)(100.0°\text{C} - 87.7°\text{C})$$

$$q = 875 \text{ J}$$

Segment 2: To vaporize the water, use the enthalpy of vaporization and Equation 12.1.

$$q = (17.0 \text{ g})\left(2260 \frac{\text{J}}{\text{mol}}\right)$$

$$q = 38{,}420 \text{ kJ}$$

Segment 3: For heating the water vapor, use the specific heat of gaseous water and Equation 6.8.

$$q = mc(\Delta T)$$

$$q = (17.0 \text{ g})\left(\frac{2.042 \text{ J}}{\text{g} \cdot °\text{C}}\right)(121.0°\text{C} - 100.0°\text{C})$$

$$q = 729 \text{ J}$$

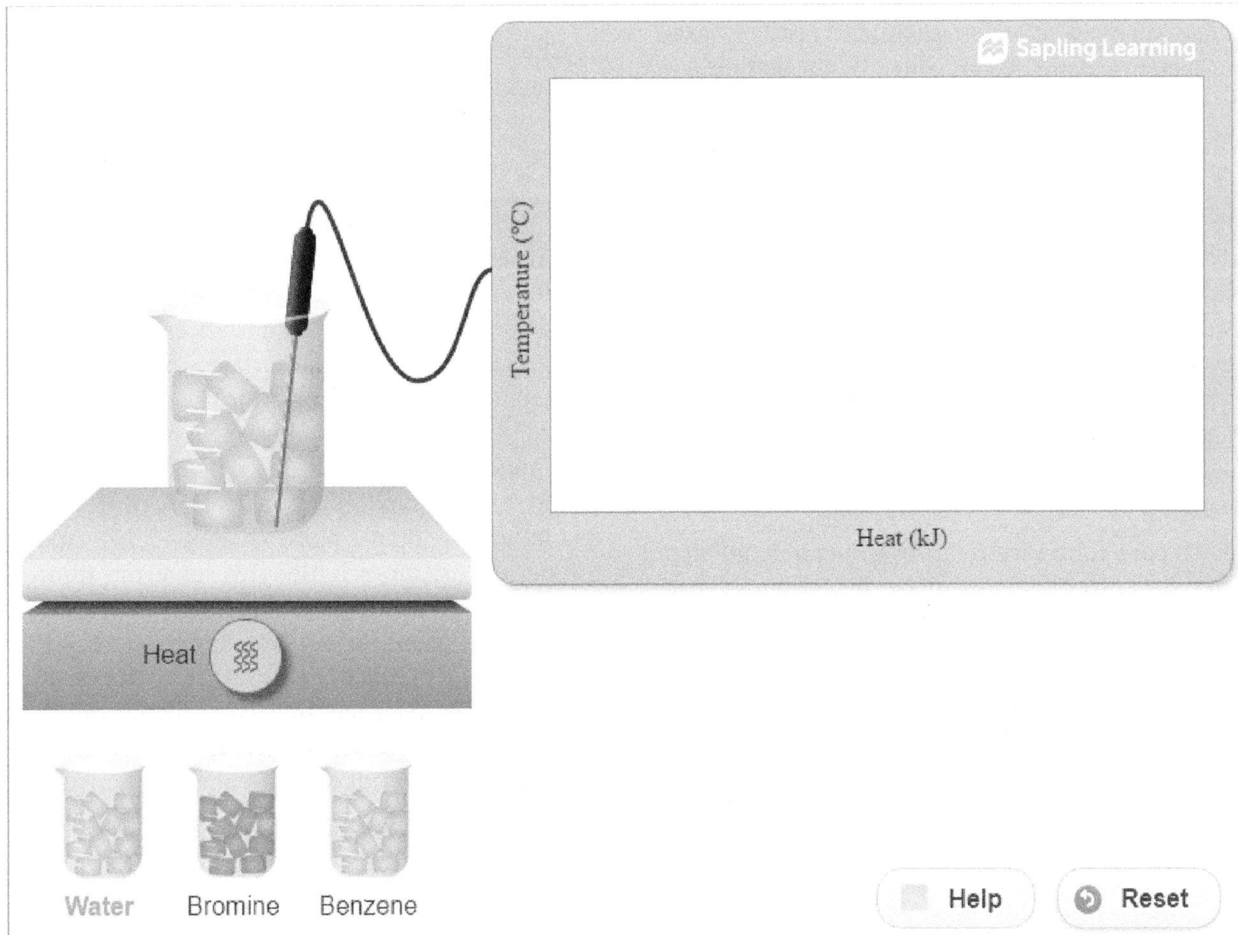

FIGURE 12.17 Changes of State for Water, H_2O, Bromine, Br_2, and Benzene, C_6H_6

NOTE: You need to be online to access this activity.

For each compound, initiate heating and note the similarities and differences between the heating curves for each substance. Click on the magnifying glass to examine the sample at the molecular level.

FIGURE 12.18 Video Tutorial: Heating Curve Calculation

NOTE: You need to be online to access this video.

This video shows how to calculate the total heat needed to go from ice to steam.

The last step is to add the energy values together.

$$q_{\text{total}} = 875\text{ J} + 38{,}420\text{ J} + 729\text{ J}$$
$$q_{\text{total}} = 40{,}020\text{ J} = 40.02\text{ kJ}$$

PRACTICE PROBLEM 12.12

Calculate q when 41.0 g of liquid water at 14.4°C is cooled to ice at −16.3°C.

Hint: Separate the process into steps: cooling the water to its freezing point, freezing the water, then cooling the ice. Calculate q for each step, then sum the individual q values. Since cooling and freezing are exothermic processes, you will need to reverse the sign of ΔH_{fus}.

SECTION REVIEW

- Phase changes refer to transitions between states of matter and are accompanied by the addition or release of energy.
- Transitions from solid to liquid (fusion), liquid to gas (vaporization), and solid to gas (sublimation) have positive enthalpy values (they are endothermic).
- Transitions from gas to liquid (condensation), liquid to solid (freezing), and gas to solid (deposition) have negative enthalpy values (they are exothermic).
- The magnitude of the enthalpy changes associated with fusion, vaporization, and sublimation depend on the strengths of the intermolecular attractions between the particles of the substance.
- Each pure substance requires a specific enthalpy change per mole for a phase transition. These enthalpy changes are denoted as ΔH_{fus}, ΔH_{vap}, and ΔH_{sub}.
- The temperature of a substance does not change during phase changes because the heat that is added or removed is used to change the phase of the substance, rather than to increase or decrease its temperature.
- Heating curves show the temperature and phase transitions for a pure substance as heat energy is added.

12.4 Vapor Pressure, Boiling Point, and the Clausius–Clapeyron Equation

GOALS

- Describe and explain the relationship between temperature and vapor pressure.
- Predict relative vapor pressures based on intermolecular forces.
- Calculate the enthalpy of vaporization from vapor pressure and temperature data using the Clausius–Clapeyron equation.
- Calculate the vapor pressure at various temperatures using the Clausius–Clapeyron equation.

Background Review

Chapter 7 Gases: Section 7.7—Dalton's Law of Partial Pressures

VAPOR PRESSURE

Substances that vaporize easily are said to be **volatile**, whereas substances that do not easily vaporize are said to be **nonvolatile**. Volatile substances have more gas-phase molecules above the surface of the liquid, creating vapor pressure (Section 7.7). The vapor pressure of a pure liquid is determined by the temperature, which determines the proportion of molecules with sufficient energy to overcome the attractive forces of the liquid and move into the gas phase (Figure 12.19). At higher temperatures, more molecules have the minimum kinetic energy needed to escape the liquid phase and enter the gas phase. At any given temperature, different liquids have different vapor pressures, determined by the strength of their intermolecular forces. Substances with stronger attractive forces have lower vapor pressures than do liquids with weaker attractive forces because there are fewer molecules in the gas phase.

Example 12.13

Use the Lewis structures of acetone, 2-propanol, and methylpropane,

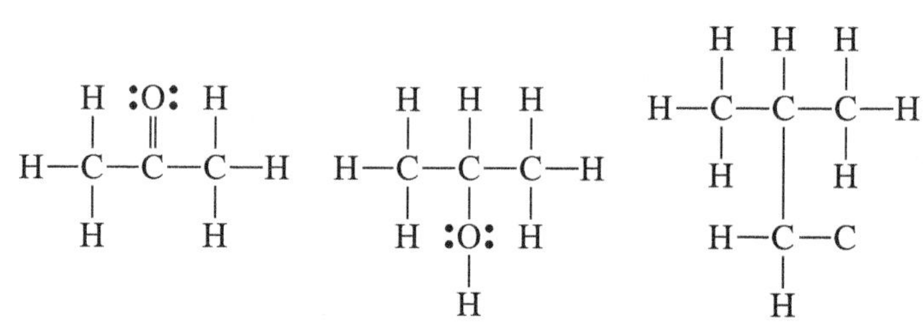

Acetone 2-Propanol Methylpropane

to rank these substances in order from lowest vapor pressure to highest vapor pressure at room temperature.

Solution

Vapor pressure depends on temperature and the strength of the intermolecular forces in the pure substance. The samples of these three compounds are at the same temperature, though, so you can ignore temperature and use just the intermolecular forces to determine their relative vapor pressures. The three molecules are similar in size and structure but differ in polarity, so molecules of the substances interact via different

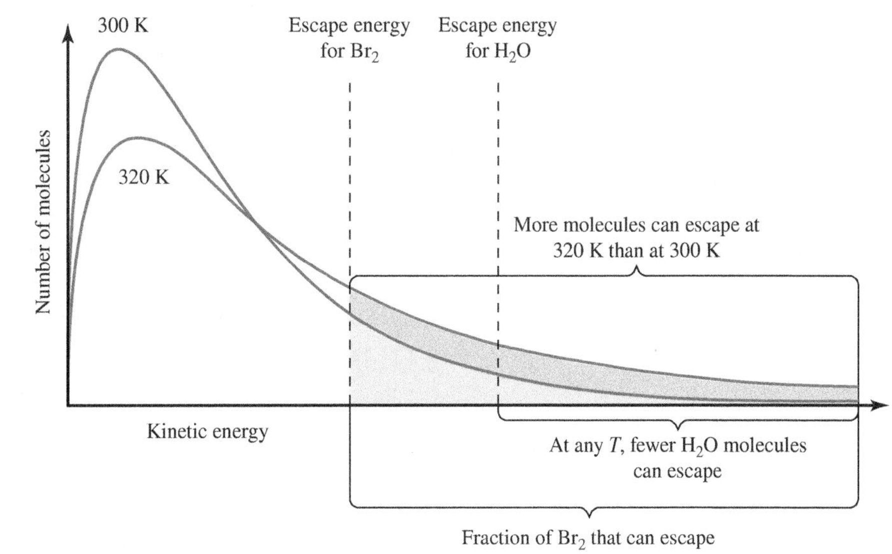

FIGURE 12.19 Distribution of Energy

A kinetic-energy distribution of molecules at two different temperatures shows that, as temperature increases, the range of energy widens, and that the percentage of molecules above a set point, such as the energy required to escape to the gas phase, increases. The escape energy is different for different substances.

intermolecular forces. Acetone is polar, and its molecules interact via dipole–dipole forces, while 2-propanol molecules interact via hydrogen bonds and methylpropane molecules interact via dispersion forces.

Vapor pressure *decreases* as the strength of intermolecular forces *increases*. Because dispersion forces are the weakest intermolecular forces, methylpropane has the highest vapor pressure, followed by acetone. Because of the relative strength of hydrogen bonding, 2-propanol has the lowest vapor pressure of the three substances.

PRACTICE PROBLEM 12.13

Use the Lewis structures of butane, propanal, and acetic acid,

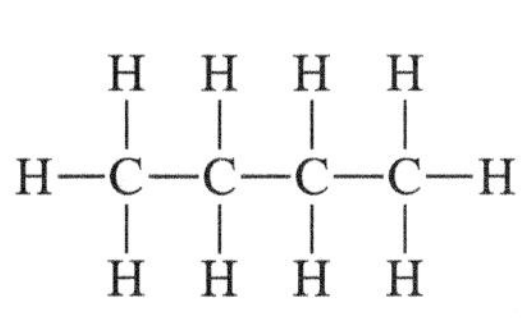

Butane

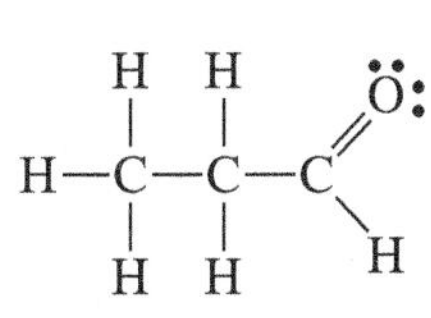

Propanal

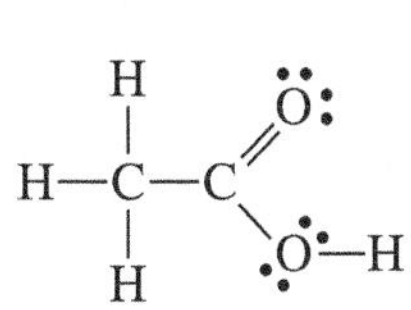

Acetic acid

to rank these substances in order from lowest vapor pressure to highest vapor pressure at room temperature.

Hint: Use the Lewis structures to identify the predominant intermolecular force for a sample of each pure substance. What, then, is the relationship between vapor pressure and the strength of intermolecular forces?

HEAT OF VAPORIZATION

The amount of energy needed to vaporize one mole of a substance—the enthalpy of vaporization (Section 12.3)—is also called the **heat of vaporization** and is always a positive value. Heats of vaporization are slightly temperature dependent and are generally reported at two temperatures—namely, 25°C and the normal boiling point of the substance (Table 12.4).

Example 12.14

How much energy is absorbed when 355 g of acetone is vaporized at 56.1°C?

Solution

According to Table 12.4, the boiling point of acetone is 56.1°C, so the enthalpy of vaporization to use is the 29.1 kJ/mol value. Convert the mass of

TABLE 12.4 Heats of Vaporization of Several Liquids

Liquid	Molecular Formula	Normal Boiling Point, °C	ΔH_{vap} (kJ/mol) at Boiling Point	ΔH_{vap} (kJ/mol) at 25°C
Water	H_2O	100.0	40.7	44.0
2-Propanol	C_3H_8O	82.3	39.9	45.4
Acetone	C_3H_6O	56.1	29.1	31.0
Ethyl acetate	$C_4H_8O_2$	77.0	31.9	34.1

acetone to moles of acetone, using the molecular formula of acetone provided in the table.

$$q = (355 \text{ g acetone})\left(\frac{1 \text{ mol acetone}}{58.0791 \text{ g acetone}}\right)\left(\frac{29.1 \text{ kJ}}{1 \text{ mol acetone}}\right)$$
$$= 178 \text{ kJ}$$

PRACTICE PROBLEM 12.14

Calculate q when 1.355 g of water condenses at 25°C.

Hint: First, convert the mass of water to moles and then use the appropriate value for the enthalpy of vaporization (Table 12.4) at the given temperature (25°C). Remember to change the sign because condensation is the reverse process of vaporization.

Example 12.15

How many grams of ethyl acetate will vaporize with the addition of 226 kJ of energy at 25°C?

Solution

Use the enthalpy of vaporization in Table 12.4 to convert kilojoules to moles of ethyl acetate and then use the molar mass to convert moles of ethyl acetate to mass.

$$m = (226 \text{ kJ})\left(\frac{1 \text{ mol ethyl acetate}}{34.1 \text{ kJ}}\right)$$
$$\left(\frac{88.1051 \text{ g ethyl acetate}}{1 \text{ mol ethyl acetate}}\right) = 584 \text{ g ethyl acetate}$$

PRACTICE PROBLEM 12.15

Calculate the mass of acetone that will vaporize when 86.5 kJ of heat energy is added to a sample of acetone at 25°C.

Hint: Use the enthalpy of vaporization in Table 12.4 to convert kilojoules to moles of acetone and then convert moles to mass of acetone.

CLAUSIUS–CLAPEYRON EQUATION

You can calculate the enthalpy of vaporization of a liquid by measuring its vapor pressure at different temperatures and then applying the **Clausius–Clapeyron equation** (Equation 12.3). The relationship between vapor pressure and temperature is exponential and is most useful in a linear format as shown in Equation 12.3, where P_{vap} is the vapor pressure in atmospheres, R is the gas law constant (8.3145 J/mol · K), T is the temperature in kelvins, and β is a constant specific for each liquid.

$$\ln P_{vap} = \frac{-\Delta H_{vap}}{R}\left(\frac{1}{T}\right) + \ln \beta \qquad (12.3)$$

The notation "ln" indicates the natural logarithm function (Section 0.5). A plot of ln P_{vap} versus $1/T$ allows you to determine the value of the enthalpy of vaporization from the slope of the line (Figure 12.20).

There is also a two-point version of the Clausius–Clapeyron equation (Equation 12.4) that allows you to calculate the enthalpy of vaporization by measuring the vapor pressure, P, at only two temperatures.

$$\ln \frac{P_2}{P_1} = \frac{\Delta H_{vap}}{R}\left(\frac{1}{T_1} - \frac{1}{T_2}\right) \qquad (12.4)$$

The *normal boiling point* of a liquid is the temperature at which its vapor pressure equals 1 atm of

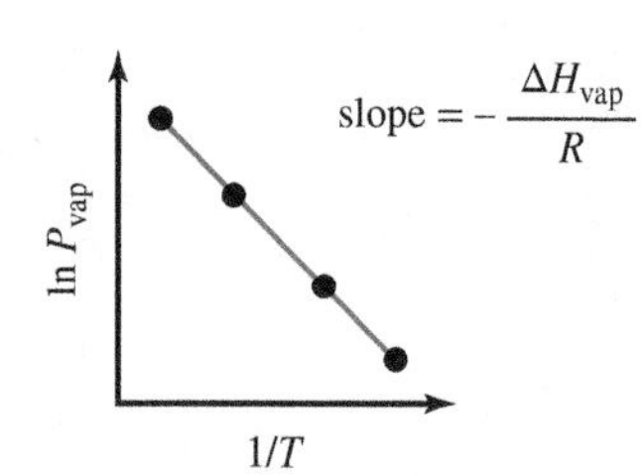

FIGURE 12.20 Clausius–Clapeyron Plot
A plot of the natural log of the vapor pressure of a liquid versus the inverse of the temperature in kelvins yields a straight-line plot with a slope equal to $-\Delta H_{vap}/R$.

Steve Lemon, Macmillan Learning

FIGURE 12.21 Video Tutorial: Clausius–Clapeyron Equation

NOTE: You need to be online to access this video.

This video shows how to calculate the heat of vaporization from vapor pressure and temperature data.

pressure, or 760 mmHg. This information can be very useful when working with the Clausius–Clapeyron equation. The video in Figure 12.21 demonstrates how to use both forms of the equation.

Example 12.16

Methanol has a normal boiling point of 64.60°C and a heat of vaporization of 35.2 kJ/mol. What is the vapor pressure of methanol at 25.00°C in mmHg?

Solution

Substitute into the two-point version of the Clausius–Clapeyron equation (Equation 12.4) using $T_2 = 64.60°\text{C}$, $P_2 = 760\ \text{mmHg}$, and $T_1 = 25.00°\text{C}$. Start by rewriting $\left(\ln \frac{P_2}{P_1}\right)$ as $(\ln P_2 - \ln P_1)$.

$$\ln P_2 - \ln P_1 = \frac{\Delta H_{\text{vap}}}{R}\left(\frac{1}{T_1} - \frac{1}{T_2}\right)$$

Express ΔH_{vap} in joules per mole, rather than kilojoules per mole, to be consistent with the units for R.

$$\ln(760\ \text{mmHg}) - \ln P_1 = \frac{35{,}200\frac{\text{J}}{\text{mol}}}{8.3145\frac{\text{J}}{\text{K}\cdot\text{mol}}}\left(\frac{1}{298.15\ \text{K}} - \frac{1}{337.75\ \text{K}}\right)$$

Remember to take the reciprocals of the temperatures before subtracting.

$$6.633 - \ln P_1 = 1.66$$

$$\ln P_1 = 6.633 - 1.66 = 4.97$$

$$P_2 = e^{4.97} = 144\ \text{mmHg}$$

PRACTICE PROBLEM 12.16

Propanol has a normal boiling point of 97.00°C and a heat of vaporization of 41.2 kJ/mol. What is the vapor pressure of propanol at 61.00°C, in mmHg?

Hint: Use the two-point version of the Clausius–Clapeyron equation, where 97.00°C and 760 mmHg are T and P for one of the points. Be sure to convert them to appropriate units first.

Example 12.17

If the vapor pressure of diethyl ether is 401 mmHg at 18.00°C and 660 mmHg at 32.00°C, then what is ΔH_{vap} for diethyl ether?

Solution

Use the two-point version of the Clausius–Clapeyron equation (Equation 12.4), where the lower temperature and pressure are T_1 and P_1, respectively. Substitute the data from the problem after converting all temperatures to kelvins.

$$\ln\frac{P_2}{P_1} = \frac{\Delta H_{\text{vap}}}{R}\left(\frac{1}{T_1} - \frac{1}{T_2}\right)$$

$$\ln\frac{660\ \text{mmHg}}{401\ \text{mmHg}} = \frac{\Delta H_{\text{vap}}}{8.3145\frac{\text{J}}{\text{K}\cdot\text{mol}}}\left(\frac{1}{291.15\ \text{K}} - \frac{1}{305.15\ \text{K}}\right)$$

Carry out the mathematical operations carefully, making sure to take the reciprocals of the temperatures before subtracting.

$$0.498 = \frac{\Delta H_{\text{vap}}}{8.3145\frac{\text{J}}{\text{K}\cdot\text{mol}}}(1.5758 \times 10^{-4})$$

$$\Delta H_{\text{vap}} = 26300\frac{\text{J}}{\text{mol}} = 26.3\ \text{kJ/mol}$$

PRACTICE PROBLEM 12.17

What is the vapor pressure of diethyl ether at 25.00°C?

Hint: Substitute T_1, P_1, and ΔH_{vap} from Example 12.17 into the Clausius–Clapeyron equation and solve for P_2.

BOILING AND DISTILLATION

Boiling occurs when the vapor pressure of the liquid equals the pressure of the surroundings. At that point, bubbles appear within the liquid itself. The boiling point of a liquid is the temperature at which the vapor pressure of the liquid equals the surrounding pressure on the system. The **normal boiling point** is the boiling point of a liquid at a pressure of 1.00 atm. For example, when liquid water at 100°C and 1.00 atm is heated, it boils.

Liquids can boil at temperatures other than their normal boiling points if the surrounding pressure is different from 1.00 atm. For example, water can boil at 25°C if the surrounding pressure is about 24 torr (0.0316 atm) (Figure 12.22). Such a low pressure allows the water to boil at a low temperature. In contrast, pressure cookers and autoclaves create high pressure to allow water to boil at a higher temperature so that food in the cooker will cook faster and medical instruments in the autoclave will be sterilized.

Volatile substances can be separated from a liquid-phase mixture using **distillation**. The liquid mixture is heated to vaporize the volatile components, and then the vapor is directed away from the original liquid and cooled to condense it back to a liquid (Figure 12.23). Components with higher boiling points and those that are nonvolatile are left behind

FIGURE 12.22 Water Boiling at Room Temperature under Reduced Pressure

Vapor is pumped out of the jar through the opening on the top left, lowering the vapor pressure in the jar. The evaporation has cooled the water sufficiently for some of it to turn to frost, resulting in thin pieces of ice at the surface.

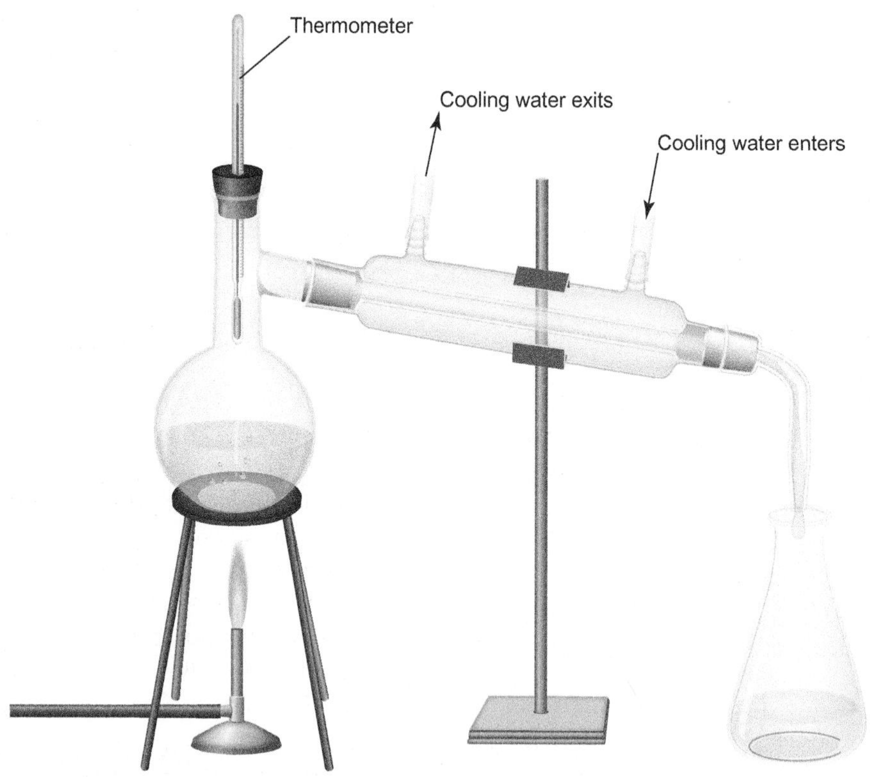

FIGURE 12.23 Distillation Apparatus

Upon heating, volatile components of a liquid mixture vaporize and flow through a tube in which they are cooled, causing them to condense back to a liquid and drip into in a separate container.

EVERYDAY CONNECTION

Distillation is used to separate the components of crude oil into many commercially important components, such as kerosene, gasoline, and diesel fuel. Some of these components, such as gasoline, require further processing.

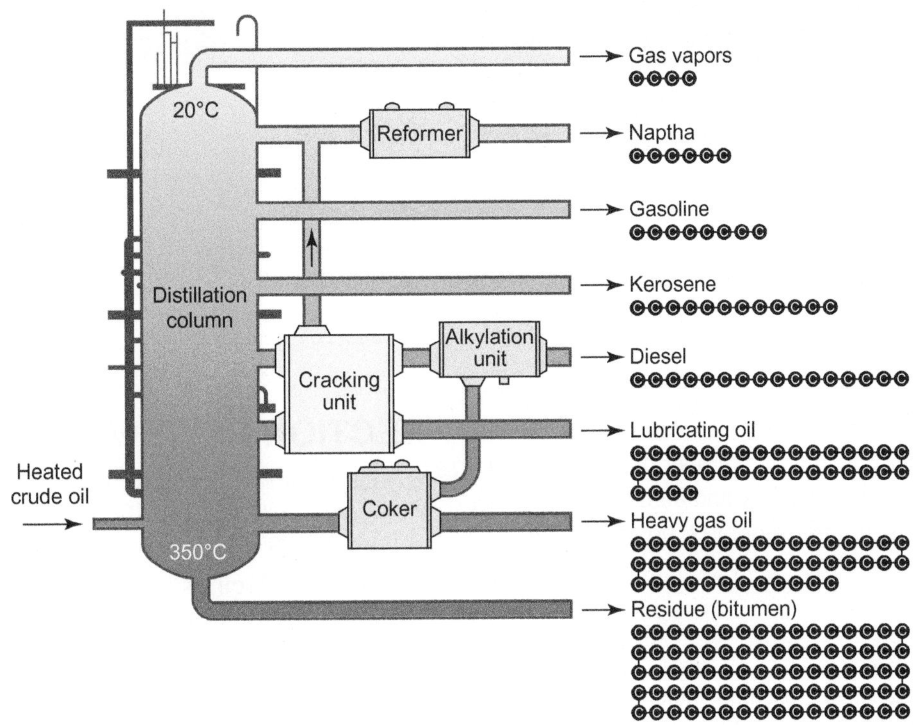

Crude oil is heated and the vapors are separated by their different boiling temperatures into fractions containing hydrocarbon molecules of similar sizes.

in the original container. For example, a salt-water solution can be purified by vaporizing the water and then cooling and condensing the vapor into another container, leaving the nonvolatile salt in the original container. A mixture of liquids can be separated into its individual components using distillation if the various components have different boiling points. The components with the lower boiling points will vaporize and be condensed and collected in another container first, while those with the higher boiling points either remain in the distillation flask or are distilled at higher temperatures. A common example of this is the use of distillation to increase the alcohol content of fermented grains and fruits in the production of whiskey and other spirits. Another common use is to purify a solvent by vaporizing it, leaving any nonvolatile components behind.

VAPOR PRESSURE AND DYNAMIC EQUILIBRIUM

As liquid molecules escape into the gas phase in a closed system at constant temperature, the pressure of the vapor builds up and condensation will occur (Figure 12.24). As the vapor pressure increases, the rate of condensation increases. At some point, the rate of evaporation of liquid molecules will be equal to the rate of condensation of gas molecules, forming an **equilibrium**. There is no longer any net change in the vapor pressure or in the amount of liquid, even though the two processes (vaporization and condensation) continue to occur.

If the temperature of the system is increased, the number of liquid molecules with sufficient energy to escape into the gas phase will increase, but the number of gas molecules available to condense will not immediately

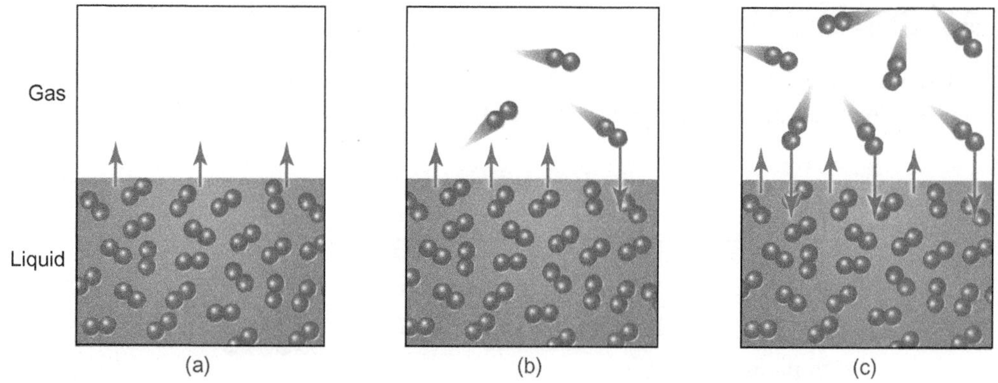

FIGURE 12.24 Vapor Pressure Equilibrium

(a) Evaporation begins. (b) Once some vapor exists, condensation occurs, but at a slower rate than evaporation. As vapor builds up, the condensation rate steadily increases. (c) At equilibrium, the condensation rate equals the evaporation rate and the vapor pressure is constant.

be affected. Therefore, the rate of evaporation will exceed the rate of condensation until the number of molecules in the gas phase builds up and a new and higher vapor pressure results. If all the liquid evaporates, no equilibrium is possible.

Example 12.18

A sample of water in a closed container is at equilibrium at room temperature. What will happen to the amount of water in the liquid phase, the amount of water in the gas phase, and the vapor pressure when the sample is placed in the refrigerator?

Solution

Before the sample is refrigerated, the rate of evaporation equals the rate of condensation. As the sample cools, though, the rate of vaporization will decrease compared with the rate of condensation. This will cause the amount of water in the gas phase to decrease, which will lower the vapor pressure. The amount of water in the liquid phase will increase. Eventually, a new equilibrium will be established at a lower vapor pressure.

PRACTICE PROBLEM 12.18

A sample of water in a closed container is at equilibrium at room temperature. What will happen to the amount of water in the liquid phase, the amount of water in the gas phase, and the vapor pressure when this container is placed in a car on a sunny day?

Hint: How will the change in temperature affect the rates of vaporization and condensation?

SECTION REVIEW

- Liquids and molecular solids can be in equilibrium with their molecules in the gas phase at the same temperature because, in any sample, some molecules will have higher energies than will others, allowing some molecules to enter the gas phase. Similarly, some gas molecules will have lower energies than will others, and some gas molecules will re-enter the liquid or solid phase.
- At the same temperature, substances with stronger intermolecular forces are less volatile than are substances with weaker intermolecular forces. As a result, substances with stronger intermolecular forces have lower vapor pressures because fewer molecules are in the gas phase above the liquid.
- The Clausius–Clapeyron equation relates the vapor pressure of a substance at a specific temperature and its heat of vaporization.

$$\ln P_{\text{vap}} = -\frac{\Delta H_{\text{vap}}}{R}\left(\frac{1}{T}\right) + \ln \beta$$

- The heat of vaporization of a substance can be calculated from measurements of vapor pressure at two different temperatures.

$$\ln \frac{P_2}{P_1} = \frac{\Delta H_{\text{vap}}}{R}\left(\frac{1}{T_1} - \frac{1}{T_2}\right)$$

- Distillation can be used to separate substances based on differences in volatility and/or boiling points.

12.5 Phase Diagrams

GOALS

- Define, describe, and interpret phase diagrams.
- Predict phase changes from changes in temperature and/or pressure using phase diagrams.

Any one substance may exist in the solid, liquid, or gas phase depending on the temperature and pressure conditions. A **phase diagram** is a graph that shows the phase of a specific substance under all possible pressure–temperature combinations. Figure 12.25 is a general phase diagram with pressure measured on the *y*-axis and temperature on the *x*-axis. At low temperatures and high pressures (i.e., the upper-left region of the diagram), the substance is in the solid phase. At low pressures and high temperatures (i.e., the lower-right region of the diagram), the substance is in the gas phase. At moderate temperatures and pressures (i.e., the upper-middle region of the graph), the substance is a liquid.

The lines on phase diagrams indicate the conditions at which different phases are in equilibrium.

- The line separating the solid and liquid regions represents all of the pressure–temperature, *P*–*T*, conditions under which the liquid and solid states are both present and in equilibrium.
- The line separating the liquid and gas phase regions represents the *P*–*T* conditions under which the liquid and gas states are both present and in equilibrium.
- The line between the solid and vapor regions indicates the *P*–*T* conditions under which the solid is in equilibrium with the vapor phase.

The single point at which these three lines intersect is called the **triple point**, and it indicates the pressure and temperature at which all three phases of the substance are in equilibrium. The **critical point** occurs at the pressure and temperature conditions (called the **critical pressure** and **critical temperature**) above which the substance no longer exists as either a liquid or gas, but as a **supercritical fluid**, a fourth phase that has properties common to both liquids and gases. Supercritical fluids can effuse through solids as gases do but can also dissolve substances as liquids do.

Another common feature found on phase diagrams is a line indicating 1 atm pressure (see the horizontal dashed line in Figure 12.25). The temperatures at which this line crosses the solid–liquid and the liquid–gas equilibrium lines are the normal melting and boiling points, respectively. Although phase diagrams for different substances have different values corresponding to the triple point, critical point, and normal melting and boiling points, the general shape of the phase diagram remains the same for most substances.

The video in Figure 12.26 uses phases diagrams to solve some example problems.

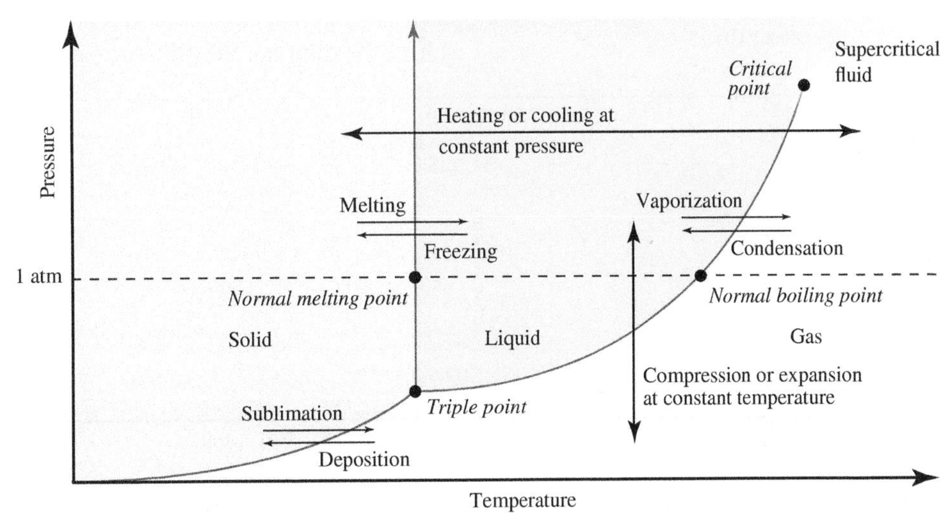

FIGURE 12.25 A Generic Phase Diagram

A phase diagram shows all the different temperature and pressure conditions possible for a substance and indicates the phase for each. Solid lines represent the conditions under which two phases are in equilibrium. The temperature and pressure at the triple point are the conditions at which all three phases are in equilibrium. At temperatures and pressures above the critical point, the substance exists as a supercritical fluid.

FIGURE 12.26 Video Tutorial: Phase Diagrams

NOTE: You need to be online to access this video.
This video shows how to label the regions and points of a phase diagram and answer questions related to it.

Example 12.19

Use the given phase diagram to identify the following items.

a. the phase(s) present in regions A, B, and C
b. the line where the solid and gas phases are in equilibrium
c. the point indicating the normal boiling point

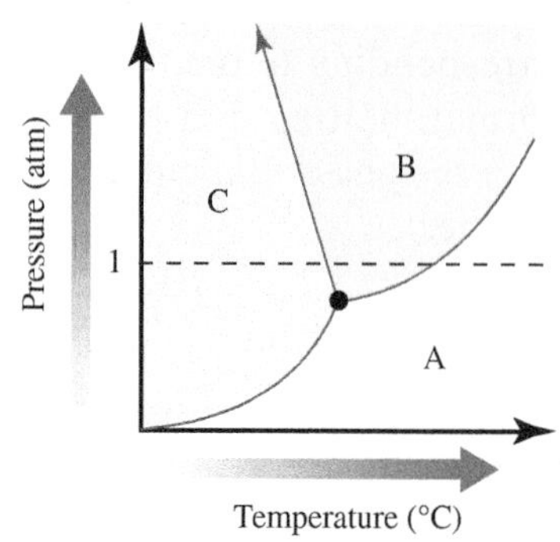

Solution

Study the phase diagram and think about what phases are present at extremes of pressure and temperatures.

a. The substance is a gas in region A, a liquid in region B, and a solid in region C.
b. The solid and gas phases are in equilibrium along the line between regions A and C.
c. The normal boiling point is the point at which the dotted line (1 atm) crosses the line between regions A and B (the liquid–gas equilibrium line).

PRACTICE PROBLEM 12.19

Identify the following items in the phase diagram from Example 12.19.

a. the line where the liquid and gas phases are in equilibrium
b. the point where the solid, liquid, and gas phases are in equilibrium
c. the point indicating the normal melting point

Hint: The lines between regions represent the equilibrium between two phases. The point at which all three regions meet represents the equilibrium between all three phases. Normal boiling and melting points occur at 1 atm.

The phase diagram for carbon dioxide, CO_2, (Figure 12.27a) shows that the line separating the solid and liquid regions has a positive slope, which is a common feature of phase diagrams for most substances. Water, H_2O, however, has many unusual properties. It has a high density for such a small molecule, as well as high melting and boiling temperatures; it is a liquid

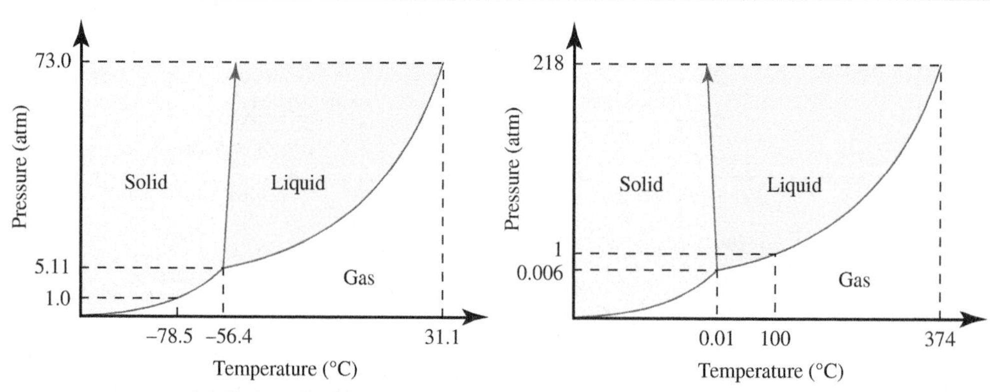

FIGURE 12.27 Phase Diagrams of Carbon Dioxide and Water

(a) The line between the solid and liquid phases for CO_2 has a slight positive slope, which is typical of most substances. Applying pressure to solid CO_2 does *not* change its phase. (b) The line between the solid and liquid phases has a negative slope for H_2O, which is highly unusual. Compressing solid H_2O causes it to melt.

over a very broad temperature range; and it is less dense as a solid than as a liquid. These unusual properties are reflected in water's phase diagram (Figure 12.27b).

Note that the line indicating equilibrium conditions between the solid and liquid phases has a positive slope for CO_2 (and most substances) and a negative slope for H_2O. When pressure is applied to solids such as CO_2, the particles are forced closer together, forming a solid of greater density. Solid H_2O (ice) is less dense than liquid H_2O, however, so applying pressure to ice causes it to melt, forming the denser liquid. When you walk on ice, you cause it to melt slightly, forming a slippery layer of water on top of the ice. Ice skaters, skiers, snowboarders, and other outdoor winter enthusiasts take advantage of this unique property of water.

Example 12.20

Use Figure 12.27 to describe what happens to a sample of carbon dioxide at 20 atm of pressure when its temperature is increased from −90°C to 25°C.

Solution

Find the region on the phase diagram that represents 20 atm and −90°C and then trace a horizontal line from that position across the diagram, approximating temperatures from the *x*-axis. At 20 atm and −90°C, carbon dioxide is a solid. As it is heated under 20 atm of pressure, it will remain a solid until about −60°C, at which point it will melt to form a liquid. The sample will remain a liquid until the temperature is somewhere close to 0°C, at which point it will vaporize to form gaseous carbon dioxide. It will remain a gas as heat is added to reach 25°C.

PRACTICE PROBLEM 12.20

Use Figure 12.27 to describe what happens to a sample of water at 5 atm of pressure when its temperature is increased from −10°C to 350°C.

Hint: Find the region on the phase diagram that represents 5 atm and −10°C and then trace a horizontal line from that position across the diagram, approximating temperatures from the *x*-axis.

SECTION REVIEW

- Phase diagrams show the states of matter for pure substances at all possible temperatures and pressures.
- Features of phase diagrams include lines indicating the temperature and pressure conditions at which two phases are in equilibrium; the triple point, which is the temperature and pressure where all three phases are in equilibrium; and the critical point, which is the temperature and pressure above which the substance exists as a supercritical fluid.
- Phase diagrams can be used to predict the transition(s) that a substance will undergo if temperature and/or pressure is changed.

12.6 Classification of Solids

GOALS

- Define and describe the various types of solids.
- Classify solids based on their chemical formula.
- Describe relative trends in physical properties based on the type of solid.

Solids are classified first by how organized their particles are and then by the type of particles that make up the solid and the connections between these particles.

Crystalline solids, such as an ice cube or a sodium chloride crystal, have definite melting points, while **amorphous solids**, such as a chocolate bar or glass, get softer as the temperature is raised and gradually form a liquid. The structures of crystalline solids feature regularly repeating arrangements of the constituent particles, whereas the structure of amorphous solids is not regular. Instead, it is less organized and more like the structure of particles in liquids.

Solids have relatively strong forces holding the particles in their proper positions, and the strength of those forces depends on the type of particle making up the solid. The particles in **molecular solids**, such as water or carbon dioxide, are molecules, so they interact via intermolecular forces and melt at relatively low temperatures. **Ionic solids**, such as sodium chloride, are composed of ions interacting via ionic bonds, so they have quite high melting points. Graphite and quartz are **covalent-network solids**, also known as macromolecular solids. They consist of atoms connected by covalent bonds throughout the solid, so they have extremely high melting points. **Metallic solids**, such as iron or mercury, are composed of metal ions loosely held together by their valence electrons, so they have a broad range of melting points. Examples of all four types of solids and their melting points are

TABLE 12.5 Melting Points of Various Types of Solids

Solid Type	Example	Formula	Melting Point (°C)
Molecular	Aspirin	$C_9H_8O_4$	135
	Benzoic acid	$HC_6H_5CO_2$	122.4
	Carbon tetrabromide	CBr_4	90.1
	Carbon tetrachloride	CCl_4	−23
	Carbon tetrafluoride	CF_4	−184
	Helium	He	−272.2 (at 26 atm)
	Naphthalene	$C_{10}H_8$	80.22
	Tetrasulfur tetranitride	S_4N_4	179 (sublimes)
	Water	H_2O	0.00
Ionic	Aluminum oxide	Al_2O_3	2045
	Magnesium oxide	MgO	2800
	Potassium carbonate	K_2CO_3	891
	Sodium chloride	NaCl	801
Covalent Network	Diamond	C	>3550
	Graphite	C	3652 (sublimes)
	Quartz	SiO_2	1610
Metallic	Cesium	Cs	28.4
	Iron	Fe	1535
	Mercury	Hg	−38.87
	Sodium	Na	97.8
	Tungsten	W	3410

listed in Table 12.5. It takes a great deal of energy to disrupt ionic or covalent bonds, which explains why ionic and covalent-network solids have melting points in the hundreds or thousands of degrees Celsius. Much less energy is needed to disrupt intermolecular forces, so molecular solids have melting points below about 200°C. Substances that exist as liquids at these relatively low temperatures are composed of molecules, uncombined atoms (noble gases), or weakly bonded atoms (metals such as mercury). See Table 12.6 for a description of the four types of crystalline solids.

Crystalline solids are characterized by the regular arrangement of units. The sodium chloride structure is an example of an ionic lattice (Figure 12.28). Diamond, graphite (pencil "lead"), and silica (sand) are examples of covalent-network lattices (Figure 12.29). Molecular solids include such solids as ice and naphthalene, $C_{10}H_8$, the major component in mothballs. Most elemental metals are examples of metallic solids. Regardless of their specific classifications, all crystalline solids are characterized by regularly repeating arrangements of their component particles (Table 12.6).

TABLE 12.6 Types of Crystalline Solids

Type	Units	Relative Melting and Boiling Points	Picture
Molecular	Small molecules	Very low to moderate	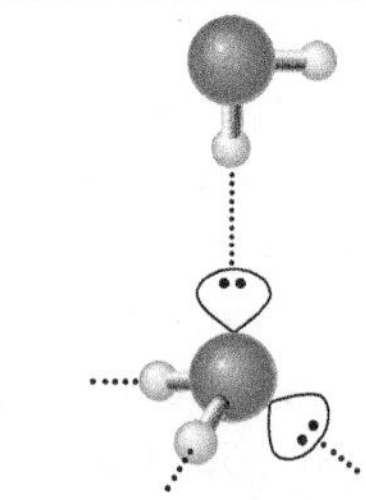
Ionic	Ions	High to very high	
Network	Atoms covalently bonded throughout	Very high	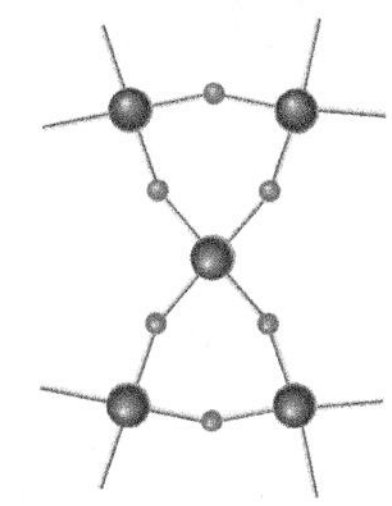
Metallic	Metal atoms bonded by mobile valence electrons	Low to very high	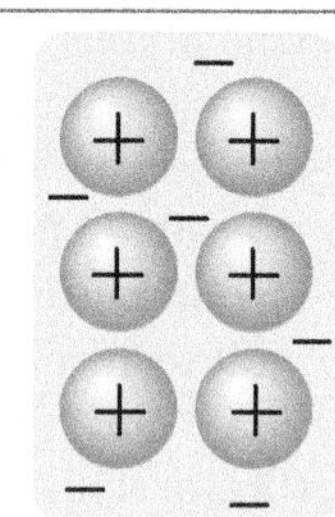

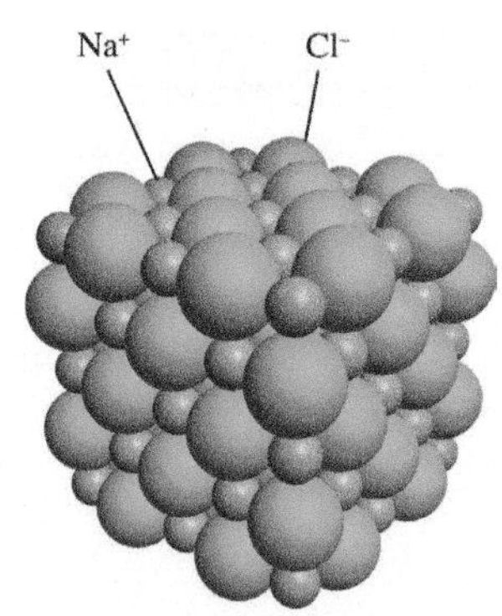

FIGURE 12.28 Sodium Chloride Structure

NOTE: You need to be online to access this video.
Click the image to launch the three-dimensional model.
This illustration represents a very small portion of a sodium chloride, NaCl, crystal, whose actual structure extends for a very large number of ions outward in each of the three directions.

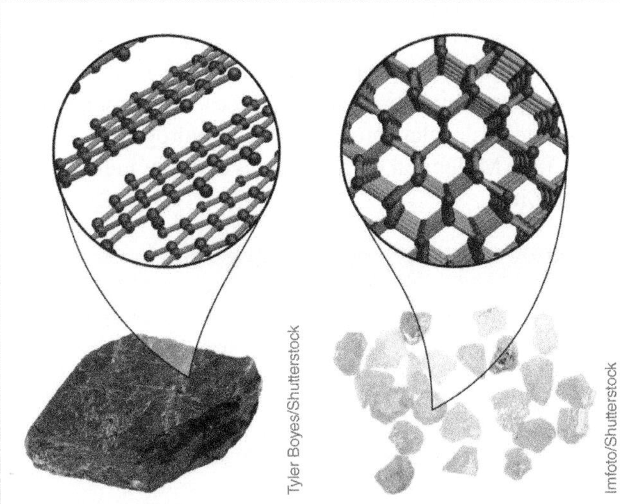

FIGURE 12.29 Structures of Two Covalent-Network Solids

NOTE: You need to be online to access this video.

The bonds in covalent-network solids such as graphite (left) and diamond (right) extend in all directions. Pencil graphite consists of large macromolecules that exist in layers that are scraped off onto the paper as it writes. A quarter-carat diamond is made up of more than 2.5×10^{21} carbon, C, atoms—more than a billion trillion atoms.

An ionic substance is composed of individual positive and negative ions that form a three-dimensional lattice. The attraction of one ion is not limited to any single other ion but extends to all the oppositely charged ions around it. Thus, the attractive forces throughout the lattice are strong, which makes the structure hard to break up. Ionic substances are solids at room temperature.

Example 12.21

How many pairs of ions are included in a tiny cube of rock salt, if 250,000 sodium ions occur on each edge in the three perpendicular directions?

Solution

The volume of a cube is its edge length cubed (raised to the third power). In this case, the edge length is being measured in units of cations. The cube contains $(2.5 \times 10^5)^3 = 1.6 \times 10^{16}$ sodium ions. There are also 1.6×10^{16} chloride ions in this tiny particle of NaCl. A salt cube this size would be invisibly small. Remember that 1.00 mol, or 58.5 g, NaCl includes 6.02×10^{23} formula units of NaCl, which is about 38 million times as many as in this tiny cube.

PRACTICE PROBLEM 12.21

How many iodine molecules and how many iodine atoms are included in a cube of solid I_2 with 250,000 molecules on each edge?

Hint: Cube the number of molecules along an edge to get the total number of molecules. Each I_2 molecule consists of two I atoms.

Example 12.22

a. The atoms in both simple molecular solids (such as ice) and covalent-network solids (such as diamond) are covalently bonded. What is the difference in their structures?
b. Compare HBr with KBr. Which has a higher melting point? Why?

Solution

a. In molecular solids, such as I_2, P_4O_{10}, or $C_6H_{12}O_6$, a few to hundreds of atoms, or even thousands of atoms in polymeric substances such as plastics, are bonded into each molecule. These individual molecules are held together by intermolecular forces. In covalent-network solids, covalent bonds connect all the atoms—many millions of them—in an extended network (see Figure 12.29).
b. HBr is a covalent compound consisting of individual molecules loosely held together into a solid by weak electrostatic interactions known as intermolecular forces (dipole–dipole forces, to be specific). KBr, in contrast, is an ionic compound consisting of oppositely charged ions held together in a solid by very strong electrostatic forces. The melting point of a compound is determined by the strength of the forces holding the individual particles together. Thus, KBr has a much higher melting point than does HBr.

PRACTICE PROBLEM 12.22

What type of solid is described by each of the following statements?

a. Fourteen atoms are covalently bonded in each molecule.
b. A billion billion ions are bonded to one another in a crystal lattice.
c. A billion billion atoms are bonded to one another with covalent bonds.

Hint: Refer to Table 12.6 for the properties of the different types of solids.

EVERYDAY CONNECTION

In 1985, Robert Curl, Harold Kroto, and Richard Smalley found that carbon, C, exists in a previously undiscovered form, with 60 atoms covalently bonded in the shape of a ball. The 60-carbon molecule in the shape of a geodesic dome is named buckminsterfullerene, C_{60} ("buckyball" for short), after Buckminster Fuller, the architect who designed the geodesic dome. Since the discovery of buckminsterfullerene, many other similar molecules have been identified in what is now known as the *fullerene* family of C compounds. The alternating hexagons and pentagons in the C_{60} structure resemble the pattern on a soccer ball.

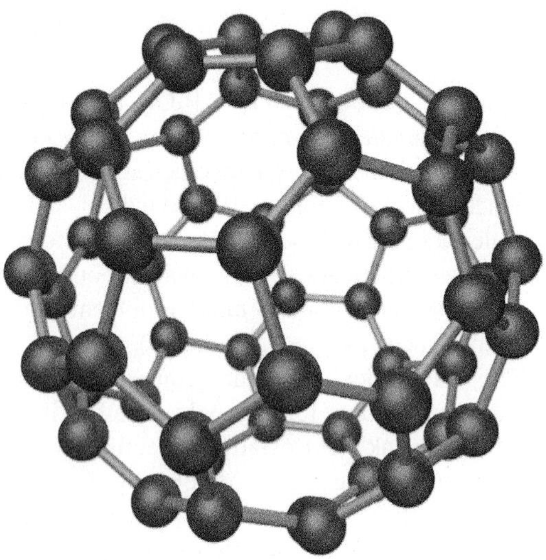

NOTE: You need to be online to access this 3D molecule.
Click the molecule for a three-dimensional view.

Example 12.23

State the type of bonding or force holding together each of the following solids and indicate whether the melting point is low or high.

a. silica, SiO_2
b. potassium chloride, KCl
c. ammonia, NH_3

Solution

a. Silica is a covalent-network solid, so it is held together by covalent bonds. The vast array of covalent bonds means SiO_2 has a high melting point.
b. Potassium chloride is an ionic solid, so it is held together by ionic bonds. Because the electrostatic attractions between opposite charges tend to be strong, KCl has a high melting point.
c. Ammonia is a molecular solid, so it is held together by intermolecular forces. The strongest intermolecular force for NH_3 is hydrogen bonding. Molecular solids have very low melting points.

PRACTICE PROBLEM 12.23

If the melting points for three solids are 90°C, 801°C, and 1475°C, which one is molecular?

Hint: Do molecular solids have high or low melting points? What kind of forces hold molecular solids together?

METALLIC SOLIDS

Metal atoms in a metallic solid do not transfer electrons to form oppositely charged ions, and they do not share electrons to form individual covalent bonds. Instead, the valence electrons of the metal atoms in a metallic solid form a sea of electrons that surrounds the collection of metal cations. This **electron-sea model** of metallic bonding is illustrated for sodium and calcium in Figure 12.30. Sodium, Na, is a group 1 metal and has one valence electron, so each Na atom contributes one electron and becomes a +1 ion. Calcium, Ca, is a group 2 metal, so each Ca atom contributes its two valence electrons and becomes a +2 ion. According

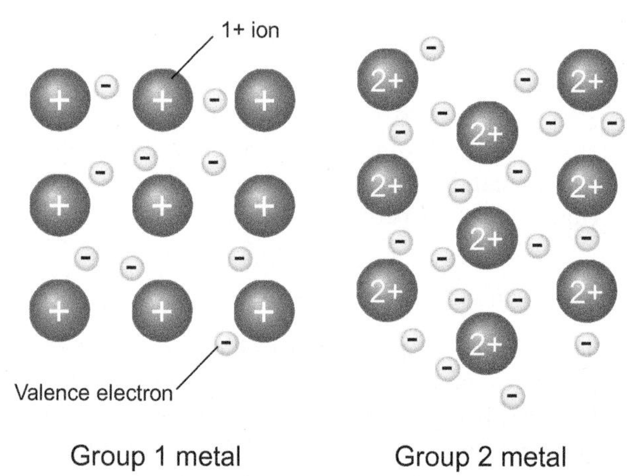

FIGURE 12.30 Electron-Sea Model of Metallic Bonding in Group 1 and Group 2 Solids

NOTE: You need to be online to access this video.
In a solid made up of a group 1 metal such as sodium, Na, each atom contributes one electron, and the solid metal is made up of +1 ions in a sea of freely moving electrons. In a group 2 metal such as magnesium, Mg, each atom contributes two electrons and becomes a +2 ion.

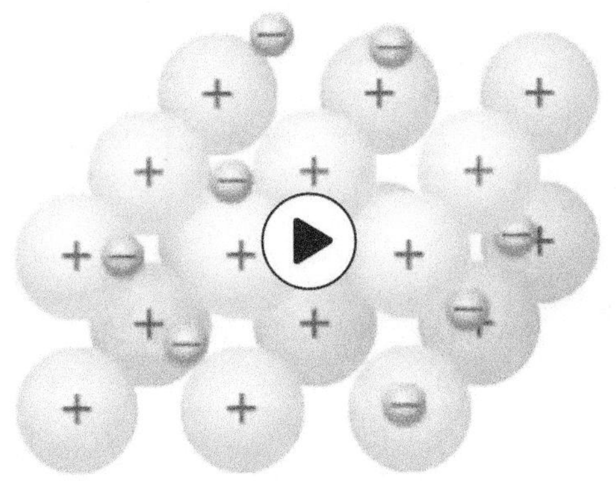

FIGURE 12.31 Electron-Sea Model

NOTE: You must be online to access this video.
In the electron-sea model of metallic bonding, each atom contributes one or more electrons, which are free to move about in the solid or liquid metal.

to the electron-sea model, the valence electrons are not bound to any particular ion but are capable of moving throughout the structure. The electron-sea model helps to explain many of the properties of metals, but it is incomplete. A more complete model, called *band theory*, describes the valence electrons as existing in delocalized, overlapping orbitals (Section 11.5) that extend throughout the metal solid.

The animation in Figure 12.31 shows how electrons can move freely among the metal ions in a metal solid.

Example 12.24

Describe what a diagram similar to those in Figure 12.30 would look like for aluminum. In particular, what charge would the ions have, and how many electrons would there be?

Solution

Aluminum (group 13) has three valence electrons that it can lose to achieve an electron configuration that is isoelectronic with its nearest noble gas (neon). The charge on the ions would be +3. Since each of the aluminum atoms contributes three electrons to the sea of electrons, the diagram would have three electrons for each +3 ion. If the diagram had nine ions like those in Figure 12.30, there would be $9 \times 3 = 27$ electrons.

PRACTICE PROBLEM 12.24

Describe what a diagram similar to those in Figure 12.30 would look like for scandium, assuming that its 4*s* and 3*d* electrons are mobile or delocalized. In particular, what charge would the ions have, and how many electrons would there be per ion?

Hint: Locate scandium in the periodic table to determine the number of 4*s* and 3*d* electrons it has and use that information to determine the ionic charge it forms.

Metal atoms in the solid state are arranged in an orderly array. In a molten (liquid) metal, the atoms are still attracted to one another through metallic bonding, but the metal ions are mobile and randomly scattered, just like the electrons. Metallic bonds are not broken until the metal is vaporized, in which case each ion takes the necessary number of electrons with it and evaporates as a neutral gaseous atom.

Although the individual atoms in a solid or liquid metal are each in ionic form, they have not really "lost" their electrons because all of the electrons are still present in the metal. Even though a piece of aluminum, for example, is made up of an array of ions in a sea of electrons, the metal is still described as neutral Al and not as Al^{3+}. The formula unit for an elemental metal is just the symbol for the element, so a piece of aluminum of any size would be represented simply as Al.

The unique properties of metals are a direct result of metallic bonding. Metals are **malleable**, which means they can be hammered or bent into different shapes without breaking. Metals are also **ductile**, which means they can be drawn into long, thin wires. These properties are possible because metallic bonds do not have a specific direction. The electrons can flow within whatever shape the metal takes, which also allows metals to conduct heat and electricity well.

SECTION REVIEW

- Crystalline solids consist of regularly arranged particles, whereas amorphous solids have particles that are more randomly arranged.
- There are four types of crystalline solids, as determined by the type of particle and bonding between the particles: molecular, ionic, covalent-network, and metallic.
- The melting point of a solid substance depends largely on the type of bond that is holding the particles of the solid together. The general order is molecular solids < metallic solids < ionic and covalent-network solids.
- Metallic solids are composed of metal cations surrounded by a sea of mobile valence electrons that are not associated with any specific ion and are free to move about the entire solid.

12.7 The Unit Cell and the Structure of Crystalline Solids

GOALS

- Describe the structure of various cubic unit cells.
- Perform calculations involving the number of atoms per unit cell as a conversion factor.

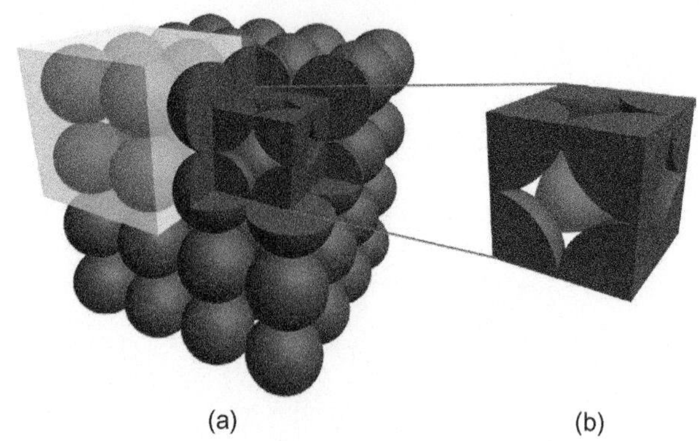

FIGURE 12.32 Simplest Arrangement for Atoms in a Metal Crystal

(a) Atoms are arranged in a very simple array with the second layer superimposed exactly upon the first. (b) The smallest repeating unit is called the unit cell.

The particles in crystalline solids are highly organized (Section 12.6). There are many types of crystal structures, not only because they contain different particles, but also because those particles are organized into different unit cells. The **unit cell** is the simplest repeating unit of a crystal structure. Unit cells arise from how the layers of particles are arranged on top of one another in the solid. Imagine, for example, a layer of atoms arranged in simple rows and columns. When you add more layers directly on top of the first layer, you form the simple three-dimensional array shown in Figure 12.32(a). The smallest repeating unit, the unit cell, is depicted in Figure 12.32(b).

Scientists who study the structure of solids refer to the ways that the layers of atoms are arranged in the three-dimensional structure as **packing**. In the simplest packing arrangement, the atoms in each layer are located immediately above (or below) the atoms of adjacent layers. Other types of packing lead to different three-dimensional structures with different unit cells. There are seven different categories of unit cells, but this text focuses on just **cubic unit cells** (Figure 12.33), which have 90° angles and edges of equal length. They consist of the **simple cubic unit cell** or primitive unit cell,

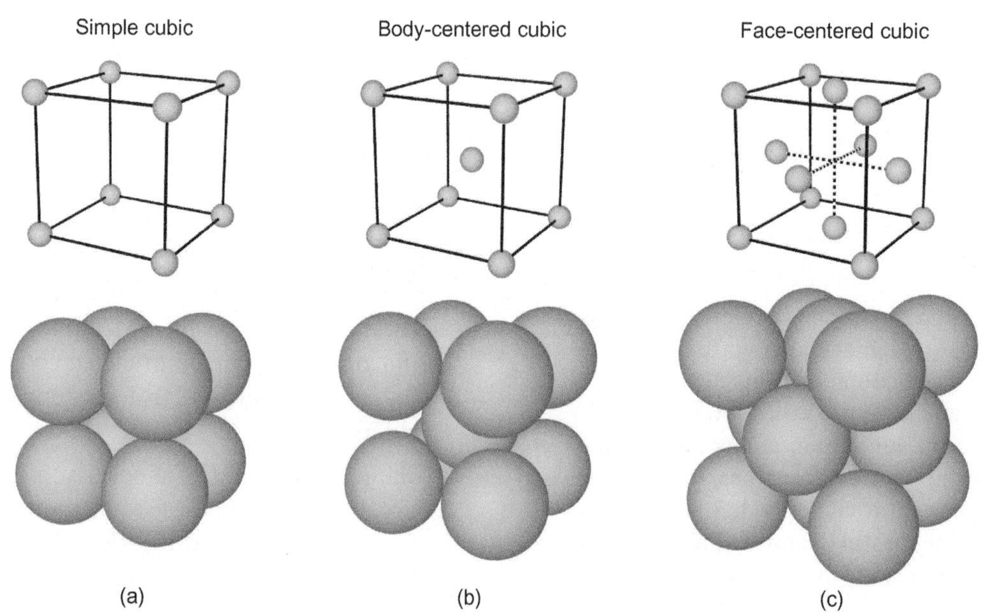

FIGURE 12.33 Cubic Unit Cells

(a) In a simple cubic unit cell, there are atoms at the corners of a cube. (b) A body-centered cubic unit cell has atoms at each corner, too, as well as an atom in the center of the cube. (c) A face-centered cubic unit cell has atoms at each corner and an atom in the center of each face of the cube.

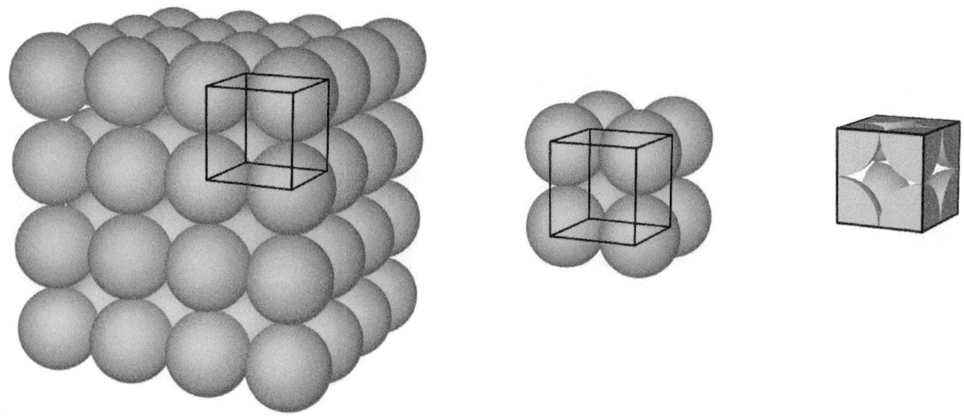

FIGURE 12.34 Counting Atoms in a Simple Cubic Unit Cell
Each atom is on the corner of the unit cell, with one-eighth of the atom contained within the volume of the unit cell. Eight corners times one-eighth of an atom in each corner gives $8(1/8) = 1$ atom per simple cubic unit cell.

the **body-centered cubic, bcc, unit cell**, and the **face-centered cubic, fcc, unit cell**.

Figure 12.34 shows how to count the number of atoms in a simple cubit unit cell. In this unit cell, there is an atom located at each of the eight corners of the cube, but only one-eighth of each atom is located within the boundaries of the unit cell.

Body-centered cubic unit cells form when the layers of atoms do not stack directly on top of each other but alternate in offset layers as shown in Figure 12.35. Notice that the atoms in the second layer are located above the spaces between the atoms of the first layer and that the layers alternate these two positions. That same figure also shows how to count the number of atoms in a body-centered cubic unit cell. In this unit cell, there is an atom located at each of the eight corners of the cube, but just like the simple cubic unit cell, only one-eighth of each atom is located within the boundaries of the unit cell. Unlike the simple cubic unit cell, though, the body-centered cubic unit cell also has an atom located at the center of the cube that is completely within the boundaries of the unit cell.

Figure 12.36 shows how to count the number of atoms in a face-centered cubic unit cell. In this unit cell, there is an atom located at each of the eight corners of the cube, but just like the simple cubic and body-centered cubic unit cells, only one-eighth of

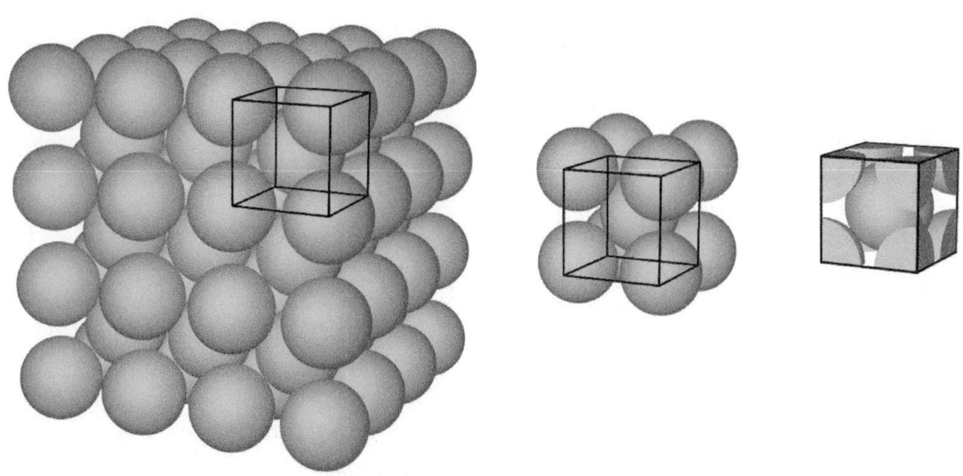

FIGURE 12.35 Counting Atoms in a Body-Centered Cubic Unit Cell
There is an atom at each corner of the unit cell, with one-eighth of each corner atom contained within the volume of the unit cell. The central "body" atom is completely within the boundaries of the unit cell. One body atom plus eight corners (at one-eighth of an atom each) gives $1 + 8(1/8) = 2$ atoms per body-centered cubic unit cell.

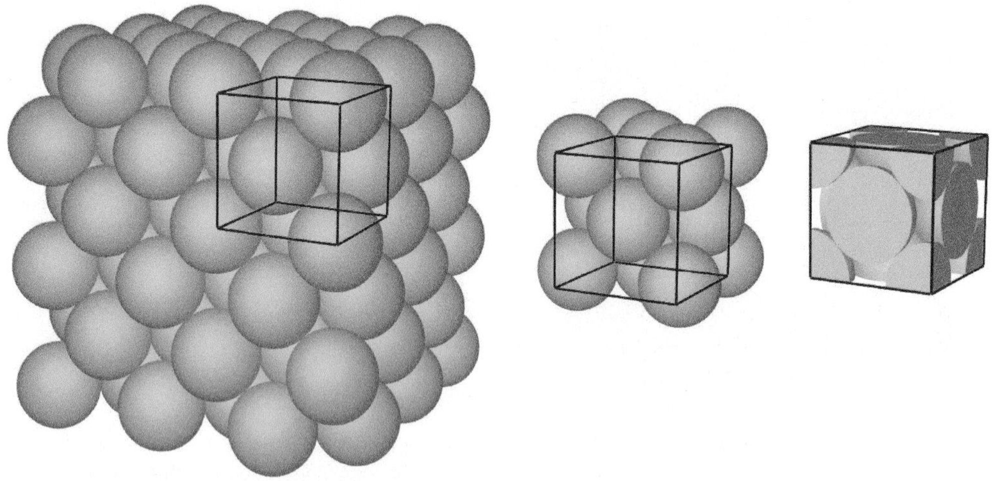

FIGURE 12.36 Counting Atoms in a Face-Centered Cubic Unit Cell

There is an atom at each corner of the unit cell, with one-eighth of each corner atom contained within the volume of the unit cell. Each "face" atom is shared with one other unit cell, so one-half is contained within the volume of a given unit cell. Six face atoms times one-half of an atom plus eight corners times one-eighth of an atom gives $6(1/2) + 8(1/8) = 4$ atoms per face-centered cubic unit cell.

each atom is located within the boundaries of the unit cell. The face-centered cubic unit cell also has an atom in the center of each face of the cube. Only one-half of each of these six atoms, though, is located within the boundaries of the unit cell.

Both the simple cubic unit cell and the body-centered unit cell include a great deal of empty space between the atoms. Other types of packing, called **close-packing**, result in a solid structure that uses space more effectively. One type of close-packing, called **hexagonal close-packing, hcp**, involves a two-layer repeat and forms a hexagonal unit cell (Figure 12.37a). These two layers start with an array of atoms in which each atom is in close contact with six other atoms. This arrangement forms six triangular-shaped empty spaces (holes) around each atom. The atoms in the second layer are arranged in a similar array but rotated to locate the atoms above the triangular holes. The second layer fills three of the six triangular holes around each atom. These layers alternate to form the crystal.

Atoms in the **cubic close-packing, ccp**, arrangement (Figure 12.37b) form layers similar to the ones in hexagonal close-packing. The atoms in each layer are in close contact with six neighboring atoms, forming the six triangular holes around each atom. The second

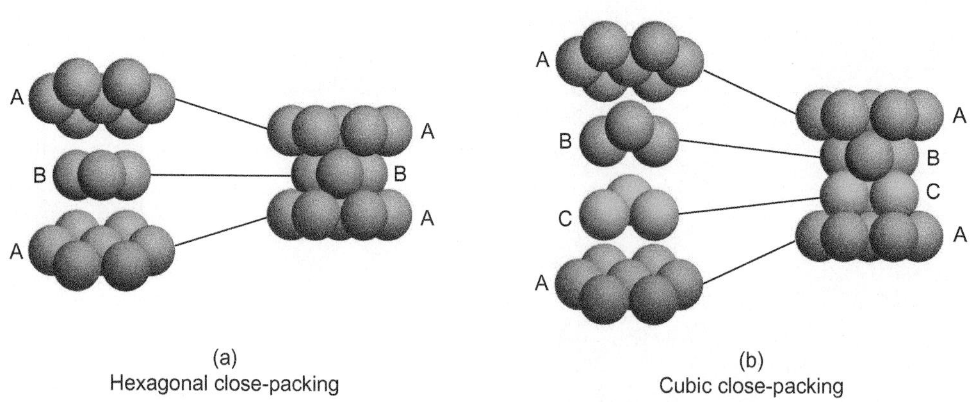

FIGURE 12.37 Close-Packing of Atoms in a Metal Crystal: Hexagonal versus Cubic

(a) In hexagonal close-packing, hcp, the B layer is rotated with respect to the A layer, and these two layers repeat to form the crystal.
(b) In cubic close-packing, ccp, the B layer is rotated with respect to the A layer, and a third layer, the C layer, places the atoms over the other half of the triangular holes from the A layer. These three layers repeat to form the crystal.
NOTE: The spheres all represent the same type of atom (the colors are meant only to distinguish layers).

TABLE 12.7 Summary of Cubic Unit Cells

Unit Cell	Atoms per Unit Cell	Packing Efficiency	Coordination Number	Relation of Edge Length and Radius
Simple cubic	1	52%	6	$l = 2r$
Body-centered cubic	2	68%	8	$l = \frac{4r}{\sqrt{3}}$
Face-centered cubic	4	74%	12	$l = \sqrt{8} \cdot r$

layer is rotated with respect to the first, locating atoms above half of the triangular holes. Cubic close-packing involves a third layer, rotated to place the atoms over the other three triangular holes from the first layer. These three layers are repeated to form a face-centered cubic unit cell.

Example 12.25

Compare a hypothetical form of copper composed of simple cubic unit cells and another hypothetical form of copper composed of face-centered cubic, fcc, unit cells. Would these two solids have the same density?

Solution

The simple unit cell (Figure 12.34), with an atom at each corner, contains only one complete atom per unit cell, so it contains a lot of empty space.

$$\frac{8 \text{ corners}}{1 \text{ unit cell}} \times \frac{\frac{1}{8} \text{ atom}}{1 \text{ corner}} = 1 \frac{\text{atom}}{\text{unit cell}}$$

The face-centered cubic unit cell (Figure 12.36), with an atom on each corner and an atom on each face, contains four complete atoms per unit cell, so it has closer packing than does the simple unit cell.

$$\frac{8 \text{ corners}}{1 \text{ unit cell}} \times \frac{\frac{1}{8} \text{ atom}}{1 \text{ corner}} + \frac{6 \text{ faces}}{1 \text{ unit cell}} \times \frac{\frac{1}{2} \text{ atom}}{1 \text{ face}} = 4 \frac{\text{atoms}}{\text{unit cell}}$$

The solid composed of face-centered cubic unit cells, with more atoms per unit cell and less empty space per unit cell, would have a higher density.

PRACTICE PROBLEM 12.25

Compare a hypothetical form of iron composed of face-centered cubic, fcc, unit cells and another hypothetical form of iron composed of body-centered cubic, bcc, unit cells. Would these two solids have the same density?

Hint: Compare the number of atoms in each unit cell. Unit cells containing more atoms have more mass and less empty space.

Table 12.7 summarizes important information about the different unit cells, such as the number of atoms and the use of space in the different unit cells. The table includes the **packing efficiency**, which is the fraction of the volume of the unit cell occupied by atoms, and the **coordination number**, which tells you the number of nearest neighbor atoms for each atom in the structure. Another very useful bit of information in the table is the relationship between the atomic radius, r, and the edge length, l, of the unit cell.

Example 12.26

Copper has an atomic radius of 128 pm. Using the information in Table 12.7, calculate and compare the densities of two hypothetical forms of copper, (a) one consisting of simple unit cells and (b) the other of face-centered cubic unit cells.

Solution

Density is the mass per unit volume. It is typically given in units of grams per cubic centimeters for solids.

a. Start by finding the mass of one unit cell. Recall that for a simple cubic unit cell, there is 1 atom per unit cell. Convert the number of atoms to number of moles, and finally to grams.

$$m = \frac{1 \text{ atom}}{\text{unit cell}} \times \frac{1 \text{ mol}}{6.022 \times 10^{23} \text{ atoms}} \times \frac{63.546 \text{ g Cu}}{1 \text{ mol Cu}}$$
$$= 1.055 \times 10^{-22} \frac{\text{g}}{\text{unit cell}}$$

Now find the volume of a unit cell. Since the desired unit of density is g/cm^3, start by converting the radius from picometers to centimeters.

$$r = 128 \text{ pm} \times \frac{1 \text{ m}}{1 \times 10^{12} \text{ pm}} \times \frac{100 \text{ cm}}{1 \text{ m}}$$
$$= 1.28 \times 10^{-8} \text{ cm}$$

Use the formula for edge length found in Table 12.7.

$$l = 2r = 2(1.28 \times 10^{-8} \text{ cm}) = 2.56 \times 10^{-8} \text{ cm}$$

Recall that volume is length cubed.

$$V = l^3 = (2.56 \times 10^{-8} \text{ cm})^3 = 1.68 \times 10^{-23} \text{ cm}^3$$

Calculate the density, $d = m/V$.

$$d = \frac{m}{V} = \frac{1.055 \times 10^{-22}\ \text{g}}{1.68 \times 10^{-23}\ \text{cm}^3} = 6.29\ \text{g/cm}^3$$

b. A face-centered cubic unit cell contains four atoms.

$$m = \frac{4\ \text{atoms}}{\text{unit cell}} \times \frac{1\ \text{mol}}{6.022 \times 10^{23}\ \text{atoms}} \times \frac{63.546\ \text{g Cu}}{1\ \text{mol Cu}}$$
$$= 4.221 \times 10^{-22} \frac{\text{g}}{\text{unit cell}}$$

Calculate the length of one side of the cube from the radius in centimeters.

$$l = \sqrt{8}r = \sqrt{8}(1.28 \times 10^{-8}\ \text{cm}) = 3.62 \times 10^{-8}\ \text{cm}$$

Find the volume from the length, then calculate the density from the mass and volume.

$$V = l^3 = (3.62 \times 10^{-8}\ \text{cm})^3 = 4.75 \times 10^{-23}\ \text{cm}^3$$

$$d = \frac{m}{V} = \frac{4.221 \times 10^{-22}\ \text{g}}{4.75 \times 10^{-23}\ \text{cm}^3} = 8.89\ \text{g/cm}^3$$

The density of the fcc form of copper ($8.9\ \text{g/cm}^3$) is 41% greater than the density of the simple cubic form of copper ($6.3\ \text{g/cm}^3$).

PRACTICE PROBLEM 12.26

Use the information in Table 12.7 to calculate the density of a hypothetical form of copper that consists of body-centered cubic, bcc, unit cells. Compare it with the densities calculated in Example 12.26 for the other hypothetical forms of copper.

Hint: First, determine the mass of a unit cell in grams. Then, use the atomic radius and the relationship between unit cell length and atomic radius for a body-centered cubic unit cell to determine the edge length and to determine the volume of a unit cell. Finally, use $d = m/V$ to calculate the density.

The measured density of copper, Cu, is $8.96\ \text{g/cm}^3$, suggesting that copper atoms pack in cubic close-packing layers to form a face-centered cubic unit cell. Copper is one of 19 elements that form face-centered cubic unit cells as solids. Approximately 15 elements form crystalline solids with body-centered cubic unit cells, and only one, polonium, Po, forms a solid with a simple unit cell. The remaining elements form crystalline solids that consist of noncubic unit cells.

Example 12.27

Determine the radius of barium in picometers, given that it forms a body-centered cubic, bcc, crystal structure with a density of $3.59\ \text{g/cm}^3$.

Solution

First, find the mass per unit cell.

$$m = \frac{2\ \text{atoms}}{1\ \text{unit cell}} \times \frac{1\ \text{mol}}{6.022 \times 10^{23}\ \text{atoms}} \times \frac{137.33\ \text{g Ba}}{1\ \text{mol Ba}}$$
$$= 4.561 \times 10^{-22} \frac{\text{g}}{\text{unit cell}}$$

Next, use the density as a conversion factor between mass and volume.

$$V = 4.561 \times 10^{-22}\ \text{g} \times \frac{1\ \text{cm}^3}{3.59\ \text{g}} = 1.27 \times 10^{-22}\ \text{cm}^3$$

Determine the length of the unit cell by taking the cube root of the volume.

$$l = \sqrt[3]{V} = \sqrt[3]{1.27 \times 10^{-22}\ \text{cm}^3} = 5.03 \times 10^{-8}\ \text{cm}$$

Convert the edge length from centimeters to picometers.

$$5.03 \times 10^{-8}\ \text{cm} \times \frac{1\ \text{m}}{100\ \text{cm}} \times \frac{10^{12}\ \text{pm}}{1\ \text{m}} = 503\ \text{pm}$$

The length of the unit cell is related to the radius by the equation given in Table 12.7, $l = \frac{4r}{\sqrt{3}}$. Rearrange this relationship and then substitute in the values to calculate the radius of the barium atom.

$$l = \frac{4r}{\sqrt{3}}$$

$$r = \frac{\sqrt{3}l}{4} = \frac{\sqrt{3}(503\ \text{pm})}{4} = 218\ \text{pm}$$

PRACTICE PROBLEM 12.27

Determine the radius of rhodium in picometers, given that it forms a face-centered cubic, fcc, crystal structure with a density of $12.41\ \text{g/cm}^3$.

Hint: Find the mass of one unit cell in grams, then use the density to find the volume of the unit cell. The cube root of the volume is the length of the unit cell, which is related to the radius by the relationship given in Table 12.7, $l = \sqrt{8}r$.

Ionic solids consist of cations and anions of very different sizes, with the anions typically much larger than the cations. In the case of sodium chloride, NaCl (Figure 12.38), the larger Cl^- ions adopt a face-centered unit cell arrangement with the Na^+ ions occupying the spaces between the Cl^- ions. The Na^+ ions are also in a face-centered unit cell arrangement with the Cl^- ions occupying the spaces between the Na^+ ions.

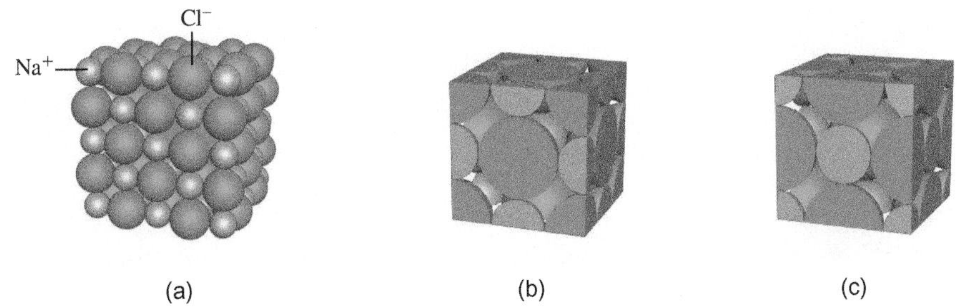

FIGURE 12.38 Sodium Chloride Unit Cell
(a) Na^+ cations are smaller than Cl^- anions. (b) The larger Cl^- anions form a face-centered cubic unit cell, and the smaller Na^+ cations fit in the spaces between Cl^- ions. (c) From the perspective of the cations, Na^+ also forms a face-centered cubic unit cell, with the Cl^- ions occupying the spaces in between.

EVERYDAY CONNECTION

Alloys, which are homogeneous mixtures of metals, form solid structures in much the same way that pure metals do—namely, in layers of atoms. One example is nitinol, a mixture of nickel, Ni, and titanium, Ti, in which alternating layers of Ni and Ti form a body-centered cubic unit cell.

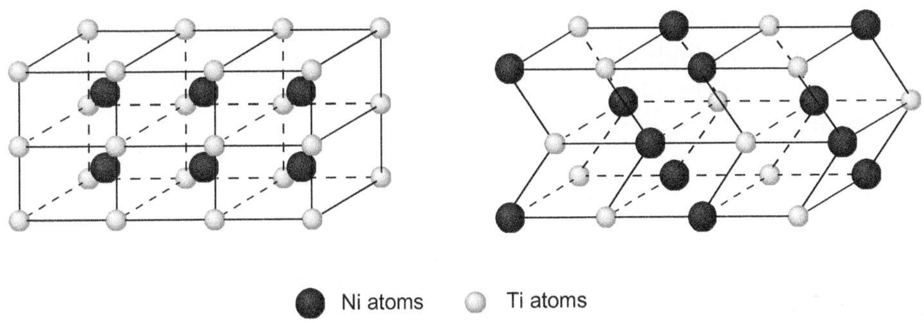

The body-centered cubic unit cell version undergoes a phase change when cooled to form a hexagonal unit cell version, which changes its overall shape. When the nitinol is rewarmed, however, it undergoes a phase change back to the body-centered cubic unit cell structure, thus reverting to the shape that it originally had at the higher temperature. This memory-shape property makes nitinol useful in many applications, including surgical implants and braces for orthodontia.

The anions and the cations in cesium chloride, CsCl, each form a simple unit cell with the other ion in the body position as shown in Figure 12.39.

SECTION REVIEW

- Unit cells, the smallest repeating unit of a crystal structure, form based on how the layers of particles are arranged or packed upon each other.
- Different packing arrangements result in
  - the formation of different unit cells, such as simple cubic unit cells, body-centered cubic (bcc) unit cells, and face-centered cubic (fcc) unit cells; and
  - differences in the use of space, with the simple cubic unit cell being the least efficient and the face-centered cubic unit cell being one of the most efficient, and different coordination numbers.
- Close-packing of spheres involves layering atoms in the depressions (holes) of the previous layer. Some examples of close-packing arrangements are cubic close-packing (ccp) and hexagonal close-packing (hcp).
- Density, unit cell type, and atomic radius are related mathematically.
- Anions and cations form unit cells in ionic solids.

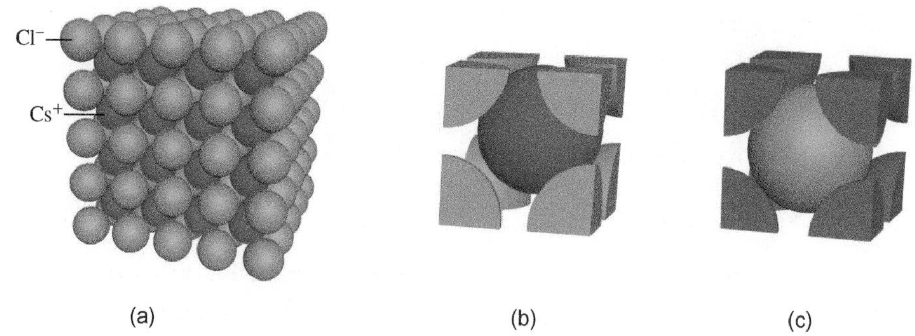

FIGURE 12.39 Cesium Chloride Unit Cell

(a) Cs^+ cations and Cl^- anions are approximately the same size. (b) The Cl^- anions form a simple cubic unit cell with the Cs^+ cations occupying the body space. (c) From the perspective of the cations, Cs also forms a simple cubic unit cell with the Cl^- ions occupying the body space.

Putting It Together

The example problems in earlier sections of this chapter focus on just the new skills acquired in that section, but homework and exam questions in chemistry often require more than just one skill at a time. In fact, you will likely be expected to apply knowledge from across the entire chapter, or even multiple chapters, in a single problem. This final example problem is meant to help you prepare for these types of multiconcept questions. Additional examples can be found in the end-of-chapter exercises.

Example 12.28

Use the data provided to estimate the normal boiling point of octane, C_8H_{18}.

Hydrocarbon, Formula	Normal Boiling Point, °C
Propane, C_3H_8	−42.1
Butane, C_4H_{10}	−0.5
Pentane, C_5H_{12}	36.1
Hexane, C_6H_{14}	68.7
Heptane, C_7H_{16}	98.4
Octane, C_8H_{18}	?

Draw structures to help explain your reasoning (in each structure, the carbon atoms will all be connected in one long chain).

Solution

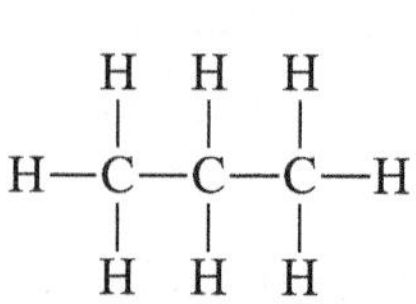

Propane

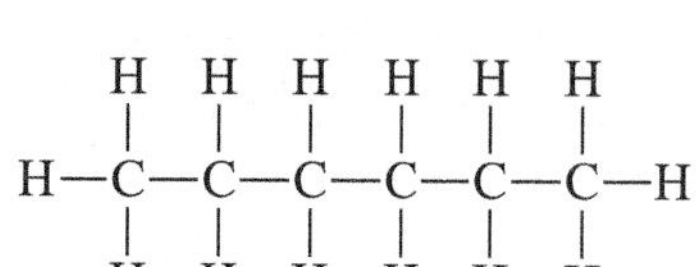

Hexane

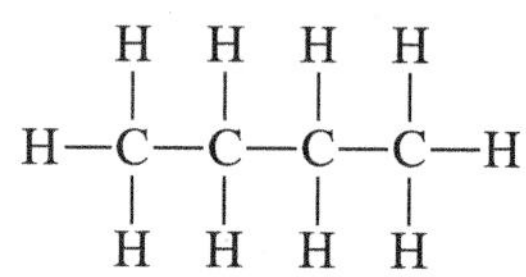

Butane

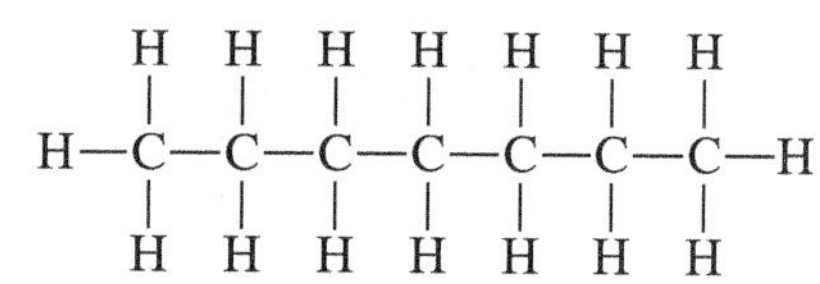

Heptane

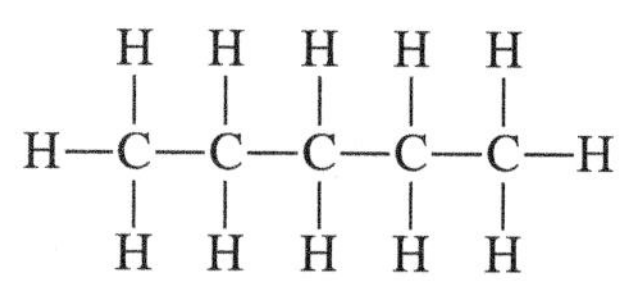

Pentane

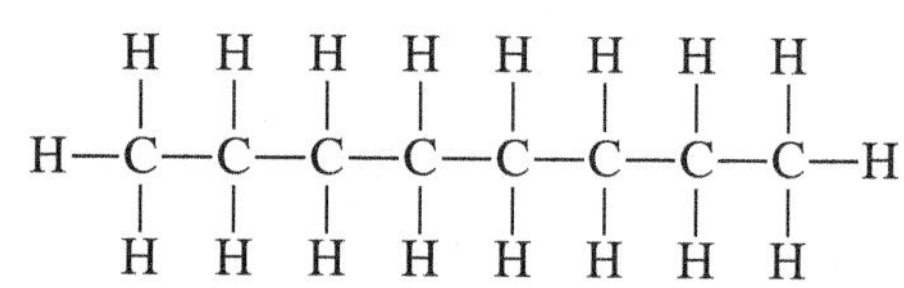

Octane

These hydrocarbons have very symmetrical shapes and are nonpolar. As the number of atoms in the molecules increases from propane to heptane, the strength of the dispersion forces between molecules increases. Based on this trend, the dispersion forces in octane should be stronger than those in heptane. Each added CH_2 unit adds to the strength of the dispersion forces.

This added strength is reflected in the normal boiling-point data, which show a higher temperature with each CH_2 unit added to the molecular formula. For example, the ΔT column in the following table shows that the boiling point increases 41.6°C between propane, C_3H_8, and butane, C_4H_8.

Hydrocarbon, Formula	Normal Boiling Point, °C	ΔT, °C
Propane, C_3H_8	−42.1	—
Butane, C_4H_{10}	−0.5	41.6
Pentane, C_5H_{12}	36.1	36.6
Hexane, C_6H_{14}	68.7	32.6
Heptane, C_7H_{16}	98.4	29.7
Octane, C_8H_{18}	? (predicted)	? (predicted)

Notice, however, that the increase in boiling point, ΔT, decreases by a few degrees as the molecular size increases. Therefore, a reasonable prediction for the normal boiling point for octane is the boiling point of heptane $+28°C$. This gives a predicted normal boiling point of 126°C for octane. The measured normal boiling point of octane is 125°C—quite close to the value predicted from the trends in the data.

PRACTICE PROBLEM 12.28

The data in the table are for a series of alcohols, a family of compounds similar to the hydrocarbons in Example 12.28 but with one H atom replaced by O—H.

Alcohol, Formula	Normal Boiling Point, °C
Propanol, C_3H_8O	97
Butanol, $C_4H_{10}O$	117
Pentanol, $C_5H_{12}O$	138
Hexanol, $C_6H_{14}O$	158
Heptanol, $C_7H_{16}O$	176
Octanol, $C_8H_{18}O$	?

a. Why are the boiling points for these alcohols so much higher than the boiling points of the hydrocarbons in Example 12.28? Draw structures to help explain your reasoning.

b. Use the data provided to estimate the normal boiling point of octanol, $C_8H_{18}O$.

The increase in boiling point, ΔT, may decrease slightly as the molecular size increases (see how the increase from hexanol to heptanol is only 18°C), but there are insufficient data to draw that conclusion. Therefore, the prediction for the normal boiling point for octanol is the boiling point of heptanol + 18–20°C = 176°C + 18–20°C = 194–196°C. The measured normal boiling point of octanol is 195°C, which falls within the values predicted from the trends in the data.

Hint: What intermolecular force can form between molecules containing an O—H group that is not possible with the hydrocarbon compounds?

Alcohol, Formula	Normal Boiling Point, °C	ΔT, °C
Propanol, C_3H_8O	97	—
Butanol, $C_4H_{10}O$	117	20
Pentanol, $C_5H_{12}O$	138	21
Hexanol, $C_6H_{14}O$	158	20
Heptanol, $C_7H_{16}O$	176	18
Octanol, $C_8H_{18}O$	? (predicted)	? (predicted)

Key Terms, Symbols, and Equations

KEY TERMS

adhesion (12.2): Attraction to different particles.

amorphous solid (12.6): A solid whose structure consists of irregular arrangements of the constituent particles.

body-centered cubic, bcc, unit cell (12.7): A cubic unit cell with one atom in the center of the cell and atoms at the eight corners.

capillary action (12.2): The ability to flow against gravity up a narrow tube.

Clausius–Clapeyron equation (12.4): The relationship among vapor pressure, temperature, and enthalpy of vaporization.

close-packing (12.7): A packing arrangement that uses space efficiently.

cohesion (12.2): Attraction to like particles.

condensation (12.3): The transition from gas to liquid phase.

coordination number (12.7): The number of nearest neighbors for each atom in a crystalline structure.

covalent-network solid (12.6): A solid whose constituent particles are atoms that interact via covalent bonds. Also called a macromolecular solid.

critical point (12.5): The pressure and temperature above which a substance no longer exists as either a liquid or a gas.

critical pressure (12.5): The pressure above which a substance no longer exists as either a liquid or a gas.

critical temperature (12.5): The temperature above which a substance no longer exists as either a liquid or a gas.

crystalline solid (12.6): A solid whose structure consists of regular repeating arrangements of the constituent particles.

cubic close-packing, ccp (12.7): A three-layer, efficient packing arrangement that forms a face-centered cubic unit cell.

cubic unit cell (12.7): A unit cell with equal length edges and 90° angles.

deposition (12.3): The transition between gas and solid phase.

dipole–dipole attraction (12.1): The temporary attraction between polar molecules.

dispersion forces (12.1): The temporary, weak attraction between an instantaneous dipole and an induced dipole. Also called London forces or London dispersion forces.

distillation (12.4): The process of vaporizing a liquid and collecting its vapors.

ductile (12.6): Able to be drawn into a thin wire.

electron-sea model (12.6): The model in which the valence electrons of atoms in a metallic solid form a sea of mobile electrons surrounding the metal cations.

enthalpy of fusion, ΔH_{fus} (12.3): The energy required for the fusion or melting of 1 mol of a solid.

enthalpy of sublimation, ΔH_{sub} (12.3): The energy required for the sublimation of 1 mol of a solid.

enthalpy of vaporization, ΔH_{vap} (12.3): The energy required for the vaporization of 1 mol of a liquid.

equilibrium (12.4): The dynamic situation in which two opposing processes occur at the same rate, resulting in no net change.

face-centered cubic, fcc, unit cell (12.7): The cubic unit cell with an atom on each of the six faces and an atom at each of the eight corners.

freezing (12.3): The transition from liquid to solid phase.

fusion (12.3): The transition from solid to liquid phase (melting).

heat of vaporization (12.4): The energy required for the vaporization of 1 mol of a liquid.

heating curve (12.3): A graph showing how the temperature and phase change as energy is added to a pure substance.

hexagonal close-packing, hcp (12.7): A two-layer, efficient packing arrangement that forms a hexagonal unit cell.

hydrogen bond (12.1): The unusually strong dipole–dipole attraction formed between partially positive hydrogen atoms and a highly electronegative atom (fluorine, oxygen, or nitrogen) with a lone pair of electrons.

hydrogen bond acceptor (12.1): A molecule containing a highly electronegative atom (fluorine, oxygen, or nitrogen) with a lone pair of electrons.

hydrogen bond donor (12.1): A molecule containing an H—N, H—O, or H—F bond.

induced dipole (12.1): A temporarily uneven distribution of electrons caused by the proximity of a spontaneous dipole.

instantaneous dipole (12.1): A temporarily uneven distribution of electrons caused by a spontaneous shift in electron density.

intermolecular force (12.1): An attractive force that forms between particles in the liquid and solid phases.

ion–dipole attraction (12.1): The temporary attraction between ions and a polar molecule; important in the formation of solutions.

ionic solid (12.6): A solid whose constituent particles are ions that interact via ionic bonds.

malleable (12.6): Able to bend or change shape without breaking when force is applied.

metallic solid (12.6): A solid whose constituent particles are metal atoms that are loosely held by their valence electrons.

molecular solid (12.6): A solid whose constituent particles are molecules that interact via intermolecular forces.

nonvolatile (12.4): Refers to a substance that does not easily vaporize.

normal boiling point (12.4): The boiling point of a liquid at a pressure of 1.00 atm.

packing (12.7): How layers of atoms are arranged in a crystalline solid.

packing efficiency (12.7): The fraction of the volume of the unit cell occupied by atoms.

phase diagram (12.5): A graph showing the phase of a substance under all possible pressure and temperature combinations.

polarizability (12.1): The measure of how readily an electron cloud can become asymmetric.

simple cubic unit cell (12.7): The simplest form of cubic unit cell, with one atom at each corner. Also called a primitive unit cell.

sublimation (12.3): The direct transition from solid phase to gas phase.

supercritical fluid (12.5): The fourth phase of matter, existing at pressures and temperatures above the critical point.

surface tension (12.2): The tendency of a liquid to minimize its surface area.

triple point (12.5): The pressure and temperature at which all three phases of the substance are in equilibrium.

unit cell (12.7): The simplest repeating unit of a crystal structure.

van der Waals forces (12.1): Sometimes used as a general term for any intermolecular force and sometimes used as a synonym for dispersion forces.

vapor (12.3): A gas in contact with its liquid phase.

vaporization (12.3): The transition from liquid to gas phase (evaporation).

viscosity (12.2): The resistance to flow of a liquid.

volatile (12.4): Refers to a substance that can easily vaporize.

SYMBOLS AND ABBREVIATIONS

bcc (body-centered cubic) (12.7)

ccp (cubic close-packing) (12.7)

ΔH_{fus} (enthalpy of fusion) (12.3)

ΔH_{sub} (enthalpy of sublimation) (12.3)

ΔH_{vap} (enthalpy of vaporization) (12.3)

fcc (face-centered cubic) (12.7)

hcp (hexagonal close-packing) (12.7)

l (edge length) (12.7)

r (radius) (12.7)

EQUATIONS

$q = n(\Delta H)$ (12.1)

$q = m(\Delta H)$ (12.2)

$$\ln P_{vap} = \frac{-\Delta H_{vap}}{R}\left(\frac{1}{T}\right) + \ln \beta \quad (12.3)$$

$$\ln \frac{P_2}{P_1} = \frac{\Delta H_{vap}}{R}\left(\frac{1}{T_1} - \frac{1}{T_2}\right) \quad (12.4)$$

Chapter Summary

The attractive forces that hold particles together in the solid and liquid phases are weak and temporary, which distinguishes them from chemical bonds. These forces are generally known as intermolecular forces, even if particles other than molecules are involved. These intermolecular forces are based on weak, temporary electrical attractions between particles and are divided into four groups, based on the types of particles involved. Ions and polar molecules, such as water, interact via ion–dipole forces, the strongest of the intermolecular forces. Polar molecules contain partially positive and partially negative regions, thus forming dipoles. Oppositely charged ends of neighboring dipoles interact via dipole–dipole attractions. Hydrogen bonds are unusually strong dipole–dipole attractions that form between hydrogen bond donors and hydrogen bond acceptors. Hydrogen bond donor molecules contain a strongly partially positive hydrogen, H, atom bonded to fluorine, F, oxygen, O, or nitrogen, N, whereas hydrogen bond acceptor molecules contain a highly electronegative F, O, or N atom with at least one available lone pair of electrons. The hydrogen bond forms between the partially positive H of the donor and a lone pair of electrons on the F, O, or N atom of the acceptor. When a molecule is nonpolar, momentary asymmetry in the distribution of electrons around the molecule causes weak dipoles to exist briefly. These instantaneous dipoles can induce the formation of temporary dipoles in adjacent molecules, resulting in short-lived instantaneous dipole–induced dipole attractions known as dispersion forces. Dispersion forces are generally the weakest intermolecular forces, though they become stronger as the number of polarizable electrons in a molecule increases (Section 12.1).

Attractions between particles give liquids unique properties such as viscosity, surface tension, and capillary action. The viscosity of a liquid, which is the resistance to flow, depends on the strength of the intermolecular forces and the temperature. Stronger intermolecular forces increase viscosity, whereas higher temperatures decrease viscosity.

Surface tension is the tendency of a liquid to reduce its surface area, and it also depends on the strengths of the intermolecular forces. Capillary action, the ability of a liquid to move up a narrow tube, involves cohesion (the attraction between molecules of a liquid) and adhesion (the attraction between molecules of a liquid and the surface of the tube). Both cohesion and adhesion involve the formation of intermolecular forces (Section 12.2).

Transitions between states of matter, or phase changes, are accompanied by the addition or release of energy. Transitions from solid to liquid (fusion), liquid to gas (vaporization), and solid to gas (sublimation) have positive enthalpy values (they absorb heat). The reverse transitions, from gas to liquid (condensation), liquid to solid (freezing), and gas to solid (deposition), have negative enthalpy values (they release heat). The magnitude of the enthalpy changes associated with fusion, vaporization, and sublimation depends on the strengths of the intermolecular attractions between the particles of the substance. Each pure substance requires a specific enthalpy change per mole for a phase transition. These enthalpy changes are denoted as ΔH_{fus}, ΔH_{vap}, and ΔH_{sub}. The temperature of a substance does not change during phase changes because the heat that is added is used to overcome intermolecular forces, rather than to increase its temperature. Heating curves show the temperature and phase transitions for a pure substance as heat energy is added (Section 12.3).

Liquids and molecular solids can be in equilibrium with their molecules in the gas phase at the same temperature because, in any sample, some molecules will have higher energies than do others, allowing some molecules to enter the gas phase. Similarly, some gas molecules will have lower energies than do others, so some gas molecules will re-enter the liquid or solid phase. The Clausius–Clapeyron equation relates the vapor pressure of a substance at a specific temperature with its heat of vaporization:

$$\ln P_{vap} = -\frac{\Delta H_{vap}}{R}\left(\frac{1}{T}\right) + \ln \beta$$

This equation can be used to calculate the heat of vaporization of a substance from measurements of vapor pressure at different temperatures. The two-point version of the equation is useful when data are available for only two temperatures:

$$\ln \frac{P_2}{P_1} = \frac{\Delta H_{vap}}{R}\left(\frac{1}{T_1} - \frac{1}{T_2}\right)$$

Substances with different heats of vaporization, and therefore different volatilities, can be separated by distillation (Section 12.4).

Phase diagrams show the states of matter for a pure substance at all possible temperatures and pressures. Features of phase diagrams include lines indicating the temperature and pressure conditions at which two phases are in equilibrium; the triple point, which is the temperature and pressure where all three phases are in equilibrium; and the critical point, which is the point on the liquid–gas equilibrium line above which the substance exists as a supercritical fluid. Phase diagrams can be used to predict the transition(s) that a substance will undergo if its temperature and/or pressure is changed (Section 12.5).

Crystalline solids consist of regularly arranged particles, whereas amorphous solids have particles that are more randomly arranged. There are four types of crystalline solids, as determined by the type of particle and bonding between the particles: molecular, ionic, covalent-network, and metallic. Metallic solids are composed of metal cations surrounded by a sea of mobile valence electrons that are not associated with any specific ion and are free to move about the entire solid. The melting point of a solid substance depends largely on the type of bond that is holding the particles in the solid together. The melting points of crystalline solids generally increase as follows: molecular solids < metallic solids < ionic and covalent-network solids (Section 12.6).

Unit cells, the smallest repeating unit of a crystal structure, are formed by the way that the layers of particles are arranged or packed upon each other. Different packing arrangements result in the formation of different unit cells, such as simple cubic unit cells; body-centered cubic, bcc, unit cells; and face-centered cubic, fcc, unit cells. Different packing arrangements also result in differences in coordination numbers and the use of space. The simple cubic unit cell is the least efficient, whereas the face-centered unit cell is one of the most efficient. Density, unit cell type, and atomic radius are related mathematically. Anions and cations are arranged in unit cells in ionic solids (Section 12.7).

END OF CHAPTER QUESTIONS

12.1 Intermolecular Forces

1. Name the intermolecular force that corresponds to:
   a. an attraction between a partially positive region in one molecule and a partially negative region in another molecule.
   b. an attraction between two temporarily polarized molecules.
   c. an attraction between a negatively charged particle and a partially positive region in a molecule.
   d. an attraction between a partially positive hydrogen atom in a molecule and a partially negative and highly electronegative atom on another molecule.

2. Explain how you can tell that the BCl_3 molecule, which has a trigonal planar molecular geometry, has no net dipole.

3. State all the types of intermolecular forces present (dispersion forces, dipole–dipole, hydrogen bonding) in each of the following pure substances. If a substance has more than one type of intermolecular force, identify the predominant one.
   a. CH_3OH
   b. Ne
   c. F_2
   d. CH_2F_2
   e. BCl_3
   f. CBr_4

4. In which of the diatomic elemental gases (H_2, N_2, O_2, F_2, Cl_2) are dispersion forces the strongest? the weakest? Explain.

5. Using knowledge of periodic trends in electronegativity values, determine the formulas of two binary compounds of nonmetals that have only nonpolar bonds.

6. Would you expect HCl or HI to have a higher normal boiling point? Explain.

7. Explain why, under ordinary conditions, elemental fluorine and chlorine both exist as gases, bromine exists as a liquid, and iodine exists as a solid.

8. Use knowledge of intermolecular forces to determine which of the seven diatomic elements has the lowest melting point.

9. Which of the following compounds has the highest boiling point?
   a. SF_2
   b. SF_4
   c. CF_4

10. Refer to the data in the table below to answer the questions.

	H_2O	H_2S	H_2Se	H_2Te	H_2Po
Melting point (°C)	0.0	−85.6	−65.7	−51	−35.3
Boiling point (°C)	100.0	−60.3	−41.3	−4	36.1

   a. The compounds in the table are hydrogen chalcogenides, meaning that they are composed of hydrogen and a chalcogen. Which periodic table group number corresponds to the name *chalcogen*?
   b. Describe the trend in melting and boiling points for the hydrogen chalcogenides in periods 3 to 6.
   c. Explain why the properties of H_2O are so different from the rest of the hydrogen chalcogenides.

11. Explain why 1-propanol has a boiling point of 97°C while 2-propanol has a boiling point of 77°C.

12.2 Properties of Liquids

12. Describe how the viscosity of a liquid substance is related to the strength of the intermolecular forces of that substance.

13. Select the liquid substance with the higher viscosity from each of the following pairs.
   a. H_2S and H_2Se
   b. NH_3 and NCl_3

14. Explain your choices in the previous problem.

15. Select the liquid substance with the higher viscosity from each of the following pairs, and explain your reasoning.
   a. 1-propanol and ethylene glycol

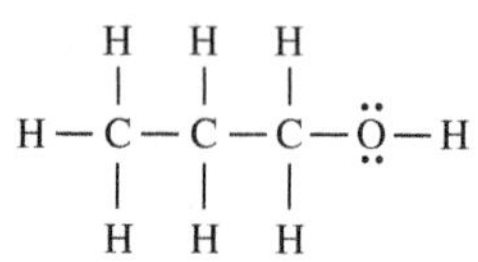

1-propanol

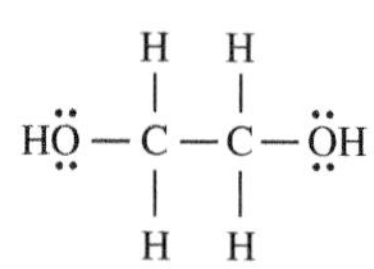

Ethylene glycol

   b. octane and 2,3,3-trimethylpentane

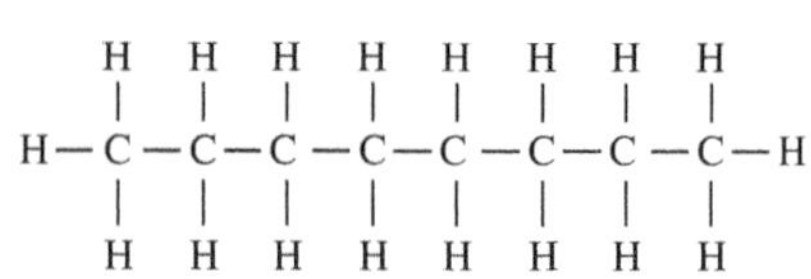

Octane

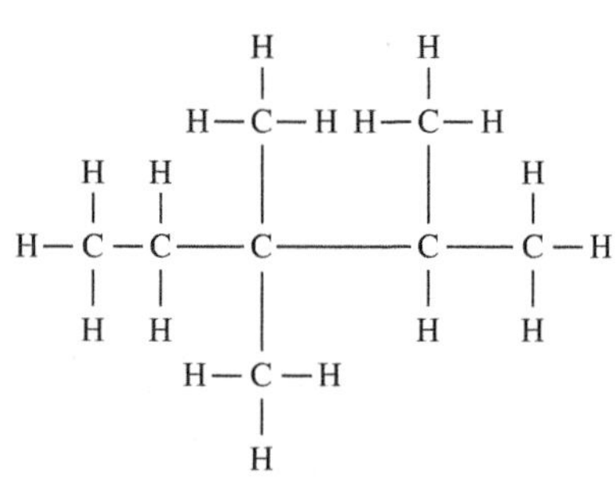

2,3,3-trimethylpentane

16. Select which of each pair has the stronger intermolecular forces.
   a. water molecules at 25°C and water molecules at 5°C
   b. water molecules in the center of the sample and water molecules at the surface

17. Select which of each pair has the higher surface tension.
   a. water molecules at 25°C and water molecules at 5°C
   b. water molecules in the center of the sample and water molecules at the surface

18. Explain the property or properties of liquids that are at work in an aroma diffuser, which consists of reeds (narrow, hollow wooden tubes) placed in a scented liquid. The liquid rises in the tubes to evaporate and, with time, the scent becomes detectable throughout the room.

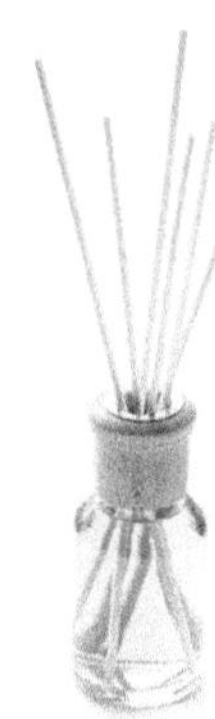

matka_Wariatka/Shutterstock

19. If you fill a drinking glass with water and continue to add water drop by drop, the surface of the water will become convex before it overflows. Explain.

20. Which, if any, of these liquids is likely to form a convex surface when poured into a cylinder?
   a. CH_3CH_2OH
   b. Br_2
   c. $HOCH_2CH_2OH$
   d. $CH_3CH_2CH_2CH_2CH_2CH_2CH_2CH_3$
   e. NH_3

12.3 Phase Changes and Heating Curves

21. The specific heat of water vapor is 2.042 $J/g \cdot °C$, and that of water is 4.184 $J/g \cdot °C$. The heat of vaporization of water is 2260 J/g.
   a. Calculate the heat required to warm 16.9 g of water from 87.4°C to 100.0°C.
   b. Calculate the heat required to vaporize the water.
   c. Calculate the heat required to warm the resulting water vapor to 122.2°C.
   d. Calculate the total heat required for all three processes.

22. What types of calculations would you make to find the energy required to change 14.8 g of ice at $-15.0°C$ to water vapor at 119°C?

23. Use the graph in Figure 12.16 to answer the following.
    a. What will happen first to liquid water at 100°C as heat is added to it?
    b. What will happen first to liquid water at 0°C as heat is added to it?

24. Use the graph in Figure 12.16 to answer the following.
    a. What will happen first to liquid water at 100°C as heat is removed from it?
    b. What will happen first to liquid water at 0°C as heat is removed from it?

25. Which of the following will increase the vapor pressure of water?
    a. increasing the surface area of the liquid
    b. increasing the temperature
    c. increasing the volume of the liquid
    d. increasing the volume occupied by the vapor

26. A sealed rectangular box is half-filled with water and has water vapor in the upper half at a pressure equal to the vapor pressure of water. Will the pressure change if the box is placed horizontally, thereby changing the surface area of the water? See the accompanying illustrations.

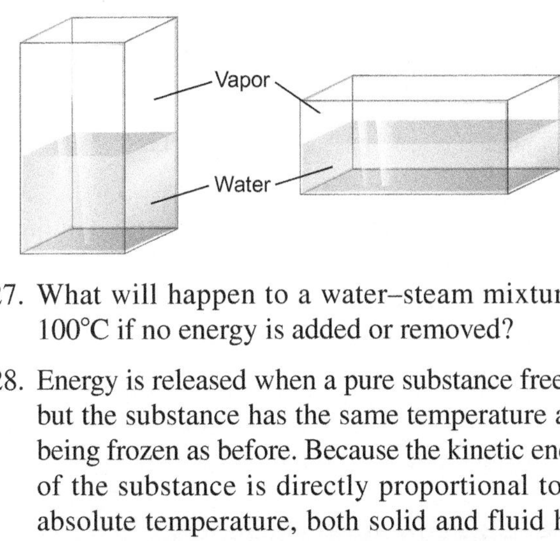

27. What will happen to a water–steam mixture at 100°C if no energy is added or removed?

28. Energy is released when a pure substance freezes, but the substance has the same temperature after being frozen as before. Because the kinetic energy of the substance is directly proportional to the absolute temperature, both solid and fluid have the same kinetic energy. Where did the released energy come from?

29. Calculate the energy change, q, associated with converting 50.5 g of water at 23.5°C to ice at $-4.2°C$.

30. Calculate the energy change, q, associated with converting 26.4 g of water at 4.5°C to steam at 115°C.

12.4 Vapor Pressure, Boiling Point, and the Clausius–Clapeyron Equation

31. As liquids, the smaller hydrocarbons such as hexane, C_6H_{14}, and octane, C_8H_{18}, are volatile, while the larger ones, such eicosane, $C_{20}H_{42}$, are nonvolatile.
    a. What does this mean about the various substances?
    b. Explain the differences.

32. Rank these substances, which have similar molar masses, from lowest to highest vapor pressure and explain your reasoning.
    a. butane, $CH_3CH_2CH_2CH_3$
    b. 1-propanol, $CH_3CH_2CH_2OH$
    c. ethylene glycol, $HOCH_2CH_2OH$

33. How much energy is absorbed when 235 g of ethyl acetate is vaporized at the following temperatures? Refer to Table 12.4 for additional information.
    a. 77.0°C
    b. 25.0°C

34. How much energy is released when 235 g of 2-propanol condenses at the following temperatures? Refer to Table 12.4 for additional information.
    a. 23.7°C
    b. 82.3°C

35. How many grams of 2-propanol can be vaporized at the following temperatures by the addition of 100 kJ of energy?
    a. 33.5°C
    b. 82.3°C

36. How many grams of ethyl acetate can be vaporized at the following temperatures by the addition of 35.5 kJ of energy?
    a. 77.0°C
    b. 35.0°C

37. Calculate the vapor pressure of 2-propanol at 35°C using information from Table 12.4 and the Clausius–Clapeyron equation.

38. Calculate the ΔH_{vap} of diethyl ether, given that its vapor pressure is 518 mmHg at 25°C and 660 mmHg at 32°C.

39. Plot the vapor pressure data for acetone shown here using the Clausius–Clapeyron equation (Equation 12.4) and determine the ΔH_{vap} for acetone.

P_{vap} (mmHg)	760	1520	3800	7600	15,200	30,400
T (°C)	56.5	78.6	113.0	144.5	181.0	214.5

40. Plot the vapor pressure data for octane shown here using the Clausius–Clapeyron equation (Equation 12.4) and determine the ΔH_{vap} for acetone.

P_{vap} (mmHg)	13.6	45.3	127.2	310.8
T (°C)	25	50	75	100

12.5 Phase Diagrams

41. Define these terms.
    a. phase diagram
    b. triple point
    c. critical point

42. Explain what the curved lines on a phase diagram indicate.

43. What kind of change does a horizontal line represent across a phase diagram? What is held constant?

44. What kind of change does a vertical line represent across a phase diagram? What is held constant?

45. Consider this phase diagram for nitrogen.

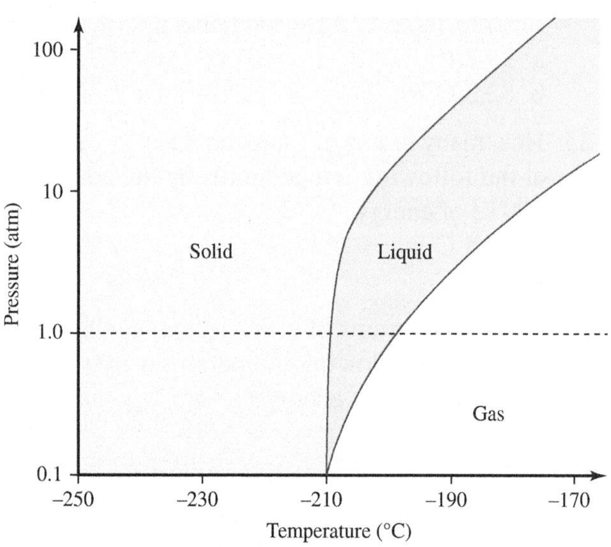

a. Label the triple point.
b. Estimate the normal melting and boiling points of nitrogen.
c. Identify the phase of nitrogen at 10 atm and −190°C.

46. Use the phase diagram for nitrogen in the previous problem to
    a. describe what happens to solid nitrogen when it is heated at pressures below 0.1 atm.
    b. describe what happens to solid nitrogen when it is heated at pressures above 0.1 atm.

47. The phase diagram for sulfur is shown here, with three triple points labeled.

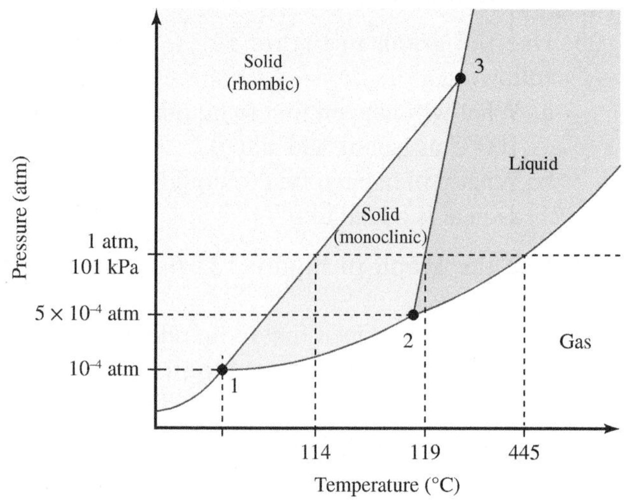

a. How many solid phases are possible for sulfur?
b. What phases are in equilibrium at triple point 1?

48. Use the phase diagram for sulfur in the previous problem to answer these questions.
    a. What phases are in equilibrium at triple point 2?
    b. What phases are in equilibrium at triple point 3?

49. Hypothetical substance Q has a normal melting point of −35°C and a normal boiling point of 68°C. At 0.05 atm and −52°C, Q exists in solid, liquid, and gas phases. Use this information to sketch out a phase diagram for Q.

50. Use Figure 12.27a to identify the phase for carbon dioxide under the following conditions.
    a. −5°C and 1 atm pressure
    b. −60°C and 5 atm pressure
    c. −40°C and 10 atm pressure

51. Use Figure 12.27b to describe what happens to water at 0.01°C when the pressure is increased from 0.002 atm pressure to 100 atm pressure.

12.6 Classification of Solids

52. List the types of forces that hold particles of various types of solids together, and give an example of a solid held together by each type.

53. Explain why solid LiF and solid CF_4 melt at such widely different temperatures: 870°C and −184°C, respectively.

54. Which has the higher melting point—an ionic compound in which the ions have +1 and −1 charges or an analogous ionic compound in which the ions have +2 and −2 charges?

55. Carbon dioxide, CO_2, sublimates at −78°C, and silicon dioxide, SiO_2, melts at 1713°C. What type of solid is each of these?

56. Glass softens over a wide range of temperatures. Ice melts at a precise temperature. Explain the difference.

57. Which of the following substances would you expect to have the lowest melting point?
a. NaCl
b. SCl_4
c. graphite, a network solid

58. Br_2 and ICl have the same total number of electrons and approximately the same molar mass. Which has the higher normal boiling point? Explain.

59. Which of the noble gases would you expect to have the lowest normal boiling point?

60. Diphosphorus trioxide, P_2O_3, melts at 23.8°C, and aluminum oxide, Al_2O_3, melts at 2045°C. What type of solid is each of these?

61. Compare and contrast ionic and metallic crystals.

62. How many oxygen atoms are covalently bonded to each silicon atom in SiO_2?

63. In SiO_2, how many silicon atoms are bonded to each oxygen atom?

64. How many carbon atoms are bonded to a given carbon atom in diamond?

12.7 The Unit Cell and the Structure of Crystalline Solids

65. Define these terms.
a. unit cell
b. packing
c. cubic unit cell

66. Show the math required to count the number of atoms present in each type of unit cell. Include atoms and fractions of atoms present in the centers, corners, and faces.
a. simple cubic unit cell
b. body-centered cubic unit cell
c. face-centered cubic unit cell

67. Describe how layers of atoms pack to form a simple cubic unit cell.

68. Describe how layers of atoms pack to form a body-centered cubic unit cell.

69. Describe how layers of atoms pack to form a face-centered cubic unit cell.

70. Polonium is the only element known to exist in the solid state as a simple cubic unit cell. Calculate the radius of a polonium atom, given that the density of polonium is $9.20\ g/cm^3$.

71. Cesium metal typically forms a solid with a body-centered unit cell with a density of $1.88\ g/cm^3$. Answer these questions for a hypothetical, face-centered unit cell form of Cs.
a. Would you expect the density of the hypothetical form to be less or greater than $1.88\ g/cm^3$?
b. Calculate the density of the hypothetical form.
c. Determine the percent difference between the two density values.

72. Calculate the radius of a cesium atom, given that it exists as a body-centered unit cell with a density of $1.88\ g/cm^3$.

73. Gold atoms pack in a cubic close-packing arrangement to form a material with a density of $19.3\ g/cm^3$. Calculate the radius of a gold atom.

74. Rhodium atoms pack in a cubic close-packing arrangement to form a unit cell with an edge length of 380.34 pm. Calculate the density of rhodium.

75. Molybdenum atoms pack in a body-centered packing arrangement to form a unit cell with an edge length of 314.7 pm. Calculate the density of molybdenum.

76. Describe how the ions are arrayed in an ionic compound with a 1:1 ratio of cation to anion in a
a. face-centered cubic unit cell.
b. body-centered cubic unit cell.

Putting It Together

77. Deduce the bond type (ionic, polar covalent, nonpolar covalent) in each of the following.
a. $SeCl_2$
b. CO_2
c. $AlBr_3$

78. Plot the normal boiling points of H_2S (−60.7°C), H_2Se (−42°C), and H_2Te (−2°C) versus the atomic number of the central atom. Extrapolate the line to atomic number 8, for H_2O, to predict the normal boiling point that water would have if not for hydrogen bonding.

79. Hydrogen bonding in water raises the expected boiling point 1½ to 2 times more than it raises the expected boiling point in HF or NH_3. Give a possible explanation.

80. Figure 12.7 shows how the four base pairs of DNA pair up via hydrogen bonding to hold the DNA strands together. The figure shows the hydrogen-bonding geometry of G with C and A with T. Mentally rearrange the bases, mirror imaging them if necessary, and compare how effectively each base would form hydrogen bonds with other bases. Are there any combinations other than G with C or A with T that would be equally effective in hydrogen bonding?

81. Explain why both NH_3 and AsH_3 boil at higher temperatures than PH_3 does.

82. It takes energy to boil a pure liquid substance, but the substance has the same temperature after being boiled as before. Because the kinetic energy of the substance is directly proportional to the absolute temperature, both liquid and vapor have the same kinetic energy. What happened to the energy that was used to change the liquid to vapor?

83. Explain why exposure to 5 g of water vapor, or steam, at 100°C causes more damage to skin than exposure to 5 g of liquid water at 100°C, even though they are both at the same temperature. *Hint:* Look at Table 12.3 and Figure 12.16.

84. Paper is composed mainly of cellulose, which is a very large molecule. A small portion of a cellulose molecule is shown below.

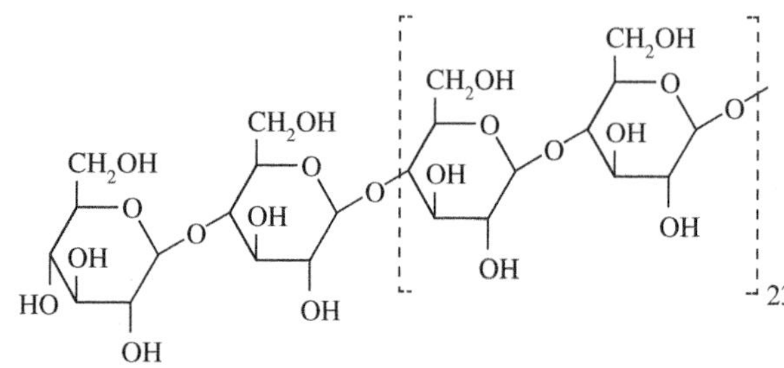

Use the intermolecular forces to explain whether you would expect paper towels to be effective at soaking up a spill of cooking oil, which is composed mainly of triglyceride molecules. An example of a triglyceride molecule is shown below.

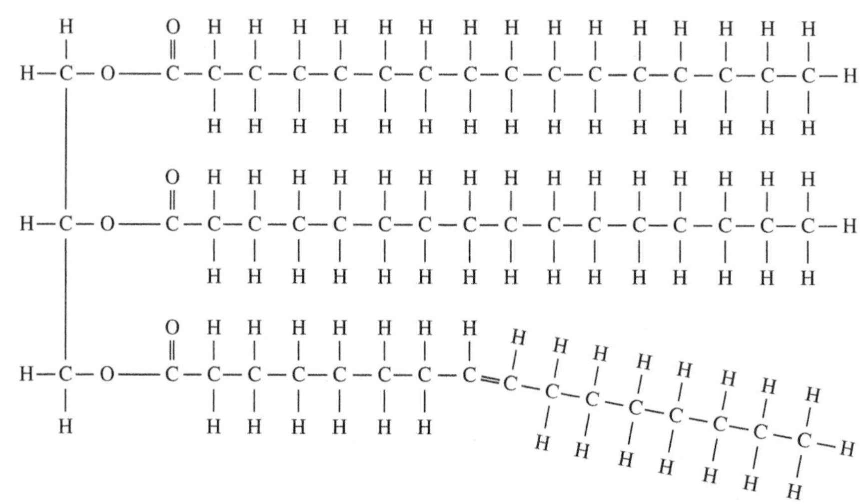

85. Refer to the phase diagram of sulfur from problem 47.
   a. In what state of matter is sulfur in the areas labeled *rhombic* and *monoclinic*?
   b. Describe the phases sulfur passes through when heated from room temperature to 500°C at 1 atm of pressure.
   c. Describe the phases that sulfur passes through when heated at very high pressure.
   d. Predict which form of sulfur has a higher density: rhombic or monoclinic. Explain your reasoning.

PRACTICE PROBLEM SOLUTIONS

Practice Problem 12.1 Solution

a. KBr and NH_3: Potassium bromide is ionic, and ammonia is polar, so ion–dipole attractions are possible.

b. NH_3 and Cl_2: Ammonia is polar, but chlorine is nonpolar. Without any ions present, ion–dipole attractions are not possible.

c. KBr and Cl_2: Potassium bromide is ionic, but chlorine is nonpolar. Ion–dipole attractions are not possible without a polar compound.

Practice Problem 12.2 Solution

a. CH_2Cl_2: Dichloromethane has a tetrahedral shape, two polar C—Cl bonds, and is asymmetric, making the overall molecule polar. CH_2Cl_2 molecules can form dipole–dipole attractions with each other.

b. Br_2: Bromine has a linear shape and a nonpolar bond, making Br_2 nonpolar and incapable of forming dipole–dipole attractions.

Practice Problem 12.3 Solution

a. H_2O: The Lewis structure of water is

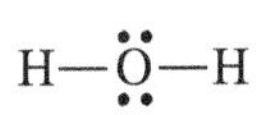

H_2O has an H—O bond, and the O atom has lone-pair electrons, so it is both a hydrogen bond donor and a hydrogen bond acceptor. Therefore, H_2O molecules can form hydrogen bonds to other H_2O molecules. Water molecules can also donate and accept hydrogen bonds to/from other compounds.

b. CH_2O: The Lewis structure of formaldehyde is

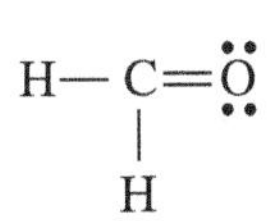

CH_2O does not contain an H bonded to O, so it not a hydrogen bond donor, and a sample of pure CH_2O will not contain any hydrogen bonds. However, the O atom does have available lone-pair electrons, so it can act as a hydrogen bond acceptor and could form hydrogen bonds with a molecule that is a hydrogen bond donor, such as water.

c. CH_3OH: The Lewis structure of methanol is

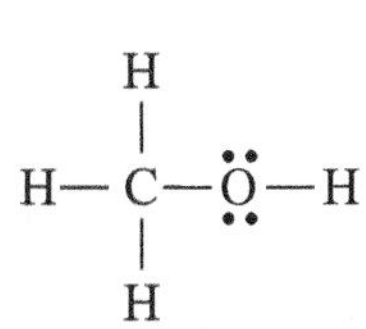

CH_3OH is both a hydrogen bond donor (it has an H—O bond) and a hydrogen bond acceptor (the O atom has lone-pair electrons). Therefore, CH_3OH molecules can form hydrogen bonds to other CH_3OH molecules and to other molecules that are either hydrogen bond donors or hydrogen bond acceptors.

d. NH_3: The Lewis structure of ammonia is

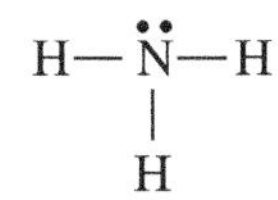

NH_3 is both a hydrogen bond donor (it has an H—N bond) and a hydrogen bond acceptor (the N atom has lone pair electrons). Therefore, NH_3 molecules can form hydrogen bonds to other NH_3 molecules and to other molecules that are either hydrogen bond donors or hydrogen bond acceptors.

Practice Problem 12.4 Solution

Choices (a) and (c) show a hydrogen bond. One side of the bond must be an H atom that is covalently bonded to N, O, or F, and the other side of the bond must be an N, O, or F atom with a lone pair. Choice (b) meets the second criterion but not the first. Choice (d) does not meet either of the criteria.

Practice Problem 12.5 Solution

Of the three factors that affect the strength of dispersion forces—namely, polarizability, the number of bonds, and molecular shape—polarizability is the most important for small diatomic molecules like F_2, Cl_2, O_2, H_2, and N_2. Based on periodic trends in atomic radius, the relative sizes of these molecules are $H_2 < F_2 < O_2 < N_2 < Cl_2$.

As a result, the electron cloud of H_2 is the least likely to polarize, which means that H_2 should form the weakest dispersion forces of the five substances. Cl_2, by contrast, has the largest electron cloud, so it should polarize the most readily. Cl_2, then, should form the strongest dispersion forces of these five substances.

Practice Problem 12.6 Solution

The only intermolecular forces that occur in these substances are dispersion forces. Dispersion forces form when the electron cloud of a bond polarizes. Larger electron clouds polarize more readily. Cl_2 is the largest of these five molecules, so its electron cloud should polarize the most readily and form the strongest dispersion forces of these five substances. Dispersion forces must be overcome to allow a liquid substance to enter the gas phase, so Cl_2 should have the highest boiling temperature.

Practice Problem 12.7 Solution

a. CH_3OH: The Lewis structure is

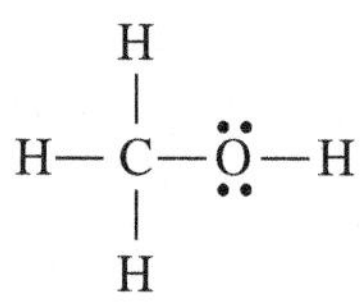

CH$_3$OH has an O—H bond, with lone pairs on the O, so it is both a hydrogen bond donor and a hydrogen bond acceptor. Hydrogen bonds are a type of dipole–dipole force, so CH_3OH exhibits dispersion forces and dipole–dipole forces as well, but its predominant intermolecular force is hydrogen bonding.

b. CBr_4: The Lewis structure is

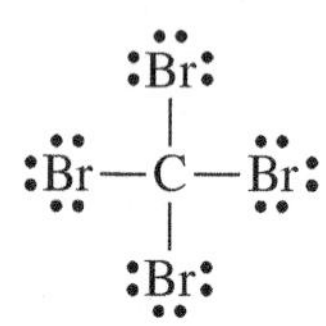

$\Delta EN = 0.4$ for each C—Br bond, making these bonds weakly polar. CBr_4 has a symmetrical tetrahedral shape, however, so those bond dipoles will cancel. CBr_4, then, is a nonpolar molecule, making dispersion forces its only intermolecular force.

Practice Problem 12.8 Solution

Both substances are at the same temperature, so any differences in their viscosities will depend on differences in their intermolecular forces.

Pentane and decane are both nonpolar hydrocarbons, so dispersion forces are their most important intermolecular forces. Because decane is a larger molecule, it forms stronger dispersion forces with other decane molecules, giving it a higher viscosity than pentane.

Practice Problem 12.9 Solution

The predominant intermolecular forces for each substance are as follows:

- CBr_4 is nonpolar and interacts with other CBr_4 molecules via dispersion forces.
- H_2O is strongly polar and forms hydrogen bonds with other H_2O molecules.
- CH_2Cl_2 is a polar molecule that interacts with other CH_2Cl_2 molecules via dipole–dipole forces but not hydrogen bonds.

Since dispersion is the weakest intermolecular force, CBr_4 will have low surface tension as a liquid. Since hydrogen bonding is the strongest of the intermolecular forces in these examples, H_2O will have high surface tension as a liquid. The ranking is $CBr_4 < CH_2Cl_2 < H_2O$.

Practice Problem 12.10 Solution

a. The transition from a liquid to a solid is called *freezing*.

b. The transition from a solid directly to a gas is called *sublimation*.

c. The transition from a gas to a liquid is called *condensation*.

Practice Problem 12.11 Solution

The heat of vaporization of water is 40.7 kJ/mol. First, convert the mass of water to moles:

$$16.4\ \text{g}\left(\frac{1\ \text{mol}}{18.02\ \text{g}}\right) = 0.910\ \text{mol}$$

Then use Equation 12.1 to calculate q:

$$q = 0.910\ \text{mol}\left(40.7\frac{\text{kJ}}{\text{mol}}\right)$$

$$q = 37.0\ \text{kJ}$$

The amount of heat needed to vaporize 16.4 g of water (37.0 kJ) is much greater than the amount of heat needed to melt 16.4 g of water (5.47 kJ).

Practice Problem 12.12 Solution

Calculate each segment separately.

- Segment 1: The liquid water at 14.4°C is cooled to its freezing point, 0°C.
- Segment 2: It then freezes, producing ice at 0°C.
- Segment 3: The ice is then cooled to −16.3°C.

Since the amount of water is given in grams, use the "per gram" values of enthalpy and specific heat from Table 12.3.

Segment 1: Cooling the liquid water involves the use of the specific heat capacity of water and Equation 6.8.

$$q = mc(\Delta T)$$

$$q = (41.0\ \text{g})\left(\frac{4.184\ \text{J}}{\text{g}\cdot{}^\circ\text{C}}\right)(0.00^\circ\text{C} - 14.4^\circ\text{C})$$

$$q = -2{,}470\ \text{J}$$

Segment 2: To freeze the water, use the enthalpy of fusion with the sign changed to indicate an exothermic process.

$$q = (41.0\ \text{g})\left(-334\frac{\text{J}}{\text{mol}}\right)$$

$$q = -13{,}700\ \text{J}$$

Segment 3: For cooling the solid water, use the specific heat of ice and Equation 6.8.

$$q = mc(\Delta T)$$

$$q = (41.0\ \text{g})\left(\frac{2.087\ \text{J}}{\text{g}\cdot{}^\circ\text{C}}\right)(-16.3^\circ\text{C} - 0.0^\circ\text{C})$$

$$q = -1395\ \text{J}$$

The last step is to add the various energy values together:

$$q_{\text{total}} = -2470\ \text{J} + (-13{,}700\ \text{J}) + (-1395\ \text{J})$$

$$q_{\text{total}} = -17{,}600\ \text{J} = -17.6\ \text{kJ}$$

Practice Problem 12.13 Solution

Vapor pressure depends upon temperature and the strength of the predominant intermolecular force in the substance. The samples of these three compounds are at the same temperature, though, so you can ignore temperature and use just the intermolecular forces to determine their relative vapor pressures. The three molecules are similar in size and structure but differ in polarity, so molecules of these substances interact via different intermolecular forces.

Butane molecules are nonpolar and interact via dispersion forces, while propanal molecules are polar and interact via dipole–dipole forces. Acetic acid is both a hydrogen bond donor and a hydrogen bond acceptor, so hydrogen bonding will give its molecules the strongest intermolecular forces of these three substances. Butane has the highest vapor pressure because it has the weakest intermolecular forces, followed by propanal and then acetic acid.

Practice Problem 12.14 Solution

$$q = (1.355\ \text{g water})\left(\frac{1\ \text{mol water}}{18.0153\ \text{g water}}\right)\left(\frac{-44.0\ \text{kJ}}{1\ \text{mol water}}\right)$$

$$= -3.31\ \text{kJ}$$

Practice Problem 12.15 Solution

$$m = (86.5\ \text{kJ})\left(\frac{1\ \text{mol acetone}}{31.0\ \text{kJ}}\right)\left(\frac{58.0791\ \text{g acetone}}{1\ \text{mol acetone}}\right)$$

$$= 162\ \text{g acetone}$$

Practice Problem 12.16 Solution

Substitute into the Clausius–Clapeyron equation using $T_2 = 97.00^\circ\text{C} = 370.15\ \text{K}$, $P_2 = 760\ \text{mmHg}$, and $T_1 = 61.00^\circ\text{C} = 334.15\ \text{K}$. Start by rewriting $\left(\ln \frac{P_2}{P_1}\right)$ as $(\ln P_2 - \ln P_1)$.

$$\ln P_2 - \ln P_1 = \frac{\Delta H_{\text{vap}}}{R}\left(\frac{1}{T_1} - \frac{1}{T_2}\right)$$

Express the ΔH_{vap} in joules per mole, rather than kilojoules per mole, to be consistent with the units for R.

$$\ln(760\ \text{mmHg}) - \ln P_1 = \frac{41{,}200\frac{\text{J}}{\text{mol}}}{8.3145\frac{\text{J}}{\text{K}\cdot\text{mol}}}\left(\frac{1}{334.15\ \text{K}} - \frac{1}{370.15\ \text{K}}\right)$$

Remember to take the reciprocals of the temperatures before subtracting.

$$6.633 - \ln P_1 = 1.442$$

$$\ln P_1 = 6.633 - 1.442 = 5.191$$

$$P_2 = e^{5.191} = 180\ \text{mmHg}$$

Practice Problem 12.17 Solution

Substitute into the Clausius–Clapeyron equation using T_1, P_1, and ΔH_{vap} from Example 12.17 and $T_2 = 25.00^\circ\text{C}$. Rewrite $\left(\ln \frac{P_2}{P_1}\right)$ as $(\ln P_2 - \ln P_1)$ and convert all temperatures to kelvins.

$$\ln P_2 - \ln P_1 = \frac{\Delta H_{\text{vap}}}{R}\left(\frac{1}{T_1} - \frac{1}{T_2}\right)$$

$$\ln P_2 - \ln(401\ \text{mmHg}) = \frac{26{,}300\frac{\text{J}}{\text{mol}}}{8.3145\frac{\text{J}}{\text{K}\cdot\text{mol}}}\left(\frac{1}{291.15\ \text{K}} - \frac{1}{298.15\ \text{K}}\right)$$

Remember to take the reciprocals of the temperatures before subtracting.

$$\ln P_2 - 5.994 = 0.25507$$

$$\ln P_2 = 6.249$$

$$P_2 = e^{6.249} = 518\ \text{mmHg}$$

A vapor pressure of 518 mmHg at 25°C makes sense because it falls in between the vapor pressures given for 18°C (401 mmHg) and 32°C (660 mmHg).

Practice Problem 12.18 Solution

Before the sample is placed in a hot car, the rate of evaporation equals the rate of condensation. As the sample warms, though, the rate of vaporization will increase compared with the rate of condensation. This will cause the amount of water in the gas phase to increase, which will raise the vapor pressure. The amount of water in the liquid phase will decrease. Eventually, a new equilibrium will be established at a higher vapor pressure.

Practice Problem 12.19 Solution

a. The liquid and gas phases are in equilibrium along the line between regions A and B.

b. The pressure and temperature at which all three phases are present in equilibrium is called the triple point, and it occurs where regions A, B, and C meet.

c. The normal melting point is the point at which the dotted line (1 atm) crosses the line between regions B and C (the solid–liquid equilibrium line).

Practice Problem 12.20 Solution

At 5 atm and −10°C, water is a solid. As it is heated under 5 atm of pressure, it will remain a solid until about −5°C, at which point it will melt to form a liquid. The sample will remain a liquid until the temperature is somewhere close to 200°C, at which point it will vaporize to form gaseous water vapor. It will remain a gas as heat is added to reach 350°C.

Practice Problem 12.21 Solution

$(2.5 \times 10^5)^3 = 1.6 \times 10^{16}\ I_2$ molecules

$2(1.6 \times 10^{16}) = 3.2 \times 10^{16}$ I atoms

Practice Problem 12.22 Solution

a. A molecule containing only 14 atoms is a molecular solid.

b. Huge numbers of ions that form a crystal lattice are an ionic solid.

c. Huge numbers of atoms that are covalently bonded to each other are a covalent-network solid.

Practice Problem 12.23 Solution

Molecular solids have relatively weak intermolecular forces, so the molecular solid must be the one with the melting point of 90°C.

Practice Problem 12.24 Solution

Scandium (group 3) has two 4*s* electrons and one 3*d* electron that it can lose to achieve a stable electron configuration that is isoelectronic with argon. The charge on the ions would be +3. Since each scandium atom contributes three electrons to the sea of electrons, the diagram would have three electrons for each +3 ion. If the diagram had nine ions like those in Figure 12.30, there would be 27 electrons.

Practice Problem 12.25 Solution

The face-centered unit cell (Figure 12.36), with an atom on each corner and an atom in each face, contains four complete atoms per unit cell.

$$\frac{8 \text{ corners}}{1 \text{ unit cell}} \times \frac{\frac{1}{8} \text{ atom}}{1 \text{ corner}} + \frac{6 \text{ faces}}{1 \text{ unit cell}} \times \frac{\frac{1}{2} \text{ atom}}{1 \text{ face}} = 4\frac{\text{atoms}}{\text{unit cell}}$$

The body-centered unit cell (Figure 12.35), with an atom at each corner and one in the center, contains only two complete atoms per unit cell, so it contains less empty space than does the simple unit cell (Example 12.25) but more than does the face-centered unit cell.

$$\frac{8 \text{ corners}}{1 \text{ unit cell}} \times \frac{\frac{1}{8} \text{ atom}}{1 \text{ corner}} + \frac{1 \text{ atom}}{1 \text{ center}} = 2\frac{\text{atoms}}{\text{unit cell}}$$

The solid composed of face-centered unit cells, with more atoms per unit cell and less empty space per unit cell, would have a higher density.

Practice Problem 12.26 Solution

Body-centered cubic unit cell: A body-centered cubic unit cell contains two atoms and has a length equal to $4r/\sqrt{3}$.

Convert the mass from atomic mass units to grams.

$$m = \frac{2 \text{ atoms}}{1 \text{ unit cell}} \times \frac{1 \text{ mol}}{6.022 \times 10^{23} \text{ atoms}} \times \frac{63.546 \text{ g}}{1 \text{ mol}} = 2.110 \times 10^{-22} \frac{\text{g}}{\text{unit cell}}$$

Calculate the length of one side of the cube from the radius in centimeters.

$$l = \frac{4r}{\sqrt{3}} = \frac{4(1.28 \times 10^{-8} \text{ cm})}{\sqrt{3}} = 2.96 \times 10^{-8} \text{ cm}$$

Find the volume from the length, then calculate the density from the mass and volume.

$$V = l^3 = (2.96 \times 10^{-8} \text{ cm})^3 = 2.58 \times 10^{-23} \text{ cm}^3$$

$$d = \frac{m}{V} = \frac{2.110 \times 10^{-22} \text{ g}}{2.58 \times 10^{-23} \text{ cm}^3} = 8.17 \text{ g/cm}^3$$

The density of the body-centered cubic unit cell form of copper (8.2 g/cm^3) is in between the density of the face-centered unit cell form (8.9 g/cm^3) and the density of the simple cell form (6.3 g/cm^3).

Practice Problem 12.27 Solution

Find the mass per unit cell. An face-centered cubic unit cell contains four atoms.

$$m = \frac{4\text{ atoms}}{1\text{ unit cell}} \times \frac{1\text{ mol}}{6.022 \times 10^{23}\text{ atoms}} \times \frac{102.91\text{ g Rh}}{1\text{ mol Rh}}$$
$$= 6.836 \times 10^{-22}\,\frac{\text{g}}{\text{unit cell}}$$

Use the density to convert mass to volume.

$$V = 6.836 \times 10^{-22} \times \frac{1\text{ cm}^3}{12.41\text{ g}} = 5.508 \times 10^{-23}\text{ cm}^3$$

Determine the length of the unit cell by taking the cube root of the volume.

$$l = \sqrt[3]{V} = \sqrt[3]{5.508 \times 10^{-23}\text{ cm}^3} = 3.8048 \times 10^{-8}\text{ cm}$$

Convert the length from centimeters to picometers.

$$3.805 \times 10^{-8}\text{ cm} \times \frac{1\text{ m}}{100\text{ cm}} \times \frac{10^{12}\text{ pm}}{1\text{ m}} = 380.5\text{ pm}$$

Rearrange the relationship between length and radius and then substitute in the values to calculate the radius of the barium atom.

$$l = \sqrt{8}r$$

$$r = \frac{l}{\sqrt{8}} = \frac{(380.5\text{ pm})}{\sqrt{8}} = 134.5\text{ pm}$$

Practice Problem 12.28 Solution

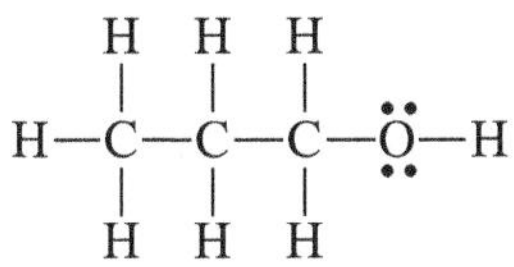

Propanol

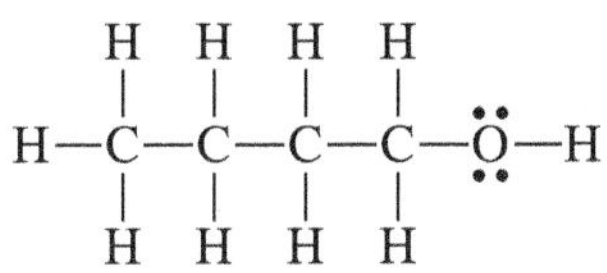

Butanol

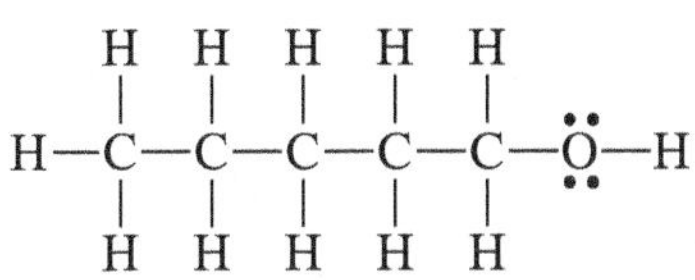

Pentanol

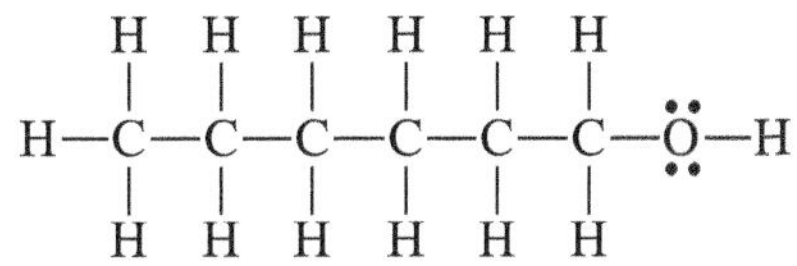

Hexanol

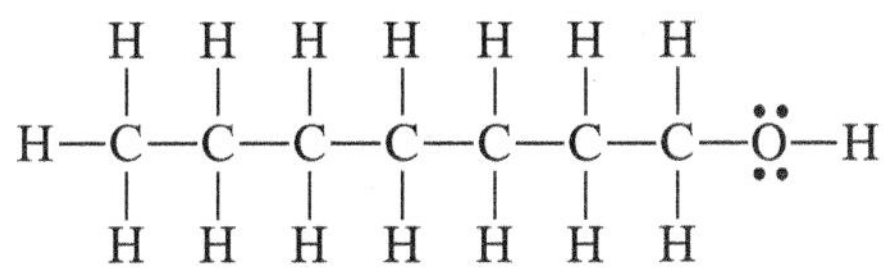

Heptanol

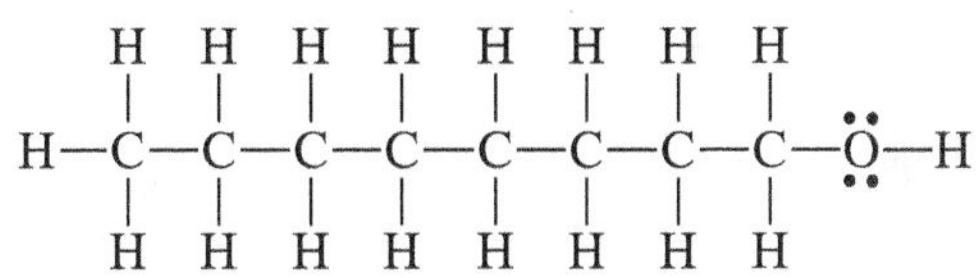

Octanol

a. Alcohol molecules can form hydrogen bonds to each other as well as dispersion forces. Hydrogen bonds are much stronger than dispersion forces, so a lot more energy is needed to break these molecules away from each other, giving alcohols much higher boiling points than those for the hydrocarbons in Example 12.28.

b. The ΔT column in the table shows that the normal boiling points of the alcohols increase by around 20°C for each CH_2 group added to the molecular formula.

CHAPTER 13 Solutions

Macmillan Learning

A mixture of table salt, NaCl, and water, H_2O, is an example of a solution. Although you are likely most familiar with this type of solution made up of a solid dissolved in a liquid, there are other types of solutions as well. Other common solution types include a gas dissolved in a liquid (carbonated beverages), two or more gases (air), or even two solids (alloys such as brass).

Chapter Outline

GOALS

- Explain, using the energetics of the solution process, how to predict which types of solvents are most likely to dissolve a given solute.
- Determine if more solute can be dissolved in a given solution from its concentration, the solubility of the solute at various temperatures, and the temperature.
- Perform calculations involving percent by mass, molality, and mole fraction as measures of concentration.
- Perform calculations using some of the properties of solutions of nonelectrolytes that depend on the concentrations of the dissolved particles rather than their nature.
- Extend the discussion of solution properties of nonelectrolytes to include electrolyte solutions.

13.1 The Solution Process

GOAL

- Explain, using the energetics of the solution process, how to predict which types of solvents are most likely to dissolve a given solute.

Background Review

Chapter 1 Science and Measurement: Section 1.1—Classification of Matter

Chapter 6 Thermochemistry: Section 6.7—Enthalpy in Chemical Reactions

Chapter 11 Molecular Shape and Bonding Theories: Section 11.2—Polar and Nonpolar Molecules

Chapter 12 Liquids and Solids: Section 12.1—Intermolecular Forces

Solutions are commonly thought of as solids dissolved in liquids, such as saltwater or sugared tea, but a solution is any homogeneous mixture, and homogeneous mixtures can be made up of almost any two phases of matter mixed together. In solutions, one substance is dissolved in another, where the dissolved substance is known as the **solute** and the substance it is dissolved in is the **solvent**. These two terms apply regardless of the phases of the two substances. Table 13.1 lists a variety of solutions composed of different phases of matter.

Metal **alloys** such as brass are solid–solid solutions of different metals (Figure 13.1).

TABLE 13.1 Examples of Different Types of Solutions

Solution Type	Example
Solid in solid	Brass, a mixture of zinc and copper (Figure 13.1)
Solid in liquid	Sugar water
Liquid in solid	Mercury in silver (dental amalgam)
Liquid in liquid	Gasoline (a mixture of hydrocarbons)
Gas in solid	Hydrogen in platinum
Gas in liquid	Carbonated soft drinks (CO_2 in water)
Gas in gas	Air (O_2 in N_2)

Substances dissolve in one another if the solute and solvent are able to form intermolecular attractions. When the solvent and solute participate in similar types of intermolecular forces, the energy released by the newly formed solvent–solute attractions can help offset the energy required to overcome solute–solute attractions and solvent–solvent attractions, making the dissolving process more energetically favorable than it would otherwise be if the solute and solvent did not share similar types of intermolecular forces.

Many ionic compounds dissolve in water due to the formation of ion–dipole forces between the charged ions and the polar water molecules (Section 12.1). The solvent molecules generally must be polar (Section 11.2) to be able to exert significant attractions on the charged ions in a way that solvents with nonpolar molecules cannot. In fact, nonpolar solvents are more apt to dissolve nonpolar solutes. The general rule is that "like dissolves like." That is, polar solvents are more likely to dissolve ionic and polar covalent solutes, whereas nonpolar solvents are more likely to dissolve nonpolar covalent solutes.

Like dissolves like.

FIGURE 13.1 Copper and Zinc Mix to Form Brass

(a) Since 1983, pennies have been made of zinc coated in an outer layer of copper. (b) If the pennies are coated in an additional layer of zinc and heated, (c) the zinc atoms blend with the copper atoms to form a gold-colored solid–solid solution called brass.

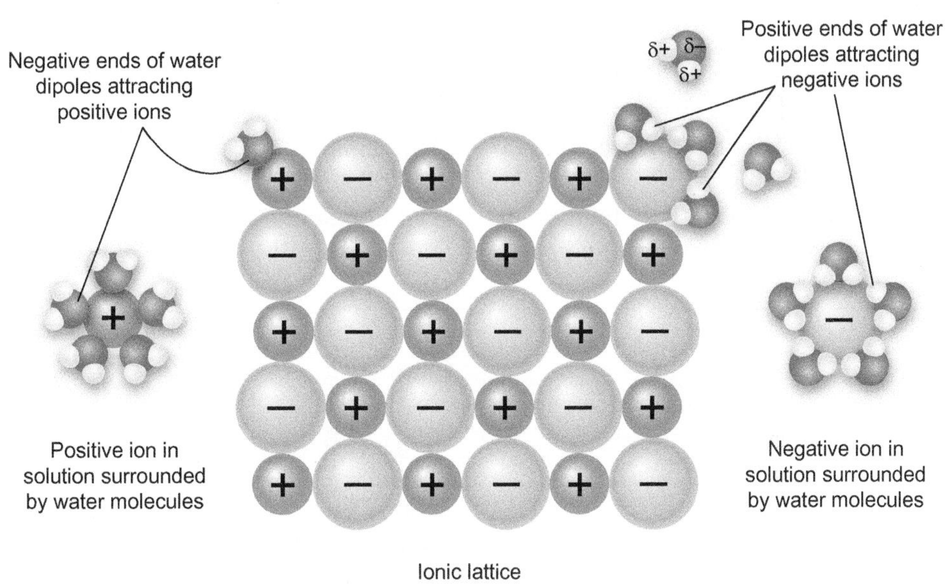

FIGURE 13.2 Dissolving Action of Water on an Ionic Solid

The negative pole of a polar water molecule (the oxygen end) is attracted to the cations, and the positive pole of the water molecule (the hydrogen end) is attracted to the anions.

When a salt dissolves in water, the H_2O molecules orient their dipoles around the cations and anions so that their oppositely charged ends are adjacent to each ion (Figure 13.2).

Example 13.1

Which solvent—liquid ammonia, NH_3, or benzene, C_6H_6—is more likely to dissolve each of the following solutes?

a. H_2O
b. C_6H_{12}
c. AgCl

Solution

Ammonia is a polar molecule, whereas benzene is nonpolar.

a. H_2O is more likely to dissolve in NH_3 because both substances are polar and capable of hydrogen bonding.
b. C_6H_{12} is a nonpolar covalent solute, so it is more likely to dissolve in the nonpolar solvent, C_6H_6.
c. AgCl is an ionic compound, so it is more likely to dissolve in the polar solvent, NH_3.

PRACTICE PROBLEM 13.1

Which type of solvent—polar or nonpolar—is most likely to dissolve methyl alcohol, CH_3OH?

Hint: A solute will dissolve best in a solvent whose intermolecular forces best match those of the solute itself. Like dissolves like.

ENERGETICS OF SOLUTION FORMATION

In aqueous solutions, water molecules surround solute particles in a process called hydration (Chapter 4). The term **solvation** means the same thing as hydration, but it applies to any solvent, not just water. For a solution to form, three processes must occur: (1) the intermolecular forces between solute particles must be broken, (2) the intermolecular forces between solvent particles must be broken, and (3) new intermolecular forces must form between the solute and solvent particles during solvation. The overall energy change, known as enthalpy of solution, ΔH_{sol} (Section 6.5), is the sum of these three steps, as shown in Figure 13.3.

Steps 1 and 2 are endothermic—they require an input of energy, E, as indicated by the upward-pointing arrows. The energy required to break solute–solute attractions in an ionic compound can be significant. When an ionic compound forms, energy is given off. The lattice energy, ΔH_L, of an ionic solid is the amount of energy given off when the solid compound forms from ions in the gas phase (Section 9.5). To dissolve an ionic compound, an amount of energy equal to the lattice energy must be added to the system to overcome the ionic attractions and separate the ions in solution.

Step 3 in the dissolution process (solvation) is exothermic—it releases energy, E, as indicated by the downward-pointing arrow. If the energy released in the solvation step is *greater* than the sum of the energies absorbed in steps 1 and 2, then the overall enthalpy of solution, ΔH_{sol}, will be *exothermic*. If the energy released in the solvation step is *less* than the sum of the two endothermic steps, however, then the enthalpy of solution will be *endothermic*. Figure 13.3 shows the case where ΔH_{sol} is exothermic. Note that when the solvent is water, the heat of solution is called the **hydration energy**, also known as the enthalpy of hydration.

Like any other chemical or physical process, dissolution is more likely to occur if energy is given off by the overall process, because that means the final

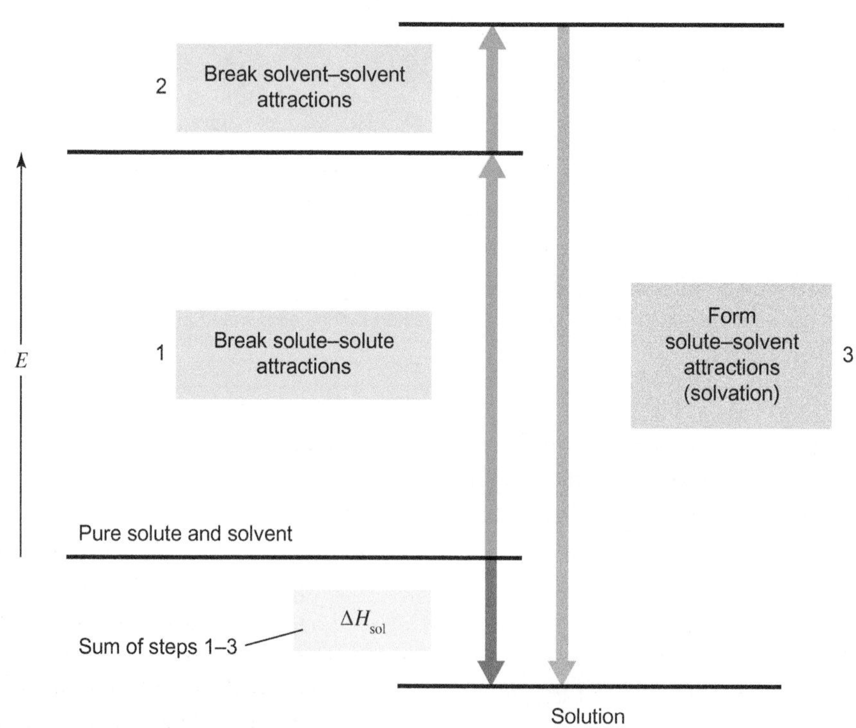

FIGURE 13.3 Steps in the Enthalpy of Solution
The enthalpy of solution depends on the strength of the intermolecular forces in the solute, the solvent, and the solution.

state has less energy, and is therefore more stable, than the initial state. When ΔH_{sol} is exothermic, energy is given off by the dissolution process, so dissolution of the solute is more likely to occur. Dissolution is less likely to occur when ΔH_{sol} is negative. However, there is another factor that also affects solubility. **Entropy** is a measure of the randomness or disorder in a system (it is discussed in more detail in Chapter 18). If a process results in an increase in entropy, that process is more favorable and more likely to occur. The ions in a salt crystal are positioned in a highly ordered state, but ions in solution are scattered randomly over a much larger volume. This is a significant increase in entropy, and it makes the dissolution of ionic compounds in water more favorable even when the enthalpy of solution for that salt is positive.

SECTION REVIEW

- Solutions are homogeneous mixtures that can be made up of almost any combination of phases of matter.
- Any solute will dissolve best in a solvent whose intermolecular forces best match those of the solute itself. This is often stated as "like dissolves like."
- Solution formation involves the breaking of the intermolecular attractions within the pure solute and pure solvent and the formation of new intermolecular attractions between the solute and solvent molecules. The enthalpy of solution, ΔH_{sol}, is the sum of the enthalpies of these individual steps.

13.2 Saturated, Unsaturated, and Supersaturated Solutions

GOAL

- Determine if more solute can be dissolved in a given solution from its concentration, the solubility of the solute at various temperatures, and the temperature.

Background Review

Chapter 5 Stoichiometry: Section 5.5—Definition and Uses of Molarity

Chapter 7 Gases: Section 7.7—Dalton's Law of Partial Pressures

Most gaseous and solid solutes will dissolve only to a certain extent in a given liquid solvent at a given temperature. For example, only 6.35 g of solid boric acid, H_3BO_3 (commonly used as a roach killer and also used medicinally at higher purification to bathe infected eyes), will dissolve in 100 g of water at 30°C. If you add more than 6.35 g of H_3BO_3 to the water at that temperature, the excess quantity H_3BO_3 will not dissolve. The **solubility** of H_3BO_3 in water at 30°C is therefore 6.35 g per 100 g of water.

A solution that contains the maximum amount of dissolved solute at a given temperature is said to be **saturated**. If the solution contains less than the maximum amount of solute, it is **unsaturated**. Thus, a solution containing 2.00 g of H_3BO_3 in 100 g of water at 30°C is unsaturated.

SOLUBILITY OF SOLIDS

A change in temperature affects the solubility of a solute in a given solvent (Figure 13.4). Most solid solutes become *more* soluble in liquid solvents as the temperature rises, whereas gases dissolved in liquids become *less* soluble. Some solid compounds, such as hydrated metal sulfate salts, become *less* soluble at higher temperatures. This is partly because the dissolution of those salts is exothermic and partly because the crystal lattice changes with increasing temperature, altering the dissolution process from the crystal.

Figure 13.5 allows you to qualitatively explore the solubilities of four different solutes (glucose, sucrose, iodine, and naphthalene) in two different solvents (water and benzene) at various temperatures. Be sure to make predictions about which solutes will be most soluble in each solvent and whether that solubility will increase or decrease with temperature. Are the changes in solubility what you expected them to be after performing the experiment?

If you have a saturated solution of a solid solute at a high temperature and you lower the temperature of the solution, the solvent will be unable to hold that much solute in solution, and the excess solute will normally crystallize from the solution as the temperature is lowered. At 100°C, for example, the solubility of H_3BO_3 in water is 27.53 g per 100 g of water. If a solution containing 27.53 g of H_3BO_3 in 100 g of water at 100°C is cooled to 30°C, then only 6.35 g of the H_3BO_3 will continue to be soluble, and 21.18 g of H_3BO_3 will crystallize from the solution. This type of process, called **recrystallization**, is commonly used to purify solid substances.

When saturated solutions of certain solutes, such as sodium acetate, are gently cooled, the solute often

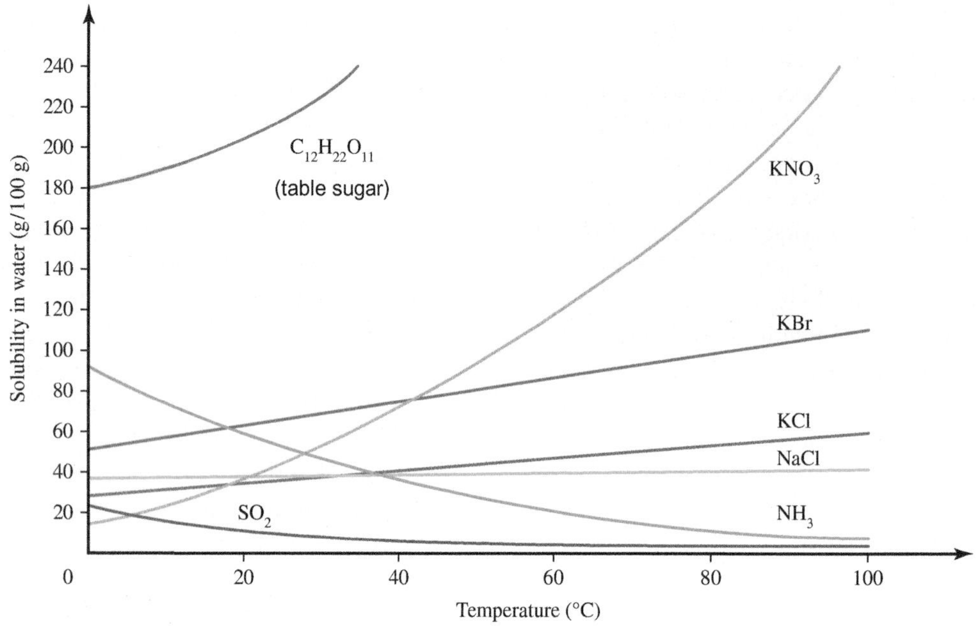

FIGURE 13.4 Solubility Versus Temperature for Some Solid Solutes in Water

The solubility of a solid in a liquid typically increases with increasing temperature, and the solubility of a gas decreases with increasing temperature.

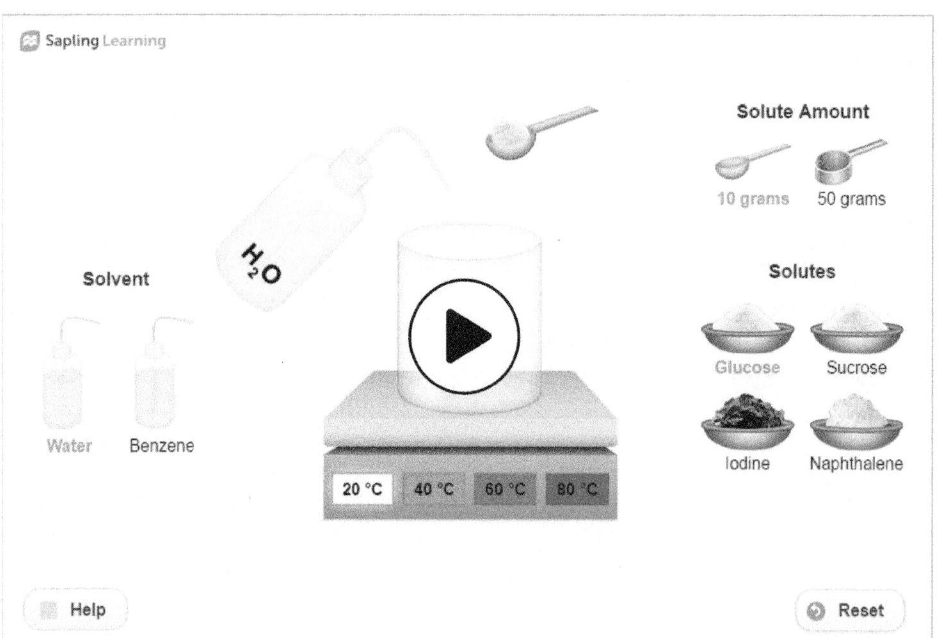

FIGURE 13.5 Solid Solubility Lab

NOTE: You need to be online to access this activity.

First, choose a solvent and a solute and mix them. If all the solute dissolves, keep adding more solute until you reach the saturation point for the selected temperature. Then, determine the saturation point at a different temperature.

FIGURE 13.6 Crystallization of a Solute from a Supersaturated Solution

NOTE: You need to be online to access this video.
Supersaturated solutions contain too much dissolved solute and are unstable. If a supersaturated solution is disturbed, the excess solute will crystallize (solidify) out of solution.

has difficulty forming the first crystal. If the temperature continues to decrease without the formation of that first crystal, all of the solute remains dissolved. This results in a situation in which more solute is dissolved in the solvent than is stable at the lower temperature. This type of solution is said to be **supersaturated**. If a supersaturated solution is disturbed, such as by shaking or by scratching the inner surface of the container with a glass rod, the excess solute will usually rapidly crystallize out. A more certain way to get a supersaturated solution to crystallize is to add a tiny crystal of the solid solute. The excess solute crystallizes out from this "seed crystal" (Figure 13.6).

The activity in Figure 13.5 allows you to qualitatively explore the solubilities of four different solutes (glucose, sucrose, iodine, and naphthalene) in two different solvents (water and benzene) at various temperatures. Open the activity and predict which of the solutes will be most soluble in each of the solvents at 20°C, then carry out the simulated experiments to see if your predictions were correct. Then increase the temperature to 80°C and compare the solubilities of each solute with their solubility at 20°C. Are the increases in solubility what you expected them to be?

EVERYDAY CONNECTION

Rock candy is another example of recrystallizing a solute from a supersaturated solution. To make rock candy, a solution of sugar water is saturated at high temperatures. A string or wooden stick is inserted into the solution, sometimes after being rolled in sugar to provide seed crystals. The recrystallization process is slow with sugar, and it can take a few days to a week for the excess dissolved sugar to recrystallize out of the supersaturated solution onto the string or stick. Eventually when enough sugar has crystallized out of the solution, the solution reaches its saturation point and the recrystallization process stops. The excess sugar has recrystallized out as rock candy.

torbakhopper/Flickr

Artificial colors and flavors can be added to the solution to give the rock candy a bright color, such as the one shown here.

Example 13.2

The mass of sodium acetate that will dissolve in 100 g of water is 119 g at 0°C and 170 g at 100°C.

a. If 170 g of sodium acetate is placed in 100 g of water at 0°C, how much will dissolve?
b. Is the resulting system homogeneous or heterogeneous?
c. Is the solution saturated, unsaturated, or supersaturated?
d. If the system is then raised to 100°C, will the mixture be homogeneous or heterogeneous?
e. Is the solution at 100°C saturated, unsaturated, or supersaturated?
f. If the system is then carefully cooled back to 0°C and no crystals appear, is the system homogeneous or heterogeneous?
g. Is the solution saturated, unsaturated, or supersaturated?

Solution

a. The solubility of sodium acetate is 119 g per 100 g of water at 0°C, so only 119 g of sodium acetate will dissolve in 100 g of water at 0°C.
b. The system is heterogeneous—it is a mixture of the solution and the excess solid.

c. The solution part is saturated—it holds as much solute as it stably can hold at 0°C.
d. When the system is heated to 100°C, all 170 g of solute will dissolve, so the mixture will be homogeneous.
e. The solution is saturated—it holds 170 g in 100 g of water, which is the maximum it can hold stably *at this temperature.*
f. The system is homogeneous. Because no solute crystallizes, the system is still a solution.
g. The solution is supersaturated because the 170 g of solute that it holds is more than the 119 g that would be stable at this temperature. If a small crystal of sodium acetate is added, the excess sodium acetate will crystallize out (see Figure 13.6).

PRACTICE PROBLEM 13.2

a. What would your answer to part (e) of Example 13.2 be if only 161 g of sodium acetate had been used?
b. What would your answer to part (d) be if 90.0 g of water had been used?

Hint:
a. Compare 161 g of sodium acetate to the solubility of sodium acetate at 100°C as given in Example 13.2.
b. This is less volume than was used in Example 13.2. How does using less solvent affect the mass of solute that can be dissolved?

Cameron Whitman/Shutterstock

FIGURE 13.7 Supersaturated CO_2 in a Carbonated Soft Drink

Shaking or pouring disturbs the solution, causing the excess dissolved CO_2 to come out of solution quickly.

SOLUBILITY OF GASES

A solution made up of a gas dissolved in a liquid behaves differently. Whereas solids generally become more soluble at higher temperatures, gases become less soluble because at higher temperatures the gas molecules have greater kinetic energy and are more easily able to escape the liquid into the gas phase. You may have experienced this with carbonated soft drinks which go "flat" (lose carbonation) faster at room temperature than they do when refrigerated.

Carbonated soft drinks are another example of a supersaturated solution, but here pressure is used to form the supersaturated solution, not temperature. In the manufacturing process, carbon dioxide, CO_2, gas is dissolved in the drink solution at high pressures, where the gas is more soluble. When the container is opened and the pressure above the solution is reduced to ordinary atmospheric pressure, the CO_2 gas is less soluble. Some escapes the solution, creating the familiar hiss of opening a carbonated beverage, but some of the excess (supersaturated) dissolved CO_2 remains in solution. Disturbing the solution by shaking or pouring causes more of the supersaturated CO_2 to come out of solution (Figure 13.7).

At any given temperature, the solubility of a gas in a liquid is directly proportional to the partial pressure of the gas above the surface of the liquid. This statement is known as **Henry's law**. Mathematically,

$$\text{Concentration of dissolved gas in solution} = kP \tag{13.1}$$

where k is the Henry's law constant, which depends on temperature and is different for each combination of gas and solvent, and P is the partial pressure (Section 7.7) of the gas above the liquid. Thus, to determine the saturated solution concentration of a gas in a liquid, you must know which gas and liquid are involved, along with both the temperature and the partial pressure of the gas above the liquid. Figure 13.8 allows you to see how the concentration of a dissolved gas in solution changes as the pressure above the gas is changed, and it also shows the effect of changing the temperature on the concentration of a dissolved gas.

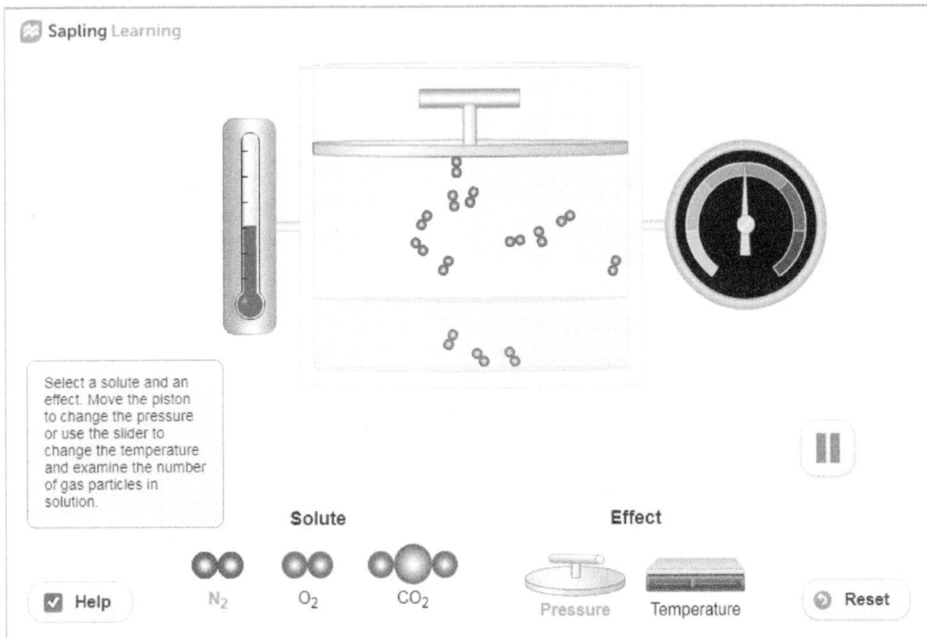

FIGURE 13.8 Gas Solubility Simulation

NOTE: You need to be online to access this activity.

First, take note of the number of molecules within the liquid layer. This represents the relative solubility of the selected gas under the selected conditions. Second, move the piston up or down to change the pressure and notice how the solubility of the gas changes. Third, select "Temperature" mode, and use the slider to adjust temperature. Finally, select a different gas and redo the same experiments involving pressure and temperature.

Example 13.3

At atmospheric pressure, the partial pressure of oxygen in air is 0.21 atm. At this pressure and 25°C, water contains 2.73×10^{-4} M dissolved oxygen gas. What is the Henry's law constant for oxygen in water at 25°C?

Solution

According to Henry's law (Equation 13.1), concentration = kP. And, since we are dealing with a concentration in molarity, we can use M as the symbol for concentration.

$$M = kP$$

Isolate k, and substitute the given pressure and molarity.

$$k = \frac{M}{P}$$

$$k = \frac{2.73 \times 10^{-4}\,\text{M}}{0.21\ \text{atm}} = 0.0013\ \text{M/atm}$$

PRACTICE PROBLEM 13.3

Use the Henry's law constant for oxygen gas in water at 25°C that you determined in Example 13.3 ($k = 0.0013$ M/atm) to calculate the molarity of oxygen in water in a hyperbaric chamber, where the partial pressure of oxygen is 0.30 atm.

Hint: Since you are asked for molarity, you can use M as the symbol for concentration in Equation 13.1 (Henry's law). Substitute the given values for k and P, and solve for M.

The terms *saturated*, *unsaturated*, and *supersaturated* are normally reserved for a solid or a gas dissolved in a liquid and do not apply to solutions that are made up of a gas dissolved in another gas, a liquid dissolved in another liquid, or a solid dissolved in another solid, because there is no upper limit to the solubility in these cases. When a liquid is mixed with a solid or a gas, the liquid is typically considered to be the solvent. The distinction between solute and solvent for other combinations is somewhat arbitrary, however, so the substance present in the greater amount is considered to be the solvent. When air is described as a solution of oxygen dissolved in nitrogen, nitrogen is the solvent simply because there is more nitrogen than oxygen.

Two liquid substances that are infinitely soluble like this are said to be **miscible**. Liquids that have the same type of intermolecular forces between their

EVERYDAY CONNECTION

Decompression sickness, also known as "the bends," can occur when scuba divers ascend from deep dives where the higher pressure makes the gases they breathe more soluble in blood and tissues (Henry's law). If a diver ascends too quickly toward the lower-pressure surface, the excess gas that dissolved in his or her tissues under higher pressure conditions can come out of solution to form gas bubbles, similar to when a carbonated beverage is opened at ordinary atmospheric pressure. Decompression sickness can result in excruciating joint pain along with other symptoms, including itching, headache, and seizures. To avoid decompression sickness, divers who are ascending from deep dives stop their ascent at designated depths for "decompression stops" of 10 minutes or more to allow the gases that dissolved in their tissues at higher pressure to gradually escape their tissues. Scuba divers use dive tables or dive computers to determine how long they can safely dive at various depths and whether or not decompression stops are necessary.

U.S. Navy photo by Mass Communication Specialist 1st Class Jayme Pastoric

molecules, such as water and ethanol, which both form hydrogen bonds, are usually miscible. When two liquids have very different intermolecular forces between their particles and do not dissolve in one another, such as nonpolar oil and highly polar water, the two liquids are said to be **immiscible**.

SECTION REVIEW

- A saturated solution holds the maximum quantity of solute that will dissolve in a given quantity of solvent at a particular temperature. The easiest way to tell that a solution is saturated is if excess solute is present that will not dissolve.
- Supersaturated solutions, which contain more solute than is stable at the temperature of the system, will likely crystallize when disturbed if the solute is solid, or erupt like a shaken soda bottle if the solute is gaseous.
- The concentration of a gas dissolved in a liquid is directly proportional to the partial pressure of the gas above the liquid (Henry's law, Equation 13.1). If a gas is supersaturated in a solution, the gas will slowly escape from the solution until its concentration reaches a point where Henry's law is satisfied.
- The terms *saturated*, *unsaturated*, and *supersaturated* do not apply to mixtures of gases or to miscible liquids or solid solutions because there is no upper limit of solubility in these cases. Instead, the substance present in the greater amount is defined as the solvent, and the other is the solute.

13.3 Concentration Units

GOAL

- Perform calculations involving percent by mass, molality, and mole fraction as measures of concentration.

Background Review

Chapter 5 Stoichiometry: Section 5.5—Definition and Uses of Molarity

The concentration of a solute in a solution can be represented in a number of different ways, but all concentration units are a ratio of the amount of solute divided by either the amount of solvent or the amount of solution.

Molarity, which is the number of moles of solute per liter of solution (Section 5.5), is usually the most convenient concentration unit in chemistry, but there are circumstances, such as those discussed in Section 13.4, where another concentration unit is more appropriate. This chapter introduces three additional concentration units: *percent by mass*, *molality*, and *mole fraction*.

PERCENT BY MASS

The **percent by mass** of a solute is simply the mass of the solute divided by the mass of the entire solution (solute plus solvent), times 100%:

$$\text{Percent by mass} = \left(\frac{\text{Mass of solute}}{\text{Total mass of solution}}\right) \times 100\% \qquad (13.2)$$

The 100% in this equation is not a measurement, so it does not limit the number of significant digits in the calculation.

Another way to think of percent by mass is that if you had a 100 gram sample of a solution, the percent by mass would be the number of grams of solute dissolved in that sample.

Percent by mass is calculated using the total mass of the *solution* rather than the mass of the solvent itself, so if you are given the mass of the *solvent*, be sure to first calculate the total mass of the solution and then use that figure in your calculations.

Be sure to distinguish between the mass of *solvent* and the mass of *solution*.

Example 13.4

What is the percent by mass of a 285 g solution that contains 85.0 g of solute?

Solution

The percent by mass is calculated using Equation 13.2:

$$\text{Percent by mass} = \left(\frac{\text{Mass of solute}}{\text{Total mass of solution}}\right) \times 100\%$$

$$\text{Percent by mass} = \left(\frac{85.0\text{ g}}{285\text{ g}}\right) \times 100\% = 29.8\%$$

Note that the actual identity of the solute and solvent do not matter for this calculation. Only the mass of each one is required.

PRACTICE PROBLEM 13.4

A chemist adds 0.18 g of a red powder to 50.0 g of water and shakes the solution until all of the powder is dissolved. What is the percent by mass of the resulting solution?

Hint: Use Equation 13.2. The mass of the solution is the sum of the mass of the solute and the mass of the solvent.

The percent by mass is equal to the mass of solute in exactly 100 g of solution, so the percent by mass can be rewritten as a fraction with the percent by mass expressed in grams instead and with "100 g solution" in the denominator. For example,

$$7.2\% \text{ by mass} = \frac{7.2\text{ g solute}}{100\text{ g solution}}$$

When the percent by mass is expressed as a fraction, it can be used as a conversion factor to convert between the mass of solute and the mass of solution.

Example 13.5

Calculate the mass of NaCl in 46.6 g of a 3.00% by mass saline solution.

Solution

Rewriting the percent by mass as a fraction allows you to use it as a conversion factor between grams of solution and grams of solvent:

$$3.00\% \text{ by mass} = \frac{3.00\text{ g solute}}{100\text{ g solution}}$$

$$46.6\text{ g solution}\left(\frac{3.00\text{ g NaCl}}{100\text{ g solution}}\right) = 1.40\text{ g NaCl}$$

PRACTICE PROBLEM 13.5

Suppose you are asked to prepare 5.00 kg of a 12.0% solution of hydroxylamine, NH_2OH, but you only have 434 g of NH_3OH. Do you have enough hydroxylamine to make the solution? If not, what mass of 12.0% by mass hydroxylamine solution can you prepare?

Hint: Turn the percent by mass into a fraction, which can be used as a conversion factor, then calculate the mass of solute that would be required to prepare 5.00 kg of solution.

MOLALITY

Because molarity is based on the volume of the solution and because temperature changes can result in volume changes, the molarity of a solution can change with temperature even when no other changes are made to the solution. When an experiment involves temperature changes, the unit molality is often used instead of molarity. **Molality** is the number of moles of solute per *kilogram of solvent* rather than per liter of solution.

$$\text{Molality} = \frac{\text{Moles of solute}}{\text{Kilogram of solvent}} \quad (13.3)$$

Molality is the number of moles of solute per kilogram of solvent.

In discussions of concentration, molality is symbolized by an italicized lowercase *m*. The concentration unit of molality is called **molal** and is also symbolized with an italicized lowercase *m* or by mol/kg. The similarities in name and meaning between molarity and molality can be confusing. However, the concepts differ in two ways: For molality, (1) *mass* is used in the denominator instead of volume and (2) the amount of *solvent* is measured, rather than the total amount of solution.

In most solutions, especially dilute ones, the concentration in molarity and the concentration in molality are nearly equal. The differences become greater as the solutions become more concentrated. Additionally, the use of mass instead of volume in the unit becomes more important for measurements that take place over a range of temperatures, since the volume of a substance may change with temperature but its mass does not.

Example 13.6

Calculate the molality of a solution prepared by dissolving 29.5 g NaCl in 212.7 g of water.

Solution

First, calculate the number of moles of solute. The molar mass of NaCl is 22.99 g/mol + 35.453 g/mol = 58.44 g/mol.

$$29.5 \text{ g NaCl}\left(\frac{1 \text{ mol NaCl}}{58.44 \text{ g NaCl}}\right) = 0.505 \text{ mol NaCl}$$

Next, calculate the number of kilograms of solvent. Recall that 1 kg = 1000 g.

$$212.7 \text{ g } H_2O\left(\frac{1 \text{ kg}}{1000 \text{ g}}\right) = 0.2127 \text{ kg } H_2O$$

Finally, divide the number of moles of NaCl by the number of kilograms of H_2O to obtain the molality.

$$m = \frac{0.505 \text{ mol NaCl}}{0.2127 \text{ kg } H_2O} = 2.37 \text{ mol/ kg} = 2.37\ m$$

PRACTICE PROBLEM 13.6

The solubility of $MgSO_4$ in water at 0°C is 26 g per 100.0 g of water. What is this solubility in molality?

Hint: Molality is moles of solute per kilograms of solvent, so convert 26 g $MgSO_4$ to moles and 100.0 g of water to kilograms (1 kg = 1000 g).

In some problems, you will not be given the mass of solvent directly. For example, you may be given the *volume* of solvent, in which case you will need to use the density to convert it to mass. Alternatively, you may be given the mass of the solution, in which case you will need to subtract out the mass of the solute to find the mass of just the solvent.

Example 13.7

Calculate the molality of a solution prepared by dissolving 28.2 g C_3H_8O in 207 mL of water (density = 1.00 g/mL).

Solution

Convert grams of solute to moles of solute. The molar mass of C_3H_8O is 3(12.011 g/mol) + 8(1.008 g/mol) + 15.999 g/mol = 60.095 g/mol.

$$28.2 \text{ g } C_3H_8O\left(\frac{1 \text{ mol}}{60.095 \text{ g}}\right) = 0.469 \text{ mol } C_3H_8O$$

Convert volume of H_2O to kilograms. The density of water is 1.00 g/mL.

$$207 \text{ mL } H_2O\left(\frac{1.00 \text{ g } H_2O}{1.00 \text{ mL } H_2O}\right)\left(\frac{1 \text{ kg}}{1000 \text{ g}}\right)$$
$$= 0.207 \text{ kg } H_2O$$

Divide moles of solute by kilogram of solvent to determine the molality.

$$m = \frac{0.469 \text{ mol } C_3H_8O}{0.207 \text{ kg } H_2O} = 2.27 \text{ mol/kg} = 2.27\ m$$

PRACTICE PROBLEM 13.7

A saturated solution of $Na_2S_2O_3$ at 80°C was determined to be 47.6% by mass. What is this concentration expressed in molality?

Hint: Remember that 46.7% by mass means there are 46.7 g of solute in 100 g of *solution*. So, you will need to subtract 46.7 g from 100 g to find the mass of *solvent*.

Like other concentration units, molality can be used as a conversion factor. For example, if you are given the molal concentration of a solution and the mass of solvent, you can calculate the number of moles of solute. Similarly, if you are given the molal concentration and the amount of solute, you can calculate the mass of solvent.

Example 13.8

Calculate the mass of $HClO_4$ needed to make a 5.13 *m* solution in 239 g of water.

Solution

First calculate the number of moles of solute using molality as a conversion factor.

239 g of H_2O is 0.239 kg of H_2O.

$$0.239 \text{ kg } H_2O\left(\frac{5.13 \text{ mol } HClO_4}{1 \text{ kg } H_2O}\right) = 1.23 \text{ mol } HClO_4$$

Then convert the moles of $HClO_4$ to grams. The molar mass of $HClO_4$ is 1.008 g/mol + 35.453 g/mol + 4(15.999 g/mol) = 100.457 g/mol.

$$1.23 \text{ mol } HClO_4\left(\frac{100.457 \text{ g } HClO_4}{1 \text{ mol } HClO_4}\right) = 124 \text{ g } HClO_4$$

PRACTICE PROBLEM 13.8

Calculate the number of kilograms of water that must be mixed with 0.334 mol acetaldehyde, C_2H_4O, to make 1.68 *m* C_2H_4O.

Hint: Use the molality, 1.68 mol/kg, as a conversion factor between moles of acetaldehyde and kilograms of water.

MOLE FRACTION

The **mole fraction** of a component of a solution is the number of moles of that component divided by the total number of moles of everything in the solution. Mole fraction is represented by the Greek letter chi, X, and the mole fraction of a component A in a solution would be represented as X_A. For a solution made up of two components, A and B, the mole fraction of A, X_A, is given by Equation 13.4:

$$X_A = \frac{\text{Moles of A}}{\text{Moles of A} + \text{Moles of B}} \qquad (13.4)$$

If there were any additional components in the solution, such as C, D, and E, the denominator would also include the number of moles of C, D, and E in the sum.

A mole fraction is similar to a percentage in that it represents a part of a whole. The sum of the mole fractions of all the components of a solution ($X_A + X_B + \cdots$) is equal to 1, just as the sum of the percentages of all components of a whole must be 100%. With mole fraction, no distinction is made between the solute and the solvent in the calculations; the mole fraction of every component of the solution is calculated the same way. A mole fraction has no units because it is obtained by dividing moles by moles. If you are given the masses of the components, you must first convert mass to moles using the molar mass of each component as a conversion factor and then calculate the mole fractions.

Example 13.9

Calculate the mole fraction of methyl alcohol, CH_3OH, in a solution composed of 1.46 mol methyl alcohol and 2.19 mol ethyl alcohol, C_2H_5OH. What is the mole fraction of C_2H_5OH in the same solution?

Solution

Using Equation 13.4, the mole fraction of CH_3OH is

$$X_{CH_3OH} = \frac{1.46 \text{ mol}}{1.46 \text{ mol} + 2.19 \text{ mol}} = 0.400$$

The mole fraction of C_2H_5OH can be determined either by calculating it from the moles of each component as you did for CH_3OH or by subtracting X_{CH_3OH} from 1, since the sum of the mole fractions of the two components must equal 1.

$$X_{C_2H_5OH} = \frac{2.19 \text{ mol}}{1.46 \text{ mol} + 2.19 \text{ mol}} = 0.600$$

or

$$X_{C_2H_5OH} = 1 - X_{CH_3OH} = 1 - 0.400 = 0.600$$

PRACTICE PROBLEM 13.9

Calculate the mole fractions of CH_2O and C_3H_8O in a solution containing equal masses of both.

Hint: Assume some mass, such as 10.00 g of each. You can use any mass as long as the two masses are equal. Determine the molar masses of CH_2O and C_3H_8O, and calculate the moles of each component.

CONVERTING FROM ONE CONCENTRATION UNIT TO ANOTHER

All concentration units are a ratio of the amount of solute to the amount of either solution or solvent. Table 13.2 summarizes the ratios of the four concentration units used in this text.

TABLE 13.2 Summary of Concentration Units

Unit	Molarity	Percent by Mass	Molality	Mole Fraction
Symbol	*M*	%	*m*	*X*
Numerator	Moles of solute	Grams of solute	Moles of solute	Moles of solute
Denominator	Liters of solution	Grams of solution	Kilograms of solvent	Total moles of solute plus moles of solvent

Steve Lemon, Macmillan Learning

FIGURE 13.9 Video Tutorial: Concentration Units

NOTE: You need to be online to access this video.
This video shows how to convert a concentration in percent by mass to molality and mole fraction.

To convert a concentration from one unit to another, you must convert both the numerator and the denominator of the initial concentration unit to those of the final concentration unit. Converting between grams and moles of solute in the numerator is done using the molar mass of solute as a conversion factor. Converting the denominator sometimes requires additional information. For example, to convert molarity to molality, you must know how much solvent was used in preparing the solution, and to convert between molarity and percent by mass, you must know the density of the solution.

Note that when converting between concentration units, you can choose an arbitrary total amount of solution to begin the calculation. Remember that concentration is an intensive property (Section 1.2), which means that it does not change when you change the amount of material present. The video in Figure 13.9 demonstrates conversions between various units of concentration.

Example 13.10

Calculate the molality of a solution of methyl alcohol, CH_3OH, in water in which the alcohol has a mole fraction of 0.133.

Solution

Molality is moles of solute (alcohol) divided by kilograms of solvent (water), so you need to determine those two quantities from the mole fraction.

Begin by assuming you have 1.00 mol total in the solution. In that case you have 0.133 mol alcohol and the rest is water.

$$1.00 \text{ mol solution} - 0.133 \text{ mol alcohol} = 0.867 \text{ mol water}$$

Convert 0.867 mol of water to kilograms. The molar mass of H_2O is 2(1.008 g/mol) + 15.999 g/mol = 18.0148 g/mol.

$$0.867 \text{ mol } H_2O\left(\frac{18.0148 \text{ g}}{1 \text{ mol}}\right)\left(\frac{1 \text{ kg}}{1000 \text{ g}}\right) = 0.0156 \text{ kg}$$

$$m = \frac{0.133 \text{ mol alcohol}}{0.0156 \text{ kg } H_2O} = 8.53 \text{ mol/kg} = 8.53\ m$$

PRACTICE PROBLEM 13.10

Calculate the mole fractions for both components of a 1.27 m solution of methyl alcohol in water.

Hint: A 1.27 m solution contains 1.27 moles of alcohol per 1 kg of water. Convert the mass of water to moles, then compute the mole fractions.

Example 13.11

What is the mole fraction NaCl in a salt solution that is 22% NaCl by mass?

Solution

Percent by mass is the ratio of grams of solute to grams of *solution*, so a 22% solution has 22 g NaCl in every 100 g of solution. Since the mass of the solution includes the mass of the salt, 100 g of solution contains 100 g solution − 22 g NaCl = 78 g water.

Mole fraction is the ratio of moles of solute to total moles of solute plus solvent. The number of moles of NaCl and of water can be calculated from their masses using their respective molar masses:

$$22 \text{ g NaCl} \times \frac{1 \text{ mol NaCl}}{58.443 \text{ g NaCl}} = 0.376 \text{ mol NaCl}$$

$$78 \text{ g } H_2O \times \frac{1 \text{ mol } H_2O}{18.0148 \text{ g } H_2O} = 4.33 \text{ mol } H_2O$$

The mole fraction of NaCl, X_{NaCl}, is the moles of NaCl divided by the total number of moles of NaCl plus H_2O:

$$X_{NaCl} = \frac{0.376 \text{ mol NaCl}}{0.376 \text{ mol NaCl} + 4.33 \text{ mol } H_2O} = 0.080$$

PRACTICE PROBLEM 13.11

What is the molality of a salt solution that is 22% NaCl by mass?

Hint: Determine how many grams of NaCl and how many grams of water are in a 100 g sample of the solution. Then convert grams of NaCl to moles of NaCl and convert grams of water to kilograms of water to determine the molality.

Example 13.12

For aqueous solutions at low concentrations, molality and molarity are approximately equal because 1 L of solution contains approximately 1 kg of solvent, but at high concentrations, these values can be very different. What is the molality of a concentrated phosphoric acid solution that is 14.8 M and has a density of 1.685 g/mL?

Solution

A 14.8 M solution contains 14.8 mol of solute in 1.00 L of *solution*. To calculate molality, you need to know the mass of *solvent*. The density of the solution can be used as a conversion factor between the volume of the solution and the mass of the solution:

$$1.00\text{ L solution} \times \frac{1000\text{ mL}}{1\text{ L}} \times \frac{1.685\text{ g solution}}{1\text{ mL solution}}$$
$$= 1685\text{ g solution}$$

The mass of the solvent can now be determined by subtracting the mass of the solute from the total mass of the solution. Because 1 L of solution contains 14.8 mol H_3PO_4 (molar mass 97.9937 g/mol), the mass of solute is

$$14.8\text{ mol H}_3\text{PO}_4 \times \frac{97.9937\text{ g H}_3\text{PO}_4}{1\text{ mol H}_3\text{PO}_4} = 1450\text{ g H}_3\text{PO}_4$$

The mass of the solvent is the mass of the solution minus the mass of the solute:

$$\text{Mass of solvent} = 1685\text{ g} - 1450\text{ g} = 235\text{ g}$$

Molality is the moles of solute per kilogram of solvent, so convert the mass of solvent from grams to kilograms, then divide moles of solute by kilograms of solvent:

$$235\text{ g solvent} \times \frac{1\text{ kg}}{1000\text{ g}} = 0.235\text{ kg solvent}$$

$$\text{molality} = \frac{14.8\text{ mol}}{0.235\text{ kg}} = 63.0\ m$$

PRACTICE PROBLEM 13.12

What is the molality of a phosphoric acid solution that is 1.00 M and has a density of 1.0303 g/mL? Compare the similarities of the molality and molarity values for this solution to those of the concentrated H_3PO_4 solution in Example 13.12.

Hint: Use the volume and density of the solution to calculate the mass of the solution, then subtract the mass of the solute from the mass of the solution to determine the mass of the solvent. Molality is the moles of solute divided by the mass of the solvent in kilograms.

SECTION REVIEW

- The concentration unit of percent by mass is the mass of the solute divided by the mass of the solution, times 100%.
- Percent by mass is also the number of grams of solute in exactly 100 g of solution. Unlike molarity (Section 5.5), the denominator of this ratio is a mass, not a volume.
- Molality is the number of moles of solute per *kilogram of solvent,* whereas molarity is the number of moles of solute per *liter of solution.*
- Because molality is based on the *mass* of solvent rather than the *volume* of solution, molality is temperature independent—it does *not* change as the solution is warmed or cooled.
- The mole fraction of a substance in a solution is the number of moles of the substance divided by the total number of moles of all of the components in the solution.
- Mole fraction is represented by the Greek letter chi, X, and the mole fraction of a component A in the solution would be represented as X_A. Component A could be either a solute or the solvent, because the solvent and solutes are all treated simply as components of the mixture.
- When converting from one concentration unit to another, both the solute and the solvent or solution must be converted to the proper units. This sometimes requires additional information, such as the density of the solution.

13.4 Colligative Properties of Nonelectrolytes

GOAL

- Perform calculations using some of the properties of solutions of nonelectrolytes that depend on the concentrations of the dissolved particles rather than their nature.

Background Review

Chapter 7 Gases: Section 7.6—Ideal Gas Law

Colligative properties of solutions are properties that depend on the concentration of solute particles in the solution but do not depend on what those particles are.

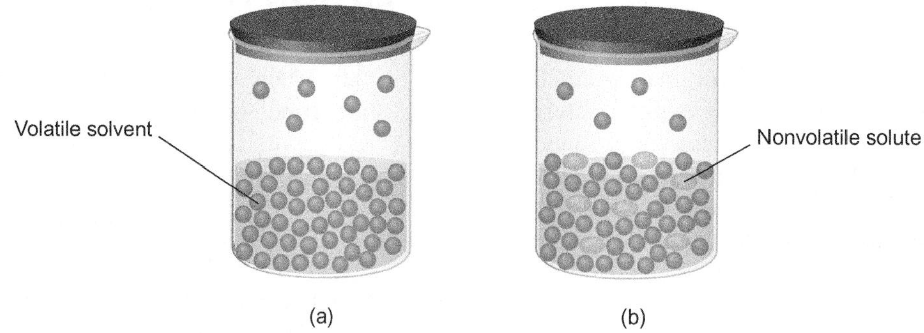

FIGURE 13.10 Vapor-Pressure Lowering

A volatile solvent (a) has a higher vapor pressure than a solution containing a nonvolatile solute (b) because the solute occupies some of the surface area of the solution, decreasing vaporization of the solvent and thereby lowering the vapor pressure above the solution. The nonvolatile solute itself does not vaporize and therefore does not contribute to the vapor pressure of the solution.

The four colligative properties covered in this chapter are *vapor-pressure lowering*, *freezing-point depression*, *boiling-point elevation*, and *osmotic pressure*.

All of the solutes in this section are assumed to be nonelectrolyte compounds, so they do not dissociate when dissolved in the solvent (Section 4.3). Colligative properties involving electrolyte solutions are covered in Section 13.5.

VAPOR-PRESSURE LOWERING

Chapter 12 describes how intermolecular forces are always at work in a liquid, attracting the atoms or molecules to other atoms or molecules of the liquid. If an atom or molecule at the surface of a liquid has sufficient kinetic energy to overcome those attractive forces, it can escape the liquid as vapor in the gas phase.

When solute particles are present, they disrupt the ability of the surface molecules to vaporize by occupying some of the surface area (Figure 13.10). Thus, if you add a solid solute to the liquid, its vapor pressure will decrease. The **vapor-pressure lowering, ΔP,** depends on the *concentration* of the solute particles, but not on their identity. Substances that evaporate easily, and thus have a measurable vapor pressure, have relatively weak intermolecular forces and are said to be **volatile** (Chapter 12). Most liquid solvents, such as water, are volatile. Solid solutes, on the other hand, are **nonvolatile**, meaning they do not easily vaporize and therefore do not contribute to the vapor pressure of the solution.

Raoult's law states that the vapor pressure of a volatile component of a solution is equal to the mole fraction of the component times its vapor pressure when it is a pure liquid. That is, for volatile component Z,

$$P_Z = X_Z P_Z^\circ \qquad (13.5)$$

where P_Z is the vapor pressure of the component in the solution and P_Z° is the vapor pressure of the pure substance at the same temperature. A solution that follows Raoult's law exactly is called an **ideal solution**. In an ideal solution, the intermolecular attractions between any two particles are equally strong, whether they are two solute particles, a solute and solvent particle, or two solvent particles. Since like dissolves like, the strengths of the intermolecular attractions between the particles in many solutions are close enough to ideal that many solutions follow Raoult's law approximately.

Solutions that deviate from Raoult's law are those in which the solute–solvent attraction is much stronger or weaker than the attractions between solvent–solvent or solute–solute. If the solute–solvent attraction is very strong, such as when there is extensive hydrogen bonding between the solute and solvent, the vapor pressure will be lower than predicted by Raoult's law. If the solute–solvent attraction is weaker than the solute–solute or solvent–solvent attractions, the presence of weaker attractions in the mixture allows particles to escape into the vapor phase more easily, and the vapor pressure of the solution will be higher than predicted by Raoult's law. The problems that follow, however, will all deal with ideal solutions.

Example 13.13

The vapor pressure of ethyl alcohol at 25°C is 58.7 torr. Calculate the vapor pressure of the ethyl alcohol in solution at 25°C if 0.175 mol glucose is dissolved in 0.909 mol of the alcohol.

Solution

The total number of moles in the solution is $0.175 + 0.909 = 1.084$ mol.

The mole fraction of the alcohol is

$$X_{\text{alcohol}} = \frac{0.909 \text{ mol}}{1.084 \text{ mol}} = 0.839$$

Remember that mole fraction is unitless.

The vapor pressure of the alcohol in the solution is

$$P_{\text{alcohol}} = X_{\text{alcohol}} P^\circ_{\text{alcohol}} = (0.839)(58.7 \text{ torr}) = 49.2 \text{ torr}$$

PRACTICE PROBLEM 13.13

Calculate the vapor pressure of benzene in a solution at 25°C in which the mole fraction of benzene is 0.820. The vapor pressure of pure benzene at 25°C is 94.8 torr.

Hint: Use Raoult's law: $P_Z = X_Z P^\circ_Z$ (Equation 13.5).

Vapor-pressure lowering is defined as the vapor pressure of the pure substance, P°, minus its vapor pressure in the solution, P. It is symbolized ΔP.

$$\Delta P = P^\circ - P \qquad (13.6)$$

Be sure to distinguish between the vapor pressure of a solvent and the vapor-pressure lowering.

Example 13.14

Calculate the vapor-pressure lowering of the alcohol in Example 13.13.

Solution

The vapor pressure of the pure alcohol, P°, was given in Example 13.13 as 58.7 torr, and the vapor pressure of the solution, P, was calculated to be 49.2 torr. Use Equation 13.6 to calculate the vapor-pressure lowering.

$$\Delta P = P^\circ - P$$

$$\Delta P = 58.7 \text{ torr} - 49.2 \text{ torr} = 9.5 \text{ torr}$$

PRACTICE PROBLEM 13.14

Calculate the vapor-pressure lowering of the benzene solution in Practice Problem 13.13.

Hint: Subtract the calculated vapor pressure for the solution from the vapor pressure of pure benzene, as given in the problem.

Steve Lemon, Macmillan Learning

FIGURE 13.11 Video Tutorial: Raoult's Law

NOTE: You need to be online to access this video.

This video shows how to calculate the vapor pressure of two solutions, one with a single volatile component and one with multiple volatile components.

The examples presented so far have all involved solutions with nonvolatile solutes and a volatile solvent, such as a solid dissolved in a liquid. If the solute is nonvolatile, it has no vapor pressure of its own to include in the calculations.

If a solution is made up of two volatile components (such as two liquids), the total vapor pressure above the solution is the sum of the vapor pressures of each of the components. Raoult's law (Equation 13.5) can be expanded to apply to each volatile component in the solution. For example, in a solution made up of volatile substances A and Z, the total vapor pressure is

$$P_{\text{total}} = P_A + P_Z = X_A P^\circ_A + X_Z P^\circ_Z \qquad (13.7)$$

The video in Figure 13.11 demonstrates both applications of Raoult's law.

Example 13.15

Calculate the total pressure of benzene and toluene over a solution consisting of 0.661 mol benzene and 0.227 mol toluene at 252°C. Their vapor pressures when pure are $P^\circ_{\text{benzene}} = 94.8$ torr and $P^\circ_{\text{toluene}} = 28.4$ torr.

Solution

Vapor pressures are given for both substances, so you can assume they are both volatile. First, find the mole fraction of each component.

$$X_{\text{benzene}} = \frac{0.661}{0.661 + 0.227} = 0.744$$

$$X_{\text{toluene}} = 1 - X_{\text{benzene}} = 1 - 0.744 = 0.256$$

Each substance follows Raoult's law (Equation 13.5). Therefore,

$$P_{\text{benzene}} = X_{\text{benzene}}P^{\circ}_{\text{benzene}} = (0.744)(94.8 \text{ torr}) = 70.5 \text{ torr}$$

$$P_{\text{toluene}} = X_{\text{toluene}}P^{\circ}_{\text{toluene}} = (0.256)(28.4 \text{ torr}) = 7.27 \text{ torr}$$

$$P_{\text{total}} = P_{\text{benzene}} + P_{\text{toluene}} = 70.5 \text{ torr} + 7.27 \text{ torr} = 77.8 \text{ torr}$$

PRACTICE PROBLEM 13.15

A mixture of carbon tetrachloride, CCl_4, and chloroform, $CHCl_3$, at 20°C has a total pressure of 111 torr. If the mole fraction of chloroform in the vapor is 0.402 and the vapor pressure of pure chloroform is 160 torr, what is the vapor pressure of pure carbon tetrachloride at that temperature?

Hint: Determine the mole fraction of carbon tetrachloride in the vapor, then use Equation 13.7 to solve for $P^{\circ}_{CCl_4}$.

VAPOR COMPOSITION

Because each volatile component in a solution has a different vapor pressure, some components will evaporate more readily than others, and the mole fraction of the components in the vapor will not be the same as the mole fraction of the components in the solution. The partial pressures in a gas mixture are proportional to the mole ratios of the gases that make up the mixture (Section 7.7). This means that the mole ratio in the vapor phase can be determined from the ratio of partial pressures of the gases, and the mole fraction of each gas can be determined from its partial pressure and the total vapor pressure. For any two volatile components A and Z in the vapor above a solution,

$$\frac{\text{Moles of A in vapor phase}}{\text{Moles of Z in vapor phase}} = \frac{P_A}{P_Z} \qquad (13.8)$$

$$X_{Z\text{(gas phase)}} = \frac{P_Z}{P_{\text{total}}} \qquad (13.9)$$

Example 13.16

Calculate the mole fraction of benzene in the vapor phase of the system in Example 13.15.

Solution

The mole fraction of any component of a mixed gas is equal to the partial pressure of that gas divided by the total pressure of the gas (Equation 13.9). In Example 13.15, the partial pressure of benzene was determined to be 70.5 torr and the total pressure was 77.8 torr, so the mole fraction of benzene in the vapor phase is

$$X_{\text{benzene(gas phase)}} = \frac{P_{\text{benzene}}}{P_{\text{total}}} = \frac{70.5 \text{ torr}}{77.8 \text{ torr}} = 0.906$$

Note that the mole fraction of the more volatile substance has increased from 0.744 in the liquid phase to 0.906 in the gas phase. The process of distillation (Section 12.4) is used to separate mixtures of volatile substances based on differences in their boiling points and vapor pressures.

PRACTICE PROBLEM 13.16

A mixture of carbon tetrachloride, CCl_4, with mole fraction 0.300, and chloroform, $CHCl_3$, at 30°C has a total vapor pressure of 215 torr. If the mole fraction of chloroform in the vapor phase is 0.800, what is the vapor pressure of each pure substance at that temperature?

Hint: Use the mole fractions in the vapor phase to calculate the partial pressure of each substance (Equation 13.9), then use Raoult's law (Equation 13.5) with the mole fraction in the liquid to calculate the vapor pressure of the pure substances.

FREEZING-POINT DEPRESSION AND BOILING-POINT ELEVATION

Addition of a solute to a solvent will cause the freezing point of the solution to be lowered compared to that of the pure solvent. For a liquid to freeze and become a solid, the randomly ordered molecules in the liquid phase must form an orderly array in the solid phase. The solute particles interfere with the process of making the orderly array of molecules and therefore prevent freezing from occurring at the liquid's normal freezing point temperature (Figure 13.12).

Antifreeze is added to car radiators to lower the freezing point of the water and help prevent the liquid in the radiator from freezing in the winter. Salt is spread on icy sidewalks and roads to make the freezing point of the salt solution lower than the outdoor temperature and thus remove the ice (Section 13.5).

The **freezing-point depression, ΔT_f**, represents how much *lower* the freezing point of the solution is compared to that of the pure solvent.

$$T_{\text{solution}} = T_{\text{solvent}} - \Delta T_f \qquad (13.10)$$

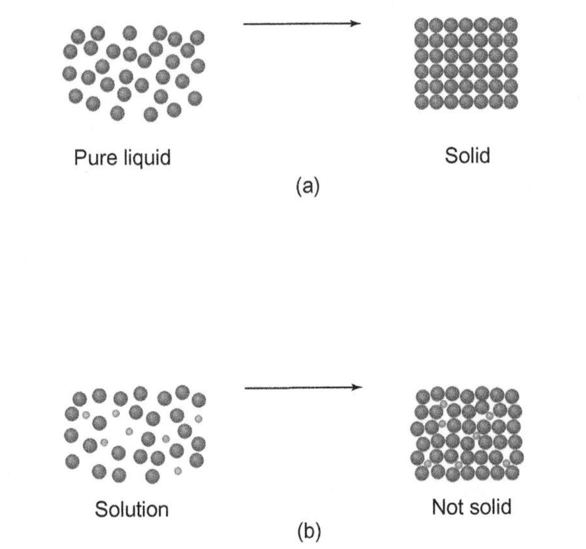

FIGURE 13.12 Freezing-Point Depression

In a pure liquid (a), the solvent molecules form an orderly array at the solvent's freezing point and the solvent becomes a solid, but in a solution (b), the solute particles interfere with the formation of an orderly array of molecules, so the solution remains in the liquid phase at the solvent's freezing point.

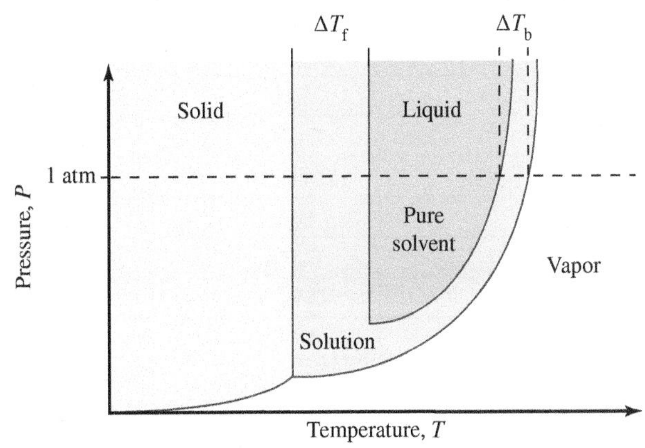

FIGURE 13.13 Liquid Range of a Nonvolatile Solvent and Its Solution

The freezing point of the solution is lower than that of the solvent, and the boiling point of the solution is higher than that of the solvent. Therefore, the liquid range in the phase diagram is larger for the solution than it is for the pure solvent.

In contrast, dissolving a nonvolatile solute in a solvent causes the boiling point of the solution to be *raised* compared to that of the pure solvent. The antifreeze added to water in car radiators causes the solution in the radiator to boil at a temperature higher than 100°C, which is important in summertime to avoid radiator boilover and the engine overheating that would result.

The **boiling-point elevation, ΔT_b,** is defined similarly to the freezing-point depression as the difference between the boiling point of the solution and the boiling point of the solvent, but in this case the difference is always positive.

$$T_{\text{solution}} = T_{\text{solvent}} + \Delta T_b \qquad (13.11)$$

Thus, the presence of a solute makes the liquid temperature range of a solution larger, extending it at both the freezing-point end and the boiling-point end. That is, the solution is in the liquid state over a wider range of temperatures than is the pure solvent (Figure 13.13).

Since boiling is defined as the temperature at which the vapor pressure of the liquid is equal to the surrounding pressure, the reason for boiling-point elevation is the same as that for vapor-pressure lowering (Figure 13.10). Solvent molecules that have sufficient kinetic energy to escape the liquid phase are blocked from escaping by solute particles at the surface and remain in the liquid. Greater kinetic energy (and therefore a higher temperature) is required before enough solvent molecules escape so that the vapor pressure is equal to the surrounding pressure.

The equations that relate freezing-point depression and boiling-point elevation to molality are similar to one another except for the constants used.

$$\Delta T_f = K_f m \qquad (13.12)$$

$$\Delta T_b = K_b m \qquad (13.13)$$

In these equations, m is the molality of the solution (moles of solute per kilogram of solvent), K_f is the freezing-point depression constant for the solvent in question, and K_b is the boiling-point elevation constant for the solvent, in units of °C/m.

The values of K_f and K_b depend on the solvent, but K_f is larger than K_b for almost all solvents, which means dissolving a solute in most solvents will lower the freezing point more than it raises the boiling point. Some freezing-point depression and boiling-point elevation data are given in Table 13.3. The values of K_f and K_b depend on the nature of the *solvent* and are independent of the solute.

The video in Figure 13.14 shows how to calculate both the freezing-point depression and the boiling-point elevation for solutions of nonelectrolyte solutes.

TABLE 13.3 Some Freezing-Point Depression and Boiling-Point Elevation Data

Solvent	Formula	Freezing Point (°C)	K_f (°C/m)	Boiling Point (°C)	K_b (°C/m)
Benzene	C_6H_6	5.5	5.12	80.1	2.53
Naphthalene	$C_{10}H_8$	80.22	6.85	218	5.80
Phenol	C_6H_5OH	43	7.40	182	3.60
Water	H_2O	0.00	1.86	100.00	0.512
Cyclohexane	C_6H_{12}	6.59	20.8	80.7	2.92
Ethanol	C_2H_6O	−117.3	1.99	78.4	1.22
Carbon tetrachloride	CCl_4	−22.9	29.8	76.8	5.03

Steve Lemon, Macmillan Learning

FIGURE 13.14 Video Tutorial: Freezing-Point Depression and Boiling-Point Elevation

NOTE: You need to be online to access this video.
This video shows how to calculate the freezing and boiling points of solutions of nonelectrolyte solutes.

Example 13.17

Calculate the freezing point of a solution containing 0.135 mol of a nonelectrolyte solute in 2.50 kg of benzene.

Solution

The concentration of the solute must be in units of molality. The molality is

$$m = \frac{0.135 \text{ mol}}{2.50 \text{ kg}} = 0.0540\ m$$

Use Equation 13.12 to calculate the freezing-point depression. The value of K_f for benzene is found in Table 13.3 to be 5.12°C/m.

$$\Delta T_f = K_f m$$

$$\Delta T_f = (5.12°\text{C}/m)(0.0540\ m) = 0.276°\text{C}$$

Now use Equation 13.10 to find the freezing point of the solution. Use the $T_{solvent}$ value from Table 13.3,

$$T_{solution} = T_{solvent} - \Delta T_f$$

$$T_{solution} = 5.5°\text{C} - 0.276°\text{C} = 5.2°\text{C}$$

PRACTICE PROBLEM 13.17

Calculate the boiling points for

a. a 0.650 m solution of fructose, also known as fruit sugar, $C_6H_{12}O_6$, in water.

b. a 0.650 m solution of ethylene glycol, the main component of automotive antifreeze, $C_2H_4(OH)_2$, in water.

Hint: Use the data in Table 13.3 and Equation 13.13 to determine the boiling-point elevation, then use Equation 13.11 to determine the boiling point of the solution.

If you know how many grams of a solute are dissolved in a given mass of solvent, the molar mass of the solute can be determined by measuring the freezing point or boiling point. The freezing-point depression (Equation 13.12) or boiling-point elevation (Equation 13.13) provides a way of calculating the molal concentration of the solute. Then, multiplying the molal concentration by the mass of the solvent in kilograms gives you the number of moles of solute. The mass of solute divided by the moles of solute gives you the molar mass of the solute.

Example 13.18

An absent-minded chemist pours 575 g of alcohol into 1.00 L of water, then leaves for lunch. When he returns, he cannot remember if the alcohol was methanol, CH_3OH, ethanol, C_2H_5OH, or butanol, C_4H_9OH. If the solution boils at 106.40°C, which alcohol did he add?

Solution

Use the boiling-point elevation of the solution to determine the molecular weight of the solute and compare it to that of CH_3OH (about 32 g/mol), C_2H_5OH (about 46 g/mol), and C_4H_9OH (about 74 g/mol).

The molality of the solution is determined from the boiling-point elevation and the value of

K_b for water. The boiling-point elevation for this solution is 6.40°C. Rearranging Equation 13.13 yields

$$m = \frac{\Delta T_b}{K_b} = \frac{6.40°\text{C}}{0.512°\text{C}/m} = 12.5\ m = 12.5\ \text{mol/kg}$$

The density of water is 1.00 g/mL, or 1.00 kg/L, so 1.00 L of water has a mass of 1.00 kg.

Multiplying this concentration by the mass of water present in kilograms yields the number of moles of solute in the solution:

$$\frac{12.5\ \text{mol solute}}{1\ \text{kg water}} \times 1.00\ \text{kg water} = 12.5\ \text{mol solute}$$

Divide the mass of solute (575 g) by the moles of solute (12.5 mol) to determine the molar mass:

$$\frac{575\ \text{g solute}}{12.5\ \text{moles solute}} = 46.0\ \text{g/mol}$$

The molar mass matches that of C_2H_5OH, so the solute is ethanol.

PRACTICE PROBLEM 13.18

A 100.0 g sample of a nonelectrolyte white crystalline solute is dissolved in 500.0 g of water, and the resulting solution freezes at −1.09°C. Determine the molar mass of the solute.

Hint: Use Equation 13.12 to determine the molality of the solution, then multiply that by the mass of solvent in kilograms to determine the number of moles of solute. With the mass and number of moles of solute, calculate the molar mass.

OSMOTIC PRESSURE

A **semipermeable membrane** allows some, but not all, molecules to pass through. For example, a semipermeable membrane might have very small pores that allow water molecules to freely pass through but completely block larger molecules such as glucose, $C_6H_{12}O_6$.

When a volume of aqueous sugar solution and a volume of pure water solvent are separated by a semipermeable membrane, the solvent molecules can pass freely through the membrane in either direction, but the solute particles cannot pass through the membrane from the solution side of the membrane to the solvent side. You might expect that the volumes of the liquids on the two sides of the membrane would remain essentially unchanged, since the water molecules can move freely back and forth through the membrane. It turns out, though, that a greater number of water molecules will move from the pure solvent side to the solution side than from the solution side to the pure solvent side. This is because the presence of the solute particles on the solution side of the membrane reduces the number of solvent molecules at the membrane and helps keep them in the solution side. Therefore, if all other factors are equal, the volume of the liquid will increase on the solution side (Figure 13.15).

> **Osmosis** is the flow of solvent from a solution of lower concentration to a solution of higher concentration through a semipermeable membrane.

The more concentrated the solute, the higher the liquid level rises on the solution side. The effect can be best measured by seeing how much external pressure it takes to keep the liquid levels even on the two sides, which keeps the concentration of the solution constant. That pressure is equal to the **osmotic pressure** of the solution. Osmotic pressure is symbolized by the Greek letter pi, Π, to distinguish it from gas pressure, P, and it is governed by an equation analogous to the ideal gas law,

$$\Pi V = nRT \qquad (13.14)$$

where Π is the osmotic pressure, V is the volume of the solution, n is the number of moles of solute, R is the gas constant, and T is the absolute temperature. If $0.08206\ \text{L} \cdot \text{atm/mol} \cdot \text{K}$ is used for the value of R and the volume is given in liters, then Π is in atmospheres. Equation 13.14 can be rearranged to relate the osmotic pressure to *molarity*—the number of moles of solute per liter of solution, $n/V = M$.

$$\Pi = \frac{nRT}{V} = \left(\frac{n}{V}\right)RT = MRT$$

Thus,

$$\Pi = MRT \qquad (13.15)$$

Example 13.19

Calculate the osmotic pressure of a 0.0150 M solution of glucose, $C_6H_{12}O_6$, in water at 25°C.

Solution

First convert T to Kelvins.

$$25°\text{C} + 273.15 = 298\ \text{K}$$

Then calculate the osmotic pressure.

$$\Pi = MRT$$

$$\Pi = (0.0150\ \text{M})\left(0.08206\frac{\text{L} \cdot \text{atm}}{\text{mol} \cdot \text{K}}\right)(298\ \text{K})$$

$$= 0.367\ \text{atm}$$

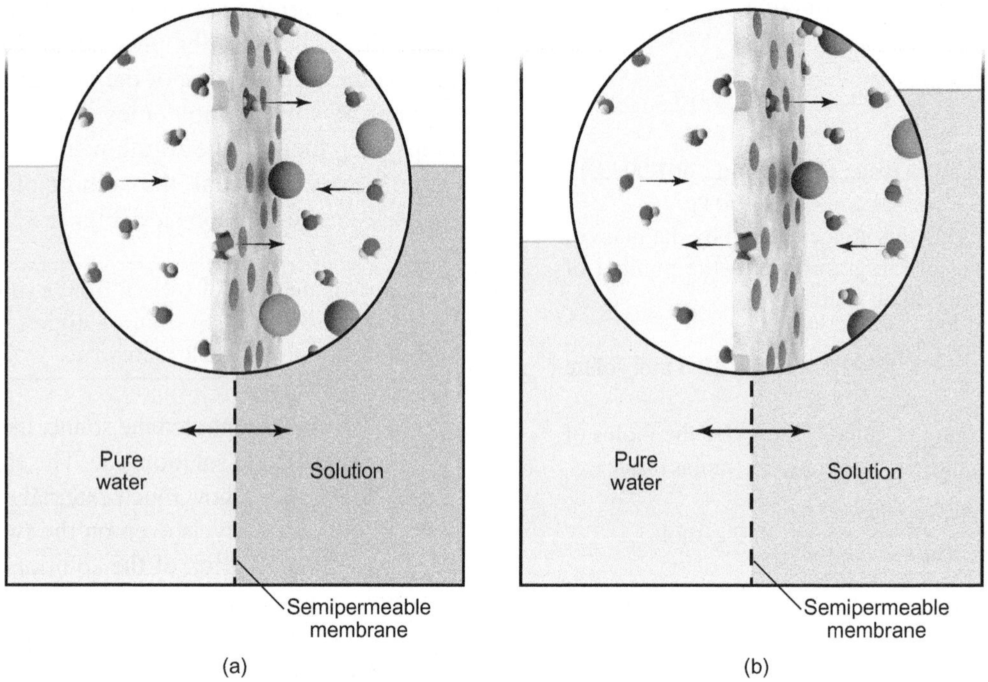

FIGURE 13.15 Osmotic Pressure

Water molecules can pass through the semipermeable membrane but solute molecules cannot. (a) Initially, the net flow of water is toward the solution of higher concentration, which causes the water level to drop and the solution level to rise. (b) Eventually, gravity counteracts the osmotic pressure, causing the net flow to be the same in both directions. At this point, the liquid levels are still at different heights, but they are no longer changing. The difference in the heights of the levels corresponds to Π, the osmotic pressure of the solution, just as the height of the mercury in a barometer corresponds to the surrounding atmospheric pressure (Figure 7.2).

EVERYDAY CONNECTION

Osmosis is the tendency of the solvent molecules to move preferentially through a semipermeable membrane toward the solution side. Applying pressure to the solution side can stop solvent molecules from migrating to the solution side, and applying even more pressure can force solvent molecules to move from the solution side to the solvent side. Applying excess pressure to remove solvent from the solution side of the membrane is called reverse osmosis. This process is used as a water purification technique to produce fresh drinking water from seawater. Reverse osmosis is an energy-intensive (and therefore expensive) way to produce fresh water, but as the cost of water increases and the availability decreases, more and more municipalities are relying on reverse osmosis plants like the one shown here as a source for some of their drinking water. Reverse osmosis is also part of many home water purification systems.

ETAJOE/Shutterstock

PRACTICE PROBLEM 13.19

Calculate the concentration of sucrose in water at 298 K that would yield an osmotic pressure of 68.3 torr.

Hint: Use Equation 13.15 to solve for molarity.

Example 13.19 showed that a solution that was only 0.015 M created an osmotic pressure of more than one-third of atmospheric pressure. Thus, the osmotic pressure is rather high, even for a very dilute solution.

SECTION REVIEW

- Vapor-pressure lowering, freezing-point depression, boiling-point elevation, and osmotic pressure are known as colligative properties. The magnitude of change for each one is directly proportional to the number of solute particles in a given quantity of solution. All are independent of the identity of the solute.
- Vapor-pressure lowering is calculated using mole fraction, freezing-point depression and boiling-point elevation are calculated with molality, and osmotic pressure is calculated with molarity.

EVERYDAY CONNECTION

Osmotic pressure is extremely important in biological systems. In humans, water returns from tissues to blood capillaries because of the greater concentration of solutes in the blood. The use of saline solution in intravenous, IV, solutions must be carefully controlled so that the fluid's osmotic pressure is the same as that of blood.

Normal blood cells are shaped like disks with shallow indentations on both sides. But if a patient is given an IV solution with a lower osmotic pressure than blood (such as pure water) their cells would expand and eventually burst, which is known as hemolysis. If given an IV solution with higher osmotic pressure than blood, the cells would begin to shrivel, which is known as crenation.

Hemolysis Normal Crenation

13.5 Colligative Properties of Electrolytes

GOAL

- Extend the discussion of solution properties of nonelectrolytes to include electrolyte solutions.

Background Review

Chapter 5 Stoichiometry: Section 5.6—Molarities of Ions

The calculations in Section 13.4 were based on *nonelectrolyte* solutes, so that each mole of solute that dissolved resulted in 1 mol of solute particles in the solution. However, when *electrolytes* (e.g., ionic compounds) dissolve in water, they dissociate into ions. For example, 1 mol NaCl will dissociate into 1 mol of Na^+ ions and 1 mol of Cl^- ions, for a total of 2 mol of solute particles. Thus, the concentration of particles in 1 M NaCl is double that of 1 M sucrose (Section 5.6). Aqueous ionic compounds (compounds containing a metal or the ammonium ion) are strong electrolytes. Strong acids (HCl, HBr, HI, HNO_3, $HClO_4$, $HClO_3$, and H_2SO_4) are strong electrolytes, too, and they ionize 100% in aqueous solution (Section 4.3).

Colligative properties depend on the number of solute particles dissolved in solution, so an electrolyte that dissociates into two ions will have twice the effect on colligative properties as a nonelectrolyte that remains as a single particle. An electrolyte that dissociates into three ions will have three times the effect on colligative properties as a nonelectrolyte, and so on.

Example 13.20

Rank the following aqueous solutions in order from largest freezing-point depression to smallest.

a. 1.0 M CH_3CH_2OH
b. 1.0 M $Al_2(SO_4)_3$
c. 1.0 M NaBr
d. 1.0 M $CaCl_2$

Solution

a. Although CH_3CH_2OH looks like it might be a hydroxide, it does not contain a metal or the ammonium ion, so it is molecular, not ionic. Molecular compounds are nonelectrolytes (they do not dissociate in water), so 1.0 M CH_3CH_2OH contains 1.0 M solute particles.

b. $Al_2(SO_4)_3$ is soluble in water and dissociates into 2 Al^{3+} ions and 3 SO_4^{2-} ions, so 1.0 M $Al_2(SO_4)_3$ contains 5.0 M solute particles.
c. NaBr dissociates in water into 1 Na^+ ion and 1 Br^- ion, so 1.0 M NaBr contains 2.0 M solute particles.
d. $CaCl_2$ dissociates in water into 1 Ca^{2+} ion and 2 Cl^- ions, so 1.0 M $CaCl_2$ contains 3.0 M solute particles.

The magnitude of freezing-point depression increases as the number of solute particles increases. Thus, the order from largest freezing-point depression to smallest is 1.0 M $Al_2(SO_4)_3$ > 1.0 M $CaCl_2$ > 1.0 M NaBr > 1.0 M CH_3CH_2OH.

PRACTICE PROBLEM 13.20

One mole of KCl, $AlCl_3$, and $BaCl_2$ are dissolved in enough water to make 1 L of each solution. Rank the resulting solutions from highest boiling point to lowest.

Hint: Colligative properties depend on the number of solute particles in solution, not the identity of the solute. Thus, the boiling-point elevation will increase as the number of solute particles dissolved in the solution increases. All of these solutes are ionic and strong electrolytes. Determine the number of ions each one dissociates into.

Equation 13.12, Equation 13.13, and Equation 13.15 can be modified to take into account the additional particles that result when ionic compounds dissociate in solution. The ratio of the number of moles of particles in solution to the number of moles of solute dissolved is called the **van't Hoff factor, *i***:

$$i = \frac{\text{Moles of particles in solution}}{\text{Moles of solute dissolved}} \qquad (13.16)$$

When the solute is a strong electrolyte, the van't Hoff factor is included as a multiplier on the concentration of the solute in the equations for freezing-point depression, boiling-point elevation, and osmotic pressure. For freezing-point depression and boiling-point elevation calculations with ionic solutes, Equation 13.12 and Equation 13.13 become

$$\Delta T_f = iK_f m \qquad (13.17)$$

$$\Delta T_b = iK_b m \qquad (13.18)$$

Example 13.21

Calculate the freezing-point depression and boiling-point elevation of a 0.53 *m* NaCl solution in water, assuming 100% dissociation of the solute.

Solution

When NaCl dissociates completely, it forms two ions per formula unit, so $i = 2$. From Table 13.3, K_f for water is 1.86°C/*m* and K_b for water is 0.512°C/*m*.

$$\Delta T_f = iK_f m = 2(1.86°\text{C}/m)(0.53\ m) = 2.0°\text{C}$$

$$\Delta T_b = iK_b m = 2(0.512°\text{C}/m)(0.53\ m) = 0.54°\text{C}$$

The freezing point of the solution drops 2.0°C compared to pure water, and the boiling point increases by 0.54°C.

PRACTICE PROBLEM 13.21

Calculate the freezing-point depression and boiling-point elevation of a 0.53 *m* $CaCl_2$ solution in water. Assume 100% dissociation of the solute.

Hint: When $CaCl_2$ dissociates completely, it forms three ions per formula unit (one calcium ion and two chloride ions). Use Equation 13.17 and Equation 13.18, where $i = 3$, and data from Table 13.3.

The measured freezing points and boiling points of solutions of strong electrolytes agree most closely with the calculated values when $i = 2$, when the ions are singly charged (+1 and −1), and when the solute concentration is low (less than 0.05 *m*). At higher *i* values, higher ionic charges, and higher concentrations, the oppositely charged ions in the solution begin to interact with one another and form something called ion pairs. **Ion pairs** form when dissolved ions of opposite charge, each surrounded by solvent molecules, nevertheless feel a sufficient attraction to one another that they move in tandem in the solution as though the two ions were one large, loosely bound particle. Ion pairs continually break apart and re-form, but ion pair formation effectively reduces the number of solute particles in the solution, leading to apparent van't Hoff factors that are *less* than the expected values. In this text, you can ignore ion pairing and assume that electrolyte solutes dissociate 100% unless explicitly given a different value for *i*.

For osmotic pressure calculations with electrolytes, the van't Hoff factor is similarly included in the equation as a multiplier to the number of moles of solute.

$$\Pi = iMRT \qquad (13.19)$$

If the solute is a nonelectrolyte, then $i = 1$ in Equation 13.17, Equation 13.18, and Equation 13.19, and the van't Hoff factor can be ignored.

EVERYDAY CONNECTION

The road salt normally used to remove ice from wintery roads is impure rock salt, NaCl, but calcium chloride, $CaCl_2$, is often sold to homeowners as an alternative for de-icing sidewalks and driveways. You have already seen that on a mole-to-mole basis, $CaCl_2$ reduces the freezing point 1.5 times as much as NaCl does, but $CaCl_2$ has other advantages as well. It removes ice faster than NaCl does and can effectively de-ice pavement at lower temperatures than NaCl can. $CaCl_2$ is also less harmful to plants, animals, and concrete surfaces. NaCl salt is much less expensive than $CaCl_2$, however, so NaCl is still widely used on roads.

Macmillan Learning (template courtesy GraphicBurger)

Although it appears as though salt melts ice, what it actually does is prevent melted ice from refreezing. Ice at any temperature has a microscopically thin layer of liquid water on top that is continually melting and refreezing. Salt dissolves in this thin layer of liquid and prevents it from refreezing. When solid ice under the liquid saltwater layer melts, the salt prevents that from refreezing as well, and the process continues until gradually all the ice has melted and is unable to refreeze.

The video in Figure 13.16 demonstrates how to use the van't Hoff factor in an osmotic pressure calculation.

Steve Lemon, Macmillan Learning

FIGURE 13.16 Video Tutorial: Van't Hoff Factor

NOTE: You need to be online to access this video.

This video shows how to calculate osmotic pressure for a solution of a strong electrolyte.

Example 13.22

Compare the osmotic pressure of a 0.015 M solution of sugar and a 0.015 M solution of table salt at 25°C, assuming 100% dissociation of the salt.

Solution

For sugar, $i = 1$:

$$\Pi = iMRT$$

$$\Pi = 1\left(0.015\frac{\text{mol}}{\text{L}}\right)\left(0.08206\frac{\text{L}\cdot\text{atm}}{\text{mol}\cdot\text{K}}\right)(298\text{ K})$$

$$= 0.37\text{ atm}$$

For table salt, NaCl, $i = 2$:

$$\Pi = 2\left(0.015\frac{\text{mol}}{\text{L}}\right)\left(0.08206\frac{\text{L}\cdot\text{atm}}{\text{mol}\cdot\text{K}}\right)(298\text{ K})$$

$$= 0.73\text{ atm}$$

The osmotic pressure of the salt solution is twice that of the sugar solution. If these solutions were placed in apparatuses similar to that shown in Figure 13.15, the level of the liquid for the salt solution would be about twice as high as that for the sugar solution apparatus.

PRACTICE PROBLEM 13.22

If the measured value of i for a 0.015 M NaCl solution is 1.9, what is the osmotic pressure, taking into account the ion pairing?

Hint: Use Equation 13.19 with $i = 1.9$ instead of $i = 2$ for NaCl.

Calculating the vapor-pressure lowering in an electrolyte solution involves more than just adding the van't Hoff factor to the equation because the dissociation of electrolytes affects the mole fractions of every component in the solution. The vapor-pressure lowering is calculated exactly as before, but the denominator in the mole fraction calculation includes the number of moles of each ion in addition to the moles of water.

$$X_A = \frac{\text{Moles of A}}{\text{Moles of A} + \text{Moles of B} + \text{Moles of C} + \cdots}$$

For example, if 150.0 g of $Ni(NO_3)_2$ is dissolved in 500.0 g of water, you would calculate the number of moles of $Ni(NO_3)_2$ and the number of moles of water, but since 1 molecule of $Ni(NO_3)_2$ dissociates into 1 Ni^{2+} and 2 NO_3^- ions, the mole fractions of all the components would be calculated using the moles of the solute particles rather than the moles of $Ni(NO_3)_2$.

Example 13.23

The vapor pressure of pure water at 25°C is 23.756 torr. Calculate the vapor pressure above the solution at 25°C if 150.0 g of $Ni(NO_3)_2$ is dissolved in 500.0 g of water.

Solution

The mole fraction of water, the solvent, is needed in order to use Raoult's law (Equation 13.5) to calculate the vapor pressure of water above the solution. To determine the mole fraction, the number of moles of each component of the solution must first be calculated.

The molar mass of $Ni(NO_3)_2$ = 58.693 g/mol + 2(14.007 g/mol) + 6(15.999 g/mol) = 182.701 g/mol.

$$150.0 \text{ g Ni(NO}_3)_2 \times \frac{1 \text{ mol}}{182.701 \text{ g}} = 0.8210 \text{ mol Ni(NO}_3)_2$$

Since 1 $Ni(NO_3)_2$ dissociates into 1 Ni^{2+} and 2 NO_3^-, there are 0.8210 moles of Ni^{2+} in the solution and 1.642 moles of NO_3^- in the solution.

$$0.8210 \text{ mol Ni(NO}_3)_2\left(\frac{1 \text{ mol Ni}^{2+}}{1 \text{ mol Ni(NO}_3)_2}\right)$$
$$= 0.8210 \text{ mol Ni}^{2+}$$

$$0.8210 \text{ mol Ni(NO}_3)_2\left(\frac{2 \text{ mol NO}_3^-}{1 \text{ mol Ni(NO}_3)_2}\right)$$
$$= 1.642 \text{ mol NO}_3^-$$

The molar mass of H_2O is 2(1.008 g/mol) + 15.999 g/mol = 18.0148 g/mol.

$$500.0 \text{ g H}_2\text{O} \times \frac{1 \text{ mol}}{18.0148 \text{ g}} = 27.755 \text{ mol H}_2\text{O}$$

The mole fraction of water, X_{H_2O}, is calculated by dividing the moles of H_2O by the sum of the number of moles of *all* components of the mixture:

$$X_{H_2O} = \frac{\text{Moles of H}_2\text{O}}{\text{Moles of H}_2\text{O} + \text{Moles of Ni}^{2+} + \text{Moles of NO}_3^-}$$

$$X_{H_2O} = \frac{27.755 \text{ mol}}{27.755 \text{ mol} + 0.8210 \text{ mol} + 1.642 \text{ mol}} = 0.9185$$

Finally, use Raoult's law (Equation 13.5) to find the vapor pressure.

$$P_{H_2O} = X_{H_2O}P^{\circ}_{H_2O} = (0.9185)(23.756 \text{ torr}) = 21.82 \text{ torr}$$

SECTION REVIEW

- When the solute is an electrolyte and dissociates into ions in solution, the colligative properties are determined based on the total number of solute particles.
- The van't Hoff factor, i, is equal to the number of individual ions that one formula unit of an ionic compound dissociates into in solution. For a nonelectrolyte, the van't Hoff factor is 1.
- For freezing-point depression, boiling-point elevation, and osmotic pressure, the only change in the calculations for an electrolyte solute compared to a nonelectrolyte solute is that the solute concentration is multiplied by the van't Hoff factor, i.
- Vapor-pressure lowering due to an electrolyte solute is calculated the same way it is calculated for a nonelectrolyte, but the mole fraction calculations take into account each of the ionic species as well as the solvent.

Putting It Together

The example problems in earlier sections of this chapter focus on just the new skills acquired in that section, but homework and exam questions in chemistry often require more than just one skill at a time. In fact, you will likely be expected to apply knowledge from across the entire chapter, or even multiple chapters in a single problem. This final example problem is meant to help you prepare for these types of multi-concept questions. Additional examples can be found in the end of chapter exercises.

Example 13.24

The solubility of sodium chlorate, $NaClO_3$, at 20°C is 959 g $NaClO_3$ per 1.000 kg of water.

a. What is this concentration in molality, *m*?
b. Assuming 100% dissociation, what is the boiling point of this solution?
c. If this solution is made using 1.00 kg of water, how much more water would have to be added in order to give a solution that boils at 105.0°C?

Solution

a. Molality is moles of solute per kilogram of solvent, so first determine how many moles of $NaClO_3$ are in 959 g, then divide by the mass of the water.

Molar mass of $NaClO_3$ = 22.99 g/mol + 35.453 g/mol + 3(15.999 g/mol) = 106.44 g/mol

$$959 \text{ g NaClO}_3\left(\frac{1 \text{ mol NaClO}_3}{106.44 \text{ g NaClO}_3}\right) = 9.010 \text{ mol NaClO}_3$$

$$\frac{9.010 \text{ mol NaClO}_3}{1.000 \text{ kg H}_2\text{O}} = 9.010 \text{ mol/kg NaClO}_3$$

b. $\Delta T_b = iK_b m$
For $NaClO_3$, $i = 2$.

$$K_b = 0.512°\text{C}/m$$

$$\Delta T_b = (2)(0.512°\text{C}/m)(9.010\ m) = 9.23°\text{C}$$

The boiling point T_b = 100.00 + 9.23 = 109.23°C.

c. Boiling-point elevation is directly proportional to concentration, so if a 9.010 *m* solution increases the boiling point by 9.23°C, then to get a boiling-point elevation of 5.00°C, you would need a concentration of

$$\frac{5.00°\text{C}}{9.23°\text{C}} \times 9.010\ m = 4.881\ m$$

The mass of water in the diluted solution can be calculated using an equation analogous to $M_1V_1 = M_2V_2$ from Chapter 5, but using molality instead of molarity and the mass of solvent instead of the volume of solution. The equation still works because the product on each side is the number of moles, which does not change during dilution.

$$(\text{Molality})_1(\text{Solvent mass})_1 = (\text{Molality})_2(\text{Solvent mass})_2$$

$$(9.010\ m)(1.00 \text{ kg}) = (4.881\ m)(x)$$

$$x = 1.846 \text{ kg H}_2\text{O}$$

Since a final solvent mass of 1.846 kg is required, 0.846 kg of water must be added to the original solution.

PRACTICE PROBLEM 13.23

The solubility of calcium chloride, $CaCl_2$, at 0°C is 59.5 g per 100 g of water. If a homeowner salts her driveway with excess $CaCl_2$ during the day when the temperature is 30°F and then the temperature drops to 10°F at night, will her driveway refreeze? Assume that the solubility of $CaCl_2$ remains constant over this temperature range.

Hint: Determine the concentration of a saturated $CaCl_2$ solution in mol/kg, then use data from Table 13.3 to calculate the freezing-point depression. Convert the Fahrenheit temperatures to Celsius (Section 1.10) to compare the freezing point of the solution to the outside temperatures.

Key Terms, Symbols, and Equations

KEY TERMS

alloy (13.1): A homogeneous mixture of two or more metals; an example of a solid–solid solution.

boiling-point elevation, ΔT_b (13.4): An increase in the boiling point of a solution compared to the pure solvent, due to the presence of a solute.

colligative properties (13.4): Properties of a liquid that change when a solute is dissolved in a pure solvent to create a solution. The four most common colligative properties are vapor-pressure lowering, freezing-point depression, boiling-point elevation, and osmotic pressure.

entropy (13.1): A measure of the randomness or disorder in a system.

freezing-point depression, ΔT_f (13.4): A decrease in the freezing point of a solution compared to the pure solvent, due to the presence of a solute.

Henry's law (13.2): The solubility of a gas in a liquid is directly proportional to its partial pressure above the liquid.

hydration energy (13.1): The amount of energy given off when 1 mole of a substance is solvated in water. Another term for hydration energy is enthalpy of hydration.

ideal solution (13.4): A solution that obeys Raoult's law exactly.

immiscible (13.2): Describes two liquids that do not mix to form a solution, such as oil and water, because they have different intermolecular forces between their particles.

ion pair (13.5): Two oppositely charged ions in solution that feel a sufficiently strong attraction toward one another that they behave as one larger solute particle instead of as two separate solute particles.

miscible (13.2): Describes two liquids that readily mix in any proportion to form a solution, such as ethanol and water, because they have very similar intermolecular forces between their particles.

molal, *m* or mol/kg (13.3): The unit of molality.

molality, *m* (13.3): A measure of solute concentration defined as the number of moles of solute per kilogram of solvent.

mole fraction, *X* (13.3): The ratio of the number of moles of a component of a solution to the total number of moles of all components in the solution.

nonvolatile (13.4): Not easily vaporized.

osmosis (13.4): The movement of solvent molecules through a semipermeable membrane from a pure liquid or a lower concentration solution into a higher concentration solution.

osmotic pressure, Π (13.4): The amount of pressure required to maintain a constant concentration of solution when it is separated from a pure solvent by a semipermeable membrane.

percent by mass (13.3): One hundred percent times the mass of the solute divided by the mass of the entire solution.

Raoult's law (13.4): The vapor pressure of a solute in a solution (P_A) is equal to its mole fraction in the solution times the vapor pressure of the pure solute: $P_A = X_A P_A^\circ$.

recrystallization (13.2): A purification process carried out by dissolving a substance in a solvent at one temperature and then reducing the temperature so that the (purified) substance crystallizes out, leaving impurities in the solution.

saturated solution (13.2): A solution that holds as much dissolved solute as it is capable of holding stably at a given temperature.

semipermeable membrane (13.4): A membrane that allows some types of molecules to pass through but not others, often based on their size. Typically a semipermeable membrane allows solvent molecules to freely pass through in either direction but blocks solute particles.

solubility (13.2): The concentration of a saturated solution at a given temperature.

solute (13.1): The substance that is dissolved in another substance to create a solution.

solvation (13.1): The process of forming solute–solvent attractions.

solvent (13.1): The substance that has another substance dissolved in it to create a solution.

supersaturated solution (13.2): A solution holding more dissolved solute than it can hold stably at a given temperature.

unsaturated solution (13.2): A solution that contains less dissolved solute than it can hold stably at a given temperature.

van't Hoff factor, *i* (13.5): The number of particles produced when one formula unit of a substance is dissolved in solution. For nonelectrolytes, $i = 1$, and for strong electrolytes i = the number of ions the electrolyte breaks into.

vapor-pressure lowering, ΔP (13.4): A decrease in the vapor pressure of a solution compared to that of the pure solvent due to the presence of a solute.

volatile (13.4): Easily vaporized.

SYMBOLS AND ABBREVIATIONS

ΔP (vapor-pressure lowering) (13.4)

ΔT_b (boiling-point elevation) (13.4)

ΔT_f (freezing-point depression) (13.4)
i (van't Hoff factor) (13.5)
K_b (boiling-point elevation constant) (13.4)
K_f (freezing-point depression constant) (13.4)
m (molal) (13.3)
m (molality) (13.3)
$P°$ (vapor pressure of pure substance) (13.4)
P_Z (vapor pressure of volatile component Z in solution) (13.4)
Π (osmotic pressure) (13.4)
X (mole fraction) (13.3)
X_A (mole fraction of component A) (13.3)

EQUATIONS

Concentration of dissolved gas in solution $= kP$ (13.1)

$$\text{Percent by mass} = \left(\frac{\text{Mass of solute}}{\text{Total mass of solution}}\right) \times 100\% \quad (13.2)$$

$$\text{Molality} = \frac{\text{Moles of solute}}{\text{Kilogram of solvent}} \quad (13.3)$$

$$X_A = \frac{\text{Moles of A}}{\text{Moles of A} + \text{Moles of B}} \quad (13.4)$$

$$P_Z = X_Z P^\circ_Z \quad (13.5)$$

$$\Delta P = P^\circ - P \quad (13.6)$$

$$P_{\text{total}} = P_A + P_Z = X_A P^\circ_A + X_Z P^\circ_Z \quad (13.7)$$

$$\frac{\text{Moles of A in vapor phase}}{\text{Moles of Z in vapor phase}} = \frac{P_A}{P_Z} \quad (13.8)$$

$$X_{Z(\text{gas phase})} = \frac{P_Z}{P_{\text{total}}} \quad (13.9)$$

$$T_{\text{solution}} = T_{\text{solvent}} - \Delta T_f \quad (13.10)$$

$$T_{\text{solution}} = T_{\text{solvent}} + \Delta T_b \quad (13.11)$$

$$\Delta T_f = K_f m \quad (13.12)$$

$$\Delta T_b = K_b m \quad (13.13)$$

$$\Pi V = nRT \quad (13.14)$$

$$\Pi = MRT \quad (13.15)$$

$$i = \frac{\text{Moles of particles in solution}}{\text{Moles of solute dissolved}} \quad (13.16)$$

$$\Delta T_f = iK_f m \quad (13.17)$$

$$\Delta T_b = iK_b m \quad (13.18)$$

$$\Pi = iMRT \quad (13.19)$$

Chapter Summary

Substances dissolve in solvents to form solutions because the attractions between solute particles and solvent particles are at least as strong as the attractions holding the solute or solvent particles together. In general, nonpolar solutes tend to dissolve in nonpolar solvents, and polar and ionic solutes tend to dissolve in polar solvents—like dissolves like (Section 13.1).

Most solutes have a certain limit to their solubility in a given solvent at a given temperature. A solution at that upper limit of concentration is said to be saturated. If less of the solute is dissolved in the solvent at that temperature, the solution is unsaturated. If more is dissolved, the solution is supersaturated. A change in temperature changes the solubility of a solute in a given solvent. Raising the temperature makes most solids more soluble in liquids but makes all gases less soluble in liquids. Greater pressure makes gases more soluble.

Supersaturated solutions are unstable; the excess solute is likely to crystallize out of solution if the solution is shaken, if the inside of the container is scratched, or especially if a seed crystal of the solute is added. Supersaturated solutions are typically prepared by dissolving a large quantity of solute in a given quantity of solvent at a high temperature, then carefully cooling the resulting solution. If the solute has difficulty crystallizing, a supersaturated solution can be obtained (Section 13.2).

Percent by mass is a measure of concentration, defined as 100% times the mass of a component of the solution divided by the total mass of the solution. It is a temperature-independent concentration unit. It is often used for solutions in applied chemistry situations, such as medical laboratories and hospitals.

Molality, m, is a temperature-independent measure of concentration, defined as the number of moles of solute per kilogram of solvent. It differs from molarity, M, in that it is based on a *mass* of *solvent*, rather than a volume of solution. Like molarity, molality can be used as a conversion factor to solve problems.

Molality is also used in problems involving freezing-point depression and boiling-point elevation.

A third temperature-independent measure of concentration is mole fraction.The mole fraction is defined as the number of moles of one component, say component A, divided by the total number of moles in the solution.

$$X_A = \frac{\text{Number of moles of A}}{\text{Total number of moles}}$$

Mole fraction does not distinguish between solute and solvent (Section 13.3).

Colligative properties, such as vapor-pressure lowering, freezing-point depression, boiling-point elevation, and osmotic pressure, are physical properties of a solution that are affected by the presence of a nonvolatile solute, but not by the identity of the solute.

The vapor pressure of a solvent that contains a nonvolatile solute is given by Raoult's law,

$$P_A = X_A P_A^\circ$$

where P_A is the vapor pressure of the solvent in the solution, X_A is the mole fraction of A, and P_A° is the vapor pressure of the solvent when pure. Because X_A must be less than 1 in a solution of A, P_A must be lower than P_A°; thus, a vapor-pressure lowering has resulted because of the presence of the solute.

The freezing point of a solution compared to the freezing point of the pure solvent is lowered by the presence of a solute, and the boiling point of a solution is raised by the presence of a nonvolatile solute. The freezing-point depression and the boiling-point elevation are both directly proportional to the molality of the solute particles. Determining the molality therefore allows you to calculate the freezing point or boiling point of a solution; conversely, if you know the freezing point or boiling point of the pure solvent and of the solution, you can calculate the molality of the solution. With the molality and other data, you can also calculate the number of moles and the molar mass of the solute.

Osmotic pressure is another colligative property that results from dissolved substances in solution. The presence of solute particles lowers the ability of solvent molecules to pass through a semipermeable membrane. Osmotic pressure is very important in biological systems because living cells, for example, are lined with semipermeable membranes. The theory behind osmotic pressure can also be used to purify seawater through a process called reverse osmosis. The osmotic pressure of a solution, Π, is proportional to the molarity (the number of moles per liter) of the dissolved solutes:

$$\Pi V = nRT$$

or

$$\Pi = \left(\frac{n}{V}\right)RT = MRT$$

where R is the ideal gas law constant. Measuring the osmotic pressure is a sensitive means of determining the number of moles of solute in a given volume of solution and, together with other data, the molar mass.

Vapor-pressure lowering is calculated using a solute concentration expressed as a mole fraction; freezing-point depression and boiling-point elevation are calculated with the solute concentration given in molality (mol/kg), and osmotic pressure is calculated with the solute concentration expressed in molarity (Section 13.4).

When the solute is an electrolyte and dissociates into ions, 1 mole of solute results in more than 1 mole of solute particles. The van't Hoff factor, *i*, is equal to the number of individual ions that one formula unit of an ionic compound dissociates into in solution. (For nonelectrolytes, $i = 1$.) For freezing-point depression, boiling-point elevation, and osmotic pressure, the only change in the calculations for an electrolyte solute compared to a nonionic solute is that the solute concentration is multiplied by the van't Hoff factor. Vapor-pressure lowering due to an electrolyte solute is calculated the same way as it is for a nonelectrolyte, but the mole fraction calculations take into account each of the ionic species as well as the solvent (Section 13.5).

END OF CHAPTER QUESTIONS

13.1 The Solution Process

1. How would you define the term *solution* to a student struggling with the concept? Be sure that your definition is applicable not only to a solution made up of a solid dissolved in a liquid, but also to solutions made up of other phases, such as a gas dissolved in another gas.

2. Describe the energy changes that occur during the formation of a solution (see Figure 13.3).
   a. Which step(s) is/are endothermic?
   b. Which step(s) is/are exothermic?

3. What must be true about the steps in the formation of a solution (see Figure 13.3) if
   a. the beaker feels warmer as the solute dissolves?
   b. the beaker feels cooler as the solute dissolves?

4. Explain why NH_3 is soluble in water but C_6H_6 is not.

5. Explain why octane, C_8H_{18}, is soluble in C_6H_6, but Na_2SO_4 is not.

6. Explain why methyl alcohol, CH_3OH, is soluble in water, but iodine, I_2, is not.

7. Which substance would you expect to be more soluble in water: chloroform, $CHCl_3$, or carbon tetrachloride, CCl_4? Which would you expect to be more soluble in C_6H_6? Explain your reasoning.

8. A molecule of sucrose (table sugar), $C_{12}H_{22}O_{11}$, contains many covalently bonded —OH groups. Explain why sucrose is so soluble in water.

9. When water dissolves $MgCl_2(s)$, which end, if either, of a water molecule's dipole is expected to be nearer to
   a. a Mg^{2+} ion?
   b. a Cl^- ion?

10. When water dissolves liquid formaldehyde, which part of a water molecule is expected to be nearer to the oxygen atom of the CH_2O molecule? Why?

11. Draw diagrams of the solute–solvent interactions described in
    a. Question 9a.
    b. Question 9b.
    c. Question 10.

13.2 Saturated, Unsaturated, and Supersaturated Solutions

12. A 15.00 g sample of a solid substance is placed in 100.0 g of water at 25°C, and all of the solid dissolves. Then another 2.00 g of the substance is added, and all of it dissolves. A final 2.00 g is added, and none of it dissolves.
    a. Is the first solution saturated, unsaturated, or supersaturated?
    b. Is the second solution saturated, unsaturated, or supersaturated?
    c. What can you tell about the final solution that is in contact with the solid?

13. Using the solubility curve (see Figure 13.4), determine whether KNO_3 or KCl is more soluble in water at the following temperatures.
    a. 10°C
    b. 40°C

14. Explain how to prepare 500 mL of a saturated solution of a given salt in water.

15. Refer to Figure 13.4. At what temperature are the solubilities of KNO_3 and KBr equal?

16. A tiny crystal of a solid substance is added to an aqueous solution of the same substance. What would happen if the original solution was
a. unsaturated?
b. supersaturated?
c. saturated?

17. When a 3 teaspoon sample of table sugar is placed in a glass of iced tea, some of it falls to the bottom of the glass. If sugar is not very soluble in water, then stirring the tea will not cause more solid to dissolve. If sugar is soluble in water, but slow to dissolve, stirring the tea will speed up the dissolution process. Examine Figure 13.4 to determine if the sugar, $C_{12}H_{22}O_{11}$, is not very soluble or does not dissolve very quickly.

18. Which compound in Figure 13.4 changes solubility most with increasing temperature?

19. Which solute in Figure 13.4 has the solubility that is the least temperature-dependent?

20. Using Figure 13.4, determine the solubility of KNO_3 in water at 80°C.

21. Using Figure 13.4, determine whether a solution of 25.0 g of NaCl in 100 g of water at 50°C is saturated, unsaturated, or supersaturated.

22. Using Figure 13.4, determine whether each of the following solutions is saturated, unsaturated, or supersaturated.
a. 80 g KBr in 100 g of water at 50°C
b. 70 g KBr in 100 g of water at 33°C
c. 85 g KBr in 100 g of water at 80°C

23. Describe the effect of increasing temperature on the solubility of
a. most solid solutes.
b. gaseous solutes.

24. How does the preparation of a supersaturated solution of a gas in a liquid differ from the preparation of a supersaturated solution of a solid in a liquid?

25. At 0°C and 1 atm of pressure, 23.5 mL of neon gas dissolves in each liter of aqueous solution.
a. Determine the value of the Henry's law constant for neon.
b. Calculate the concentration of dissolved neon in an aqueous solution subjected to neon gas at 3.75 atm pressure.

13.3 Concentration Units

26. Calculate the mass of NaCl required to make a 2.00% by mass saline solution with 55.7 g of water.

27. Calculate the mass of NaCl in 156.2 g of 15.50% by mass saline solution.

28. Using Figure 13.4, calculate the approximate percent by mass of saturated NaCl at 0°C.

29. A chemist wants to prepare 75.0 g of a 1.75% solution of NaCl by diluting a 5.00% stock solution, but she only has 30.0 g of stock solution available. Does she have enough stock solution to make the 1.75% solution she needs?

30. An incompetent lab assistant sees that he only has 11.8 g of 25.0% stock solution left, but rather than make up a new solution, he simply refills the container with water up to 100.0 g. What is the concentration of the resulting solution?

31. State exactly how to prepare 200.0 g of a 1.750% by mass KNO_3 solution.

32. A careless lab assistant is asked to make a 1.50% solution by diluting 10.0 g of a 15.0% stock solution to 100.0 g. Instead of diluting the solution to 100.0 g, he *adds* 100.0 g of water to the solution. What is the concentration of the resulting solution?

33. Calculate the molality of a solution of 6.17 g of acetic acid, $HC_2H_3O_2$, in 72.3 g of water.

34. Calculate the molality of a solution containing 0.527 mol of MgF_2 and 700.0 g of water.

35. Calculate the number of moles of solute in a 2.73 *m* solution that was made with 139 g of water.

36. Calculate the mass of solvent in a 1.33 *m* solution containing 0.707 mol of solute.

37. Calculate the number of moles of Na^+ ions in a 0.507 *m* solution of Na_2SO_4 containing 1.33 kg of water.

38. A student is asked to calculate the molality of a solution made up of 17.4 g of NaCl in 135 g of water. He divides the mass of NaCl, 17.4 g, by the kilograms of water, 0.135 kg, and reports his answer as 129 *m*. What has he done wrong, and what is the actual molality of the solution?

39. Calculate the number of moles of $Mg(NO_3)_2$ needed to make a solution with 14.9 g of water that is 0.600 *m* in NO_3^-.

40. Two chemists are in a heated argument over whose solution has a higher molality of chloride ions. The first chemist made his solution using 6.75 g of $AlCl_3$ in 195 g of water. The second chemist made his solution using 5.55 g of $CaCl_2$ in 125 g of water. Which chemist wins the argument?

41. Calculate the molality of 1.000 kg of solution containing 1.62 mol of glycerol, also called glycerine, $C_3H_5(OH)_3$, in water.

42. Calculate the mass of solvent in a 1.18 *m* solution containing 0.697 mol of solute.

43. Calculate the molarity and molality of
   a. a 207 mL solution consisting of 0.515 mol of a covalent compound in 182 g of benzene.
   b. a 191 mL solution consisting of 0.515 mol of an ionic compound with the generic formula MX_2 in 182 g of water.
   c. Compare the answers of the previous two problems and explain any major differences.

44. Calculate the molarity and molality of 268.3 mL of a solution containing 0.5142 mol of CsCl and 197.5 g of water.

45. A solution of density 1.03 g/mL contains 0.363 mol of an inorganic compound (molar mass = 73.2 g/mol) in 417 g of water. Calculate its molarity and its molality.

46. Calculate the molality of an aqueous solution 7.50% by mass ethylene glycol, $C_2H_4(OH)_2$.

47. Calculate the percent by mass of a 3.00 *m* solution of benzoic acid, $HC_6H_5CO_2$, in benzene, C_6H_6.

48. A solution of density 0.903 g/mL contains 0.255 mol of an organic compound (molar mass = 165 g/mol) in 298 g of benzene. Calculate its molarity and its molality.

49. Calculate the mole fraction of water in each of the following solutions.
   a. 1.50 mol of $C_2H_4(OH)_2$, 2.50 mol of CH_2O, and 6.00 mol of H_2O
   b. 1.50 g of $C_2H_4(OH)_2$, 2.50 g of CH_2O, and 6.00 g of H_2O

50. Calculate the mole fraction of water in each of the following solutions.
   a. 95.5 g H_2O and 1.25 mol CH_3OH
   b. 49.2 g C_2H_5OH and 74.8 g H_2O

51. Calculate the mole fraction of ammonia in a 7.50 *m* aqueous solution of ammonia.

52. Calculate the mole fraction of each component in a solution that is 15.7% by mass methyl alcohol, CH_3OH, in water.

53. Calculate the percent by mass of an alcohol–water solution with a mole fraction of water equal to 0.912. The alcohol is C_2H_5OH.

54. Calculate the mole fraction of glycerine in 715 g of solution containing 1.50 mole of glycerine, $C_3H_5(OH)_3$, in water.

55. Calculate the molality of alcohol in water if the mole fraction of alcohol is 0.180.

56. Calculate the mole fraction of NaCl in a solution containing 12.6 g NaCl and 21.3 g KCl in 122 g of water.

57. Calculate the molality of CH_2O in CH_3OH, with $X_{CH_2O} = 0.200$.

58. Determine the molality of chloride ions in a 10.0% by mass $AlCl_3$ solution in water.

59. Calculate the molarity of a 2.50% by mass aqueous NaCl solution whose density is 1.03 g/mL.

13.4 Colligative Properties of Nonelectrolytes

60. Calculate the following.
   a. The vapor pressure of benzene, C_6H_6, at 25°C in an ideal solution containing 1.66 mol of benzene and 0.313 mol of toluene. The vapor pressure of pure benzene is 96.0 torr.
   b. The vapor pressure of toluene, C_7H_8, at 25°C in an ideal solution containing 1.66 mol of benzene and 0.313 mol of toluene. The vapor pressure of pure toluene is 27.0 torr.
   c. The total vapor pressure at 25°C above a solution containing 1.66 mol benzene and 0.313 mol toluene

61. At 25°C, the vapor pressure of pure benzene, C_6H_6, is 96.0 torr. The vapor pressure of pure ethanol, C_2H_5OH, is 44.0 torr at the same temperature. Assuming ideal behavior, calculate the vapor pressure at 25°C of a solution that contains an equal mass of each.

62. A solution of a nonionic solute in benzene freezes at 4.02°C. Calculate its molality (see Table 13.3).

63. A solution of a nonionic solute in naphthalene freezes at 74.12°C. Calculate its molality (see Table 13.3).

64. Sucrose, $C_{12}H_{22}O_{11}$, is nonvolatile and nonionic. For a 3.15 m solution of sucrose in water, calculate the following (see Table 13.3):
a. the freezing point of the solution
b. the boiling point of the solution at 1.0000 atm

65. An aqueous solution freezes at −1.51°C. Calculate the molality of the nonionic solute (see Table 13.3).

66. Calculate the freezing point of
a. 0.529 m benzene in naphthalene.
b. 0.529 m naphthalene in benzene.

67. The freezing point of pure ethylene glycol, $C_2H_6O_2$, which is used in automotive antifreeze, is −11.5°C. Would a solution of 17.3 g of water in 1.00 kg of ethylene glycol freeze below −11.5°C, at −11.5°C, or above −11.5°C? Explain.

68. Calculate the freezing-point depression of an 0.800 m aqueous solution of
a. CH_3OH.
b. C_2H_5OH.
c. C_3H_7OH.

69. Calculate the number of moles of nonionic solute in 125 g of water if the solution freezes at −1.02°C.

70. Fructose, also called fruit sugar, $C_6H_{12}O_6$, is nonvolatile and nonionic. For a 2.46 m solution of fructose in water, calculate the following:
a. the freezing point of the solution
b. the boiling point of the solution at exactly 1 atm

71. At 30°C, the vapor pressure of methanol, CH_3OH, is 0.211 atm. What is the mole fraction of CH_3OH in a solution in which the partial pressure of CH_3OH is 0.157 atm at 30°C?

72. An aqueous solution freezes at −0.908°C. Calculate the molality of the nonionic solute.

73. Calculate the freezing point of
a. 0.200 m benzene in naphthalene.
b. 0.200 m naphthalene in benzene.

74. Calculate the osmotic pressure of a 0.0100 M solution of glucose in water at 25°C.

75. Calculate the osmotic pressure in torr of a 0.1033 M solution of sucrose, or table sugar, in water at 25°C.

13.5 Colligative Properties of Electrolytes

76. The temperature of a sample of pure water is −1°C.
a. Is the sample in the liquid or solid state?
b. If the freezing point of a sample of water is depressed to −3°C by the addition of $CaCl_2$, in what state will the sample be at −1°C?
c. Explain why a salt is used on icy streets and sidewalks.

77. Determine the van't Hoff factor for the following solutions.
a. 0.25 M KCl
b. 0.0017 M $CaCl_2$
c. 1.116 M $C_6H_{12}O_6$
d. 0.075 M $(NH_4)_2SO_4$

78. Which of the following 0.250 m solutions has the greatest freezing-point depression?
a. KCl
b. CH_2O
c. $CaCl_2$

79. Calculate the freezing point of 0.250 m aqueous solutions of the following.
a. KCl
b. $CaCl_2$

80. The vapor pressure of water at 25°C is 23.756 torr. Calculate the vapor pressure at 25°C of the solutions prepared by dissolving 75.0 g of solute in 500 g of water.
a. KCl
b. $CaCl_2$

81. Which of the following 0.150 m solutions has the greatest boiling-point elevation?
a. $Mg(NO_3)_2$
b. $NaNO_3$
c. $C_2H_4(OH)_2$

82. Calculate the boiling point of 0.150 m aqueous solutions of the following.
a. $Mg(NO_3)_2$
b. $NaNO_3$

Putting It Together

83. Calculate the concentration of a 7.500% by mass solution of NaCl in water in the following.
a. Molality NaCl
b. Mole fraction NaCl

84. An aqueous solution of glucose, $C_6H_{12}O_6$, has a mole fraction of glucose equal to 0.175.

a. Calculate the percent by mass glucose.
b. Calculate the percent glucose, $C_6H_{12}O_6$, by mass in a 4.68 *m* solution in water.

85. A solution contains 7.04 g of CH_2O and 80.0 g of C_2H_5OH.
a. Calculate the percent by mass of CH_2O in the solution.
b. Calculate the molality of CH_2O in C_2H_5OH.
c. Calculate the molality of C_2H_5OH in CH_2O.
d. Calculate the mole fraction of each component.
e. What does identifying the solvent have to do with determining the percent by mass or the mole fractions?

86. A solution contains 42.7 g of ethylene glycol, $C_2H_4(OH)_2$, and 89.6 g of H_2O.
a. Calculate the percent of $C_2H_4(OH)_2$.
b. Calculate the molality of $C_2H_4(OH)_2$ in the water.
c. Calculate the molality of H_2O in the $C_2H_4(OH)_2$.
d. Calculate the mole fraction of each component.
e. What does identifying the solvent have to do with determining the percent by mass or the mole fractions?

87. A 14.5 g sample of a nonionic solute is dissolved in 50.0 g of water. The solution freezes at −2.50°C. Calculate the molar mass of the solute.

88. Calculate the number of moles of solute in 400.0 g of water if the solution boils at 104.0°C and 1.000 atm.

89. Which compound in Figure 13.4 could be purified best by recrystallization (dissolving it in hot water and cooling the solution)?

90. Calculate the total pressure of an ideal solution consisting of 1.13 mol of benzene and 1.87 mol of toluene. The vapor pressures of the pure components are 105 torr and 34.0 torr, respectively.

91. Calculate the total pressure of an ideal solution consisting of 0.678 mol of benzene and 0.414 mol of toluene. The vapor pressures of the pure components are 105 torr and 34.0 torr, respectively.

92. A 4.73 g sample of a nonionic solute is dissolved in 50.5 g of water. The solution freezes at −1.73°C. Calculate the molar mass of the solute.

93. Calculate the freezing point of 60.0 mL of an aqueous solution of density 1.01 g/mL if its osmotic pressure at 25°C is 27.1 torr. The molar mass of the solute is 78.0 g/mol.

94. A solution contains a solute with molar mass 94.5 g/mol. The solution is 1.77 *m* and also 1.70 M. Calculate the density of the solution.

95. Calculate the freezing point of an aqueous solution that boils at 102.60°C at 1.00 atm.

96. The molality of a solution can be calculated from its molarity if the density of the solution is known. In such a calculation, you must keep track of not only of the units involved but also of the materials to which the units apply. Calculate the molality of a 0.503 M $Sn(NO_3)_2$ solution that has a density of 1.083 g/mL.

97. The percent composition of a solute is 93.71% C and 6.29% H. If a solution containing 18.6 g of this substance in 86.6 g of benzene freezes at −2.90°C, calculate the molecular formula of the substance. (For a review of determining empirical formulas and molecular formulas, see Section 3.10 and Section 3.11.)

98. Calculate the molar mass of a nonionic solute if a solution containing 6.11 g in 250.0 g of water freezes at −0.42°C.

99. Calculate the molar mass of a nonionic solute if a solution containing 1.61 g in 81.4 g of benzene freezes at 4.3°C.

100. Calculate the molality of methyl alcohol, CH_3OH, in ethyl alcohol, C_2H_5OH, in which the mole fraction of methyl alcohol is 0.319.

101. The vapor pressure of pure benzene, C_6H_6, at 50°C is 268 torr. How many moles of nonvolatile solute per mole of benzene is needed to prepare a solution with a vapor pressure of 231 torr at 50°C?

102. The boiling point at 1.00 atm of a solution containing 1.71 g of a nonionic solute and 8.14 g of water is 100.44°C. Calculate the molar mass of the solute.

103. The percent composition of a nonionic substance is 40.0% C, 6.7% H, and 53.3% O. If a solution containing 9.298 g of this substance in 340.7 g of water freezes at −0.42°C, calculate the molecular formula of the substance.

104. Calculate the mole fraction of CH_3OH in a solution containing 70.0% by mass CH_3OH and 30.0% CH_2O.

105. Calculate the mole fraction of C_2H_5OH in a solution containing 45.0% by mass C_2H_5OH in CH_3OH.

106. Calculate the vapor-pressure lowering of an aqueous solution of density 1.02 g/mL if its osmotic pressure at 25°C is 98.0 torr. The molar mass of the nonvolatile solute is 125 g/mol.

107. The boiling point at 1.00 atm of a solution containing 70.2 g of a nonionic solute and 482 g of water is 101.32°C. Calculate the molar mass of the solute.

108. Adding 42.0 g of a nonvolatile solute to 2.15 mol of benzene lowers the vapor pressure of the benzene from 105.0 torr to 95.1 torr. Calculate the molar mass of the solute.

109. The vapor pressure of pure chloroform at 40°C is 366 torr, and that of pure carbon tetrachloride is 143 torr. A solution with mole fraction 0.180 in chloroform is allowed to evaporate, the vapor phase is separated from the solution and condensed, and the resulting solution is allowed to evaporate. What would be the mole fraction of the vapor phase after the second evaporation?

110. A saturated solution of ammonia in water is about 15 M at 25°C and 1.0 atm. Calculate the ratio of moles of ammonia per liter of this solution to moles per liter of ammonia gas at 25°C and 1.00 atm.

111. A solution is described as 55.2 *m* CH_3OH in water. Calculate the molality of water in CH_3OH.

112. A solution is described as 16.5 *m* acetone, C_3H_6O, in ethyl alcohol, C_2H_5OH. Calculate the molality of ethyl alcohol in C_3H_6O.

113. Calculate the molality of methyl alcohol, CH_3OH, in an aqueous solution in which the mole fraction of methyl alcohol is 0.191.

114. Calculate the percent by mass of a solution prepared from a 12.00% solution and a 2.00% solution of the same solute by combining
   a. equal masses of the two solutions.
   b. samples of each solution containing equal masses of water.

115. The molality of a solution can be calculated from its molarity if the density of the solution is known. In such a calculation, you must keep track not only of the units involved but also of the materials to which the units apply. Calculate the molality of a 0.333 M $CaCl_2$ solution that has a density of 1.031 g/mL.

116. The density of 10.00% by mass KCl solution in water is 1.06 g/mL. Calculate the molarity, molality, and mole fraction of KCl in this solution.

117. Peptides, which are short chains of amino acids, have many important functions in living things. A 3.51 g sample of an unknown peptide was dissolved to form 200 mL of a solution with an osmotic pressure of 557 mmHg. What is the molar mass of the unknown peptide?

118. Another way of expressing concentration is in units of % *m/V*, which is the number of grams of solute per 100 milliliters of solution. One example of % *m/V* solutions are intravenous, IV, solutions, which must contain similar total solute concentrations as body fluids. Two commonly used IV solutions are *normal saline*, which is 0.9% *m/V* NaCl(aq), and *5DW*, which is 5.0% *m/V* dextrose in water (dextrose is another term used for glucose, $C_6H_{12}O_6$). Determine the osmotic pressure of these two solutions and comment on the results.

119. A bottle of whiskey is labeled "80 proof," which means that it contains 40% ethanol, C_2H_6O, *by volume (v/v)*. Calculate the molarity of ethanol in a 750 mL bottle of 80 proof whiskey. The density of ethanol is 0.789 g/mL.

120. For trace levels of contaminants in soil, the unit *parts per million*, ppm, is often used. Parts per million is the mass of the substance of interest, in mg, divided by the mass of the entire sample, in kg, so 1 ppm = 1 mg/kg. If a soil sample has a lead content of 15.5 ppm, what is the mass percent lead in the soil?

PRACTICE PROBLEM SOLUTIONS

Practice Problem 13.1 Solution

CH_3OH is polar and contains an H atom bonded to an O atom with lone pairs, so it is capable of hydrogen bonding. Thus, a polar solvent that is also capable of hydrogen bonding would be the most effective solvent for CH_3OH.

Practice Problem 13.2 Solution

a. The solution would be unsaturated because it would be holding less solute (161 g) than the maximum amount that is stable at 100°C (170 g).

b. The 170 g of solute needs 100 g of water to dissolve completely at 100°C. Thus, not all of the solute will dissolve in 90.0 g of water, and a heterogeneous mixture will still be present.

Practice Problem 13.3 Solution

Using M as the symbol for concentration in Henry's law, Equation 13.1 becomes $M = kP$. Substitute the given values, and solve for M.

$$M = kP$$

$$M = \left(0.0013 \frac{\text{M}}{\text{atm}}\right)(0.30 \text{ atm}) = 3.9 \times 10^{-4} \text{ M}$$

Practice Problem 13.4 Solution

The percent by mass is calculated using Equation 13.2:

$$\text{Percent by mass} = \left(\frac{\text{Mass of solute}}{\text{Total mass of solution}}\right) \times 100\%$$

The mass of the solution is the sum of the mass of the solute and the mass of the solvent.

$$\text{Percent by mass} = \left(\frac{0.18 \text{ g}}{50.0 \text{ g} + 0.18 \text{ g}}\right) \times 100\% = 0.36\%$$

Practice Problem 13.5 Solution

First convert the mass of solution to grams.

$$5.00 \text{ kg}\left(\frac{1000 \text{ g}}{1 \text{ kg}}\right) = 5.00 \times 10^3 \text{ g}$$

Now write the percentage as a conversion factor.

$$12.0\% \text{ by mass} = \frac{12.0 \text{ g solute}}{100 \text{ g solution}}$$

Use the conversation factor to find the mass of solute.

$$5.00 \times 10^3 \text{ g solution}\left(\frac{12.0 \text{ g solute}}{100 \text{ g solution}}\right) = 6.00 \times 10^2 \text{ g solute}$$

Although 600 g of NH_2OH is required, you have only 434 g, so you are unable to make the solution.

Use the inverted conversion factor to find the mass of solution that you can prepare.

$$434 \text{ g } NH_2OH \times \left(\frac{100 \text{ g solution}}{12.0 \text{ g } NH_2OH}\right) = 3620 \text{ g of solution}$$

Practice Problem 13.6 Solution

Convert the mass of solute to moles. The molar mass of $MgSO_4$ is 24.305 g/mol + 32.066 g/mol + 4(15.999 g/mol) = 120.367 g/mol.

$$26 \text{ g } MgSO_4\left(\frac{1 \text{ mol } MgSO_4}{120.367 \text{ g } MgSO_4}\right) = 0.22 \text{ mol } MgSO_4$$

Convert the mass of solvent to kilograms, given that 1 kg = 1000 g.

$$100.0 \text{ g } H_2O\left(\frac{1 \text{ kg}}{1000 \text{ g}}\right) = 0.1000 \text{ kg } H_2O$$

Finally, calculate the molality.

$$m = \frac{0.22 \text{ mol } MgSO_4}{0.1000 \text{ kg } H_2O} = 2.2 \text{ mol/ kg} = 2.2\ m$$

Practice Problem 13.7 Solution

$$\text{Mass of the solvent} = \text{Total mass of the solution} - \text{Mass of the solute}$$

$$\text{Mass of } H_2O = 100.0 \text{ g} - 47.6 \text{ g} = 52.4 \text{ g } H_2O = 0.0524 \text{ kg } H_2O$$

Molar mass of

$$Na_2S_2O_3 = 2(22.99 \text{ g/mol}) + 2(32.066 \text{ g/mol}) + 3(15.999 \text{ g/mol}) = 158.109 \text{ g/mol}$$

$$47.6 \text{ g } Na_2S_2O_3\left(\frac{1 \text{ mol } Na_2S_2O_3}{158.109 \text{ g } Na_2S_2O_3}\right) = 0.301 \text{ mol } Na_2S_2O_3$$

$$m = \frac{0.301 \text{ mol } Na_2S_2O_3}{0.0524 \text{ kg } H_2O} = 5.74 \text{ mol/kg} = 5.74\ m$$

Practice Problem 13.8 Solution

Use the concentration in molality to convert from moles of solute to kilograms of solvent. Since you are solving for the mass of the solvent, put the mass of the solvent in the numerator of the conversion factor.

$$0.334 \text{ mol } C_2H_4O\left(\frac{1 \text{ kg } H_2O}{1.68 \text{ mol } C_2H_4O}\right) = 0.199 \text{ kg } H_2O$$

Practice Problem 13.9 Solution

Molar mass of CH_2O = 12.011 g/mol + 2(1.008 g/mol) + 15.999 g/mol = 30.0258 g/mol

Molar mass of C_3H_8O = 3(12.011 g/mol) + 8(1.008 g/mol) + 15.999 g/mol = 60.0952 g/mol

Assume some mass, such as 10.00 g of each. You can use any mass as long as the two masses are equal.

$$10.00\ \text{g}\ CH_2O\left(\frac{1\ \text{mol}\ CH_2O}{30.0258\ \text{g}\ CH_2O}\right) = 0.3330\ \text{mol}\ CH_2O$$

$$10.00\ \text{g}\ C_3H_8O\left(\frac{1\ \text{mol}\ C_3H_8O}{60.0952\ \text{g}\ C_3H_8O}\right) = 0.1664\ \text{mol}\ C_3H_8O$$

$$X_{CH_2O} = \frac{0.3330\ \text{mol}}{0.3330\ \text{mol} + 0.1664\ \text{mol}} = 0.6668$$

$$X_{C_3H_8O} = \frac{0.1664\ \text{mol}}{0.3330\ \text{mol} + 0.1664\ \text{mol}} = 0.3332$$

Since there are only two components in the solution and their mole fractions must add up to 1, $X_{C_3H_8O}$ can also be calculated by subtracting X_{CH_2O} from 1:

$$X_{C_3H_8O} = 1 - X_{CH_2O} = 1 - 0.6668 = 0.3332$$

Practice Problem 13.10 Solution

To calculate mole fraction, you need to know the number of moles of alcohol (the solute) and the number of moles of water (the solvent). A 1.27 *m* solution contains 1.27 moles of alcohol in exactly 1 kg of water, so convert 1.000 kg of water to moles of water, then calculate mole fraction from the number of moles of alcohol and water.

Start by converting the mass of water to moles. The molar mass of H_2O is 2(1.008 g/mol) + 15.999 g/mol = 18.0148 g/mol.

$$1.000\ \text{kg}\ H_2O\left(\frac{1000\ \text{g}}{1\ \text{kg}}\right)\left(\frac{1\ \text{mol}}{18.0148\ \text{g}}\right) = 55.51\ \text{mol}\ H_2O$$

Now calculate the mole fraction of alcohol.

$$X_{CH_3OH} = \frac{1.27\ \text{mol}}{1.27\ \text{mol} + 55.51\ \text{mol}} = 0.0224$$

X_{H_2O} can be calculated from the moles of each component or by the difference from a total mole fraction of 1:

$$X_{H_2O} = 1 - X_{CH_3OH} = 1 - 0.0224 = 0.9776$$

or

$$X_{H_2O} = \frac{55.51\ \text{mol}}{1.27\ \text{mol} + 55.51\ \text{mol}} = 0.9776$$

Practice Problem 13.11 Solution

Percent by mass is the ratio of grams of solute to grams of *solution*, so a 22% solution has 22 g NaCl in every 100 g of solution. Since the mass of the solution includes the mass of the salt, 100 g of solution contains 100 g solution − 22 g NaCl = 78 g water.

Molality is moles of solute divided by kilograms of solvent, so convert grams of NaCl to moles of NaCl and grams of water to kilograms of water.

$$22\ \text{g NaCl} \times \frac{1\ \text{mol NaCl}}{58.443\ \text{g NaCl}} = 0.376\ \text{mol NaCl}$$

$$78\ \text{g}\ H_2O \times \frac{1\ \text{kg}}{1000\ \text{g}} = 0.078\ \text{kg}\ H_2O$$

$$\text{Molality} = \frac{0.376\ \text{mol NaCl}}{0.078\ \text{kg}\ H_2O} = 4.8\ m$$

Practice Problem 13.12 Solution

A 1.00 *M* solution contains 1.00 mol of solute in 1.00 L of *solution*. To calculate molality, you need to know the mass of *solvent*. The density of the solution can be used as a conversion factor between the volume of the solution and the mass of the solution:

$$1.00\ \text{L solution} \times \frac{1000\ \text{mL}}{1\ \text{L}} \times \frac{1.0303\ \text{g solution}}{1\ \text{mL solution}}$$
$$= 1030.3\ \text{g solution}$$

The mass of the solvent can now be determined by subtracting the mass of the solute from the total mass of the solution. Because 1 L of solution contains 1.00 mol H_3PO_4 (molar mass 97.9937 g/mol), the mass of solute is

$$1.00\ \text{mol}\ H_3PO_4 \times \frac{97.9937\ \text{g}\ H_3PO_4}{1\ \text{mol}\ H_3PO_4}$$
$$= 97.9937\ \text{g}\ H_3PO_4$$

The mass of the solvent is the mass of the solution minus the mass of the solute:

$$\text{Mass of solvent} = 1030.3\ \text{g} - 97.9937\ \text{g} = 932.3\ \text{g}$$

Molality is the moles of solute per kilogram of solvent, so convert the mass of the solvent from grams to kilograms, then divide moles of solute by kilograms of solvent:

$$932.3\ \text{g solvent} \times \frac{1\ \text{kg}}{1000\ \text{g}} = 0.9323\ \text{kg solvent}$$

$$\text{Molality} = \frac{1.00\ \text{moles}}{0.9323\ \text{kg}} = 1.07\ m$$

For the dilute H_3PO_4 solution, the numerical values for molarity and molality are very close (1.00 M = 1.07 *m*), but for the concentrated H_3PO_4 solution, the numerical values are much different (14.8 M = 63.0 *m*). This is because 1 L of a dilute aqueous solution contains about 1 kg of water. For higher concentrations, however, the mass of solvent in the solution decreases as the mass of solute increases, resulting in values for molality that are much higher than their corresponding molarity values.

Practice Problem 13.13 Solution

According to Raoult's law, the vapor pressure above the solution is equal to the vapor pressure of the pure liquid at that temperature times the mole fraction of the liquid.

$$P_Z = X_Z P^\circ_Z$$
$$P_Z = (0.820)(94.8 \text{ torr}) = 77.7 \text{ torr}$$

Practice Problem 13.14 Solution

The vapor pressure of the pure benzene, P°, was given in Practice Problem 13.13 as 94.8 torr, and the vapor pressure of the solution, P, was calculated to be 77.7 torr. Using Equation 13.6,

$$\Delta P = P^\circ - P$$
$$\Delta P = 94.8 \text{ torr} - 77.7 \text{ torr} = 17.1 \text{ torr}$$

Practice Problem 13.15 Solution

$$X_{CCl_4} = 1 - X_{CHCl_3} = 1 - 0.402 = 0.598$$
$$P_{\text{total}} = X_{CCl_4}P^\circ_{CCl_4} + X_{CHCl_3}P^\circ_{CHCl_3}$$
$$111 \text{ torr} = (0.598)P^\circ_{CCl_4} + (0.402)(160 \text{ torr})$$
$$P^\circ_{CCl_4} = 78.1 \text{ torr}$$

Practice Problem 13.16 Solution

The mole fraction of $CHCl_3$ in the vapor phase is 0.800, so the mole fraction of CCl_4 in the vapor phase is 0.200. The partial pressure of each gas is equal to the mole fraction of each gas times the total pressure (Equation 13.9), so

$$P_{CHCl_3} = 0.800(215 \text{ torr}) = 172 \text{ torr}$$
$$P_{CCl_4} = 0.200(215 \text{ torr}) = 43.0 \text{ torr}$$

According to Raoult's law, the vapor pressure of each component of the solution is equal to the mole fraction in the solution times the vapor pressure of the pure substance (Equation 13.5):

$$P_{CCl_4} = X_{CCl_4}P^\circ_{CCl_4}$$
$$P_{CHCl_3} = X_{CHCl_3}P^\circ_{CHCl_3}$$

The mole fraction of CCl_4 in the solution is given as 0.300, so the mole fraction of $CHCl_3$ in the solution is $1 - 0.300 = 0.700$.

For CCl_4:

$$P_{CCl_4} = X_{CCl_4}P^\circ_{CCl_4}$$
$$43.0 \text{ torr} = (0.300)P^\circ_{CCl_4}$$
$$P^\circ_{CCl_4} = \frac{43.0 \text{ torr}}{0.300} = 143 \text{ torr}$$

For $CHCl_3$:

$$P_{CHCl_3} = X_{CHCl_3}P^\circ_{CHCl_3}$$
$$172 \text{ torr} = (0.700)P^\circ_{CHCl_3}$$
$$P^\circ_{CCl_4} = \frac{172 \text{ torr}}{0.700} = 246 \text{ torr}$$

Practice Problem 13.17 Solution

The boiling-point elevation constant for water is $0.512°C/m$, and its normal boiling point is 100.00°C (see Table 13.3).

a. Use Equation 13.13 to calculate the boiling-point elevation.

$$\Delta T_b = K_b m$$
$$\Delta T_b = (0.512°C/m)(0.650\ m) = 0.333°C$$

Then use Equation 13.11 to find the boiling point of the fructose solution.

$$T_{\text{solution}} = T_{\text{solvent}} + \Delta T_b$$
$$T_{\text{solution}} = 100.00°C + 0.333°C = 100.33°C$$

b. Colligative properties such as boiling-point elevation depend on the *number* of solute particles, not on the *identity* of the solute. So, even though the solutes are different, the solutions will have the same boiling point because they have the same solvent and the same concentration of solute. $T_{\text{solution}} = 100.33°C$.

Practice Problem 13.18 Solution

The molality of the solution is determined from the freezing-point depression and the value of K_f for water. The freezing-point depression for this solution is 1.09°C. Rearranging Equation 13.12 yields

$$m = \frac{\Delta T_f}{K_f} = \frac{1.09°C}{1.86°C/m} = 0.586\ m = 0.586 \text{ mol/kg}$$

Multiplying this concentration by the mass of water present in kilograms yields the number of moles of solute in the solution:

$$\frac{0.586 \text{ mol solute}}{1 \text{ kg water}} \times 0.5000 \text{ kg water} = 0.293 \text{ mol solute}$$

Divide the mass of solute (100.0 g) by the moles of solute (0.293 mol) to determine the molar mass:

$$\frac{100.0 \text{ g solute}}{0.293 \text{ mol solute}} = 341 \text{ g/mol}$$

Practice Problem 13.19 Solution

Equation 13.15, $\Pi = MRT$, provides the necessary relationship between concentration and osmotic pressure. To use $R = 0.08206 \text{ L} \cdot \text{atm/mol} \cdot \text{K}$, first convert the osmotic pressure from torr to atmospheres.

$$68.3 \text{ torr}\left(\frac{1 \text{ atm}}{760 \text{ torr}}\right) = 0.0899 \text{ atm}$$

Next, rearrange the osmotic pressure formula to isolate M.

$$\Pi = MRT$$

$$M = \frac{\Pi}{RT} = \frac{0.0899 \text{ atm}}{\left(0.08206\frac{\text{L} \cdot \text{atm}}{\text{mol} \cdot \text{K}}\right)(298 \text{ K})} = 0.00368 \text{ M}$$

Practice Problem 13.20 Solution

The order from highest boiling point to lowest is $AlCl_3 > BaCl_2 > KCl$. $AlCl_3$ dissociates into 4 moles of particles per mole of $AlCl_3$, $BaCl_2$ dissociates into 3 moles of particles per mole of $BaCl_2$, and KCl dissociates into 2 moles of particles per mole of KCl.

Practice Problem 13.21 Solution

Since $CaCl_2$ is a strong electrolyte, it will completely dissociate in water into one Ca^{2+} and two Cl^- ions, so the van't Hoff factor for $CaCl_2$ is $i = 3$. From Table 13.3, K_f for water is 1.86°C/m and K_b for water is 0.512°C/m.

$$\Delta T_f = iK_fm = 3(1.86°\text{C}/m)(0.53\ m) = 3.0°\text{C}$$

$$\Delta T_b = iK_bm = 3(0.512°\text{C}/m)(0.53\ m) = 0.81°\text{C}$$

The freezing point of the solution drops 3.0°C compared to water, and the boiling point increases by 0.81°C.

Practice Problem 13.22 Solution

Ion pairing has reduced the van't Hoff factor from $i = 2$ to $i = 1.9$, but the problem is still solved with Equation 13.19, just as it was in Example 13.22.

$$\Pi = 1.9\left(0.015\frac{\text{mol}}{\text{L}}\right)\left(0.08206\frac{\text{L} \cdot \text{atm}}{\text{mol} \cdot \text{K}}\right)(298 \text{ K})$$
$$= 0.70 \text{ atm}$$

Thus, the osmotic pressure decreases from 0.73 atm to 0.70 atm when i decreases from 2 to 1.9 due to ion pairing.

Practice Problem 13.23 Solution

First calculate the concentration of a saturated solution of $CaCl_2$ in molality by dividing the moles of $CaCl_2$ by the mass of solvent in kilograms:

$$\text{Molar mass of } CaCl_2 = 40.078 \text{ g/mol} + 2(35.453 \text{ g/mol}) = 110.984 \text{ g/mol}$$

$$\text{Moles of } CaCl_2 \text{ in } 100 \text{ g } H_2O = \frac{59.5 \text{ g}}{110.984 \text{ g/mol}} = 0.5361 \text{ mol}$$

$$\text{Molality} = \frac{0.5361 \text{ mol } CaCl_2}{0.100 \text{ kg } H_2O} = 5.361\ m$$

Now calculate the freezing-point depression using data from Table 13.3 and the molal concentration you just calculated.

$$\Delta T_f = iK_fm$$

For $CaCl_2$, $i = 3$.

$$K_f = 1.86°\text{C}/m$$

$$\Delta T_f = (3)(1.86°\text{C/m})(5.361\ m) = 29.91°\text{C}$$

The freezing point of the solution on the roads will be −29.91°C.

To convert temperature from Fahrenheit to Celsius, use the equation from Section 1.10.

$$T_C = \frac{5}{9}(T_F - 32)$$

Daytime temperature:

$$T_C = \frac{5}{9}(30 - 32) = -1.1°\text{C}$$

Nighttime temperature:

$$T_C = \frac{5}{9}(10 - 32) = -12.2°\text{C}$$

Since the $CaCl_2$ solution freezes at −29.91°C, the driveway will remain unfrozen in both the daytime and nighttime temperatures. This question told you to assume the solubility of $CaCl_2$ is roughly constant over this temperature range. In reality, the solubility of $CaCl_2$ decreases slightly as the temperature decreases over this range, but the freezing-point depression will not change enough to allow the solution to refreeze.

CHAPTER 14

Chemical Kinetics

Charles Knowles/Shutterstock; Tamisclao/Shutterstock

Chemical kinetics is the study of reaction rates. The reaction between iron and oxygen to produce rust is quite slow, whereas combustion occurs very quickly. Knowing what factors affect reaction rates is useful if you want to slow down or speed up a reaction. For example, the spoiling of food can be slowed by keeping it cold and the dissolving of sugar into a cold beverage can be sped up by using finer-grain sugar. Additionally, knowing how to quantify and measure reaction rates is useful for industrial processes such as the production of plastics.

Chapter Outline

GOALS

- List and describe the factors that affect reaction rates.
- Express reaction rates in relation to reaction stoichiometry.
- Use experimental data to write rate laws for chemical reactions.
- Predict the concentration and time values of reactions using first- and second-order integrated rate laws.
- Graph data to identify the order of a reaction.
- Define and apply the terms *half-life*, *first-order reaction*, and *second-order reaction*.
- Explain collision theory using appropriate terminology.
- Apply the Arrhenius equation to calculate activation energy and/or the value of the rate constant at various temperatures.
- Define and discuss *reaction mechanism*.
- Write rate laws for elementary steps.
- Identify intermediates in a reaction mechanism.
- Analyze steps in a reaction mechanism to determine if the mechanism is consistent with the experimentally determined rate low.
- Discuss how catalysts work to speed up chemical reactions.
- Provide examples of both homogeneous and heterogeneous catalysts.
- Identify catalysts in reaction mechanisms.

14.1 Rates of Reactions

GOALS

- List and describe the factors that affect reaction rates.
- Express reaction rates in relation to reaction stoichiometry.

Background Review

Chapter 5 Stoichiometry: Section 5.1—Mole Calculations for Chemical Reactions; Section 5.5—Definition and Uses of Molarity

CHANGING REACTION RATES

The **rate** of a chemical reaction, or **reaction rate**, is defined as the change in the concentration of a reactant or product per unit time. For example, the rate may be described as the disappearance of 0.300 mol/L of a certain reactant per hour or the appearance of 0.00100 mol/L of a certain product per second. The units used reflect how rapidly or slowly a reaction occurs. The rates of slower reactions are expressed using longer units of time or smaller units of concentration, such as mmol/L or μmol/L.

There are five factors that can alter the rate of a reaction: (1) the particle size of solid reactants, (2) the concentration of reactants, (3) the temperature, (4) the nature of the reactants, and (5) the presence of a **catalyst**. Some reactions, such as the explosion of nitroglycerine, proceed rapidly due to the unstable, high-energy nature of the reactants. Others, such as the reaction of low-energy, stable limestone with carbon dioxide and water to form soluble calcium hydrogen carbonate, tend to proceed slowly. It can take many centuries for underground streams to form caverns in limestone bedrock.

$$\underset{\text{nitroglycerin}}{4\,C_3H_5N_3O_9(s)} \xrightarrow{\text{rapid decomposition}} 6\,N_2(g) + 12\,CO_2(g) + 10\,H_2O(g) + 7\,O_2(g)\underset{\text{limestone}}{CaCO_3(s)} + H_2O(l) + CO_2(aq) \xrightarrow{\text{slow combination}} Ca(HCO_3)_2(aq)$$

During a reaction, the reactant atoms, molecules, or ions must come in contact or collide with each other with enough energy for chemical bond rearrangements to occur. When you increase the concentration (or for solids, the surface area), you make it more likely that particles will collide with each other.

Both endothermic and exothermic chemical reactions require a certain amount of energy to initiate the rearrangement of chemical bonds, that is, a chemical reaction. Increasing the temperature of the reaction will increase the kinetic energy of the reactant molecules and enhance the rate of all reactions. Note in the graph in Figure 14.1 that the reactant is used up more rapidly when the reaction occurs at a higher temperature. In fact, raising the temperature by 10°C causes the rates of many reactions to double. The last factor, adding a catalyst, provides a lower-energy pathway for

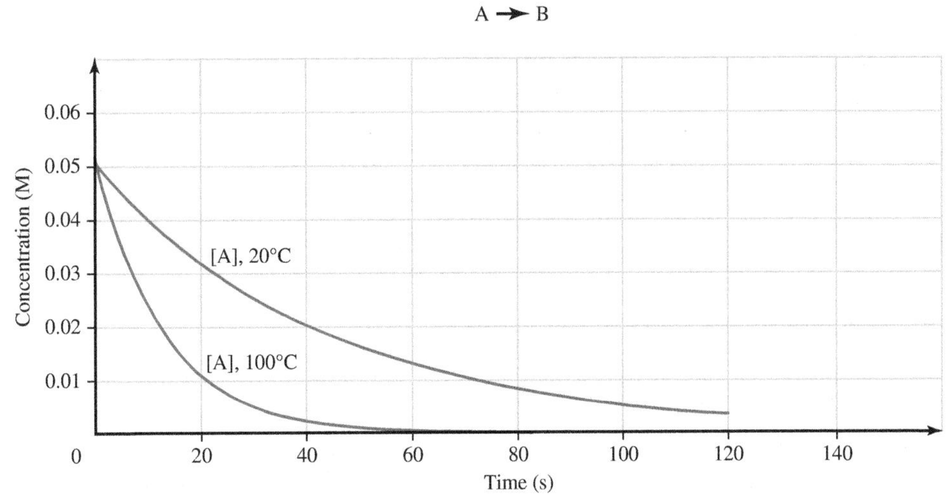

FIGURE 14.1 Temperature and Reaction Rate

The rate of the reaction A → B is monitored by the decrease in the concentration of A over time. The reaction rate is much higher at 100°C than at 20°C as seen in the more rapid decrease in the concentration of A.

the chemical bond rearrangement, allowing reactions to happen more quickly at lower temperatures. Catalysts will be discussed in greater detail in Section 14.6.

STOICHIOMETRY AND REACTION RATES

Reaction rates are measured by monitoring the change in concentration of a reactant or product over time, *t*. The rate of the generic reaction A → B can be expressed as the rate at which the concentration of the reactant, A, *decreases* or as the rate at which the concentration of the product, B, *increases* (Figure 14.2).

In the following equation, the molar concentrations of A and B are shown as [A] and [B], and the change in concentration is shown as Δ[A] or Δ[B].

$$\text{Rate} = \frac{\text{change in concentration}}{\text{change in time}} = \frac{\Delta\text{concentration}}{\Delta t}$$

$$= -\frac{\Delta[\text{A}]}{\Delta t} = \frac{\Delta[\text{B}]}{\Delta t}$$

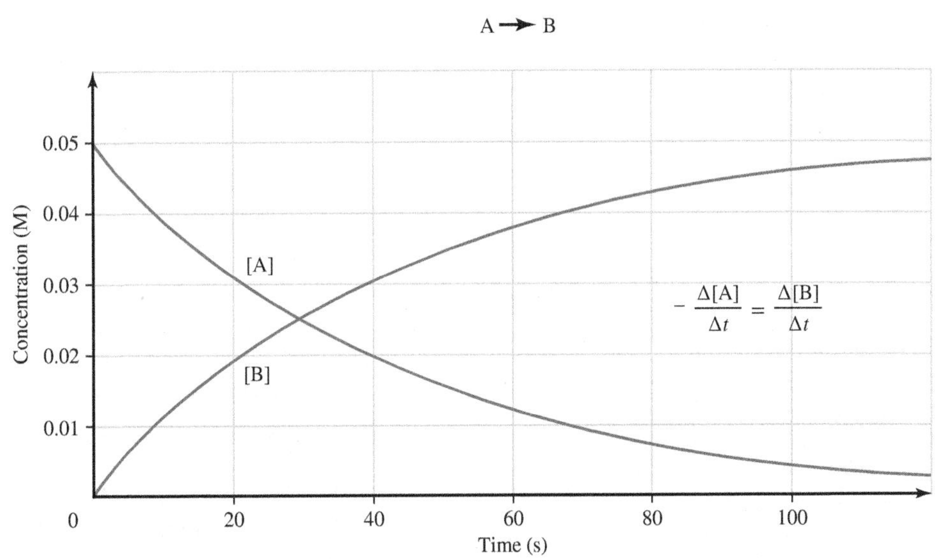

FIGURE 14.2 Stoichiometry and Reaction Rate: A → B

The rate of the reaction, A → B, can be monitored by the decrease in the concentration of A, [A], or the increase in the concentration of B, [B]. Reaction rates are depicted as changes in these concentrations over time. Rate = $-\Delta[\text{A}]/\Delta t = \Delta[\text{B}]/\Delta t$.

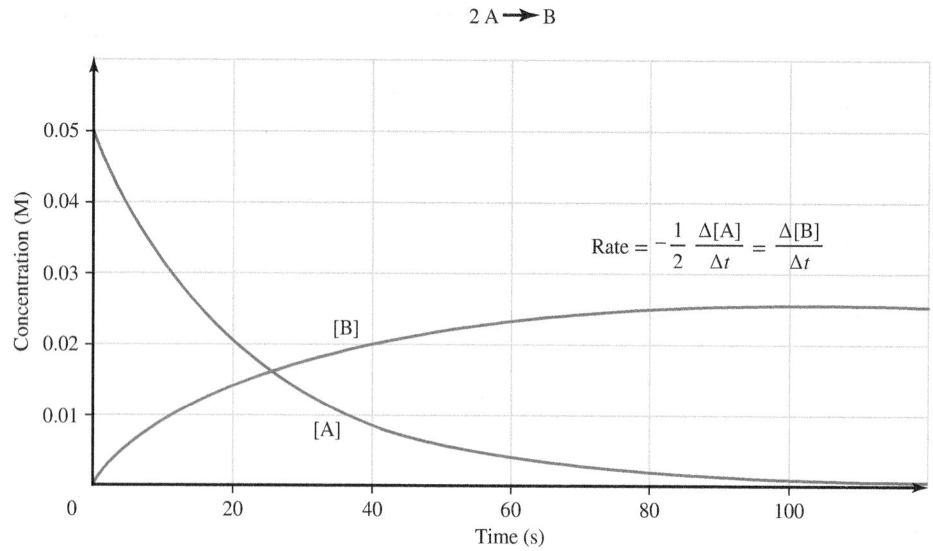

FIGURE 14.3 Stoichiometry and Reaction Rate: 2 A → B

The rate of the reaction, 2 A → B, can be monitored by the decrease in the concentration of A, [A], or the increase in the concentration of B, [B]. Because two molecules of A are consumed for each molecule of B produced, the reaction rate is expressed as $\text{Rate} = -\frac{1}{2}\frac{\Delta[A]}{\Delta t} = \frac{\Delta[B]}{\Delta t}$.

The units used for rate are typically molar per second, abbreviated as M/s or $M \cdot s^{-1}$. Slower reactions may be expressed in M/min or even M/h. The rates of reactions slow over time as the reactant concentration decreases.

In the simple generic reaction shown graphically in Figure 14.2, A → B, there is a 1:1 relationship between the disappearance of A and the appearance of B. In the generic reaction 2 A → B, 2 molecules (or moles) of A disappear for every molecule (or mole) of B that is produced. Thus, the rate of disappearance of A is twice the rate of appearance of B (Figure 14.3).

$$\text{Rate} = -\frac{1}{2}\frac{\Delta[A]}{\Delta t} = \frac{\Delta[B]}{\Delta t}$$

Many reactions involve more than one reactant or product, such as the reaction A → B + 2 C. You could follow the progress of this reaction by monitoring the concentration of A, B, or C as shown in the following rate equation and in Figure 14.4.

$$\text{Rate} = -\frac{\Delta[A]}{\Delta t} = \frac{\Delta[B]}{\Delta t} = \frac{1}{2}\frac{\Delta[C]}{\Delta t}$$

For the reaction $a\text{A} \rightarrow b\text{B}$, where a and b are stoichiometric coefficients in the balanced chemical equation, the rate is expressed as

$$\text{Rate} = -\frac{1}{a}\frac{\Delta[A]}{\Delta t} = \frac{1}{b}\frac{\Delta[B]}{\Delta t} \quad (14.1)$$

Example 14.1

For the generic reaction A → 2 B, express the reaction rate as an equation in terms of rate of change of A and the rate of change of B. Also express in words how the rates of change of A and B are related.

Solution

In A → 2 B, one molecule (or mole) of the reactant A is consumed for every two molecules (or moles) of the product B that are made in the reaction. Therefore, the rate of disappearance of A is one-half the rate of appearance of B.

$$\text{Rate} = -\frac{\Delta[A]}{\Delta t} = \frac{1}{2}\frac{\Delta[B]}{\Delta t}$$

PRACTICE PROBLEM 14.1

For each of the following chemical equations, use words and an equation to express the reaction rate in terms of the changes in concentration of both the reactants and products(s).

a. 2 A → 3 B
b. 3 A → 2 B
c. $3\,O_2 \rightarrow 2\,O_3$
d. $2\,NO_2(g) \rightarrow N_2O_4(g)$

Hint: Use the coefficients from each chemical equation to express the relative rate of change. And don't forget that the sign of the rate of change of a reactant is opposite that of a product.

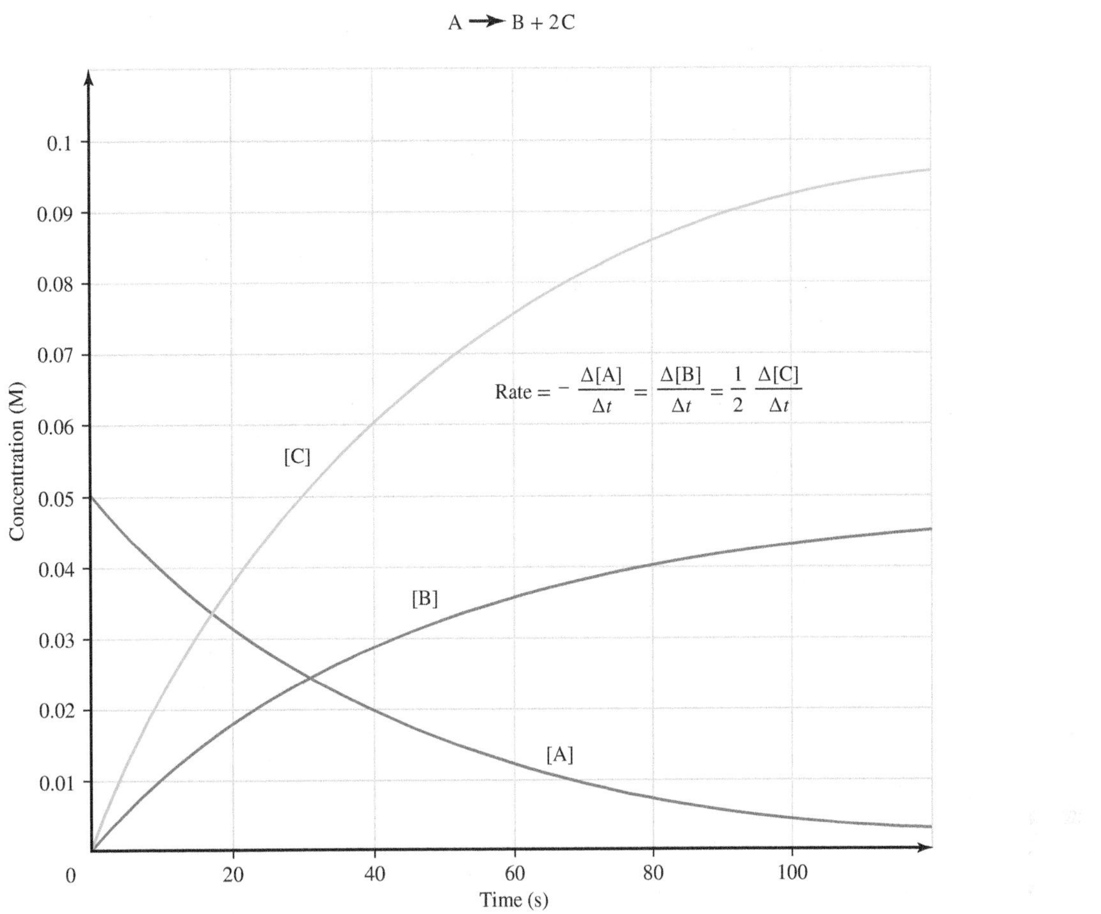

FIGURE 14.4 Stoichiometry and Reaction Rate: A → B + 2 C

The rate of the reaction, A → B + 2 C, can be monitored by the decrease in [A] or the increase in [B] or [C]. Because two molecules of C are produced for each molecule of B produced and each molecule of A consumed, the reaction rate is expressed as Rate $= -\frac{\Delta[A]}{\Delta t} = \frac{\Delta[B]}{\Delta t} = \frac{1}{2}\frac{\Delta[C]}{\Delta t}$.

MEASURING CONCENTRATIONS

How are the changes in the concentration of the reactants and products monitored during a reaction? Many substances absorb electromagnetic radiation, which can be measured in a lab (Figure 14.5). Colorful substances absorb visible light, and many seemingly colorless substances do absorb light in the ultraviolet range. As the concentration of a substance increases, more

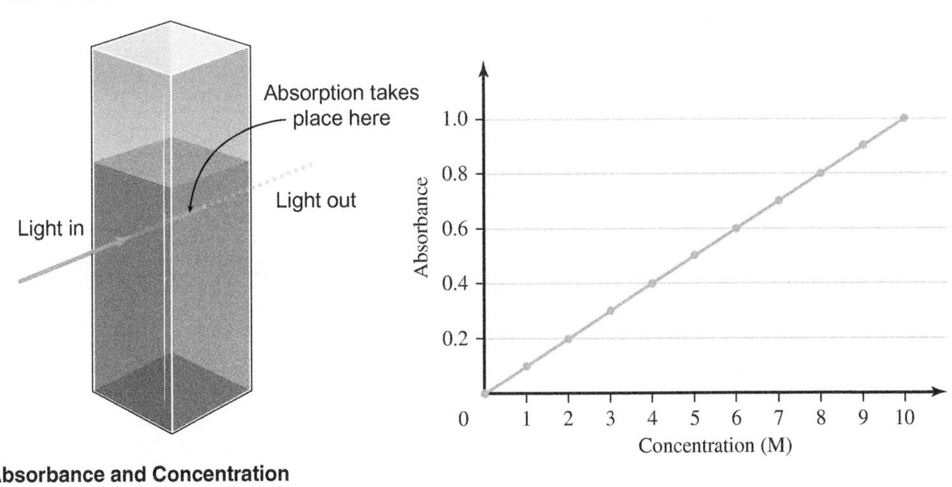

FIGURE 14.5 Absorbance and Concentration

For many solutions, the amount of light absorbed (absorbance) is directly proportional to concentration.

electromagnetic radiation is absorbed, making it possible to monitor changes in concentration in real time.

SECTION REVIEW

- Reaction rates are affected by five factors: the nature of the reactants, the particle size of a solid, the concentration of a reactant, temperature, and the presence of a catalyst.
- All chemical reactions require energy to initiate the reaction.
- Increasing the temperature increases the rates of all chemical reactions.
- Increasing the concentration of reactants increases the reaction rate.
- Catalysts provide a lower-energy pathway for the reaction.
- Reaction rates can be measured by the disappearance of a reactant or the appearance of a product. For the reaction $a\text{A} \rightarrow b\text{B}$, where a and b are stoichiometric coefficients in a balanced chemical equation,

$$\text{Rate} = -\frac{1}{a}\frac{\Delta[\text{A}]}{\Delta t} = \frac{1}{b}\frac{\Delta[\text{B}]}{\Delta t}.$$

- The concentrations of reactants and/or products in many reactions can be measured spectroscopically, because many compounds absorb electromagnetic radiation.

14.2 Reaction Rates and Concentration: Rate Laws

GOAL

- Use experimental data to write rate laws for chemical reactions.

Background Review

Chapter 5 Stoichiometry: Section 5.1—Mole Calculations for Chemical Reactions; Section 5.5—Definition and Uses of Molarity

MEASURING REACTION RATES

There are several ways of using the changing concentrations of reactants or products to measure reaction rates. One way is to use **average rates**, measuring the concentrations at two times and dividing the change in concentration by the change in time. Another way is to use **instantaneous rates**, which are measured by finding the slope of the tangent to the concentration versus time graph. A quick look at Figure 14.6 will show you that these instantaneous rates vary as the overall rate of the reaction slows.

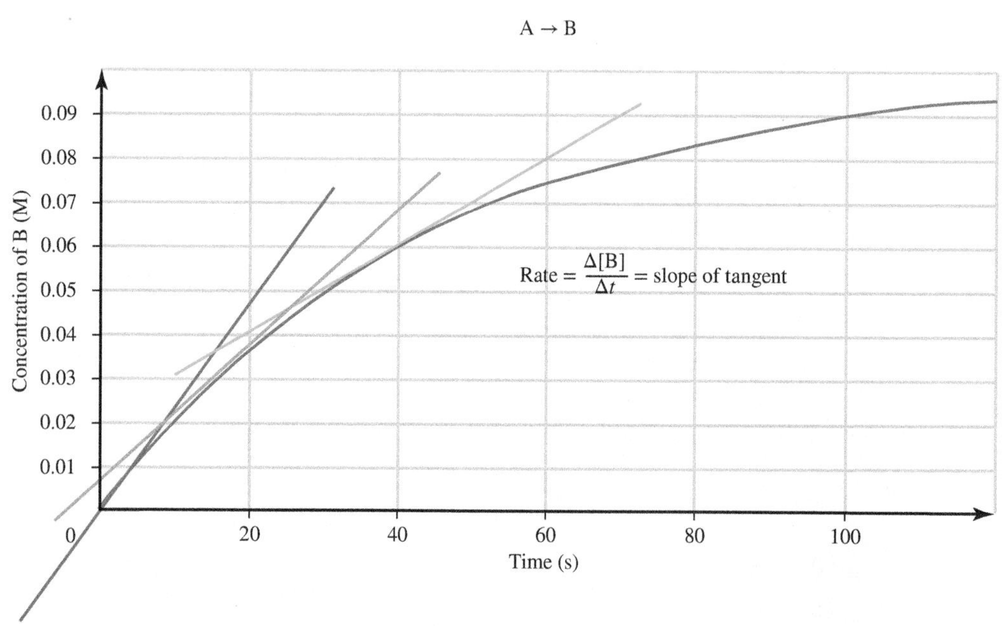

FIGURE 14.6 Instantaneous Rate

In contrast to rates measured over a period of time, an instantaneous rate is the slope of the tangent to the curve at a given instant. The slope of the tangent at time zero is called the initial rate.

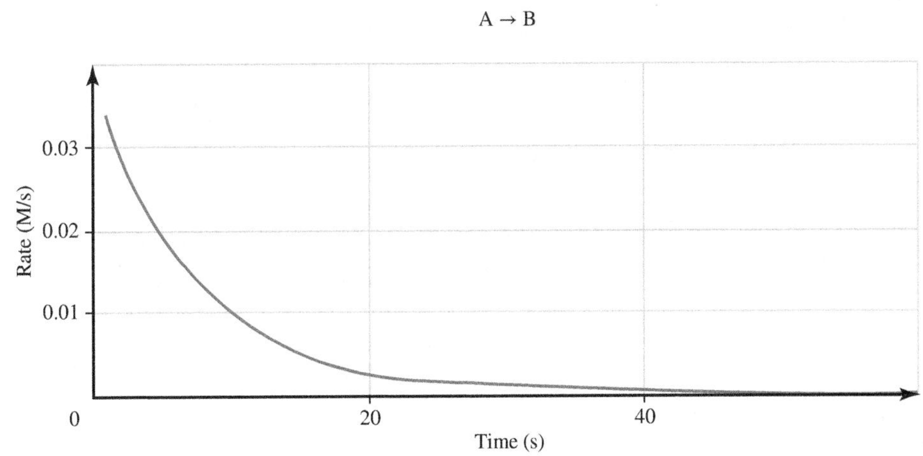

FIGURE 14.7 Reaction Rate Versus Time

Reaction rate is highest at the beginning of the reaction and drops off as the reactant concentration decreases. For this reason, initial reaction rates are commonly used to study the kinetics of chemical reactions.

Most often, chemists determine the instantaneous rates as close as possible to the start of the reaction (time zero) and refer to these measurements as **initial rates**. This is important because, in most cases, the rate of reaction slows over time as the reactant concentration decreases (Figure 14.7).

Example 14.2

Use the concentration and time data for the reaction A → B to determine

a. the average rate between 10.0 s and 30.0 s.
b. the instantaneous rate at 20.0 s.

Time (s)	[B] (M)
0	0
5.0	0.0160
10.0	0.0295
20.0	0.0503
30.0	0.0650
40.0	0.0753

Solution

a. Determine the average rate.

$$\text{Rate} = \frac{\Delta[\text{B}]}{\Delta t} = \frac{0.0650\text{ M} - 0.0295\text{ M}}{30.0\text{ s} - 10.0\text{ s}}$$

$$\text{Rate} = \frac{0.0355\text{ M}}{20.0\text{ s}} = 0.00178\text{ M/s}$$

b. To determine the instantaneous rate at 20.0 s, first plot the data either by hand or by using graphing software:

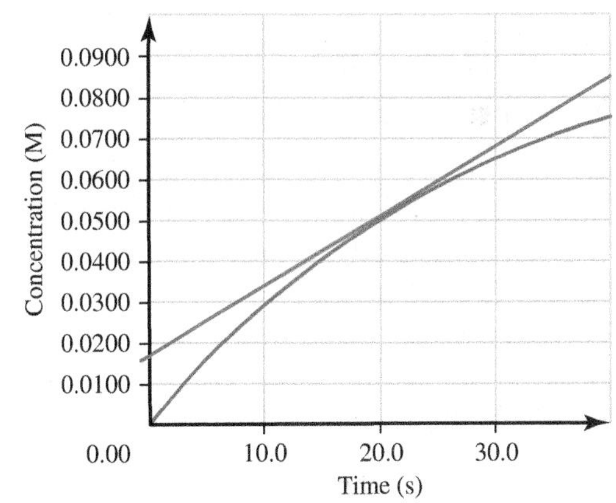

Then draw a tangent to the curve at the 20.0-s point. The slope of the tangent is the instantaneous rate at 20.0 s. Using (x, y) points (40.0, 0.0850) and (0, 0.0160), the slope (m) is calculated as rise over run:

$$m = \frac{(y_2 - y_1)}{(x_2 - x_1)}$$

$$m = \frac{(0.0850 - 0.0160)\text{ M}}{(40.0 - 0)\text{ s}} = 0.00173\text{ M/s}$$

PRACTICE PROBLEM 14.2

Given the concentration and time data shown in the following table for the reaction A → B, determine

a. the average reaction rate between 5.0 s and 30.0 s.
b. the instantaneous rate at 10.0 s.

Time (s)	[B] (M)
0	0
5.0	0.050
10.0	0.091
20.0	0.148
30.0	0.185
40.0	0.209
60.0	0.233

Hint:

a. Plug values from two rows of the table (at 5.0 s and 30.0 s) into the formula Rate $= \frac{\Delta[B]}{\Delta t}$.

b. Plot all the data from the table, either by hand or by using a graphing program. Then estimate the slope of the tangent line at 10.0 s with a "rise over run" calculation.

REACTION RATES AND RATE LAWS

You now know that the rate of a reaction depends upon the concentration of the reactant or reactants. The basic mathematical expression for this relationship is called a **rate law**. Rate laws include a proportionality constant called a **rate constant, k**, and a term for the concentration of each reactant raised to the power of its order. The following rate law is for the very basic reaction aA → products,

$$\text{Rate} = -\frac{1}{a}\frac{\Delta[\text{A}]}{\Delta t} = k[\text{A}]^n \qquad (14.2)$$

where a represents the coefficient in the balanced chemical equation and *does not appear in the rate law*. The rate constant, k, is determined experimentally. The units of k depend on the **reaction order, n**, which is also determined experimentally. Common values for n are 0, 1, and 2, although negative and fractional values are possible. When $n = 0$, the reaction is **zero order** with respect to A, and when $n = 1$, the reaction is **first order** with respect to A. When $n = 2$, the reaction is **second order** with respect to A.

When a reaction has multiple reactants, each reactant has its own order, and the **overall reaction order** is the sum of the orders with respect to each reactant.

For the generic reaction aA + bB → products, start with the following general rate law,

$$\text{Rate} = -\frac{1}{a}\frac{\Delta[\text{A}]}{\Delta t} = k[\text{A}]^n[\text{B}]^m \qquad (14.3)$$

then determine the values of k, n, and m experimentally. If you found that both n and m were equal to 1, you would say that the reaction is first order with respect to each reactant and second order overall. The reaction order for each reactant describes how the rate of the reaction responds to or depends upon changes in the concentration of that reactant.

In first-order reactions, $n = 1$, the rate law is simply rate $= k[\text{A}]$. When the concentration of the reactant A increases by a factor of 2, the rate also increases by a factor of 2. As first-order reactions continue, their rates decrease as the reactant is used up. The rate at half the initial concentration will be half of the initial rate.

In a second-order reaction with a single reactant, $n = 2$ and rate $= k[\text{A}]^2$. When the concentration of A is doubled, the rate of the reaction increases by a factor of $2^2 = 4$. Consequently, reaction rates of second-order reactions increase greatly when the concentration of the reactant is doubled but also decrease very quickly when the concentration drops. The reaction rate at one-half of the initial concentration of reactant is one-quarter of the initial reaction rate.

In zero-order reactions, changing the concentration of the reactant has no effect on the rate of the reaction. Figure 14.8 illustrates the effect of reaction order on the concentration of a reactant over time.

Example 14.3

The rate law for the reaction aA + bB → cC + dD is shown below:

$$\text{Rate} = k[\text{A}]^2[\text{B}]$$

At certain concentrations of A and B, the reaction has an initial rate of 0.220 M/s. Calculate the new initial rate when the concentration of A is doubled and the concentration of B is tripled.

Solution

The reaction is second order in A, so doubling the concentration of A will increase the reaction rate by a factor of $2^2 = 4$.

The reaction is first order in B, so tripling the concentration of will increase the reaction rate by a factor of $3^1 = 3$.

Therefore, the original rate must increase by a factor of $4 \times 3 = 12$.

$$\frac{\text{New rate}}{\text{Old rate}} = \frac{k[2\text{A}]^2[3\text{B}]}{k[\text{A}]^2[\text{B}]} = 12$$

$$\text{New rate} = 12(\text{Old rate}) = 12(0.220\ \text{M/s}) = 2.64\ \text{M/s}$$

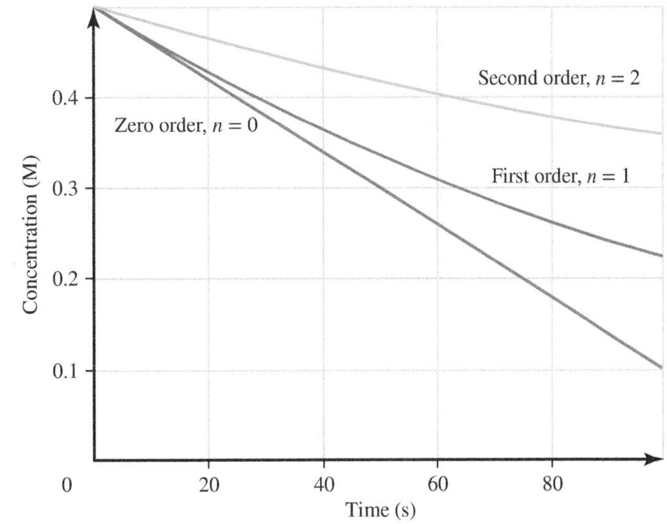

FIGURE 14.8 Effect of Reaction Order on Rate

This graph shows the change in concentration of reactant over time for reactions of different reaction order (n) but with identical rate constants (k). For the zero-order reaction, there is no change in the rate of disappearance of reactant over time, even though the reactant concentration is decreasing. The first- and second-order reactions show a slowing of the reaction rate (reactant disappears more slowly) as the reactant is used up. Notice that the second-order reaction's rate slows in a more pronounced manner as the reactant concentration decreases.

PRACTICE PROBLEM 14.3

The rate law for the reaction $a\text{A} + b\text{B} \rightarrow c\text{C} + d\text{D}$ is rate $= k[\text{A}]^2[\text{B}]$. At certain concentrations of A and B, the initial rate is 0.110 M/s. What is the new initial rate when the concentration of

a. A is unchanged and B is doubled?
b. both A and B are doubled?
c. A is tripled and B is doubled?

Hint: Each case involves doubling [B]. The reaction is first order in B, so when [B] doubles, the rate doubles. If [A] also changes by some factor, the rate changes even further, by the square of that factor (because the reaction is second order in A).

DETERMINING REACTION ORDER

Reaction orders are determined by carefully measuring a reaction's initial rate at different concentrations of the reactant, while keeping all other conditions unchanged. For example, the general rate law for the reaction $a\text{A} \rightarrow$ products is given by Equation 14.2.

$$\text{Rate} = -\frac{1}{a}\frac{\Delta[\text{A}]}{\Delta t} = k[\text{A}]^n$$

You can use the data in Table 14.1 to determine the values of n and k.

Take a close look at the data in the table. Note that the concentration of A doubles between experiments 1 and 2 and again between experiments 2 and 3. Notice, also, that the rate of experiment 2 is double the rate of experiment 1, and that the rate of experiment 3 is double the rate of experiment 2.

TABLE 14.1 Rate Data

Experiment	[A] (M)	Initial Rate (M/s)
1	0.050	3.14×10^{-2}
2	0.100	6.28×10^{-2}
3	0.200	0.125

$$\frac{\text{Rate}_2}{\text{Rate}_1} = \frac{6.28 \times 10^{-2}\ \text{M/s}}{3.14 \times 10^{-2}\ \text{M/s}} = 2.00$$

$$\frac{[\text{A}]_2}{[\text{A}]_1} = \frac{0.100\ \text{M}}{0.050\ \text{M}} = 2.0$$

Since both concentration and rate increase by the same factor, the value of n must be 1. For this reaction, the reaction rate is proportional to [A] raised to the first power, $[\text{A}]^1$. Thus, the rate law for this reaction is Rate $= k[\text{A}]^1 = k[\text{A}]$.

This equation can then be rearranged to show that $k = \text{Rate}/[\text{A}]$. You can now use the data for any one experiment to determine the value of the rate constant as follows:

$$k = \frac{\text{Rate}}{[\text{A}]}$$

$$k = \frac{3.14 \times 10^{-2}\ \text{M/s}}{0.050\ \text{M}} = 0.63\ \text{s}^{-1}$$

The unit M cancels, leaving reciprocal seconds, s^{-1}, as the unit for this rate constant. All first-order rate

TABLE 14.2 Rate Data

Experiment	[A] (M)	[B] (M)	Initial Rate (M/s)
1	0.0250	0.0250	2.04×10^{-3}
2	0.0500	0.0250	8.16×10^{-3}
3	0.0500	0.0500	1.63×10^{-2}
4	0.100	0.100	0.130

constants have units of s^{-1}. The final form of the rate law for this reaction is shown below:

$$\text{Rate} = (0.63\ \text{s}^{-1})[\text{A}]$$

Rate constants vary with temperature, which is why the data used to determine a rate law must be collected at a specific temperature that does not change from one experiment to the next.

Another common generic reaction, $a\text{A} + b\text{B} \rightarrow$ products, has the following rate law:

$$\text{Rate} = k[\text{A}]^n[\text{B}]^m$$

Table 14.2 contains rate data collected by measuring the amount of product produced per second at a constant temperature. Examine the rate data for each reactant separately to determine the values of m and n and then determine the rate constant.

By comparing experiments 1 and 2, you can determine how the concentration of A affects the reaction rate, because [A] changes between these two experiments, but [B] is held constant.

$$\frac{\text{Rate}_2}{\text{Rate}_1} = \frac{k[\text{A}]_2^n}{k[\text{A}]_1^n}$$

$$\frac{8.16 \times 10^{-3}\ \text{M/s}}{2.04 \times 10^{-3}\ \text{M/s}} = \frac{k(0.0500\ \text{M})^n}{k(0.0250\ \text{M})^n}$$

$$4 = 2^n$$

$$n = 2$$

The data show that when [A] doubles, the rate increases by a factor of 4. This corresponds to $n = 2$. For this reaction, then, the rate is proportional to the concentration of A raised to the second power, $[\text{A}]^2$. So far, the rate law for this reaction is:

$$\text{Rate} = k[\text{A}]^2[\text{B}]^m$$

To determine how [B] affects the rate, you must compare the data from experiments 2 and 3, because [B] changes between these two experiments, and [A] is held constant.

$$\frac{\text{Rate}_3}{\text{Rate}_2} = \frac{k[\text{B}]_3^m}{k[\text{B}]_2^m}$$

$$\frac{1.63 \times 10^{-2}\ \text{M/s}}{8.16 \times 10^{-3}\ \text{M/s}} = \frac{k(0.0500\ \text{M})^m}{k(0.0250\ \text{M})^m}$$

$$2 = 2^m$$

$$m = 1$$

In this case, when [B] doubles, the rate also doubles, indicating that $m = 1$. The rate is proportional to the concentration of B raised to the first power, $[\text{B}]^1$, or [B]. Insert the values of n and m into the general rate equation to yield the specific rate law for the reaction:

$$\text{Rate} = k[\text{A}]^2[\text{B}]$$

Thus, the reaction is second order with respect to A and first order with respect to B, making it a third-order reaction overall.

This specific rate law and the data from any one experiment in Table 14.2 can now be used to determine the value of the rate constant. Below, the data from experiment 2, where $[\text{A}] = 0.0500$ M, $[\text{B}] = 0.0250$ M, and Rate $= 8.16 \times 10^{-3}$ M/s, are used to yield a value for the rate constant:

$$k = \frac{\text{Rate}}{[\text{A}]^2[\text{B}]} = \frac{8.16 \times 10^{-3}\ \text{M/s}}{(0.0500\ \text{M})^2(0.0250\ \text{M})}$$

$$k = 131\ \text{M}^{-2}\text{s}^{-1}$$

According to this calculation, third-order rate constants have the units $\text{M}^{-2}\text{s}^{-1}$. The final form of the rate law for this reaction is shown here:

$$\text{Rate} = (131\ \text{M}^{-2}\text{s}^{-1})[\text{A}]^2[\text{B}]$$

The next example involves another general chemical reaction with two reactants and the same general rate law.

$$a\text{A} + b\text{B} \rightarrow \text{product}$$

$$\text{Rate} = \frac{\Delta[\text{product}]}{\Delta t} = k[\text{A}]^n[\text{B}]^m$$

Table 14.3 lists rate data for this new reaction, obtained at a constant temperature.

The rate data in experiments 1 and 2 show that when [A] doubles and [B] is constant, the rate quadruples, indicating that $n = 2$. However, the rate data in experiments 2 and 3 show that when [B] doubles and [A] is constant, there is *no change* in the rate. This corresponds to $m = 0$. Thus, this reaction is second order

TABLE 14.3 Rate Data

Experiment	[A] (M)	[B] (M)	Initial Rate (M/s)
1	0.0250	0.0250	1.15×10^{-5}
2	0.0500	0.0250	4.60×10^{-5}
3	0.0500	0.0500	4.60×10^{-5}

TABLE 14.4 Summary of Reaction Orders and Rate Laws

Reaction order	Example Chemical Equation	Example Rate Law	Units of *k*
0	$aA \rightarrow$ products	Rate = $k[A]^0$ Rate = k	$M \cdot s^{-1}$
1	$aA \rightarrow$ products	Rate = $k[A]$	s^{-1}
2	$aA \rightarrow$ products	Rate = $k[A]^2$	$M^{-1}s^{-1}$
2	$aA + bB \rightarrow$ products	Rate = $k[A][B]$	$M^{-1}s^{-1}$
3	$aA + bB \rightarrow$ products	Rate = $k[A]^2[B]$	$M^{-2}s^{-1}$

with respect to A and zero order with respect to B, making it second order overall:

$$\text{Rate} = k[A]^2[B]^0$$
$$\text{Rate} = k[A]^2$$

You can now determine the rate constant by rearranging the rate law and using data from a single experiment, experiment 2 in this case. Second-order rate constants always have the units $\frac{1}{M \cdot s}$, which is also written as $M^{-1}s^{-1}$.

$$k = \frac{\text{Rate}}{[A]^2} = \frac{4.60 \times 10^{-5}\ M/s}{(0.0500\ M)^2}$$
$$k = 1.8 \times 10^{-2}\ M^{-1}s^{-1}$$

Table 14.4 summarizes the basic types of rate laws and the corresponding units for the rate constants.

Figure 14.9 and the next example problem demonstrate the techniques discussed above for the experimental determination of order, rate law, and rate constant.

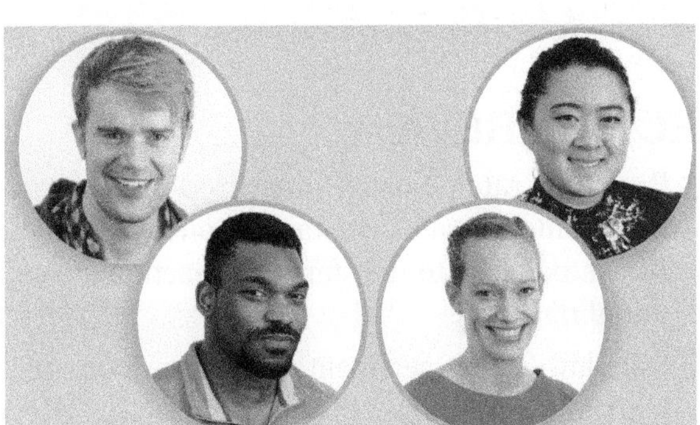

Steve Lemon, Macmillan Learning

FIGURE 14.9 Video Tutorial: Concentration and Rate

NOTE: You need to be online to access this video.

This video shows how to determine a rate law and rate constant from concentration and rate data.

Example 14.4

Nitrogen dioxide gas decomposes at high temperatures according to this reaction.

$$2\ NO_2(g) \rightarrow 2\ NO(g) + O_2(g)$$

The following data were collected at 300°C.

Experiment	$[NO_2]$ (M)	Initial Rate (M/s)
1	0.0075	3.01×10^{-6}
2	0.010	5.40×10^{-5}
3	0.020	2.15×10^{-4}

Determine the reaction order and the value of the rate constant.

Solution

A comparison of the rates for experiments 3 and 2 shows that the rate increases by a factor of 4 while the concentration of NO_2 doubles. This indicates that the reaction is second order with respect to NO_2, and has the following rate law:

$$\text{Rate} = k[NO_2]^2$$

Rearranging the rate equation to solve for *k* and using the specific data from experiment 2 (although any of the three experiments would work) gives

$$k = \frac{\text{Rate}}{[NO_2]^2} = \frac{5.40 \times 10^{-5}\ M/s}{(0.010\ M)^2}$$
$$k = 0.54\ M^{-1}s^{-1}$$

PRACTICE PROBLEM 14.4

Cyclopropane, C_3H_6, is an unstable, cyclic molecule that rearranges to form propene rather slowly at room temperature, which is why the rates in the table are measured in molarity per *hour* and not in molarity per *second*.

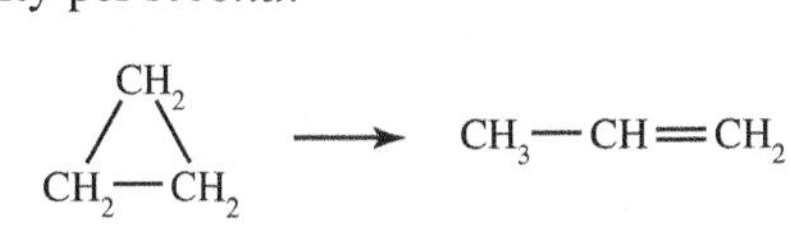

Cyclopropane Propene

Experiment	[cyclopropane] (M)	Rate (M/h)
1	0.31	0.017
2	0.16	0.0086
3	0.62	0.033

a. Write the rate law.
b. Determine the value of the rate constant.
c. Determine the reaction rate when the cyclopropane concentration is 0.44 M.

Hint:

a. The rate law has the form Rate = k[cyclopropane]^x, where x is the order. You just need to determine x to complete the rate law. Choose any two rows in the table, and determine the factor by which [cyclopropane] changes. By what factor does the rate change for those same two rows?
b. Once you have the complete rate law, you can use it as a formula. Pick any row of the table, plug those values into the rate law, and solve for k.
c. Once you have the rate law and the value of k, plug in 0.44 M for [cyclopropane] and solve for the rate.

Example 14.5

One component of photochemical smog is nitrogen dioxide, NO_2, which can be formed in the presence of ultraviolet light according to the following equation:

$$2\,NO(g) + O_2(g) \rightarrow 2\,NO_2(g)$$

Rate data for this reaction were measured at a constant temperature and appear in the table.

Experiment	[NO] (M)	$[O_2]$ (M)	Initial Rate (M/s)
1	0.0021	0.0032	8.8×10^{-5}
2	0.0021	0.0016	4.4×10^{-5}
3	0.0042	0.0016	1.8×10^{-4}

a. Determine the rate law for the reaction.
b. Determine the value of the rate constant.
c. Determine the rate of the reaction when [NO] = 0.0015 M and $[O_2]$ = 0.0024 M.

Solution

a. Comparing experiments 1 and 2 shows that the rate doubles when $[O_2]$ is doubled and [NO] is held constant. The reaction is, therefore, first order with respect to oxygen. Comparing experiments 2 and 3 shows that the rate increases by a factor of 4 when [NO] is doubled and $[O_2]$ is held constant. Thus, the reaction is second order with respect to NO, and third order overall.

$$\text{Rate} = k[NO]^2[O_2]$$

b. The rate constant is calculated here using the data from experiment 1. Since the data were recorded to only two significant figures, all calculations involving these data must be rounded to two significant figures.

$$k = \frac{\text{Rate}}{[NO]^2[O_2]}$$

$$k = \frac{8.8 \times 10^{-5}\ \text{M/s}}{(0.0021\ \text{M})^2(0.0032\ \text{M})}$$

$$k = 6.2 \times 10^3\ \text{M}^{-2}\text{s}^{-1}$$

c. Substitute the given concentration values into the rate law.

$$\text{Rate} = (6.2 \times 10^3\ \text{M}^{-2}\text{s}^{-1})[NO]^2[O_2]$$

$$\text{Rate} = (6.2 \times 10^3\ \text{M}^{-2}\text{s}^{-1})(0.0015\ \text{M})^2\,(0.0024\ \text{M})$$

$$\text{Rate} = 3.3 \times 10^{-5}\ \text{M}\cdot\text{s}^{-1}$$

PRACTICE PROBLEM 14.5

The explosive compound, nitryl fluoride, NO_2F, is formed by the reaction of nitrogen dioxide and fluorine.

$$2\,NO_2(g) + F_2(g) \rightarrow 2\,NO_2F(g)$$

Rate data for this reaction were measured at a constant temperature, and appear in the table.

Experiment	$[NO_2]$ (M)	$[F_2]$ (M)	Initial Rate (M/s)
1	0.00130	0.00479	2.16×10^{-4}
2	0.00259	0.00479	4.30×10^{-4}
3	0.00612	0.00123	2.61×10^{-4}
4	0.00612	0.00246	5.22×10^{-4}

a. Determine the rate law for the reaction.
b. Calculate the value of the rate constant.
c. Determine the rate when $[NO_2]$ = 0.00722 M and $[F_2]$ = 0.00479 M.

Hint:

a. The rate law has the form Rate = $k[NO_2]^n[F_2]^m$, where n and m are the orders with respect to each reactant. Choose two rows in the table where one reactant changes but the other does not. By what factor does the rate change for those same two rows?
b. Once you have the rate law with the proper orders, you can use it as a formula. Pick any row of the table, plug those values into the rate law and solve for k.
c. Once you have the rate law and the value of k, plug in the given concentrations and solve for the rate.

SECTION REVIEW

- Reaction rates can be measured as average or instantaneous rates. Instantaneous rates that are measured close to the start of a reaction are called initial rates.
- Rate laws are experimentally determined, mathematical relationships between the reaction rate and the concentrations of the reactants.
- For a reaction with a single reactant, A, rate = $k[A]^n$, where k is the rate constant and n is the order with respect to A as well as the overall reaction order.

- For a reaction with multiple reactants, A and B, rate = $k[A]^n[B]^m$, where k is the rate constant, n is the order with respect to A, and m is the order with respect to B.
- The order of the overall reaction is $n + m$, the sum of the orders with respect to each reactant.
- Common reaction orders are 0, 1, and 2. Negative and fractional orders are possible but less common.
- The units of the rate constant depend upon the overall reaction order.

14.3 Integrated Rate Laws and Half-Lives

GOALS

- Predict the concentration and time values of reactions using first- and second-order integrated rate laws.
- Graph data to identify the order of a reaction.
- Define and apply the terms *half-life*, *first-order reaction*, and *second-order reaction*.

Background Review

Chapter 0 Math Review: Section 0.5—Logarithms and Antilogs

Section 14.1 states that reaction rates decrease over time as the concentration of the reactants decreases (Figures 14.2 and 14.7) and that this decrease in concentration depends on the order of the reaction (Section 14.2, Figure 14.8). In this section you will learn how to use the integrated version of first- and second-order rate laws to predict the concentration of a reactant at any time and how to use the concentration of a reactant to determine how much time has passed since the start of the reaction. A brief discussion of integrated rate laws for zero-order reactions appears at the end of this section.

FIRST-ORDER REACTIONS: INTEGRATED RATE LAW

First-order reactions are reactions in which the rate of the reaction depends directly on the concentration of one reactant. You saw in Figure 14.8 that the decrease in reactant concentration over time in a first-order reaction is not linear. This makes it inconvenient to try to predict the reactant concentration at any future time or to know how long to allow a reaction to proceed to use up a certain percentage of the reactant. To be able to make these types of predictions, use the **integrated rate law**. Using calculus, a first-order rate law can be converted into an equation that can then be rearranged to follow the linear, $y = mx + b$, format.

First-order rate law: $-\dfrac{\Delta[A]}{\Delta t} = k[A]$

Integrated version of the rate law: $\ln\dfrac{[A]_t}{[A]_0} = -kt$

$y = mx + b$ format: $\ln[A]_t = -kt + \ln[A]_0$ (14.4)

In the integrated rate law, $[A]_t$, represents the concentration of the reactant at time t (any time after the start of the reaction), while $[A]_0$ is the initial concentration of the reactant. Plotting the natural logarithm of the reactant concentration, $\ln[A]_t$, versus time will give you a straight line (Figure 14.10).

The slope of that straight line (m) is equal to $-k$, giving you a second way to determine the rate constant for a reaction. For information and examples about how to calculate slope for linear data, see Section 0.7. For information and examples about natural logarithms, see Section 0.5.

Example 14.6

The thermal decomposition of phosphine, PH_3, displays first-order kinetics. The data listed in the table were collected at 680°C with $[PH_3]_0 = 2.50$ M. Notice that the data are recorded to three significant figures.

$$4\ PH_3 \rightarrow P_4 + 6\ H_2$$

Time (s)	$[PH_3]$ (M)
0	2.50
10.0	2.05
20.0	1.68
30.0	1.38
40.0	1.13

a. Determine the value of the rate constant.
b. Determine the concentration of phosphine remaining after 60.0 s.

Solution

a. There are two possible ways to find the rate constant. One method is to plug values directly into the first-order integrated rate law. $[A]_0 = 2.50$ M

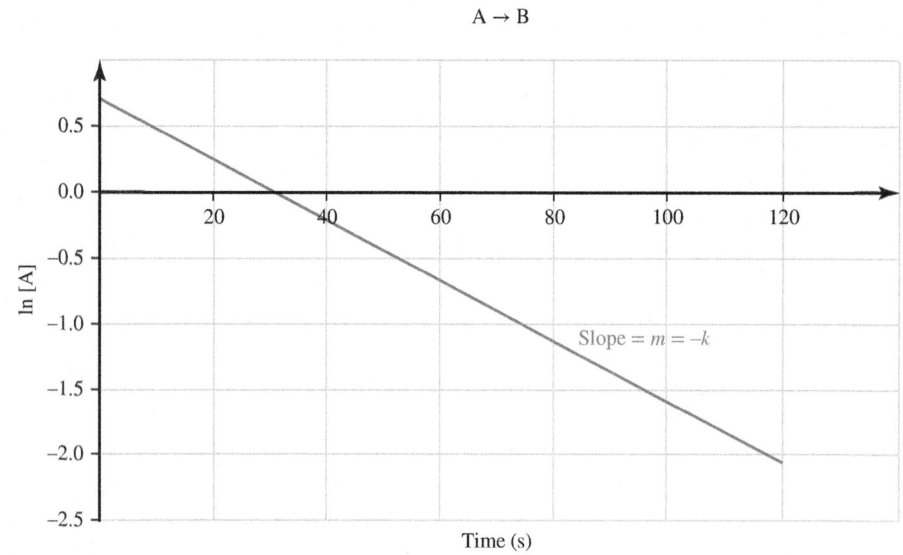

FIGURE 14.10 First-Order Reaction: ln[A] Versus *t*

For first-order reactions, a plot of ln[A] versus time yields a straight line with the slope equal to $-k$, utilizing the linear version of the integrated, first-order rate law, $\ln[A]_t = -kt + \ln[A]_0$.

is given in the first row of the table (at $t = 0$). Use any row of the table (other than the first row) for the values of t and $[A]_t$.

$$\ln[A]_t = -kt + \ln[A]_0$$
$$\ln(1.38\ M) = -k(30.0\ s) + \ln(2.50\ M)$$
$$k = 0.0198\ s^{-1}$$

The other method is to plot $\ln[PH_3]$ versus time and determine the slope of the line. You can do this by calculating rise over run as shown in Example 14.2 or by using graphing software, such as Microsoft Excel. The slope of the line is equal to $-k$.

$$m = 0.0198\ s^{-1} \quad k = 0.0198\ s^{-1}$$

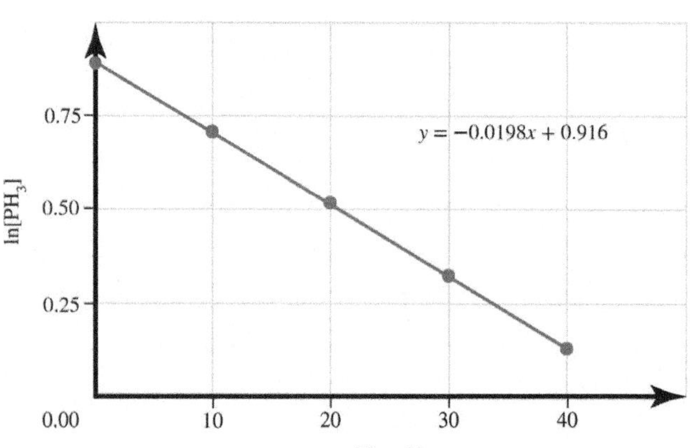

b. To determine the concentration of phosphine at a specific time, use the integrated rate law including the rate constant calculated in part (a). Recall that if $\ln x = y$, then $x = e^y$.

$$\ln[A]_t = -kt + \ln[A]_0$$
$$\ln[PH_3]_{60.0\ s} = -(0.0198\ s^{-1})(60.0\ s) + \ln(2.50\ M)$$
$$\ln[PH_3]_{60.0\ s} = -1.19 + 0.916 = -0.27$$
$$[PH_3]_{60.0\ s} = e^{-0.27} = 0.76\ M$$

PRACTICE PROBLEM 14.6

Data were collected for the first-order reaction $A \rightarrow B$ at 500°C.

Time (s)	[A] (M)
0.00	0.350
2.00	0.308
3.00	0.289
4.00	0.271
5.00	0.254
10.00	0.185

Use the data in the table to determine

a. the value of the rate constant.
b. [A] at 30 s.

Hint: For both parts, plug values into the first-order integrated rate law:

$$\ln[A]_t = -kt + \ln[A]_0$$

a. Get $[A]_0$ from the first row of the table, and use any other row for the values of t and $[A]_t$. Solve for k.
b. Again, get $[A]_0$ from the first row of the table, use the value of k you calculated in part (a), and use the given value of t ($t = 30$ s). Solve for $[A]_t$.

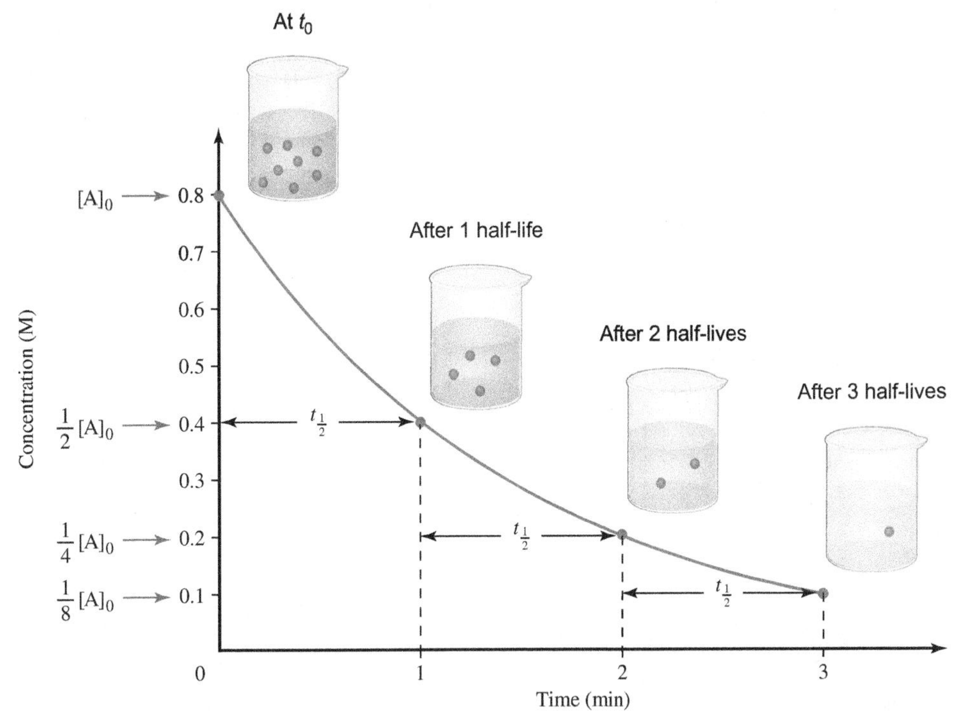

FIGURE 14.11 Half-Life for a First-Order Reaction

This graph depicts a first-order reaction with a half-life of $t_{1/2} = 1$ min. Notice that the increment of change on the vertical axis gets smaller and smaller while the increment of change on the horizontal axis stays the same.

FIRST-ORDER REACTIONS: HALF-LIFE

Another way to describe the rate of a reaction is by using its **half-life**. The half-life, $t_{1/2}$, of a reaction is the time it takes for one-half of the reactant to be used up. The graph in Figure 14.11 shows that the concentration of the reactant decreases by a factor of 2 with each half-life.

The integrated rate law can be used to develop an expression for $t_{1/2}$ for a first-order reaction as follows:

Integrated rate law: $$\ln\frac{[A]_t}{[A]_0} = -kt$$

Rearrange to solve for t: $$t = \frac{1}{k}\ln\frac{[A]_0}{[A]_t}$$

Substitute definition of $[A]_t$ at $t_{1/2}$: $$t = \frac{1}{k}\ln\frac{[A]_0}{\frac{1}{2}[A]_0}$$

Simplify: $$t = \frac{\ln 2}{k} \qquad (14.5)$$

For *first-order reactions*, the half-life is *constant* and is *independent* of the initial concentration of the reactant. Thus, the time needed for a reactant's concentration to drop from 0.8 M to 0.4 M is exactly the same as that needed to drop from 0.2 M to 0.1 M. Notice, too, that $t_{1/2}$ is *inversely proportional* to k. That is, the slower the reaction, the longer the half-life. The relationship between $t_{1/2}$ and k gives you yet another way to determine the rate constant of a first-order reaction, by measuring its half-life. When you study nuclear chemistry in Chapter 20, you will apply first-order rate laws and half-lives to nuclear decay processes.

> The half-life of a first-order reaction depends on only the rate constant and is inversely proportional to the rate constant.

Example 14.7

A first-order reaction has a half-life of 63.4 min at 225°C.

a. Calculate the rate constant for the reaction.
b. Determine the percentage of reactant remaining after 25.0 min at 225°C.

Solution

Why is the temperature included in these problems when it is not used in the calculations? Rate constants are temperature dependent. That means that the value of the rate constant in the problem is only true at the specified temperature. Kinetic studies always include the temperature at which the experiments were carried out.

a. For a first-order reaction, the rate constant and half-life are inversely proportional to each other:

$$t_{1/2} = \frac{\ln 2}{k}$$

$$k = \frac{\ln 2}{t_{1/2}}$$

$$k = \frac{\ln 2}{63.4 \text{ min}} = 0.0109 \text{ min}^{-1}$$

b. Use the integrated rate law to determine the fraction of reactant remaining, which is expressed mathematically as the ratio $[A]_t/[A]_0$.

$$\ln\frac{[A]_t}{[A]_0} = -kt$$

$$\ln\frac{[A]_t}{[A]_0} = (-0.0109 \text{ min}^{-1})(25.0 \text{ min}) = -0.2725$$

$$\frac{[A]_t}{[A]_0} = e^{-0.2725} = 0.761$$

The ratio $[A]_t/[A]_0$ is equal to 0.761, which is the same as 76.1/100 or 76.1%. That tells you that 76% of the reactant is present after 25 min of the reaction. Note that the final answer has been rounded to three significant figures, based upon the number of significant figures present in the original data.

PRACTICE PROBLEM 14.7

A first-order reaction has a half-life of 28.0 seconds at 655°C.

a. Calculate the rate constant for the reaction.
b. Determine the percentage of reactant remaining after 35.0 seconds at that same temperature.

Hint: Start by using the half-life formula to find k. For a first-order reaction, $t_{1/2} = \frac{\ln 2}{k}$. Then use the first-order integrated rate law to find $[A]_t/[A]_0$ (the fraction remaining), and convert that fraction to a percentage by multiplying by 100.

SECOND-ORDER REACTIONS: INTEGRATED RATE LAW

Second-order reactions come in two types, one in which the reaction rate depends on the concentration of a single reactant raised to the second power, rate = $k[A]^2$, and another in which the reaction rate depends on the concentrations of two reactants, rate = $k[A]^n[B]^m$, where $n + m = 2$. The focus here is on the less complex type, the second-order reactions with a single reactant in the rate law, rate = $k[A]^2$.

Again, calculus is used to obtain the integrated rate law for the second-order reaction.

Second-order rate law: $$-\frac{\Delta[A]}{\Delta t} = k[A]^2$$

Integrated rate law: $$\frac{1}{[A]_t} = kt + \frac{1}{[A]_0} \quad (14.6)$$

To obtain a linear graph, plot 1/[A] versus time with the slope of the resulting line being equal to the value of the rate constant.

Example 14.8

Data for the second-order reaction A → products were collected and are listed in the table below.

t (s)	[A] (M)
0	0.750
5.00	0.728
10.0	0.708
20.0	0.670
30.0	0.636
40.0	0.605
50.0	0.577

a. Determine the value of the rate constant.
b. Determine the concentration of the reactant at 90 seconds after the reaction has begun.

Solution

a. Since this is a second-order reaction, the appropriate integrated rate law is $\frac{1}{[A]_t} = kt + \frac{1}{[A]_0}$

Calculate values of 1/[A] (shown in the table below) and plot 1/[A] versus time to obtain a straight line, with a slope equal to the rate constant, k. Determine the slope of the line by using a rise over run calculation or graphing software.

t (s)	[A] (M)	1/[A] (M^{-1})
0.00	0.750	1.33
5.00	0.728	1.37
10.0	0.708	1.41
20.0	0.670	1.49
30.0	0.636	1.57
40.0	0.605	1.65
50.0	0.577	1.73

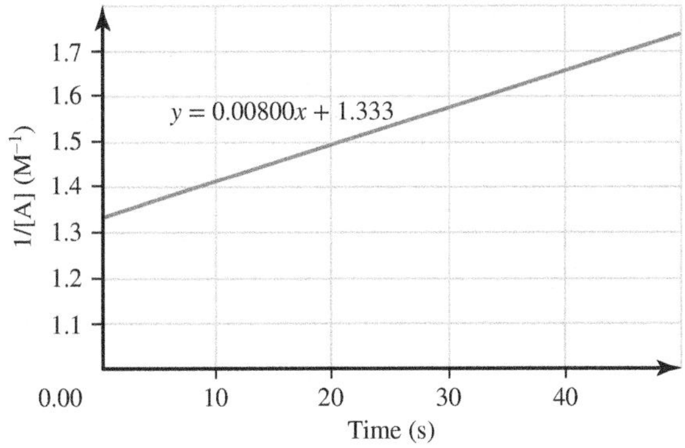

The slope is $0.00800\ M^{-1}s^{-1}$.

b. According to the table, the initial concentration, [A] at $t = 0$, is 0.750 M. Use the integrated rate law and the rate constant calculated previously to determine $[A]_t$ at $t = 90$ s.

$$\frac{1}{[A]_t} = kt + \frac{1}{[A]_0}$$

$$\frac{1}{[A]_t} = 0.00800\ M^{-1}s^{-1}(90\ s) + \frac{1}{0.750}\ M^{-1}$$

$$\frac{1}{[A]_t} = 2.05\ M^{-1}$$

$$[A]_t = 0.488\ M$$

PRACTICE PROBLEM 14.8

The rate constant for the second-order reaction of nitryl bromide is $1.55\ M^{-1}s^{-1}$ at 20°C.

$$2\ NOBr(g) \rightarrow 2\ NO(g) + Br_2(l)$$

Given that the reaction starts with [NOBr] = 0.0480 M,

a. calculate [NOBr] after 10.0 s.
b. determine how long it will take to reduce the initial concentration of NOBr by 90.0%.

Hint: Use the second-order integrated rate law, $\frac{1}{[A]_t} = kt + \frac{1}{[A]_0}$ for both parts. In part (a), you are solving for $[A]_t$. In part (b), you are solving for t. If 90% has reacted, then 10% remains, so use 10% of 0.0480 M (0.10×0.0480 M) as the value of $[A]_t$.

SECOND-ORDER REACTIONS: HALF-LIFE

Second-order reactions have half-lives as well. The half-life relationship for a second-order reaction is obtained as follows:

Integrated rate law: $$\frac{1}{[A]_t} = kt + \frac{1}{[A]_0}$$

Substitute $\frac{1}{2}[A]_0$ for $[A]_t$: $$\frac{1}{\frac{1}{2}[A]_0} = kt_{1/2} + \frac{1}{[A]_0}$$

Rearrange and simplify: $$t_{1/2} = \frac{1}{k[A]_0} \quad (14.7)$$

The half-life of a second-order reaction depends upon both the rate constant and the initial concentration of the reactant, $[A]_0$ (it is inversely proportional to both).

Example 14.9

The compound AB decomposes via a second-order process with a rate constant equal to $5.13 \times 10^{-4}\ M^{-1}s^{-1}$ at 35°C.

a. Calculate the half-life of the reaction with an initial concentration of [AB] = 0.230 M.
b. This same reaction has a half-life of 45.0 minutes when carried out at 55°C with an initial concentration of 0.230 M. What is the rate constant at 55°C?
c. Compare the rate constants at the two temperatures.

Solution

a. The problem indicates that the reaction follows second-order kinetics. Therefore, use the half-life expression for a second-order reaction and substitute the values for the rate constant and initial concentration given in the problem statement.

$$t_{1/2} = \frac{1}{k[A]_0}$$

$$t_{1/2} = \frac{1}{(5.13 \times 10^{-4}\ M^{-1}s^{-1})(0.230\ M)}$$

$$t_{1/2} = 8.48 \times 10^3\ s$$

The half-life of this reaction at 35°C is 8480 seconds. This value might have more meaning to you if expressed in hours, but this is not required by the problem.

$$8.48 \times 10^3\ s\left(\frac{1\ min}{60\ s}\right)\left(\frac{1\ h}{60\ min}\right) = 2.35\ h$$

b. The value of the rate constant depends upon the temperature. To calculate the rate constant at the higher temperature, rearrange the half-life expression to solve for k.

$$k = \frac{1}{t_{1/2}[A]_0}$$

$$k = \frac{1}{(45.0\ min)(0.230\ M)} = 0.0966\ M^{-1}min^{-1}$$

c. Because this rate constant is expressed in terms of reciprocal minutes, it is difficult to compare it with the rate constant at the lower temperature. Convert the new rate constant to reciprocal seconds (alternatively, you could convert the original rate constant to reciprocal minutes for the comparison):

$$0.0966\ \text{M}^{-1}\text{min}^{-1}\left(\frac{1\ \text{min}}{60\ \text{s}}\right) = 1.61 \times 10^{-3}\ \text{M}^{-1}\text{s}^{-1}$$

Comparing two values is most easily done as a ratio.

$$\frac{k_{55°\text{C}}}{k_{35°\text{C}}} = \frac{1.61 \times 10^{-3}\ \text{M}^{-1}\text{s}^{-1}}{5.13 \times 10^{-4}\ \text{M}^{-1}\text{s}^{-1}} = 3.13$$

Thus, raising the temperature by 20°C approximately triples the rate of this reaction.

PRACTICE PROBLEM 14.9

A second-order reaction was started with 0.050 M reactant. When checked exactly 35 minutes later, 0.025 M reactant remained. Calculate the rate constant for the reaction.

Hint: Notice that you have been given the half-life. Since 0.025 M is exactly half of 0.050 M, $t_{1/2} = 35$ min. Use the second-order half-life formula to find k.

$$t_{1/2} = \frac{1}{k[\text{A}]_0}$$

where $[\text{A}]_0$ is the initial concentration.

ZERO-ORDER REACTIONS: INTEGRATED RATE LAW

In the case of a zero-order reaction A → products, the rate is equal to the rate constant, Rate = $k[\text{A}]^0 = k$. Using calculus, a zero-order rate law can be converted into a linear equation.

Rate law:

$$-\frac{\Delta[\text{A}]}{\Delta t} = k$$

Linear format:

$$[\text{A}]_t = -kt + [\text{A}]_0$$

The half-life expression for a zero-order reaction is obtained by substituting $\frac{1}{2}[\text{A}]_0$ for $[\text{A}]_t$ and rearranging.

Substitution:

$$\frac{1}{2}[\text{A}]_0 = -kt + [\text{A}]_0$$

Rearranged and simplified:

$$t_{1/2} = \frac{[\text{A}]_0}{2k} \tag{14.8}$$

The half-life of a zero-order reaction depends upon both the rate constant and the initial concentration of the reactant, $[\text{A}]_0$. But unlike the second-order half-life, the zero-order half-life is *directly* proportional to the initial reactant concentration.

GRAPHICAL DETERMINATION OF REACTION ORDER

So far you have used the integrated rate laws to determine the rate constant, k. You can also use them to determine whether a reaction follows first- or second-order kinetics. Simply take the concentration versus time data for a reaction and plot the data in two ways: (1) ln [reactant] versus time and (2) 1/[reactant] versus time. If the natural log plot is linear, the reaction is first order, at least with respect to that reactant. If the reciprocal plot is linear, then the reaction is second order with respect to that reactant. Table 14.5 summarizes the

TABLE 14.5 Summary of Rate Laws, A → products

Reaction Order	Rate Law	Units of k	Integrated Rate Law	Straight Line Plot	Half-Life Expression
0	Rate = $k[\text{A}]^0$	$\text{M}\cdot\text{s}^{-1}$	$[\text{A}]_t = -kt + [\text{A}]_0$	[A] vs. t slope = $-k$	$t_{1/2} = \frac{[\text{A}]_0}{2k}$
1	Rate = $k[\text{A}]$	s^{-1}	$\ln[\text{A}]_t = -kt + \ln[\text{A}]_0$	ln[A] vs. t slope = $-k$	$t_{1/2} = \frac{\ln 2}{k}$
2	Rate = $k[\text{A}]^2$	$\text{M}^{-1}\text{s}^{-1}$	$\frac{1}{[\text{A}]_t} = kt + \frac{1}{[\text{A}]_0}$	1/[A] vs. t slope = k	$t_{1/2} = \frac{1}{k[\text{A}]_0}$

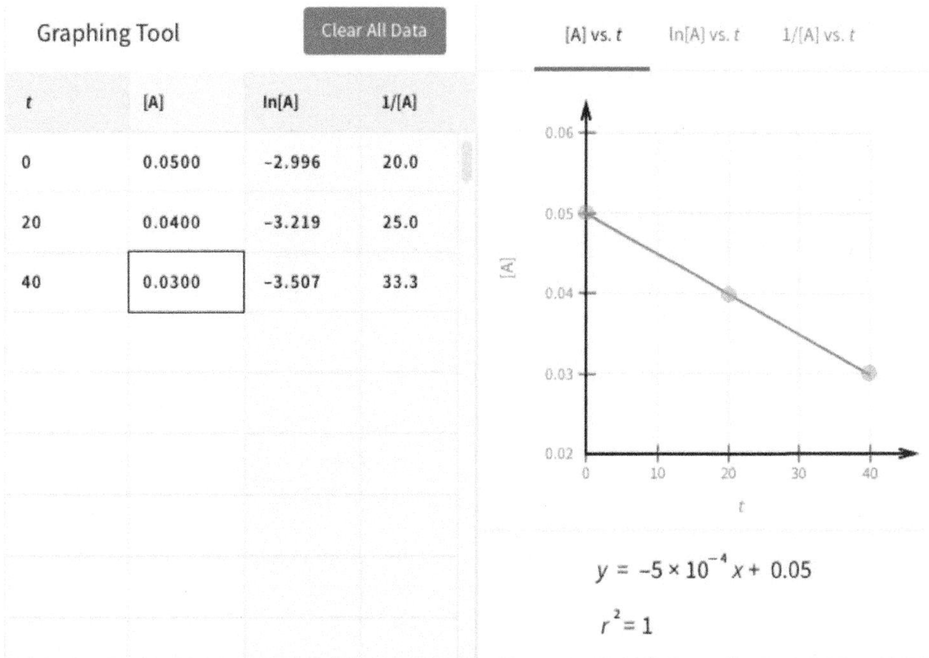

FIGURE 14.12 Kinetics Graphing Tool

NOTE: You need to be online to access this video.

Enter the time and concentration data given in any relevant homework or example problem (such as Example 14.10). Identify which of the three graphs (shown in different tabs) is linear (or closest to linear), and consult Table 14.5 for the corresponding order. The r^2 value is a measure of how linear the data are, where $r^2 = 1$ is perfectly linear. The equation of the line provides the slope value, which you can use to determine k. Consult Table 14.5 for the relation between slope and k for a particular reaction order.

basic relationships between reactant concentration, rate constants, and half-lives. It includes zero-order reactions, even though these have not been discussed in detail. As you can see from the table, a plot of [reactant] versus time is linear for a zero-order reaction.

The Kinetics Graphing Tool (Figure 14.12) allows you to plot concentration and time data, which may come in handy if you do not have access to or do not know how to use graphing software. Use it when solving homework and practice problems that provide these data and that ask you determine the reaction order and/or rate constant. Try it with the data from Example 14.6 and again with the data from Example 14.8 to illustrate the difference between a first-order reaction and a second-order reaction.

Figure 14.13 and the subsequent example problem demonstrate how to determine reaction order graphically.

Steve Lemon, Macmillan Learning

FIGURE 14.13 Video Tutorial: Concentration and Time

NOTE: You need to be online to access this video.

This video shows how to determine reaction order and rate constant from concentration and time data.

Example 14.10

Data were collected for the reaction A → products by monitoring the concentration of the reactant, A, over time.

t (s)	[A] (M)
0	0.350
3.00×10^2	0.282
6.00×10^2	0.236
9.00×10^2	0.203
1.20×10^3	0.178
1.50×10^3	0.159
1.80×10^3	0.143

a. Determine the reaction order with respect to A.
b. Calculate the rate constant for this reaction.

Solution

a. To determine the reaction order, plot the data in three different ways using the graphing tool in Figure 14.12. Option (1) plots [A] versus t to test for zero order, option (2) plots ln[A] versus t to test for first order, and option (3) plots $\frac{1}{[A]}$ versus t to test for second order. Use the linear graph and the information in Table 14.5 to help identify the order of the reaction.

t (s)	[A] (M)	1/[A]	ln[A]
0	0.350	2.86	−1.05
3.00×10^2	0.282	3.55	−1.27
6.00×10^2	0.236	4.24	−1.44
9.00×10^2	0.203	4.93	−1.59
1.20×10^3	0.178	5.62	−1.73
1.50×10^3	0.159	6.31	−1.84
1.80×10^3	0.143	7.00	−1.95

Option 1

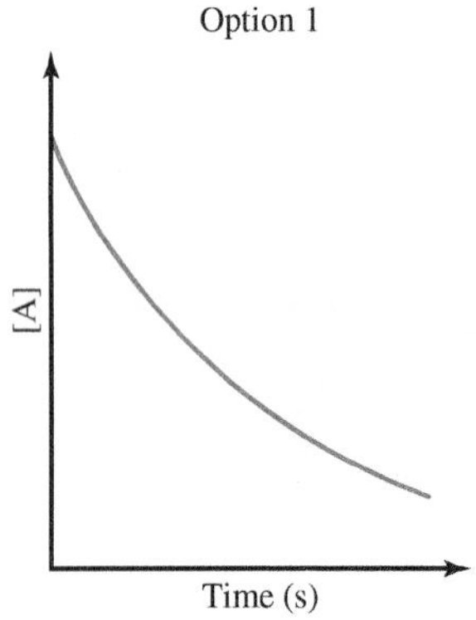

Option 2

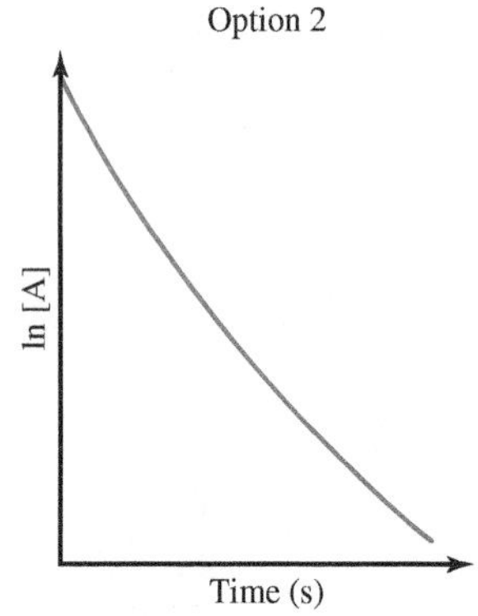

Option 3

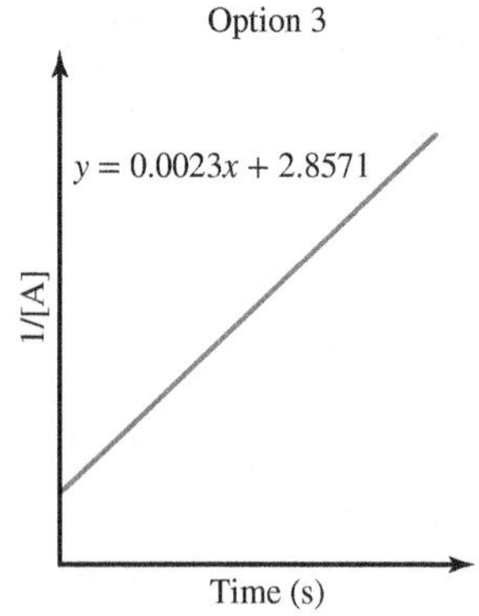

The graph of $\frac{1}{[A]}$ versus t is the only linear graph, indicating that this reaction is second order with respect to A.

b. Now that the reaction order is known, plug values into the appropriate integrated rate law.

$$\frac{1}{[A]_t} = kt + \frac{1}{[A]_0}$$

$$\frac{1}{0.282\text{ M}} = k(3.00 \times 10^2\text{ s}) + \frac{1}{0.350\text{ M}}$$

$$k = 0.00230\text{ M}^{-1}\text{s}^{-1}$$

Alternatively, use a rise over run calculation or the graphing tool in Figure 14.12 to determine the slope of the line. The graphing tool yields a best-fit line of $y = 0.0023x + 2.86$. The slope and, therefore, the rate constant, is equal to $k = 0.00230\text{ M}^{-1}\text{s}^{-1}$.

PRACTICE PROBLEM 14.10

Data were collected for the reaction A → products by monitoring the concentration of the reactant, A, over time and are listed in the table below.

t (s)	[A] (M)
0.0	1.50
10.0	0.963
20.0	0.464
30.0	0.224
40.0	0.108
50.0	0.0520
60.0	0.0251

a. Determine the order with respect to A.
b. Determine the rate constant of the reaction.

Hint: Start by making three plots, [A] versus t, ln[A] versus t, and 1/[A] versus t, to see which is linear. You'll need to expand the data table, making new columns for ln[A] and 1/[A], and filling in those values.

SECTION REVIEW

- For zero-order reactions, the integrated rate law is $[A]_t = -kt + [A]_0$ and the half-life expression is $t_{1/2} = \frac{[A]_0}{2k}$.
- For first-order reactions, the integrated rate law is $\ln[A]_t = -kt + \ln[A]_0$ and the half-life expression is $t_{1/2} = \frac{\ln 2}{k}$.
- For second-order reactions, the integrated rate law is $\frac{1}{[A]_t} = kt + \frac{1}{[A]_0}$ and the half-life expression is $t_{1/2} = \frac{k}{[A]_0}$.

- The integrated rate laws are used to determine the concentration of reactant at any time or the time needed to reach a certain concentration of reactant.
- Reaction order and the value of the rate constant can be determined graphically using the integrated rate laws.

14.4 Reaction Rates and Temperature: Activation Energy

GOALS

- Explain collision theory using appropriate terminology.
- Apply the Arrhenius equation to calculate activation energy and/or the value of the rate constant at various temperatures.

Background Review

Chapter 6 Thermochemistry: Section 6.4—Energy and Enthalpy

Chapter 10 Covalent Bonding: Section 10.6—Bond Enthalpy

As you learned at the beginning of this chapter, increasing temperature increases the rate of chemical reactions, and a certain amount of energy is needed to initiate a chemical reaction. In Section 14.2, you learned that rate constants are temperature-dependent. In this section you will learn about the other factors that determine the magnitude of the rate constant: activation energy, collision frequency, and collision orientation. You will also learn how to use the Arrhenius equation to calculate the activation energy and to predict the effect of a change in temperature on the rate constant for a chemical reaction.

ACTIVATION ENERGY

Figure 14.14 shows the progress of a reaction from reactants to products in terms of the potential energy of the molecules involved.

The reactant molecules must reach a higher energy state to begin the bond-breaking and bond-making processes that make up a chemical reaction. The minimum amount of energy needed to reach that state is

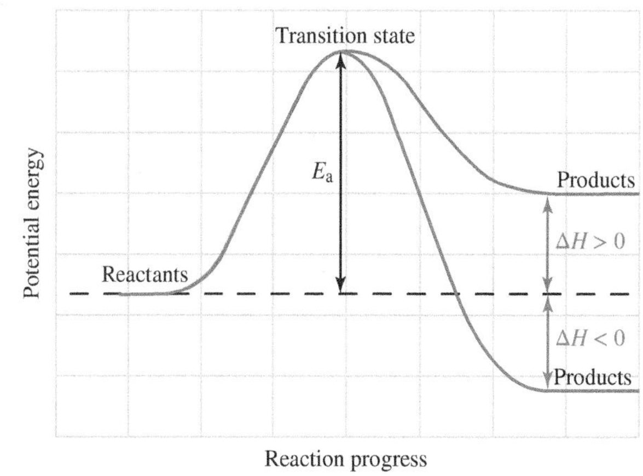

FIGURE 14.14 Energy Diagram for an Endothermic Reaction and an Exothermic Reaction

Activation energy, E_a, is the energy difference between the reactants and the transition state. Enthalpy, ΔH, is the energy difference between reactants and products.

called the **activation energy, E_a**, and is represented by the symbol. Activation energy represents a barrier to the formation of products and is sometimes referred to as barrier energy. Molecules that have reached that barrier energy through a successful collision and have begun the rearrangement of chemical bonds are said to be in the **transition state**, upon which they can then form the products. Another name for the transition state is an activated complex. Note in Figure 14.14 that the transition state is higher in energy than both the reactants and products regardless of the overall energy change, ΔH, of the reaction. Recall from Chapter 6 that $\Delta H \approx \Delta U$ for reactions at constant pressure.

The magnitude of the activation energy is inversely related to the magnitude of the rate constant. As the activation energy increases, the rate constant decreases and the reaction proceeds more slowly.

There are many factors that contribute to the size of the activation energy, including the nature of the reactants and the types of bonds being rearranged during the reaction.

Figure 14.15 shows the decomposition of nitrogen monoxide to form oxygen and nitrogen. In this reaction, which has a high activation energy, the double bond between N and O atoms in NO must break and a new triple bond must form between nitrogen atoms in N_2, as well as a double bond between oxygen atoms in O_2. In Section 14.6, you will learn how catalytic converters work to speed up the decomposition of NO in automobile exhaust.

One of the primary reasons the transition state has such a high potential energy is the bonds that are in the process of being broken are strained and, therefore, of

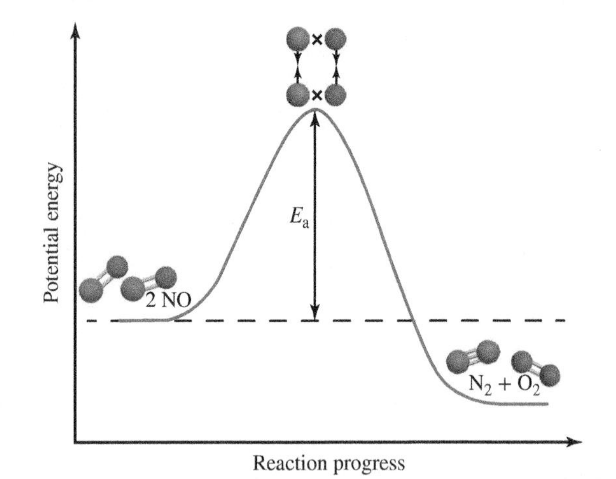

FIGURE 14.15 Energy Diagram for the Decomposition of NO
The reactant molecules must achieve a high-energy transition state before the reaction can occur, allowing products to form.

higher energy. Although there are other factors involved, the number of bonds that need to be broken can be used to predict the relative size of a reaction's activation energy.

Example 14.11

Hydrogen gas reacts with many other substances, such as chlorine or oxygen. You can predict which has a higher activation energy by comparing the number of reactant bonds that must be broken in each situation, counting a double bond as two bonds and a triple bond as three bonds.

Reaction A: $H_2(g) + Cl_2(g) \rightarrow 2\ HCl(g)$

Reaction B: $2\ H_2(g) + 2\ O_2(g) \rightarrow 2\ H_2O(l)$

Draw Lewis structures for the reactants to identify the bonds that must be broken (assume all reactant bonds are broken) and predict which reaction has a higher activation energy.

Solution

Reaction A: The Lewis structures show that one mole of H—H single bonds and one mole of Cl—Cl single bonds must be broken for a total of two moles of bonds.

H—H :C̈l—C̈l:

Reaction B: The Lewis structures indicate that two moles of H—H single bonds and one mole of O—O double bonds (counts as two) must be broken for a total of four moles of bonds.

H—H Ö=Ö
H—H

Reaction B involves breaking more moles of bonds than reaction A. Therefore, you would predict that the reaction of hydrogen and oxygen has a higher activation energy than the reaction of hydrogen and chlorine.

PRACTICE PROBLEM 14.11

Fluorine is a very reactive element. Examine the two reactions of fluorine shown below and predict which has the higher activation energy.

Reaction A: $N_2(g) + 3\ F_2(g) \rightarrow 2\ NF_3(g)$

Reaction B: $Cl_2(g) + F_2(g) \rightarrow 2\ ClF(g)$

Hint: Start by identifying the bonds that need to break in each reaction. This is a good predictor of activation energy, where a greater number of reactant bonds tends to correspond to a higher activation energy for the reaction.

COLLISION THEORY: ARRHENIUS EQUATION

According to **collision theory**, reactions occur when reactants collide with each other, but only when the reactants have the appropriate amount of energy and are in the correct orientation. The **Arrhenius equation**, developed in the late 1800s by Svante Arrhenius, a Swedish chemist, describes the relationship among these factors.

$$k = Ae^{-E_a/RT} \qquad (14.9)$$

In the Arrhenius equation, k represents the rate constant and A is known as the **frequency factor**. In the exponential component of the equation, E_a is the activation energy, R is the gas law constant in the form $8.3145\ J/mol \cdot K$, and T is the absolute temperature (in kelvins). Note that R is the same gas constant that you saw in Chapter 7, but converted to different units.

The frequency factor, A, varies little with temperature, and is related to both how often collisions occur and the probability that the collision will occur with the reactants in the appropriate **orientation**. In Section 14.1, you learned that reactions occur more readily in the gas state or in solution. In both of those situations, the reactants take up only a small percentage of the volume of the sample. In a gas, most of the sample is empty space, and in a solution, most of the volume is occupied by the solvent molecules. Therefore, even in the best circumstances for reactions, collisions between reactants are not expected to occur all that frequently. You can increase the rate of collisions by increasing the concentration of reactants and, to a

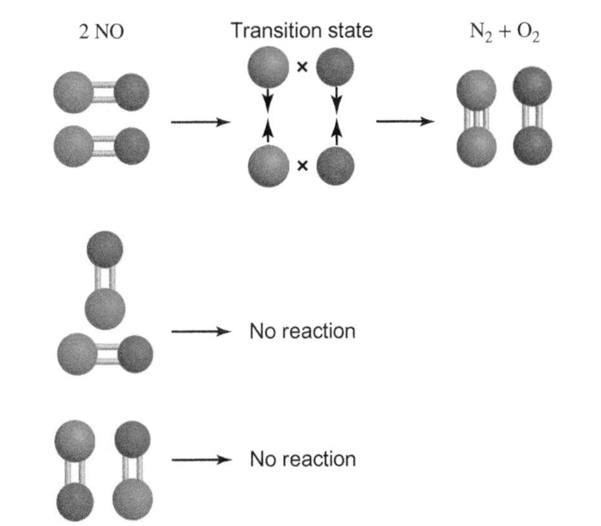

FIGURE 14.16 Collision Orientation for 2 NO → N_2 + O_2
NO molecules collide with each other in many orientations, only a small percentage of which lead to the formation of the transition state.

much smaller extent, by increasing the temperature. Regardless of the collision rate, only a percentage of the collisions will be in the correct orientation for the necessary bond-making and bond-breaking processes to occur. Consider the decomposition of NO previously shown in Figure 14.15. To achieve the transition state, the molecules of NO must line up so that like atoms are next to each other. Figure 14.16 shows that this orientation is only one of many other ways for the molecules to bump into each other.

Thus, there are many more orientations that do *not* lead to reaction than there are orientations that do lead to reaction.

Example 14.12

The reactants and products of a chemical reaction are shown here.

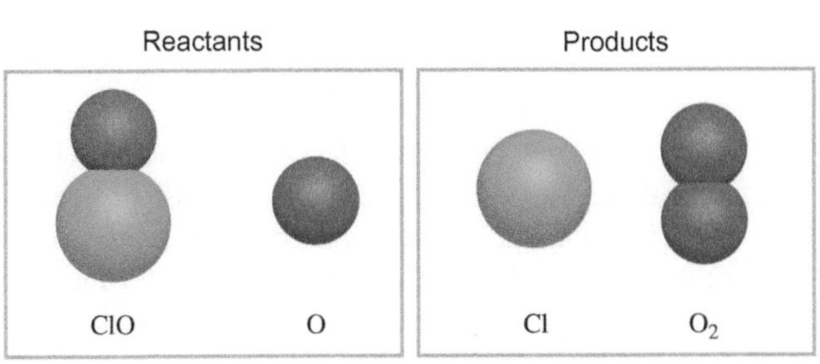

Draw models of the most likely orientation between reactant molecules for this chemical reaction to proceed successfully to products.

Solution

First, identify which bonds change between the reactants and products. In this case, the O atom from the ClO molecule combines with a free O atom to form a diatomic O_2 molecule and a free Cl atom. The most likely orientation for this reaction allows for the free O atom to collide with the bound O atom. If the free O atom collided with the Cl atom, the reaction would not occur.

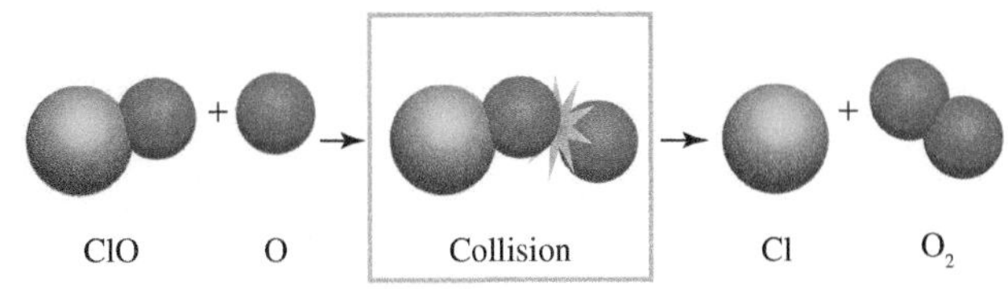

PRACTICE PROBLEM 14.12

The reactants and products of a chemical reaction are shown here.

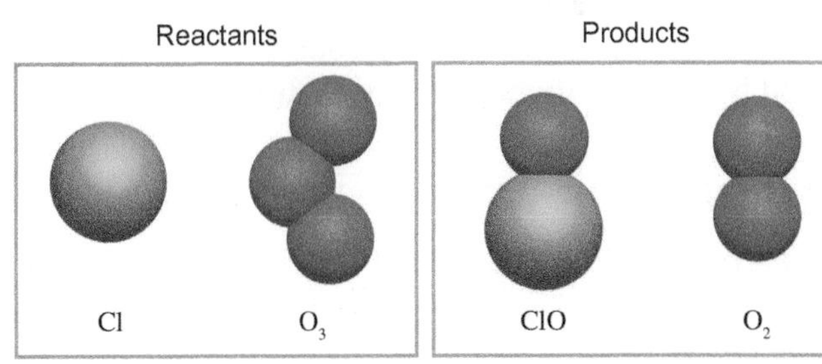

Draw models of the most likely orientation between reactant molecules for this chemical reaction to form products.

Hint: Identify which atoms need to connect to others and which atoms need to separate. Find the best possible orientation for a single collision to result in the products.

Not only must collisions occur in the right orientation, but they also must be of sufficient energy to overcome the activation energy. Chapter 7 states that the kinetic energy of molecules is proportional to the absolute (in kelvins) temperature. You can see in Figure 14.17 that the percentage of molecules with a particular energy is highly temperature dependent. You can also see that as activation energy increases, the percentage of molecules that exceed this energy decreases, regardless of temperature.

In summary, the frequency factor indicates the number of correctly oriented reactions per unit time and the exponential factor indicates the percentage of those reactions that have sufficient energy to reach the

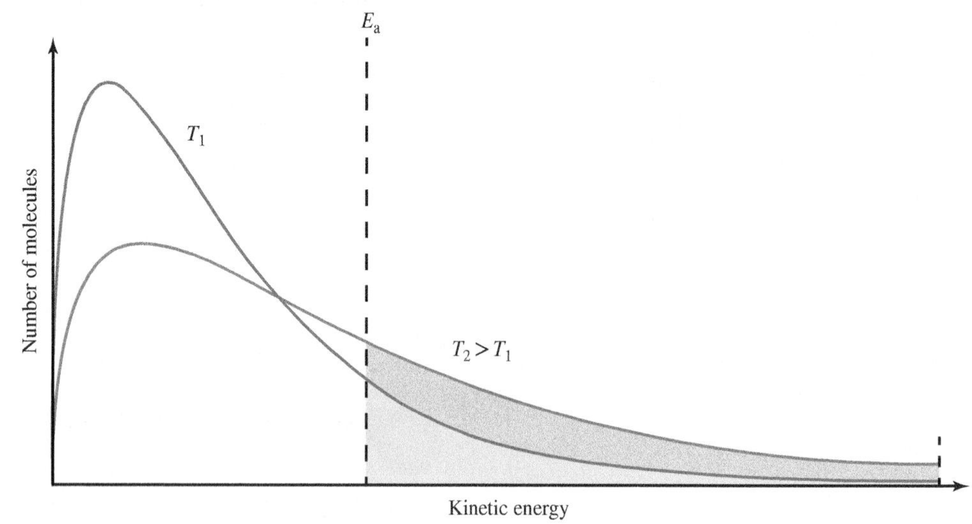

FIGURE 14.17 Effect of Temperature on Kinetic Energy

At T_1, some fraction of molecules has kinetic energy greater than E_a, as represented by the shaded region. At the higher temperature, T_2, the shaded region is larger. The reaction proceeds more rapidly when more molecules can overcome the activation energy.

transition state. Unlike the frequency factor, the exponential factor is affected by changes in temperature and by the magnitude of the activation energy.

USING THE ARRHENIUS EQUATION

The frequency factor is difficult to measure, which limits the usefulness of the basic form of the Arrhenius equation.

$$k = Ae^{-E_a/RT}$$

A more useful form arises when the equation is modified and rearranged into straight line ($y = mx + b$) format.

Take the natural log of both sides of the equation:

$$\ln k = \ln A - \frac{E_a}{RT}$$

Rearrange into $y = mx + b$ format:

$$\ln k = -\frac{E_a}{R}\left(\frac{1}{T}\right) + \ln A \qquad (14.10)$$

Rate constants for a reaction can be determined at several different temperatures. A plot of the natural log of those rate constants ($\ln k$) versus $1/T$ yields a straight line with the slope equal to $-\frac{E_a}{R}$, allowing you to determine the activation energy.

Example 14.13

Use the experimental rate constant data shown in the table to calculate the activation energy for the following reaction.

$$2\,N_2O(g) \rightarrow 2\,N_2(g) + O_2(g)$$

T (K)	k ($M^{-1}s^{-1}$)
850	0.0018
975	0.175
1040	1.22
1120	9.75

Solution

Activation energy involves the Arrhenius equation:

$$\ln k = -\frac{E_a}{R}\left(\frac{1}{T}\right) + \ln A$$

Plot $\ln k$ versus $1/T$ either by hand or by using graphing software to give a straight line with a slope equal to $-E_a/R$. Determine the slope by a rise over run calculation or use the slope of the best-fit line given by the graphing software. The slope units can be confusing in these plots as the y-axis has no units and the unit for the x-axis is K^{-1}, which results in the slope having units of K.

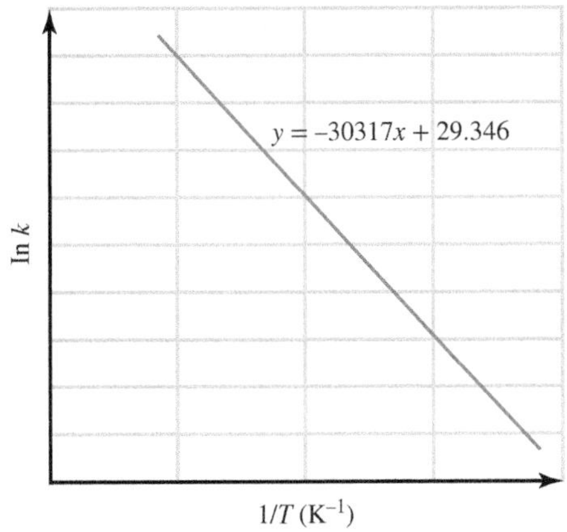

$$\text{Slope} = \frac{-E_a}{R} = -30{,}317\ \text{K}$$

$$E_a = -\text{slope} \times R$$

$$E_a = -(-30{,}317\ \text{K})\left(8.3145\ \frac{\text{J}}{\text{mol}\cdot\text{K}}\right)$$

$$E_a = 252{,}000\ \frac{\text{J}}{\text{mol}} = 250\ \text{kJ/mol}$$

The final answer is adjusted to reflect the two significant figures present in some of the data points because a calculation can only be as good as the data used to obtain it. This result is fairly high for an activation energy, which makes sense given the high temperatures required for the reaction.

PRACTICE PROBLEM 14.13

Use the experimental rate constant data in the table to calculate the activation energy for the following generic reaction.

$$\text{A} \rightarrow \text{B} + \text{C}$$

T (K)	k (s^{-1})
308	1.35×10^{-4}
318	4.98×10^{-4}
328	1.50×10^{-3}
338	4.87×10^{-3}

Hint: Start by adding new columns to the data table for ln k and $1/T$, and fill in those values. Then make a plot of ln k versus $1/T$, either by hand or with graphing software. The slope of the line will be equal to $-E_a/R$.

Yet another form of the Arrhenius equation, sometimes called the two-point version, is useful for comparing rate constants at two different temperatures. To derive the new form, first write the Arrhenius equation for each temperature, subtract one equation from the other, and simplify.

Two equations:

$$\ln k_1 = -\frac{E_a}{R}\left[\frac{1}{T_1}\right] + \ln A$$

$$\ln k_2 = -\frac{E_a}{R}\left[\frac{1}{T_2}\right] + \ln A$$

Subtract:

$$\ln k_1 - \ln k_2 = \left[-\frac{E_a}{R}\left(\frac{1}{T_1}\right) + \ln A\right] - \left[-\frac{E_a}{R}\left(\frac{1}{T_2}\right) + \ln A\right]$$

Rearrange, factor, and simplify:

$$\ln\frac{k_1}{k_2} = \frac{E_a}{R}\left(\frac{1}{T_2} - \frac{1}{T_1}\right) \tag{14.11}$$

This version of the Arrhenius equation allows you to determine the activation energy if you know the rate constant at two temperatures. Similarly, if you know the activation energy and the rate constant at one temperature, you can predict the rate constant at a different temperature.

Example 14.14

Calculate the activation energy for the decomposition of HI given the following values for the rate constant: $k_1 = 8.15 \times 10^{-8}\ M^{-1}s^{-1}$ at $T_1 = 655$ K; $k_2 = 1.39 \times 10^{-6}\ M^{-1}s^{-1}$ at $T_2 = 705$ K.

$$2\,\text{HI(g)} \rightarrow \text{H}_2\text{(g)} + \text{I}_2\text{(g)}$$

Solution

Use the two-point version of the Arrhenius equation, and substitute the given values for k and T. Be sure carry out the division indicated by $\frac{1}{T_1}$ and $\frac{1}{T_2}$ *before* you subtract them. This example shows one of several correct approaches to resolving this equation. Make sure to round to the correct number of significant figures in your final answer and not in any earlier steps.

$$\ln\frac{k_1}{k_2} = \frac{E_a}{R}\left(\frac{1}{T_2} - \frac{1}{T_1}\right)$$

Substitute the given values.

$$\ln\frac{8.15 \times 10^{-8}\ M^{-1}s^{-1}}{1.39 \times 10^{-6}\ M^{-1}s^{-1}} = \frac{E_a}{8.3145\ \frac{\text{J}}{\text{mol}\cdot\text{K}}}\left(\frac{1}{705\ \text{K}} - \frac{1}{655\ \text{K}}\right)$$

Begin the calculation by determining the natural log and carrying out the math within the parentheses.

$$-2.83646 = \frac{E_a}{8.3145\frac{\text{J}}{\text{mol}\cdot\text{K}}}(-1.082778\times10^{-4}\,\text{K}^{-1})$$

Rearrange to solve for E_a.

$$E_a = \frac{-2.83646\left(8.3145\frac{\text{J}}{\text{mol}\cdot\text{K}}\right)}{-1.082778\times10^{-4}\,\text{K}^{-1}}$$

Complete the math, rounding the final answer.

$$E_a = 217{,}807\ \text{J/mol} = 218\ \text{kJ/mol}$$

PRACTICE PROBLEM 14.14

Given the data in Example 14.14, use the two-point version of the Arrhenius equation to determine the value of the rate constant for the decomposition of HI at 805 K.

Hint: The hardest part of this problem is the algebra to solve for k_2. Recall that $\ln\frac{k_1}{k_2} = \ln k_1 - \ln k_2$ and pay close attention to minus signs. Once you rearrange the equation, the rest is plugging in values. For T_1 and k_1, you can use either set of values from the previous example (705 K and $1.39\times10^{-6}\,\text{M}^{-1}\text{s}^{-1}$, or 655 K and $8.15\times10^{-8}\,\text{M}^{-1}\text{s}^{-1}$). For E_a, use 218,000 J/mol, and for T_2, use 805 K.

SECTION REVIEW

- Activation energy, E_a, is the energy needed to initiate a reaction, the energy needed to begin the bond-making and bond-breaking processes. It is the difference between the potential energy of the reactants and the transition state.
- There is an inverse relationship between the values of the activation energy and the rate constant. That is, as activation energy increases, reaction rate decreases.
- Reaction rates are affected by the frequency of collisions, the percentage of collisions with appropriate orientation, and the size of the activation energy.
- The Arrhenius equation, $k = Ae^{-E_a/RT}$, describes the relationship between the rate constant and the activation energy of a chemical reaction.
- The two-point version of the Arrhenius equation, $\ln\frac{k_1}{k_2} = \frac{E_a}{R}\left(\frac{1}{T_1} - \frac{1}{T_2}\right)$, is used to calculate E_a from rate constants measured at two temperatures and to predict rate constants at different temperatures.

14.5 Reaction Mechanisms

GOALS

- Define an discuss *reaction mechanism*.
- Write rate laws for elementary steps.
- Identify intermediates in a reaction mechanism.
- Analyze steps in a reaction mechanism to determine if the mechanism is consistent with the experimentally determined rate low.

ELEMENTARY STEPS

Chemical reactions can happen in just one step, with the old bonds breaking and new bonds forming during an infinitesimally brief time known as the transition state. However, many reactions involve more than one molecular event and are best described as a series of **elementary steps** or elementary reactions, each of which has its own transition state. These elementary steps often occur as follows: (1) a portion of the reactant molecules react to produce a short-lived, unstable intermediate form that (2) reacts with the remaining reactant molecules to produce the final product. Consider the reaction AB + C → AC + B, which occurs in the two elementary steps shown here:

Step 1: AB → A + B

Step 2: A + C → AC

In step 1, the reactant separates into A and B. In step 2, A combines with C to form the product. Figure 14.18 shows reaction energy diagrams of the two steps in this reaction.

Together, the elementary steps in a reaction make up the **reaction mechanism**. The chemical equations that you have been working with up to now represent the sum of the elementary steps, or the overall, stoichiometric equation for the reaction. The experimentally determined rate law for a reaction tells us something about the slowest step of the mechanism, which is called the **rate-determining step**.

The reaction of nitrogen dioxide with carbon monoxide is thought to occur via the following two-step mechanism:

Elementary step 1: $NO_2(g) + NO_2(g) \rightarrow NO(g) + NO_3(g)$

Elementary step 2: $NO_3(g) + CO(g) \rightarrow NO_2(g) + CO_2(g)$

Overall equation: $NO_2(g) + CO(g) \rightarrow NO(g) + CO_2(g)$

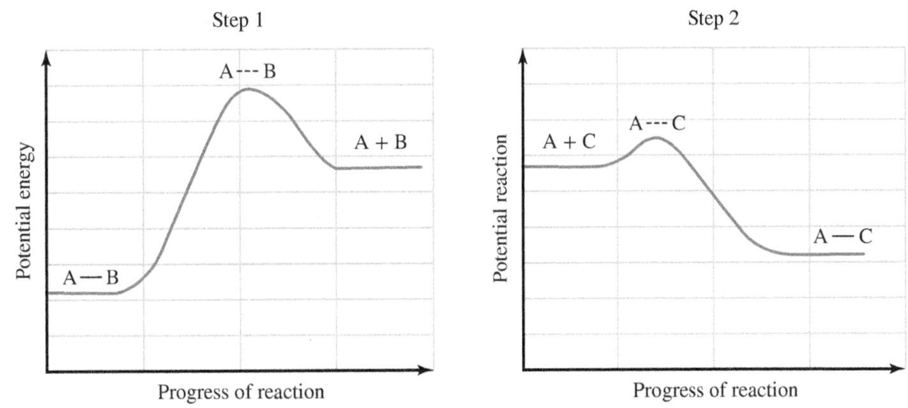

FIGURE 14.18 Energy Diagrams for Two Elementary Steps in a Mechanism

Step 1 of the mechanism has a higher activation energy than step 2. Thus, step 1 is slower at any temperature and is the rate-determining step.

In the first elementary step, two molecules of the reactant, NO_2, collide to form one molecule of NO and another of NO_3. This collision breaks the N—O bond in one NO_2, thereby releasing an oxygen atom, which then forms a bond with another NO_2 molecule to form NO_3. In the second step, NO_3 collides with CO, thereby releasing an oxygen atom, which then forms a bond to CO to make CO_2.

Notice that NO_3 is produced in the first elementary step and then consumed in the second. A substance that appears as a product in one step of a mechanism and as a reactant in a subsequent step is called an **intermediate**. Because intermediates are first produced and then consumed again, they do not appear in the overall equation for the reaction. Notice, too, that although two molecules of NO_2 are required for step 1, only one molecule is consumed overall because one is produced in step 2.

Example 14.15

The decomposition of N_2O into oxygen and nitrogen is thought to occur via a two-step mechanism:

Step 1: $N_2O(g) \rightarrow N_2(g) + O(g)$

Step 2: $N_2O(g) + O(g) \rightarrow N_2(g) + O_2(g)$

Write the overall equation for this reaction and identify any intermediates.

Solution

The overall equation is the sum of the two elementary steps after combining like terms and removing any species that appear on both sides of the arrow.

Add steps 1 and 2 together.

$$N_2O(g) + N_2O(g) + O(g) \rightarrow N_2(g) + O(g) + N_2(g) + O_2(g)$$

Simplify to give the overall equation.

$$2\,N_2O(g) \rightarrow 2\,N_2(g) + O_2(g)$$

The species, O(g), appears as a product in step 1 and is used as a reactant in step 2, making it an intermediate in this mechanism.

PRACTICE PROBLEM 14.15

The reaction of NO with chlorine is believed to occur via a two-step mechanism:

Step 1: $NO(g) + Cl_2(g) \rightarrow NOCl_2(g)$

Step 2: $NOCl_2(g) + NO(g) \rightarrow 2\,NOCl(g)$

Write the overall equation for this reaction and identify any intermediates.

Hint: Write all reactants from both steps together as the reactants of the overall reaction. Then write all products from both steps as the products of the overall reaction. Combine species that appear multiple times on the same side (e.g., A + A should be rewritten as 2A) and cancel species that appear multiple times on opposite sides (e.g., A + B → B + C should be rewritten as A → C). Species that cancel out completely are called intermediates if they are produced in one step and consumed in a later step.

MOLECULARITY

The reactions used at the beginning of this section to explain the elementary steps in a reaction mechanism are reproduced here, along with their molecularities:

- $AB \rightarrow A + B$

  One reactant molecule = unimolecular
- $A + C \rightarrow AC$

  Two reactant molecules = bimolecular
- $2\,A \rightarrow A_2$

  Two identical reactant molecules = bimolecular

The **molecularity** identifies the number of reactant molecules in an elementary step. Thus, the first step is unimolecular (one reactant molecule), whereas the second step is bimolecular (two reactant molecules). Elementary steps with three reactant molecules—known as **termolecular**—are possible but rare.

Because each elementary step represents an individual molecular event, you can write the rate law for an elementary step directly from the balanced equation, as shown here.

- $AB \rightarrow A + B$ rate $= k[AB]$
- $A + C \rightarrow AC$ rate $= k[A][C]$
- $2\,A \rightarrow A_2$ rate $= k[A]^2$

> Be careful! Unless you are explicitly told that a reaction is an elementary step, you cannot assume that the rate law follows the reaction stoichiometry.

Example 14.16

N_2O decomposes into oxygen and nitrogen, which is thought to occur via a two-step mechanism.

Step 1: $N_2O(g) \rightarrow N_2(g) + O(g)$

Step 2: $N_2O(g) + O(g) \rightarrow N_2(g) + O_2(g)$

For each elementary step,

a. identify the molecularity.
b. write the rate law.

Solution

a. Step 1 has a single reactant molecule, so it is unimolecular. Step 2 has two reactant molecules, so it is bimolecular.
b. Rate laws for elementary steps can be written directly from the balanced elementary reaction.

$$\text{Rate}_{\text{step 1}} = k_1[N_2O]$$
$$\text{Rate}_{\text{step 2}} = k_2[N_2O][O]$$

PRACTICE PROBLEM 14.16

NO reacts with chlorine in a reaction that is thought to occur via a two-step mechanism.

Step 1: $NO(g) + Cl_2(g) \rightarrow NOCl_2(g)$

Step 2: $NOCl_2(g) + NO(g) \rightarrow 2NOCl(g)$

For each elementary step,

a. identify the molecularity.
b. write the rate law.

Hint:
a. Count the number of reactant molecules in each step.
b. Since these are elementary steps, we can use the coefficients in the chemical equation to determine the rate law. The rate law begins with k times a term for each reactant in brackets, raised to the power of its coefficient.

RATE-DETERMINING STEP

Because the individual steps in a reaction mechanism have different rate laws, you would also expect them to have different rates. The rate of the overall reaction can be no faster than the slowest elementary step, which is referred to as the rate-determining step.

Figure 14.19 shows a reaction energy diagram for a two-step reaction in which the activation energy for step 1 is higher than it is for step 2. This tells us that step 1 is the slow step—the rate-determining step—in this mechanism at any temperature.

Consider again the reaction of NO_2 and CO, which is thought to occur via a two-step mechanism:

Step 1: $NO_2(g) + NO_2(g) \xrightarrow{k_1} NO(g) + NO_3(g)$ (slow)

Step 2: $NO_3(g) + CO(g) \xrightarrow{k_2} NO_2(g) + CO_2(g)$ (fast)

Overall equation: $NO_2(g) + CO(g) \longrightarrow NO(g) + CO_2(g)$

Step 1 of the mechanism is believed to be the slower step of the mechanism, suggesting that the overall reaction has a reaction energy diagram similar to the one shown in Figure 14.19. For that to be true, k_2 must be greater than k_1. If step 2 is faster than step 1, then as soon as the intermediate, NO_3, is produced by step 1, it is immediately consumed in step 2. Step 2 and the overall reaction are entirely dependent upon the rate of step 1, the rate-determining step. Therefore, you

EVERYDAY CONNECTION

You have likely experienced rate-determining steps frequently in your life. Imagine that you are in the airport and trying to get to your gate on time but you have to check your bag and get through the security check. Typically, people move through the check-in process fairly quickly but get bogged down in the security line. The security checkpoint is the rate-determining step in the process of reaching the gate.

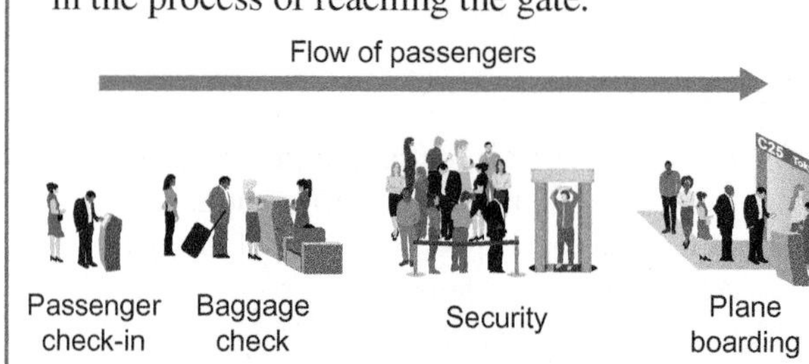

Getting through airport security, then, is the rate-determining step in the overall process of reaching the gate.

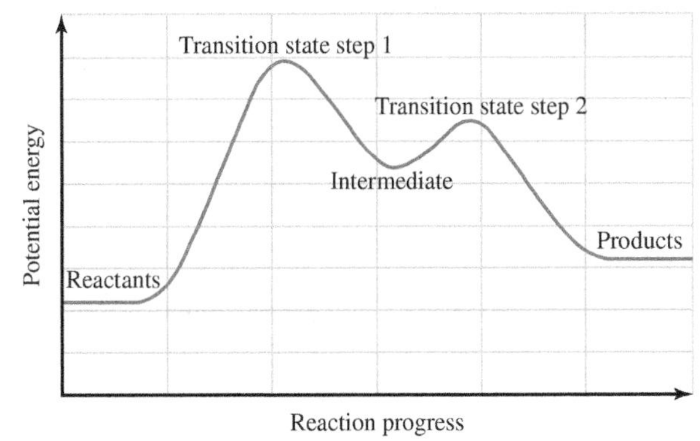

FIGURE 14.19 Two-Step Mechanism
In this reaction energy diagram for a two-step mechanism, the first step has a high activation energy and produces the intermediate, which is the reactant for the second, faster step.

would predict that the rate law for the overall reaction is identical to the rate law for step 1. The experimentally determined rate law is

$$\text{Rate} = k[NO_2]^2$$

and is consistent with the slower step 1 mechanism. Keep in mind that you cannot prove that a proposed mechanism is correct. You can only show that the mechanism is consistent with the existing observations.

Any proposed mechanism must (1) account for the overall stoichiometry of the reaction and (2) have a rate-determining step that is consistent with the observed rate law.

In the reaction of NO_2 and CO, the first step in the mechanism is the rate-determining step. So, what happens when the second step is the slow step in a mechanism? Steps other than the first step of a mechanism will contain intermediates as their reactants, which should never appear in a rate law. You saw a reaction that follows this type of mechanism in Practice Problem 14.15—the reaction of nitrogen monoxide with chlorine. The overall reaction has the following stoichiometry and observed rate law:

$$2\,NO(g) + Cl_2(g) \rightarrow N_2(g) + 2\,NOCl(g)$$

$$\text{Rate} = k[NO]^2[Cl_2]$$

If this happened in one step, the elementary reaction would be termolecular.

$$NO(g) + NO(g) + Cl_2(g) \rightarrow N_2(g) + 2\,NOCl(g)$$

$$\text{Rate} = k[NO]^2[Cl_2]$$

Although the rate law is consistent with this mechanism, termolecular reactions are rare because they require three molecules to collide simultaneously with the correct orientation and sufficient energy to reach the transition state. Another possible mechanism is a two-step mechanism with a fast first step:

$$\text{Step 1:} \quad NO(g) + Cl_2(g) \underset{k_{-1}}{\overset{k_1}{\rightleftharpoons}} NOCl_2(g) \quad \text{(fast)}$$

$$\text{Step 2:} \quad NOCl_2(g) + NO(g) \xrightarrow{k_2} 2\,NOCl(g) \quad \text{(slow)}$$

The rate law for rate-determining step is $k_2[NOCl_2][NO]$.

The rate law for the slow step must be consistent with the observed rate law, and it should not contain intermediates. To account for this, take advantage of a phenomenon called equilibrium (Chapter 15), where the forward and reverse reactions occur simultaneously at identical rates. The double arrows in step 1 indicate that it is reversible. At equilibrium, the rate of the forward reaction equals the rate of the reverse reaction.

You can obtain the following expression for $[NOCl_2]$ by following this process:

$$\text{Step 1 (forward):} \quad NO(g) + Cl_2(g) \xrightarrow{k_1} NOCl_2(g)$$

$$\text{Rate}_{\text{forward}} = k_1[NO][Cl_2]$$

$$\text{Step 1 (reverse):} \quad NOCl_2(g) \xrightarrow{k_{-1}} NO(g) + Cl_2(g)$$

$$\text{Rate}_{\text{reverse}} = k_{-1}[NOCl_2]$$

$$\text{At equilibrium:} \quad k_1[NO][Cl_2] = k_{-1}[NOCl_2]$$

$$\text{Rate}_{\text{forward}} = \text{Rate}_{\text{reverse}}$$

$$\text{Solve for } [NOCl_2]\text{:} \quad [NOCl_2] = \frac{k_1}{k_{-1}}[NO][Cl_2]$$

Substitute the above expression for $[NOCl_2]$ into the rate law for step 2 to obtain a rate law for the mechanism that is consistent with the observed rate law:

Step 2 rate law:

$$\text{Rate} = k_2[NOCl_2][NO]$$

Replace $[NOCl_2]$:

$$\text{Rate} = \frac{k_1}{k_{-1}}[NO][Cl_2]k_2[NO]$$

Combine constants and like terms:

$$\text{Rate} = \frac{k_1k_2}{k_{-1}}[NO]^2[Cl_2]$$

The rate constant for the overall reaction is expressed as k, which in this case is equal to $\frac{k_1k_2}{k_{-1}}$.

Steve Lemon, Macmillan Learning

FIGURE 14.20 Video Tutorial: Rate Determining Step

NOTE: You need to be online to access this video.
This video shows how to determine the rate law for an overall reaction based on its mechanism with an initial fast step.

Figure 14.20 and the subsequent example problem demonstrate how to solve problems involving the rate-determining step.

Example 14.17

$Co(CN)_5(H_2O)^{2-}(aq)$ is a coordination complex (see Chapter 22) in which a Co^{3+} ion is bonded to five CN^- ions and a molecule of H_2O. When this complex is reacted with iodide ion, I^- displaces the water molecule as shown in the following balanced chemical equation:

$$Co(CN)_5(H_2O)^{2-}(aq) + I^- \rightarrow Co(CN)_5I^{3-}(aq) + H_2O(l)$$

The rate law for this reaction,

$$\text{Rate} = k[Co(CN)_5(H_2O)^{2-}]$$

is zero order with respect to iodide ion. Suggest a possible reaction mechanism to account for the observed rate law.

Solution

Since the observed rate law does not involve the iodide ion, I^-, must be a reactant in a step other than the rate-determining step, suggesting at least a two-step mechanism. One possibility is that the water separates from the coordination complex first and the iodide reacts in a second, fast step.

Step 1: $Co(CN)_5(H_2O)^{2-}(aq) \rightarrow Co(CN)_5^{2-} + H_2O(l)$ (slow)

Step 2: $Co(CN)_5^{2-} + I^- \rightarrow Co(CN)_5I^{3-}(aq)$ (fast)

The rate law for the elementary reaction in step 1, the rate-determining step, is consistent with the observed rate law for the overall reaction.

PRACTICE PROBLEM 14.17

The reaction of NO with oxygen has several proposed mechanisms, one of which is the following:

Step 1: $NO(g) + O_2(g) \rightleftharpoons NO_3(g)$ (fast, equilibrium)

Step 2: $NO(g) + NO_3(g) \longrightarrow 2NO_2(g)$ (slow)

Overall: $2NO(g) + O_2(g) \longrightarrow 2NO_2(g)$ Rate $= k[NO]^2[O_2]$

Show that the mechanism is consistent with the observed rate law.

Hint: Start by writing the rate law for the slow step. This is equal to the rate law for the overall reaction, but contains intermediates. Use the equilibrium step to identify an equivalent expression for the intermediate, and substitute it in the overall rate law.

SECTION REVIEW

- Chemical reactions occur via a series of molecular events called elementary steps, which together make up the reaction mechanism.
- Elementary steps are categorized as unimolecular, bimolecular, or termolecular based on the number of reactant molecules.
- The rate laws of elementary steps are derived directly from the stoichiometry of their equations.
- The rate of the slowest step of the mechanism determines the overall reaction rate, so the slowest step is referred to as the rate-determining step.
- Intermediate species are the products of one elementary step and the reactants of a subsequent elementary step. They must not appear in the rate law for the overall reaction.
- A mechanism for a reaction must satisfy the following criteria:
  - the elementary steps must sum up to the overall equation and
  - the rate law for the rate-determining step must be consistent with the observed rate law, which cannot contain intermediates.

14.6 Catalysis

GOALS

- Discuss how catalysts work to speed up chemical reactions.
- Provide examples of both homogeneous and heterogeneous catalysts.
- Identify catalysts in reaction mechanisms.

Up to now, you have studied how to increase the rate of a reaction by increasing the temperature or concentration of the reactants (Sections 14.1 and 14.2). You also learned in Section 14.4 that the size of the activation energy is the major factor in determining rate. There are very real limitations to increasing temperature because it can be quite costly (in terms of both energy and the need for high-temperature equipment), and it can increase the rate of unwanted side reactions. Higher temperatures may also decompose reactants and/or products. There are similar economic and practical limitations to increasing the concentration of reactants.

CATALYSTS FACILITATE REACTIONS

Another way to speed up chemical reactions, first mentioned in Section 14.1, is to use catalysts, which generally work by lowering the activation energy of the reaction. How is this possible? Consider the airport analogy again. While you are waiting in the security line and watching the people ahead of you take their computers out of the bags; empty their pockets; and take off shoes, jewelry, watches, and so on, you might notice that some people are going to separate lines, sending closed computer bags through the scanner and walking through the security checkpoint with their shoes on. This alternative pathway through security, the TSA pre-check line, allows people to move more quickly through the security checkpoint than you are able to. Catalysts work in much the same way by providing an alternative pathway with a lower activation energy, as shown in Figure 14.21.

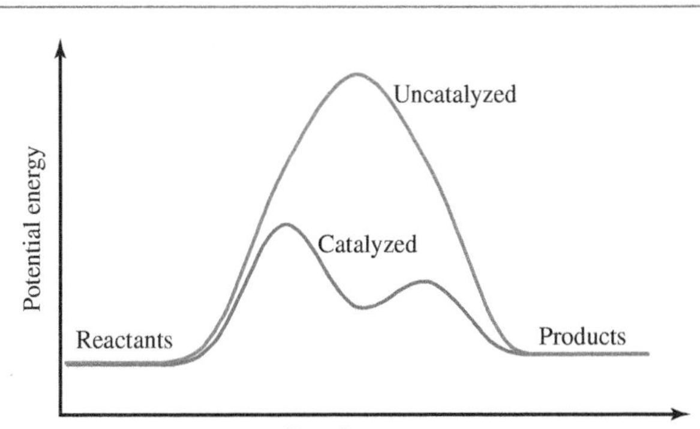

FIGURE 14.21 Activation Energy of Catalyzed Reaction Compared to Uncatalyzed Reaction

The catalyst changes the reaction mechanism to one with lower activation energy in all steps.

When a catalyst is present, a reaction follows a different set of elementary reactions. Catalysts facilitate chemical reactions but are not consumed by them. That is, the catalyst is consumed in one step and produced in a later step.

The decomposition of hydrogen peroxide has a very high activation energy in the absence of a catalyst.

$$2\,H_2O_2(aq) \rightarrow 2\,H_2O(l) + O_2(g)$$

However, in the presence of bromide ions and under acidic conditions (i.e., in the presence of H^+), the reaction occurs quite readily. So one way to catalyze this reaction is to add HBr(aq).

Step 1: $H_2O_2(aq) + 2\,HBr(aq) \rightarrow Br_2(aq) + 2\,H_2O(l)$

Step 2: $\underline{Br_2(aq) + H_2O_2(aq) \rightarrow O_2(g) + 2\,HBr(aq)}$

$$2\,H_2O_2(aq) + \cancel{2\,HBr(aq)} + \cancel{Br_2(aq)} \rightarrow \cancel{Br_2(aq)} + 2\,H_2O(l) + O_2(g) + \cancel{2\,HBr(aq)}$$

Overall equation: $2\,H_2O_2(aq) \rightarrow 2\,H_2O(l) + O_2(g)$

Both H^+ and Br^- ions are consumed in the rate-determining step (step 1) but are produced in step 2. As a result, neither H^+ nor Br^- is consumed in the overall reaction.

> Neither catalysts nor intermediates appear in the overall reaction. Catalysts are consumed and then later produced, whereas intermediates are produced and then later consumed.

Example 14.18

The accepted mechanism for the hydration of propene, C_3H_6, consists of the following three steps.

Step 1: $C_3H_6 + H^+ \rightarrow C_3H_7^+$

Step 2: $C_3H_7^+ + H_2O \rightarrow C_3H_9O^+$

Step 3: $C_3H_9O^+ \rightarrow C_3H_8O + H^+$

Use these elementary reactions to:

a. write the balanced equation for the overall reaction, and

b. identify any intermediates and catalysts.

Solution

a. To determine the overall equation, add the three equations together, combining any like terms and removing any species that appears on both sides of the reaction arrow.

The combined equation, before simplifying, is:

Combined: $C_3H_6 + H^+ + C_3H_7{}^+ + H_2O + C_3H_9O^+ \rightarrow C_3H_7{}^+ + C_3H_9O^+ + C_3H_8O + H^+$

Simplify by combining like terms and removing any species that appear as both products and reactants:

$$C_3H_6 + \cancel{H^+} + \cancel{C_3H_7^+} + H_2O + \cancel{C_3H_9O^+} \rightarrow \cancel{C_3H_7^+} + \cancel{C_3H_9O^+} + C_3H_8O + \cancel{H^+}$$

After simplifying, this equation reduces to this overall equation:

$$C_3H_6 + H_2O \rightarrow C_3H_8O$$

b. To identify any intermediates and catalysts, you need to look at each step carefully. $C_3H_7^+$ appears as a product in step 1 and as a reactant in step 2. Similarly, $C_3H_9O^+$ appears as a product in step 2 and as a reactant in step 3. Both species are produced in one step and consumed in a subsequent step. These are intermediates. H^+ is a reactant in step 1 and a product in step 3. It is consumed in an early step and produced in a subsequent step. H^+ is a catalyst.

Step 1: $C_3H_6 + H^+ \rightarrow C_3H_7^+$

Step 2: $C_3H_7^+ + H_2O \rightarrow C_3H_9O^+$

Step 3: $C_3H_9O^+ \rightarrow C_3H_8O + H^+$

PRACTICE PROBLEM 14.18

Sulfur oxides and nitrogen oxides are components of air pollution. One of the reactions they undergo together consists of the following two-step mechanism:

Step 1: $2\,SO_2(g) + 2\,NO_2(g) \rightarrow 2\,SO_3(g) + 2\,NO(g)$

Step 2: $2\,NO(g) + O_2(g) \rightarrow 2\,NO_2(g)$

Use this proposed mechanism to:

a. write the balanced equation for the overall reaction.
b. identify any intermediates and catalysts.

Hint: Write all reactants from both steps together as the reactants of the overall reaction. Then write all products from both steps as the products of the overall reaction. Combine species that appear multiple times on the same side (e.g., A + A should be rewritten as 2A) and cancel species that appear multiple times on opposite sides (e.g., A + B → B + C should be rewritten as A → C). A species that cancels out completely is an intermediate if it is produced and then consumed, but a catalyst if it is consumed and then produced.

Figure 14.22 allows you to explore the effect of a catalyst, and the amount of catalyst, on the concentrations of the reactants and products over the course of a reaction.

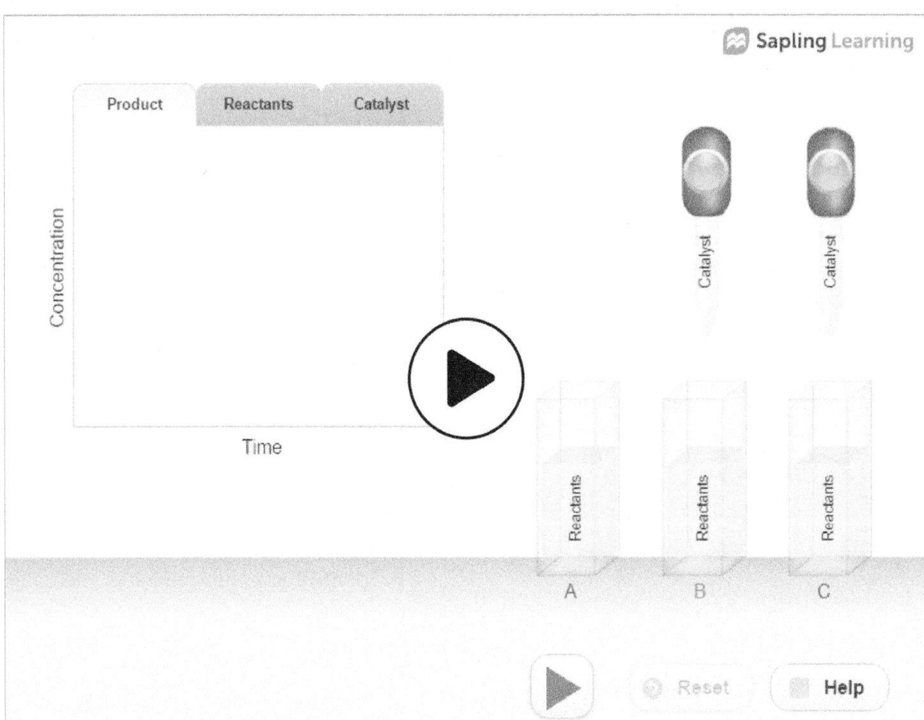

FIGURE 14.22 Catalyst Simulation Activity

NOTE: You need to be online to access this activity.

Start the reaction, and add different amounts of catalyst to the second and third reaction vessels. Then compare the rate of reaction among the three reactions.

TYPES OF CATALYSTS

In the decomposition of hydrogen peroxide, the reactant and the catalysts are all in the same phase—namely, aqueous solution. This is an example of **homogeneous catalysis**, which is very common. Many homogeneous catalysts work to speed up aqueous- or gas-phase reactions.

Heterogeneous catalysts, in contrast, are in a different phase than the reactants, and are usually solids that provide a surface for the reactants to adsorb (adhere) onto. This adsorption often weakens bonds within one of the reactants, making it easier for the reaction to proceed. An example of this is the catalytic converter in automobiles. One function of the catalytic converter is to convert carbon monoxide in exhaust to carbon dioxide, $2\,CO(g) + O_2(g) \rightarrow 2\,CO_2(g)$. Once oxygen molecules in the engine exhaust adsorb to the surface of the catalytic converter, the bond between oxygen atoms is weakened, enabling the formation of a bond between adsorbed CO molecules and oxygen atoms. Another component in catalytic converters works to catalyze the decomposition of NO to oxygen and nitrogen, by adsorbing the NO molecules and weakening the N—O bonds. All of this happens quickly, in 100 to 400 ms, and efficiently, with up to 96% of CO and 76% of NO being removed from the exhaust.

Catalysis is profoundly important in modern industrial processes and has always been an integral part of living things. All of the reactions of metabolism in living things are catalyzed by a class of proteins known as enzymes. These enzymes enable biological reactions to happen under physiological conditions, which are quite mild when compared to the conditions commonly used in the chemical industry. An example of this is the conversion of nitrogen in the atmosphere to ammonia, NH_3. This process is carried out in nature by the enzyme nitrogenase, in soil bacteria at ambient temperatures and pressures. On a nice spring day, ambient temperature and pressure might be 20°C and 0.93 atm (only 78% of which is nitrogen gas). Contrast this with the conditions needed for the Haber process, which combines nitrogen and hydrogen gases at 200 atm and 450°C in the presence of an iron catalyst to produce ammonia for commercial purposes.

SECTION REVIEW

- Catalysts speed up chemical reactions by providing an alternative reaction pathway with a lower activation energy.
- Catalysts are part of the elementary steps but do not appear in the overall reaction. They participate

EVERYDAY CONNECTION

The catalytic converter in an automobile converts the toxic gases and pollutants in exhaust (such as CO and NO_x) to less harmful emissions. It contains a solid surface, the catalyst, onto which the gaseous reactants adsorb. Since the catalyst is in a different phase than the reactants, it is an example of a heterogeneous catalyst.

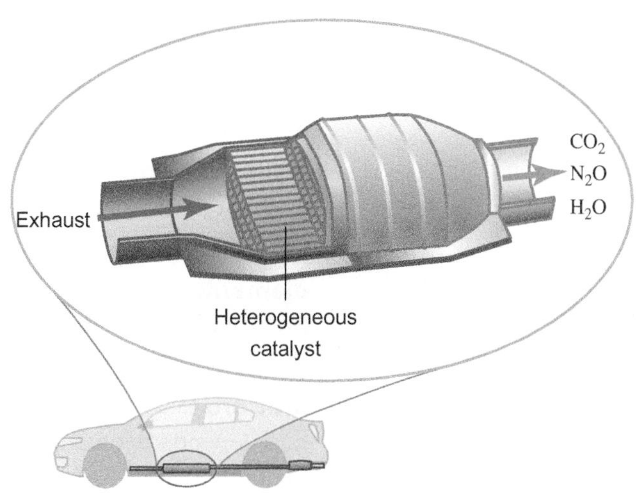

in the reaction by being consumed on one step and produced in a later step.

- Homogeneous catalysts are in the same phase as the reactants, whereas heterogeneous catalysts are in a different phase.
- Catalysts are involved in many industrial processes and all metabolic processes.

Putting It Together

The example problems in earlier sections of this chapter focus on just the new skills acquired in that section. But homework and exam questions in chemistry often require more than just one skill at a time. In fact, you will likely be expected to apply knowledge from across the entire chapter, or even multiple chapters, in a single problem. This final example problem is meant to help you prepare for these types of multi-concept questions. Additional examples can be found in the end-of-chapter exercises.

Example 14.19

Initial rate and concentration data for $A \rightarrow B$ were collected for a reaction at two different temperatures.

Temperature (K)	[A] (M)	Rate (M/s)
298 K	0.310 M	0.120
298 K	0.620 M	0.480
375 K	0.310 M	0.230
375 K	0.620 M	0.920

Determine the activation energy, and propose a plausible mechanism.

Solution

The rate quadruples when the concentration doubles, indicating that the reaction is second order with a rate law of Rate $= k[A]^2$.

Plug values from the table into the rate law to determine the rate constant at each temperature.

$$0.120\ \text{M/s} = k_1(0.310\ \text{M})^2$$
$$k_1 = 1.25\ \text{M}^{-1}\text{s}^{-1}$$
$$0.230\ \text{M/s} = k_2(0.310\ \text{M})^2$$
$$k_2 = 2.39\ \text{M}^{-1}\text{s}^{-1}$$

Use the two-point version of the Arrhenius equation to determine the activation energy.

$$\ln\frac{1.25\ \text{M}^{-1}\text{s}^{-1}}{2.39\ \text{M}^{-1}\text{s}^{-1}} = \frac{E_a}{8.3145\frac{\text{J}}{\text{mol}\cdot\text{K}}}\left(\frac{1}{375} - \frac{1}{298}\right)$$
$$E_a = 7820\ \text{J/mol}$$

The mechanism must show a bimolecular slow step to be consistent with the observed rate law. One possible mechanism for an overall reaction of $A \rightarrow B$ and a rate law of Rate $= k[A]^2$ is

Step 1: $A + A \rightarrow C$ (slow)

Step 2: $C \rightarrow B + A$ (fast)

PRACTICE PROBLEM 14.19

A proposed mechanism for the reaction $A \rightarrow B + C$ is

Step 1: $A \rightarrow C + D$ (slow)

Step 2: $D \rightarrow B$ (fast)

Determine the half-life of the reaction if the initial rate is 0.025 M/s when the initial concentration of A is 0.50 M.

Hint: Use the slow step to determine the rate law, then plug values into the rate law to find *k*. Finally, use *k* to determine the half-life.

Key Terms, Symbols, and Equations

KEY TERMS

activation energy, E_a (14.4): The minimum amount of energy needed for the reactant to reach the transition state; also called barrier energy.

Arrhenius equation (14.4): An equation relating the rate constant, activation energy, frequency of collisions, orientation, and temperature.

average rates (14.2): Reaction rates determined by measuring the concentration at two different times and dividing the change in concentration by the change in time.

catalyst (14.1): A substance that provides an alternative, lower-energy path for a reaction to occur but is not consumed by the reaction.

collision theory (14.4): Theory that describes chemical reactions as occurring when reactants collide with sufficient energy and in the correct orientation.

elementary step (14.5): An individual molecular event with a transition state and rate law, typically part of a series that makes up a reaction mechanism.

first order (14.2): A type of reaction in which the rate depends upon a reactant's concentration raised to the first power.

frequency factor (14.4): Indicates the number of correctly oriented reactions per unit time.

half-life (14.3): The time needed for one-half of the reactant to be consumed by a reaction.

heterogeneous catalyst (14.6): A catalyst in a different phase than the reactants.

homogeneous catalyst (14.6): A catalyst in the same phase as the reactants.

initial rate (14.2): The instantaneous rate measured at time zero.

instantaneous rates (14.2): Reaction rates determined by graphing concentration versus time, drawing a tangent to the curve, and determining the slope of the tangent.

integrated rate law (14.3): Version of the rate law that allows for the calculation of changes in reactant concentration over time and for graphical determination of the rate constant.

intermediate (14.5): A high-energy, unstable species formed by one intermediate step and consumed by the next intermediate step in a reaction mechanism.

molecularity (14.5): Identifies the number of reactant molecules in an elementary step.

orientation (14.4): The arrangement of molecules as they approach for a collision, where the proximity of certain atoms dictates whether the reaction can occur.

overall reaction order (14.2): The sum of the reaction orders for the individual reactants.

rate (14.1): In a chemical reaction, the change in the concentration of a reactant or product per unit time.

rate constant, *k* (14.2): A proportionality constant used in the rate law.

rate law (14.2): A mathematical expression for the relationship between reaction rate and the concentrations of reactants that includes a proportionality constant.

rate-determining step (14.5): The slowest elementary step in a reaction mechanism.

reaction mechanism (14.5): A series of elementary steps that make up a chemical reaction.

reaction order, *n* (14.2): The power to which a reactant's concentration is raised in a rate law.

reaction rate (14.1): The change in the concentration of a reactant or product per unit time.

second order (14.2): A type of reaction in which the rate depends upon a reactant's concentration raised to the second power.

termolecular (14.5): Elementary steps with three reactant molecules.

transition state (14.4): A high-energy state associated with rearrangement of bonds that occurs during chemical reactions; also called activated complex.

zero order (14.2): A type of reaction in which the rate does not depend upon a reactant's concentration.

SYMBOLS AND ABBREVIATIONS

A (frequency factor) (14.4)

[A] (concentration of A) (14.1)

$\frac{\Delta[\text{A}]}{\Delta t}$ (a rate, change in concentration per change in time) (14.1)

Δ ("change in") (14.1)

E_a (activation energy) (14.4)

k (rate constant) (14.2)

m (slope in the equation for a line, $y = mx + b$) (14.3)

M/s or $\text{M} \cdot \text{s}^{-1}$ (molar per second, units of rate) (14.1)

R (gas constant, 8.3145 J/mol · K) (14.4)

t (time) (14.1)

$t_{1/2}$ (half-life) (14.3)

EQUATIONS

$$\text{Rate} = -\frac{1}{a}\frac{\Delta[\text{A}]}{\Delta t} = \frac{1}{b}\frac{\Delta[\text{B}]}{\Delta t} \quad (14.1)$$

$$\text{Rate} = -\frac{1}{a}\frac{\Delta[\text{A}]}{\Delta t} = k[\text{A}]^n \quad (14.2)$$

$$\text{Rate} = -\frac{1}{a}\frac{\Delta[\text{A}]}{\Delta t} = k[\text{A}]^n[\text{B}]^m \quad (14.3)$$

$$\ln[\text{A}]_t = -kt + \ln[\text{A}]_0 \quad (14.4)$$

$$t = \frac{\ln 2}{k} \quad (14.5)$$

$$\frac{1}{[\text{A}]_{-t}} = kt + \frac{1}{[\text{A}]_{-0}} \quad (14.6)$$

$$t_{1/2} = \frac{1}{k[\text{A}]_0} \quad (14.7)$$

$$t_{1/2} = \frac{[\text{A}]_0}{2k} \quad (14.8)$$

$$k = Ae^{-E_a/RT} \quad (14.9)$$

$$\ln k = -\frac{E_a}{R}\left(\frac{1}{T}\right) + \ln A \quad (14.10)$$

$$\ln\frac{k_1}{k_2} = \frac{E_a}{R}\left(\frac{1}{T_2} - \frac{1}{T_1}\right) \quad (14.11)$$

Chapter Summary

Reaction rates are affected by five factors: the nature of the reactants, the particle size of a solid, the concentration of a reactant, temperature, and the presence of a catalyst. Increasing the particle size of solids or the concentration of aqueous or gaseous reactants increases the reaction rate. Since all chemical reactions require energy to initiate the reaction, increasing the temperature increases the rates of all chemical reactions. Catalysts speed up reactions by providing a lower-energy pathway for the reaction. Reaction rates can be monitored by the disappearance of a reactant or the appearance of a product. For the reaction $aA \rightarrow bB$, where a and b are stoichiometric coefficients in a balanced chemical equation, Rate $= -\frac{1}{a}\frac{\Delta[A]}{\Delta t} = \frac{1}{b}\frac{\Delta[B]}{\Delta t}$. The concentrations of reactants and/or products in many reactions can be measured spectroscopically, because many compounds absorb electromagnetic radiation (Section 14.1).

Reaction rates can be measured as average or instantaneous rates. Initial rates—instantaneous rates measured close to the start of a reaction—are most common. Reaction rates depend upon the molar concentration of a specific reactant or reactants raised to a power, which identifies the reaction as zero, first, or second order. Rate laws are experimentally determined, mathematical relationships between the reaction rate and the concentrations of the reactants. The rate law for a reaction expresses the relationship between rate and reaction concentration and includes a proportionality constant called the rate constant, k, which is temperature-dependent.

- For a reaction with a single reactant, A, rate $= k[A]^n$, where k is the rate constant and n is the order with respect to A as well as the overall reaction order.
- For a reaction with multiple reactants, A and B, rate $= k[A]^n[B]^m$, where k is the rate constant, n is the order with respect to A, and m is the order with respect to B.

The order of the overall reaction is the sum of the orders with respect to each reactant. Common reaction orders are 0, 1, and 2. Negative and fractional orders are possible but less common. The units of the rate constant depend upon the overall reaction order (Section 14.2).

Integrated versions of zero-, first-, and second-order rate laws allow you to calculate changes in reaction concentration over time and to graphically determine rate constants and reaction order. You can also use half-lives of reactions to determine rate constants.

- For zero-order reactions, the integrated rate law is $[A]_t = -kt + [A]_0$ and the half-life expression is $t_{1/2} = \frac{[A]_0}{2k}$.
- For first-order reactions, the integrated rate law is $\ln[A]_t = -kt + \ln[A]_0$ and the half-life expression is $t_{1/2} = \frac{\ln 2}{k}$.
- For second-order reactions, the integrated rate law is $\frac{1}{[A]_t} = kt + \frac{1}{[A]_0}$ and the half-life expression is $t_{1/2} = \frac{k}{[A]_0}$ (Section 14.3).

Activation energy, E_a, is the energy needed to initiate a reaction, the energy needed to begin the bond-making and bond-breaking processes. It is the difference between the potential energy of the reactants and the transition state. Rate constants, therefore, are temperature-dependent. As temperature increases, a higher percentage of molecules have sufficient energy (activation energy, E_a) to react. However, even in collisions with sufficient energy, molecules must have the correct orientation before a reaction can occur. These various parameters are combined in the Arrhenius equation, $k = Ae^{-\frac{E_a}{RT}}$. Taking the natural log of this relationship yields a linear equation that allows you to calculate E_a given values of the rate constant at various temperatures. The two-point version of the Arrhenius equation, $\ln \frac{k_1}{k_2} = \frac{E_a}{R}\left(\frac{1}{T_2} - \frac{1}{T_1}\right)$, is used to calculate activation energy from rate constants measured at two temperatures and also to predict rate constants at different temperatures (Section 14.4).

Stoichiometric or overall equations typically represent a series of individual molecular events known as elementary steps or elementary reactions, which are categorized as unimolecular, bimolecular, or termolecular based on the number of reactant molecules. The rate laws of elementary steps are derived directly from the stoichiometry of the elementary step equations. Intermediate species are the products of one elementary step and the reactants of a subsequent elementary step. Together, the elementary steps make up the reaction mechanism. The slowest step, the one with the highest activation energy, is the rate-determining step and determines the rate law for the overall reaction. Neither intermediates nor catalysts appear in the rate law for the overall reaction. A proposed mechanism for a reaction must satisfy the following criteria:

- the elementary steps must sum up to the overall equation and
- the rate law for the rate-determining step must be consistent with the observed rate law, which cannot contain intermediates (Section 14.5).

Catalysts facilitate reactions by providing an alternative reaction pathway with a lower activation energy. Catalysts interact with reactants, where they are consumed in one step and produced in a later step. Thus, catalysts are *not* consumed by the overall reaction. Catalysts, which play important roles in all biological and many industrial processes, can be homogeneous (in the same phase as the reactants) or heterogeneous (in a different phase than the reactants) (Section 14.6).

END OF CHAPTER QUESTIONS

14.1 Rates of Reaction

1. For the generic reaction $A \rightarrow B$, state whether the following changes will result in an increase in the reaction rate, a decrease in the reaction rate, or whether the reaction rate will be unaffected.
   a. Increasing the concentration of A
   b. Decreasing the temperature
   c. Adding a catalyst
   d. Increasing the concentration of B

2. State whether the following changes will result in an increase in the reaction rate, a decrease in the reaction rate, or whether the reaction rate will be unaffected.
   a. Decreasing the surface area of a reactant
   b. Decreasing the concentration of a product
   c. Increasing the temperature
   d. Adding a catalyst

3. For each of the following chemical equations, use words and an equation to express the reaction rate in terms of the changes in concentration of both the reactants and products.
   a. $2\,A + B \rightarrow C + 3\,D$
   b. $A + 3\,B \rightarrow 2\,C + 2\,D$
   c. $2\,NO(g) + O_2(g) \rightarrow 2\,NO_2(g)$
   d. $2\,H_2O_2(aq) \rightarrow 2\,H_2O(l) + O_2(g)$

4. For each of the following chemical equations, use words and an equation to express the reaction rate in terms of the changes in concentration of both the reactants and products.
   a. $A \rightarrow 2\,B + C$
   b. $2\,A + 3\,B \rightarrow C + 2\,D$
   c. $2\,NO(g) + Br_2(g) \rightarrow 2\,NOBr(g)$
   d. $H_2(g) + 2\,ICl(g) \rightarrow 2\,HCl(g) + I_2(g)$

5. For the reaction $3\,A + B \rightarrow 2\,C + 2\,D$, the rate of change of reactant A is determined to be $-3.56 \times 10^{-3}\ M \cdot s^{-1}$.
   a. What is the rate of the reaction at this point?
   b. What is the rate of change of reactant B?
   c. What is the rate of change of product D?

6. For the reaction $A \rightarrow B + 2\,C$, the rate of change of product B is determined to be $7.42 \times 10^{-4}\ M \cdot s^{-1}$.
   a. What is the rate of the reaction at this point?
   b. What is the rate of change of product C?
   c. What is the rate of change of reactant A?

14.2 Reaction Rates and Concentration: Rate Laws

7. Chlorine gas, Cl_2, reacts with chloroform, $CHCl_3$, to form carbon tetrachloride, CCl_4, and hydrogen chloride gas, HCl.

$$Cl_2(g) + CHCl_3(g) \rightarrow HCl(g) + CCl_4(g)$$

Calculate the average rate of reaction based on the following time and concentration data.

Time (s)	$[CCl_4]$ (M)
7.00	0.167
148.0	0.374

8. Given the concentration and time data for the reaction $A \rightarrow 2\,B$, determine the average rate of change of B from $t = 0.00$ s to $t = 332.0$ s.

Time (s)	[A] (M)
0.00	0.780
166.0	0.480
332.0	0.180

9. Concentration and time data for the reaction $A \rightarrow B$ are given below.
   a. Calculate the average rate of change from $t = 0.00$ s to $t = 100.0$ s.
   b. Calculate the instantaneous rate of change at $t = 40.0$ s.

Time (s)	[B] (M)
0.00	0.00
20.0	0.0231
40.0	0.0398
60.0	0.0513
80.0	0.0589
100.0	0.0635

10. Given the concentration and time data for the reaction $A \rightarrow$ products, calculate
    a. the average rate of change from $t = 0.00$ s to $t = 50.0$ s.
    b. the instantaneous rate of change at $t = 20.0$ s.

Time (s)	[A] (M)
0.00	0.54
5.00	0.45
10.0	0.39
20.0	0.31
30.0	0.26
40.0	0.22
50.0	0.19

11. The reaction $2\,A + 2\,B \rightarrow$ products has a rate law of rate $= k[A]$.
    a. What is the order of the reaction with respect to A?
    b. What is the order of the reaction with respect to B?
    c. What is the overall reaction order?

12. The reaction $2\,A + 3\,B \rightarrow$ products has a rate law rate $= k[A]^2[B]$.
    a. What is the order of the reaction with respect to A?
    b. What is the order of the reaction with respect to B?
    c. What is the overall reaction order?

13. The reaction

$$A + B \rightarrow C + D \quad \text{rate} = k[A][B]^2$$

has an initial rate of 0.0470 M/s.
    a. What will the initial rate be if [A] is halved and [B] is tripled?
    b. What will the initial rate be if [A] is tripled and [B] is halved?

14. Consider the initial rate data at a certain temperature for the reaction

$$2\,NO(g) + 2\,H_2(g) \rightarrow N_2(g) + 2\,H_2O(g)$$

Experiment	$[H_2]$ (M)	[NO] (M)	Initial rate (M/s)
1	0.200	0.200	2.06×10^{-4}
2	0.200	0.400	8.24×10^{-4}
3	0.400	0.400	1.65×10^{-3}

    a. Determine the rate law for the reaction.
    b. Calculate the rate constant.

15. The initial rate data at a certain temperature were collected for the reaction

$$NO_2(g) + CO(g) \rightarrow NO(g) + CO_2(g)$$

Experiment	$[NO_2]$ (M)	[CO] (M)	Initial rate (M/s)
1	0.0250	0.0250	2.12×10^{-3}
2	0.0250	0.0500	2.12×10^{-3}
3	0.0500	0.0500	8.48×10^{-3}

a. Determine the rate law for the reaction.
b. Calculate the rate constant.

16. Using the given information for each reaction, provide the overall reaction order, the rate law, and the units of k.
a. For the reaction $2\,A(g) \rightarrow 4\,B(g) + C(g)$, the rate doubles when [A] is doubled.
b. The reaction $A(aq) + B(aq) \rightarrow C(aq) + D(aq)$ is first order with respect to A and first order with respect to B.
c. For the reaction $2\,A(g) \rightarrow 2\,B(g) + C(g)$, the reaction rate quadruples when the concentration of A is doubled.
d. The reaction $2\,A(g) + 2\,B(g) \rightarrow C(g) + 2\,D(g)$ is first order with respect to B and second order with respect to A.

17. The following initial rate data at 600 K were collected for the reaction

$$H_2(g) + I_2(g) \rightarrow 2\,HI(g)$$

Experiment	$[H_2]$ (M)	$[I_2]$ (M)	Initial rate (M/s)
1	0.300	0.300	3.96×10^{-5}
2	0.600	0.300	7.92×10^{-5}
3	0.600	0.600	1.58×10^{-4}

a. Write the rate law.
b. Calculate the rate constant.
c. What is the rate when $[H_2] = 0.250$ M and $[I_2] = 0.800$ M?

18. Consider the initial rate data collected at 298 K for the reaction

$$CH_3Br(aq) + OH^-(aq) \rightarrow CH_3OH(aq) + Br^-(aq)$$

Experiment	$[CH_3Br]$ (M)	$[OH^-]$ (M)	Initial rate (M/s)
1	0.40	0.40	4.48×10^{-5}
2	0.80	0.40	8.96×10^{-5}
3	0.40	0.20	2.24×10^{-5}
4	0.40	0.80	8.96×10^{-5}
5	0.20	0.20	1.12×10^{-5}

a. Write the rate law.
b. Calculate the rate constant.
c. What is the rate when $[CH_3Br] = 0.350$ M and $[OH^-] = 0.950$ M?

19. The initial rate data were collected for the reaction $A(g) + B(g) \rightarrow C(g) + D(g)$ at 300 K.

Experiment	[A] (M)	[B] (M)	Initial rate (M/s)
1	0.650	0.800	3.12×10^{4}
2	1.10	0.800	5.28×10^{4}
3	1.76	1.40	14.78×10^{4}

a. Write the rate law.
b. Calculate the rate constant.
c. What is the rate when $[A] = 1.25$ M and $[B] = 1.50$ M?

20. Given the initial rate data, calculate the rate constant for the reaction $A(g) + B(g) \rightarrow$ products.

Experiment	[A] (M)	[B] (M)	Initial rate (M/s)
1	0.200	0.210	0.0186
2	0.200	0.462	0.0900
3	0.280	0.210	0.0260

14.3 Integrated Rate Laws and Half-Lives

21. The decomposition of sulfuryl chloride, SO_2Cl_2, is a first-order process with a rate constant of $4.50 \times 10^{-2}\ s^{-1}$ at 660 K.

$$SO_2Cl_2(g) \rightarrow SO_2(g) + Cl_2(g)$$

The initial concentration of SO_2Cl_2 is 0.693 M.
a. Calculate the concentration of SO_2Cl_2 after 24.5 s.
b. How many seconds does it take for the concentration of SO_2Cl_2 to drop to 3.59×10^{-3} M?

22. The first-order reaction $A \rightarrow B$ has a rate constant of $0.0793\ s^{-1}$. How many seconds will it take for 65.7% of A to react?

23. The rearrangement of cyclopropane to propene is a first-order reaction. If it takes 13.92 min for the concentration of cyclopropene to decrease from 0.56 M to 0.32 M, how many minutes will it take for the concentration of cyclopropene to decrease from 0.39 M to 0.16 M?

24. The following data were collected for the first-order decomposition of acetone, CH_3COCH_3, at a certain temperature.

Time (s)	$[CH_3COCH_3]$ (M)
0.00	0.583
40.0	0.429
80.0	0.302
120.0	0.209
160.0	0.148
200.0	0.101

a. Calculate the value of the rate constant.
b. Calculate the concentration of acetone remaining after 93.0 s.

25. A first-order reaction has a rate constant of $4.38 \times 10^{-4}\ s^{-1}$ at a certain temperature. Calculate the half-life for this reaction in minutes.

26. The rearrangement of methyl isonitrile (CH_3NC) to acetonitrile (CH_3CN) is a first-order reaction and has a half-life of 3.77 hours at 472 K. Calculate the rate constant for this reaction in inverse seconds.

27. For the first order reaction $A \rightarrow B$, 21.2% of A remains after 32.8 min. Calculate the half-life in minutes.

28. Sucrose reacts with water in an acidic solution to produce glucose and fructose.

$$C_{12}H_{22}O_{11}(aq) + H_2O(l) \rightarrow$$
$$C_6H_{12}O_6(aq)(\text{glucose}) + C_6H_{12}O_6(aq)(\text{fructose})$$

The reaction is first order with a rate constant of $5.78 \times 10^{-5}\ s^{-1}$ at 25°C.
a. Calculate the half-life for this reaction at 25°C in hours.
b. If the initial concentration of sucrose is 0.958 M, calculate the concentration of sucrose that remains after 5.82 hours.

29. The decomposition reaction $A \rightarrow B + C$ is a second-order process with a rate constant of $6.92 \times 10^{-3}\ M^{-1} \cdot s^{-1}$. The initial concentration of A is 0.0248 M.
a. Calculate the concentration of A after 78.9 min.
b. How many minutes does it take for the concentration of A to drop to 4.28×10^{-3} M?

30. The decomposition of HI to H_2 and I_2 is a second-order reaction with a rate constant of $9.7 \times 10^{-6}\ M^{-1} \cdot s^{-1}$ at 600 K. If the initial concentration of HI is 0.137 M, calculate the amount of time (in days) it will take to reduce the initial concentration to 85.9% of the initial concentration.

31. For the second-order reaction $2\,A \rightarrow B + C$, 4.58 hours is required for the concentration of A to decrease from an initial concentration of 0.398 M to 0.183 M at 40°C. Calculate the rate constant for this reaction at 40°C.

32. The dimerization of butadiene is a second-order reaction.

$$2\,C_4H_6(g) \rightarrow C_8H_{12}(g)$$

The following data were collected at 500 K.

Time (s)	$[C_4H_6]$ (M)
0.00	0.158
579.0	0.0799
1452	0.0407
3157	0.0203
4639	0.0146
6179	0.0109

a. Calculate the value of the rate constant.
b. Determine the concentration of butadiene remaining after 37.55 min.

33. The half-life of a second-order decomposition reaction is 278 s when the initial concentration of the reactant is 0.059 M. Calculate the rate constant for this reaction.

34. At a certain temperature, the second-order reaction $2\,NOBr(g) \rightarrow 2\,NO(g) + Br_2(g)$ has a rate constant of $0.489\ M^{-1} \cdot s^{-1}$ when the initial concentration of NOBr is 0.692 M.
a. Calculate the half-life for this reaction.
b. Calculate the amount of time required for the concentration of NOBr to decrease to 0.0379 M.

35. The rate constant for this zero-order reaction is 0.0271 M/s at a certain temperature.

$$2\,NH_3(g) \rightarrow 3\,H_2(g) + N_2(g)$$

How long would it take for the concentration of NH_3 to decrease from 0.850 M to 0.320 M?

36. For the zero-order reaction $A \rightarrow B + C$, the rate constant at 300 K is 0.0711 M/s. If the initial concentration of A is 0.671 M, calculate the half-life.

37. The time and concentration data for the reaction A → products are shown below.

t (s)	[A] (M)
0.00	0.750
30.0	0.596
60.0	0.473
90.0	0.376

a. Determine the reaction order with respect to A.
b. Calculate the rate constant for the reaction.

38. Time and concentration data were collected for the reaction A → B.

t (s)	[A] (M)
0.00	0.600
30.0	0.484
60.0	0.405
90.0	0.349

a. Determine the reaction order with respect to A.
b. Calculate the rate constant for the reaction.

14.4 Reaction Rates and Temperature: Activation Energy

39. For a certain reaction, the activation energy and enthalpy of reaction were determined to be 245 kJ/mol and 56 kJ/mol, respectively. Sketch an energy diagram for this reaction that shows the potential energy of the reactants, products, and transition state, and include labels for E_a and ΔH.

40. Use the energy diagrams to determine the activation energy, E_a, and enthalpy of reaction, ΔH, for each reaction.

Reaction A

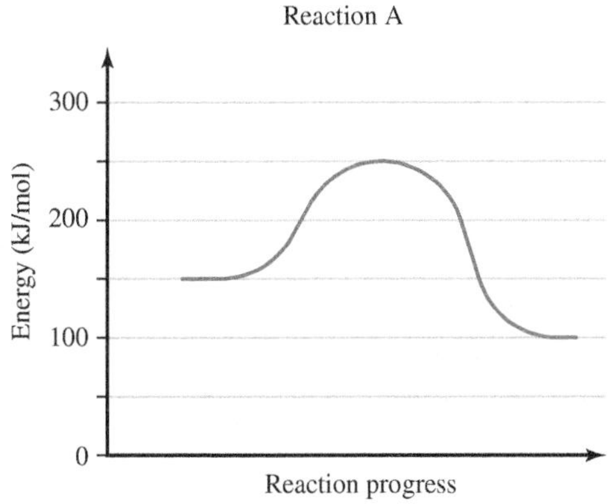

Reaction B

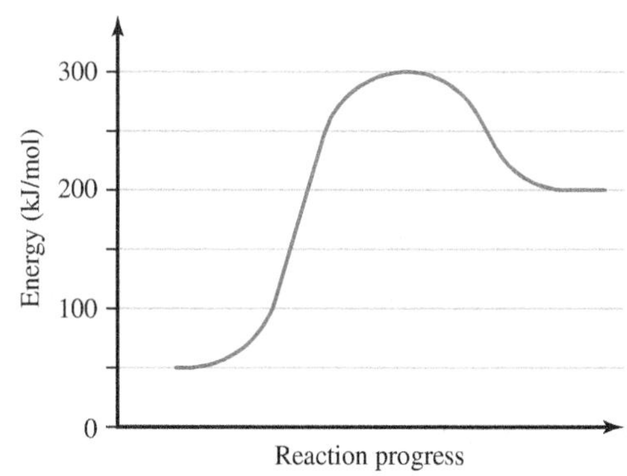

41. Based on the energy diagrams in the previous problem, predict which reaction will proceed at the higher rate or whether they will proceed at the same rate. Explain your reasoning.

42. Predict which reaction will have the higher activation energy.
a. $N_2(g) + 3\,H_2(g) \rightarrow 2\,NH_3(g)$
b. $CH_4(g) + 2\,O_2(g) \rightarrow CO_2(g) + 2\,H_2O(g)$

43. The reactants and products of a chemical reaction are shown here. Draw models of the most likely orientation between the reactant molecules for this chemical reaction to proceed successfully to products. (Reaction: $N_2O + NO \rightarrow N_2 + NO_2$)

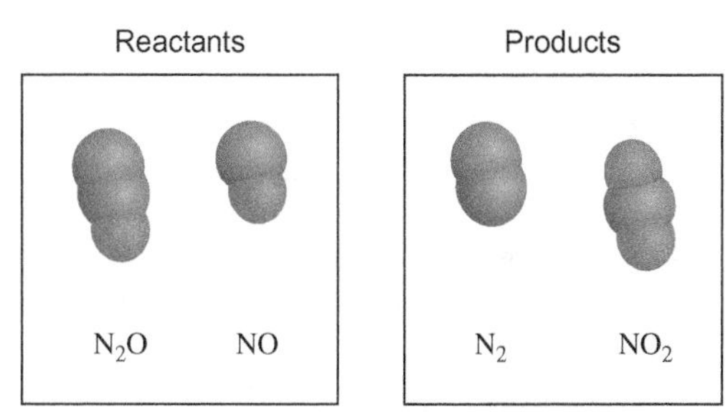

44. The reactants and products of a chemical reaction are shown here. Draw models of the most likely orientation between the reactant molecules for this chemical reaction to proceed successfully to products. [Reaction: $NO(g) + O_3(g) \rightarrow O_2(g) + NO_2(g)$]

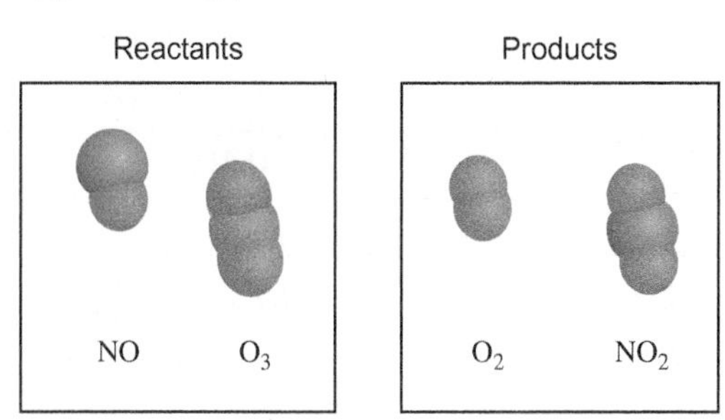

45. Calculate the rate constant for a reaction at 75°C that has an activation energy of 80.2 kJ/mol and a frequency factor of $3.58 \times 10^{11}\ s^{-1}$.

46. Calculate the activation energy, in kJ/mol, for a reaction at 57°C that has a rate constant of $0.224\ s^{-1}$ and a frequency factor of $7.30 \times 10^{11}\ s^{-1}$.

47. The rate constant of a certain reaction was experimentally determined at several temperatures. Use the data in the table to determine the activation energy and frequency factor for this reaction.

T (K)	*k* (s^{-1})
500.0	0.0000105
520.0	0.0000658
540.0	0.000348
560.0	0.00159
580.0	0.00643
600.0	0.0232
620.0	0.0758
640.0	0.227
660.0	0.629
680.0	1.62

48. Use the experimental rate constant data shown in the table to calculate the activation energy for the following reaction.

$$2\ HI(g) \rightarrow H_2(g) + I_2(g)$$

T (°C)	*k* ($M^{-1} \cdot s^{-1}$)
283.0	9.42×10^{-7}
302.0	3.26×10^{-6}
356.0	8.09×10^{-5}
374.0	2.30×10^{-4}
393.0	5.88×10^{-4}
410.0	1.37×10^{-3}
427.0	3.10×10^{-3}
443.0	6.70×10^{-3}
508.0	0.1059

49. Rate constants for the reaction $2\ NO_2(g) \rightarrow 2\ NO(g) + O_2(g)$ are $0.77\ M^{-1} \cdot s^{-1}$ at 603 K and $4.7\ M^{-1} \cdot s^{-1}$ at 656 K.
   a. Calculate the value of the activation energy in kJ/mol.
   b. Calculate the rate constant at 626 K.

50. The rate constant for the reaction $2\ N_2O_5(g) \rightarrow 4\ NO_2(g) + O_2(g)$ is 5.2×10^{-3} at 65°C. Calculate the rate constant for the reaction at 85°C.

51. A certain reaction has an activation energy of 32.98 kJ/mol. At what temperature in kelvins will the reaction proceed 6 times faster than it did at 345 K?

52. A certain reaction proceeds 3 times faster at 465 K than it did at 435 K. Calculate the activation energy in kJ/mol for this reaction.

14.5 Reaction Mechanisms

53. Write the overall balanced reaction and identify any intermediates for the following reaction mechanism.

   Step 1: $O_2(g) \rightleftharpoons 2\ O(g)$
   Step 2: $O(g) + N_2(g) \longrightarrow NO(g) + N(g)$
   Step 3: $N(g) + O(g) \longrightarrow NO(g)$

54. Write the overall balanced reaction and identify any intermediates for the following reaction mechanism.

   Step 1: $N_2O_5(g) \rightarrow NO_3(g) + NO_2(g)$
   Step 2: $NO_3(g) \rightarrow NO_2(g) + O(g)$
   Step 3: $2\ O(g) \rightarrow O_2(g)$

55. What is the relationship between molecularity and order in an elementary step? Does that same relationship hold true for an overall reaction?

56. Write the rate law and identify the molecularity of the following elementary reactions.
   a. $NO_2(g) \rightarrow NO(g) + O(g)$
   b. $ClO(g) + O(g) \rightarrow Cl(g) + O_2(g)$
   c. $2\ NO(g) + Br_2(g) \rightarrow 2\ NOBr(g)$
   d. $I_2(g) \rightarrow 2\ I(g)$

57. Write the rate law and identify the molecularity of the following elementary reactions.
   a. $2\ NO_2(g) \rightarrow NO_3(g) + NO(g)$
   b. $SO_2Cl_2(g) \rightarrow SO_2(g) + Cl_2(g)$
   c. $Cl(g) + Cl(g) + N_2(g) \rightarrow Cl_2(g) + N_2(g)$
   d. $O_3(g) + Cl(g) \rightarrow O_2(g) + ClO(g)$

58. The formation of nitryl fluoride, NO_2F, is thought to occur by the following two-step mechanism.

Step 1: $NO_2(g) + F_2(g) \rightarrow NO_2F(g) + F(g)$ (slow)
Step 2: $F(g) + NO_2(g) \rightarrow NO_2F(g)$ (fast)

Write the overall balanced reaction and rate law.

59. The decomposition of hydrogen peroxide is thought to occur by the following three-step mechanism.

Step 1: $H_2O_2(g) \rightarrow 2\,OH(g)$ (slow)

Step 2: $H_2O_2(g) + OH(g) \rightarrow H_2O(g) + HO_2(g)$ (fast)

Step 3: $HO_2(g) + OH(g) \rightarrow H_2O(g) + O_2(g)$ (fast)

Write the overall balanced equation and rate law.

60. The thermal decomposition of nitryl chloride, NO_2Cl, is described by the following overall reaction and rate law.

$2\,NO_2Cl(g) \rightarrow 2\,NO_2(g) + Cl_2(g)$
Rate $= k[NO_2Cl]$

Propose a mechanism that is consistent with this rate law.

61. Propose a mechanism that is consistent with the rate law for the reaction

$H_2(g) + 2\,ICl(g) \rightarrow I_2(g) + 2\,HCl(g)$
Rate $= k[H_2][ICl]$

62. The reaction $NO(g) + NO_2(g) + O_2(g) \rightarrow N_2O_5(g)$ is experimentally determined to obey this rate law: Rate $= k[NO][NO_2]$. Propose a mechanism that is consistent with this rate law.

63. The following mechanism has been proposed for the formation of HI(g), which has a rate law of Rate $= k[H_2][I_2]$.

Step 1: $I_2(g) \rightleftharpoons 2\,I(g)$ (fast, equilibrium)

Step 2: $H_2(g) + 2\,I(g) \longrightarrow 2\,HI(g)$ (slow)

a. Write the overall balanced reaction.
b. Show that the proposed mechanism is consistent with the rate law.
c. Express the overall rate constant k in terms of the rate constants for the elementary reactions.

64. The following three-step mechanism has been proposed for the reaction of nitric oxide with hydrogen, which has a rate law of Rate $= k[NO]^2[H_2]$.

Step 1: $2\,NO(g) \rightleftharpoons N_2O_2(g)$ (fast, equilibrium)

Step 2: $N_2O_2(g) + H_2(g) \longrightarrow N_2O(g) + H_2O(g)$ (slow)

Step 3: $N_2O(g) + H_2(g) \longrightarrow N_2(g) + H_2O(g)$ (fast)

a. Write the overall balanced reaction.
b. Show that the proposed mechanism is consistent with the rate law.
c. Express the overall rate constant k in terms of the rate constants for the elementary reactions.

65. In an acidic solution, the reaction

$NH_4^+ + HNO_2 \rightarrow N_2 + 2\,H_2O + H^+$

has been proposed to proceed by the following mechanism.

Step 1: $HNO_2 + H^+ \rightleftharpoons H_2O + NO^+$ (fast, equilibrium)

Step 2: $NH_4^+ \rightleftharpoons NH_3 + H^+$ (fast, equilibrium)

Step 3: $NO^+ + NH_3 \longrightarrow NH_3NO^+$ (slow)

Step 4: $NH_3NO^+ \longrightarrow H_2O + H^+ + N_2$ (fast)

Determine the rate law.

14.6 Catalysis

66. Determine whether the following aspects of a reaction are increased, decreased, or unaffected by the addition of a catalyst.
a. rate of the forward reaction
b. rate of the reverse reaction
c. activation energy of the forward reaction
d. activation energy of the reverse reaction
e. enthalpy of the reaction

67. Identify whether the following statements are true or false.
a. A catalyst lowers the activation energy of a chemical reaction.
b. A reaction follows the same set of elementary reactions in the presence of a catalyst.
c. The enthalpy of a reaction is the same for a catalyzed reaction and an uncatalyzed reaction.
d. The overall reaction in the presence of a catalyst is different from the uncatalyzed reaction.
e. A catalyst is not consumed in the reaction.

68. What is the difference between a homogeneous catalyst and a heterogeneous catalyst?

69. The decomposition of acetaldehyde, CH_3CHO, in the presence of iodine is thought to occur by the following two-step mechanism.

Step 1: $CH_3CHO(g) + I_2(g) \rightarrow CH_3I(g) + HI(g) + CO(g)$

Step 2: $CH_3I(g) + HI(g) \rightarrow CH_4(g) + I_2(g)$

a. Write the balanced equation for the overall reaction.
b. Identify any intermediates and catalysts.

70. The destruction of ozone, O_3, by Cl atoms in the upper atmosphere is thought to occur by the following two-step mechanism.

Step 1: $O_3(g) + Cl(g) \rightarrow ClO(g) + O_2(g)$
Step 2: $ClO(g) + O(g) \rightarrow Cl(g) + O_2(g)$

Write the balanced equation for the overall reaction.
a. Identify any intermediates and catalysts.
b. Identify whether the catalyst is a heterogeneous or homogeneous catalyst.

71. The decomposition of nitramide, NH_2NO_2, in aqueous solution is thought to occur through the following two-step mechanism.

Step 1: $NH_2NO_2(aq) + OH^-(aq) \rightarrow NHNO_2^-(aq) + H_2O(l)$
Step 2: $NHNO_2^-(aq) \rightarrow N_2O(g) + OH^-(aq)$

a. Write the balanced equation for the overall reaction.
b. Identify any intermediates and catalysts.

72. Write the overall balanced reaction and identify any intermediates and catalysts for the following reaction mechanism.

Step 1: $ClO^-(aq) + H_2O(l) \rightarrow HClO(aq) + OH^-(aq)$
Step 2: $I^-(aq) + HClO(aq) \rightarrow HIO(aq) + Cl^-(aq)$
Step 3: $OH^-(aq) + HIO(aq) \rightarrow H_2O(l) + IO^-(aq)$

Putting It Together

73. A first-order reaction has a half-life of 36.7 min at 60°C and a half-life of 23.5 min at 75°C.
a. Calculate the activation energy of this reaction in kJ/mol.
b. Calculate the half-life of the reaction at 85°C.

74. For the reaction A → B, the concentration of A and the time required to decrease that concentration to one-half of the initial concentration, $t_{1/2}$, are directly proportional.
a. What is the order of the reaction?
b. The rate constant for the reaction is 0.0426 M/s at 350 K. Given an initial concentration of 0.385 M, calculate the half-life of the reaction.

75. A reactant with an initial concentration of 0.310 M decomposes with a half-life of 105 s. The same reactant decomposes with a half-life of 221 s when its initial concentration is 0.147 M.
a. What is the order of the reaction?
b. Calculate the rate constant.

76. A first-order reaction A → products has a rate constant of $k = 4.7 \times 10^{-4}$ at 298 K. Calculate the rate of reaction at $t = 580$ s when the initial concentration of A is 3.2×10^{-2} M.

77. A certain reactant, A, decomposes spontaneously to B and C.

$$A \rightarrow B + C$$

The activation energy for the reaction is 19 kJ/mol. The presence of a catalyst lowers the activation energy to 7.5 kJ/mol. At what temperature would the uncatalyzed reaction have a rate equal to that of the catalyzed reaction at 298 K?

78. A three-step mechanism has been proposed for the reaction between chlorine and chloroform.

Step 1: $Cl_2(g) \rightleftharpoons 2\,Cl(g)$ (fast)
Step 2: $Cl(g) + CHCl_3(g) \longrightarrow HCl(g) + CCl_3(g)$ (slow)
Step 3: $Cl(g) + CCl_3(g) \longrightarrow CCl_4(g)$ (fast)

a. Write the balanced equation for the overall reaction.
b. Identify any intermediates and catalysts.
c. Write the rate law for the reaction.
d. Express the overall rate constant k in terms of the rate constants for the elementary reactions.

79. Time and concentration data were collected for the reaction $C_4H_8 \rightarrow 2\,C_2H_4$ at a certain temperature.

Time (s)	$[C_4H_8]$ (M)
0.00	0.942
25.0	0.805
50.0	0.703
75.0	0.612
100.0	0.528
125.0	0.459
150.0	0.403
175.0	0.345
200.0	0.304

a. Determine the order of the reaction and rate constant at this temperature.
b. Determine the half-life for the reaction at the initial concentration.
c. Determine the amount of time it will take for 75.2% of the C_4H_8 to convert to C_2H_4.

80. For the decomposition reaction $A_2B \rightarrow 2\ A + B$, the following time and concentration data were collected at a certain temperature.

Time (min)	$[A_2B]$ (M)
0.00	0.238
15.0	0.216
45.0	0.187
75.0	0.166
105.0	0.15
135.0	0.136

a. Determine the order of the reaction and rate constant at this temperature.
b. Determine the half-life for the reaction at the initial concentration.
c. Determine the concentration of A after 175 min.

81. The fraction of molecules at or above the activation energy is equal to k/A (the rate constant divided by the frequency factor). The activation energy for a particular reaction is $E_a = 11.10$ kJ. What percentage of molecules are at or above the activation energy at 450.0 K?

82. At 30.0°C, milk sours in 24 hours. If kept refrigerated at 5.0°C, the same milk takes 6 days to sour. Estimate the activation energy in kJ/mol for the reaction that leads to the souring of the milk.

83. The first-order reaction $AB_2(g) \rightarrow A(g) + 2\ B(g)$ has a half-life of 1.36 hours at 35°C. A 2.5 L vessel initially contains 0.923 atm of AB_2. Calculate the partial pressure of B in the vessel after 159 minutes.

84. The first-order reaction $A(g) \rightarrow B(g)$ has a rate constant of 3.45×10^{-3} at 225°C. A 2.0 L vessel initially contains 0.856 atm of A. Calculate the amount of time it will take to reduce the partial pressure of A to 0.284 atm.

85. The rate constant of the reaction $A(g) + B(g) \rightarrow AB(g)$ was experimentally determined at several temperatures. The reaction is first order for each reactant and second order overall.

T (°C)	k ($M^{-1} \cdot s^{-1}$)
125.0	0.00478
150.0	0.00729
175.0	0.0113
200.0	0.0178
225.0	0.0267

a. Calculate the activation energy and frequency factor for this reaction.
b. Determine the rate constant at 100.0°C.
c. If the reaction mixture contains 0.0178 M A and 0.0317 M B, calculate the initial rate of the reaction at 250°C.

86. The following three-step mechanism has been proposed for the formation of phosgene gas (Cl_2CO) from Cl_2 and CO.

Step 1: $Cl_2 \rightleftharpoons 2\ Cl$ (fast, equilibrium)

Step 2: $Cl + CO \rightleftharpoons ClCO$ (fast, equilibrium)

Step 3: $ClCO + Cl_2 \longrightarrow Cl_2CO + Cl$ (slow)

a. Write the balanced equation for the overall reaction.
b. Identify any intermediates and catalysts.
c. Write the rate law for the reaction.
d. Express the overall rate constant k in terms of the rate constants for the elementary reactions.

87. The rate law for the reaction

$$A + B + C \rightarrow D + E$$

is Rate $= [A]^2[B]^{1/2}/[C]$. The rate of the reaction is 0.0385 M/s at certain initial concentrations of A, B, and C. Calculate the rate of the reaction if the concentration of A is tripled, the concentration of B is doubled, and the concentration of C is halved.

PRACTICE PROBLEM SOLUTIONS

Practice Problem 14.1 Solution

For $2\ A \rightarrow 3\ B$, two reactant molecules A are consumed for every three molecules of the product B that appear. These rates can be written as

$$\text{Rate} = -\frac{1}{2}\frac{\Delta[A]}{\Delta t} = \frac{1}{3}\frac{\Delta[B]}{\Delta t}$$

For $3\ A \rightarrow 2\ B$, three reactant molecules A are consumed for every two molecules of the product B that appear. These rates can be written as

$$\text{Rate} = -\frac{1}{3}\frac{\Delta[A]}{\Delta t} = \frac{1}{2}\frac{\Delta[B]}{\Delta t}$$

For $3\ O_2 \rightarrow 2\ O_3$, the reaction consumes three oxygen molecules, O_2, for every two molecules of ozone, O_3, that appear. These rates can be written as

$$\text{Rate} = -\frac{1}{3}\frac{\Delta[O_2]}{\Delta t} = \frac{1}{2}\frac{\Delta[O_3]}{\Delta t}$$

For $2\ NO_2 \rightarrow N_2O_4$, two molecules of nitrogen dioxide, NO_2, are consumed for every one molecule of dinitrogen tetroxide, N_2O_4, produced. Therefore, the rate of disappearance of NO_2 is twice the rate of appearance of N_2O_4.

$$\text{Rate} = -\frac{1}{2}\frac{\Delta[NO_2]}{\Delta t} = \frac{\Delta[N_2O_4]}{\Delta t}$$

Practice Problem 14.2 Solution

a. Determine the average rate.

$$\text{Rate} = \frac{\Delta[B]}{\Delta t}$$

$$\text{Rate} = \frac{0.185\ \text{M} - 0.050\ \text{M}}{30.0\ \text{s} - 5.0\ \text{s}}$$

$$\text{Rate} = \frac{0.135\ \text{M}}{25.0\ \text{s}} = 0.00540\ \text{M/s}$$

b. To determine the instantaneous rate at 10.0 s, plot the data, draw a tangent to the curve at the 10.0 s point, and determine the slope of that tangent line.

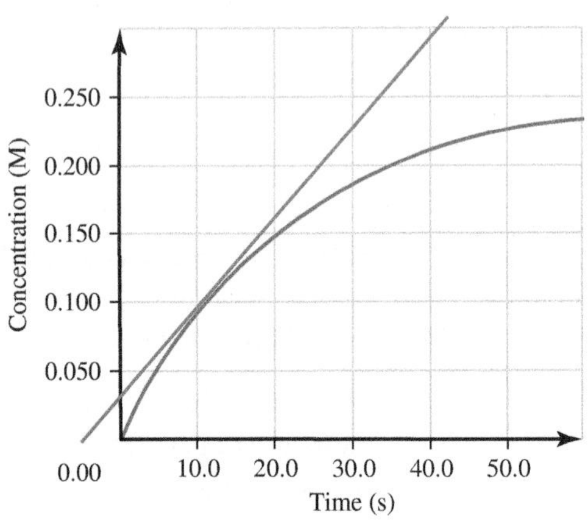

Choose two points from the tangent line: (30.0, 0.225) and (10.0, 0.091).

$$m = \frac{(0.225 - 0.091)\ \text{M}}{(30.0 - 10.0)\ \text{s}} = 0.0067\ \text{M/s}$$

The instantaneous rate at 10.0 s is 0.0067 M/s.

Practice Problem 14.3 Solution

a. [A] is unchanged and [B] is doubled.

The reaction is second order in A but there is no change in [A] to alter the rate: $1^2 = 1$.

The reaction is first order in B, so doubling [B] will increase the reaction rate by a factor of $2^1 = 2$.

Therefore, the original rate must increase by a factor of $1 \times 2 = 2$.

$$2(0.110\ \text{M/s}) = 0.220\ \text{M/s}$$

b. Both [A] and [B] are doubled.

The reaction is second order in A, so doubling [A] will increase the reaction rate by a factor of $2^2 = 4$.

The reaction is first order in B, so doubling [B] will increase the reaction rate by a factor of $2^1 = 2$.

Therefore, the original rate must increase by a factor of $4 \times 2 = 8$.

$$8(0.110\ \text{M/s}) = 0.880\ \text{M/s}$$

c. [A] is tripled and [B] is doubled.

The reaction is second order in A, so tripling [A] will increase the reaction rate by a factor of $3^2 = 9$.

The reaction is first order in B, and doubling [B] will increase the reaction rate by a factor of $2^1 = 2$.

Therefore, the original rate must increase by a factor of $9 \times 2 = 18$.

$$18(0.110\ \text{M/s}) = 1.98\ \text{M/s}$$

Practice Problem 14.4 Solution

a. To write the rate law, compare the data between two experiments. If you compare either experiments 1 and 2 or 1 and 3, then you will find that the rate doubles when the concentration of cyclopropane is doubled. The rearrangement of cyclopropane to propene, then, is a first-order reaction.

$$\text{Rate} = k[\text{cyclopropane}]$$

b. To calculate the rate constant, rearrange the rate law to solve for k and use the rate and concentration data from any one of the three experiments. The following calculation uses the data from experiment 3. Since the data were recorded to only two significant figures, all calculations involving these data must be rounded to two significant figures.

$$k = \frac{\text{Rate}}{[\text{cyclopropane}]} = \frac{0.033\ \text{M/h}}{0.62\ \text{M}} = 0.053\ \text{h}^{-1}$$

c. Now that you know k, calculate the reaction rate at any given concentration of cyclopropane.

$$\text{Rate} = 0.053\ \text{h}^{-1}[\text{cyclopropane}]$$

$$\text{Rate} = 0.053\ \text{h}^{-1}(0.44\ \text{M}) = 0.023\ \text{M}\cdot\text{h}^{-1}$$

Practice Problem 14.5 Solution

a. Experiments 1 and 2 show that the rate doubles when $[NO_2]$ doubles and $[F_2]$ is held constant. The reaction, then, is first order with respect to NO_2. Experiments 3 and 4 show that the rate doubles when $[F_2]$ doubles and $[NO_2]$ is held constant. The reaction, then, is also first order with respect to F_2 and second order overall. Now write the rate law.

$$\text{Rate} = k[NO_2][F_2]$$

b. Calculate the rate constant using the data from any experiment. Experiment 2 is used here. Since the data were recorded to only three significant figures, all calculations involving these data must be rounded to three significant figures.

$$k = \frac{\text{Rate}}{[NO_2][F_2]}$$

$$k = \frac{4.30 \times 10^{-4}\ \text{M/s}}{(0.00259\ \text{M})(0.00479\ \text{M})}$$

$$k = 34.7\ \text{M}^{-1}\text{s}^{-1}$$

c. Use the completed rate law and the concentrations provided in the problem:

$$\text{Rate} = (34.7\ \text{M}^{-1}\text{s}^{-1})[NO_2][F_2]$$

$$\text{Rate} = (34.7\ \text{M}^{-1}\text{s}^{-1})(0.00722\ \text{M})(0.00479\ \text{M})$$

$$\text{Rate} = 1.20 \times 10^{-3}\ \text{M}\cdot\text{s}^{-1}$$

Practice Problem 14.6 Solution

a. Apply the linear form of the integrated rate law for first-order reactions. $[A]_0 = 0.350$ M is given in the first row of the table (at $t = 0$). Use any other row of the table for the values of t and $[A]_t$.

$$\ln[A]_t = -kt + \ln[A]_0$$

$$\ln(0.271\ \text{M}) = -k(4.00\ \text{s}) + \ln(0.350\ \text{M})$$

$$k = 0.0640\ \text{s}^{-1}$$

Alternatively, you could plot ln[A] versus time, then use "rise over run" or graphing software to determine the slope of the line, where slope $= m = -k$.

$$m = -0.0640\ \text{s}^{-1} \qquad k = 0.0640\ \text{s}^{-1}$$

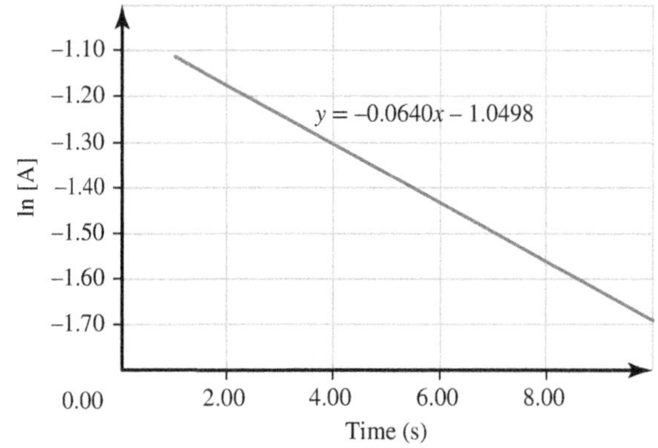

To determine the concentration of A at a specific time, use the integrated rate law including the rate constant calculated in part 1. $[A]_0$ is provided in the data table and the specific time is provided in the problem statement.

b. Again use the first-order integrated rate law, with the value of k calculated in part (a).

$$\ln[A]_t = -kt + \ln[A]_0$$

$$\ln[A]_{30.0\ \text{s}} = -(0.0640\ \text{s}^{-1})(30.0\ \text{s}) + \ln(0.350\ \text{M})$$

$$\ln[A]_{30.0\ \text{s}} = -1.92 + (-1.05) = -2.97$$

$$[A]_{30.0\ \text{s}} = e^{-2.97} = 0.051\ \text{M}$$

Practice Problem 14.7 Solution

a. For a first-order reaction, the rate constant and half-life are related as follows.

$$t_{1/2} = \frac{\ln 2}{k}$$

Rearrange the equation to isolate k.

$$k = \frac{\ln 2}{t_{1/2}}$$

$$k = \frac{\ln 2}{26.0\ \text{s}} = 0.0267\ \text{s}^{-1}$$

b. Use the integrated rate law to determine the fraction of reactant remaining.

$$\ln\frac{[A]_t}{[A]_0} = -kt$$

$$\ln\frac{[A]_t}{[A]_0} = (-0.0267\ \text{s}^{-1})(35.0\ \text{s})$$

$$\ln\frac{[A]_t}{[A]_0} = -0.9345$$

$$\frac{[A]_t}{[A]_0} = e^{-0.9345}$$

$$\frac{[A]_t}{[A]_0} = 0.393$$

The ratio $[A]_t/[A]_0$ equals 0.393, which can be rewritten as 39.3/100. Thus, 39.3% of the reactant is present after the reaction has proceeded for 35.0 s.

Practice Problem 14.8 Solution

a. To calculate the concentration of a reactant after a certain period of time, use the integrated rate law for second-order reactions, and substitute the values given for the rate constant, the time, and the initial concentration.

$$\frac{1}{[A]_t} = kt + \frac{1}{[A]_0}$$

$$\frac{1}{[A]_{10\ s}} = 1.55\ M^{-1}s^{-1}(10.0\ s) + \frac{1}{0.0480\ M}$$

$$\frac{1}{[A]_{10\ s}} = 36.3\ M^{-1}$$

$$[A]_{10\ s} = 0.0275\ M$$

b. To determine how long it will take to reduce the concentration of a reactant by a certain percentage, use the integrated rate law for a second-order reaction and substitute for $[A]_t$ based on the information in the problem. When the initial concentration is reduced by 90.0%, 10.0% of the initial 0.0480 M is left. $[A]_t = 0.1[A]_0$

$$[A]_t = 0.100(0.048\ M) = 0.00480\ M$$

Rearrange the integrated rate law to solve for t:

$$t = \frac{1}{k}\left(\frac{1}{[A]_t} - \frac{1}{[A]_0}\right)$$

$$t = \frac{1}{1.55\ M^{-1}s^{-1}}\left(\frac{1}{0.0048\ M} - \frac{1}{0.048\ M}\right)$$

$$t = 121\ s$$

After 121 seconds, the initial concentration of NOBr will be reduced by 90%.

Practice Problem 14.9 Solution

The concentration of reactant decreases from 0.050 M to 0.025 M, which is a drop of one-half. That means that the half-life under these conditions is 35 min. This allows us to use the half-life expression for a second-order reaction to determine the rate constant.

$$k = \frac{1}{t_{1/2}[A]_0}$$

$$k = \frac{1}{(35\ min)(0.050\ M)} = 0.57\ M^{-1}min^{-1}$$

Practice Problem 14.10 Solution

a. To determine the reaction order, plot the data three ways. Option (1) plots [A] versus t to test for zero order, option (2) plots ln[A] versus t to test for first order, and option (3) plots $\frac{1}{[A]}$ versus t to test for second order. Use the linear graph and the information in Table 14.5 to help identify the order of the reaction.

t (s)	[A] (M)	ln[A]	1/[A]
0.0	2.00	0.693	0.667
10.0	0.963	−0.0377	1.04
20.0	0.464	−0.768	2.16
30.0	0.224	−1.50	4.46
40.0	0.108	−2.23	9.26
50.0	0.0520	−2.96	19.2
60.0	0.0251	−3.68	39.8

Option 1

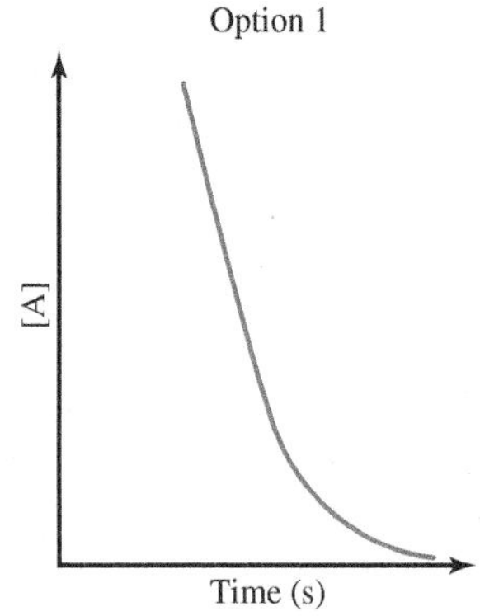

Option 2

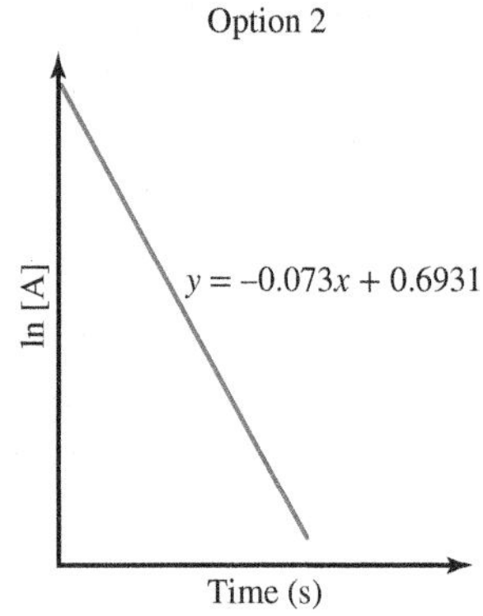

Option 3

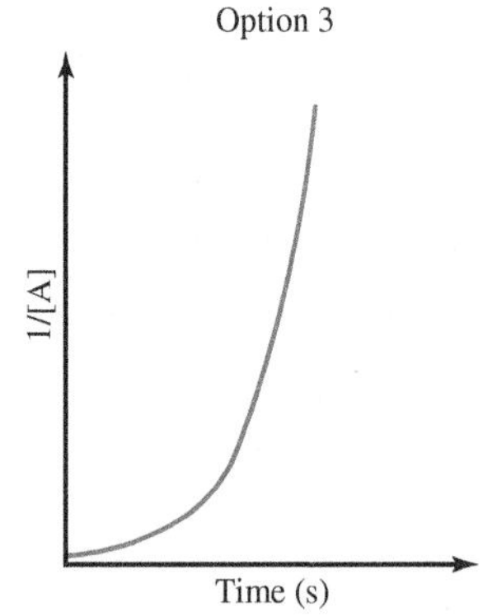

Option 2 gives the only linear result. This reaction is first order with respect to A.

b. Now that the reaction order is known, plug values into the appropriate integrated rate law.

$$\ln[A]_t = -kt + \ln[A]_0$$

$$\ln(0.963\ M) = -k(10.0\ s) + \ln(2.00\ M)$$

$$k = 0.0730\ s^{-1}$$

Alternatively, determine the slope of the line for the ln[A] plot where $m = -k$. The graphing tool (Figure 14.12) gives a slope of $-0.073\ s^{-1}$ for the best-fit line ($y = -0.073x + 0.693$). After adjusting this calculation to three significant figures to reflect the significant figures in the data table, the rate constant is $k = 0.0730\ s^{-1}$.

Practice Problem 14.11 Solution

Reaction A: The Lewis structures show that one mole of N—N triple bonds (counts as 3) and 3 moles of F—F single bonds must be broken for a total of 6 moles of bonds.

:N≡N: :F̤̈—F̤̈:   :F̤̈—F̤̈:   :F̤̈—F̤̈:

Reaction B: The Lewis structures indicate that one mole of Cl—Cl single bonds and 1 mole of F—F single bonds must be broken for a total of 2 moles of bonds.

:C̤̈l—C̤̈l: :F̤̈—F̤̈:

Reaction A involves breaking more moles of bonds. Therefore, you would predict that the reaction of nitrogen and fluorine has a higher activation energy than the reaction of chlorine and fluorine.

Practice Problem 14.12 Solution

A new bond must form between Cl and O, breaking one bond between O atoms and leaving two O atoms still bonded to each other. The most likely orientation for this reaction is a collision between Cl and one of the end O atoms, not the central O atom.

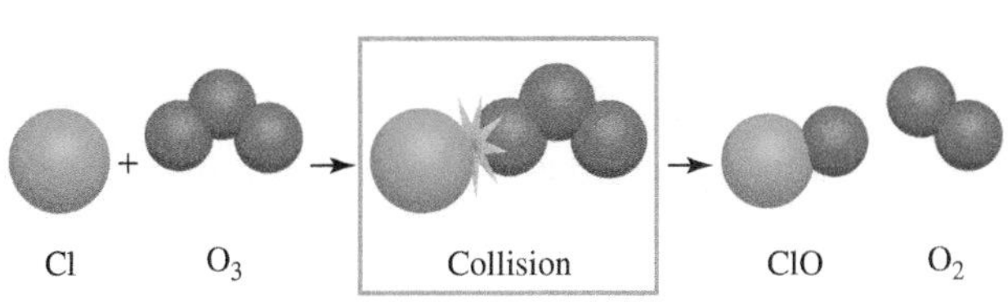

Practice Problem 14.13 Solution

This reaction was carried out at much lower temperatures than the one in Example 14.13, which tells us to expect a lower value for the activation energy. As before, use the Arrhenius equation and plot ln k versus $1/T$. This should produce a straight line with a slope equal to $-E_a/R$.

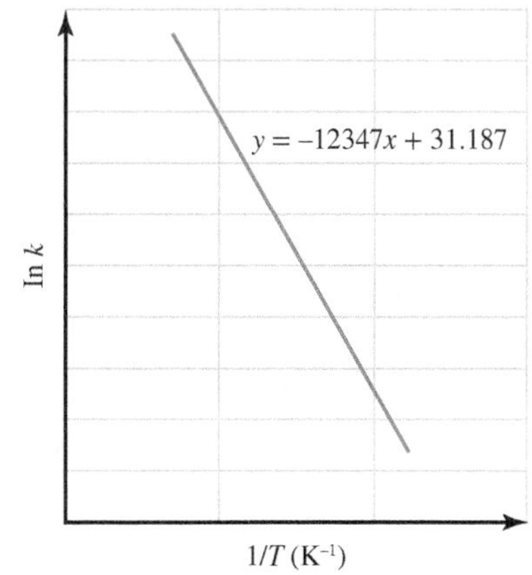

$$\text{Slope} = -\frac{E_a}{R} = -12{,}347\ \text{K}$$

$$E_a = -\text{slope} \times R$$

$$E_a = -(-12{,}347\ \text{K})\left(8.3145 \frac{\text{J}}{\text{mol} \cdot \text{K}}\right)$$

$$E_a = 103{,}000 \frac{\text{J}}{\text{mol}} = 103\ \text{kJ/mol}$$

As predicted, E_a is lower for this reaction than the one in Example 14.13.

Practice Problem 14.14 Solution

For T_1, use either of the temperatures given in the previous example, and use its corresponding rate constant value as k_1. The solution here uses $T_1 = 705$ K. Then rearrange the two-point version of the Arrhenius equation to solve for k_2.

$$\ln \frac{k_1}{k_2} = \frac{E_a}{R}\left(\frac{1}{T_2} - \frac{1}{T_1}\right)$$

Separate the rate constants.

$$\ln k_1 - \ln k_2 = \frac{E_a}{R}\left(\frac{1}{T_2} - \frac{1}{T_1}\right)$$

Solve for $\ln k_2$.

$$\ln k_2 = -\left[\frac{E_a}{R}\left(\frac{1}{T_2} - \frac{1}{T_1}\right) - \ln k_1\right]$$

Substitute values. Remember to divide by the temperatures before subtracting.

$$\ln k_2 = -\left(\frac{218{,}000 \frac{\text{J}}{\text{mol}}}{8.3145 \frac{\text{J}}{\text{mol} \cdot \text{K}}}\left(\frac{1}{805\ \text{K}} - \frac{1}{705\ \text{K}}\right) - \ln 1.39 \times 10^{-6}\ \text{M}^{-1}\text{s}^{-1}\right)$$

$$\ln k_2 = -8.866$$

Finally, solve for k_2. Recall that if $\ln x = y$, then $x = e^y$:

$$k_2 = e^{-8.866} = 1.4 \times 10^{-4}\,M^{-1}s^{-1}$$

Rate constants are temperature-dependent so, as expected, the rate constant at 805 K is greater than the rate constant at 705 K.

Practice Problem 14.15 Solution

The overall equation is the sum of the two elementary steps after combining like terms and removing any species that appear on both sides of the arrow.

Add steps 1 and 2 together:

$$NO(g) + Cl_2(g) + NOCl_2(g) + NO(g) \rightarrow NOCl_2(g) + 2\,NOCl(g)$$

Simplify to give the overall equation:

$$2\,NO(g) + Cl_2(g) \rightarrow 2\,NOCl(g)$$

$NOCl_2(g)$ is a product in step 1 and a reactant in step 2, and it does not appear in the overall balanced equation. $NOCl_2(g)$ is an intermediate in this mechanism.

Practice Problem 14.16 Solution

a. Both elementary steps have two molecules as their reactants, so both are bimolecular.

b. Rate laws for elementary steps can be written directly from the balanced equation.

$$\text{Rate}_{\text{step 1}} = k_1[NO][Cl_2]$$
$$\text{Rate}_{\text{step 2}} = k_2[NOCl_2][NO]$$

Practice Problem 14.17 Solution

The goal is to show that the rate law for step 2, the rate-determining step, is consistent with the overall rate law. Start by writing the rate law for the slow step.

$$\text{Rate} = k_2[NO][NO_3]$$

$[NO_3]$ does not appear in the rate law for the overall reaction, so you must use the equilibrium step of the mechanism to find an equivalent expression for $[NO_3]$ that contains only those species that do appear in the overall reaction.

The rate law for step 1 in the forward direction is Rate $= k_1[NO][O_2]$ and the rate law for step 1 in the reverse direction is Rate $= k_{-1}[NO_3]$. At equilibrium, the forward and reverse rates are equal.

$$k_1[NO][O_2] = k_{-1}[NO_3]$$

Rearrange to solve for $[NO_3]$.

$$[NO_3] = \frac{k_1}{k_{-1}}[NO][O_2]$$

Substitute for $[NO_3]$ in the rate law for the slow step and simplify.

$$\text{Rate} = k_2[NO][NO_3]$$
$$\text{Rate} = k_2[NO]\frac{k_1}{k_{-1}}[NO][O_2]$$
$$\text{Rate} = \frac{k_1k_2}{k_{-1}}[NO]^2[O_2]$$

Making the substitution yields a rate law for the rate-determining step that is consistent with the observed rate law, where $\frac{k_1k_2}{k_{-1}} = k$.

Practice Problem 14.18 Solution

a. Add the equations together, combining all reactants and combining all products. Simplify by combining like terms and removing any species appearing as both a product and a reactant.

Combined: $2\,SO_2(g) + 2\,NO_2(g) + 2\,NO(g) + O_2(g) \rightarrow 2\,SO_3(g) + 2\,NO(g) + 2\,NO_2(g)$

Simplified: $2\,SO_2(g) + 2\,NO_2(g) + 2\,NO(g) + O_2(g) \rightarrow 2\,SO_3(g) + 2\,NO(g) + 2\,NO_2(g)$

The overall reaction is

$$2\,SO_2(g) + O_2(g) \rightarrow 2\,SO_3(g)$$

b. To identify any intermediates and catalysts, you need to look at each step carefully. NO appears as a product in step 1 and a reactant in step 2 (it is produced and then consumed), so it must be an intermediate. NO_2 is present at the start and end of the reaction (it is consumed and then produced), so it must be a catalyst.

Step 1: $2\,SO_2(g) + 2\,NO_2(g) \rightarrow 2\,SO_3(g) + 2\,NO(g)$

Step 2: $2\,NO(g) + O_2(g) \rightarrow 2\,NO_2(g)$

Practice Problem 14.19 Solution

Use the slow step to determine the rate law.

$$\text{Rate} = k[A]$$

Now substitute the given values into this rate law to find k.

$$0.025\text{ M/s} = k(0.50\text{ M})$$
$$k = 0.50\text{ s}^{-1}$$

The rate law indicates that the reaction is first order, so use the first-order half-life formula.

$$t_{1/2} = \frac{\ln 2}{k}$$

$$t_{1/2} = \frac{\ln 2}{0.50\text{ s}^{-1}} = 1.4\text{ s}$$

CHAPTER 15

Chemical Equilibrium

Fotokostic/Shutterstock

The equilibrium system for the combination of hydrogen and nitrogen is economically very important. It is difficult to get nitrogen gas to react to form compounds, yet compounds of nitrogen are necessary for preparing fertilizers and explosives, among many other useful products. The German chemist Fritz Haber (1868–1934) devised the Haber process to "fix" nitrogen (convert it to a compound). The process was first used to produce explosives during World War I, when Germany was cut off from imports of natural nitrates by a shipping blockade. The process is now used to produce 500 million tons of ammonia-based fertilizers every year for use on crops as shown here.

Chapter Outline

GOALS

- Define and explain the condition of equilibrium.
- Determine equilibrium expressions and constants.
- Use equilibrium expressions as formulas.
- Manipulate equilibrium expressions based on changes to the chemical equation.
- Define and explain the reaction quotient.
- Predict the direction of a reaction using the relationship of the reaction quotient to the equilibrium constant.
- Use ICE tables to solve equilibrium problems.
- Identify the reaction conditions that shift the equilibrium position of a reaction.

15.1 Introduction to Equilibrium

GOAL

- Define and explain the condition of equilibrium.

Background Review

Chapter 14 Chemical Kinetics: Section 14.2—Reaction Rates and Concentration: Rate Laws

What would happen if some nitrogen gas, N_2, and some hydrogen gas, H_2, were placed in a vessel along with a catalyst (such as specially treated porous iron) and the temperature of the system was increased to 500°C? The nitrogen would begin to react with the hydrogen to form ammonia, NH_3:

$$3\,H_2(g) + N_2(g) \rightarrow 2\,NH_3(g)$$

The rate of the reaction would be rapid at first, but it would slow down as some of the reactants are used up. Because the pressures of the nitrogen and the hydrogen both decrease as the reaction progresses, the rate of combination also decreases (Section 14.1).

Now suppose that some ammonia gas was introduced into a similar vessel with the same catalyst and the temperature of the system was increased to 500°C. In this case, the ammonia would begin to decompose to hydrogen and nitrogen:

$$2\,NH_3(g) \rightarrow 3\,H_2(g) + N_2(g)$$

The rate of this reaction would decrease from the initial rate as some of the ammonia is used up to form the products. As hydrogen and nitrogen are produced, however, they begin to react to form ammonia, because the reaction of hydrogen and nitrogen to form ammonia is reversible. Whether you start with nitrogen and hydrogen and allow them to form ammonia, or you start with ammonia and allow it to form nitrogen and hydrogen, you will end up with a mixture of nitrogen, hydrogen, and ammonia (Figure 15.1).

When the rate at which hydrogen and nitrogen combine to form ammonia equals the rate at which ammonia decomposes to hydrogen and nitrogen (Figure 15.2), a state of **equilibrium** exists. Equilibrium is a **dynamic state**, which means that *both reactions continue to occur*. The rate of combination equals the rate of decomposition, though, so no *net* change occurs. The decomposition of ammonia, NH_3, continues to occur, but once the reaction reaches equilibrium, new NH_3 is being produced as quickly as the existing NH_3 is decomposing. Therefore, the reaction never goes to completion. Neither reaction stops, but the pressures of nitrogen gas, N_2, and hydrogen gas,

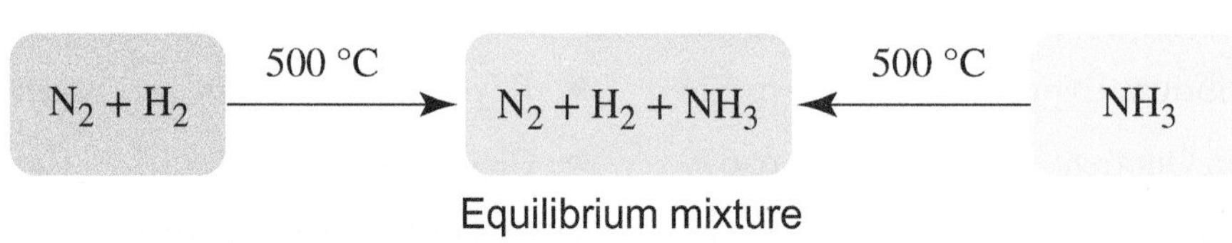

FIGURE 15.1 Approaching Equilibrium from Either Direction

Because the reaction of nitrogen and hydrogen to form ammonia is reversible, the reactants are forming product at the same time the product is decomposing to form reactants. When both reactions occur at the same rate, the system is at equilibrium.

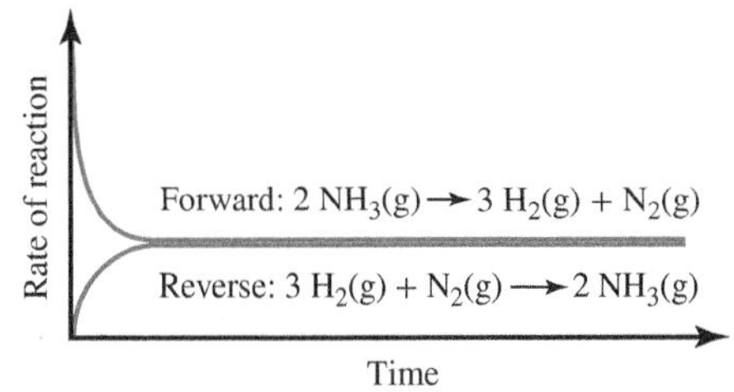

FIGURE 15.2 Rates of Forward and Reverse Reactions
The initial rate of decomposition of NH_3 to form N_2 and H_2 is high because the concentration of NH_3 is high, but as the reaction proceeds, the NH_3 concentration and the reaction rate decrease. Meanwhile, the concentrations of N_2 and H_2, which started at 0, are increasing, as is the rate at which they combine to form NH_3. These reaction rates will continue to change until they are equal, at which point equilibrium is reached. Both reactions continue to occur at the same rate, but no further change in concentrations is observed.

H_2, in the vessel increase to a certain point and go no further, so the effect of the two opposing reactions makes it *appear* as though the decomposition reaction has stopped. No matter how long this system exists, as long as the conditions imposed on the system are not changed, none of the pressures of any of the gases will change.

For efficiency, both the forward and reverse reactions of an equilibrium system can be written in one equation, using a double arrow ($\rightleftharpoons$) to denote that the reaction is occurring in both directions at the same time. For example,

$$2\ NH_3(g) \rightleftharpoons 3\ H_2(g) + N_2(g)$$

If the reaction is started with the substance on the left, it produces the substances on the right. If the reaction is started with the substances on the right, it produces the substance on the left. Because either set of substances produces the other, either set can be placed on the left. The substances written on the left side are conventionally called the reactants, and those written on the right side are called the products. When the substances on the left react to produce those on the right—called the *forward reaction*—the reaction is said to *proceed to the right*. When the substances on the right react to produce those on the left—called the *reverse reaction*—the reaction is said to *proceed to the left*.

SECTION REVIEW

- Equilibrium can occur when a reaction is reversible: The products can react with one another to re-form the reactants.
- In an equilibrium reaction, the forward and reverse reactions occur at the same time.
- When the forward and reverse reactions occur at the same rate, the system is in a state of chemical equilibrium.

15.2 Equilibrium Constants

GOAL

- Determine equilibrium expressions and constants.

Background Review

Chapter 7 Gases: Section 7.6—Ideal Gas Law

Because equilibrium occurs when the forward and reverse reaction rates are equal (Section 15.1), and because reaction rates can be expressed in terms of the concentrations of the reactants (Section 14.2), equilibrium can be described mathematically in terms of concentration. For example, two gaseous iodine atoms at high temperature can combine to form iodine, I_2.

$$2\ I(g) \rightleftharpoons I_2(g)$$

The forward and reverse reactions are described as follows, where k_1 and k_{-1} are their respective rate constants. Concentrations are represented within brackets.

$$2\ I(g) \xrightarrow{k_1} I_2(g) \qquad \text{rate}_{\text{forward}} = k_1[I]^2$$

$$I_2(g) \xrightarrow{k_{-1}} 2\ I(g) \qquad \text{rate}_{\text{reverse}} = k_{-1}[I_2]$$

When this reaction reaches equilibrium (Figure 15.3), the rates of the forward and reverse reactions are equal.

$$k_1[I]^2 = k_{-1}[I_2]$$

Rearranging the expression to put the constants on one side gives

$$\frac{k_1}{k_{-1}} = \frac{[I_2]}{[I]^2}$$

This ratio of rate constants is called the **equilibrium constant, K**. (In some sources, K is denoted as K_{eq}.)

$$K = \frac{k_1}{k_{-1}} \qquad (15.1)$$

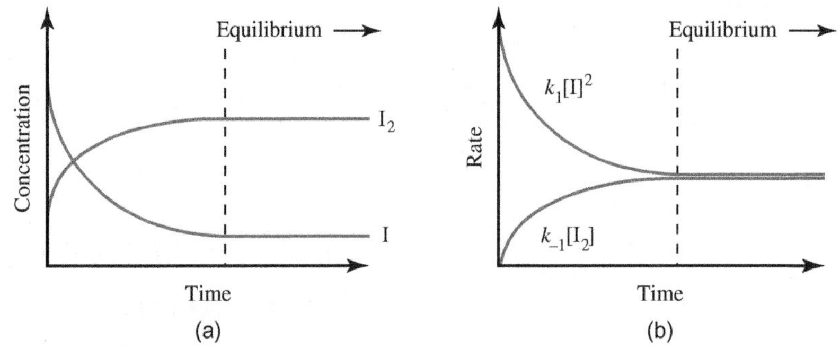

FIGURE 15.3 Chemical Equilibrium of $2\,I(g) \rightleftharpoons I_2(g)$

(a) Equilibrium is achieved when the concentrations of I_2 and I no longer change. (b) The rate of formation of I_2 (k_1) and the rate of formation of I (k_{-1}) are equal at equilibrium.

For the reaction $2\,I(g) \rightleftharpoons I_2(g)$, the equilibrium constant is $K = [I_2]/[I]^2$, but this relationship can be generalized for any reaction.

> The equilibrium constant, K, is expressed as the concentrations of the products over the concentrations of the reactants, each raised to the power of its coefficient in the balanced chemical equation.

For the general reaction

$$a\,A + b\,B \rightleftharpoons c\,C + d\,D$$

the equilibrium constant is expressed as

$$K = \frac{[C]^c[D]^d}{[A]^a[B]^b} \tag{15.2}$$

The entire equation is known as the **equilibrium constant expression**, or an equilibrium expression. No matter what the *initial* concentrations of reactants or products are, *at equilibrium* the ratio of the concentrations (raised to the appropriate power) will always be the same value, K. This phenomenon is sometimes called the **law of mass action**.

The value of K depends only on the specific chemical equation and on the temperature. It does not depend on any of the other factors that can affect the rate of a reaction, such as the concentrations of the species in the reaction, the particle size of a solid in a reaction, or the presence of a catalyst (Section 14.1).

Equilibrium constant expressions *do not include any solids or pure liquids*. Only aqueous and gaseous species have concentrations that can change, so only these species are included in equilibrium constant expressions. Pay close attention to the phases when writing equilibrium expressions, particularly for **heterogeneous equilibria**, which are equilibria in which more than one phase is present.

> Solids and pure liquids are *not* included in equilibrium constant expressions.

Example 15.1

Write equilibrium constant expressions for the following reactions:

a. $Ag_2S(s) \rightleftharpoons 2\,Ag^+(aq) + S^{2-}(aq)$

b. $CO_2(aq) + H_2O(l) \rightleftharpoons H_2CO_3(aq)$

Solution

According to Equation 15.2, equilibrium constants are expressed with the concentrations of the right side of the reaction (products) in the numerator and the concentrations on the left side of the reaction (reactants) in the denominator. Each concentration is raised to a power equal to its coefficient in the balanced chemical equation. Therefore, these chemical equations should be balanced before doing anything else.

a. Solids are not included in equilibrium expressions, so $Ag_2S(s)$ is omitted and only the aqueous products are included. The $[Ag^+]$ term must also be squared because there is a coefficient of 2 in front of Ag^+ in the balanced equation:

$$K = [Ag^+]^2[S^{2-}]$$

b. Pure liquids are not included in equilibrium expressions, so $H_2O(l)$ is omitted, but the aqueous reactant and product are included:

$$K = \frac{[H_2CO_3]}{[CO_2]}$$

PRACTICE PROBLEM 15.1

Write equilibrium constant expressions for the following reactions:

a. $PCl_5(g) \rightleftharpoons PCl_3(g) + Cl_2(g)$

b. $2\ H_2O(l) \rightleftharpoons 2\ H^+(aq) + 2\ OH^-(aq)$

Hint: The general expression for the equilibrium constant is given in Equation 15.2. Any solids and pure liquids in the reaction are not included.

THE MAGNITUDE OF *K* AND ITS MEANING

The value of K for a reaction gives quantitative information about the extent of the reaction. For the reaction $A \rightleftharpoons B$, if the forward and reverse reactions are equally favored, then $[A] = [B]$ at equilibrium, and $K = 1$. When K is greater than 1, it means that there are more molecules of products than reactants at equilibrium, which means the forward reaction is favored. When K is less than 1, it means there are more molecules of reactants than products at equilibrium, which means the reverse reaction is favored. For more complicated reactions than $A \rightleftharpoons B$, $K = 1$ is not an exact cut-off, but the general trend still applies where $K \gg 1$ indicates a product-favored reaction and $K \ll 1$ indicates a reactant-favored reaction.

Example 15.2

The equilibrium constant, K, is 1.5×10^{-5} for the following generic reaction:

$$A \rightleftharpoons B$$

Is there more of A or B at equilibrium?

Solution

A small value of K (i.e., <1) means that the reverse reaction is favored. Therefore, there is more of A than B present at equilibrium.

PRACTICE PROBLEM 15.2

In each of the following reactions, determine whether the reaction favors the forward or reverse reaction.

a. $2\ H_2(g) + S_2(g) \rightleftharpoons 2\ H_2S(g)$

$K = 1.1 \times 10^7$ at 700°C

b. $SO_2Cl_2(g) \rightleftharpoons SO_2(g) + Cl_2(g)$

$K = 2.99 \times 10^{-7}$ at 500 K

c. $2\ H_2S(g) \rightleftharpoons 2\ H_2(g) + S_2(g)$

$K = 2.4 \times 10^{-4}$ at 800°C

Hint: The equilibrium constant expression is a ratio of the products of the reaction to the reactants. Therefore, $K > 1$ indicates that the forward reaction is favored, whereas $K < 1$ indicates that the reverse reaction is favored.

K EXPRESSED IN TERMS OF PRESSURE

Equilibrium constants expressed in terms of concentration (molarity) are sometimes denoted as K_c to distinguish them from K_p. K_p is the equilibrium constant of a gaseous system in which the species involved in the equilibrium are expressed as their partial pressures. For the following equilibrium of gases,

$$2\ CO(g) + O_2(g) \rightleftharpoons 2\ CO_2(g)$$

K_c is given by

$$K_c = \frac{[CO_2]^2}{[CO]^2[O_2]}$$

The form of K_p is analogous to that of K_c, but K_p uses partial pressures in place of concentrations.

$$K_p = \frac{(P_{CO_2})^2}{(P_{CO})^2 P_{O_2}}$$

In general, for the equilibrium,

$$a\ A(g) + b\ B(g) \rightleftharpoons c\ C(g) + d\ D(g)$$

K_p is given by Equation 15.3:

$$K_p = \frac{(P_C)^c(P_D)^d}{(P_A)^a(P_B)^b} \tag{15.3}$$

K_p and K_c can be interconverted using the ideal gas law (Section 7.6).

$$PV = nRT$$

Rearrange the ideal gas law to isolate the quantity $\frac{n}{V}$, which is equal to molarity.

$$\frac{n}{V} = \frac{P}{RT}$$

Now substitute $\frac{P}{RT}$ for each concentration in the K_c expression (Equation 15.2).

$$K_c = \frac{\left(\frac{P_C}{RT}\right)^c \left(\frac{P_D}{RT}\right)^d}{\left(\frac{P_A}{RT}\right)^a \left(\frac{P_B}{RT}\right)^b}$$

Factor the constant $\frac{1}{RT}$.

$$K_c = \frac{P_C{}^c P_D{}^d \left(\frac{1}{RT}\right)^{c+d}}{P_A{}^a P_B{}^b \left(\frac{1}{RT}\right)^{a+b}} = \frac{P_C{}^c P_D{}^d}{P_A{}^a P_B{}^b}\left(\frac{1}{RT}\right)^{(c+d)-(a+b)}$$

Substitute K_p for the collection of partial pressure terms (Equation 15.3).

$$K_c = K_p\left(\frac{1}{RT}\right)^{(c+d)-(a+b)}$$

Rearrange to solve for K_p,

$$K_p = K_c(RT)^{(c+d)-(a+b)}$$

Finally, the exponential term $(c + d) - (a + b)$ represents the total number of moles of products minus the total number of moles of reactants for this particular reaction. This is equivalent to the change in the number of moles of gas during the reaction and can be represented by Δn.

$$K_p = K_c(RT)^{\Delta n} \qquad (15.4)$$

The Δn term in Equation 15.4 is unitless.

Example 15.3

Molecular fluorine gas is in equilibrium with gaseous fluorine atoms:

$$F_2(g) \rightleftharpoons 2\,F(g)$$

The equilibrium constant for this reaction is $K_c = 1.2 \times 10^{-4}$ at 1000.0°C. Calculate K_p for this equilibrium.

Solution

First, convert the temperature to kelvins.

$$T = 1000.0°C + 273.15 = 1273.2\ K$$

Next, find the change in moles of gas by looking at the coefficients from the balanced chemical equation.

$$\Delta n = 2 - 1 = 1$$

Use Equation 15.4 to solve for K_p. Recall from Chapter 7 that the gas constant R is 0.08206 L · atm/mol · K.

$$K_p = K_c(RT)^{\Delta n}$$

$$K_p = (1.2 \times 10^{-4})\left[\left(0.08206\frac{L \cdot atm}{mol \cdot K}\right)(1273.2\ K)\right]^1$$

$$K_p = 1.3 \times 10^{-2}$$

PRACTICE PROBLEM 15.3

The equilibrium between nitrogen gas, hydrogen gas, and gaseous ammonia is established in a sealed container at 25.0°C:

$$N_2(g) + 3\,H_2(g) \rightleftharpoons 2\,NH_3(g)$$

$K_p = 6.8 \times 10^5$ for this reaction at 25.0°C. Calculate K_c for this equilibrium.

Hint: Use Equation 15.4 to convert from K_p to K_c.

SECTION REVIEW

- For the general reaction $a\,A + b\,B \rightleftharpoons c\,C + d\,D$, the equilibrium constant K_c has the form

$$K_c = \frac{[C]^c[D]^d}{[A]^a[B]^b}$$

  where the brackets around each species denote the concentration of that species in units of molarity.
- For reactions in the gas phase, the equilibrium constant K_p is expressed in terms of the partial pressure of each gas (P).

$$K_p = \frac{[P_C]^c[P_D]^d}{[P_A]^a[P_B]^b}$$

- For a gaseous reaction, K_p and K_c are related as follows,

$$K_p = K_c(RT)^{\Delta n}$$

  where Δn is the change in the number of moles of gas. For the general reaction

$$a\,A(g) + b\,B(g) \rightleftharpoons c\,C(g) + d\,D(g)$$

  $\Delta n = (c + d) - (a + b)$.
- Species that are in the solid or pure liquid phase are *not* included in equilibrium expressions.

15.3 Using Equilibrium Expressions

GOALS

- Use equilibrium expressions as formulas.
- Manipulate equilibrium expressions based on changes to the chemical equation.

Background Review

Chapter 6 Thermochemistry: Section 6.7—Enthalpy in Chemical Reactions

CALCULATING EQUILIBRIUM CONSTANTS

The values used in the equilibrium constant expression are concentrations (in molarity) or pressures (in atmospheres). Moreover, they are concentrations or pressures of the reactants and products *at equilibrium.* Equilibrium constants are temperature-dependent, so the equilibrium constant for a given reaction changes depending on the temperature at which the reaction is carried out.

> The values used to calculate K are the concentrations or pressures at *equilibrium.*

Example 15.4

For the following reaction at a particular high temperature

$$CO(g) + H_2O(g) \rightleftharpoons CO_2(g) + H_2(g)$$

the concentrations of the reactants and products at equilibrium are CO(g), 0.0600 M; H_2O(g), 0.120 M; CO_2(g), 0.150 M; and H_2(g), 0.300 M. Calculate the value of the equilibrium constant, K_c, at this temperature.

Solution

The equilibrium constant expression for this reaction is

$$K_c = \frac{[CO_2][H_2]}{[CO][H_2O]}$$

Substituting the equilibrium concentrations yields the value of the equilibrium constant.

$$K_c = \frac{[CO_2][H_2]}{[CO][H_2O]} = \frac{[0.150\ M][0.300\ M]}{[0.0600\ M][0.120\ M]} = 6.25$$

PRACTICE PROBLEM 15.4

The following equilibrium is established in a sealed container at 25°C:

$$N_2O_4(g) \rightleftharpoons 2\ NO_2(g)$$

The equilibrium pressures of N_2O_4 and NO_2 are 1.74 atm and 0.512 atm, respectively. Calculate the equilibrium constant, K_p, at 25°C.

Hint: Use Equation 15.3 to write the equilibrium constant expression for the reaction in terms of the pressures of N_2O_4 and NO_2.

> By convention, equilibrium constants are expressed without units.

USING THE *K* EXPRESSION AS A FORMULA

The concentration of a single reactant or product at equilibrium can be determined by using the reaction's equilibrium constant and the concentrations of the other species at equilibrium.

Example 15.5

The equilibrium between N_2O_4 and NO_2 has a K_p value of 47.9 at 400 K.

$$N_2O_4(g) \rightleftharpoons 2\ NO_2(g)$$

If the partial pressure of N_2O_4 in a sealed reaction vessel at 400 K is 0.335 atm, then what is the partial pressure of NO_2 in the vessel?

Solution

First, write the equilibrium constant expression:

$$K_p = \frac{(P_{NO_2})^2}{P_{N_2O_4}}$$

Then rearrange the equation to solve for the partial pressure of NO_2:

$$(P_{NO_2})^2 = K_p \cdot P_{N_2O_4}$$

Finally, insert the known values and solve:

$$P_{NO_2} = \sqrt{K_p \cdot P_{N_2O_4}} = \sqrt{(47.9)(0.335\ atm)}$$
$$= 4.01\ atm$$

PRACTICE PROBLEM 15.5

The reaction between sulfur dioxide and molecular oxygen has a K_c value of 1.7×10^6 at 700 K.

$$2\ SO_2(g) + O_2(g) \rightleftharpoons 2\ SO_3(g)$$

If this reaction is carried out in a sealed reaction vessel and the equilibrium concentrations of O_2 and SO_3 are 2.1×10^{-3} M and 3.8 M, respectively, then what is the concentration of SO_2 in the vessel at equilibrium?

Hint: First, write the equilibrium constant expression for this reaction. Then rearrange that equation to solve for $[SO_2]$.

MANIPULATING EQUILIBRIUM CONSTANTS

When a chemical equation is manipulated, its equilibrium constant also changes to represent the new reaction. Knowing how to manipulate equations and their equilibrium constants is often useful because it allows you to use the known equilibrium constants of reactions to predict unknown equilibrium constants of different reactions. Three common manipulations are described here.

Reversing the equation yields the inverse equilibrium constant. For example,

$$A \rightleftharpoons B \qquad K = \frac{[B]}{[A]}$$

$$B \rightleftharpoons A \qquad K' = \frac{[A]}{[B]} = \frac{1}{K}$$

If two or more equations are added together, the equilibrium constant for the overall reaction is the product of the individual equations. For example,

$$2\,A \rightleftharpoons \cancel{B} \qquad K_1 = \frac{[B]}{[A]^2}$$

$$+\cancel{B} \rightleftharpoons C \qquad K_2 = \frac{[C]}{[B]}$$

$$2\,A \rightleftharpoons C \qquad K_{overall}$$

$$K_{overall} = K_1 \cdot K_2 = \left(\frac{[\cancel{B}]}{[A]^2} \cdot \frac{[C]}{[\cancel{B}]}\right) = \frac{[C]}{[A]^2}$$

When the coefficients of a reaction are multiplied by a factor, the equilibrium constant is raised to the power of the same factor. For example,

$$A \rightleftharpoons B \qquad K = \frac{[B]}{[A]}$$

$$2\,A \rightleftharpoons 2\,B \qquad K' = \frac{[B]^2}{[A]^2} = K^2$$

$$\frac{1}{2}A \rightleftharpoons \frac{1}{2}B \qquad K'' = \frac{[B]^{1/2}}{[A]^{1/2}} = K^{1/2}$$

Example 15.6

Write the equilibrium expressions, K_c, for the following reactions.

a. $3\,H_2(g) + N_2(g) \rightleftharpoons 2\,NH_3(g)$

b. $2\,NH_3(g) \rightleftharpoons 3\,H_2(g) + N_2(g)$

How are the answers to parts (a) and (b) related?

Solution

The equilibrium constant expression is the ratio of the products to the reactants with each species raised to the power of its stoichiometric coefficient in the balanced equation.

a. $K_c = \dfrac{[NH_3]^2}{[H_2]^3[N_2]}$

b. $K_c = \dfrac{[H_2]^3[N_2]}{[NH_3]^2}$

The chemical equation in part (b) is the *reverse* of the one in part (a), so the equilibrium constant expression in part (b) is the *reciprocal* of the one in part (a).

PRACTICE PROBLEM 15.6

Write an equilibrium constant expression for the following reactions, and explain how the constants are related.

a. $2\,N_2(g) + O_2(g) \rightleftharpoons 2\,N_2O(g)$

b. $N_2(g) + \frac{1}{2}O_2(g) \rightleftharpoons N_2O(g)$

Hint: Use Equation 15.2 to write the equilibrium constant expressions for the two reactions. How, then, can you mathematically transform the equilibrium constant expression in part (a) to the one in part (b)?

Example 15.7

Use the following equilibrium constants to determine K_c for the reaction $2\,A + 2\,B \rightleftharpoons D$.

$$A + B \rightleftharpoons C \qquad K_c = 0.80$$

$$D \rightleftharpoons 2\,C \qquad K_c = 2.5$$

Solution

Manipulate the reactions described, much like a Hess's law problem (Section 6.7).

The desired reaction has 2 mol A and 2 mol B, so multiply the first reaction by 2, then adjust the equilibrium constant accordingly. Multiplying the coefficients by 2 means K_c should be raised to a power of 2.

$$2\,A + 2\,B \rightleftharpoons 2\,C \qquad K_c = (0.80)^2 = 0.64$$

The desired reaction shows D as a product. Reversing the second reaction accomplishes this, and it also removes the unwanted species C from the desired reaction. When you reverse a reaction, the equilibrium constant of the reversed reaction is the inverse of the original equilibrium constant.

$$2\,\mathrm{C} \rightleftharpoons \mathrm{D} \qquad K_c = \frac{1}{2.5} = 0.40$$

Adding the two modified equations gives the desired equation: $2\,\mathrm{A} + 2\,\mathrm{B} \rightleftharpoons \mathrm{D}$.

$$\begin{array}{lll} & 2\,\mathrm{A} + 2\,\mathrm{B} \rightleftharpoons \cancel{2\mathrm{C}} & K_c = 0.64 \\ + & \cancel{2\mathrm{C}} \rightleftharpoons \mathrm{D} & K_c = 0.40 \\ \hline & 2\,\mathrm{A} + 2\,\mathrm{B} \rightleftharpoons \mathrm{D} & \end{array}$$

When two or more equations are added together, the equilibrium constant for the overall reaction is the product of the individual equations:

$$K_c = (0.64)(0.40) = 0.26$$

PRACTICE PROBLEM 15.7

Nitrosyl bromide, NOBr, can be formed from the reaction of NO and Br_2:

$$\mathrm{NO}(g) + \frac{1}{2}\mathrm{Br_2}(g) \rightleftharpoons \mathrm{NOBr}(g) \qquad K_1 = 1.41$$

Nitrosyl bromide also readily decomposes to give N_2, O_2, and Br_2:

$$2\,\mathrm{NOBr}(g) \rightleftharpoons \mathrm{N_2}(g) + \mathrm{O_2}(g) + \mathrm{Br_2}(g) \qquad K_2 = 1.05 \times 10^{30}$$

Use these reactions to calculate K for the decomposition of nitric oxide, NO, into N_2 and O_2:

$$2\,\mathrm{NO}(g) \rightleftharpoons \mathrm{N_2}(g) + \mathrm{O_2}(g)$$

Hint: When you reverse a reaction, you must take the reciprocal of its equilibrium constant, and when the coefficients of a reaction are multiplied by a factor, the equilibrium constant is raised to the power of that same factor.

SECTION REVIEW

- The equilibrium constant expression, like any mathematical formula, can be used to calculate one of the terms if the values for all the other terms are known.
  - The value of K can be calculated if the equilibrium concentrations of all species are known.
  - Alternatively, the equilibrium concentration of one species can be calculated if K and the equilibrium concentrations of all the other species are known.
- When manipulating a chemical equation, the K value of the new equation is related to that of the original equation in predictable ways.
  - When a reaction is reversed, its K value is inverted.
  - When the coefficients of a reaction are multiplied by a factor, the K value is raised to the power of that factor.
  - When reactions are summed, their K values are multiplied.

15.4 The Reaction Quotient

GOALS

- Define and explain the reaction quotient.
- Predict the direction of a reaction using the relationship of the reaction quotient to the equilibrium constant.

Equilibrium constants are a ratio of the concentrations (or partial pressure) of the products of an equilibrium system to the concentrations (or partial pressures) of the reactants (Section 15.1). The larger the equilibrium constant, the more the equilibrium is shifted to the right (in which case more products than reactants are present at equilibrium). Conversely, a small equilibrium constant means that the equilibrium is shifted to the left (in which case more reactants than products are present at equilibrium). Figure 15.3 shows, however, that there is a period of time, such as immediately after the equilibrium species are mixed together, when the reaction system is not at equilibrium. Because the system is not at equilibrium, a K value cannot be determined.

What can be determined, though, is the reaction quotient. The **reaction quotient, Q**, is defined as the ratio of the products to the reactants, where each species is raised to its stoichiometric coefficient from the balanced chemical equation. Unlike K, Q describes the ratio of products to reactants *at any time during the reaction.* For the general reaction

$$a\,\mathrm{A} + b\,\mathrm{B} \rightleftharpoons c\,\mathrm{C} + d\,\mathrm{D}$$

Q can be defined in units of molarity (Equation 15.5) or units of partial pressure (Equation 15.6).

$$Q_c = \frac{[\mathrm{C}]^c[\mathrm{D}]^d}{[\mathrm{A}]^a[\mathrm{B}]^b} \qquad (15.5)$$

$$Q_p = \frac{(P_\mathrm{C})^c(P_\mathrm{D})^d}{(P_\mathrm{A})^a(P_\mathrm{B})^b} \qquad (15.6)$$

> Although K and Q take the same form, K describes the ratio of products to reactants at *equilibrium*, whereas Q describes the ratio of products to reactants at *any time* during the reaction.

PREDICTING THE DIRECTION OF A REACTION

The reaction quotient can be used to determine how the concentrations of reactants and products at a particular time in the reaction will change as the reaction reaches equilibrium. You can predict the direction in which the reaction will shift by comparing the values of Q and K:

- If $Q = K$, the current ratio of products to reactants is equivalent to the equilibrium ratio, so the reaction is at equilibrium (no shift occurs).
- If $Q > K$, the current ratio of products to reactants is greater than the equilibrium ratio, so more reactants must be formed to achieve equilibrium (i.e., the reaction shifts left).
- If $Q < K$, the current ratio of products to reactants is less than the equilibrium ratio, so more products must be formed to achieve equilibrium (i.e., the reaction shifts right).

These points are depicted graphically in Figure 15.4.

Example 15.8

$K_c = 377$ at 22°C for the decomposition of BrCl gas to give gaseous bromine and chlorine.

$$2\,BrCl(g) \rightleftharpoons Br_2(g) + Cl_2(g)$$

Calculate Q_c for this reaction when the reaction mixture contains 0.32 M Br_2, 0.37 M Cl_2, and 0.15 M BrCl. Is the reaction at equilibrium? If not, will it proceed to form more reactants or more products?

Solution

First, write the reaction quotient expression, Q_c. Then calculate Q_c using the given concentrations of each gas:

$$Q_c = \frac{[Br_2][Cl_2]}{[BrCl]^2} = \frac{(0.32\,M)(0.37\,M)}{(0.15\,M)^2} = 5.3$$

$Q_c\,(5.3) < K_c\,(377)$, so the reaction will form more products, Br_2 and Cl_2 (i.e., will proceed to the right), until equilibrium is reached.

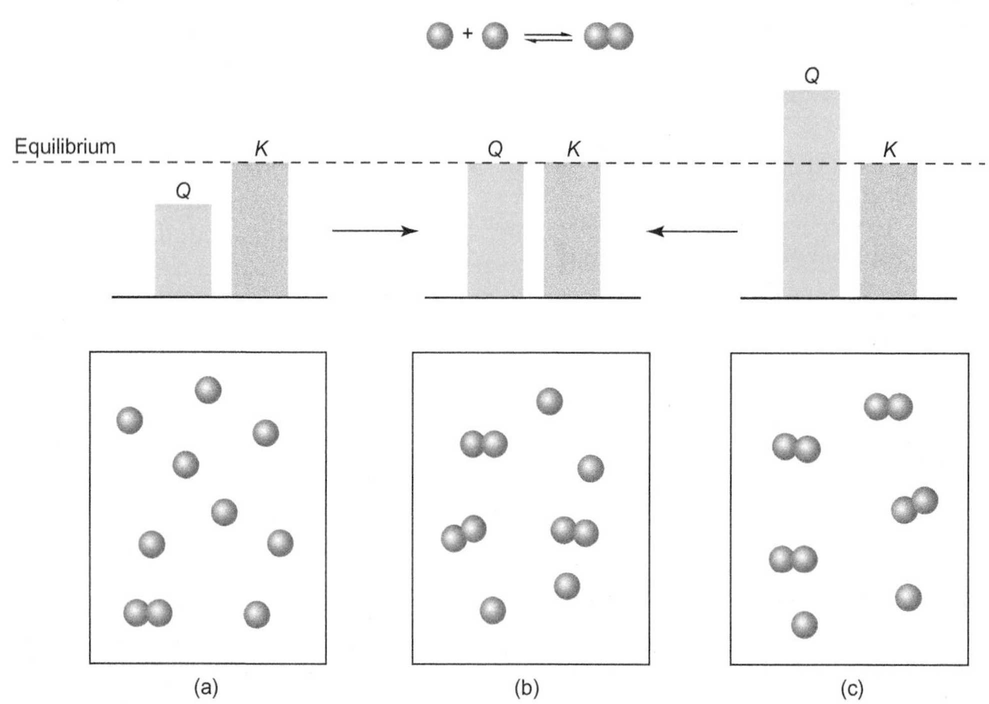

FIGURE 15.4 Q, K, and the Direction of a Reaction

(a) When $Q < K$, the reaction proceeds in the forward direction (producing more products) to achieve equilibrium. (b) When $Q = K$, the reaction is at equilibrium. (c) When $Q > K$, the reaction proceeds in the reverse direction (producing more reactants) to reach equilibrium.

PRACTICE PROBLEM 15.8

At 400 K, $K_p = 41$ for the formation of gaseous ammonia from nitrogen and hydrogen gas.

$$N_2(g) + 3\,H_2(g) \rightleftharpoons 2\,NH_3(g)$$

Calculate Q_p for this reaction when the reaction mixture contains 0.124 atm N_2, 0.113 atm H_2, and 0.00682 atm NH_3. Is the reaction at equilibrium? If not, will it proceed to form more reactants or more products?

Hint: Use Equation 15.6 to write the expression for Q_p. Calculate Q_p, and determine whether it is larger or smaller than K_p (41). If $Q_p > K_p$, the reaction will proceed to the left. If $Q_p < K_p$, the reaction will proceed to the right.

SECTION REVIEW

- The reaction quotient, Q, is the ratio of the products to the reactants, where each species is raised to its stoichiometric coefficient.
- For the general reaction $a\,A + b\,B \rightleftharpoons c\,C + d\,D$,

$$Q_c = \frac{[C]^c[D]^d}{[A]^a[B]^b}$$

$$Q_p = \frac{(P_D)^d(P_C)^d}{(P_A)^a(P_B)^b}$$

- Unlike the equilibrium constant, the reaction quotient describes the ratio of products to reactants *at any time during the reaction*. The reaction quotient is used to predict how the concentrations or partial pressures of products and reactants must change to reach equilibrium.
- If $Q = K$, the reaction is at equilibrium. If $Q > K$, the reaction will shift back toward the left (i.e., will form more reactants) to achieve equilibrium. If $Q < K$, the reaction will shift toward the right (i.e., will form more products) to achieve equilibrium.

15.5 Calculations Using ICE Tables

GOAL

- Use ICE tables to solve equilibrium problems.

Background Review

Chapter 0 Math Review: Section 0.10—The Quadratic Formula

Chapter 5 Stoichiometry

Section 5.3 introduced the strategy of making a table of initial and final amounts in a chemical reaction for the purpose of solving limiting reactant problems. All reactions were assumed to go to completion—that is, at least one reactant was assumed to be completely used up. For a reversible reaction, however, that is generally not the case (some amount of every reactant and product is present at equilibrium). Thus, a strategy for tabulating amounts becomes even more important. But instead of labeling the rows as initial, change, and final, as was done in Chapter 5, the rows for reversible reactions are typically labeled initial (I), change (C), and equilibrium (E), and this type of table is known as an **ICE table**.

FINDING *K* FROM INITIAL CONDITIONS

When the equilibrium constant of a reaction is unknown and only the *initial* conditions of one or more reactants and the equilibrium condition of one or more products are known, you can determine the equilibrium conditions of the species present in the reaction from the reaction stoichiometry. Once the equilibrium conditions of all species are known, the equilibrium constant can be calculated. For example, consider the reaction of hydrogen gas, H_2, and iodine gas, I_2, to give gaseous hydrogen iodide, HI.

$$H_2(g) + I_2(g) \rightleftharpoons 2\,HI(g)$$

If 0.500 mol H_2 and 0.500 mol I_2 react at high temperature at a constant volume of 1.00 L, and the amount of HI present at equilibrium is 0.900 mol, then this information and the stoichiometry of the reaction can be used to fill in the ICE table.

	$H_2(g)$	+	$I_2(g)$	$\rightleftharpoons$	$2\,HI(g)$
Initial (M)					
Change (M)					
Equilibrium (M)					

The ICE table consists of a column for each species in the reaction (i.e., the two reactants and the single product) and three rows. The first row represents the initial concentrations of all species, the second row represents how the species will change based on the reaction stoichiometry, and the final row represents the concentrations of all species at equilibrium. For this particular reaction, the units for every cell in the ICE table are molarity. While molarity is a common unit that is used in ICE tables, other units such as moles or partial pressures can be used, too.

Begin by filling in the initial row of the ICE table using information given in the problem. There are 0.500 mol of each reactant in a 1.00 L container, so the molarity of each reactant is 0.500 M. There is no product present initially, so that is recorded as 0 M. The amount of product at equilibrium is also given, 0.900 mol in a 1.00 L container, or 0.900 M.

	$H_2(g)$ +	$I_2(g)$ $\rightleftharpoons$	2 HI(g)
Initial (M)	0.500	0.500	0
Change (M)			
Equilibrium (M)			0.900

Next, identify the direction in which the reaction will proceed to reach equilibrium. In this case, there are no products present initially, so the net reaction is in the forward direction. In the forward direction, the change to the reactants is negative, and the change to the products is positive. Looking at the balanced equation, for every mole of I_2 consumed, 1 mol H_2 is also consumed. If the variable x is arbitrarily assigned to represent the amount H_2 that reacts, then the change in H_2 is $-x$.

	$H_2(g)$ +	$I_2(g)$ $\rightleftharpoons$	2 HI(g)
Initial (M)	0.500	0.500	0
Change (M)	$-x$		
Equilibrium (M)			0.900

Now use the stoichiometric coefficients from the balanced equation to complete the change line of the table. I_2 is also a reactant and has the same coefficient as H_2, so I_2 also changes by $-x$. The balanced equation shows that 2 mol HI are formed per 1 mol H_2 and 1 mol I_2. Therefore, the formation of HI is represented algebraically as $+2x$.

	$H_2(g)$ +	$I_2(g)$ $\rightleftharpoons$	2 HI(g)
Initial (M)	0.500	0.500	0
Change (M)	$-x$	$-x$	$+2x$
Equilibrium (M)			0.900

Complete the equilibrium row using the mathematical expressions. In this case, if a reactant starts at 0.500 M and changes by $-x$, then the resulting amount is $0.500 - x$.

	$H_2(g)$ +	$I_2(g)$ $\rightleftharpoons$	2 HI(g)
Initial (M)	0.500	0.500	0
Change (M)	$-x$	$-x$	$+2x$
Equilibrium (M)	$0.500-x$	$0.500-x$	0.900

The value of x can be determined from the product column.

$$0 + 2x = 0.900\text{ M}$$
$$x = (0.900\text{ M})/2 = 0.450\text{ M}$$

Substituting this value for x gives the equilibrium concentrations for both H_2 and I_2 as 0.500 M − 0.450 M = 0.050 M. These values can be substituted back into the ICE table to show the complete reaction values.

	$H_2(g)$ +	$I_2(g)$ $\rightleftharpoons$	2 HI(g)
Initial (M)	0.500	0.500	0
Change (M)	−0.450	−0.450	+0.900
Equilibrium (M)	0.050	0.050	0.900

You can now determine the equilibrium constant, K_c, at this particular temperature by substituting the equilibrium concentration values into the K_c expression for this reaction.

$$K_c = \frac{[HI]^2}{[H_2][I_2]} = \frac{(0.900)^2}{(0.050)(0.050)} = 324$$

When calculating K_c, use the *molarities* of the species at equilibrium, *not* the number of moles of each species.

Example 15.9

Consider the following equilibrium.

$$2\,SO_3(g) \rightleftharpoons 2\,SO_2(g) + O_2(g)$$

Suppose that 0.0150 mol SO_3 is placed in a 1.00 L vessel and allowed to come to equilibrium at a high temperature. When equilibrium is achieved, 0.0076 mol SO_3 remains. Calculate the value of the equilibrium constant for the reaction.

Solution

First, construct an ICE table for the reaction.

	$2\,SO_3(g)$ $\rightleftharpoons$	$2\,SO_2(g)$ +	$O_2(g)$
Initial (M)	0.150	0	0
Change (M)			
Equilibrium (M)			

In this equilibrium, 2 mol SO_3 react to form 2 mol SO_2 and 1 mol O_2. Using this stoichiometry, the amount of SO_3 lost can be represented by the variable $2x$ and the amounts of SO_2 and O_2 formed can be represented by $2x$ and x, respectively.

	$2\,SO_3(g)$ $\rightleftharpoons$	$2\,SO_2(g)$ +	$O_2(g)$
Initial (M)	0.150	0	0
Change (M)	$-2x$	$+2x$	$+x$
Equilibrium (M)			

At equilibrium, the concentration of SO_3 is $0.150 - 2x$ and the amounts of SO_2 and O_2 present are $2x$ and x, respectively.

	$2\,SO_3(g)$ $\rightleftharpoons$	$2\,SO_2(g)$ +	$O_2(g)$
Initial (M)	0.150	0	0
Change (M)	$-2x$	$+2x$	$+x$
Equilibrium (M)	$0.150 - 2x$	$2x$	x

Because 0.0076 mol SO_3 remains at equilibrium in a 1.00 L vessel, the equilibrium concentration of SO_3 is 0.0076 M. In other words,

$$0.150 - 2x = 0.0076$$
$$0.150 - 0.0076 = 2x$$
$$2x = 0.142$$
$$x = 0.142/2 = 0.0710$$

Substituting these values for x and $2x$ into the change and equilibrium rows of the ICE table yields the following:

	$2\,SO_3(g)$ $\rightleftharpoons$	$2\,SO_2(g)$ +	$O_2(g)$
Initial (M)	0.150	0	0
Change (M)	−0.142	+0.142	+0.0710
Equilibrium (M)	0.0076	0.142	0.0710

Now write the equilibrium constant expression for the reaction, and determine K_c:

$$K_c = \frac{[SO_2]^2[O_2]}{[SO_3]^2}$$

$$K_c = \frac{(0.142)^2(0.0710)}{(0.0076)^2} = 25$$

PRACTICE PROBLEM 15.9

Consider the following equilibrium.

$$CO(g) + H_2O(g) \rightleftharpoons H_2(g) + CO_2(g)$$

Suppose that 0.00925 mol carbon monoxide gas and 0.0200 mol water vapor are placed in a 0.500 L flask and allowed to come to equilibrium at a high temperature. At equilibrium, 0.00825 mol CO_2 are present. Calculate the value of K_c at this temperature.

Hint: First, convert the number of moles of all species to concentrations in units of molarity. Then construct an ICE table, and determine the concentrations of all four species at equilibrium. Finally, write the equilibrium constant expression, and insert the equilibrium concentrations to determine K_c.

FINDING EQUILIBRIUM CONDITIONS FROM INITIAL CONDITIONS

In most cases, you know the initial conditions of a reaction and the equilibrium constant for the reaction at a particular temperature but need to determine the concentrations or partial pressures of all species at equilibrium.

Consider the reaction from Practice Problem 15.9 at the same temperature but with different initial concentrations. Suppose that you want to calculate the concentration of all four species at equilibrium if the initial concentration of carbon monoxide, CO, is 0.0125 M and the initial concentration of water, H_2O, is 0.0125 M. The value of K_c determined earlier is 5.8.

$$CO(g) + H_2O(g) \rightleftharpoons H_2(g) + CO_2(g)$$

The first step in solving a problem like this is to determine which way the reaction proceeds by calculating Q.

$$Q_c = \frac{[H_2][CO_2]}{[CO][H_2O]} = \frac{(0.00)(0.00)}{(0.0125)(0.0125)} = 0$$

Since $Q_c < K_c$, as it will be for any reaction conditions where no product is present, the equilibrium proceeds to the right (toward product formation). Now construct an ICE table.

	$CO(g)$ +	$H_2O(g)$ $\rightleftharpoons$	$H_2(g)$ +	$CO_2(g)$
Initial (M)	0.0125	0.0125	0	0
Change (M)	$-x$	$-x$	$+x$	$+x$
Equilibrium (M)	$0.0125 - x$	$0.0125 - x$	x	x

Since all species have a 1:1 stoichiometry, the amounts of CO and H_2O that react are equal to x and the amounts of H_2 and CO_2 that form are also equal to x. Now, set up the equilibrium constant expression to solve for x:

$$K_c = \frac{[H_2][CO_2]}{[CO][H_2O]} = \frac{(x)(x)}{(0.0125 - x)(0.0125 - x)} = 5.8$$

$$K_c = 5.8 = \frac{x^2}{(0.125 - x)^2}$$

Steve Lemon, Macmillan Learning

FIGURE 15.5 Video Tutorial: Using an ICE Table

NOTE: You need to be online to access this video.

This video shows how to determine equilibrium pressures from initial pressures and the value of K_p.

$$\sqrt{5.8} = \frac{x}{0.0125 - x}$$

$$\sqrt{5.8} \cdot (0.0125 - x) = x$$

$$0.030 - 2.4x = x$$

$$0.030 = 3.4x$$

$$x = 0.0088 \text{ M}$$

Therefore, at equilibrium,

$$[H_2] = x = 0.0088 \text{ M}$$

$$[CO_2] = x = 0.0088 \text{ M}$$

$$[CO] = 0.0125 - x = 0.0125 - 0.0088 \text{ M} = 0.0037 \text{ M}$$

$$[H_2O] = 0.0125 - x = 0.0125 - 0.0088 \text{ M} = 0.0037 \text{ M}$$

The video in Figure 15.5 demonstrates the use of K and an ICE table to determine equilibrium amounts from initial amounts.

THE QUADRATIC FORMULA IN EQUILIBRIUM CALCULATIONS

Sometimes, the equilibrium expression that results from an ICE table will be a quadratic equation, meaning that it involves an x^2 term, and thus requires a specific mathematical technique to solve. For example, consider the following chemical equation where $I_2(g)$ is in equilibrium with I(g):

$$I_2(g) \rightleftharpoons 2\,I(g)$$

$K_p = 0.260$ at 1000 K for this equilibrium. Suppose that this equilibrium originally contains I at a partial pressure of 0.200 atm and I_2 at a partial pressure of 0.00500 atm. Determine the partial pressures of I_2 and I at equilibrium.

As in the previous example, calculate Q to determine the direction of the reaction:

$$Q_p = \frac{P_I^2}{P_{I_2}} = \frac{(0.200)^2}{(0.00500)} = 8$$

Under these conditions, $Q_p > K_p$, so the reaction proceeds to the left (i.e., to form more I_2). The ICE table is

	$I_2(g)$	$\rightleftharpoons$	$2\,I(g)$
Initial (atm)	0.00500		0.200
Change (atm)	$+x$		$-2x$
Equilibrium (atm)	$0.00500 + x$		$0.200 - 2x$

Substitute the equilibrium pressures into the K_p expression.

$$K_p = \frac{P_I^2}{P_{I_2}} = \frac{(0.200 - 2x)^2}{(0.00500 + x)} = 0.260$$

Unlike the previous example, this equation cannot be simplified by taking the square root of both sides. Instead, the next step is to get the equation into the general form of $ax^2 + bx + c$.

$$\frac{0.0400 - 0.800x + 4x^2}{(0.00500 + x)} = 0.260$$

$$0.0400 - 0.800x + 4x^2 = 0.00130 + 0.260x$$

$$4x^2 - 1.06x + 0.0387 = 0$$

Now use the quadratic formula (Equation 0.2) to solve for x. As discussed in Section 0.10, the quadratic equation for the general equation $ax^2 + bx + c$ is

$$x = \frac{-b \pm \sqrt{b^2 - 4ac}}{2a}$$

For the equation $4x^2 - 1.06x + 0.0387 = 0$, $a = 4$, $b = -1.06$, and $c = 0.0387$:

$$x = \frac{-(-1.06) \pm \sqrt{(-1.06)^2 - 4(4)(0.0387)}}{2(4)}$$

$$x = \frac{1.06 \pm \sqrt{1.1236 - 0.6192}}{8} = \frac{1.06 \pm 0.710}{8}$$

$$x = 0.221 \text{ atm or } 0.0437 \text{ atm}$$

The $x = 0.221$ atm value will give a negative partial pressure of I, so it should be disregarded. That leaves $x = 0.0437$ atm. At equilibrium, therefore,

$$P_{I_2} = 0.0050 + 0.0437 = 0.0487 \text{ atm}$$

$$P_I = 0.200 - 2(0.0437) = 0.113 \text{ atm}$$

You can check your work by inserting these numbers back into the equilibrium constant expression:

$$K_p = \frac{P_I^2}{P_{I_2}} = \frac{(0.113)^2}{(0.0487)} = 0.262$$

The calculated equilibrium constant (0.262) is close to the expected value (0.260), so these equilibrium pressures make sense.

Example 15.10

CO gas reacts with Cl_2 gas to form gaseous phosgene ($COCl_2$):

$$CO(g) + Cl_2(g) \rightleftharpoons COCl_2(g)$$

If a 1.00 L reaction vessel at 1000°C contains 0.150 mol CO, 0.100 mol Cl_2, and 0.0500 mol $COCl_2$, then determine the equilibrium concentration of $COCl_2$. $K_c = 255$ at 1000°C for this reaction.

Solution

First, convert the amounts of CO and Cl_2 from moles to molarity. The volume of the reaction vessel is 1.00 L, so the initial concentrations are

$$[CO] = 0.150\text{ M}$$
$$[Cl_2] = 0.100\text{ M}$$
$$[COCl_2] = 0.0500\text{ M}$$

Calculate Q to determine the direction of the reaction:

$$Q_c = \frac{[COCl_2]}{[CO][Cl_2]} = \frac{(0.0500)}{(0.150)(0.100)} = 3.33$$

$Q_c < K_c$, so the reaction proceeds to the right (i.e., to form more $COCl_2$). Construct an ICE table for this system, and solve for x.

	$CO(g)$	+ $Cl_2(g)$	$\rightleftharpoons$ $COCl_2(g)$
Initial (M)	0.150	0.100	0.0500
Change (M)	$-x$	$-x$	$+x$
Equilibrium (M)	$0.150 - x$	$0.100 - x$	$0.0500 + x$

Substitute the equilibrium concentrations into the K_c expression.

$$K_c = \frac{[COCl_2]}{[CO][Cl_2]} = \frac{(0.0500 + x)}{(0.150 - x)(0.100 - x)} = 255$$
$$(0.0500 + x) = 255(x^2 - 0.250x + 0.0150)$$
$$(0.0500 + x) = 255x^2 - 63.75x + 3.825$$
$$0 = 255x^2 - 64.75x + 3.775$$

Solve for x using the quadratic equation.

$$x = \frac{-b \pm \sqrt{b^2 - 4ac}}{2a}$$
$$x = \frac{-(-64.75) \pm \sqrt{(-64.75)^2 - 4(255)(3.775)}}{2(255)}$$
$$x = \frac{64.75 \pm \sqrt{342}}{510}$$
$$x = 0.1632\text{ M or } 0.09070\text{ M}$$

The $x = 0.1632$ value gives negative concentrations for both CO and Cl_2, so $x = 0.09070$ M. At equilibrium, the concentrations are

$$[CO] = 0.150 - x = 0.150 - 0.09070 = 0.059\text{ M}$$
$$[Cl_2] = 0.100 - x = 0.100 - 0.09070 = 0.009\text{ M}$$
$$[COCl_2] = 0.0500 + x = 0.0500 + 0.09070 = 0.141\text{ M}$$

Now, check your work by inserting the calculated values of each species back into the equilibrium expression:

$$K_c = \frac{[COCl_2]}{[CO][Cl_2]} = \frac{(0.141)}{(0.059)(0.009)} = 265$$

The value of K_c calculated with x (265) is close to the given value of K_c (255), so the calculated values are reasonable. The values do not agree to three significant figures because the calculated K_c value uses a $[Cl_2]$ with only one significant digit (0.009 M). If the K_c value is calculated with the chlorine concentration expressed as two significant digits (0.0093 M), a value of 257 is obtained, which is much closer to the given value of 255.

PRACTICE PROBLEM 15.10

$K_p = 794$ at 25°C for the following equilibrium:

$$H_2(g) + I_2(g) \rightleftharpoons 2\,HI(g)$$

If a reaction vessel at 25°C contains 0.350 atm H_2, 0.275 atm I_2, and 1.500 atm HI, then what is the partial pressure of each species at equilibrium?

Hint: First, calculate Q_p under the given conditions to determine the direction that the reaction proceeds. Then construct an ICE table, and solve for x using the quadratic equation. Use your calculated value of x to determine the partial pressure of each species at equilibrium.

SIMPLIFIED EQUILIBRIUM CALCULATIONS

The quadratic equations used to solve Example Problem 15.10 and Practice Problem 15.10 are time consuming to solve and, in many cases, unnecessary. When the change in concentration or pressure is relatively small, you can often simplify the equilibrium expression to avoid solving a quadratic equation. This tends to occur when the initial concentrations or pressures of reactants are large and the equilibrium constant is relatively small. For the simplification to be valid, the change in amount (x, $2x$, etc.) must be less than 5% of the initial value of the reactant.

The ionization of formic acid, HCO_2H, in water can be used to demonstrate this method:

$$HCO_2H(aq) + H_2O(l) \rightleftharpoons H_3O^+(aq) + CO_2H^-(aq)$$

Suppose that you are asked to calculate the concentration of hydronium ion, H_3O^+, at equilibrium at 25°C if the initial concentration of HCO_2H is 0.250 M. $K_c = 1.80 \times 10^{-4}$ for this reaction at 25°C. The equilibrium constant expression is

$$K_c = \frac{[H_3O^+][CO_2H^-]}{[HCO_2H]} = 1.80 \times 10^{-4}$$

Water is not included in the equilibrium constant expression because it is a pure liquid (its concentration also has negligible change during the reaction). The ICE table is as follows:

	$HCO_2H(aq)$	+ $H_2O(l)$	$\rightleftharpoons$ $H_3O^+(aq)$	+ $HCO_2^-(aq)$
Initial (M)	0.250	—	0	0
Change (M)	$-x$	—	$+x$	$+x$
Equilibrium (M)	$0.250 - x$	—	x	x

The value of K_c is very small, so the value of x will also be quite small—so small, in fact, that $0.250 - x$ will be essentially equal to 0.250 M. Proceeding with that assumption allows you to replace the $0.250 - x$ term in the equilibrium constant expression with 0.250, which simplifies the math dramatically (i.e., no quadratic equation is required).

$$K_c = \frac{[H_3O^+][CO_2H^-]}{[HCO_2H]} = \frac{(x)(x)}{(0.250 - x)} \approx \frac{x^2}{0.250}$$
$$= 1.80 \times 10^{-4}$$
$$x = \sqrt{(0.250)(1.80 \times 10^{-4})} = 6.71 \times 10^{-3}$$
$$x = [H_3O^+] = 6.71 \times 10^{-3}\ \text{M}$$

You can now check to see if the assumption was valid by determining whether x is less than 5% of 0.250 M.

$$\frac{6.71 \times 10^{-3}}{0.250} \times 100\% = 2.68\%$$

Since x is less than 5%, the simplification is valid for this problem. To double-check, you can enter the calculated value of x back into the equilibrium expression and calculate the equilibrium constant. The calculated equilibrium constant should be very close in value to 1.80×10^{-4}.

$$K_c = \frac{[H_3O^+][CO_2H^-]}{[HCO_2H]} = \frac{x^2}{(0.250 - x)}$$
$$\approx \frac{(6.71 \times 10^{-3})^2}{(0.250 - 6.71 \times 10^{-3})} = 1.85 \times 10^{-4}$$

The calculated value of K_c is very close to the given value, indicating that the simplification is valid.

Example 15.11

Benzoic acid, $HC_7H_5O_2$, ionizes in water to give H_3O^+ and $C_7H_5O_2^-$:

$$HC_7H_5O_2(aq) + H_2O(l) \rightleftharpoons H_3O^+(aq) + C_7H_5O_2^-(aq)$$

If a solution of 0.100 M benzoic acid dissolves in water at a particular temperature, then what are the concentrations of benzoic acid, $HC_7H_5O_2$, benzoate ion, $C_7H_5O_2^-$, and hydronium ion, H_3O^+, at equilibrium? $K_c = 6.31 = 10^{-5}$ at this particular temperature.

Solution

The equilibrium constant expression is

$$K_c = \frac{[H_3O^+][C_7H_5O_2^-]}{[HC_7H_5O_2]} = 6.31 \times 10^{-5}$$

The ICE table for this reaction is as follows:

	$HC_7H_5O_2(aq)$	+ $H_2O(l)$	$\rightleftharpoons$ $H_3O^+(aq)$	+ $C_7H_5O_2^-(aq)$
Initial (M)	0.100		0	0
Change (M)	$-x$		$+x$	$+x$
Equilibrium (M)	$0.100 - x$		x	x

To simplify the equilibrium expression, assume that x is small compared to 0.100 M.

$$K_c = \frac{[H_3O^+][C_7H_5O_2^-]}{[HC_7H_5O_2]} = \frac{x^2}{(0.100 - x)} \approx \frac{x^2}{(0.100)}$$

$$= 6.31 \times 10^{-5}$$

$$x = \sqrt{(0.100)(6.31 \times 10^{-5})} = 2.512 \times 10^{-3}$$

Check that x is indeed less than 5% of 0.100 M.

$$\frac{2.512 \times 10^{-3}}{0.100} \times 100\% = 2.51\%$$

The simplification is valid in this case, and the equilibrium concentrations are

$$[HC_7H_5O_2] = 0.100 - x = 0.100\ \text{M} - 2.512 \times 10^{-3}\ \text{M} = 0.097\ \text{M}$$

$$[C_7H_5O_2^-] = x = 2.51 \times 10^{-3}\ \text{M}$$

$$[H_3O^+] = x = 2.51 \times 10^{-3}\ \text{M}$$

PRACTICE PROBLEM 15.11

The decomposition of gaseous ammonia into nitrogen gas and hydrogen gas has $K_p = 1.47 \times 10^{-6}$ at 25°C:

$$2\,NH_3(g) \rightleftharpoons N_2(g) + 3\,H_2(g)$$

If a reaction vessel at 25°C contains 1.20 atm NH_3, then what are the partial pressures of each species at equilibrium?

Hint: After writing the equilibrium constant expression, construct an ICE table and simplify the terms containing x by assuming that x is much smaller than the value that it is being added to or subtracted from. Determine whether or not the change in partial pressure of NH_3 is less than 5% of the initial value of 1.20 atm. If so, use the value of x obtained from the simplification to determine the equilibrium pressures of NH_3, N_2, and H_2. If not, solve for x by using the quadratic equation.

SECTION REVIEW

- When sufficient information is given, the equilibrium constant expression can be used to calculate the concentrations of reactants and products at equilibrium.
- ICE (initial, change, equilibrium) tables are useful for determining the concentrations of species at equilibrium, and they are particularly useful when only the initial concentrations are given.
- When both reactants and products are initially present for a reversible reaction and you need to determine their concentrations at equilibrium, you must first calculate the reaction quotient (Q) to determine the direction in which the reaction proceeds.
- In some cases, you will need to use the quadratic equation to determine the concentrations of species at equilibrium.

$$x = \frac{-b \pm \sqrt{b^2 - 4ac}}{2a}$$

- When the initial concentrations of reactants are large and the equilibrium constant is relatively small, you can often simplify the equilibrium expression to avoid solving a quadratic equation. For the simplification to be valid, the change (x, $2x$, etc.) must be less than 5% of the initial value.

15.6 Le Châtelier's Principle

GOAL

- Identify the reaction conditions that shift the equilibrium position of a reaction.

Background Review

Chapter 6 Thermochemistry: Section 6.4—Energy and Enthalpy

When a system is at equilibrium and the conditions that affect the equilibrium position of a chemical reaction are changed, the rates of the forward and reverse reactions may be affected differently. If these rates differ, more reactants or more products will be produced until the correct ratio of products to reactants, governed by K, is re-established. The direction in which a reaction shifts can be predicted qualitatively by using **Le Châtelier's principle**. Le Châtelier's principle states that if a *stress* is applied to a system *at equilibrium*, the reaction will tend to *shift* in a direction to relieve that stress.

A stress is a change of conditions imposed on the system, such as a change in the concentration or pressure of one or more of the reactants or products, or a change in the system's temperature. A shift is a net forward reaction of reactants to form products or a net reverse reaction of products to form reactants. If no further stress is applied, equilibrium will be re-established to satisfy K.

The equilibrium constant, K, for a reaction changes *only* if the temperature changes, so a reaction shift due to a change in concentration or partial pressure does *not* change K.

THE EFFECT OF A CONCENTRATION CHANGE

As described in Section 15.4, the direction of a reaction shifts to achieve equilibrium if $Q \neq K$. Consider the following reaction between A and B that is at equilibrium:

$$\mathrm{A} \rightleftharpoons \mathrm{B}$$

If more A is added to the system, then $Q < K$ and the reaction proceeds to the right (to form more B). Conversely, if the system is at equilibrium and more B is added, then $Q > K$ and the reaction shifts to the left (to form more A). Similarly, *removing* A shifts the reaction to the left and *removing* B shifts the reaction to the right. The effect of changing the concentration of a reactant or product is summarized in Table 15.1. The reaction always shifts in a way to restore an equilibrium position with concentrations (or pressures) equal to K.

Example 15.12

Hydrogen sulfide gas, H_2S, decomposes into gaseous H_2 and S_2:

$$2\,\mathrm{H_2S}(g) \rightleftharpoons 2\,\mathrm{H_2}(g) + \mathrm{S_2}(g)$$

Determine the direction in which the reaction shifts after the following changes are made to the system:

a. Increasing the concentration of H_2S
b. Increasing the concentration of H_2
c. Removing S_2 from the system

TABLE 15.1 The Effect of Concentration and Pressure Changes on Reaction Direction

Species (aq) or (g)	Change in Concentration or Pressure	Effect on Q Relative to K	Reaction Shift
Reactant	Increase	$Q<K$	To the right (more products formed)
	Decrease	$Q>K$	To the left (more reactants formed)
Product	Increase	$Q>K$	To the left (more reactants formed)
	Decrease	$Q<K$	To the right (more products formed)

Solution

The effect of a change of concentration of a reactant or product can be found in Table 15.1.

a. Increasing the concentration of a reactant (H_2S) disrupts the equilibrium of the reaction system, making $Q < K$. The reaction responds to counteract this disturbance by shifting to the right (more H_2 and S_2 are formed).
b. Increasing the concentration of a product (H_2) disrupts the equilibrium of the reaction system, making $Q > K$. To counteract the addition of H_2, the reaction shifts to the left (more H_2S formed).
c. Removing S_2 from the system has the same effect on the direction of the reaction as decreasing its concentration (making $Q < K$). To counteract this disruption of the equilibrium, the reaction shifts to the right (more H_2 and S_2 formed).

PRACTICE PROBLEM 15.12

Consider the following equilibrium:

$$2\,\mathrm{NOCl}(g) \rightleftharpoons \mathrm{Cl_2}(g) + 2\,\mathrm{NO}(g)$$

Determine the relative values of Q and K when the following changes are made to the system, and determine the direction in which the reaction shifts after these changes are made:

a. Increasing the concentration of Cl_2
b. Decreasing the concentration of NO
c. Removing NOCl from the system

Hint: The effect of change of concentration of reactants or products and the relative values of Q and K can be found in Table 15.1. The removal of a product or reactant from an equilibrium system has the same effect on the direction of the reaction as decreasing its concentration.

THE EFFECT OF VOLUME AND PRESSURE CHANGES

The pressure (P) and volume (V) of a gas, discussed in detail in Chapter 7, are related to the temperature (T) and the number of moles of gas (n) via the ideal gas law, $PV = nRT$. Thus, P and V are inversely proportional to each other when T and n are held constant. This means that *decreasing* the volume of a container of gas *increases* its pressure, whereas *increasing* the volume of the container *decreases* its pressure. This concept is illustrated in Figure 15.6 for the equilibrium between nitrogen dioxide, NO_2, and dinitrogen tetraoxide, N_2O_4.

$$2\,\mathrm{NO_2}(g) \rightleftharpoons \mathrm{N_2O_4}(g)$$

Reducing the container volume increases the total pressure (and the concentration, n/V), and the reaction

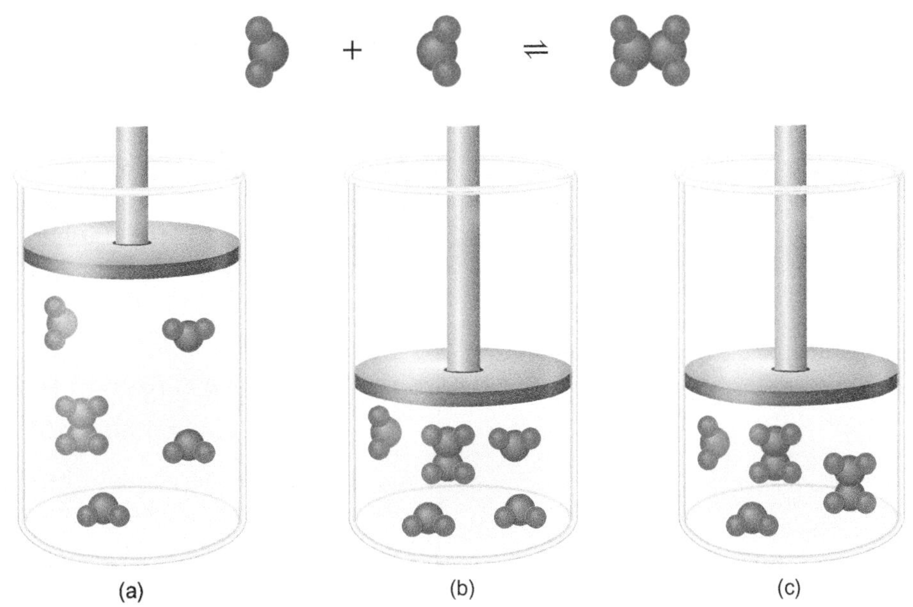

FIGURE 15.6 Le Châtelier's Principle Applied to a Volume Change

(a) NO_2 is in equilibrium with N_2O_4. (b) Decreasing the volume increases the pressure and the concentration. (c) The net reaction proceeds toward the side with fewer moles of gas, forming more N_2O_4. Increasing the volume has the opposite effect (i.e., more NO_2 forms).

shifts toward the side with *fewer* moles of gas to offset the *decrease* in volume (i.e., more N_2O_4 forms). Conversely, increasing the volume of the container decreases the total pressure (and the concentration), and the reaction shifts toward the side of the reaction with *more* moles of gas to offset the *increase* in volume (i.e., more NO_2 forms).

Based on what you now know, how do you think the following reaction shifts when the volume increases or decreases (i.e., when the pressure decreases or increases)?

$$H_2(g) + Cl_2(g) \rightleftharpoons 2\,HCl(g)$$

Because both sides of the equilibrium contain the same number of moles of gas ($\Delta n = 0$), changing the volume or pressure will *not* shift the position of this reaction. Table 15.2 summarizes these effects for the various values of Δn.

TABLE 15.2 Volume Changes and Δn

Δn	Change	Reaction
<0 (i.e., more gaseous reactants than products)	Increase V	Shift left
	Decrease V	Shift right
0	Increase or decrease V	No change
>0 (i.e., more gaseous products than reactants)	Increase V	Shift right
	Decrease V	Shift left

If an inert (unreactive) gas is added to the system, and if the volume does not change, then the total pressure increases, but *the reaction position does not shift at all*. You may find this counterintuitive at first, but the reason is that the partial pressures (and concentrations) of the reactants and products do not change.

Finally, a change in the volume or pressure of the reaction *does not* change the value of the reaction's equilibrium constant. The equilibrium constant is *only* affected by temperature.

To summarize the effects of pressure and volume changes:

- A *decrease* in reaction volume results in an *increase* in pressure, and this shifts the equilibrium position toward the side of the reaction that has the *fewest* number of moles of gas.
- An *increase* in reaction volume results in a *decrease* in pressure, and this shifts the equilibrium position toward the side of the reaction that has the *largest* number of moles of gas.
- A change in reaction volume has *no effect* on a reaction in which the same number of moles of gas are present on both sides of the reaction.
- The addition of an inert gas to a reaction at equilibrium *will not* shift the equilibrium position, provided that the reaction volume does not change.
- Pressure and volume changes *do not affect* the value of the reaction's equilibrium constant.

Example 15.13

The formation of gaseous NH_3 from N_2 and H_2 gas is carried out in a sealed container of variable volume.

$$N_2(g) + 3\,H_2(g) \rightleftharpoons 2\,NH_3(g)$$

Determine the direction in which the equilibrium position shifts after the following changes are made to the system:

a. The volume of the container is decreased.
b. The volume of the container is increased.
c. Gaseous helium is added to the container while the volume is held constant.

Solution

In total there are 4 moles of gaseous reactants and 2 moles of gaseous product. This will determine the direction in which the reaction shifts in parts (a) and (b) (see Table 15.2).

a. A decrease in the volume of the container is accompanied by an increase in pressure. The increase in pressure will cause the equilibrium position to shift to the side of the reaction that has fewer moles of gas. Therefore, the reaction shifts to the right (more NH_3 is formed).
b. An increase in the volume of the container is accompanied by a decrease in pressure. The decrease in pressure will cause the equilibrium position to shift to the side of the reaction that has more moles of gas. Therefore, the reaction shifts to the left (more N_2 and H_2 are formed).
c. Helium is a noble gas (Section 2.2) and is inert. If the volume is held constant, the addition of an inert gas will not shift the reaction one way or the other. This is because the relative partial pressures of the three gases do not change.

PRACTICE PROBLEM 15.13

The following reaction is carried out in a sealed container of variable volume:

$$Ni(CO)_4(g) \rightleftharpoons Ni(s) + 4\,CO(g)$$

Determine the direction in which the reaction shifts after the following changes are made to the system:

a. Neon is added to the container while the volume is held constant.
b. The volume of the container is increased.
c. The mass of Ni(s) is increased (assume a negligible volume change).

Hint: Review Table 15.2 to determine how a change in the volume of a reaction shifts the equilibrium. Also, noble gases are unreactive, and only gaseous species and species in solution enter the equilibrium expression.

EVERYDAY CONNECTION

In humans, oxygen, O_2, is carried from the lungs to tissues by the protein hemoglobin (Hb; Section 22.7). Hemoglobin contains four Fe^{2+} ions that can each bind an O_2 molecule, forming $Fe^{3+}—O_2$ adducts. The equilibrium constant for the formation of oxyhemoglobin, $Hb(O_2)_4$, from hemoglobin and four O_2 molecules is very large ($K = 1.86 \times 10^{44}$).

$$Hb(aq) + 4\,O_2(g) \rightleftharpoons Hb(O_2)_4(aq)$$
$$K_{O_2} = 1.86 \times 10^{44}$$

Despite the large equilibrium constant for oxyhemoglobin formation, some molecules, such as carbon monoxide, CO, can bind more strongly to hemoglobin than oxygen and disrupt the transport of blood in the body. Exposure to lower levels of CO causes headaches and dizziness, but higher levels result in asphyxiation and death.

$$Hb(aq) + 4CO(g) \rightleftharpoons Hb(CO)_4(aq) \quad K_{CO} \approx 10^{54}$$

Carbon monoxide poisoning results from the equilibrium constant for carboxyhemoglobin, $Hb(CO)_4$, formation being substantially larger than the equilibrium constant for $Hb(O_2)_4$ formation ($K_{CO} > K_{O_2}$). One way to treat patients suffering from carbon monoxide poisoning is to expose them to pure O_2 gas. The large excess of O_2 shifts the following equilibrium to the right according to Le Châtelier's principle, favoring $Hb(O_2)_4$ over $Hb(CO)_4$.

$$Hb(CO)_4(aq) + 4O_2(g) \rightleftharpoons Hb(O_2)_4(aq) + 4CO(g)$$
$$\rightarrow$$
$$(\text{excess } O_2)$$

For this reason, carbon monoxide alarms are often used in homes and other buildings in addition to smoke detectors.

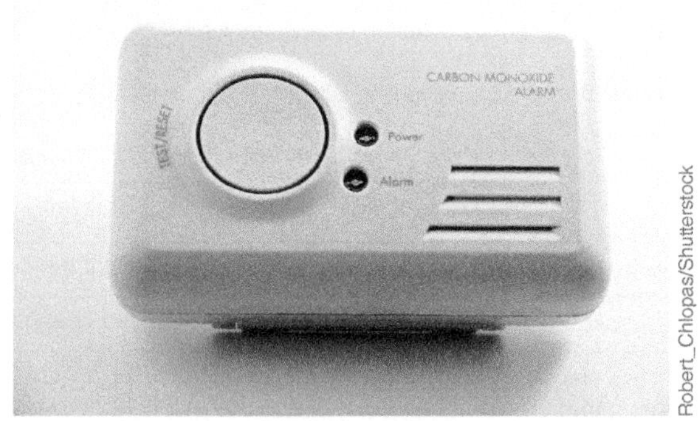

Robert_Chlopas/Shutterstock

THE EFFECT OF TEMPERATURE

Changes in concentration, volume, or pressure do not change the equilibrium constant, but changes in temperature do (Section 15.1). The sign of the enthalpy of the reaction (Section 6.4) dictates whether *K* is directly or inversely related to *T*.

For endothermic reactions (i.e., when $\Delta H > 0$), *K* and *T* are directly related (*K* increases when *T* increases and *K* decreases when *T* decreases). For exothermic reactions (i.e., when $\Delta H < 0$), *K* and *T* are inversely related (*K* decreases when *T* increases and *K* increases when *T* decreases). In each case, the reaction shifts left or right until *Q* is equal to the new *K* value. These trends are summarized in Table 15.3.

At constant pressure, a reaction that *absorbs* heat is *endothermic*.

$$2\,SO_3(g) + \text{heat} \rightleftharpoons 2\,SO_2(g) + O_2(g) \qquad \Delta H = 197\text{ kJ (endothermic)}$$

Thus, heat can be treated as a reactant in an endothermic reaction. The addition of heat, like the addition of more reactant, causes the reaction to shift to the right (producing more products). Similarly, cooling an endothermic reaction (effectively removing heat from the reaction), causes the reaction to shift to the left, producing more reactants (Figure 15.7).

Conversely, a reaction that *releases* heat at constant pressure is *exothermic*.

$$CO(g) + 2\,H_2(g) \rightleftharpoons CH_3OH(g) + \text{heat} \qquad \Delta H = -91\text{ kJ (exothermic)}$$

Thus, heat can be treated as a product in an exothermic reaction. The addition of heat, like the addition of more $CH_3OH(g)$ to the reaction, causes the reaction to shift to the left (producing more reactants). Similarly, cooling an exothermic reaction (effectively removing heat from the reaction) causes the reaction to shift to the right, producing more products.

TABLE 15.3 The Effect of Temperature on Endothermic and Exothermic Equilibria

Reaction Type	Temperature Change	Change in *K*	Result	Reaction Shift
Endothermic ($\Delta H > 0$)	*T* increases	*K* increases	$Q < K$	To the right (products)
	T decreases	*K* decreases	$Q > K$	To the left (reactants)
Exothermic ($\Delta H < 0$)	*T* increases	*K* decreases	$Q > K$	To the left (reactants)
	T decreases	*K* increases	$Q < K$	To the right (products)

A video summarizing Le Châtelier's principle is shown in Figure 15.8.

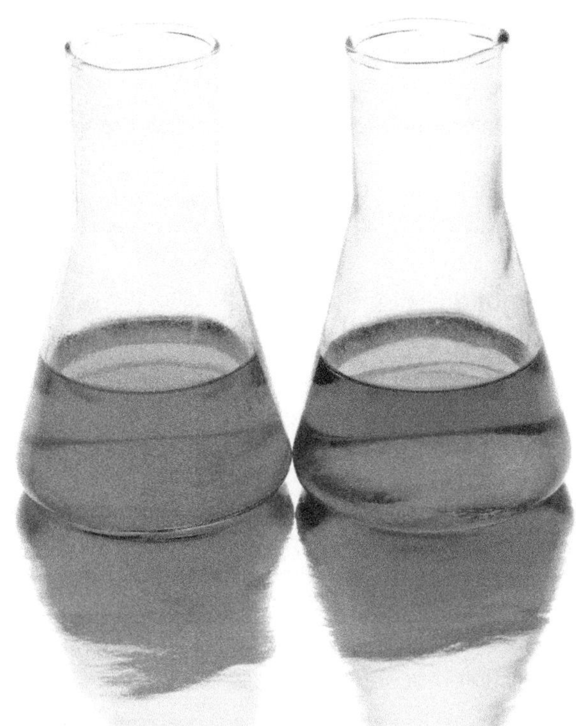

Alexander Ishchenko/Shutterstock

FIGURE 15.7 The Effect of Temperature on an Endothermic Reaction

The reaction between aqueous $Co(H_2O)_6^{2+}$ (pink) and aqueous $CoCl_4^{2-}$ (blue) is endothermic ($\Delta H > 0$).

$$\underset{\text{pink}}{Co(H_2O)_6^{2+}(aq)} + 4\,Cl^-(aq) + \text{heat} \rightleftharpoons \underset{\text{blue}}{CoCl_4^{2-}(aq)} + 6\,H_2O(l)$$

When the solution is at room temperature (left flask), the equilibrium favors $Co(H_2O)_6^{2+}$. When the solution is heated (right flask), the equilibrium favors $CoCl_4^{2-}$.

Steve Lemon, Macmillan Learning

FIGURE 15.8 Video Tutorial: Le Châtelier's Principle

NOTE: You need to be online to access this video.

This video shows how to determine the direction of a reaction shift based on changes to concentration, volume, and temperature.

Example 15.14

The decomposition of NH_3 into N_2 and H_2 is endothermic.

$$2\,NH_3(g) \rightleftharpoons 3\,H_2(g) + N_2(g)$$

a. How is K for this reaction affected by an increase in temperature?
b. Determine the direction in which the system shifts after the change in K.
c. Identify how the partial pressure of each gas is affected by the reaction shift.

Solution

a. For endothermic reactions, K and T are directly related (Table 15.3), so an increase in T causes an increase in K, in which case $Q < K$.
b. When $Q < K$, the reaction shifts to the right, toward the products.
c. Because more products are formed, the partial pressure of NH_3 decreases and the partial pressures of H_2 and N_2 both increase.

To double-check your answer, recall that heat can be treated as a reactant in an endothermic reaction.

$$\text{heat} + 2\,NH_3(g) \rightleftharpoons 3\,H_2(g) + N_2(g)$$

Thus, increasing the temperature (i.e., adding heat) will cause the same type of shift as would increasing the concentration of a reactant.

PRACTICE PROBLEM 15.14

The following reaction is exothermic.

$$Cl_2(g) + 2\,NO(g) \rightleftharpoons 2\,NOCl(g)$$

a. How is K for this reaction affected by an increase in temperature?
b. Determine the direction in which the system shifts after the change in K.
c. Identify how the partial pressure of each gas is affected by the reaction shift.

Hint: Heat can be treated as a product in an exothermic reaction.

$$Cl_2(g) + 2\,NO(g) \rightleftharpoons 2\,NOCl(g) + \text{heat}$$

Thus, increasing the temperature (i.e., adding heat) will cause the same type of shift as would increasing the concentration of a product.

The Le Châtelier's Principle Activity (Figure 15.9) allows you to explore how various changes to a system can disturb equilibrium by altering the value of Q or K.

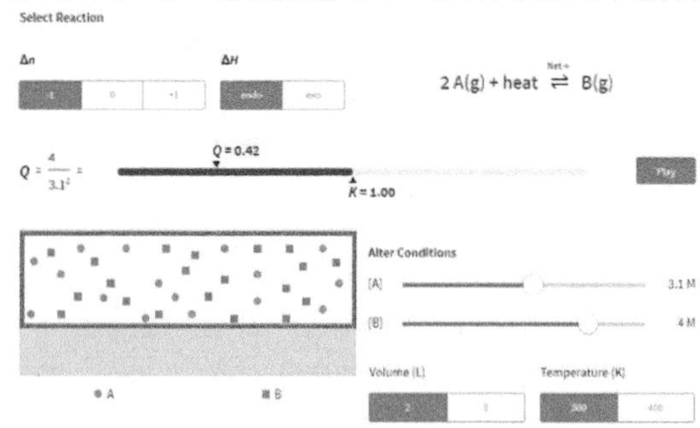

FIGURE 15.9 Le Châtelier's Principle Activity

NOTE: You need to be online to access this tool.

For the given reaction, adjust concentration, volume, or temperature to observe the effect on Q or K. Then press Play to observe how the system responds to re-establish equilibrium. Then, start over with a different reaction by adjusting Δn and/or ΔH, and again test the effects of changing concentration, volume, and temperature.

EVERYDAY CONNECTION

As mentioned in the chapter opener, the industrial production of ammonia uses the Haber process.

$$3\,H_2(g) + N_2(g) \rightleftharpoons 2\,NH_3(g)$$

Since the reaction is exothermic, you would expect a lower temperature to be used to increase reaction yield. However, colder temperatures decrease the reaction rate significantly, and so higher temperatures (about 400°C) are preferred. To increase yield, the reaction is carried out at high pressure (about 250 atm) and the product that forms is continuously removed from the reaction chamber, both of which shift the reaction to the right according to Le Châtelier's principle.

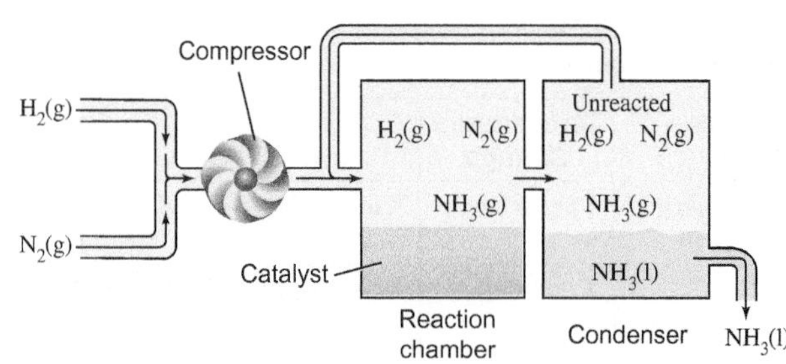

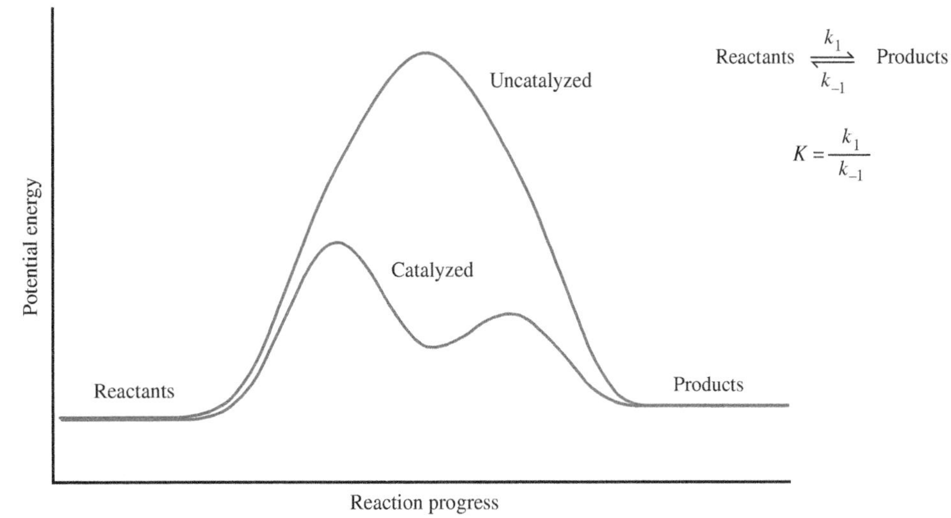

FIGURE 15.10 The Equilibrium Constant Does Not Change in the Presence of a Catalyst

A catalyst increases the rates of both the forward and reverse reactions proportionally, so $\frac{k_1}{k_{-1}}$ does not change. In other words, a catalyzed reaction reaches equilibrium faster, but the ratio of products to reactants at equilibrium remains the same.

THE EFFECT OF A CATALYST

Catalysts, which increase the rate of a chemical reaction, are discussed in detail in Section 14.6. Unlike temperature, volume, pressure, and concentration, the presence of a catalyst does *not* affect the equilibrium position, Q, or the equilibrium constant, K, for a reaction.

Recall that K is the ratio of the rate constants for the forward and reverse reactions (Equation 15.2):

$$K = \frac{k_1}{k_{-1}}$$

Catalysts lower the activation energies of both the forward and reverse reactions, which increases the forward and reverse rate constants proportionally. Equilibrium is established more quickly in the presence of a catalyst, but the *ratio* of k_1 and k_{-1} does not change. Therefore, K for the reaction is not altered by the presence of a catalyst (Figure 15.10).

SECTION REVIEW

- Le Châtelier's principle states that if a stress is placed on a system at equilibrium, the reaction will shift to reduce the stress.
- If the concentration of a reactant is increased or the concentration of a product is decreased, then $Q < K$ and the reaction shifts to the right to form more product. If the concentration of a product is increased or the concentration of a reactant is decreased, then $Q > K$ and the reaction shifts to the left to form more reactant.
- For a reaction of gases at equilibrium, an increase in pressure (i.e., a decrease in volume) favors the side of the reaction in which there are the fewest moles of gas. A decrease in pressure (i.e., an increase in volume) favors the side of the reaction in which there is the greatest number of moles of gas.
- Heating an endothermic reaction (a reaction that absorbs heat) shifts the equilibrium toward the products. Cooling an endothermic reaction shifts the equilibrium toward the reactants.
- Heating an exothermic reaction (a reaction that produces heat) shifts the equilibrium toward the reactants. Cooling an exothermic reaction shifts the equilibrium toward the products.
- The equilibrium constant for a reaction depends *only* on the temperature at which the reaction is carried out. The equilibrium constant is *not* altered by other reaction conditions such as concentration, volume, pressure, or the presence of a catalyst.

Putting It Together

The example problems in earlier sections of this chapter focus on just the new skills acquired in that section, but homework and exam questions in chemistry often require more than just one skill at a time. In fact, you will likely be expected to apply knowledge from across the entire chapter, or even multiple chapters in a single problem. This final example problem is meant to help you prepare for these types of multi-concept questions. Additional examples can be found in the end of chapter exercises.

Example 15.15

Phosgene, $COCl_2$, was used as a chemical weapon during World War I and is currently used as a starting material for the synthesis of other chemical compounds. Phosgene decomposes into carbon monoxide and chlorine gas.

$$COCl_2(g) \rightleftharpoons CO(g) + Cl_2(g)$$

Suppose that 0.250 mol $COCl_2$ decomposes in a sealed 1.00 L container at 1000 K to give 0.0294 mol CO at equilibrium.

a. Determine the equilibrium constant for the decomposition of phosgene at 1000 K.
b. Calculate the equilibrium concentration of $COCl_2$ after the volume of the container has been doubled.

Solution

The volume of the container is 1.00 L, so the initial $COCl_2$ concentration is 0.250 M and the equilibrium CO concentration is 0.0294 M.

a. The equilibrium constant expression is

$$K_c = \frac{[CO][Cl_2]}{[COCl_2]}$$

The following ICE table can be constructed for this reaction:

	$COCl_2(g)$ $\rightleftharpoons$	$CO(g)$ +	$Cl_2(g)$
Initial (M)	0.250	0	0
Change (M)	$-x$	$+x$	$+x$
Equilibrium (M)	$0.250 - x$	x	x

Because the equilibrium concentration of CO is 0.0294 M, the equilibrium concentration of Cl_2 is also 0.0294 M. This value is represented by x in the preceding ICE table. The equilibrium concentration of $COCl_2$ is $0.250 - x = 0.250 - 0.0294 = 0.2206$ M.

	$COCl_2(g)$ $\rightleftharpoons$	$CO(g)$ +	$Cl_2(g)$
Initial (M)	0.250	0	0
Change (M)	−0.0294	+0.0294	+0.0294
Equilibrium (M)	0.2206	0.0294	0.0294

Substituting the equilibrium values into the equilibrium constant expression gives K_c for the decomposition of phosgene at 1000 K:

$$K_c = \frac{[CO][Cl_2]}{[COCl_2]} = \frac{[0.0294][0.0294]}{[0.2206]} = 0.00392$$

b. After the volume of the container doubles, the concentration of $COCl_2$ is $0.2206/2 = 0.1103$ M and the concentrations of CO and Cl_2 are $0.0294/2 = 0.0147$ M. According to Le Châtelier's principle, increasing the volume of the container means that the equilibrium will now shift toward the side of the reaction with *more* gaseous species (the products, in this case). A new ICE table can now be constructed.

	$COCl_2(g)$ $\rightleftharpoons$	$CO(g)$ +	$Cl_2(g)$
Initial (M)	0.1103	0.0147	0.0147
Change (M)	$-x$	$+x$	$+x$
Equilibrium (M)	$0.1103 - x$	$0.0147 + x$	$0.0147 + x$

Now set up the equilibrium constant expression for these new conditions, and solve for x.

$$K_c = \frac{[CO][Cl_2]}{[COCl_2]} = \frac{(0.0147 + x)^2}{(0.1103 - x)}$$

$$= \frac{(x^2 + 0.0294x + 0.0002161)}{(0.1103 - x)} = 0.00392$$

$$(x^2 + 0.0294x + 0.0002161) = 0.0004324 - 0.00392x$$

$$x^2 + 0.03332x - 0.0002163 = 0$$

Using the quadratic formula to solve this equation yields $x = 0.005563$ M or -0.03888 M.

The negative value of x would result in negative CO and Cl_2 concentrations, so x must be 0.05563 M. The equilibrium concentration of $COCl_2$ is then $0.1103 - 0.005563 = 0.1047$ M.

You can check your work by substituting the value of x back into the equilibrium expression shown here and recalculating K_c.

$$K_c = \frac{[CO][Cl_2]}{[COCl_2]} = \frac{(0.0147 + 0.005563)^2}{(0.1103 - 0.005563)}$$

$$= \frac{(0.0203)^2}{0.1047} = 0.00394$$

The recalculated K_c value is very close to the value calculated in part (a), so you can be confident that the calculated value of x for part (b) is correct.

PRACTICE PROBLEM 15.15

The decomposition of N_2O_4 into NO_2 is carried out in a sealed container at 25°C.

$$N_2O_4(g) \rightleftharpoons 2\ NO_2(g)$$

$K_p = 0.15$ for this reaction at 25°C.

a. The initial partial pressures of this reaction are 0.100 atm N_2O_4 and 0.500 atm NO_2. Determine the direction in which the reaction shifts.
b. Determine the equilibrium partial pressures of N_2O_4 and NO_2.
c. The standard enthalpies of formation, ΔH°_f, (Section 6.8) of N_2O_4 and NO_2 are 9.66 kJ/mol and 33.84 kJ/mol, respectively. Is the reaction endothermic or exothermic?
d. Given your answer to part (c), how will lowering the temperature from 25°C to 0°C affect the equilibrium?
e. Does changing the temperature from 25°C to 0°C affect K_p? Explain your answer.

Hint: First, calculate Q with the given partial pressures. After you know the direction in which the reaction proceeds, set up an ICE table and use the quadratic equation to determine the partial pressures of the gases. To determine whether the reaction is endothermic or exothermic, calculate the standard enthalpy of reaction, ΔH°_{rxn}, from the standard enthalpies of formation, $\Delta H^\circ_{rxn} = \sum \Delta H^\circ_f(\text{products}) - \sum \Delta H^\circ_f(\text{reactants})$. The information in Table 15.3 may be helpful for answering parts (d) and (e).

Key Terms, Symbols, and Equations

KEY TERMS

dynamic state (15.1): A state in which two opposite processes occur at equal rates.

equilibrium (15.1): The situation in which the forward and reverse reactions are occurring *at the same rate.*

equilibrium constant, *K* (15.2): A constant that tells how far a reaction will proceed until it reaches equilibrium.

equilibrium constant expression (15.2): The ratio of the product of the concentrations of the products divided by the product of the concentrations or partial pressures of the reactants, each raised to the power corresponding to its coefficient in the balanced equation. Also referred to as an equilibrium expression.

heterogeneous equilibrium (15.2): An equilibrium in which the species are in different phases.

ICE table (15.5): A table that shows the initial, change, and equilibrium values of the species in an equilibrium.

law of mass action (15.2): The ratio of products to reactants in the equilibrium constant expression does *not* change as long as the system is at equilibrium.

Le Châtelier's principle (15.6): When a stress is applied to a system at equilibrium, the reaction shifts in a direction to relieve that stress.

reaction quotient, *Q* (15.4): The ratio of the products to the reactants, where each species is raised to its stoichiometric coefficient, at any time in an equilibrium.

SYMBOLS AND ABBREVIATIONS

$\rightleftharpoons$ (equilibrium) (15.1)

[A] (molar concentration of A) (15.2)

K (equilibrium constant) (15.2)

Q (reaction quotient) (15.4)

EQUATIONS

$$K = \frac{k_1}{k_{-1}} \quad (15.1)$$

$$K_c = \frac{[C]^c[D]^d}{[A]^a[B]^b} \quad (15.2)$$

$$K_p = \frac{(P_C)^c(P_D)^d}{(P_A)^a(P_B)^b} \quad (15.3)$$

$$K_p = K_c(RT)^{\Delta n} \quad (15.4)$$

$$Q_c = \frac{[C]^c[D]^d}{[A]^a[B]^b} \quad (15.5)$$

$$Q_p = \frac{(P_C)^c(P_D)^d}{(P_A)^a(P_B)^b} \quad (15.6)$$

Chapter Summary

Equilibrium is a dynamic process that can occur when a reaction is reversible: the products can react with one another to re-form the reactants. In an equilibrium reaction, the forward and reverse reactions occur at the same time. When the forward and reverse reactions are occurring at the same rate, the system is in a state of chemical equilibrium (Section 15.1).

The general reaction $a\,A + b\,B \rightleftharpoons c\,C + d\,D$ is represented by the equilibrium constant expression

$$K_c = \frac{[C]^c[D]^d}{[A]^a[B]^b}$$

K_c is the molar equilibrium constant, and the brackets around each species denote the molar concentration of that species. For reactions in the gas phase, the equilibrium constant, K_p, is expressed in terms of the partial pressure of each gas, P.

$$K_p = \frac{(P_C)^c(P_D)^d}{(P_A)^a(P_B)^b}$$

Species that are in the solid or pure liquid phase are *not* included in equilibrium expressions. K_p and K_c are related to one another as follows

$$K_p = K_c(RT)^{\Delta n}$$

where Δn is the change in the number of moles of gas, $\Delta n = (c + d) - (a + b)$ (Section 15.2).

When a chemical equation is reversed, its equilibrium constant is inverted. When the coefficients of a chemical equation are multiplied by a factor, its equilibrium constant is raised to the power of that factor. When chemical equations are summed, the equilibrium constant of the overall equation is the product of the equilibrium constants of the component reactions (Section 15.3).

The reaction quotient, Q, is the ratio of the products to the reactants, where each species is raised to its stoichiometric coefficient in the balanced chemical equation. Unlike the equilibrium constant, K, Q describes the ratio of products to reactants *at any time during the reaction*. Q can be used to predict the direction of a reaction based on the current conditions of the system.

For the general reaction $a\,A + b\,B \rightleftharpoons c\,C + d\,D$,

$$Q_c = \frac{[C]^c[D]^d}{[A]^a[B]^b}$$

$$Q_p = \frac{(P_C)^c(P_D)^d}{(P_A)^a(P_B)^b}$$

If $Q = K$, the reaction is at equilibrium. If $Q > K$, the reaction will shift back to the left (will form reactants) to achieve equilibrium. If $Q < K$, the reaction will shift to the right (will form products) to achieve equilibrium (Section 15.4).

When both reactants and products are present in an equilibrium reaction and you need to determine their concentrations at equilibrium, you must first calculate the reaction quotient, Q, to determine the direction in which the reaction proceeds. It often helps to use an ICE table in these calculations, particularly when only the initial concentrations of reactants are known. In some cases, you will need to use the quadratic equation to determine the concentrations of species at equilibrium.

$$x = \frac{-b \pm \sqrt{b^2 - 4ac}}{2a}$$

When the initial concentrations of reactants are large and the equilibrium constant is relatively small, you can often simplify the equilibrium expression to avoid solving a quadratic equation. For the simplification to be valid, the change (x, $2x$, etc.) must be less than 5% of the initial amount that it is being subtracted from (Section 15.5).

Le Châtelier's principle states that if a stress is placed on a system at equilibrium, the equilibrium position will shift to reduce the stress. If the concentration of a reactant is increased or the concentration of a product is decreased, the reaction will shift to the right to form more product. If the concentration of a product is increased or the concentration of a reactant is decreased, the reaction will shift to the left to form more reactant.

For an equilibrium reaction of gases, an increase in pressure (i.e., a decrease in volume) favors the side of the reaction with the fewest moles of gas. A decrease in pressure (i.e., an increase in volume) favors the side of the reaction with the greatest number of moles of gas.

Heating an endothermic reaction (i.e., increasing T) shifts the equilibrium toward the products. Cooling an endothermic reaction (i.e., decreasing T) shifts the equilibrium toward the reactants. Heating an exothermic reaction shifts the equilibrium toward the reactants, and cooling an exothermic reaction shifts the equilibrium toward the products.

The equilibrium constant for a reaction depends *only* on the temperature at which the reaction is carried out. The equilibrium constant is *not* altered by other reaction conditions such as concentration, volume, pressure, or the presence of a catalyst (Section 15.6).

END OF CHAPTER QUESTIONS

15.1 Introduction to Equilibrium

1. Give an example of a reversible reaction and an irreversible reaction. Explain how they are fundamentally different.

2. Equilibrium is a dynamic process. Explain what this means.

3. Determine whether the following statements are true or false. Correct the false statements.
   a. When a chemical reaction reaches equilibrium, the reaction completely stops.
   b. When a chemical reaction reaches equilibrium, the forward reaction stops and the reverse reaction begins.

4. Determine whether the following statements are true or false. Correct the false statements.
   a. The concentrations of the products are equal to the concentrations of the reactants at equilibrium.
   b. The rates of the forward and reverse reactions are the same at equilibrium.

5. Consider the reversible reaction
   $A + B \rightleftharpoons C + D$
   a. If A and B are placed together in a flask and allowed to react, which species will be present at equilibrium?
   b. If C and D are placed together in a flask and allowed to reaction, which species will be present at equilibrium?

15.2 Equilibrium Constants

6. For the following reactions, determine whether the forward or reverse reaction is favored.
   a. $2\ SO_3(g) \rightleftharpoons 2\ SO_2(g) + O_2(g)$ $K = 2.5 \times 10^{25}$
   b. $N_2(g) + O_2(g) \rightleftharpoons 2\ NO(g)$ $K = 4.1 \times 10^{-31}$
   c. $H_2(g) + Cl_2(g) \rightleftharpoons 2\ HCl(g)$ $K = 5.1 \times 10^{8}$

7. For the following reactions, determine whether the forward or reverse reaction is favored.
   a. $Ag_2CrO_4(s) \rightleftharpoons 2\ Ag^+(aq) + CrO_4^{2-}(aq)$ $K = 1.1 \times 10^{-12}$
   b. $2\ NO(g) + O_2(g) \rightleftharpoons 2\ NO_2(g)$ $K = 2.5 \times 10^{10}$
   c. $HCN(aq) + OH^-(aq) \rightleftharpoons CN^-(aq) + H_2O(l)$ $K = 4.9 \times 10^{4}$

8. Write the equilibrium expression, K_p, for each of the following reactions.
   a. $2\ SO_3(g) \rightleftharpoons 2\ SO_2(g) + O_2(g)$
   b. $N_2(g) + O_2(g) \rightleftharpoons 2\ NO(g)$
   c. $H_2(g) + Cl_2(g) \rightleftharpoons 2\ HCl(g)$

9. Write the equilibrium expression, K_c, for each of the following reactions.
   a. $Ag_2CrO_4(s) \rightleftharpoons 2\ Ag^+(aq) + CrO_4^{2-}(aq)$
   b. $2\ NO(g) + O_2(g) \rightleftharpoons 2\ NO_2(g)$
   c. $HCN(aq) + OH^-(aq) \rightleftharpoons CN^-(aq) + H_2O(l)$

10. Determine whether the following statements are true or false. Correct the false statements.
    a. Equilibrium constants are ratios of the concentrations (or partial pressures) of reactants over the concentrations (or partial pressures) of products, each multiplied by the value of its coefficient in the balanced chemical reaction.
    b. Solids and pure liquids are always omitted from equilibrium expressions.
    c. Species dissolved into a solvent are always omitted from equilibrium expressions.

11. Explain the difference between K_c and K_p.

12. N_2O_4 gas dissociates into NO_2 via the following reaction:

    $N_2O_4(g) \rightleftharpoons 2\ NO_2(aq)$

    $K_c = 6.1 \times 10^{23}$ at 298 K

    Calculate K_p for this reaction at 298 K.

13. $SOCl_2$ gas dissociates into SO_2 and Cl_2 via the following reaction:

    $SOCl_2(g) \rightleftharpoons SO_2(aq) + Cl_2(g)$

    $K_p = 1.23 \times 10^{-6}$ at 500 K

    Calculate K_c for this reaction at 500 K.

14. Determine whether the following statements are true or false. Correct the false statements.
    a. When the coefficients of an equation are multiplied by two, the equilibrium constant of the resulting reaction is the square of the original equilibrium constant.
    b. When a reaction is reversed, its equilibrium constant can be obtained by multiplying the equilibrium constant of the original reaction by -1.
    c. If two equations are added, the equilibrium constant of the resulting equation is the sum of the original equations' equilibrium constants.

15. Gaseous H_2 and Br_2 react to form HBr gas:

    $H_2(g) + Br_2(g) \rightleftharpoons 2\ HBr(g)$

    The equilibrium partial pressures of H_2 and Br_2 are 1.25×10^{-5} atm and 2.25×10^{-5} atm, respectively, at 300 K. The equilibrium partial pressure of HBr under these conditions is 7310 atm. Calculate K_p for this reaction at 300 K.

16. Consider the equilibrium between acetylene, C_2H_2, and benzene, C_6H_6.

    $3\ C_2H_2(g) \rightleftharpoons C_6H_6(l)$

    a. Write the equilibrium expression for this reaction.
    b. Write the equilibrium expression for the reverse reaction

    $C_6H_6(l) \rightleftharpoons 3\ C_2H_2(g)$

15.3 Using Equilibrium Expressions

17. Aqueous Fe^{3+} reacts with aqueous SCN^- to give $FeSCN^{2+}$:

    $Fe^{3+}(aq) + SCN^-(aq) \rightleftharpoons FeSCN^{2+}(aq)$

    At 25°C, the concentrations of Fe^{3+} and SCN^- are 0.0015 M and the concentration of $FeSCN^{2+}$ is 2.5×10^{-8} M. Calculate the equilibrium constant, K_c, at 25°C.

18. At 800°C, the following reaction has a K_p value of 14.1.

    $C(s) + H_2O(g) \rightleftharpoons CO(g) + H_2(g)$

    If the equilibrium pressures of CO and H_2 are both 0.920 at this temperature, what is the pressure of H_2O?

19. Consider the reaction of gaseous S_2 and H_2 to form gaseous H_2S.

    $2\ H_2(g) + S_2(g) \rightleftharpoons 2\ H_2S(g)$

    $K = 1.1 \times 10^7$ at 700°C

    Calculate K for the following reaction at 700°C.

    $H_2S(g) \rightleftharpoons H_2(g) + \frac{1}{2} S_2(g)$

20. Diatomic fluorine gas is in equilibrium with gaseous fluorine atoms at high temperature.

    $F_2(g) \rightleftharpoons 2\ F(g) \quad K_p = 0.020$ at 700 K

    Suppose that a sealed flask initially contains 0.75 atm of gaseous F_2. Calculate the partial pressure of F(g) present at equilibrium at 700 K.

21. Gaseous BrCl decomposes into bromine and chlorine gas:

$$2\,BrCl(g) \rightleftharpoons Br_2(g) + Cl_2(g) \qquad K_p = 377 \text{ at } 300\text{ K}$$

Cl_2 (1.5 atm) and Br_2 (1.0 atm) are added to a sealed flask and are allowed to come to equilibrium at 300 K. Calculate the partial pressure of BrCl present at equilibrium.

22. Oxygen and fluorine react to form OF_2.

$$\frac{1}{2}O_2(g) + F_2(g) \rightleftharpoons OF_2(g) \quad K = 40 \text{ at } 25°C$$

Given the information above, calculate the equilibrium constant for the following reaction at 25°C:

$$O_2(g) + 2F_2(g) \rightleftharpoons 2\,OF_2(g) \quad K' = ?$$

23. Consider the following reaction.

$$2\,COF_2(g) \rightleftharpoons CF_4(g) + CO_2(g) \qquad K = 2 \times 10^6 \text{ at } 25°C$$

Given the preceding information, calculate the equilibrium constant for the following reaction at 25°C:

$$\frac{1}{2}CF_4(g) + \frac{1}{2}CO_2(g) \rightleftharpoons COF_2(g) \quad K' = ?$$

24. Consider the following reactions:

$$2\,A + B \rightleftharpoons D \quad K_1 = 0.250$$
$$C \rightleftharpoons D \quad K_2 = 575$$

Use the information above to calculate the equilibrium constant for the following reaction:

$$C \rightleftharpoons 2\,A + B \quad K = ?$$

25. Consider the following reactions:

$$\frac{1}{2}A + B \rightleftharpoons \frac{1}{2}C \quad K_1 = 115$$
$$3\,D \rightleftharpoons 3\,C \quad K_2 = 1.12 \times 10^4$$
$$E \rightleftharpoons C \quad K_3 = 0.0278$$

Use the information above to calculate the equilibrium constant for the following reaction:

$$A + 2B \rightleftharpoons E \quad K = ?$$

26. Consider the following reactions:

$$CO(g) + 2\,H_2S(g) \rightleftharpoons CS_2(g) + H_2O(g) + H_2(g) K_1 = 1.3 \times 10^5$$

$$\frac{1}{2}CH_4(g) + H_2S(g) \rightleftharpoons \frac{1}{2}CS_2(g) + 2\,H_2(g) \qquad K_2 = 180$$

Use the information above to calculate the equilibrium constant for the following reaction:

$$2\,CO(g) + 6\,H_2(g) \rightleftharpoons 2\,CH_4(g) + 2\,H_2O(g) \qquad K = ?$$

15.4 The Reaction Quotient

27. How does Q compare to K at the beginning of a chemical reaction when only the reactants are present?

28. Consider the reaction $X + Y \rightleftharpoons Z$. Determine the direction in which the reaction will proceed when
    a. $Q > K$.
    b. $Q < K$.
    c. $Q = K$.

29. Balance the equation and write the reaction quotient expression, Q_c, for the following synthesis of carbon disulfide, CS_2:

$$CH_4(g) + H_2S(g) \rightleftharpoons CS_2(g) + H_2(g)$$

30. Consider the following reaction between reactants X and Y to give product Z:

$$X_2(g) + Y(g) \rightleftharpoons Z(g) \quad K_c = 1.00 \text{ at } 300\text{ K}$$

    a. Predict the direction in which the reaction will proceed if the concentrations of X, Y, and Z are all 2.00 M.
    b. Predict the direction in which the reaction will proceed if the partial pressures of X, Y, and Z are all 1.00 atm.

31. Consider the following reaction of carbon monoxide and hydrogen to form gaseous methanol, CH_3OH. The equilibrium constant, K_c, is 0.0334 at a particular temperature:

$$CO(g) + 2\,H_2(g) \rightleftharpoons CH_3OH(g)$$

Suppose that $[CO] = 0.0500$ M, $[H_2] = 0.150$ M, and $[CH_3OH] = 0.000250$ M at a particular point in the reaction. Determine which direction the reaction will shift to re-establish equilibrium.

32. Consider the following reaction:

$$CO(g) + H_2O(g) \rightleftharpoons CO_2(g) + H_2(g) \qquad K_p = 2.0 \text{ at } 25°C$$

At a particular point in the reaction, suppose that CO has a partial pressure of 3.5 atm, H_2O has a partial pressure of 0.71 atm, CO_2 has a partial pressure of 2.6 atm, and H_2 has a partial pressure of 0.86 atm. Determine which direction the reaction will shift to re-establish equilibrium.

33. Methane, CH_4, can react with oxygen to give carbon dioxide and water vapor:

$$CH_4(g) + 2\,O_2(g) \rightleftharpoons CO_2(g) + 2\,H_2O(g) \quad K_p = 1 \times 10^4$$

At a particular point in the reaction, suppose that CH_4 has a partial pressure of 0.86 atm, O_2 has a partial pressure of 1.2 atm, CO_2 has a partial pressure of 1.4 atm, and H_2O has a partial pressure of 0.97 atm. Determine which direction the reaction will shift to re-establish equilibrium.

34. Nitrogen and hydrogen gases can react to give gaseous ammonia:

$$N_2(g) + 3\,H_2(g) \rightleftharpoons 2\,NH_3(g) \quad K_p = 5.3 \times 10^5 \text{ at } 25°C$$

At a particular point in the reaction, suppose that N_2 has a partial pressure of 1.5 atm, H_2 has a partial pressure of 0.57 atm, and NH_3 has a partial pressure of 0.78 atm. Determine which direction the reaction will shift to re-establish equilibrium.

35. Consider the following theoretical reaction, where A and B react to form C and D:

$$2\,A + B \rightleftharpoons 2\,C + D \quad K_c = 0.50$$

Determine which direction the reaction will shift to re-establish equilibrium when

a. $[A] = 1.0$ M, $[B] = 1.5$ M, $[C] = 1.5$ M, and $[D] = 1.0$ M.

b. $[A] = 0.75$ M, $[B] = 1.75$, $[C] = 0.35$ M, and $[D] = 2.25$ M.

c. $[A] = 2.25$ M, $[B] = 0.65$, $[C] = 2.25$ M, and $[D] = 0.65$ M.

15.5 Calculations Using ICE Tables

36. Nitrogen and oxygen gas react to form nitric oxide, NO, at high temperature:

$$N_2(g) + O_2(g) \rightleftharpoons 2\,NO(g) \quad K_p = 0.0025 \text{ at } 2100°C$$

Suppose that a sealed reaction vessel contains 1.3 atm of N_2 and 0.70 atm of O_2. Calculate the partial pressure of NO at equilibrium at 2100°C.

37. Phosphine, PH_3, dissociates to give H_2 and P_4. The equilibrium constant, K_c, for this reaction at a particular temperature is 0.353. If the concentration of H_2 is 0.105 M and the concentration of P_4 is 0.575 M at equilibrium, calculate the equilibrium concentration of PH_3.

38. At high temperature, P_4 decomposes into P_2:

$$P_4(g) \rightleftharpoons 2\,P_2(g) \quad K_p = 0.10 \text{ at } 1050°C$$

If a sealed container initially contains 0.225 atm of P_4, calculate the equilibrium partial pressures of P_4 and P_2 at 1050°C.

39. Hydrogen sulfide gas decomposes into gaseous hydrogen and sulfur at a particular temperature:

$$H_2S(g) \rightleftharpoons H_2(g) + S(g) \quad K_p = 0.749$$

Suppose that a sealed container initially contains 0.445 atm of H_2S. Calculate the equilibrium partial pressures of H_2S, H_2, and S at this temperature.

40. At a particular temperature, CO_2 and H_2 can react to give CO and H_2O with an equilibrium constant, K_c, of 1.7:

$$CO_2(g) + H_2(g) \rightleftharpoons H_2O(g) + CO(g) \quad K_c = 1.7$$

A sealed reaction vessel initially contains 0.15 M CO_2, 0.075 M H_2, 0 M H_2O, and 0 M CO at that temperature, and the reaction is allowed to achieve equilibrium. Determine the equilibrium concentrations of all four species.

41. Gaseous I_2 and Cl_2 react to form ICl:

$$I_2(g) + Cl_2(g) \rightleftharpoons ICl(g) \quad K_c = 9.1$$

Suppose that a sealed container initially contains 0.250 M I_2 and 0.150 M Cl_2. Calculate the concentration of all three species at equilibrium.

42. At 25°C, gaseous H_2 and I_2 react to form gaseous HI:

$$2\,H_2(g) + I_2(g) \rightleftharpoons 2\,HI(g) \quad K_p = 794$$

A sealed reaction vessel initially contains 0.550 atm H_2 and 0.125 atm I_2. Calculate the concentration of all three species at equilibrium.

43. At 500 K, gaseous BrCl decomposes into gaseous bromine and chlorine:

$$2\,BrCl(g) \rightleftharpoons Br_2(g) + Cl_2(g) \quad K_p = 32$$

Suppose that a sealed container initially contains 1.75 atm BrCl, 0.750 atm Br_2, and 1.15 atm Cl_2. Calculate the concentrations of all three gases at equilibrium.

44. Aqueous iodine reacts with aqueous iodide ion to give triiodide ion, I_3^-:

$$I_2(aq) + I^-(aq) \rightleftharpoons I_3^-(aq) \quad K_c = 721 \text{ at } 25°C$$

Suppose that a reaction in 0.250 M I^- produces 0.0228 M I_2. Calculate the amount of I_3^- present in the reaction system when equilibrium is reached.

45. Gaseous sulfuryl chloride, SO_2Cl_2, decomposes into gaseous SO_2 and Cl_2:

$$SO_2Cl_2(g) \rightleftharpoons SO_2(g) + Cl_2(g) \quad K_p = 2.4 \text{ at } 373 \text{ K}$$

A sealed reaction vessel contains 0.0028 atm SO_2, 0.0025 atm Cl_2, and 0.0034 atm SO_2Cl_2 at a particular point in the reaction. Calculate the concentrations of all three gases at equilibrium.

15.6 Le Châtelier's Principle

46. For the reversible reaction $X(g) + Y(g) \rightleftharpoons Z(g)$, explain how the following affects Q.
   a. an increase in volume
   b. a decrease in volume
   c. an increase in the amount of Z
   d. a decrease in the amount of Z
   e. an increase in the amount of X
   f. a decrease in the amount of X

47. For the reversible reaction $X(s) + Y(g) \rightleftharpoons Z(g)$, explain how the following affects Q.
   a. an increase in volume
   b. a decrease in volume
   c. an increase in the amount of Z
   d. a decrease in the amount of Z
   e. an increase in the amount of X
   f. a decrease in the amount of X

48. Suppose that the reaction $X(g) + Y(g) \rightleftharpoons Z(g)$ is carried out in a sealed container. Determine the direction in which the reaction will proceed when
   a. the volume of the container is increased.
   b. the volume of the container is reduced.

49. Suppose that the reaction $X(g) + Y(g) \rightleftharpoons 3\,Z(g)$ is carried out in a sealed container. Determine the direction in which the reaction will proceed when
   a. the volume of the container is increased.
   b. the volume of the container is reduced.

50. Carbon monoxide reacts with water to form carbon dioxide in a sealed container:

$$CO(g) + O_2(g) \rightleftharpoons CO_2(g)$$

Determine the direction in which the reaction will shift in order to re-establish equilibrium if
   a. the concentration of CO increases.
   b. the concentration of CO_2 increases.
   c. the concentration of CO_2 decreases.
   d. the volume of the container is increased.

51. Sulfur reacts with oxygen to form gaseous sulfur dioxide, SO_2, in a sealed container:

$$S(s) + O_2(g) \rightleftharpoons SO_2(g)$$

Determine the direction in which the reaction will shift in order to re-establish equilibrium if
   a. the partial pressure of O_2 increases.
   b. some sulfur is removed from the container.
   c. the partial pressure of SO_2 increases.
   d. the volume of the container decreases.

52. For an endothermic reaction,
   a. state how Q and K are affected by a temperature increase.
   b. state how Q and K are affected by a temperature decrease.

53. For an exothermic reaction,
   a. state how Q and K are affected by a temperature increase.
   b. state how Q and K are affected by a temperature decrease.

54. The formation of gaseous NH_3 from N_2 and H_2 is exothermic:

$$N_2(g) + 3\,H_2(g) \rightleftharpoons 2\,NH_3(g) \quad \Delta H = -92 \text{ kJ/mol at } 25°C$$

Determine how the reaction will shift when its temperature is changed from 25°C to
   a. 100°C.
   b. −20°C.

55. Answer the questions about the following reaction that occurs at high temperature:

$$C(s) + H_2O(g) \rightleftharpoons CO(g) + H_2(g) \quad K = 2.6 \text{ at } 1000 \text{ K}$$

   a. How will the reaction shift if carbon is removed from the reaction?
   b. If the reaction is carried out in a sealed vessel, how will the reaction position shift if the volume of the vessel is reduced?
   c. If the reaction is carried out at 800 K instead, will K change? Explain.

56. One of the reactions that occurs in a car's catalytic converter is the conversation of highly toxic

carbon monoxide, CO, produced during gasoline combustion, to carbon dioxide, CO_2.

$$2\,CO(g) + O_2(g) \rightleftharpoons 2\,CO_2(g)$$

The forward reaction is facilitated by palladium and platinum catalysts inside the catalytic converter. Do the contents of the catalytic converter affect the equilibrium constant of this reaction? Explain.

57. Consider the following reaction, where methanol (CH_4O) is produced from the reaction of CO with H_2:

$$CO(g) + 2\,H_2(g) \rightleftharpoons CH_4O(g)$$

Answer the following questions about this reaction:
a. How will the reaction shift if CO is removed from the system?
b. How will the equilibrium constant change if an inert gas such as Ar is added to the reaction and the reaction volume does not change.

58. The following reaction is exothermic:

$$CO(g) + 2\,H_2(g) \rightleftharpoons CH_4O(g) \qquad \Delta H = -91\ \text{kJ/mol}$$

a. How would raising the temperature of the reaction affect its equilibrium constant?
b. Would lowering the temperature increase or decrease K?

59. The equilibrium between solid calcium chloride and its constituent aqueous ions is as follows:

$$CaCl_2(s) \rightleftharpoons Ca^{2+}(aq) + 2\,Cl^-(aq) \quad \Delta H > 0$$

Given this information, select the statement or statements that are true.
a. The reaction is endothermic.
b. The reaction is exothermic.
c. K increases with increasing temperature.
d. K decreases with increasing temperature.

60. The equilibrium between solid barium nitrate and its constituent aqueous ions is as follows:

$$Ba(NO_3)_2(s) \rightleftharpoons Ba^{2+}(aq) + 2\,NO_3^-(aq) \qquad K = 4.64 \times 10^{-3} \text{ at } 25°C$$

Answer the following questions about this equilibrium:
a. How will the reaction shift if solid $Ba(NO_3)_2$ is removed from the reaction?
b. How will the reaction shift if the volume of the reaction container is expanded?
c. The solubility of barium nitrate increases as the temperature of the reaction increases. Does this mean that the dissolution of solid $Ba(NO_3)_2$ is endothermic or exothermic?
d. Given that the solubility of barium nitrate increases as the temperature of the reaction increases, would K for this equilibrium be larger at 25°C or 100°C?

Putting It Together

61. Consider the following sets of reactions:

$$Cl_2(g) \rightleftharpoons 2\,Cl(g) \quad \text{At 1000 K,} \quad K_p = 1.23 \times 10^{-6} \text{ and } K_c = 1.2 \times 10^{-7}$$

$$H_2(g) + I_2(g) \rightleftharpoons 2\,HI(g) \quad \text{At 700 K,} \quad K_p = K_c = 54$$

Explain why the K_p and K_c values differ from each other in the first reaction, but not in the second reaction.

62. Phosphorus pentachloride, PCl_5, decomposes into phosphorus trichloride, PCl_3, and Cl_2 in a 2.0 L container at 250°C:

$$PCl_5(g) \rightleftharpoons PCl_3(g) + Cl_2(g)$$

a. If 0.98 moles of PCl_5 and 0.188 moles of PCl_3 are present at equilibrium, calculate the equilibrium constant, K_c, of this reaction at 250°C.
b. Calculate K_p for this reaction at 250°C.

63. Dinitrogen tetroxide, N_2O_4, decomposes into nitrogen dioxide, NO_2, at 25°C with the following equilibrium constant:

$$N_2O_4(g) \rightleftharpoons 2\,NO_2(g) \quad K_c = 5.9 \times 10^{-3}$$

Calculate the percent decomposition of N_2O_4 molecules at equilibrium at 25°C.

64. Gaseous hydrogen iodide, HI, dissociates into hydrogen and iodine gas at 25°C with the following equilibrium constant:

$$2\,HI(g) \rightleftharpoons H_2(g) + I_2(g) \quad K_c = 0.0013$$

Calculate the percent decomposition of HI molecules at equilibrium at 25°C.

65. Nitrogen dioxide, NO_2, dissociates into nitric oxide, NO, and oxygen gas:

$$2\,NO_2(g) \rightleftharpoons 2\,NO(g) + O_2(g) \qquad K_p = 5.9 \times 10^{-13} \text{ at } 25°C$$

a. Determine the effect of adding 0.50 atm helium to the system.

b. Determine how the total pressure of the system will be affected if the volume of the reaction system is reduced to half of the original volume.
c. Determine how the reduction in volume will affect the direction of the reaction.

66. Gaseous carbonyl fluoride, COF_2, dissociates into carbon dioxide and carbon tetrafluoride gas.

$$2\,COF_2(g) \rightleftharpoons CO_2(g) + CF_4(g) \qquad K_p = 2.00 \text{ at } 1000°C$$

a. Suppose that a sealed flask of variable volume initially contains 1.50 atm COF_2, 0.135 atm CO_2, and 0.255 atm CF_4. Determine the equilibrium concentrations of all three species.
b. Suppose that the volume of the flask is doubled after equilibrium has been reached in part (a). Determine the concentration of the three species after equilibrium has been re-established.

67. Gaseous chlorine and fluorine react to form ClF gas:

$$Cl_2(g) + F_2(g) \rightleftharpoons 2\,ClF(g) \qquad K_p = 8.6 \times 10^{19} \text{ at } 25°C$$

a. The reaction is carried out in a sealed vessel with Cl_2 and F_2 having initial partial pressures of 0.50 atm. In which direction does the reaction proceed?
b. If the sealed vessel had a variable volume, how would decreasing the reaction volume after equilibrium was established shift the reaction? Explain.
c. The standard enthalpy of formation, ΔH_f°, of ClF(g) is −56.5 kJ/mol. Is this reaction endothermic or exothermic?

68. Gaseous ammonia, NH_3, and oxygen react to form nitrogen gas and steam:

$$NH_3(g) + O_2(g) \rightleftharpoons N_2(g) + H_2O(g) \qquad \text{(unbalanced)}$$

a. Balance the chemical reaction.
b. If the sealed vessel had a variable volume, how would decreasing the reaction volume after equilibrium was established shift the reaction? Explain.
c. The standard enthalpy of formation, ΔH_f°, of $NH_3(g)$ is −46.1 kJ/mol and the standard enthalpy of formation of $H_2O(g)$ is −241.8 kJ/mol. Determine whether the equilibrium constant of this reaction would increase or decrease if the reaction temperature were raised from 100°C to 200°C.

69. Phosgene, $COCl_2$, can be synthesized by the reaction of carbon monoxide, CO, with chlorine:

$$CO(g) + Cl_2(g) \rightleftharpoons COCl_2(g)$$

The standard enthalpy of formation, ΔH_f°, of CO(g) is −137.2 kJ/mol and the standard enthalpy of formation of $COCl_2(g)$ is −220.1 kJ/mol. Given this information and the balanced reaction above, determine whether the synthesis of phosgene will be maximized at low or high temperature. Also, determine how altering the volume of the reaction vessel could maximize the amount of phosgene at equilibrium.

70. State what effect the addition of a catalyst has on each of the following for a reversible reaction.
a. the concentrations of the species at equilibrium
b. the value of K
c. the enthalpy change for the forward reaction
d. the enthalpy change for the reverse reaction
e. the activation energy for the forward reaction
f. the activation energy for the reverse reaction
g. the reaction mechanism
h. the rate of the forward reaction
i. the rate of the reverse reaction

PRACTICE PROBLEM SOLUTIONS

Practice Problem 15.1 Solution

According to Equation 15.2, equilibrium constants are expressed as the concentrations of the right side of the reaction (products) divided by the concentrations of the left side of the reaction (reactants), with equation concentration raised to a power equal to the coefficient from the balanced chemical equation.

a. All of the species are gases, so all appear in the equilibrium expression:

$$K = \frac{[PCl_3][Cl_2]}{[PCl_5]}$$

b. Pure liquids are not included in equilibrium constant expressions, so water is omitted from this one. Both the $[H^+]$ and $[OH^-]$ terms are squared because each has a coefficient of 2 in the balanced equation.

$$K = [H^+]^2[OH^-]^2$$

Practice Problem 15.2 Solution

a. $K > 1$, so the forward reaction is favored.

b. $K < 1$, so the reverse reaction is favored.

c. $K < 1$, so the reverse reaction is favored.

Practice Problem 15.3 Solution

$$T_K = T_C + 273.15$$
$$T_K = 25.0 + 273.15 = 298.2\ K$$
$$\Delta n = 2 - (3 + 1) = -2$$
$$K_p = K_c(RT)^{\Delta n}$$
$$K_c = \frac{K_p}{(RT)^{\Delta n}}$$
$$K_c = \frac{6.8 \times 10^5}{\left[\left(0.08206 \frac{L \cdot atm}{mol \cdot K}\right)(298.2\ K)\right]^{-2}} = 4.1 \times 10^8$$

Practice Problem 15.4 Solution

The equilibrium expression for this reaction is

$$K_p = \frac{(P_{NO_2})^2}{P_{N_2O_4}}$$

Substituting the concentrations of N_2O_4 and NO_2 at equilibrium into the equilibrium expression gives

$$K_p = \frac{(0.512)^2}{(1.74)} = 0.151$$

Although the ratio $\frac{(P_{NO_2})^2}{P_{N_2O_4}}$ would appear to have units of $\frac{atm^2}{atm}$ = atm, equilibrium constants are unitless by convention (for reasons that are beyond the scope of this text).

Practice Problem 15.5 Solution

Write the equilibrium expression for this reaction, and rearrange it to solve for $[SO_2]$:

$$K_c = \frac{[SO_3]^2}{[SO_2]^2[O_2]}$$
$$[SO_2]^2 = \frac{[SO_3]^2}{K_c[O_2]}$$
$$[SO_2] = \sqrt{\frac{[SO_3]^2}{K_c[O_2]}} = \sqrt{\frac{(3.8\ M)^2}{(1.7 \times 10^6)(2.1 \times 10^{-3}\ M)}}$$
$$= 0.064\ M$$

Practice Problem 15.6 Solution

The equilibrium constant expression is the ratio of the products to the reactants, with each species raised to the power of its stoichiometric coefficients in the balanced chemical equation.

a. $K_c = \frac{[N_2O]^2}{[N_2]^2[O_2]}$

b. $K_c = \frac{[N_2O]}{[N_2][O_2]^{1/2}}$

The equation in part (b) can be obtained by multiplying all of the coefficients in the equation in part (a) by $\frac{1}{2}$. When the coefficients of a reaction are multiplied by a factor such as $\frac{1}{2}$, the equilibrium constant is raised to the power of the same factor. As a result, the equilibrium constant expression in part (b) is the square root of the one in part (a). That is, raising the expression in part (a) to the $\frac{1}{2}$ power yields the expression in part (b).

Practice Problem 15.7 Solution

The desired equation needs 2 mol NO reactant, so multiplying the equation represented by K_1 by 2 gives the following:

$$2\ NO(g) + Br_2(g) \rightleftharpoons 2\ NOBr(g)$$
$$K_1' = (K_1)^2 = (1.41)^2 = 1.99$$

If the K_1' equation is added to the K_2 equation, then the NOBr and Br_2 species cancel each other out, leaving the desired reaction. The value for K is the product of K_1' and K_2:

$$2\ NO(g) + \cancel{Br_2(g)} \rightleftharpoons \cancel{2\ NOBr(g)}$$
$$\cancel{2\ NOBr(g)} \rightleftharpoons N_2(g) + O_2(g) + \cancel{Br_2(g)}$$
$$2\ NO \rightleftharpoons N_2(g) + O_2(g)$$
$$K = (1.99)(1.05 \times 10^{30}) = 2.09 \times 10^{30}$$

Practice Problem 15.8 Solution

$$Q_p = \frac{[NH_3]^2}{[N_2][H_2]^3}$$
$$Q_p = \frac{(0.00682\ atm)^2}{(0.124\ atm)(0.113\ atm)^3} = 0.260$$

Under the given conditions, Q_p (0.260) < K_p (41), so the reaction proceeds to the right to form more NH_3 product until equilibrium is established.

Practice Problem 15.9 Solution

First, convert the number of moles of each species to molarities. The reaction vessel has a volume of 0.500 L, so dividing the number of moles of each species by 0.500 L gives their molar concentrations.

$$\text{Initial }[CO] = \left(\frac{0.00925\text{ mol}}{0.500\text{ L}}\right) = 0.0185\text{ M}$$

$$\text{Initial }[H_2O] = \left(\frac{0.0200\text{ mol}}{0.500\text{ L}}\right) = 0.0400\text{ M}$$

$$\text{Equilibrium }[CO_2] = \left(\frac{0.00825\text{ mol}}{0.500\text{ L}}\right) = 0.0165\text{ M}$$

Next, construct an ICE table, and enter the given values.

	$CO(g)$	+ $H_2O(g)$ ⇌	$H_2(g)$	+ $CO_2(g)$
Initial (M)	0.0185	0.0400	0	0
Change (M)				
Equilibrium (M)				0.0165

All species in this table have a 1:1 stoichiometry, so the change in concentration of each can be represented by the variable x.

	$CO(g)$	+ $H_2O(g)$ ⇌	$H_2(g)$	+ $CO_2(g)$
Initial (M)	0.0185	0.0400	0	0
Change (M)	$-x$	$-x$	$+x$	$-x$
Equilibrium (M)				0.0165

At equilibrium, the concentrations of CO and H_2O are $0.0185 - x$ and $0.0400 - x$, respectively, whereas the concentrations of H_2 and CO_2 are both x.

	$CO(g)$	+ $H_2O(g)$ ⇌	$H_2(g)$	+ $CO_2(g)$
Initial (M)	0.0185	0.0400	0	0
Change (M)	$-x$	$-x$	$+x$	$+x$
Equilibrium (M)	$0.0185 - x$	$0.0400 - x$	x	0.0165

Use the last column (the one with a known equilibrium concentration) to solve for x.

$$0 + x = 0.0165$$
$$x = 0.0165$$

Plug this x value into the expressions for the other species.

$$\text{Equilibrium }[CO] = 0.0185 - 0.0165 = 0.0020\text{ M}$$
$$\text{Equilibrium }[H_2O] = 0.0400 - 0.0165 = 0.0235\text{ M}$$
$$\text{Equilibrium }[H_2] = 0 + 0.0165 = 0.0165\text{ M}$$

Substitute these values back into the table.

	$CO(g)$	+ $H_2O(g)$ ⇌	$H_2(g)$	+ $CO_2(g)$
Initial (M)	0.0185	0.0400	0	0
Change (M)	−0.0165	−0.0165	+0.0165	+0.0165
Equilibrium (M)	0.0020	0.0235	0.0165	0.0165

Calculate K_c by inserting the equilibrium concentrations into the equilibrium expression:

$$K_c = \frac{[H_2][CO_2]}{[CO][H_2O]} = \frac{(0.0165)(0.0165)}{(0.0020)(0.0235)} = 5.8$$

Practice Problem 15.10 Solution

Calculate Q to determine the direction of the reaction:

$$Q_p = \frac{P_{HI}^2}{P_{H_2}P_{I_2}} = \frac{(1.500)^2}{(0.350)(0.275)} = 23.4$$

$Q_p < K_p$, so the reaction proceeds to the right (i.e., more HI is produced). The ICE table for this equilibrium is

	$H_2(g)$	+ $I_2(g)$ ⇌	$2\,HI(g)$
Initial (atm)	0.350	0.275	1.500
Change (atm)	$-x$	$-x$	$+2x$
Equilibrium (atm)	$0.350 - x$	$0.275 - x$	$1.500 + 2x$

Substitute the equilibrium pressures into the K_p expression.

$$K_p = \frac{P_{HI}^2}{P_{H_2}P_{I_2}} = \frac{(1.500 + 2x)^2}{(0.350 - x)(0.275 - x)} = 794$$

$$K_p = \frac{4x^2 + 6.00x + 2.250}{x^2 - 0.625x + 0.09625} = 794$$

$$K_p = 4x^2 + 6.00x + 2.250 = 794x^2 - 496.3x + 76.42$$
$$0 = 790x^2 - 502.3x + 74.17$$
$$x = 0.4027 \text{ or } 0.2332$$

If $x = 0.4027$, both reactants would have a negative partial pressure at equilibrium. As a result, $x = 0.2332$ and the equilibrium pressures are as follows:

$$[H_2] = 0.350 - x = 0.350\text{ atm} - 0.2332\text{ atm} = 0.117\text{ atm}$$

$[I_2] = 0.275 - x = 0.275 \text{ atm} - 0.2332 = 0.042 \text{ atm}$

$[HI] = 1.500 + 2x = 1.500 \text{ atm} + (2)(0.2332 \text{ atm})$
$= 1.966 \text{ atm}$

Check your work by inserting the calculated values of each species back into the equilibrium expression:

$$K_p = \frac{[HI]^2}{[H_2][I_2]} = \frac{[1.966]^2}{(0.117)(0.042)} = 787$$

The calculated K_p value of 787 is close to the given value of 794, so the pressures are reasonable. Note that a significant digit was lost when the partial pressure of iodine was rounded to 0.042 atm. If the unrounded value of 0.0418 atm were used instead, the calculated K_p would have been 790, which is closer to the given value of 794.

Practice Problem 15.11 Solution

The equilibrium constant expression is

$$K_p = \frac{P_{N_2}(P_{H_2})^3}{(P_{NH_3})^2} = 1.47 \times 10^{-6}$$

The ICE table for this reaction is

	$2NH_3(g)$ ⇌	$N_2(g)$ +	$3H_2(g)$
Initial (atm)	1.20	0	0
Change (atm)	$-2x$	$+x$	$+3x$
Equilibrium (atm)	$1.20 - 2x$	x	$3x$

Simplify the equilibrium expression by assuming that $1.20 - 2x \approx 1.20$.

$$K_p = \frac{P_{N_2}(P_{H_2})^3}{(P_{NH_3})^2} = \frac{(x)(3x)^3}{(1.20 - 2x)^2} \approx \frac{27x^4}{(1.20)^2}$$
$$= 1.47 \times 10^{-6}$$

$$x = \sqrt[4]{\frac{(1.47 \times 10^{-6})(1.20)^2}{27}} = 0.01673$$

Determine whether $2x$ is less than 5% of 1.20.

$$\frac{2(0.01673)}{1.20} \times 100\% = 2.79\%$$

In this case, the simplification is valid, so the equilibrium partial pressures are

$$P_{NH_3} = 1.20 - 2x = 1.20 - (2)(0.01673) = 1.17 \text{ atm}$$
$$P_{N_2} = x = 0.01673 \text{ atm}$$
$$P_{H_2} = 3x = (3)(0.01673 \text{ atm}) = 0.0502 \text{ atm}$$

Practice Problem 15.12 Solution

The effect of change of concentration of reactants or products and the relative values of Q and K can be found in Table 15.1.

a. Increasing the concentration of a product (Cl_2) makes $Q > K$, so the equilibrium position would shift to the left (more NOCl would form).

b. Decreasing the concentration of a product (NO) makes $Q < K$, so the equilibrium position would shift to the right (more NO and Cl_2 would form).

c. Removing a reactant from the system has the same effect on the direction of the reaction as decreasing its concentration. Therefore, $Q > K$, and the equilibrium position would shift to the left (more NOCl would form).

Practice Problem 15.13 Solution

a. Neon is a noble gas and is inert. If the volume is held constant, the addition of an inert gas will not shift the reaction one way or the other.

b. An increase in the volume of the container is accompanied by a decrease in pressure, which shifts the equilibrium position to the side of the reaction that has more moles of gas (Table 15.2). As a result, the reaction in the problem shifts to the right (more CO is formed).

c. Nickel is a solid and does not enter the equilibrium expression. Because the addition of more nickel has a negligible effect on the volume, the reaction does not shift one way or the other.

Practice Problem 15.14 Solution

a. For exothermic reactions, K and T are inversely related (Table 15.3), so an increase in T causes a decrease in K, in which case $Q > K$.

b. When $Q > K$, the reaction shifts to the left, toward the reactants.

c. Because more reactants form, the partial pressure of NOCl decreases and the partial pressures of Cl_2 and NO both increase.

Practice Problem 15.15 Solution

a. Calculate Q to determine the direction of the reaction.

$$Q_p = \frac{(P_{NO_2})^2}{P_{N_2O_4}} = \frac{(0.500)^2}{(0.100)} = 2.50$$

$Q_p > K_p$, so the reaction proceeds to the left (more N_2O_4 is produced).

b. The ICE table for this equilibrium is

	$N_2O_4(g)$ ⇌	$2\,NO_2(g)$
Initial (M)	0.100	0.500
Change (M)	$+x$	$-2x$
Equilibrium (M)	$0.100 + x$	$0.500 - 2x$

Solve for x.

$$K_p = \frac{P_{NO_2}{}^2}{P_{N_2O_4}} = \frac{(0.500 - 2x)^2}{(0.100 + x)} = 0.15$$

$$K_p = \frac{4x^2 - 2x + 0.250}{(0.100 + x)} = 0.15$$

$$4x^2 - 2x + 0.250 = 0.0150 + 0.150x$$

$$4x^2 - 2.150x + 0.235 = 0$$

$$x = 0.385 \text{ M or } 0.153 \text{ M}$$

The correct value of x to use for this calculation is 0.153 M because $x = 0.385$ M would give a negative partial pressure of NO_2. Thus, the equilibrium partial pressures are

$$P_{N_2O_4} = 0.100 + x = 0.100 \text{ atm} + 0.153 \text{ atm} = 0.253 \text{ atm}$$

$$P_{NO_2} = 0.500 - 2x = 0.500 \text{ atm} - 2(0.153 \text{ atm}) = 0.194 \text{ atm}$$

c. From Section 6.8, the enthalpy of reaction is the enthalpy of formation of the products minus that of the reactants, taking into account the coefficients from the balanced equation.

$$\Delta H^\circ_{rxn} = 2[\Delta H^\circ_f(NO_2)] - [\Delta H^\circ_f(N_2O_4)]$$

$$\Delta H^\circ_{rxn} = 2 \text{ mol}\left(\frac{33.84 \text{ kJ}}{\text{mol}}\right) - \left[1 \text{ mol}\left(\frac{9.66 \text{ kJ}}{\text{mol}}\right)\right]$$

$$\Delta H^\circ_{rxn} = 67.68 \text{ kJ} - 9.66 \text{ kJ} = 58 \text{ kJ}$$

ΔH°_{rxn} is positive, so the reaction is endothermic (heat is absorbed).

d. In an endothermic reaction, heat can be treated as a reactant:

$$N_2O_4(g) + \text{heat} \rightleftharpoons 2\, NO_2(g)$$

Cooling the reaction from 25°C to 0°C effectively removes heat from the equilibrium. Therefore, cooling the reaction causes the equilibrium to shift to the left (more N_2O_4 is formed).

e. Equilibrium constants are temperature dependent, so K_p has a different value at 0°C than it does at 25°C.

CHAPTER 16

Acid–Base Theory

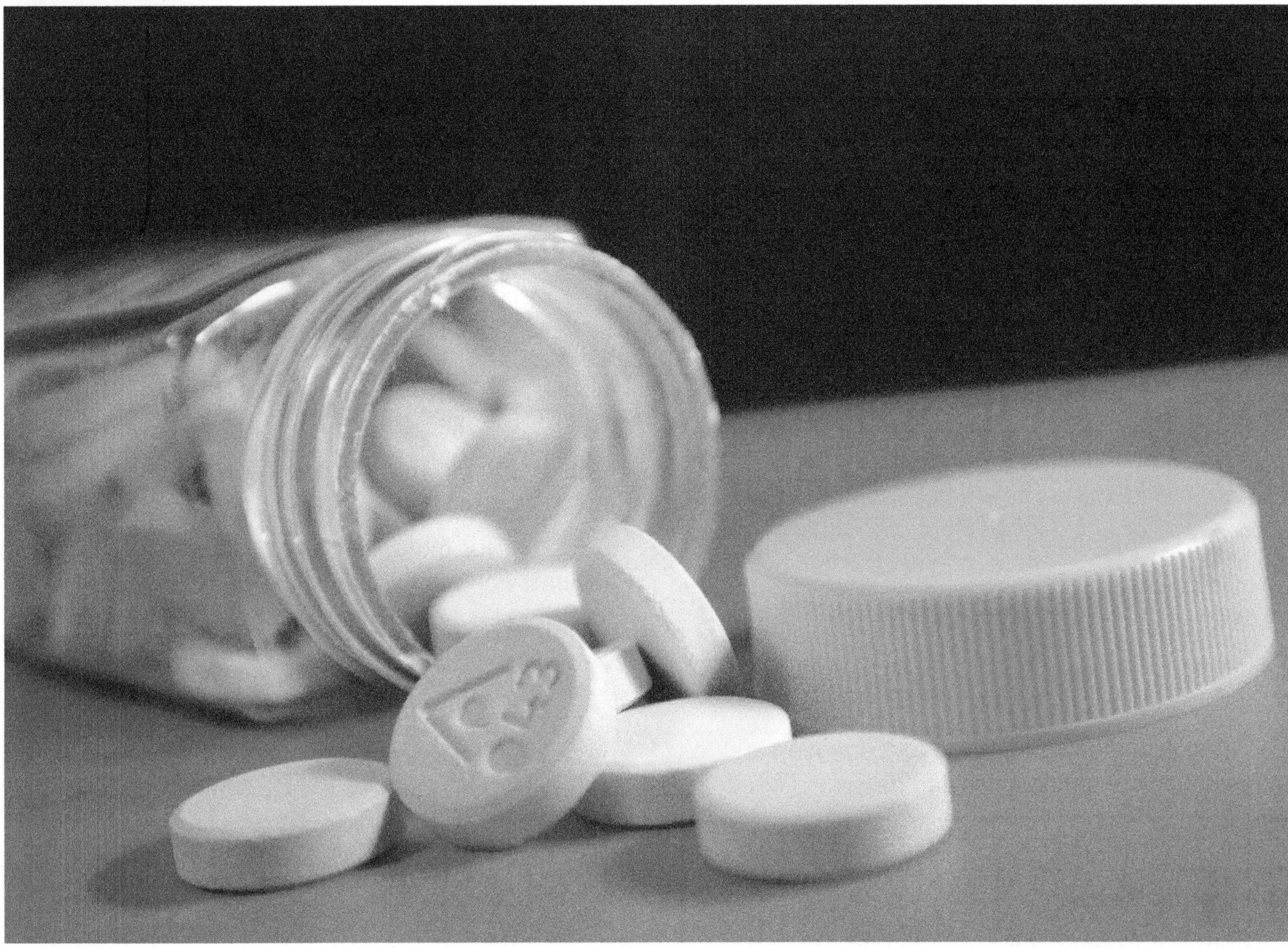

Treasure/Flickr

You are likely familiar with the names of a few acids, such as the hydrochloric acid in your stomach, the sulfuric acid in a car battery, and the citric acid in fruits such as oranges, lemons, and pineapple. Bases are less identifiable in everyday life because they do not have "base" in their names, but ammonia in household cleaners is a base, as is the caustic lye found in drain cleaners and oven cleaners. Salts can also have acid–base properties. For example, antacid tablets contain calcium carbonate, which is a salt that acts as a base, to neutralize stomach acid.

Chapter Outline

GOALS

- Write ionization reactions for strong and weak acids and bases.
- Calculate the hydrogen ion concentration in solutions of strong acids and the hydroxide ion concentration in solutions of strong bases.
- Identify conjugate acids and bases using the Brønsted–Lowry definitions of acids and bases.
- Describe the relationship between the ionization of water and the concentrations of acidic and basic species in solution.
- Calculate the pH of a solution.
- Explain how pH describes the acidity of a solution.
- Demonstrate how the equilibrium constants for weak acid and weak bases can be used to calculate pH.
- Calculate the pH of acids with more than one ionizable hydrogen atom.
- Identify from their formulas which salts have acidic or basic properties.
- Calculate the pH of salt solutions.
- Predict relative acid strengths based on the structures of acid molecules.
- Extend the definitions of acids and bases to include reactions that do not involve H^+.

16.1 Ionization Reactions of Acids and Bases

GOALS

- Write ionization reactions for strong and weak acids and bases.
- Calculate the hydrogen ion concentration in solutions of strong acids and bases.

Background Review

Chapter 4 Chemical Reactions and Aqueous Solutions: Section 4.3—Compounds in Aqueous Solution

Chapter 5 Stoichiometry: Section 5.6—Molarities of Ions

The first modern definition of acids and bases—the **Arrhenius theory**—is based directly on the concentration of H^+ and OH^- ions. An **Arrhenius acid** is a compound that increases the concentration of hydrogen ions, H^+, when it is dissolved in water, and an **Arrhenius base** is a compound that increases the concentration of hydroxide ions, OH^-, when it is dissolved in water. The H^+ and OH^- ions are formed by the ionization or dissociation of electrolytes, where a neutral compound is broken into ions (Section 4.3).

Ionization and *dissociation* are widely used as synonyms, but some chemists prefer to reserve the term *ionization* for molecular compounds and *dissociation* for ionic compounds. This text largely adheres to that convention but does not expect students to do so.

A hydrogen ion, H^+, consists only of a **proton**. It is a highly reactive chemical species that does not actually exist as a freely moving proton in solution. Instead, the H^+ released by an acid attaches to a water molecule to form H_3O^+, which is known as the **hydronium ion**.

$$H^+(aq) + H_2O(l) \rightarrow H_3O^+(aq)$$

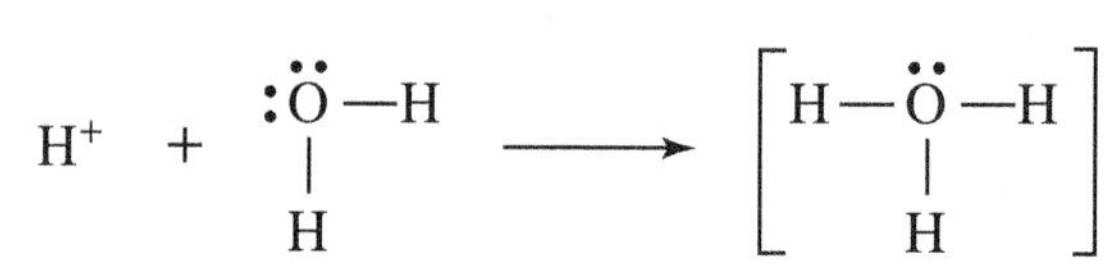

Hydronium ion

The terms *hydrogen ion* and *hydronium ion* and the formulas H^+ and H_3O^+ are all used synonymously in this text.

> H^+ is a common shorthand notation for H_3O^+.

ACID IONIZATION

As discussed in Section 3.5 and Section 4.3, the chemical formulas for acids typically begin with H to indicate that the hydrogen atom ionizes when the acid is dissolved in water. For example, hydrochloric acid, HCl(aq), does not exist as intact hydrogen chloride,

HCl, molecules in solution, but rather as its ions according to the following equation.

$$HCl(aq) \rightarrow H^+(aq) + Cl^-(aq)$$

or

$$HCl(aq) + H_2O(l) \rightarrow H_3O^+(aq) + Cl^-(aq)$$

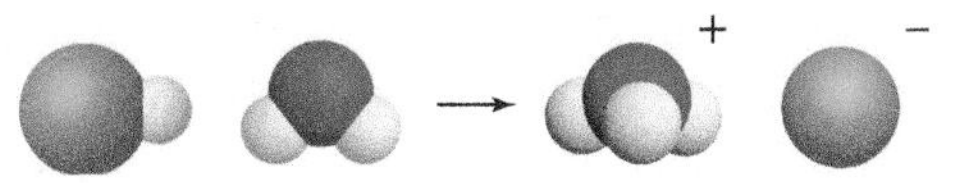

Notice that H_3O^+ can be substituted for H^+ in the products as long as H_2O is included as a reactant to balance the equation. HCl is a strong acid, which is why the reaction is shown with a right-pointing arrow to indicate that the reaction goes to completion. Hydrofluoric acid, HF, by contrast, is a weak acid, so it does not ionize completely, as indicated by the equilibrium arrows.

$$HF(aq) \rightleftharpoons H^+(aq) + F^-(aq)$$

or

$$HF(aq) + H_2O(l) \rightleftharpoons H_3O^+(aq) + F^-(aq)$$

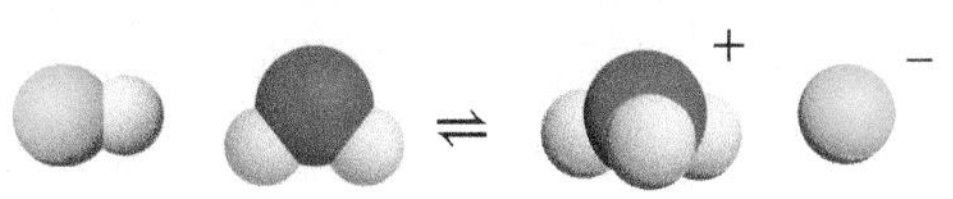

Strong acid ionization reactions, which go to completion, are shown with a regular reaction arrow. Weak acid ionization reactions, which do not go to completion, are shown with equilibrium arrows.

As shown in Figure 16.1, a strong acid exists entirely as ions in solution, whereas a weak acid exists mostly as intact molecules.

The seven strong acids are HCl, HBr, HI, HNO_3, H_2SO_4, $HClO_4$, and $HClO_3$.*

*$HClO_3$ is considered a weak acid in some sources.

Methane, CH_4, ammonia, NH_3, and sucrose (table sugar, $C_{12}H_{22}O_{11}$) contain H atoms but are *not* acids because they do not generate free hydrogen ions when dissolved in aqueous solutions. Their hydrogen atoms are therefore not written first in their formulas. For certain acids, such as acetic acid, $HC_2H_3O_2$, and citric acid, $H_3C_6H_5O_7$, only the hydrogen atoms that are written first are capable of being ionized; the other hydrogen atoms are no more ionizable than the ones in CH_4, NH_3, or $C_{12}H_{22}O_{11}$ (Section 3.5).

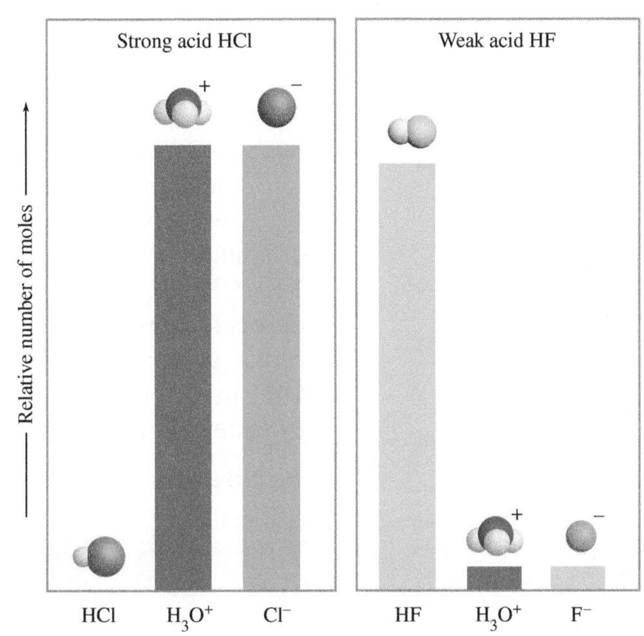

FIGURE 16.1 Strong Versus Weak Acid Ionization

Given the same number of moles of dissolved acid initially, a strong acid will yield more hydronium ions than a weak acid.

Example 16.1

a. Write the ionization reaction for $HNO_3(aq)$.
b. Calculate the H^+ concentration in 1.77 M HNO_3.
c. Write the ionization reaction for $HNO_2(aq)$.
d. How does the H^+ concentration in 1.77 M HNO_2 compare to that in 1.77 M HNO_3?

Solution

a. HNO_3 (nitric acid) is a strong acid, so it is 100% ionized in aqueous solution. There are two valid ways to write the ionization reaction, both of which use a regular reaction arrow.

$$HNO_3(aq) \rightarrow H^+(aq) + NO_3^-(aq)$$

or

$$HNO_3(aq) + H_2O(l) \rightarrow H_3O^+(aq) + NO_3^-(aq)$$

b. Because the ionization reaction goes to completion, the H^+ concentration (or H_3O^+ concentration) in 1.77 M HNO_3 is 1.77 M. (The nitrate ion concentration is also 1.77 M.)
c. HNO_2 (nitrous acid) is a weak acid, so it is only partially ionized in aqueous solution. There are two valid ways to write the ionization reaction, both of which use equilibrium arrows.

$$HNO_2(aq) \rightleftharpoons H^+(aq) + NO_2^-(aq)$$

or

$$HNO_2(aq) + H_2O(l) \rightleftharpoons H_3O^+(aq) + NO_2^-(aq)$$

d. Because the ionization reaction does not go to completion, the H^+ concentration (or H_3O^+ concentration) in 1.77 M HNO_2 is less than 1.77 M. (The nitrite ion concentration is also less than 1.77 M.)

PRACTICE PROBLEM 16.1

a. Write the ionization reaction for $HClO_4(aq)$.
b. What is the H^+ concentration in 0.0015 M $HClO_4$?
c. Write the ionization reaction for $HClO(aq)$.
d. How does the H^+ concentration in 0.0015 M $HClO_4$ compare to that in 0.0015 M $HClO$?

Hint: $HClO_4$ is a strong acid, but $HClO$ is not. Strong acids ionize completely, whereas weak acids do not.

A strong acid ionizes completely in water, regardless of its concentration. That is, even a very dilute solution of HCl, which would contain a relatively small amount of H^+, is still a solution of a strong acid. Do not confuse a *strong acid* with a *concentrated acid*. Similarly, do not confuse a *weak acid* with a *dilute acid*. An acid, whether it is strong or weak, can be either concentrated or dilute.

BASE IONIZATION

A strong base is a compound that dissociates completely in water, yielding OH^- and the **counterion**, which is the cation that balances the charge of the OH^- in the base. For example, sodium hydroxide, NaOH, ionizes completely in water into OH^- and Na^+. Notice the use of a regular, right-pointing arrow to signify that the reaction goes to completion.

$$NaOH(aq) \rightarrow Na^+(aq) + OH^-(aq)$$

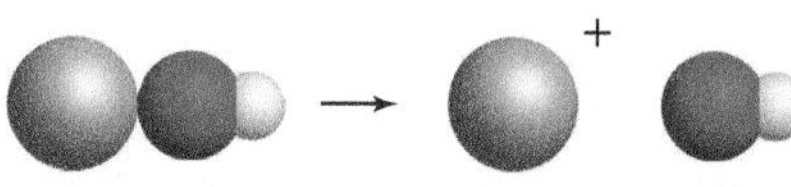

The strong bases are the group 1 hydroxides and heavier group 2 hydroxides. The group 1 hydroxides are strong electrolytes that are highly soluble in water, but the heavier group 2 hydroxides—namely, $Ca(OH)_2$, $Ba(OH)_2$, and $Sr(OH)_2$—are only slightly soluble. To the extent that they dissolve, they completely dissociate, so they are considered strong bases even though their solubilities are low compared to the group 1 hydroxides.

> Strong bases: LiOH, NaOH, KOH, RbOH, CsOH, $Ca(OH)_2$, $Ba(OH)_2$, $Sr(OH)_2$

The group 2 hydroxides such as $Ba(OH)_2$ are said to be **dibasic** because each formula unit of the base releases 2 OH^-. The concentration of OH^- is therefore double the concentration of the dissolved base.

A weak base, in contrast, is typically a derivative of ammonia, NH_3. Examples of weak bases include NH_3, CH_3NH_2, and any molecule that contains a nitrogen atom surrounded by H atoms and/or hydrocarbon groups. Although a weak base does not contain OH^- in its formula, its ionization produces OH^- ions by taking H^+ ions from water.

$$NH_3(aq) + H_2O(l) \rightleftharpoons NH_4^+(aq) + OH^-(aq)$$

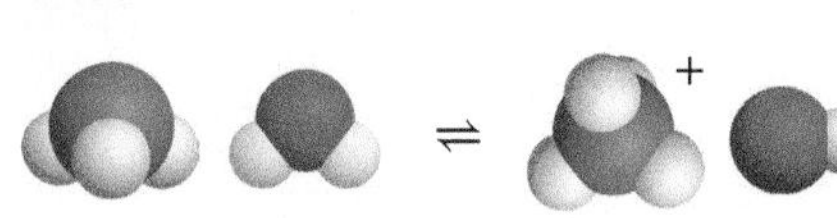

This is an example of a hydrolysis reaction. A **hydrolysis** reaction is one in which a water molecule is broken into H^+ and OH^- (*hydrolysis* literally means "breaking water"). As with weak acids, the ionization of a weak base does not go to completion, so it is shown with equilibrium arrows.

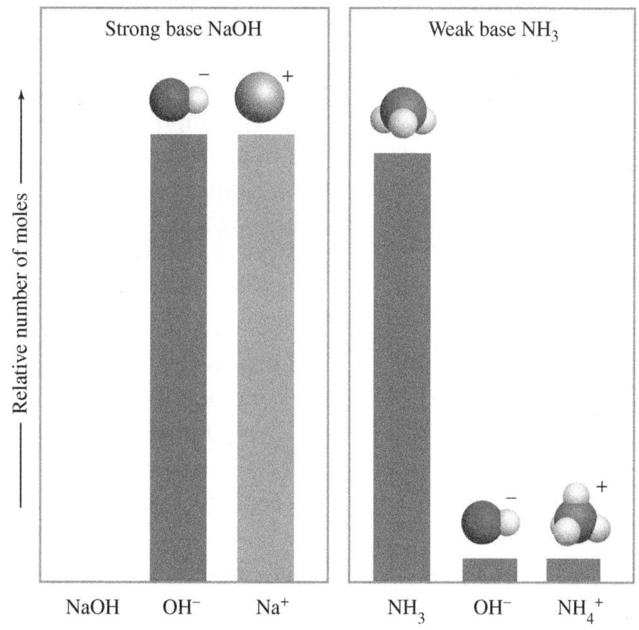

FIGURE 16.2 The Ionization of a Strong Base Versus a Weak Base

Given the same number of moles of dissolved base initially, a strong base will produce more hydroxide ions than a weak base.

Figure 16.2 shows that a strong base exists entirely as dissociated ions in solution, whereas a weak base exists mostly as intact molecules.

Example 16.2

a. Write ionization reactions for KOH(aq), $Ba(OH)_2$(aq), and CH_3NH_2(aq).

b. Given equal concentrations of these bases, rank them by their OH^- concentration.

Solution

a. KOH and $Ba(OH)_2$ are strong bases, whereas CH_3NH_2 is a weak base.

$$KOH(aq) \rightarrow K^+(aq) + OH^-(aq)$$

$$Ba(OH)_2(aq) \rightarrow Ba^{2+}(aq) + 2\,OH^-(aq)$$

$$CH_3NH_2(aq) + H_2O(l) \rightleftharpoons CH_3NH_3^+(aq) + OH^-(aq)$$

b. CH_3NH_2 is a weak base, so its OH^- concentration will be the lowest of the three choices. KOH and $Ba(OH)_2$ both dissociate 100%, but the stoichiometry of the $Ba(OH)_2$ dissociation shows that its OH^- concentration will be double that of the KOH solution. In order of increasing OH^- concentration, the bases are

$$CH_3NH_2 < KOH < Ba(OH)_2.$$

PRACTICE PROBLEM 16.2

a. What is the OH^- concentration in 0.34 M KOH?

b. What is the OH^- concentration in 0.34 M $Ba(OH)_2$?

Hint: Strong bases dissociate 100% in aqueous solution. Are KOH and $Ba(OH)_2$ strong or weak bases? How many OH^- per formula unit do KOH and $Ba(OH)_2$ have?

Just as with strong acids, a *strong base* ionizes completely in water, regardless of its concentration. Thus, a strong base is not necessarily a *concentrated base*. A very dilute solution of a strong base contains relatively few OH^-, but it is still a solution of a strong base.

SECTION REVIEW

- According to the Arrhenius definitions of acid and base, an acid is a compound that increases the H^+ concentration when dissolved in water, and a base is a compound that increases the OH^- concentration.
- The terms *hydrogen ion* and *hydronium ion* and the formulas H^+ and H_3O^+ are all used synonymously in this text.
- Strong acids and strong bases ionize completely, so their ionization reactions are written with a normal, right-pointing arrow.

- Weak acids and weak bases ionize only partially, so their ionization reactions are written with equilibrium arrows.
- The concentration of H_3O^+ in a strong acid solution is equal to the initial concentration of the acid.
- The concentration of OH^- in a strong base solution is either equal to the initial concentration of the base or, in the case of a dibasic strong base, equal to double the initial concentration of the base.
- The concentration of H_3O^+ or OH^- in a weak acid or weak base solution is less than the initial concentration of the acid or base.

16.2 Brønsted–Lowry Theory

GOAL

- Identify conjugate acids and bases using the Brønsted–Lowry definitions of acids and bases.

Background Review

Chapter 4 Chemical Reactions and Aqueous Solutions: Section 4.5—Acid–Base Reactions

Although the Arrhenius definitions of an acid as a compound that produces H^+ in aqueous solution and a base as a compound that produces OH^- are adequate for many purposes, they proved limiting when chemists began developing a more comprehensive understanding of acid–base chemistry.

In 1923, Johannes Brønsted (1879–1947) and Thomas Lowry (1874–1936) independently proposed modified definitions for acids and bases. According to the resulting **Brønsted–Lowry theory**, a **Brønsted acid** is a *proton donor*, and a **Brønsted base** is a *proton acceptor*. A **proton donor** is a molecule or ion that is capable of releasing H^+ into solution, and a **proton acceptor** is a molecule or ion that is capable of forming a chemical bond with available H^+.

In this context, *proton* is a synonym for H^+ (the hydrogen atom of an acid that is stripped of its electrons upon ionization), but not for the protons in the nucleus of any larger atom in the molecule.

An acid is a proton donor; a base is a proton acceptor.

The Brønsted–Lowry definitions of acid and base are the ones most commonly used today, and unless otherwise indicated, the terms *acid* and *base* refer to a Brønsted acid and a Brønsted base.

An important aspect of the Brønsted definitions is that if there is a proton donor in a solution, there must also be a proton acceptor, and vice versa. If there is not a specific compound added to the solution to serve as a proton acceptor from an acid or as a proton donor to a base, the solvent (usually water) can serve that role. Thus, water can act as a Brønsted acid or a Brønsted base.

In the following reaction, the acetic acid molecule, $HC_2H_3O_2$, donates H^+ to the H_2O molecule, so acetic acid acts as the Brønsted acid. The water molecule accepts that proton, so water acts as the Brønsted base.

$$\underset{\text{Acid}}{HC_2H_3O_2(aq)} + \underset{\text{Base}}{H_2O(l)} \rightleftharpoons \underset{\text{Acid}}{H_3O^+(aq)} + \underset{\text{Base}}{C_2H_3O_2^-(aq)}$$

Conjugate Pair (H_2O / H_3O^+)

Conjugate Pair ($HC_2H_3O_2$ / $C_2H_3O_2^-$)

In the reverse reaction, the hydronium ion donates a proton to the acetate ion, so the hydronium ion is the acid and the acetate ion is the base. $HC_2H_3O_2$ and $C_2H_3O_2^-$ differ from each other by only a single proton, H^+. This relationship makes them a **conjugate acid–base pair**. H_2O and H_3O^+ are a conjugate acid–base pair, too.

Every Brønsted acid has a **conjugate base**, and every Brønsted base has a **conjugate acid**. The reaction of the weak base ammonia with water also illustrates this concept, but in this case, water acts as an acid rather than a base.

$$\underset{\text{Base}}{NH_3(aq)} + \underset{\text{Acid}}{H_2O(l)} \rightleftharpoons \underset{\text{Acid}}{NH_4^+(aq)} + \underset{\text{Base}}{OH^-(aq)}$$

Conjugate Pair (H_2O / OH^-)

Conjugate Pair (NH_3 / NH_4^+)

In the forward reaction, the ammonia molecule accepts a proton from the water molecule and is therefore a Brønsted base. The water molecule donates the proton, so in this reaction, water acts as a Brønsted acid. In the reverse reaction, the ammonium ion acts as an acid, and the hydroxide ion acts as a base.

All Arrhenius acids are also Brønsted acids and all Arrhenius bases are also Brønsted bases, but the Brønsted definitions include compounds that are neither acids nor bases according to the Arrhenius definition.

For example, water is not normally thought of as being either an acid or a base, but under the Brønsted definition it can behave as both. It acts as an acid in the presence of a stronger base and as a base in the presence of a stronger acid. A compound that is capable of acting as both an acid and a base is said to be **amphoteric**. Within the context of Brønsted–Lowry theory, where an acid is a proton donor and a base is a proton acceptor, an amphoteric compound is sometimes referred to as **amphiprotic**.

Example 16.3

Classify each species in the following reactions as a Brønsted acid or a Brønsted base, and identify each conjugate pair.

a. $H_2PO_4^-(aq) + H_2O(l) \rightleftharpoons HPO_4^{2-}(aq) + H_3O^+(aq)$

b. $HPO_4^{2-}(aq) + H_2O(l) \rightleftharpoons H_2PO_4^-(aq) + OH^-(aq)$

Solution

The proton donor is the acid (loses H^+), and the proton acceptor is the base (gains H^+). A conjugate acid–base pair differs only by H^+.

a. In the forward reaction, H^+ is transferred from $H_2PO_4^-$ (acid) to H_2O (base). In the reverse reaction, H^+ is transferred from H_3O^+ (acid) to HPO_4^{2-} (base).

$$H_2PO_4^-(aq) + H_2O(l) \rightleftharpoons HPO_4^{2-}(aq) + H_3O^+(aq)$$

Acid Base Base Acid

Conjugate Pair

Conjugate Pair

a. In the forward reaction, H^+ is transferred from H_2O (acid) to HPO_4^{2-} (base). In the reverse reaction, H^+ is transferred from $H_2PO_4^-$ (acid) to OH^- (base).

$$HPO_4^{2-}(aq) + H_2O(l) \rightleftharpoons H_2PO_4^-(aq) + OH^-(aq)$$

Base Acid Acid Base

Conjugate Pair

Conjugate Pair

Notice that H_2O is amphiprotic—whether it behaves as an acid or a base depends on the relative acid or base strength of the other species present in the reaction. HPO_4^{2-} and $H_2PO_4^-$ are also amphiprotic. In a reaction with a weaker acid than themselves, they would act as acids and donate a proton, but in a reaction with a stronger acid than themselves, they would behave as bases and accept a proton.

PRACTICE PROBLEM 16.3

Classify each species in the following reactions as a Brønsted acid or a Brønsted base, and identify each conjugate acid–base pair.

a. $SO_4^{2-}(aq) + H_2O(l) \rightleftharpoons HSO_4^-(aq) + OH^-(aq)$

b. $HSO_4^-(aq) + H_2O(l) \rightleftharpoons SO_4^{2-}(aq) + H_3O^+(aq)$

Hint: To identify the conjugate acid–base pairs, look for a species in the reactants that differs only by H^+ from a species in the products. In each pair, the species with more H^+ is the acid.

CONJUGATE ACID AND BASE STRENGTH

Acid strength determines to what extent an acid reacts with water to form hydronium ions. Strong acids react entirely with water to form H_3O^+, whereas weak acids ionize to varying degrees. As a result, some weak acids are stronger than others, but they are never as strong as strong acids. Because different weak acids ionize to different extents, their conjugate bases also have different tendencies to react with hydronium ions or with water. Similarly, **base strength** determines the extent to which a base interacts with water to form ions. Strong bases react entirely with water to form ions, whereas weak bases react to varying degrees. The *stronger* the weak acid or weak base, the *weaker* its conjugate base or conjugate acid, and the *weaker* the weak acid or weak base, the *stronger* its conjugate base or conjugate acid.

Example 16.4

The following weak acids are listed in order of acid strength:

$$HClO > HBrO > HIO$$

Identify their conjugate bases and list them in order of base strength from strongest to weakest.

Solution

The conjugate base is the anion that results when one H^+ ion is removed from the weak acid molecule. Thus, the conjugate bases are ClO^-, BrO^-, and IO^-, respectively.

The stronger the weak acid, the weaker its conjugate base. Thus, the conjugate base strength from strongest to weakest is $IO^- > BrO^- > ClO^-$.

PRACTICE PROBLEM 16.4

The following weak bases are listed in order of base strength:

$$(CH_3)_2NH > CH_3NH_2 > NH_3$$

Identify their conjugate acids, and list them in order of acid strength from strongest to weakest.

Hint: A conjugate acid–base pair differs from each other by only a single proton (H^+). To write the conjugate acid, then, add H^+ to the formula of the base. The stronger the weak base, the weaker its conjugate acid.

ACIDS AND BASES WITHOUT WATER

The Brønsted theory extends the concepts of acid and base beyond reactions in aqueous solution. For example, it describes the gas-phase reaction of ammonia gas with hydrogen chloride gas to form solid ammonium chloride.

$$NH_3(g) + HCl(g) \rightleftharpoons NH_4Cl(s)$$

Here, hydrogen chloride donates its proton to the lone pair of electrons on the ammonia molecule and is therefore a Brønsted acid. The ammonia molecule is a Brønsted base because it accepts that proton. The resulting ions from the acid–base reaction, NH_4^+ and Cl^-, form an ionic bond, resulting in the formation of $NH_4Cl(s)$.

SECTION REVIEW

- In the Brønsted–Lowry definitions of acids and bases, an acid is a species that donates a proton, and a base is a species that accepts a proton.
- In the Brønsted–Lowry theory, every reaction that includes an acid must also include a base.
- When a weak acid donates a proton, the remaining part of the acid is the conjugate base, which can now accept a proton. When a weak base accepts a proton, it becomes the conjugate acid of that base and can now donate a proton.
- The Brønsted–Lowry theory expands the definitions of acids and bases to explain the acidity or basicity of solutions previously regarded as salts and to explain reactions other than those in aqueous solutions.

16.3 Autoionization of Water

GOAL

- Describe the relationship between the ionization of water and the concentrations of acidic and basic species in solution.

Water can act as either a proton donor or a proton acceptor (Section 16.2). In fact, water can act as both an acid and a base *in the same reaction*:

$$H_2O(l) + H_2O(l) \rightleftharpoons H_3O^+(aq) + OH^-(aq)$$

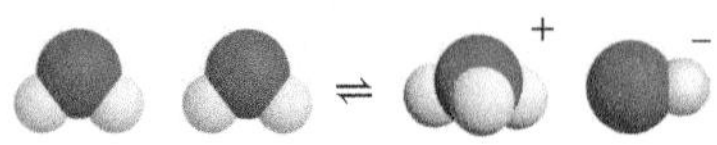

This reaction, which is an example of **autoionization**, proceeds to the right to only a tiny extent because water is such a weak acid and a weak base. Because this is an equilibrium reaction, you can construct an ICE (initial, change, equilibrium) table for this reaction and determine the form of the equilibrium-constant expression (Section 15.2). The equilibrium constant for this reaction is called the **water ionization constant** and is denoted K_w.

$$K_w = [H_3O^+][OH^-]$$

	$H_2O(l)$ +	$H_2O(l)$ ⇌	$H_3O^+(aq)$ +	$OH^-(aq)$
Initial	—	—	0	0
Change	—	—	$+x$	$+x$
Equilibrium	—	—	x	x

Pure liquids and solids are not included in K expressions, which is why the K_w expression has no denominator. At 25°C, the value of K_w is 1.0×10^{-14}. Therefore, for any aqueous solution at 25°C,

$$K_w = [H_3O^+][OH^-] = 1.0 \times 10^{-14} \quad (16.1)$$

Like all equilibrium constants, K_w is temperature dependent. The value of K_w is smaller at lower temperatures (e.g., $K_w = 0.68 \times 10^{-14}$ at 10°C), so water autoionizes to a lesser extent at colder temperatures. The value of K_w is larger at higher temperatures (e.g., $K_w = 5.48 \times 10^{-14}$ at 50°C), so water dissociates more at higher temperatures. Unless otherwise indicated, assume all solutions are at 25°C, and $K_w = 1.0 \times 10^{-14}$.

In pure water, $[H_3O^+] = [OH^-]$. Therefore, at 25°C,

$$K_w = x^2 = 1.0 \times 10^{-14}$$
$$x = \sqrt{1.0 \times 10^{-14}} = 1.0 \times 10^{-7}$$

In pure water at 25°C, $[H_3O^+] = [OH^-] = 1.0 \times 10^{-7}$ M.

Because of the 1:1 stoichiometry of the autoionization reaction, a solution of pure water (at any temperature) has equal concentrations of hydronium and hydroxide ions. In fact, that is the definition of a **neutral solution**. An aqueous solution is **acidic** if the hydrogen ion concentration is greater than the hydroxide ion concentration, and a solution is **basic** if the hydroxide ion concentration is greater than the hydrogen ion concentration.

$[H_3O^+] > [OH^-]$	Acidic solution
$[H_3O^+] = [OH^-]$	Neutral solution
$[H_3O^+] < [OH^-]$	Basic solution

If acid is added to water, causing $[H_3O^+]$ to increase, or if base is added, causing $[OH^-]$ to increase, the autoionization equilibrium will shift to the left according to Le Châtelier's principle until equilibrium is reestablished. After such a shift, $[H_3O^+]$ no longer equals $[OH^-]$, but the product $[H_3O^+][OH^-]$ again equals K_w. Because the product $[H_3O^+][OH^-]$ at a given temperature is equal to a constant, the concentration of hydronium ion in any aqueous solution can be calculated from the concentration of hydroxide ion, and vice versa.

Example 16.5

Calculate $[OH^-]$ in the following solutions at 25°C, and classify each as acidic, basic, or neutral.

a. Ketchup: $[H_3O^+] = 1.3 \times 10^{-4}$ M
b. Ocean water: $[H_3O^+] = 7.9 \times 10^{-9}$ M

Solution

a. Use the K_w expression (Equation 16.1) and solve for the concentration of hydroxide.

$$K_w = [H_3O^+][OH^-]$$
$$[OH^-] = \frac{K_w}{[H_3O^+]} = \frac{1.0 \times 10^{-14}}{1.3 \times 10^{-4}} = 7.7 \times 10^{-11}\text{ M}$$

$[H_3O^+] > [OH^-]$, so the solution is acidic.

b. Use the K_w expression (Equation 16.1) and solve for the concentration of hydroxide.

$$K_w = [H_3O^+][OH^-]$$
$$[OH^-] = \frac{K_w}{[H_3O^+]} = \frac{1.0 \times 10^{-14}}{7.9 \times 10^{-9}} = 1.3 \times 10^{-6}\text{ M}$$

$[H_3O^+] < [OH^-]$, so the solution is basic.

PRACTICE PROBLEM 16.5

Calculate $[H_3O^+]$ in the following solutions at 25°C, and classify each as acidic, basic, or neutral.

a. A soft drink that has $[OH^-] = 7.1 \times 10^{-12}$
b. Laundry bleach that has $[OH^-] = 2.9 \times 10^{-3}$

Hint: Use Equation 16.1, $K_w = [H_3O^+][OH^-] = 1.0 \times 10^{-14}$, to solve for $[H_3O^+]$.

The K_w equilibrium must always be satisfied for any aqueous solution regardless of temperature, so $[H_3O^+]$ and $[OH^-]$ are inversely proportional. That is, if the H_3O^+ concentration increases, the OH^- concentration must decrease by an equal factor.

SECTION REVIEW

- There are always some hydronium ions and some hydroxide ions present in every aqueous solution, whether it is acidic, basic, or neutral.
- In any aqueous solution, $[H_3O^+][OH^-] = 1.0 \times 10^{-14}$ at 25°C. This constant is known as the water ionization constant, K_w.

16.4 pH Calculations

GOALS

- Calculate the pH of a solution.
- Explain how pH describes the acidity of a solution.

Background Review

Chapter 0 Math Review: Section 0.1—Using a Calculator; Section 0.5—Logarithms and Antilogs

The concentration of H_3O^+ and OH^- in a solution can be expressed as a molar concentration, but these concentrations are typically low, so scientific notation is often required. This can be cumbersome, so the **pH scale** was developed as a more convenient way to express H_3O^+ concentration. The pH of a solution is the negative logarithm (Section 0.5) of the hydrogen ion molar concentration.

$$pH = -\log[H^+] = -\log[H_3O^+] \qquad (16.2)$$

The pH scale results in a number that is usually between 1 and 14. A solution that is neither acidic nor basic is referred to as a neutral solution, and it has a pH of 7.00 (the reason for this is explained shortly). Solutions with a pH value lower than 7 are acidic, and those with pH values above 7 are basic. The abbreviation *p* in pH stands for *power*, as in "power of 10," and the H represents $[H^+]$, which, as noted earlier, is a shorter way to indicate $[H_3O^+]$. pH is a unitless number.

$pH < 7$	Acidic solution
$pH = 7$	Neutral solution
$pH > 7$	Basic solution

Example 16.6

Determine the pH of each of the following solutions, and classify each as acidic, basic, or neutral.

a. 1.0×10^{-5} M HCl
b. 0.100 M HNO_3
c. 7.2×10^{-2} M NaOH

Solution

Use Equation 16.2: $pH = -\log[H_3O^+]$.

a. $pH = -\log[H_3O^+] = -\log(1.0 \times 10^{-5}\text{ M}) =$ 5.00; acidic ($pH < 7.00$)
b. $pH = -\log(0.100\text{ M}) = -\log(1.00 \times 10^{-1}\text{ M}) =$ 1.000; acidic ($pH < 7.00$)
c. NaOH is a strong base, so in 7.2×10^{-2} M NaOH, $[OH^-] = 7.2 \times 10^{-2}$ M. Use Equation 16.1 to calculate $[H_3O^+]$ in this solution:

$$K_w = [H_3O^+][OH^-]$$

$$[H_3O^+] = \frac{K_w}{[OH^-]} = \frac{1.0 \times 10^{-14}}{7.2 \times 10^{-2}} = 1.4 \times 10^{-13}\text{ M}$$

Now use Equation 16.2 to calculate pH:

$$pH = -\log(1.4 \times 10^{-13}\text{ M}) = 12.90;$$
basic ($pH > 7.00$)

PRACTICE PROBLEM 16.6

Determine the pH of each of the following solutions, and classify each as acidic, basic, or neutral.

a. 8.0×10^{-4} M KOH
b. 0.0015 M HCl
c. 6.6×10^{-5} M NaOH

Hint: If the compound is an acid, calculate pH from $[H_3O^+]$ using Equation 16.2. If the compound is a base, first calculate $[H_3O^+]$ using Equation 16.1, then calculate pH using Equation 16.2.

EVERYDAY CONNECTION

The relationship between the H_3O^+ concentration and the pH is logarithmic, similar to the Richter scale used for measuring earthquakes. Each step *up* by one on the Richter scale indicates an earthquake that is 10 times more powerful than the step below. For example, a 5 on the Richter scale is an earthquake that is 10 times more powerful than a 4, and a 6 on the Richter scale is 100 times more powerful than a 4. The pH scale is a log scale, too, but pH is a *negative* log scale—that is, each step *down* on the pH scale indicates a solution that has an H_3O^+ concentration 10 times greater than the one before. Thus, a 5 on the pH scale is a solution whose H_3O^+ concentration is 10 times that of a solution with pH 6, and a solution with pH 4 has 100 times the H_3O^+ concentration of a solution with pH 6. Because pH is a log scale, a range of H_3O^+ concentrations from 0.1 M to 1×10^{-14} M can be conveniently represented by a number between 1 and 14.

U.S. Geological Survey/photo by R.B. Colton

Only the digits that come after the decimal point in a pH value are significant—that is, a pH of 6.23 has two significant figures, not three. (The digits that come before the decimal point in the pH come from the exponent, not from the coefficient, and are not significant.) Thus, the number of significant digits in the concentration determines the number of digits after the decimal point in the pH value—that is, $[H_3O^+] = 0.00157$ M (three significant figures) corresponds to pH = 2.804, not 2.80.

When the H_3O^+ concentration of a solution is an exact power of 10, such as 0.001 M or 1.0×10^{-9} M, the pH is simply the positive value of the exponent of the concentration expressed in scientific notation. For example, 0.001 M (one significant figure) is the same as 1×10^{-3} M, so the pH is 3.0. For a concentration of 1.0×10^{-9} M (two significant figures), the pH is 9.00.

pH is not directly proportional to H_3O^+ concentration, however, so when the concentration is *not* an exact power of 10 or the pH is *not* an exact integer, use a calculator to determine the corresponding pH or $[H_3O^+]$. For a review of calculations using logarithms and inverse logarithms on a calculator, see Section 0.1 and Section 0.5.

If the pH of a solution is known, the H_3O^+ concentration can be determined by taking the inverse log (also called the antilog) of the negative pH.

$$[H_3O^+] = 10^{-pH} \tag{16.3}$$

The H_3O^+ concentration can also be quickly determined from the pH if the pH is an exact integer value such as 5.00 or 12.0. A solution with pH = 5.00 (two significant figures) has $[H_3O^+] = 1.0 \times 10^{-5}$ M, and a solution with pH = 12.0 (one significant figure) has $[H_3O^+] = 1 \times 10^{-12}$ M. If a pH value is reported with no digits after the decimal point (e.g., pH = 12), use only one significant digit in the H_3O^+ concentration (i.e., $[H_3O^+] = 1 \times 10^{-12}$ M).

Example 16.7

Determine $[H_3O^+]$ for a solution with each of the following pH values, and classify each as acidic, basic, or neutral.

a. pH = 10
b. pH = 1.0
c. pH = 6.00

Solution

Use Equation 16.3: $[H_3O^+] = 10^{-pH}$.

a. $[H_3O^+] = 10^{-pH} = 10^{-10} = 1 \times 10^{-10}$ M; basic (pH > 7.00)
b. $[H_3O^+] = 10^{-1.0} = 1 \times 10^{-1}$ M = 0.1 M; acidic (pH < 7.00)
c. $[H_3O^+] = 10^{-6.00} = 1.0 \times 10^{-6}$ M; acidic (pH < 7.00)

PRACTICE PROBLEM 16.7

Determine $[H_3O^+]$ for a solution with each of the following pH values, and classify each as acidic, basic, or neutral.

a. pH = 12.3
b. pH = 7.05
c. pH = 1.4

Hint: Equation 16.3 relates a given pH value to the corresponding $[H_3O^+]$ value.

The pH values for some common solutions are listed in Table 16.1. Notice that foods tend to be acidic and household cleaners tend to be basic.

The neutral point of water at pH = 7 is a direct result of the fact that $K_w = 1.0 \times 10^{-14}$ at 25°C. At higher or lower temperatures, where K_w has different values, the pH of neutral water (defined as $[H_3O^+] = [OH^-]$) has different values, too.

Example 16.8

Calculate the H_3O^+ concentration in dill pickle juice that has a pH of 3.22.

TABLE 16.1 Approximate pH Values for Some Common Solutions

Solution	pH	Classification	$[H_3O^+]$ (M)
Stomach acid	1–2		1×10^{-1} to 1×10^{-2}
Soft drinks	3		1×10^{-3}
Vinegar	3	Acidic	1×10^{-3}
Orange juice	3.5		3×10^{-2}
Tomatoes	4		1×10^{-4}
Rainwater	6		1×10^{-6}
Pure water	7	Neutral	1×10^{-7}
Human blood	7.3		5×10^{-8}
Seawater	8.5		3×10^{-9}
Baking soda, aqueous	8.5		3×10^{-9}
Ammonia, aqueous	11–12	Basic	1×10^{-11} to 1×10^{-12}
Washing soda, aqueous	12		1×10^{-12}
Laundry bleach	11–13		1×10^{-11} to 1×10^{-13}

Solution

Use Equation 16.3:

$$[H_3O^+] = 10^{-pH} = 10^{-3.22} = 6.0 \times 10^{-4}\,M$$

The calculated concentration has two significant digits because there are two digits after the decimal point in the value given for the pH.

PRACTICE PROBLEM 16.8

Calculate the H_3O^+ concentration in a sample of peanut butter that has a pH of 6.3.

Hint: Use $[H_3O^+] = 10^{-pH}$ (Equation 16.3). Go to Section 0.1 for help using a calculator, and go to Section 0.5 for help with antilogs. Only the digits after the decimal point in the pH are significant.

Analogous to pH, the pOH of a solution is defined as the negative of the logarithm of the hydroxide ion concentration:

$$pOH = -\log[OH^-] \qquad (16.4)$$

Recall from Equation 16.1 (the K_w expression) that for any aqueous solution at 25°C,

$$[H_3O^+][OH^-] = 1.0 \times 10^{-14}$$

Taking the negative logarithm of both sides gives

$$-\log[H_3O^+] + -\log[OH^-] = -\log(1.0 \times 10^{-14})$$

because $-\log(A \times B) = -\log(A) + -\log(B)$; $-\log[H_3O^+] = pH$, $-\log[OH^-] = pOH$, and $-\log(1.0 \times 10^{-14}) = 14.00$, so

$$pH + pOH = 14.00 \qquad (16.5)$$

Figure 16.3 shows the relationship between pH and pOH on the scale from most acidic to most basic.

Example 16.9

Calculate the pH of a solution that is $6.9 \times 10^{-2}\,M$ in NaOH.

Solution

NaOH is a strong base, so $[OH^-] = [NaOH] = 6.9 \times 10^{-2}\,M$. There are two ways to use this value to solve for pH.

In the first method, use $[OH^-]$ in Equation 16.4 to calculate pOH, and then rearrange Equation 16.5 to isolate pH: pH = 14.00 − pOH.

$$pOH = -\log(6.9 \times 10^{-2}) = 1.16$$
$$pH = 14.00 - 1.16 = 12.84$$

In the second method, use the K_w expression (Equation 16.1) to solve for the hydronium ion concentration, then use Equation 16.2 to solve for pH.

$$K_w = [H_3O^+][OH^-] = 1.0 \times 10^{-14}$$
$$[H_3O^+] = \frac{1.0 \times 10^{-14}}{[OH^-]}$$
$$[H_3O^+] = \frac{1.0 \times 10^{-14}}{6.9 \times 10^{-2}}$$
$$[H_3O^+] = 1.45 \times 10^{-13}\,M$$
$$pH = -\log[H_3O^+] = -\log(1.45 \times 10^{-13}\,M) = 12.84$$

PRACTICE PROBLEM 16.9

Calculate the pH of a solution with a hydroxide ion concentration of $7.7 \times 10^{-10}\,M$.

Hint: There are two ways to determine pH from $[OH^-]$. The first uses Equation 16.4 to calculate pOH and then Equation 16.5 to get the pH. The second uses Equation 16.1 to determine $[H_3O^+]$ and then Equation 16.2 to get the pH.

Example 16.10

Calculate the hydronium ion concentration and the pH in

a. a 0.1 M HCl solution.
b. a 0.1 M NaOH solution.

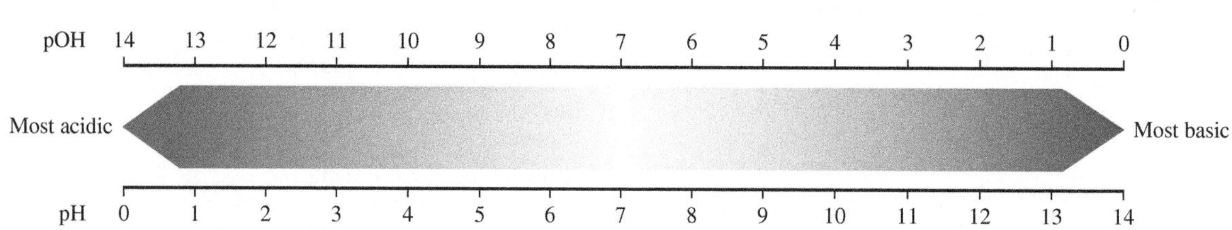

FIGURE 16.3 pH and pOH Scales at 25°C

pH + pOH = 14.00 at 25°C. On the acidic end of the scale, pH is low and pOH is high. On the basic end of the scale, pH is high and pOH is low.

Solution

a. HCl is a strong acid, so 0.1 M HCl consists of 0.1 M H^+ (i.e., H_3O^+) and 0.1 M Cl^-. $[H_3O^+] =$ 0.1 M $= 1 \times 10^{-1}$ M. Using Equation 16.2,

$$pH = -\log[H_3O^+] = -\log(1 \times 10^{-1}) = 1.0$$

b. NaOH is a strong, soluble base, so $[OH^-] =$ 0.1 M. To find $[H_3O^+]$, use the K_w expression (Equation 16.1):

$$K_w = [H_3O^+][OH^-] = 1.0 \times 10^{-14}$$

$$[H_3O^+] = \frac{1.0 \times 10^{-14}}{[OH^-]} = \frac{1.0 \times 10^{-14}}{0.1}$$
$$= 1 \times 10^{-13}\text{ M}$$

Then use Equation 16.2 to calculate the pH:

$$pH = -\log[H_3O^+] = -\log(1 \times 10^{-13}) = 13.0$$

PRACTICE PROBLEM 16.10

Calculate the hydroxide ion concentration and the pH of

a. 0.005 M HCl.
b. 0.005 M NaOH.

Hint: HCl and NaOH are both strong electrolytes, so use their concentrations to determine $[H_3O^+]$ and $[OH^-]$, respectively. Use Equation 16.1 to determine $[OH^-]$ from $[H_3O^+]$ for the acid and $[H_3O^+]$ from $[OH^-]$ for the base. Once you have $[H_3O^+]$ for each solution, use Equation 16.2 to calculate the pH.

MEASURING pH

The pH of a solution is usually determined using an *indicator* or a *pH meter*.

An acid–base indicator (Section 5.9) is a soluble colored dye that changes color depending on the pH of the solution. Indicators are themselves weak acids or bases that alter their molecular bonding configuration depending on the acidity of the solution. **Litmus** is a common indicator that appears pink in acidic solution and blue in basic solution. Litmus is often infused into paper strips, and a drop of solution can be added to litmus paper for a quick check to determine if the solution is acidic or basic. **Universal indicator** is a mixture of acid–base indicators that changes color multiple times across a wide range of pH, such that each pH value from 1 to 14 turns universal indicator a different color. Whereas litmus allows you to determine only whether a solution is acidic or basic, universal indicator gives an estimate of the actual pH. Figure 16.4 is a short video that demonstrates some of the color changes universal indicator undergoes at various pH levels.

Paper that has been infused with universal indicator is known as **pH paper** (Figure 16.5).

A pH meter (Figure 16.6) is a standard laboratory electronic device used for measuring the pH of a solution more precisely. When a probe attached to the pH meter is submerged in the solution, the H_3O^+ concentration is measured electrochemically and

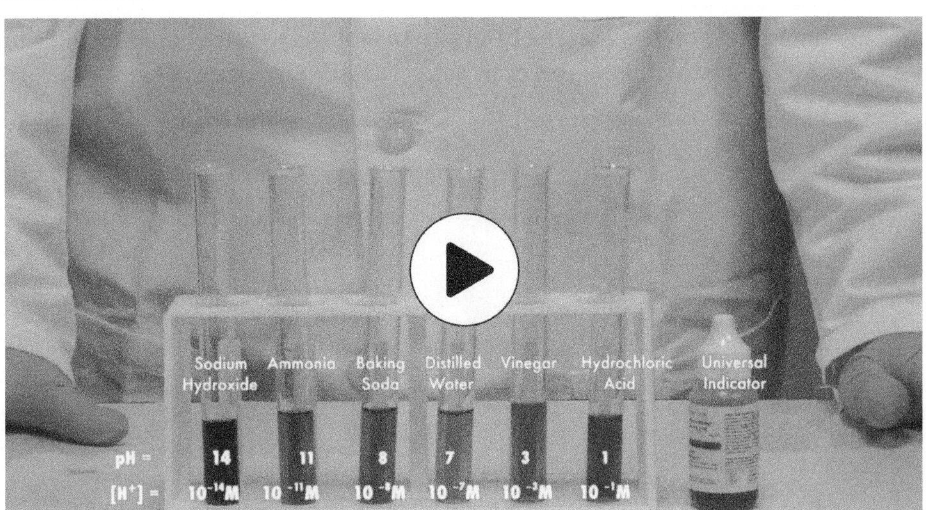

FIGURE 16.4 Universal Indicator and pH

NOTE: You need to be online to access this video.

One or two drops of universal indicator can be added directly to a solution, so the color of the solution itself indicates its pH. This video shows the color of universal indicator in six solutions with different pH values.

posterize/Deposit Photos

FIGURE 16.5 Universal Indicator Colors

A mixture of acid–base indicators known as universal indicator can be infused into paper that can be used to estimate the pH of a sample solution.

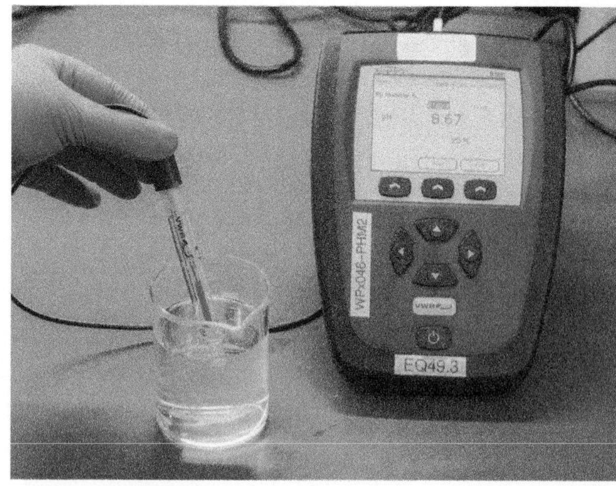

Steve Lemon, Macmillan Learning

FIGURE 16.6 pH Meter

A pH meter has a probe that is submerged into the solution. The H_3O^+ ion concentration of the solution is determined electrochemically and is displayed on a digital readout, usually to two decimal places. A pH meter must be calibrated using solutions with known pH values (called pH standards) before it is used to make a measurement.

a readout of pH, usually to two decimal places, is displayed.

Figure 16.7 is an interactive simulation of a solution in which you can change the solution pH by dragging any of three sliders up and down. Notice how pH, $[H_3O^+]$, and $[OH^-]$ are all interrelated and how changing any one of them changes all three. The acidity or basicity of the solution can be tested using red and blue litmus paper, and a better idea of the actual pH can be obtained by using universal indicator.

EVERYDAY CONNECTION

The pH of swimming pools and hot tubs must be carefully monitored to prevent harmful bacteria from growing. Test kits use indicators, either in liquid form or in paper strips, to measure pH and chlorine levels.

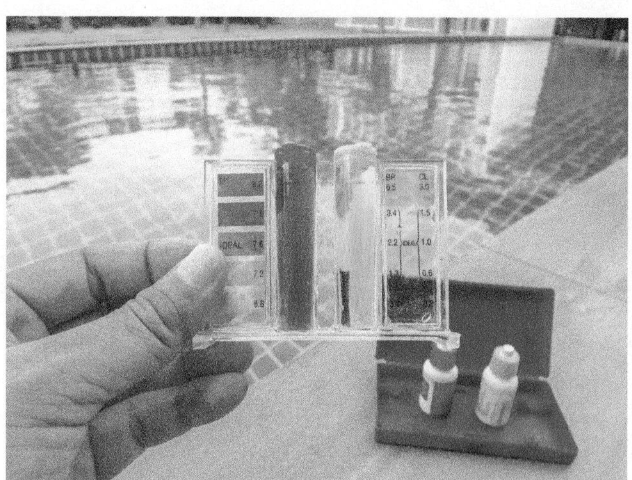

oneSHUTTER oneMEMORY/Shutterstock

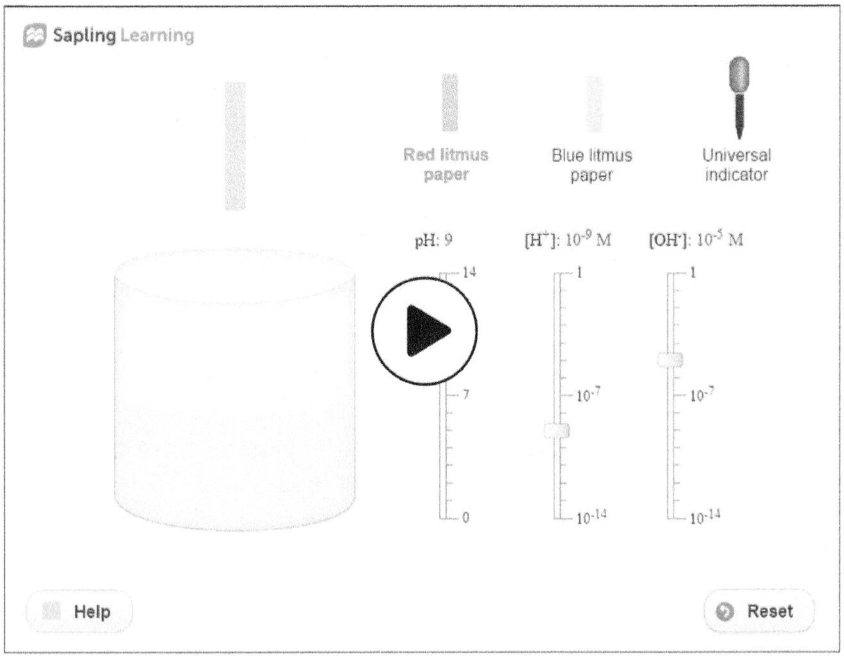

FIGURE 16.7 pH Simulation

NOTE: You need to be online to access this activity.

Use the sliders to adjust pH, $[H_3O^+]$, and $[OH^-]$ of the solution to see how the other variables respond. For example, how do $[H_3O^+]$ and $[OH^-]$ change as the pH is raised or lowered, and how do pH and $[OH^-]$ change as $[H_3O^+]$ is increased or decreased? Test the solution with litmus paper and with universal indicator to see how changes in pH affect those indicators.

SECTION REVIEW

- pH is another way to express the concentration of H_3O^+ in solution, and $pH = -\log[H_3O^+]$ (Equation 16.2).
- A $pH < 7$ means the solution is acidic, a $pH > 7$ means the solution is basic, and a $pH = 7$ means the solution is neutral.
- If the pH is known, $[H_3O^+]$ can be calculated by taking the inverse log of the negative pH: $[H_3O^+] = 10^{-pH}$ (Equation 16.3).
- Analogous to pH, $pOH = -\log[OH^-]$ (Equation 16.4).
- Because $[H_3O^+][OH^-] = 1.0 \times 10^{-14}$, $pH + pOH = 14$ (Equation 16.5). This relationship can sometimes be used to simplify pH calculations involving basic solutions.

16.5 Weak Acids and Bases

GOAL

- Demonstrate how the equilibrium constants for weak acid and weak bases can be used to calculate pH.

Background Review

Chapter 15 Chemical Equilibrium:
Section 15.5—Calculations Using ICE Tables

Strong acids and bases ionize completely in water (Section 16.1). This means that $[H_3O^+]$ in a solution of a monoprotic strong acid such as $HClO_4$ is always equal to the concentration of the acid. What, then, is $[H_3O^+]$ in solutions of the majority of acids, which are *weak* acids?

A weak acid, such as acetic acid, $HC_2H_3O_2$, only partially ionizes in water, forming an equilibrium.

$$HC_2H_3O_2(aq) + H_2O \rightarrow H_3O^+(aq) + C_2H_3O_2^-(aq)$$

A small percentage of the acid molecules ionize, but most of them remain intact in their molecular form. Two competing reactions occur—namely, the ionization of the acid (the forward reaction) and the formation of the acid and water from the ions (the reverse reaction).

Since this is an *equilibrium reaction*, it has an equilibrium-constant expression (Chapter 15).

$$K_a = \frac{[H_3O^+][C_2H_3O_2^-]}{[HC_2H_3O_2]}$$

TABLE 16.2 Selected K_a and K_b Values

Acid	Formula	K_a	Base	Formula	K_b
Acetic acid	$HC_2H_3O_2$	1.8×10^{-5}	Ammonia	NH_3	1.8×10^{-5}
Boric acid	HBH_2O_3	5.8×10^{-10}	Methylamine	CH_3NH_2	5.0×10^{-4}
Formic acid	$HCHO_2$	1.7×10^{-4}	Dimethylamine	$(CH_3)_2NH$	5.4×10^{-4}
Hydrofluoric acid	HF	6.8×10^{-4}	Trimethylamine	$(CH_3)_3N$	6.3×10^{-5}
Nitrous acid	HNO_2	4.0×10^{-4}	Pyridine	C_5H_5N	1.7×10^{-9}
Phenol	HOC_6H_5	1.1×10^{-10}	Hydrazine	H_2NNH_2	1.3×10^{-6}

A longer list of ionization constants can be found in Appendix A.3.

The equilibrium constant K_a is called the **acid ionization constant**. The subscript "a" indicates that the constant is for the ionization of an acid. The general expression for a weak acid, HA, ionization is written as

$$HA(aq) \rightleftharpoons H^+(aq) + A^-(aq)$$

or

$$HA(aq) + H_2O(l) \rightleftharpoons H_3O^+(aq) + A^-(aq)$$

where A^- is the counterion. The general form of the K_a expression for any weak acid is therefore

$$K_a = \frac{[H^+][A^-]}{[HA]} \quad (16.6)$$

or

$$K_a = \frac{[H_3O^+][A^-]}{[HA]} \quad (16.7)$$

where [HA] is the equilibrium concentration of the weak acid, $[A^-]$ is the equilibrium concentration of its conjugate base, and $[H^+]$ or $[H_3O^+]$ is the equilibrium concentration of hydrogen ion or hydronium ion. Equation 16.6 and Equation 16.7 are equivalent ways of writing the same expression.

Similarly, a weak base such as ammonia exists in water in equilibrium with its ionization products.

$$NH_3(aq) + H_2O(l) \rightleftharpoons NH_4^+(aq) + OH^-(aq)$$

It also has an equilibrium-constant expression.

$$K_b = \frac{[NH_4^+][OH^-]}{[NH_3]}$$

The constant K_b is called the **base ionization constant**. The subscript "b" indicates that the constant is for the ionization of a base. The general expression for a weak base, B, ionization is

$$B(aq) + H_2O(l) \rightleftharpoons BH^+(aq) + OH^-(aq)$$

and the general form of the K_b expression for any weak base is

$$K_b = \frac{[BH^+][OH^-]}{[B]} \quad (16.8)$$

where [B] is the equilibrium concentration of the weak base, $[BH^+]$ is the equilibrium concentration of its conjugate acid, and $[OH^-]$ is the equilibrium concentration of hydroxide ion. K_a and K_b are often referred to as **ionization constants** for the weak acid or weak base because ions are formed in ionization reactions. Despite this special name, they are still equilibrium constants, K_c, that follow the rules first explained in Chapter 15.

Selected values of K_a and K_b are listed in Table 16.2. Although the reactions are equilibria and can therefore be written with either set of species on the left, the equilibrium constant values in such tables represent the equations with the molecular acid or base on the *left* and the ions on the *right*. A larger K value indicates more complete ionization, so acetic acid ($K_a = 1.8 \times 10^{-5}$) is much stronger than boric acid ($K_a = 5.8 \times 10^{-10}$), even though both are weak acids.

Many online sources of equilibrium constants list pK_a values instead of K_a values. The relationship between K_a and pK_a is the same as that between $[H_3O^+]$ and pH.

$$pK_a = -\log K_a$$

To calculate K_a from a given pK_a value, take the inverse log of $-pK_a$.

$$K_a = 10^{-pK_a} \quad (16.9)$$

Example 16.11

Complete the following table, then rank these weak acids from weakest to strongest.

Acid	Formula	K_a	pK_a
Chlorous	$HClO$		1.96
Oxalic	$H_2C_2O_4$		1.25
Periodic	HIO_4	7.3×10^{-2}	
Phosphoric	H_3PO_4		2.16
Sulfurous	H_2SO_3	1.4×10^{-2}	

Solution

First fill in the missing information using the formulas $pK_a = -\log K_a$ and $K_a = 10^{-pK_a}$.

Acid	Formula	K_a	pK_a
Chlorous	$HClO$	1.1×10^{-2}	1.96
Oxalic	$H_2C_2O_4$	5.6×10^{-2}	1.25
Periodic	HIO_4	7.3×10^{-2}	1.14
Phosphoric	H_3PO_4	6.9×10^{-3}	2.16
Sulfurous	H_2SO_3	1.4×10^{-2}	1.85

As K_a increases, so does the strength of the weak acid. Because pK_a is the *negative* log of K_a, a large K_a corresponds to a *small* pK_a. You can use either K_a or pK_a to compare the strengths of these weak acids.

In order of increasing K_a or decreasing pK_a, the strengths of the acids from weakest to strongest are phosphoric < chlorous < sulfurous < oxalic < periodic. For the polyprotic acids (i.e., phosphoric and sulfurous), this ranking compares only the acid strength of the first hydrogen ionized. Subsequent ionizations have different (and much smaller) K_a values.

PRACTICE PROBLEM 16.11

Complete the following table, then rank these weak bases from weakest to strongest.

Base	Formula	K_b	pK_b
Ethylamine	$CH_3CH_2NH_2$		3.20
Diethylamine	$(C_2H_5)_2NH$		3.16
Triethylamine	$(C_2H_5)_3N$		3.25
Methylamine	CH_3NH_2	5.0×10^{-4}	
Dimethylamine	$(CH_3)_2NH$	5.4×10^{-4}	

Hint: Fill in the missing information using the formulas $pK_b = -\log K_b$ and $K_b = 10^{-pK_b}$. If you compare K_b values, the base strength increases as K_b increases. If you compare pK_b values, the base strength increases as pK_b decreases.

ICE TABLES IN ACID–BASE CALCULATIONS

To find the equilibrium concentrations of ions in a weak acid or weak base, ICE tables (initial, change, equilibrium) are a useful tool (Section 15.5). Because these are aqueous solutions, it is important to remember that pure water contains a small amount (1.0×10^{-7} M) of hydronium and hydroxide even before the ionization of the acid or base (Section 16.3). However, since this low concentration is generally negligible compared to the amount of H_3O^+ or OH^- produced by the reaction, the ICE tables shown here will approximate the initial 1.0×10^{-7} M concentration as ~0 (approximately 0).

Example 16.12

When 0.1000 mol of an unknown acid, represented as HA, is dissolved in enough water to make 1.000 L of solution, the resulting pH is 2.20. Calculate the value of K_a for HA.

$$HA(aq) + H_2O \rightleftharpoons H_3O^+(aq) + A^-(aq)$$

Solution

Set up an ICE table as discussed in Section 15.5. Include the initial concentration for HA and the known concentration of hydronium in pure water.

	$HA(aq)$ + H_2O $\rightleftharpoons$	$H_3O^+(aq)$ +	$A^-(aq)$
Initial	0.1000	~0	0
Change			
Equilibrium			

The initial $[H_3O^+]$ is 1×10^{-7} M, but this will be a negligible contribution to the final $[H_3O^+]$, so it is approximated as 0 M to simplify the table.

The equilibrium concentration for H_3O^+ can be calculated from the pH value given.

$$[H_3O^+] = 10^{-2.20} = 0.0063\ M$$

Add that value to the ICE table.

	$HA(aq)$ + H_2O $\rightleftharpoons$	$H_3O^+(aq)$ +	$A^-(aq)$
Initial	0.1000	~0	0
Change			
Equilibrium		0.0063	

Starting with the change in H_3O^+, fill in the remaining values. Because each HA molecule that ionizes produces one H_3O^+ and one A^-, $[A^-] = [H_3O^+]$.

	$HA(aq)$ + H_2O $\rightleftharpoons$	$H_3O^+(aq)$ +	$A^-(aq)$
Initial	0.1000	~0	0
Change	−0.0063	+0.0063	+0.0063
Equilibrium	0.0937	0.0063	0.0063

As noted previously, the amount of H_3O^+ produced by the reaction (in this case, 0.0063 M) is far greater than the initial amount present in the water (1.0×10^{-7} M), so the initial concentration of $[H_3O^+]$ is negligible and can be treated as 0. It is generally safe to make this assumption when the initial concentration of acid is significantly greater than 10^{-7} M.

Calculate the value of K_a using the equilibrium concentrations and the K_a expression for HA (Equation 16.7).

$$K_a = \frac{[H_3O^+][A^-]}{[HA]} = \frac{(0.0063)^2}{(0.0937)} = 4.24 \times 10^{-4}$$

PRACTICE PROBLEM 16.12

Caffeine, $C_8H_{10}N_4O_2$, is a weak base that reacts with water according to the following chemical equation.

$$C_8H_{10}N_4O_2(aq) + H_2O(l) \rightleftharpoons HC_8H_{10}N_4O_2^{\ +}(aq) + OH^-(aq)$$

A solution that is 0.00155 M caffeine (about the same concentration as that found in a carbonated energy drink) has an OH^- concentration of 6.18×10^{-4} M. Calculate the K_b of caffeine.

Hint: Set up an ICE table using the concentrations given in the problem. Once you've determined the equilibrium concentrations, plug them into the K_b expression.

EVERYDAY CONNECTION

Caffeine is a weak base.

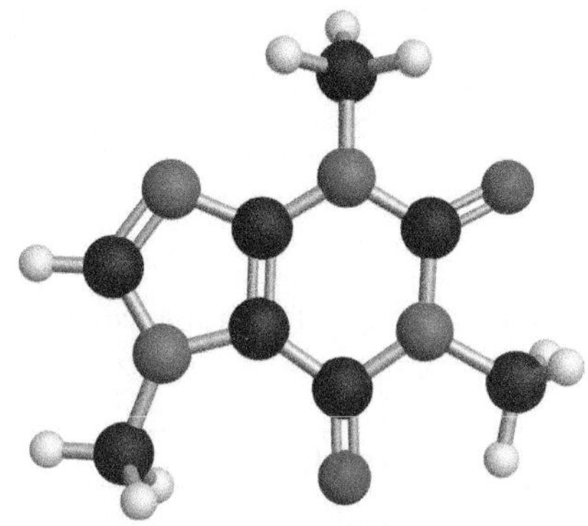

However, caffeinated beverages are often acidic because of their other ingredients. For example, soda contains phosphoric acid. Coffee contains small amounts of several different acids that can vary depending on where the coffee beans were grown and how they were roasted.

Petr Kratochvil/Shutterstock

Figure 16.8 is an interactive activity in which you can compare the pH and ionization of a strong acid, a strong base, a weak acid, and a weak base, all at the same concentration. The pH can be tested using pH paper (Figure 16.5) and a pH meter (Figure 16.6). The extent of ionization in each solution can be explored by testing the conductivity of the solution and by zooming to a molecular view of the acid or base in solution. While pH paper and a pH meter provide a measure of how acidic or basic the solution is, conductivity indicates only the extent of ionization in the solution—the greater the ion concentration, the brighter the light. Conductivity does not distinguish between acids and bases (or salts) and does not provide any quantitative information that can be used to calculate pH or $[H_3O^+]$. The molecular-level view qualitatively shows the extent to which each acid or base has dissociated into ions or remains in its molecular form. (In the molecular-level view, water molecules are removed whenever possible, so H_3O^+ is represented as H^+.)

pH CALCULATIONS FOR WEAK ACIDS AND BASES

To determine the pH of a weak acid or base, you must know the concentration of the acid or base and its ionization constant, K_a or K_b. Then, make an ICE table using x as the change in concentration. As described in Section 15.5, this technique often results in a quadratic equation once the equilibrium values (in terms of x) are plugged into the K expression. Luckily, in cases

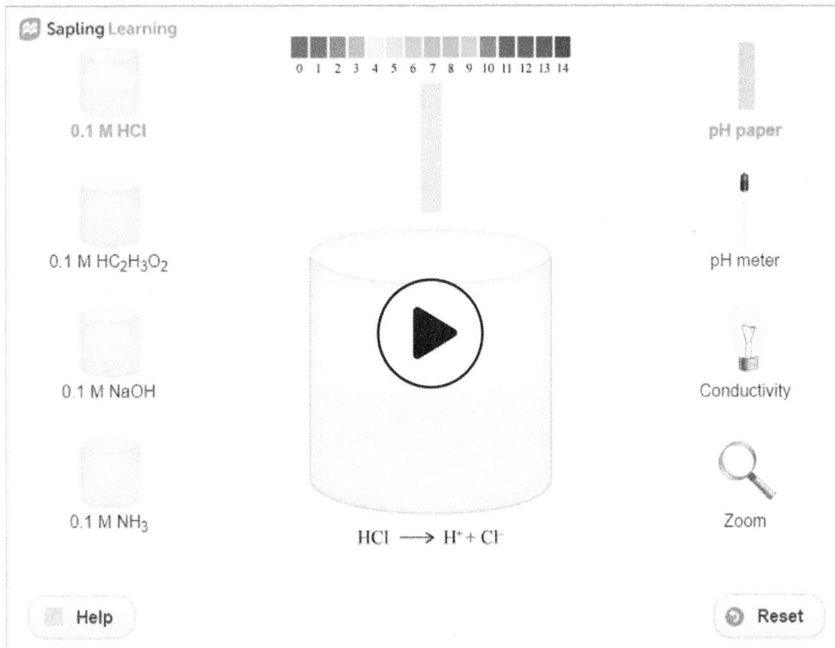

FIGURE 16.8 Comparison of Strong and Weak Acids and Bases

NOTE: You need to be online to access this activity.

Use the three detection methods on the right to see how the extent of ionization of an acid or base affects the pH and the conductivity of the different solutions provided. Zoom in with the molecular-level viewer to get a relative idea of which types of particles are present in each solution.

of weak acid or weak base ionization, the value of K_a or K_b is usually small compared to the initial concentration, so the extent of ionization is so small that the amount of acid or base lost to ionization is negligible (less than about 5% of the initial concentration). Ignoring the amount of acid or base lost to ionization greatly simplifies the math, but always check the result to ensure that the approximation was valid.

Figure 16.9 is a video demonstration of how to calculate the pH of a weak acid solution and how to calculate the pH of a weak base solution when you know the initial concentration and the ionization constant of the weak acid or weak base.

Steve Lemon, Macmillan Learning

FIGURE 16.9 Video Tutorial: Weak Acid and Weak Base pH Calculations

NOTE: You need to be online to access this activity.

This video shows how to calculate the pH of a weak acid solution and a weak base solution, given the initial concentration and the ionization constant.

Example 16.13

Calculate the pH of a solution made from dissolving 0.100 mol acetic acid ($HC_2H_3O_2$) in enough water to make 1.00 L of solution.

Solution

The ionization equation for acetic acid is

$$HC_2H_3O_2(aq) + H_2O(l) \rightleftharpoons H_3O^+(aq) + C_2H_3O_2^-(aq)$$

The initial concentration of acetic acid (before ionization) is 0.100 M. The initial concentration of the conjugate base, $C_2H_3O_2^-$, is 0. The initial concentration of hydronium ion is 1.0×10^{-7} M, which is essentially zero in this context. Use x as the change in concentration.

	$HC_2H_3O_2$ (aq) + H_2O ⇌	H_3O^+ (aq) +	$C_2H_3O_2^-$ (aq)
Initial	0.100	~0	0
Change	$-x$	$+x$	$+x$
Equilibrium	$0.100 - x$	x	x

Use the K_a expression and the value of K_a for acetic acid (Table 16.2) to solve for x.

$$K_a = \frac{[H_3O^+][C_2H_3O_2^-]}{[HC_2H_3O_2]} = \frac{x^2}{(0.100 - x)} = 1.8 \times 10^{-5}$$

K_a is much smaller than the initial concentration, so assume that x is very small compared to 0.100 and that the amount of acid lost to ionization is negligible. Therefore, $0.100 - x \approx 0.100$.

$$\frac{x^2}{(0.100 - x)} \approx \frac{x^2}{0.100} = 1.8 \times 10^{-5}$$

$$x^2 = 1.8 \times 10^{-6}$$

Take the square root of both sides.

$$x = 1.3 \times 10^{-3}$$

Because x represents both $[H_3O^+]$ and $[C_2H_3O_2^-]$, both of these concentrations equal 1.3×10^{-3} M. Finally, 1.3×10^{-3} M is about 1% of 0.100 M, so the approximation that $0.100 - x \approx 0.100$ is acceptable.

$$pH = -\log[H_3O^+] = -\log(1.3 \times 10^{-3}\ M) = 2.87$$

PRACTICE PROBLEM 16.13

Calculate the pH of the solution that results when 0.100 mol NH_3 is dissolved in enough water to make 1.00 L of solution.

Hint: Write the ionization reaction for NH_3, and use it to fill out an ICE table. Once you have expressions for the equilibrium concentrations in terms of x, plug them into the K_b expression and solve for x, which is equal to $[OH^-]$. Use $[OH^-]$ to find either pOH or $[H_3O^+]$, then use that value to find pH.

In Example 16.13 and Practice Problem 16.13, the assumption that x was negligible compared to the initial acid or base concentration was valid, so the denominator of the equilibrium expression in both cases simplified to the initial concentration of the acid or base. This situation results in a predictable formula for hydronium or hydroxide, $x = \sqrt{K \cdot C_{initial}}$, where $C_{initial}$ is the initial concentration of the weak acid or base. In some situations, however, such as when you are working with a large K_a or K_b value (typically about 10^{-4} or greater) or a low initial concentration (typically less than 0.001 M), the change will *not* be negligible compared to the initial concentration. In these cases the denominator of the equilibrium expression will be $C_{initial} - x$, and solving for x means solving a quadratic equation of the form $x^2 + Kx - KC_{initial} = 0$. To review using the quadratic formula to solve quadratic equations, see Section 0.10.

REACTIONS INVOLVING WEAK ACIDS AND WEAK BASES

The equilibria that have been described so far for the dissociation ionization of weak acids and bases apply only to a weak acid or weak base dissolving in water. An acid–base reaction always goes to completion, even if one of the reactants is a weak acid or a weak base. For example, ammonia reacts with hydrochloric acid to form the ammonium ion and the chloride ion.

$$NH_3(aq) + HCl(aq) \rightarrow NH_4^+(aq) + Cl^-(aq)$$

This is not an equilibrium reaction. Ammonium, NH_4^+, and chloride, Cl^-, do not react with each other to form NH_3 and HCl. However, the NH_4^+ produced by this reaction is itself a weak acid, so the (nonequilibrium) acid–base reaction results in a product that then participates in a separate equilibrium ionization:

$$NH_4^+(aq) + H_2O(l) \rightleftharpoons H_3O^+(aq) + NH_3(aq)$$

The acidic and basic properties of salts such as NH_4Cl are discussed in further detail in Section 16.7.

SECTION REVIEW

- The ionization constants K_a and K_b are equilibrium constants for the ionization of a weak acid or weak base when it is dissolved in water.
- As K_a or K_b increases, the strength of the weak acid or weak base increases. Correspondingly, as the pK_a or pK_b decreases, the strength of the weak acid or weak base increases.
- The ionization constant expression for the ionization of an acid or base does *not* include a term for the concentration of water because pure liquids are never included in equilibrium-constant expressions.
- Equilibrium-constant expressions for weak acid or weak base ionizations always involve four variables: the molecular acid or base, the two ions formed as products, and the equilibrium constant. Unless there is an additional source of ions, the concentrations of the ions formed as products will be equal.

- In most cases of weak acid or weak base ionization, the extent of ionization is so small that the concentration of acid or base lost to ionization is a negligible amount (less than about 5% of the initial concentration). Ignoring the concentration lost to ionization greatly simplifies the math, but always check the result to ensure that the approximation was valid.
- When you are solving for $[H_3O^+]$ or $[OH^-]$ and the extent of ionization is greater than about 5% of the initial acid or base concentration, the equilibrium expression becomes a quadratic equation and is most easily solved using the quadratic formula.
- Acid–base reactions involving weak acids or weak bases are not equilibrium reactions, but they will produce a weak acid or weak base as a product that can then undergo an equilibrium ionization.

16.6 Polyprotic Acids

GOAL

- Calculate the pH of acids with more than one ionizable hydrogen atom.

Background Review

Chapter 15 Chemical Equilibrium:
Section 15.5—Calculations Using ICE Tables

A **polyprotic acid** is an acid that has more than one ionizable hydrogen atom per molecule, such as sulfuric acid, H_2SO_4, or phosphoric acid, H_3PO_4. Polyprotic acids do not release all of their ionizable hydrogen atoms at once—they ionize in steps.

$$H_3PO_4(aq) + H_2O(l) \rightleftharpoons H_2PO_4^-(aq) + H_3O^+(aq) \quad K_{a1} = 6.9 \times 10^{-3}$$

$$H_2PO_4^-(aq) + H_2O(l) \rightleftharpoons HPO_4^{2-}(aq) + H_3O^+(aq) \quad K_{a2} = 6.2 \times 10^{-8}$$

$$HPO_4^{2-}(aq) + H_2O(l) \rightleftharpoons PO_4^{3-}(aq) + H_3O^+(aq) \quad K_{a3} = 4.8 \times 10^{-13}$$

Each ionization has its own ionization constant, usually labeled with 1, 2, and so on in the subscript. The second (or third) ionization has a much lower ionization constant than does the prior ionization for two reasons: (1) The prior ionization produces hydronium ions that repress further ionization, in accordance with Le Châtelier's principle, and (2) the conjugate base that results from the loss of the first ionizable hydrogen is usually a negative ion, and it is more difficult to remove a positive H^+ from a negative ion. The hydrogen ions in a solution of a polyprotic acid therefore come mainly from the first step in the ionization.

TABLE 16.3 Ionization Constants of Selected Polyprotic Acids

Acid Name	Formula	K_{a1}	K_{a2}	K_{a3}
Ascorbic acid	$H_2C_6H_6O_6$	8.0×10^{-5}	1.6×10^{-12}	
Citric acid	$H_3C_6H_5O_7$	7.4×10^{-4}	1.7×10^{-5}	4.0×10^{-7}
Hydrosulfuric acid	H_2S	8.9×10^{-8}	1.0×10^{-19}	
Malic acid	$H_2C_4H_4O_5$	4.0×10^{-4}	6.3×10^{-6}	
Oxalic acid	$H_2C_2O_4$	6.0×10^{-2}	6.1×10^{-5}	
Phosphoric acid	H_3PO_4	6.9×10^{-3}	6.2×10^{-8}	4.8×10^{-13}

Ionization constants for additional polyprotic acids can be found in Appendix A.3.

Table 16.3 lists the ionization constants for a number of common polyprotic acids. In each case, the ionization constant for the first ionization is greater than the second, and the second is greater than the third (if present). In many cases, the ionization constants of two successive ionizations differ by a factor of 1000 or more. In those cases, a double greater-than sign is often used to express such a large difference: $K_{a1} \gg K_{a2} \gg K_{a3}$.

A polyprotic acid with exactly two ionizable protons is known as a **diprotic acid**, and one with exactly three ionizable protons is known as a **triprotic acid**. The acids in Table 16.3 that have a value for K_{a3} are triprotic, and those that stop at K_{a2} are diprotic.

Finding the equilibrium concentrations of all ions in a polyprotic acid solution requires the use of multiple ICE tables, one for each ionization step. The initial values in the second ICE table come from the equilibrium values in the first ICE table. In other words, when the second ionizable hydrogen atom on a polyprotic acid ionizes, the second ionization occurs in a solution that already contains H_3O^+ ions from the first ionization.

Example 16.14

Using the ionization constants for hydrosulfuric acid in Table 16.3, calculate the pH and sulfide ion concentration of a 0.100 M H_2S solution.

Solution

Start with an ICE table for the first ionization.

	$H_2S(aq)$ + H_2O	$\rightleftharpoons$ $H_3O^+(aq)$	+ $HS^-(aq)$
Initial	0.100	~0	0
Change	$-x$	$+x$	$+x$
Equilibrium	$0.100 - x$	x	x

Assume $x \ll 0.100$, so $0.100 - x \approx 0.100$.

$$K_{a1} = \frac{[H_3O^+][HS^-]}{[H_2S]} = \frac{x^2}{0.100 - x} \approx \frac{x^2}{0.100}$$

$$= 8.9 \times 10^{-8}$$

$$x^2 = 0.1008.9 \times 10^{-8} = 8.9 \times 10^{-9}$$

$$x = \sqrt{8.9 \times 10^{-9}} = 9.4 \times 10^{-5}$$

Because 9.4×10^{-5} M is much less than 0.100 M, the assumption that $x \ll 0.100$ M is valid.

Now, make an ICE table for the second ionization using the final values from the first ionization. Use y as the change to distinguish from x in the previous ionization.

	$HS^-(aq)$ + H_2O	$\rightleftharpoons$ $H_3O^+(aq)$	+ $S^{2-}(aq)$
Initial	9.4×10^{-5}	9.4×10^{-5}	0
Change	$-y$	$+y$	$+y$
Equilibrium	$9.4 \times 10^{-5} - y$	$9.4 \times 10^{-5} + y$	y

Assume $y \ll 9.4 \times 10^{-5}$, so $(9.4 \times 10^{-5} - y) \approx 9.4 \times 10^{-5}$.

$$K_{a2} = \frac{[H_3O^+][S^{2-}]}{[HS^-]} = \frac{9.4 \times 10^{-5} y}{9.4 \times 10^{-5} - y}$$

$$\approx \frac{9.4 \times 10^{-5} y}{9.4 \times 10^{-5}} = 1.0 \times 10^{-19}$$

$$y = [S^{2-}] = 1.0 \times 10^{-19}$$

1.0×10^{-19} M $\ll 9.4 \times 10^{-5}$, so the assumption is valid.

$$[H_3O^+] = 9.4 \times 10^{-5} + y = 9.4 \times 10^{-5}$$

$$pH = -\log[H_3O^+] = -\log 9.4 \times 10^{-5} = 4.03$$

The hydronium ion concentration that is provided by the second step of the ionization (also equal to 1.0×10^{-19} M) is totally insignificant compared with that provided by the first step. There are two reasons for that: (1) The value of the equilibrium constant is much smaller, and (2) the hydronium ion provided by the first step represses the ionization of the second.

The second ionization of H_2S is not needed to calculate the pH of a 0.100 M solution of the acid because the H_3O^+ contribution from the second ionization, y, is negligible compared to that from the first, x. Had you calculated the pH after the first ICE table, namely, $-\log(x)$, you would have gotten the same answer as you did after the second, namely, $-\log(x + y)$.

The second equilibrium step is needed to calculate $[S^{2-}]$ because that is the only step that produces sulfide ions. $[S^{2-}]$, however, was equal to K_{a2}. It is a general rule, in fact, that $y = K_{a2}$ for diprotic acids where $K_{a1} \gg K_{a2}$.

PRACTICE PROBLEM 16.14

Ascorbic acid, $H_2C_6H_6O_6$, also known as vitamin C, is a diprotic acid. Using the ionization constants in Table 16.3, calculate the pH and ascorbate ion concentration, $[C_6H_6O_6{}^{2-}]$, of a 0.25 M ascorbic acid solution.

Hint: From Table 16.3, $K_{a1} = 8.0 \times 10^{-5}$ and $K_{a2} = 1.6 \times 10^{-12}$. $K_{a1} \gg K_{a2}$, so assume that $[H_3O^+] = x$ from the first ionization and that $[C_6H_6O_6{}^{2-}] = K_{a2}$.

SECTION REVIEW

- Polyprotic acids ionize in steps, each having its own value for the ionization constant.
- The successive ionization constants are smaller than the preceding ones, so the second (or third) ionization does not contribute appreciably to the hydronium ion concentration of the solution in water, but is the only source of the doubly (and triply) charged anion.
- For a diprotic acid where $K_{a1} \gg K_{a2}$, you can calculate $[H_3O^+]$ from the first ionization only and assume that $[A^{2-}] = K_{a2}$.

16.7 Acid–Base Properties of Salts

GOALS

- Identify from their formulas which salts have acidic or basic properties.
- Calculate the pH of salt solutions.

Background Review

Chapter 15 Chemical Equilibrium:
Section 15.5—Calculations Using ICE Tables

The term *salt* is sometimes used as a synonym for an ionic compound because nearly all ionic compounds are salts. In this text, however, *salt* refers only to ionic compounds that do not contain H^+ as the cation or OH^- as the anion (Section 4.2). For this reason, you might expect that all salts form neutral solutions when dissolved in water. To the contrary, many salts have acidic or basic properties. This occurs if the anion or cation in the salt is the conjugate of a weak acid or a weak base, or if the cation in the salt is a small, highly charged metal ion.

FIGURE 16.10 Video Tutorial: Acidic, Basic, and Neutral Salts

NOTE: You need to be online to access this video.
This video shows how to classify a salt as acidic, basic, or neutral.

ACIDIC OR BASIC NATURE OF SALT SOLUTIONS

If the salt is made up of a cation from a strong base and an anion from a strong acid, such as NaCl, it will have no acid–base character. Table 16.4 lists the ions that meet these criteria.

Any combination of cation and anion from Table 16.4, such as sodium chloride, NaCl, or strontium chlorate, $Sr(ClO_3)_2$, forms a neutral salt with no acidic or basic qualities. If one of the ions in Table 16.4 combines with the conjugate of a weak acid or weak base, however, such as ammonium chloride, NH_4Cl, or sodium acetate, $NaC_2H_3O_2$, the resulting salt will have acidic or basic qualities.

- Anions of strong acids and cations of strong bases have no acid–base character.
- Cations that are conjugate acids of weak bases are acidic.
- Anions that are conjugate bases of weak acids are basic.

For example, an aqueous solution of sodium acetate, $NaC_2H_3O_2$, turns red litmus paper blue, indicating that the solution is basic. This salt consists of Na^+ and the acetate ion, $C_2H_3O_2^-$. Na^+ has no acid–base properties because it is the cation of a strong base. $C_2H_3O_2^-$ is the conjugate base of the weak acid $HC_2H_3O_2$ (acetic acid), however, so the acetate ion behaves as a weak base.

$$C_2H_3O_2^-(aq) + H_2O(l) \rightleftharpoons HC_2H_3O_2(aq) + OH^-(aq)$$

The combination of a cation that is neither acidic nor basic and a basic anion in $NaC_2H_3O_2(aq)$ makes the solution basic.

Figure 16.10 is a video demonstration of how to classify a salt as acidic, basic, or neutral.

TABLE 16.4 Counterions from Strong Acids and Strong Bases

Strong Acid	Anion	Strong Base	Cation
HCl	Cl^-	LiOH	Li^+
HBr	Br^-	NaOH	Na^+
HI	I^-	KOH	K^+
HNO_3	NO_3^-	RbOH	Rb^+
$HClO_4$	ClO_4^-	CsOH	Cs^+
$HClO_3$	ClO_3^-	$Ca(OH)_2$	Ca^{2+}
H_2SO_4	*	$Sr(OH)_2$	Sr^{2+}
		$Ba(OH)_2$	Ba^{2+}

*As the anion of a polyprotic acid, HSO_4^- is a special case and is therefore excluded from this list.

Example 16.15

Is ammonium nitrate, NH_4NO_3, acidic, basic, or neutral in aqueous solution?

Solution

The ammonium ion, NH_4^+, is the conjugate acid of the weak base ammonia, so it is a weak acid.

$$NH_4^+(aq) + H_2O(l) \rightleftharpoons NH_3(aq) + H_3O^+(aq)$$

The nitrate ion, NO_3^-, is the anion of the strong acid nitric acid (Table 16.4), so it behaves as neither an acid nor a base.

The combination of an acidic cation, NH_4^+, and an anion with no acid–base character, NO_3^-, means that this salt solution is acidic.

PRACTICE PROBLEM 16.15

Are the following solutions acidic, basic, or neutral?

a. NaCl(aq)
b. NaF(aq)

Hint: Anions of strong acids and cations of strong bases are neither acidic nor basic. Cations that are conjugate acids of weak bases are acidic, whereas anions that are conjugate bases of weak acids are basic.

SO_4^{2-} has basic properties because its conjugate acid is HSO_4^- (a weak acid), not H_2SO_4 (a strong acid). HSO_4^- is also a tricky case, because as the conjugate base of a strong acid, it does not hydrolyze water like the conjugate base of a weak acid would. It has an ionizable proton, however, which makes it a weak acid.

It is also possible for both of the ions in a salt to be the conjugate acid or base of a weak base or acid. The salt ammonium phosphate, for example, $(NH_4)_3PO_4$, is made up of a conjugate weak acid, NH_4^+, and a conjugate weak base, PO_4^{3-}. In cases like this, whichever ion has stronger acid or base properties will dominate, and will drive the pH of the solution in the corresponding direction. In $(NH_4)_3PO_4$, the K_b of the phosphate ion ($K_b = 2.1 \times 10^{-2}$) is much larger than the K_a of the ammonium ion ($K_a = 5.6 \times 10^{-10}$), so despite having a weak acid in its formula, this salt has overall basic properties and a solution of ammonium phosphate would be basic.

EVERYDAY CONNECTION

The chlorine in bleach is not Cl_2, but rather part of the salt sodium hypochlorite, NaClO. The hypochlorite ion, ClO^-, acts as a base because it is the conjugate of the weak acid hypochlorous acid, HClO.

design56/Shutterstock

ACIDIC NATURE OF METAL CATIONS

Certain metal cations that have a high charge density (a high positive charge combined with a small ionic diameter) can also act as acids. For example, a 0.1 M solution of $AlCl_3$ has a pH of about 3.0. There are no ionizable hydrogen atoms in aluminum chloride, $AlCl_3$, but when aluminum ion, Al^{3+}, is dissolved in water, it is hydrated by six water, H_2O, molecules.

$$Al^{3+}(aq) + 6\,H_2O(l) \rightleftharpoons Al(H_2O)_6^{3+}(aq)$$

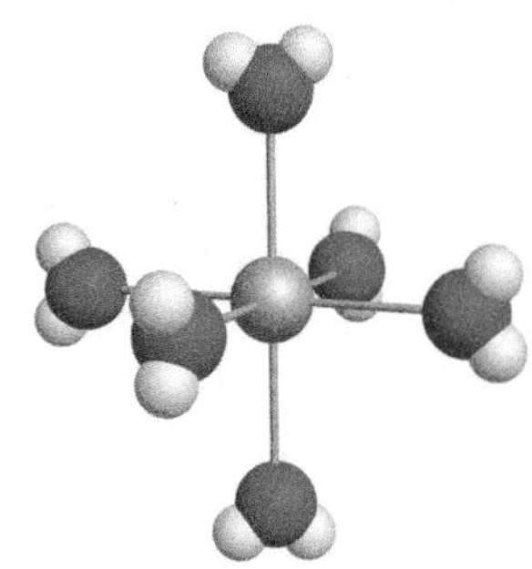

The dense positive charge on the hydrated Al^{3+} ion is able to hydrolyze one of the hydrating water molecules to release H^+.

$$Al(H_2O)_6^{3+}(aq) \rightleftharpoons Al(H_2O)_5(OH)^{2+}(aq) + H^+(aq)$$

Adding these two equations and canceling out the $Al(H_2O)_6^{3+}(aq)$ term from both sides shows how Al^{3+} can act as an acid.

$$Al^{3+}(aq) + 6\,H_2O(l) \rightleftharpoons Al(H_2O)_5(OH)^{2+}(aq) + H^+(aq)$$

Only a few metal ions—notably Al^{3+}, Fe^{3+}, Cr^{3+}, Cu^{2+}, Zn^{2+}, and Cd^{2+}—are capable of hydrolyzing water like this. These hydrated metal ions are proton donors, which makes them Brønsted acids.

Example 16.16

Will dissolving each of the following salts in water raise the pH, lower the pH, or have no effect?

a. $Ba(ClO_4)_2$
b. $Fe(NO_3)_3$
c. $CuSO_4 \cdot 5\,H_2O$

Solution

a. pH will *not change*: $Ba(ClO_4)_2$ is made up of the cation of a strong base and the anion of a monoprotic strong acid (Table 16.4), so neither the cation nor the anion has acid–base properties.

b. pH will *decrease*: The Fe^{3+} ion is a small, highly charged cation, so it will hydrolyze water, releasing H^+ ions.

c. pH will *decrease*: $CuSO_4 \cdot 5\,H_2O$ contains Cu^{2+}, which is capable of hydrolyzing water, releasing H^+ ions.

PRACTICE PROBLEM 16.16

Will dissolving each of the following salts in water raise the pH, lower the pH, or have no effect?

a. $CrCl_3$

b. $SrCl_2$

c. $Ca(C_2H_3O_2)_2$

Hint: Analyze the cation and the anion separately. If the cation is one of the acidic metal cations, or if it is the conjugate acid of a weak base, then it is acidic. If it is derived from a strong base, it has no acid–base character.

If the anion is the conjugate base of a weak acid, it is basic. If not, the anion has no acid–base character. If the salt contains acidic ions, the pH will decrease, and if it contains basic ions, the pH will increase.

CALCULATING CONJUGATE ACID AND BASE STRENGTH

The strength of an acid or base is inversely proportional to the strength of its conjugate base or conjugate acid (Section 16.2). That is, the stronger the weak acid, the weaker its conjugate base, and vice versa.

The strength of a weak acid and that of its conjugate base are related through the K_w equilibrium, so if you know the value of K_a, then it is possible to calculate K_b for the conjugate base. To see how, begin with the equilibrium expression for the ionization of a weak acid HA to form its conjugate base A^-:

$$HA(aq) + H_2O(l) \rightleftharpoons H_3O^+(aq) + A^-(aq)$$

$$K_a = \frac{[H_3O^+][A^-]}{[HA]}$$

If the weak base, A^-, ionizes in water, it forms its conjugate weak acid, HA. The equation for the weak base ionization and the corresponding K_b expression are

$$A^-(aq) + H_2O(l) \rightleftharpoons HA(aq) + OH^-(aq)$$

$$K_b = \frac{[HA][OH^-]}{[A^-]}$$

The product of $K_a \times K_b$ is

$$\frac{[H_3O^+][A^-]}{[HA]} \times \frac{[HA][OH^-]}{[A^-]} = [H_3O^+][OH^-] = K_w$$

Therefore, for any acid–base conjugate pair,

$$K_a \times K_b = K_w \qquad (16.10)$$

If you know the K_a for any weak acid or the K_b for any weak base, you can use K_w to calculate the corresponding K_b or K_a for the conjugate base or conjugate acid.

Example 16.17

Formic acid, $HCHO_2$, is the compound in fire ant bites that makes them so painful. The K_a of formic acid is 1.7×10^{-4}. Calculate K_b of the formate ion, CHO_2^-.

Solution

The K_a of formic acid is provided, so use Equation 16.10 to determine K_b of CHO_2^-:

$$K_a \times K_b = K_w$$

$$K_b = \frac{K_w}{K_a} = \frac{1.0 \times 10^{-14}}{1.7 \times 10^{-4}} = 5.9 \times 10^{-11}$$

PRACTICE PROBLEM 16.17

Sodium benzoate, $NaC_7H_5O_2$, is used as a preservative in acidic foods such as salad dressing, carbonated drinks, jams, and fruit juices, because in acidic environments it helps prevent bacteria and fungi from reproducing. The benzoate ion, $C_7H_5O_2^-$, is the conjugate base of the benzoic acid, $K_a = 6.3 \times 10^{-5}$. Calculate K_b for the benzoate ion.

Hint: For any conjugate acid–base pair $K_a \times K_b = K_w$ (Equation 16.10), where $K_w = 1.0 \times 10^{-14}$.

Example 16.18

In Example 16.4, you used the K_a values of the following weak oxyacids to predict the relative strengths of their conjugate bases.

Acid	K_a
HClO	4.0×10^{-8}
HBrO	2.8×10^{-9}
HIO	3.2×10^{-11}

This time, use the K_a values to calculate the K_b values for their conjugate bases.

Solution

For any conjugate acid–base pair, $K_a \times K_b = K_w$ (Equation 16.10), where $K_w = 1.0 \times 10^{-14}$.

$$K_b = \frac{K_w}{K_a} = \frac{1.0 \times 10^{-14}}{K_a}$$

Acid	K_a	Conjugate Base	K_b
HClO	4.0×10^{-8}	ClO^-	$\frac{1.0 \times 10^{-14}}{4.0 \times 10^{-8}} = 2.5 \times 10^{-7}$
HBrO	2.8×10^{-9}	BrO^-	$\frac{1.0 \times 10^{-14}}{2.8 \times 10^{-9}} = 3.6 \times 10^{-6}$
HIO	3.2×10^{-11}	IO^-	$\frac{1.0 \times 10^{-14}}{3.2 \times 10^{-11}} = 3.1 \times 10^{-4}$

The calculated K_b values confirm the earlier prediction that the conjugate base strength from strongest to weakest is $IO^- > BrO^- > ClO^-$.

PRACTICE PROBLEM 16.18

In Practice Problem 16.4, you used the K_b values of the following weak bases to predict the relative strengths of their conjugate acids.

Base	K_b
NH_3	1.8×10^{-5}
CH_3NH_2	5.0×10^{-4}
$(CH_3)_2NH$	5.4×10^{-4}

This time, use the K_b values to calculate the K_a values for their conjugate acids.

Hint: Equation 16.10 relates K_a and K_b for any conjugate acid–base pair.

pH OF SALT SOLUTIONS

The pH of a salt can be calculated if you know its concentration and the K_a or K_b for the acidic or basic ions that make up the salt. The calculation follows the same procedure as that of a weak acid or weak base (Section 16.5). In some cases you will need to determine the ionization constant for an ion from the K_a or K_b of its conjugate weak acid or base using $K_a \times K_b = K_w$ (Equation 16.10).

Figure 16.11 is a video demonstration of how to calculate the pH of a salt solution when the salt is the conjugate acid or conjugate base of a weak base or weak acid.

Steve Lemon, Macmillan Learning

FIGURE 16.11 Video Tutorial: pH of Salt Solutions

NOTE: You need to be online to access this video.

This video shows how to calculate the pH of a 0.10 M solution of methylammonium bromide, CH_3NH_3Br, and of a 0.10 M solution of sodium hypochlorite, NaClO.

Example 16.19

Determine the pH of a 1.0 M solution of sodium acetate ($NaC_2H_3O_2$). $K_a = 1.8 \times 10^{-5}$ for acetic acid.

Solution

The acetate ion is the conjugate base of acetic acid (a weak acid), so sodium acetate will hydrolyze water to produce OH^- ions.

$$C_2H_3O_2^-(aq) + H_2O(l) \rightleftharpoons HC_2H_3O_2(aq) + OH^-(aq)$$

The ionization constant K_b can be determined from K_w and K_a for acetic acid (Equation 16.10).

$$K_b = \frac{K_w}{K_a} = \frac{1.0 \times 10^{-14}}{1.8 \times 10^{-5}} = 5.6 \times 10^{-10}$$

Set up an ICE table the same way you would for a weak base.

	$C_2H_3O_2^-$ (aq)	+ H_2O(l) ⇌	$HC_2H_3O_2$ (aq)	+ OH^-(aq)
Initial	1.0	—	0	~0
Change	$-x$	—	$+x$	$+x$
Equilibrium	$1.0 - x$	—	x	x

K_b is small, indicating that the hydrolysis occurs only to a small extent, so assume that x is small compared to 1.0, in which case $1.0 - x \approx 1.0$.

$$K_b = \frac{[HC_2H_3O_2][OH^-]}{[C_2H_3O_2^-]} = 5.6 \times 10^{-10} = \frac{x^2}{1.0 - x} \approx \frac{x^2}{1.0}$$

$$5.6 \times 10^{-10} = \frac{x^2}{1.0}$$

$$x^2 = (1.0)(5.6 \times 10^{-10}) = 5.6 \times 10^{-10}$$

Take the square root of both sides to get $[OH^-]$.

$$x = [OH^-] = [HC_2H_3O_2] = 2.4 \times 10^{-5}\ M$$

Because 2.4×10^{-5} is much less than 1.0, the assumption that x is small compared to 1.0 is valid. Now use $[OH^-]$ in Equation 16.1 to get $[H_3O^+]$, then Equation 16.2 to get the pH.

$$[H_3O^+] = \frac{K_w}{[OH^-]} = \frac{1.0 \times 10^{-14}}{2.4 \times 10^{-5}} = 4.2 \times 10^{-10}$$

$$pH = -\log[H_3O^+] = -\log(4.2 \times 10^{-10}) = 9.37$$

PRACTICE PROBLEM 16.19

Determine the pH of a 1.0 M solution of $(CH_3)_3NHCl$. $K_b = 6.3 \times 10^{-5}$ for trimethylamine, $(CH_3)_3N$.

Hint: $(CH_3)_3NH^+$ is the conjugate acid of $(CH_3)_3N$, a weak base, so it behaves as a weak acid. Begin by determining the ionization constant for $(CH_3)_3NH^+$ using Equation 16.10, then set up an ICE table for the ionization of $(CH_3)_3NH^+$.

SECTION REVIEW

- If the cation or anion in a salt is a weak base or weak acid, the salt will have acidic or basic properties.
- The anion of monoprotic strong acids and the group 1 and 2 cations have no acid–base properties, so salts made up of these ions do not affect the solution pH.
- Some metal cations with high charge and/or small diameters can act as proton donors in solution by hydrolyzing water molecules.
- The K_a and K_b for any conjugate acid–base pair are related by the expression $K_a \times K_b = K_w$.
- The pH for a salt can be calculated in a manner similar to that used to calculate the pH of a weak acid or a weak base, given its concentration and ionization constant.

16.8 Relating Acid Strength to Structure

GOAL

- Predict relative acid strengths based on the structures of acid molecules.

Background Review

Chapter 10 Covalent Bonding: Section 10.5—Polar Bonds and the Bonding Continuum

Some acids are stronger than others, which means they ionize to a greater extent and release H^+ more readily into solution. Moreover, acids such as acetic acid, $HC_2H_3O_2$, have one H atom that is ionizable but other H atoms that are not. The hydrogen atoms that ionize from an acid are sometimes referred to as **labile hydrogen atoms**. Whether an H atom is ionizable and how easily ionizable it is are both related to the structure of the molecule.

BOND STRENGTH

Generally speaking, bond strength and acid strength are inversely related. The stronger the chemical bond is that holds a hydrogen atom to the rest of the molecule, the less likely that bond is to break and form H^+ ions—therefore, the less acidic the compound will be. For example, compare the bond energies in the hydrogen halides to the acidity of those compounds in water (Table 16.5).

As the bond energy between the hydrogen and halide atom increases going from hydroiodic acid, HI, to hydrogen fluoride, HF, indicating a stronger bond between the two atoms, the acid strength gets progressively weaker. Thus, the strength of an acid increases as it becomes easier to break the bond between hydrogen and its neighboring atom.

The relative strength of an acid can often be determined based on the structure of the molecule, even without knowing bond energies. There are two main considerations when comparing the relative acid strength of two similar compounds: the size of the anion in a binary acid and the electronegativity of the environment around the hydrogen atom.

TABLE 16.5 pK_a and Bond Energy for Hydrogen Halides

	HI	HBr	HCl	HF
Bond energy (kJ/mol)	299	366	431	562
Increasing bond strength	→			
pK_a	−9.3	−8.7	−6.3	3.2
Increasing acid strength	←			

ANION SIZE

When hydrogen forms a bond to another nonmetal atom, they share an electron pair by overlapping electron orbitals. In HF, for example, the 1*s* orbital of the hydrogen atom overlaps with the 2*p* orbital of the fluorine atom and the two unpaired electrons, one from each atom, are shared to form a bond. In HI, however, the 1*s* orbital of the hydrogen atom overlaps with the significantly larger 5*p* orbital of the iodine. Because the 5*p* orbital is so much larger than the 1*s*, the extent of overlap between the two orbitals is much less than it was with the 2*p* orbital in HF. This smaller overlap results in a weaker bond. That makes the hydrogen atom in HI more easily ionizable than is the hydrogen in HF. As a result, HI is a stronger acid than HF.

Table 16.6 shows how the increasing size of the anion in a binary acid relates to the increasing acid strength of the molecule. Although HCl, hydrogen bromide, HBr, and HI are all considered strong acids that completely ionize in water, using specialized instrumental techniques it is possible to measure the extremely small trace amounts of molecular acid remaining in solution and determine a K_a for the dissociation of the strong acid. Although the amount of unionized strong acid in solution is immeasurably small for most purposes, these techniques allow scientists to determine that the K_a of HI is about 3 trillion times greater than that of HF.

A similar trend is seen with the group 16 binary hydrogen compounds (i.e., H_2O, H_2S, H_2Se, and H_2Te)—as the anion size increases going down the column, so does the acid strength of the compound.

ELECTRONEGATIVITY

Acid molecules lose ionizable hydrogens as H^+ ions, so if the bond that holds the hydrogen atom to the molecule is highly polar, the hydrogen atom will already have some partial positive character, making it easier to fully ionize. The more polar the bond between hydrogen and its bonding partner, the more easily ionizable the hydrogen atom will be. For example, acetic acid contains four hydrogen atoms, but only one of them is ionizable. Looking at the Lewis structure, it becomes easier to see why.

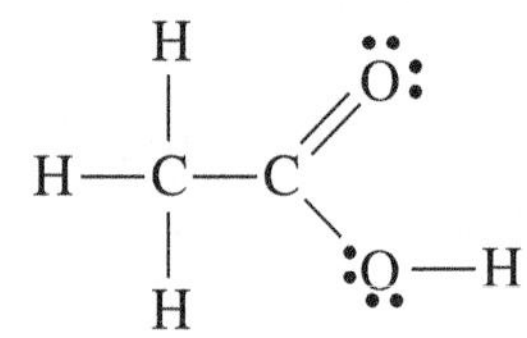

One of those hydrogen atoms is bonded to the highly electronegative oxygen atom, and the other three are bonded to carbon. The hydrogen atoms in nonpolar bonds with the carbon atom are not ionizable hydrogen atoms.

The polarity of the bond between a hydrogen atom and its bonding partner can be influenced by the surrounding atoms. If the surrounding atoms are highly electronegative (Figure 10.7), they draw electron density away from hydrogen's bonding partner, and that atom in turn pulls electrons more strongly from hydrogen. This gives the hydrogen atom a stronger partial positive charge and makes it more easily ionizable. The magnitude of the effect can be seen in Table 16.7 by comparing the strength of acetic acid with the strengths of

TABLE 16.6 pK_a and Anion Size for Hydrogen Halides

	HI	HBr	HCl	HF
Anion size (pm)	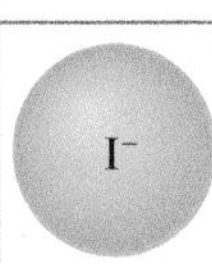 I^- 220	 Br^- 196	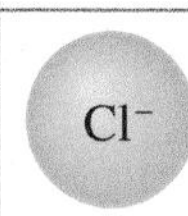 Cl^- 181	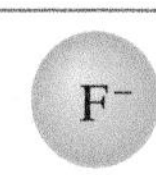 F^- 133
Increasing anion size	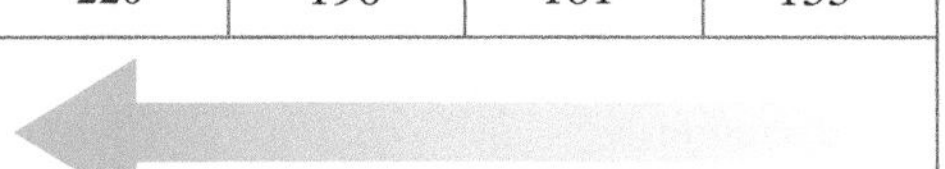			
pK_a	−9.3	−8.7	−6.3	3.2
Increasing acid strength	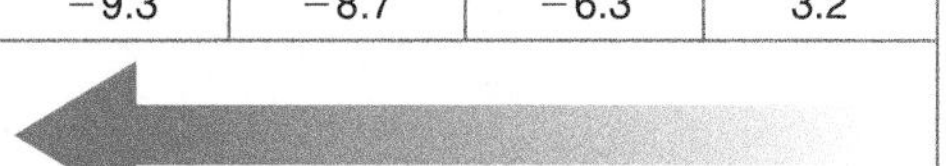			

TABLE 16.7 K_a Values for the Chloroacetic Acid Series

Acid	Structure	K_a
Acetic acid	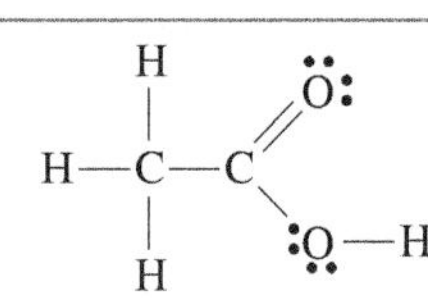	1.8×10^{-5}
Chloroacetic acid	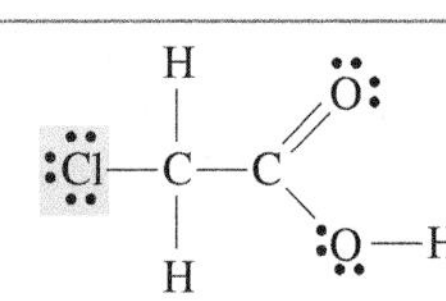	1.4×10^{-3}
Dichloroacetic acid	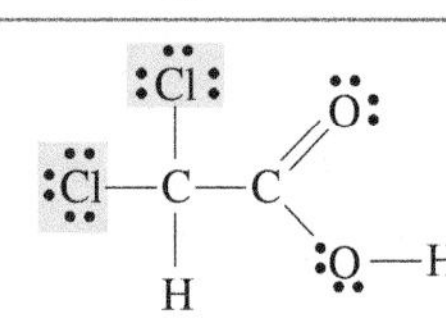	4.5×10^{-2}
Trichloroacetic acid	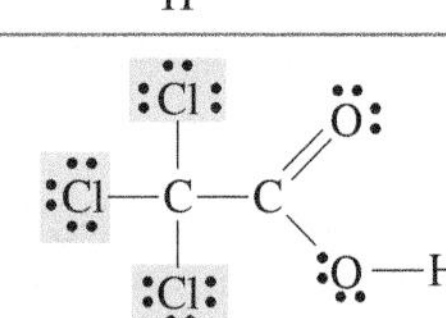	2.2×10^{-1}

the acids that result as each of the three nonionizable hydrogen atoms (electronegativity = 2.1) is replaced one by one with a more highly electronegative chlorine atom (electronegativity = 3.0).

The addition of the first chlorine atom to the molecule increases the strength of the acid by a factor of almost 100, and when the third chlorine atom has been added, the acid is more than 10,000 times stronger than acetic acid. This is because the more electronegative chlorine atoms draw electron density away from the ionizable hydrogen atom, giving it a more positive partial charge within the molecule and making it more easily ionizable.

The same trend is seen with acids that contain varying numbers of oxygen atoms, such as the oxyacids. Acid strength steadily increases going from hypochlorous acid, $HClO$ (weak), to perchloric acid, $HClO_4$ (strong). Similarly, nitrous acid, HNO_2, and sulfurous acid, H_2SO_3, are both weak acids, but the addition of one oxygen atom to each to form nitric acid, HNO_3, and sulfuric acid, H_2SO_4, respectively, produces strong acids.

Even in binary compounds, the electronegativity of the bonding partner affects how easily ionizable the hydrogen atom is. Electronegativity increases as you move to the right in the periodic table (Section 10.3), and this is consistent with NH_3 being a weak base, H_2O being amphiprotic, and HF being a weak acid. That is, this increase in acid strength with increasing electronegativity of the bonded atom is a direct result of the polarity of the bond between hydrogen and the other atom.

Figure 16.12 summarizes the effects of both electronegativity and anion size in binary hydrogen compounds. Going from left to right across a row in the periodic table, the acid strength of binary hydrogen compounds increases with increasing electronegativity of the other atom. Going down a column in the periodic table, the acid strength of binary hydrogen compounds increases with increasing anion size.

Although the polarity of the hydrogen bond in an oxyacid is a good indicator of acid strength, there are sometimes unexpected additional considerations that can affect the extent of ionization of an acid. For example, phosphorous acid, H_3PO_3, is stronger than phosphoric acid, H_3PO_4, even though H_3PO_4 has one more oxygen atom than H_3PO_3. In the case of H_3PO_3, the $H_2PO_3^-$ anion derives additional stability from resonance structures, resulting in greater ionization. In general, however, bond polarity is a good predictor of acid strength.

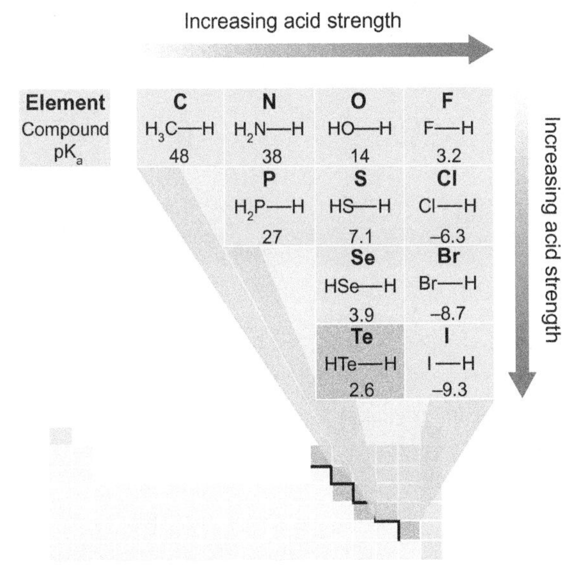

FIGURE 16.12 Effect of Electronegativity and Anion Size on Binary Acid Strength

Moving left to right across a row in the periodic table, the acid strength of binary hydrogen compounds increases with increasing electronegativity of the other atom. This is because an increasingly polar bond makes H easier to ionize. Moving down a column in the periodic table, the acid strength of binary hydrogen compounds increases with increasing anion size. This is because a longer bond is generally a weaker bond, which is easier to ionize.

Example 16.20

Rank the following acids from weakest to strongest.

a. HIO_4
b. HIO_3
c. HIO_2
d. HIO

Solution

In general, the strength of the acid increases as the bond to the ionizable hydrogen becomes more polar, and that is the case here. Adding more oxygen atoms to the central iodine atom draws electron density away from the hydrogen atom, leading to a more highly polarized bond and a stronger acid. The acid strength is $HIO < HIO_2 < HIO_3 < HIO_4$.

PRACTICE PROBLEM 16.20

Rank the following acids from weakest to strongest.

a. trifluoroacetic acid, $HC_2F_3O_2$
b. bromoacetic acid, $HC_2BrH_2O_2$
c. acetic acid, $HC_2H_3O_2$
d. trichloroacetic acid, $HC_2Cl_3O_2$

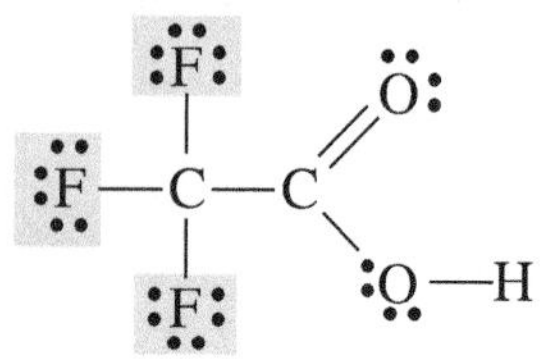

(a)

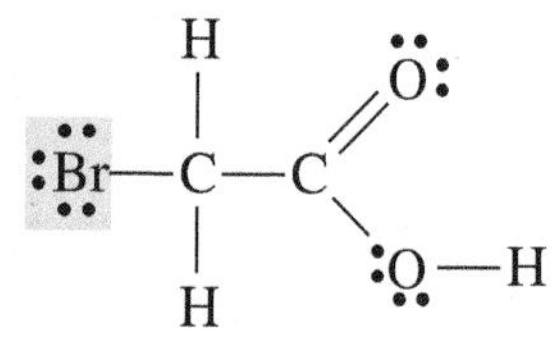

(b)

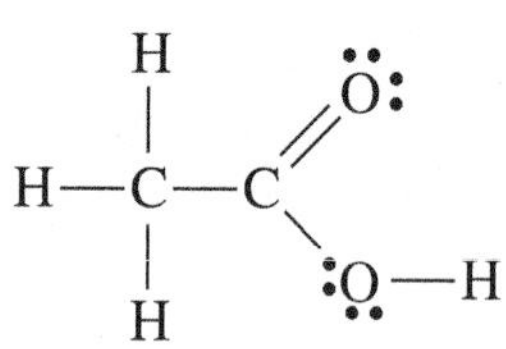

(c)

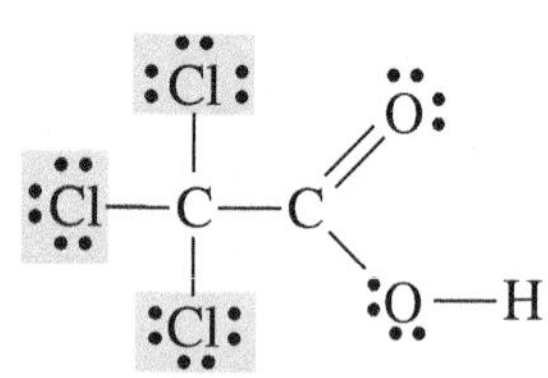

(d)

Hint: This group of acids includes acetic acid and three acids where one or more nonionizable hydrogen atoms have been replaced by a more electronegative atom (Figure 10.7). The strength of the acid should increase as the electronegativity of the replacement atoms increases.

When an acid contains oxygen, the ionizable hydrogen atoms are always bonded directly to oxygen atoms. Any hydrogen atom in an oxyacid that is *not* bonded to an oxygen atom is a nonionizable hydrogen atom. Knowing this, you can determine from the structure alone whether an oxyacid is monoprotic, diprotic, or triprotic.

Example 16.21

How many ionizable hydrogen atoms does each of the following acids have?

a. H_3PO_4
b. H_3PO_3
c. $H_4P_2O_5$

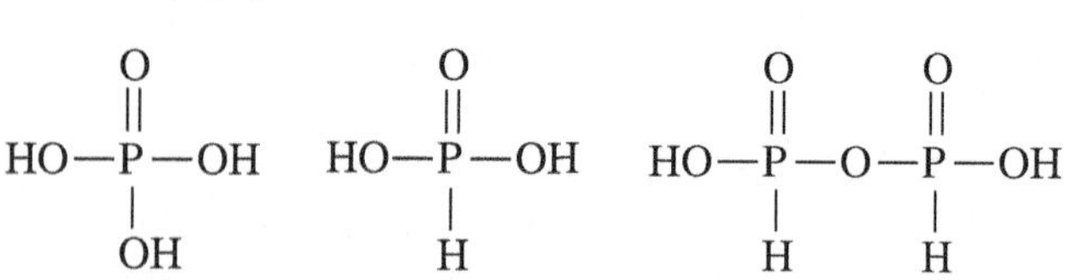

(a) (b) (c)

Solution

The hydrogen atoms that are bonded to oxygen atoms are ionizable, so

a. H_3PO_4 has three.
b. H_3PO_3 has two.
c. $H_4P_2O_5$ has two.

PRACTICE PROBLEM 16.21

How many ionizable hydrogen atoms does each of the following acids have?

a. H_3PO_2
b. H_2SO_2
c. H_2SO

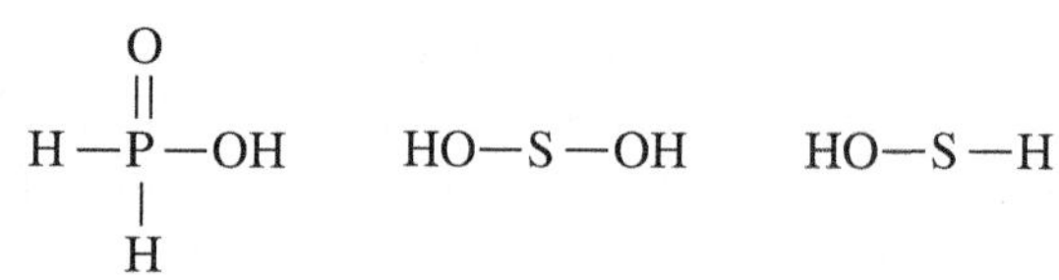

(a) (b) (c)

Hint: Hydrogen atoms that are bonded to oxygen atoms are ionizable.

SECTION REVIEW

- In binary hydrogen compounds, acid strength increases with both anion size and the electronegativity of the atom bonded to hydrogen.
- A hydrogen atom is more easily ionized as the polarity of its bond to the rest of the acid molecule increases.
- The bond to an ionizable hydrogen in an acid is made more polar by increasing the number of highly electronegative atoms near the hydrogen atom in the molecule.
- Sometimes unique situations arise that result in an acid being weaker or stronger than would be predicted based on bond polarities alone, but bond polarity is usually a reliable indicator of relative acid strength.
- In an acid that contains oxygen, all of the ionizable hydrogen atoms are bonded to oxygen atoms, and all hydrogen atoms that are bonded to oxygen atoms are ionizable.

16.9 Lewis Acids and Bases

GOAL

- Extend the definitions of acids and bases to include reactions that do not involve H^+.

Background Review

Chapter 10 Covalent Bonding: Section 10.2—Lewis Structures; Section 10.4—Exceptions to the Octet Rule

A Brønsted base is a proton acceptor because it has a nonbonding pair of electrons.

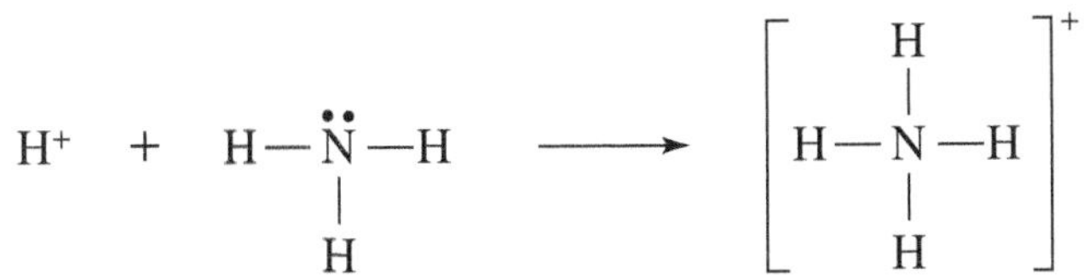

G. N. Lewis used this fact to redefine acids and bases. A **Lewis base** is an **electron pair donor**, and a **Lewis acid** is an **electron pair acceptor**. Just as all Arrhenius acids (Section 16.1) are also Brønsted acids (Section 16.2), all Brønsted acids are also Lewis acids, but the new definition again broadens the scope of what can be considered an acid because many species besides H^+ can accept an electron pair. All Lewis bases are also Brønsted bases, because Brønsted bases must have an available electron pair so that they can accept a proton.

In addition to the wider array of compounds that can be considered acids under the Lewis definition, there are two important differences between the **Lewis theory** of acid–base chemistry and the Brønsted theory. A Brønsted acid is a proton donor such as HCl, but a Lewis acid is the donated proton itself, rather than the molecule it came from. Also, the reaction of a Brønsted acid and a Brønsted base produces a salt and water, but the reaction of a Lewis acid and a Lewis base forms a **Lewis adduct**, which is a combination of the acid and base as a single compound (Figure 16.13). Lewis acid–base chemistry is therefore a type of synthesis reaction (Section 4.2).

Just as Arrhenius and Brønsted acids and bases have different strengths, so too do Lewis acids and bases. For example, both ammonia, NH_3, and nitrogen gas, N_2, have nonbonding electron pairs that can be donated, but the nonbonding pairs in N_2 are held much more tightly to the molecule and are much less likely to be shared with the electron pair acceptor. Because N_2 is such an extremely weak Lewis base and forms adducts only in very rare cases, some texts do not consider N_2 to be a Lewis base at all, even though it has nonbonding electron pairs.

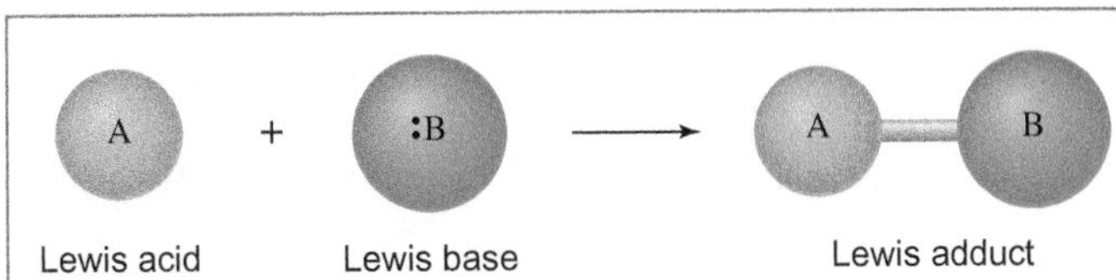

FIGURE 16.13 Formation of an Adduct

The reactants are a Lewis acid, which has an unfilled outer shell, and a Lewis base, which has a lone pair in its outer shell. The product is a single compound called an adduct, which is made up of the Lewis acid and Lewis base covalently bonded together.

Lewis acids must be able to accept an electron pair, so Lewis acids must have an incomplete octet (or duet in the case of H^+) in their valence shell. Any species with an incomplete outer shell can act as a Lewis acid. For example, the boron atom in boron trifluoride, BF_3, has only six electrons in its outer shell and can act as an electron pair acceptor. Ammonia has a nonbonding electron pair on the central nitrogen atom and can act as an electron pair donor. The reaction of BF_3 with NH_3 is a Lewis acid–base reaction that results in the formation of an adduct, BF_3NH_3.

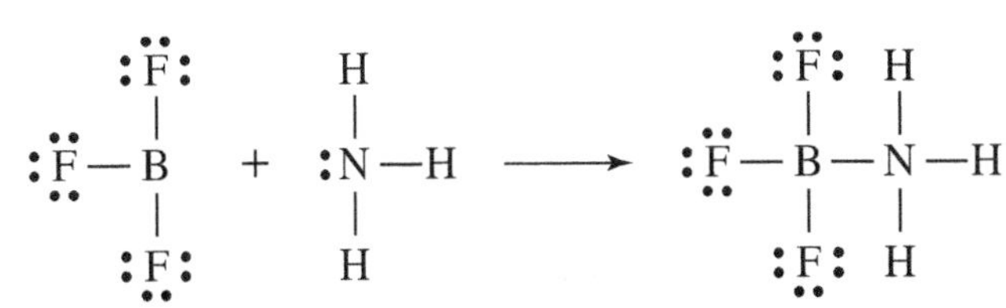

In a Lewis adduct, a covalent bond forms in which both shared electrons come from the same atom. This type of bond is called a **coordinate covalent bond**. These compounds can be solid, liquid, gas, or aqueous, so Lewis acid–base reactions can take place in any physical phase. The complex ions discussed in Section 16.7 are all Lewis acid–base adducts.

Al^{3+} is a weak Brønsted acid (Section 16.7). Cations like Al^{3+} can act as electron pair acceptors, which make them Lewis acids as well. The reaction of the Lewis acid Al^{3+} with the Lewis base H_2O forms the adduct $Al(H_2O)_6{}^{3+}$:

$$Al^{3+}(aq) + 6\,H_2O(l) \rightarrow Al(H_2O)_6{}^{3+}(aq)$$

Compounds containing double bonds can often shift a bonding pair of electrons to one atom as a nonbonding pair, creating an unfilled outer electron shell that can then accept an electron pair. For example, carbon dioxide, CO_2 is a Brønsted acid because when CO_2 dissolves in water a reaction occurs that releases H^+ into solution:

$$CO_2(g) + H_2O(l) \rightarrow H_2CO_3(aq)$$
$$H_2CO_3(aq) \rightarrow H^+(aq) + HCO_3{}^-(aq)$$

CO_2 is also a Lewis acid. Each atom in CO_2 has a filled outer shell of electrons, but if a bonding pair of electrons is moved to one of the oxygen atoms, the central carbon is left with only six electrons in its outer shell.

The central atom in CO_2 can now accept an electron pair, such as when it reacts with water (a Lewis base) to form H_2CO_3 (the adduct).

Example 16.22

Classify each of the following as a Lewis acid, a Lewis base, or neither.

a. Fe^{3+}
b. CH_4
c. Cl^-
d. NH_3
e. H_2
f. Fe

Solution

a. Fe^{3+} is a Lewis acid because metal cations are electron pair acceptors.
b. CH_4 is neither a Lewis base nor a Lewis acid because all of its electrons are in single bonds and each atom has a filled outer shell, so CH_4 can neither donate nor accept an electron pair.
c. Cl^- is a Lewis base because monoatomic anions always have nonbonding electron pairs to donate.
d. NH_3 is a Lewis base because it has a nonbonding electron pair on the central nitrogen that it can donate.
e. H_2 is neither a Lewis base nor a Lewis acid because it can neither accept nor donate an electron pair.
f. Fe is neither a Lewis base nor a Lewis acid because neutral metal atoms do not donate or accept electron pairs to form covalent bonds.

PRACTICE PROBLEM 16.22

Identify the Lewis acid and Lewis base in each of the following reactions.

a. $Cu^{2+} + 6\,CN^- \rightarrow Cu(CN)_6{}^{4-}$
b. $H_2O + CH_3{}^+ \rightarrow CH_3OH + H^+$

Hint: Lewis bases have a nonbonding electron pair that can be donated to form a covalent bond. Lewis acids have an unfilled outer electron shell and can accept an electron pair.

SECTION REVIEW

- A Lewis acid is a species that is able to accept an electron pair from another chemical species, thus forming a coordinate covalent bond.
- A Lewis base is a species that is able to donate a nonbonding pair of electrons to another chemical species, thus forming a coordinate covalent bond.
- A Lewis acid–base reaction occurs when a Lewis base donates a pair of electrons to a Lewis acid, creating a coordinate covalent bond in the process. The product of the reaction is called a Lewis adduct.
- All Brønsted bases are also Lewis bases. Brønsted acids must be proton donors, but Lewis acids do not have to be able to donate a proton, so Lewis acids include many species that are not Brønsted acids.

Putting It Together

The example problems in earlier sections of this chapter focus on just the new skills acquired in that section, but homework and exam questions in chemistry often require more than just one skill at a time. In fact, you will likely be expected to apply knowledge from across the entire chapter, or even multiple chapters, in a single problem. This final example problem is meant to help you prepare for these types of multi-concept questions. Additional examples can be found in the end-of-chapter exercises.

Example 16.23

Equal volumes of 0.80 M acetic acid and 0.80 M NaOH are mixed together.

a. What is the initial pH of the NaOH solution?
b. What is the initial pH of the acetic acid solution?
c. What is the final pH after the two solutions have been mixed?
d. When the two solutions are mixed, the acetic acid is completely neutralized. Is the final solution pH equal to 7? If not, why not?

Solution

a. As a strong base, NaOH completely dissociates to produce 0.80 M OH^-.

$$[H_3O^+][OH^-] = K_w = 1.0 \times 10^{-14}$$

$$[H_3O^+] = \frac{1.0 \times 10^{-14}}{[OH^-]} = \frac{1.0 \times 10^{-14}}{[0.80]} = 1.25 \times 10^{-14}\text{M}$$

$$\text{pH} = -\log[H_3O^+] = -\log(1.25 \times 10^{-14}) = 13.90$$

Alternatively, you could calculate pOH from the OH^- concentration and then calculate pH from that.

$$\text{pOH} = -\log[OH^-] = -\log(0.80) = 0.097$$
$$\text{pH} = 14.00 - \text{pOH} = 14.00 - 0.097 = 13.90$$

b. Acetic acid is a weak acid ($K_a = 1.8 \times 10^{-5}$), so set up an ICE table.

	$HC_2H_3O_2$ (aq)	+ $H_2O(l)$ $\rightleftharpoons$	H_3O^+ (aq) +	$C_2H_3O_2^-$ (aq)
Initial	0.80	—	~0	0
Change	$-x$	—	$+x$	$+x$
Equilibrium	$0.80 - x$	—	x	x

Assume that x is small compared to 0.80, so $0.80 - x \approx 0.80$.

$$K_a = \frac{[H_3O^+][C_2H_3O_2^-]}{[HC_2H_3O_2]} = \frac{x^2}{(0.80 - x)} \approx \frac{x^2}{0.80}$$
$$= 1.8 \times 10^{-5}$$
$$x^2 = (0.80)(1.8 \times 10^{-5}) = 1.4 \times 10^{-5}$$
$$x = [H_3O^+] = 3.8 \times 10^{-3}\text{ M}$$

This is small compared to 0.80, so the assumption was valid.

$$\text{pH} = -\log[H_3O^+] = -\log(3.8 \times 10^{-3}) = 2.43$$

c. An acid and a base react completely to form a salt.

$$HC_2H_3O_2(aq) + NaOH(aq) \rightarrow NaC_2H_3O_2(aq) + H_2O(l)$$

The stoichiometry of the reaction is 1:1, and equal volumes and equal concentrations of acid and base were mixed, so there is no limiting reactant. The number of moles of each product formed is equal to the initial number of moles of each reactant.

The total volume of the solution is now twice what it was initially, which halves the concentrations. The solution contains no acetic acid, no NaOH, and 0.80 M/2 = 0.40 M $NaC_2H_3O_2$. The acetate ion is the conjugate base of acetic acid, a weak acid, so it will hydrolyze water, producing OH^- ions:

$$C_2H_3O_2^-(aq) + H_2O(l) \rightleftharpoons HC_2H_3O_2(aq) + OH^-(aq)$$

The equilibrium constant for this reaction, K_b, can be determined from K_a for the conjugate acid and K_w for water, according to Equation 16.10.

$$K_b = \frac{K_w}{K_a} = \frac{1.0 \times 10^{-14}}{1.8 \times 10^{-5}} = 5.6 \times 10^{-10}$$

	$C_2H_3O_2^-$ (aq)	+ $H_2O(l)$ $\rightleftharpoons$	$HC_2H_3O_2$ (aq)	+ OH^- (aq)
Initial	0.40	—	0	~0
Change	$-x$	—	$+x$	$+x$
Equilibrium	$0.40 - x$	—	x	x

K_b is very small, indicating that the hydrolysis occurs only to a small extent, so assume that x is small compared to 0.40, in which case $0.40 - x \approx 0.40$.

$$K_b = \frac{[HC_2H_3O_2][OH^-]}{[C_2H_3O_2^-]} = \frac{x^2}{(0.40 - x)} \approx \frac{x^2}{0.40}$$
$$5.6 \times 10^{-10} = \frac{x^2}{0.40}$$
$$x^2 = (0.40)(5.6 \times 10^{-10}) = 2.2 \times 10^{-10}$$

Taking the square root of both sides, $x = [OH^-] = [HC_2H_3O_2] = 1.5 \times 10^{-5}\text{ M}$

$$\text{pOH} = -\log(1.5 \times 10^{-5}) = 4.82$$
$$\text{pH} = 14.00 - \text{pOH} = 14.00 - 4.82 = 9.18$$

d. The final pH of the neutralized weak acid solution is *not* equal to 7, because acetate ion (the conjugate base of acetic acid) is the product when acetic acid is neutralized, and acetate ion hydrolyzes water, which raises the pH above 7.

PRACTICE PROBLEM 16.23

Hydrazine (N_2H_4) is a weak base with $K_b = 1.3 \times 10^{-6}$. Equal volumes of 0.080 M hydrazine and 0.080 M HCl are mixed together.

a. What is the initial pH of the HCl solution?
b. What is the initial pH of the hydrazine solution?
c. What is the final pH after the two solutions have been mixed?
d. When the two solutions are mixed, the weak base hydrazine is completely neutralized. Is the final solution pH equal to 7? If not, why not?

Hint: In part (a), use the concentration of the strong acid to determine $[H_3O^+]$. For the weak acid in part (b), use the K_b expression for a weak base, with 0.080 M as the initial concentration of N_2H_4. In part (c), calculate K_a for $N_2H_5^+$ from Equation 16.10. For part (d), look at the products of the neutralization reaction and determine whether the products of the reaction themselves have acid–base properties.

Key Terms, Symbols, and Equations

KEY TERMS

acid ionization constant, K_a (16.5): The equilibrium constant that describes the extent of ionization of a weak acid in water.

acid strength (16.2): The tendency for a certain percentage of acid molecules to ionize in water; the higher the acid strength, the higher the percentage of ionization.

acidic (16.3): A solution in which the H_3O^+ concentration is greater than the OH^- concentration.

amphiprotic (16.2): The ability of a molecule or ion to act as both a proton donor and a proton acceptor. This definition is specific to Brønsted acids and bases.

amphoteric (16.2): The ability of a molecule or ion to act as an acid or as a base. This is a general term that is used in any acid–base theory.

Arrhenius acid (16.1): A compound that releases H^+ into solution.

Arrhenius base (16.1): A compound that releases OH^- into solution.

Arrhenius theory (16.1): The acid–base theory that defines acids as compounds that increase the H^+ concentration when dissolved in water, and bases as compounds that increase the OH^- concentration when dissolved in water.

autoionization (16.3): A reaction of two molecules of a single substance to produce both positive and negative ions; for example, water can autoionize to turn two H_2O molecules into one H_3O^+ and one OH^-.

base ionization constant, K_b (16.5): The equilibrium constant that describes the extent of ionization of a weak base in water.

base strength (16.2): The tendency for a certain percentage of molecules of a base to ionize in water; the higher the base strength, the greater the percent ionization.

basic (16.3): A solution in which the OH^- concentration is greater than the H_3O^+ concentration.

Brønsted acid (16.2): A substance that can donate H^+ to another substance.

Brønsted base (16.2): A substance that can accept H^+ from another substance.

Brønsted–Lowry theory (16.2): A theory of acids and bases based on the exchange of H^+ ions between two species. In Brønsted–Lowry theory, anytime an acid is in solution, by definition there must also be a base, and vice versa.

conjugate acid (16.2): The Brønsted weak acid that results from the gain of a proton by a weak base.

conjugate acid–base pair (16.2): A Brønsted weak acid and weak base that are related by the gain or loss of one proton.

conjugate base (16.2): The Brønsted weak base that results from the loss of a proton by a weak acid.

coordinate covalent bond (16.9): A covalent bond in which both shared electrons come from the same atom.

counterion (16.1): The ion that accompanies another ion of opposite charge in an ionic compound.

dibasic (16.1): Describes an Arrhenius strong base, such as $Ba(OH)_2$, that releases two OH^- ions per formula unit.

diprotic acid (16.6): An acid with two ionizable hydrogen atoms.

electron pair acceptor (16.9): A Lewis acid.

electron pair donor (16.9): A Lewis base.

hydrolysis (16.1): The breaking up of water into H^+ and OH^-. One of these ions ends up bonded to the species doing the hydrolysis, and the other ion is released into solution, potentially changing the pH of the solution.

hydronium ion (16.1): H_3O^+, a water molecule that has accepted an H^+. In this text *hydronium ion* is used synonymously with *hydrogen ion.*

ionization constant (16.5): A generic term that can mean either an acid ionization constant (K_a) or a base ionization constant (K_b).

labile hydrogen atom (16.8): An ionizable hydrogen atom on an acid.

Lewis acid (16.9): In Lewis acid–base theory, a species that does not have a filled outer valence electron shell and is capable of forming a coordinate covalent bond by accepting an electron pair from an atom in another substance. Also called an electron pair acceptor.

Lewis adduct (16.9): The product formed in a Lewis acid–base reaction in which the acid and base are bonded together via a coordinate covalent bond.

Lewis base (16.9): In Lewis acid–base theory, a species that has a nonbonding electron pair in its outer valence shell and is capable of forming a coordinate covalent bond by sharing its electron pair with an atom in another substance. Also called an electron pair donor.

Lewis theory (16.9): An expanded theory of acid–base chemistry in which an acid is a substance that accepts an electron pair from a base, forming a Lewis adduct as the product.

litmus (16.4): An acid–base indicator that is pink in acidic solution and blue in basic solution. Litmus paper is often used to make a quick assessment of whether a solution is acidic or basic.

neutral solution (16.3): A solution in which $[H_3O^+] = [OH^-]$. A neutral solution is neither acidic nor basic.

pH paper (16.4): Paper that has been infused with universal indicator so that it can be used to make quick assessments of the approximate pH of a solution. pH paper provides more information about the pH of a solution than litmus paper.

pH scale (16.4): A scale of acidity that typically goes from 1 to 14, with 7 indicating a neutral solution. $pH < 7$ indicates an acidic solution, and $pH > 7$ indicates a basic solution. Mathematically equal to the negative logarithm of the hydrogen ion concentration.

polyprotic acid (16.6): An acid that has more than one ionizable proton per molecule.

proton (16.1): In the context of acid–base chemistry, a proton refers only to a hydrogen atom that has been stripped of its electron, and not to any of the protons in the nucleus of a larger atom.

proton acceptor (16.2): A Brønsted base.

proton donor (16.2): A Brønsted acid.

triprotic acid (16.6): An acid with three ionizable hydrogen atoms.

universal indicator (16.4): A mixture of acid–base indicators that results in a different color for each pH from 1 to 14 and can therefore be used to provide a rough estimate of the pH of a solution.

water ionization constant, K_w (16.3): The equilibrium constant describing the autoionization of water into H_3O^+ and OH^-.

SYMBOLS AND ABBREVIATIONS

K_a (acid ionization constant) (16.5)

K_{a1} (first ionization constant of a polyprotic acid) (16.6)

K_{a2} (second ionization constant of a polyprotic acid) (16.6)

K_{a3} (third ionization constant of a polyprotic acid) (16.6)

K_b (base ionization constant) (16.5)

K_w (water ionization constant) (16.3)

p ($-\log_{10}$ of) (16.4)

EQUATIONS

$K_w = [H_3O^+][OH^-] = 1.0 \times 10^{-14}$ (at 25°C) (16.1)

$pH = -\log[H^+] = -\log[H_3O^+]$ (16.2)

$[H_3O^+] = 10^{-pH}$ (16.3)

$pOH = -\log[OH^-]$ (16.4)

$pH + pOH = 14.00$ (at 25°C) (16.5)

$$K_a = \frac{[H^+][A^-]}{[HA]} \quad (16.6)$$

$$K_a = \frac{[H_3O^+][A^-]}{[HA]} \quad (16.7)$$

$$K_b = \frac{[BH^+][OH^-]}{[B]} \quad (16.8)$$

$K_a = 10^{-pKa}$ (16.9)

$K_a \times K_b = K_w$ (16.10)

Chapter Summary

The earliest definitions of acid and base were offered by Arrhenius and were based simply on whether a compound increased the H^+ or OH^- concentration when dissolved in water. Strong acids were compounds that ionized completely into ions, so for a monoprotic strong acid, the resulting H^+ concentration was equal to the acid concentration. Strong bases were metal hydroxides that dissociated completely into a metal cation and OH^-. The reaction of a strong acid with a strong base is a double-displacement reaction that produces a soluble salt and water, so the net ionic equation for any strong acid–strong base reaction is $H^+ + OH^- \rightarrow H_2O$. H^+ does not exist freely in solution but is instead bonded to a water molecule to form the hydronium ion (H_3O^+), but for simplicity and convenience H_3O^+ is often written as H^+ (hydrogen ion), and those terms are used synonymously in this text (Section 16.1).

The Brønsted–Lowry theory of acids and bases redefines acids as proton (H^+) donors and bases as proton acceptors. When a weak acid molecule donates a proton, the remaining portion becomes capable of accepting a proton, and is therefore a weak base, known as the conjugate base of the acid. Every weak acid and base is part of a conjugate weak acid–base pair. The stronger the weak acid is, the weaker its conjugate base, and vice versa. A compound that can act as either a proton donor or a proton acceptor is called amphoteric or amphiprotic. The Brønsted definitions of acid and base are the ones most often used, and unless otherwise indicated, *acid* should be interpreted as a proton donor and *base* as a proton acceptor (Section 16.2).

Water is amphiprotic and can act as an acid and a base in the same reaction, known as the autoionization of water: $2\,H_2O(l) \rightleftharpoons H_3O^+(aq) + OH^-(aq)$. This ionization is governed by the equilibrium $K_w = [H_3O^+][OH^-] = 1.0 \times 10^{-14}$. The relative strengths of a weak acid and its conjugate base are also linked by K_w: $K_a \times K_b = K_w$ (Section 16.3).

Because the H_3O^+ concentration can vary over a wide range, H_3O^+ concentrations are more conveniently written as the pH, which is the negative logarithm of the H_3O^+ concentration. In water at 25°C, pH varies over a range of about 1 to 14. A pH of 7 means the H_3O^+ and OH^- concentrations are equal, and the solution is neutral. A pH below 7 means the solution is acidic ($[H_3O^+] > [OH^-]$), and a pH above 7 means the solution is basic ($[OH^-] > [H_3O^+]$) (Section 16.4).

Weak acids and bases are those that ionize only partially in water, so the H_3O^+ and OH^- concentrations are typically much less than the concentration of the actual acid or base itself. Weak acids and bases ionize according to an equilibrium relationship between the ions and the acid or base. The equilibrium is governed by an ionization constant—namely, K_a for weak acids and K_b for weak bases. The larger the ionization constant, the greater the extent of ionization, and therefore the stronger the weak acid or base (Section 16.5).

Polyprotic acids are acids that have more than one ionizable hydrogen atom. The ionizable hydrogen atoms are released in a stepwise fashion, not all at once. The first ionization always occurs to a greater extent than the second, and if there is a third ionization, it occurs to a lesser extent than the second. The subsequent ionizations are decreased, in part because the most easily ionizable H^+ always comes off first, so any subsequent H^+ ions that are released are necessarily more difficult to ionize, and in part by the presence of H^+ in solution from the prior ionizations (Section 16.6).

Many soluble salts will change the pH of a solution, and this can be explained by considering the acid–base properties of the cation and anion that make up the salt. If the cation in a salt is a group 1 or 2 metal and the anion is the anion of a strong acid, neither the cation nor the anion will have acid–base properties, and a solution of that salt will remain neutral. If the anion in a salt is the anion of a weak acid, the anion will be a weak base and will therefore drive the pH up. The cation can have acidic properties, such as NH_4^+, which is the conjugate acid of the weak base ammonia, or small, dense metal ions such as Al^{3+}, which can hydrolyze water to produce H_3O^+ ions (Section 16.7).

The strength of an acid is related to its molecular structure. In general, the more polar the bond that holds an H atom to the molecule, the more easily ionizable that H atom will be and the stronger the acid will be. This is why acid strength almost always increases in an oxyacid sequence as more oxygens are added to the acid. A hydrogen atom that is surrounded by more electronegative atoms in an acid molecule will tend to be more easily ionized in water, and a hydrogen atom that is part of a nonpolar covalent bond will not be ionizable in water at all (Section 16.8).

Lewis acid–base theory redefined acids and bases and broadened the scope of acid–base chemistry in a number of ways. Rather than focus on the H^+ ion that is exchanged in a Brønsted acid–base reaction, Lewis focused on the nonbonding electron pair that is present on the base that allows it to accept the proton. Lewis defined a base as an electron pair donor and an acid as an electron pair acceptor. In Lewis acid–base theory, H^+ is no longer required to play any role at all, so a much wider range of reactions can be regarded as acid–base reactions. In addition, the product of a Lewis acid–base reaction is an adduct formed by a bond between the acid and the base. Lewis acid–base reactions are therefore synthesis reactions that always form one product from two or more reactants (Section 16.9).

END OF CHAPTER QUESTIONS

16.1 Ionization Reactions of Acids and Bases

1. Which of the following are weak acids and which are strong acids?
   a. HNO_3
   b. H_2S
   c. H_2SO_3
   d. H_2SO_4

2. Which of the following are weak acids and which are strong acids?
   a. H_3PO_4
   b. HBr
   c. HIO
   d. HI

3. Write the ionization reaction for each of these acids.
   a. $HClO_4$
   b. $HClO_2$

4. Write the ionization reaction for each of these acids.
   a. HClO
   b. HCl

5. Write the ionization reaction for each of these bases.
   a. $Ba(OH)_2$
   b. NH_3

6. Write the ionization reaction for each of these bases.
   a. KOH
   b. CH_3NH_2

7. Which ions or molecules are 0.1 M after 0.100 mol of each of the following is dissolved in enough water to make 1.00 L of solution?
   a. HNO_2
   b. $NaNO_3$
   c. HClO
   d. NaClO

8. Which ions or molecules are 0.1 M or greater after 0.100 mol of each of the following is dissolved in enough water to make 1.00 L of solution?
   a. $Mg(ClO_2)_2$
   b. HNO_2
   c. $KClO_2$
   d. $(NH_4)_2SO_4$
   e. NH_3

16.2 Brønsted–Lowry Theory

9. Classify each species in each reaction as a Brønsted acid or Brønsted base, and identify the conjugate pairs.
   a. $HCN(aq) + H_2O(l) \rightleftharpoons CN^-(aq) + H_3O^+(aq)$
   b. $NH_4^+(aq) + OH^-(aq) \rightleftharpoons NH_3(aq) + H_2O(l)$

10. Classify each species in each reaction as a Brønsted acid or Brønsted base, and identify the conjugate pairs.
    a. $HNO_2(aq) + H_2O(l) \rightleftharpoons NO_2^-(aq) + H_3O^+(aq)$
    b. $C_5H_5N(aq) + H_2O(l) \rightleftharpoons C_5H_5NH^+(aq) + OH^-(aq)$

11. Classify each species in each reaction as a Brønsted acid or Brønsted base, and identify the conjugate pairs.
   a. $H_3PO_4(aq) + OH^-(aq) \rightleftharpoons H_2PO_4^- + H_2O(l)$
   b. $H_2PO_4^-(aq) + OH^-(aq) \rightleftharpoons HPO_4^{2-}(aq) + H_2O(l)$
   c. $HPO_4^{2-}(aq) + OH^-(aq) \rightleftharpoons PO_4^{3-}(aq) + H_2O(l)$

12. Classify each species in each reaction as a Brønsted acid or Brønsted base, and identify the conjugate pairs.
   a. $SO_3^{2-}(aq) + H_2O(l) \rightleftharpoons HSO_3^-(aq) + OH^-(aq)$
   b. $NH_4^+(aq) + H_2O(l) \rightleftharpoons NH_3(aq) + H_3O^+(aq)$

13. Classify each species in each reaction as a Brønsted acid or Brønsted base, and identify the conjugate pairs.
   a. $HSO_3^-(aq) + H_3O^+(aq) \rightleftharpoons H_2SO_3(aq) + H_2O(l)$
   b. $HSO_3^-(aq) + OH^-(aq) \rightleftharpoons SO_3^{2-}(aq) + H_2O(l)$

14. Write the formula for the conjugate base of each of the following.
   a. HNO_2
   b. H_2SO_3
   c. H_2SO_4

15. Write the formula for the conjugate base of each of the following.
   a. $HClO_2$
   b. H_3O^+
   c. NH_4^+

16. Write the formula for the conjugate acid of each of the following.
   a. CH_3NH_2
   b. PO_4^{3-}
   c. CN^-
   d. OH^-
   e. NO_2^-

17. Write the formula for the conjugate acid of each of the following.
   a. CO_3^{2-}
   b. ClO_2^-
   c. NO_3^-
   d. BrO^-

18. Write formulas for the conjugate acid and the conjugate base of each of the following.
   a. H_2O
   b. HSO_3^-

19. Write formulas for the conjugate acid and the conjugate base of each of the following.
   a. HPO_4^{2-}
   b. $H_2PO_4^-$

16.3 Autoionization of Water

20. Write the equation for the autoionization of water.

21. What is the symbol for the equilibrium constant for the autoionization of water, and what is its value at 25°C?

22. Determine $[H_3O^+]$ at 25°C for an aqueous solution with
   a. $[OH^-] = 2.4 \times 10^{-9}$ M.
   b. $[OH^-] = 1.77 \times 10^{-7}$ M.
   c. $[OH^-] = 6.94 \times 10^{-3}$ M.

23. Determine $[OH^-]$ at 25°C for an aqueous solution with
   a. $[H_3O^+] = 4.68 \times 10^{-11}$ M.
   b. $[H_3O^+] = 3.15 \times 10^{-3}$ M.
   c. $[H_3O^+] = 6.05 \times 10^{-4}$ M.

24. Classify each solution in problem 22 as acidic, basic, or neutral.

25. Classify each solution in problem 23 as acidic, basic, or neutral.

26. At some temperature other than 25°C, the concentrations of $[H_3O^+]$ and $[OH^-]$ in pure water are each 1.8×10^{-7} M. What is the value of K_w at this temperature?

27. At some temperature other than 25°C, $K_w = 1.14 \times 10^{-14}$. What are the concentrations of $[H_3O^+]$ and $[OH^-]$ in pure water at this temperature?

16.4 pH Calculations

28. Calculate the pH of a solution having each of the following hydronium ion concentrations.
   a. 4.56×10^{-4} M
   b. 3.33×10^{-9} M
   c. 1.00 M

29. Calculate the pH of a solution having each of the following hydronium ion concentrations.
   a. 1.29×10^{-6} M
   b. 7×10^{-12} M
   c. 2.00 M

30. Classify the following solutions as acidic, basic, or neutral at 25°C.
   a. pH = 13.00
   b. $[H_3O^+] = 1.0 \times 10^{-4}$ M
   c. pOH = 8.00
   d. $[OH^-] = 1.0 \times 10^{-7}$ M

31. Classify the following solutions as acidic, basic, or neutral at 25°C.
   a. pH = 7.00
   b. $[H_3O^+] = 1.0 \times 10^{-12}$ M
   c. pOH = 5.00
   d. $[OH^-] = 1.0 \times 10^{-9}$ M

32. Calculate the hydronium ion concentration of a solution having each of the following pH values.
   a. 7.33
   b. 6.44
   c. 13.33
   d. 4.22
   e. 0.99

33. Calculate the hydronium ion concentration of a solution having each of the following pOH values.
   a. 2.00
   b. 12.00
   c. 0.00
   d. 14.00
   e. 7.00

34. Calculate the pH of a solution having each of the following hydroxide ion concentrations.
   a. 1.1×10^{-6} M
   b. 5.0×10^{-13} M
   c. 4.1×10^{-7} M

35. Calculate the pOH of a solution having each of the following hydroxide ion concentrations.
   a. 6.2×10^{-4} M
   b. 9.93×10^{-8} M
   c. 4.55×10^{-12} M

36. Calculate the hydroxide ion concentration of a solution having each of the following pOH values.
   a. 4.419
   b. 12.509
   c. 6.39
   d. 5.113
   e. 13.017

37. Calculate the hydroxide ion concentration of a solution having each of the following pH values.
   a. 3.41
   b. 8.01
   c. 13.59
   d. 0.50
   e. 9.73

38. Calculate the pH of each of the following solutions.
   a. 0.300 M H_3O^+
   b. 0.300 M HCl

39. Calculate the pH of each of the following solutions.
   a. 0.100 M OH^-
   b. 0.100 M NaOH

40. Calculate the pH of each of the following solutions.
   a. 6.16×10^{-3} M KOH
   b. 1.73×10^{-4} M $HClO_4$
   c. 5.00×10^{-3} M $Ba(OH)_2$

41. Calculate the pH of each of the following solutions.
   a. 0.0010 M HCl
   b. 0.025 M NaOH
   c. 0.33 M $Sr(OH)_2$

42. Calculate the pH of each of the following solutions.
   a. 7.15×10^{-3} M HNO_3
   b. 2.42×10^{-3} M $Ba(OH)_2$

43. Calculate the pH of each of the following solutions.
   a. 0.010 M HBr
   b. 0.010 M KOH

16.5 Weak Acids and Bases

44. A 0.100 M solution of which substance in Table 16.2 has the highest pH?

45. A 0.100 M solution of which substance in Table 16.2 has the lowest pH?

46. Calculate $[H_3O^+]$ and pH for a 0.350 M solution of $HCHO_2$; $K_a = 1.7 \times 10^{-4}$.

47. Calculate $[H_3O^+]$ and pH for a 0.317 M solution of HF; $K_a = 6.8 \times 10^{-4}$.

48. Calculate $[OH^-]$ and pH for a 0.228 M solution of NH_3; $K_b = 1.8 \times 10^{-5}$.

49. Calculate the pH of 0.0100 M HNO_2; $K_a = 4.0 \times 10^{-4}$.

50. Calculate the pH of 0.100 M HOC_6H_5; $K_a = 1.1 \times 10^{-10}$.

51. Calculate the pH of 0.180 M NH_3; $K_b = 1.8 \times 10^{-5}$.

52. A 0.100 M solution of a weak acid, represented as HA, has a hydronium ion concentration of 2.50×10^{-5} M. Calculate the value of K_a for HA.

53. A 0.200 M solution of a weak base, represented as B, has a hydroxide ion concentration of 6.74×10^{-5} M. Calculate the value of K_b for B.

54. A 0.100 M solution of a weak acid, represented as HA, has a pH of 3.88. Calculate the value of K_a for HA.

55. A 0.110 M solution of a weak acid, represented as HA, has a pH of 4.35. Calculate the value of K_a for HA.

56. A 0.199 M solution of a weak base, represented as B, has a pH of 11.57. Calculate the value of K_b for B.

57. A 0.344 M solution of a weak base, represented as B, has a pH of 10.23. Calculate the value of K_b for B.

16.6 Polyprotic Acids

58. Citric acid, $H_3C_6H_5O_7$, is triprotic.
   a. Write the three ionization reactions for citric acid.
   b. Write the K_{a1}, K_{a2}, and K_{a3} expressions for citric acid.

59. Oxalic acid, $H_2C_2O_4$, is diprotic.
   a. Write the two ionization reactions for oxalic acid.
   b. Write the K_{a1} and K_{a2} expressions for oxalic acid.

60. Since the first ionization of H_2S in 0.100 M solution produces 9.5×10^{-5} M H_3O^+, why don't the first and second ionization steps together produce twice that concentration?

61. H_2SO_4 is a strong acid, but only its first ionization goes to completion (i.e., HSO_4^- is a weak acid). Estimate the hydronium ion concentration of 0.1 M H_2SO_4.
   a. below 0.1 M
   b. 0.1 M
   c. between 0.1 M and 0.2 M
   d. 0.2 M
   e. above 0.2 M

62. Calculate the pH and carbonate ion concentration of a solution of 0.100 M carbonic acid. See Table 16.3 for K_a values.

63. Calculate the pH and sulfite ion concentration of a solution of 0.100 M sulfurous acid. See Appendix A.2 for K_a values.

64. Estimate the sulfide ion concentration in 0.200 M H_2S. See Table 16.3 for K_a values.

65. Estimate the ascorbate ion concentration in 0.200 M ascorbic acid (vitamin C) solution. See Table 16.3 for K_a values.

16.7 Acid–Base Properties of Salts

66. Which of the following 0.100 M solutions are acidic, which are basic, and which are neutral?
   a. $NaC_2H_3O_2$
   b. K_2S
   c. $NaNO_2$
   d. $LiClO_3$
   e. NH_4ClO_3

67. Which of the following 0.100 M solutions are acidic, which are basic, and which are neutral?
   a. $BaCl_2$
   b. NH_4Br
   c. K_2CO_3
   d. NH_4NO_3
   e. $CaSO_3$
   f. $LiNO_3$

68. What is the pH of an 8.14×10^{-4} M KCl solution?

69. What is the approximate pH of a solution of ammonium acetate? See Table 16.2 for K values as needed.

70. Explain why a small, highly charged metal cation such as Al^{3+} has acidic properties.

71. If the K_a for a weak acid, HA, is 4.5×10^{-6}, what is the K_b for its conjugate base, A^-?

72. If the K_b for a weak base, B, is 9.2×10^{-8}, what is the K_a for its conjugate acid, BH^+?

73. Calculate the pH of 0.0470 M LiBrO. See Appendix A.3 for K values as needed.

74. Calculate the pH of 0.160 M KCN. See Table 16.2 for K values as needed.

75. Calculate the pH of 0.290 M NH_4Cl. See Table 16.2 for K values as needed.

76. Calculate the pH of 0.0880 M $(CH_3)_2NH_2Cl$. See Table 16.2 for K values as needed.

16.8 Relating Acid Strength to Structure

77. Rank the acid strength of HClO, $HClO_2$, and HBrO from weakest to strongest.

78. Rank the acid strength of H_2SO_4, H_2SO_3, and HSO_3F from weakest to strongest.

79. Rank the acid strength of HIO_2, HNO_2, and HNO_3 from weakest to strongest.

80. Use the following structure of phthalic acid to predict which of its six hydrogen atoms are ionizable.

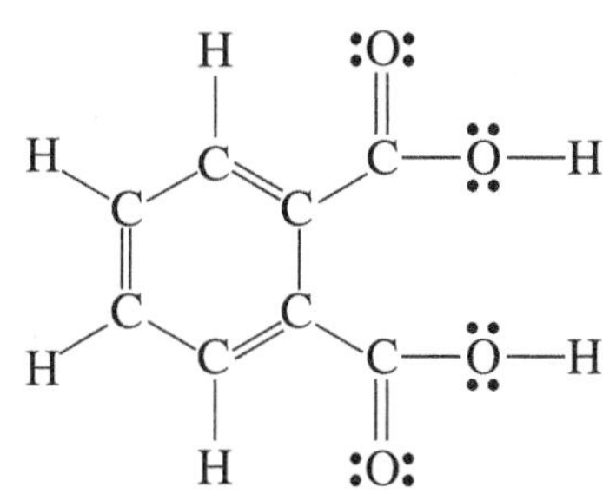

81. Use the following structure of formic acid to explain why it is monoprotic instead of diprotic.

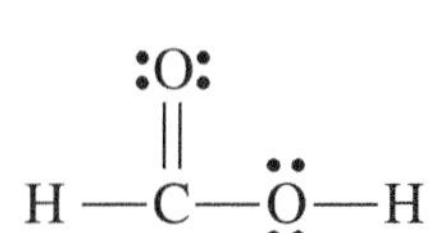

82. Complete each of these sentences with "increases" or "decreases." All other factors being equal,
   a. as the strength of the bond to H increases, the strength of the acid ________.
   b. as the polarity of the bond to H increases, the strength of the acid ________.
   c. as the size of the anion bonded to H increases, the strength of the acid ________.

16.9 Lewis Acids and Bases

83. Which of the following are common characteristics of Lewis bases? Select all that apply.
   a. lone pair
   b. incomplete valence shell
   c. positive charge
   d. negative charge
   e. double bonds

84. Which of the following are common characteristics of Lewis acids? Select all that apply.
   a. lone pair
   b. less than octet
   c. positive charge
   d. negative charge
   e. double bonds

85. Classify the following species as Lewis acids or Lewis bases.
   a. NH_3
   b. BH_3
   c. Al^{3+}
   d. S^{2-}
   e. CO_2

86. Classify the following species as Lewis acids or Lewis bases.
   a. H_2O
   b. BF_3
   c. Sn^{2+}
   d. F^-
   e. SO_2

87. Identify the Lewis acid and the Lewis base in the following reaction.

$$Al^{3+} + 6\,H_2O \rightarrow Al(H_2O)_6{}^{3+}$$

88. Identify the Lewis acid and the Lewis base in the following reaction.

$$O^{2-} + SO_3 \rightarrow SO_4{}^{2-}$$

89. Identify the Lewis acid and the Lewis base in the following reaction.

$$H^+ + H_2O \rightarrow H_3O^+$$

90. Identify the Lewis acid and the Lewis base in the following reaction.

$$H^+ + NH_3 \rightarrow NH_4{}^+$$

Putting It Together

91. At normal human body temperature, 37°C, the pH of a neutral solution is 6.81. Based on this information, is the autoionization of water endothermic or exothermic? Hint: See Table 15.3.

92. Calculate the pH of a solution prepared by mixing equal volumes of 0.500 M HNO_3 and 0.150 M $Ba(OH)_2$. Hint: This is a limiting reactant problem.

93. In a titration of 175 mL of HCl(aq) with 0.120 M NaOH(aq), 107 mL of NaOH was needed to reach the equivalence point. What was the pH of the original HCl solution?

94. For NH_3 and CH_3NH_2:
 a. Draw the Lewis structure for each molecule.
 b. Explain how each can act as a Lewis base.
 c. Explain how each can act as a Brønsted base.
 d. Draw the Lewis structure for the conjugate acid of each.

95. Citric acid has the formula $H_3C_6H_5O_7$. What is the name of the compound with the formula $Na_3C_6H_5O_7$?

96. Sodium hydrogen glutamate, $NaHC_5H_7NO_4$, is commonly called monosodium glutamate, or MSG. What is the formula for glutamic acid?

97. Complete each of these sentences with "increases" or "decreases."
 a. As K_a increases, acid strength ______.
 b. As pK_a increases, acid strength ______.
 c. As the acidity of a solution increases, the pH ______.
 d. As the acidity of a solution increases, the pOH ______.
 e. As the strength of an acid increases, the strength of its conjugate base ______.

PRACTICE PROBLEM SOLUTIONS

Practice Problem 16.1 Solution

a. $HClO_4$ (perchloric acid) is a strong acid, so it is 100% ionized in aqueous solution. There are two valid ways to write the ionization reaction, both of which use a regular reaction arrow.

$$HClO_4(aq) \rightarrow H^+(aq) + ClO_4^-(aq)$$

or

$$HClO_4(aq) + H_2O(l) \rightarrow H_3O^+(aq) + ClO_4^-(aq)$$

b. Because the ionization reaction goes to completion, the H^+ concentration (or H_3O^+ concentration) in 0.0015 M $HClO_4$ is 0.0015 M. (The perchlorate ion concentration is also 0.0015 M.)

c. HClO (chlorous acid) is a weak acid, so it is only partially ionized in aqueous solution. There are two valid ways to write the ionization reaction, both of which use equilibrium arrows.

$$HClO(aq) \rightleftharpoons H^+(aq) + ClO^-(aq)$$

or

$$HClO(aq) + H_2O(l) \rightleftharpoons H_3O^+(aq) + ClO^-(aq)$$

d. Because the ionization reaction does not go to completion, the H^+ concentration (or H_3O^+ concentration) in 0.0015 M HClO is less than 0.0015 M. (The chlorite ion concentration is also less than 0.0015 M.)

Practice Problem 16.2 Solution

Both KOH and $Ba(OH)_2$ are strong bases, so both dissociate 100% in aqueous solution.

a. Because KOH contains one OH^- per formula unit, the OH^- concentration equals the initial concentration of KOH: 0.34 M KOH gives 0.34 M OH^-.

b. $Ba(OH)_2$ is dibasic, so the concentration of OH^- is twice the initial concentration of the $Ba(OH)_2$: 0.34 M $Ba(OH)_2$ gives 0.68 M OH^-.

Practice Problem 16.3 Solution

The proton donor is the acid (loses H^+), and the proton acceptor is the base (gains H^+). A conjugate acid–base pair differs only by H^+.

a. In the forward reaction, H^+ is transferred from H_2O (acid) to SO_4^{2-} (base). In the reverse reaction, H^+ is transferred from HSO_4^- (acid) to OH^- (base).

$$SO_4^{2-}(aq) + H_2O(l) \rightleftharpoons HSO_4^-(aq) + OH^-(aq)$$

Base — Acid — Acid — Base

Conjugate Pair (H_2O / OH^-)

Conjugate Pair (SO_4^{2-} / HSO_4^-)

b. In the forward reaction, H^+ is transferred from HSO_4^- (acid) to H_2O (base). In the reverse reaction, H^+ is transferred from H_3O^+ (acid) to SO_4^{2-} (base).

$$HSO_4^-(aq) + H_2O(l) \rightleftharpoons SO_4^{2-}(aq) + H_3O^+(aq)$$

Acid — Base — Base — Acid

Conjugate Pair (H_2O / H_3O^+)

Conjugate Pair (HSO_4^- / SO_4^{2-})

Notice again that H_2O is amphiprotic—whether it behaves as an acid or a base depends on the relative acid or base strength of the other species present in the reaction. HSO_4^- is also amphiprotic. In a reaction with a weaker acid than itself (such as water), it will act as an acid and donate a proton, but in a reaction with a stronger acid than itself (such as HCl), it will behave as a base and accept a proton. SO_4^{2-} can only accept a proton, so it is not amphiprotic and in aqueous solution can only behave as a weak base.

Practice Problem 16.4 Solution

The conjugate acid is the species that results when H^+ is added to the formula of the base. Thus, the conjugate acids are $(CH_3)_2NH_2^+$, $CH_3NH_3^+$, and NH_4^+, respectively.

The strength of the conjugate acid increases as the strength of its weak base decreases. Thus, the conjugate acid strength is $NH_4^+ > CH_3NH_3^+ > (CH_3)_2NH_2^+$.

Practice Problem 16.5 Solution

a. Use the K_w expression (Equation 16.1) and solve for the hydronium ion concentration.

$$K_w = [H_3O^+][OH^-] = 1.0 \times 10^{-14}$$

$$[H_3O^+] = \frac{K_w}{[OH^-]} = \frac{1.0 \times 10^{-14}}{7.1 \times 10^{-12}} = 1.4 \times 10^{-3}\text{ M}$$

$[H_3O^+] > [OH^-]$, so the solution is acidic.

b. Use the K_w expression (Equation 16.1) and solve for the hydronium ion concentration.

$$K_w = [H_3O^+][OH^-] = 1.0 \times 10^{-14}$$

$$[H_3O^+] = \frac{K_w}{[OH^-]} = \frac{1.0 \times 10^{-14}}{2.9 \times 10^{-3}} = 3.4 \times 10^{-12}\text{ M}$$

$[H_3O^+] < [OH^-]$, so the solution is basic.

Practice Problem 16.6 Solution

Use Equation 16.2: $pH = -\log[H_3O^+]$.

a. KOH is a strong base, so in 8.0×10^{-4} M KOH, $[OH^-] = 8.0 \times 10^{-4}$ M. Use Equation 16.1 to calculate $[H_3O^+]$ in this solution:

$$K_w = [H_3O^+][OH^-]$$

$$[H_3O^+] = \frac{K_w}{[OH^-]} = \frac{1.0 \times 10^{-14}}{8.0 \times 10^{-4}} = 1.25 \times 10^{-11}\text{ M}$$

Now use Equation 16.2 to calculate pH:

$$pH = -\log(1.25 \times 10^{-11}\text{ M}) = 10.90;\quad \text{basic (pH} > 7.00)$$

b. $pH = -\log(0.0015\text{ M}) = 2.82$; acidic ($pH < 7.00$)

c. NaOH is a strong base, so first calculate $[H_3O^+]$ using Equation 16.1:

$$K_w = [H_3O^+][OH^-]$$

$$[H_3O^+] = \frac{K_w}{[OH^-]} = \frac{1.0 \times 10^{-14}}{6.6 \times 10^{-5}} = 1.52 \times 10^{-10}\text{ M}$$

Then use Equation 16.2 to calculate pH:

$$pH = -\log(1.52 \times 10^{-10}\text{ M}) = 9.82;\quad \text{basic (pH} > 7.00)$$

Practice Problem 16.7 Solution

Use Equation 16.3:

$$[H_3O^+] = 10^{-pH}$$

a. $[H_3O^+] = 10^{-pH} = 10^{-12.3} = 5 \times 10^{-13}$ M; basic ($pH > 7.00$)

b. $[H_3O^+] = 10^{-pH} = 10^{-7.05} = 8.9 \times 10^{-8}$ M; nearly neutral but just barely basic ($pH > 7.00$)

c. $[H_3O^+] = 10^{-pH} = 10^{-1.4} = 4 \times 10^{-2}\text{ M} = 0.04$ M; acidic ($pH < 7.00$)

Practice Problem 16.8 Solution

Use Equation 16.3:

$$[H_3O^+] = 10^{-pH} = 10^{-6.3} = 5 \times 10^{-7}\text{ M}$$

There is only one digit after the decimal point in the pH, so the calculated $[H_3O^+]$ concentration can have only one significant figure.

Practice Problem 16.9 Solution

$[OH^-] = 7.7 \times 10^{-10}$ M, so use Equation 16.4 to calculate pOH and then rearrange Equation 16.5 to determine the pH:

$$pOH = -\log[OH^-] = -\log(7.7 \times 10^{-10}) = 9.11$$

$$pH = 14.00 - pOH = 14.00 - 9.11 = 4.89$$

Alternatively, use Equation 16.1 to determine $[H_3O^+]$, then use Equation 16.2 to calculate the pH from that:

$$K_w = [H_3O^+][OH^-] = 1.0 \times 10^{-14}$$

$$[H_3O^+] = \frac{1.0 \times 10^{-14}}{[OH^-]} = \frac{1.0 \times 10^{-14}}{7.7 \times 10^{-10}} = 1.30 \times 10^{-5}\text{ M}$$

$$pH = -\log[H_3O^+] = -\log(1.30 \times 10^{-5}) = 4.89$$

Practice Problem 16.10 Solution

a. 0.005 M HCl ionizes completely to yield 0.005 M $[H_3O^+]$. Equation 16.2 gives the pH:

$$pH = -\log[H_3O^+] = -\log(0.005) = 2.3$$

$$K_w = [H_3O^+][OH^-] = 1.0 \times 10^{-14}$$

$$[OH^-] = \frac{1.0 \times 10^{-14}}{[H_3O^+]} = \frac{1.0 \times 10^{-14}}{0.005} = 2 \times 10^{-12}\text{ M}$$

b. 0.005 M NaOH dissociates completely to yield 0.005 M $[OH^-]$.

$$K_w = [H_3O^+][OH^-] = 1.0 \times 10^{-14}$$

$$[H_3O^+] = \frac{1.0 \times 10^{-14}}{[OH^-]} = \frac{1.0 \times 10^{-14}}{0.005} = 2 \times 10^{-12}\ M$$

$$pH = -\log[H_3O^+] = -\log(2 \times 10^{-12}) = 11.7$$

Practice Problem 16.11 Solution

Fill in the missing information using the formulas $pK_b = -\log K_b$ and $K_b = 10^{-pK_b}$.

Base	Formula	K_b	pK_b
Ethylamine	$CH_3CH_2NH_2$	6.3×10^{-4}	3.20
Diethylamine	$(C_2H_5)_2NH$	6.9×10^{-4}	3.16
Triethylamine	$(C_2H_5)_3N$	5.6×10^{-4}	3.25
Methylamine	CH_3NH_2	5.0×10^{-4}	3.30
Dimethylamine	$(CH_3)_2NH$	5.4×10^{-4}	3.27

The strength of a weak base increases as K_b increases. Because pK_b is the *negative* log of K_b, a large K_b corresponds to a *small* pK_b. You can use either K_b or pK_b to compare the strengths of these bases.

In order of increasing K_b or decreasing pK_b, the strengths of the bases from weakest to strongest are methylamine < dimethylamine < triethylamine < ethylamine < diethylamine.

Practice Problem 16.12 Solution

Rather than write out the entire chemical formula for caffeine throughout the problem, abbreviate it as B (for base) and abbreviate its conjugate acid as BH^+. The reaction then becomes

$$B(aq) + H_2O(l) \rightleftharpoons BH^+(aq) + OH^-(aq)$$

Set up an ICE table using the concentrations given in the problem.

	B(aq) + H_2O(l) ⇌	BH^+(aq) +	OH^-(aq)
Initial	0.00155	0	~0
Change			
Equilibrium			6.18×10^{-4}

Fill in the remaining values starting with the change in OH^-.

	B(aq)	+ H_2O(l) ⇌	BH^+(aq)	+ OH^-(aq)
Initial	0.00155		0	~0
Change	-6.18×10^{-4}		$+6.18 \times 10^{-4}$	$+6.18 \times 10^{-4}$
Equilibrium	9.32×10^{-4}		6.18×10^{-4}	6.18×10^{-4}

The change in $[OH^-]$ is much greater than 1×10^{-7} M, so the assumption that the initial $[OH^-]$ is negligible compared to the change in $[OH^-]$ is valid.

Now plug the equilibrium concentrations into the K_b expression.

$$K_b = \frac{[BH^+][OH^-]}{[B]} = \frac{(6.18 \times 10^{-4})(6.18 \times 10^{-4})}{(9.32 \times 10^{-4})}$$
$$= 4.10 \times 10^{-4}$$

Practice Problem 16.13 Solution

The ionization equation for ammonia is

$$NH_3(aq) + H_2O(l) \rightleftharpoons NH_4^+(aq) + OH^-(aq)$$

The initial concentration of ammonia (before ionization) is 0.100 M. The initial concentration of the conjugate acid (NH_4^+) is 0. The initial concentration of OH^- is 1.00×10^{-7} M, which is essentially zero in this context because the ionization of NH_3 will produce far more than that. Use x as the change in concentration.

	NH_3(aq) + H_2O(l) ⇌	NH_4^+ (aq) +	OH^- (aq)
Initial	0.100	0	~0
Change	$-x$	$+x$	$+x$
Equilibrium	$0.100 - x$	x	x

Use the K_b expression and the value of K_b for ammonia (Table 16.2) to solve for x.

$$K_b = \frac{[NH_4^+][OH^-]}{[NH_3]} = \frac{x^2}{(0.100 - x)} = 1.8 \times 10^{-5}$$

K_b is much smaller than the initial concentration, so assume that x is very small compared to 0.100 and that the amount of base lost to ionization is negligible. Therefore, $0.100 - x \approx 0.100$.

$$\frac{x^2}{(0.100 - x)} \approx \frac{x^2}{0.100} = 1.8 \times 10^{-5}$$
$$x^2 = 1.8 \times 10^{-6}$$

Take the square root of both sides.

$$x = 1.3 \times 10^{-3}$$

Because x represents both $[OH^-]$ and $[NH_4^+]$, both of these concentrations are 1.3×10^{-3} M. Finally, 1.3×10^{-3} M is about 1% of 0.100 M, so the approximation that $0.100 - x \approx 0.100$ is acceptable.

$$pOH = -\log[OH^-] = -\log(1.3 \times 10^{-3}\ M) = 2.87$$
$$pH = 14.00 - pOH = 14.00 - 2.87 = 11.13$$

Practice Problem 16.14 Solution

Start with an ICE table for the first ionization. Ascorbic acid has been abbreviated as H_2A for simplicity.

	$H_2A(aq)$ + $H_2O(l)$ ⇌	H_3O^+ (aq)	+ HA^- (aq)
Initial	0.25	~0	0
Change	$-x$	$+x$	$+x$
Equilibrium	$0.25 - x$	x	x

Assume $x \ll 0.25$, so $0.25 - x \approx 0.25$.

$$K_{a1} = \frac{[H_3O^+][HA^-]}{[H_2A]} = \frac{x^2}{0.25 - x} \approx \frac{x^2}{0.25}$$
$$= 8.0 \times 10^{-5}$$
$$x^2 = 0.258.0 \times 10^{-5} = 2.0 \times 10^{-5}$$
$$x = \sqrt{2.0 \times 10^{-5}} = 0.0045$$

0.0045 M is much less than 0.25 M, so the assumption that $x < 0.25$ M is valid.

As in Example 16.14, nearly all of the H_3O^+ came from the first ionization, so pH can be calculated from x.

$$[H_3O^+] = x = 0.0045\ M$$
$$pH = -\log(0.0045\ M) = 2.35$$

$K_{a1} \gg K_{a2}$, so you can assume that $[C_6H_6O_6^{2-}] = K_{a2} = 1.6 \times 10^{-12}$ M. Nevertheless, the calculations are shown here to verify this. Make an ICE table for the second ionization using the final values from the first ionization. Use y as the change to distinguish it from x in the previous ionization.

	HA^- (aq) + $H_2O(l)$ ⇌	H_3O^+ (aq)	+ A^{2-} (aq)
Initial	~0.0045	0.0045	0
Change	$-y$	$+y$	$+y$
Equilibrium	$0.0045 - y$	$0.0045 + y$	y

Assume $y \ll 0.0045$, so $(0.0045 - y) \approx 0.0045$ and $(0.0045 + y) \approx 0.0045$.

$$K_{a2} = \frac{[H_3O^+][A^{2-}]}{[HA^-]} = \frac{(0.0045 + y)y}{0.0045 - y} \approx \frac{0.0045y}{0.0045}$$
$$= 1.6 \times 10^{-12}$$
$$y = [A^{2-}] = 1.6 \times 10^{-12}$$

$1.6 \times 10^{-12}\ M < 0.0045$, so the assumption is valid.

$$[C_6H_6O_6^{2-}] = [A^{2-}] = 1.6 \times 10^{-12}$$

Practice Problem 16.15 Solution

a. NaCl is made up of the cation of a strong base (sodium hydroxide, NaOH) and the anion of a strong acid (hydrochloric acid, HCl), so neither Na^+ nor Cl^- will exhibit any acid–base character.

b. NaF is made up of the cation of a strong base (sodium hydroxide, NaOH) and the anion of a weak acid (hydrofluoric acid, HF). As the conjugate base of a weak acid, F^- behaves as a weak base.

$$F^-(aq) + H_2O(l) \rightleftharpoons HF(aq) + OH^-(aq)$$

The combination of a cation that is neither acidic nor basic (Na^+) and a basic anion (F^-) results in a basic salt.

Practice Problem 16.16 Solution

a. pH will decrease: Cr^{3+} is one of the acidic metal ions listed earlier, and Cl^- is neutral.

b. pH will not change: Sr^{2+} is a group 2 metal ion (the cation of a strong base) and Cl^- is the anion of a monoprotic strong acid, so neither ion has acid–base properties.

c. pH will increase: Ca^{2+} has no acid–base properties, but the acetate anion ($C_2H_3O_2^-$) is the conjugate base of acetic acid, a weak acid.

Practice Problem 16.17 Solution

The K_a of benzoic acid is provided, so use Equation 16.10 to determine K_b of $C_7H_5O_2^-$:

$$K_a \times K_b = K_w$$

$$K_b = \frac{K_w}{K_a} = \frac{1.0 \times 10^{-14}}{6.3 \times 10^{-5}} = 1.6 \times 10^{-10}$$

Practice Problem 16.18 Solution

For any conjugate acid–base pair, $K_a \times K_b = K_w$ (Equation 16.10), where $K_w = 1.0 \times 10^{-14}$.

$$K_a = \frac{K_w}{K_b} = \frac{1.0 \times 10^{-14}}{K_b}$$

Base	K_b	Conjugate Acid	K_a
NH_3	1.8×10^{-5}	NH_4^+	$\frac{1.0 \times 10^{-14}}{1.8 \times 10^{-5}} = 5.6 \times 10^{-10}$
CH_3NH_2	5.0×10^{-4}	$CH_3NH_3^+$	$\frac{1.0 \times 10^{-14}}{5.0 \times 10^{-4}} = 2.0 \times 10^{-11}$
$(CH_3)_2NH$	5.4×10^{-4}	$(CH_3)_2NH_2^+$	$\frac{1.0 \times 10^{-14}}{5.4 \times 10^{-4}} = 1.9 \times 10^{-11}$

Placing these K_a values in order from largest to smallest confirms the prediction in Practice Problem 16.4 that the conjugate acid strength from strongest to weakest is $NH_4^+ > CH_3NH_3^+ > (CH_3)_2NH_2^+$.

Practice Problem 16.19 Solution

$(CH_3)_3NH^+$ is the conjugate acid of $(CH_3)_3N$, a weak base, so it behaves as a weak acid.

$$(CH_3)_3NH^+(aq) + H_2O \rightleftharpoons H_3O^+(aq) + (CH_3)_3N(aq)$$

K_a for $(CH_3)_3NH^+$ can be calculated from K_b for $(CH_3)_3N$ and Equation 16.10.

$$K_a = K_w/K_b = (1.0 \times 10^{-14})/(6.3 \times 10^{-5})$$
$$= 1.6 \times 10^{-10}$$

Now set up an ICE table for the ionization of $(CH_3)_3NH^+$.

	$(CH_3)_3NH^+$ (aq)	+ $H_2O(l)$ $\rightleftharpoons$	H_3O^+ (aq) +	$(CH_3)_3N$ (aq)
Initial	1.0		~0	0
Change	$-x$		$+x$	$+x$
Equilibrium	$1.0 - x$		x	x

Assume $x \ll 1.0$, so $1.0 - x \approx 1.0$

$$K_a = \frac{[H_3O^+][(CH_3)_3N]}{[(CH_3)_3NH^+]} = \frac{x^2}{1.0 - x} \approx \frac{x^2}{1.0}$$
$$= 1.6 \times 10^{-10}$$
$$x^2 = (1.0)(1.6 \times 10^{-10}) = 1.6 \times 10^{-10}$$

Because $x = [H_3O^+] = 1.3 \times 10^{-5}$ M, which is much less than 1.0, the assumption that $x \ll 1.0$ M is valid.

$$pH = -\log[H_3O^+] = -\log(1.3 \times 10^{-5}) = 4.90$$

Practice Problem 16.20 Solution

Replacing one hydrogen atom (electronegativity = 2.1) in acetic acid with a more electronegative atom creates a more polar bond to the ionizable hydrogen atom and therefore increases the acid strength. Replacing three hydrogen atoms with more electronegative atoms creates an even more polar bond to the ionizable hydrogen atom and results in an even stronger acid. Thus, the strength of the acid increases as the electronegativity of the atoms bonded to carbon increases. Electronegativity increases up a column of the periodic table, so fluorine (electronegativity = 4.0) > chlorine (3.0) > bromine (2.8). The order from weakest acid to strongest acid is therefore acetic acid < bromoacetic acid < trichloroacetic acid < trifluoroacetic acid.

Practice Problem 16.21 Solution

The hydrogen atoms that are bonded to oxygen atoms are ionizable, so

a. H_3PO_2 has one.
b. H_2SO_2 has two.
c. H_2SO has one.

Practice Problem 16.22 Solution

a. CN^- has nonbonding electron pairs available and is the electron pair donor—the Lewis base. Cu^{2+} accepts an electron pair from each CN^- and is an electron pair acceptor—the Lewis acid.

b. H_2O has two nonbonding electron pairs on the oxygen atom that can be donated, so H_2O is the Lewis base. CH_3^+ does not have an octet on the carbon atom and can accept an electron pair, so CH_3^+ is the Lewis acid.

Practice Problem 16.23 Solution

a. HCl is a strong acid, so it ionizes completely: $[H_3O^+] = 0.080$ M.

$$pH = -\log[H_3O^+] = -\log(0.080) = 1.10$$

b. A solution of the weak base hydrazine hydrolyzes water, producing $N_2H_5^+$ and OH^- ions.

$$N_2H_4(aq) + H_2O(l) \rightleftharpoons N_2H_5^+(aq) + OH^-(aq)$$

Initially, $[N_2H_4] = 0.080$ M, and $[N_2H_5^+] = [OH^-] = 0$.

K_b for this reaction is 1.3×10^{-6}.

	$N_2H_4(aq)$ +	$H_2O(l)$ $\rightleftharpoons$	$N_2H_5^+(aq)$ +	$OH^-(aq)$
Initial	0.80	—	0	~0
Change	$-x$	—	$+x$	$+x$
Equilibrium	$0.80 - x$	—	x	x

K_b is small, indicating that the ionization occurs only to a small extent, so assume that x is small compared to 0.080, in which case $0.080 - x \approx 0.080$.

$$K_b = \frac{[N_2H_5^+][OH^-]}{[N_2H_4]} = \frac{x^2}{(0.080 - x)} \approx \frac{x^2}{0.080}$$

$$1.3 \times 10^{-6} = \frac{x^2}{0.080}$$

$$x^2 = (0.080)(1.3 \times 10^{-6}) = 1.0 \times 10^{-7}$$

Taking the square root of both sides,

$$x = [OH^-] = [N_2H_5^+] = 3.2 \times 10^{-4}\text{ M}$$

Because 3.2×10^{-4} is less than 1% of 0.080, the assumption that x is small is valid.

$$pOH = -\log[OH^-] = -\log(3.2 \times 10^{-4}) = 3.49$$

$$pH = 14.00 - pOH = 14.00 - 3.49 = 10.51$$

c. Hydrazine and H^+ react in a 1:1 mole ratio according to the following neutralization reaction.

$$N_2H_4(aq) + HCl(aq) \rightleftharpoons N_2H_5Cl(aq)$$

The base and the acid are both 0.080 M and equal volumes are mixed, so an equal number of moles of acid and base are present, and the neutralization reaction goes to completion. The total volume of the solution is now twice what it was initially, so the solution contains no hydrazine, no HCl, and 0.040 M protonated hydrazine ($N_2H_5^+$). $N_2H_5^+$ is the conjugate acid of hydrazine, so it is a weak acid and will ionize in water, producing H_3O^+ ions.

$$N_2H_5^+(aq) + H_2O \rightleftharpoons H_3O^+(aq) + N_2H_4(aq)$$

The equilibrium constant for this reaction, K_a, can be determined from K_b for hydrazine and K_w for water (Equation 16.10).

$$K_a = \frac{K_w}{K_b} = \frac{1.0 \times 10^{-14}}{1.3 \times 10^{-6}} = 7.7 \times 10^{-9}$$

	$N_2H_5^+(aq)$ +	$H_2O(l)$ $\rightleftharpoons$	$H_3O^+(aq)$ +	$N_2H_4(aq)$
Initial	0.040	—	~0	0
Change	$-x$	—	$+x$	$+x$
Equilibrium	$0.040 - x$	—	x	x

Assume that x is small compared to 0.040, so $0.040 - x \approx 0.040$.

$$K_a = \frac{[N_2H_4][H_3O^+]}{[N_2H_5^+]} = \frac{x^2}{(0.040 - x)} \approx \frac{x^2}{0.040}$$

$$7.7 \times 10^{-9} = \frac{x^2}{0.040}$$

$$x^2 = (0.040)(7.7 \times 10^{-9}) = 3.08 \times 10^{-10}$$

Taking the square root of both sides,

$$x = [H_3O^+] = [N_2H_4] = 1.75 \times 10^{-5}\text{ M}$$

$$pH = -\log[H_3O^+] = -\log(1.75 \times 10^{-5}) = 4.76$$

d. The final pH of the neutralized weak base solution is *not* equal to 7, because $N_2H_5^+$ (the conjugate acid of hydrazine) is the product when hydrazine is neutralized, and $N_2H_5^+$ ionizes to produce H_3O^+, which lowers the pH below 7.

CHAPTER 17

Aqueous Equilibria

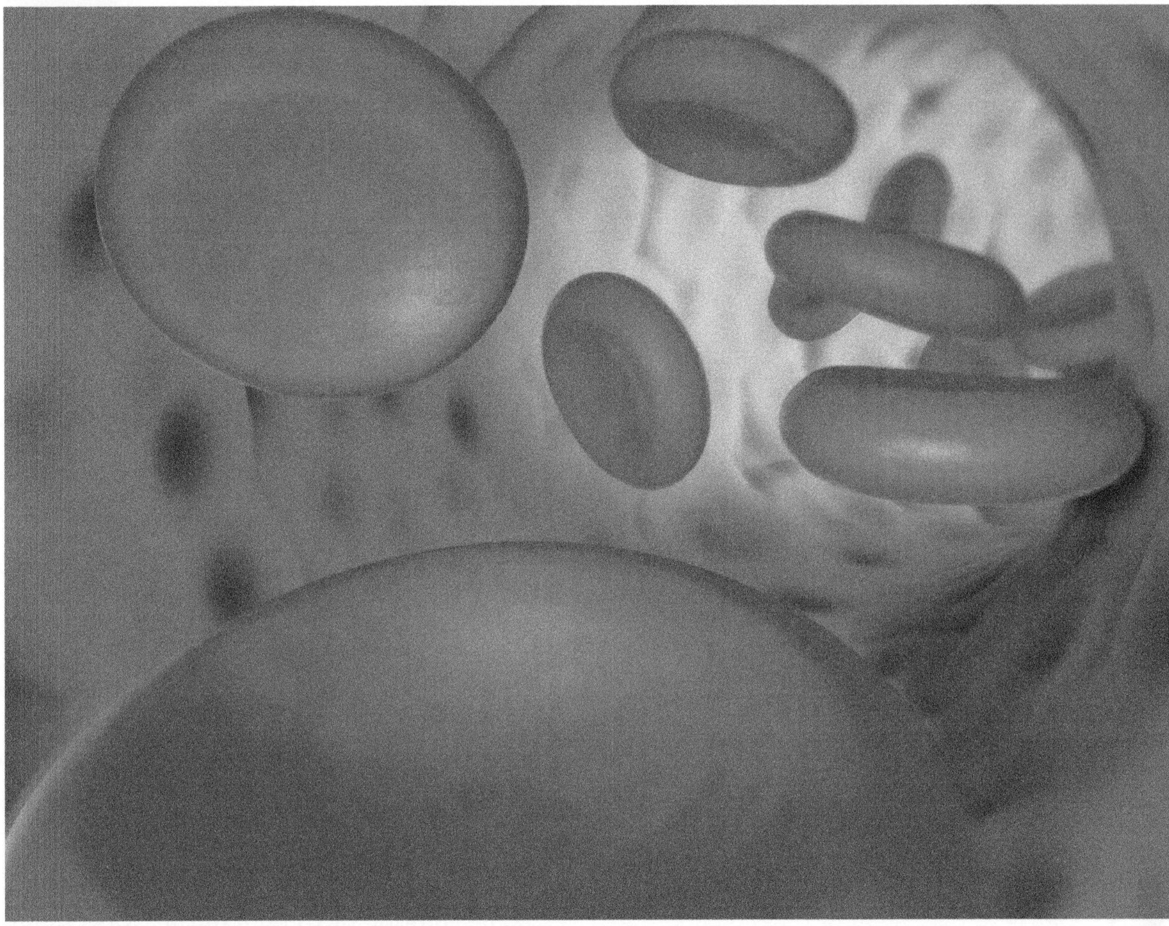

The term *aqueous equilibria* describes equilibrium reactions that occur in aqueous solution. These include the reactions that occur in a type of solution called a buffer. Buffers are important in biological systems because they regulate pH. For example, human blood is buffered at a pH of 7.4.

Chapter Outline

GOALS

- Explain how buffer solutions work.
- Calculate pH changes in buffer solutions after adding a strong acid or a strong base.
- Apply the Henderson–Hasselbalch equation to calculate the pH of buffer solutions.
- Compare and contrast the titration curves of strong acids and strong bases.
- Calculate the pH values and/or concentrations of relevant species at different areas along the titration curves.
- Compare and contrast the titration curves of weak acids and weak bases.
- Select an appropriate indicator for an acid–base titration.
- Explain the difference between solubility and the solubility product constant.
- Solve solubility equilibrium calculations using the solubility product constant.
- Explain how a common ion affects solubility.
- Explain how pH affects solubility.
- Explain the relationship between the reaction quotient and the solubility product constant.
- Identify methods to selectively precipitate ionic compounds from solution.
- Apply the concept of selective precipitation to systematically isolate and identify the metal ions present in a sample.
- Define *complex ion*.
- Apply the complex ion formation constant in the calculation of the concentrations of free metal ion and ligand in solution.

17.1 Introduction to Buffer Solutions

GOALS

- Explain how buffer solutions work.
- Calculate pH changes in buffer solutions after adding a strong acid or a strong base.

Background Review

Chapter 15 Chemical Equilibrium:
Section 15.5—Calculations Using ICE Tables;
Section 15.6—Le Châtelier's Principle

Chapter 16 Acid–Base Theory

From human blood to our oceans and our soil, the regulation of pH is critical to the survival of organisms. Solution pH is controlled via the presence of one or more *buffer* solutions. Buffer solutions, described in greater detail later in this section, resist changes in pH by neutralizing added acid or base. The mechanism for this neutralization is the equilibrium of a weak acid and its conjugate base (Section 16.2), governed by the common-ion effect.

THE COMMON-ION EFFECT

Chapter 16 discussed Brønsted acids and bases, as well as their ionization constants. Consider an aqueous solution of nitrous acid, HNO_2. HNO_2 ionizes into the nitrite ion, NO_2^-, and the hydronium ion, H_3O^+.

$$HNO_2(aq) + H_2O(l) \rightleftharpoons NO_2^-(aq) + H_3O^+(aq)$$

The addition of sodium nitrite, $NaNO_2$, produces additional NO_2^-. $NaNO_2$ is a salt and a strong electrolyte, so it dissociates completely.

$$NaNO_2(aq) \rightarrow Na^+(aq) + NO_2^-(aq)$$

When an aqueous solution of $NaNO_2$ is added to an aqueous solution of HNO_2, the high concentration of NO_2^- shifts the equilibrium back toward HNO_2. This suppresses the ionization of nitrous acid. (Na^+ is a spectator ion that does not take part in this equilibrium.)

$$HNO_2(aq) + H_2O(l) \rightleftharpoons \underset{\leftarrow}{\overset{\text{(excess)}}{NO_2^-(aq)}} + H_3O^+(aq)$$

(equilibrium shift towards HNO_2)

When a weak electrolyte is combined with a strong electrolyte that contains a common ion, the ionization of the weak electrolyte is suppressed. This phenomenon is known as the **common-ion effect**. The common-ion effect is an observation that can be explained via Le Châtelier's principle (Section 15.5). In the preceding equation, the equilibrium shifts to counteract the addition of NO_2^- (in the form of $NaNO_2$).

Example 17.1

Calculate the pH of an aqueous solution containing

a. 0.30 M HNO_2;

b. a mixture of 0.30 mol of HNO_2 and 0.20 mol of $NaNO_2$, with a total solution volume of 1.0 L. The K_a of HNO_2 is 5.6×10^{-4}.

Solution

a.

	HNO_2 (aq)	$+\ H_2O(l) \rightleftharpoons$	NO_2^- (aq)	+	H_3O^+ (aq)
Initial	0.30		0		0
Change	$-x$		$+x$		$+x$
Equilibrium	$0.30 - x$		x		x

Use the equilibrium expression to solve for x.

$$K_a = \frac{[NO_2^-][H_3O^+]}{[HNO_2]} = 5.6 \times 10^{-4}$$

$$K_a = \frac{x^2}{(0.30 - x)} = 5.6 \times 10^{-4}$$

If x is less than 5% of the number that it is being subtracted from (0.150, in this case), the preceding equation can be simplified to avoid solving a quadratic equation (Section 15.5). For now, assume that the assumption is valid and simplify the denominator to 0.150.

$$\frac{x^2}{0.30} = 5.6 \times 10^{-4}$$

$$x^2 = (0.30)(5.6 \times 10^{-4})$$

$$x = [H_3O^+] = 0.013 \text{ M}$$

Now check to be sure that the simplification is valid by dividing x by the original concentration of nitrous acid.

$$\frac{0.013}{0.30} \times 100\% = 4.3\%$$

Because x is less than 5% of the concentration of the acid, the simplification is valid. Now calculate the solution pH.

$$\text{pH} = -\log(0.013) = 1.89$$

b. Prior to equilibrium, the concentration of nitrous acid is 0.30 M and the concentration of sodium nitrite is 0.20 M.

	HNO_2 (aq)	$+\ H_2O(l) \rightleftharpoons$	NO_2^- (aq)	+	H_3O^+ (aq)
Initial	0.30		0.20		0
Change	$-x$		$+x$		$+x$
Equilibrium	$0.30 - x$		$0.20 + x$		x

Use the equilibrium expression to solve for x.

$$K_a = \frac{[NO_2^-][H_3O^+]}{[HNO_2]} = 5.6 \times 10^{-4}$$

$$K_a = \frac{(0.20 + x)(x)}{(0.30 - x)} = 5.6 \times 10^{-4}$$

As in part (a), assume that the value of x is less than 5% of the original concentrations of HNO_2 and NO_2^-, and simplify the $(0.20 + x)$ and $(0.30 - x)$ terms to 0.20 and 0.30, respectively:

$$\frac{(0.20)(x)}{0.30} = 5.6 \times 10^{-4}$$

$$x = \frac{(0.30)(5.6 \times 10^{-4})}{0.20}$$

$$x = [H_3O^+] = 0.00084 \text{ M}$$

Now check to be sure that the simplification is valid by dividing x by the original concentrations of nitrous acid and nitrite ion.

$$\text{For nitrous acid: } \frac{0.00084}{0.30} \times 100\% = 0.28\%$$

$$\text{For nitrite ion: } \frac{0.00084}{0.200} \times 100\% = 0.42\%$$

Because x is less than 5% of the concentrations of both nitrous acid and nitrite ion, the simplification is valid. Now calculate the solution pH.

$$\text{pH} = -\log(0.00084) = 3.08$$

Note that the pH of the solution containing nitrous acid and sodium nitrite (3.08) is higher than that of the solution containing only nitrous acid (1.89). The presence of excess nitrite ion suppresses the formation of H_3O^+ and shifts the equilibrium towards the left. This renders the buffer solution less acidic than the solution of pure nitrous acid.

PRACTICE PROBLEM 17.1

Calculate the pH of a solution of 0.16 mol of hydrazoic acid, HN_3, and 0.19 mol of sodium azide, NaN_3, in 1.00 L of solution. The K_a of hydrazoic acid is 2.5×10^{-5}.

Hint: Start by filling in an ICE table for the ionization.

$$HN_3(aq) + H_2O(l) \rightleftharpoons N_3^-(aq) + H_3O^+(aq)$$

Then, plug the equilibrium values into the K_a expression and solve for x, using the simplifying assumption.

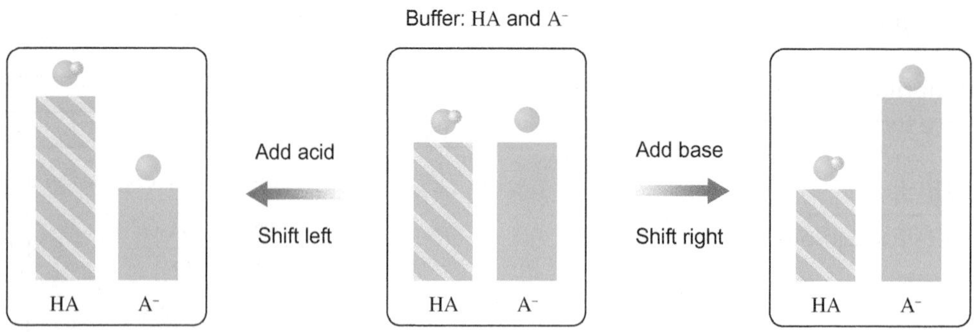

FIGURE 17.1 How a Buffer Works

When an acid is added to a buffer solution, $[H_3O^+]$ increases and the equilibrium shifts to the left.

$$HA(aq) + H_2O(l) \rightleftharpoons H_3O^+(aq) + A^-(aq)$$

In contrast, when a base is added, $[H_3O^+]$ decreases, and the equilibrium shifts to the right.

BUFFER SOLUTIONS

A solution containing both a weak acid and its conjugate base is called a **buffer solution**. Buffer solutions *resist a change in pH*, even when an appreciable quantity of a strong acid or strong base is added. The following equation shows the equilibrium of generic weak acid, HA, in water, as well as the equivalent expression where water is omitted for simplicity.

$$HA(aq) + H_2O(l) \rightleftharpoons H_3O^+(aq) + A^-(aq) \quad (17.1)$$

$$HA(aq) \rightleftharpoons H^+(aq) + A^-(aq) \quad (17.2)$$

A buffer has significant quantities of both HA and its conjugate base, A^-, allowing it to shift in either direction according to Le Châtelier's principle when either acid or base is added. In contrast, a weak acid by itself has the capacity to shift right, but not left, because it lacks a significant quantity of A^-. Figure 17.1 shows how a buffer solution works to resist a change in solution pH.

The solution containing nitrous acid, HNO_2, and nitrite, NO_2^-, which you saw in Example 17.1b is an example of a buffer. Buffer solutions can also be formed from the combination of a weak base and its conjugate acid. For example, a weak base such as ammonia, NH_3, could be combined with ammonium ion, NH_4^+, to produce a buffer solution.

Example 17.2

Determine which of the following combinations of species will result in a buffer solution.

a. HCl and NaOH
b. HCO_3^- and CO_3^{2-}
c. HBr and NaBr

Solution

a. HCl is a strong acid, and NaOH is a strong base. There is no conjugate acid–base pair, so the combination of HCl and NaOH will not result in a buffer solution.
b. HCO_3^{2-} is a weak acid. CO_3^{2-} is the conjugate base of HCO_3^{2-}, so the combination of HCO_3^- and CO_3^{2-} will result in a buffer solution.
c. NaBr is a strong electrolyte. Despite the fact that Br^- is the conjugate base of HBr, hydrobromic acid is a strong acid and fully dissociates in solution. Therefore, the combination of HBr and NaBr will not result in a buffer solution.

PRACTICE PROBLEM 17.2

Determine which of the following combinations of species will result in a buffer solution.

a. HF and NaF
b. CH_3NH_2 and $CH_3NH_3^+$
c. HI and I_2

Hint: Look for a weak acid paired with its conjugate base, or a weak base paired with its conjugate acid. To identify whether an acid is strong or weak, recall the list of seven strong acids: HCl, HBr, HI, HNO_3, H_2SO_4, $HClO_4$, and $HClO_3$. To identify whether a base is strong or weak, remember that hydroxides of group 1 and group 2 metals tend to be strong bases, whereas ammonia derivatives tend to be weak bases.

To summarize the important facts about buffer solutions:

- Buffer solutions are prepared by combining, in aqueous solution, a weak acid and its conjugate base, or a weak base and its conjugate acid.

EVERYDAY CONNECTION

Human blood is buffered at a pH of 7.4, and if the pH varies more than ±0.2 units (i.e., if it dips below 7.2 or rises above 7.6), then dire results—even death—may occur. The principle of buffering is even used in a commercial pain reliever to reduce the acidity of plain aspirin and lessen the possibility of stomach upset.

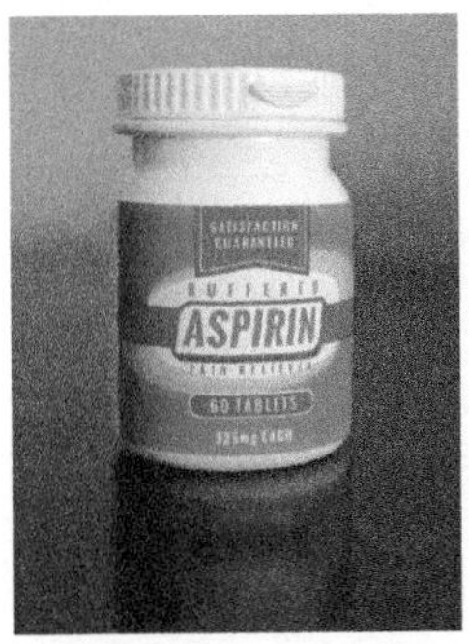

Thomas Turner, Macmillan Learning

- Buffer solutions resist changes in their pH values, even if a limited quantity of a strong acid or strong base is added.
- The pH of a buffer solution does not change appreciably when the solution is diluted.

Example 17.3

Explain how a weak base, B, and its conjugate acid, BH^+, form a buffer solution.

Solution

B and BH^+ are in equilibrium according to the equation

$$B(aq) + H_2O(l) \rightleftharpoons BH^+(aq) + OH^-(aq)$$

The equilibrium will shift left or right, in accordance with Le Châtelier's principle, reducing any added acid or base, so the pH does not change much. Adding strong base increases OH^- so the equilibrium shifts to the left. Adding strong acid decreases OH^- so the equilibrium shifts to the right.

PRACTICE PROBLEM 17.3

Explain why a solution of the strong acid $HClO_4$ and its conjugate base, ClO_4^-, does *not* act as a buffer solution.

Hint: $HClO_4$ is a strong acid. Consider the type of arrow used in the equation for the ionization of a strong acid.

Example 17.4

a. Ammonia, NH_3, and ammonium chloride, NH_4Cl, are combined to form a buffer with initial concentrations of $[NH_3] = 0.21$ M and $[NH_4^+] = 0.14$ M. The K_b of NH_3 is 1.8×10^{-5}. Calculate the pH of this buffer.

b. How does your answer change if you treat the initial concentrations as equilibrium concentrations, and plug them directly into the K_b expression?

Solution

a. Construct an ICE table (Section 15.4) that includes the initial concentrations of both NH_3 and NH_4^+.

	NH_3 (aq)	+ H_2O(l) $\rightleftharpoons$	NH_4^+ (aq)	+ OH^- (aq)
Initial (M)	0.21		0.14	0
Change (M)	$-x$		$+x$	$+x$
Equilibrium (M)	$0.21 - x$		$0.14 + x$	x

Use the equilibrium expression to solve for x.

$$K_b = \frac{[NH_4^+][OH^-]}{[NH_3]} = 1.8 \times 10^{-5}$$

$$K_b = \frac{(0.14 + x)(x)}{(0.21 - x)} = 1.8 \times 10^{-5}$$

Assume that the value of x is less than 5% of the original concentrations of NH_3 and NH_4^+, so the $(0.14 + x)$ and $(0.21 - x)$ terms simplify to 0.14 and 0.21, respectively:

$$\frac{(0.14)(x)}{(0.21)} = 1.8 \times 10^{-5}$$

$$x = \frac{(0.21)(1.8 \times 10^{-5})}{(0.14)}$$

$$x = [OH^-] = 2.7 \times 10^{-5}\ \text{M}$$

Now calculate the solution pOH and finally pH.

$$pOH = -\log(2.7 \times 10^{-5}) = 4.57$$

$$pH = 14.00 - pOH$$

$$pH = 14.00 - 4.57 = 9.43$$

b. Equilibrium concentrations can be plugged directly into the K_b expression.

$$K_b = \frac{[NH_4^+][OH^-]}{[NH_3]} = 1.8 \times 10^{-5}$$

$$\frac{(0.14)[OH^-]}{(0.21)} = 1.8 \times 10^{-5}$$

$$[OH^-] = \frac{(0.21)(1.8 \times 10^{-5})}{(0.14)} = 2.7 \times 10^{-5}\ \text{M}$$

The answer is the same. In a buffer, you can generally assume that the ionization, x, will be minimal, meaning that the equilibrium concentrations are nearly equal to the initial concentrations.

PRACTICE PROBLEM 17.4

Cyanic acid, HCNO, and cyanate ion, CNO^-, are combined to make a buffer with initial concentrations of $[HCNO] = 0.125$ M and $[CNO^-] = 0.160$ M. The K_a of cyanic acid is 3.5×10^{-4}. Calculate the pH of this buffer.

Hint: Start by writing the K_a expression for the ionization.

$$HCNO(aq) + H_2O(l) \rightleftharpoons CNO^-(aq) + H_3O^+(aq)$$

Assume that the initial concentrations are approximately equal to the equilibrium concentrations, such that you can substitute them directly into the K_a expression.

> Because of the common-ion effect, buffers ionize very little, making the starting concentrations of the conjugate pair a very good approximation for the equilibrium concentrations.

SECTION REVIEW

- The common-ion effect is a phenomenon in which the ionization of a weak electrolyte is suppressed when a weak electrolyte and a strong electrolyte that contains a common ion are combined.
- A buffer solution consists of a weak acid and its conjugate base, or a weak base and its conjugate acid. Buffer solutions resist changes in pH.

17.2 The Henderson–Hasselbalch Equation

GOAL

- Apply the Henderson–Hasselbalch equation to calculate the pH of buffer solutions.

Background Review

Chapter 0 Math Review: Section 0.5—Logarithms and Antilogs

Chapter 16 Acid–Base Theory

For buffer solutions, you have determined $[H_3O^+]$ by constructing an ICE table, and approximated $[H_3O^+]$ by plugging initial concentrations into the K_a expression. Building on the latter method, consider a weak acid, HA, and its conjugate base, A^-.

$$HA(aq) + H_2O(l) \rightleftharpoons H_3O^+(aq) + A^-(aq)$$

$$K_a = \frac{[H_3O^+][A^-]}{[HA]}$$

The equilibrium expression for the preceding reaction can be rearranged to relate the H_3O^+ concentration to the rest of the variables.

$$[H_3O^+] = K_a\frac{[HA]}{[A^-]}$$

Taking the negative logarithm of both sides of the equation gives an expression relating the pH to the pK_a of the acid and the relative concentrations of the acidic and basic components of the buffer:

$$-\log[H_3O^+] = -\log(K_a) - \log\frac{[HA]}{[A^-]}$$

Recalling that $pH = -\log[H_3O^+]$ and that $pK_a = -\log(K_a)$,

$$pH = pK_a - \log\frac{[HA]}{[A^-]}$$

Now,

$$-\log\frac{[HA]}{[A^-]} = -(\log[HA] - \log[A^-])$$

$$= -\log[HA] + \log[A^-]$$

$$-\log[HA] + \log[A^-] = \log\frac{[A^-]}{[HA]}$$

Therefore,

$$pH = pK_a + \log\frac{[A^-]}{[HA]} \quad (17.3)$$

This equation is known as the **Henderson–Hasselbalch equation**. It can be used to calculate the pH of a buffer with specific concentrations of HA and A^-.

> Notice that the concentration terms in the Henderson–Hasselbalch equation are in a ratio, $\frac{[A^-]}{[HA]}$.
>
> $$pH = pK_a + \log\frac{[A^-]}{[HA]}$$
>
> Since $\frac{n/V}{n/V} = \frac{n}{n}$, it is appropriate to use either concentrations or moles of HA and A^- in this equation.

The Henderson–Hasselbalch equation uses the assumption that the equilibrium concentrations are approximately equal to the initial concentrations. Therefore, it is only useful in cases in which ionization is less than 5%. Although this criterion is satisfied in most situations, buffers in which the initial concentrations are less than 200 times greater than K_a may deviate from what the Henderson–Hasselbalch equation would predict. For example, the equilibrium concentrations and pH of a buffer containing 0.010 M chlorous acid, $HClO_2$, ($K_a = 1.12 \times 10^{-2}$) and 0.012 M chlorite ion, ClO_2^-, would be most accurately determined using the ICE table method *without* making the simplifications outlined in Section 15.5. For the sake of simplicity, you should assume that the subsequent buffer examples and problems in this section have sufficiently low K_a values and sufficiently high acid and conjugate base concentrations that the use of the Henderson–Hasselbalch equation is appropriate.

Example 17.5

a. Calculate the pH of a buffer that contains 0.170 M formic acid and 0.120 M sodium formate. The K_a of formic acid is 1.8×10^{-4}.

b. Calculate the pH of a buffer that contains 0.100 mol formic acid and 0.150 mol sodium formate.

Solution

a. The pK_a of formic acid is $-\log K_a = -\log(1.8 \times 10^{-4}) = 3.74$. You are given the concentration of the acid and its conjugate base, so use the Henderson–Hasselbalch equation to solve for the pH.

$$pH = pK_a + \log\frac{[A^-]}{[HA]}$$

$$pH = 3.74 + \log\frac{0.120}{0.170}$$

$$pH = 3.74 + (-0.151) = 3.59$$

b. Moles can be used in the Henderson–Hasselbalch equation instead of concentrations.

$$pH = 3.74 + \log\frac{0.150}{0.100}$$

$$pH = 3.74 + 0.176 = 3.92$$

Note in part (a), where there is more formic acid than formate ion, that the solution pH is *lower* than the pK_a of formic acid. In part (b), on the other hand, where there is more conjugate base than acid, the solution pH is *higher* than the pK_a.

PRACTICE PROBLEM 17.5

Calculate the pH of a buffer that contains 0.220 M NH_3 and 0.150 M NH_4Cl. The K_a of the ammonium ion is 5.65×10^{-10}.

Hint: Use the Henderson–Hasselbalch equation.

$$pH = pK_a + \log\frac{[A^-]}{[HA]}$$

In this case, the acid, HA, is NH_4^+, and the conjugate base, A^-, is NH_3.

The Henderson–Hasselbalch equation can also be used to determine the relative concentrations of HA and A^- that are necessary to make a buffer solution with a specific pH value as shown in Figure 17.2 and Example 17.6.

Example 17.6

Calculate the relative concentrations of acetate ion and acetic acid that must be used to make a buffer solution with a pH of 4.00. The K_a of acetic acid is 1.8×10^{-5}.

Solution

The pK_a of acetic acid is $-\log(1.8 \times 10^{-5}) = 4.74$.

$$pH = pK_a + \log\frac{[A^-]}{[HA]}$$

$$4.00 = 4.74 + \log\frac{[\text{acetate ion}]}{[\text{acetic acid}]}$$

$$-0.74 = \log\frac{[\text{acetate ion}]}{[\text{acetic acid}]}$$

$$\frac{[\text{acetate ion}]}{[\text{acetic acid}]} = 10^{-0.74} = 0.18$$

The concentration of acetate ion in the buffer must be 0.18 times the concentration of acetic acid.

Steve Lemon, Macmillan Learning

FIGURE 17.2 Video Tutorial: Buffer Preparation

NOTE: You need to be online to access this video.

This video shows how to calculate the $[A^-]/[HA]$ ratio for a buffer with a specified pH.

PRACTICE PROBLEM 17.6

Calculate the relative concentrations of bicarbonate ion, HCO_3^-, and carbonate ion, CO_3^{2-}, that must be used to make a buffer solution with a pH of 10.0. The K_a of the bicarbonate ion is 5.0×10^{-11}.

Hint: Use the Henderson–Hasselbalch equation (Equation 17.3) to solve for the ratio $\frac{[A^-]}{[HA]}$.

BUFFER CAPACITY

The effectiveness of a buffer solution is based on two factors: buffer capacity and effective pH range. **Buffer capacity** refers to the ability of the buffer solution to resist a change in pH when an acid or base is added. A buffer that has a higher concentration of conjugate acid and conjugate base will resist a pH change more strongly than a buffer with a lower concentration of conjugate acid and conjugate base.

The effectiveness of a buffer also depends on the pH range over which the buffer can usefully resist a change in pH. As you will see later in this section, buffers resist a pH change most effectively when the concentrations of the acid and conjugate base components of the buffer are equal. In other words, buffers are optimally effective at a pH that is numerically equal to the pK_a of the buffer's conjugate acid. (Recall that the pK_a of a weak acid is equal to $-\log K_a$.) Buffers are typically useful at pH values that are within ± 1 units of the conjugate acid's pK_a. For example, acetic acid has a pK_a of 4.75. Therefore, you could expect an acetic acid buffer solution to be effective between pH 3.75 and 5.75.

> An effective buffer has a pH within 1 unit of the conjugate acid's pK_a and has significant quantities of both the conjugate acid and base.

Example 17.7

Use Table 16.2 to select the weak acid(s) that could be used to buffer a solution at pH 5.5.

Solution

The pK_a of the acid should be within 1 unit of the pH, that is, between 4.5 and 6.5. Convert these pK_a values to K_a values so that you can compare them to the acids in the table.

$$10^{-6.5} = 3.16 \times 10^{-7}$$
$$10^{-4.5} = 3.16 \times 10^{-5}$$

Acetic acid has a K_a of 1.76×10^{-5}, which is a pK_a of 4.75. This is the only acid in the table with a pK_a value that is within 1 unit of pH 5.5. Therefore, a buffer containing acetic acid and its conjugate base, acetate ion, will work effectively at pH 5.5.

PRACTICE PROBLEM 17.7

Use Table 16.2 to select the weak acid that could be used to buffer a solution at pH 10.8.

Hint: The pK_a of the acid should be within 1 pH unit of the pH, that is, between 9.8 and 11.8. Recall that $pK_a = -\log K_a$ and $K_a = 10^{-pK_a}$.

Example 17.8

a. Calculate the pH of 1.00 L of a buffer containing 0.150 mol of acetic acid ($HC_2H_3O_2$) and 0.195 mol of sodium acetate ($NaC_2H_3O_2$).
b. Calculate the new pH after 0.0300 mol of solid NaOH is added to the buffer from part (a). Assume that the volume of the solution does not change.
c. Calculate the pH after 0.0300 mol of solid NaOH is added to 1.000 L of pure water.

Solution

a. Use the Henderson–Hasselbalch equation with either concentrations or moles.

$$pH = pK_a + \log\frac{[A^-]}{[HA]}$$

$$pH = -\log(1.8 \times 10^{-5}) + \log\frac{0.195}{0.150} = 4.86$$

b. An acid and a base will react to completion. In this case, there is some acetic acid left over after the neutralization because NaOH is the limiting reactant.

	$HC_2H_3O_2$ (aq)	+	NaOH (aq)	→	$NaC_2H_3O_2$ (aq)	+	H_2O (l)
Initial	0.150				0.0300		0.195
Change	−0.0300				−0.0300		+0.0300
Final	0.120				0		0.225

$$pH = -\log(1.8 \times 10^{-5}) + \log\frac{0.225}{0.120} = 5.02$$

The buffer pH rose only slightly after the addition of NaOH, from 4.86 to 5.02, a difference of only 0.16 pH units.

c. If 0.030 mol of NaOH were added to 1.00 L of pure water, the resulting solution would contain 0.030 M OH^-. This pH of 0.0300 M NaOH in pure water is

$$pOH = -\log(0.030) = 1.52$$
$$pH + pOH = 14.00$$
$$pH + 1.52 = 14.00$$
$$pH = 12.48$$

The unbuffered solution pH rose from 7.00 to 12.48, a difference of 5.48 pH units.

PRACTICE PROBLEM 17.8

a. Find the pH of a buffer solution containing 0.250 M $H_2PO_4^-$ and 0.200 M HPO_4^{2-}. The K_a of $H_2PO_4^-$ is 6.32×10^{-8}.

b. Find the pH after 50.0 mL of 0.500 M KOH is added to the buffer from part (a).

c. Find the pH after 50.0 mL of 0.500 M KOH is added to 500.0 mL of pure water.

Hint: For parts (b) and (c), you'll need to account for the volume change. In the previous example, solid base was added so the volume did not change. This time, the new volume is 50.0 mL + 500.0 mL = 550.0 mL and all the concentrations change accordingly. Use $M_1V_1 = M_2V_2$ to find the new concentrations immediately after mixing. Alternatively, you can do the entire calculation in moles instead.

EVERYDAY CONNECTION

It is critical that human blood pH is 7.4 ± 0.2. Blood contains three main buffer systems that maintain this pH. The first is a phosphate buffer system.

$$H_2PO_4^-(aq) + H_2O(l) \rightleftharpoons HPO_4^{2-}(aq) + H_3O^+(aq) \quad pK_a \approx 6.8$$

Proteins contain many ionizable groups that also allow them to be involved in buffering.

$$HProtein(aq) + H_2O(l) \rightleftharpoons Protein^-(aq) + H_3O^+(aq) \quad pK_a \approx 7$$

Carbon dioxide and the bicarbonate ion make up the third and most important buffering system. When gaseous CO_2 dissolves in water, it is hydrated to form carbonic acid, H_2CO_3. This hydration is catalyzed by the enzyme carbonic anhydrase.

$$CO_2(g) + H_2O(l) \rightleftharpoons H_2CO_3(aq) \rightleftharpoons H^+(aq) + HCO_3^-(aq)$$

The concentration of H_2CO_3 in blood is very low, so the effective equilibrium is

$$CO_2(g) + H_2O(l) \rightleftharpoons H^+(aq) + HCO_3^-(aq) \quad pK_a \approx 6.1$$

Despite the pK_a of this third buffer system being relatively far-removed from the target pH of 7.4, the buffer is still effective because a large number of human metabolic by-products are acidic and the relatively high concentration of HCO_3^- at pH 7.4 is effective at neutralizing them. The resulting H_2CO_3 product is then recycled into the buffer system. This buffer system also allows for the regulation of pH by the partial pressure of CO_2 in the blood. In the medical field, the partial pressures of gases in blood are denoted by the letter p preceding the formula (e.g., pCO_2), as shown in this photo of an analysis of blood.

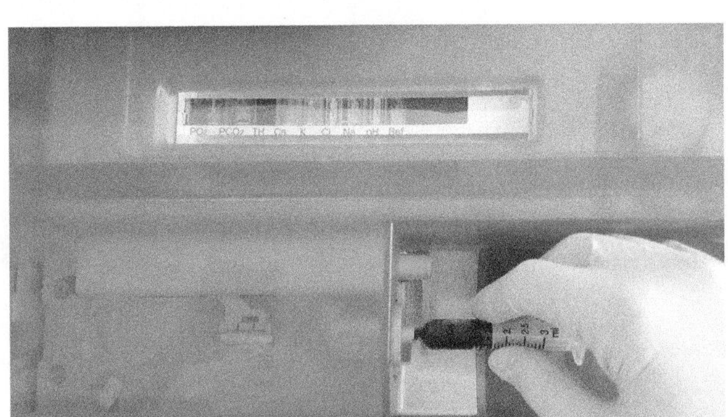

Chamaiporn Naprom/Shutterstock

SECTION REVIEW

- Buffer capacity is the ability of the buffer solution to resist a change in pH when an acid or base is added.
- Buffers resist a pH change most effectively when the concentrations of the weak acid and conjugate base components of the buffer are equal, when the conjugate acid and base concentrations are appreciably high compared to the conjugate acid's K_a value, and when the pH of the solution is ± 1 unit from the acid's pK_a.
- The Henderson–Hasselbalch equation relates the pH of a buffer solution to the pK_a of the acid, the concentration of the acid, HA, and the concentration of its conjugate base, A^-:

$$pH = pK_a + \log\frac{[A^-]}{[HA]}$$

17.3 Titrations of Strong Acids and Strong Bases

GOALS

- Compare and contrast the titration curves of strong acids and strong bases.
- Calculate the pH values and/or concentrations of relevant species at different areas along the titration curves.

Background Review

Chapter 5 Stoichiometry: Section 5.9—Titration

Chapter 16 Acid–Base Theory

Section 5.9 introduced titrations, in which a solution of known concentration (the **titrant**) is added to a solution of unknown concentration (the **analyte**). An indicator (Figure 17.3) was used to determine the stoichiometric equivalence point of the titration, which allows you to calculate the number of moles of titrant, and finally the concentration of the analyte.

This section focuses on the change in pH during a titration, which requires a modified lab setup (Figure 17.4). Here, a pH meter monitors the analyte pH as it changes, allowing you to plot a graph, called a **titration curve**, for pH versus the volume of titrant added.

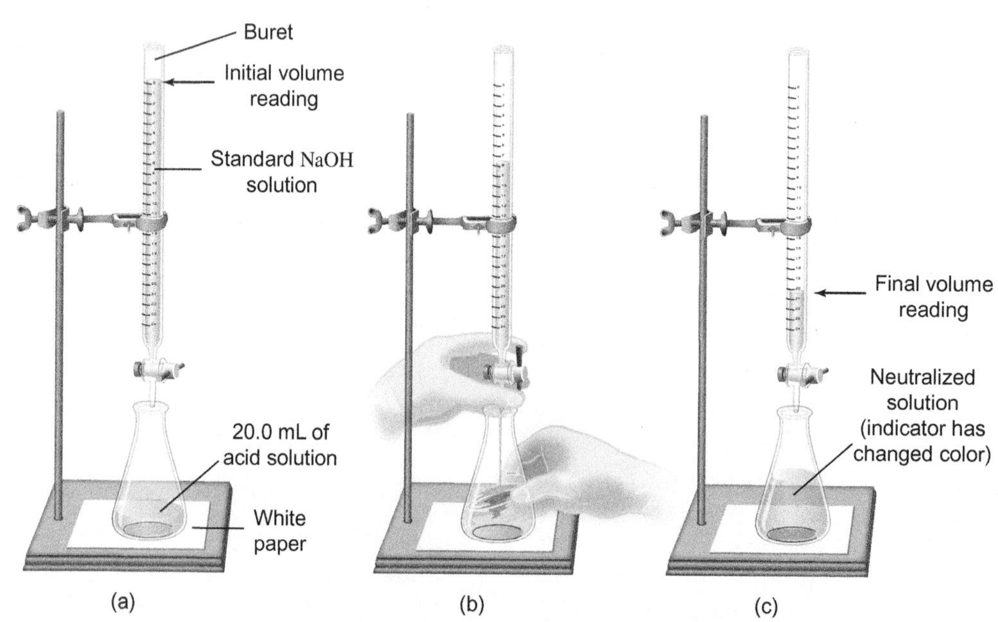

FIGURE 17.3 Titration with an Indicator

NOTE: You need to be online to access this video.

A beaker contains an unknown concentration of HCl. An NaOH solution of known concentration is added via a buret. The HCl solution contains the indicator phenolphthalein, which changes from colorless to pink very near the equivalence point of the titration. The use of indicators is discussed in greater detail later in this section.

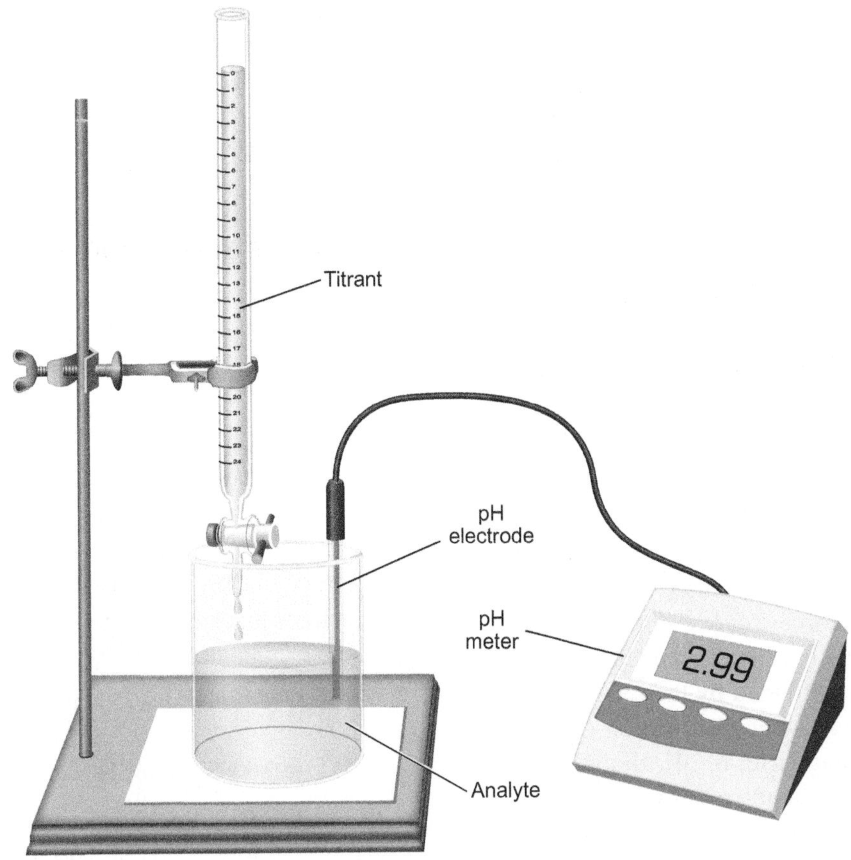

FIGURE 17.4 Titration with a pH Meter
As an alternative to an indicator, a pH meter can be used to monitor the solution pH and identify the equivalence point of a titration. In the case of a strong acid–strong base titration, such as the titration of HCl with NaOH, the equivalence point is at pH 7.0.

STRONG ACID–STRONG BASE TITRATIONS

A plot of pH versus volume of titrant for a typical strong acid–strong base titration is shown in Figure 17.5.

The focus of this section will be on the four different regions of these titration curves.

Region A: The initial pH of the solution
This is the pH of the acid or base prior to the addition of titrant. For the titration of a strong acid, HX, with a strong base, MOH, the initial solution pH is

$$pH = -\log[H_3O^+] = -\log[HX]$$

Region B: The segment of the curve between the initial pH and the equivalence point
This is the point of the titration where some titrant has been added, but the equivalence point has not been reached. The pH can be directly calculated by the amount of acid (or base, when a strong base is titrated with a strong acid) in the flask that has not yet been neutralized by the titrant. Note that the pH change at

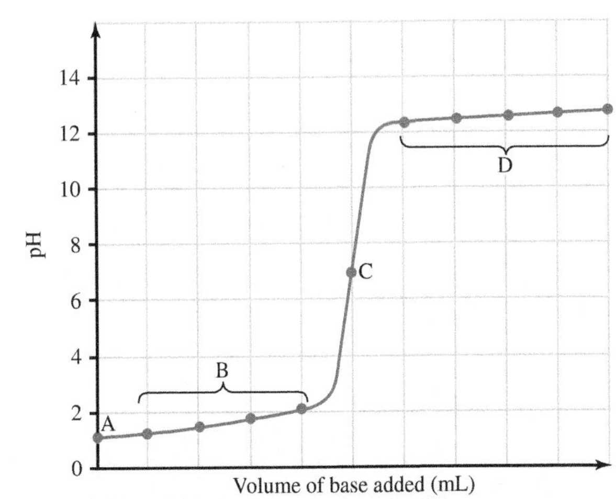

FIGURE 17.5 Titration of a Strong Acid with a Strong Base
This titration curve shows how the pH changes as a strong base is added to a strong acid. The four regions are A, the initial pH of the acid alone; B, after some base has been added but before the equivalence point; C, the equivalence point at pH = 7.0; and D, after the equivalence point where excess base determines the pH.

this point of the curve is slow at first, but then changes rapidly as the equivalence point is reached. For the titration of a strong acid with a strong base, the pH of the titration curve prior to the equivalence point is the concentration of H_3O^+ that has not been neutralized.

$$pH = -\log[H_3O^+]$$

Region C: The equivalence point
This is the point in the titration where the number of moles of added strong base is equal to the number of moles of strong acid. For a strong acid–strong base titration, the pH of the equivalence point is exactly 7.0.

Region D: The segment of the curve after the equivalence point
This is the region of the titration curve where all of the acid or base in the flask has been neutralized and the titrant is in excess. The portion of the curve near the equivalence point is steep, but then the pH change afterwards becomes far less abrupt. The pH at this point of the curve is calculated as the number of moles of excess titrant divided by the total volume of solution inside the flask. For the titration of a strong acid, HX, with a strong base, MOH, the pOH of the solution after the equivalence point is the concentration of excess OH^- in solution. The pH is then calculated from the pOH.

$$pOH = -\log[OH^-]$$
$$pH = 14.00 - pOH$$

An animation of the species present in each region of a strong acid–strong base titration curve is shown in Figure 17.6.

FIGURE 17.6 Molecular View of a Titration of a Strong Acid with a Strong Base

NOTE: You need to be online to access this video.

When strong base, NaOH, is added to strong acid, HCl, OH^- combines with H^+ to form water until the equivalence point is reached, where all the H^+ has reacted. After the equivalence point, OH^- accumulates. Note that H_3O^+ is shown as H^+ for simplicity.

Example 17.9

Suppose that 25.00 mL of a 0.255 M HCl solution is titrated with a 0.150 M solution of the strong base KOH. Determine the pH at these points:

a. before KOH is added
b. after 4.00 mL of KOH solution is added
c. at the equivalence point
d. after 50.00 mL of KOH solution is added

Solution

a. The initial pH is determined from the concentration of HCl. HCl is a strong acid, so its concentration is equal to the concentration of H^+ in solution.

$$pH = -\log(0.255) = 0.593$$

b. First, calculate the number of moles of HCl inside the flask (prior to the addition of any KOH solution) and the number of moles of KOH that are added to the flask at this point in the titration.

$$0.02500\text{ L HCl}\left(\frac{0.255\text{ mol HCl}}{1\text{ L}}\right) = 0.006375\text{ mole HCl inside the flask}$$

$$0.00400\text{ L KOH}\left(\frac{0.150\text{ mol KOH}}{1\text{ L}}\right) = 0.0006000\text{ mol KOH}$$

Then calculate the number of moles of H^+ (as HCl) remaining after the addition of KOH.

	$H^+(aq)$	+	$OH^-(aq)$	$\rightarrow H_2O(l)$
Initial	0.006375 mol		0 mol	
Addition of KOH			0.000600 mol	
Reaction change	−0.000600 mol		−0.000600 mol	
Final	0.005775 mol		0 mol	

Determine the molarity of H^+ at equilibrium. Be sure to account for the change in volume that comes with adding KOH solution.

$$[H^+] = \frac{0.005775\text{ mol}}{(0.02500\text{ L} + 0.00400\text{ L})} = 0.199\text{ M H}^+$$

Finally, calculate the pH of the solution.

$$pH = -\log(0.199) = 0.701$$

c. This is a strong acid–strong base titration and, by definition, the equivalence point is at pH 7.0.

d. Calculate the number of moles of KOH that have been added to the flask.

$$0.05000\text{ L KOH}\left(\frac{0.150\text{ mol KOH}}{1\text{ L}}\right) = 0.007500\text{ mol KOH}$$

Recall from part (a) that there are 0.006375 mol of H^+ inside the flask prior to the addition of KOH. You can see that this value is less than the number of moles of KOH added to the flask, so the titration is past the equivalence point and an excess of OH^- is present.

	$H^+(aq)$	+	$OH^-(aq)$	$\rightarrow H_2O(l)$
Initial	0.006375 mol		0 mol	
Addition of KOH			0.007500 mol	
Reaction change	−0.006375 mol		−0.006375 mol	
Final	0 mol		0.001125 mol	

Determine the concentration of OH^-. Be sure once again to account for the volume of KOH solution added.

$$[OH^-] = \frac{0.001125 \text{ mol}}{(0.02500 \text{ L} + 0.05000 \text{ L})} = 0.0150 \text{ M OH}^-$$

Now that $[OH^-]$ is known, you can calculate the pOH and then use the relationship, pH + pOH = 14.000, from Section 16.4 to calculate the pH:

$$pOH = -\log[OH^-]$$
$$pOH = -\log(0.0150) = 1.824$$
$$pH = 14.000 - 1.824 = 12.176$$

PRACTICE PROBLEM 17.9

Suppose that 25.00 mL of a 0.300 M solution of the strong acid $HClO_4$ is titrated with a 0.225 M solution of NaOH. Determine the pH at these points:

a. before NaOH is added
b. after 25.00 mL of NaOH solution is added
c. at the equivalence point
d. after 40.00 mL of NaOH solution is added

Hint: Part 9a) is a typical strong acid calculation, $pH = -\log[H_3O^+]$, where the concentration of H_3O^+ is equal to the concentration of $HClO_4$.

Part (b) is also a strong acid calculation, but you first need to use stoichiometry (NaOH is the limiting reactant) to determine the amount of acid remaining. You also need to take into account the total volume: 25.00 mL + 25.00 mL = 50.00 mL.

Part (c) does not require a calculation. At the equivalence point of a strong acid–strong base titration, the solution is always neutral.

Part (d) is a typical strong base calculation, $pOH = -\log[OH^-]$, $pH = 14.00 - pOH$, where the concentration of hydroxide is equal to the concentration of NaOH. However, a stoichiometry step is required first to determine how much NaOH is in excess after all the $HClO_4$ is used up ($HClO_4$ is the limiting reactant). Don't forget to account for the total volume: 25.00 mL + 40.00 mL = 65.00 mL.

STRONG BASE–STRONG ACID TITRATIONS

The titration of a strong base with a strong acid shown in Figure 17.7 gives a titration curve with a similar shape to the titration curve of a strong acid with a strong base (see Figure 17.5). As with the titration of a strong acid with a strong base, the titration of a strong base with a strong acid has a pH of 7.0 at the equivalence point. The main difference between the titration curves in Figure 17.5 and Figure 17.7 is that the starting and ending pH values are on opposite ends of the pH scale. In the titration of a strong base with a strong acid, the initial pH is basic and the pH past the equivalence point is acidic.

Example 17.10

Suppose that 35.00 mL of a 0.180 M NaOH solution is titrated with a 0.150 M solution of HCl.

a. Determine the pH before any HCl is added.
b. Determine the pH after 15.75 mL of HCl solution is added.
c. Determine the volume of HCl that is needed to reach the equivalence point.
d. Determine the pH of the solution after 43.25 mL of HCl solution is added.

Solution

a. NaOH is a strong base, so it dissociates completely to Na^+ and OH^-.

$$pOH = -\log(0.180) = 0.745$$
$$pH = 14.000 - 0.745 = 13.255$$

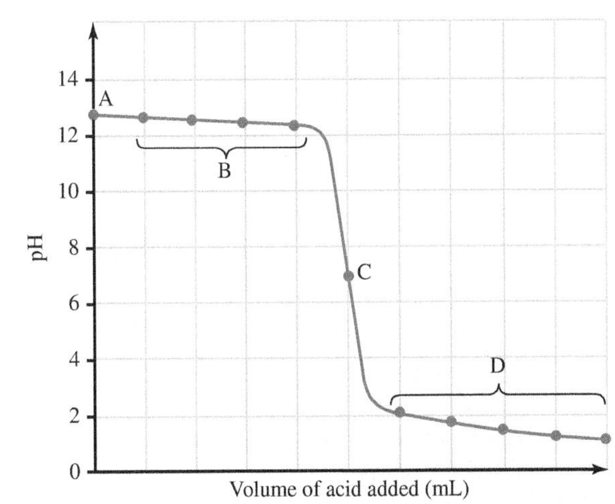

FIGURE 17.7 Titration of a Strong Base with a Strong Acid
The titration curve represents the addition of a strong acid to a solution of a strong base. The four regions are A, the initial pH of the base alone; B, after some acid has been added but before the equivalence point; C, the equivalence point at pH = 7.0; and D, after the equivalence point where excess acid determines the pH.

b. First, calculate the number of moles of NaOH inside the flask (prior to the addition of any HCl solution) and the number of moles of HCl that are added to the flask at this point in the titration.

$$0.03500 \text{ L NaOH}\left(\frac{0.180 \text{ mol NaOH}}{1 \text{ L}}\right)$$
$$= 0.006300 \text{ mol NaOH inside the flask}$$

$$0.01575 \text{ L HCl}\left(\frac{0.150 \text{ mol HCl}}{1 \text{ L}}\right)$$
$$= 0.002363 \text{ mol HCl}$$

Then calculate the number of moles of OH^- (as NaOH) remaining after the addition of HCl.

	$H^+(aq)$	+	$OH^-(aq)$	$\rightarrow H_2O(l)$
Initial	0 mol		0.006300 mol	
Addition of HCl	0.002363 mol			
Reaction change	−0.002363 mol		−0.002363 mol	
Final	0 mol		0.003937 mol	

Determine the concentration of OH^-. Be sure to account for the volume of HCl solution added.

$$[OH^-] = \frac{0.003937 \text{ mol}}{(0.03500 \text{ L} + 0.01575 \text{ L})} = 0.07758 \text{ M } OH^-$$

$$pOH = -\log[OH^-]$$
$$pOH = -\log(0.07758) = 1.110$$
$$pH = 14.000 - 1.110 = 12.890$$

c. From part (a), there are 0.006300 moles of NaOH inside the flask. Because HCl reacts with NaOH in a 1:1 molar ratio, 0.006300 moles of HCl must be added to reach the equivalence point of the titration. The volume of HCl needed to reach the equivalence point is the number of moles of HCl divided by the concentration of HCl.

$$0.006300 \text{ mol HCl}\left(\frac{1 \text{ L}}{0.150 \text{ mol HCl}}\right)$$
$$= 0.04200 \text{ L} = 42.00 \text{ mL}$$

Thus, 42.00 mL of the HCl solution must be added to reach the equivalence point.

d. Calculate the number of moles of HCl that have been added to the flask.

$$0.04325 \text{ L HCl}\left(\frac{0.150 \text{ mol HCl}}{1 \text{ L}}\right) = 0.006488 \text{ mol HCl}$$

Recall from part (a) that the flask contained 0.006300 mol OH^- prior to the addition of HCl. This value is less than the number of moles of HCl that have been added to the flask, so the titration is past the equivalence point.

	$H^+(aq)$	+	$OH^-(aq)$	$\rightarrow H_2O(l)$
Initial	0 mol		0.006300 mol	
Addition of KOH	0.006488 mol			
Reaction change	−0.006300 mol		−0.006300 mol	
Final	0.0001880 mol		0 mol	

Determine the concentration of H^+. Be sure once again to account for the volume of HCl solution added.

$$[H^+] = \frac{0.0001880 \text{ mol}}{(0.03500 \text{ L} + 0.04325 \text{ L})} = 0.002403 \text{ M } H^+$$

Calculate the pH of the solution.

$$pH = -\log(0.002403) = 2.619$$

PRACTICE PROBLEM 17.10

Suppose that 25.00 mL of a 0.200 M KOH solution is titrated with a 0.150 M solution of the strong acid HBr. Determine the pH of the solution at each of these points.

a. before any HBr is added
b. at half of the equivalence point
c. at the equivalence point
d. at 1.00 mL of HBr past the equivalence point

Hint: Part (a) is a typical strong base calculation, $pOH = -\log[OH^-]$, $pH = 14.00 - pOH$, where the concentration of OH^- is equal to the concentration of KOH.

Part (b) is also a strong base calculation, but you first need to use stoichiometry (HBr is the limiting reactant) to determine the amount of base remaining. You also need to take into account the total volume, which requires determining the volume of HBr added at the equivalence point, so you can halve it for the half-equivalence point.

Part (c) does not require a calculation. At the equivalence point of a strong base–strong acid titration, the solution is always neutral.

Part (d) is a typical strong acid calculation $pH = -\log[H_3O^+]$, where the concentration of hydronium is equal to the concentration of HBr. However, a stoichiometry step is required first to determine how much HBr is in excess after all the KOH is used up (KOH is the limiting reactant). Don't forget to account for the total volume.

SECTION REVIEW

- There are four general areas of a titration curve: the initial pH, the area after the initial point and prior to the equivalence point, the equivalence point, and the area after the equivalence point. You have been shown how to calculate the pH in all four areas.
- The equivalence point of a strong acid–strong base titration or a strong base–strong acid titration is 7.0.

17.4 Titrations of Weak Acids and Weak Bases

GOALS

- Compare and contrast the titration curves of weak acids and weak bases.
- Calculate the pH values and/or concentrations of relevant species at different areas along the titration curves.

Background Review

Chapter 5 Stoichiometry: Section 5.9—Titration

Chapter 16 Acid–Base Theory

WEAK ACID–STRONG BASE TITRATIONS

Figure 17.8 shows a titration curve of a weak acid with a strong base. The titration curve represents the addition of NaOH (a strong base) to a solution of acetic acid, HCH_3CO_2 (a weak acid). The pH of the equivalence point is greater than 7 (i.e., basic).

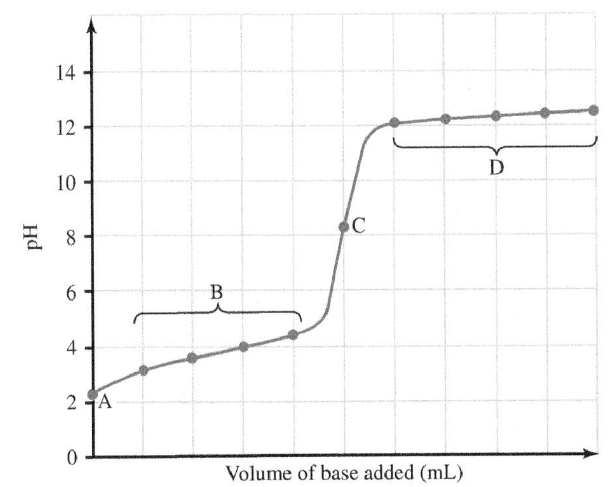

FIGURE 17.8 Titration of a Weak Acid with a Strong Base
This titration curve shows how the pH changes as strong base is added to a weak acid. The four regions are A, the initial pH of the acid alone; B, the buffer range, where some conjugate base has been produced from the reaction, but not all the weak acid has been consumed; C, the equivalence point at pH > 7.0; and D, after the equivalence point where excess base determines the pH.

As shown in Figure 17.9, a weak acid–strong base titration curve is different from a strong acid–strong base curve in several ways.

- The pH of the equivalence point is >7. This is because weak acids do not release as much H^+ into solution as strong acids, and also because the conjugate bases of weak acids are appreciably basic. In contrast, the equivalence points of strong acid–strong base titrations are always 7 because conjugate bases of strong acids have negligible basicity. The weaker the acid, the higher the pH at the equivalence point.
- The initial pH of a weak acid, before the titration begins, is higher than that of a strong acid. The weaker the acid (i.e., the lower the K_a value), the higher the initial pH of the titration. It is difficult to titrate weak acids with K_a values smaller than 10^{-10}, because the pH change at the equivalence point is small and gradual.
- Weak acids titrated with strong bases display a less abrupt pH change near the equivalence point than strong acids titrated with strong bases. The lower the K_a of the acid, the more "elongated" the titration curve.
- The lower the K_a of a weak acid, the higher the initial rise in pH when base is added. This is due in part to the fact that acids become increasingly poor at resisting pH changes from the addition of base as their K_a values decrease.

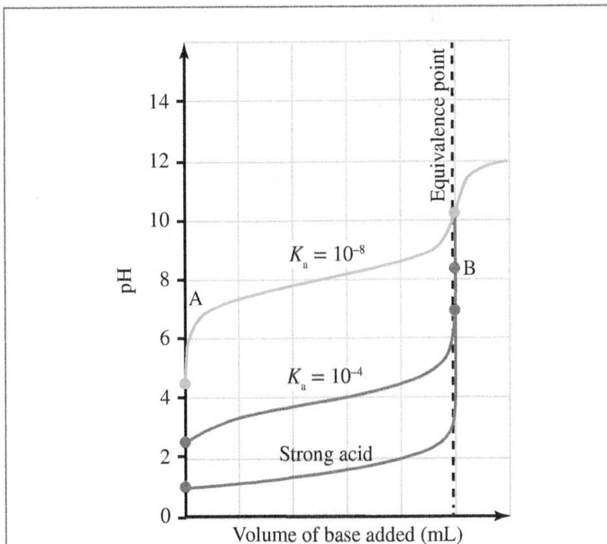

FIGURE 17.9 Titrations of Acids of Variable Strength with a Strong Base
The initial pH and the pH at the equivalence point both increase as the K_a of the weak acid decreases. The titration curve for a strong acid is provided for comparison.

Example 17.11

An equal amount of each of the following weak acids is titrated with 0.100 M NaOH. Determine which acid would have the highest pH at the equivalence point of the titration and which acid would have the lowest pH at the equivalence point.

0.100 M acetic acid ($pK_a = 4.75$)
0.100 M benzoic acid ($pK_a = 4.20$)
0.100 M pyridinium ion ($pK_a = 5.23$)

Solution

Recall that as acid strength decreases, the acid releases less H^+ into solution and its conjugate base increases in strength. Consequently, when a weak acid is titrated with a strong base, the pH of the equivalence point increases with decreasing acid strength. Also recall that as the K_a of an acid decreases, its pK_a increases. Therefore, pyridinium ion (highest pK_a) is the weakest of the three acids, while benzoic acid (lowest pK_a) is the strongest of the three acids. Given that the acid and base concentrations are equal in all three titrations, benzoic acid would have the lowest pH at the equivalence point of its titration because it is the strongest of the three acids. The pyridinium ion would have the highest pH at the equivalence point of its titration because it is the weakest acid.

PRACTICE PROBLEM 17.11

An equal amount of each of the weak acids below is titrated with 0.100 M NaOH. Determine which acid would have the lowest pH at the equivalence point of the titration and which acid would have the highest pH at the equivalence point.

0.100 M ammonium ion ($pK_a = 9.24$)
0.100 M phenol ($pK_a = 9.98$)
0.100 M hypobromous acid ($pK_a = 8.63$)

Hint: Recall that acidity is inversely related to pH, so the weakest acid will result in the highest pH.

When determining the pH values at different points during a weak acid–strong base titration (Figure 17.8), there are again four main regions.

Region A: The initial pH of the solution

The initial pH of a weak acid (HA), before the addition of a strong base (MOH), is calculated from the acid's equilibrium expression, as described in Section 16.5. The equilibrium expression can be simplified in cases where less than 5% of the weak acid ionizes.

$$HA(aq) + H_2O(l) \rightleftharpoons A^-(aq) + H_3O^+(aq)$$

$$K_a = \frac{[A^-][H_3O^+]}{[HA]} \approx \frac{x^2}{[HA]}$$

$$[H_3O^+] = x = \sqrt{K_a \cdot [HA]} \qquad (17.4)$$

$$pH = -\log[H_3O^+] = -\log\sqrt{K_a \cdot [HA]}$$

Region B: The segment of the curve between the initial pH and the equivalence point

After strong base is added but before the equivalence point, you have a buffer because some A^- has been produced but not all the HA is used up. Stoichiometry dictates the concentrations of weak acid and conjugate base, which can be plugged into the Henderson–Hasselbalch equation.

$$\begin{array}{ccccccc} HA(aq) & + & OH^-(aq) & \rightarrow & A^-(aq) & + & H_2O(l) \\ -x & & -x & & +x & & \end{array}$$

$$pH = pK_a + \log\frac{[A^-]}{[HA]}$$

Note that *all* of the strong base reacts, so x is equal to the amount of OH^-.

Region C: The equivalence point

At the equivalence point, only the conjugate base remains. The pH calculation is the same as that of a basic salt from Section 16.7.

$$A^-(aq) + H_2O(l) \rightleftharpoons HA(aq) + OH^-(aq)$$

$$K_b = \frac{K_w}{K_a}$$

$$K_b \approx \frac{x^2}{[A^-]}$$

$$[OH^-] = x = \sqrt{K_b \cdot [A^-]} \qquad (17.5)$$

$$pOH = -\log[OH^-] = -\log\sqrt{K_b \cdot [A^-]}$$

$$pH = 14.00 - pOH$$

Region D: The segment of the curve after the equivalence point

Past the equivalence point, the solution pH depends almost completely on the concentration of excess OH^- added. The contribution of the conjugate base to the solution pH at this point in the titration can be assumed to be negligible.

$$pOH = -\log[OH^-]$$

$$pH = 14.00 - pOH$$

The implementation of these steps to determine the pH at different points of a weak acid–strong base titration curve is described in detail in Figure 17.10 and Example 17.12.

Steve Lemon, Macmillan Learning

FIGURE 17.10 Video Tutorial: Weak Acid Titration Calculations

NOTE: You need to be online to access this video.

This video shows how to calculate pH at various points in the titration of a weak acid with strong base.

Example 17.12

Suppose that 40.0 mL of a 0.500 M formic acid ($HCHO_2$, $K_a = 1.8 \times 10^{-4}$) solution is titrated with a 0.500 M solution of NaOH. Assume that less than 5% of the acid ionizes in solution. Determine the pH at these points.

a. prior to the addition of NaOH

b. at half of the equivalence point

c. at the equivalence point

d. when the equivalence point has been reached and 2.0 mL of excess NaOH has been added to the solution

See the ICE table below.

Solution

a. Prior to the addition of titrant, this is a typical weak acid pH calculation (Equation 17.4).

$$\text{pH} = -\log\sqrt{K_a \cdot [\text{HCHO}_2]}$$
$$= -\log\sqrt{(1.8 \times 10^{-4})(0.500)} = 2.02$$

b. The concentrations of the acid and base are equal, and the stoichiometry is 1:1, so the equivalence point will be at 40.0 mL (0.0400 L) of NaOH added.

$$0.0400\text{ L HCHO}_2\left(\frac{0.500\text{ mol HCHO}_2}{1\text{ L}}\right)\left(\frac{1\text{ mol NaOH}}{1\text{ mol HCHO}_2}\right)\left(\frac{1\text{ L}}{0.500\text{ mol NaOH}}\right) = 0.0400\text{ L NaOH}$$

The equivalence point is at 40.0 mL (0.0400 L), so the half-equivalence point is 20.0 mL (0.0200 L). Since volumes change with the addition of titrant, it can be helpful to do the stoichiometry step with moles.

$$0.0400\text{ L}\left(\frac{0.500\text{ mol HCHO}_2}{1\text{ L}}\right) = 0.0200\text{ mol HCHO}_2$$

$$0.0200\text{ L}\left(\frac{0.500\text{ mol NaOH}}{1\text{ L}}\right) = 0.0100\text{ mol NaOH}$$

Use the Henderson–Hasselbalch equation to determine the pH of the solution at half of the equivalence point. Recall that moles can be used in place of concentrations in this equation.

$$\text{pH} = \text{p}K_a + \log\frac{[\text{CHO}_2^-]}{[\text{HCHO}_2]}$$

$$\text{pH} = -\log(1.8 \times 10^{-4}) + \log\frac{0.0100}{0.0100}$$

$$\text{pH} = 3.74 + \log(1)$$

$$\text{pH} = 3.74 + 0 = 3.74$$

At half the equivalence point of a weak acid–strong base titration, the amounts of acid and conjugate base are equal, rendering the log term of the Henderson–Hasselbalch equation equal to zero. When the amount of acid and conjugate base are equal, the solution pH is equal to the $\text{p}K_a$ of the acid.

For any weak acid–strong base titration, the pH at the half-equivalence point of the titration is equal to the $\text{p}K_a$ of the weak acid.

c. At the equivalence point of the titration, all of the formic acid (0.0200 mol) has been converted to formate ion. Determine the concentration of formate in the new total volume: 40.0 mL + 40.0 mL = 80.0 mL (0.0800 L).

$$[\text{CHO}_2^-] = \frac{0.0200\text{ mol}}{0.0800\text{ L}} = 0.250\text{ M}$$

The pH calculation is done in the same manner as that of a basic salt (as seen in Section 16.7),

	$HCHO_2(aq)$	+	OH^-	→	$CHO_2^-(aq)$	+	$H_2O(l)$
Initial	0.0200 mol				0		
Addition of NaOH			0.0100 mol				
Reaction change	−0.0100 mol		−0.0100 mol		+0.0100 mol		
Final	0.0100 mol		0		0.0100 mol		

which is similar to that of a weak base but with a calculation to find the K_b.

$$K_b = \frac{K_w}{K_a} = \frac{1.0 \times 10^{-14}}{1.8 \times 10^{-4}} = 5.6 \times 10^{-11}$$

$$\text{pOH} = -\log\sqrt{K_b \cdot [CHO_2^-]}$$

$$= -\log\sqrt{(5.6 \times 10^{-11})(0.250)} = 5.43$$

$$\text{pH} = 14.00 - 5.43 = 8.57$$

d. Past the equivalence point, the contribution of OH^- from the excess NaOH dominates. For titrations of weak acids with strong bases, you can generally ignore the OH^- produced by the reaction of the acid's conjugate base with water. Therefore, this step is a strong base pH calculation. First, calculate the number of moles of excess OH^- present.

$$0.0020\text{ L}\left(\frac{0.500\text{ mol OH}^-}{1\text{ L}}\right) = 0.00100\text{ mol OH}^-$$

The number of moles of hydroxide ion is now divided by the total solution volume. This includes the 40.0 mL of formic acid, the 40.0 mL of NaOH needed to reach the equivalence point, and the 2.00 mL of NaOH added past the equivalence point.

$$[OH^-] = \left(\frac{0.00100\text{ mol OH}^-}{0.0820\text{ L}}\right) = 0.0122\text{ M}$$

$$\text{pOH} = -\log(0.0122) = 1.91$$

$$\text{pH} = 14.00 - 1.91 = 12.09$$

PRACTICE PROBLEM 17.12

If 30.0 mL of 0.100 M weak acid (HA, $K_a = 3.5 \times 10^{-4}$) is titrated with a 0.120 M solution of KOH, determine the pH at these points. Assume that less than 5% of the acid ionizes in solution.

a. before any KOH is added
b. after 15.0 mL of KOH has been added
c. at the equivalence point
d. after 30.0 mL of KOH has been added

Hint: The concentrations of the acid and base are not equal, so the equivalence point will *not* be at 30.0 mL of KOH added. Instead, it will occur at 25.0 mL.

$$0.0300\text{ L HA}\left(\frac{0.100\text{ mol HA}}{1\text{ L HA}}\right)\left(\frac{1\text{ mol KOH}}{1\text{ mol HA}}\right)\left(\frac{1\text{ L}}{0.120\text{ mol KOH}}\right)$$

$$= 0.0250\text{ L} = 25.0\text{ mL}$$

The half-equivalence point would be at 12.5 mL KOH added.

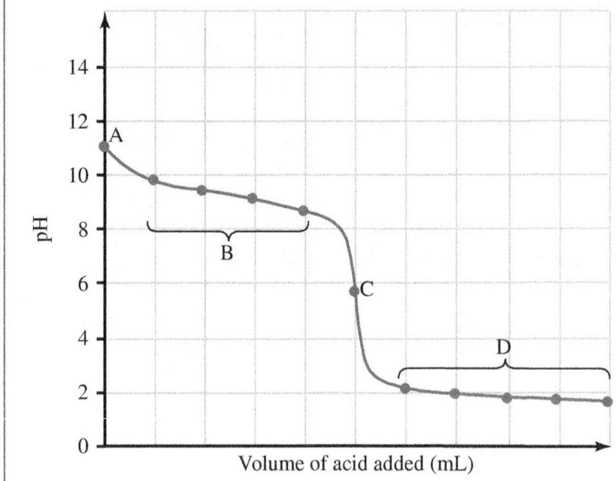

FIGURE 17.11 Titration of a Weak Base with a Strong Acid
This titration curve shows how the pH changes as strong acid is added to a weak base. The four regions are A, the initial pH of the base alone; B, the buffer range, where some conjugate acid has been produced from the reaction, but not all the weak base has been consumed; C, the equivalence point at pH > 7.0; and D, after the equivalence point where excess acid determines the pH.

WEAK BASE–STRONG ACID TITRATIONS

Figure 17.11 shows a titration curve of a weak base with a strong acid. Weak base–strong acid titrations are conceptually similar to the weak acid–strong base titrations that were just discussed. The main difference is that the initial pH is basic, rather than acidic, and the pH at the equivalence point is acidic, rather than basic. The pH at the half-equivalence point is equal to the pK_a of the conjugate acid of the weak base being titrated.

Example 17.13

Suppose that 20.0 mL of a 0.150 M solution of ammonia (NH_3, $K_b = 1.8 \times 10^{-5}$) is titrated with a 0.200 M solution of HCl. Assume that less than 5% of NH_3 ionizes in solution. Determine the pH at these points:

a. prior to the addition of HCl
b. at half of the equivalence point
c. at the equivalence point
d. when the equivalence point has been reached and 1.2 mL of excess HCl has been added to the solution

Solution

a. Calculate the pH of the NH_3 solution like a typical weak base.

$$\text{pOH} = -\log\sqrt{K_b \cdot [NH_3]}$$

$$= -\log\sqrt{(1.8 \times 10^{-5})(0.150)} = 2.78$$

$$\text{pH} = 14.00 - 2.78 = 11.22$$

b. The pH of the solution at the half-equivalence point is equal to the pK_a of NH_4^+.

$$pH = pK_a = -\log K_a$$
$$= -\log\frac{K_w}{K_b} = -\log\frac{1.0 \times 10^{-14}}{1.8 \times 10^{-5}} = 9.26$$

c. At the equivalence point, the pH is dictated by the concentration of conjugate acid, NH_4^+. Start by finding the moles of NH_4^+.

$$0.02000\ \text{L}\ NH_3\left(\frac{0.150\ \text{mol}\ NH_3}{1\ \text{L}}\right)\left(\frac{1\ \text{mol}\ NH_4^+}{1\ \text{mol}\ NH_3}\right)$$
$$= 0.00300\ \text{mol}\ NH_4^+$$

Now, determine the total solution volume. The number of moles of HCl added to reach the equivalence point (0.00300 mol) divided by the concentration of HCl gives the volume of HCl added.

$$0.00300\ \text{mol HCl}\left(\frac{1\ \text{L}}{0.200\ \text{mol HCl}}\right) = 0.0150\ \text{L HCl}$$

Determine the concentration of NH_4^+ at the equivalence point, accounting for the total volume.

$$[NH_4^+] = \frac{0.00300\ \text{mol}}{(0.0200\ \text{L} + 0.0150\ \text{L})} = 0.0857\ \text{M}$$

Calculate the pH as you would for any acidic salt, where the K_a of NH_4^+ is calculated from the K_b of NH_3.

$$K_a = \frac{K_w}{K_b} = \frac{1.0 \times 10^{-14}}{1.8 \times 10^{-5}} = 5.6 \times 10^{-10}$$
$$pH = -\log\sqrt{K_a \cdot [NH_4^+]}$$
$$= -\log\sqrt{(5.6 \times 10^{-10})(0.0857)} = 5.16$$

d. Past the equivalence point, the contribution of H_3O^+ from the excess HCl dominates, and you can generally ignore the H_3O^+ produced by the reaction of NH_4^+ with water. First, calculate the number of moles of excess H_3O^+ present.

$$0.0012\ \text{L}\left(\frac{0.200\ \text{mol HCl}}{1\ \text{L}}\right) = 2.4 \times 10^{-4}\ \text{mol HCl}$$
$$= 2.4 \times 10^{-4}\ \text{mol}\ H_3O^+$$

Find the concentration accounting for the total volume. This includes the 20.0 mL of NH_3, the 15.0 mL of HCl needed to reach the equivalence point, and the 1.2 mL of HCl added past the equivalence point. Note that 20.0 mL + 15.0 mL + 1.2 mL = 36.2 mL.

$$[H_3O^+] = \left(\frac{2.4 \times 10^{-4}\ \text{mol}\ H_3O^+}{0.0362\ \text{L}}\right) = 0.0066\ \text{M}$$
$$pH = -\log(0.0066) = 2.18$$

PRACTICE PROBLEM 17.13

Suppose 25.0 mL of a 0.200 M solution of methylamine (CH_3NH_2; $K_b = 4.3 \times 10^{-4}$) is titrated with a 0.150 M solution of HCl. Assume that less than 5% of 0.200 M CH_3NH_2 ionizes to $CH_3NH_3^+$ in solution. Determine the pH at these points:

a. before any HCl is added
b. at half of the equivalence point
c. at the equivalence point
d. after 35.00 mL of HCl has been added

Hint:

a. Treat part (a) as a typical weak base calculation using a variant of Equation 17.4.

$$pOH = \sqrt{K_b \cdot [B]}$$

b. $pH = pK_a$ at the half-equivalence point. Also recall that $pK_a = -\log K_a$ and $K_a = \frac{K_w}{K_b}$.

c. Treat part (c) as a typical acidic salt calculation using a variant of Equation 17.3.

$$pH = \sqrt{K_a \cdot [BH^+]}\ \text{where}\ K_a = \frac{K_w}{K_b}.$$

The moles of conjugate acid produced are equal to the moles of titrant consumed. Don't forget to account for the total volume.

d. First, use stoichiometry to find the moles of excess HCl (CH_3NH_2 is the limiting reactant). Then divide the moles of HCl by the total volume, and treat this as a typical strong acid calculation.

TITRATION OF POLYPROTIC ACIDS

Many weak acids have more than one ionizable proton. These include many important biological species, such as amino acids and nucleic acids. The titration curves of polyprotic acids are similar in shape to those of monoprotic weak acids, but they contain more than one equivalence point. For example, the diprotic malonic acid, $H_2CH_3H_2O_4$, has two acidic groups.

$$H_2CH_3H_2O_4(aq) + H_2O(l) \rightleftharpoons HCH_3H_2O_4^-(aq) + H_3O^+(aq) \quad K_{a1} = 1.42 \times 10^{-3}$$

$$HCH_3H_2O_4^-(aq) + H_2O(l) \rightleftharpoons CH_3H_2O_4^{2-}(aq) + H_3O^+(aq) \quad K_{a2} = 2.01 \times 10^{-6}$$

A titration curve of a generic diprotic acid, H_2A, is shown in Figure 17.12.

SECTION REVIEW

- Weak acid–strong base titration curves differ from strong acid–strong base titration curves in that the equivalence points are at pH > 7, and they display a less abrupt pH change near the equivalence point.

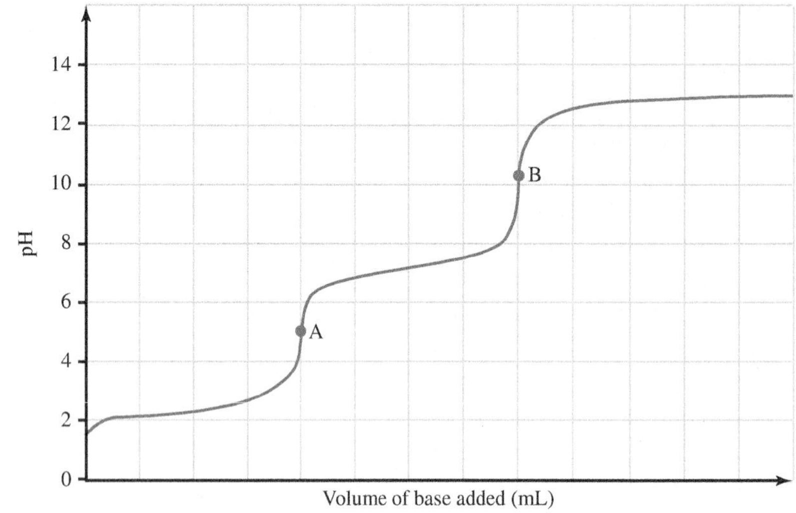

FIGURE 17.12 Titration Curve of a Diprotic Acid

This titration curve shows how the pH changes as a strong base is added to a diprotic acid. Point A is the first equivalence point, where H_2A has been completely converted to HA^-. Point B is the second equivalence point where HA^- has been completely converted to A^{2-}.

- In weak acid–strong base titration curves, the weaker the acid (i.e., the lower the K_a value), the higher the initial pH of the titration. Acids with lower K_a values also exhibit a more pronounced initial pH change when base is first added.
- For any weak acid–strong base titration, the pH at the half-equivalence point of the titration is equal to the pK_a of the weak acid.
- Weak base–strong acid titrations are conceptually similar to the weak acid–strong base titrations that were just discussed. The main difference is that the initial pH is basic, rather than acidic, and the pH at the equivalence point is acidic, rather than basic. The pH at the half-equivalence point is equal to the pK_a of the conjugate acid of the weak base being titrated.

17.5 Indicators in Acid–Base Titrations

GOAL

- Select an appropriate indicator for an acid–base titration.

Background Review

Chapter 5 Stoichiometry: Section 5.9—Titration

Chapter 16 Acid–Base Theory

An indicator can be used to determine the equivalence point of a titration (Section 5.9). For titrations of acids and bases, phenolphthalein is often used for this purpose. Phenolphthalein solution is colorless in acidic solution and exhibits a pink color near pH 9. Indicators work by having two forms in equilibrium with each other, where each form is a different color. In fact, most of the indicators used for acid–base titrations are weak acids, where the protonated (acidic) form is one color and the unprotonated (basic) form is another color.

$$\underset{\text{color 1}}{HA(aq)} + H_2O(l) \rightleftharpoons \underset{\text{color 2}}{A^-(aq)} + H_3O^+(aq)$$

When $\frac{[A^-]}{[HA]} < 10$, color 1 predominates. When $\frac{[A^-]}{[HA]} > 10$, color 2 predominates. The color change of an indicator occurs near its pK_a, where the $\frac{[A^-]}{[HA]}$ ratio approaches 1. Although they are often weak acids, indicators do not affect titration end points because they are relatively weak and because only a drop or two of dilute indicator solution is needed to produce the necessary color change.

Note that the color change of the indicator in a titration is known as the *end point*, which is different than the *equivalence point* of the titration (Section 5.9). When a titration is carried out with an appropriate indicator, the end point of the titration is a good approximation for the equivalence point. The rapid pH change near the equivalence point often allows for an indicator to be used that does not change pH exactly at the equivalence point of the titration.

An appropriate indicator for a particular titration must change color over a range that either overlaps with or is close to the equivalence point.

The equivalence points of many weak acid–strong base titrations are in the pH range of phenolphthalein's color change (8.2–10). Phenolphthalein is also satisfactory for titrations of strong acids with strong bases. Despite the pH range of phenolphthalein's color change being 8.2–10 and the equivalence point being 7.0, the pH change around the equivalence point of a strong acid–strong base titration is so large that one drop of titrant can change the pH from 5 to 10. Therefore, phenolphthalein effectively changes color at the measured equivalence point, as shown in Figure 17.13.

However, phenolphthalein is not useful for all acid–base titrations. For example, it is not an appropriate indicator for the titration of many weak bases with strong acids because the equivalence points for these titrations are at $pH < 7$. Therefore, the measured end point of such a titration with phenolphthalein would occur prior to the equivalence point. Some common indicators and the pH ranges of their color changes are listed in Table 17.1.

Figure 17.14 is an interactive simulation of all the titration types discussed in this chapter, with options for various indicators. Note the pH at the equivalence point and the shape of the curve for each analyte. The relative concentrations of the ions (shown in the bar graph) will give you an idea of the solution composition at any point during the titration. For example, in the titration of the weak acid or the weak base, you can identify the buffer region of the curve by watching where the conjugate acid and conjugate base concentrations are approximately equal to each other.

In choosing an indicator for a titration, the goal is that it changes color within the most vertical portion of the titration curve. For titrations of a weak acid or weak base, that is typically within ± 1 pH unit of the equivalence point. For titrations of a strong acid or strong base, the end-point pH can be ± 2 pH units from the equivalence point and still be effective; that tolerance increases to ± 3 for sufficiently concentrated solutions.

TABLE 17.1 pH Ranges of Selected Indicator Color Changes

Indicator Name	pH Range and Color Change
Methyl Orange	(red) 3.2–4.4 (yellow)
Bromocresol Green	(yellow) 3.8–5.4 (blue)
Methyl Red	(red) 4.8–6.0 (yellow)
Bromothymol Blue	(yellow) 6.0–7.6 (blue)
Phenolphthalein	(colorless) 8.2–10.0 (pink)*
Alizarin Yellow R	(yellow) 10.1–12.0 (red)

*At $pH > 13$, phenolpthalein will fade back to colorless, but the transition takes several minutes.

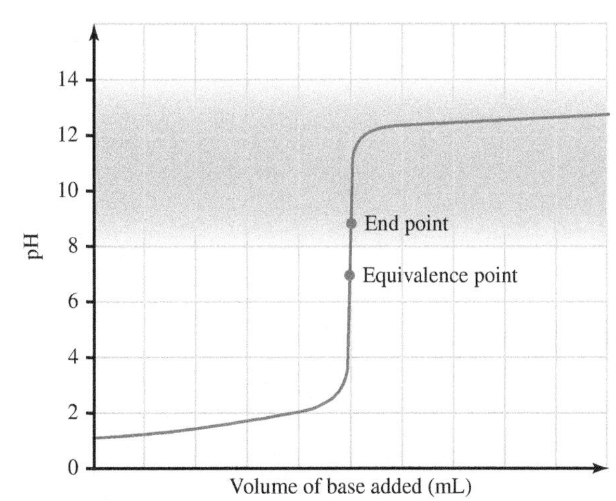

FIGURE 17.13 Equivalence Point versus End Point in a Strong Acid–Strong Base Titration

With phenolphthalein as the indicator, the pH range of the color change does not overlap the equivalence point at pH = 7.0. However, the volume of titrant at the end point is nearly identical to the volume at the equivalence point.

Example 17.14

Select an appropriate indicator from Table 17.1 for the titration of the weak acid $As(OH)_3$ with a strong base. The expected equivalence point of this titration is at pH 9.3.

Solution

Since this is a weak acid, the ideal indicator would change color within ± 1 unit of the equivalence point pH of 9.3, so somewhere between 8.3 and 10.3. At first glance, phenolphthalein looks like the best choice because its color-change range nearly completely overlaps the end-point range. But since you are starting with an acid and adding base, the pH will start low and increase, approaching this range from the lower end. The lower bound of the phenolphthalein range is 8.2, which is just outside of the target end-point range. Using phenolphthalein for this titration is still feasible, however, if you continue titrating to a bright pink color rather than stopping at pale pink. The lower bound for color change of alizarin yellow R is at pH = 10.1, which is within the target end-point range, so it is also a reasonable choice for this titration.

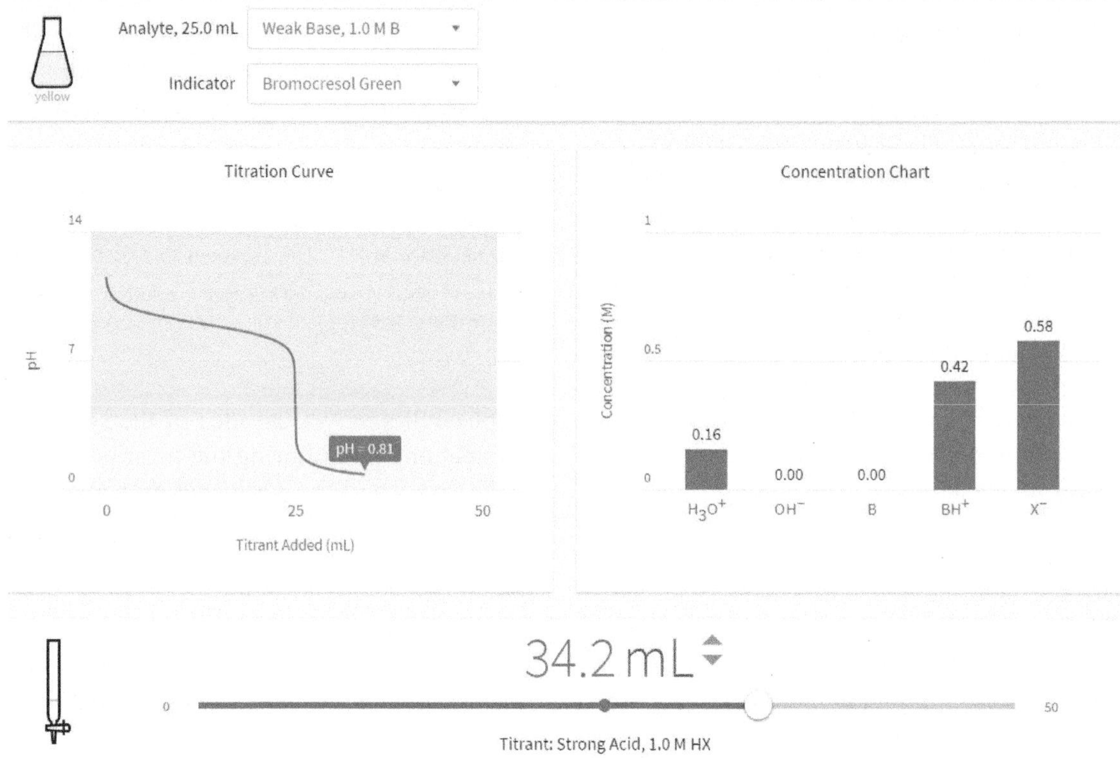

FIGURE 17.14 Titration Interactive

NOTE: You need to be online to access this interactive.

Select an analyte and an indicator, then move the volume slider to produce the titration curve.

PRACTICE PROBLEM 17.14

A KOH solution is titrated with an HCl solution. Other than phenolphthalein, select the most appropriate indicator from Table 17.1 for this titration.

Hint: KOH is a strong base and HCl is a strong acid. Consider how this affects the equivalence-point pH, as well as the end-point pH range.

SECTION REVIEW

- Indicators that are used in acid–base titrations produce visible color changes that mark the end point of the titration. An appropriate indicator can be used to show the visible end point of the titration, which is near the equivalence point of the titration.
- An appropriate indicator for a particular titration must change color over a range that either overlaps with or is close to the equivalence point.

17.6 Solubility Product Constant, K_{sp}

GOALS

- Explain the difference between solubility and the solubility product constant.
- Solve solubility equilibrium calculations using the solubility product constant.

Background Review

Chapter 3 Compounds and the Mole: Section 3.8—Molar Mass

Chapter 4 Chemical Reactions and Aqueous Solutions: Section 4.4—Precipitation Reactions

Chapter 13 Solutions: Section 13.2—Saturated, Unsaturated, and Supersaturated Solutions

Chapter 15 Chemical Equilibrium

THE SOLUBILITY PRODUCT CONSTANT DEFINED

You have learned about the equilibria of numerous homogeneous systems, but in this section you will see examples of *heterogeneous* equilibria. In a heterogeneous system, species in different phases interact with one another. Section 13.2 introduced the concepts of solubility, saturated solutions, unsaturated solutions, and supersaturated solutions. In this section, you will learn further details about the solubility of ionic compounds in aqueous solution, also discussed in Section 4.4.

Figure 17.15 shows a saturated aqueous solution of lead(II) iodide. Solid lead(II) iodide forms from the reaction of aqueous Pb^{2+} ions and aqueous I^- ions.

$$Pb^{2+}(aq) + 2\,I^-(aq) \rightleftharpoons PbI_2(s)$$

In such a solution, there is a solid component of lead(II) iodide and an aqueous component that contains Pb^{2+} and I^- ions, as well as any spectator ions that may be present. Solid PbI_2 is in equilibrium with Pb^{2+} and I^-. When equilibrium exists between an ionic solid and a solution containing the constituent ions, the solid compound is conventionally written on the left side of the equilibrium double-arrow and the ions are written on the right side.

$$PbI_2(s) \rightleftharpoons Pb^{2+}(aq) + 2\,I^-(aq)$$

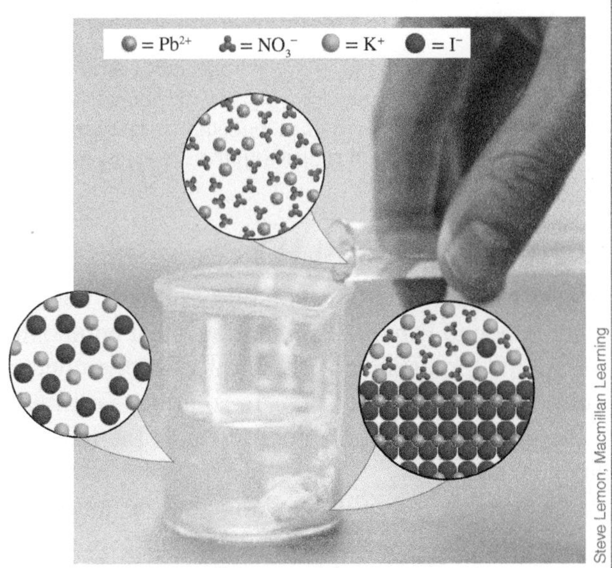

FIGURE 17.15 A Precipitation Reaction
The mixture of aqueous Pb^{2+} and aqueous I^- forms solid PbI_2. K^+ and NO_3^- are spectator ions.

The equilibrium constant for this equation is known as the **solubility product constant, K_{sp}**.

$$K_{sp} = [Pb^{2+}][I^-]^2$$

Note that solids do not appear in equilibrium expressions because their concentrations are considered constant. Therefore, $PbI_2(s)$ does not appear in the K_{sp} expression. As in other equilibrium expressions, the species are taken to the powers of their coefficients in the balanced chemical equation. Here is another example showing the K_{sp} expression for barium phosphate.

$$Ba_3(PO_4)_2(s) \rightleftharpoons 3\,Ba^{2+}(aq) + 2\,PO_4^{3-}(aq)$$

$$K_{sp} = [Ba^{2+}]^3[PO_4^{3-}]^2$$

The K_{sp} values of several ionic compounds in water are listed in Table 17.2. A more complete list can be found in Appendix A.4.

Example 17.15

A saturated solution of iron(II) sulfide contains 4.0×10^{-10} M Fe^{2+} and 4.0×10^{-10} M S^{2-}. Calculate K_{sp} for iron(II) sulfide.

Solution

A saturated solution is at equilibrium, so the given concentrations can be substituted directly into the K_{sp} expression.

$$FeS(s) \rightleftharpoons Fe^{2+}(aq) + S^{2-}(aq)$$
$$K_{sp} = [Fe^{2+}][S^{2-}]$$
$$K_{sp} = (4.0 \times 10^{-10})(4.0 \times 10^{-10})$$
$$K_{sp} = 1.6 \times 10^{-19}$$

PRACTICE PROBLEM 17.15

A different saturated solution of iron(II) sulfide contains 7.0×10^{-11} M Fe^{2+}. Use the K_{sp} value to calculate the concentration of S^{2-}.

Hint: A saturated solution is at equilibrium, so the known values can be substituted directly into the K_{sp} expression.

K_{sp} is a measure of a compound's solubility. Lower K_{sp} values are generally indicative of lower solubility, but this is not always the case. The situations in which the relative solubility of two compounds can be compared by their K_{sp} values are restricted to cases where their reaction stoichiometries are the same. In other words, the K_{sp} values of two compounds are comparable

TABLE 17.2 Some Solubility Product Constants at 25°C

Formula	K_{sp}	Formula	K_{sp}	Formula	K_{sp}
AgCl	1.77×10^{-10}	$Cr(OH)_3$	3×10^{-29}	$MgCO_3$	6.82×10^{-6}
$Al(OH)_3$	4.6×10^{-33}	$Co(OH)_2$	5.92×10^{-15}	$Mg(OH)_2$	5.61×10^{-12}
$BaCO_3$	2.58×10^{-9}	CoS	4.0×10^{-21}	$Mg_3(PO_4)_2$	1.04×10^{-24}
BaF_2	1.84×10^{-7}	CuBr	6.27×10^{-9}	$Mn(OH)_2$	2×10^{-13}
$Ba(NO_3)_2$	4.64×10^{-3}	CuCl	1.72×10^{-7}	MnS	4.6×10^{-14}
$Ba_3(PO_4)_2$	3.40×10^{-23}	CuI	1.27×10^{-12}	$Ni(OH)_2$	5.48×10^{-16}
$BaSO_4$	1.08×10^{-10}	CuS	6.3×10^{-26}	NiS	1.1×10^{-21}
$BaSO_3$	5.0×10^{-10}	Cu_2S	2.5×10^{-48}	PbS	8.9×10^{-29}
CdF_2	6.44×10^{-3}	FeF_2	2.36×10^{-6}	$PbCl_2$	1.70×10^{-5}
CdS	1×10^{-27}	$Fe(OH)_2$	4.87×10^{-17}	PbI_2	9.8×10^{-9}
$CaCO_3$	3.36×10^{-9}	FeS	1.6×10^{-19}	$SrCO_3$	5.60×10^{-10}
$Ca(OH)_2$	5.02×10^{-6}	$Fe(OH)_3$	2.79×10^{-39}	$Sr_3(PO_4)_2$	1×10^{-31}
$Ca(IO_3)_2$	6.47×10^{-6}	$Hg(OH)_2$	3.6×10^{-26}	SnS	3.2×10^{-28}
$Ca_3(PO_4)_2$	2.07×10^{-33}	HgS	4×10^{-53}	SnS_2	1×10^{-70}
$CaSO_4$	4.93×10^{-5}	KIO_4	3.71×10^{-4}	$Zn(OH)_2$	3×10^{-17}

when each produces the same number of ions in solution. For example, the K_{sp} values of CaS and MgS are comparable because these solids dissociate into one cation and one anion. However, the K_{sp} values of CaS and Na_2S are *not* comparable because Na_2S dissociates into *two* cations and one anion.

> Although the solubility product constant of a compound is related to the solubility of that compound, the two terms are not mathematically equal and should not be used interchangeably.

Example 17.16

Use the K_{sp} values in Table 17.2 to predict the relative solubilities of CuCl, CuBr, and CuI in water.

Solution

Table 17.2 gives the following K_{sp} values:

$$CuCl(s) \rightleftharpoons Cu^+(aq) + Cl^-(aq) \quad K_{sp} = 1.72 \times 10^{-7}$$

$$CuBr(s) \rightleftharpoons Cu^+(aq) + Br^-(aq) \quad K_{sp} = 6.27 \times 10^{-9}$$

$$CuI(s) \rightleftharpoons Cu^+(aq) + I^-(aq) \quad K_{sp} = 1.27 \times 10^{-12}$$

Given that these compounds all produce the same number of ions, it is likely that the compound with the highest K_{sp} is the most soluble and the compound with the lowest K_{sp} is the least soluble. Therefore, the predicted solubility in water is CuCl > CuBr > CuI.

PRACTICE PROBLEM 17.16

Use the K_{sp} values in Table 17.2 to comment on the relative solubilities of $Ca(OH)_2$, $Ca(IO_3)_2$ and $CaCO_3$ in water.

Hint: Relative solubility can be predicted from relative K_{sp} only for compounds with the same stoichiometry. The stoichiometry of $CaCO_3$ is different than that of the other two compounds.

K_{sp} AND SOLUBILITY

It bears repeating that the solubility product constant of a compound is *not* the solubility of that compound. The K_{sp} of a substance is the product of the concentration of the substance's ions in solution, each raised to the power of the ion's coefficient in the balanced chemical equation.

Conversely, solubility is defined as the amount of a substance that is dissolved in a saturated solution of that substance. The **molar solubility** of a compound is the number of moles of a substance that can dissolve into 1 L of solution. The solubility of a compound is also often expressed as the number of grams of substance that can dissolve into 1 L of solution.

Steve Lemon, Macmillan Learning

FIGURE 17.16 Video Tutorial: Molar Solubility

NOTE: You need to be online to access this video.
This video shows how to derive the formulas for K_{sp} in terms of x (molar solubility) for various stoichiometries.

For example, the molar solubility, x, of $Ca(OH)_2$ is calculated as follows:

	$Ca(OH)_2(s)$ $\rightleftharpoons$	$Ca^{2+}(aq)$ +	$2\,OH^-(aq)$
Initial	excess	0	0
Change	$-x$	$+x$	$+2x$
Equilibrium		x	$2x$

$$K_{sp} = [Ca^{2+}][OH^-]^2$$
$$K_{sp} = [x][2x]^2$$
$$K_{sp} = (x)(4x^2) = 4x^3$$
$$\text{Molar solubility} = x = \sqrt[3]{\frac{K_{sp}}{4}}$$

In fact, $K_{sp} = 4x^3$ for any compound with AB_2 stoichiometry. However, compounds with a different stoichiometry (such as AB or AB_3) will have a different relationship between K_{sp} and molar solubility, as shown in Figure 17.16.

Example 17.17

Calculate the molar solubility of BaF_2. The K_{sp} of BaF_2 is listed in Table 17.2.

Solution

Construct the following ICE table:

	$BaF_2(s)$ $\rightleftharpoons$	$Ba^{2+}(aq)$ +	$2\,F^-(aq)$
Initial	excess	0	0
Change	$-x$	$+x$	$+2x$
Equilibrium		x	$2x$

Here, x represents the molar solubility of BaF_2, because every mole of BaF_2 that dissolves forms 1 mol Ba^{2+} ions and 2 mol F^- ions.

$$K_{sp} = [Ba^{2+}][F^-]^2$$
$$K_{sp} = [x][2x]^2$$
$$K_{sp} = 4x^3 = 1.84 \times 10^{-7}$$
$$x = \sqrt[3]{\frac{1.84 \times 10^{-7}}{4}}$$
$$x = 3.58 \times 10^{-3}\,\text{M}$$

The molar solubility of barium fluoride is 3.58×10^{-3} M. A saturated solution of BaF_2 contains 3.58×10^{-3} M Ba^{2+} ions and $2(3.58 \times 10^{-3}) = 7.16 \times 10^{-3}$ M F^- ions.

It may seem that substituting $2x$ into the F^- term of the equilibrium expression *and* squaring the term is "double counting," but it is indeed the correct way to do the calculation. (You can prove this to yourself by calculating K_{sp} while using 3.58×10^{-3} as x in the equilibrium expression.)

PRACTICE PROBLEM 17.17

Calculate a. the molar solubility and b. the solubility (in units of g/L) of barium phosphate. The K_{sp} of $Ba_3(PO_4)_2$ is listed in Table 17.2.

Hint: Start by making an ICE table for the dissociation reaction

$$Ba_3(PO_4)_2(s) \rightleftharpoons 3\,Ba^{2+}(aq) + 2\,PO_4^{3-}(aq)$$

where the initial concentrations of the ions are both zero. Then express K_{sp} in terms of x. Solve for x, which is equal to the molar solubility in M (mol/L). To convert from mol/L to g/L, use the molar mass of barium phosphate.

Example 17.18

The solubility of $Ba(NO_3)_2$ is 27.50 g/L. Calculate the K_{sp} of $Ba(NO_3)_2$.

Solution

First, convert the molar solubility of $Ba(NO_3)_2$ to units of mol/L. The molar mass of $Ba(NO_3)_2$ is

$$137.33\,\text{g/mol} + 2(14.007\,\text{g/mol}) + 6(15.999\,\text{g/mol}) = 261.338\,\text{g/mol}$$

$$\frac{27.50\,\text{g}}{1\,\text{L}}\left(\frac{1\,\text{mol}}{261.338\,\text{g}}\right) = 0.1052\,\text{mol/L}$$

Next, construct an ICE table and give the equilibrium expression for $Ba(NO_3)_2$. The molar solubility of $Ba(NO_3)_2$ is represented by x:

	$Ba(NO_3)_2(s)$ $\rightleftharpoons$	$Ba^{2+}(aq)$ +	$2\,NO_3^-(aq)$
Initial	excess	0	0
Change	$-x$	$+x$	$+2x$
Equilibrium		x	$2x$

$$K_{sp} = [Ba^{2+}][NO_3^-]^2$$
$$K_{sp} = (x)(2x)^2 = 4x^3$$

Substituting the molar solubility of $Ba(NO_3)_2$, 0.1052 M, into the equation,

$$K_{sp} = 4(0.1052)^3 = 4.66 \times 10^{-3}$$

PRACTICE PROBLEM 17.18

The solubility of $Fe(OH)_3$ is 1.08×10^{-8} g/L. Calculate the K_{sp} of $Fe(OH)_3$.

Hint: Convert the solubility (in g/L) to a *molar* solubility (in mol/L) using the molar mass of $Fe(OH)_3$. Then make an ICE table for the dissociation reaction

$$Fe(OH)_3(s) \rightleftharpoons Fe^{3+}(aq) + 3\,OH^-(aq)$$

and express K_{sp} in terms of x. Finally, substitute the molar solubility for x and solve for K_{sp}.

SECTION REVIEW

- The solubility product constant, K_{sp}, of an ionic compound is the product of that compound's ion concentrations in solution, each raised to the power of its coefficient in the balanced chemical equation.
- The molar solubility of a compound is the number of moles of a substance that can dissolve into 1 L of solution. The molar solubility of a compound should not be confused with its solubility product constant.
- In general, lower K_{sp} values indicate lower solubility, whereas higher K_{sp} values indicate higher solubility.
- The situations in which the relative solubilities of two compounds can be compared by their K_{sp} values are restricted to cases where their reaction stoichiometries are the same.

17.7 The Common-Ion Effect and the Effect of pH on Solubility

GOALS

- Explain how a common ion affects solubility.
- Explain how pH affects solubility.

Background Review

Chapter 15 Chemical Equilibrium:
Section 15.6—Le Châtelier's Principle

THE COMMON-ION EFFECT ON SOLUBILITY

As discussed in Section 17.1, the common-ion effect is a phenomenon whereby the ionization of a weak electrolyte is suppressed when a weak electrolyte and a strong electrolyte that contain a common ion are combined. Rooted in Le Châtelier's principle (Section 15.6), the common-ion effect works to resist a change in the equilibrium of buffer solutions. Here, you will see how the common-ion effect lowers the solubility of an ionic compound.

Consider a solution of silver chloride, AgCl, in pure water. At 25°C, the molar solubility of AgCl is 1.33×10^{-5} M.

$$AgCl(s) \rightleftharpoons Ag^+(aq) + Cl^-(aq)$$

Consider what happens when solid AgCl is dissolved into a 0.200 M NaCl solution.

$$\underset{\leftarrow}{AgCl(s) \rightleftharpoons Ag^+(aq) + \overset{\text{(common ion)}}{Cl^-(aq)}}$$

(equilibrium shifts toward solid AgCl)

The common-ion effect limits the solubility of AgCl in 0.200 M NaCl solution by shifting the equilibrium back toward AgCl(s). The net result is a dissolution reaction that proceeds to the right, but to a lesser extent than it would have without the common ion present.

Example 17.19

Calculate the molar solubility of AgCl in a solution of 0.200 M NaCl, and compare it to the molar solubility of AgCl in pure water (1.33×10^{-5} M). The K_{sp} of AgCl is listed in Table 17.2.

Solution

Construct the following ICE table:

	$AgCl(s) \rightleftharpoons$	$Ag^{+}(aq)$ +	$Cl^{-}(aq)$
Initial	excess	0.00	0.200
Change	$-x$	$+x$	$+x$
Equilibrium		x	$0.200 + x$

In this expression, x represents the molar solubility of AgCl. Note that 1 mol of chloride ions is formed per 1 mol of silver ion.

$$K_{sp} = [Ag^{+}][Cl^{-}]$$
$$K_{sp} = [x][0.200 + x]$$

You can simplify this expression for K_{sp} because x is much smaller than 0.200 M.

$$K_{sp} = [x][0.200] = 1.77 \times 10^{-10}$$
$$x = 8.85 \times 10^{-10}\ M$$

The molar solubility of AgCl in an aqueous solution of 0.200 M NaCl (8.85×10^{-10} M) is much lower than the molar solubility of AgCl in pure water (1.33×10^{-5} M).

PRACTICE PROBLEM 17.19

Calculate the molar solubility of FeF_2 in

a. pure water.
b. a 0.100 M solution of NaF.

The K_{sp} of FeF_2 is listed in Table 17.2.

Hint: Part (a) is done exactly like Example 17.17, where the ICE table has initial concentrations of zero for both ions. In part (b), the initial concentration of F^{-} in the ICE table is 0.100 M.

THE EFFECT OF pH ON SOLUBILITY

The pH of a solution will affect the solubility of an ionic compound that has a basic anion. When acid is added to a saturated solution of magnesium hydroxide, $Mg(OH)_2$, for example, the acid reacts with (neutralizes) the hydroxide ion in the equilibrium. Le Châtelier's principle forces the equilibrium towards the right, decreasing the amount of solid $Mg(OH)_2$ and increasing the concentration of Mg^{2+} and OH^{-} ions. The overall effect is that more solid $Mg(OH)_2$ dissolves.

$$\text{H}_3\text{O}^{+} \text{ reacts with } \text{OH}^{-}$$
$$Mg(OH)_2(s) \rightleftharpoons Mg^{2+}(aq) + 2\,OH^{-}(aq)$$
$$\rightarrow$$
$$\text{equilibrium shifts toward } Mg^{2+}(aq) \text{ and } OH^{-}(aq)$$

Note that the anion of the ionic compound need not be a strong base such as hydroxide. Recall that the conjugate of a weak acid is a weak base, so in general, the solubility of an electrolyte that contains the conjugate base of a weak acid is enhanced in acidic solution. Calcium carbonate, $CaCO_3$, is an example of this, where CO_3^{2-} is a weak base, the conjugate of the weak acid HCO_3^{-}.

The photo below of a statue that is constructed of limestone shows the erosion by acid rain.

In contrast, the solubility of compounds with a neutral anion is not enhanced in acidic solution. Recall that the conjugate bases of strong acids are extremely weak (so weak they are essentially neutral). NaCl is an example, where Cl^{-} is the conjugate of the strong acid HCl.

EVERYDAY CONNECTION

Many statues are constructed of limestone, a type of $CaCO_3$, which is a relatively insoluble compound near the natural pH of rainwater (5.0–5.5). However, acidic rainwater produced by sulfur and nitrogen oxide pollutants can be closer to pH 4. The solubility of $CaCO_3$ in this pH range is enhanced, so limestone statues slowly dissolve in areas where acid rain is common.

CSP_Dserra1/AGE Fotostock

Example 17.20

Determine which of the following compounds will be more soluble in acidic solution than in neutral or basic solution.

a. $Hg(OH)_2$
b. CuBr and
c. CdF_2

Solution

a. $Hg(OH)_2$ will be more soluble in acidic solution because H^+ will remove the strong base OH^- from the equilibrium, forcing more $Hg(OH)_2$ to dissolve according to Le Châtelier's principle.
b. CuBr will not be more soluble in acidic solution because Br^- is an extremely weak base (effectively neutral) and will not appreciably react with H^+. Recall that HBr is a strong acid and that Br^- is its conjugate base. All conjugate bases of strong acids are so weak they are effectively neutral (Section 16.7).
c. CdF_2 will be more soluble in acidic solution because F^-, unlike Cl^- and Br^-, is appreciably basic. F^- is the conjugate base of the weak acid HF. H^+ will remove F^- from the equilibrium, forcing more CdF_2 to dissolve.

PRACTICE PROBLEM 17.20

Determine which of the following compounds will be more soluble in acidic solution than in neutral or basic solution.

a. KI
b. $KClO_4$
c. $MgCO_3$

Hint: First, look at the anion of each compound (I^-, ClO_4^-, CO_3^{2-}) and determine whether the acid of that anion (HI, $HClO_4$, H_2CO_3) is strong or weak. The anion of a strong acid is effectively neutral, and so the acidity of the solution will not affect its solubility.

SECTION REVIEW

- The common-ion effect limits the solubility of an ionic compound that is dissolved in a solution containing a common ion.
- The pH of a solution will affect the solubility of an ionic compound that has a basic anion. The addition of an acid will increase the solubility of these compounds, while the addition of a base will decrease the solubility of these compounds.

17.8 Precipitation: Q versus K_{sp}

GOALS

- Explain the relationship between the reaction quotient and the solubility product constant.
- Identify methods to selectively precipitate ionic compounds from solution.

Background Review

Chapter 15 Chemical Equilibrium:
Section 15.4—The Reaction Quotient

THE REACTION QUOTIENT, Q

As discussed in Section 17.6, the solubility product constant, K_{sp}, is a measure of a compound's solubility. When several ions are present in solution, you can determine which compounds precipitate by comparing K_{sp} values to the reaction quotient, Q, which was introduced in Section 15.4. The reaction quotient for a heterogeneous system is mathematically similar to the solubility product constant.

$$CdF_2(s) \rightleftharpoons Cd^{2+}(aq) + 2\,F^-(aq)$$
$$Q = [Cd^{2+}][F^-]^2$$

The major difference between Q and K_{sp} is that K_{sp} is a measurement of the product of ion concentrations *at equilibrium*, whereas Q is a measurement of the product of ion concentrations under *any conditions*. The relationships between Q and K_{sp}, along with the physical meaning of those relationships, are as follows:

- If $Q < K_{sp}$, the solution is not yet saturated. More of the solid ionic compound can be dissolved.
- If $Q = K_{sp}$, the solution is saturated and at equilibrium.
- If $Q > K_{sp}$, the solution is past the point of saturation and the excess ionic compound will precipitate from solution until $Q = K_{sp}$.

As an example, when excess solid CdF_2 is first added to water, $Q < K_{sp}$. As a result, solid CdF_2 will dissolve into solution, and the net reaction is to the right. As the solid CdF_2 continues to dissolve, the concentrations of Cd^{2+} and F^- will eventually reach the point where the solution is saturated. At this point, $Q = K_{sp}$, and the forward and reverse reactions proceed at the same rate (equilibrium).

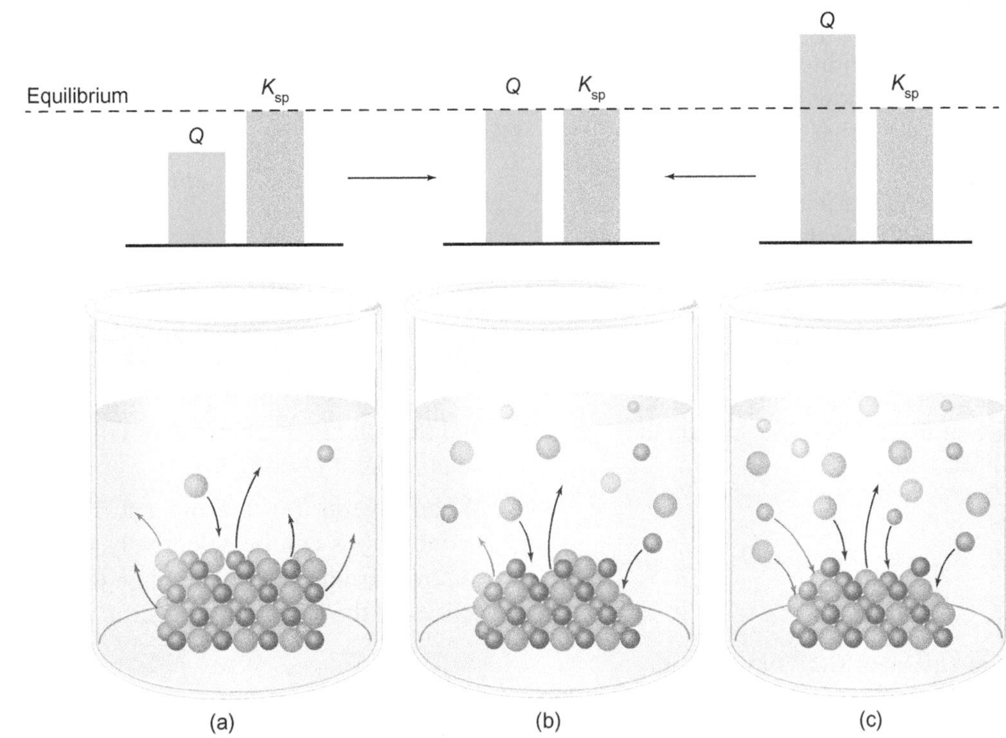

FIGURE 17.17 Solubility Equilibrium

(a) When $Q < K_{sp}$, the net reaction is to the right and the solid dissolves. (b) When $Q = K_{sp}$, the solution is saturated and at equilibrium. (c) When $Q > K_{sp}$, the net reaction is to the left and the solid precipitates.

If enough dissolved Cd^{2+} and F^- ions are present such that $Q > K_{sp}$ (this can be accomplished by mixing soluble salts of each ion, such as $Cd(NO_3)_2$ and NaF), the net reaction is to the left and solid CdF_2 precipitates. Figure 17.17 shows the relationship between Q and K_{sp} for a generic salt.

Example 17.21

Suppose that equal volumes of a solution of 0.0015 M $AgClO_4$ and a solution of 0.0015 M NaCl are mixed. Determine whether or not AgCl precipitates from solution. K_{sp} values are listed in Table 17.2.

Solution

First, determine the post-mixing concentrations. Given that equal volumes of each solution are mixed, their concentrations in the resulting solution are $0.00150/2 = 7.50 \times 10^{-4}$ M.

Now, write the equilibrium expression for the formation of AgCl and calculate Q.

$$AgCl(s) \rightleftharpoons Ag^+(aq) + Cl^-(aq)$$

$$Q = [Ag^+][Cl^-]$$

$$Q = (7.50 \times 10^{-4})(7.50 \times 10^{-4}) = 5.63 \times 10^{-7}$$

Q, which is equal to 5.63×10^{-7}, is greater than K_{sp}, which is equal to 1.77×10^{-10}, so AgCl precipitates.

PRACTICE PROBLEM 17.21

Suppose that solutions of $Cd(NO_3)_2$ and NaF are mixed to form a solution that is 0.00250 M $Cd(NO_3)_2$ and 0.00500 M NaF at the moment of mixing. Determine whether a precipitate will form. K_{sp} values are listed in Table 17.2.

Hint: The possible products of this reaction are $NaNO_3$ and CdF_2. $NaNO_3$ is highly soluble so the potential precipitate is CdF_2. Use the given concentrations to calculate Q, then compare Q to K_{sp}.

SELECTIVE PRECIPITATION OF IONS

In cases where several ions are present in a solution, one or more ions can be selectively precipitated and removed from solution with a specific reagent, based on the different solubilities of the compounds. For example, consider a solution that contains the environmentally toxic silver ion, Ag^+, and the relatively non-toxic magnesium ion, Mg^{2+}. To selectively remove Ag^+ via precipitation, you add an anion that forms an insoluble compound with Ag^+, but a soluble compound (or a less insoluble compound) with Mg^{2+}. Table 17.2 does not show a listed K_{sp} value for $MgCl_2$, but it does show that AgCl has limited solubility ($K_{sp} = 1.77 \times 10^{-10}$). Therefore, a source of chloride ion, such as HCl or NaCl can be used to selectively precipitate AgCl from the solution, leaving Mg^{2+} behind.

Example 17.22

Suppose you have a solution containing Ba^{2+} and Mg^{2+} ions. Which of these salts could you add to selectively precipitate barium?

a. Na_2CO_3
b. Na_3PO_4

Solution

a. The addition of sufficient CO_3^{2-} to the solution will cause the precipitation of $BaCO_3$ ($K_{sp} = 2.58 \times 10^{-9}$) and $MgCO_3$ ($K_{sp} = 6.82 \times 10^{-6}$). Since $BaCO_3$ has the lower K_{sp} value (by several orders of magnitude), it is more insoluble and will precipitate first. In other words, Ba^{2+} can be selectively precipitated using $NaCO_3$.
b. The addition of sufficient PO_4^{3-} to the solution will cause the precipitation of $Ba_3(PO_4)_2$ ($K_{sp} = 3.40 \times 10^{-23}$) and $Mg_3(PO_4)_2$ ($K_{sp} = 1.04 \times 10^{-24}$). These K_{sp} values are relatively close (only one order of magnitude), meaning you would not get much of the first ion to precipitate before the second ion began to precipitate as well. Furthermore, $Mg_3(PO_4)_2$ has the lower K_{sp} value and would precipitate first. In other words, Ba^{2+} cannot be selectively precipitated using Na_3PO_4.

PRACTICE PROBLEM 17.22

Suppose you have a solution containing Ba^{2+} and Ca^{2+} ions. Which of these salts could you add to selectively precipitate calcium?

a. Na_2CO_3
b. Na_3PO_4

Hint: In both cases, sodium is a spectator ion. Look up the K_{sp} values for the carbonate and phosphate salts of barium and calcium. If the calcium salt has a significantly lower K_{sp} value than the barium salt of that same anion, then that anion can be used to selectively precipitate calcium. K_{sp} values are listed in Table 17.2.

SECTION REVIEW

- In heterogeneous equilibrium systems between an ionic solid and a solution, K_{sp} is a measurement of the product of the ion concentrations at equilibrium. In contrast, Q is a measurement of the product of the ion concentrations under any conditions.
- When $Q < K_{sp}$, the solution is not yet saturated and more solid ionic compound can be dissolved into the solution. When $Q = K_{sp}$, the solution is saturated and the system is at equilibrium. When $Q > K_{sp}$, the solution is past the point of saturation, and the solid ionic compound will precipitate from solution until $Q = K_{sp}$.
- When several ions are present in a solution, one or more ions can be selectively precipitated and removed from solution based on the different solubilities of the ions with a specific reactant.

17.9 Qualitative Analysis

GOAL

- Apply the concept of selective precipitation to systematically isolate and identify the metal ions present in a sample.

Background Review

Chapter 4 Chemical Reactions and Aqueous Solutions: Section 4.4—Precipitation Reactions

QUALITATIVE AND QUANTITATIVE ANALYSIS

There are two basic types of chemical analyses: qualitative and quantitative. **Qualitative analysis** tests for the presence or absence of chemical species (regardless of their amounts), whereas **quantitative analysis** determines the quantity or amount of a chemical substance present. Modern chemical analysis methods, such as high-performance liquid chromatography and mass spectrometry, can be used simultaneously to determine the presence of chemical species *and* to quantify them. You will learn more about these analytical methods if you go on to take organic chemistry and analytical chemistry.

The focus in this section is on the *qualitative* analysis of metal ions. The selective precipitation reactions discussed in Section 17.8 are known as *wet chemistry* techniques, and you will learn about the use of these techniques to systematically determine the presence of metal ions in aqueous solution. Although these wet chemistry techniques have been replaced by modern instrumental analysis, they are historically important, inexpensive, and frequently used in general chemistry labs to teach solubility rules.

SYSTEMATIC IDENTIFICATION OF METAL IONS VIA PRECIPITATION

The systematic qualitative analysis process for the identification of metal ions in aqueous solution is shown in Figure 17.18. Note that the order of this process is very important. In this scheme, five different precipitation reactions are performed to identify five specific groups of metal ions.

The five different groups of metal ions from the series of precipitation reactions shown in Figure 17.18 are described here. Precipitates from each of these groups are filtered out and can be further analyzed with specific tests to determine the identity of the metal ion(s) present.

1. Insoluble chlorides
   The addition of HCl solution precipitates chloride salts of Ag^+, Pb^{2+}, and Hg_2^{2+}. If no precipitate forms, it is reasonable to conclude that none of these three ions is present in the sample. If a precipitate forms, it is filtered out before proceeding to the next step.
2. Acid-insoluble sulfides
   The remaining solution is treated with the weak acid H_2S, which will precipitate Cu^{2+}, Bi^{3+}, Cd^{2+}, Pb^{2+}, Hg^{2+}, As^{3+}, Sb^{3+}, and Sn^{4+}. Due to the acidic conditions from the previous step, the concentration of S^{2-} in solution is low. Therefore, only metal ions that form very insoluble sulfide salts will precipitate during this step. Other metal sulfides with higher K_{sp} values precipitate at a later point.

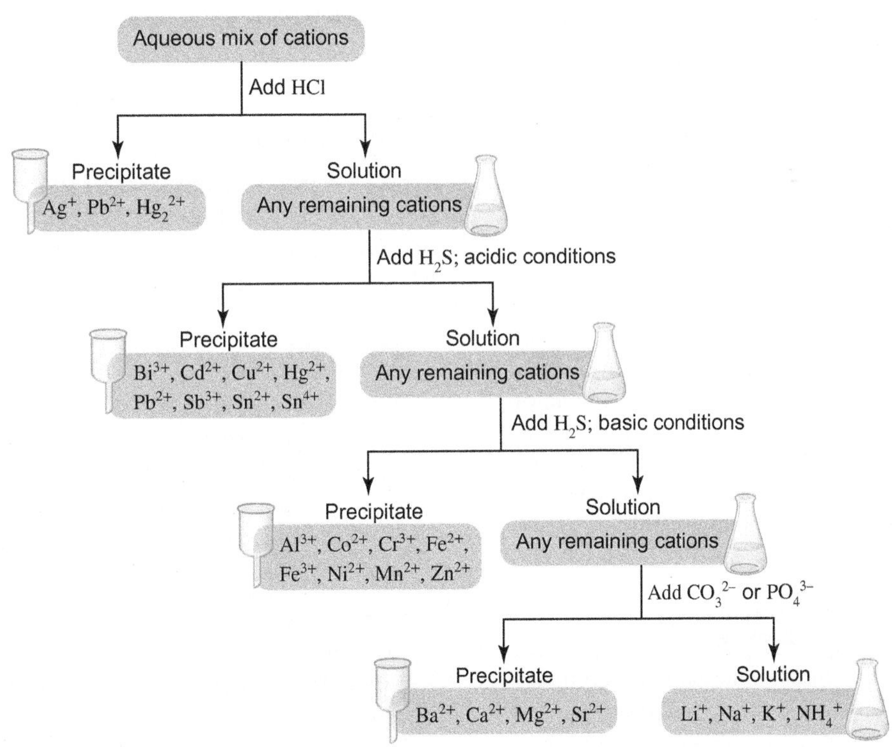

FIGURE 17.18 Separation of Common Cations

Starting with an unknown aqueous solution, a series of tests are performed, each for a specific group of cations. The formation of a precipitate at any given step confirms the presence of at least one ion in that group. The lack of a precipitate confirms the absence of all ions from that group.

3. Base-insoluble sulfides and hydroxides
At this point, base and either $(NH_4)_2S$ or additional H_2S are added to the solution. The base drastically increases the concentration of S^{2-} and OH^-. If Zn^{2+}, Ni^{2+}, Co^{2+}, or Mn^{2+} are present, they precipitate as sulfide salts. Any Al^{3+}, Cr^{3+}, or Fe^{3+} in solution will precipitate as hydroxide salts.
4. Insoluble phosphates
At this point, only group 1 and group 2 metal ions are present in solution. The group 2 metals Mg^{2+}, Ca^{2+}, Sr^{2+}, and Ba^{2+} all form insoluble phosphate compounds, and are precipitated by the addition of $(NH_4)_2HPO_4$.
5. The alkali metal ions and NH_4^+
The remaining ions in solution should only be group 1 (alkali) metals or NH_4^+ at this point. Some of these ions can be distinguished from one another via a simple flame test (see Figure 8.8). When a solution containing K^+ is held in a flame, the potassium ion displays a distinct violet color. Sodium ion produces a yellow-orange flame.

Example 17.23

A precipitate formed when dilute HCl was added to an unknown aqueous solution, but no more precipitates formed during the remaining precipitation steps of the qualitative analysis process. What conclusions can be made about the species present in the original solution?

Solution

The formation of a precipitate upon the addition of HCl means the original solution contained at least one of the ions that form insoluble chlorides (Ag^+, Pb^{2+}, and Hg_2^{2+}). The lack of any further precipitate means the solution contained none of the ions that form acid-insoluble sulfides, base-insoluble sulfides and hydroxides, or insoluble phosphates. The solution may have also contained ammonium or any of the alkali metal ions, which do not precipitate.

PRACTICE PROBLEM 17.23

While testing an unknown solution, no precipitates formed during any of the precipitation steps of the qualitative analysis process, but a purple color was observed during the flame test at the end. What conclusions can be made about the species present in the original solution?

Hint: Refer to Figure 17.18. The lack of a precipitate in any given step confirms the absence of all ions from that group.

SECTION REVIEW

- Qualitative analysis tests for the presence or absence of chemical species, whereas quantitative analysis determines the quantity or amount of a chemical substance present.
- Five different groups of metal ions—insoluble chlorides, acid-insoluble sulfides, base-insoluble sulfides and hydroxides, insoluble phosphates, and group 1 ions—can be selectively precipitated based on their solubilities with different anions. Precipitates from each of these groups can be further analyzed with specific tests to determine the identity of the metal ion(s) present.

17.10 Complex Ion Equilibria, K_f

GOALS

- Define *complex ion*.
- Apply the complex ion formation constant in the calculation of the concentrations of free metal ion and ligand in solution.

Background Review

Chapter 15 Chemical Equilibrium: Section 15.5—Calculations Using ICE Tables

COMPLEX IONS

Transition metal ions can act as Lewis acids (Section 16.9). In aqueous solution, transition metal ions bond to water molecules, where water acts as a Lewis base. These water molecules can be displaced by stronger Lewis bases, such as NH_3 and CN^-. These complexes of metal ions bonded to Lewis bases, such as $Cu(NH_3)_4^{2+}$, are known as **complex ions**. Some common complex ions are listed in Table 17.3. The Lewis bases that bond to complex ions are known as **ligands**.

THE FORMATION CONSTANT

The equilibrium constant for the formation of a complex ion is the **formation constant, K_f**. Think of the formation constant as the opposite of a dissociation

TABLE 17.3 Formation Constants of Some Common Complex Ions at 25°C

Complex Ion	Formation Constant, K_f
$Ag(CN)_2^-$	1.0×10^{21}
$Ag(NH_3)_2^+$	2.00×10^7
$Co(NH_3)_6^{2+}$	5.0×10^{31}
$Cu(NH_3)_2^+$	6.3×10^{10}
$Cu(NH_3)_4^{2+}$	1.7×10^{13}
$Ni(NH_3)_6^{2+}$	5.5×10^8
PbI_4^{2-}	3.0×10^4

constant. (Indeed, it is the mathematical inverse of a dissociation constant.)

$$Cu^{2+}(aq) + 4\,NH_3(aq) \rightleftharpoons Cu(NH_3)_4^{2+}$$

$$K_f = \frac{[Cu(NH_3)_4^{2+}]}{[Cu^{2+}][NH_3]^4} = 5 \times 10^{12}$$

As shown in Table 17.3, formation constants of complex ions are generally large, indicating that these complexes are strongly favored in solution. Consequently, the presence of Lewis bases can significantly increase the solubility of transition metal ions in aqueous solution.

Example 17.24

The complex ion $Ni(NH_3)_6^{2+}$ is formed from a solution that originally contains 5.00×10^{-4} M $Ni(ClO_4)_2$ and 0.100 M NH_3. Determine the concentration of free Ni^{2+} that remains in solution under these conditions. The K_f value of $Ni(NH_3)_6^{2+}$ is listed in Table 17.3.

Solution

The ICE table equilibrium method that you have seen in other contexts took advantage of extremely small equilibrium constants to make the simplifying assumption that the change was very small. In this case, you must make the opposite assumption: The change is so large that the reaction goes nearly to completion, leaving a very small amount of the limiting reactant.

	Ni^{2+} (aq)	+	$6\,NH_3$ (aq)	$\rightleftharpoons$	$Ni(NH_3)_6^{2+}$ (aq)
Initial	5.00×10^{-4}		0.100		0
Change	-5.00×10^{-4}		$-6(5 \times 10^{-4})$		$+5.00 \times 10^{-4}$
Equilibrium	x		0.0970		5.00×10^{-4}

Ni^{2+} is the limiting reactant, so the final concentration of product is 5.00×10^{-4} M. Use x to represent the very small amount of Ni^{2+} that remains in solution.

$$K_f = \frac{[Ni(NH_3)_6^{2+}]}{[Ni^{2+}][NH_3]^6}$$

$$1.2 \times 10^9 = \frac{5.00 \times 10^{-4}}{x(0.0970)^6}$$

$$x = \frac{5.00 \times 10^{-4}}{(1.2 \times 10^9)(0.0970)^6}$$

$$x = [Ni^{2+}] = 5.0 \times 10^{-7}\ M$$

PRACTICE PROBLEM 17.24

The complex ion $Fe(CN)_6^{3-}$ is formed from a solution that originally contained 1.00×10^{-3} M $Fe(NO_3)_3$ and 0.150 M CN^-. Determine the concentration of free Fe^{3+} that remains in solution under these conditions. The K_f value of $Fe(CN)_6^{3-}$ is listed in Table 17.3.

Hint: Make an ICE table for the K_f reaction

$$Fe^{3+}(aq) + 6\,CN^-(aq) \rightleftharpoons Fe(CN)_6^{3-}(aq)$$

where x is the equilibrium concentration of Fe^{3+}. The limiting reactant is Fe^{3+} so fill in the *Change* row as if all 1.00×10^{-3} M of it reacts.

SECTION REVIEW

- Complex ions consist of ligands (Lewis bases) that bond to a metal ion (Lewis acid).
- The formation constant, K_f, of a complex ion is the equilibrium constant for the formation of the complex from the metal ion and its ligands.

Putting It Together

The example problems in earlier sections of this chapter focus on just the new skills acquired in that section, but homework and exam questions in chemistry often require more than just one skill at a time. In fact, you will likely be expected to apply knowledge from across the entire chapter, or even multiple chapters in a single problem. This final example problem is meant to help you prepare for these types of multi-concept questions. Additional examples can be found in the end of chapter exercises.

Example 17.25

Determine the solubility of $Mg(OH)_2$ in a solution buffered at pH = 11.00.

Solution

First use the pH to find $[OH^-]$.

$$pOH = 14.00 - 11.00 = 3.00$$
$$[OH^-] = 10^{-pOH} = 10^{-3.00} = 1.0 \times 10^{-3}$$

This becomes the initial concentration of $[OH^-]$ in the ICE table for the solubility of $Mg(OH)_2$.

	$Mg(OH)_2(s)$ $\rightleftharpoons$	$Mg^{2+}(aq)$ +	$2\,OH^-(aq)$
Initial	excess	0	0.0010
Change	$-x$	$+x$	$+2x$
Equilibrium		x	$0.0010 + 2x$

Finally, express K_{sp} in terms of x and solve for x.

$$K_{sp} = [Mg^{2+}][OH^-]^2$$
$$K_{sp} = x(0.0010 + 2x)^2 \approx x(0.0010)^2$$
$$x = \frac{K_{sp}}{(0.0010)^2} = \frac{5.61 \times 10^{-12}}{(0.0010)^2} = 5.6 \times 10^{-6}\ M$$

PRACTICE PROBLEM 17.25

Suppose you create a buffer from the partial titration of HCN ($K_a = 6.2 \times 10^{-10}$) with strong base, stopping at the half-equivalence point. In this buffer, what concentration of Mg^{2+} would be necessary (assuming no volume change) to precipitate $Mg(OH)_2$?

Hint: First, determine the pH. Recall that pH = pK_a at the half-equivalence point of a weak-acid titration. Then, use pH to find $[OH^-]$. Finally, plug $[OH^-]$ into the K_{sp} expression for $Mg(OH)_2$ and solve for $[Mg^{2+}]$.

Key Terms, Symbols, and Equations

KEY TERMS

analyte (17.3): A solution of unknown concentration, to which titrant is added during a titration.

buffer capacity (17.2): The ability of a buffer solution to resist a change in pH when an acid or base is added.

buffer solution (17.1): A solution consisting of a weak acid and its conjugate base (or a weak base and its conjugate acid) that resists changes in pH.

common-ion effect (17.1): A phenomenon whereby the addition of a strong electrolyte containing a common ion suppresses the ionization of a weak electrolyte.

complex ion (17.10): A compound consisting of a metal ion that is bound to one or more ligands.

formation constant, K_f (17.10): The equilibrium constant for the formation of a complex ion.

Henderson–Hasselbalch equation (17.2): An equation that relates the pH of a buffer solution to the pK_a of the weak acid and the concentrations of its acidic and basic components.

ligand (17.10): A Lewis base that bonds to the metal ion of a complex ion.

molar solubility (17.6): The number of moles of a substance that can dissolve into 1 L of solution.

qualitative analysis (17.9): The determination of the identity of chemical species present in a sample.

quantitative analysis (17.9): The determination of the amounts of chemical species present in a sample.

solubility product constant, K_{sp} (17.6): The equilibrium constant for the dissolution of an ionic compound. It is a measure of the compound's solubility and is equal to the product of that compound's ion concentrations in a saturated solution, each raised to the power of its coefficient in the balanced chemical equation.

titrant (17.3): A solution of known concentration, typically delivered via buret in a titration.

titration curve (17.3): A plot of pH versus volume of titrant added over the course of a titration.

SYMBOLS AND ABBREVIATIONS

A^- (a weak base) (17.1)

HA (a weak acid) (17.1)

K_{sp} (solubility product constant) (17.6)

K_f (formation constant) (17.10)

EQUATIONS

$HA(aq) + H_2O(l) \rightleftharpoons H_3O^+(aq) + A^-(aq)$ (17.1)

$HA(aq) \rightleftharpoons H^+(aq) + A^-(aq)$ (17.2)

$pH = pK_a + \log\frac{[A^-]}{[HA]}$ (17.3)

$[H_3O^+] = x = \sqrt{K_a \cdot [HA]}$ (17.4)

$[OH^-] = x = \sqrt{K_b \cdot [A^-]}$ (17.5)

Chapter Summary

The ionization of a weak electrolyte is suppressed when a strong electrolyte that contains a common ion is added. This phenomenon is known as the common-ion effect, and it is the basis for the action of a buffer solution. Buffer solutions, which consist of a weak acid and its conjugate base, utilize the common-ion effect to suppress changes in pH (Section 17.1).

The Henderson–Hasselbalch equation relates the pH of a buffer solution to the pK_a of the weak acid and the concentrations of its acidic and basic components. Buffer capacity is highest when the concentrations of the buffer components are high and the pH of the solution is within ± 1 unit of the weak acid's pK_a (Section 17.2).

$$\mathrm{pH} = \mathrm{p}K_a + \log\frac{[\mathrm{A^-}]}{[\mathrm{HA}]}$$

In a strong acid–strong base or strong base–strong acid titration, the pH of the equivalence point is exactly 7. In a weak acid–strong base titration, the equivalence point is greater than pH 7, and in a weak base–strong acid titration, it is less than pH 7 (Section 17.3).

In a weak acid–strong base titration, the pH at the half-equivalence point is equal to the pK_a of the acid. Similarly, in a weak base–strong acid titration, the pH at the half-equivalence point is equal to the pK_b of the base. In weak acid–strong base titration curves, the weaker the acid, the higher the initial pH of the titration and the higher the pH at the equivalence point (Section 17.4).

An appropriate indicator for a particular titration must change color over a range that either overlaps with or is close to the equivalence point (Section 17.5).

The solubility product constant, K_{sp}, of an ionic compound is a measure of that compound's solubility. It is the product of that compound's ion concentrations in solution, each raised to the power of its coefficient in the balanced chemical equation. The solubility product constant differs from the molar solubility of a compound, which is the number of moles of a substance that can dissolve into 1 L of solution. In general, lower K_{sp} values indicate lower solubility, whereas higher K_{sp} values indicate higher solubility (Section 17.6).

The common-ion effect limits the solubility of an ionic compound that is dissolved in a solution that contains a common ion. The pH of a solution also affects the solubility of an ionic compound that has a basic anion. The addition of an acid will increase the solubility of these compounds, while the addition of a base will decrease their solubility (Section 17.7).

In heterogeneous equilibrium systems between an ionic solid and a solution, K_{sp} is a measurement of the product of ion concentrations at equilibrium, whereas the reaction quotient, Q, is a measurement of the product of ion concentrations under any conditions. When $Q < K_{sp}$, the solution is not yet saturated and more solid ionic compound can be dissolved into the solution. When $Q = K_{sp}$, the solution is saturated and the system is at equilibrium. When $Q > K_{sp}$, the solution is past the point of saturation and precipitate will form until $Q = K_{sp}$.

When several ions are present in a solution, one or more ions can be selectively precipitated and removed from solution based on the different solubilities of the ions with a specific reagent (Section 17.8).

Qualitative analysis is the determination of the presence or absence of chemical species in a sample, regardless of amounts. Quantitative analysis is the determination of the amount of specific chemical species present in a sample.

Five different groups of metal ions in aqueous solution can be systematically precipitated based on their solubilities with different anions. Precipitates from each of these groups can be further analyzed with specific tests to determine the identity of the metal ion(s) present (Section 17.9).

Complex ions consist of Lewis bases known as ligands that coordinate to a Lewis acid metal ion. The formation constant, K_f, of a complex ion is the equilibrium constant for the formation of the complex from the metal ion and its ligands (Section 17.10).

END OF CHAPTER QUESTIONS

17.1 Introduction to Buffer Solutions

1. Describe the common-ion effect.

2. Explain which types of electrolytes, when combined, exhibit the common-ion effect.

3. Explain how a buffer solution works.

4. Determine which of the following compounds would form a buffer solution when dissolved in water:
   a. HCl and NaCl
   b. HClO and NaCl
   c. HClO and NaClO
   d. CO and CO_2

5. Select the statement or statements that are true about buffer solutions
   a. Buffer solutions consist of a strong acid and its conjugate base.
   b. The pH of a buffer solution never changes, even when a large amount of strong acid or base is added.
   c. Buffer solutions resist a change in pH by shifting the position of their equilibria to counteract the addition of H_3O^+ or OH^-.

6. Use an ICE table to calculate the pH of a buffer solution that contains 0.150 M benzoic acid, $HO_2C_7H_5$, and 0.200 M benzoate ion, $O_2C_7H_5^-$. The K_a of benzoic acid is 6.3×10^{-5}.

7. Use an ICE table to calculate the pH of a buffer solution that contains 0.100 M diethylammonium ion, $HNC_2H_6^+$, and 0.0900 M diethylamine, NC_2H_6. The K_a of the diethylammonium ion is 1.2×10^{-11}.

17.2 The Henderson–Hasselbalch Equation

8. Calculate the pH of a buffer that contains 0.125 M cyanic acid, HCNO ($K_a = 3.5 \times 10^{-4}$), with 0.220 M potassium cyanate, KCNO.

9. Calculate the pH of a buffer that contains 0.390 M hydrazine, N_2H_4 ($K_b = 1.3 \times 10^{-6}$), with 0.264 M hydrazinium ion, $N_2H_5^+$.

10. Calculate the ratio of conjugate base to weak acid, $[A^-]/[HA]$, needed to make a buffer at pH = 5.00 if the pK_a of the acid is 4.20.

11. How many moles of ammonium nitrate, NH_4NO_3, must be added to a solution containing 0.0750 mol of ammonia, NH_3 ($K_b = 1.8 \times 10^{-5}$), to produce a buffer with a pH of 9.00?

12. Assuming no volume change, calculate the pH of:
    a. a solution made from 0.0500 mol of NaOH(s) added to 1.00 L of pure water.
    b. a solution made from 0.0500 mol of NaOH(s) added to 1.00 L of a buffer containing 0.100 mol each of weak acid (pK_a = 5.00) and its conjugate base.

13. Which of the following weak acids would be suitable for making a buffer at pH = 3.50?
    a. chlorous acid ($K_a = 1.1 \times 10^{-2}$)
    b. formic acid ($K_a = 1.8 \times 10^{-4}$)
    c. hydrofluoric acid ($K_a = 6.3 \times 10^{-4}$)
    d. hypobromous acid ($K_a = 2.8 \times 10^{-9}$)

14. Which of the following sets of acids and conjugate bases would buffer most effectively at biological pH (7.4)?
    a. acetic acid ($K_a = 1.6 \times 10^{-5}$) and its conjugate base
    b. benzoic acid ($K_a = 6.3 \times 10^{-5}$) and its conjugate base

c. hypoiodous acid ($K_a = 2.5 \times 10^{-11}$) and its conjugate base
d. dihydrogen phosphate ($K_a = 6.3 \times 10^{-8}$) and its conjugate base

15. A 1.00 L buffer solution consists of 0.100 M formic acid ($pK_a = 3.7$) and its conjugate base, 0.100 M sodium formate. Specify whether the pH will increase, decrease, or stay the same after the addition of the following:
a. 0.0500 mol of formic acid
b. 0.150 mol of sodium formate
c. 1 mL of 0.001 M HCl
d. 50 mL of pure water

16. What is the pH of a buffer solution when its weak acid and conjugate base components are in equal concentrations?

17. Select the solution of formic acid ($pK_a = 3.74$) and formate ion that would most effectively buffer a solution at pH 3.5:
a. 0.100 M formic acid and 0.100 M formate ion
b. 0.100 M formic acid and 0.569 M formate ion
c. 0.176 M formic acid and 0.100 M formate ion

17.3 Titrations of Strong Acids and Strong Bases

18. What is the pH at the equivalence point of a strong acid–strong base titration? Explain how this might differ from the pH at the end point of this type of titration.

19. A strong acid is titrated with a strong base. Which of the following pH values can be determined without knowing the concentrations or volumes used in the titration.
a. the initial pH, before the base is added
b. the pH at half of the equivalence point
c. the pH at the equivalence point
d. the pH immediately after the equivalence point

20. In the titration of 375 mL of 0.400 M HCl with 0.250 M NaOH, calculate the pH at each of these points:
a. before the addition of NaOH
b. after the addition of 375 mL of NaOH
c. at the equivalence point
d. after the addition of 650 mL of NaOH

21. In the titration of 225 mL of 0.200 M KOH with 0.300 M HBr, calculate the pH at each of these points:
a. before the addition of HBr
b. after the addition of 125 mL of HBr
c. at the equivalence point
d. after the addition of 175 mL of HBr

22. Compare and contrast the titration curves resulting from:
a. strong acid titrated with strong base.
b. strong base titrated with strong acid.

23. In the titration of 0.500 L of 0.200 M monoprotic strong acid with 0.100 M strong base, determine the volume of strong base needed to reach the equivalence point if the base is:
a. NaOH.
b. $Ba(OH)_2$.

17.4 Titrations of Weak Acids and Weak Bases

24. Compare and contrast the titration curves resulting from:
a. strong monoprotic acid titrated with strong base.
b. weak monoprotic acid titrated with strong base.
c. weak diprotic acid titrated with strong base.

25. Is the pH at the equivalence point of a weak acid–strong base titration lower, higher, or the same as the pH at the equivalence point of a strong acid–weak base titration? Explain.

26. How is the pH at the equivalence point of a weak acid–strong base titration related to the ionization constant (K_a) of the weak acid?

27. For the titration of 405 mL of 0.100 M weak acid HA with 0.125 M NaOH, what volume of NaOH is needed
a. to reach the point where $pH = pK_a$?
b. to reach the equivalence point?

28. In the titration of 375 mL of 0.400 M HNO_2 ($K_a = 5.6 \times 10^{-4}$) with 0.250 M NaOH, calculate the pH at each of these points:
a. before the addition of NaOH
b. after the addition of 375 mL of NaOH
c. at the equivalence point
d. after the addition of 650 mL of NaOH

29. In the titration of 225 mL of 0.200 M weak base ($K_b = 6.0 \times 10^{-6}$) with 0.300 M HBr, calculate the pH at each of these points:
a. before the addition of HBr
b. after the addition of 125 mL of HBr
c. at the equivalence point
d. after the addition of 175 mL of HBr

30. Determine the pH at the half-equivalence point for each of these weak acids titrated with strong base.
a. chlorous acid ($K_a = 1.1 \times 10^{-2}$)
b. formic acid ($K_a = 1.8 \times 10^{-4}$)
c. hydrofluoric acid ($K_a = 6.3 \times 10^{-4}$)
d. hypobromous acid ($K_a = 2.8 \times 10^{-9}$)

31. Describe how the equivalence point pH of a weak acid–strong base titration changes as the K_a of the acid decreases. (Hint: See Figure 17.9.)

32. Describe how the shape of a weak acid–strong base titration curve changes as the K_a of the acid decreases. What causes the shape to change with decreasing K_a? (Hint: See Figure 17.9.)

33. Solutions of acetic acid ($pK_a = 4.74$) and 4-methylphenol ($pK_a = 10.26$) are each titrated with NaOH, using a pH meter to monitor the solution pH. Explain why it is easier to obtain an accurate equivalence point in the acetic acid titration than in the 4-methylphenol titration. (Hint: See Figure 17.9.)

34. A compound with three ionizable acidic groups is titrated with a strong base. How many equivalence points would be encountered during the titration?

17.5 Indicators in Acid–Base Titrations

35. Describe the difference between the end point and the equivalence point of an acid–base titration. Which of these does a colorimetric indicator detect?

36. What is the pH at the *equivalence point* of a strong acid–strong base titration? Is the pH at the *end point* of a strong acid–strong base titration the same? Explain.

37. A particular indicator with a pK_a of 4 is red in its protonated form and yellow in its unprotonated form. What color will this indicator be at
a. pH = 1?
b. pH = 4?
c. pH = 7?

38. Using Table 17.1, choose an appropriate indicator for the titration of a weak acid with NaOH, where the expected equivalence point of the titration is at pH 6.5.

39. Using Table 17.1, choose an appropriate indicator for the titration of a weak base with HCl, where the expected equivalence point of the titration is at pH 5.5.

40. An HCl solution is titrated with NaOH solution, using phenolphthalein as the indicator. Explain why the solution pH is usually slightly basic when the indicator has turned the solution a very faint pink color. (Hint: See Figure 17.14.)

41. True or false: In a strong acid–strong base titration, if the pH values at the equivalence point and end point differ significantly, the volumes of titrant added at these points must also differ significantly. (Hint: See Figure 17.14.)

42. A solution of methylamine, a weak base, is titrated with HCl solution. Explain why phenolphthalein would not be a good indicator for this titration.

17.6 The Solubility Product Constant, K_{sp}

43. Explain the difference between the solubility of a compound and its solubility product constant.

44. A solution of $Zn(OH)_2$ contains 2×10^{-6} M Zn^{2+} and 4×10^{-6} M OH^-. Calculate the K_{sp} of $Zn(OH)_2$.

45. Consider the K_{sp} values of the following compounds:
a. $MgCO_3$ $K_{sp} = 6.8 \times 10^{-6}$
b. $CdCO_3$ $K_{sp} = 1.0 \times 10^{-12}$
c. $SrCO_3$ $K_{sp} = 5.6 \times 10^{-10}$

Comment on the relative solubilities of these three compounds.

46. Calculate $[Br^-]$ in a saturated $PbBr_2$ solution where $[Pb^{2+}] = 9.71 \times 10^{-4}$ M. The K_{sp} of $PbBr_2$ is 6.60×10^{-6}.

47. Calculate the molar solubility of Li_3PO_4, $K_{sp} = 2.37 \times 10^{-11}$ in pure water.

48. Calculate the solubility, in grams per liter, of PbI_2, $K_{sp} = 9.8 \times 10^{-9}$ in pure water.

49. For a salt with a molar solubility of 0.0033 M, calculate its K_{sp} if its formula is
a. AB.
b. AB_2.
c. AB_3.
d. A_2B_3.

50. Express K_{sp} in terms of molar solubility, x, for salts with the following formulas. If each of these compounds has the same K_{sp} value, which has the highest molar solubility?
a. AB
b. AB_2
c. AB_3
d. A_2B_3

51. The solubility of CuI is 2.15×10^{-4} g/L. Calculate the K_{sp} of CuI.

52. The solubility of $Ni_3(PO_4)_2$ is 9.71×10^{-5} g/L. Calculate the K_{sp} of $Ni_3(PO_4)_2$.

17.7 The Common-Ion Effect and the Effect of pH on Solubility

53. Suggest two ways in which the dissolution of each of the following compounds could be suppressed:
    a. ZnF_2
    b. $KClO_4$
    c. $Ba(NO_3)_2$

54. Calculate the molar solubility of Li_3PO_4, $K_{sp} = 2.37 \times 10^{-11}$, in a solution containing 8.0×10^{-5} M LiCl. Compare your answer to that of problem 47.

55. Calculate the solubility, in grams per liter, of PbI_2, $K_{sp} = 9.8 \times 10^{-9}$, in a solution containing 0.100 M $Pb(NO_3)_2$. Compare your answer to that of problem 48.

56. The K_{sp} of $Ca(OH)_2$ is 5.02×10^{-6}. Calculate the molar solubility of $Ca(OH)_2$ in:
    a. pure water
    b. a solution buffered at pH 10.00

57. Calculate the molar solubility of $Ca(OH)_2$ in a solution buffered at pH 7.00 and compare it to the molar solubility of $Ca(OH)_2$ in pure water (see previous problem). Explain how Le Châtelier's principle can be used to explain the differing solubilities.

58. Calculate the mass of $CaSO_4$ that can dissolve into 250.0 mL of a 0.0200 M Na_2SO_4 solution. The K_{sp} of $CaSO_4$ is 4.93×10^{-5}.

59. Determine which of the following compounds will be more soluble in acidic solution than in basic or neutral solution:
    a. $Mg(OH)_2$
    b. $MgCO_3$
    c. $MgCl_2$
    d. MgF_2

60. Determine which of the following compounds will be more soluble in basic solution than in acidic or neutral solution:
    a. acetic acid ($HC_2H_3O_2$)
    b. sodium acetate ($NaC_2H_3O_2$)
    c. phenol (HC_6H_5O, $pK_a = 9.99$)
    d. $CaCO_3$

17.8 Precipitation: Q versus K_{sp}

61. Will a precipitate form when equal volumes of 1.0×10^{-4} M $AgNO_3$ and 5.0×10^{-4} M Na_2CO_3 are mixed? See Appendix A.4 for K_{sp} values as needed.

62. A scientist attempts to prepare a 0.00500 M solution of AgI ($K_{sp} = 8.52 \times 10^{-17}$). Does all of the AgI precipitate?

63. A scientist attempts to prepare a 1.0×10^{-3} M solution of $KClO_4$ ($K_{sp} = 1.05 \times 10^{-2}$). Does all of the $KClO_4$ precipitate?

64. A scientist attempts to prepare 500.00 mL of a 0.100 M LiF solution ($K_{sp} = 1.84 \times 10^{-3}$). What mass of solid LiF does not dissolve?

65. A scientist attempts to prepare 50.00 mL of a 5.00×10^{-4} M MgF_2 solution ($K_{sp} = 5.16 \times 10^{-11}$). What mass of solid MgF_2 does not dissolve?

17.9 Qualitative Analysis

66. What can be added to a solution containing Pb^{2+}, Cu^{2+}, Co^{2+}, and Fe^{2+} to selectively precipitate the Pb^{2+}?

67. A chemist is given an aqueous sample containing several soluble perchlorate salts of metal ions. The addition of HCl to the solution did not result in a precipitate. The addition of H_2S under acidic conditions *did* result in a precipitate. Which of the following compounds could have been present in the original solution?
    a. $AgClO_4$
    b. $Hg(ClO_4)_2$
    c. $Ba(ClO_4)_2$
    d. $Fe(ClO_4)_2$

68. A chemist is given an aqueous sample containing several soluble nitrate salts of metal ions. The addition of HCl to the solution did not result in a precipitate. The addition of H_2S under acidic conditions also did not result in a precipitate. However, the addition of H_2S under basic conditions *did* result in a precipitate. Which of the following compounds could have been present in the original solution?
    a. $Cu(NO_3)_2$
    b. $Ni(NO_3)_2$
    c. $Mg(NO_3)_2$
    d. $LiNO_3$

69. While testing an unknown solution, no precipitates formed during any of the precipitation steps of the qualitative analysis process, but there was a yellow-orange color observed during the flame test at the end. What conclusions can be made about the species present in the original solution?

70. While testing an unknown aqueous solution containing metal ions, a precipitate forms after the addition of HCl. No precipitate forms upon the addition of H_2S under acidic or basic conditions. A precipitate forms upon the addition of Na_3PO_4. Select the true statement(s).
a. Ag^+ is likely present.
b. Hg_2^{2+} is possibly present.
c. A group 1 ion is possibly present.
d. A group 2 ion is possibly present.

71. Describe procedures for the following qualitative analysis tests
a. Detect the presence of Sr^{2+} in an aqueous solution containing Ag^+ and Cd^{2+}.
b. Detect the presence of Hg^{2+} in an aqueous solution containing Hg_2^{2+}.
c. Detect the presence of K^+ in an aqueous solution containing Na^+, Li^+, and Fe^{3+}.

72. An aqueous solution was treated with HCl and no precipitate was formed. Addition of H_2S under both acidic and basic conditions also yielded no precipitate. The addition of Na_2CO_3 resulted in the formation of a precipitate. Name the metals that may be present in the precipitate.

73. A chemist treats an aqueous solution with HCl and a precipitate forms. Select the possible identity of the precipitate.
a. NaCl
b. HgCl
c. $HgCl_2$
d. PbS
e. CuS

74. An aqueous solution was treated with HCl and no precipitate was formed. The addition of H_2S under acidic conditions yielded no precipitate. H_2S was then bubbled through the solution under basic conditions and a precipitate formed. A subsequent addition of Na_2CO_3 did not result in a precipitate. Identify whether each of the following ions are definitely present, possibly present, or definitely absent.
a. Pb^{2+}
b. Sn^{4+}
c. Mn^{2+}
d. Ca^{2+}
e. NH_4^+

75. An aqueous solution was treated with HCl and a precipitate was formed. The addition of H_2S under acidic conditions also yielded a precipitate. H_2S was then bubbled through the solution under basic conditions and no precipitate formed. A subsequent addition of Na_2CO_3 resulted in a precipitate. Identify whether each of the following ions are definitely present, possibly present, or definitely absent.
a. Cu^{2+}
b. Ag^+
c. Li^+
d. Ba^{2+}
e. Cr^{3+}

17.10 Complex Ion Equilibria, K_f

76. Write the balanced chemical equation and the formation constant expression, K_f, for each of the following complex ions in aqueous solution:
a. $Fe(OH)_6^{2+}$
b. $Co(NH_3)_6^{3+}$
c. $Fe(CN)_6^{4-}$

77. Write the formation constant equilibrium expressions for the following reactions:
a. $Co^{2+}(aq) + 4\,SCN^-(aq) \rightleftharpoons Co(SCN)^{4-}(aq)$
b. $Mo^{4+}(aq) + 8\,CN^-(aq) \rightleftharpoons Mo(CN)_8^{4-}(aq)$
c. $Ni^{2+}(aq) + 4\,F^-(aq) \rightleftharpoons NiF_4^{2-}(aq)$

78. The complex ion $Ag(NH_3)^{2+}$ is formed from a solution that initially contains 1.00×10^{-3} M $AgNO_3$ and 0.100 M NH_3. Determine the concentration of free Ag^+ that remains in solution under these conditions. The K_f value of $Ni(NH_3)_6^{2+}$ is 1.7×10^7.

79. The complex ion $Cr(OH)_4^-$ is formed from a solution that initially contains 5.0×10^{-5} M $Cr(ClO_4)_3$ and is buffered at pH 10. Determine the concentration of free Cr^{3+} that remains in solution under these conditions. The K_f value of $Cr(OH)_4^-$ is 8×10^{29}.

80. Write the formation constant equilibrium expression for $CuCl_2^-$ from its constituent ions and determine the concentrations of free Cu^+, Cl^-, and $CuCl_2^-$ at equilibrium. The formation constant for $CuCl_2^-$ is 3.0×10^5.

81. Consider the following reactions to form complex ions. Assuming that all metal ions are initially the same concentration and all anions are initially the same concentration, determine which of the three complex ions is present in the highest concentration at equilibrium. Which is present at the lowest concentration?
    a. $Hg^{2+}(aq) + 4\ Br^-(aq) \rightleftharpoons HgBr_4^{2-}(aq) \quad K_f = 3.0 \times 10^4$
    b. $Zn^{2+}(aq) + 4\ Cl^-(aq) \rightleftharpoons ZnCl_4^{2-}(aq) \quad K_f = 1.6$
    c. $Hg^{2+}(aq) + 4\ I^-(aq) \rightleftharpoons MgI_4^{2-}(aq) \quad K_f = 1.9 \times 10^{30}$

82. In cases when a complex ion's formation constant is relatively small, chemists sometimes use a large excess of anion to shift the reaction position toward the formation of more complex ion. Consider the following reaction between Co^{2+} and SCN^-:

    $$Co^{2+}(aq) + 4\ SCN^-(aq) \rightleftharpoons Co(SCN)_4^{2-}(aq) \quad K_f = 1.0 \times 10^3$$

    Determine the concentration of free Co^{2+} present at equilibrium when the initial Co^{2+} concentration is 0.020 M and the initial SCN^- concentration is:
    a. 0.085 M
    b. 0.50 M

Putting It Together

83. A chemist mixes 250 mL of 0.100 M weak acid, HA, ($pK_a = 4.5$) with 150 mL of 0.150 M NaOH.
    a. Identify the limiting reactant.
    b. Calculate the amount of each product formed and the amount of excess reactant left over when the reaction is complete.
    c. Is the resulting solution a buffer?
    d. Calculate the pH of the resulting solution.

84. Based on the titration curve shown in Figure 17.8, approximate the pK_a of the acid.

85. Calculate the pH of a solution of calcium hydroxide, $Ca(OH)_2$ ($K_{sp} = 5.02 \times 10^{-6}$), made by dissolving solid $Ca(OH)_2$ in pure water until the solution is saturated.

86. An excess of an unknown metal hydroxide, $M(OH)_2$, is added to pure water. The resulting pH of the water is 8.66. Determine the K_{sp} of $M(OH)_2$.

87. Aqueous $Co(NO_3)_2$ is added to an unbuffered solution at pH 12, and $Co(OH)_2$ precipitate forms. Determine whether each of the following methods will dissolve the solid $Co(OH)_2$, and explain why or why not:
    a. addition of HCl solution
    b. addition of KOH solution
    c. addition of NH_3 solution
    d. addition of NO_3^- solution

88. Suppose that 20.00 mL of a 0.100 M strong acid is titrated with 0.100 M strong base. Now suppose that 20.00 mL of a weak acid is titrated with 0.100 M strong base. Which of the following are the same in the two titrations?
    a. the initial pH of the titration, before any base is added
    b. the pH of the titration at the half equivalence point
    c. the pH of the titration at the equivalence point
    d. the volume of strong base needed to reach the equivalence point

89. A 0.125 M solution of a diprotic weak acid, H_2A, is titrated with a 0.100 M strong base. A volume of 16.25 mL of strong base is needed to reach the first equivalence point. What volume of this strong base would be needed to reach the second equivalence point?

90. A weak acid is titrated with a strong base and the pH rises rapidly three times during the titration. What can be said about the polyprotic acid?
    a. It is diprotic.
    b. It is triprotic.
    c. It is tetraprotic.

91. Suppose that 20 mL of a 0.1 M weak acid is diluted by adding 20 mL of water. Would you expect the weak acid to dissociate more or less after the water is added? (Hint: Consider the role that Le Châtelier's principle plays.)

92. The concentration of a strong acid needs to be measured. Explain why titration of the strong acid with 1.000 M strong base and a buret that is accurate to ± 0.01 mL can give a more precise concentration than measuring the pH of the strong acid with a pH meter that is accurate to ± 0.01 pH units.

PRACTICE PROBLEM SOLUTIONS

Practice Problem 17.1 Solution

First, set up an ICE equilibrium table.

	HN_3 (aq)	+ $H_2O(l)$ $\rightleftharpoons$	N_3^- (aq)	+	H_3O^+ (aq)
Initial	0.16		0.19		0
Change	$-x$		$+x$		$+x$
Equilibrium	$0.16 - x$		$0.19 + x$		x

Then use the following equilibrium expression to solve for x:

$$K_a = \frac{[N_3^-][H_3O^+]}{[HN_3]} = 2.5 \times 10^{-5}$$

$$K_a = \frac{(0.19 + x)(x)}{(0.16 - x)} = 2.5 \times 10^{-5}$$

Assume that the value of x is less than 5% of the original concentrations of HN_3 and N_3^-, and simplify the $(0.19 + x)$ and $(0.16 - x)$ terms to 0.19 and 0.16, respectively:

$$\frac{(0.19)(x)}{0.16} = 2.5 \times 10^{-5}$$

$$x = \frac{(0.16)(2.5 \times 10^{-5})}{0.19}$$

$$x = [H_3O^+] = 2.1 \times 10^{-5}\text{ M}$$

Now compare the original concentrations of hydrazoic acid, HN_3, and azide ion, N_3,

$$\text{For hydrazoic acid: } \frac{2.1 \times 10^{-5}}{0.16} \times 100\% = 0.013\%$$

$$\text{For azide ion: } \frac{2.1 \times 10^{-5}}{0.19} \times 100\% = 0.011\%$$

Because x is far less than 5% of the original concentrations of both hydrazoic acid and azide ion, the simplification is valid. Now calculate the solution pH.

$$\text{pH} = -\log(2.1 \times 10^{-5}) = 4.68$$

Practice Problem 17.2 Solution

a. Unlike the other hydrogen halides, HF is a weak acid in solution. NaF dissolves to produce F^-, which is the conjugate base of HF. Therefore, the combination of HF and NaF will result in a buffer solution.

b. CH_3NH_2 is a weak base. $CH_3NH_3^+$ is the conjugate acid of CH_3NH_2, so the combination of these two species will result in a buffer solution.

c. HI is a strong acid. Therefore, the combination of HI and I_2 does not result in a buffer solution.

Practice Problem 17.3 Solution

$HClO_4$ is a strong acid that fully ionizes in solution. The reaction is

$$HClO_4(aq) + H_2O(l) \rightarrow H_3O^+(aq) + ClO_4^-(aq)$$

With strong acids, there is no equilibrium. When strong base is added, it will react with $HClO_4$, but if strong acid is added, no reverse reaction can occur.

Practice Problem 17.4 Solution

The ionization reaction is

$$HCNO(aq) + H_2O(l) \rightleftharpoons CNO^-(aq) + H_3O^+(aq)$$

Assume that the initial concentrations are approximately equal to the equilibrium concentrations, which can be substituted directly into the K_a expression.

$$K_a = \frac{[CNO^-][H_3O^+]}{[HCNO]} = 3.5 \times 10^{-4}$$

$$\frac{(0.160)[H_3O^+]}{(0.125)} = 3.5 \times 10^{-4}$$

$$[H_3O^+] = \frac{(3.5 \times 10^{-4})(0.125)}{(0.160)}$$

$$[H_3O^+] = 2.7 \times 10^{-4}\text{ M}$$

Compare $[H_3O^+]$ to the original concentrations.

$$\text{For HCNO: } \frac{2.7 \times 10^{-4}}{0.125} \times 100\% = 0.22\%$$

$$\text{For CNO}^-\text{: } \frac{2.7 \times 10^{-4}}{0.160} \times 100\% = 0.17\%$$

Because $[H_3O^+]$ is far less than 5% of the original concentrations, the simplification is valid.

Now calculate the solution pH:

$$\text{pH} = -\log(2.7 \times 10^{-4}) = 3.56$$

Practice Problem 17.5 Solution

In this problem, the conjugate acid is NH_4^+ and the conjugate base is NH_3.

The pK_a of NH_4^+ is $-\log(5.65 \times 10^{-10}) = 9.248$.

$$\text{pH} = pK_a + \log\frac{[A^-]}{[HA]}$$

$$\text{pH} = 9.248 + \log\frac{[0.220]}{[0.150]}$$

$$\text{pH} = 9.248 + 0.166$$

$$\text{pH} = 9.414$$

Practice Problem 17.6 Solution

In this problem, the conjugate acid is HCO_3^- and the conjugate base is CO_3^{2-}.

The pK_a of HCO_3^- is $-\log(5.0 \times 10^{-11}) = 10.30$.

$$pH = pK_a + \log\frac{[A^-]}{[HA]}$$

$$10.0 = 10.30 + \log\frac{[CO_3^{2-}]}{[HCO_3^-]}$$

$$-0.3 = \log\frac{[CO_3^{2-}]}{[HCO_3^-]}$$

$$\frac{[CO_3^{2-}]}{[HCO_3^-]} = 10^{-0.3} = 0.5$$

The concentration of carbonate ion in the buffer must be half the concentration of bicarbonate ion.

Practice Problem 17.7 Solution

Phenol has a K_a of 1.1×10^{-10}, which is a pK_a of 9.96. This is the only acid in the table with a pK_a value that is within 1 unit of pH 10.8. Therefore, a buffer containing phenol and its conjugate base, phenolate ion, will work effectively at pH 10.8.

Practice Problem 17.8 Solution

a. Use the Henderson–Hasselbalch equation. The pK_a of $H_2PO_4^-$ is $-\log(6.32 \times 10^{-8}) = 7.20$.

$$pH = pK_a + \log\frac{[HPO_4^{2-}]}{[H_2PO_4^-]}$$

$$pH = 7.20 + \log\frac{[0.200]}{[0.250]} = 7.10$$

b. First, convert the amount of each species to moles.

$$0.500\ L\left(\frac{0.250\ mol}{1\ L}\right) = 0.125\ mol\quad H_2PO_4^-$$

$$0.500\ L\left(\frac{0.200\ mol}{1\ L}\right) = 0.100\ mol\quad HPO_4^{2-}$$

$$0.0500\ L\left(\frac{0.500\ mol}{1\ L}\right) = 0.0250\ mol\quad KOH$$

KOH is a strong base and the neutralization of $H_2PO_4^-$ proceeds to completion.

	$H_2PO_4^-$ (aq)	+	KOH (aq)	→	HPO_4^{2-} (aq)	+	H_2O (l)
Initial	0.125 mol		0.0250 mol		0.100 mol		
Change	−0.0250 mol		−0.0250 mol		+0.0250 mol		
Final	0.100 mol		0 mol		0.125 mol		

Now use the Henderson–Hasselbalch equation to determine the pH of the solution. Recall that moles can be used in place of concentrations in this equation.

$$pH = pK_a + \log\frac{[HPO_4^{2-}]}{[H_2PO_4^-]}$$

$$pH = 7.20 + \log\frac{(0.125)}{(0.100)}$$

$$pH = 7.20 + (0.097) = 7.30$$

c. The total volume is 50.0 mL + 500.0 mL = 550.0 mL. Determine the new concentration of KOH using $M_1V_1 = M_2V_2$.

$$M_2 = \frac{M_1V_1}{V_2} = \frac{(0.500\ M)(50.0\ mL)}{550.0\ mL} = 0.0455\ M\ KOH$$

Since KOH is a strong base, 0.0455 M KOH contains 0.0455 M OH^-.

$$pOH = -\log(0.0455) = 1.342$$

$$pH + pOH = 14.000$$

$$pH + (-1.342) = 14.000$$

$$pH = 14.000 - 1.342 = 12.658$$

Practice Problem 17.9 Solution

a. The initial pH is determined from the concentration of $HClO_4$. $HClO_4$ is a strong acid, so its concentration is equal to the concentration of H^+ in solution.

$$pH = -\log(0.225) = 0.648$$

b. First, calculate the number of moles of $HClO_4$ inside the flask (prior to the addition of any NaOH solution) and the number of moles of NaOH that are added to the flask at this point in the titration.

$$0.02500\ L\ HClO_4\left(\frac{0.300\ mol\ HClO_4}{L}\right)$$

$$= 0.007500\ mol\ HClO_4$$

$$0.02500\ L\ NaOH\left(\frac{0.225\ mol\ NaOH}{L}\right)$$

$$= 0.005625\ mol\ NaOH$$

Then calculate the number of moles of H^+ (as $HClO_4$) remaining after the addition of NaOH.

	H^+(aq)	+	OH^-(aq)	→ H_2O(l)
Initial	0.007500 mol		0 mol	
Addition of NaOH			0.005625 mol	
Reaction change	−0.005625 mol		−0.005625 mol	
Final	0.001875 mol		0 mol	

Determine the molarity of H^+ at equilibrium. Be sure to account for the change in volume that comes with adding NaOH solution.

$$[H^+] = \frac{0.007500 \text{ mol}}{(0.02500 \text{ L} + 0.02500 \text{ L})} = 0.150 \text{ M H}^+$$

Finally, calculate the pH of the solution.

$$\text{pH} = -\log(0.150) = 0.824$$

c. Given that $HClO_4$ is a strong acid and NaOH is a strong base, the pH of this titration at the equivalence point is 7.0.

d. Calculate the number of moles of NaOH that have been added to the flask.

$$0.04000 \text{ L}\left(\frac{0.225 \text{ mol NaOH}}{\text{L}}\right) = 0.009000 \text{ mol NaOH}$$

Recall from part (a) that there are 0.005625 mol of H^+ inside the flask prior to the addition of NaOH. You can see that this value is less than the number of moles of NaOH that have been added to the flask, so the titration is past the equivalence point and excess OH^- is present.

	$H^+(aq)$	+	$OH^-(aq)$	$\rightarrow H_2O(l)$
Initial	0.005625 mol		0 mol	
Addition of NaOH			0.009000 mol	
Reaction change	−0.005625 mol		−0.005625 mol	
Final	0 mol		0.003375 mol	

Determine the concentration of OH^-. Be sure once again to account for the volume of NaOH solution added.

$$[OH^-] = \frac{0.003375 \text{ mol OH}^-}{(0.02500 + 0.04000 \text{ L})} = 0.05192 \text{ M OH}^-$$

Now that $[OH^-]$ is known, you can calculate the pOH and then the pH.

$$\text{pOH} = -\log[OH^-]$$
$$\text{pOH} = -\log(0.0519) = 1.285$$
$$\text{pH} = 14.000 - 1.285 = 12.715$$

Practice Problem 17.10 Solution

a. $\text{pOH} = 14.00 - (-\log[0.200]) = 13.30$

b. First, determine the equivalence point of HBr. HBr reacts with KOH in a 1:1 molar ratio.

$$0.02500 \text{ L KOH}\left(\frac{0.200 \text{ mol KOH}}{1 \text{ L}}\right)\left(\frac{1 \text{ mol HBr}}{1 \text{ mol KOH}}\right)$$
$$= 0.00500 \text{ mol HBr}$$

$$0.00500 \text{ mol HBr} = \frac{1 \text{ L}}{0.150 \text{ mol HBr}} = 0.03333 \text{ L}$$
$$= 33.33 \text{ mL}$$

Half of the equivalence point is 33.3 mL/2 = 16.7 mL of HBr added.

Now determine the number of moles of KOH in the flask and the number of moles of HBr added.

$$0.02500 \text{ L}\frac{0.200 \text{ mol KOH}}{\text{L}} = 0.005000 \text{ mol KOH in flask}$$

$$0.0167 \text{ L}\frac{0.150 \text{ mol}}{\text{L}} = 0.002505 \text{ mol HBr}$$

	$H^+(aq)$	+	$OH^-(aq)$	$\rightarrow H_2O(l)$
Initial	0 mol		0.00500 mol	
Addition of NaOH	0.002505 mol			
Reaction change	−0.002505 mol		−0.002505 mol	
Final	0 mol		0.002495 mol	

$$[OH^-] = \frac{0.002505 \text{ mol}}{(0.02500 \text{ L} + 0.01667 \text{ L})} = 0.0601 \text{ M}$$
$$\text{pOH} = -\log(0.0601) = 1.221$$
$$\text{pH} = 14.000 - 1.221 = 12.779$$

c. For any strong acid–strong base titration, the pH at the equivalence point is exactly 7.

d. The KOH has been completely neutralized, so the 1.00 mL of HBr is in excess. First determine how many moles of acid that is, then determine the concentration of that acid.

$$0.00100 \text{ L}\frac{0.150 \text{ mol HBr}}{\text{L}} = 0.000150 \text{ mol HBr}$$
$$= 0.000150 \text{ mol H}^+$$

Divide the number of moles of H^+ by the total volume of solution (25.00 mL of KOH + 33.3 mL of HBr + 1.00 mL of HBr added after the equivalence point).

$$[H^+] = \frac{0.000150 \text{ mol H}^+}{(0.0333 \text{ L} + 0.02500 \text{ L} + 0.00100 \text{ L})}$$
$$= 0.002530 \text{ M H}^+$$
$$\text{pH} = -\log(0.002530) = 2.597$$

Practice Problem 17.11 Solution

As acid strength increases, the acid releases more H^+ into solution and its conjugate base decreases in strength. Acid strength increases with decreasing pK_a.

Hypobromous acid (lowest pK_a) is the strongest of the three acids, and phenol (highest pK_a) is the weakest of the three acids. Given that the acid and base concentrations are equal in all three titrations, hypobromous acid would have the lowest pH at the equivalence point of its titration because it is the strongest of the three acids. Phenol would have the highest pH at the equivalence point of its titration because it is the weakest of the three acids.

Practice Problem 17.12 Solution

a. $\text{pH} = -\log\sqrt{K_a \cdot [\text{HA}]} = -\log\sqrt{(3.5 \times 10^{-4})(0.100)} = 2.23$

b. After 15.0 mL, the solution is a buffer. Calculate the moles of HA and A^-.

$$\text{mol A}^- = \text{mol OH}^- = 0.0150\ \text{L}\left(\frac{0.120\ \text{mol}}{1\ \text{L}}\right) = 0.00180\ \text{mol}$$

$$\text{mol HA} = 0.0300\ \text{L}\left(\frac{0.100\ \text{mol}}{1\ \text{L}}\right) - 0.00180 = 0.00120\ \text{mol}$$

Find the pH using the Henderson–Hasselbalch equation.

$$\text{pH} = pK_a + \log\frac{[\text{A}^-]}{[\text{HA}]}$$

$$\text{pH} = -\log(3.5 \times 10^{-4}) + \log\frac{0.00180}{0.00120} = 3.63$$

c. The volume of KOH added at the equivalence point is 25.0 mL.

$$0.0300\ \text{L HA}\left(\frac{0.100\ \text{mol HA}}{1\ \text{L HA}}\right)\left(\frac{1\ \text{mol KOH}}{1\ \text{mol HA}}\right)\left(\frac{1\ \text{L}}{0.120\ \text{mol KOH}}\right) = 0.0250\ \text{L} = 25.0\ \text{mL}$$

All the HA ($0.0300\ \text{L} \times 0.100\ \text{M} = 0.00300$ mol) has been converted to A^-. Convert the moles of A^- to a concentration taking into account the total volume.

$$[\text{A}^-] = \frac{0.00300\ \text{mol}}{(0.0300\ \text{L} + 0.0250\ \text{L})} = 0.0545\ \text{M}$$

Convert the ionization constant, K_a, for the acid to K_b.

$$K_b = \frac{K_w}{K_a} = \frac{1.0 \times 10^{-14}}{3.5 \times 10^{-4}} = 2.9 \times 10^{-11}$$

$$\text{pOH} = -\log\sqrt{K_b \cdot [\text{A}^-]} = -\log\sqrt{(2.9 \times 10^{-11})(0.0545)} = 5.90$$

d. The equivalence point occurs at 25.0 mL, so at 30.0 mL, the amount of excess OH^- is 30.0 mL = 25.0 mL = 5.0 mL. Calculate the total number of moles of excess OH^-.

$$0.0050\ \text{L}\left(\frac{0.120\ \text{mol KOH}}{1\ \text{L}}\right) = 0.00060\ \text{mol OH}^-$$

Now determine the concentration of OH^-, accounting for the total volume.

$$[\text{OH}^-] = \frac{0.00060\ \text{mol}}{(0.0300\ \text{L} + 0.0250\ \text{L})} = 0.011\ \text{M}$$

Finally, calculate the pH.

$$\text{pOH} = -\log(0.011) = 1.96$$
$$\text{pH} = 14.00 - 1.96 = 12.04$$

Practice Problem 17.13 Solution

a. $\text{pOH} = -\log\sqrt{K_b \cdot [\text{CH}_3\text{NH}_2]} = -\log\sqrt{(4.3 \times 10^{-4})(0.200)} = 2.03$

$$\text{pH} = 14.00 - \text{pOH} = 14.00 - 2.03 = 11.97$$

b. The pH of the solution at the half-equivalence point is equal to the pK_a of the base's conjugate acid ($CH_3NH_3^+$).

$$\text{pH} = pK_a = -\log K_a = -\log\frac{K_w}{K_b} = -\log\frac{1.0 \times 10^{-14}}{4.3 \times 10^{-4}} = 10.63$$

c. At the equivalence point of the titration, all CH_3NH_2 ($0.0250\ \text{mL} \times 0.500\ \text{M} = 0.0125$ mol) has been converted to $CH_3NH_3^+$. First, determine the volume of HCl needed to produce 0.0125 mol of $CH_3NH_3^+$.

$$0.0125\ \text{mol HCl}\left(\frac{1\ \text{L}}{0.150\ \text{mol HCl}}\right) = 0.0833\ \text{L HCl}$$

Next, calculate the concentration of $CH_3NH_3^+$ at the equivalence point, accounting for the increase in volume from the added HCl (0.0833 L).

$$[\text{CH}_3\text{NH}_3^+] = \frac{0.0125\ \text{mol}}{(0.0250\ \text{L} + 0.0833\ \text{L})} = 0.115\ \text{M}$$

Calculate the pH as you would for a typical acidic salt, where $K_a = K_w/K_b$.

$$K_a = \frac{K_w}{K_b} = \frac{1.0 \times 10^{-14}}{4.3 \times 10^{-4}} = 2.33 \times 10^{-11}$$

$$\text{pH} = -\log\sqrt{K_a \cdot [\text{CH}_3\text{NH}_3^+]} = -\log\sqrt{(2.33 \times 10^{-11})(0.115)} = 5.79$$

d. First, calculate the total number of moles of H_3O^+ added to the solution.

$$0.0350\ \text{L}\left(\frac{0.150\ \text{mol HCl}}{1\ \text{L}}\right) = 0.00525\ \text{mol } H_3O^+ \text{ added}$$

As calculated in part (a), there are initially 0.00500 mol of CH_3NH_2. All CH_3NH_3 reacts with HCl. The number of moles of excess H_3O^+ is

$$0.00525\ \text{mol OH}^- - 0.00500\ \text{mol OH}^-$$
$$= 0.00025\ \text{mol of excess } H_3O^+$$

Now determine the concentration of H_3O^+ at equilibrium, accounting for dilution.

$$[H_3O^+] = \frac{0.00025\ \text{mol}}{(0.0250\ \text{L} + 0.0350\ \text{L})} = 0.0042\ \text{M}$$
$$\text{pH} = -\log(0.0042) = 2.38$$

Practice Problem 17.14 Solution

Since this is a strong base being titrated with strong acid, the ideal indicator will begin to change color within ±2 units of the equivalence point pH of 7, so somewhere between 5 and 9. Several indicators from Table 17.1 will either begin changing color or finish changing color within this end-point range. Of these, bromothymol blue is the best choice because its entire color-change range (6.0–7.6) is within the end-point range.

Practice Problem 17.15 Solution

From the previous example or from Table 17.2, the K_{sp} value for iron(II) sulfide is 1.6×10^{-19}. A saturated solution is at equilibrium, so the known concentration can be substituted directly into the K_{sp} expression.

$$FeS(s) \rightleftharpoons Fe^{2+}(aq) + S^{2-}(aq)$$
$$K_{sp} = [Fe^{2+}][S^{2-}]$$
$$1.6 \times 10^{-19} = (7.0 \times 10^{-11})[S^{2-}]$$
$$[S^{2-}] = \frac{1.6 \times 10^{-19}}{7.0 \times 10^{-11}} = 2.3 \times 10^{-9}\ \text{M}$$

Practice Problem 17.16 Solution

Table 17.2 gives the following K_{sp} values:

$$Ca(OH)_2(s) \rightleftharpoons Ca^{2+}(aq) + 2\ OH^-(aq) \qquad K_{sp} = 5.02 \times 10^{-6}$$

$$Ca(IO_3)_2(s) \rightleftharpoons Ca^{2+}(aq) + 2\ IO_3^-(aq) \qquad K_{sp} = 6.47 \times 10^{-6}$$

$$CaCO_3(s) \rightleftharpoons Ca^{2+}(aq) + CO_3^{2-}(aq) \qquad K_{sp} = 3.36 \times 10^{-9}$$

The relative solubilities of $Ca(OH)_2$ and $Ca(IO_3)_2$ can be predicted based on their respective K_{sp} values because 1 mol of each compound dissolves to produce 1 mol of Ca^{2+} and 2 mol of anion. $Ca(OH)_2$ has a slightly higher K_{sp} than $Ca(IO_3)_2$, so it is likely that $Ca(OH)_2$ has a higher solubility than $Ca(IO_3)_2$. However, 1 mol of $CaCO_3$ dissolves to produce 1 mol of Ca^{2+} and 1 mol of CO_3^{2-}. Therefore, the solubility of $CaCO_3$ relative to $Ca(OH)_2$ and $Ca(IO_3)_2$ cannot be predicted.

Practice Problem 17.17 Solution

a.

	$Ba_3(PO_4)_2(s) \rightleftharpoons$	$3Ba^{2+}(aq)$ +	$2\ PO_4^{3-}(aq)$
Initial	excess	0	0
Change	$-x$	$+3x$	$+2x$
Equilibrium		$3x$	$2x$

$$K_{sp} = [Ba^{2+}]^3[PO_4^{3-}]^2$$
$$K_{sp} = [3x]^3[2x]^2$$
$$K_{sp} = (9x^3)(4x^2)$$
$$K_{sp} = 36x^5 = 3.40 \times 10^{-23}$$
$$x = \sqrt[5]{\frac{3.40 \times 10^{-23}}{36}}$$
$$x = 1.57 \times 10^{-5}$$

The molar solubility of barium phosphate is 1.57×10^{-5} M.

b. To calculate the solubility in grams of barium phosphate per liter of solution, use the molar mass of $Ba_3(PO_4)_2$ to convert mol/L to g/L. The molar mass of $Ba_3(PO_4)_2$ is

$$3(137.33\ \text{g/mol}) + 2(30.974\ \text{g/mol}) + 8(15.999\ \text{g/mol}) = 601.93\ \text{g/mol}$$

$$\frac{1.57 \times 10^{-5}\ \text{mol}}{1\ \text{L}}\left(\frac{601.93\ \text{g}}{1\ \text{mol}}\right) = 0.00943\ \text{g/L}$$

Practice Problem 17.18 Solution

First, calculate the molar solubility of $Fe(OH)_3$ in units of mol/L. The molar mass of $Fe(OH)_3$ is

$$55.847\ \text{g/mol} + 3(15.999\ \text{g/mol}) + 3(1.008\ \text{g/mol}) = 106.8677\ \text{g/mol}$$

$$\frac{1.08 \times 10^{-8}\ \text{g}}{1\ \text{L}}\left(\frac{1\ \text{mol}}{106.8677\ \text{g}}\right) = 1.01 \times 10^{-10}\ \text{mol/L}$$

Next, construct an ICE table and give the equilibrium expression for $Fe(OH)_3$. The molar solubility of $Fe(OH)_3$ is represented by x:

	$Fe(OH)_3(s)$ $\rightleftharpoons$	$Fe^{3+}(aq)$ +	$3\ OH^-(aq)$
Initial	excess	0	0
Change	$-x$	$+x$	$+3x$
Equilibrium		x	$3x$

$$K_{sp} = [Fe^{3+}][OH^-]^3$$

$$K_{sp} = (x)(3x)^3 = 27x^4$$

Substituting the molar solubility of $Fe(OH)_3$, 1.01×10^{-10} M, into the equation,

$$K_{sp} = 27(1.01 \times 10^{-10})^4 = 2.82 \times 10^{-39}$$

Practice Problem 17.19 Solution

a. The molar solubility of FeF_2 in pure water is calculated as follows:

	$FeF_2(s)$ $\rightleftharpoons$	$Fe^{2+}(aq)$ +	$2\ F^-(aq)$
Initial	excess	0	0
Change	$-x$	$+x$	$+2x$
Equilibrium		x	$2x$

$$K_{sp} = [Fe^+][F^-]^2$$

$$K_{sp} = [x][2x]^2$$

$$K_{sp} = 4x^3 = 2.36 \times 10^{-6}$$

$$x = \sqrt[3]{\frac{2.36 \times 10^{-6}}{4}}$$

$$x = 8.39 \times 10^{-3}$$

The molar solubility of FeF_2 in pure water is 8.39×10^{-3} M.

b. The molar solubility of FeF_2 in 0.100 M NaF is calculated as shown below.

	$FeF_2(s)$ $\rightleftharpoons$	$Fe^{2+}(aq)$ +	$2\ F^-(aq)$
Initial	excess	0	0.100
Change	$-x$	$+x$	$+2x$
Equilibrium		x	$0.100 + 2x$

Considering that $2x$ is much smaller than 0.100 M, the $0.100 + 2x$ term in the equilibrium expression can be simplified to 0.100.

$$K_{sp} = [Fe^+][F^-]^2$$

$$K_{sp} = [x][0.100]^2 = 2.36 \times 10^{-6}$$

$$x = \frac{2.36 \times 10^{-6}}{0.0100} = 0.000236\ \text{M}$$

The molar solubility of FeF_2 in 0.100 M NaF solution is 2.36×10^{-4} M, which is less than its solubility in pure water.

Practice Problem 17.20 Solution

a. KI will *not* be more soluble in acidic solution because I^- is an extremely weak base and will not appreciably react with H^+. HI is a strong acid and I^- is its conjugate base. All conjugate bases of strong acids are extremely weak (so weak that they are effectively neutral).

b. $KClO_4$ will *not* be more soluble in acidic solution because ClO_4^- is an extremely weak base and will not appreciably react with H^+. $HClO_4$ is a strong acid and ClO_4^- is its conjugate base. All conjugate bases of strong acids are extremely weak (so weak they are effectively neutral).

c. $MgCO_3$ will be more soluble in acidic solution because CO_3^{2-} is a weak base (it is the conjugate base of HCO_3^-, which is the conjugate base of H_2CO_3). In fact, the acidification of $MgCO_3$ will also produce a gas, since H_2CO_3 rapidly dehydrates to form CO_2. As CO_2 bubbles out of solution, it is removed from the equilibrium and the solubility of $MgCO_3$ is further enhanced via Le Châtelier's principle.

Practice Problem 17.21 Solution

The possible products of this reaction are $NaNO_3$ and CdF_2. $NaNO_3$ is highly soluble, as you may recall from the solubility rules presented in Section 4.4 or deduce from its absence in K_{sp} tables (Table 17.2 and the extended K_{sp} list in Appendix A.4). However, CdF_2 is less soluble, with a listed K_{sp} of 6.44×10^{-3}.

$$CdF_2(s) \rightleftharpoons Cd^{2+}(aq) + 2\ F^-(aq)$$

$$Q = [Cd^{2+}][F^-]^2$$

$$Q = (0.00250)(0.00500)^2 = 6.30 \times 10^{-8}$$

Q, which is equal to 6.30×10^{-8} is less than K_{sp}, which is equal to 6.44×10^{-3}, so CdF_2 does *not* precipitate.

Practice Problem 17.22 Solution

a. The addition of sufficient CO_3^{2-} to the solution will cause the precipitation of $BaCO_3$ ($K_{sp} = 2.58 \times 10^{-9}$) and $CaCO_3$ ($K_{sp} = 3.36 \times 10^{-9}$). These K_{sp} values are not significantly different (same order of magnitude), and $CaCO_3$ has the higher K_{sp} value, so Na_2CO_3 cannot be used to selectively precipitate calcium.

b. The addition of sufficient PO_4^{3-} to the solution will cause the precipitation of $Ba_3(PO_4)_2$ ($K_{sp} = 3.40 \times 10^{-23}$) and $Ca_3(PO_4)_2$ ($K_{sp} = 2.07 \times 10^{-33}$). The K_{sp} value of $Ca_3(PO_4)_2$ is several orders of magnitude lower, so Na_3PO_4 can indeed be used to selectively precipitate calcium.

Practice Problem 17.23 Solution

The lack of any precipitate means the solution contained none of the ions that form insoluble chlorides, acid-insoluble sulfides, base-insoluble sulfides and hydroxides, or insoluble phosphates. The purple color that appeared during the flame tests suggests the presence of the potassium ion, K^+, but does not rule out the presence of other alkali metal ions or ammonium.

Practice Problem 17.24 Solution

Use the ICE equilibrium method, treating the reaction as if it goes to completion.

	Fe^{3+} (aq)	+	$6\ CN^-$ (aq)	$\rightleftharpoons$	$Fe(CN)_6^{3-}$ (aq)
Initial	1.00×10^{-3}		0.150		0
Change	-1.00×10^{-3}		$-6(1.00 \times 10^{-3})$		$+1.00 \times 10^{-3}$
Equilibrium	x		0.144		1.00×10^{-3}

Fe^{3+} is the limiting reactant, so the concentration of product is 1.00×10^{-3} M. Use x to represent the miniscule amount of Fe^{3+} that remains in solution.

$$K_f = \frac{[Fe(CN)_6^{3-}]}{[Fe^{3+}][CN^-]^6}$$

$$1 \times 10^{42} = \frac{1.00 \times 10^{-3}}{x(0.144)^6}$$

$$x = \frac{1.00 \times 10^{-3}}{(1 \times 10^{42})(0.144)^6}$$

$$x = [Fe^{3+}] = 1 \times 10^{-40}\ M$$

This extremely small concentration of Fe^{3+} makes sense, given the very large K_f value of 1×10^{42}.

Practice Problem 17.25 Solution

First, determine the pH. At the half-equivalence point of a weak-acid titration, pH = pK_a.

$$pH = pK_a = -\log K_a = -\log(6.2 \times 10^{-10}) = 9.21$$

Use the pH to find $[OH^-]$.

$$pOH = 14.00 - 9.21 = 4.79$$

$$[OH^-] = 10^{-pOH} = 10^{-4.79} = 1.6 \times 10^{-5}$$

Finally, plug this value into the K_{sp} expression.

$$K_{sp} = [Mg^{2+}][OH^-]^2$$

$$5.61 \times 10^{-12} = [Mg^{2+}](1.6 \times 10^{-5})^2$$

$$[Mg^{2+}] = \frac{5.61 \times 10^{-12}}{(1.6 \times 10^{-5})^2} = 0.022\ M$$

CHAPTER 18

Chemical Thermodynamics

Robert74/Shutterstock

Given a spark to overcome its activation energy, combustion (burning) is a spontaneous chemical reaction. The reverse reaction, however, simply does not occur. That is, ashes will not spontaneously "unburn" to form wood. In contrast, freezing (liquid → solid) and melting (solid → liquid) are reversible processes, where temperature dictates the direction. This chapter explores the concept of spontaneity to explain why some reactions and physical processes are reversible, whereas others favor one direction.

Chapter Outline

GOALS

- State the second law of thermodynamics.
- Define *entropy*.
- Identify the sign of ΔS from chemical equations or changes of state.
- Demonstrate a qualitative understanding of the relationship between entropy and probability.
- State the third law of thermodynamics.
- Determine ΔS for both chemical reactions and changes of state using standard molar entropies.
- Compare and contrast ΔS_{univ}, ΔS_{sys}, and ΔS_{surr}.
- Calculate ΔS_{surr} from ΔH_{sys} and temperature data for chemical and physical changes.
- Define *Gibbs free energy*.
- Describe how the signs of ΔH and ΔS affect the sign of ΔG.
- Calculate $\Delta G°$ for chemical and physical processes using $\Delta H_f°$, $S°$, and $\Delta G_f°$ data and interpret the results.
- Calculate ΔG at nonstandard temperatures.
- Determine the equilibrium temperature of a reaction and interpret the results.
- Calculate $\Delta G°$ at nonstandard concentrations.
- Apply the relationship between $\Delta G°$ and the equilibrium constant, K.

18.1 Entropy and Spontaneity

GOALS

- State the second law of thermodynamics.
- Define *entropy*.
- Identify the sign of ΔS from chemical equations or changes of state.
- Demonstrate a qualitative understanding of the relationship between entropy and probability.

Background Review

Chapter 6 Thermochemistry: Section 6.4—Energy and Enthalpy

Chapter 7 Gases: Section 7.10—Kinetic Molecular Theory of Gases

Chapter 12 Liquids and Solids: Section 12.3—Phase Changes and Heating Curves

INTRODUCTION

Chemical thermodynamics is the study of how heat and work are involved in chemical reactions and in physical changes, such as changes of state. Much of the work of chemists, and other scientists who apply chemical principles in their fields, seeks to answer questions and make predictions about chemical and physical processes. In your studies thus far, you have learned how to answer some questions and make some predictions. Chapter 4 and Chapter 5 described *what happens* in a chemical reaction and *in what proportions*. Chapter 14 discussed the factors that affect *how fast* a chemical reaction occurs. Chapter 15 introduced equilibrium constants, which indicate *to what extent* a reaction will proceed.

The focus of this chapter is distinguishing spontaneous from nonspontaneous processes. **Spontaneous processes** happen under the indicated conditions; they may occur quickly or slowly, but the process occurs. Nonspontaneous processes do not happen under the indicated conditions, no matter how long you might wait. You will learn how to predict whether a process is spontaneous, and what conditions might be needed to make a process happen spontaneously. For this, you will need to review the concept of enthalpy (Section 6.4) and you will need to learn about a new concept called entropy.

FIRST LAW OF THERMODYNAMICS

The first law of thermodynamics states that the total energy of the universe is constant: Energy is neither created nor destroyed, but it can be transformed from one form to another. When discussing matters of energy, enthalpy, and—as you will see—entropy, it is important to remember that the process under study is referred to as the system and everything else is the surroundings. Together, the system and the surroundings make up the universe (Section 6.2).

The first law was applied in Chapter 6 for carrying out enthalpy, ΔH, calculations for calorimetry and

Hess's law, and again in Chapter 12 for performing enthalpy calculations for phase changes. Recall that a process that absorbs heat is endothermic ($\Delta H > 0$), whereas a process that releases heat is exothermic ($\Delta H < 0$). Whenever a process is reversed, the sign of ΔH for that process changes because the amount of energy absorbed or released in the forward direction of the process is the same as the amount released or absorbed when the same process is reversed. However, knowing the enthalpy change alone does not make it possible to predict the conditions under which a process will occur spontaneously.

For example, the melting of ice, $H_2O(s) \rightarrow H_2O(l)$, is endothermic and spontaneous at temperatures above the melting point, whereas the reverse reaction, the freezing of water, is exothermic and spontaneous at temperatures below the melting point. Other processes are spontaneous in only one direction. For example, if you provide the appropriate spark to a hydrocarbon fuel such as gasoline, it will burn spontaneously to produce carbon dioxide and water in a combustion reaction that happens only in the forward direction.

Steve Lemon, Macmillan Learning

FIGURE 18.1 Phase Changes and Entropy

NOTE: You need to be online to access this video.
The particles of a solid are close together and cannot move past each other. The particles of a liquid are still close together, but can move past each other. The particles of a gas are spread out and move more quickly, with complete freedom of movement. Entropy increases going from solid to liquid to gas, and decreases going from gas to liquid to solid.

SECOND LAW OF THERMODYNAMICS

The **second law of thermodynamics** states that spontaneous processes always result in an overall increase in **entropy**, S, of the universe. Entropy is a measure of the degree of disorder or randomness in a system. Another way to think of entropy is that it describes how spread out a system's energy is.

A positive value for ΔS of the process, ΔS, indicating an increase in entropy, results when there is

- a phase change from solid to liquid,
- a phase change from solid or liquid to gas,
- the dissolution of a solid into an aqueous solution,
- an increase in temperature within a phase, or
- an increase in the number of gas particles.

Chapter 12 indicated that the solid state of matter is highly organized, whereas liquids are less organized, but still more organized than gases. According to the kinetic molecular theory (Section 7.10), gases move randomly and an increase in the temperature of a gaseous sample increases the kinetic energy of the particles. Increasing kinetic energy causes particles to move faster, which disperses their energy more throughout the system and increases their entropy (Figure 18.1). To a lesser extent, increases in temperature also increase the movement of particles in liquids and solids and increase randomness. Any increase in the number of particles provides more ways for the system's energy to be distributed. Because the gas phase has the highest entropy of any state, any reaction that produces more gas particles than it started with is likely to have an especially high increase in entropy.

Example 18.1

Determine the sign of ΔS for the following processes:

a. $2\ KClO_3(s) \rightarrow 2\ KCl(s) + 3\ O_2(g)$
b. $CO_2(g) \rightarrow CO_2(s)$

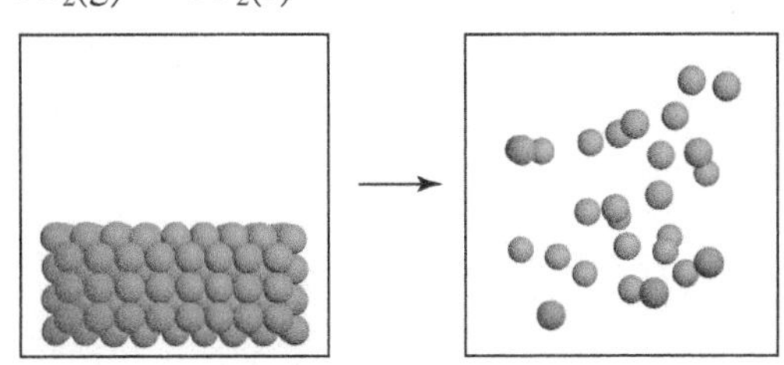

c.
d. condensation appearing on bathroom mirror after a shower

Solution

a. ΔS is positive (+). The process starts with 2 moles of a solid but yields 2 moles of a solid and 3 moles of a gas. The increase in the number of moles and the formation of a gas both are associated with increases in entropy.

b. ΔS is negative (−). The process starts with a gas and ends with a solid (dry ice).
c. ΔS is positive (+). The process starts with particles clustered together on the bottom of a container but with a definite shape, indicating a solid, and ends with particles dispersed throughout the container, indicating a gas.
d. ΔS is negative (−). The process starts with a gas (water vapor) and ends with a liquid.

PRACTICE PROBLEM 18.1

Determine the sign of ΔS for the following processes:

a. $2\,Na(s) + Cl_2(g) \rightarrow 2\,NaCl(s)$
b. the sublimation of ice
c.

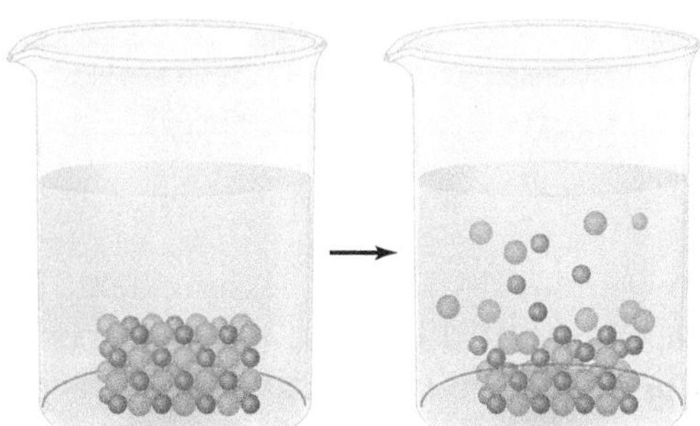

d. frost forming on a windshield

Hint: For a positive ΔS, the product particles are more dispersed or disordered than the reactant particles. For a negative ΔS, the product particles are less dispersed or disordered than the reactant particles.

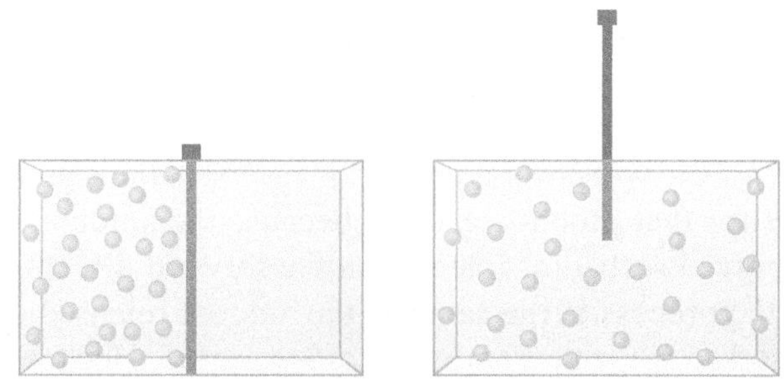

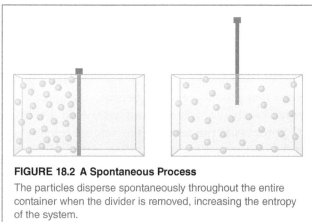

FIGURE 18.2 A Spontaneous Process
The particles disperse spontaneously throughout the entire container when the divider is removed, increasing the entropy of the system.

ENTROPY AND PROBABILITY

Entropy, as a measure of the dispersal of a system's energy, increases when there are more energetically equivalent ways to arrange the components of that system. Ludwig Boltzmann proposed the following mathematical definition of entropy in the 1870s.

$$S = k \ln W \qquad (18.1)$$

The symbol k is the **Boltzmann constant, k**, (1.38×10^{-23} J/K). It is derived from the gas law constant, R, and Avogadro's number, N_A, by the relationship $k = \frac{R}{N_A}$. The symbol W is the number of energetically equivalent arrangements, called **microstates**, which are possible for the system.

Consider the rectangular box shown in Figure 18.2. It has a removable divider in the center, and gaseous particles are initially confined to the left side of the divider. When the divider is removed, you fully expect that the particles will disperse spontaneously throughout the entire container. Scientists use probability to explain this and to derive mathematical relationships to calculate ΔS.

The challenge now is to understand how to determine W, the number of possible equivalent arrangements. Consider first a box like the one shown in Figure 18.3. The box has a divider down the middle and each side has two possible locations within it (top and bottom). When there is just one particle in the box (Figure 18.3a), there are two possible arrangements—namely, the particle on the top and the particle on the bottom. With two particles, A and B, the four arrangements shown in Figure 18.3b are possible—namely, particle A on top, particle B on bottom; B on top, A on bottom; both A and B on top; and both A and B on bottom. Thus, a situation with two particles and two locations results in four possible arrangements, $W = 4$.

When the divider is removed and the two particles each have four possible locations, the number of possible arrangements increases. The same 4 arrangements shown in Figure 18.3b are still possible, but Figure 18.4 shows that 12 additional arrangements are also possible, giving 16 total arrangements for 2 particles in 4 locations, $W = 16$.

The equation used to determine W in the Boltzmann equation is $W = X^n$, where X is the number of locations and n is the number of molecules. You can use the examples in Figure 18.3 and Figure 18.4 to confirm this.

- In Figure 18.3a, $X = 2$ and $n = 1$, so $W = X^n = 2^1 = 2$.
- In Figure 18.3b, $X = 2$ and $n = 2$, so $W = X^n = 2^2 = 4$.
- In Figure 18.4, $X = 4$ and $n = 2$, so $W = X^n = 4^2 = 16$.

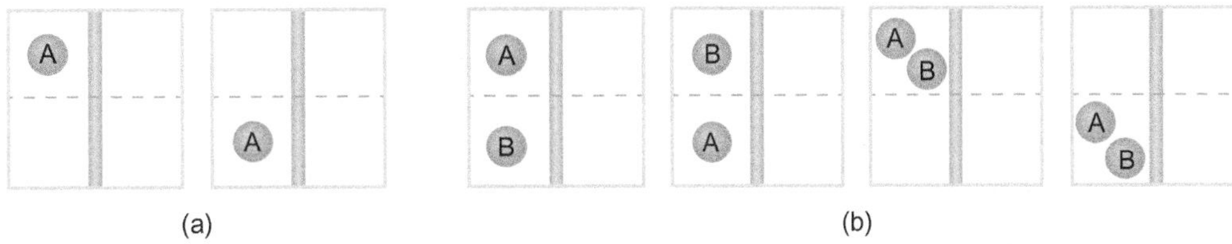

FIGURE 18.3 Systems with Two and Four Possible Arrangements

(a) The particle is restricted to one side by a divider and can be located in either the top or the bottom. This creates two possible arrangements, so $W = 2$ for this system. (b) The particles are restricted to one side be the divider, leaving two of the possible four locations empty. Each side has two possible locations, upper and lower. The two particles each have two possible locations, which gives four possible arrangements, so $W = 4$ for this system.

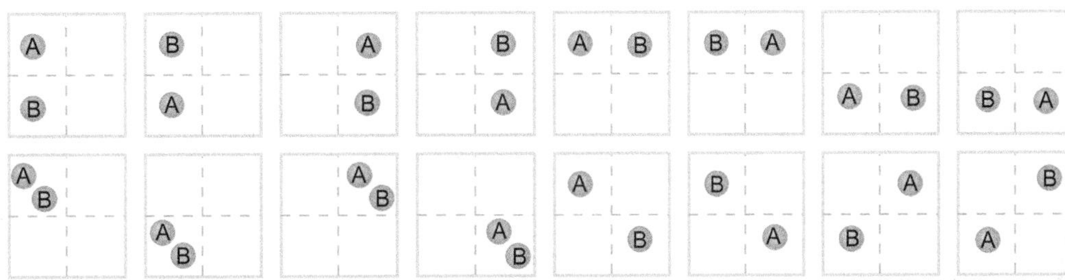

FIGURE 18.4 A System with 16 Possible Arrangements

With the divider removed, there are four possible locations for each of the two particles, giving 16 arrangements. $W = 16$ for this system.

Each of these possible arrangements represents a microstate of the system, with equivalent microstates forming a **macrostate**. The most likely macrostate is the one that has the most possible microstates. The example in Figure 18.4, with 2 particles and 4 locations, has 3 possible macrostates:

- both particles on the left (4 of the 16 microstates);
- both particles on the right (4 of the 16 microstates); and
- one particle on the left and one on the right (8 of the 16 microstates).

The most probable macrostate, the one with the higher number of microstates, is the one with one molecule on each side of the container. This use of probability illustrates why a system will spontaneously move toward a more spread-out arrangement. Real systems contain huge numbers of particles, and as the number of particles increases, the number of possible arrangements also increases. The most probable state, however, is always the one with the highest number of equivalent microstates.

> The tendency toward disorder is a statistical probability.

Example 18.2

Predict the sign of ΔS for the following change between macrostates.

Particles on both sides → All particles on the left

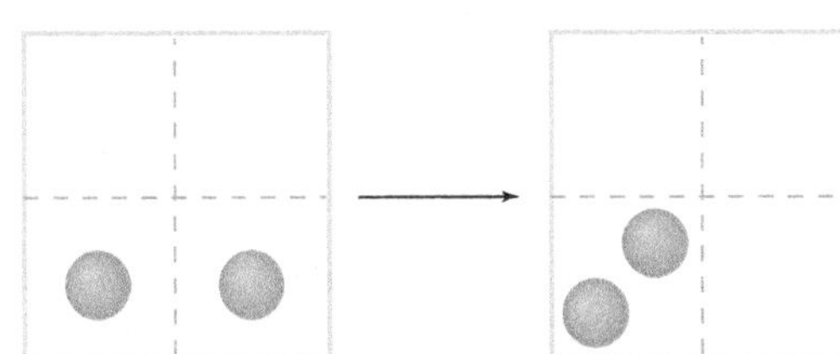

Solution

As in Figure 18.4, there are 16 total microstates possible for 2 particles and 4 possible locations ($W = X^n = 4^2 = 16$). Out of those 16, there are 8 possible microstates in which the 2 particles are located on separate sides of the box, as shown on the reactant side. This is the most probable macrostate.

On the product side, both particles are located on the left side only, which has only 4 possible microstates. Overall, then, there is a decrease in entropy, so the sign of ΔS is negative (−). Another way to think about this is that the particles have become less dispersed, indicating a decrease in entropy.

PRACTICE PROBLEM 18.2

Predict the sign of ΔS for the following change between macrostates.

All particles on the left → Particles on both sides

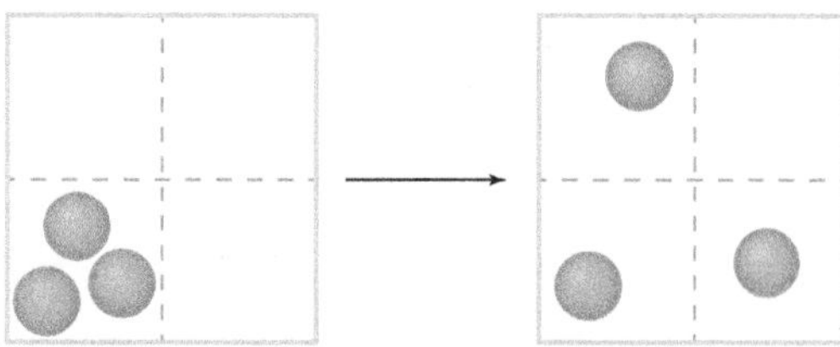

Hint: To answer this question, you could consider the fraction of microstates that match each macrostate. Alternatively, you could apply what you know about entropy and the dispersal of particles.

SECTION REVIEW

- Chemical thermodynamics deals with predicting the conditions necessary for a process to occur, which is not possible using enthalpy changes alone.
- The second law of thermodynamics states that all spontaneous processes result in an increase in entropy, S, of the universe, where entropy is the degree of disorder or randomness.
- Positive changes in entropy accompany phase changes from solid to liquid to gas, increases in temperature within a phase, and processes that result in an increase in the total number of moles of particles.
- The mathematical definition of entropy is $S = k \ln W$ (Equation 18.1), where k is the Boltzmann constant (1.38×10^{-23} J/K), and W is the number of energetically equivalent arrangements (microstates) possible for the system.
- Equivalent microstates form a macrostate, and the most probable macrostate is the one containing the highest number of microstates.

18.2 Entropy Changes—Both Chemical and Physical

GOALS

- State the third law of thermodynamics.
- Determine ΔS for both chemical reactions and changes of state using standard molar entropies.

Background Review

Chapter 6 Thermochemistry: Section 6.8—Standard Enthalpies of Formation

THIRD LAW OF THERMODYNAMICS

Section 18.1 showed how to predict the sign of ΔS based on a few guidelines. In this section, you will learn how to calculate ΔS based on the **third law of thermodynamics**, which states that the entropy of a pure, perfectly ordered, crystalline substance at absolute zero is zero: $S\,(0\text{ K}) = 0$.

At absolute zero, which is impossible to achieve, there would be no thermal energy to cause the particles in a solid to move. A perfectly ordered crystal in which the particles have no ability to move has only one microstate. Substituting 1 for W in the Boltzmann equation (Equation 18.1) yields

$$S = k \ln 1$$
$$S = 0$$

Experimental measurements of entropy can be used to determine absolute values of entropy based on the zero point established by the third law. These tabulated values (see Table 18.1 or Appendix A.2) are called **standard molar entropies, S_f°**, which have units of J/(mol·K). Recall from Chapter 6 that the ° symbol indicates measurements made under standard thermodynamic conditions, generally 298 K (or other specified temperature) and 1 atm of pressure. Standard molar entropies can be used to calculate standard entropy changes, ΔS°, for chemical and physical

TABLE 18.1 Standard Entropies at 298 K of Selected Substances

Compound(state)	S° (J/mol·K)
CO_2(g)	213.8
CaO(s)	38.1
$CaCO_3$(s)	91.7
H_2(g)	130.7
H_2O(l)	70.0
H_2O(g)	188.8
HCl(g)	186.9
Hg(l)	75.9
Hg(g)	175.0
I_2(s)	116.1
I_2(g)	260.7
O_2(g)	205.2

processes by subtracting the sum of the molar entropies of the reactants from the sum of the molar entropies of the products.

$$\Delta S^\circ_{rxn} = \Sigma m[S^\circ_f(\text{products})] - \Sigma n[S^\circ_f(\text{reactants})] \quad (18.2)$$

The m and n in this equation are the coefficients of the products and reactants, respectively, from the balanced chemical equation. You may remember using a similar equation, Equation 6.14, to calculate standard changes in enthalpy, ΔH°_{rxn}, from standard enthalpies of formation, ΔH°_f. Recall also that ΔH values are generally reported in units of kilojoules per mole (kJ/mol), which means that any calculations involving both ΔS and ΔH will require conversions to the same energy unit.

Additional values can be found in Appendix A.2.

Example 18.3

Predict the sign of ΔS and calculate the standard entropy change associated with the reaction of gaseous hydrogen and gaseous oxygen to form water vapor.

Solution

The first step is to write the balanced chemical equation.

$$2\,H_2(g) + O_2(g) \rightarrow 2\,H_2O(g)$$

Prediction: The number of moles of gases decreases in the reaction, so ΔS will be negative (−).

Use Equation 18.2 and the standard entropy values provided in Table 18.1 to calculate the standard entropy change for the balanced chemical equation (note that "moles" will cancel).

$$\Delta S^\circ_{rxn} = \Sigma m[S^\circ_f(\text{products})] - \Sigma n[S^\circ_f(\text{reactants})]$$

$$\Delta S^\circ_{rxn} = [2S^\circ_f(H_2O(g))] - [2S^\circ_f(H_2(g)) + S^\circ_f(O_2(g))]$$

$$\Delta S^\circ_{rxn} = \left[2\text{ mol}\left(188.8\frac{\text{J}}{\text{mol}\cdot\text{K}}\right)\right] - \left[2\text{ mol}\left(130.7\frac{\text{J}}{\text{mol}\cdot\text{K}}\right) + 1\text{ mol}\left(205.2\frac{\text{J}}{\text{mol}\cdot\text{K}}\right)\right]$$

$$\Delta S^\circ_{rxn} = 377.6\frac{\text{J}}{\text{K}} - 466.6\frac{\text{J}}{\text{K}}$$

$$\Delta S^\circ_{rxn} = -89.0\frac{\text{J}}{\text{K}}$$

The standard entropy change is negative, indicating that the products are less disordered than the reactants. This is consistent with a reaction in which the number of moles of gases decreases.

PRACTICE PROBLEM 18.3

Predict the sign of ΔS and calculate the standard entropy change associated with the reaction of solid calcium carbonate to produce calcium oxide and carbon dioxide according to the following balanced chemical equation.

$$CaCO_3(s) \rightarrow CaO(s) + CO_2(g)$$

Hint: There is an increase in the moles of gas in this reaction, implying an increase in entropy. To calculate ΔS°_{rxn}, use the values in Table 18.1. Sum the S°_f values of the products, then subtract the S°_f value of the reactant.

Example 18.4

Predict the sign of ΔS and calculate the change in entropy when 72.85 g of liquid mercury is vaporized.

Solution

The equation for the vaporization of mercury is

$$Hg(l) \rightarrow Hg(g)$$

Prediction: ΔS will be positive (+) because this is a phase change from liquid to gas.

Calculation: Although this is a physical change and not a chemical reaction, the mathematical process for calculating the standard entropy change is identical to that used for a chemical reaction—it's just limited to one mole of the substance:

$$\Delta S^\circ = S^\circ_f(\text{product}) - S^\circ_f(\text{reactant})$$

$$\Delta S^\circ = S^\circ_f(Hg(g)) - S^\circ_f(Hg(l))$$

$$\Delta S^\circ = \left[1\text{ mol}\left(175.0\frac{\text{J}}{\text{mol}\cdot\text{K}}\right)\right] - \left[1\text{ mol}\left(75.9\frac{\text{J}}{\text{mol}\cdot\text{K}}\right)\right]$$

$$\Delta S^\circ = 99.1\frac{\text{J}}{\text{K}}$$

You know from the balanced equation that this entropy value is for the vaporization of 1 mole of mercury (i.e., 99.1 J/K per 1 mol Hg). Multiply this conversation factor by the number of moles present in the 72.85 g sample to obtain the overall entropy change.

$$\Delta S = 72.85\text{ g Hg}\left(\frac{1\text{ mol Hg}}{200.59\text{ g Hg}}\right)\left(\frac{99.1\frac{\text{J}}{\text{K}}}{1\text{ mol Hg}}\right)$$

$$= 36.0\frac{\text{J}}{\text{K}}$$

PRACTICE PROBLEM 18.4

Predict the sign of ΔS and calculate the change in entropy for the deposition of 117.4 g of iodine vapor, $I_2(g) \rightarrow I_2(s)$.

SECTION REVIEW

- The third law of thermodynamics states that the entropy of a pure crystalline substance at absolute zero is zero, $S\,(0\text{ K}) = 0$.
- Standard molar entropies for substances are measured at 298 K, and can be found in Table 18.1 and Appendix A.2.
- Equation 18.2 can be used to calculate the standard entropy change for chemical reactions and phase changes.

$$\Delta S^\circ = \Sigma m[S_f^\circ(\text{products})] - \Sigma n[S_f^\circ(\text{reactants})]$$

18.3 Entropy and Temperature

GOALS

- Compare and contrast ΔS_{univ}, ΔS_{sys}, and ΔS_{surr}.
- Calculate ΔS_{surr} from ΔH_{sys} and temperature data for chemical and physical changes.

Background Review

Chapter 6 Thermochemistry: Section 6.2—Energy, Heat, and Work

Section 6.2 stated that any process currently being studied is called the *system* and everything else is the *surroundings*. Together, the system and surroundings make up the *universe*. An overall change in the entropy, then, is described by Equation 18.3.

$$\Delta S_{univ} = \Delta S_{sys} + \Delta S_{surr} \qquad (18.3)$$

According to the second law of thermodynamics, ΔS_{univ} must be positive for a process to be spontaneous. ΔS_{univ} will be positive if

- both ΔS_{sys} and ΔS_{surr} are positive;
- ΔS_{sys} is negative but is offset by a larger, positive change in ΔS_{surr}; or
- ΔS_{surr} is negative but is offset by a larger, positive change in ΔS_{sys}.

Section 18.2 showed how to use tabulated standard entropies to calculate ΔS_{sys} (ΔS_{rxn}), so the focus now turns to ΔS_{surr}.

In chemistry, the reaction being studied (the system) is typically very small compared to the surroundings, which means that enthalpy changes in the system, ΔH_{sys}, have a very minimal effect on the temperature of the surroundings. That is, a burning candle releases heat energy, but it is unlikely to change the temperature in the building, let alone the temperature of the neighborhood. For these situations, known as **isothermal processes** (no temperature change in the surroundings), the entropy change of the surroundings is related to the thermal energy change of the system.

$$\Delta S_{surr} = \frac{-q_{sys}}{T} \qquad (18.4)$$

Because many chemical reactions occur at constant pressure, q_{sys} is simply the enthalpy change for the reaction. The following equation results when you substitute ΔH for q_{sys} in Equation 18.4.

$$\Delta S_{surr} = \frac{-\Delta H_{sys}}{T} \qquad (18.5)$$

This equation shows that the entropy change of the surroundings is inversely proportional to the temperature. Therefore, the effect of the enthalpy change of the system on the entropy of the surroundings is smaller at higher temperatures than at lower temperatures. At lower temperatures, the surroundings have lower kinetic energy. The release of heat energy by the system increases that kinetic energy and causes the particles in the surroundings to become more dispersed. At higher temperatures, the surroundings have higher kinetic energy and the release of heat energy by the system will increase that kinetic energy by a much lower percentage than at lower temperatures. That is, the heat released or absorbed by a chemical reaction alters the randomness of the surroundings by a much smaller factor at high temperatures than it does at low temperatures.

Example 18.5

a. Calculate ΔS_{surr} for the reaction of gaseous hydrogen and gaseous oxygen to form 2 mol of water vapor at 298 K.

b. Use the results from Example 18.3 to calculate ΔS_{univ} for this same reaction.

Solution

First, attempt to predict the sign of ΔS_{univ}. Example 18.3 indicates that ΔS_{sys} is negative, but what about ΔS°_{surr}? You may recall that this is a highly exothermic reaction (i.e., $\Delta H \ll 0$). Moreover, 298 K is a fairly low temperature, so these circumstances would indicate that ΔS°_{surr} is positive. Since the two components of ΔS°_{univ} have opposite signs, you cannot readily make a prediction.

a. Write the balanced chemical equation.

$$2\,H_2(g) + O_2(g) \rightarrow 2\,H_2O(g)$$

Calculate the standard enthalpy change using ΔH°_f data from Appendix A.2.

$$\Delta H^\circ_{rxn} = \Sigma m[\Delta H^\circ_f(\text{products})] - \Sigma n[\Delta H^\circ_f(\text{reactants})]$$

$$\Delta H^\circ_{rxn} = [2\Delta H^\circ_f(H_2O(g))] - [2\Delta H^\circ_f(H_2(g)) + \Delta H^\circ_f(O_2(g))]$$

$$\Delta H^\circ_{rxn} = \left[2\text{ mol}\left(-241.8\frac{\text{kJ}}{\text{mol}}\right)\right] - \left[2\text{ mol}\left(0\frac{\text{kJ}}{\text{mol}}\right) + 1\text{ mol}\left(0\frac{\text{kJ}}{\text{mol}}\right)\right]$$

$$\Delta H^\circ_{rxn} = -483.6\text{ kJ}$$

Use Equation 18.5 and the value of ΔH°_{rxn} to calculate ΔS°_{surr}.

$$\Delta S^\circ_{surr} = \frac{-\Delta H^\circ_{rxn}}{T}$$

$$\Delta S^\circ_{surr} = \frac{-(-483.6\text{ kJ})}{298\text{ K}} \times \frac{1000\text{ J}}{1\text{ kJ}}$$

$$\Delta S^\circ_{surr} = 1.62 \times 10^3\frac{\text{J}}{\text{K}}$$

b. Calculate ΔS_{univ} using Equation 18.3.

$$\Delta S_{univ} = \Delta S_{sys} + \Delta S_{surr}$$

The value of ΔS_{sys} was found to be -89.0 J/K in Example 18.3. Therefore,

$$\Delta S_{univ} = -89.0\frac{\text{J}}{\text{K}} + 1620\frac{\text{J}}{\text{K}}$$

$$\Delta S_{univ} = 1530\frac{\text{J}}{\text{K}}$$

The reaction of hydrogen and oxygen to form water vapor is accompanied by a large increase in the overall entropy, even though the entropy change for the reaction itself is negative. Although this reaction is spontaneous, it also has a very high activation energy and occurs quite slowly unless it is run at high temperatures or a spark is introduced. Thus, thermodynamics tells you if something will happen spontaneously, but it does not tell you how quickly it will happen. To predict the rates of reactions, chemists rely on kinetics, as described in Chapter 14.

PRACTICE PROBLEM 18.5

a. Calculate ΔS_{surr} for the reaction of solid calcium carbonate to produce calcium oxide and carbon dioxide at 298 K.

b. Use the results from Practice Problem 18.3 to calculate ΔS_{univ} for this same reaction.

Hint:

a. First, use the data in Appendix A.2 to calculate ΔH°_{rxn} for this reaction. Then use Equation 18.5 to calculate the entropy change for the surroundings, ΔS_{surr}, where $T = 298$ K.

$$\Delta S^\circ_{surr} = \frac{-\Delta H^\circ_{rxn}}{T}$$

b. Keep in mind that the reaction is the system. Use Equation 18.3 with $\Delta S_{sys} = \Delta S_{rxn} = 160.2$ J/K (from Practice Problem 18.3) and the ΔS_{surr} value from part (a).

$$\Delta S_{univ} = \Delta S_{sys} + \Delta S_{surr}$$

SECTION REVIEW

- The overall entropy change is written according to Equation 18.3, where $\Delta S_{sys} = \Delta S_{rxn}$.

$$\Delta S_{univ} = \Delta S_{sys} + \Delta S_{surr}$$

- ΔS_{univ} is positive for all spontaneous processes.
- ΔS_{surr} is calculated using tabulated data for changes in enthalpy and Equation 18.5.

$$\Delta S_{surr} = \frac{-\Delta H_{sys}}{T}$$

- Negative ΔS_{rxn} values can be offset by large increases in ΔS_{surr}, making ΔS_{univ} positive overall.

18.4 Gibbs Free Energy

GOALS

- Define *Gibbs free energy*.
- Describe how the signs of ΔH and ΔS affect the sign of ΔG.
- Calculate ΔG° for chemical and physical processes using ΔH°_f, S°, and ΔG°_f data and interpret the results.

Background Review

Chapter 6 Thermochemistry: Section 6.3—Energy as a State Function

Chapter 13 Solutions: Section 13.1—The Solution Process

FREE ENERGY, ENTHALPY, AND ENTROPY

Up to now, you have learned the definition of entropy and a little about probability and entropy (Section 18.1), how to calculate standard changes in entropy for a process, and how to calculate changes in entropy for the surroundings and the overall change in entropy at 298 K (Section 18.2). However, you still have no way to predict if a process will be spontaneous at a particular temperature, or at what temperature it will become spontaneous. For this, you need a different state function, **Gibbs free energy, *G***, named for J. Willard Gibbs (Figure 18.5) who first described it in the 1870s.

A state function is a property of a system that depends only on the current state of the system and not on any changes that might have occurred prior to the system's current state (Section 6.3). Gibbs free energy is a defined quantity used to predict if a process is spontaneous under the given conditions and is derived as follows.

$$\Delta S_{univ} = \Delta S_{sys} + \Delta S_{surr}$$

Substitute $-\Delta H_{sys}/T$ for ΔS_{surr}.

$$\Delta S_{univ} = \Delta S_{sys} + \left(\frac{-\Delta H_{sys}}{T}\right)$$

Multiply by $-T$.

$$-T\Delta S_{univ} = \Delta H_{sys} - T\Delta S_{sys}$$

FIGURE 18.5 J. Willard Gibbs
Gibbs free energy, *G*, is named for Josiah Willard Gibbs (1839–1903).

According to the second law of thermodynamics, ΔS_{univ} must be positive for a spontaneous process, so $-T\Delta S_{univ}$ must then be negative. Gibbs free energy, defined as $-T\Delta S_{univ}$, provides chemists with a way to determine if a process is spontaneous under constant temperature and pressure conditions. The formal definition of Gibbs free energy is given here, with *H* being enthalpy, *S* being entropy, and *T* representing the absolute temperature.

$$G = H - TS$$

For processes occurring at constant temperature and pressure, the change in free energy of the system, ΔG, is given by

$$\Delta G = \Delta H - T\Delta S \qquad (18.6)$$

- A decrease in Gibbs free energy, $\Delta G < 0$, corresponds to a spontaneous process, i.e., spontaneous in the forward direction.
- An increase in Gibbs free energy, $\Delta G > 0$, indicates a nonspontaneous process, i.e., spontaneous in the reverse direction.
- When $\Delta G = 0$, the system is at equilibrium.

For a process occurring under standard conditions, the Gibbs free-energy change is

$$\Delta G^\circ = \Delta H^\circ - T\Delta S^\circ \qquad (18.7)$$

ΔG° can be calculated by first calculating ΔH° and ΔS° using thermodynamic data for ΔH°_f and S°_f, which are available in Appendix A.2.

Example 18.6

Determine ΔG° for the reaction of hydrogen and oxygen to form water.

$$2\ H_2(g) + O_2(g) \rightarrow 2\ H_2O(g)$$

Solution

From previous examples or experience, you know that both ΔS° and ΔH° for this reaction are negative. Therefore, the sign of the free-energy change depends upon *T* and the relative sizes of the enthalpy and entropy, and thus cannot be readily predicted.

Use Equation 18.7 to calculate ΔG°.

$$\Delta G^\circ = \Delta H^\circ - T\Delta S^\circ$$

From Example 18.5, you know that $\Delta H^\circ = -483.6$ kJ, and from Example 18.3, you know that $\Delta S^\circ = -89.0\,\frac{\text{J}}{\text{K}}$. Be sure to convert the entropy to kilojoules, and use standard temperature (T = 298 K, unless indicated otherwise).

$$\Delta G^\circ = -483.6\text{ kJ} - 298\text{ K}\left(-89.0\,\frac{\text{J}}{\text{K}}\right)\left(\frac{1\text{ kJ}}{1000\text{ J}}\right)$$

$$\Delta G^\circ = -457.1\text{ kJ}$$

The large, negative value for ΔG° indicates that this process is spontaneous under standard conditions. Hydrogen and oxygen can react together to produce explosions, but these explosions do not happen at room temperature (298 K) unless a spark provides the very high activation energy or a catalyst is present to lower the activation energy. In the absence of a spark or a catalyst, this reaction happens very, very slowly at room temperature. Remember that thermodynamics only tells you if a process is spontaneous—it does not provide any information about the *rate* of that process. Insight into the rate of the reaction requires kinetics (Chapter 14).

PRACTICE PROBLEM 18.6

Determine ΔG° for the reaction of calcium carbonate to form calcium oxide and carbon dioxide:

$$CaCO_3(s) \rightarrow CaO(s) + CO_2(g)$$

Hint: Use Equation 18.7 to calculate ΔG°.

$$\Delta G^\circ = \Delta H^\circ - T\Delta S^\circ$$

From Practice Problem 18.5, you know that ΔH° = 179.2 kJ, and from Practice Problem 18.3, you know that ΔS° = 160.2 J/K. Be sure to convert the entropy from J/K to kJ/K, and use standard temperature (T = 298 K, unless indicated otherwise).

FREE ENERGY OF FORMATION

When using the table of thermodynamic data in Appendix A.2, you may have noticed a column headed ΔG°_f. These data represent the molar free-energy changes of

EVERYDAY CONNECTION

Glycolysis is the process by which energy is harvested from glucose by living things. Several of the reactions of glycolysis are thermodynamically unfavorable (nonspontaneous) but proceed when they are coupled with other spontaneous reactions. For example, the conversion of adenosine triphosphate, ATP, to adenosine diphosphate, ADP, has a Gibbs free energy of −30.5 kJ. When coupled with a nonspontaneous reaction with a ΔG value of less than +30.5 kJ, the overall process is spontaneous because the sum of the ΔG values is negative. The ADP molecules can be converted back to ATP with an input of energy and then be used to power other metabolic reactions. In this way, ATP is like a rechargeable battery within your body.

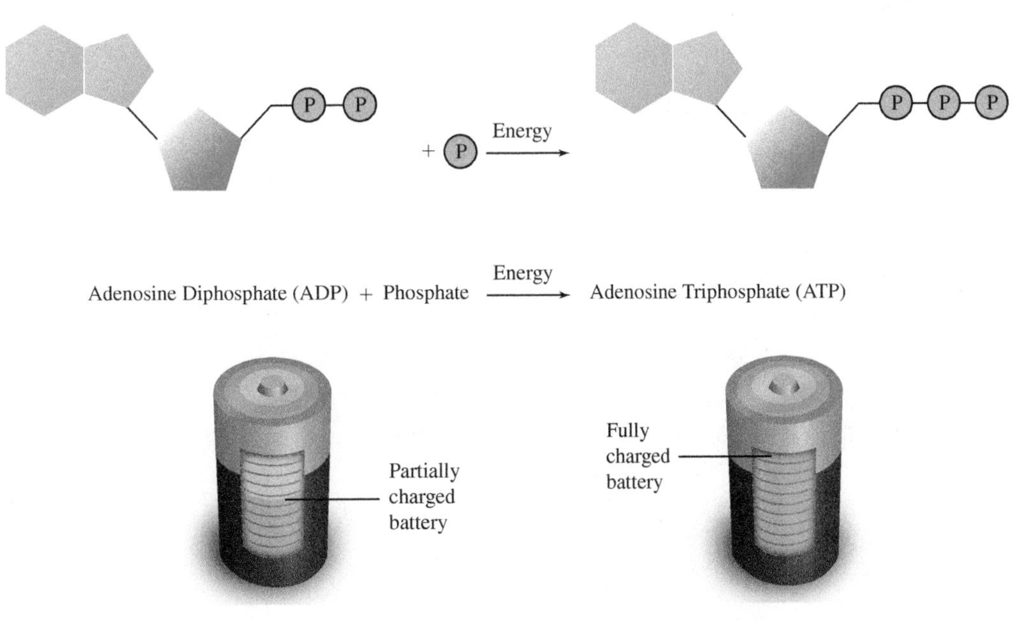

formation at 298 K—the **standard free energies of formation, ΔG_f°**, for various substances. Note that ΔG_f° for elements in their standard states is 0 and that these measurements adhere to the same standard conditions as for standard enthalpies and entropies—namely, pure liquids and solids, 1 atm of pressure, and, generally, 298 K. You can use these ΔG_f° values to calculate the standard free-energy change for a reaction using Equation 18.8.

$$\Delta G^\circ_{rxn} = \Sigma m[\Delta G_f^\circ(\text{products})] - \Sigma n[\Delta G_f^\circ(\text{reactants})] \quad (18.8)$$

Example 18.7

Calculate ΔG°_{rxn} for the combustion of propane.

$$C_3H_8(g) + 5\,O_2(g) \rightarrow 3\,CO_2(g) + 4\,H_2O(l)$$

Solution

The value of ΔG°_{rxn} can be obtained from Equation 18.8.

$$\Delta G^\circ_{rxn} = \Sigma m[\Delta G_f^\circ(\text{products})] - \Sigma n[\Delta G_f^\circ(\text{reactants})]$$

For the combustion of propane, this equation becomes

$$\Delta G^\circ_{rxn} = [3\Delta G_f^\circ(CO_2(g)) + 4\Delta G_f^\circ(H_2O(g))] - [\Delta G_f^\circ(C_3H_8(g)) + 5\Delta G_f^\circ(O_2(g))]$$

The appropriate values for ΔG_f° can be obtained from Appendix A.2.

$$\Delta G^\circ_{rxn} = \left[3\text{ mol}\left(-394.4\frac{\text{kJ}}{\text{mol}}\right) + 4\text{ mol}\left(-237.1\frac{\text{kJ}}{\text{mol}}\right)\right] - \left[1\text{ mol}\left(-23.4\frac{\text{kJ}}{\text{mol}}\right) + 5\text{ mol}\left(0\frac{\text{kJ}}{\text{mol}}\right)\right]$$

$$\Delta G^\circ_{rxn} = (-2131.6\text{ kJ}) - (-23.4\text{ kJ}) = -2108.2\text{ kJ}$$

The large, negative free-energy change indicates that this reaction is spontaneous at 298 K. As with most combustion reactions, though, it has a high activation energy and requires a spark or other ignition source to initiate the reaction.

PRACTICE PROBLEM 18.7

Calculate ΔG°_{rxn} for the following reaction of white phosphorus with HCl.

$$2\,P(s, \text{white}) + 10\,HCl(g) \rightarrow 2\,PCl_5(g) + 5\,H_2(g)$$

Hint: Sum the ΔG_f° values of the products, then subtract the sum of the ΔG_f° values of the reactants (see Appendix A.2). Be sure to take into account the coefficients in the balanced equation.

EVERYDAY CONNECTION

Experience and advertising tell us that diamonds are forever. But according to the negative value of the Gibbs free energy, diamonds spontaneously turn to graphite at room temperature.

$$C(\text{diamond}) \rightarrow C(\text{graphite})$$

$$\Delta G^\circ_{rxn} = \Delta G_f^\circ(C(\text{graphite})) - \Delta G_f^\circ(C(\text{diamond})) = 0 - 1\text{ mol}\left(2.9\frac{\text{kJ}}{\text{mol}}\right) = -2.9\text{ kJ}$$

This illustrates an important point, that *spontaneous* does not mean *instantaneous*. Although this reaction occurs, it does so extremely slowly—so slowly, in fact, that it is imperceptible. The structures of graphite and diamond are shown here.

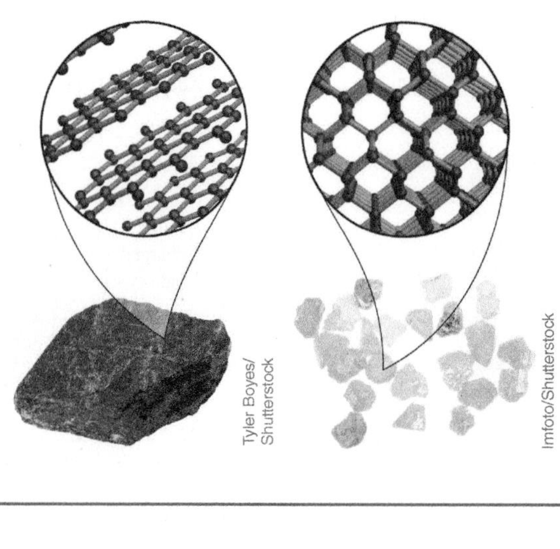

Steve Lemon, Macmillan Learning

FIGURE 18.6 Endothermic Dissolution

NOTE: You need to be online to access this video.

When ammonium nitrate is dissolved in water, the temperature of the surroundings decreases enough to freeze the water below the beaker. But even though the process is endothermic, it still occurs (i.e., is spontaneous) because of the significant increase in entropy associated with dissolving.

FREE ENERGY OF SOLUTION

Free energy and entropy are also relevant to the formation of solutions. For example, the dissolution of ammonium nitrate, NH_4NO_3, in water is highly endothermic, as shown in Figure 18.6. You may also recall from Figure 6.9 that ammonium nitrate is often used in instant cold packs. But if ΔH_{soln} is positive, it means the total energy needed to separate the particles of each substance is greater than the energy released by solvation (Section 13.1). So why would this process occur spontaneously? The answer is entropy. The solid ionic compound is highly ordered, but in solution, the particles are dispersed. This increase in entropy is sufficient to overcome the positive enthalpy changes associated with the dissolution of many solutes.

Example 18.8

Calculate $\Delta G°$ from $\Delta H°$ and $\Delta S°$ for the dissolution of NH_4Cl in water under standard conditions according to this equation.

$$NH_4Cl(s) \rightarrow NH_4^+(aq) + Cl^-(aq)$$

Solution

Calculate $\Delta H°$ and $\Delta H°$ using the $\Delta H_f°$ values and $S_f°$ values found in Appendix A.2.

$$\Delta G° = \Delta H° - T\Delta S°$$

Calculate the enthalpy change first.

$$\Delta H°_{soln} = \Sigma m[\Delta H_f°(\text{products})] - \Sigma n[\Delta H_f°(\text{reactants})]$$

$$\Delta H°_{soln} = [\Delta H_f°(NH_4^+(aq)) + \Delta H_f°(Cl^-(aq))] - [\Delta H_f°(NH_4Cl(s))]$$

$$\Delta H°_{soln} = \left[1\ \text{mol}\left(-133.3\frac{\text{kJ}}{\text{mol}}\right) + 1\ \text{mol}\left(-167.1\frac{\text{kJ}}{\text{mol}}\right)\right] - \left[1\ \text{mol}\left(-314.4\frac{\text{kJ}}{\text{mol}}\right)\right]$$

$$\Delta H°_{soln} = 14.0\ \text{kJ}$$

The positive result for $\Delta H°_{soln}$ tells you that this is an endothermic process.

Calculate the entropy change in a similar manner.

$$\Delta S°_{soln} = \Sigma m[S_f°(\text{products})] - \Sigma n[S_f°(\text{reactants})]$$

$$\Delta S°_{soln} = [S_f°(NH_4^+(aq)) + S_f°(Cl^-(aq))] - [S_f°(NH_4Cl(s))]$$

$$\Delta S°_{soln} = \left[1\ \text{mol}\left(111.2\frac{\text{J}}{\text{K}\cdot\text{mol}}\right) + 1\ \text{mol}\left(56.6\frac{\text{J}}{\text{K}\cdot\text{mol}}\right)\right] - \left[1\ \text{mol}\left(94.6\frac{\text{J}}{\text{K}\cdot\text{mol}}\right)\right]$$

$$\Delta S°_{soln} = 73.2\frac{\text{J}}{\text{K}}$$

Now calculate the free-energy change using Equation 18.7.

$$\Delta G° = \Delta H° - T\Delta S°$$

$$\Delta G°_{soln} = 14.0\ \text{kJ} - (298\ \text{K})\left(73.2\frac{\text{J}}{\text{K}} \times \frac{1\ \text{kJ}}{1000\ \text{J}}\right)$$

$$\Delta G°_{soln} = -7.8\ \text{kJ}$$

The negative free-energy change indicates that the dissolution of ammonium chloride, despite being an endothermic process, is spontaneous under standard conditions.

PRACTICE PROBLEM 18.8

Calculate $\Delta G°$ from $\Delta H°$ and $\Delta S°$ for the dissolution of KBr in water under standard conditions according to this equation.

$$KBr(s) \rightarrow K^+(aq) + Br^-(aq)$$

Hint: Calculate $\Delta H°$ and $\Delta S°$ using the $\Delta H_f°$ values and $S_f°$ values found in Appendix A.2. Then use $\Delta G° = \Delta H° - T\Delta S°$ (Equation 18.7).

SECTION REVIEW

- Gibbs free energy, G, is a defined state function that enables scientists to determine if a process is spontaneous or nonspontaneous based on the

enthalpy and entropy changes of the system only.
- When $\Delta G < 0$, the process is spontaneous as written.
- When $\Delta G > 0$, the process is nonspontaneous as written, but spontaneous in the reverse direction.
- When $\Delta G = 0$, the system is at equilibrium.

- Gibbs free energy for a system is defined by several related equations.
  - Basic definition: $G = H - TS$
  - Definition for changes in free energy: $\Delta G = \Delta H - T\Delta S$ (Equation 18.6)
  - Definition for standard free-energy changes: $\Delta G° = \Delta H° - T\Delta S°$ (Equation 18.7)
- The $\Delta H°$ and $\Delta S°$ values found using the data in Appendix A.2 can be used to calculate $\Delta G°$ for reactions at any temperature using according Equation 18.6.
- $\Delta G°$ for chemical reactions and physical processes can be calculated using $\Delta G_f°$ data and Equation 18.8.

$$\Delta G°_{rxn} = \Sigma m[\Delta G_f°(\text{products})] - \Sigma n[\Delta G_f°(\text{reactants})]$$

18.5 Free-Energy Changes and Temperature

GOALS

- Calculate ΔG at nonstandard temperatures.
- Determine the equilibrium temperature of a reaction and interpret the results.

Section 18.4 discussed how the signs of ΔH and ΔS affect the sign of ΔG according to Equation 18.6 ($\Delta G = \Delta H - T\Delta S$). Table 18.2 summarizes the conditions under which ΔG is negative or positive.

Another way to think about this table is that negative ΔH (release of energy) and positive ΔS (increase in disorder) are favored and drive the spontaneity of a reaction. When both quantities are favorable, the reaction is spontaneous as written at all temperatures. When neither quantity is favorable, the reaction is nonspontaneous as written, but spontaneous in the reverse direction at all temperatures. When one quantity is favorable but the other is not, the reaction is enthalpy-driven in one direction but entropy-driven in the other, so the direction of spontaneity depends on the temperature.

TABLE 18.2 Signs of ΔH, ΔS, and ΔG

ΔH	ΔS	$-T\Delta S$	$\Delta G = \Delta H - T\Delta S$	Reaction Characteristics
−	+	−	−	Spontaneous at all temperatures
+	−	+	+	Nonspontaneous at all temperatures
−	−	+	+ or −	Spontaneous at low temperatures Nonspontaneous at high temperatures
+	+	−	+ or −	Spontaneous at high temperatures Nonspontaneous at low temperatures

Note that the tabulated thermodynamic data in Appendix A.2 are specifically for 298 K. The values of ΔH and ΔS vary with temperature, but they vary only a little bit. Therefore, it is possible to use the tabulated data to calculate ΔG for temperatures other than 298 K, as shown in Example 18.9.

Example 18.9

The formation of $TiCl_4$ is an important step in the production of titanium metal and the white pigment, TiO_2. $TiCl_4$ is an unusual metal halide because it is a volatile liquid.

$$TiCl_4(l) \rightarrow TiCl_4(g)$$

Using the data in Appendix A.2, determine ΔG for the vaporization of $TiCl_4$ at the following temperatures:

a. 298 K
b. 775 K

Solution

a. There are two ways to calculate ΔG at 298 K. One is to use the $\Delta G_f°$ data and the other is to determine $\Delta H°$ and $\Delta S°$ for the reaction and use the definition of $\Delta G°$: $\Delta G° = \Delta H° - T\Delta S°$. The second option is used here. Notice that the entropy value must be converted from J/K to kJ/K.

$$\begin{aligned}\Delta H° &= H_f°(TiCl_4(g)) - H_f°(TiCl_4(l)) \\ &= 1\text{ mol}\left(-763.2\frac{\text{kJ}}{\text{mol}}\right) - 1\text{ mol}\left(-804.2\frac{\text{kJ}}{\text{mol}}\right) \\ &= 41.0\text{ kJ}\end{aligned}$$

$$\begin{aligned}\Delta S° &= S_f°(TiCl_4(g)) - S_f°(TiCl_4(l)) \\ &= 1\text{ mol}\left(353.2\frac{\text{J}}{\text{mol}\cdot\text{K}}\right) \\ &\quad - 1\text{ mol}\left(252.3\frac{\text{J}}{\text{mol}\cdot\text{K}}\right) = 100.9\frac{\text{J}}{\text{K}}\end{aligned}$$

$$\Delta G° = \Delta H° - T\Delta S°$$

$$\Delta G° = 41.0\ \text{kJ} - 298\ \text{K}\left(100.9\ \frac{\text{J}}{\text{K}}\right)\left(\frac{1\ \text{kJ}}{1000\ \text{J}}\right)$$

$$\Delta G° = 10.9\ \frac{\text{kJ}}{\text{mol}}$$

At 298 K, the sign of ΔG is positive, indicating a nonspontaneous process. Since this calculation was carried out at 298 K, it is correct to call this a standard free-energy change, $\Delta G°$.

b. Because ΔH and ΔS vary only slightly with temperature, calculating the free-energy change at 775 K is just a matter of substituting 775 K for the 298 K in the calculation carried out in part (a).

$$\Delta G = 41.0\ \text{kJ} - 775\ \text{K}\left(100.9\ \frac{\text{J}}{\text{K}}\right)\left(\frac{1\ \text{kJ}}{1000\ \text{J}}\right)$$

$$\Delta G = -37.2\ \frac{\text{kJ}}{\text{mol}}$$

At 775 K, the sign of ΔG is negative, indicating that the vaporization of $TiCl_4$ is spontaneous at this temperature.

PRACTICE PROBLEM 18.9

Consider once again the reaction of calcium carbonate to form calcium oxide and carbon dioxide, which you have seen previously in practice problems.

Based on the values of $\Delta H°$ from Practice Problem 18.5 and $\Delta S°$ from Practice Problem 18.3,

a. determine ΔG at 1150 K, and
b. compare that to the value of $\Delta G°$ that you calculated in Practice Problem 18.6.

Hint: Use Equation 18.6

$$\Delta G = \Delta H - T\Delta S$$

where $\Delta H° = 179.2$ kJ and $\Delta S° = 160.2$ J/K. Be sure to convert the entropy from J/K to kJ/K.

Consider again the vaporization of $TiCl_4$ from Example 18.9, which was nonspontaneous at 298 K and spontaneous at 775 K. At what temperature between 298 K and 775 K does the process becomes spontaneous? That is, at what temperature does ΔG change sign from positive to negative? You can determine that temperature using Equation 18.6 when the system is at equilibrium. At equilibrium, the rate of the forward reaction equals the rate of the reverse reaction and there is no net change in the system. Therefore, there is no free-energy change, $\Delta G = 0$.

$$\Delta G = \Delta H - T\Delta S = 0$$

$$\Delta H = T\Delta S$$

$$T = \frac{\Delta H}{\Delta S} \qquad (18.9)$$

For the vaporization of $TiCl_4$,

$$T = \frac{\Delta H}{\Delta S} = \frac{41.0\ \text{kJ}}{100.9\ \frac{\text{J}}{\text{K}}\left(\frac{1\ \text{kJ}}{1000\ \text{J}}\right)} = 406\ \text{K}$$

At any temperature below this equilibrium temperature, the sign of ΔG is positive and the process is not spontaneous. At higher temperatures, ΔG is negative and the process is spontaneous. Figure 18.7 shows the effect of changing the temperature on the sign of ΔG.

Figure 18.8 and the subsequent example problem demonstrate how to calculate the temperature range over which a particular reaction is spontaneous.

Example 18.10

Determine the minimum temperature for the spontaneous vaporization of liquid mercury using data from Example 18.3 and Appendix A.2.

Solution

The equation for the vaporization of liquid mercury is

$$Hg(l) \rightarrow Hg(g)$$

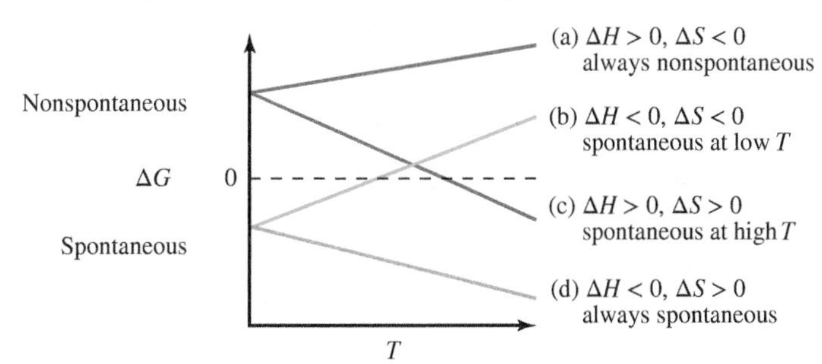

FIGURE 18.7 Spontaneity and Temperature

The effect of temperature on spontaneity varies with the signs of ΔH and ΔS. Spontaneity is temperature-dependent in cases (b) and (c).

Steve Lemon, Macmillan Learning

FIGURE 18.8 Video Tutorial: Gibbs Free Energy and Temperature

NOTE: You need to be online to access this video.
This video shows how to calculate the temperature at which a reaction becomes spontaneous.

Example 18.3 indicates that the entropy for the vaporization of mercury is $\Delta S° = 99.1\frac{J}{K}$. The data for mercury in Appendix A.2 give $\Delta H_f° = 0$ for Hg(l) and $\Delta H_f° = 61.4\frac{kJ}{mol}$ for Hg(g), which means that the standard enthalpy for the vaporization of mercury is $\Delta H° = 1\ mol(61.4\frac{kJ}{mol}) - 0 = 61.4\ kJ$. Now you can use Equation 18.9 to find the temperature where $\Delta G = 0$.

$$T = \frac{\Delta H}{\Delta S}$$

$$T = \frac{61.4\ kJ}{99.1\frac{J}{K}\left(\frac{1\ kJ}{1000\ J}\right)}$$

$$T = 620\ K$$

According to Table 18.2, processes with positive enthalpy and entropy values tend to be spontaneous only at high temperatures. At any temperature above 620 K, then, the vaporization of mercury is spontaneous. At any temperature below 620 K, the process is nonspontaneous.

PRACTICE PROBLEM 18.10

Determine the minimum temperature at which the reaction from Practice Problem 18.9 is spontaneous.

$$CaCO_3(s) \rightarrow CaO(s) + CO_2(g)$$

Hint: Use Equation 18.9

$$T = \frac{\Delta H}{\Delta S}$$

where $\Delta H° = 179.2\ kJ$ and $\Delta S° = 160.2\frac{J}{K}$. Be sure to convert the entropy from J/K to kJ/K.

The second law of thermodynamics tells you that the entropy of the *universe* must increase for a process (chemical or physical) to be spontaneous. The Gibbs free energy allows chemists to predict spontaneity using data for the *system* under consideration, without having to calculate ΔS_{surr} or ΔS_{univ}. The values of ΔH and ΔS used to calculate the free energy are those of the system—the chemical reaction or physical process being studied.

SECTION REVIEW

- ΔH and ΔS do not change greatly with temperature, so Gibbs free-energy changes at temperatures other than 298 K can be calculated using $\Delta H°$ and $\Delta S°$ value via the following equation.

$$\Delta G = \Delta H° - T\Delta S°$$

- At equilibrium, $\Delta G = 0$. Setting the Gibbs free-energy equation equal to zero gives an equation for the temperature at which the sign of ΔG changes.

$$T = \frac{\Delta H}{\Delta S}$$

18.6 Gibbs Free Energy and Equilibrium

GOALS

- Calculate $\Delta G°$ at nonstandard concentrations.
- Apply the relationship between $\Delta G°$ and the equilibrium constant, *K*.

Background Review

Chapter 15 Equilibrium

In Section 18.5, you calculated free-energy changes at temperatures other than 298 K using standard enthalpy and entropy changes found in thermodynamic data tables, which are based on very specific standard conditions. Standard conditions are that liquids and solids are present as pure substances, solutes are present at 1 M concentrations, any gases are at 1 atmosphere of pressure, and the temperature is defined—usually 298 K. To determine changes in free energy, ΔG, under nonstandard conditions, scientists use Equation 18.10:

$$\Delta G = \Delta G° + RT \ln Q \qquad (18.10)$$

where ΔG° is the standard free-energy change, R is the universal gas constant ($8.3145 \frac{\text{J}}{\text{mol} \cdot \text{K}}$), T is the absolute (Kelvin) temperature, and Q is the reaction quotient. R is the gas constant converted to energy units to make it compatible with thermodynamic calculations. Note that ln is the natural logarithm function (Section 0.5).

Recall from Section 15.4 that the reaction quotient, Q_c or Q_p, has the same expression as the equilibrium constant, K_c or K_p, but with non-equilibrium concentrations or pressures. However, the Q in Equation 18.10 contains a pressure term for all gaseous species and a concentration term for all aqueous species. Therefore, Q is equal to Q_p for gaseous reactions and Q_c for aqueous reactions. For example, the balanced chemical equation and the corresponding expression for Q for the production of ammonia by the Haber process are as follows.

$$N_2(g) + 3\,H_2(g) \rightleftharpoons 2\,NH_3(g)$$

$$Q = Q_p = \frac{(P_{NH_3})^2}{(P_{N_2})(P_{H_2})^3}$$

For heterogeneous systems, the Q expression may contain both pressure and concentration terms.

Example 18.11

Calculate ΔG for the Haber process at 365 K for a mixture of 1.5 atm N_2, 4.5 atm H_2, and 0.75 atm NH_3.

$$N_2(g) + 3\,H_2(g) \rightleftharpoons 2\,NH_3(g)$$

Solution

The given temperature and pressures are nonstandard states, so use Equation 18.10.

$$\Delta G = \Delta G^\circ + RT \ln Q$$

Calculate ΔG° for the Haber process from the ΔG_f° values from Appendix A.2.

$$\Delta G^\circ = 2\text{ mol}\left(-16.4\frac{\text{kJ}}{\text{mol}}\right) - [0 + 0] = -32.8\text{ kJ}$$

Use the partial pressures of N_2, H_2, and NH_3 given in the problem statement to calculate Q.

$$Q = \frac{(P_{NH_3})^2}{(P_{N_2})(P_{H_2})^3}$$

$$Q = \frac{(0.75)^2}{(1.5)(4.5)^3} = 4.1 \times 10^{-3}$$

You now have values for ΔG° and Q, so you can plug them into the equation for ΔG along with the value for R (8.3145 J/mol·K) and the temperature given in the problem statement (365 K).

$$\Delta G = \Delta G^\circ + RT \ln Q$$

$$\Delta G = -32.8\text{ kJ/mol} + \left(8.3145\frac{\text{J}}{\text{mol}\cdot\text{K}} \times \frac{1\text{ kJ}}{1000\text{ J}}\right)(365\text{ K})\ln(4.1 \times 10^{-3})$$

$$\Delta G = -49.5\frac{\text{kJ}}{\text{mol}}$$

Under these particular conditions, the reaction has a greater free-energy change than it does under standard conditions. What does this mean in terms of Le Châtelier's principle? The negative sign of ΔG° indicates that the reaction is not at equilibrium and that $Q < K$. Hence, the forward direction is favored when all components are present at partial pressures of 1 atm (standard conditions). In the problem, the partial pressures of the reactants are higher than 1 atm, while the partial pressure of the product is lower than 1 atm. These amounts indicate a situation that is further from equilibrium than the standard state, and thus favors the forward reaction even more strongly.

PRACTICE PROBLEM 18.11

Calculate ΔG for the vaporization of $TiCl_4(l)$ at 298 K and 0.250 atm to $TiCl_4(g)$.

$$TiCl_4(l) \rightleftharpoons TiCl_4(g)$$

Hint: Use $\Delta G = \Delta G^\circ + RT \ln Q$ (Equation 18.10). You know from Example 18.9 that $\Delta G^\circ = 10.9$ kJ/mol for this reaction. Recall that liquids are not included in reaction quotient expressions, so $Q = P_{TiCl_4(g)}$. Be sure to convert R to kJ/mol · K.

When a reaction is at equilibrium, $\Delta G = 0$ and $Q = K$, where K is the equilibrium constant for the reaction. Making these substitutions into Equation 18.10 yields Equation 18.11.

$$\Delta G = \Delta G^\circ + RT \ln Q$$

$$0 = \Delta G^\circ + RT \ln K$$

$$\Delta G^\circ = -RT \ln K \qquad (18.11)$$

Note that K in Equation 18.11 is equal to K_p for gaseous reactions and K_c for aqueous reactions. For heterogeneous systems, the K expression would contain a pressure term for all gaseous species and a concentration term for all aqueous species.

The relationship between the value of K and the sign of ΔG° is summarized in Table 18.3. When the equilibrium constant is greater than 1, ΔG° is negative, indicating that the forward reaction is spontaneous under

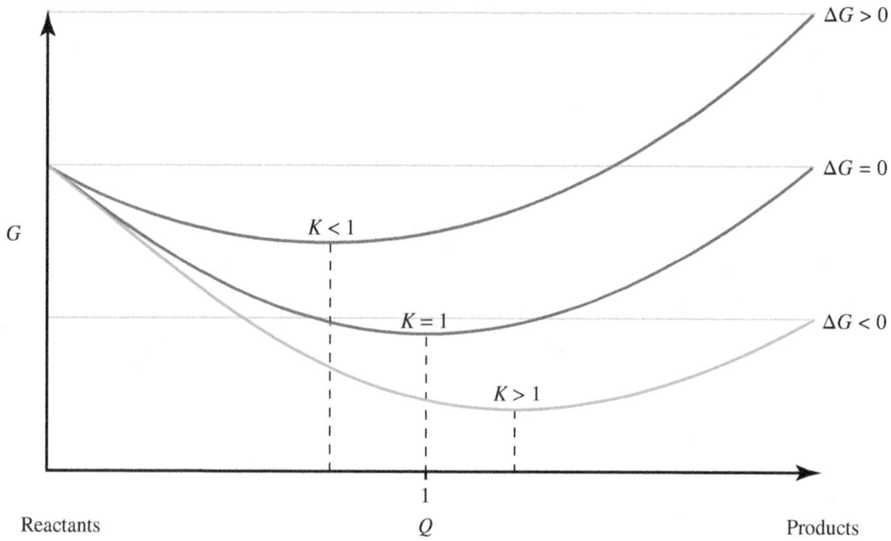

FIGURE 18.9 Free Energy and the Approach to Equilibrium

The sign of ΔG predicts the direction of the reaction starting from $Q = 1$. When $\Delta G > 0$ and $Q = 1$, the reaction proceeds in the reverse direction until $Q = K$. When $\Delta G = 0$ and $Q = 1$, the reaction is at equilibrium because K is also equal to 1. When $\Delta G < 0$ and $Q = 1$, the reaction proceeds in the forward direction until $Q = K$.

TABLE 18.3 The Relationship of ΔG and K

$\Delta G°$	K
<0	>1
$=0$	$=1$
>0	<1

standard conditions. When the equilibrium constant is less than 1, $\Delta G°$ is positive, indicating that the forward reaction is not spontaneous under standard conditions.

Systems proceed spontaneously until they reach equilibrium (where $\Delta G = 0$) because that is the most stable, lowest energy situation for that system (Figure 18.9).

- For systems with $\Delta G < 0$, the equilibrium position lies closer to the lower-energy products, resulting in a large equilibrium constant, $K > 1$. Starting from standard conditions ($Q = 1$), the forward process is spontaneous and the system proceeds in the forward direction toward equilibrium.
- When $\Delta G = 0$, the system is at equilibrium. Under standard conditions, both Q and K are equal to 1. Hence, there is no net change in the forward or reverse direction.
- When $\Delta G > 0$, the equilibrium position lies closer to the lower-energy reactants, resulting in a small equilibrium constant, $K < 1$. Starting from standard conditions ($Q = 1$), the forward process is nonspontaneous and the system proceeds in the reverse direction toward equilibrium.

Equation 18.11 can be rearranged to isolate the equilibrium constant.

$$\Delta G° = -RT \ln K$$

$$\ln K = \frac{\Delta G°}{-RT}$$

The inverse operation of a natural logarithm is the exponential function e (Section 0.5).

$$K = e^{-\frac{\Delta G°}{RT}} \tag{18.12}$$

Equation 18.12 makes it possible to calculate equilibrium constants from $\Delta G°$, as shown in Figure 18.10.

FIGURE 18.10 Video Tutorial: Gibbs Free Energy and Temperature

NOTE: You need to be online to access this video.
This video shows how to calculate K from $\Delta G°$.

Example 18.12

Calculate the equilibrium constant for the Haber process (Example 18.10) at 298 K.

Solution

Recall from Example 18.11 that $\Delta G^\circ = -32.8\ \text{kJ/mol}$ for the Haber process. This value was calculated from ΔG°_f data.

The negative value for ΔG° tells you that the forward reaction is spontaneous under standard conditions, thus favoring the products at equilibrium. This suggests that the equilibrium constant will be greater than 1. During the calculation, make sure that *all the energy units are the same.*

Use Equation 18.12.

$$K = e^{-\frac{\Delta G^\circ}{RT}}$$

It can be easier to calculate the exponent separately.

$$-\frac{\Delta G^\circ}{RT} = \frac{-(-32.8\ \text{kJ/mol})}{\left(8.3145\frac{\text{J}}{\text{mol}}\cdot\text{K}\right)(298\ \text{K})} \times \frac{1000\ \text{J}}{1\ \text{kJ}}$$

$$= 13.24$$

$$K = e^{13.24}$$

$$K = 5.62 \times 10^5$$

This is a large value for an equilibrium constant, indicating that the system favors the products, as predicted from the negative ΔG°.

PRACTICE PROBLEM 18.12

Recall from Practice Problem 18.6 that $\Delta G^\circ = 131.5\ \text{kJ/mol}$ for the following reaction:

$$CaCO_3(s) \rightarrow CaO(s) + CO_2(g)$$

Use that value to

a. predict the relative size of the equilibrium constant and
b. calculate K.

Hint:

a. A positive ΔG value means the reaction is nonspontaneous as written, but spontaneous in the reverse direction. In other words, it favors reactants. Is K greater than or less than 1 if reactants are favored at equilibrium?
b. To calculate K, use $K = e^{-\frac{\Delta G^\circ}{RT}}$ (Equation 18.12). Be sure to convert R to kJ/mol · K.

SECTION REVIEW

- Free-energy changes under nonstandard conditions are calculated according to Equation 18.10, where Q is the reaction quotient, R is the gas constant ($8.3145\ \frac{\text{J}}{\text{mol}\cdot\text{K}}$), and T is the absolute temperature.

$$\Delta G = \Delta G^\circ + RT\ln Q$$

- Standard free-energy changes are related to the equilibrium constant by Equation 18.11.

$$\Delta G^\circ = -RT\ln K$$

- The sign of ΔG indicates the direction the system will proceed to equilibrium from a given starting point, Q.
  - $\Delta G < 0$; forward direction
  - $\Delta G = 0$; at equilibrium, no net change
  - $\Delta G > 0$; reverse direction
- Equilibrium constants can be calculated from thermodynamic data using Equation 18.12.

$$K = e^{-\frac{\Delta G^\circ}{RT}}$$

Putting It Together

The example problems in earlier sections of this chapter focus on just the new skills acquired in that section, but homework and exam questions in chemistry often require more than just one skill at a time. In fact, you will likely be expected to apply knowledge from across the entire chapter, or even multiple chapters, in a single problem. This final example problem is meant to help you prepare for these types of multi-concept questions. Additional examples can be found in the end-of-chapter exercises.

Example 18.13

Calculate the K_{sp} of AgI at 298 K using Appendix A.2 and compare it to the value in Appendix A.4.

Solution

You can use ΔG to find the equilibrium constant, K, of any reaction. The K_{sp} of AgI is the equilibrium constant for this reaction.

$$AgI(s) \rightleftharpoons Ag^+(aq) + I^-(aq)$$

To find ΔG for the reaction, use the ΔG°_f values from Appendix A.2.

$$\Delta G^\circ = \left[1\ \text{mol}\left(77.107\frac{\text{kJ}}{\text{mol}}\right) + 1\ \text{mol}\left(-51.57\frac{\text{kJ}}{\text{mol}}\right)\right] - \left[1\ \text{mol}\left(-66.2\frac{\text{kJ}}{\text{mol}}\right)\right]$$

$$= 91.737\ \text{kJ}$$

Now find K.

$$\Delta G = -RT \ln K$$

$$K = e^{-\frac{\Delta G}{RT}}$$

$$\frac{\Delta G}{RT} = \frac{91.737 \text{ kJ/mol}}{\left(8.3145 \dfrac{\text{J}}{\text{mol} \cdot \text{K}}\right)\left(\dfrac{1 \text{ kJ}}{1000 \text{ J}}\right)(298 \text{ K})} = 37.0$$

$$K = e^{-\frac{\Delta G}{RT}} = e^{-37.0} = 8.53 \times 10^{-17}$$

The K_{sp} value for AgI listed in Appendix A.4 is 8.52×10^{-17}.

PRACTICE PROBLEM 18.13

Calculate the K_{sp} of AgI at 355 K.

Hint: The K_{sp} of AgI is the equilibrium constant for $AgI(s) \rightleftharpoons Ag^+(aq) + I^-(aq)$. Start by finding $\Delta H°$ and $\Delta S°$ using Appendix A.2. Then use $\Delta G = \Delta H - T\Delta S$ to find ΔG at a nonstandard temperature. Finally, use $\Delta G = -RT \ln K$ to find K.

Key Terms, Symbols, and Equations

KEY TERMS

Boltzmann constant, k (18.1): The proportionality constant relating entropy to the natural log of the number of microstates for the system; equal to 1.38×10^{-23} J/K.

chemical thermodynamics (18.1): The study of how heat and work are involved in chemical reactions and in physical changes, such as changes of state.

entropy, S (18.1): The degree of disorder or randomness of a system's energy.

Gibbs free energy, G (18.4): A state function defined in terms of the enthalpy, entropy, and temperature of the system, and used to determine if a process is spontaneous.

isothermal process (18.3): A process or reaction for which the temperature of the surroundings does not change.

macrostate (18.1): A set of energetically equivalent microstates.

microstate (18.1): A specific energetic state possible for a system.

second law of thermodynamics (18.1): All spontaneous changes result in an increase in the entropy of the universe.

spontaneous process (18.1) A process or reaction that occurs.

standard free energy of formation, $\Delta G_f°$ (18.4) The free-energy change in the formation of a substance from its elements in their standard states.

standard molar entropy, $S_f°$ (18.2) The entropy of 1 mol of substance under standard conditions.

third law of thermodynamics (18.2) The entropy of a pure, perfectly ordered, crystalline substance at 0 K is 0.

SYMBOLS AND ABBREVIATIONS

G (Gibbs free energy) (18.4)

ΔG (Gibbs free-energy change) (18.4)

$\Delta G°$ (standard Gibbs free-energy change) (18.4)

$\Delta G_f°$ (standard free energy of formation) (18.4)

H (enthalpy) (18.1)

ΔH (enthalpy change) (18.1)

$\Delta H°$ (standard enthalpy change) (18.3)

$\Delta H_f°$ (standard enthalpy change of formation) (18.3)

k (Boltzmann constant, 1.38×10^{-23} J/K) (18.1)

K (equilibrium constant) (18.6)

Q (reaction quotient) (18.6)

R (gas law constant, 8.3145 J/mol · K) (18.6)

S (entropy) (18.1)

ΔS (change in entropy) (18.1)

$\Delta S°$ (standard entropy change) (18.2)

$S_f°$ (standard molar entropy) (18.2)

ΔS_{surr} (change in entropy of the surroundings) (18.3)

ΔS_{sys} (change in entropy of the system) (18.3)

ΔS_{rxn} (change in entropy for a reaction, also used for change in entropy of the system) (18.3)

ΔS_{univ} (change in entropy of the universe) (18.3)

W (number of microstates) (18.1)

EQUATIONS

$S = k \ln W$ (18.1)

$\Delta S_{rxn}° = \Sigma m[S_f°(\text{products})] - \Sigma n[S_f°(\text{reactants})]$ (18.2)

$\Delta S_{univ} = \Delta S_{sys} + \Delta S_{surr}$ (18.3)

$\Delta S_{surr} = \dfrac{-q_{sys}}{T}$ (18.4)

$\Delta S_{surr} = \frac{-\Delta H_{sys}}{T}$ (18.5)

$\Delta G = \Delta H - T\Delta S$ (18.6)

$\Delta G^\circ = \Delta H^\circ - T\Delta S^\circ$ (18.7)

$\Delta G^\circ_{rxn} = \Sigma m[\Delta G^\circ_f(\text{products})] - \Sigma n[\Delta G^\circ_f(\text{reactants})]$ (18.8)

$T = \frac{\Delta H}{\Delta S}$ (18.9)

$\Delta G = \Delta G^\circ + RT \ln Q$ (18.10)

$\Delta G^\circ = -RT \ln K$ (18.11)

$K = e^{-\frac{\Delta G^\circ}{RT}}$ (18.12)

Chapter Summary

Chemical thermodynamics deals with predicting the conditions necessary for a process to occur spontaneously, which is not possible using enthalpy changes alone. Entropy, S, is the degree of disorder or randomness. The second law of thermodynamics states that all spontaneous processes result in an increase in the entropy of the universe. Positive changes in entropy accompany phase changes from solid to liquid to gas, increases in temperature within a phase, and processes that result in an increase in the overall number of moles of species, particularly gases.

The mathematical definition of entropy is given by Equation 18.1.

$$S = k \ln W$$

where k is the Boltzmann constant $(1.38 \times 10^{-23} \text{J/K})$ and W is the number of energetically equivalent arrangements (microstates) possible for the system. Equivalent microstates form a macrostate; the most probable macrostate is the one containing the largest number of microstates (Section 18.1).

The third law of thermodynamics states that the entropy of a pure crystalline substance at absolute zero is zero, $S\,(0\text{ K}) = 0$. Standard molar entropy values for substances are measured at 298 K, so changes in standard entropy for chemical processes can be calculated using Equation 18.2.

$$\Delta S^\circ_{rxn} = \Sigma m[S^\circ_f(\text{products})] - \Sigma n[S^\circ_f(\text{reactants})]$$

where m and n are the coefficients of the products and reactants, respectively, in the balanced chemical equation for the process. Changes in entropy can also be calculated for physical processes using the same equation (Section 18.2).

To determine if a process is spontaneous, you can determine the overall entropy change, which is calculated by Equation 18.3, in which $\Delta S_{sys} = \Delta S_{rxn}$.

$$\Delta S_{univ} = \Delta S_{sys} + \Delta S_{surr}$$

ΔS_{univ} is positive for all spontaneous processes. ΔS_{surr} is calculated as follows (Equation 18.5)

$$\Delta S_{surr} = \frac{-\Delta H_{sys}}{T}$$

using tabulated data for changes in enthalpy (Section 18.3).

Gibbs free energy, G, is a state function that enables scientists to determine if a process is spontaneous or nonspontaneous based on the enthalpy and entropy changes of the system only, and is defined by several related equations.

- Basic definition: $G = H - TS$
- Definition for changes in free energy: $\Delta G = \Delta H - T\Delta S$ (Equation 18.6).
- Definition for standard free-energy changes: $\Delta G^\circ = \Delta H^\circ - T\Delta S^\circ$ (Equation 18.7).

$\Delta G°$ values for reactions are calculated in two ways—first using $\Delta H°$ (enthalpy) and $\Delta S°$ (entropy) changes, and second using $\Delta G°_f$ (standard free-energy changes of formation) data and Equation 18.8.

$$\Delta G°_{rxn} = \Sigma m[\Delta G°_f(\text{products})] - \Sigma n[\Delta G°_f(\text{reactants})]$$

where m and n are the coefficients of the products and reactants, respectively, in the balanced chemical equation for the process (Section 18.4).

Because ΔH and ΔS do not change greatly with temperature, it is possible to calculate Gibbs free-energy changes at temperatures other than 298 K using $\Delta H°$ and $\Delta S°$ data and Equation 18.7.

$$\Delta G = \Delta H° - T\Delta S°$$

At equilibrium, $\Delta G = 0$. Setting the Gibbs free energy equation equal to zero yields Equation 18.9

$$T = \frac{\Delta H}{\Delta S}$$

which makes it possible to calculate the temperature at which the sign of ΔG changes (Section 18.5).

Free-energy changes under nonstandard conditions are calculated according to Equation 18.10, where Q is the reaction quotient, R is the gas constant ($8.3145 \frac{\text{J}}{\text{mol} \cdot \text{K}}$), and T is the absolute temperature.

$$\Delta G = \Delta G° + RT \ln Q$$

At equilibrium, where $\Delta G = 0$ and $Q = K$, Equation 18.10 simplifies to Equation 18.11.

$$\Delta G° = -RT \ln K$$

Thus, standard free-energy changes ($\Delta G°$) are related to the size of the equilibrium constant. Negative values of $\Delta G°$ correspond to large equilibrium constants ($K > 1$), positive values of $\Delta G°$ correspond to small equilibrium constants ($K < 1$), and $\Delta G° = 0$ corresponds to $K = 1$.

The sign of ΔG indicates the direction in which the system will proceed to equilibrium.

- $\Delta G < 0$; forward direction
- $\Delta G = 0$; at equilibrium, no net change
- $\Delta G > 0$; reverse direction

Equilibrium constants can also be calculated from thermodynamic data using Equation 18.12

$$K = e^{-\frac{\Delta G°}{RT}}$$

(Section 18.6).

END OF CHAPTER QUESTIONS

18.1 Entropy and Spontaneity

1. List at least three factors that result in a positive sign for the change in entropy.

2. Which of the following processes have a positive change in entropy?
   a. $A(g) + B(g) \rightarrow C(g)$
   b. $A(g) + B(s) \rightarrow 2\,C(g)$
   c. $A(g) + B(g) \rightarrow 3\,C(g)$
   d. $2\,A(g) + B(g) \rightarrow 5\,C(g)$

3. Which of the following processes have a negative change in entropy?
   a. $A(g) + B(g) \rightarrow C(s)$
   b. $A(g) + B(g) \rightarrow 2\ C(g) + D(s)$
   c. $A(g) + 2\ B(g) \rightarrow 2\ C(g)$
   d. $A(g) + B(l) \rightarrow C(g)$

4. Predict the sign of ΔS for these processes:
   a. $2\ H_2(g) + O_2(g) \rightarrow 2\ H_2O(l)$
   b. $H_2O(l) \rightarrow H_2O(s)$
   c. $CaCO_3(s) \rightarrow CaO(s) + CO_2(g)$
   d. $CO_2(s) \rightarrow CO_2(g)$
   e. $2\ C_8H_{18}(l) + 25\ O_2(g) \rightarrow 16\ CO_2(g) + 18\ H_2O(l)$

5. Explain why entropy decreases during these processes:
   a. C(s, amorphous) → C(s, diamond)
   b. $Si(s) + 2\ Cl_2(g) \rightarrow SiCl_4(l)$
   c. H_2O(l, 55°C) → H_2O(l, 23°C)
   d. $2\ Fe(s) + 3\ O_2(g) \rightarrow Fe_2O_3(s)$

6. Predict the sign of ΔS for these processes:
   a. $KClO_3(s) \rightarrow KCl(s) + O_2(g)$
   b. $Zn(s) + 2\ HCl(aq) \rightarrow ZnCl_2(aq) + H_2(g)$
   c. $S(s) + O_2(g) \rightarrow SO_2(g)$
   d. $2\ KI(aq) + Pb(NO_3)_2(aq) \rightarrow PbI_2(s) + 2\ KNO_3(aq)$
   e. $C_3H_8(g) + 5\ O_2(g) \rightarrow 3\ CO_2(g) + 4\ H_2O(l)$

7. Predict the sign of ΔS for these processes:
   a. $MgI_2(aq) + 2\ AgNO_3(aq) \rightarrow 2\ AgI(s) + Mg(NO_3)_2(aq)$
   b. $2\ CoCl_2(aq) + Cl_2(g) \rightarrow 2\ CoCl_3(aq)$
   c. $2\ KCl(s) \rightarrow 2\ K(s) + Cl_2(g)$
   d. $2\ Li(s) + 3\ N_2(g) \rightarrow 2\ Li_3N(s)$
   e. $(NH_4)_2S(aq) + CuCl_2(aq) \rightarrow CuS(s) + 2\ NH_4Cl(aq)$

8. Predict the sign of ΔS for these processes:
   a. $H_2O(l) + N_2O_5(g) \rightarrow 2\ HNO_3(aq)$
   b. $NH_4NO_3(s) \rightarrow N_2O(g) + 2\ H_2O(l)$
   c. $2\ Mg(s) + O_2(g) \rightarrow 2\ MgO(s)$
   d. $2\ C_2H_6(g) + 7\ O_2(g) \rightarrow 4\ CO_2(g) + 6\ H_2O(l)$
   e. $2\ NH_4I(aq) + Pb(NO_3)_2(aq) \rightarrow 2\ NH_4NO_3(aq) + PbI_2(s)$

9. Explain why entropy increases during these processes:
   a. C(s, 35°C) → C(s, 335°C)
   b. 25 g NaCl(s, single crystal) → 25 g NaCl(s, many small crystals)
   c. $Hg(l) \rightarrow Hg(g)$
   d. $NaCl(s) \rightarrow NaCl(aq)$
   e. $CO_2(s) \rightarrow CO_2(g)$

10. Predict the sign of ΔS for these processes:
    a. $Ca(s) + 2\ HBr(aq) \rightarrow CaBr_2(aq) + H_2(g)$
    b. $2\ HgO(s) \rightarrow 2\ Hg(l) + O_2(g)$
    c. $H_2O(g) \rightarrow H_2O(s)$
    d. $Ca(NO_3)_2(s) \rightarrow Ca(NO_3)_2(aq)$
    e. $2NO_2(g) \rightarrow N_2O_4(g)$

11. Imagine that you are rolling *three* typical six-sided dice. Each way that you can roll a particular outcome using these three dice represents a microstate for that outcome.
    a. How many ways can you roll a five with these three dice? That is, how many microstates exist for a roll of five with three dice?
    b. What is the entropy associated with an outcome of five in this situation?

18.2 Entropy Changes—Both Chemical and Physical

12. Calculate the standard entropy change for these physical changes using values found in Appendix A.2:
    a. $NaCl(s) \rightarrow NaCl(aq)$
    b. $CO_2(s) \rightarrow CO_2(g)$

13. Calculate ΔS° for these chemical changes using values found in Appendix A.2:
    a. $Si(s) + 2\ Cl_2(g) \rightarrow SiCl_4(l)$
    b. $2\ HgO(s) \rightarrow 2\ Hg(l) + O_2(g)$

14. Calculate ΔS° for these physical changes using values found in Appendix A.2:
    a. $H_2O(l) \rightarrow H_2O(s)$
    b. C(s, graphite) → C(s, diamond)

15. Calculate the standard entropy change for these reactions using values found in Appendix A.2:
    a. $2\ KClO_3(s) \rightarrow 2\ KCl(s) + 3\ O_2(g)$
    b. $S_8(s) + 8\ O_2(g) \rightarrow 8\ SO_2(g)$

16. Calculate the standard entropy change for these reactions using values found in Appendix A.2:
    a. $C_3H_8(g) + 5\ O_2(g) \rightarrow 3\ CO_2(g) + 4\ H_2O(l)$
    b. $2NO_2(g) \rightarrow N_2O_4(g)$

17. Calculate ΔS° for these physical changes using values found in Appendix A.2:
    a. $H_2O(g) \rightarrow H_2O(l)$
    b. $Br_2(l) \rightarrow Br_2(g)$

18. Calculate $\Delta S°$ for these chemical changes using values found in Appendix A.2:
a. $2\ HgO(s) \rightarrow 2\ Hg(l) + O_2(g)$
b. $2\ KCl(s) \rightarrow 2\ K(s) + Cl_2(g)$

19. Calculate the standard entropy change for these reactions using values found in Appendix A.2:
a. $2\ H_2(g) + O_2(g) \rightarrow 2\ H_2O(l)$
b. $2\ LiCl(s) \rightarrow 2\ Li(s) + Cl_2(g)$

20. Calculate $\Delta S°$ for these reactions using values found in Appendix A.2:
a. $CaCO_3(s) \rightarrow CaO(s) + CO_2(g)$
b. $CH_4(g) + 2\ O_2(g) \rightarrow CO_2(g) + 2\ H_2O(l)$

21. Calculate the standard entropy change for these reactions using values found in Appendix A.2:
a. $2\ Mg(s) + O_2(g) \rightarrow 2\ MgO(s)$
b. $2\ C_2H_6(g) + 7\ O_2(g) \rightarrow 4\ CO_2(g) + 6\ H_2O(l)$

18.3 Entropy and Temperature

22. How does an enthalpy change in the system affect the entropy of the surroundings?

23. The heat released by burning a candle has an impact on the entropy of the surroundings. Will this impact be greater when the surroundings are cold or when the surroundings are hot? Explain your reasoning.

24. Use the standard entropy change calculated in question 12 to calculate ΔS_{surr} and ΔS_{univ} for these physical changes that occur at 298 K:
a. $NaCl(s) \rightarrow NaCl(aq)$
b. $CO_2(s) \rightarrow CO_2(g)$

25. Use the standard entropy change calculated in question 13 to calculate ΔS_{surr} and ΔS_{univ} for these reactions at 298 K:
a. $Si(s) + 2\ Cl_2(g) \rightarrow SiCl_4(l)$
b. $2\ HgO(s) \rightarrow 2\ Hg(l) + O_2(g)$

26. Use the standard entropy change calculated in question 14 to calculate ΔS_{surr} and ΔS_{univ} for these physical changes that occur at 298 K:
a. $H_2O(l) \rightarrow H_2O(s)$
b. C(s, graphite) → C(s, diamond)

27. Use the standard entropy change calculated in question 15 to calculate ΔS_{surr} and ΔS_{univ} for these reactions at 298 K:
a. $KClO_3(s) \rightarrow KCl(s) + O_2(g)$
b. $S(s) + O_2(g) \rightarrow SO_2(g)$

28. Use the standard entropy change calculated in question 16 to calculate ΔS_{surr} and ΔS_{univ} for these reactions at 298 K:
a. $C_3H_8(g) + 5\ O_2(g) \rightarrow 3\ CO_2(g) + 4\ H_2O(l)$
b. $2NO_2(g) \rightarrow N_2O_4(g)$

29. Use the standard entropy change calculated in question 17 to calculate ΔS_{surr} and ΔS_{univ} for these physical changes that occur at 298 K:
a. $H_2O(g) \rightarrow H_2O(l)$
b. $Br_2(l) \rightarrow Br_2(g)$

30. Use the standard entropy change calculated in question 18 to calculate ΔS_{surr} and ΔS_{univ} for these reactions at 298 K:
a. $2\ HgO(s) \rightarrow 2\ Hg(l) + O_2(g)$
b. $2\ KCl(s) \rightarrow 2\ K(s) + Cl_2(g)$

31. Use the standard entropy change calculated in question 19 to calculate ΔS_{surr} and ΔS_{univ} for these reactions at 298 K:
a. $2\ H_2(g) + O_2(g) \rightarrow 2\ H_2O(l)$
b. $2\ Li(s) + Cl_2(g) \rightarrow LiCl(s)$

32. Use the standard entropy change calculated in question 20 to calculate ΔS_{surr} and ΔS_{univ} for these reactions at 298 K:
a. $CaCO_3(s) \rightarrow CaO(s) + CO_2(g)$
b. $CH_4(g) + 2\ O_2(g) \rightarrow CO_2(g) + 2\ H_2O(l)$

33. Use the standard entropy change calculated in question 21 to calculate ΔS_{surr} and ΔS_{univ} for these reactions at 298 K:
a. $2\ Mg(s) + O_2(g) \rightarrow 2\ MgO(s)$
b. $2\ C_2H_6(g) + 7\ O_2(g) \rightarrow 4\ CO_2(g) + 6\ H_2O(l)$

18.4 Gibbs Free Energy

34. How is the sign of ΔG used to predict if a process is spontaneous or not?

35. How do the signs of ΔS and ΔH affect the sign of ΔG?

36. Use the $\Delta S°$ and $\Delta H°$ values calculated in questions 12 and 24 to calculate the Gibbs free-energy change for these physical changes that occur at 298 K:
a. $NaCl(s) \rightarrow NaCl(aq)$
b. $CO_2(s) \rightarrow CO_2(g)$

37. Use the $\Delta S°$ and $\Delta H°$ values calculated in questions 13 and 25 to calculate the Gibbs free-energy change for these reactions at 298 K:
a. $Si(s) + 2\ Cl_2(g) \rightarrow SiCl_4(l)$
b. $2\ HgO(s) \rightarrow 2\ Hg(l) + O_2(g)$

38. Use the $\Delta S°$ and $\Delta H°$ values calculated in questions 14 and 26 to calculate the Gibbs free-energy change for these physical changes that occur at 298 K:
a. $H_2O(l) \rightarrow H_2O(s)$
b. C(s, graphite) $\rightarrow$ C(s, diamond)

39. Use the $\Delta S°$ and $\Delta H°$ values calculated in questions 15 and 27 to calculate the Gibbs free-energy change for these reactions at 298 K:
a. $KClO_3(s) \rightarrow KCl(s) + O_2(g)$
b. $S(s) + O_2(g) \rightarrow SO_2(g)$

40. Use the $\Delta S°$ and $\Delta H°$ values calculated in questions 16 and 28 to calculate the Gibbs free-energy change for these reactions at 298 K:
a. $C_3H_8(g) + 5\ O_2(g) \rightarrow 3\ CO_2(g) + 4\ H_2O(l)$
b. $2NO_2(g) \rightarrow N_2O_4(g)$

41. Use the $\Delta S°$ and $\Delta H°$ values calculated in questions 17 and 29 to calculate the Gibbs free-energy change for these physical changes that occur at 298 K:
a. $H_2O(g) \rightarrow H_2O(s)$
b. $Br_2(l) \rightarrow Br_2(g)$

42. Use the $\Delta S°$ and $\Delta H°$ values calculated in questions 18 and 30 to calculate the Gibbs free-energy change for these reactions at 298 K:
a. $2\ HgO(s) \rightarrow 2\ Hg(l) + O_2(g)$
b. $2\ KCl(s) \rightarrow 2\ K(s) + Cl_2(g)$

43. Use the $\Delta S°$ and $\Delta H°$ values calculated in questions 19 and 31 to calculate the Gibbs free-energy change for these reactions at 298 K:
a. $2\ H_2(g) + O_2(g) \rightarrow 2\ H_2O(l)$
b. $2\ Li(s) + 3\ N_2(g) \rightarrow 2\ Li_3N(s)$

44. Use the $\Delta S°$ and $\Delta H°$ values calculated in questions 20 and 32 to calculate the Gibbs free-energy change for these reactions at 298 K:
a. $CaCO_3(s) \rightarrow CaO(s) + CO_2(g)$
b. $CH_4(g) + 2\ O_2(g) \rightarrow CO_2(g) + 2\ H_2O(l)$

45. Use the $\Delta S°$ and $\Delta H°$ values calculated in questions 21 and 33 to calculate the Gibbs free-energy change for these reactions at 298 K:
a. $2\ Mg(s) + O_2(g) \rightarrow 2\ MgO(s)$
b. $2\ C_2H_6(g) + 7\ O_2(g) \rightarrow 4\ CO_2(g) + 6\ H_2O(l)$

46. In human history, copper and tin (bronze) were made from their ores before iron, and the common use of aluminum came about in only the last century. Assuming that these metals are all found as oxide ores in nature, use the standard free energies of formation for these metal oxides, CuO, SnO_2, Fe_2O_3 and Al_2O_3, in Appendix A.2 to propose a reason for this order of development.

18.5 Free-Energy Changes and Temperature

47. What signs of ΔS and ΔH are associated with processes that are spontaneous
a. at temperatures above a specific threshold?
b. at temperatures below a specific threshold?

48. Use the values of $\Delta S°$ and $\Delta H°$ calculated in questions 12 and 24 (assume that these values are not affected much by changes in temperature) to determine the temperature range in which these processes are spontaneous.
a. $NaCl(s) \rightarrow NaCl(aq)$
b. $CO_2(s) \rightarrow CO_2(g)$

49. Use the values of $\Delta S°$ and $\Delta H°$ calculated in questions 13 and 25 (assume that these values are not affected much by changes in temperature) to determine the temperature range in which these processes are spontaneous.
a. $Si(s) + 2\ Cl_2(g) \rightarrow SiCl_4(l)$
b. $2\ HgO(s) \rightarrow 2\ Hg(l) + O_2(g)$

50. Use the values of $\Delta S°$ and $\Delta H°$ calculated in questions 14 and 26 (assume that these values are not affected much by changes in temperature) to determine the temperature range in which these processes are spontaneous.
a. $H_2O(l) \rightarrow H_2O(s)$
b. C(s, graphite) $\rightarrow$ C(s, diamond)

51. Use the values of $\Delta S°$ and $\Delta H°$ calculated in questions 15 and 27 (assume that these values are not affected much by changes in temperature) to determine the temperature range in which these processes are spontaneous.
a. $KClO_3(s) \rightarrow KCl(s) + O_2(g)$
b. $S(s) + O_2(g) \rightarrow SO_2(g)$

52. Use the values of $\Delta S°$ and $\Delta H°$ calculated in questions 16 and 28 (assume that these values are not affected much by changes in temperature) to determine the temperature range in which these processes are spontaneous.
a. $C_3H_8(g) + 5\ O_2(g) \rightarrow 3\ CO_2(g) + 4\ H_2O(l)$
b. $2NO_2(g) \rightarrow N_2O_4(g)$

53. Use the values of $\Delta S°$ and $\Delta H°$ calculated in questions 17 and 29 (assume that these values are

not affected much by changes in temperature) to determine the temperature range in which these processes are spontaneous.

a. $H_2O(g) \rightarrow H_2O(s)$
b. $Br_2(l) \rightarrow Br_2(g)$

54. Use the values of $\Delta S°$ and $\Delta H°$ calculated in questions 18 and 30 (assume that these values are not affected much by changes in temperature) to determine the temperature range in which these processes are spontaneous.
a. $2\ HgO(s) \rightarrow 2\ Hg(l) + O_2(g)$
b. $2\ KCl(s) \rightarrow 2\ K(s) + Cl_2(g)$

55. Use the values of $\Delta S°$ and $\Delta H°$ calculated in questions 19 and 31 (assume that these values are not affected much by changes in temperature) to determine the temperature range in which these processes are spontaneous.
a. $2\ H_2(g) + O_2(g) \rightarrow 2\ H_2O(l)$
b. $2\ Li(s) + 3\ N_2(g) \rightarrow 2\ Li_3N(s)$

56. Use the values of $\Delta S°$ and $\Delta H°$ calculated in questions 20 and 32 (assume that these values are not affected much by changes in temperature) to determine the temperature range in which these processes are spontaneous.
a. $CaCO_3(s) \rightarrow CaO(s) + CO_2(g)$
b. $CH_4(g) + 2\ O_2(g) \rightarrow CO_2(g) + 2\ H_2O(l)$

57. Use the values of $\Delta S°$ and $\Delta H°$ calculated in questions 21 and 33 (assume that these values are not affected much by changes in temperature) to determine the temperature range in which these processes are spontaneous.
a. $2\ Mg(s) + O_2(g) \rightarrow 2\ MgO(s)$
b. $2\ C_2H_6(g) + 7\ O_2(g) \rightarrow 4\ CO_2(g) + 6\ H_2O(l)$

18.6 Gibbs Free Energy and Equilibrium

58. At 25°C, the equilibrium partial pressures for the following reaction were measured as P_A = 0.230 atm, P_B = 0.155 atm, P_C = 0.482 atm, and P_D = 0.776 atm. Calculate the standard free-energy change.

$$2\ A(g) + B(g) \rightleftharpoons C(g) + 3\ D(g)$$

59. Sulfur dioxide reacts with oxygen gas to produce sulfur trioxide gas according to the following reaction:

$$2\ SO_2(g) + O_2(g) \rightleftharpoons 2\ SO_3(g)$$

a. Calculate the standard free-energy change for this process (Appendix A.2).
b. Calculate the free-energy change at 298 K when the partial pressure of SO_2 is 0.250 atm, the partial pressure of O_2 is 0.500 atm, and the partial pressure of SO_3 is 0.400 atm.

60. Refer to the equation and your answers from question 59 for this question.
a. Calculate the equilibrium constant for the reaction at 298 K.
b. Use the Le Châtelier principle to explain the difference in value between ΔG (from the previous question) and $\Delta G°$.

61. Given this equilibrium

$$NO(g) + O_2(g) \rightleftharpoons 2\ NO_2(g)$$

a. calculate the standard free energy change for this process (Appendix A.2).
b. calculate the free-energy change at 298 K when the partial pressure of NO is 0.375 atm, the partial pressure of O_2 is 0.250 atm, and the partial pressure of NO_2 is 0.0500 atm.

62. Refer to the equation and your answers from question 61 for the following:
a. Calculate the equilibrium constant at 298 K for the reaction (Appendix A.2).
b. Use the Le Châtelier principle to explain the difference in value between ΔG (from the previous question) and $\Delta G°$.

63. Given this equilibrium

$$C_2H_4(g) + H_2O(g) \rightleftharpoons C_2H_5OH(g)$$

a. calculate the standard free-energy change for this process (Appendix A.2).
b. calculate the free-energy change at 298 K when the partial pressure of C_2H_4 is 0.275 atm, the partial pressure of H_2O is 0.350 atm, and the partial pressure of $C_2H_5OH_2$ is 0.100 atm.

64. Refer to the equation and your answers from question 63 for this question.
a. Calculate the equilibrium constant at 298 K for the reaction.
b. Use the Le Châtelier principle to explain the difference in value between ΔG (from the previous question) and $\Delta G°$.

Putting It Together

65. Consider the reaction of ammonia with water

$$NH_3(aq) + H_2O(l) \rightleftharpoons NH_4^+(aq) + OH^-(aq)$$

a. Use Appendix A.2 to calculate the standard free-energy change associated with this reaction.
b. Calculate the equilibrium constant for the reaction and compare it to the K_b given in Appendix A3.

66. Calculate the free-energy change of the reaction of ammonia with water (see previous problem) under these conditions:
a. 325 K.
b. 298 K with 0.130 M NH_3, 0.065 M NH_4^+, and 0.045 M OH^-

67. Calculate the K_{sp} of $CaSO_4$ at 298 K using Appendix A.2, and compare it to the value in Appendix A.4.

68. Calculate the K_{sp} of $CaSO_4$ at 455 K.

69. Calculate the K_{sp} of $Ca(OH)_2$ at 298 K using Appendix A.2, and compare it to the value in Appendix A.4.

70. Calculate the K_{sp} of $Ca(OH)_2$ at 275 K.

71. Calculate the K_{sp} of AgCl at 298 K using Appendix A.2, and compare it to the value in Appendix A.4.

72. Calculate the K_{sp} of AgCl at 455 K.

PRACTICE PROBLEM SOLUTIONS

Practice Problem 18.1 Solution

a. ΔS is negative $(-)$. The process starts with a gaseous reactant and yields only solid products, for an overall decrease in the moles of gas.
b. ΔS is positive $(+)$. The process starts with a solid and ends with a gas.
c. ΔS is positive $(+)$. The process starts with a solid and a liquid, and ends with a solution in which the solid is dispersed.
d. ΔS is negative $(-)$. The process starts with gaseous water vapor and ends with ice (solid water).

Practice Problem 18.2 Solution

For the reactants, the 3 particles are located on the left side of the box only (fewer microstates possible), whereas the particles on the product side are located on both sides (more microstates possible). The particles have become more dispersed, indicating an increase in entropy, so the sign of ΔS is positive $(+)$.

Use $W = X^n$ to confirm that the total number of microstates possible for this system is $4^3 = 64$. Of those 64, there are 8 possible microstates with the three particles confined to the left side, 8 with the three particles on the right side, and 48 with particles on both sides.

Practice Problem 18.3 Solution

Prediction: ΔS will be positive $(+)$, because the number of moles of gases increases.

Calculation:

$$\Delta S^\circ_{rxn} = [S^\circ_f(CaO(s)) + S^\circ_f(CO_2(g))] - [S^\circ_f(CaCO_3(s))]$$

$$\Delta S^\circ_{rxn} = \left[1\ \text{mol}\left(38.1\ \frac{\text{J}}{\text{mol}\cdot\text{K}}\right) + 1\ \text{mol}\left(213.8\frac{\text{J}}{\text{mol}\cdot\text{K}}\right)\right] - \left[1\ \text{mol}\left(91.7\ \frac{\text{J}}{\text{mol}\cdot\text{K}}\right)\right]$$

$$\Delta S^\circ_{rxn} = 160.2\frac{\text{J}}{\text{K}}$$

Practice Problem 18.4 Solution

Prediction: The entropy change for the phase change from a gas to a solid is negative.

$$\Delta S^\circ = S^\circ_f(I_2(s)) - S^\circ_f(I_2(g))$$

$$\Delta S^\circ = 1\ \text{mol}\left(116.1\frac{\text{J}}{\text{mol}\cdot\text{K}}\right) - 1\ \text{mol}\left(260.7\frac{\text{J}}{\text{mol}\cdot\text{K}}\right)$$

$$\Delta S^\circ = -144.6\frac{\text{J}}{\text{K}}$$

$$\Delta S = 117.4\ \text{g}\ I_2\left(\frac{1\ \text{mol}\ I_2}{253.8\ \text{g}\ I_2}\right)\left(\frac{-144.6\ \text{J/K}}{1\ \text{mol}\ I_2}\right) = -66.89\ \frac{\text{J}}{\text{K}}$$

Practice Problem 18.5 Solution

First, attempt to predict the sign of ΔS_{univ}. You know from Practice Problem 18.3 that ΔS_{sys} is positive, but what about ΔS°_{surr}? You would have to know the sign of ΔH for the reaction, which is likely to be positive because the reaction involves the production of a gas from a solid. Endothermic reactions decrease the entropy of the surroundings, making ΔS°_{surr} negative. Since the two components of ΔS_{univ} have opposite signs, you cannot readily make a prediction.

The balanced chemical equation was given in Practice Problem 18.3.

$$CaCO_3(s) \rightarrow CaO(s) + CO_2(g)$$

Use the data in Appendix A.2 to calculate ΔH°_{rxn} for this reaction.

$$\Delta H^\circ_{rxn} = [\Delta H^\circ_f(CaO(s)) + \Delta H^\circ_f(CO_2(g))] - [\Delta H^\circ_f(CaCO_3(s))]$$

$$\Delta H^\circ_{rxn} = \left[1\ mol\left(-634.9\frac{kJ}{mol}\right) + 1\ mol\left(-393.5\frac{kJ}{mol}\right)\right] - \left[1\ mol\left(-1207.6\frac{kJ}{mol}\right)\right]$$

$$\Delta H^\circ_{rxn} = 179.2\ kJ$$

Then use that value in Equation 18.5 to calculate ΔS°_{surr}.

$$\Delta S^\circ_{surr} = \frac{-\Delta H^\circ_{rxn}}{T}$$

$$\Delta S^\circ_{surr} = \frac{-179.2\ kJ}{298\ K} \times \frac{1000\ J}{1\ kJ}$$

$$\Delta S^\circ_{surr} = -601.3\frac{J}{K}$$

Use Equation 18.3 with $\Delta S_{sys} = 160.2\ J/K$ (from Practice Problem 18.3) and $\Delta S_{surr} = -601.3\ J/K$ (from part a).

$$\Delta S_{univ} = \Delta S_{sys} + \Delta S_{surr}$$

$$\Delta S_{univ} = 160.2\frac{J}{K} + \left(-601.3\frac{J}{K}\right)$$

$$\Delta S_{univ} = -441.1\frac{J}{K}$$

Because the change in entropy of the universe is negative, this reaction is not spontaneous at 298 K.

Practice Problem 18.6 Solution

Use Equation 18.7 to calculate ΔG°.

$$\Delta G^\circ = \Delta H^\circ - T\Delta S^\circ$$

From Practice Problem 18.5, you know that $\Delta H^\circ = 179.2\ kJ$, and from Practice Problem 18.3, you know that $\Delta S^\circ = 160.2\ J/K$. Be sure to convert the entropy from J/K to kJ/K, and use standard temperature ($T = 298$ K, unless indicated otherwise).

$$\Delta G^\circ = 179.2\ kJ - 298\ K\left(160.2\frac{J}{K}\right)\left(\frac{1\ kJ}{1000\ J}\right)$$

$$\Delta G^\circ = 131.5\ kJ$$

The positive value for ΔG° indicates that this reaction is not spontaneous under standard conditions.

Practice Problem 18.7 Solution

Use Equation 18.8 to calculate ΔG°_{rxn}.

$$\Delta G^\circ_{rxn} = \Sigma m[\Delta G^\circ_f(\text{products})] - \Sigma n[\Delta G^\circ_f(\text{reactants})]$$

Rewrite the equation to include the species in the reaction of phosphorus with HCl.

$$\Delta G^\circ_{rxn} = [2\Delta G^\circ_f(PCl_5(g)) + 5\Delta G^\circ_f(H_2(g))] - [2\Delta G^\circ_f(P(s,\ white)) + 10\Delta G^\circ_f(HCl(g))]$$

Substitute the appropriate values from the table of thermodynamic data in Appendix A.2.

$$\Delta G^\circ_{rxn} = \left[2\ mol\left(-305.0\frac{kJ}{mol}\right) + 5\ mol\left(0\frac{kJ}{mol}\right)\right] - \left[2\ mol\left(0\frac{kJ}{mol}\right) + 10\ mol\left(-95.3\frac{kJ}{mol}\right)\right]$$

$$\Delta G^\circ_{rxn} = (-610.0\ kJ) - (-953.0\ kJ) = 343.0\ kJ$$

The positive free-energy change indicates that this reaction is not spontaneous at 298 K.

Practice Problem 18.8 Solution

Calculate the enthalpy change first.

$$\Delta H^\circ_{soln} = \Sigma m[\Delta H^\circ_f(\text{products})] - \Sigma n[\Delta H^\circ_f(\text{reactants})]$$

$$\Delta H^\circ_{soln} = [\Delta H^\circ_f(K^+(aq)) + \Delta H^\circ_f(Br^-(aq))] - [\Delta H^\circ_f(KBr(s))]$$

$$\Delta H^\circ_{soln} = \left[1\ mol\left(-252.1\frac{kJ}{mol}\right) + 1\ mol\left(-121.4\frac{kJ}{mol}\right)\right] - \left[1\ mol\left(-393.8\frac{kJ}{mol}\right)\right]$$

$$\Delta H^\circ_{soln} = 20.3\ kJ$$

The positive result for ΔH°_{soln} indicates that this is an endothermic process.

Calculate the entropy change in a similar manner.

$$\Delta S^\circ_{soln} = \Sigma m[S^\circ_f(\text{products})] - \Sigma n[S^\circ_f(\text{reactants})]$$

$$\Delta S^\circ_{soln} = [S^\circ_f(K^+(aq)) + S^\circ_f(Br^-(aq))] - [S^\circ_f(KBr(s))]$$

$$\Delta S^\circ_{soln} = \left[1\ mol\left(101.2\frac{J}{K\cdot mol}\right) + 1\ mol\left(82.4\frac{J}{K\cdot mol}\right)\right] - \left[1\ mol\left(95.9\frac{J}{K\cdot mol}\right)\right]$$

$$\Delta S^\circ_{soln} = 87.7\frac{J}{K}$$

The positive entropy change is favorable, but you must calculate the free-energy change under standard conditions to know if this solution will form.

$$\Delta G^\circ = \Delta H^\circ - T\Delta S^\circ$$

$$\Delta G^\circ_{soln} = 20.3 \text{ kJ} - (298 \text{ K})\left(87.7\frac{\text{J}}{\text{K}} \times \frac{1 \text{ kJ}}{1000 \text{ J}}\right)$$

$$\Delta G^\circ_{soln} = -5.8 \text{ kJ}$$

The negative free-energy change indicates that the dissolution of potassium bromide, despite being endothermic, is spontaneous under standard conditions.

Practice Problem 18.9 Solution

a. The balanced chemical equation is

$$CaCO_3(s) \rightarrow CaO(s) + CO_2(g)$$

To calculate ΔG, use Equation 18.6.

$$\Delta G = \Delta H - T\Delta S$$

From Practice Problem 18.5, $\Delta H^\circ = 179.2$ kJ, and from Practice Problem 18.3, $\Delta S^\circ = 160.2\frac{\text{J}}{\text{K}}$. Because enthalpy and entropy values do not change much with temperature, you can use these standard values to calculate ΔG at 1150 K.

$$\Delta G = 179.2 \text{ kJ} - 1150 \text{ K}\left(160.2\frac{\text{J}}{\text{K}}\right)\left(\frac{1 \text{ kJ}}{1000 \text{ J}}\right)$$

$$\Delta G = -5.03 \text{ kJ}$$

b. The standard free-energy change calculated in Practice Problem 18.5 is 131.5 kJ, which means the reaction is *not* spontaneous at 298 K. At the much higher temperature of 1150 K, however, the reaction has a small negative ΔG of -5.03 kJ and is spontaneous.

Practice Problem 18.10 Solution

Use Equation 18.9 where $\Delta G = 0$, and substitute the data for ΔH and ΔS from previous practice problems.

$$T = \frac{\Delta H}{\Delta S}$$

Recall from Practice Problem 18.9 that $\Delta H =$ 179.2 kJ and $\Delta S = 160.2$ J/K for this reaction:

$$T = \frac{179.2 \text{ kJ}}{160.2\frac{\text{J}}{\text{K}}\left(\frac{1 \text{ kJ}}{1000 \text{ J}}\right)}$$

$$T = 1119 \text{ K}$$

Thus, the reaction is at equilibrium at 1119 K, it is spontaneous at $T > 1119$ K, and it is nonspontaneous at $T < 1119$ K.

Practice Problem 18.11 Solution

Use Equation 18.10.

$$\Delta G = \Delta G^\circ + RT \ln Q$$

You know from Example 18.9 that $\Delta G^\circ = 10.9 \frac{\text{kJ}}{\text{mol}}$ for this reaction. From the chemical equation, you can get the reaction quotient expression: $Q_p = P_{TiCl_4(g)}$. $TiCl_4(l)$ does not appear in the Q expression because it is a pure liquid.

$$\Delta G = 10.9\frac{\text{kJ}}{\text{mol}} + \left(8.3145\frac{\text{J}}{\text{mol}\cdot\text{K}} \times \frac{1 \text{ kJ}}{1000 \text{ J}}\right)(525 \text{ K}) \ln (0.250)$$

$$\Delta G = 4.85\frac{\text{kJ}}{\text{mol}}$$

A positive value for ΔG means the vaporization of $TiCl_4(l)$ is nonspontaneous under these particular conditions of temperature and pressure. Instead, the condensation of $TiCl_4(g)$ to $TiCl_4(l)$ is spontaneous.

Practice Problem 18.12 Solution

a. ΔG° is a large positive number, so the forward process (the decomposition of solid $CaCO_3$) is nonspontaneous at 298 K, whereas the reverse process (the formation of solid $CaCO_3$) is spontaneous. Therefore, reactants are favored for this process, which means that $K < 1$ is expected.

Calculate K using Equation 18.12.

$$K = e^{-\frac{\Delta G^\circ}{RT}}$$

$$-\frac{\Delta G^\circ}{RT} = \frac{-131.5 \text{ kJ/mol}}{\left(8.3145\frac{\text{J}}{\text{mol}\cdot\text{K}}\right)(298 \text{ K})} \times \frac{1000 \text{ J}}{1 \text{ kJ}}$$

$$-\frac{\Delta G^\circ}{RT} = -53.07$$

$$K = e^{-53.07} = 8.95 \times 10^{-24}$$

b. This is a very small equilibrium constant, indicative of a reaction that favors the reactants at equilibrium.

Practice Problem 18.13 Solution

Start by finding ΔH° and ΔS° using Appendix A.2.

$$\Delta H^\circ = \left[1 \text{ mol}\left(105.8\frac{\text{kJ}}{\text{mol}}\right) + 1 \text{ mol}\left(-56.78\frac{\text{kJ}}{\text{mol}}\right)\right] - \left[1 \text{ mol}\left(-61.8\frac{\text{kJ}}{\text{mol}}\right)\right]$$

$$= 110.82 \text{ kJ}$$

$$\Delta S^\circ = \left[1\ \text{mol}\left(73.4\frac{\text{J}}{\text{mol}\cdot\text{K}}\right) + 1\ \text{mol}\left(106.5\frac{\text{J}}{\text{mol}\cdot\text{K}}\right)\right] - \left[1\ \text{mol}\left(115.5\frac{\text{J}}{\text{mol}\cdot\text{K}}\right)\right]$$

$$= 64.4\,\frac{\text{J}}{\text{K}}$$

Now find ΔG at 355 K.

$$\Delta G = \Delta H - T\Delta S$$

$$\Delta G = 110.82\ \text{kJ} - (355\ \text{K})\left(64.4\,\frac{\text{J}}{\text{K}}\right)\left(\frac{1\ \text{kJ}}{1000\ \text{J}}\right)$$

$$= 87.958\ \text{kJ}$$

Finally, find K.

$$\Delta G = -RT\ln K$$

$$K = e^{-\frac{\Delta G}{RT}}$$

$$\frac{\Delta G}{RT} = \frac{87.958\ \text{kJ/mol}}{\left(8.3145\,\frac{\text{J}}{\text{mol}\cdot\text{K}}\right)\left(\frac{1\ \text{kJ}}{1000\ \text{J}}\right)(355\ \text{K})} = 29.8$$

$$K = e^{-\frac{\Delta G}{RT}} = e^{-29.8} = 1.14 \times 10^{-13}$$

As expected, the solubility of a solid increases with temperature.

CHAPTER 19

Electrochemistry

mariva2017/Shutterstock

Batteries use spontaneous redox reactions to produce electricity, which is the flow of electrons. The reactants in a battery are separated so that electrons can't flow until the battery is placed in an appliance, such as a flashlight or a cell phone, which completes the circuit. Once the reactants are used up, the battery no longer produces electricity. Some batteries can be recharged by applying an external voltage to cause the reaction to occur in the reverse, replenishing the reactants.

Chapter Outline

GOALS

- Write half-reactions from overall redox reactions and vice versa.
- Identify oxidizing and reducing agents in disproportionation reactions.
- Balance redox equations in acidic solution.
- Balance redox equations in basic solution.
- Determine the concentration of solutions based on redox titration data.
- Describe the components of voltaic cells using appropriate terminology and notation.
- Calculate cell potential using tables of standard reduction potentials.
- Compare the strengths of substances as oxidizing and reducing agents using tables of standard reduction potentials.
- Describe the relationships between standard free energy, standard cell potential, and the equilibrium constant.
- Perform calculations involving standard free energy, standard cell potential, and the equilibrium constant.
- Calculate the effect of the reactant concentration on cell potential using the Nernst equation.
- Use voltaic cell concepts to describe specific batteries, fuel cells, and corrosion.
- Describe how electricity can be used to drive redox reactions.
- Perform stoichiometric calculations involving mass and current in electrolytic applications.
- Describe relevant applications of electrolysis in the production or refining of specific substances.

19.1 Redox Reactions

GOALS

- Write half-reactions from overall redox reactions and vice versa.
- Identify oxidizing and reducing agents in disproportionation reactions.

Background Review

Chapter 4 Chemical Reactions and Aqueous Solutions: Section 4.6—Oxidation States and Redox Reactions

Electrochemistry is the branch of chemistry that studies the relationship between chemistry and electricity. Electrochemistry involves using either spontaneous redox reactions to create electricity or electricity to cause non-spontaneous electron transfer reactions to occur. Redox reactions always involve the simultaneous oxidation of one reactant and reduction of another (Section 4.6).

- Oxidation = Increase in oxidation state = Loss of electrons
- Reduction = Decrease in oxidation state = Gain of electrons

HALF-REACTIONS

You can separate a redox reaction into two **half-reactions**, one which depicts the reduction and the other which depicts the oxidation. In the synthesis of aluminum chloride, $AlCl_3$, aluminum is oxidized from Al to Al^{3+}, while chlorine is reduced from Cl_2 to Cl^- (Section 3.3):

$$\text{Oxidation half-reaction: } Al \rightarrow Al^{3+} + 3\,e^-$$

$$\text{Reduction half-reaction: } Cl_2 + 2\,e^- \rightarrow 2\,Cl^-$$

The charge is balanced in each half-reaction using an appropriate number of electrons, e^-. To combine these half-reactions into the overall reaction, the electrons gained and lost must be equal. The lowest common multiple of $2\,e^-$ and $3\,e^-$ is $6\,e^-$. Thus, doubling the oxidation (Al) half-reaction and tripling the reduction (Cl_2) half-reaction balances the electron transfer.

$$2(Al \rightarrow Al^{3+} + 3\,e^-) = 2\,Al \rightarrow 2\,Al^{3+} + 6\,e^-$$

$$3(Cl_2 + 2\,e^- \rightarrow 2\,Cl^-) = 3\,Cl_2 + 6\,e^- \rightarrow 6\,Cl^-$$

Now, when the half-reactions are summed, the electrons cancel.

$$2\,Al + 3\,Cl_2 + \cancel{6\,e^-} \rightarrow 2\,Al^{3+} + 6\,Cl^- + \cancel{6\,e^-}$$

Any reaction involving the transfer of electrons can be written and balanced as half-reactions.

Example 19.1

Separate the following redox reactions into their half-reactions, and classify those half-reactions as oxidation or reduction.

a. $2\,Mg + O_2 \rightarrow 2\,MgO$
b. $2\,RbF \rightarrow 2\,Rb + F_2$

Solution

When only two elements are involved, as in parts (a) and (b), each one will have its own half-reaction. You can either assign oxidation states (Section 4.6) or use the periodic table (Figure 3.7) to predict the charges on the monoatomic ions.

a. Magnesium is converted from Mg to Mg^{2+}.

$$Mg \rightarrow Mg^{2+}$$

Balance the charge by adding electrons to the more positive side.

$$Mg \rightarrow Mg^{2+} + 2\,e^-$$

Electrons are lost in this reaction, so it is the *oxidation* half-reaction.

Oxygen is converted from O_2 to O^{2-}. A coefficient of 2 is needed on the right to balance the number of O atoms.

$$O_2 \rightarrow 2\,O^{2-}$$

Balance the charge by adding electrons to the more positive side.

$$O_2 + 4\,e^- \rightarrow 2\,O^{2-}$$

Electrons are gained in this reaction, so it is the *reduction* half-reaction.

b. Rubidium is converted from Rb^+ to Rb.

$$Rb^+ \rightarrow Rb$$

Add an appropriate number of electrons to the more positive side to balance the charge.

$$Rb^+ + e^- \rightarrow Rb$$

Electrons are gained, so this is the *reduction* half-reaction.

Fluoride is converted from F^- to F_2. A coefficient of 2 is needed to balance the F atoms.

$$2\,F^- \rightarrow F_2$$

Add an appropriate number of electrons to the more positive side to balance the charge.

$$2\,F^- \rightarrow F_2 + 2\,e^-$$

Electrons are lost, so this is the *oxidation* half-reaction.

PRACTICE PROBLEM 19.1

Balance the following half-reactions, then combine each pair of half-reactions into a balanced overall redox equation.

a. $Cl^- \rightarrow Cl_2$
$K^+ \rightarrow K$

b. $Al \rightarrow Al^{3+}$
$Ag^+ \rightarrow Ag$

Hint: Use coefficients to balance the elements and electrons to balance the charge in each individual half-reaction. Before adding the two balanced half-reactions together, you may need to multiply one or both reactions by a factor so that the electrons cancel.

DISPROPORTIONATION

Sometimes, a single reactant can be both oxidized and reduced in the same reaction. Such a reactant is said to undergo **disproportionation**. Copper(I), Cu^+, for example, disproportionates in water.

$$2\,Cu^+(aq) \rightarrow Cu(s) + Cu^{2+}(aq)$$

Two copper(I) ions react, transferring an electron between them such that one ion is oxidized and the other is reduced. The Cu^+ that is reduced to Cu is called the *oxidizing agent* because it causes another Cu^+ to be oxidized to Cu^{2+}. Similarly, the Cu^+ that is oxidized to Cu^{2+} is called the *reducing agent* because it causes another Cu^+ to be reduced to Cu. This redox terminology is summarized in Table 4.6.

Example 19.2

When Cl_2 gas is dissolved in a concentrated NaOH solution, the following reaction occurs.

$$3\,Cl_2(g) + 6\,NaOH(aq) \rightarrow 5\,NaCl(aq) + NaClO_3(aq) + 3\,H_2O(l)$$

Identify the oxidizing and reducing agents.

Solution

Assign oxidation numbers to determine which elements change oxidation state.

$$\underset{0}{3\,Cl_2(g)} + \underset{+1\,-2\,+1}{6\,NaOH(aq)} \rightarrow \underset{+1\,-1}{5\,NaCl(aq)} + \underset{+1\,+5\,-2}{NaClO_3} + \underset{+1\,-2}{3\,H_2O(l)}$$

The oxidation states for Na, O, and H are unchanged, but the oxidation state for Cl increases from 0 to +5 to form $NaClO_3$ and decreases from 0 to −1 to form NaCl. $Cl_2(g)$ has undergone disproportionation, so it is both oxidizing agent and reducing agent.

PRACTICE PROBLEM 19.2

If exposed to heat or light, or even if left standing long enough, hydrogen peroxide decomposes into oxygen gas and hydrogen gas.

$$H_2O_2(aq) \rightarrow H_2(g) + O_2(g)$$

Identify the oxidizing and reducing agents.

Hint: Assign an oxidation number to H and O in both the reactants and products to determine which elements are oxidized and which are reduced.

SECTION REVIEW

- A redox reaction can be separated into an oxidation half-reaction and a reduction half-reaction.
- To combine two half-reactions into a balanced overall equation, first balance the electron transfer.
- Disproportionation reactions are redox reactions in which one reactant is both oxidized and reduced to form the products.

19.2 Balancing Redox Equations

GOALS

- Balance redox equations in acidic solution.
- Balance redox equations in basic solution.

Background Review

Chapter 4 Chemical Reactions and Aqueous Solutions: Section 4.5—Acid–Base Reactions; Section 4.6—Oxidation States and Redox Reactions

Many redox equations, such as the following, are so complex that they are tedious to balance by trial-and-error methods.

$$S_2O_3^{2-}(aq) + Cl_2(g) \rightarrow SO_4^{2-}(aq) + Cl^-(aq)$$

The key to balancing these equations is to identify the oxidation and reduction processes and to balance the transfer of electrons. Additionally, you may need to account for H and O, the process for which depends on whether the reaction occurs under acidic or basic conditions.

BALANCING REDOX REACTIONS IN ACIDIC SOLUTION

Use the steps in Table 19.1 to balance the preceding redox reaction in acidic solution.

$$S_2O_3^{2-}(aq) + Cl_2(g) \rightarrow SO_4^{2-}(aq) + Cl^-(aq)$$

Example 19.3

Balance the equation for the reaction of dichromate ion with tin(II) ion in acidic solution to produce chromium(III) ion, $SnO_2(s)$, and other products.

$$Cr_2O_7^{2-}(aq) + Sn^{2+}(aq) \rightarrow Cr^{3+}(aq) + SnO_2(s)$$

Solution

1. *Add coefficients to balance any elements other than H and O.*

$$Cr_2O_7^{2-}(aq) + Sn^{2+}(aq) \rightarrow 2\,Cr^{3+}(aq) + SnO_2(s)$$

2. *Assign oxidation numbers to all elements in the equation.*

$$\underset{+6\ \ -2}{Cr_2O_7^{2-}}(aq) + \underset{+2}{Sn^{2+}}(aq) \rightarrow 2\,\underset{+3}{Cr^{3+}}(aq) + \underset{+4\ -2}{SnO_2}(s)$$

3. *Identify the elements that undergo oxidation and reduction.* Cr is reduced from +6 to +3, a gain of three electrons. Sn is oxidized from +2 to +4, a loss of two electrons.
4. *Determine the coefficients needed to balance the electron transfer, and place these coefficients in the equation.* The least common multiple of 3 and 2 is 6, which means that a total of six electrons must be exchanged to balance the electron transfer. To transfer six electrons, two Cr must be reduced and three Sn must be oxidized.

$$Cr_2O_7^{2-}(aq) + 3\,Sn^{2+}(aq) \rightarrow 2\,Cr^{3+}(aq) + 3\,SnO_2(s)$$

5. *Balance any missing O atoms by adding water molecules.* There are seven O atoms on the reactant side and only six on the product side. Add one water molecule to the product side.

$$Cr_2O_7^{2-}(aq) + 3\,Sn^{2+}(aq) \rightarrow 2\,Cr^{3+}(aq) + 3\,SnO_2(s) + H_2O(l)$$

6. *Balance any missing H atoms by adding H^+ ions.* There are two hydrogen atoms on the product side and none on the reactant side. Add two H^+ to the reactant side.

$$Cr_2O_7^{2-}(aq) + 3\,Sn^{2+}(aq) + 2\,H^+(aq) \rightarrow 2\,Cr^{3+}(aq) + 3\,SnO_2(s) + H_2O(l)$$

TABLE 19.1 Steps for Balancing Redox Reactions in Acidic Solution

Step	Example
1. Add coefficients to balance any elements other than H and O.	$S_2O_3^{2-}(aq) + Cl_2(g) \rightarrow 2\ SO_4^{2-}(aq) + 2\ Cl^-(aq)$ Coefficients must be added to balance S and Cl.
2. Assign oxidation numbers to all elements in the equation.	$S_2O_3^{2-}(aq) + Cl_2(g) \rightarrow 2\ SO_4^{2-}(aq) + 2\ Cl^-(aq)$ +2 −2 0 +6 −2 −1
3. Identify the elements that undergo oxidation and reduction.	The oxidation state of S changes from +2 to +6, so S loses four electrons and is oxidized. The oxidation state of Cl changes from 0 to −1, so Cl gains one electron and is reduced. The oxidation state of O does not change.
4. Determine the coefficients needed to balance the electron transfer, and place these coefficients in the equation.	The least common multiple of 4 and 1 is 4. Therefore, four Cl must be reduced for every S that is oxidized to balance the electron transfer. Note that Cl appears as the diatomic chlorine molecule in the reactants and that the sodium thiosulfate reactant contains two S. Placing a 4 in front of the chlorine gives 8 Cl and 2 S, which is the needed 4:1 ratio of Cl to S. $S_2O_3^{2-}(aq) + 4\ Cl_2(g) \rightarrow 2\ SO_4^{2-}(aq) + 8\ Cl^-(aq)$
5. Balance any missing O atoms by adding water molecules.	There are three O atoms on the reactant side and eight on the product side. Add five water molecules to the reactant side. $S_2O_3^{2-}(aq) + 4\ Cl_2(g) + 5\ H_2O(l) \rightarrow 2\ SO_4^{2-}(aq) + 8\ Cl^-(aq)$
6. Balance any missing H atoms by adding H^+ ions.	There are 10 H atoms on the reactant side and none on the product side. Add 10 hydrogen ions to the product side. $S_2O_3^{2-}(aq) + 4\ Cl_2(g) + 5\ H_2O(l) \rightarrow 2\ SO_4^{2-}(aq) + 8\ Cl^-(aq) + 10\ H^+(aq)$
7. Verify that all atoms and charges are balanced.	All atoms are balanced: 2 S, 8 Cl, 10 H, and 8 O on each side. Total charge of reactants is $1(-2) = -2$. Total charge of products is $2(-2) + 8(-1) + 10(+1) = -2$. Charge is balanced.

7. *Verify that all atoms and charges are balanced.*
   All atoms are balanced: 2 Cr, 3 Sn, 7 O, and 2 H on each side.
   Total charge of reactants is $1(-2) + 3(+2) + 2(+1) = +6$.
   Total charge of products is $2(+3) = +6$. Charge is balanced.

PRACTICE PROBLEM 19.3

Complete and balance the equation for the following redox reaction in acidic solution:

$$MnO_4^-(aq) + Cl^-(aq) \rightarrow Mn^{2+}(aq) + ClO^-(aq)$$

Hint: Use the seven-step method outlined in Table 19.1.

BALANCING REDOX REACTIONS IN BASIC SOLUTION

The procedure for balancing in basic solution (Figure 19.1) uses the first six steps for balancing in acidic solution and then continues with the following three steps:

7. Neutralize the H^+ ions by adding the same number of OH^- ions to each side of the equation.
8. Combine any H^+ and OH^- ions on the same side to form water molecules, and then remove any water molecules appearing on both sides of the equation.
9. Finish by verifying that all atoms and charges are balanced.

Steve Lemon, Macmillan Learning

FIGURE 19.1 Video Tutorial: Balancing Redox Reactions
NOTE: You need to be online to access this video.
This video shows how to balance a redox reaction in basic solution.

Example 19.4

Balance the reaction of hydrogen peroxide and chlorine dioxide, which occurs in basic solution.

$$H_2O_2(aq) + ClO_2(aq) \rightarrow ClO_2^-(aq) + O_2(g)$$

Solution

1. *Add coefficients to balance any elements other than H and O.* No coefficients are needed.

$$H_2O_2(aq) + ClO_2(aq) \rightarrow ClO_2^-(aq) + O_2(g)$$

2. *Assign oxidation numbers to all elements in the equation.* The oxidation state of O in peroxide compounds is -1.

$$H_2O_2(aq) + ClO_2(aq) \rightarrow ClO_2^-(aq) + O_2(g)$$

$+1 \; -1 \qquad +4 \; -2 \qquad +3 \; -2 \qquad 0$

3. *Identify the elements that undergo oxidation and reduction.* O is oxidized from -1 (in H_2O_2) to 0 (in O_2), a loss of one electron, while Cl is reduced from $+4$ to $+3$, a gain of one electron.
4. *Determine the coefficients needed to balance the electron transfer, and place these coefficients in the equation.* Therefore, one O must be oxidized for each Cl that is reduced for a total of one electron transferred. Because two O atoms are oxidized, two Cl atoms must be reduced.

$$H_2O_2(aq) + 2\,ClO_2(aq) \rightarrow 2\,ClO_2^-(aq) + O_2(g)$$

5. *Balance any missing O atoms by adding water molecules.* There are six O atoms on each side of the equation, so no additional water molecules are needed.

$$H_2O_2(aq) + 2\,ClO_2(aq) \rightarrow 2\,ClO_2^-(aq) + O_2(g)$$

6. *Balance any missing H atoms by adding H^+ ions.* Add two hydrogen ions to the product side.

$$H_2O_2(aq) + 2\,ClO_2(aq) \rightarrow 2\,ClO_2^-(aq) + O_2(g) + 2\,H^+(aq)$$

7. *Neutralize the H^+ ions by adding the same number of OH^- ions to each side of the equation.* Add two OH^- to each side.

$$H_2O_2(aq) + 2\,ClO_2(aq) + 2\,OH^-(aq) \rightarrow 2\,ClO_2^-(aq) + O_2(g) + 2\,H^+(aq) + 2\,OH^-(aq)$$

8. *Combine any H^+ and OH^- ions on the same side to form water molecules, and then remove any water molecules appearing on both sides of the equation.* Form two water molecules on the product side.

$$H_2O_2(aq) + 2\,ClO_2(aq) + 2\,OH^-(aq) \rightarrow 2\,ClO_2^-(aq) + O_2(g) + 2\,H_2O(l)$$

9. *Verify that all atoms and charges are balanced.*
   All atoms are balanced: 4 H, 8 O, and 2 Cl on each side.
   The total charge of reactants is $2(-1) = -2$.
   The total charge of products is $2(-1) = -2$.
   Therefore, the charge is balanced.

PRACTICE PROBLEM 19.4

Balance the following redox reaction in basic solution:

$$NO_2^-(aq) + Al(s) \rightarrow NH_3(g) + AlO_2^-(aq)$$

Hint: Use the nine-step method outlined in Table 19.1 and Example 19.4.

SECTION REVIEW

- A systematic approach is used to balance complex redox reactions in acidic solution:
  - Add coefficients to balance any elements other than H and O.
  - Assign oxidation numbers to all elements in the equation.
  - Identify the elements that undergo oxidation and reduction.
  - Determine the total number of electrons transferred during the reaction and the coefficients needed to balance the electron transfer, and place these coefficients in the equation.
  - Balance any missing O atoms by adding water molecules.
  - Balance any missing H atoms by adding H^+ ions.
  - Verify that all atoms and charges are balanced.
- A separate, but related, systematic approach is used to balance redox reactions in basic solution. Use the first six steps for acidic conditions, then finish with the following:
  - Neutralize any added H^+ ions by adding the same number of OH^- ions to *both* sides of the equation.
  - Combine any H^+ and OH^- ions on the same side to form water molecules, and remove any water molecules appearing on both sides of the equation.
  - Verify that all atoms and charges are balanced.

19.3 Redox Titrations

GOAL

- Determine the concentration of solutions based on redox titration data.

Background Review

Chapter 5 Stoichiometry: Section 5.6—Molarities of Ions; Section 5.9—Titration

Titration is a laboratory technique for measuring the concentration of a base (or acid) by the extent to which it reacts with an acid (or base) of known concentration (Section 5.9). Redox titrations use the same procedure of reacting a solution of known concentration with a solution of unknown concentration, except the reaction is a redox reaction instead of an acid–base reaction.

The permanganate ion, MnO_4^-, which is deep purple in acidic solution, is a powerful oxidizing agent that turns colorless once its Mn^{7+} is reduced to Mn^{2+}.

$$\underset{\text{purple}}{MnO_4^-(aq)} \rightarrow \underset{\text{colorless}}{Mn^{2+}(aq)}$$

This color change is used in redox titrations, which involve adding a known volume of permanganate solution of known concentration to a sample containing an unknown quantity of reactant.

The titration of Fe^{2+} with potassium permanganate, $KMnO_4$, (Figure 19.2) begins with a dark purple solution of permanganate ion in a buret and a colorless Fe^{2+} solution in a flask. As the purple solution is slowly added to the flask, a reaction occurs, and the purple color first fades and then disappears. Once all the Fe^{2+} has been oxidized, any added MnO_4^- causes the solution to turn purple. This color change marks the end point of the titration, the point at which all the Fe^{2+} has been oxidized to Fe^{3+}. At this point, the concentration of the permanganate solution and the known ratios of reactants from the balanced chemical equation can be used to determine the amount of reactant in the unknown solution.

FIGURE 19.2 Redox Titration

NOTE: You need to be online to access this video.

In this video, Fe^{2+} is oxidized to Fe^{3+} while the Mn^{7+} in MnO_4^- is reduced to Mn^{2+}. MnO_4^- is a powerful oxidizing agent commonly used in chemistry labs. It is identified by its deep purple color, which makes it easy to visualize the end point of a redox titration.

FIGURE 19.3 Diphenylamine, a Redox Indicator

NOTE: You need to be online to access this video.

Indicators are used to identify the end points of redox titrations. Diphenylamine, a commonly used redox indicator, is green in the reduced state and a deep purple when oxidized.

Other redox titrations require indicators, analogous to the pH indicators used in acid–base titrations (Section 17.3). In the reaction of dichromate ion, $Cr_2O_7^{2-}$, with aqueous methanol, $CH_4O(aq)$, to form Cr^{3+}, for example, a small amount of diphenylamine, $C_{12}H_{11}N$, is added to the methanol solution at the beginning of the titration. The formation of a deep purple color (Figure 19.3) indicates that the end point has been reached.

Example 19.5

A 25.00 mL solution of Fe^{2+} required 13.65 mL of 0.103 M $KMnO_4$ to reach the end point.

$$Fe^{2+}(aq) + MnO_4^-(aq) \rightarrow Fe^{3+}(aq) + Mn^{2+}(aq) \quad \text{(unbalanced)}$$

Balance the equation in acidic solution, and calculate the concentration of the Fe^{2+} solution.

Solution

Start by balancing the redox equation in acidic solution.

1. *Add coefficients to balance any elements other than H and O.* No coefficients are needed.

$$Fe^{2+}(aq) + MnO_4^-(aq) \rightarrow Fe^{3+}(aq) + Mn^{2+}(aq)$$

2. *Assign oxidation numbers to all elements in the equation.*

$$\underset{+2}{Fe^{2+}}(aq) + \underset{+7\ -2}{MnO_4^-}(aq) \rightarrow \underset{+3}{Fe^{3+}}(aq) + \underset{+2}{Mn^{2+}}(aq)$$

3. *Identify the elements that undergo oxidation and reduction.* Fe is oxidized from +2 to +3, a loss of one electron, while Mn is reduced from +7 to +2, a gain of five electrons.
4. *Determine the coefficients needed to balance the electron transfer, and place these coefficients in the equation.* The least common multiple of 5 and 1 is 5, so a total of five electrons are transferred during this reaction. Therefore, five Fe must be oxidized for each Mn that is reduced for a total of five electrons transferred.

$$5\,Fe^{2+}(aq) + MnO_4^-(aq) \rightarrow 5\,Fe^{3+}(aq) + Mn^{2+}(aq)$$

5. *Balance any missing O atoms by adding water molecules.* Four water molecules must be added to the product side to balance the four O atoms present on the reactant side.

$$5\,Fe^{2+}(aq) + MnO_4^-(aq) \rightarrow 5\,Fe^{3+}(aq) + Mn^{2+}(aq) + 4\,H_2O(l)$$

6. *Balance any missing H atoms by adding H^+ ions.* Eight hydrogen ions must be added to the reactant side.

$$5\,Fe^{2+}(aq) + MnO_4^-(aq) + 8\,H^+ \rightarrow 5\,Fe^{3+}(aq) + Mn^{2+}(aq) + 4\,H_2O(l)$$

7. *Verify that all atoms and charges are balanced.*

All atoms are balanced: 5 Fe, 1 Mn, 4 O, and 8 H on each side.

The total charge of reactants is $5(+2) + 1(-1) + 8(+1) = +17$.

The total charge of products is $5(+3) + 1(+2) = +17$.

Charge is balanced.

Now apply stoichiometric principles. Use molarity and volume to determine the number of moles of $KMnO_4$ present in the volume used in the titration. Then use the mole ratio from the balanced equation to find the corresponding moles of Fe^{2+}.

$$13.65\text{ mL } KMnO_4\left(\frac{1\text{ L}}{1000\text{ mL}}\right)\left(\frac{0.103\text{ mol } KMnO_4}{1\text{ L}}\right)\left(\frac{5\text{ mol } Fe^{2+}}{1\text{ mol } KMnO_4}\right) = 0.00703\text{ mol } Fe^{2+}$$

Finally, use the moles and volume of Fe^{2+} solution to calculate molarity.

$$\frac{0.00703\text{ mol } Fe^{2+}}{25.00\text{ mL } Fe^{2+} \times \dfrac{1\text{ L}}{1000\text{ mL}}} = 0.281\text{ M } Fe^{2+}$$

PRACTICE PROBLEM 19.5

A 15.00 mL solution of methanol, CH_4O, required 7.35 mL of 0.0887 M sodium dichromate, $Na_2Cr_2O_7$, to reach the end point using diphenylamine as the indicator.

$$CH_4O(aq) + Cr_2O_7^{2-}(aq) \rightarrow CH_2O_2(aq) + 2\,Cr^{3+}(aq) \qquad \text{(unbalanced)}$$

Balance the equation in acidic solution, and calculate the concentration of methanol.

Hint: Use the volume and concentration of $Na_2Cr_2O_7$ to calculate the number of moles of $Cr_2O_7^{2-}$. Then use stoichiometry of the *balanced* equation to find the corresponding number of moles of CH_4O. Finally, use the volume and number of moles of CH_4O to determine the concentration of methanol.

SECTION REVIEW

- A redox titration is similar to an acid–base titration but with a redox reaction instead of an acid–base reaction.
- Some redox titrations require an indicator to identify the end point, whereas others take advantage of the natural color change associated with many redox reactions.

19.4 Voltaic Cells

GOAL

- Describe the components of voltaic cells using appropriate terminology and notation.

Background Review

Chapter 4 Chemical Reactions and Aqueous Solutions: Section 4.7—Predicting the Products of Redox Reactions

There are two main types of **electrochemical cells**: **voltaic cells**, which use spontaneous chemical reactions to create a flow of electrons (electricity), and **electrolytic cells**, which use electricity to cause a nonspontaneous chemical reaction to occur. Both involve redox reactions separated into half-reactions.

VOLTAIC CELLS

The activity series you saw in Figure 4.23 showed that placing a bar of zinc into a solution of Cu^{2+} ions causes a displacement reaction to occur. This reaction is a combination of a reduction and an oxidation in which two electrons are transferred from each atom of solid zinc to each Cu^{2+} (Figure 4.22).

$$\text{Reduction: } Cu^{2+}(aq) + 2\,e^- \rightarrow Cu(s)$$

$$\text{Oxidation: } Zn(s) \rightarrow Zn^{2+}(aq) + 2\,e^-$$

$$\text{Net ionic equation: } Cu^{2+}(aq) \cancel{+ 2e^-} + Zn(s) \rightarrow Zn^{2+}(aq) \cancel{+ 2e^-} + Cu(s)$$

You can cause this reaction to occur with the zinc and copper bars in separate containers, provided that the metal bars are connected by a wire for electron flow. This is the arrangement used in the Daniell cell (Figure 19.4), which was invented by John Frederic Daniell (1790–1845).

In the Daniell cell (or any electrochemical cell), the metal bars where the redox reactions take place are called **electrodes**. In Figure 19.4, electrons move from the Zn electrode over the wire to the Cu electrode. Because the Zn electrode is the source of the electrons, it is the **negative electrode**, which is called the **anode**. The electrons move toward the **positive electrode**, the Cu electrode, which is called the **cathode**.

The terms *anode* and *cathode* follow a similar naming convention as anions and cations—that is, the negative charge is associated with the prefix *an-*, whereas the positive charge is associated with the prefix *cat-*. Reduction always occurs at the cathode in an electrochemical cell, and oxidation always occurs at the anode. Electrodes can be involved in the chemical reaction, as in the Daniell cell, or they can be inert materials that conduct electricity, such as a platinum wire or a carbon rod.

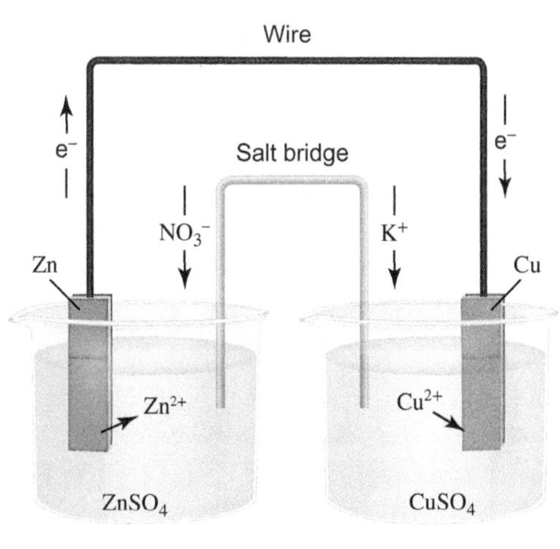

FIGURE 19.4 The Daniell Cell

The Daniell cell consists of a wire that connects the anode (the Zn electrode, where oxidation occurs) to the cathode (the Cu electrode, where reduction occurs), and a salt bridge to complete the circuit.

If the Daniell cell consisted *only* of an anode, a cathode, and a wire connecting them, Zn would be oxidized to Zn^{2+} (making the anode more positive), and Cu^{2+} would be reduced to Cu (making the cathode more negative). Eventually, though, the electrons would stop flowing because they will not flow from a positive environment (the zinc solution) to a negative one (the copper solution). This charge build-up is eliminated by adding a **salt bridge** containing an electrolyte solution such as $KNO_3(aq)$. When the salt bridge is in place, Zn^{2+} and K^+ from the salt bridge flow toward the copper side, and SO_4^{2-} and NO_3^- from the salt bridge flow toward the zinc side, completing an **electrical circuit**.

Electricity is produced by the movement of electrons through the wire from the zinc atoms to the copper ions. This system is an example of a *voltaic cell*, also known as a *galvanic cell*. A voltaic cell is a spontaneous oxidation–reduction reaction set up in separate compartments, or **half-cells**, to produce electricity, as the reactants transfer electrons to form products. The driving force for the flow of electrons is called the electrical **potential,** ***E***, or electromotive force, emf. The energy associated with the electrical potential can be used to do work, such as causing a lightbulb to glow. A voltmeter connected between the two half-cells can measure this potential in **volts, V**.

The Daniell cell and all voltaic cells have the following important features:

1. Both oxidation and reduction are taking place at the same time, though not in the same place.
2. The same overall reaction is taking place as if the two reactants (the zinc bar and Cu^{2+} solution in this example) were in direct contact.
3. The reaction is spontaneous; electrons move from the anode to the cathode spontaneously.
4. The chemical energy of the reaction is transformed into electrical energy, which can then be further transformed into light energy or mechanical energy.

In voltaic cells, spontaneous oxidation–reduction reactions are used to produce electricity.

A convenient way to show what is happening in a voltaic cell, such as the Daniell cell, is to use standard cell notation, which shows the composition of the two half-cells and the direction of electron movement, from left (anode) to right (cathode). Single vertical lines indicate a phase separation such as a solid in contact with a solution, while double vertical lines indicate the salt bridge.

$$\text{Zn(s)}\,|\,\text{Zn}^{2+}(1\ \text{M})\,\|\,\text{Cu}^{2+}(1\ \text{M})\,|\,\text{Cu(s)}$$

The notation shown here indicates that zinc metal releases electrons to form zinc ions, which under standard conditions are present in a 1 molar solution. These electrons flow to copper ions, also present in a 1 molar solution, and reduce those ions to form copper metal.

Example 19.6

Write the cell notation based on the description of the following voltaic cells:

a. Silver ions, Ag^+, are reduced to silver metal, and copper metal is oxidized to Cu^{2+} under standard conditions.
b. Iron(III) ions are reduced to iron(II) ions in the presence of a platinum electrode, and tin is oxidized to tin(II) under standard conditions.

Solution

The source of the electrons, which is the substance being oxidized at the anode, goes on the left; the substance being reduced at the cathode goes on the right. Use single vertical lines to indicate a phase separation and double vertical lines to indicate the salt bridge.

a. Copper metal releases electrons to form Cu^{2+}. These electrons travel over the wire to Ag^+, forming silver atoms. At the same time, cations and anions are flowing through the salt bridge to complete the electrical circuit. Standard conditions dictate that the ions are present in molar concentrations.

$$\text{Cu(s)}\,|\,\text{Cu}^{2+}(1\ \text{M})\,\|\,\text{Ag}^{+}(1\ \text{M})\,|\,\text{Ag(s)}$$

b. Tin metal releases electrons to form Sn^{2+}. These electrons travel over the wire to the platinum electrode, which is in contact with Fe^{3+} in solution. Fe^{3+} accepts the electrons to form Fe^{2+} in solution. At the same time, cations and anions are flowing through the salt bridge to complete the electrical circuit. Standard conditions dictate that the ions are present in molar concentrations. The two iron ions are in the same phase, so they are separated by a comma and not a vertical line.

$$\text{Sn(s)}\,|\,\text{Sn}^{2+}(1\ \text{M})\,\|\,\text{Pt(s)}\,|\,\text{Fe}^{3+}(1\ \text{M}),\ \text{Fe}^{2+}(1\ \text{M})$$

PRACTICE PROBLEM 19.6

Write the cell notation based on the description of the following voltaic cells:

a. Lead(II) ions are reduced to form lead, and magnesium is oxidized to Mg^{2+} under standard conditions.
b. Cobalt(III) ions are reduced to cobalt(II) ions in the presence of a Pt electrode, and nickel is oxidized to nickel(II) under standard conditions.

Hint: Start with the source of the electrons, which is the substance being oxidized. Single vertical lines are used to indicate different phases, such as a solid in contact with a solution.

Example 19.7

Draw a figure like Figure 19.4 for the cell in Example 19.6a with a KNO_3 salt bridge.

$$\text{Cu(s)}\,|\,\text{Cu}^{2+}(1\ \text{M})\,\|\,\text{Ag}^{+}(1\ \text{M})\,|\,\text{Ag(s)}$$

Use arrows to indicate the direction of spontaneous electron flow, as well as cation and anion flow in the salt bridge. Label the anode and the cathode.

Solution

The cell notation for Example 19.6a indicates that Cu(s) is oxidized at the anode and Ag^+ is reduced at the cathode. Electrons move through the wire from the anode (oxidation = loss of electrons) to the cathode (reduction = gain of electrons).

For the electrical circuit to be complete, you must also include a salt bridge. To maintain electrical neutrality, the positive ions from the salt bridge move toward the side that is gaining electrons (the cathode), and negative ions from the salt bridge move toward the side that is losing electrons (the anode). In other words, cations flow through the salt bridge in the same direction as the electrons through the wire, while anions flow in the opposite direction.

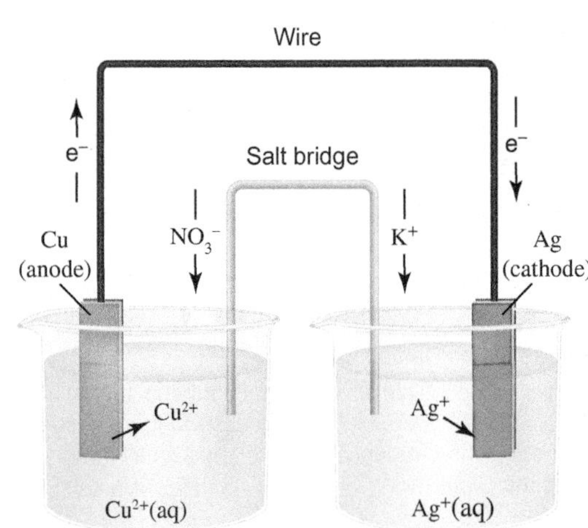

PRACTICE PROBLEM 19.7

Draw a figure like Figure 19.4 for the cell in Example 19.6b with a KNO_3 salt bridge.

$$Sn(s)|Sn^{2+}(1\ M)||Pt(s)|Fe^{3+}(1\ M), Fe^{2+}(1\ M)$$

Use arrows to indicate the direction of spontaneous electron flow, as well as cation and anion flow in the salt bridge. Label the anode and the cathode.

Hint: In cell notation, the anode is written on the left, so you know that tin is the anode and platinum is the cathode. Based on that information, you can determine which metal is losing electrons and which is gaining electrons, in order to identify the direction of electron flow through the wire. From there, you can determine the direction of flow of the anions and cations from the salt bridge to offset the increase or decrease in charge that would otherwise result from the flow of electrons.

SECTION REVIEW

- Reactants that undergo spontaneous redox reactions when in direct contact with each other also react spontaneously when suitably connected electrochemically.
- A complete circuit is necessary for a voltaic cell to operate, requiring a metal wire for the flow of electrons and a salt bridge for the flow of ions.
- A voltaic (or galvanic) cell produces electricity from a spontaneous redox reaction.
- The oxidation half-reaction occurs in the anode half-cell, while the reduction half-reaction occurs in the cathode half-cell.
- Standard cell notation summarizes the flow of electrons in a complete electrochemical circuit.

19.5 Cell Potential

GOALS

- Calculate cell potential using tables of standard reduction potentials.
- Compare the strengths of substances as oxidizing and reducing agents using tables of standard reduction potentials.

Background Review

Chapter 4 Chemical Reactions and Aqueous Solutions: Section 4.7—Predicting the Products of Redox Reactions

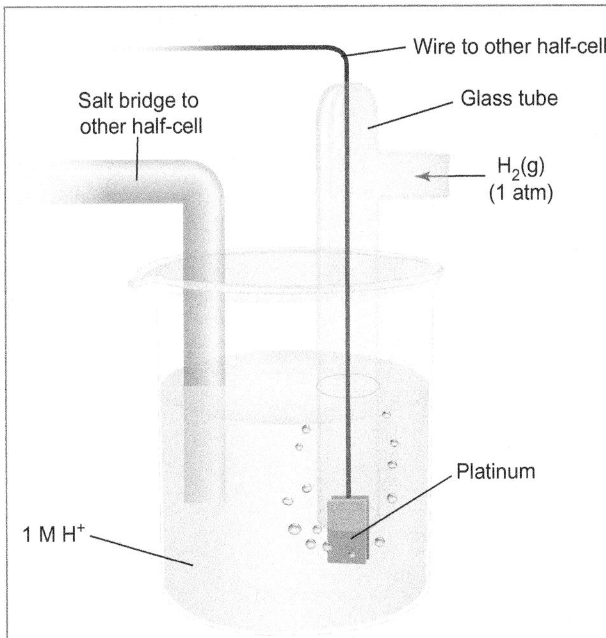

FIGURE 19.5 The Standard Hydrogen Electrode, SHE
Hydrogen gas at 1 atm pressure flows around a platinum wire (needed for electrical contact) immersed in a 1 M H^+ solution. Platinum, an unreactive metal, is frequently used as an inert electrode that provides electrical contact with ions in solution. Electrons from the other half-cell reduce the H^+ to hydrogen gas, provided the other half-cell is composed of materials with higher potential than the SHE.

$$2\,H^+(aq) + 2\,e^- \rightleftharpoons H_2(g) \qquad E^\circ = 0.000\ V$$

If the other half-cell is composed of materials with lower potential than the SHE, the opposite reaction occurs, oxidizing hydrogen gas to H^+.

Section 19.4 explained that voltaic cells produce a flow of electrons by separating a redox reaction into half-reactions connected by a wire and a salt bridge. Section 19.4 also explained that the electromotive force associated with the flow of electrons is measured as the cell potential, or voltage. Each unique combination of half-reactions is associated with its own cell potential.

Chemists chose a specific half-cell to be the standard half-cell and set its voltage at 0.000 V. This standard half-cell, the **standard hydrogen electrode, SHE**, is shown in Figure 19.5. **Standard reduction potentials** of various half-cell reactions are measured with the SHE as the other half-cell, some of which are listed in Table 19.2 and Appendix A.5.

The *standard* in standard reduction potentials tells you that the voltage is measured by a chemical

TABLE 19.2 Selected Standard Reduction Potentials (25°C)

Half-Reaction	E°_{red}(V)
$F_2(g) + 2\,e^- \rightarrow 2\,F^-(aq)$	2.87
$Co^{3+}(aq) + e^- \rightarrow Co^{2+}(aq)$	1.92
$MnO_4^-(aq) + 8\,H^+(aq) + 5\,e^- \rightarrow Mn^{2+}(aq) + 4\,H_2O(l)$	1.51
$Pb^{4+}(aq) + 2\,e^- \rightarrow Pb^{2+}(aq)$	1.46
$Cl_2(g) + 2\,e^- \rightarrow 2\,Cl^-(aq)$	1.36
$Cr_2O_7^{2-}(aq) + 14\,H^+(aq) + 6\,e^- \rightarrow 2\,Cr^{3+}(aq) + 7\,H_2O(l)$	1.23
$Ag^+(aq) + e^- \rightarrow Ag(s)$	0.80*
$Fe^{3+}(aq) + e^- \rightarrow Fe^{2+}(aq)$	0.77
$Cu^+(aq) + e^- \rightarrow Cu(s)$	0.52
$Cu^{2+}(aq) + 2\,e^- \rightarrow Cu(s)$	0.34*
$Cu^{2+}(aq) + e^- \rightarrow Cu^+(aq)$	0.15
$Sn^{4+}(aq) + 2\,e^- \rightarrow Sn^{2+}(aq)$	0.15
$2\,H^+(aq) + 2\,e^- \rightarrow H_2(g)$	0.000
$Pb^{2+}(aq) + 2\,e^- \rightarrow Pb(s)$	−0.13
$Sn^{2+}(aq) + 2\,e^- \rightarrow Sn(s)$	−0.14
$Ni^{2+}(aq) + 2\,e^- \rightarrow Ni(s)$	−0.25
$Cr^{3+}(aq) + e^- \rightarrow Cr^{2+}(aq)$	−0.41
$Fe^{2+}(aq) + 2\,e^- \rightarrow Fe(s)$	−0.44
$Zn^{2+}(aq) + 2\,e^- \rightarrow Zn(s)$	−0.76*
$2\,H_2O(l) + 2\,e^- \rightarrow H_2(g) + 2\,OH^-(aq)$	−0.83
$Al^{3+}(aq) + 3\,e^- \rightarrow Al(s)$	−1.66
$Mg^{2+}(aq) + 2\,e^- \rightarrow Mg(s)$	−2.38*
$Na^+(aq) + e^- \rightarrow Na(s)$	−2.71

*Indicates half-cells available in the simulation presented in Figure 19.6.

reaction under standard conditions (Section 6.8 and Chapter 18):

1. Any solids and liquids are pure substances.
2. Any solutes are 1.000 M.
3. Any gases are at 1.000 atm pressure.

Once E° values are known for various half-cell reactions, any two of them can be combined to calculate the potential of a cell formed by combining those two half-cells.

CALCULATING CELL POTENTIAL

The standard reduction potential or voltage of a voltaic cell, E°_{cell}, is the standard reduction potential of the cathode half-cell, $E^\circ_{cathode}$, *minus* the standard reduction potential of the anode half-cell, E°_{anode}.

$$E^\circ_{cell} = E^\circ_{cathode} - E^\circ_{anode} \qquad (19.1)$$

Any reactant (or set of reactants) on the *left* side of an equation in Table 19.2 will react spontaneously with any product (or set of products) on the *right* side of an equation with a lower potential in the table. When E° for the lower equation is subtracted from E° for the higher equation (Equation 19.1), the difference of the two potentials will be positive. For example, Fe^{3+} reacts with Ni to produce Fe^{2+} and Ni^{2+}, with a standard potential of $0.77\ V - (-0.26\ V) = +1.03\ V$. Positive cell potentials are associated with a spontaneous redox reaction. Negative cell potentials indicate that the reverse direction is spontaneous.

$$Fe^{3+} + e^- \rightarrow Fe^{2+} \qquad E^\circ = 0.77\ V$$
$$Ni^{2+} + 2e^- \rightarrow Ni \qquad E^\circ = -0.26\ V$$

The *reactants* near the top of Table 19.2 are powerful oxidizing agents, and the *products* near the bottom of the table are powerful reducing agents (Section 4.6).

Example 19.8

Calculate the cell potential of the Daniell cell, which consists of a Zn/Zn^{2+} half-cell and a Cu/Cu^{2+} half-cell.

Solution

Find the standard reduction potential values in Table 19.2 for the two half-cells.

$$Zn^{2+} + 2\,e^- \rightarrow Zn \qquad E^\circ = -0.76\ V$$
$$Cu^{2+} + 2\,e^- \rightarrow Cu \qquad E^\circ = +0.34\ V$$

Copper ions are more readily reduced, making the copper half-cell the cathode and the zinc half-cell the anode (see Figure 19.4). Use Equation 19.1 to combine the standard potentials of the two half-cells to arrive at E°_{cell} for the Daniell cell.

$$Zn + Cu^{2+} \rightarrow Zn^{2+} + Cu$$
$$E^\circ_{cell} = E^\circ_{cathode} - E^\circ_{anode}$$
$$E^\circ_{cell} = 0.34\ V - (-0.76\ V) = 1.10\ V$$

This reaction has a positive cell potential, indicating that it is spontaneous in the forward direction.

PRACTICE PROBLEM 19.8

Calculate the cell potential of the Cu/Cu^{2+} and Ag/Ag^+ cell from Example 19.6a.

Hint: Use Table 19.2 to determine which half-cell is the cathode and which is the anode. Then use Equation 19.1 to determine E°_{cell}.

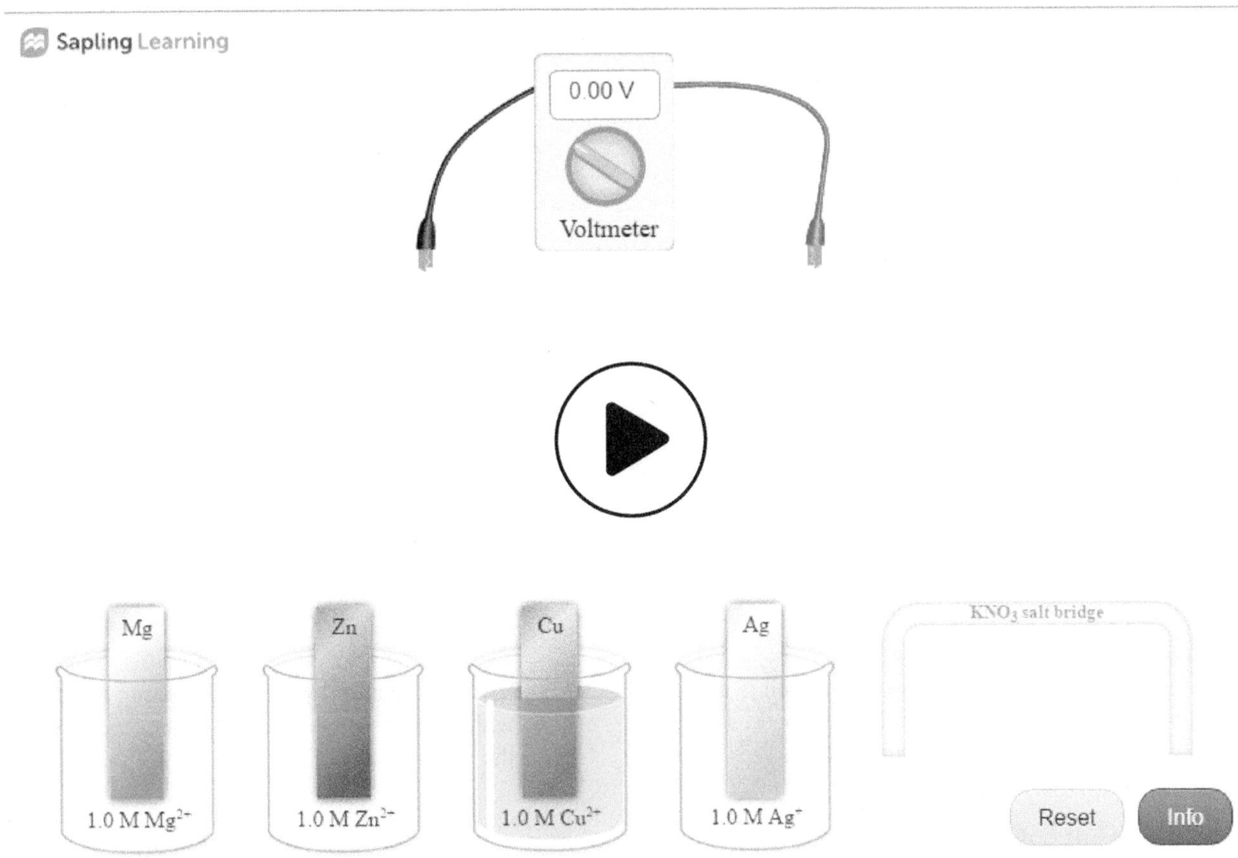

FIGURE 19.6 Voltaic Cell Simulation

NOTE: You need to be online to access this activity.

Select two half-cells and construct a voltaic cell from them. Check the voltage reading to see if the voltage is the same as you calculated using the values in Table 19.2.

Figure 19.6 is a simulation in which four different half-cells can be paired in any combination to create voltaic cells. The cell potential of each voltaic cell is then displayed on the voltmeter readout. The four half-cells available—Ag^+/Ag, Cu^{2+}/Cu, Zn^{2+}/Zn, and Mg^{2+}/Mg—are identified with an asterisk in Table 19.2. Before you begin the simulation, select two of these half-reactions and calculate the cell potential (voltage) of a voltaic cell composed of these two half-cells. Then construct these same cells in the activity, and check your work. Select another pair of half-cells and repeat the process until you are comfortable using the standard reduction potentials to determine cell voltage. A negative potential indicates that the reverse reaction is spontaneous and that you must switch the positions of the half-cells.

Refer to Figure 19.7 for additional examples of how to sketch voltaic cells, write cell notation, and calculate cell potentials.

Steve Lemon, Macmillan Learning

FIGURE 19.7 Video Tutorial: Voltaic Cell Calculations

NOTE: You need to be online to access this video.

This video shows you how to sketch a voltaic cell, how to indicate the flow of electrons from the anode to the cathode (both on the sketch and using cell notation), and how to calculate the cell potential.

Example 19.9

Calculate the cell potential, and write the cell notation for voltaic cells composed of the following sets of half-cells:

a. Sn^{4+}/Sn^{2+} and Cr^{3+}/Cr^{2+}
b. Al/Al^{3+} and Pb/Pb^{2+}

Solution

Locate the standard reduction potentials for the two half-cells in Table 19.2. The one with the greater $E°$ value is the cathode, because the larger $E°$ value means this half-reaction is more easily reduced. The other half-cell is the anode, the location where oxidation occurs and the origin of the flow of electrons.

a. The two half-cells and their potentials are

$$Sn^{4+}(aq) + 2\,e^- \rightarrow Sn^{2+}(aq) \quad E° = 0.15\text{ V}$$
$$Cr^{3+}(aq) + e^- \rightarrow Cr^{2+}(aq) \quad E° = -0.41\text{ V}$$

Based on the $E°$ values, the tin half-cell is the cathode and the chromium half-cell is the anode. The cell voltage can be calculated using Equation 19.1:

$$E°_{cell} = E°_{cathode} - E°_{anode}$$
$$E°_{cell} = 0.15\text{ V} - (-0.41\text{ V}) = 0.56\text{ V}$$

When writing cell notation, place the anode on the left and the cathode on the right. Because neither of these half-reactions includes a solid, both half-cells must include a platinum electrode. The two chromium ions are in the same phase, so they are separated by a comma and not a vertical line. The same is true of the two tin ions.

$$Pt(s)\,|\,Cr^{2+}(1\text{ M}), Cr^{3+}(1\text{ M})\,\|\,Pt(s)\,|\,Sn^{4+}(1\text{ M}), Sn^{2+}(1\text{ M})$$

b. The two half-cells and their potentials are

$$Al^{3+}(aq) + 3\,e^- \rightarrow Al(s) \quad E° = -1.66\text{ V}$$
$$Pb^{2+}(aq) + 2\,e^- \rightarrow Pb(s) \quad E° = -0.13\text{ V}$$

The Pb^{2+} ion is more easily reduced, so lead is the cathode and aluminum is the anode. The resulting cell voltage is

$$E°_{cell} = E°_{cathode} - E°_{anode}$$
$$E°_{cell} = -0.13\text{ V} - (-1.66\text{ V}) = 1.53\text{ V}$$

For the cell notation, the anode goes on the left and the cathode on the right. No Pt electrodes are needed because both half-reactions include a solid.

$$Al(s)\,|\,Al^{3+}(1\text{ M})\,\|\,Pb^{2+}(1\text{ M})\,|\,Pb(s)$$

PRACTICE PROBLEM 19.9

Calculate the cell potential, and write the cell notation for voltaic cells composed of the following sets of half-cells:

a. Sn/Sn^{2+} and Fe^{3+}/Fe^{2+}
b. Co^{2+}/Co^{3+} and Mg/Mg^{2+}

Hint: The half-cell with the greater standard reduction potential (Table 19.2) is the cathode.

Example 19.10

Write balanced net ionic equations for the cell reactions from Example 19.9.

Solution

a. The two half-cells are shown here along with the cell notation from Example 19.9. The half-cells show the number of electrons involved in each half-cell reaction, while the notation indicates which direction the half-cell reactions occur in the voltaic cell.

$$Sn^{4+}(aq) + 2\,e^- \rightarrow Sn^{2+}(aq)$$
$$Cr^{3+}(aq) + e^- \rightarrow Cr^{2+}(aq)$$
$$Pt(s)\,|\,Cr^{2+}(1\text{ M}), Cr^{3+}(1\text{ M})\,\|\,Pt(s)\,|\,Sn^{4+}(1\text{ M}), Sn^{2+}(1\text{ M})$$

For the electron transfer to be balanced, two Cr^{2+} ions must be oxidized for every Sn^{4+} ion that is reduced, for a total of 2 moles of electrons transferred.

$$Sn^{4+}(aq) + 2\,e^- \rightarrow Sn^{2+}(aq) \quad \text{and}$$
$$2\,Cr^{2+}(aq) \rightarrow 2\,Cr^{3+}(aq) + 2\,e^-$$
$$2\,Cr^{2+}(aq) + Sn^{4+}(aq) \rightarrow 2\,Cr^{3+}(aq) + Sn^{2+}(aq)$$

b. The two half-cells for the cell are shown here along with the cell notation from Example 19.9.

$$Al^{3+}(aq) + 3\,e^- \rightarrow Al(s)$$
$$Pb^{2+}(aq) + 2\,e^- \rightarrow Pb(s)$$
$$Al(s)\,|\,Al^{3+}(1\text{ M})\,\|\,Pb^{2+}(1\text{ M})\,|\,Pb(s)$$

For the electron transfer to be balanced, two Al atoms must be oxidized for every three Pb^{2+} ions that are reduced, making a total of 6 moles of electrons transferred.

$$2\,Al^{3+}(aq) + 6\,e^- \rightarrow 2\,Al(s) \quad \text{and}$$
$$3\,Pb(s) \rightarrow 3\,Pb^{2+}(aq) + 6\,e^-$$
$$2\,Al(s) + 3\,Pb^{2+}(aq) \rightarrow 2\,Al^{3+}(aq) + 3\,Pb(s)$$

PRACTICE PROBLEM 19.10

Write balanced net ionic equations for the cell reactions from Practice Problem 19.9.

Hint: Use the half-cell reactions and cell notation from Practice Problem 19.9 to determine the reactants, products, and coefficients in the cell reaction.

SECTION REVIEW

- Tables of standard reduction potentials can be used to determine the tendencies of redox reactions to proceed and to calculate the cell potential: $E^\circ_{\text{cell}} = E^\circ_{\text{cathode}} - E^\circ_{\text{anode}}$.
- A positive cell potential indicates a spontaneous reaction, whereas a negative cell potential indicates a nonspontaneous reaction.

19.6 Free Energy and Cell Potential

GOALS

- Describe the relationships between standard free energy, standard cell potential, and the equilibrium constant.
- Perform calculations involving standard free energy, standard cell potential, and the equilibrium constant.

Background Review

Chapter 18 Chemical Thermodynamics:
Section 18.4—Gibbs Free Energy; Section 18.6—Gibbs Free Energy and Equilibrium

Positive cell potentials ($E > 0$) and negative free energies ($\Delta G < 0$) (Section 18.4) both indicate that a reaction proceeds spontaneously in the forward direction. These two quantities are related according to Equation 19.2,

$$\Delta G = -nFE \tag{19.2}$$

where n is the number of moles of electrons transferred, and F is the Faraday constant. The **Faraday constant, F,** is the charge, in **coulombs, C,** of a mole of electrons; $F = 96{,}485\ \text{C/mol}$. The relationship between free energy and potential holds true when they are expressed using standard values, too.

$$\Delta G^\circ = -nFE^\circ$$

The units of the quantity nFE are coulomb-volts, $\text{C}\cdot\text{V}$, which are equivalent to joules.

$$1\ \text{J} = 1\ \text{C}\cdot\text{V}$$

Example 19.11

Calculate the standard free energy change for the Daniell cell in Example 19.8.

Solution

Refer to the work done in Example 19.8. Combine the half-cell reactions to yield a balanced net ionic equation for the cell reaction to determine the number of moles of electrons transferred in a balanced equation for the value of n.

$$Zn + Cu^{2+} \rightarrow Zn^{2+} + Cu$$

Zinc atoms lose two electrons and copper ions gain two electrons in the balanced net ionic equation, so $n = 2$. The cell potential is 1.10 V. Use these values in Equation 19.2.

$$\Delta G^\circ = -nFE^\circ$$

$$\Delta G^\circ = -(2\ \text{mol e}^-)\left(\frac{96{,}485\ \text{C}}{1\ \text{mol e}^-}\right)(1.10\ \text{V})$$

$$\Delta G^\circ = -212{,}000\ \text{C}\cdot\text{V} = -212{,}000\ \text{J} = -212\ \text{kJ}$$

The large, negative value of ΔG° indicates a spontaneous reaction, as does the positive value of the potential.

PRACTICE PROBLEM 19.11

Calculate the standard free energy change of the Cu/Cu^{2+} and Ag/Ag^+ cell from Practice Problem 19.8.

Hint: Refer to the work done in Practice Problem 19.8. Combine the half-cell reactions to yield a balanced net ionic equation for the cell reaction to determine n, the number of moles of electrons transferred in the balanced equation. Use Equation 19.2 to calculate ΔG°.

Standard free energy changes are also related to the equilibrium constant via Equation 18.11.

$$\Delta G^\circ = -RT\ln K$$

Combining this with Equation 19.2 and rearranging a bit yields a relationship between standard cell potential and the equilibrium constant.

$$E^\circ = \frac{RT}{nF}\ln K \tag{19.3}$$

Example 19.12

Calculate the value of the equilibrium constant using the standard potential of the Daniell cell in Example 19.8.

Solution

Example 19.8 provides the standard potential ($E° = 1.10$ V) and Example 19.10 provides the number of electrons transferred in the reaction ($n = 2$). Rearrange Equation 19.3 to solve for K, and substitute in the values of $E°$, F, R, and n, remembering that $T = 298$ K under standard conditions.

$$E° = \frac{RT}{nF} \ln K$$

$$\ln K = \frac{nFE°}{RT}$$

$$K = e^{\frac{nFE°}{RT}}$$

You might find it easier to solve for the value of the exponent separately.

$$\frac{nFE°}{RT} = \frac{2 \text{ mol e}^-\left(\frac{96{,}485 \text{ C}}{1 \text{ mol e}^-}\right)(1.10 \text{ V})}{8.3145\frac{\text{J}}{\text{K}\cdot\text{mol}}(298 \text{ K})} = 85.7$$

$$K = e^{85.7}$$

$$K = 2 \times 10^{37}$$

For logarithms, the number of significant figures equals the number of digits after the decimal point (Section 0.5). Once the exponent was correctly rounded to three significant digits, only one digit past the decimal point was left. The result, 2×10^{37}, is a huge value for an equilibrium constant and is consistent with the large, positive cell potential and the large, negative $\Delta G°$ value from Example 19.11.

PRACTICE PROBLEM 19.12

Calculate the value of the equilibrium constant from the standard potential of the Cu/Cu^{2+} and Ag/Ag^+ cell in Practice Problem 19.8.

Hint: Refer to Practice Problem 19.8 and Practice Problem 19.10 to find the standard potential, $E°$, and the number of electrons transferred, n. Then rearrange Equation 19.3 to solve for K. Remember that $T = 298$ K under standard conditions.

Example 19.13

A certain redox process that involves a transfer of 1 mole of electrons has an equilibrium constant of $K = 230$. What standard potential is associated with this process?

Solution

Use the given values for n and K in Equation 19.3. Because $K > 1$, the process is expected to be spontaneous (i.e., $\Delta G < 0$ and $E° > 0$). This is still a relatively small equilibrium constant, though, so $E°$ should be a relatively small positive value.

$$E° = \frac{RT}{nF} \ln K$$

$$E° = \frac{8.3145\frac{\text{J}}{\text{K}\cdot\text{mol}}(298 \text{ K})}{1 \text{ mol e}^-\left(\frac{96{,}485 \text{ C}}{1 \text{ mol e}^-}\right)} \ln 230$$

$$E° = 0.14 \text{ V}$$

The small positive value for the standard cell potential is as predicted for the small positive equilibrium constant value.

PRACTICE PROBLEM 19.13

A certain redox process that involves a transfer of 1 mole of electrons has an equilibrium constant of $K = 3.5 \times 10^6$. What standard potential is associated with this process?

Hint: Use the given values for n and K in Equation 19.3.

Under standard conditions (1 atm, 298 K, and $Q = 1$), spontaneous processes have positive values for $E°$, negative values for $\Delta G°$, and K values greater than 1.

Figure 19.8 summarizes the relationships among the standard cell potential, $E°$, the standard change in free energy, $\Delta G°$, and the equilibrium constant, K.

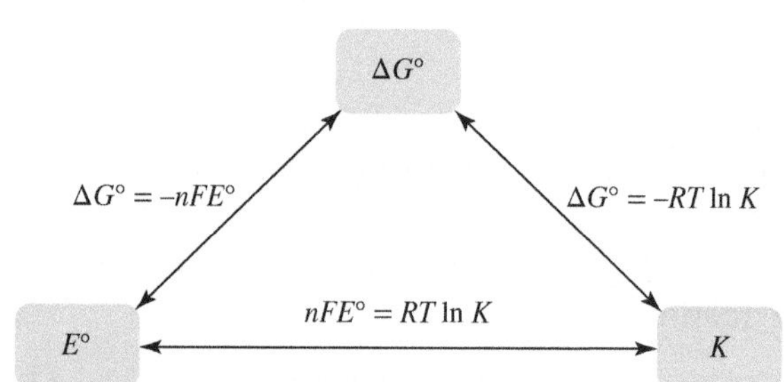

FIGURE 19.8 Equations Relating $E°$, $\Delta G°$, and K
Standard cell potentials, standard changes in free energy, and equilibrium constants can be calculated from one another using the equations shown here.

SECTION REVIEW

- Cell potentials are related to changes in free energy by $\Delta G = -nFE$ or, in the standard state, by $\Delta G^\circ = -nFE^\circ$.
- In these equations, n is the number of moles of electrons transferred in the balanced chemical equation, and F is the Faraday constant, or the charge, in coulombs, of a mole of electrons.
- Spontaneous processes are associated with positive values of E and negative values of ΔG.
- Cell potentials are related to equilibrium constants by $E^\circ = \frac{RT}{nF} \ln K$.

19.7 The Nernst Equation and Concentration Cells

GOAL

- Calculate the effect of the reactant concentration on cell potential using the Nernst equation.

Background Review

Chapter 15 Chemical Equilibrium: Section 15.4—The Reaction Quotient

Chapter 16 Acid–Base Theory: Section 16.4—pH Calculations

In a *standard* cell, all solid and liquid reagents are pure, all solutes are 1.000 M, and all gases are at 1.000 atm (Section 6.8). It is unlikely, however, that these conditions will be met very often in real situations. Changes in free energy under nonstandard conditions can be calculated using Equation 18.10.

$$\Delta G = \Delta G^\circ + RT \ln Q$$

Substituting Equation 19.2, $\Delta G = -nFE$, into this equation yields

$$-nFE = -nFE^\circ + RT \ln Q$$

which can be simplified by factoring to form the **Nernst equation**.

$$E = E^\circ - \frac{RT}{nF} \ln Q \qquad (19.4)$$

The Nernst equation can be used to calculate the cell potential under nonstandard conditions (i.e., solute concentrations are something other than 1.00 M). In a cell containing reactants at concentrations lower than 1.0 M, the reaction should proceed to a lesser degree, in which case $E < E^\circ$. If the concentrations of solutes are higher than 1.0 M, then $E > E^\circ$.

Example 19.14

Calculate the potential of a Zn/Zn^{2+} half-cell in which the pure zinc electrode is immersed in a 0.100 M Zn^{2+} solution.

Solution

The standard reduction potential is achieved when $[Zn^{2+}] = 1.0\,M$, but this half-cell has $[Zn^{2+}] = 0.1$ M. Thus, E for this half-cell should be lower than E°. To determine E, write the equation for the Zn/Zn^{2+} half-cell (Table 19.2) and use it to determine the expression for Q and the value for n.

$$Zn^{2+}(aq) + 2\,e^- \rightarrow Zn(s) \qquad n = 2$$

$$Q = \frac{1}{[Zn^{2+}]} = \frac{1}{0.100\text{ M}} = 10.0\text{ M}^{-1}$$

Use the Nernst equation (Equation 19.4) to determine the voltage under these nonstandard conditions. You can find the standard potential (E°) for this half-cell in Table 19.2.

$$E = E^\circ - \frac{RT}{nF} \ln Q$$

$$E = -0.76\text{ V} - \left[\frac{8.3145 \frac{\text{J}}{\text{K}\cdot\text{mol}}(298\text{ K})}{(2\text{ mol e}^-)\left(\frac{96{,}485\text{ C}}{1\text{ mol e}^-}\right)}\right] \ln 10$$

$$E = -0.79\text{ V}$$

As predicted, $E < E^\circ$.

PRACTICE PROBLEM 19.14

Calculate the potential of an Ag/Ag^+ half-cell in which the silver electrode is immersed in a solution of 0.100 M silver nitrate.

Hint: Start by writing the chemical equation for the half-cell and finding the standard potential in Table 19.2. Use the chemical equation to determine the values of n and Q in the Nernst equation (Equation 19.4).

The Nernst equation can also be used for complete cell reactions. The value of n in this case is the number of moles of electrons transferred in the balanced net ionic equation for the cell.

Example 19.15

Calculate the potential of a zinc/silver cell in which the zinc electrode is immersed in 0.100 M zinc nitrate and the silver electrode is in 0.500 M silver nitrate. Which species is reduced spontaneously?

Solution

First, calculate the standard potential for the cell, as shown in Section 19.2. $E°(Ag^+) > E°(Zn^{2+})$, so zinc metal is oxidized at the anode and Ag^+ is reduced at the cathode.

Start with the half-reactions, and determine the standard cell potential using Table 19.2 and Equation 19.1.

$$Zn^{2+}(aq) + 2\,e^- \rightarrow Zn(s) \quad E° = -0.76\text{ V}$$
$$Ag^+(aq) + e^- \rightarrow Ag(s) \quad E° = +0.80\text{ V}$$
$$E°_{cell} = E°_{cathode} - E°_{anode}$$
$$E° = 0.80\text{ V} - (-0.76\text{ V}) = 1.56\text{ V}$$

Combine the half-cell equations to form a cell equation with a *balanced* transfer of electrons.

$$Zn^{2+}(aq) + 2\,e^- \rightarrow Zn(s) \quad \text{and}$$
$$2\,Ag^+(aq) + 2\,e^- \rightarrow 2\,Ag(s)$$
$$Zn + 2\,Ag^+ \rightarrow Zn^{2+} + 2\,Ag \qquad n = 2$$

Write the expression for Q, and substitute the concentrations into the expression. The concentration of Ag^+ (a reactant) is much higher than the concentration of Zn^{2+} (a product), which favors the forward reaction. You might predict, then, that $E > E°$.

$$Q = \frac{[Zn^{2+}]}{[Ag^+]^2} = \frac{0.100}{(0.500)^2} = 0.400$$

Now, use the Nernst equation (Equation 19.4) to calculate E of the given cell.

$$E = E° - \frac{RT}{nF}\ln Q$$

$$E = 1.56\text{ V} - \left[\frac{\left(8.3145\frac{\text{J}}{\text{K}\cdot\text{mol}}\right)(298\text{ K})}{(2\text{ mol e}^-)\left(\frac{96{,}485\text{ C}}{1\text{ mol e}^-}\right)}\right]\ln(0.400)$$

$$E = 1.57\text{ V}$$

The positive potential means the reaction is spontaneous under these conditions. That is, zinc atoms are oxidized, and silver ions are reduced. The slightly increased cell potential agrees with the prediction made earlier that higher concentrations of reactants versus products result in a reaction that favors products.

PRACTICE PROBLEM 19.15

Calculate the potential of a cell in which a lead electrode is immersed in 0.200 M lead(II) nitrate and a copper electrode is immersed in 0.100 M copper(II) sulfate. Which metal is reduced spontaneously?

Hint: Use Table 19.2 to determine which half-cell is reduced and which is oxidized. Calculate the standard potential, then balance the electron transfer to write the overall cell equation and obtain the values of n and Q. Finally, use the Nernst equation (Equation 19.4) to determine the cell potential.

$E > 0$, so the reaction is spontaneous under these conditions, in which case copper ions are reduced. $E < E°$, moreover, as predicted based on the relative concentrations of the reactants and products.

If $E° > 0$, the cell reaction is spontaneous under standard conditions. When the conditions are *not* standard, then the Nernst equation is used to determine the cell potential (E). If $E > 0$, the reaction proceeds in the forward direction (i.e., is spontaneous) under those nonstandard conditions.

CONCENTRATION CELLS

Because concentration affects potential, it is possible to make a cell in which both half-cells are identical except for the concentration of the ions. The difference in concentrations then drives the redox reactions according to Le Châtelier's principle (Section 15.6). Consider a **concentration cell** composed of two Cu/Cu^{2+} half-cells of varying concentration. The standard half-cell potential for the reduction of Cu^{2+} to Cu is 0.34 V (Table 19.2). Because $E° > 0$, the reduction of Cu^{2+} is spontaneous and the oxidation of Cu is nonspontaneous under standard conditions. If both cells have identical concentrations of Cu^{2+}, the potential is 0 V, because the cell is at equilibrium. When the concentration of Cu^{2+} is different in the two half-cells, however, the cell is no longer at equilibrium and a potential exists. The magnitude of the difference in concentration between the half-cells is directly related to the magnitude of the cell potential. Because the reduction of Cu^{2+} is energetically favored, the half-cell with the higher concentration of Cu^{2+} is the site of reduction (the cathode).

$$Cu^{2+}(aq, x\text{ M}) + Cu(s) \rightarrow Cu^{2+}(aq, y\text{ M}) + Cu(s) \qquad Q = \frac{y}{x}$$

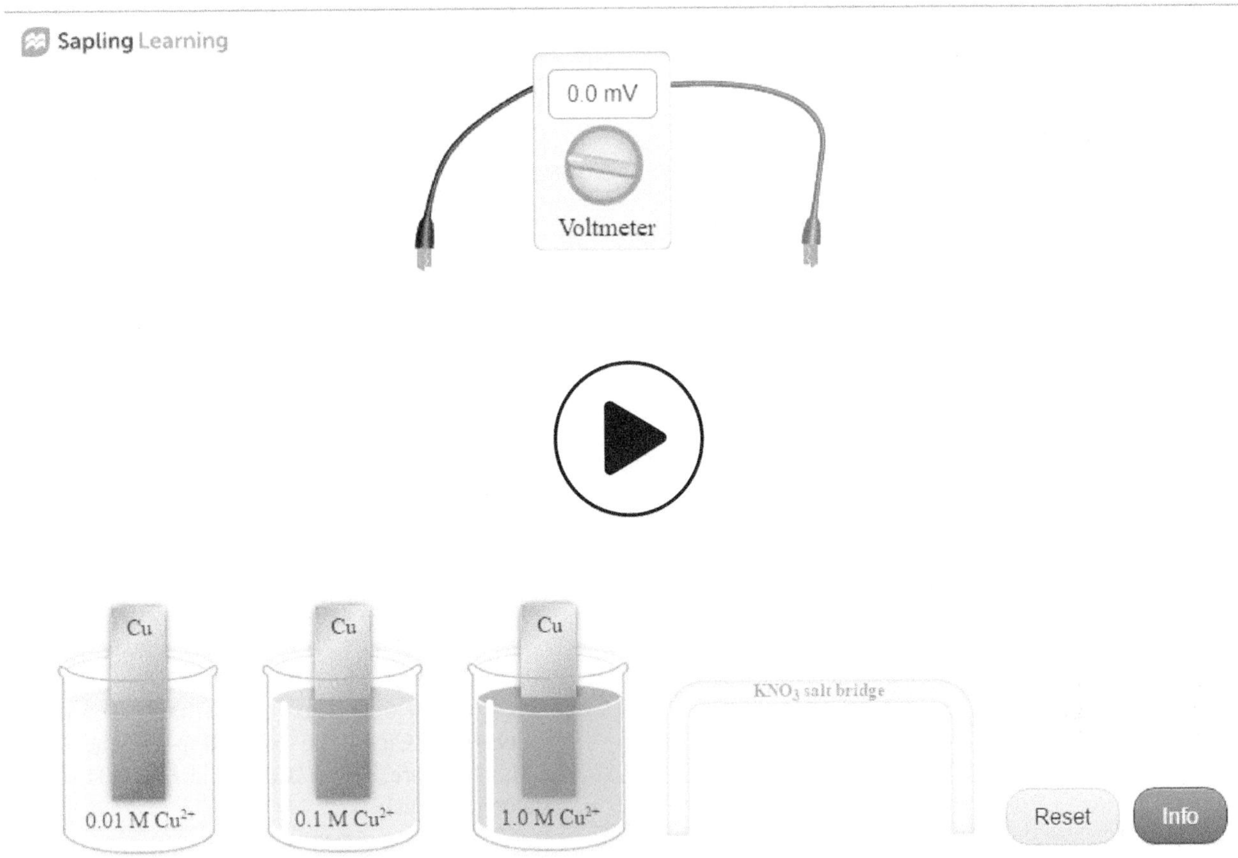

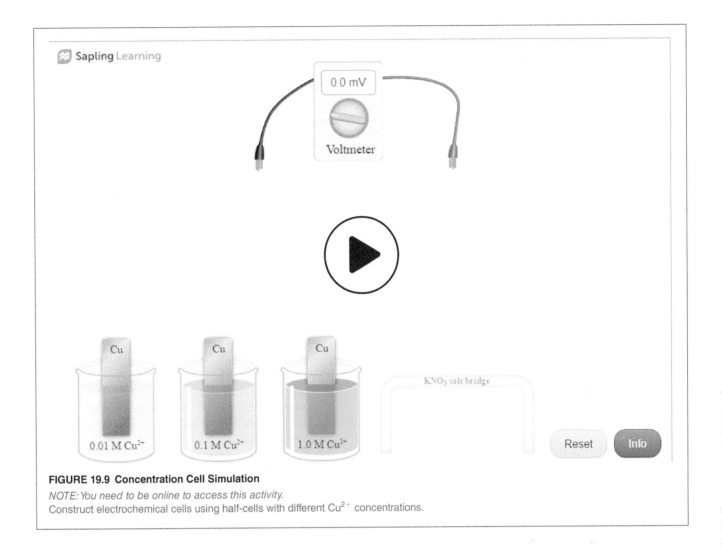

FIGURE 19.9 Concentration Cell Simulation

NOTE: You need to be online to access this activity.

Construct electrochemical cells using half-cells with different Cu^{2+} concentrations.

If x represents the cathode ion concentration and y represents the anode ion concentration, then according to Le Châtelier's principle, the reaction is spontaneous when $x > y$ (which means that Q is always less than 1). In this way, $[Cu^{2+}]$ simultaneously increases in one half-cell (the anode) and decreases in the other half-cell (the cathode), bringing the two half-cell concentrations closer to the same level. Reactions in concentration cells move spontaneously in the direction that brings the cell closer to equilibrium.

You can explore these aspects of concentration cells using the Concentration Cell Simulation (Figure 19.9), which simulates a voltaic cell composed of two Cu^{2+}/Cu half-cells with different concentrations. Notice that the cell potential (voltage) increases as the difference in $[Cu^{2+}]$ in the two half-cell solutions increases. That is, for each factor of 10 difference in concentration between the half-cells, the cell potential is 29.6 mV greater. Typically, the voltages produced by concentration cells are much smaller than the voltages produced by other cells and are more likely to be expressed in millivolts (mV) rather than volts (V).

You can use the Nernst equation to determine the voltage of a concentration cell by placing the different cell concentrations in the Q expression. Here, $E° = 0$ because the two cell reactions are identical and, under standard conditions, would not undergo any transfer of electrons. Also, when the half-cells contain different concentrations of the same ion, the ions in the more concentrated half-cell are reduced (cathode), and metal atoms in the less concentrated half-cell are oxidized (anode).

In a concentration cell, $E° = 0$ and $Q < 1$.

Example 19.16

Calculate the voltage of a concentration cell consisting of two $Cu(s)/Cu^{2+}(aq)$ half-cells. One contains 1.0 M Cu^{2+}, and the other contains 0.20 M Cu^{2+}.

Solution

Because both cells contain the same ions, $E° = 0$. The reaction will occur spontaneously in the direction that decreases the higher concentration and increases the lower concentration.

$$Cu^{2+}(aq, 1.0\ M) + Cu(s) \rightarrow Cu^{2+}(aq, 0.20\ M) + Cu(s)$$

Thus, $Q = 0.20\ M/1.0\ M = 0.20$. Each half-reaction involves Cu/Cu^{2+}, so $n = 2\ mol\ e^-$.

$$E = E° - \frac{RT}{nF}\ln Q$$

$$E = 0 - \frac{8.3145\frac{J}{K \cdot mol}(298\ K)}{(2\ mol\ e^-)\left(\frac{96{,}485\ C}{1\ mol\ e^-}\right)}\ln 0.20$$

$$E = 0.021\ V$$

PRACTICE PROBLEM 19.16

Calculate the voltage of a concentration cell consisting of two Pb/Pb^{2+} half-cells. One contains 1.0 M Pb^{2+}, and the other contains 0.020 M Pb^{2+}.

Hint: Use the Nernst equation to determine the cell potential with $E° = 0$ and $Q < 1$.

EVERYDAY CONNECTION

Ion-selective electrodes are specially designed electrochemical probes that work as concentration cells but are designed to be sensitive to a specific ion. Each probe contains a half-cell of known concentration of the ion in question and an electrode that is placed into an unknown solution that acts as the other half-cell to complete the voltaic cell. Ion-selective electrons are used to make on-site measurements of chloride ions, ammonium ions, and nitrate ions to monitor water quality in streams and wetlands.

I. Noyan Yilmaz/Shutterstock

Example 19.17

A concentration cell consists of two $Cu(s)/Cu^{2+}(aq)$ half-cells. One has a concentration of 1.0 M $Cu^{2+}(aq)$, and the other has an unknown $Cu^{2+}(aq)$ concentration. If the potential of the cell is 0.046 V, what is the unknown $Cu^{2+}(aq)$ concentration?

Solution

Begin with the Nernst equation with $E° = 0$ and $n = 2$, and rearrange it to solve for Q.

$$E = E° - \frac{RT}{nF}\ln Q$$

$$\ln Q = -\frac{nFE}{RT}$$

$$Q = e^{-nFE/RT}$$

Because $E = 0.046$ V (i.e., $E > 0$), the two half-cells must have different Cu^{2+} concentrations. Assuming that the unknown half-cell concentration is less than 1.0 M, Cu^{2+} in this half-cell will be reduced and Cu will be oxidized in the other half-cell. Therefore, $Q = x/1.0\ M$ and $E = 0.046$ V as stated previously.

Solve the exponent separately.

$$-\frac{nFE}{RT} = -\frac{(2\ mol\ e^-)\left(\frac{96{,}485\ C}{mol\ e^-}\right)(0.046\ V)}{\left(8.3145\frac{J}{K \cdot mol}\right)(298\ K)} = -3.58$$

$$Q = e^{-3.58} \text{ and } Q = \frac{x}{1.0\ M}$$

$$x = e^{-3.58} \cdot 1.0\ M$$

$$x = 0.028\ M$$

PRACTICE PROBLEM 19.17

A concentration cell consists of two $Pb(s)/Pb^{2+}(aq)$ half-cells. One has a concentration of 1.0 M $Pb^{2+}(aq)$, and the other has an unknown $Pb^{2+}(aq)$ concentration. If the potential of the cell is 0.065 V, what is the unknown Pb^{2+} concentration?

Hint: Rearrange the Nernst equation to solve for Q; use $E° = 0$ and $n = 2$. Write an expression for Q based on the data given in the problem.

SECTION REVIEW

- The Nernst equation, $E = E° - \frac{RT}{nF}\ln Q$, is used to calculate the electrochemical potential of a voltaic cell under nonstandard conditions.

- Concentration cells are voltaic cells composed of half-cells containing identical components at different concentrations; they exhibit a potential based on those differences in concentration.
- Concentration cells can be used to determine unknown concentrations of specific ions.

19.8 Voltaic Cell Applications: Batteries, Fuel Cells, and Corrosion

GOAL

- Use voltaic cell concepts to describe specific batteries, fuel cells, and corrosion.

BATTERIES

Lead Storage Battery

A car battery is made up of six lead storage cells linked in series. Each lead storage cell (Figure 19.10) consists of a lead electrode coated with a paste of lead(II) sulfate and another electrode that has lead(IV) oxide as the active oxidizing agent. It is also coated with lead(II) sulfate. The electrolyte is concentrated sulfuric acid, in which $PbSO_4$ is insoluble. Both electrodes are placed in the same solution. The half-reactions are

Anode (oxidation): $Pb(s) + SO_4^{2-}(aq) \rightarrow PbSO_4(s) + 2\,e^-$

Cathode (reduction): $PbO_2(s) + SO_4^{2-}(aq) + 4\,H^+(aq) + 2\,e^- \rightarrow PbSO_4(s) + 2\,H_2O(l)$

Overall: $PbO_2(s) + 2\,SO_4^{2-}(aq) + 4\,H^+(aq) + Pb(s) \rightarrow 2\,PbSO_4(s) + 2\,H_2O(l)$

The SO_4^{2-} and H^+ in these equations are due to the concentrated sulfuric acid solution. As the discharge reaction proceeds, sulfuric acid ($2\,SO_4^{2-} + 4\,H^+$) is consumed and water is produced. The solution becomes diluted, and the state of the charge of the cell was at one time determined by measuring the density of the solution (sulfuric acid has a higher density than water). Car batteries now are manufactured as sealed devices to prevent injuries from the sulfuric acid.

In the lead storage cell, both electrodes are in the same solution. This is possible because both the oxidizing agent, PbO_2, and the reducing agent, Pb, as well as the products of the oxidation and reduction processes, $PbSO_4$, are all solids. As solids, these reactants cannot migrate to the opposite electrode and react directly.

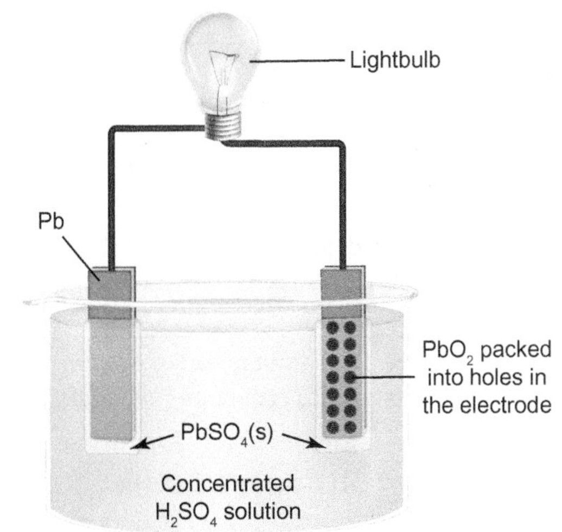

FIGURE 19.10 Lead Storage Cell
Electrons flow from the lead electrode to the lead(IV) oxide electrode.

Example 19.18

The lead storage battery consists of six cells linked in a series and is commonly referred to as a 12 V battery. When linked in this manner, the cell potentials combine to form a battery with a voltage equal to the sum of the component cells.

a. Calculate the potential of a single cell of the lead storage battery.
b. Calculate the total potential of the six cells. Is it really a 12 V battery?

Solution

a. The standard reduction potential for the anode and cathode reactions can be found in the Appendix A.5. Combine that value with the standard reduction potential for the anode reaction to determine the cell potential.

Anode:

$$Pb(s) + SO_4^{2-}(aq) \rightarrow PbSO_4(s) + 2\,e^- \quad E^\circ = -0.3588\text{ V}$$

Cathode:

$$PbO_2(s) + SO_4^{2-}(aq) + 4\,H^+(aq) + 2\,e^- \rightarrow PbSO_4(s) + 2\,H_2O(l) \quad E^\circ = 1.6913\text{ V}$$

$$E^\circ_{cell} = E^\circ_{cathode} - E^\circ_{anode}$$

$$E^\circ_{cell} = 1.6913\text{ V} - (-0.3588\text{ V}) = 2.0501\text{ V}$$

b. For cells linked in a series, the voltages of the individual cells are added together to give the total voltage of the battery.

$$E_{total} = 6 \text{ cells}\left(\frac{2.0501 \text{ V}}{1 \text{ cell}}\right) = 12.301 \text{ V}$$

Based on this result, the 12 volt car battery has a total potential slightly higher than 12 volts.

PRACTICE PROBLEM 19.18

The electrode reactions for a nickel–cadmium cell, as well as their standard reduction potentials, are as follows:

Anode: $Cd(s) + 2\,OH^-(aq) \rightarrow Cd(OH)_2(s) + 2\,e^-$

Cathode: $Ni(OH)_2(s) + 2\,e^- \rightarrow Ni(s) + 2\,OH^-(aq)$

a. Calculate the cell voltage using data found in Appendix A.5.
b. Calculate the voltage for a battery consisting of four nickel–cadmium cells.
c. Determine the overall reaction for the cell.

Hint: Combine the half-cell potentials to yield a positive value for the cell potential for one cell, and then multiply that potential by 4 to determine the total potential of the battery.

The car battery recharges as you drive the car. The car's alternator sends electricity through the lead storage battery in the reverse direction, and this external source of electricity forces the chemical reactions of the lead storage cell to go in the reverse direction, thus regenerating the original reactants. Recharging of a lead storage cell proceeds as follows:

Cathode (reduction): $PbSO_4(s) + 2\,e^- \rightarrow Pb(s) + SO_4^{2-}(aq)$

Anode (oxidation): $PbSO_4(s) + 2\,H_2O(l) \rightarrow PbO_2(s) + SO_4^{2-}(aq) + 4\,H^+(aq) + 2\,e^-$

Overall: $2\,PbSO_4(s) + 2\,H_2O(l) \rightarrow PbO_2(s) + 2\,SO_4^{2-}(aq) + 4\,H^+(aq) + Pb(s)$

When the battery is being recharged, the cathode and anode are switched. The electron flow in an electrochemical cell is always from the anode to the cathode, so if the flow of electrons is reversed by the application of an external source of electricity, the electrode designations are also reversed. Reduction always occurs at the cathode, and oxidation always occurs at the anode.

Not all batteries can be recharged. The Daniell cell, for example, cannot be recharged in this manner. If you were to apply electricity to that cell to try to reverse the chemical reaction, copper(II) ions would migrate to the zinc electrode solution, where they would react directly with the zinc and produce a copper-plated electrode. Once the surface of the zinc electrode was plated with copper, the cell would no longer function.

Dry Cells

Lead storage batteries and the voltaic cells described in Section 19.2 have an aqueous electrolyte solution or salt bridge connecting the half-cells. The cells that are used in electronic appliances, on the other hand, are **dry cells**, which contain mobile ions in a paste or gel. The first commonly used dry cell, which is still in use today, consists of a small zinc case that acts as the anode. Immediately inside the zinc is a layer of coated paper surrounding an acidic paste containing MnO_2 plus NH_4Cl with a carbon rod down the middle to act as the cathode. The half-cell reactions for this dry cell are

Anode: $Zn(s) \rightarrow Zn^{2+}(aq) + 2\,e^-$

Cathode: $2\,MnO_2(s) + 2\,NH_4^+(aq) + 2\,e^- \rightarrow Mn_2O_3(s) + 2\,NH_3(g) + H_2O(l)$

Alkaline cells involve zinc as the anode and MnO_2 as the cathode with a basic electrolyte paste (Figure 19.11). The half-cell reactions under these conditions are

Anode: $Zn(s) + 2\,OH^-(aq) \rightarrow Zn(OH)_2(s) + 2\,e^-$

Cathode: $MnO_2(s) + H_2O(l) + e^- \rightarrow MnO(OH)(s) + OH^-(aq)$

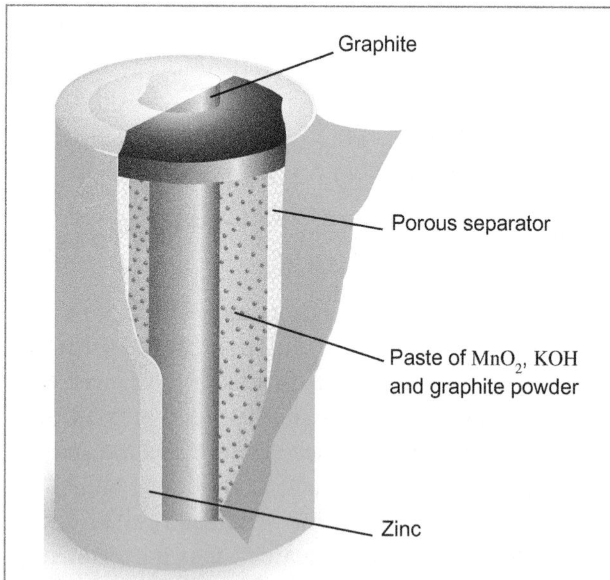

FIGURE 19.11 Alkaline Dry Cell

The alkaline dry cell is composed of a zinc anode and a graphite cathode, with an electrolyte paste containing KOH, MnO_2, and graphite powder.

Neither the simple dry cell nor the alkaline dry cell can be recharged. There are rechargeable dry cells, however, such as the nickel–cadmium (Ni–Cd) cell described in Practice Problem 19.18, lithium ion cells, and nickel–metal hydride cells.

Example 19.19

The simple zinc–carbon dry cell has a potential of 1.5 V.

a. Write the balanced equation for the cell.
b. What is the half-cell potential for the cathode?

Solution

a. The oxidation reaction at the anode releases 2 moles of electrons for each mole of zinc that is oxidized, and the reduction reaction at the cathode involves 2 moles of electrons. The electron flow is balanced.

Anode: $Zn(s) \rightarrow Zn^{2+}(aq) + 2\,e^-$

Cathode: $2\,MnO_2(s) + 2\,NH_4^+(aq) + 2\,e^- \rightarrow Mn_2O_3(s) + 2\,NH_3(g) + H_2O(l)$

Combine the reactants of both half-cells and the products of both half-cells, and eliminate any components that appear as both reactants and products.

$$Zn(s) + 2\,MnO_2(s) + 2\,NH_4^+(aq) + \cancel{2\,e^-} \rightarrow Zn^{2+}(aq) + \cancel{2\,e^-} + Mn_2O_3(s) + 2\,NH_3(g) + H_2O(l)$$

Overall reaction:

$$Zn(s) + 2\,MnO_2(s) + 2\,NH_4^+(aq) \rightarrow Zn^{2+}(aq) + Mn_2O_3(s) + 2\,NH_3(g) + H_2O(l)$$

b. Find the standard reduction potentials for the anode half-cell in Table 19.2 or Appendix A.5, and use this information along with the full cell potential to determine the half-cell potential for the cathode.

$$E^\circ_{cell} = E^\circ_{cathode} - E^\circ_{anode}$$
$$E^\circ_{cathode} = E^\circ_{cell} + E^\circ_{anode}$$
$$E^\circ_{cathode} = 1.5\text{ V} + (-0.76\text{ V}) = 0.74\text{ V}$$

PRACTICE PROBLEM 19.19

a. Write the balanced equation for the alkaline dry cell.
b. What is the half-cell potential of the cathode reaction?

Hint: Combine the half-cell reactions using coefficients to balance the redox process. Then refer to the data in Appendix A.5 to determine the cell potential.

FUEL CELLS

Up to now, all the voltaic cells that you have encountered in the text have been closed systems, where the reactants and products are at finite concentrations within the cell. In these cases, the cell's potential declines as the reactant concentrations decrease, eventually becoming zero when the reactants are depleted. There is a type of voltaic cell, however, called a **fuel cell**, which generates a continuous flow of electricity. Fuel cells require an ongoing supply of reactants, fuel, and a means of dispersing the resulting products.

The most common fuel used in fuel cells is gaseous hydrogen, which reacts with oxygen in the air in an explosive reaction that releases a great deal of energy (Figure 19.12).

$$2\,H_2(g) + O_2(g) \rightarrow 2\,H_2O(g)$$

When this same reaction is separated into half-reactions in a hydrogen fuel cell (Figure 19.13), that energy can be released in a more controlled and useful form—namely, electrical energy. At the anode, hydrogen gas is oxidized to H^+ and electrons, as per the standard hydrogen electrode (SHE).

$$H_2(g) \rightarrow 2\,H^+(aq) + 2\,e^-$$

The electrons flow to the cathode while H^+ travels through the electrolyte to the cathode, where they combine with oxygen and the released electrons to form water molecules.

$$O_2(g) + 4\,H^+(aq) + 4\,e^- \rightarrow 2\,H_2O(l)$$

Combining and balancing the two processes yields the same overall reaction as the direct reaction of the two gases.

$$2\,H_2(g) + O_2(g) \rightarrow 2\,H_2O(g)$$

FIGURE 19.12 Reaction of Hydrogen and Oxygen

NOTE: You need to be online to access this activity.

When hydrogen and oxygen gases are combined and a spark or other source of activation energy is applied, they react together to release energy in the form of heat, light, and sound.

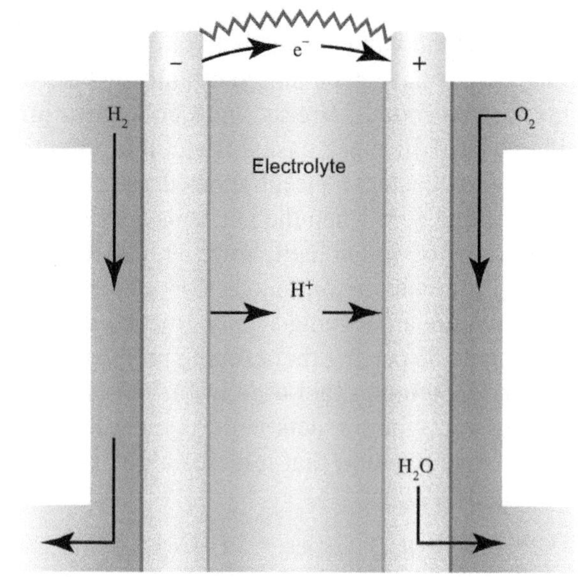

FIGURE 19.13 Hydrogen Fuel Cell

The diagram shows the continuous input of hydrogen fuel and atmospheric oxygen in a hydrogen fuel cell and the continuous output of water. The hydrogen gas is oxidized as it passes over a catalytic surface. Oxygen gas is reduced by the electrons from the hydrogen. Reduced oxygen combines with H^+ to form water.

Example 19.20

What is the standard potential of a hydrogen fuel cell?

Solution

Refer to Appendix A.5 to find the half-cell potentials.

Anode: $H_2(g) \rightarrow 2\,H^+(aq) + 2\,e^- \quad E^\circ_{anode} = 0$

Cathode: $O_2(g) + 4\,H^+(aq) + 4\,e^- \rightarrow 2\,H_2O(l) \quad E^\circ_{cathode} = 1.23\text{ V}$

$$E^\circ_{cell} = E^\circ_{cathode} - E^\circ_{anode}$$
$$E^\circ_{cell} = 1.23\text{ V} - 0\text{ V} = 1.23\text{ V}$$

PRACTICE PROBLEM 19.20

Another type of hydrogen fuel cell is the alkaline fuel cell. Use the following half-reactions to

a. write the balanced overall equation and
b. calculate the standard cell potential.

Anode: $H_2(g) + 2\,OH^-(aq) \rightarrow 2\,H_2O(l) + 2\,e^-$

Cathode: $O_2(g) + 2\,H_2O(l) + 4\,e^- \rightarrow 4\,OH^-(aq)$

Hint: Start by balancing the electron transfer process. Then combine all reactants and all products, eliminating any components that appear on both sides of the equation. Use the half-cell potentials available in Appendix A.5 to calculate the standard cell potential.

CORROSION

The oxidation of metal structures, known as **corrosion**, occurs more quickly when those structures are in wet, salty locations and in areas that receive acidic rainfall. Corrosion can be sped up in these circumstances due to the formation of electrochemical cells on the surface of the metal (Figure 19.14).

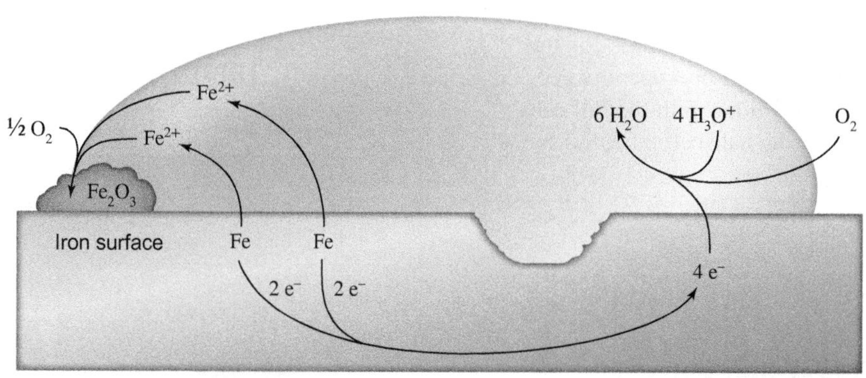

FIGURE 19.14 The Corrosion of Iron

Corrosion occurs via an electrochemical cell that forms when mildly acidic water, such as normal rainfall, encounters exposed metal surfaces. Iron atoms oxidize to form Fe^{2+} (anode reaction), which dissolves in the water droplet. The electrons provided by the iron move through the metal to reduce oxygen gas (cathode reaction), which combines with H_3O^+ to form H_2O. The aqueous Fe^{2+} then reacts directly with additional oxygen in the air to form Fe_2O_3.

Oxidation: $Fe(s) \rightarrow Fe^{2+}(aq) + 2\,e^-$

Reduction: $O_2(g) + 4\,H_3O^+(aq) + 4\,e^- \rightarrow 6\,H_2O(l)$

Further redox: $2\,Fe^{2+}(aq) + 6\,H_2O(l) + \frac{1}{2}\,O_2(g) \rightarrow Fe_2O_3(s) + 4\,H_3O^+(aq)$

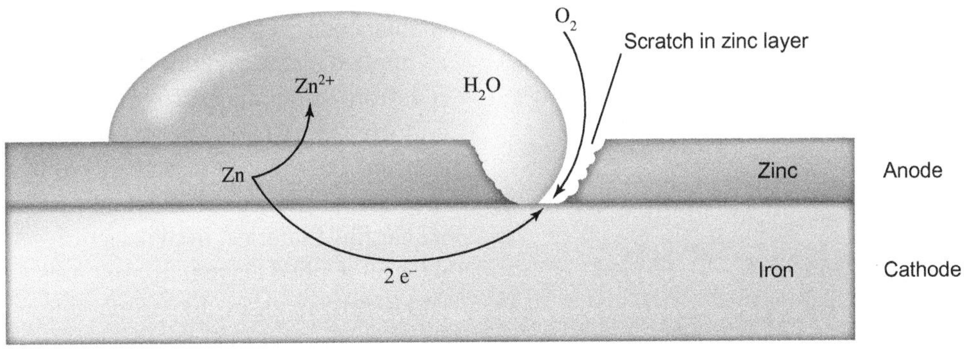

FIGURE 19.15 Cathodic Protection

Putting a more active metal in contact with iron prevents corrosion of the iron. The active metal, zinc, oxidizes readily and serves as the anode. Electrons flow through the protected iron metal, which acts as the electrical connection to the cathode. At the cathode, oxygen is reduced and combines with H_3O^+ to form water. Should any Fe^{2+} form, it is reduced back to iron metal at the cathode.

Oxidation: $Zn(s) \rightarrow Zn^{2+}(aq) + 2\ e^-$

Reduction: $O_2(g) + 4\ H_3O^+(aq) + 4\ e^- \rightarrow 6\ H_2O(l)$

All rain is mildly acidic, which allows H_3O^+ to play a role in the process. Any salt dissolved in the water on the surface of the metal acts as an electrolyte.

The reactions responsible for the corrosion of iron are shown in Figure 19.14. Iron atoms on the surface of a bridge or other structure undergo oxidation to form Fe^{2+}, which dissolves in a drop of water on the surface of the metal. The electrons released by the oxidation of the iron are conducted through the metal to a site near the edge of the water drop, where oxygen from the air is reduced by the electrons and combines with H_3O^+ to form water molecules (cathode). The site at which the iron metal is being oxidized, the anode, causes a small pit to form on the surface of the iron. The ultimate product of corrosion, iron(III) oxide, forms when the dissolved Fe^{2+} reacts directly with oxygen in the air, causing the rust to deposit at a site nearby but separate from the anode. Because of the electrochemical behavior of corrosion, it is most prevalent in wet areas where the pH is acidic.

Electrochemistry can be used to prevent corrosion by connecting a more active metal to the metal structure in need of protection. This more active metal becomes the anode via **cathodic protection** (Figure 19.15).

Metals such as zinc and magnesium are frequently used as **sacrificial anodes** by connecting them to an iron structure. By doing so, the iron structure becomes the cathode in any corrosion electrochemical cell. That is, the zinc or magnesium oxidizes more readily, so they transfer electrons to any Fe^{2+} that may form.

EVERYDAY CONNECTION

Steel is an alloy of iron, so steel nails and screws are prone to rust, which is a type of corrosion.

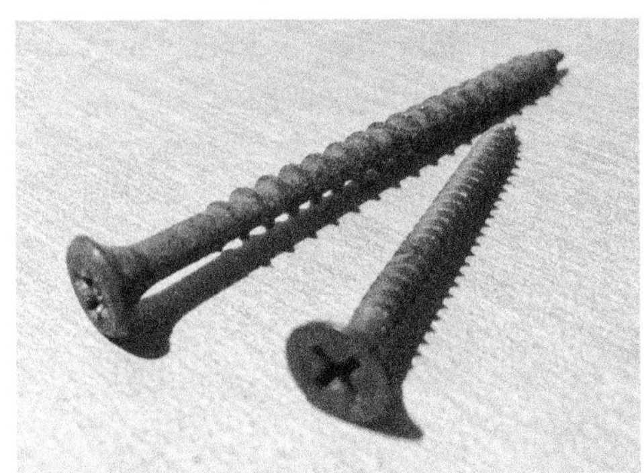

Sara Egner, Macmillan Learning

Galvanized nails are made of steel coated in zinc. Even if there is a scratch in the zinc coating, zinc acts as a sacrificial anode, protecting the steel from corrosion until all of the zinc has been oxidized.

SECTION REVIEW

- Dry cells and lead storage cells are voltaic cells commonly used in batteries.
- The reactions of some voltaic cells are readily reversible, making it possible to recharge them by applying an outside source of electricity.
- Fuel cells are voltaic cells with a continuous input of reactants and outflow of products, thus allowing for a continuous production of electricity.

- Corrosion is an electrochemical process in which a metal structure acts as an anode and is oxidized upon exposure to air and mildly acidic conditions. Cathodic protection converts the structure to a cathode to prevent corrosion.

19.9 Electrolytic Cells and Applications of Electrolysis

GOALS

- Describe how electricity can be used to drive redox reactions.
- Perform stoichiometric calculations involving mass and current in electrolytic applications.
- Describe relevant applications of electrolysis in the production or refining of specific substances.

Background Review

Chapter 5 Stoichiometry: Section 5.2—Mass Calculations for Chemical Reactions

Voltaic cells involve the production of electricity from spontaneous chemical reactions. It is also possible to use an applied electrical current to cause a nonspontaneous reaction to occur, a process known as **electrolysis** (Figure 19.16). As mentioned in Section 19.5, an applied current is used to drive a nonspontaneous reaction to reform the reactants during the process of recharging batteries. In the electrolysis of water (Figure 4.6), an applied current decomposes water into oxygen and hydrogen gases. Experimenting with the electrolysis of molten salts led Sir Humphry Davy (1778–1829) to isolate and, therefore, discover potassium, sodium, calcium, strontium, barium, magnesium, and boron.

Even today, some of the most reactive elements, such as sodium and fluorine, are produced from their naturally occurring compounds by electrolysis.

ELECTROLYSIS CALCULATIONS

Section 5.2 explains how to calculate the amount of product that would be formed in a chemical reaction, and Section 5.3 describes how to base yield calculations on the limiting amount of a specific reactant. The yield of most electrolysis reactions depends not upon the mass or number of moles of reactants but, instead upon the number of moles of electrons passing through the electrolytic cell. It is possible to calculate the amount of product formed in an electrolysis reaction based on how

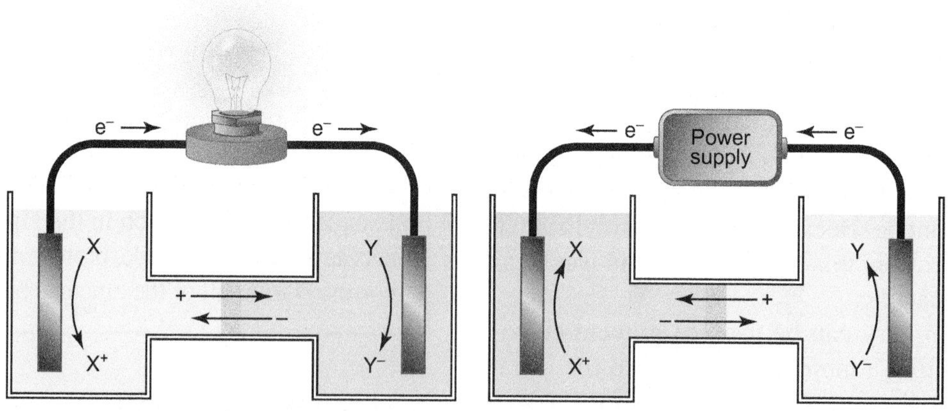

Voltaic cell
(a)

Electrolytic cell
(b)

FIGURE 19.16 Voltaic and Electrolytic Cells

(a) Voltaic cells use a spontaneous chemical reaction to create a flow of electrons that can do work. Substance X is oxidized and supplies electrons to reduce substance Y.

$$X + Y \rightarrow X^+ + Y^-$$

(b) Electrolytic cells apply a flow of electrons (an external current) to cause a nonspontaneous chemical reaction to occur. An external source of electrical potential causes substance Y^- to oxidize, thus providing electrons to reduce substance X^+.

$$X^+ + Y^- \rightarrow X + Y$$

Steve Lemon, Macmillan Learning

FIGURE 19.17 Video Tutorial: Electrolysis Calculations

NOTE: You need to be online to access this video.
This video shows how to calculate the mass of metal plated or the time required to plate a certain mass of metal.

many electrons are consumed by the reaction and the stoichiometry of the redox process (Figure 19.17).

The number of electrons consumed by a reaction can be calculated because electrical current, I, and electrical charge, q, are related. Electrical current is measured in **amperes, A**, which are defined as the amount of electrical charge in coulombs, C, that passes a point in one second.

$$1\ \text{A} = 1\ \text{C/s}$$
$$1\ \text{C} = 1\ \text{A}\cdot\text{s}$$

One electron has an electrical charge of 1.60×10^{-19} C, and 1 mole of electrons has a total charge of 96,485 C. This amount of charge is known as the Faraday constant, F (Section 19.6), and is the charge on 1 mole of electrons.

$$1\ \text{mol e}^- = 96{,}485\ \text{C}$$

If you know the current and the time it passes through an electrolytic cell, you can use the relationship between charge, current, and time,

$$q = I \cdot t \qquad (19.5)$$

to calculate the total electrical charge (in coulombs) that was consumed by the reaction. You can then use the Faraday constant to calculate the number of moles of electrons consumed. In a final step, you can use the stoichiometry of the electron transfer process to calculate how much product is formed.

Example 19.21

Calculate the mass of copper metal that will be deposited by passing a 10.0 A current through a solution of copper(II) sulfate for 3.00 h.

Solution

Use the current and the duration to determine the total charge consumed by the reaction. Then convert that charge to moles of electrons and use the stoichiometry of the chemical reaction to determine the number of moles of electrons per mole of copper deposited.

$$\text{Cu}^{2+}(aq) + 2\ \text{e}^- \rightarrow \text{Cu}(s)$$

According to the stoichiometry of this half-reaction, 2 moles of electrons produce 1 mole of copper metal. You can combine the calculation for total charge and the stoichiometry of the redox process along with molar mass to obtain the answer.

$$\overbrace{3.00\ \text{h}\left(\frac{60.0\ \text{min}}{1\ \text{hr}}\right)\left(\frac{60.0\ \text{s}}{1\ \text{min}}\right)\left(\frac{10.0\ \text{C}}{1\ \text{s}}\right)}^{\text{Total charge consumed: } q = I\cdot t}\underbrace{\left(\frac{1\ \text{mol e}^-}{96{,}485\ \text{C}}\right)}_{\substack{\text{Converting charge}\\ \text{to moles of electrons}\\ \text{(Faraday constant)}}}\overbrace{\left(\frac{1\ \text{mol Cu}}{2\ \text{mol e}^-}\right)}^{\text{Redox stoichiometry}}\underbrace{\left(\frac{63.546\ \text{g Cu}}{1\ \text{mol Cu}}\right)}_{\text{Molar mass}} = 35.6\ \text{g Cu}$$

PRACTICE PROBLEM 19.21

Calculate the mass of silver metal that will be deposited by passing a 10.0 A current through a solution of silver nitrate for 3.00 h.

Hint: Calculate the charge by multiplying the amps by the time in seconds. Then convert to moles of electrons using the Faraday constant. Lastly, use the stoichiometry of the electron transfer to relate the moles of electrons to the mass of silver.

Example 19.22

Calculate the time required to produce 2.50 g of hydrogen gas by the electrolysis of water with a current of 5.00 A. The water must contain an ionic compound, such as sodium sulfate, to act as an electrolyte.

Solution

Calculate the total charge needed to produce 2.50 g using the stoichiometry of the redox process, and use the given current as a conversion factor to obtain time. The equation for the reduction of water shows that 2 moles of electrons are needed for each mole of hydrogen gas produced.

$$2\,H_2O(l) + 2\,e^- \rightarrow H_2(g) + 2\,OH^-(aq)$$

$$2.50\text{ g } H_2\left(\frac{1\text{ mol } H_2}{2.0159\text{ g } H_2}\right)\left(\frac{2\text{ mol } e^-}{1\text{ mol } H_2}\right)\left(\frac{96{,}485\text{ C}}{1\text{ mol } e^-}\right)\left(\frac{1\text{ s}}{5.00\text{ C}}\right) = 4.79 \times 10^4\text{ s} = 13.3\text{ h}$$

PRACTICE PROBLEM 19.22

Calculate the time required to produce 1.00 kg of lead metal by passing a 25.0 A current through a solution of lead(II) nitrate.

Hint: Calculate the total charge needed to produce 1.00 kg of lead using the stoichiometry of the redox process, and use the current as a conversion factor to obtain time.

Example 19.23

Calculate the current required to produce 2.50 g of hydrogen by the electrolysis of water (containing sodium sulfate to carry the charge) in 3.00 h.

Solution

Use the stoichiometry of the electrolysis reaction to determine the total charge needed to produce the 2.50 g of hydrogen.

$$2\,H_2O(l) + 2\,e^- \rightarrow H_2(g) + 2\,OH^-(aq)$$

$$2.50\text{ g } H_2\left(\frac{1\text{ mol } H_2}{2.0159\text{ g } H_2}\right)\left(\frac{2\text{ mol } e^-}{1\text{ mol } H_2}\right)\left(\frac{96{,}485\text{ C}}{1\text{ mol } e^-}\right) = 2.39 \times 10^5\text{ C}$$

Next, use Equation 19.5 to obtain the current from the charge and given amount of time.

$$I = \frac{q}{t} = \frac{2.39 \times 10^5\text{ C}}{3.00\text{ h}}\left(\frac{1\text{ h}}{3600\text{ s}}\right) = 22.2\text{ A}$$

Alternatively, you could forego the equation and use dimensional analysis to find the number of coulombs per second (1 C/s = 1 A).

PRACTICE PROBLEM 19.23

Calculate the current required to produce 1.00 kg of lead metal by the electrolysis of lead(II) nitrate in 24.00 h.

Hint: Determine the total charge needed to produce the 1.00 kg of lead, and divide that total charge by the time in seconds to determine the current (Equation 19.5).

Voltaic cell reactions follow the same equations that electrolytic cells do. The problems in this section deal with how much product is formed when an external current is passed into an electrolytic cell, but you could use the same equations to calculate how much reactant is used up in a galvanic cell if you knew how much current was generated by the cell over a given period.

APPLICATIONS OF ELECTROLYSIS

Electroplating is an application of electrolysis that places the decorative or protective metal as the anode in an electrolytic cell and the metal item that you want to protect as the cathode (Figure 19.18). Once the electrical current is applied, the anode metal oxidizes to form ions that migrate to and deposit as atoms on the cathode, forming a protective and/or decorative surface.

Ultrapure copper metal is prepared from impure copper metal by electrolysis—a process called **electrorefining** (Figure 19.19). The contaminants in the impure copper metal consist of other metals, some of which are more active than copper and some

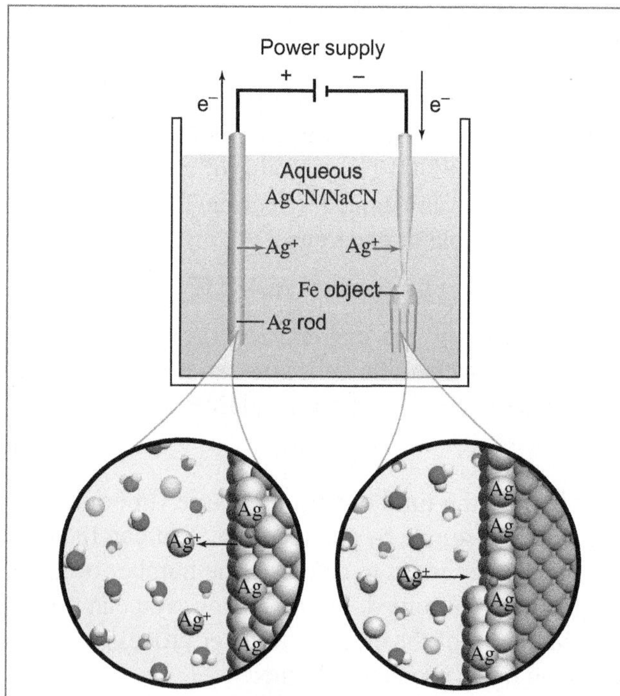

FIGURE 19.18 Electroplating

Inexpensive metals can be coated with a protective and/or decorative metal by applying an appropriate voltage to an electrolytic cell that consists of the less reactive metal as the anode and the item to be coated as the cathode. In this schematic, a steel fork is being plated with silver metal.

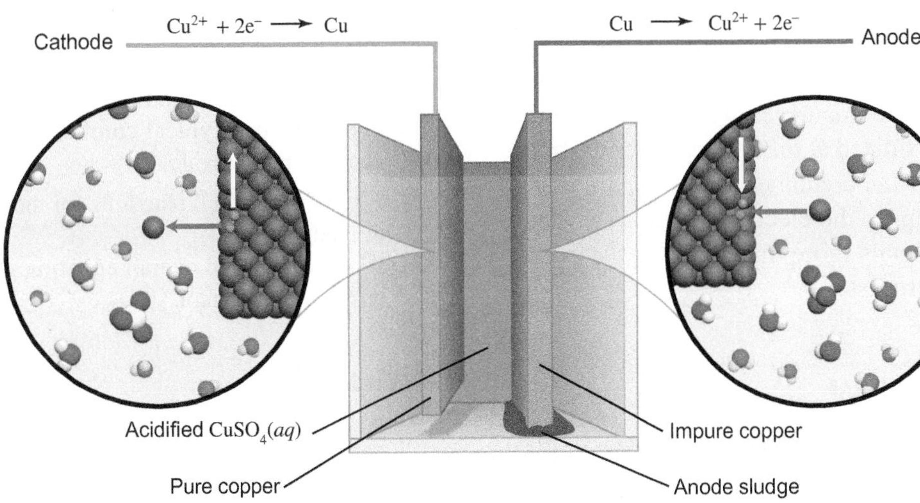

FIGURE 19.19 Electrolytic Refining of Copper

In the extraction of copper from an ore by electrolysis, pure copper is used for the cathode and the ore is used as the anode; both are placed in the same copper(II) solution. Copper from the ore is oxidized to Cu^{2+}, which dissolves in the solution then plates onto the cathode. Some impurities from the ore are oxidized and dissolve in the solution, too, while others remain solid (unoxidized) and fall to the bottom as "anode sludge" once the copper anode is used up in the electrolysis process.

EVERYDAY CONNECTION

"White gold" is less yellow than pure gold because it is a mixture of gold and other metals. However, the characteristic silvery mirror finish of white gold comes from a rhodium plating on the outside. Like most plated metal objects, white gold jewelry is *not* dipped in molten metal but rather plated using electrolysis (i.e., electroplated).

Sara Egner, Macmillan Learning

The zinc coating on galvanized nails (Section 19.8) can also be achieved using electroplating, which is why you might see them referred to as electrogalvanized.

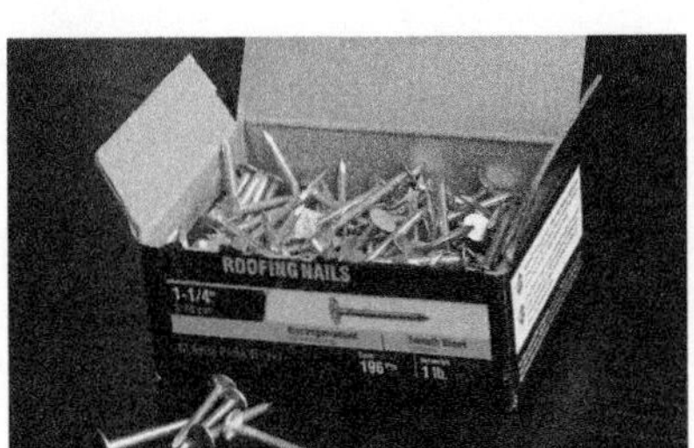

Sara Egner, Macmillan Learning

EVERYDAY CONNECTION

Copper ore is mined from the ground.

Karin Rollett-Vlcek/Getty Images

Uses of refined copper include coins and electrical wiring.

MPanchenko/Shutterstock

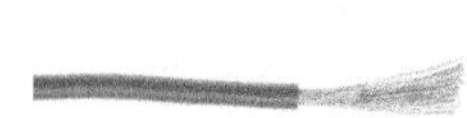

Flegere/Shutterstock

of which are less active. This impure copper is used as the anode of an electrolytic cell, with a sample of ultrapure copper metal as the cathode.

When a certain potential is applied to the cell, both the copper and the more active impurities are oxidized at the anode to form ions in solution. The copper ions migrate to the cathode, where they are reduced to copper metal, which deposits onto the cathode, while the more active metals, such as Zn^{2+} and Fe^{2+} remain in solution. The less active impurities, which include gold and silver, are not oxidized at the applied potential and fall to the bottom of the container as the impure copper anode is used up by the electrolysis process. The recovery of these metals more than pays for the costs of the purification process.

SECTION REVIEW

- Electrolysis causes a nonspontaneous chemical reaction to occur via an applied electrical potential.
- Electrolysis reactions require ions capable of movement and an external electrical current of sufficient potential to cause the desired reaction to occur.
- The species in an electrolytic cell that oxidize or reduce most easily will be the ones that are oxidized or reduced, respectively. When electrolysis is carried out in aqueous solution, water is often either oxidized or reduced.
- The amount of product produced by an electrolytic cell can be calculated from the quantity of charge that passes through the cell, combined with the stoichiometry of the redox process.
- If a specific amount of product is needed, the amount of current for a specific time or the time for a specific current can be calculated from the stoichiometry of the redox process.
- Examples of electrolysis include electrorefining and electroplating.

Putting It Together

The example problems in earlier sections of this chapter focus on the new skills acquired in that section, but homework and exam questions in chemistry often require more than just one skill at a time. In fact, you will likely be expected to apply knowledge from throughout the chapter, or even multiple chapters in a single problem. This final example problem is meant to help you prepare for these types of multi-concept questions. Additional examples can be found in the end of chapter exercises.

Example 19.24

Methanol is one of several fuels besides hydrogen that is being considered for use in fuel cells. In a methanol fuel cell, liquid methanol, CH_4O, reacts with oxygen in a typical combustion reaction to produce carbon dioxide and water.

a. Write the half-cell reactions for the combustion of methanol.

b. Write a balanced overall equation for the combustion of methanol.

Solution

a. Start by writing an unbalanced overall equation based on the description in the problem—namely, liquid methanol reacts with oxygen to produce carbon dioxide and water. Follow the first three steps used to balance a redox reaction in acidic solution.

1. *Add coefficients to balance any elements other than H and O.* No coefficients needed.

$$2\,CH_4O(l) + 3\,O_2(g) \rightarrow 2\,CO_2(g) + H_2O(l)$$

2. *Assign oxidation numbers to all elements in the equation.*

$$\underset{-2\ +1\ -2}{CH_4O(l)} + \underset{0}{O_2(g)} \rightarrow \underset{+4\ -2}{CO_2(g)} + \underset{+1\ -2}{H_2O(l)}$$

3. *Identify the elements that undergo oxidation and reduction.* C in methanol is oxidized from -2 to $+4$ in CO_2 for a loss of six electrons, and each O in O_2 is reduced from 0 to -2 in the products (CO_2 and H_2O) for a gain of two electrons. Four electrons are needed to reduce both O atoms in O_2. Use this information to write unbalanced versions of the oxidation and reduction half-reactions:

Oxidation half-reaction: $CH_4O(l) \rightarrow CO_2(g) + 6\,e^-$

Reduction half-reaction: $O_2(g) + 4\,e^- \rightarrow 2\,H_2O(l)$

These half-reactions can be completed by adding water molecules and H^+ as needed:

Oxidation half-reaction: $CH_4O(l) + H_2O(l) \rightarrow CO_2(g) + 6\,e^- + 6\,H^+(aq)$

Reduction half-reaction: $O_2(g) + 4\,e^- + 4\,H^+(aq) \rightarrow 2\,H_2O(l)$

b. You now have two options to balance the overall equation. The one shown first completes the steps as shown previously for a redox reaction in acidic solution.

4. *Determine the coefficients needed to balance the electron transfer, and place these*

coefficients in the equation. Oxidation of 1 mole of methanol provides enough electrons to reduce 3 moles of oxygen atoms, but O atoms are present as diatomic oxygen molecules. Therefore, you need twice as many moles of methanol. Two moles of methanol are needed to reduce 3 moles diatomic oxygen. In other words, the oxidation of 2 moles methanol releases 12 moles of electrons, and the reduction of 3 moles of O_2 uses 12 moles of electrons. (Omit any coefficient for water now because the O atoms are balanced in the next step.)

$$2\,CH_4O(l) + 3\,O_2(g) \rightarrow 2\,CO_2(g) + H_2O(l)$$

5. *Balance any missing O atoms by adding water molecules.* There are eight O atoms in the reactants and five O atoms in the products. Add three water molecules to the products.

$$2\,CH_4O(l) + 3\,O_2(g) \rightarrow 2\,CO_2(g) + 4\,H_2O(l)$$

6. *Balance any missing H atoms by adding* H^+. There are eight H atoms in the reactants and eight H atoms in the products, so no additional H^+ are needed.

7. *Verify that all atoms and charges are balanced.* All atoms are balanced: 2 C, 8 O, and 8 H on each side. All reactants and products are neutral, so charge is balanced.

The second method for writing a balanced overall reaction adds coefficients to the half-reactions to balance the electron transfer and then adds the half-reactions together. The least common multiple for the electron transfer is 12, so multiply the coefficients in the oxidation half-reaction by 2 and the coefficients in the reduction half-reaction by 3.

The adjusted oxidation half-reaction is

$$2\,CH_4O(l) + 2\,H_2O(l) \rightarrow 2\,CO_2(g) + 12\,e^- + 12\,H^+(aq)$$

The adjusted reduction half-reaction is

$$3\,O_2(g) + 12\,e^- + 12\,H^+(aq) \rightarrow 6\,H_2O(l)$$

Combine the half-reactions to yield this overall reaction,

$$2\,CH_4O(l) + 2\,H_2O(l) + 3\,O_2(g) \cancel{+ 12\,e^-} + \cancel{12\,H^+(aq)} \rightarrow 2\,CO_2(g) \cancel{+ 12\,e^-} + 6\,H_2O(l) \cancel{+ 12\,H^+(aq)}$$

which simplifies to give the same balanced equation for the overall reaction as the previous method.

$$2\,CH_4O(l) + 3\,O_2(g) \rightarrow 2\,CO_2(g) + 4\,H_2O(l)$$

PRACTICE PROBLEM 19.24

a. Calculate $\Delta G°$ for the methanol fuel cell reaction using the $\Delta G_f°$ values found in Appendix A.2.

b. Calculate $E°_{cell}$ for a methanol fuel cell.

Hint: Use Equation 18.8 to calculate the standard free energy change, and then apply Equation 19.2 to calculate the standard potential.

Key Terms, Symbols, and Equations

KEY TERMS

ampere, A (19.9): A unit of electrical current; 1 A = 1 C/s.

anode (19.4): The electrode at which the oxidation half-reaction occurs.

cathode (19.4): The electrode at which the reduction half-reaction occurs.

cathodic protection (19.8): Protecting a metal structure by creating an electrochemical cell in which a more active metal is the anode and the metal structure that needs to be protected is the cathode.

concentration cell (19.7): An electrochemical cell in which the half-cells undergo the same reaction but differ in ion concentrations, thus leading to a spontaneous reaction.

corrosion (19.8): The oxidation of a metal object in soil or water that is accelerated by the unintentional formation of a voltaic cell.

coulomb, C (19.6): A unit of charge; 1 C = 1 J/V.

disproportionation (19.1): A reaction in which one reactant acts as both the oxidizing and reducing agent.

dry cell (19.8): A sealed voltaic cell containing the mobile ions in a paste or gel form rather than an aqueous solution; commonly referred to as a battery.

electrical circuit (19.4): The circular connection for the free flow of electrons and ions.

electrochemical cell (19.4): A system composed of two half-cells connected by a salt bridge and a wire, thus allowing for electron transfer.

electrochemistry (19.1): The branch of chemistry that studies the relationship between electricity and chemistry.

electrode (19.4): A half-cell in an electrochemical cell; sometimes it requires an inert wire or carbon rod to make an electrical connection to the half-cell.

electrolysis (19.9): The process of applying an electrical current to a cell to cause a nonspontaneous reaction to occur.

electrolytic cell (19.4): An electrochemical cell in which an electrical current is used to cause a nonspontaneous redox reaction to occur.

electroplating (19.9): The process of using an electrical current to cause a protective or cosmetic layer of metal to form on the surface of a metal object.

electrorefining (19.9): The process of using an electrical current to remove impurities from a metal sample.

Faraday constant, *F* (19.6): The charge, in coulombs, of a mole of electrons; $F = 96{,}485\ \text{C/mol}$.

fuel cell (19.8): A voltaic cell with continuous inflow of fuel (usually hydrogen) and outflow of products (usually water) used to generate electricity.

half-cell (19.4): One section of an electrochemical cell in which either the oxidation or the reduction reaction occurs.

half-reaction (19.1): A chemical equation for just the oxidation or reduction component of a redox reaction.

ion-selective electrode (19.7): An electrochemical probe that works like concentration cells to measure the concentration of specific ions.

negative electrode (19.4): The anode in a voltaic cell; the cathode in an electrolytic cell.

Nernst equation (19.7): The equation used to calculate cell potential under nonstandard conditions.

positive electrode (19.4): The cathode in a voltaic cell; the anode in an electrolytic cell.

potential, *E* (19.4): The tendency of an electrochemical reaction or half-reaction to proceed.

sacrificial anode (19.8): A more active metal that is purposely allowed to be oxidized to prevent corrosion of a metal structure.

salt bridge (19.4): The physical connection between half-cells in both voltaic and electrolytic cells that allows for movement of ions to complete the electrical circuit.

standard hydrogen electrode, SHE (19.5): A half-cell composed of hydrogen gas and a platinum electrode in 1 M hydrogen ion solution that is assigned a voltage of zero; it is used to measure the standard reduction potentials of other half-reactions.

standard reduction potential (19.5): The voltage of a half-reaction under standard conditions measured against the standard hydrogen electrode.

volt, V (19.4): The unit used to measure electrical potential; $1\ \text{V} = 1\ \text{J/C}$.

voltaic cell (19.4): An electrochemical cell in which a spontaneous redox reaction is used to create an electrical current.

SYMBOLS AND ABBREVIATIONS

$|$ (phase separation) (19.4)

$||$ (salt bridge) (19.4)

A (amperes) (19.6)

C (coulomb) (19.6)

E (electrical potential) (19.4)

E° (standard potential) (19.5)

E°_{anode} (standard reduction potential of the anode half-cell) (19.5)

E°_{cathode} (standard reduction potential of the cathode half-cell) (19.5)

E°_{cell} (standard cell potential) (19.6)

F (Faraday constant) (19.6)

I (electrical current) (19.9)

n (number of moles of electrons) (19.6)

q (electrical charge) (19.6)

Q (reaction quotient) (19.6)

SHE (standard hydrogen electrode) (19.5)

V (volt) (19.4)

EQUATIONS

$E^\circ_{\text{cell}} = E^\circ_{\text{cathode}} - E^\circ_{\text{anode}}$ (19.1)

$\Delta G = -nFE$ (19.2)

$E^\circ = \dfrac{RT}{nF} \ln K$ (19.3)

$E = E^\circ - \dfrac{RT}{nF} \ln Q$ (19.4)

$q = I \cdot t$ (19.5)

Chapter Summary

Redox reactions can be divided into two half-reactions, one for oxidation and one for reduction. An oxidation half-reaction can be combined with a reduction half-reaction if the electrons cancel, resulting in a balanced redox reaction. Certain oxidation–reduction reactions, known as disproportionation reactions, involve only one type of reactant that is both oxidized and reduced to form the products (Section 19.1).

Redox reactions can be quite complex and are not readily balanced by the trial-and-error method used in previous chapters. The following systematic approach can be used to balance redox reactions under acidic conditions:

1. Add coefficients to balance any elements other than H and O.
2. Assign oxidation numbers to all elements in the equation.
3. Identify the elements that undergo oxidation and reduction.
4. Determine the coefficients needed to balance the electron transfer, and place those coefficients in the equation.
5. Balance any missing O atoms by adding water molecules.
6. Balance any missing H atoms by adding H^+.
7. Verify that both the atoms and the charges are balanced.

In basic conditions, start by balancing in acidic solution. Then, add OH^- to both sides to neutralize H^+, combining H^+ and OH^- into H_2O molecules (Section 19.2).

Redox reactions are frequently used in titrations to determine the amount or concentration of reactant in an unknown sample. The redox reaction must be balanced first (Section 19.3).

Reactants that undergo spontaneous redox reactions when in direct contact with each other also react spontaneously when properly connected electrochemically. These reactions can be used to create voltaic (or galvanic) cells that produce electricity from a spontaneous chemical reaction. The oxidation half-reaction occurs in the anode half-cell, while the reduction half-reaction takes place in the cathode half-cell.

A complete circuit, which involves both a metal wire for the flow of electrons and a salt bridge for the flow of ions, is needed for a voltaic cell to operate. Standard cell notation, such as the notation for a Daniell cell,

$$\mathrm{Zn(s)}\,|\,\mathrm{Zn^{2+}(1\ M)}\,||\,\mathrm{Cu^{2+}(1\ M)}\,|\,\mathrm{Cu(s)}$$

summarizes the flow of electrons in a complete electrochemical circuit (Section 19.4).

Tables of standard reduction potentials can be used to determine the tendencies of redox reactions to proceed and to calculate the cell potential: $E^\circ_{\text{cell}} = E^\circ_{\text{cathode}} - E^\circ_{\text{anode}}$ (Section 19.5).

Electrochemical (cell) potentials are related to changes in free energy by $\Delta G = -nFE$ and, in the standard state, by $\Delta G^\circ = -nFE^\circ$, where n = the number of moles of electrons transferred in the balanced chemical equation, and F is the Faraday constant, or the charge, in coulombs, of a mole of electrons. Spontaneous processes are associated with positive values of E and negative values of ΔG. Cell potentials are also related to equilibrium constants, K, by $E^\circ = \frac{RT}{nF}\ln K$ (Section 19.6).

Under nonstandard conditions, electrochemical potentials are calculated using the Nernst equation: $E = E^\circ - \frac{RT}{nF}\ln Q$. Concentration cells, which are voltaic cells composed of half-cells containing identical components at different concentrations, represent another application of the Nernst equation. The differences in concentration give rise to a cell potential. Specialized concentration cells known as ion-selective electrodes are used to determine unknown concentrations of specific ions (Section 19.7).

There are many everyday applications of voltaic cells. Dry cells and lead storage cells are voltaic cells commonly used in consumer batteries. The reactions of some voltaic cells, such as the lead storage battery, are readily reversible, making it possible to recharge them by applying an outside source of electricity. Fuel cells are voltaic cells with a continuous input of reactants and outflow of products, which results in a continuous production of electricity. Corrosion is an electrochemical process in which a metal structure acts as an anode and is oxidized upon exposure to air and mildly acidic conditions. The addition of a sacrificial anode converts the structure to a cathode to prevent corrosion (Section 19.8).

Electrolysis causes a nonspontaneous chemical reaction to occur via an applied electrical potential. An electrolysis reaction depends strongly on the conditions under which it is carried out because often more than one electrochemical reaction is possible. The species in an electrolytic cell that oxidize or reduce most easily will be the ones that are oxidized or reduced, respectively. When electrolysis is carried out in aqueous solution, water is often either oxidized or reduced. The amount of a chemical reaction occurring in an electrolytic cell can be calculated from the quantity of charge that passes through the cell, combined with the stoichiometry of the redox process. If a specific amount of product is needed, the amount of current for a specific time or the time for a specific current can be calculated from the stoichiometry of the redox process. Important applications of electrolysis include electrorefining and electroplating (Section 19.9).

END OF CHAPTER QUESTIONS

19.1 Redox Reactions

1. For each of the following equations, identify the oxidizing agent, the reducing agent, the element oxidized, and the element reduced.
   a. $Cu(s) + CuCl_2(aq) \rightarrow 2\,CuCl(s)$
   b. $Cd(s) + CuCl_2(s) \rightarrow CdCl_2(s) + Cu(s)$
   c. $4\,KI(aq) + 2\,CuCl_2(aq) \rightarrow 2\,CuI(s) + I_2(aq) + 4\,KCl(aq)$
   d. $2\,H_2(g) + O_2(g) \rightarrow 2\,H_2O(l)$
2. For each of the following equations, identify the oxidizing agent, the reducing agent, the element oxidized, and the element reduced.
   a. $4\,H^+(aq) + 2\,NO_3^-(aq) + Cu(s) \rightarrow Cu^{2+}(aq) + 2\,NO_2(g) + 2\,H_2O(l)$
   b. $Cu_2O(s) + 2\,H^+(aq) \rightarrow Cu(s) + Cu^{2+}(aq) + H_2O(l)$
   c. $Zn(s) + CuCl_2(s) \rightarrow ZnCl_2(s) + Cu(s)$
3. Separate each reaction into its half-reactions, then classify each half-reaction as oxidation or reduction.
   a. $2\,MgO(s) \rightarrow 2\,Mg(s) + O_2(g)$
   b. $Pb(s) + Cl_2(g) \rightarrow PbCl_2(s)$
   c. $16\,Na(s) + S_8(s) \rightarrow 8\,Na_2S(s)$
4. Combine each pair of unbalanced half-reactions into a balanced overall redox equation.
   a. $Fe^{2+}(aq) \rightarrow Fe^{3+}(aq)$
      $Cu^{2+}(aq) \rightarrow Cu(s)$
   b. $Al(s) \rightarrow Al^{3+}(aq)$
      $Sn^{2+}(aq) \rightarrow Sn(s)$
   c. $Ni^{2+}(aq) \rightarrow Ni(s)$
      $Pb(s) \rightarrow Pb^{4+}(aq)$

19.2 Balancing Redox Equations

5. Balance the following oxidation–reduction equations in acidic solution.
   a. $BiO_3^-(aq) + Mn^{2+}(aq) \rightarrow MnO_4^-(aq) + Bi^{3+}(aq)$
   b. $H_2SO_4(conc) + Mg(s) \rightarrow H_2S(g) + Mg^{2+}(aq)$
   c. $MnO_4^-(aq) + Pb^{2+}(aq) \rightarrow Mn^{2+}(aq) + Pb^{4+}(aq)$
   d. $MnO_4^{2-}(aq) \rightarrow MnO_4^-(aq) + MnO_2(s)$
6. Balance the following oxidation–reduction equations in acidic solution.
   a. $HAsO_2(s) + Cl_2(aq) \rightarrow Cl^-(aq) + H_3AsO_4(aq)$
   b. $Pb^{4+}(aq) + Br^-(aq) \rightarrow Pb^{2+}(aq) + BrO_3^-(aq)$

c. $Mn(s) + H^+(aq) + NO_3^-(aq) \rightarrow Mn^{2+}(aq) + NH_4^+(aq)$

d. $H_2SO_4(conc) + Ce(s) \rightarrow Ce_2(SO_4)_3(aq) + H_2S(g)$

7. Balance the following oxidation–reduction equations in basic solution.
   a. $Ce^{4+}(aq) + C_2O_4^{2-}(aq) \rightarrow CO_2(g) + Ce^{3+}(aq)$
   b. $I^-(aq) + Cu^{2+}(aq) \rightarrow CuI(s) + I_2(aq)$
   c. $Cl^-(aq) + Ce^{4+}(aq) \rightarrow Cl_2(aq) + Ce^{3+}(aq)$
   d. $H_2O_2(aq) + Co^{2+}(aq) \rightarrow Co^{3+}(aq)$

8. Balance the following oxidation–reduction equations in basic solution.
   a. $H_2O_2(aq) + Cr_2O_7^{2-}(aq) \rightarrow Mn^{2+}(aq) + Cl_2(g)$
   b. $MnO_4^-(aq) + Cl^-(aq) \rightarrow Mn^{2+}(aq) + Cl_2(g)$
   c. $MnO_2(s) + V^{2+}(aq) \rightarrow VO_3^-(aq) + Mn^{2+}(aq)$
   d. $Cl_2(aq) + C_2O_4^{2-}(aq) \rightarrow Cl^-(aq) + CO_2(g)$

19.3 Redox Titrations

9. The amount of triiodide ion, I_3^-, in a solution can be determined using a redox titration with thiosulfate ion, $S_2O_3^{2-}$, according to the net ionic equation that follows. What is the concentration of I_3^- in a solution if it takes 13.7 mL of a 0.130 M solution of $S_2O_3^{2-}$ to titrate 25.0 mL of a sample of that solution?

$$2\,S_2O_3^{2-}(aq) + I_3^-(aq) \rightarrow S_4O_6^{2-}(aq) + 3\,I^-(aq)$$

10. A 15.00 mL solution of Fe^{2+} required 17.35 mL of 0.231 M $KMnO_4$ to reach the end point. Refer to the balanced equation in Example 19.5 to calculate the concentration of the Fe^{2+} solution.

11. A 25.00 mL solution of methanol, CH_4O, required 17.85 mL of 0.1033 M sodium dichromate, $Na_2Cr_2O_7$, to reach the end point using diphenylamine as the indicator in the following equation. Calculate the concentration of methanol in the solution.

$$3\,CH_4O(aq) + 2\,Cr_2O_7^{2-}(aq) + 16\,H^+(aq) \rightarrow 3\,CH_2O_2(aq) + 4\,Cr^{3+}(aq) + 11\,H_2O(l)$$

12. Calculate the concentration of sulfite, SO_3^{2-}, in a solution given that a 25.00 mL sample of the solution required 18.35 mL of a 0.021 M $KMnO_4$ to reach the end point.

$$2\,MnO_4^-(aq) + 6\,H^+(aq) + 5\,SO_3^{2-}(aq) \rightarrow 2\,Mn^{2+}(aq) + 5\,SO_4^{2-}(aq) + 3\,H_2O(l)$$

13. A 0.1340 g sample of sodium oxalate, $Na_2C_2O_4$, is dissolved in a small amount of water and requires 30.74 mL of a potassium permanganate solution to titrate it to the end point, according to the following equation:

$$5\,C_2O_4^{2-}(aq) + 2\,MnO_4^-(aq) + 16\,H^+(aq) \rightarrow 2\,Mn^{2+}(aq) + 10\,CO_2(g) + 8\,H_2O(l)$$

   a. Calculate the number of moles of sodium oxalate present in the initial mass.
   b. Calculate the number of moles of potassium permanganate used in the titration.
   c. Determine the molarity of the potassium permanganate solution.

14. A rock sample is to be assayed for its tin content by an oxidation–reduction titration with $I_3^-(aq)$. A 12.35 g sample of the rock is crushed, dissolved in sulfuric acid, and passed over a reducing agent so that all the tin is in the form Sn^{2+}. The $Sn^{2+}(aq)$ is completely oxidized by 54.35 mL of a 0.633 M solution of NaI_3. Calculate the amount of tin in the sample and its mass percentage in the rock using the balanced net ionic equation shown here.

$$I_3^-(aq) + Sn^{2+}(aq) \rightarrow Sn^{4+}(aq) + 3\,I^-(aq)$$

15. A 25.00 mL sample of a solution of $Fe^{2+}(aq)$ requires 17.55 mL of a 0.1223 M solution of $Ce^{4+}(aq)$ according the reaction shown in the following equation.

$$Fe^{2+}(aq) + Ce^{4+}(aq) \rightarrow Fe^{3+}(aq) + Ce^{3+}(aq)$$

   a. Calculate the molarity of $Fe^{2+}(aq)$.
   b. Calculate the mass of iron in the sample.

16. A 0.1773 g sample of $As_4O_6(s)$ dissolved in 35.00 mL of water requires 42.60 mL of $I_3^-(aq)$ to reach the end point of the titration. Calculate the molarity of the $I_3^-(aq)$ solution using the information in this balanced net ionic equation:

$$4\,H_2O + As_4O_6(s) + 4\,I_3^-(aq) \rightarrow As_4O_{10}(s) + 12\,I^-(aq) + 8\,H^+$$

19.4 Voltaic Cells

17. Sketch the voltaic cell that corresponds to the following standard cell notation. Indicate the direction of electron flow, positive ion flow, and negative ion flow.

$$Cr(s)\,|\,Cr^{2+}(aq)\,||\,Pb^{2+}(aq)\,|\,Pb(s)$$

18. Consider the electrochemical reaction of copper metal in aqueous copper(II) ion with lead metal in aqueous lead(II) ion.
    a. Using the activity series in Table 4.7, predict which metal will be oxidized.
    b. Sketch the voltaic cell. Indicate the direction of electron flow, positive ion flow, and negative ion flow.
    c. Write the standard cell notation for this cell.
    d. Write the net ionic equation for the overall reaction.

19. The half-reaction of two ions such as Ce^{4+} and Ce^{3+}, neither of which can serve as an electrode, is done with an inert electrode such as a platinum bar. Diagram the apparatus for the electrochemical reaction of aqueous cerium(IV) ion and cerium(III) ion with MnO_4^- and Mn^{2+}. (Note that cerium(IV) ion is a better oxidizing agent than permanganate ion.)

20. The reaction in the Daniell cell and the direct reaction of zinc metal and copper(II) ion are the same, but the Daniell cell produces electrical energy. What happens to the chemical energy when the elements react directly?

21. Consider the voltaic cell represented by the following standard cell notation, where X and Y are generic metals:

$$X(s)\,|\,X^{2+}(aq)\,\|\,Y^{+}(aq)\,|\,Y(s)$$

    a. Write the net ionic equation for the overall reaction.
    b. Which electrode gains mass?
    c. Which electrode loses mass?

19.5 Cell Potential

22. In each part, choose which ion, if either, is easier to reduce.
    a. MnO_4^- or $Cr_2O_7^{2-}$
    b. Sn^{2+} or Pb^{2+}
    c. Fe^{3+} or Fe^{2+}

23. In each part, choose the substance, if either, that is easier to oxidize.
    a. Zn or Fe^{2+}
    b. H_2 or Fe^{2+}
    c. H_2 or Fe

24. Calculate the standard potential of each of the following cells:
    a. $Cu(s) + Fe^{2+}(aq) \rightarrow Cu^{2+}(aq) + Fe(s)$
    b. $2\,Ag(s) + Fe^{2+}(aq) \rightarrow 2\,Ag^{+}(aq) + Fe(s)$
    c. $Cu(s) + 2\,Fe^{3+}(aq) \rightarrow Cu^{2+}(aq) + 2\,Fe^{2+}(aq)$
    d. $Cu(s) + Pb^{2+}(aq) \rightarrow Cu^{2+}(aq) + Pb(s)$

25. Calculate the standard potential of each of the following cells, and identify which, if any, represent spontaneous reactions.
    a. $MnO_4^-(aq) + 8\,H^+(aq) + 5\,Fe^{2+}(aq) \rightarrow Mn^{2+}(aq) + 5\,Fe^{3+}(aq) + 4\,H_2O(l)$
    b. $2\,H^+(aq) + 2\,Fe^{2+}(aq) \rightarrow H_2 + 2\,Fe^{3+}(aq)$
    c. $Sn(s) + Pb^{2+}(aq) \rightarrow Sn^{2+}(aq) + Pb(s)$
    d. $Zn(s) + Pb^{2+}(aq) \rightarrow Zn^{2+}(aq) + Pb(s)$

26. Write the cell notation for each of the cells in problem 24.

27. Write the standard cell notation for each of the cells in problem 25.

28. Consider two hypothetical metals, X and Z.
    a. The potential of the reduction of X^{2+} to X is 0.55 V. Will X react with 1 M H^+?
    b. The potential of the reduction of Z^+ to Z is -0.55 V. Will Z react with 1 M H^+?
    c. Which is spontaneous, the reaction of X with Z^+ or the reaction of X^{2+} with Z? Calculate the cell voltage for the spontaneous reaction.

29. Use the standard reduction potential data in Appendix A.5 to
    a. explain why Cu^+ is unstable in aqueous solution.
    b. determine the products expected from the reaction of Cu_2O and dilute sulfuric acid.

30. For the following standard cell notation:

$$Mg(s)\,|\,Mg^{2+}(aq)\,\|\,H^{+}(aq)\,|\,H_2(g)\,|\,Pt(s)$$

    a. Sketch the voltaic cell. Indicate the direction of electron flow, positive ion flow, and negative ion flow.
    b. Calculate the cell potential.
    c. Does the magnesium electrode gain mass or lose mass over the course of the reaction?
    d. The mass of the platinum electrode does not change. Why?

19.6 Free Energy and Cell Potential

31. What ranges of values for $\Delta G°$, $\Delta E°$, and K indicate a spontaneous (product-favored) reaction?

32. Use the cell potentials calculated in problem 24 to calculate the standard free energy change of each reaction at 25°C.
    a. $Cu(s) + Fe^{2+}(aq) \rightarrow Cu^{2+}(aq) + Fe(s)$
    b. $2\,Ag(s) + Fe^{2+}(aq) \rightarrow 2\,Ag^{+}(aq) + Fe(s)$

c. $Cu(s) + 2\,Fe^{3+}(aq) \rightarrow Cu^{2+}(aq) + 2\,Fe^{2+}(aq)$
d. $Cu(s) + Pb^{2+}(aq) \rightarrow Cu^{2+}(aq) + Pb(s)$

33. Use the cell potentials calculated in problem 25 to calculate the standard free energy change of each reaction at 25°C.
a. $MnO_4^-(aq) + 8\,H^+(aq) + 5\,Fe^{2+}(aq) \rightarrow Mn^{2+}(aq) + 5\,Fe^{3+}(aq) + 4\,H_2O(l)$
b. $2\,H^+(aq) + 2\,Fe^{2+}(aq) \rightarrow H_2 + 2\,Fe^{3+}(aq)$
c. $Sn(s) + Pb^{2+}(aq) \rightarrow Sn^{2+}(aq) + Pb(s)$
d. $Zn(s) + Pb^{2+}(aq) \rightarrow Zn^{2+}(aq) + Pb(s)$

34. Use the standard potentials in Appendix A.5 to calculate ΔG°_{rxn} for this reaction at 25°C.

$$Br_2(l) + 2\,Cl^-(aq) \rightarrow 2\,Br^-(aq) + Cl_2(g)$$

35. Calculate the equilibrium constant for each reaction in problem 32.

36. Calculate the equilibrium constant for each reaction in problem 33.

37. Calculate the equilibrium constant for the reaction in problem 34.

38. Calculate ΔG°_{rxn} and E°_{cell} for a redox reaction with $n = 2$ and $K = 15$ at 25°C.

39. Calculate ΔG°_{rxn} and E°_{cell} for a redox reaction with $n = 6$ and $K = 0.150$ at 25°C.

40. Calculate the equilibrium constant for the reaction of $Mg(s) + Cu^{2+}(aq)$ at 25°C.

41. Calculate the equilibrium constant for the reaction of $Ni(s) + Ag^+(aq)$ at 25°C.

19.7 The Nernst Equation and Concentration Cells

42. Calculate the potential of each of the following at 25°C.
a. $Fe^{2+}(aq, 0.100\ M) + 2\,e^- \rightarrow Fe(s)$
b. $Fe^{3+}(aq, 0.100\ M) + e^- \rightarrow Fe^{2+}(aq, 0.100\ M)$
c. $Pb^{2+}(aq, 0.500\ M) + 2\,e^- \rightarrow Pb(s)$
d. $MnO_4^-(aq, 2.00\ M) + 8\,H^+(aq, 1.00\ M) + 5\,e^- \rightarrow Mn^{2+}(aq, 0.500\ M) + 4\,H_2O(l)$

43. Calculate the potential of each of the following at 25°C.
a. $Cu(s) \rightarrow Cu^{2+}(aq, 0.100\ M) + 2\,e^-$
b. $Ag(s) \rightarrow Ag^+(aq, 0.100\ M) + e^-$

44. Calculate the potential of each of the following at 25°C.
a. $Cu(s) + Fe^{2+}(aq, 0.100\ M) \rightarrow Cu^{2+}(aq, 0.100\ M) + Fe(s)$
b. $2\,Ag(s) + Fe^{2+}(aq, 0.100\ M) \rightarrow 2\,Ag^+(aq, 0.100\ M) + Fe(s)$
c. $Cu(s) + 2\,Fe^{3+}(aq, 0.100\ M) \rightarrow Cu^{2+}(aq, 0.100\ M) + 2\,Fe^{2+}(aq, 0.100\ M)$
d. $Cu(s) + Pb^{2+}(aq, 0.100\ M) \rightarrow Cu^{2+}(aq, 2.00\ M) + Pb(s)$
e. $MnO_4^-(aq, 2.00\ M) + 8\,H^+(aq, 1.00\ M) + 5\,Fe^{2+}(aq, 0.100\ M) \rightarrow Mn^{2+}(aq, 0.500\ M) + 5\,Fe^{3+}(aq, 0.100\ M) + 4\,H_2O(l)$

45. Calculate the potential of the half-cell consisting of hydrogen gas at 1.000 atm and hydrogen ion at 0.200 M at 25°C.

$$2\,H^+(aq) + 2\,e^- \rightarrow H_2(g)$$

46. Calculate the potential for each of the following reactions under the conditions given, and state whether the reaction will proceed as written or in the opposite direction.
a. $MnO_4^-(aq, 0.125\ M) + 8\,H^+(aq, 1.00\ M) + 5\,Fe^{2+}(aq, 0.600\ M) \rightarrow Mn^{2+}(aq, 0.500\ M) + 5\,Fe^{3+}(aq, 0.900\ M) + 4\,H_2O(l)$
b. $Sn(NO_3)_2(aq, 3.00\ M) + Pb(NO_3)_2(aq, 2.00\ M) \rightarrow Pb(s) + Sn(NO_3)_4(aq, 0.500\ M)$
c. $2AgNO_3(aq, 1.50\ M) + Zn(s) \rightarrow Zn(NO_3)_2(aq, 0.400\ M) + 2Ag(s)$

47. Calculate the potential for each of the following reactions under the conditions given, and state whether the reaction will proceed as written or in the opposite direction.
a. $Cu(s) + Fe^{2+}(aq, 0.200\ M) \rightarrow Cu^{2+}(aq, 0.0100\ M) + Fe(s)$
b. $2\,Ag(s) + Fe^{2+}(aq, 0.500\ M) \rightarrow 2\,Ag^+\ (aq, 1.25\ M) + Fe(s)$
c. $Cu(s) + 2\,Fe^{3+}(aq, 2.00\ M) \rightarrow Cu^{2+}(aq, 0.800\ M) + 2\,Fe^{2+}(aq, 0.00100\ M)$
d. $Cu(s) + Pb^{2+}(aq, 0.750\ M) \rightarrow Cu^{2+}(aq, 0.250\ M) + Pb(s)$

19.8 Voltaic Cell Applications: Batteries, Fuel Cells, and Corrosion

48. Consider the overall cell reaction for the small, button-shaped batteries used in watches and car fobs.

$$Zn(s) + HgO(s) \rightarrow Hg(l) + ZnO(s)$$

a. Write the half-cell reactions.
b. Write the cell notation.
c. Calculate the cell voltage.
d. Calculate the standard free energy.

49. Consider the overall cell reaction for a lithium–iodine battery.

$$2\,Li(s) + I_2(s) \rightarrow 2\,LiI(s)$$

a. Write the half-cell reactions.
b. Write the cell notation.
c. Calculate the cell voltage.
d. Calculate the standard free energy.

50. A new lithium battery with $E^\circ_{cell} = 2.87$ V consists of a redox reaction between lithium metal and peroxide ions.

$Li(s) \rightarrow Li^+(aq) + e^-$ and $O_2^{2-}(aq) + 2\,e^- \rightarrow 2\,O^{2-}(aq)$

a. Identify the anode and cathode reactions.
b. Write the balanced, overall cell equation.
c. Calculate the standard potential for the cathode half-reaction.

51. Another proposed battery is a lithium–sulfur battery, which has an average $E^\circ_{cell} = 2.3$ V. The anode half-reaction is the oxidation of lithium metal. Sulfur, however, can form several different products under these conditions. Use the information in this problem and in Appendix A.5 to determine the average standard reduction potential of the cathode in this battery.

52. Methane is proposed as an alternative fuel to hydrogen in fuel cells. Calculate E°_{cell} for a fuel cell using the combustion of methane to form gaseous products, carbon dioxide, and water.

53. Another area of fuel cell research involves using microorganisms. One proposed fuel cell couples the oxidation of sugar in one half-cell with the reduction of oxygen gas in the other, using these half-cell reactions:

$$C_{12}H_{22}O_{11}(aq) + 13\,H_2O(l) \rightarrow 12\,CO_2(g) + 48\,H^+(aq) + 48\,e^-$$

$$O_2(g) + 4\,H^+(aq) + 4\,e^- \rightarrow 2\,H_2O(l)$$

a. Write the balanced overall equation.
b. Use data from Appendix A.2 and $\Delta G^\circ_f(C_{12}H_{22}O_{11}) = -1320$ kJ/mol to calculate ΔG°_{rxn} for the reaction.
c. Calculate E°_{cell} for this fuel cell.

54. Which of the following metals could act as a sacrificial anode (cathodic protection) for iron?
a. Al
b. Cu
c. Sn
d. Pb

55. Which of the following metals could *not* act as a sacrificial anode (cathodic protection) for iron?
a. Ca
b. Ni
c. Mn
d. Ag

19.9 Electrolytic Cells and Applications of Electrolysis

56. Identify the anode and cathode in Figure 4.7.

57. State whether each of the following equations would describe the overall reaction in a voltaic cell or an electrolysis cell.
a. $Ni(s) + Cl_2(g) \rightarrow Ni^{2+}(aq) + 2\,Cl^-(aq)$
b. $NiCl_2(aq) \rightarrow Ni(s) + Cl_2(g)$
c. $Zn(s) + 2\,AgNO_3(aq) \rightarrow 2\,Ag(s) + Zn(NO_3)_2(aq)$

58. State whether each of the following equations would describe the overall reaction in a voltaic cell or an electrolysis cell.
a. $2\,H_2(g) + O_2(g) \rightarrow 2\,H_2O(l)$
b. $Al_2O_3(\text{in } Na_3AlF_6) + 3\,C(s) \rightarrow 2\,Al(l) + 3\,CO(g)$

59. Three cells are connected in series, so the same current passes through each one. The first cell contains silver electrodes in silver nitrate solution, the second contains copper electrodes in copper(II) sulfate solution, and the third contains gallium electrodes in gallium(III) chloride solution. In one experiment, 1.500 g of silver is deposited in the first cell. What masses of copper and gallium are deposited in the other cells?

60. Calculate the mass of mercury deposited by passage of 19,200 C through $Hg_2(NO_3)_2(aq)$.

61. Calculate the mass of mercury deposited by a 10.0 A current passing for 3.00 h through $Hg_2(NO_3)_2(aq)$.

62. Calculate the volume of $Cl_2(g)$ (at 1.00 atm and 298 K) produced by passing a 0.400 A current through 25.00 mL of 5.000 M NaCl solution for 500.0 s. Assume that only chlorine is produced at the anode.

63. Two pure copper electrodes are immersed in a $CuSO_4$ solution. One is connected to a battery and the other to a cell with two pure silver electrodes immersed in silver nitrate solution. The second silver electrode is also connected to the battery. If sufficient charge passes to

deposit 1.00 g of copper on the cathode of the first cell,

a. what mass of copper is "dissolved" from the anode of that cell?

b. what mass of silver is deposited on the cathode of the second cell?

Putting It Together

64. Explain how Table 4.7 can be created from the data in Table 19.2.

65. Complete and balance an equation for the reaction in which cyanate ion, CNO^-, is oxidized to CO_2 and NO_3^- by MnO_4^-. Two elements in the same chemical species are oxidized in this reaction. (Hint: The carbon-to-nitrogen ratio is set by the formula of CNO^-.)

66. Complete and balance each of the following equations, in which more than one element is oxidized.

a. $Cr_2O_7^{2-}(aq) + CNO^-(aq) \rightarrow Cr^{3+}(aq) + CO_2(g) + NO_2(g)$

b. $Cr_2O_7^{2-}(aq) + CN^-(aq) \rightarrow Cr^{3+}(aq) + CO_2(g) + NO_2(g)$

c. $Cr_2O_7^{2-}(aq) + CNS^-(aq) \rightarrow Cr^{3+}(aq) + CO_2(g) + NO_2(g) + SO_4^{2-}(aq)$

67. Consider the following equation:

$2\ KMnO_4(s) + C_2H_6O_2(l) \rightarrow K_2CO_3(s) + 2\ MnO(s) + CO_2(g) + 3\ H_2O(l)$

a. What is the change in oxidation state for manganese?

b. What is the change in oxidation state for carbon?

68. Given that a positive cell potential means that a reaction will proceed spontaneously as written, and a negative potential means that it will proceed spontaneously in the opposite direction, what does a zero potential mean?

69. To electrolyze NaCl to yield Na and Cl_2, the NaCl must be molten. Sometimes an impurity such as LiCl is added to the solid NaCl before heating.

a. What happens to the freezing point (melting point) of a solution when a solute is added?

b. Explain why the impurity is added.

c. Should the impurity have any ions that are more easily reduced than sodium?

70. In a cell composed of a Co^{3+}/Co^{2+} half-cell suitably connected to a Cr^{3+}/Cr^{2+} half-cell, each of the ions is 1.00 M.

a. Write the equation for the spontaneous reaction.

b. Write the equation for the spontaneous reaction if each ion were initially 2.00 M.

71. Consider a situation in which a current of 3.00 A is passed through 1.00 L of a solution of 1.50 M Fe^{3+} for 2.00 h.

a. Use the data in Appendix A5 to determine what product will be produced.

b. Calculate the mass of the product produced.

72. Consider a situation in which a current of 3.00 A is passed through 1.00 L of a solution of 1.50 M Cu^{2+} for 2.00 h.

a. Use the data in Appendix A.5 to determine what product will be produced.

b. Calculate the mass of the product produced.

73. The electrolytic reduction of $Cu(CN)_2^-$ to Cu (plus cyanide ion) requires vigorous stirring to be most effective.

a. How many moles of electrons are required per mole of Cu?

b. Explain why the stirring is so important.

74. State whether each of the following equations would describe the overall reaction in a voltaic cell or an electrolysis cell:

a. $2\ Fe^{2+}(aq) + Cl_2(g) \rightarrow 2\ Fe^{3+}(aq) + 2\ Cl^-(aq)$

b. $14\ H^+(aq) + Cr_2O_7^{2-}(aq) + 3\ C_2O_4^{2-}(aq) \rightarrow 2\ Cr^{3+}(aq) + 6\ CO_2(g) + 7\ H_2O(l)$

c. $MnO_4^-(aq) + 8\ H^+(aq) + 5\ Ag(s) \rightarrow 5\ Ag^+(aq) + Mn^{2+}(aq) + 4\ H_2O(l)$

PRACTICE PROBLEM SOLUTIONS

Practice Problem 19.1 Solution

a. First, balance each half-reaction. Add coefficients to the elements as necessary, then add an appropriate number of electrons to the more positive side to balance the charge.

$$2\ Cl^- \rightarrow Cl_2 + 2\ e^-$$
$$K^+ + e^- \rightarrow K$$

Now, double the potassium half-reaction so that each half-reaction transfers the same number of electrons.

$$2(K^+ + e^- \rightarrow K) = 2\ K^+ + 2\ e^- \rightarrow 2\ K$$

Combine the half-reactions to yield the balanced chemical equation.

$$2\,K^+ + \cancel{2e^-} + 2\,Cl^- \rightarrow 2\,K + Cl_2 + \cancel{2e^-}$$
$$2\,K^+ + 2\,Cl^- \rightarrow 2\,K + Cl_2$$

b. First, balance each half-reaction. Adding coefficients to the elements is unnecessary for these two half-reactions, but the appropriate number of electrons must still be added to the more positive side to balance the charge.

$$Al \rightarrow Al^{3+} + 3\,e^-$$
$$Ag^+ + e^- \rightarrow Ag$$

Now, triple the silver half-reaction so that each half-reaction transfers the same number of electrons.

$$3(Ag^+ + e^- \rightarrow Ag) = 3\,Ag^+ + 3\,e^- \rightarrow 3\,Ag$$

Combine the half-reactions to yield the balanced chemical equation.

$$Al + 3\,Ag^+ + \cancel{3e^-} \rightarrow Al^{3+} + \cancel{3e^-} + 3\,Ag$$
$$Al + 3\,Ag^+ \rightarrow Al^{3+} + 3\,Ag$$

Practice Problem 19.2 Solution

Start by assigning oxidation numbers.

$$\underset{+1\ -1}{H_2O_2}(aq) \rightarrow \underset{0}{H_2}(g) + \underset{0}{O_2}(g)$$

Hydrogen is reduced from +1 to 0 and oxygen is oxidized from −1 to 0. In this reaction, then, hydrogen peroxide disproportionates, making it both the reducing agent and the oxidizing agent. More specifically, each hydrogen atom is reduced and thereby acts as an oxidizing agent, while each oxygen atom is oxidized, acting as a reducing agent.

Practice Problem 19.3 Solution

1. *Add coefficients to balance any elements other than H and O.* No coefficients are needed.

$$MnO_4^-(aq) + Cl^-(aq) \rightarrow Mn^{2+}(aq) + ClO^-(aq)$$

2. *Assign oxidation numbers to all elements in the equation.*

$$\underset{+7\ -2}{MnO_4^-}(aq) + \underset{-1}{Cl^-}(aq) \rightarrow \underset{+2}{Mn^{2+}}(aq) + \underset{+1\ -2}{ClO^-}(aq)$$

3. *Identify the elements that undergo oxidation and reduction.* Mn is reduced from +7 to +2, which is a gain of five electrons. Cl is oxidized from a −1 to +1, which is a loss of two electrons.

4. *Determine the coefficients needed to balance the electron transfer, and place these coefficients in the equation.* The least common multiple of 5 and 2 is 10, so a total of 10 electrons must be transferred during this reaction. Thus, two Mn must be reduced for every five Cl that are oxidized.

$$2\,MnO_4^-(aq) + 5\,Cl^-(aq) \rightarrow 2\,Mn^{2+}(aq) + 5\,ClO^-(aq)$$

5. *Balance any missing O atoms by adding water molecules.* There are eight O atoms on the reactant side and five on the product side. Add three water molecules to the product side.

$$2\,MnO_4^-(aq) + 5\,Cl^-(aq) \rightarrow 2\,Mn^{2+}(aq) + 5\,ClO^-(aq) + 3\,H_2O(l)$$

6. *Balance any missing H atoms by adding H^+ ions.* There are six H on the product side and none on the reactant side. Add six H^+ to the reactant side.

$$2\,MnO_4^-(aq) + 5\,Cl^-(aq) + 6\,H^+(aq) \rightarrow 2\,Mn^{2+}(aq) + 5\,ClO^-(aq) + 3\,H_2O(l)$$

7. *Verify that all atoms and charges are balanced.*

All atoms are balanced: 2 Mn, 8 O, 5 Cl, 6 H on each side.

Total charge of reactants is $2(-1) + 5(-1) + 6(+1) = -1$.

Total charge of products is $2(+2) + 5(-1) = -1$. Charge is balanced.

Practice Problem 19.4 Solution

1. *Add coefficients to balance any elements other than H and O.* No coefficients are needed.

$$NO_2^-(aq) + Al(s) \rightarrow NH_3(g) + AlO_2^-(aq)$$

2. *Assign oxidation numbers to all elements in the equation.* The oxidation state of O in peroxide compounds is −1.

$$\underset{+3-2}{NO_2^-}(aq) + \underset{0}{Al}(s) \rightarrow \underset{-3+1}{NH_3}(g) + \underset{+3-2}{AlO_2^-}(aq)$$

3. *Identify the elements that undergo oxidation and reduction.* Al is oxidized from 0 to +3, a loss of three electrons, while N is reduced from +3 to −3, a gain of six electrons.

4. *Determine the coefficients needed to balance the electron transfer, and place these coefficients in the equation.* Therefore, two Al must be oxidized for each N that is reduced for a total of six electrons transferred.

$$NO_2^-(aq) + 2\,Al(s) \rightarrow NH_3(g) + 2\,AlO_2^-(aq)$$

5. *Balance any missing O atoms by adding water molecules.* There are two O atoms on the reactant side and four O atoms on the product side of the equation. Add two water molecules to the reactant side.

$$NO_2^-(aq) + 2\,Al(s) + 2\,H_2O(l) \rightarrow NH_3(g) + 2\,AlO_2^-(aq)$$

6. *Balance any missing H atoms by adding H^+ ions.* There are four H atoms on the reactant side and three on the product side. Add one hydrogen ion to the product side.

$$NO_2^-(aq) + 2\,Al(s) + 2\,H_2O(l) \rightarrow NH_3(g) + 2\,AlO_2^-(aq) + H^+(aq)$$

7. *Neutralize the H^+ ions by adding the same number of OH^- ions to each side of the equation.* Add one OH^- to each side.

$$NO_2^-(aq) + 2\,Al(s) + 2\,H_2O(l) + OH^-(aq) \rightarrow NH_3(g) + 2\,AlO_2^-(aq) + H^+(aq) + OH^-(aq)$$

8. *Combine any H^+ and OH^- ions on the same side to form water molecules, and then remove any water molecules appearing on both sides of the equation.* Form one water molecule on the product side, and then cancel one water molecule on each side.

$$NO_2^-(aq) + 2\,Al(s) + 2\,H_2O + OH^-(aq) \rightarrow NH_3(g) + 2\,AlO_2^-(aq) + H_2O(l)$$

$$NO_2^-(aq) + 2\,Al(s) + H_2O + OH^-(aq) \rightarrow NH_3(g) + 2\,AlO_2^-(aq)$$

9. *Verify that all atoms and charges are balanced.*

All atoms are balanced: 1 N, 4 O, 2 Al, and 3 H on each side.
The total charge of reactants is $-1 + -1 = -2$.
The total charge of products is $2(-1) = -2$.
Therefore, the charge is balanced.

Practice Problem 19.5 Solution

1. *Add coefficients to balance any elements other than H and O.* Insert a 2 to balance Cr.

$$CH_4O(aq) + Cr_2O_7^{2-}(aq) \rightarrow CH_2O_2(aq) + 2\,Cr^{3+}(aq)$$

2. *Assign oxidation numbers to all elements in the equation.*

$$\underset{-2+1-2}{CH_4O(aq)} + \underset{+6\ -2}{Cr_2O_7^{2-}(aq)} \rightarrow \underset{+2+1-2}{CH_2O_2(aq)} + \underset{+3}{2\,Cr^{3+}(aq)}$$

3. *Identify the elements that undergo oxidation and reduction.* C is oxidized from -2 to $+2$ (a loss of four electrons), while Cr is reduced from $+6$ to $+3$ (a gain of three electrons).

4. *Determine the coefficients needed to balance the electron transfer, and place these coefficients in the equation.* The least common multiple of 4 and 3 is 12, so a total of 10 electrons are transferred during this reaction. Three C must be oxidized for every four Cr that are reduced.

$$3\,CH_4O(aq) + 2\,Cr_2O_7^{2-}(aq) \rightarrow 3\,CH_2O_2(aq) + 4\,Cr^{3+}(aq)$$

5. *Balance any missing O atoms by adding water molecules.* There are 17 O atoms on the reactant side but only six on the product side, so add 11 water molecules to the products.

$$3\,CH_4O(aq) + 2\,Cr_2O_7^{2-}(aq) \rightarrow 3\,CH_2O_2(aq) + 4\,Cr^{3+}(aq) + 11\,H_2O(l)$$

6. *Balance any missing H atoms by adding H^+ ions.* There are 28 H atoms on the product side but only 12 on the reactant side, so add 16 hydrogen ions to the reactants.

$$3\,CH_4O(aq) + 2\,Cr_2O_7^{2-}(aq) + 16\,H^+(aq) \rightarrow 3\,CH_2O_2(aq) + 4\,Cr^{3+}(aq) + 11\,H_2O(l)$$

7. Verify that all atoms and charges are balanced.

All atoms are balanced: 3 C, 28 H, 17 O, and 4 Cr on each side.
Total charge of reactants is $2(-2) + 16(+1) = +12$.
Total charge of products is $4(+3) = +12$.
Charge is balanced.

Apply stoichiometric principles to calculate the number of moles of methanol.

$$7.35\ \text{mL}\ Cr_2O_7^{2-}\left(\frac{1\ \text{L}}{1000\ \text{mL}}\right)\left(\frac{0.0887\ \text{mol}\ Cr_2O_7^{2-}}{1\ \text{L}}\right)\left(\frac{3\ \text{mol}\ CH_4O}{2\ \text{mol}\ Cr_2O_7^{2-}}\right) = 9.78 \times 10^{-4}\ \text{mol}\ CH_4O$$

Calculate molarity using the moles and volume of methanol.

$$\frac{9.78 \times 10^{-4}\ \text{mol}\ CH_4O}{15.00\ \text{mL}\ CH_4O \times \dfrac{1\ \text{L}}{1000\ \text{mL}}} = 0.0652\ \text{M}\ CH_4O$$

Practice Problem 19.6 Solution

a. Magnesium metal is the anode, the site of oxidation and the source of the electrons. The electrons flow to the lead cathode, where they are accepted by lead(II) ions to form solid lead, which will deposit on the cathode. At the same time, cations and anions are flowing through the salt bridge to complete the electrical circuit. Standard conditions dictate that the ions are present in molar concentrations.

$$Mg(s)|Mg^{2+}(1\ M)\|Pb^{2+}(1\ M)|Pb(s)$$

b. The anode is the nickel metal, which oxidizes to release electrons that flow to the platinum electrode and are accepted by the Co(III) ions in solution to form Co(II) ions in solution. At the same time, cations and anions are flowing through the salt bridge to complete the electrical circuit. Standard conditions dictate that the ions are present in molar concentrations.

$$Ni(s)|Ni^{2+}(1\ M)\|Pt(s)|Co^{3+}(1\ M), Co^{2+}(1\ M)$$

Practice Problem 19.7 Solution

In Example 19.6b Sn is oxidized at the anode and Fe^{3+} is reduced at the cathode. More specifically, the anode half-cell consists of a Sn electrode suspended in Sn^{2+} solution, whereas the cathode half-cell consists of the Pt electrode suspended in Fe^{3+} solution. Cations flow through the salt bridge in the same direction as the electrons through the wire, while anions flow in the opposite direction.

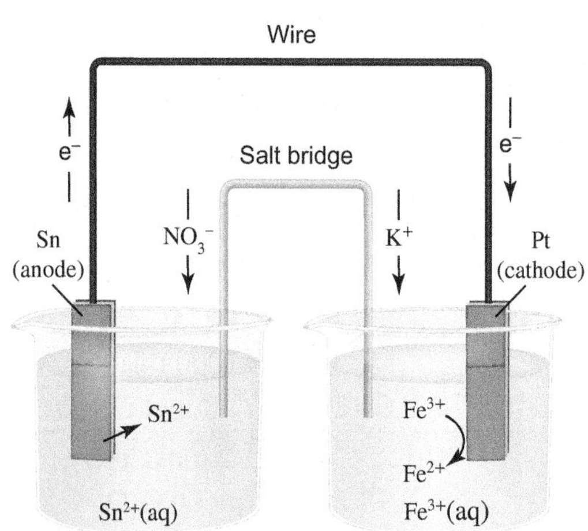

Practice Problem 19.8 Solution

Find the standard reduction potentials for each half-cell in Table 19.2:

$$Ag^+ + e^- \rightarrow Ag \quad E° = 0.80\ V$$
$$Cu^{2+} + 2\ e^- \rightarrow Cu \quad E° = 0.34\ V$$

$E°$ for Ag^+ is larger than $E°$ for Cu^{2+}, so Ag^+ is more easily reduced than Cu^{2+} and will form the cathode half-cell. Copper will oxidize at the anode.

$$Cu + 2\ Ag^+ \rightarrow Cu^{2+} + 2\ Ag$$
$$E°_{cell} = E°_{cathode} - E°_{anode}$$
$$E°_{cell} = 0.80\ V - (0.34\ V) = 0.46\ V$$

The positive value for the cell potential indicates that this combination of half-cells produces a spontaneous reaction in the forward direction.

Practice Problem 19.9 Solution

a. The two half-cells and their potentials are

$$Sn^{2+}(aq) + 2\ e^- \rightarrow Sn(s) \quad E° = -0.14\ V$$
$$Fe^{3+}(aq) + e^- \rightarrow Fe^{2+}(aq) \quad E° = 0.77\ V$$

Fe^{3+} is more easily reduced than Sn^{2+}, so the iron half-cell is the cathode and the tin half-cell is the anode. Use Equation 19.1 to calculate the cell voltage:

$$E°_{cell} = E°_{cathode} - E°_{anode}$$
$$E°_{cell} = 0.77\ V - (-0.14\ V) = 0.91\ V$$

When writing the cell notation, the anode (tin) goes on the left and the cathode (iron) on the right. A Pt electrode is needed for the iron half-cell, and a comma is used to separate the two iron ions.

$$Sn(s)|Sn^{2+}(1\ M)\|Pt(s)|Fe^{3+}(1\ M), Fe^{2+}(1\ M)$$

b. The two half-cells and their potentials are

$$Co^{3+}(aq) + e^- \rightarrow Co^{2+}(aq) \quad E° = 1.92\ V$$
$$Mg^{2+}(aq) + 2\ e^- \rightarrow Mg(s) \quad E° = -2.38\ V$$

Co^{3+} is more easily reduced than Mg^{2+}, so the cobalt half-cell is the cathode and the magnesium half-cell is the anode. The cell voltage is

$$E°_{cell} = E°_{cathode} - E°_{anode}$$
$$E°_{cell} = 1.92\ V - (-2.38\ V) = 4.30\ V$$

Correct cell notation places the anode (magnesium) on the left and the cathode (cobalt) on the right. The cathode includes a Pt electrode because the reduction of Co^{3+} does not include a solid.

$$Mg(s)|Mg^{2+}(1\ M)\|Pt(s)|Co^{3+}(1\ M), Co^{2+}(1\ M)$$

Practice Problem 19.10 Solution

a. The two half-cells for the cell are shown here along with the cell notation from Practice Problem 19.9.

$$Sn^{2+}(aq) + 2\ e^- \rightarrow Sn(s)$$
$$Fe^{3+}(aq) + e^- \rightarrow Fe^{2+}(aq)$$
$$Sn(s)|Sn^{2+}(1\ M)\|Pt(s)|Fe^{3+}(1\ M), Fe^{2+}(1\ M)$$

For the electron transfer to be balanced, one Sn atom must be oxidized for every two Fe^{3+} ions that are reduced, for a total of 2 moles of electrons transferred.

$$Sn^{2+}(aq) + 2\,e^- \rightarrow Sn(s) \quad \text{and}$$
$$2\,Fe^{2+}(aq) \rightarrow 2\,Fe^{3+}(aq) + 2\,e^-$$
$$Sn(s) + 2\,Fe^{3+}(aq) \rightarrow Sn^{2+}(aq) + 2\,Fe^{2+}(aq)$$

b. The two half-cells for the cell and the cell notation from Practice Problem 19.9 are as follows:

$$Co^{3+}(aq) + e^- \rightarrow Co^{2+}(aq)$$
$$Mg^{2+}(aq) + 2\,e^- \rightarrow Mg(s)$$
$$Mg(s)\,|\,Mg^{2+}(1\text{ M})\,\|\,Pt(s)\,|\,Co^{3+}(1\text{ M}), Co^{2+}(1\text{ M})$$

For the electron transfer to be balanced, one Mg atom must be oxidized for every two Co^{3+} ions that are reduced, making a total of 2 moles of electrons transferred.

$$2\,Co^{3+}(aq) + 2\,e^- \rightarrow 2\,Co^{2+}(aq) \quad \text{and}$$
$$Mg(s) \rightarrow Mg^{2+}(aq) + 2\,e^-$$
$$Mg(s) + 2\,Co^{3+}(aq) \rightarrow Mg^{2+}(aq) + 2\,Co^{2+}(aq)$$

Practice Problem 19.11 Solution

Practice Problem 19.8 provides the balanced net ionic equation, the number of moles of electrons transferred, and the cell voltage. Use these data in Equation 19.2 to calculate the standard free energy change.

$$Cu + 2\,Ag^+ \rightarrow Cu^{2+} + 2\,Ag \quad n = 2\text{ mol}$$
$$E^\circ_{cell} = 0.46\text{ V}$$
$$\Delta G^\circ = -nFE^\circ$$
$$\Delta G^\circ = -(2\text{ mol e}^-)\left(\frac{96{,}485\text{ C}}{1\text{ mol e}^-}\right)(0.46\text{ V})$$
$$\Delta G^\circ = -89{,}000\text{ C}\cdot\text{V} = 89{,}000\text{ J} = -89\text{ kJ}$$

Practice Problem 19.12 Solution

$$E^\circ = \frac{RT}{nF}\ln K$$
$$\ln K = \frac{nFE^\circ}{RT}$$
$$K = e^{\frac{nFE^\circ}{RT}}$$

Solve the exponent separately.

$$\frac{nFE^\circ}{RT} = \frac{2\text{ mol e}^-\left(\frac{96{,}485\text{ C}}{1\text{ mol e}^-}\right)(0.46\text{ V})}{8.3145\frac{\text{J}}{\text{K}\cdot\text{mol}}(298\text{ K})} = 36$$
$$K = e^{36}$$
$$K = 4 \times 10^{15}$$

The large, positive value of the equilibrium constant indicates a reaction that proceeds strongly in the forward direction, consistent with the positive value for the cell potential and the negative value for the free energy change calculated in Practice Problem 19.11.

Practice Problem 19.13 Solution

$K \gg 1$, so this should be a spontaneous process with a positive standard cell potential that is greater in magnitude than E° in Example 19.13.

$$E^\circ = \frac{RT}{nF}\ln K$$
$$E^\circ = \frac{8.3145\frac{\text{J}}{\text{K}\cdot\text{mol}}(298\text{ K})}{1\text{ mol e}^-\left(\frac{96{,}485\text{ C}}{1\text{ mol e}^-}\right)}\ln 3.5 \times 10^6$$
$$E^\circ = 0.387\text{ V}$$

The positive value for the standard cell potential is as predicted for the equilibrium constant value, and the magnitude is greater than that of Example 19.13.

Practice Problem 19.14 Solution

This reaction has a lower concentration of Ag^+ ions than the standard conditions, so you should expect $E < E^\circ$. To calculate the potential, write the equation for the Ag/Ag^+ half-cell, and determine the expression for Q:

$$Ag^+(aq) + e^- \rightarrow Ag(s) \quad n = 1$$
$$Q = \frac{1}{[Ag^+]} = \frac{1}{0.100\text{ M}} = 10.0\text{ M}^{-1}$$

According to Table 19.2, $E^\circ = 0.80$ V for this half-cell. Use the Nernst equation (Equation 19.4) to determine the voltage under the nonstandard conditions given.

$$E = E^\circ - \frac{RT}{nF}\ln Q$$
$$E = 0.80\text{ V} - \left[\frac{\left(8.3145\frac{\text{J}}{\text{K}\cdot\text{mol}}\right)(298\text{ K})}{(1\text{ mol e}^-)\left(\frac{96{,}485\text{ C}}{1\text{ mol e}^-}\right)}\right]\ln 10$$
$$E = 0.74\text{ V}$$

As predicted, $E < E^\circ$.

Practice Problem 19.15 Solution

Start with the half-cell reactions, and determine the standard cell potential using Table 19.2 and Equation 19.1.

$$Pb^{2+}(aq) + 2\,e^- \rightarrow Pb(s) \qquad E^\circ = -0.13\ V$$
$$Cu^{2+}(aq) + 2\,e^- \rightarrow Cu(s) \qquad E^\circ = +0.34\ V$$

$E°(Cu^{2+}) > E°(Pb^{2+})$, so Cu^{2+} is reduced at the cathode and Pb^{2+} is oxidized at the anode in this cell.

$$E°_{cell} = E°_{cathode} - E°_{anode}$$
$$E° = 0.34\text{ V} - (-0.13\text{ V}) = 0.47\text{ V}$$

Combine the half-cell equations to form a cell equation with a *balanced* transfer of electrons.

$$Pb(s) + Cu^{2+}(aq) \rightarrow Pb^{2+}(aq) + Cu(s) \qquad n = 2$$

Write the expression for Q, and substitute the concentrations into the expression.

$$Q = \frac{[Pb^{2+}]}{[Cu^{2+}]} = \frac{0.200}{0.100} = 2.00$$

In this problem, the reactant concentration ($[Cu^{2+}]$) is somewhat lower than the product concentration ($[Pb^{2+}]$), which favors the reverse reaction. Thus, you might predict that $E < E°$.

Now, use the Nernst equation (Equation 19.4) to calculate the potential of the given cell.

$$E = E° - \frac{RT}{nF}\ln Q$$

$$E = 0.47\text{ V} - \left[\frac{\left(8.3145\frac{\text{J}}{\text{K}\cdot\text{mol}}\right)(298\text{ K})}{(2\text{ mol e}^-)\left(\frac{96{,}485\text{ C}}{1\text{ mol e}^-}\right)}\right]\ln(2.00)$$

$$E = 0.46\text{ V}$$

Practice Problem 19.16 Solution

The ions in the half-cell with the higher concentration will be reduced. Thus, $Q = 0.020\text{ M}/1.0\text{ M} = 0.020$ and $n = 2$.

$$E = E° - \frac{RT}{nF}\ln Q$$

$$E = 0 - \frac{8.3145\frac{\text{J}}{\text{K}\cdot\text{mol}}(298\text{ K})}{(2\text{ mol e}^-)\left(\frac{96{,}485\text{ C}}{1\text{ mol e}^-}\right)}\ln 0.020$$

$$E = 0.050\text{ V}$$

Practice Problem 19.17 Solution

Here, as in Example 19.17, you can assume that the half-cell with the 1.0 M concentration is the higher concentration and is the site of reduction. Therefore, $Q = \frac{x}{1.0\text{ M}}$.

$$E = E° - \frac{RT}{nF}\ln Q$$

$$\ln Q = \frac{-nFE}{RT}$$
$$Q = e^{-nFE/RT}$$

Solve the exponent separately.

$$-\frac{nFE}{RT} = -\frac{(2\text{ mol e}^-)\left(\frac{96{,}485\text{ C}}{\text{mol e}^-}\right)(0.065\text{ V})}{\left(8.3145\frac{\text{J}}{\text{K}\cdot\text{mol}}\right)(298\text{ K})} = -5.06$$

$$Q = e^{-5.06} \quad Q = \frac{x}{1.0\text{ M}}$$
$$x = e^{-5.06}\cdot 1.0\text{ M}$$
$$x = 0.0063\text{ M}$$

Practice Problem 19.18 Solution

a. The standard reduction potentials for the half-cells are

Anode: $Cd(s) + 2\,OH^-(aq) \rightarrow Cd(OH)_2(s) + 2\,e^-$ $\quad E° = -0.809\text{ V}$

Cathode: $Ni(OH)_2(s) + 2\,e^- \rightarrow Ni(s) + 2\,OH^-(aq)$ $\quad E° = 0.72\text{ V}$

$$E°_{cell} = E°_{cathode} - E°_{anode}$$
$$E°_{cell} = 0.72\text{ V} - (-0.809\text{ V}) = 1.53\text{ V}$$

b. For cells linked in a series, the voltages of the individual cells are added together to obtain the total voltage of the battery.

$$E_{total} = 4\text{ cells}\left(\frac{1.53\text{ V}}{1\text{ cell}}\right) = 6.12\text{ V}$$

A battery composed of four of these nickel–cadmium cells has a total voltage of 6.12 volts.

c. Both the anode and cathode reactions involve 2 moles of electrons, so the redox process is balanced. Combine the reactants of both equations and the products of both equations, eliminating any components that appear as both reactants and products.

$$Cd(s) + \cancel{2\,OH^-(aq)} + Ni(OH)_2(s) + \cancel{2e^-} \rightarrow Cd(OH)_2(s) + \cancel{2e^-} + Ni(s) + \cancel{2\,OH^-(aq)}$$

Overall reaction: $Cd(s) + Ni(OH)_2(s) \rightarrow Cd(OH)_2(s) + Ni(s)$

Practice Problem 19.19 Solution

a. Write the anode and cathode reactions, and balance the redox processes. A coefficient of 2 is needed for every component in the cathode reaction.

Anode: $Zn(s) + 2\,OH^-(aq) \rightarrow Zn(OH)_2(s) + 2\,e^-$

Cathode: $2\,MnO_2(s) + 2\,H_2O(l) + 2\,e^- \rightarrow 2\,MnO(OH)(s) + 2\,OH^-(aq)$

Combine the anode and cathode reactions:

$$Zn(s) + \cancel{2\,OH^-(aq)} + 2\,MnO_2(s) + 2\,H_2O(l) + \cancel{2e^-} \rightarrow$$
$$Zn(OH)_2(s) + \cancel{2e^-} + 2\,MnO(OH)(s) + \cancel{2\,OH^-(aq)}$$

Cell reaction: $Zn(s) + 2\,MnO_2(s) + 2\,H_2O(l) \rightarrow Zn(OH)_2(s) + 2\,MnO(OH)(s)$

b. Find the anode half-cell potential in Appendix A.5, and use the full cell potential to calculate the cathode half-cell potential.

$$E^\circ_{cell} = E^\circ_{cathode} - E^\circ_{anode}$$
$$E^\circ_{cathode} = E^\circ_{cell} + E^\circ_{anode}$$
$$E^\circ_{cathode} = 1.5\text{ V} + (-1.249\text{ V}) = 0.251\text{ V}$$

Practice Problem 19.20 Solution

a. The coefficients in the anode half-reaction must be multiplied by 2 to balance the transfer of electrons.

$$2\,H_2(g) + 4\,OH^-(aq) \rightarrow 4\,H_2O(l) + 4\,e^-$$

Now combine this equation with that of the cathode.

$$2\,H_2(g) + \cancel{4\,OH^-(aq)} + O_2(g) + \cancel{2\,H_2O(l) + 4\,e^-} \rightarrow$$
$$2\,H_2O(l) + \cancel{4\,e^- + 4\,OH^-(aq)}$$

The balanced overall equation, therefore, is

$$2\,H_2(g) + O_2(g) \rightarrow 2\,H_2O(l)$$

b. Because this fuel cell has the same overall reaction as the fuel cell in Example 19.20, you could assume, according to Hess's law (Section 6.7), that the standard cell potential is the same. Use the half-cell potentials in Appendix A.5 to verify this.

$$E^\circ_{cell} = E^\circ_{cathode} - E^\circ_{anode}$$
$$E^\circ_{cell} = 0.401\text{ V} - (-0.83\text{ V}) = 1.23\text{ V}$$

Practice Problem 19.21 Solution

The stoichiometry of the chemical reaction of interest shows that 1 mole of electrons produces 1 mole of silver metal.

$$Ag^+(aq) + e^- \rightarrow Ag(s)$$

Combining the charge calculation with the stoichiometry gives the following equation.

$$3.00\text{ h}\left(\frac{60.0\text{ min}}{1\text{ h}}\right)\left(\frac{60.0\text{ s}}{1\text{ min}}\right)\left(\frac{10.0\text{ C}}{1\text{ s}}\right)\left(\frac{1\text{ mol e}^-}{96{,}485\text{ C}}\right)\left(\frac{1\text{ mol Ag}}{1\text{ mol e}^-}\right)\left(\frac{107.9\text{ g Ag}}{1\text{ mol Ag}}\right) = 121\text{ g Ag}$$

Practice Problem 19.22 Solution

$$Pb^{2+}(aq) + 2\,e^- \rightarrow Pb(s)$$

$$1.00\text{ kg Pb}\left(\frac{1000\text{ g Pb}}{1\text{ kg Pb}}\right)\left(\frac{1\text{ mol Pb}}{207.2\text{ g Pb}}\right)\left(\frac{2\text{ mol e}^-}{1\text{ mol Pb}}\right)\left(\frac{96{,}485\text{ C}}{1\text{ mol e}^-}\right)\left(\frac{1\text{ s}}{25.0\text{ C}}\right)$$
$$= 3.73 \times 10^4\text{ s} = 10.3\text{ h}$$

Practice Problem 19.23 Solution

$$Pb^{2+}(aq) + 2\,e^- \rightarrow Pb(s)$$

$$\frac{1.00\text{ kg Pb}}{1}\left(\frac{1000\text{ g Pb}}{1\text{ kg Pb}}\right)\left(\frac{1\text{ mol Pb}}{207.2\text{ g Pb}}\right)\left(\frac{2\text{ mol e}^-}{1\text{ mol Pb}}\right)\left(\frac{96{,}485\text{ C}}{1\text{ mol e}^-}\right) = 9.31 \times 10^5\text{ C}$$

$$I = \frac{q}{t} = \frac{9.31 \times 10^5\text{ C}}{24.00\text{ h}}\left(\frac{1\text{ h}}{3600\text{ s}}\right) = 10.8\text{ A}$$

Practice Problem 19.24 Solution

a. Start with the balanced overall reaction from Example 19.24, and use the coefficients as the molar amounts in Equation 18.8.

$$2\,CH_4O(l) + 3\,O_2(g) \rightarrow 2\,CO_2(g) + 4\,H_2O(l)$$
$$\Delta G^\circ_{rxn} = \Sigma n[\Delta G^\circ_f(\text{products})] - \Sigma n[\Delta G^\circ_f(\text{reactants})]$$
$$\Delta G^\circ_{rxn} = \left[2\text{ mol }CO_2\left(\frac{-394.4\text{ kJ}}{1\text{ mol }CO_2}\right) + 4\text{ mol }H_2O\left(\frac{-273.1\text{ kJ}}{1\text{ mol }H_2O}\right)\right] - \left[2\text{ mol }CH_4O\left(\frac{-162.3\text{ kJ}}{1\text{ mol }CH_4O}\right) + 3\text{ mol }O_2\left(\frac{0\text{ kJ}}{1\text{ mol }O_2}\right)\right]$$
$$\Delta G^\circ_{rxn} = -1556.6\text{ kJ}$$

b. Rearrange Equation 19.2 to calculate E°_{cell} from ΔG°_{rxn}. Based on the balanced half-reactions from Example 19.24, $n = 12$ mol of electrons.

$$\Delta G^\circ = -nFE^\circ$$
$$E^\circ = \frac{\Delta G^\circ}{-nF}$$
$$E^\circ = \frac{-1556.6\text{ kJ}\left(\frac{1000\text{ J}}{1\text{ kJ}}\right)}{-\left(12\text{ mol e}^-\left(\frac{96{,}485\text{C}}{1\text{ mol e}^-}\right)\right)}$$
$$E^\circ = 1.344\text{ V}$$

CHAPTER 20

Nuclear Chemistry

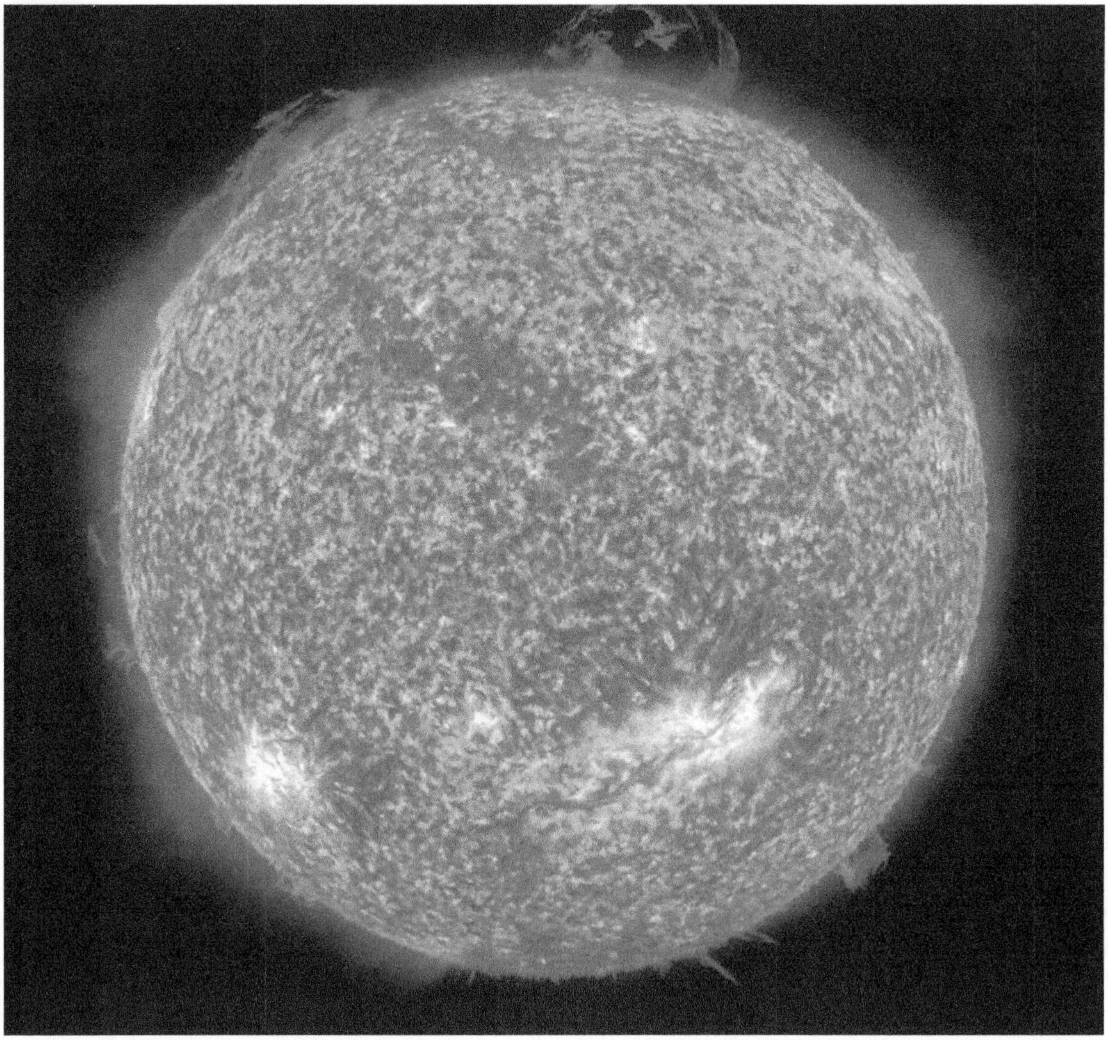

Courtesy of NASA/SDO and the AIA, EVE, and HMI science teams

The term *nuclear* means pertaining to the *nucleus* of an atom. Unlike chemical reactions that affect electrons (via changes in electron configurations or making and breaking bonds), nuclear reactions affect the protons and neutrons. As you'll see in this chapter, nuclear reactions tend to release large amounts of energy. For example, the energy of the Sun comes from nuclear reactions in the Sun's core.

Chapter Outline

GOALS

- Describe how each process of decay occurs.
- Write balanced equations for nuclear decay.
- Using the mass number and atomic number, predict whether a given isotope is likely to be radioactive.
- Using the mass number and atomic number, predict the mode of decay of a radioactive isotope.
- Calculate half-life, initial amount, final amount, or decay time given the other variables.
- Determine the age of artifacts using the concepts and equations of decay and half-life.
- Predict the products of fission reactions.
- Predict the products of fusion reactions.
- Calculate energy changes for nuclear reactions.
- Calculate nuclear binding energy.
- Compare the stabilities of different isotopes using relative binding energies.

20.1 Natural Radioactivity

GOALS

- Describe how each process of decay occurs.
- Write balanced equations for nuclear decay.

Background Review

Chapter 2 Atoms and the Periodic Table: Section 2.4—Subatomic Particles, Isotopes, and Ions

Previous chapters have discussed chemical reactions (which affect electron configurations and/or bonds within molecules) and physical processes (which affect intermolecular forces). This chapter considers the effects of **nuclear** changes in atoms. In most cases, nuclear changes alter the number of protons in the nucleus of the atom, so they cause a change from one element to another—a process called **nuclear transmutation**. Nuclear reactions differ from ordinary chemical reactions in the ways listed in Table 20.1.

Isotopes are atoms that have the same number of protons but different numbers of neutrons (Section 2.4).

TABLE 20.1 Chemical Versus Nuclear Reactions

Chemical Reactions	Nuclear Reactions
Involve electrons (e.g., making/breaking bonds).	Involve protons and neutrons.
Atomic numbers do not change.	Atomic numbers almost always change.
Isotopes of a given element behave almost identically.	Different isotopes of an element behave differently.
The total quantity of matter does not change.	A small amount of matter is converted to energy.

As a result, isotopes of an element have the same atomic number and nuclear charge, Z, but different mass numbers, A. The symbol for an isotope such as cobalt-60 may be represented as either ^{60}Co or $^{60}_{27}Co$.

> Including the Z subscript is very helpful when balancing nuclear equations.

Although "isotope" and "nuclide" are widely used as synonyms, *isotope* refers to the entire atom, including the electrons, whereas **nuclide** refers specifically to the nucleus of the isotope. When interpreting equations for nuclear reactions, assume that the species shown are nuclides.

RADIOACTIVE DECAY

The nuclei of some naturally occurring isotopes spontaneously alter their number of protons and/or neutrons to become more stable in a process called **radioactive decay** or nuclear decay. Isotopes that spontaneously undergo decay are considered **radioactive** because they emit one or more types of **nuclear radiation**—alpha particles, beta particles, positrons, and gamma particles—as well as a considerable quantity of energy during the decay process. The properties of these particles are listed in Table 20.2. Because this release of particles (radiation) occurs spontaneously, it is often called **natural radioactivity**.

Alpha particles are made up of two protons and two neutrons, so they are identical to a helium-4 nucleus. **Beta particles** are electrons with extremely high energies. **Positrons** are similar to beta particles, but with the opposite charge. **Gamma particles** are photons of **electromagnetic radiation** (i.e., a form of light), but with much higher energy and much shorter wavelengths than visible light (Figure 8.4).

TABLE 20.2 Products of Natural Radioactivity

Particle	Symbols	*A*	*Z*	Charge	Identity
Alpha	$\alpha, {}^4_2\alpha, {}^4_2\text{He}$	4	2	+2	Helium nucleus
Beta	$\beta, \beta^-, {}^{\ 0}_{-1}\beta, {}^{\ 0}_{-1}\text{e}$	0	−1	−1	Electron
Positron	$\beta^+, {}^{\ 0}_{+1}\beta$	0	1	+1	Positron
Gamma	$\gamma, {}^0_0\gamma$	0	0	0	Photon of high-energy electromagnetic radiation

Sometimes, a stream of any of these types of particles is called a ray, as in gamma ray. Once alpha and beta particles slow down after being emitted from the nucleus, they become ordinary ^{4}He nuclei and ordinary electrons, respectively.

The term *atomic number* does not easily apply to particles that are not atoms. In the context of nuclear reactions, therefore, *Z* is typically called the *charge* or *nuclear charge* (Section 9.2) rather than the atomic number. This expanded definition for *Z* explains how some particles (e.g., beta, positron, and gamma) can have a nonzero value for *Z* even though they do not contain any protons.

Nuclear reactions can be represented by equations similar to those used for chemical reactions, with the reactants on the left, the products on the right, and an arrow in the middle pointing from the reactants to the products. The total of the mass numbers and the total of the nuclear charges must always be equal on both sides of a balanced nuclear equation.

The nuclide that undergoes radioactive decay is called the **parent nuclide**, and the nuclide that is produced (along with a small particle from Table 20.2) is called the **daughter nuclide**. For example, the natural decay of ${}^{238}_{92}\text{U}$ (the parent nuclide) produces ${}^{234}_{90}\text{Th}$ (the daughter nuclide) and an alpha particle, ${}^4_2\text{He}$. In an equation written to represent this process, the sums of the subscripts on the left and right sides of the arrow are equal, as are the sums of the superscripts.

$$ {}^{238}_{92}\text{U} \rightarrow {}^{234}_{90}\text{Th} + {}^4_2\text{He} $$

$$ \text{Superscripts: } 238 = 234 + 4 $$
$$ \text{Subscripts: } 92 = 90 + 2 $$

A nuclear equation must be balanced in both mass (the superscripts) and nuclear charge (the subscripts).

ALPHA AND BETA DECAY

In **alpha decay**, the nucleus ejects an alpha particle, so its mass number decreases by 4 and its atomic number decreases by 2. In **beta decay**, a neutron becomes a proton by ejecting an electron (the beta particle), so the mass number does not change, but the atomic number increases by 1.

The video in Figure 20.1 demonstrates how to write balanced equations for alpha and beta decay.

Steve Lemon, Macmillan Learning

FIGURE 20.1 Video Tutorial: Product of Decay I

NOTE: You need to be online to access this video.

This video shows how to determine the production of nuclear decay, given the reactant and type of decay (alpha or beta).

Example 20.1

^{210}Tl decays to ^{210}Pb and one other product. What is the other product?

Solution

Balance the nuclear equation to determine what the other product is. It is easiest to balance a nuclear reaction if you include the subscripts for each isotope, because the subscript represents the charge, which must also be balanced. The atomic numbers for Pb and Tl can be determined from the periodic table and part of the nuclear equation can be written as follows:

$$ {}^{210}_{81}\text{Tl} \rightarrow {}^{210}_{82}\text{Pb} + ? $$

The total mass number for the reactant and products is already equal, so the superscript of the unknown product must be 0:

$$ {}^{210}_{81}\text{Tl} \rightarrow {}^{210}_{82}\text{Pb} + {}^0_?? $$

The parent isotope has a total positive charge of 81 and the daughter isotope has a total positive charge of 82. For the overall charges to balance between the reactants and products, the subscript of the unknown product must be −1:

$$ {}^{210}_{81}\text{Tl} \rightarrow {}^{210}_{82}\text{Pb} + {}^{\ 0}_{-1}? $$

The particle in Table 20.2 that has a single negative charge and a zero mass number is a beta particle (electron), so the complete equation is

$$ {}^{210}_{81}\text{Tl} \rightarrow {}^{210}_{82}\text{Pb} + {}^{\ 0}_{-1}\beta $$

EVERYDAY CONNECTION

Space probes that travel far from the Sun, such as the *Cassini* probe to Saturn or *New Horizons* to Pluto, cannot generate sufficient operating power using solar panels. Instead, heat generated by the natural alpha decay of plutonium-238 is converted to electrical energy to operate these probes.

NASA/JPL

Steve Lemon, Macmillan Learning

FIGURE 20.2 Video Tutorial: Product of Decay II

NOTE: You need to be online to access this video.

This video shows how to determine the production of nuclear decay, given the reactant and type of decay (positron emission of electron capture).

PRACTICE PROBLEM 20.1

What daughter nuclide is produced by the beta decay of ^{234}Th?

Hint: Write an equation for the beta decay of ^{234}Th. Balance the total mass number (the superscripts) and total charge (the subscripts) on both sides of the equation.

GAMMA EMISSION

Nearly all radioactive decay processes also give off a gamma particle, but some radioactive decay events give off *only* a gamma particle. The emission of a gamma particle does not change the atomic number or the mass number of the parent isotope because the gamma particle has zero charge and zero mass number:

$$^{119}_{50}Sn \rightarrow \, ^{119}_{50}Sn + \, ^{0}_{0}\gamma$$

Thus, in gamma particle emission, the identity of the element does not change. Instead, the daughter isotope is simply a lower-energy form of the parent isotope. Because gamma emission does not affect the mass or charge balance of the decay process, gamma particles are generally left out of radioactive decay equations.

POSITRON EMISSION AND ELECTRON CAPTURE

In both positron emission and electron capture, a proton is transformed into a neutron.

Positron emission, also called beta plus decay, is a type of beta decay in which the emitted particle is a positively charged electron, known as a positron. A positron is the antimatter equivalent of an electron, so it has all the same properties as an ordinary electron except that it has a $+1$ charge instead of a -1 charge.

In **electron capture**, also known as K-capture, the nucleus draws one of the atom's inner core electrons into the nucleus, converting a proton into a neutron. The electron that is drawn into the nucleus is shown as a reactant in the radioactive decay equation.

The video in Figure 20.2 demonstrates how to write balanced equations for positron emission and electron capture.

Example 20.2

Complete the equation for each of the following radioactive decay processes, and indicate whether it is an example of alpha decay, beta decay, positron emission, or electron capture.

a. $^{11}_{6}C + \, ^{?}_{?}? \rightarrow \, ^{11}_{5}B$

b. $^{222}_{86}Rn \rightarrow \, ^{218}_{84}Po + \, ^{?}_{?}?$

c. $^{14}_{6}C \rightarrow \, ^{14}_{7}? + \, ^{?}_{?}?$

d. $^{18}_{9}? \rightarrow \, ^{?}_{8}? + \, ^{?}_{?}?$

Solution

In each equation, the mass numbers (superscripts) and nuclear charges (subscripts) must be balanced.

a. The mass number of the unknown reactant particle must be 0 and the charge must be -1, so the particle is an electron.

$$^{11}_{6}C + \, ^{0}_{-1}e \rightarrow \, ^{11}_{5}B \qquad \text{Electron capture}$$

EVERYDAY CONNECTION

Some household smoke detectors use americium-241 to ionize the air between two electrically charged plates. The ionization of the air by the alpha particle allows a small electrical current to flow between the plates. When smoke from a fire gets between the plates, it interferes with the ionization of the air, and the current drops. The decreased current triggers the alarm. Because ionizing smoke detectors contain radioactive material, old or broken smoke detectors should never be thrown in the trash. They should be disposed of at municipal drop-off sites instead.

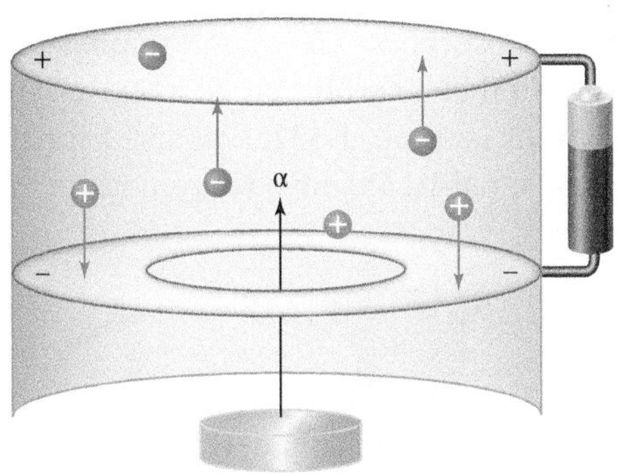

b. The emitted particle must have a mass number of 4 and a charge of 2, so it is a helium nucleus (an alpha particle).

$$^{222}_{86}Rn \rightarrow {}^{218}_{84}Po + {}^{4}_{2}He \qquad \text{Alpha decay}$$

c. The daughter nuclide has an atomic number of 7, so it is nitrogen. The other particle emitted must have a mass number of 0 and a charge of −1, so it is an electron (a beta particle).

$$^{14}_{6}C \rightarrow {}^{14}_{7}N + {}^{0}_{-1}\beta \qquad \text{Beta decay}$$

d. The parent nuclide has an atomic number of 9, so it is fluorine. The daughter nuclide has $Z = 8$ (oxygen). The charge on the emitted particle must be +1 to balance the charge, and the only particle emitted in radioactive decay with a +1 charge is a positron, which has a mass number of 0. As a result, the mass number of the daughter isotope must be the same as that of the parent.

$$^{18}_{9}F \rightarrow {}^{18}_{8}O + {}^{0}_{+1}\beta \qquad \text{Positron emission}$$

PRACTICE PROBLEM 20.2

Complete the equation for each of these radioactive decay processes, and indicate whether it is an example of alpha decay, beta decay, positron emission, or electron capture.

a. $^{23}_{12}Mg \rightarrow {}^{?}_{11}? + {}^{?}_{?}?$

b. $^{238}_{?}U \rightarrow {}^{?}_{90}? + {}^{?}_{?}?$

c. $^{40}_{19}K \rightarrow {}^{?}_{?}? + {}^{40}_{18}Ar$

d. $^{211}_{82}? \rightarrow {}^{211}_{83}? + {}^{?}_{?}?$

Hint: In each equation, balance the mass numbers (superscripts) and nuclear charges (subscripts) to determine the charge and mass number of the unknown particle. The nuclear charge for an isotope is equal to its atomic number from the periodic table.

Because the nucleus of the atom is undergoing the change, the chemical environment of the atom makes no difference to the process of radioactive decay. For example, pure uranium-238 metal or uranium-238 in any one of its compounds undergoes nuclear decay in the same manner and at the same rate.

There is no known way to control natural radioactive decay. It cannot be sped up, slowed down, or stopped.

RADIOACTIVE SERIES

When a radioactive isotope with a high atomic number decays, the daughter isotope that is produced is often itself radioactive, in which case a whole series of decay reactions can take place. All the isotopes involved form a **radioactive series**. For example, ^{235}U decay begins a series of decay reactions in which a total of seven alpha particles and four beta particles (as well as some gamma particles) are given off before a stable daughter isotope, ^{207}Pb, is formed. The decay series of ^{238}U is shown in Figure 20.3 as a graph of the mass number versus the atomic number. Gamma particle emissions are not shown in the figure. One of the isotopes in this series, $^{214}_{83}Bi$, can decay in either of two ways.

MEASURING RADIOACTIVITY

Each particle emission is referred to as a **disintegration**, so the rate of decay, called the **activity, A**, of a sample can be measured in the number of disintegrations, d, per unit time. Other units of activity are the becquerel, Bq, and the curie, Ci.

$$1 \text{ Bq} = 1\ d/\text{s}$$
$$1 \text{ Ci} = 3.7 \times 10^{10} \text{ Bq}$$

Activities are also reported on a per-gram basis, as in $d/\text{s}\cdot\text{g}$ or Ci/g, when comparing samples of different mass.

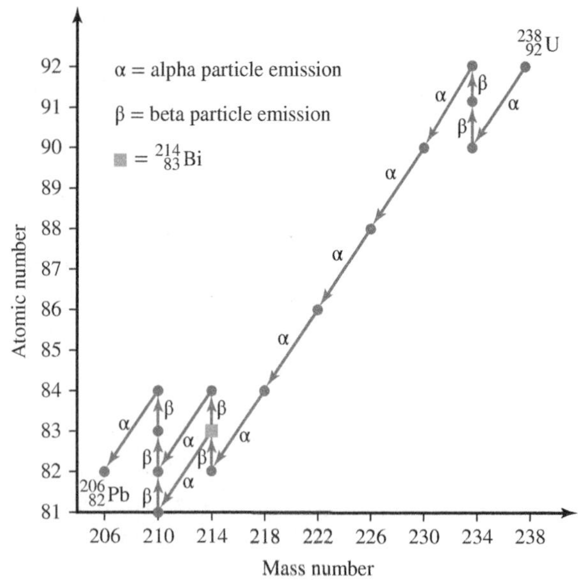

FIGURE 20.3 Radioactive Decay Series for Uranium-238

Atomic number is plotted versus mass number for each isotope in the U-238 decay series. The radioactive decay sequence begins with mass number 238 in the upper right and ends with mass number 206 in the lower left.

A **Geiger counter** is a device that can detect radioactive disintegrations (Figure 20.4). The high-energy particles emitted from a radioactive sample cause the gas in a Geiger counter's tube to be ionized and to carry an electric current for a short period

EVERYDAY CONNECTION

The thyroid gland is the only part of the human body that absorbs iodine atoms, which it uses for producing two important hormones that help regulate the body's temperature, metabolism, and heart rate. When a physician suspects that the thyroid gland is not functioning properly, he or she might administer iodine that includes a tiny fraction of I-123, a radioactive isotope of iodine. The physician can follow the path of the radioactive isotope using imaging that can detect the radiation given off when the I-123 decays. If the thyroid does *not* absorb the radioactive iodine, that means the regular iodine has not been absorbed either, and the physician has confirmed that a certain problem exists. Initially a different isotope, I-131, was used for thyroid diagnoses, but I-131 proved carcinogenic even in low doses.

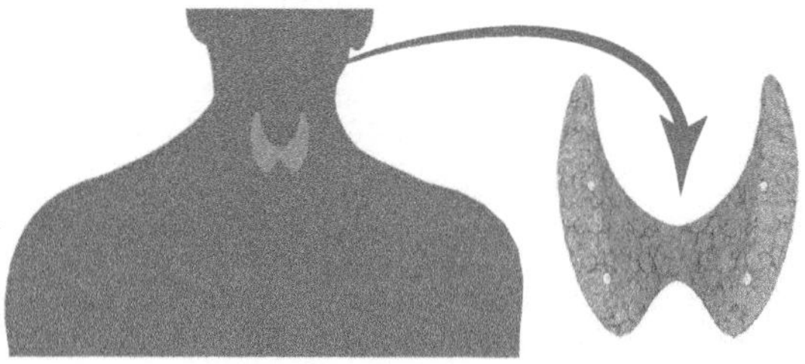

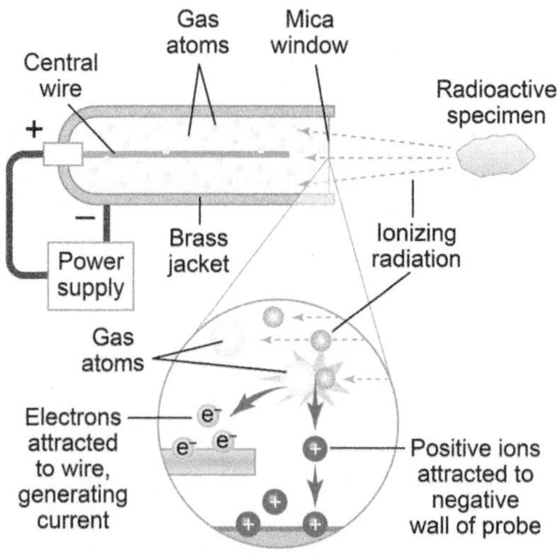

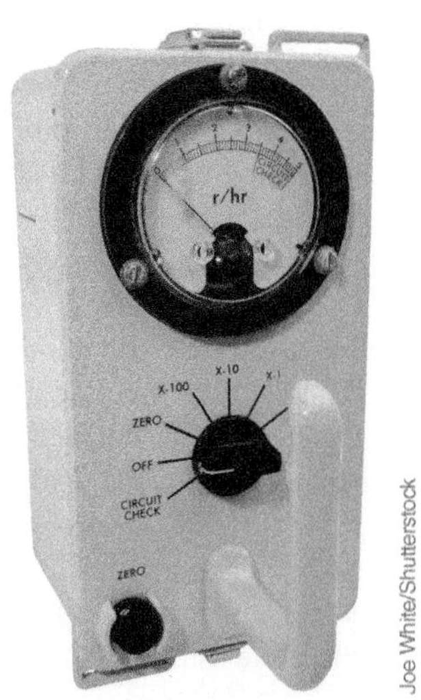

FIGURE 20.4 Simplified Diagram of a Geiger Counter

(a) The radioactive sample gives off radiation that ionizes an atom of an inert gas inside the tube, turning it into a positive ion. The ion impacts the negatively charged inside wall of the probe, generating an electrical current, which is detected and can be displayed on a readout (b) or turned into an audible click.

of time. Each clicking noise heard from the Geiger counter signals a particle (e.g., alpha, beta) entering the detector. Other, more modern devices, such as scintillation counters and film badges, are also used to detect and measure disintegrations.

Radioactive isotopes have the same chemical properties as the nonradioactive isotopes of the same element. Because they undergo the same chemical reactions, radioactive atoms are often used as **tracers** to determine what ordinary atoms are doing.Nonradioactive atoms cannot be easily traced as they move through the human body, but radioactive atoms can be traced by the energy they give off as they decay.

SECTION REVIEW

- Different types of particles can be emitted or captured during radioactive decay. These include alpha particles (^4_2He), beta particles ($^{\ 0}_{-1}\beta$), positrons ($^{\ 0}_{+1}\beta$), and gamma particles ($^0_0\gamma$).
- Nuclear equations are balanced by balancing the superscripts (mass number, *A*) and the subscripts (nuclear charge, *Z*).
- When an unstable parent nuclide decays, the daughter nuclide may also be unstable. This process may continue, forming a chain of successive daughter nuclides called a radioactive series, until a stable nuclide is reached.
- Activity is a measure of the amount of radiation. Units of activity include disintegrations per second, becquerels, and curies.

20.2 Nuclear Stability

GOALS

- Using the mass number and atomic number, predict whether a given isotope is likely to be radioactive.
- Using the mass number and atomic number, predict the mode of decay of a radioactive isotope.

Background Review

Chapter 2 Atoms and the Periodic Table: Section 2.4—Subatomic Particles, Isotopes, and Ions

Some isotopes are stable and some are radioactive. Radioactive nuclides undergo some form of radioactive decay to become stable. What makes some isotopes stable and others unstable? The answer lies in the ratio of neutrons to protons in the nucleus. Because the protons in an atomic nucleus are all positively charged, electrostatic forces between the protons repel them away from one another. The nucleus does not fly apart, however, because a force known as *the strong nuclear force* pulls the protons together to overcome the electrostatic repulsion. The strong nuclear force is an attractive force that all **nucleons** (protons and neutrons) exert on other nucleons.

The addition of neutrons to a nucleus adds strong nuclear force attraction without adding electrostatic repulsion, so it provides an overall stability to the nucleus. After a point, though, adding more neutrons *decreases* the stability of the nucleus instead because, in the same way that atoms have energy levels for electrons, there are energy levels for the nucleons within the nucleus: adding too many neutrons to a nucleus places the excess neutrons in higher energy levels, which begins to destabilize the nucleus. Thus, there is an ongoing struggle between the attractive and repulsive forces within the nucleus of each atom. If the forces are balanced, the nucleus is stable. If they are not, the nucleus eventually reaches a tipping point and releases excess energy through radioactive decay.

Eighty out of the 118 elements in the periodic table have at least one stable isotope. There are 253 stable isotopes, meaning that these nuclides have never been seen to decay, and more than 3000 radioactive isotopes.

In addition to the ratio of neutrons to protons in the nucleus, the actual number of protons and neutrons in the nucleus seems to play a role in determining the stability of the isotope. For example, the majority of stable isotopes have an even number of both protons and neutrons, and nearly all the rest have an even number of at least one nucleon. Only 5 out of the 253 stable isotopes have an odd number of both protons and neutrons (Table 20.3). Evidence suggests that a pairing of protons and a pairing of neutrons in the nucleus provides additional stability to the nucleus.

TABLE 20.3 Number of Stable Isotopes with Even and Odd Numbers of Protons and Neutrons

Number of Stable Isotopes	Number of Protons	Number of Neutrons
147	Even	Even
53	Even	Odd
48	Odd	Even
5	Odd	Odd

In the same way that certain numbers of electrons in an atom confer chemical stability (nonreactivity)—namely, the number of electrons found in the noble gases (2, 10, 18, 36, 54, and 86)—having a certain number of protons or neutrons makes it more likely that a nucleus will be stable. Nuclei with 2, 8, 20, 28, 50, or 82 protons, or with 2, 8, 20, 28, 50, 82, or 126 neutrons, tend to be more stable than isotopes that do not have these numbers. These special stability numbers are known as **magic numbers**. The magic numbers support a model in which atomic nuclei have energy levels analogous to the electronic energy levels of an atom.

BELT OF STABILITY

The relationship between the neutron-to-proton ratio and stability is shown in Figure 20.5. In this graph, each point represents a stable nuclide, and the location of that point is based on its number of neutrons and protons. The points form a region called the **belt of stability**, also called the band, island, or valley of stability.

There is no mathematical formula for calculating exactly how many neutrons provide maximum stability in a nucleus, but there are some general trends that make it possible to predict stability. At low atomic masses, the most stable nuclei tend to have equal numbers of protons and neutrons. Through the first 20 elements, for example, the atomic mass in the periodic table tends to be about double the atomic number, or double plus one. As atomic number increases from there, however, the atomic mass in the periodic table becomes increasingly greater than double the atomic number. This indicates that when there are more protons in the nucleus, a greater number of neutrons is required to balance the forces and stabilize the nucleus.

Lead ($Z = 82$) is the element with the highest atomic number that has a stable isotope.

For many years it was believed that bismuth-209 ($Z = 83$) was stable, but it was determined in 2009 that bismuth-209 decays with a half-life of 1.9×10^{19} years. Many sources still list bismuth as the element with the highest atomic number that has a stable isotope.

PREDICTING DECAY MODE

When a radioactive nuclide decays, it typically does so in a manner that brings the daughter isotope closer to the belt of stability than the parent was.

- Heavier nuclides ($Z > 82$) typically decay by alpha decay. Although this does not affect the neutron-to-proton ratio (an alpha particle contains

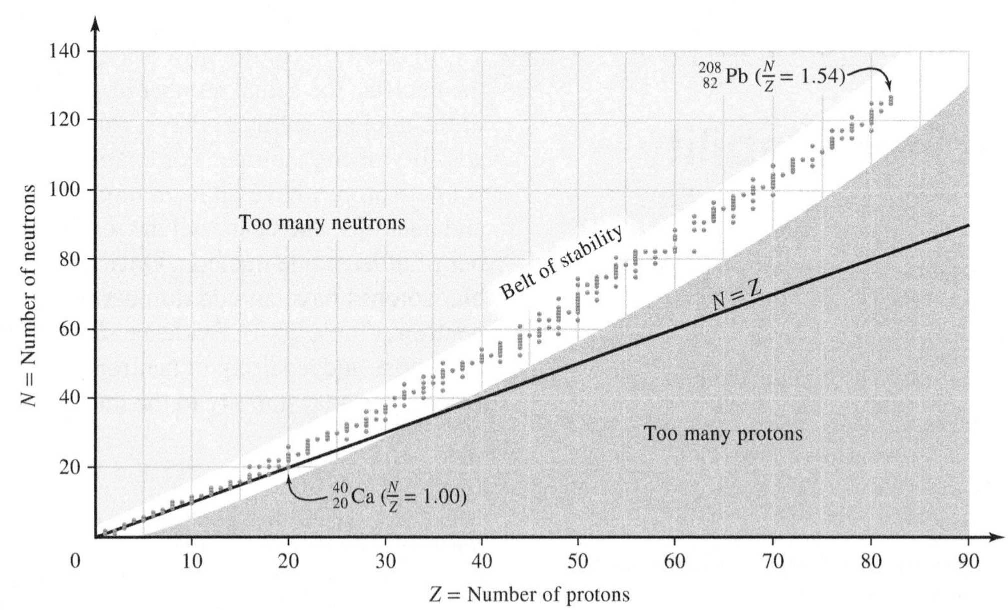

FIGURE 20.5 Nuclide Stability Plot

Each dot represents a stable nuclide. At lower atomic masses, the greatest stability is achieved when the number of neutrons is equal, or nearly equal, to the number of protons. As the atomic number increases, the number of neutrons required for a stable nuclide grows increasingly larger, causing the belt of stability to deviate further from the $N = Z$ line. Stable nuclides end at $Z = 82$; every nuclide beyond that point is radioactive.

two of each), it decreases the atomic number more drastically than other modes of decay.

- Neutron-rich nuclides (i.e., those found above the belt of stability) tend to decay by beta decay, because converting a neutron to a proton moves the nuclide down and to the right.
- Proton-rich nuclides (i.e., those found below the belt of stability) tend to decay by positron emission or electron capture, because converting a proton to a neutron moves the nuclide up and to the left.

A way to quickly tell whether an isotope lies above or below the belt of stability is to compare its mass number, A, to the atomic mass for that element given in the periodic table. This works because the average atomic mass is weighted toward the more abundant isotopes, which also tend to be the stable ones.

Example 20.3

Predict the mode of decay for each of the following unstable isotopes.

a. ^{32}P
b. ^{11}C
c. ^{15}O
d. ^{3}H

Solution

Alpha decay is ruled out for all of these isotopes because none has $Z > 82$.

a. The average atomic mass of phosphorus in the periodic table is 30.974 u. Phosphorus-32 is heavier than that, meaning it is *above* the belt of stability and will decay by converting a neutron to a proton via *beta decay*. The daughter isotope is stable sulfur-32, which has a mass very close to the average atomic mass for sulfur of 32.06.
b. The average atomic mass of carbon is 12.011 u. Carbon-11 is lighter than that, so it is *below* the belt of stability and will decay by converting a proton to a neutron via *positron decay*. The daughter isotope is stable boron-11, which has a mass very close to the average atomic mass for boron of 10.811 u.
c. The average atomic mass of oxygen is 15.999 u. Oxygen-15 is lighter than that, so it is *below* the belt of stability and will decay by converting a proton to a neutron via *positron emission*. The daughter isotope is nitrogen-15, which has a mass about one mass unit higher than the average atomic mass for nitrogen of 14.007 u. (Nitrogen-15 is stable, but it makes up only about 0.4% of naturally occurring nitrogen.)
d. The average atomic mass of hydrogen is 1.008 u. Hydrogen-3, also called tritium, is heavier than that, so it is *above* the belt of stability and will decay by converting a neutron to a proton via *beta decay*. The daughter isotope is helium-3, which has a mass about one mass unit lower than the average atomic mass for helium of 4.0026 u. (Helium-3 is stable, but it is present in only trace amounts on Earth.)

PRACTICE PROBLEM 20.3

Predict the mode of decay for each of the following unstable isotopes.

a. ^{63}Ni
b. ^{30}P
c. ^{13}N
d. ^{90}Sr

Hint: First, you can rule out alpha decay because none of these isotopes has $Z > 82$.
Next, find the average atomic mass for the element in the periodic table. If the mass number of the isotope is higher than the average atomic mass of the element, the isotope lies *above* the belt of stability. If the mass number of the isotope is lower than the average atomic mass for the element, the isotope lies *below* the belt of stability.
Finally, choose the mode of decay that will decrease the neutron-to-proton ratio (for those above the belt of stability) or increase the ratio (for those below it).

Although most radioactive isotopes decay by only one mode, some radioactive isotopes can undergo decay by more than one mode. For example, 89.1% of radioactive ^{40}K atoms undergo beta decay to form ^{40}Ca, while 10.1% undergo electron capture to form ^{40}Ar. Both of these daughter isotopes are stable.

$$^{40}_{19}K \rightarrow ^{40}_{20}Ca + ^{0}_{-1}\beta \quad (89.1\%)$$
$$^{40}_{19}K + ^{0}_{-1}e \rightarrow ^{40}_{18}Ar \quad (10.9\%)$$

A trace amount of ^{40}K decays by positron emission:

$$^{40}_{19}K \rightarrow ^{40}_{18}Ar + ^{0}_{+1}\beta \quad (\sim 0.001\%)$$

In general, however, a particular isotope decays via a single mode.

SECTION REVIEW

- A number of factors contribute to whether a nuclide is stable. Among these are the ratio of neutrons to protons, the number of each nucleon, and whether the numbers of protons and neutrons are even or odd.
- Based on the ratio of neutrons to protons, a graph can be drawn in which the stable isotopes form

a rough line, surrounded above and below by unstable nuclides.

- Radioactive nuclei tend to decay in a manner that brings them closer to a stable configuration of neutrons and protons.

20.3 Half-Life

GOAL

- Calculate half-life, initial amount, final amount, or decay time given the other variables.

Background Review

Chapter 14 Chemical Kinetics: Section 14.3—Integrated Rate Laws and Half-Lives

Radioactive isotopes have widely different stabilities, as measured by how long they take to decay. Some radioactive nuclei decay within a fraction of a second after being formed, while others persist for hours, days, years, or even billions of years or more before decaying. The atoms of a given isotope do not decay all at once. Instead, each individual disintegration occurs randomly, but if the sample is large enough, it will decay at a rate that is statistically predictable. Therefore, although scientists cannot tell how long any particular atom of an isotope will last before it decays, they can predict what fraction of the atoms in any given sample of the isotope will decay over a given period of time.

The decay rate depends not only on the relative instability of the isotope but also on the number of atoms in the sample. For any given isotope, if you have twice as many radioactive atoms in the sample, you will get twice as many disintegrations in the same amount of time. As discussed in Section 20.1, the number of disintegrations per unit time is called the activity, A. Activity is directly proportional to N, the number of atoms of the radioactive isotope present,

$$A = kN \qquad (20.1)$$

where k is a rate constant that differs for each radioactive isotope. Note the similarities between this equation and the rate laws presented in Chapter 14, such as rate $= k[\text{A}]$.

As a sample of a radioactive isotope decays, the number of atoms of that isotope decreases. As the number of atoms decreases, the number of disintegrations per second also decreases. The time it takes for a sample of an isotope to get to half of its original number of atoms is called the **half-life, $t_{1/2}$**, of the isotope. The size of the original sample does not affect the length of the half-life because all radioactive decay reactions follow first-order kinetics (Section 14.3).

Figure 20.6 shows the decay of a radioactive isotope with a 1 minute half-life over the span of three half-lives. Over the course of each half-life, half of the atoms of that isotope will decay. If the sample begins with 40 g of a radioactive isotope, then after one half-life, half of that isotope (20 g) will remain. Half of *that* sample will then decay during the next half-life, leaving 10 g of the isotope remaining. Each half-life reduces the number of radioactive atoms in the sample by half, no matter how many atoms there are in the sample.

Larger samples of a radioactive isotope contain more atoms and therefore have more disintegrations per second (Equation 20.1). This means larger samples lose mass faster than smaller samples do. Because the decay rate slows down proportionally as the number of atoms decreases, the half-life of any given isotope remains constant regardless of the sample size.

Half-lives of some radioactive isotopes are listed in Table 20.4.

Example 20.4

Using the half-life for carbon-14 from Table 20.4, calculate the time required for a 60.0 g sample of $^{14}_{6}\text{C}$ to be reduced to only 7.50 g of $^{14}_{6}\text{C}$.

Solution

From Table 20.4, the half-life of $^{14}_{6}\text{C}$ is 5730 years. That means that in 5730 years (one half-life), half of the original sample remains.

$$\frac{1}{2}(60.0\text{ g}) = 30.0\text{ g}$$

After another 5730 years, half of *that* remains.

$$\frac{1}{2}(30.0\text{ g}) = 15.0\text{ g}$$

After a third half-life, half of *that* remains.

$$\frac{1}{2}(15.0\text{ g}) = 7.50\text{ g}$$

It takes three half-lives to get to this amount, so the time required is

$$3\text{ half-lives} \times \frac{5730\text{ years}}{1\text{ half-life}} = 17{,}200\text{ years}$$

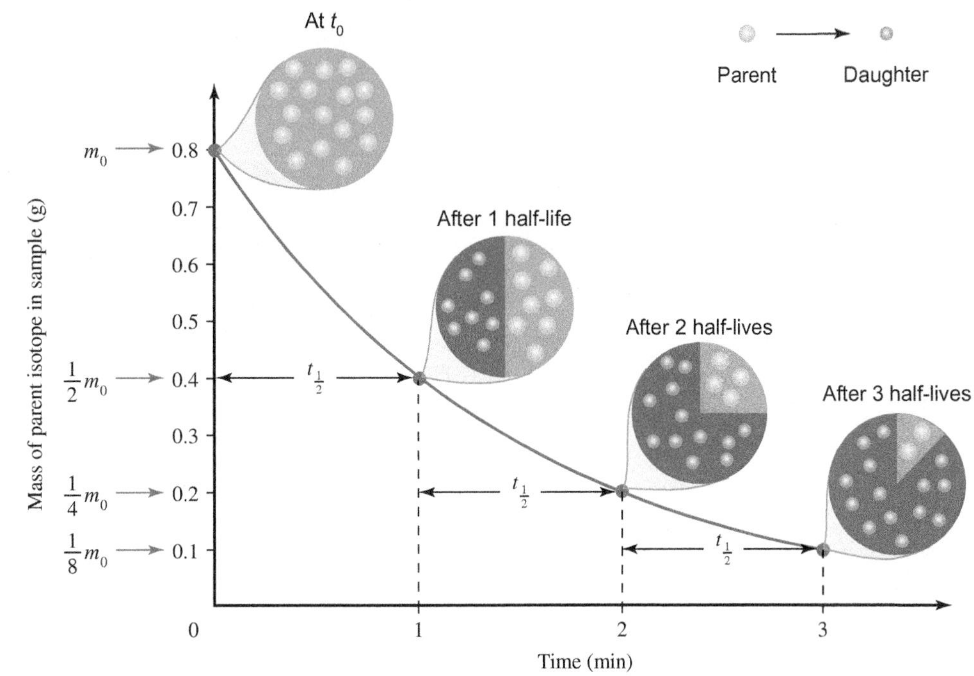

FIGURE 20.6 Decay of a Sample of Radioactive Isotope over Three Half-Lives

A graph of the decay of an isotope with a half-life of 1 min. The increment of change on the vertical axis (mass of isotope) gets smaller and smaller, while the increment of change on the horizontal axis (time) stays the same. Half-lives follow first-order reaction kinetics (Section 14.3)—compare the radioactive decay in this figure to the reactant concentration in Figure 14.11.

TABLE 20.4 Half-Lives of Some Radioactive Isotopes

Isotope	Half-Life	Particle Emitted
^{238}U	4.47×10^9 years = 4.47 billion years	Alpha
^{235}U	7.04×10^8 years = 704 million years	Alpha
^{14}C	5730 years	Beta
^{40}K	1.250×10^9 years	Beta
^{90}Sr	28.8 years	Beta
^{3}H	12.3 years	Beta
^{231}Th	25.6 hours	Beta
^{232}Th	1.41×10^{10} years = 14.1 billion years	Alpha
^{131}I	8 days	Beta
^{140}La	40 hours	Beta

PRACTICE PROBLEM 20.4

A research scientist receives a shipment of a radioactive sample containing 10.0 mg of ^{140}La, then leaves for an out-of-town conference. If the scientist returns to work exactly 5 days later, how much of the original sample of ^{140}La is left?

Hint: Use the half-life of ^{140}La in Table 20.4 to determine how many half-lives have passed after 5 days (you will need to convert days to hours). Once you know the number of half-lives, divide the mass of the sample in half that many times.

Example 20.5

If 43.2 mg of a certain radioactive isotope disintegrates to 10.8 mg in 59.6 seconds, what is the half-life of the isotope?

Solution

The fraction of the original sample remaining is

$$\frac{10.8 \text{ mg}}{43.2 \text{ mg}} = 0.250 = \frac{1}{4}$$

The isotope in the sample has disintegrated to one-fourth of its original mass, so one-fourth of its original number of atoms must remain. Two half-lives must have elapsed:

$$1 \xrightarrow[1]{} \frac{1}{2} \xrightarrow[2]{} \frac{1}{4}$$

If 59.6 seconds represents two half-lives, then one half-life is half of that, or 29.8 seconds.

PRACTICE PROBLEM 20.5

How long would it take for 64.8 g of the isotope from Example 20.5 to disintegrate to 8.10 g?

Hint: First, determine the number of half-lives it takes to go from 64.8 g to 8.10 g. Then, multiply that number by the length of one half-life, which was determined in Example 20.5.

Although the mass of the parent isotope decreases by half over the course of one half-life, the total mass of the sample might be reduced only slightly. For example, if 2.00 mole of thorium-231 ($^{231}_{90}Th$) is allowed to disintegrate for 25.6 h (one half-life), then 1.00 mole of $^{231}_{90}Th$ remains:

$$^{231}_{90}\text{Th} \rightarrow ^{231}_{91}\text{Pa} + ^{0}_{-1}\beta$$

However, 1.00 mole of protactinium-231 ($^{231}_{91}Pa$) and 1.00 mole of electrons are formed in the process, and the total mass of the remaining mixture of $^{231}_{90}Th$ and $^{231}_{91}Pa$ is only slightly less than the original mass of $^{231}_{90}Th$. Over a period of 10 half-lives, 99.9% of the parent nuclide is converted to the daughter nuclide, but the mass of the sample essentially does not change.

For decay periods that are not an integer multiple of the half-life, Equation 20.2 can be used to calculate the amount of time that has elapsed since the decay began (t), the half-life of the isotope ($t_{1/2}$), the original number of isotope atoms in the sample (N_0), or the number of isotope atoms remaining after time $t(N)$.

$$\ln\left(\frac{N_0}{N}\right) = \left(\frac{\ln 2}{t_{1/2}}\right)t \qquad (20.2)$$

Equation 20.2 is a variation on the first-order integrated rate equation (Section 14.3). Solving Equation 20.2 for t or for $t_{1/2}$ is fairly straightforward, but solving for N_0 or N requires taking the inverse natural log of both sides of the equation to remove those terms from within the natural log function. Figure 20.7 and the examples that follow demonstrate how to solve this equation for any of the four variables.

Steve Lemon, Macmillan Learning

FIGURE 20.7 Video Tutorial: Half-Life Calculations

NOTE: You need to be online to access this video.

This video shows how to calculate half-life from time and mass data, and the percentage remaining from half-life and time.

Example 20.6

Calculate the time it takes for 6.75×10^{18} atoms of an isotope to disintegrate to the point where 8.90×10^{17} atoms of the isotope remain. The half-life of the isotope is 73.5 h.

Solution

The time required to reduce the sample to a given fraction can be calculated using Equation 20.2.

$$\ln\left(\frac{N_0}{N}\right) = \left(\frac{\ln 2}{t_{1/2}}\right)t$$

The amount of time (t) can be isolated by multiplying both sides of the equation by $\left(\frac{t_{1/2}}{\ln 2}\right)$.

$$t = \ln\left(\frac{N_0}{N}\right)\left(\frac{t_{1/2}}{\ln 2}\right)$$

Plugging in the known values for N, N_0, and $t_{1/2}$ gives

$$t = \ln\left(\frac{6.75 \times 10^{18}}{8.90 \times 10^{17}}\right)\left(\frac{73.5 \text{ h}}{\ln 2}\right)$$

$$t = 215 \text{ h}$$

The time (215 h) is a little less than three half-lives, and the number of atoms remaining is a little more than 1/8 of the original number, so this answer is reasonable.

PRACTICE PROBLEM 20.6

Calculate the time it takes for a sample of an isotope to be reduced to exactly one-fifth of its original number of atoms if the half-life is 6.79 y.

Hint: Use Equation 20.2. Because one-fifth of the material remains, $\frac{N_0}{N} = \frac{1}{\frac{1}{5}} = 5$.

For calculations involving the half-life, be careful to distinguish between the *original* amount, N_0; the amount that *remains,* N; and the amount that *decays,* $N_0 - N$. For example, if 25% decays, then 75% remains, and $N_0/N = 100/75$.

If you are solving Equation 20.2 for the original number of isotope atoms (N_0) or the number of isotope atoms remaining (N), then you must take the inverse natural logarithm, e^x, of both sides of the equation to isolate them. If you have values for t and $t_{1/2}$, it is often easier to simplify the right side of the equation before taking the inverse natural log, as shown in Example 20.7.

Example 20.7

A particular isotope has a half-life of 17.9 min. How many atoms of this isotope remain after a sample containing 4.00×10^{19} atoms is left for 21.2 min?

Solution

Solve for N using Equation 20.2.

$$\ln\left(\frac{N_0}{N}\right) = \left(\frac{\ln 2}{t_{1/2}}\right)t$$

Solving for N means taking the inverse natural log of both sides of the equation, so first plug in the known values for t and ($t_{1/2}$), and simplify the right side of the equation.

$$\ln\left(\frac{N_0}{N}\right) = \left(\frac{\ln 2}{17.9 \text{ min}}\right)21.2 \text{ min} = 0.821$$

To extract N from the natural log term, take the inverse natural log of both sides (Section 0.5):

$$e^{\ln\left(\frac{N_0}{N}\right)} = e^{0.821}$$

The e and ln functions cancel each other out, leaving

$$\frac{N_0}{N} = 2.27$$

Rearrange the equation algebraically to isolate and solve for N:

$$N = \frac{N_0}{2.27} = \frac{4.00 \times 10^{19} \text{ atoms}}{2.27} = 1.76 \times 10^{19} \text{ atoms}$$

In a little more than one half-life, a little more than half of the atoms have disintegrated and fewer than half remain, so this answer is reasonable.

PRACTICE PROBLEM 20.7

a. Calculate the time it takes an isotope with a half-life of 47.2 years to disintegrate from 1.77×10^{15} atoms to 5.59×10^{14} atoms.

b. Calculate the original number of atoms of this isotope if 1.77×10^{15} atoms remain after 112 years.

Hint:

a. Use Equation 20.2. Plug in the three known variables, and solve for t.

b. Solving for N_0 means taking the inverse natural log of both sides of the equation, so simplify the right side of the equation first, using the given values for t and $t_{1/2}$.

The total mass of a radioactive isotope in a sample is proportional to the number of atoms of that isotope in the sample; likewise the activity (the rate of decay) is proportional to the number of atoms of that isotope in the sample. Therefore the ratio N_0/N is equal to the mass ratio m_0/m (where m_0 is the initial mass of the isotope, and m is the mass remaining after time t) and to the activity ratio A_0/A (where A_0 is the initial activity of the isotope, and A is the activity of the sample after time t). This means that the mass or activity of the isotope in the sample can be used in Equation 20.2 in place of the number of atoms:

$$\ln\left(\frac{m_0}{m}\right) = \left(\frac{\ln 2}{t_{1/2}}\right)t \qquad (20.3)$$

$$\ln\left(\frac{A_0}{A}\right) = \left(\frac{\ln 2}{t_{1/2}}\right)t \qquad (20.4)$$

The reason you can simply replace N_0/N with m_0/m or A_0/A in this equation is twofold: (1) mass, activity, and number of atoms are all directly proportional, and (2) these values are ratios, so the proportionality factors cancel out. In fact, any quantity (e.g., number of moles or molarity) works in this ratio as long as it is directly proportional to the number of atoms.

Example 20.8

Calculate the half-life of an isotope if the activity of a sample was reduced to 45.0% of its original activity in 1.08 years.

Solution

This problem provides information about the *activity* of the sample rather than the number of atoms. Because activity is directly proportional to the number of atoms, the ratio of A_0/A can be used in place of N_0/N, as shown in Equation 20.4.

$$\ln\left(\frac{A_0}{A}\right) = \left(\frac{\ln 2}{t_{1/2}}\right)t$$

The ratio of activities, A_0/A, is equal to 100/45.0:

$$\ln\left(\frac{100}{45.0}\right) = \left(\frac{\ln 2}{t_{1/2}}\right)(1.08 \text{ years})$$

$$0.799 = \left(\frac{\ln 2}{t_{1/2}}\right)(1.08 \text{ years})$$

Rearranging gives

$$t_{1/2} = \left(\frac{\ln 2}{0.799}\right)(1.08 \text{ years}) = 0.937 \text{ year}$$

This answer is reasonable, because more than one but less than two half-lives are required.

EVERYDAY CONNECTION

Exposure to radiation can be dangerous, but it can also be beneficial in certain situations such as radiation therapy, which is used to treat cancer. The radiation kills healthy cells as well as cancerous cells, but because the radiation can be targeted at the cancerous tissue, radiation therapy kills a greater number of cancer cells than ordinary cells. The two most common methods of delivering the radiation for radiation therapy are by ^{60}Co decay and by linear accelerator (linac). Cobalt-60 decays by beta decay, spontaneously emitting both beta particles and gamma rays, but since it has a half-life of 5.27 years, the cobalt needs to be replaced every few years. A medical linac (shown here) generates X-rays and beta particles without the use of a radioactive isotope as the fuel source.

Thomas Hecker/Shutterstock

PRACTICE PROBLEM 20.8

Calculate the half-life of an isotope if a sample was reduced to 75.0% of its original mass in 10.0 years.

Hint: Use Equation 20.3, which substitutes m_0/m in place of N_0/N.

SECTION REVIEW

- All radioactive decay reactions follow first-order kinetics.
- The time it takes for a sample of an isotope to disintegrate to half of its original number of atoms is called the half-life of the isotope.
- Different radioactive isotopes can have wildly different stabilities and, therefore, wildly different half-lives. Some radioactive half-lives are only fractions of a second, whereas others are billions of years.
- The rate of spontaneous radioactive decay for a given isotope is directly proportional to the number of atoms of the isotope present and, therefore, to the number of moles of the isotope or the mass of the isotope. Half of any given sample will disintegrate in one half-life period.

20.4 Radiometric Dating

GOAL

- Determine the age of artifacts using the concepts and equations of decay and half-life.

Background Review

Chapter 14 Chemical Kinetics: Section 14.3—Integrated Rate Laws and Half-Lives

GEOLOGIC DATING

Archaeologists and geologists apply the principles of half-life measurement to determine the age of samples of interest to them. The method they use is called **radiometric dating**. For example, a geologist might be interested in the age of a certain rock formation that contains atoms of a radioactive isotope. Any daughter atoms present can be assumed to have originally been parent atoms, allowing the geologist to determine N_0 (Figure 20.8).

For example, ^{238}U disintegrates in a series of events to ^{206}Pb, which is stable. The half-lives of the isotopes that are formed along the way from ^{238}U to ^{206}Pb are short compared to that of ^{238}U, so at any given moment nearly all of the atoms in the series are in the form of either ^{238}U or ^{206}Pb. If the rock originally contained ^{238}U but no ^{206}Pb when it solidified from a molten state, the geologist can tell how long ago the rock solidified based on the number of ^{206}Pb atoms now present. N_0 is equal to the number of atoms of ^{206}Pb plus the number of atoms of ^{238}U that are present now, and N is the number of atoms of ^{238}U present now. These values can be used in Equation 20.2 to calculate t, the age of the rock. A representative sample of the rock is analyzed to determine the numbers of atoms of each isotope present.

Another radiometric dating technique that is commonly used for determining how long ago a rock was formed is potassium–argon dating, which measures

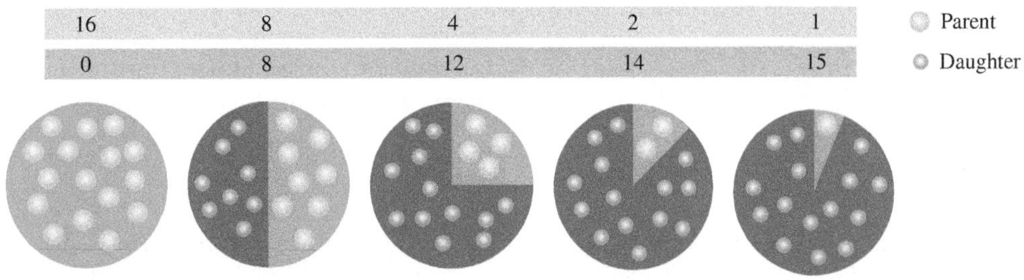

FIGURE 20.8 Numbers of Parent and Daughter Atoms

The parent atoms turn into daughter atoms, so their sum is a constant equal to the original number of parent atoms, N_0.

the amount of radioactive $^{40}_{19}K$ present relative to the amount of the stable daughter isotope, $^{40}_{18}Ar$ gas, that is trapped within the rock.

Example 20.9

A geologist analyzes a sample of rock and finds that it contains 3.40×10^{15} atoms of ^{206}Pb for every 1.32×10^{16} atoms of ^{238}U. Calculate the age of the rock, assuming that no lead was present when the rock solidified and no uranium or its daughter elements escaped from the rock.

Solution

Because all of the ^{206}Pb was originally ^{238}U, the number of atoms of ^{238}U originally present was

$$N_0 = 3.40 \times 10^{15} + 1.32 \times 10^{16} = 1.66 \times 10^{16} \text{ atoms}$$

The value of N, the number of ^{238}U atoms currently present, is given as 1.32×10^{16} atoms. These values can be used in Equation 20.2:

$$\ln\left(\frac{N_0}{N}\right) = \left(\frac{\ln 2}{t_{1/2}}\right)t$$

Isolate t by multiplying both sides of the equation by $\left(\frac{t_{1/2}}{\ln 2}\right)$.

$$t = \ln\left(\frac{N_0}{N}\right)\left(\frac{t_{1/2}}{\ln 2}\right)$$

Plug the known variables into the equation to solve it. From Table 20.4, $t_{1/2} = 4.5 \times 10^9$ y for ^{238}U.

$$t = \ln\left(\frac{1.66 \times 10^{16} \text{ atoms}}{1.32 \times 10^{16} \text{ atoms}}\right)\left(\frac{4.5 \times 10^9 \text{ y}}{\ln 2}\right)$$

$$= 1.49 \times 10^9 \text{ y}$$

This is much less than one complete half-life for ^{238}U, and almost 80% of the initial ^{238}U is still present, so this is a reasonable result for t.

PRACTICE PROBLEM 20.9

Calculate the age of a sample of rock that contains 2.57×10^{17} atoms of $^{40}_{19}K$ for every 7.71×10^{16} atoms of $^{40}_{18}Ar$. Assume that no argon was in the rock when it solidified and that no argon escaped from the rock since its solidification. The half-life of $^{40}_{19}K$ is 1.3×10^9 y.

Hint: N is the number of atoms of ^{40}K present, and N_0 is the sum of the atoms of ^{40}K and ^{40}Ar. Solve for t using Equation 20.2.

When the amounts of the parent and daughter isotopes in a sample are given in grams, you cannot always just add the amounts to determine m_0. If the parent isotope decays by alpha decay, the parent and daughter isotopes will have different mass numbers, and therefore different molar masses. In that case, equal masses of the isotopes do not correspond to an equal number of atoms, so you have to use the molar mass of each isotope to calculate the number of moles of each isotope present in the sample. If the parent and daughter isotopes do have the same mass number, however, then equal masses do correspond to an equal number of atoms, so the masses themselves can be added.

Example 20.10

Calculate the age of a sample of rock that contains 5.5 g ^{206}Pb for every 29.6 g ^{238}U.

Solution

Because the parent and daughter isotopes do not have the same mass number, the masses of the two isotopes cannot simply be added to calculate m_0. Instead, use the molar mass of each isotope to determine the number of moles of each. To three significant digits, the mass of a mole of each of the isotopes involved in this problem is equal to its mass number (in grams).

$$5.5\text{ g }^{206}\text{Pb}\left(\frac{1\text{ mol }^{206}\text{Pb}}{206\text{ g }^{206}\text{Pb}}\right) = 0.027\text{ mol }^{206}\text{Pb}$$

$$29.6\text{ g }^{238}\text{U}\left(\frac{1\text{ mol }^{238}\text{U}}{238\text{ g }^{238}\text{U}}\right) = 0.124\text{ mol }^{238}\text{U}$$

The number of moles is directly proportional to the number of atoms, so the ratio of initial moles to final moles, n_0/n, can also be used in place of N_0/N in Equation 20.2.

Initial moles of ^{238}U present = 0.124 + 0.0267 = 0.151 mol.

$$\ln\left(\frac{n_0}{n}\right) = \left(\frac{\ln 2}{t_{1/2}}\right)t$$

Isolate t by multiplying both sides of the equation by $\left(\frac{t_{1/2}}{\ln 2}\right)$.

$$t = \ln\left(\frac{n_0}{n}\right)\left(\frac{t_{1/2}}{\ln 2}\right)$$

Plug the known variables into the equation to solve for t.

$$t = \ln\left(\frac{0.151\text{ mol}}{0.124\text{ mol}}\right)\left(\frac{4.5 \times 10^9}{\ln 2}\right) = 1.3 \times 10^8\text{ y}$$

PRACTICE PROBLEM 20.10

Calculate the age of a sample of rock containing 9.61 g of $^{40}_{19}$K and 1.04 g of its stable daughter isotope, $^{40}_{18}$Ar. Assume that no argon was in the rock when it solidified and that no potassium or argon has escaped from the rock since its solidification. The half-life of $^{40}_{19}$K is 1.3×10^9 years.

Hint: Because the mass numbers of the parent and daughter isotopes are equal, the ratio of masses is equal to the ratio of atoms. As a result, the masses of the two isotopes can be added to determine n_0 for the parent isotope.

RADIOCARBON DATING

^{238}U and ^{40}K both have half-lives of more than a billion years, which makes them suitable for dating very old objects (more than 100,000 years). They do *not* provide accurate ages for objects that are less than about 100,000 years old, however, because so little of the parent isotope has decayed that the statistics are less reliable.

For dating materials such as paper and wood, which are made from once-living organisms, carbon-14 dating is used. When radiometric dating is done using ^{14}C, it is referred to as **radiocarbon dating** or just carbon dating. Radioactive carbon-14 is created continuously in the upper atmosphere by the bombardment of $^{14}_{7}$N atoms by cosmic rays:

$$^{14}_{7}\text{N} + ^{1}_{0}\text{n} \rightarrow ^{14}_{6}\text{C} + ^{1}_{1}\text{H}$$

Carbon-14 makes up only a trace amount of all the carbon in the atmosphere—only about 1 in 10^{12} carbon atoms is C-14. The half-life of ^{14}C is 5730 years (Table 20.4).

The newly formed ^{14}C finds its way into carbon dioxide and eventually into living things through the process of photosynthesis. An archaeologist can date a sample of wood by analyzing the amount of $^{14}_{6}$C in it, because after a tree has died, it no longer takes in $^{14}_{6}$C in carbon dioxide. Assuming that the ratio of $^{14}_{6}$C to $^{12}_{6}$C in the atmosphere today is the same as it was in ancient times, the ^{14}C activity in a piece of modern wood (A_0) can be compared to the ^{14}C activity in a wooden archaeological relic (A), and the ratio of activities can be used to determine the age of the relic.

Unlike the other dating methods described previously, radiocarbon dating does not use a ratio of parent isotope to daughter isotope to determine the age of the sample. Part of the reason for this is that carbon-14 decays by beta decay to the daughter isotope ^{14}N, which is by far the most common isotope of nitrogen (99.636% natural abundance), so the additional amount of ^{14}N produced by beta decay of ^{14}C is negligibly small.

Example 20.11

A wooden plank found in Norway is believed to have been part of a Viking longship built circa 1000 CE. The ^{14}C in the wood is decaying at a rate of 14.4 $d/\text{min} \cdot \text{g}$. A modern sample of carbon disintegrates at a rate of 15.3 $d/\text{min} \cdot \text{g}$. Assume that the ratio of $^{14}_{6}$C to $^{12}_{6}$C in the atmosphere was the same when the tree was alive as it is today.

Solution

Use Equation 20.4.

$$\ln\left(\frac{A_0}{A}\right) = \left(\frac{\ln 2}{t_{1/2}}\right)t$$

Isolate t by multiplying both sides of the equation by $\left(\frac{t_{1/2}}{\ln 2}\right)$.

$$t = \ln\left(\frac{A_0}{A}\right)\left(\frac{t_{1/2}}{\ln 2}\right)$$

EVERYDAY CONNECTION

Archaeologists can validate the assumption that the ratio of ${}^{14}_{6}C$ to ${}^{12}_{6}C$ was the same in ancient times as it is now by dating a sample of wood of known age. The age of a particular sample of wood from the cross section of a tree like the one shown here can be determined by counting the rings, each of which is formed during one year's growth, and then measuring the C-14 content of a portion of the wood from an inner ring.

Denis Kholyavin/Shutterstock

Plug the known variables into the equation to solve it.

$$t = \ln\left(\frac{15.3\,\frac{d}{\text{min}\cdot\text{g}}}{14.4\,\frac{d}{\text{min}\cdot\text{g}}}\right)\left(\frac{5730\text{ y}}{\ln 2}\right) = 5.01 \times 10^2\text{ y}$$

The wooden plank dates to the 16th century, making it too recent to have come from a Viking ship.

PRACTICE PROBLEM 20.11

If the wooden plank in Example 20.11 had actually been from 1000 CE, what would the measured decay rate have been in 2018?

Hint: Use Equation 20.4 to solve for A. The time elapsed from the year 1000 to 2018 is t.

SECTION REVIEW

- The process of determining the age of an object is called dating.
- Rocks can be dated by comparing the ratio of the amount of a parent radioactive isotope present in a sample to that of its final stable daughter isotope.
- Ancient objects made from wood or paper can be dated by comparing the level of radioactive activity in the object to the level of radioactivity in a modern tree.

20.5 Fission and Fusion

GOALS

- Predict the products of fission reactions.
- Predict the products of fusion reactions.

Background Review

Chapter 1 Science and Measurement:
Section 1.3—Matter and Energy

Although natural radioactive decay cannot be triggered or prevented (i.e., the rate of decay cannot be changed in any way), scientists have learned how to make some isotopes undergo other nuclear reactions. Artificial radioactivity is induced by the bombardment of certain nuclei with subatomic particles (or atoms), which are produced either by other nuclear reactions or in **particle accelerators**. Particle accelerators, also called cyclotrons or atom-smashers, are large machines containing a magnetic track where small electrically charged particles are made to impact one another at high speeds. The Large Hadron Collider in Switzerland is a particle accelerator. The magnetic track at the Large Hadron Collider is about 27 km in circumference, and it is built at an average depth of 100 m below the surface.

The first artificially induced nuclear reaction was produced by Ernest Rutherford (1871–1937) in 1919.

$${}^{14}_{7}N + {}^{4}_{2}He \rightarrow {}^{17}_{8}O + {}^{1}_{1}H$$

Nitrogen-14 was bombarded by alpha particles (helium nuclei), producing oxygen-17 and protons (hydrogen nuclei). In 1934, Irène Joliot-Curie (1897–1956), the daughter of Marie Curie, produced an isotope of phosphorus by bombarding aluminum-27 with alpha particles from polonium.

$${}^{27}_{13}Al + {}^{4}_{2}He \rightarrow {}^{30}_{15}P + {}^{1}_{0}n$$

Equations for artificial nuclear reactions are balanced the same way as natural nuclear decay equations

TABLE 20.5 Small Particles Involved in Artificial Radioactivity

Particle	Symbol	*A*	*Z*	Identity
Neutron	n, $^{1}_{0}n$, n^0	1	0	Uncharged nucleon
Proton	p, $^{1}_{1}p$, $^{1}_{1}H$	1	+1	Hydrogen nucleus
Deuteron	d, $^{2}_{1}d$, $^{2}_{1}H$	2	+1	Nucleus of ^{2}H
Positron	$^{0}_{+1}\beta$	0	+1	Positively charged electron

(Section 20.1)—that is, by making the superscripts and subscripts on the left and right sides of the equation add up to the same totals.

These reactions are examples of artificial transmutation. Several small particles, in addition to the ones you have seen already in natural radioactivity, are involved in artificial nuclear reactions. Some of these additional particles are listed in Table 20.5. These particles are used as projectiles to bombard nuclei, are produced along with other products of such reactions, or both.

After these kinds of transmutations, the product nucleus often disintegrates spontaneously in further nuclear reactions. For example, ^{30}P disintegrates by means of positron decay with a half-life of 2.50 min, producing $^{30}_{14}Si$.

$$^{30}_{15}P \rightarrow ^{30}_{14}Si + ^{0}_{+1}\beta$$

NUCLEAR FISSION

One of the projectiles most often used in modern times to initiate nuclear reactions is the neutron. To be effective, a neutron does not need as high an energy as an alpha particle or a proton because it is uncharged and can penetrate a nucleus more easily than a positively charged particle can. Some nuclear reactions initiated with neutrons produce more neutrons. For example, the bombardment of ^{235}U with a neutron produces two smaller nuclei plus two or three new neutrons (Figure 20.9).

$$^{235}_{92}U + ^{1}_{0}n \rightarrow ^{141}_{56}Ba + ^{92}_{36}Kr + 3\,^{1}_{0}n$$

This reaction of ^{235}U is an example of **nuclear fission** because one large nucleus is broken up into two smaller ones. Fission reactions do not occur naturally, as decay does. Instead, fission is triggered by firing a neutron into the nucleus of certain nuclei.

When a neutron enters a sample of ^{235}U, it may collide with the nucleus of one of the atoms, resulting in a reaction in which two or three new neutrons are produced. Each of these may react with another nucleus, causing more reactions and increasing the number of neutrons being ejected. Such reactions, all started by a single neutron, can continue until the entire sample of ^{235}U has reacted. The sequence of reactions is called a **chain reaction** (Figure 20.10) and is the process by which nuclear power plants generate energy. Atomic bombs also use a fission chain reaction.

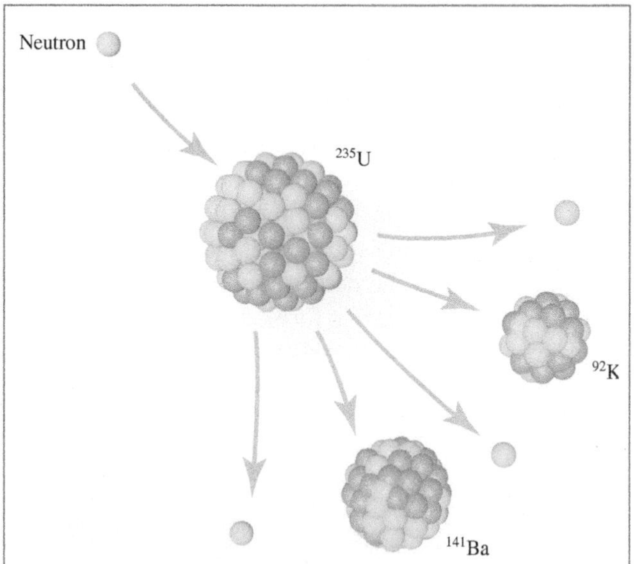

FIGURE 20.9 A Nuclear Fission Reaction

Neutron bombardment causes the ^{235}U to split into two smaller nuclei and a few neutrons.

The animation in Figure 20.10 illustrates some important differences between natural radioactive decay (Section 20.1) and nuclear fission. Radioactive decay of a parent isotope always produces the same daughter isotope, but nuclear fission creates a mixture of different product isotopes. While there is no way to cause a radioactive isotope to undergo a disintegration, nuclear fission can be triggered by impacting a nucleus with a low-energy neutron. Also, the natural decay of a radioactive atom has no effect on the decay of the surrounding atoms, but the neutrons given off by the fission of one atom can trigger fission reactions in the neighboring atoms.

Example 20.12

Use this unbalanced fission reaction to answer the questions that follow.

$$^{235}_{92}U + ^{1}_{0}n \rightarrow ^{90}_{38}Sr + ^{143}_{54}Xe + ?\,^{1}_{0}n$$

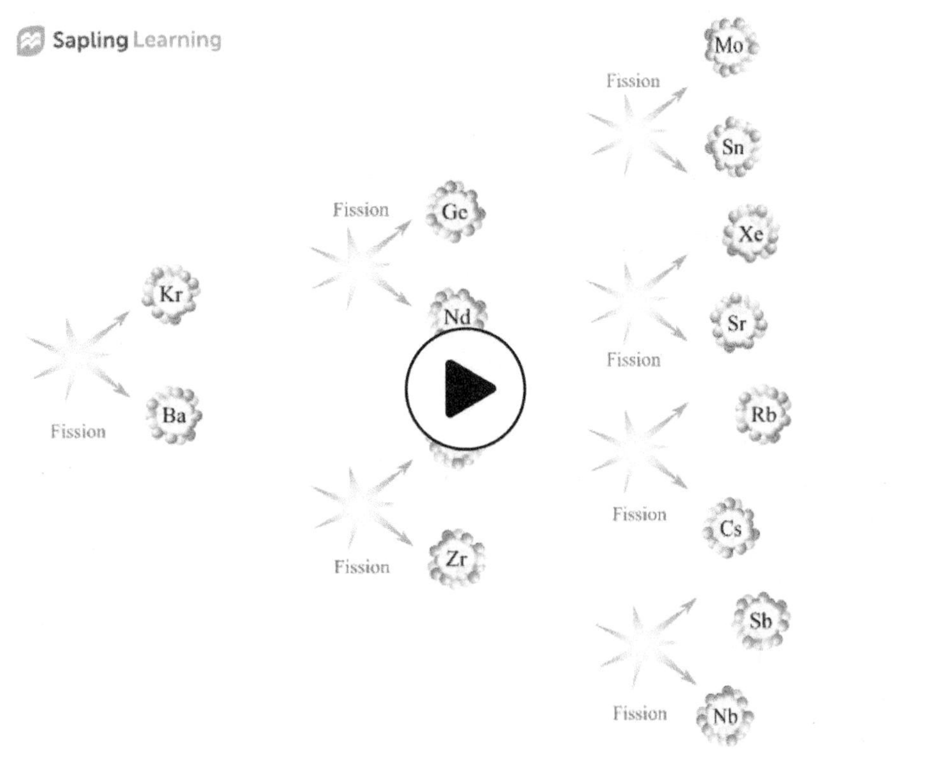

FIGURE 20.10 Fission Chain Reaction

NOTE: You need to be online to watch this video.

The initial stages of a ^{235}U fission chain reaction. Unlike radioactive decay, which always produces the same daughter isotope, fission reactions of the same isotope can produce a variety of product isotopes.

a. How many neutrons are produced in this reaction?

b. If each neutron produced in the first reaction initiates another round of the same reaction, how many total neutrons are produced?

Solution

a. As with all nuclear equations, the sum of the superscripts and subscripts on each side must be balanced. The subscripts are already balanced (92 on each side). To balance the superscripts, set up an equation where x is the missing coefficient.

$$235 + 1 = 90 + 143 + x(1)$$
$$236 = 233 + x$$
$$x = 3$$

The balanced equation is

$$^{235}_{92}U + ^{1}_{0}n \rightarrow ^{90}_{38}Sr + ^{143}_{54}Xe + 3\,^{1}_{0}n$$

b. The first reaction produces 3 neutrons, each of which initiates a second round of reactions, producing $3^2 = 9$ neutrons.

PRACTICE PROBLEM 20.12

Use this unbalanced fission reaction to answer the questions that follow.

$$^{235}_{92}U + ^{1}_{0}n \rightarrow ^{137}_{52}Te + ^{97}_{40}Zr + ?\,^{1}_{0}n$$

a. How many neutrons are produced in this reaction?

b. If each neutron produced in the first reaction initiates one additional reaction, how many total neutrons are produced?

Hint: Balance the equation so that the superscripts and subscripts are balanced.

Not all isotopes are capable of undergoing nuclear fission. Uranium-238 makes up about 99.3% of all naturally occurring uranium, but it does *not* undergo fission when impacted by neutrons. Uranium-235, which makes up about 0.7% of naturally occurring uranium, does undergo fission when triggered with a low-energy neutron. An isotope that is capable of undergoing fission in this manner is described as **fissionable**.

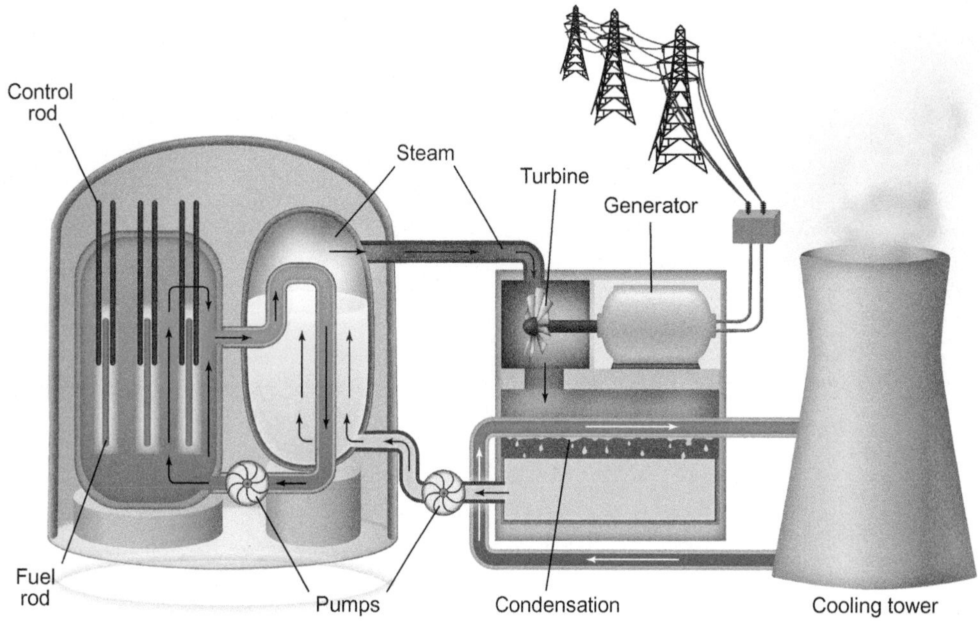

FIGURE 20.11 Simplified Diagram of a Nuclear Reactor

Heat generated by the fission of radioactive uranium atoms heats water, which produces steam to drive a turbine that produces electricity. If too much heat is being generated, control rods are lowered into the reactor to absorb some neutrons and slow down the fission reaction.

The exponential increase in the number of neutrons produced in a fission reaction means that the reaction can quickly grow out of control. This is the basis of an **atomic bomb**. In an atomic bomb, a fissionable nuclide, typically ^{235}U or ^{239}Pu, is bombarded with neutrons, triggering a chain reaction. Each fission event generates heat, and as the number of fission events escalate exponentially, an enormous amount of heat is generated in a very short period of time, resulting in an explosion.

To control such a reaction, the mass of uranium may be kept small so that many of the neutrons that are produced escape from the sample without triggering other fission events. The smallest mass in which a nuclear fission chain reaction can continue is called the **critical mass**. Another way to control a nuclear fission reaction is to interfere with the chain reaction by inserting **control rods** made of some material that can absorb neutrons without causing a reaction. Control rods are used in nuclear reactors (Figure 20.11) in which uranium is the fuel that generates heat to produce electricity. When too much heat is being generated, the reaction is slowed down by lowering the control rods farther into the sample of fuel, thus absorbing more neutrons. When more energy from the reaction is desired, the rods are withdrawn somewhat, allowing more neutrons to impact the fissionable isotope and generate more heat. The control rods are operated automatically.

Nuclear power plants (Figure 20.12) are not simply atomic bombs with control rods, however. An atomic bomb requires a fuel made up of nearly 100% fissionable material, while the fuel in a nuclear reactor is only about 4% fissionable. When a nuclear power plant overheats, it can result in fire and the release of radioactive materials into the environment, as happened at the Fukushima plant in Japan in 2011 and at the Chernobyl plant in Ukraine in 1986, but it cannot result in a nuclear explosion.

NUCLEAR FUSION

Whereas nuclear fission reactions break one large nucleus into two smaller nuclei, **nuclear fusion** reactions combine two small nuclei to form one larger one. Nuclear fusion reactions generate tremendous quantities of energy—even more than is released in fission reactions.

Tennessee Valley Authority

FIGURE 20.12 A Nuclear Power Plant

Nuclear power plants use nuclear reactors to generate power through controlled fission reactions.

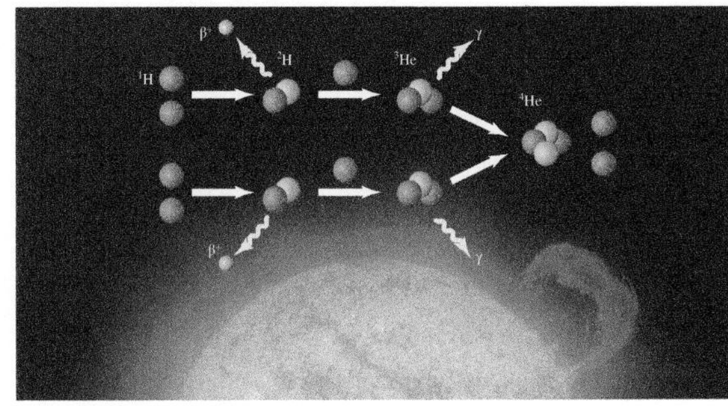

SOHO-EIT Consortium, ESA, NASA

FIGURE 20.13 Fusion Reactions in the Sun

The Sun is powered by the fusion of hydrogen to form helium.

The energy of stars comes from a series of nuclear fusion reactions. The simplest of these has the overall effect of transforming hydrogen nuclei into helium nuclei (alpha particles). Different kinds of stars are capable of fusing different nuclei, depending mainly on the temperature of the star. The Sun, a moderately small star of average temperature, is thought to be powered by the following sequence of reactions.

$$^{1}_{1}\text{H} + ^{1}_{1}\text{H} \rightarrow ^{2}_{1}\text{H} + ^{0}_{1}\beta$$
$$^{1}_{1}\text{H} + ^{2}_{1}\text{H} \rightarrow ^{3}_{2}\text{He} + ^{0}_{0}\gamma$$
$$^{3}_{2}\text{He} + ^{3}_{2}\text{He} \rightarrow ^{4}_{2}\text{He} + 2\,^{1}_{1}\text{H}$$

Each one of these reactions emits energy along with the products shown. The positron released in the first reaction can react with an electron to yield even more energy. The net reaction of this series of fusion reactions is the conversion of four protons into an alpha particle plus a great deal of energy (Figure 20.13). Hotter stars than our Sun are able to convert protons into alpha particles via another series of reactions, and they can fuse heavier elements as well (all the way to iron).

Fusion reactions in stars often create heavier isotopes of hydrogen as the first steps toward later fusion reactions. A hydrogen atom that has gained one neutron ($^{2}_{1}$H) is called **deuterium** and is given the symbol D. A deuterium nucleus is also known as a **deuteron**. A hydrogen atom that has gained two neutrons is called **tritium** ($^{3}_{1}$H), symbolized T. A tritium nucleus is also called a **triton**. Deuterium and tritium are important reactants in the fusion reactions that form helium and heavier elements. The animation in Figure 20.14 shows the fusion of deuterium and tritium to form helium.

Because neither the reactants nor the products of a fusion reaction are necessarily radioactive, fusion reactors would be an ideal source of energy for society. Unfortunately, while fission reactions can be carried out at room temperature, fusion reactions occur only at extremely high temperatures. Nuclear weapons that use fusion to generate energy actually require a small fission bomb to generate sufficient heat for the fusion reaction to occur. Fusion-based weapons are known as **thermonuclear weapons**, or **hydrogen bombs**, to distinguish them from atomic bombs, which use fission.

FIGURE 20.14 Fusion Reaction

NOTE: You need to be online to view this video.

Two isotopes of hydrogen (tritium, $^{3}_{1}$H, and deuterium, $^{2}_{1}$H) combine to produce a fusion product along with a subatomic particle as a by-product.

EVERYDAY CONNECTION

All of the atoms in you and around you that are heavier than hydrogen and helium were formed in stars that went supernova and spread those atoms across space. The Big Bang resulted in a universe that was made up of about 90% hydrogen atoms and 10% helium atoms, with traces of lithium and beryllium. A small star like our Sun will produce only helium as a fusion product. More massive stars can produce carbon and oxygen, and the most massive stars can produce elements up to iron (atomic number 26). Every atom heavier than iron was formed in a supernova such as the one shown here.

NASA/ESA, The Hubble Key Project Team and The High-Z Supernova Search Team

SECTION REVIEW

- Bombarding certain large radioactive isotopes with small particles, especially neutrons, causes the fissionable nuclei to split, producing two other elements plus other products, in a process called nuclear fission.
- Natural radioactive decay usually releases an alpha or beta particle and the parent isotope always becomes a specific daughter isotope, whereas in fission the nucleus is split into two atoms, usually with the release of a number of neutrons as well, and the elements produced by the fission of a given isotope are not always the same.
- Combining smaller nuclei together to form larger ones is called nuclear fusion. The reactions of the Sun and stars are fusion reactions.
- The parent isotope in radioactive decay and in fission is always radioactive, but in fusion, the reactant and product isotopes are not necessarily radioactive.

20.6 Energetics of Nuclear Reactions

GOAL

- Calculate energy changes for nuclear reactions.

Background Review

Chapter 1 Science and Measurement:
Section 1.3—Matter and Energy

A conventional chemical reaction that is exothermic gives off energy. This energy comes from the bonds between the atoms; more specifically, the chemical bonds in the products are overall more stable (have less potential energy) than the bonds in the reactants (Section 6.6). When nuclear reactions give off energy, it is also because the products are more stable (have less potential energy) than the reactants, but the energy does not come from chemical bonds—it comes from the nuclei of the atoms themselves. In any nuclear reaction, energy is emitted because a small amount of mass is converted into a large amount of energy according to Equation 20.5, which Albert Einstein first proposed in 1905.

$$E = mc^2 \qquad (20.5)$$

In this equation, E is the energy produced, m is the mass, and c is the speed of light in a vacuum, 2.998×10^8 m/s (Section 8.1). The c^2 term in this equation is such a large number that conversion of a small quantity of matter produces a large quantity of energy. When m is in kilograms, the units of E come out to $\text{kg} \cdot \text{m}^2/\text{s}^2$, which is equivalent to a joule.

$$1 \text{ J} = 1 \text{ kg} \cdot \text{m}^2 \cdot \text{s}^2$$

All nuclear reactions must be balanced in terms of mass numbers, which implies that the sum of the masses of the reactants is always equal to the sum of the masses of the products. This is approximately, but not exactly, true because the mass numbers used in those equations are not the exact masses of the isotopes. When more precise values are used for the masses of each reactant and product, it can be shown

Steve Lemon, Macmillan Learning

FIGURE 20.15 Video Tutorial: Energetics of Nuclear Reactions

NOTE: You need to be online to access this video.

This video shows how to calculate the energy change of a nuclear reaction based on the masses of the reactants and products.

that a small amount of mass is always missing on the product side in the final balanced equation. This missing mass was converted to energy in the nuclear process.

You can use the first radioactive decay equation listed in Section 20.1 as an example.

$$^{238}_{92}\text{U} \rightarrow {}^{234}_{90}\text{Th} + {}^{4}_{2}\text{He}$$

Nucleus or Particle	Mass (u)
U-238	238.00033
Th-234	233.99423
He-4	4.00151

Using more exact values given for the masses of each nucleus in the preceding table, the sum of the products is 237.99574 u, which is 0.00459 u *less* than the mass of the original U-238 nucleus. This difference is often symbolized as Δm and is used in Equation 20.6, a modified version of Equation 20.5.

$$\Delta E = \Delta mc^2 \qquad (20.6)$$

Note that Δm must be converted to kilograms or kilograms per mole. Recall that a mole of atomic mass units is equal to 1 g (Section 2.5), so 1 u = 1 g/mol.

Figure 20.15 demonstrates how to use Equation 20.6 to solve problems.

Example 20.13

Use the data given in the following table, to calculate the energy (in J/mol) released in this fission reaction.

$$^{235}_{92}\text{U} + {}^{1}_{0}\text{n} \rightarrow {}^{90}_{38}\text{Sr} + {}^{143}_{54}\text{Xe} + 3\,{}^{1}_{0}\text{n}$$

Nucleus or Particle	Mass (u)
U-235	234.99343
Neutron	1.00866
Sr-90	89.88688
Xe-143	142.90578

Solution

Use the values given in the table to determine the difference in mass, Δm, between the products and the reactants. The products are Sr-90, Xe-143, and three neutrons. The reactants are U-235 and one neutron.

$$\begin{aligned}\text{Products} &= 89.88688\text{ u} + 142.90578\text{ u} \\ &\quad + (3 \times 1.00866)\text{ u} \\ &= 235.81864\text{ u}\end{aligned}$$

$$\text{Reactants} = 234.99343\text{ u} + 1.00866\text{ u} = 236.00209\text{ u}$$

$$\begin{aligned}\Delta m &= m_{\text{products}} - m_{\text{reactants}} \\ &= 235.81864\text{ u} - 236.00209\text{ u} = -0.18345\text{ u}\end{aligned}$$

Convert Δm to kilograms per mole, and substitute it into Equation 20.6.

$$\begin{aligned}\Delta m &= -0.18345\text{ u}\left(\frac{1\text{ g/mol}}{1\text{ u}}\right)\left(\frac{1\text{ kg}}{1000\text{ g}}\right) \\ &= -1.8345 \times 10^{-4}\text{ kg/mol}\end{aligned}$$

$$\begin{aligned}\Delta E &= \Delta mc^2 \\ &= (-1.8345 \times 10^{-4}\text{ kg/mol})(2.998 \times 10^{8}\text{m/s})^2 \\ &= -1.649 \times 10^{13}\text{ J/mol}\end{aligned}$$

The negative sign indicates that energy is released. Each mole of U-235 that undergoes this fission reaction produces 1.652×10^{13} J of energy. That is about 7×10^{10} J per gram of U-235.

PRACTICE PROBLEM 20.13

Use the data given in the table below to calculate the energy (in J/mol) released in the following fission reaction.

$$^{235}_{92}\text{U} + {}^{1}_{0}\text{n} \rightarrow {}^{140}_{56}\text{Ba} + {}^{94}_{36}\text{Kr} + 2\,{}^{1}_{0}\text{n}$$

Nucleus or Particle	Mass (u)
U-235	234.99343
Neutron	1.00866
Ba-140	139.87988
Kr-94	93.91439

Hint: First, calculate the difference in mass, Δm, between the products and the reactants. Then convert Δm to kg/mol, and plug this value into Equation 20.6.

The energy given off by a *fusion* reaction can be calculated in the same way as for a *fission* reaction—that is, by using precise values for each of the particles and nuclei involved to determine Δm and then substituting into Equation 20.6.

Example 20.14

If scientists of the future are ever able to harness the power of fusion on Earth, it will most likely occur via the following reaction.

$$^{3}_{1}\text{H} + ^{2}_{1}\text{H} \rightarrow ^{4}_{2}\text{He} + ^{1}_{0}\text{n}$$

Calculate the energy (in J/mol) released in this fusion reaction.

Nucleus or Particle	Mass (u)
Tritium, H-3	3.01550
Deuterium, H-2	2.01355
Helium, He-4	4.00151
Neutron, $^{1}_{0}\text{n}$	1.00866

Solution

Find the difference in mass, Δm, between the products and the reactants. The products are He-4 and a neutron. The reactants are tritium and deuterium.

$$\text{Products} = 4.00151\ \text{u} + 1.00866\ \text{u} = 5.01017\ \text{u}$$

$$\text{Reactants} = 3.01550\ \text{u} + 2.01355\ \text{u} = 5.02905\ \text{u}$$

$$\Delta m = m_{\text{products}} - m_{\text{reactants}}$$
$$= 5.01017\ \text{u} - 5.02905\ \text{u} = -0.01888\ \text{u}$$

Convert Δm to kilograms per mole, and substitute it into Equation 20.6.

$$\Delta m = -0.01888\ \text{u}\left(\frac{1\ \text{g/mol}}{1\ \text{u}}\right)\left(\frac{1\ \text{kg}}{1000\ \text{g}}\right)$$
$$= -1.888 \times 10^{-5}\ \text{kg/mol}$$

$$\Delta E = \Delta mc^2$$
$$= (-1.888 \times 10^{-5}\ \text{kg/mol})(2.998 \times 10^{8}\ \text{m/s})^2$$
$$= -1.697 \times 10^{12}\ \text{J/mol}$$

The amount of energy released is 1.697×10^{12} J/mol.

PRACTICE PROBLEM 20.14

When a massive star has consumed the hydrogen in its core, it begins fusing larger nuclei. Silicon-28, a stable isotope that makes up 92% of the silicon found on Earth, is formed in massive stars through the fusion of two oxygen nuclei.

$$^{16}_{8}\text{O} + ^{16}_{8}\text{O} \rightarrow ^{28}_{14}\text{Si} + ^{4}_{2}\text{He}$$

Calculate the energy (in J/mol) released in this fusion reaction.

Particle	Mass (u)
Oxygen-16	15.99052
Silicon-28	27.96925
Helium, He-4	4.00151

Hint: First, calculate the difference in mass, Δm, between the products and the reactants. Then convert Δm to kg/mol, and plug this value into Equation 20.6.

On average, the energies produced by fusion reactions are similar to or greater than those produced by fission reactions when you compare them *per gram* of reactant rather than per mole. Fission reactants tend to be much heavier than fusion reactants, so fusion reactions produce about 10 times more energy per gram of reactant than fission reactions do, and at least 10 *million* times more than chemical reactions do.

SECTION REVIEW

- When the masses of the reactants and products in a nuclear reaction are measured precisely, the products have *less* mass than the reactants.
- The lost mass is converted to energy according to the equation $E = mc^2$ or $\Delta E = \Delta mc^2$.

20.7 Nuclear Binding Energy

GOALS

- Calculate nuclear binding energy.
- Compare the stabilities of different isotopes using relative binding energies.

Background Review

Chapter 1 Science and Measurement:
Section 1.3—Matter and Energy

The nucleus of a helium atom is made up of two protons and two neutrons.

$$^{4}_{2}\text{He} \rightarrow 2\ ^{1}_{1}\text{p} + 2\ ^{1}_{0}\text{n}$$

Using precise values for the masses of a proton, neutron, and helium nucleus, you can compare the mass of the nucleus to the total mass of its particles.

$$\text{Mass of } ^{4}_{2}\text{He nucleus} = 4.00151\ \text{u}$$

$$\text{Sum of its particles} = 2(1.00728\ \text{u}) + 2(1.00866\ \text{u})$$
$$= 4.03188\ \text{u}$$

$$\Delta m = m_{\text{particles}} - m_{\text{nucleus}} = 4.03188\ \text{u} - 4.00151\ \text{u}$$
$$= 0.03037\ \text{u}$$

Nucleus or Particle	Mass (u)
Proton, ${}^{1}_{1}\text{p}$	1.00728
Neutron, ${}^{1}_{0}\text{n}$	1.00866
Helium, ${}^{4}_{2}\text{He}$	4.00151

This calculation illustrates that the helium nucleus has *less* mass than the sum of its parts, implying that some of the mass of the reactants is lost when forming the helium nucleus. This amount of missing mass, known as the **mass defect**, is converted to energy when the helium nucleus is formed according to $E = mc^2$ (Equation 20.5). Energy is given off in the process, which means that the product is more stable than the reactants. If you were to try to disassemble the helium nucleus back into its component protons and neutrons, it would require an amount of energy equal to the amount of energy given off when the nucleus was formed. This amount of energy is known as the **binding energy**.

Binding energy is typically reported per nucleon rather than per mole. Recall that *nucleon* is the collective term for both protons and neutrons, since these are the particles that make up the nucleus. Thus, once you have found binding energy per atom by applying Equation 20.6, the final step is to divide by the mass number.

Example 20.15

Calculate and compare the binding energies per nucleon for ${}^{12}_{6}\text{C}$ and ${}^{14}_{6}\text{C}$.

Nucleus or Particle	Mass (u)
Proton, ${}^{1}_{1}\text{p}$	1.00728
Neutron, ${}^{1}_{0}\text{n}$	1.00866
Carbon-12, ${}^{12}_{6}\text{C}$	11.99671
Carbon-14, ${}^{14}_{6}\text{C}$	13.99995

Solution

${}^{12}_{6}\text{C}$ is made up of six protons and six neutrons: ${}^{12}_{6}\text{C} \rightarrow 6\,{}^{1}_{1}\text{p} + 6\,{}^{1}_{0}\text{n}$.

$$\text{Mass of } {}^{12}_{6}\text{C nucleus} = 11.99671\text{ u}$$

$$\text{Sum of its particles} = 6(1.00728\text{ u}) + 6(1.00866\text{ u}) = 12.09564\text{ u}$$

$$\Delta m = m_{\text{particles}} - m_{\text{nucleus}} = 12.09564\text{ u} - 11.99671\text{ u} = 0.09893\text{ u}$$

Convert Δm to kilograms and apply Equation 20.6.

$$\Delta m = 0.09893\text{ u}\left(\frac{1\text{ g}}{6.022 \times 10^{23}\text{ u}}\right)\left(\frac{1\text{ kg}}{1000\text{ g}}\right) = 1.643 \times 10^{-28}\text{ kg}$$

$$\Delta E = \Delta mc^2 = (1.643 \times 10^{-28}\text{ kg})(2.998 \times 10^{8}\text{ m/s})^2 = 1.477 \times 10^{-11}\text{ J}$$

The total number of nucleons is 6 protons + 6 neutrons = 12 nucleons (equal to the mass number).

$$\text{Binding energy per nucleon} = \frac{1.477 \times 10^{-11}\text{ J}}{12\text{ nucleons}} = 1.230 \times 10^{-12}\text{ J per nucleon}$$

Repeat the same calculation for ${}^{14}_{6}\text{C}$, which has six protons and eight neutrons: ${}^{14}_{6}\text{C} \rightarrow 6\,{}^{1}_{1}\text{p} + 8\,{}^{1}_{0}\text{n}$.

$$\text{Mass of } {}^{14}_{6}\text{C nucleus} = 13.99995\text{ u}$$

$$\text{Sum of its particles} = 6(1.00728\text{ u}) + 8(1.00866\text{ u}) = 14.11296\text{ u}$$

$$\Delta m = 14.11296\text{ u} - 13.99995\text{ u} = 0.11301\text{ u}$$

Convert Δm to kilograms and apply Equation 20.6.

$$\Delta m = 0.11301\text{ u}\left(\frac{1\text{ g}}{6.022 \times 10^{23}\text{ u}}\right)\left(\frac{1\text{ kg}}{1000\text{ g}}\right) = 1.877 \times 10^{-28}\text{ kg}$$

$$\Delta E = \Delta mc^2 = (1.877 \times 10^{-28}\text{ kg})(2.998 \times 10^{8}\text{ m/s})^2 = 1.687 \times 10^{-11}\text{ J}$$

The total number of nucleons is 6 protons + 8 neutrons = 14 nucleons (equal to the mass number).

$$\text{Binding energy per nucleon} = \frac{1.687 \times 10^{-11}\text{ J}}{14\text{ nucleons}} = 1.205 \times 10^{-12}\text{ J per nucleon}$$

The binding energy per nucleon is greater for ${}^{12}\text{C}$ (1.230×10^{-12} J) than it is for ${}^{14}\text{C}$ (1.205×10^{-12} J), indicating that ${}^{12}\text{C}$ is a more stable nucleus. In fact, ${}^{12}\text{C}$ is stable, whereas ${}^{14}\text{C}$ is radioactive.

PRACTICE PROBLEM 20.15

Calculate and compare the binding energies per nucleon for ${}^{15}_{8}\text{O}$ and ${}^{16}_{8}\text{O}$.

Nucleus or Particle	Mass (u)
Proton, ${}^{1}_{1}\text{p}$	1.00728
Neutron, ${}^{1}_{0}\text{n}$	1.00866
Oxygen-15, ${}^{15}_{8}\text{O}$	14.99868
Oxygen-16, ${}^{16}_{8}\text{O}$	15.99052

Hint: For each nucleus, sum the masses of the component particles, then subtract the mass of the nucleus itself. Convert this mass defect to kilograms, then plug this value into Equation 20.6. Dividing by the mass number gives the binding energy per nucleon.

SECTION REVIEW

- Binding energy is the energy required to break a nucleus into its component nucleons. It is equal to the energy equivalent of the mass defect of the nucleus.
- Binding energy per nucleon can be used to compare the relative stabilities of two nuclei. The nucleus with the greater binding energy per nucleon is the more stable nucleus.

Putting It Together

The example problems in earlier sections of this chapter focus on the new skills acquired in that section, but homework and exam questions in chemistry often require more than just one skill at a time. In fact, you will likely be expected to apply knowledge from throughout the chapter, or even multiple chapters, in a single problem. This final example problem is meant to help you prepare for these types of multi-concept questions. Additional examples can be found in the end-of-chapter exercises.

Example 20.16

Americium-241 is a synthetic isotope used in some household smoke detectors.

a. Write the balanced nuclear equation for the decay of ^{241}Am.

b. Old smoke detectors containing ^{241}Am should be brought to a hazardous waste collection site rather than thrown in the trash. If a smoke detector containing 0.290 microgram of ^{241}Am ($t_{1/2} = 432.6$ y) ends up in a landfill, how many micrograms of the daughter isotope will there be 100 years later? The masses of ^{241}Am and its daughter isotope can be treated as equal to their mass numbers for the purposes of this calculation.

c. If the daughter isotope decays by alpha decay, what is the granddaughter isotope of ^{241}Am? Based on the number of protons and neutrons in the granddaughter isotope, would you expect it to be stable or radioactive?

Solution

a. According to the periodic table, Am has an atomic number of 95. Radioactive isotopes with $Z > 82$ tend to decay by alpha decay.

$$^{241}_{95}\text{Am} \rightarrow {}^{?}_{?}? + {}^{4}_{2}\alpha$$

The missing mass number must be 237 because 241 = 237 + 4. The missing nuclear charge must be 93 because 95 = 93 + 2. The element with $Z = 93$ is Np.

$$^{241}_{95}\text{Am} \rightarrow {}^{237}_{93}\text{Np} + {}^{4}_{2}\alpha$$

b. There are two different ways (method 1 and method 2) you can approach this part.

Method 1: Convert the mass of ^{241}Am to atoms of ^{241}Am, then use Equation 20.2 to determine how many ^{241}Am atoms remain after exactly 100 years. From that you can calculate how many atoms of ^{237}Np were formed, and using the molar mass of ^{237}Np, calculate the mass of ^{237}Np present.

$$N_0 = 0.290\ \mu\text{g}\left(\frac{10^{-6}\ \text{g}}{1\ \mu\text{g}}\right)\left(\frac{1\ \text{mol}}{241\ \text{g}}\right)\left(\frac{6.022 \times 10^{23}\ \text{atoms}}{1\ \text{mol}}\right)$$
$$= 7.24 \times 10^{14}\ \text{atoms}$$

Solve for N using Equation 20.2:

$$\ln\left(\frac{N_0}{N}\right) = \left(\frac{\ln 2}{t_{1/2}}\right)t$$

Solving for N means you will have to take the inverse natural log of both sides of the equation, so first plug in the known values for t and $t_{1/2}$, and simplify the right side of the equation.

$$\ln\left(\frac{N_0}{N}\right) = \left(\frac{\ln 2}{432.6\ \text{y}}\right)100\ \text{y}$$

$$\ln\left(\frac{N_0}{N}\right) = 0.1602$$

To extract N from the natural log term, take the inverse natural log of both sides (Section 0.5).

$$e^{\ln\left(\frac{N_0}{N}\right)} = e^{0.1602}$$

The e and ln functions cancel each other out, leaving

$$\frac{N_0}{N} = 1.174$$

Rearrange the equation algebraically to isolate and solve for N.

$$N = \frac{7.24 \times 10^{14}\ \text{atoms}}{1.174} = 6.17 \times 10^{14}\ \text{atoms}$$

The number of ^{241}Am atoms that decayed is $N_0 - N = 7.24 \times 10^{14} - 6.17 \times 10^{14} = 1.07 \times 10^{14}$ atoms.

Convert this number of ^{237}Np atoms to a mass of Np in micrograms.

$$m = 1.07 \times 10^{14}\ {}^{237}\text{Np atoms}\left(\frac{1\ \text{mol}}{6.022 \times 10^{23}\ \text{atoms}}\right)\left(\frac{237\ \text{g}}{1\ \text{mol}}\right)\left(\frac{1 \times 10^{6}\ \mu\text{g}}{1\ \text{g}}\right)$$
$$= 0.0421\ \mu\text{g}\ {}^{237}\text{Np}$$

Method 2: Use Equation 20.3 (the m_0/m version of Equation 20.2) to determine the mass of ^{241}Am remaining, then calculate the mass of ^{241}Am that decayed and multiply that mass by the ratio of atomic masses to determine how many grams of ^{237}Np were formed.

Initial mass of $^{241}_{95}$Am present $= m_0 =$ 0.290 μg. Equation 20.3 is

$$\ln\left(\frac{m_0}{m}\right) = \left(\frac{\ln 2}{t_{1/2}}\right)t$$

Solving for m means you will have to take the inverse natural log of both sides of the equation, so first plug in the known values for t and $t_{1/2}$, and simplify the right side of the equation.

$$\ln\left(\frac{m_0}{m}\right) = \left(\frac{\ln 2}{432.6 \text{ y}}\right)100 \text{ y}$$

$$\ln\left(\frac{m_0}{m}\right) = 0.1602$$

To extract m from the natural log term, take the inverse natural log of both sides (Section 0.5).

$$e^{\ln\left(\frac{m_0}{m}\right)} = e^{0.1602}$$

The e and ln functions cancel each other out.

$$\frac{m_0}{m} = 1.174$$

Rearrange the equation algebraically to isolate and solve for m.

$$m = \frac{0.290\ \mu\text{g}}{1.174} = 0.247\ \mu\text{g}$$

The mass of ^{241}Am atoms that decayed is $m_0 - m = 0.290\,\mu\text{g} - 0.247\,\mu\text{g} = 0.043\,\mu\text{g}\ ^{241}\text{Am}$. Convert this value to a mass of ^{237}Np by multiplying by the mass ratio of the two isotopes.

$$m = 0.043\ \mu\text{g}\ ^{241}\text{Am}\left(\frac{237\ \mu\text{g}\ ^{237}\text{Np}}{241\ \mu\text{g}\ ^{241}\text{Am}}\right) = 0.042\ \mu\text{g}\ ^{237}\text{Np}$$

c. The unbalanced equation for the alpha decay of the daughter isotope is

$$^{237}_{93}\text{Np} \rightarrow\ ^{?}_{?}? + ^{4}_{2}\text{He}$$

Find the missing mass and charge, then locate the appropriate element in the periodic table.

$$^{237}_{93}\text{Np} \rightarrow\ ^{233}_{91}\text{Pa} + ^{4}_{2}\text{He}$$

The granddaughter isotope, protactinium-233, has an atomic number of 91, and there are no elements above atomic number 82 that have stable isotopes, so that alone indicates that $^{233}_{91}$Pa would be radioactive. Furthermore, $^{233}_{91}$Pa has an odd number of protons and an odd number of neutrons, whereas *even* numbers of nucleons tend to confer stability. Thus, having an odd–odd configuration also suggests $^{233}_{91}$Pa is probably unstable.

PRACTICE PROBLEM 20.16

The *New Horizons* space probe that took photos of the dwarf planet Pluto and its moon Charon in 2015 and 2016 was powered, appropriately enough, by radioactive plutonium.

a. Write the balanced nuclear equation for the decay of ^{238}Pu.

b. *New Horizons* left Earth in 2005 with 8.59 kg of ^{238}Pu ($t_{1/2}$ = 87.7 years) on board in the form of plutonium(IV) oxide pellets. One hundred years after liftoff, what will the mass of the daughter isotope be? (The daughter isotope has a half-life of almost 25,000 years, so ignore the decay of the daughter isotope.) The masses of ^{238}Pu and its daughter isotope can be treated as equal to their mass numbers for the purposes of this calculation.

c. If the daughter isotope decays by alpha decay, what is the granddaughter isotope of ^{238}Pu? Based on the number of protons and neutrons in the granddaughter isotope, would you expect it to be stable or radioactive?

Hint:

a. Write a nuclear decay equation and balance the mass numbers and the atomic numbers, then use the atomic number of the daughter isotope to identify which element it is.

b. Use Equation 20.2 to solve for N or Equation 20.3 to solve for m, then calculate how many atoms or how much mass of ^{238}Pu decayed. From there, calculate the mass of daughter isotope formed.

c. Write a nuclear decay equation as you did in part a, then consider the stability of the daughter isotope based on its atomic number.

Key Terms, Symbols, and Equations

KEY TERMS

activity, *A* (20.1): The number of disintegrations per unit time in a sample of a radioactive substance. The activity is proportional to the decay rate and to the number of atoms of the isotope in the sample.

alpha decay (20.1): A form of radioactive decay in which a nucleus emits an alpha particle and often a gamma ray.

alpha particle, α (20.1): A particle made up of two protons and two neutrons that is ejected from a radioactive atom's nucleus in alpha decay. Alpha particles eventually pick up two electrons from their surroundings and become helium atoms.

atomic bomb (20.5): A nuclear weapon that uses a fission reaction to release energy.

belt of stability (20.2): The area showing the stable isotopes within the plot of the number of neutrons versus the number of protons for all isotopes.

beta decay (20.1): A form of radioactive decay in which a nucleus emits a beta particle and often a gamma ray, turning a neutron into a proton.

beta particle, β (20.1): An electron that is ejected from a radioactive atom's nucleus in beta decay as a neutron in the nucleus is transformed into a proton.

binding energy (20.7): The energy required to separate an atomic nucleus into its component protons and neutrons.

chain reaction (20.5): In nuclear fission, a reaction that requires one neutron to trigger fission, but the fission process produces two or more neutrons, thereby continuing, and accelerating the rate of, the reaction.

control rod (20.5): A rod made of a material that can absorb neutrons without causing a reaction. Control rods are used in fission reactors to absorb neutrons and slow the reaction down if too much heat is being generated.

critical mass (20.5): The minimum mass of a fissionable isotope necessary to sustain a chain reaction. If less than the critical mass is present, neutrons are able to escape the sample and the reaction will eventually stop.

daughter nuclide (20.1): The product isotope that is formed as a result of a radioactive decay process.

deuterium (20.5): An isotope of hydrogen that has one proton and one neutron in the nucleus instead of the usual lone proton.

deuteron (20.5): A particle made up of one proton and one neutron (the nucleus of a deuterium atom).

disintegration (20.1): A single nuclear decay event, such as alpha decay, beta decay, electron capture, or positron emission.

electromagnetic radiation (20.1): A general term for light of all wavelengths, from radio waves to gamma rays. The gamma particles released in nuclear reactions are a form of electromagnetic radiation.

electron capture (20.1): A form of radioactive decay in which a nucleus captures an electron from one of the inner shells of the atom, turning a proton into a neutron.

fissionable (20.5): The property of an isotope that makes it capable of undergoing fission when triggered with a low-energy neutron.

gamma particle (20.1): A photon of high-energy gamma radiation emitted from the nucleus in a nuclear reaction.

Geiger counter (20.1): A device that captures the charged particles emitted by the decay of a radioactive sample and generates an electrical current to indicate the activity of the radioactive sample.

half-life, $t_{1/2}$ (20.3): The amount of time required for one-half of a radioactive isotope to decay.

hydrogen bomb (20.5): A nuclear bomb that uses a fusion reaction to release energy; also known as a thermonuclear bomb or H-bomb.

magic number (20.2): A specific number of protons or neutrons commonly found in stable atoms.

mass defect (20.7): The difference in mass between an atomic nucleus and the total mass of the protons and neutrons that make up that nucleus. The nucleus always has less mass than the sum of the constituent particles.

natural radioactivity (20.1): The spontaneous release of energy and particles from the nucleus of an atom.

nuclear (20.1): Pertaining to the nucleus of an atom.

nuclear fission (20.5): The breaking of a large nuclide into two smaller nuclides. Fission is triggered by striking the parent nuclide with a low-energy neutron.

nuclear fusion (20.5): The combining of two smaller nuclides into one larger one. Fusion requires extreme temperatures.

nuclear radiation (20.1): The energy and particles that are given off by radioactive isotopes.

nuclear transmutation (20.1): The transformation of one element into another via a nuclear reaction.

nucleons (20.2): The particles found in the nucleus of an atom (i.e., protons and neutrons).

nuclide (20.1): The nucleus of an isotope. In this chapter, *isotope* and *nuclide* are used synonymously.

parent nuclide (20.1): The radioactive atom that undergoes radioactive decay to generate a new isotope (the daughter nuclide).

particle accelerator (20.5): A large magnetic track designed for accelerating small electrically charged particles to make them impact one another at high speeds.

positron, β^+ (20.1): An antimatter particle that is identical to an electron in all its properties except that it has a +1 charge instead of a −1 charge.

positron emission (20.1): A form of radioactive decay in which a nucleus emits a positron and often a gamma ray, turning a proton into a neutron.

radioactive (20.1): The property of an unstable isotope that makes it eject particles from the nucleus.

radioactive decay (20.1): A process in which an unstable nucleus of an atom releases energy by ejecting a particle from the nucleus or by capturing an electron from the atom's inner shells.

radioactive series (20.1): A series of sequential radioactive decays from one radioactive isotope to another, ending with a stable isotope.

radiocarbon dating (20.4): Radiometric dating that uses the activity of carbon-14 to determine the age of a sample; also called carbon dating.

radiometric dating (20.4): A method of determining the age of a sample by comparing the ratios of parent and daughter isotopes in the sample (such as potassium–argon dating) or by comparing the activity of a radioactive isotope in the sample to the activity of the same isotope in a modern sample (such as carbon-14 dating).

thermonuclear weapon (20.5): A nuclear bomb that generates energy through a fusion reaction rather than through fission; also called a hydrogen bomb or H-bomb.

tracer (20.1): A radioactive isotope that is added to a medicine or procedure (often medical) so that the movement of the isotope through a system can be monitored using a Geiger counter or other means.

tritium (20.5): A radioactive isotope of hydrogen that has two neutrons and one proton in the nucleus.

triton (20.5): A particle made up of one proton and two neutrons (a tritium nucleus).

SYMBOLS

A (activity) (20.1)

$\alpha, {}^4_2\alpha, {}^4_2\text{He}$ (alpha particle) (20.1)

Bq (becquerel) (20.1)

$\beta, \beta^-, {}^{\ 0}_{-1}\beta$ (beta particle) (20.1)

$\beta^+, {}^{\ 0}_{+1}\beta$ (positron) (20.1)

Ci (curie) (20.1)

d number of disintegrations (20.1)

D (deuterium) (20.5)

γ (gamma particle) (20.1)

n (neutron) (20.5)

N (number of nuclei) (20.3)

N_0 (original number of nuclei) (20.3)

p (proton) (20.5)

T (tritium) (20.5)

$t_{1/2}$ (half-life) (20.3)

EQUATIONS

$A = kN$ (20.1)

$\ln\left(\frac{N_0}{N}\right) = \left(\frac{\ln 2}{t_{1/2}}\right)t$ (20.2)

$\ln\left(\frac{m_0}{m}\right) = \left(\frac{\ln 2}{t_{1/2}}\right)t$ (20.3)

$\ln\left(\frac{A_0}{A}\right) = \left(\frac{\ln 2}{t_{1/2}}\right)t$ (20.4)

$E = mc^2$ (20.5)

$\Delta E = \Delta mc^2$ (20.6)

Chapter Summary

Nuclear reactions, unlike ordinary chemical reactions, usually change one element into one or more other elements. The energy produced in nuclear reactions is much greater than that involved in any chemical reaction.

Natural radioactivity on Earth occurs when radioactive nuclei disintegrate spontaneously, yielding alpha, beta, and gamma particles, sometimes called rays, plus daughter isotopes almost as massive as the parent isotopes. A nuclear equation can be balanced by making both the total of the mass numbers and the total of the nuclear charges the same on both sides of the equation. When the products of a nuclear reaction are radioactive, a series of disintegrations may occur. The isotopes involved, including the original parent isotope and all daughter isotopes, constitute a radioactive series.

Radioactive isotopes react chemically just like the nonradioactive isotopes of the same element. Because of this, physicians can add a little radioactive isotope to a sample of an element, which is then ingested or injected into the body. They can then determine the element's location in the body by detecting the particles that the radioactive isotope emits. The radioactive isotope is called a tracer, and this technique is used extensively in medicine and other fields (Section 20.1).

All elements up through lead (atomic number 82) have at least one stable isotope, but there are no known isotopes with atomic number 83 or greater that are stable. A nucleus contains a balance of attractive and repulsive forces; if the forces are well balanced, the nucleus will be stable, and if not, it will be radioactive. Factors that contribute to stability include having an even number of protons, having an even number of neutrons, and having a magic number of either or both protons and neutrons. The magic numbers are 2, 8, 20, 28, 50, 82, and 126 (126 for neutrons only). The ratio of neutrons to protons also affects the stability of the nucleus—in a scatter plot of the number of neutrons versus the number of protons, a trend emerges where a certain ratio adds stability; deviating from that ratio creates instability. The ratio is not constant and changes with the atomic ratio. For the first 20 elements the ratio is approximately 1:1, but beyond that, increasing numbers of neutrons are required to stabilize larger nuclei (Section 20.2).

All the atoms of a radioactive isotope in a sample do *not* disintegrate at once, but rather in accordance with the laws of statistics. The rate of disintegration is proportional to the number of atoms of the radioactive isotope present. The time it takes for half of a given number of atoms of the isotope to disintegrate spontaneously is called the half-life of the isotope. The half-life does *not* depend on the sample size.

The following equation, which governs radioactive disintegration, can be used to calculate the half-life from data on the numbers of atoms or to calculate the number of atoms remaining from knowledge of the half-life:

$$\ln\left(\frac{N_0}{N}\right) = \left(\frac{\ln 2}{t_{1/2}}\right)t$$

Here, N_0 is the original number of atoms of the isotope, N is the number at time t, and $t_{1/2}$ is the half-life (Section 20.3).

Archaeological and geological samples can be dated by half-life measurements. Once-living objects such as wood and bone can be dated using the activity of carbon-14 remaining compared to the constant level of carbon-14 found in living things. Non-organic materials such as rocks can be dated using the relative amounts of parent and daughter isotopes present (Section 20.4).

Bombardment of certain large radioactive nuclei with small particles, such as alpha particles or neutrons, can lead to artificial nuclear reactions. The splitting of heavy atoms is one such process, called nuclear fission. Two fairly massive products plus some small particles typically result from splitting one large nucleus with a projectile particle, as shown in the following example:

$$^{235}_{92}\text{U} + ^{1}_{0}\text{n} \rightarrow ^{90}_{38}\text{Sr} + ^{143}_{54}\text{Xe} + 3\,^{1}_{0}\text{n}$$

Chain reactions result when more neutrons are produced in a step of a nuclear reaction than are used up in that step. For example, for every neutron that causes a nuclear fission reaction of $^{235}_{92}\text{U}$, two or three new neutrons are produced. If each of these product neutrons, in turn, causes another nuclear reaction, many more neutrons will be produced, creating a chain reaction. If some of the product neutrons escape from the sample or are absorbed by other nuclei that do not split, the overall reaction can be controlled. The operation of commercial nuclear reactors is based on this principle. If the neutrons produced by the reaction are not controlled, an exponential increase occurs. If a critical mass of fuel is present, this results in an explosion.

Small nuclei can be fused together to form larger ones. An example of such a nuclear fusion is one of the reactions thought to power the Sun:

$$^{1}_{1}H + ^{2}_{1}H \rightarrow ^{3}_{2}He + ^{0}_{0}\gamma$$

Fusion reactions require extremely high temperatures, and they release large amounts of energy. In contrast to radioactive decay or nuclear fission, neither the reactants nor the products in fusion reactions are necessarily radioactive (Section 20.5).

In all nuclear reactions, a certain quantity of matter is converted to energy. The mass of the matter converted is related to the energy produced by Einstein's equation, $E = mc^2$ (Section 20.6).

The formation of atomic nuclei is an exothermic process. When a nucleus is formed from protons and neutrons, a small amount of mass is lost in the form of energy. This amount of missing mass is called the mass defect, and the energy released is the binding energy of the nucleus. Binding energies are typically divided by the number of nucleons in the nucleus. The stability of the nucleus increases as the binding energy per nucleon increases (Section 20.7).

END OF CHAPTER QUESTIONS

20.1 Natural Radioactivity

1. Substitute the correct symbol for X for each of the following particles.
   a. $^{0}_{+1}X$
   b. $^{0}_{-1}X$
   c. $^{4}_{2}X$
   d. $^{0}_{0}X$

2. Complete each of the following radioactive decay equations.
   a. $^{214}Pb \rightarrow ^{214}Bi + ?$
   b. $^{13}N \rightarrow \beta^{+} + ?$
   c. $^{210}Rn \rightarrow \alpha + ?$

3. Complete each of the following radioactive decay equations.
   a. $^{230}Th \rightarrow ? + \alpha$
   b. $^{30}P \rightarrow ^{30}S + ?$
   c. $^{37}Ar + e \rightarrow ?$

4. Complete each of the following radioactive decay equations.
   a. $^{7}Be \rightarrow ^{7}Li + ?$
   b. $^{3}H \rightarrow \beta^{-} + ?$
   c. $^{64}Cu \rightarrow \beta^{+} + ?$

5. Complete each of the following radioactive decay equations.
   a. $^{210}Bi \rightarrow \beta^{-} + ?$
   b. $^{106}Ag \rightarrow ^{106}Cd + ?$
   c. $^{68}Ge + e \rightarrow ?$

6. Cobalt-60 is used for radiation treatments of certain cancers. It decays by positron emission. Write a nuclear equation for this reaction.

7. Iodine-131 was once used for medical treatment of thyroid problems. It decays by emission of a beta particle. Write a nuclear equation for this reaction.

8. Write the nuclear equation for the electron capture of chromium-51.

9. Write the nuclear equation for the alpha decay of francium-221.

10. Complete these sentences related to natural radioactivity.
    a. A neutron becomes a proton by ejecting a(n) ________.
    b. A proton becomes a neutron by ejecting a(n) ________.

11. In electron capture, does a proton become a neutron, or does a neutron become a proton?

20.2 Nuclear Stability

12. Which stable element has the highest atomic number?

13. Classify each of these statements as true or false.
    a. Elements with an equal number of protons and neutrons are always stable.
    b. Elements with an atomic number greater than 82 are always unstable.
    c. Elements with even numbers of protons and neutrons tend to be stable.

14. Identify the magic numbers for protons.

15. Identify the magic numbers for neutrons.

16. Predict whether the following isotopes are stable or radioactive.
    a. ^{80}Br
    b. ^{223}Fr
    c. ^{114}Sn

17. Predict whether the following isotopes are stable or radioactive.
    a. ^{209}Ac
    b. ^{208}Pb
    c. ^{40}K

18. Predict the mode of decay for each of these isotopes.
    a. ^{247}Cm
    b. ^{125}Xe
    c. ^{137}Xe

19. Predict the mode of decay for each of these isotopes.
    a. ^{67}Ga
    b. ^{73}Ga
    c. ^{274}Mt

20.3 Half-Life

20. If half of a radioactive sample disintegrates in 2.00 y, why does it not all disintegrate in 4.00 y?

21. The half-life of a certain isotope is 20.0 min.
    a. How many atoms of 2.50×10^9 present initially will disintegrate in the first 20.0 min?
    b. How many will remain?
    c. How many will disintegrate in the second 20.0 min?

22. Calculate the half-life of an isotope if 155.2 mg disintegrates to 19.40 mg in 12.9 min.

23. The half-life of a certain isotope is 17.5 y. Determine the time required for 74.4 g of the isotope to decay to 18.6 g.

24. The half-life of a certain isotope is 23.5 min. Calculate the original mass of a sample of the isotope if it takes 70.5 min to decay to 12.0 g.

25. A certain isotope has a half-life of 4.540 s. How much of a 29.7 mg sample of this isotope will remain after 18.16 s?

26. A certain isotope has a half-life of 25.5 min. How much of a 64.0 mg sample of this isotope will remain after 102 min?

27. The half-life of a certain isotope is 20.4 y. Calculate the original mass of a sample of the isotope if it takes 61.2 y to decay to 12 mg.

28. The half-life of a certain isotope is 7.57×10^4 years. Calculate the time required for 7.55 mg of the isotope to decay to 0.103 mg.

29. The half-life of a certain isotope is 1.70 h. Calculate the time required for 6.62 mg of the isotope to decay to 4.79 mg.

30. Calculate the half-life of a 6.90 g sample
    a. if 1.71 g remains after 6.13 h.
    b. if 1.71 g decays in 6.13 h.

31. Calculate the half-life of a 17.3 mg sample that decays to 12.9 mg in 214 y.

32. Calculate the half-life of a 6.92 mg sample if 0.955 mg decays in 17.4 min.

33. One-fourth of the radioactive atoms of a certain sample are present 120.0 min after the original measurement. How many will be present after another 60.00 min?

34. Calculate the time required for 87.5% of a sample with a 46.7 h half-life to disintegrate.

35. It takes 7.22 min for 45% of a certain isotope to disintegrate. Calculate its half-life.

36. It takes 4.94 years for 75% of a certain isotope to disintegrate. Calculate its half-life.

20.4 Radiometric Dating

37. Suppose that parent isotope X naturally decays to daughter isotope Y. If a rock originally contained only X, but now contains 0.4 mol X and 1.2 mol Y, how much X was in the rock originally? How many half-lives of X have passed?

38. Calculate the age of a sample of rock containing 1.93×10^{19} atoms of ^{40}K for every 5.79×10^{19} atoms of ^{40}Ar, its stable daughter isotope. Assume that no argon was in the rock

when it solidified and that no argon escaped from the rock since its solidification. The half-life of ^{40}K is 1.3×10^9 years.

39. If a rock has a ^{40}K to ^{40}Ar *mole* ratio of 1:3, is it older, younger, or the same age as another rock with a ^{40}K to ^{40}Ar *mass* ratio of 1:3?

40. If a rock has a ^{235}U to ^{207}Pb *mole* ratio of 1:3, is it older, younger, or the same age as another rock with a ^{235}U to ^{207}Pb *mass* ratio of 1:3?

41. A certain rock contains 3.01×10^{-4} g of ^{235}U and 7.93×10^{-4} g of ^{207}Pb. Assuming that no lead was in the rock when it solidified and that no uranium or its daughter isotopes escaped, calculate the age of the rock. (Note: To three significant digits, the masses of the atoms are equal to their mass numbers.)

42. A certain rock contains 1.58×10^{-3} g of ^{238}U and 2.49×10^{-4} g of ^{206}Pb. Assuming that no lead was in the rock when it solidified and that no uranium or its daughter isotopes escaped, calculate the age of the rock. (Note: To three significant digits, the masses of the atoms are equal to their mass numbers.)

43. Calculate the age of a piece of wood with an activity of 7.65 *d*/min per gram of carbon. A modern sample of carbon decays at a rate of 15.3 $d/\text{min} \cdot \text{g}$. Assume that the ratio of ^{14}C to ^{12}C in the atmosphere when the wood formed was the same as it is today. The half-life of ^{14}C is 5730 years.

44. An archeologist finds a figurine carved from bone. Analysis reveals the figurine to have 89% of the ^{14}C of that same type of bone in a living organism. How old is the bone in the figurine?

20.5 Fission and Fusion

45. Compare and contrast nuclear fission and nuclear fusion in terms of
   a. relative masses of reactant and product nuclei.
   b. energy output.
   c. applications (e.g., bombs, power plants).

46. Substitute the correct symbol for X for each of the following particles.
   a. $^{1}_{0}X$
   b. $^{1}_{1}X$
   c. $^{2}_{1}X$
   d. $^{3}_{1}X$

47. Complete each of the following fission equations.
   a. $^{235}U + n \rightarrow {}^{140}Ba + ? + 3\,n$
   b. $^{235}U + n \rightarrow ?\ {}^{143}Xe + 3\,n$
   c. $^{235}U + n \rightarrow {}^{139}La + ? + 2\,n$

48. Complete each of the following fission equations.
   a. $^{235}U + n \rightarrow {}^{137}Te + 2\,n + ?$
   b. $^{235}U + n \rightarrow {}^{142}Ba + 2\,n + ?$
   c. $^{235}U + n \rightarrow {}^{97}Mo + 2\,n + ?$

49. Complete each of the following fusion equations.
   a. $^{2}H + {}^{2}H \rightarrow {}^{1}H + ?$
   b. $^{2}H + ? \rightarrow {}^{3}He + n$
   c. $^{1}H + ? \rightarrow {}^{2}H + \beta^{+}$

50. Complete each of the following fusion equations.
   a. $^{1}H + ? \rightarrow {}^{3}He + \gamma$
   b. $? + {}^{4}He \rightarrow {}^{13}C + p$
   c. $^{2}H + ? \rightarrow {}^{4}He + n$

51. Complete each of the following equations and classify them as fission or fusion.
   a. $^{3}He + {}^{2}H \rightarrow {}^{4}He + ?$
   b. $^{239}Pu + n \rightarrow {}^{95}Zr + ? + 2\,n$
   c. $^{244}Am \rightarrow {}^{134}I + ? + 3\,n$
   d. $^{43}Ca + {}^{4}He \rightarrow p + ?$

52. Complete each of the following equations and classify them as fission or fusion.
   a. $? + {}^{7}Li \rightarrow {}^{4}He$
   b. $n + {}^{6}Li \rightarrow {}^{3}H + ?$
   c. $? + {}^{4}He \rightarrow {}^{13}N + n$
   d. $^{10}Be + ? \rightarrow {}^{13}C + n$

20.6 Energetics of Nuclear Reactions

53. Combustion of 1.00 kg of anthracite coal gives off about 32,500 kJ of energy. How many kilojoules of energy would be released by the conversion of 1.00 kg of matter to energy?

54. When a positron and an electron meet, the matter in both is totally converted to energy; they annihilate each other and no mass remains. The mass of each of these particles is 9.10×10^{-31} kg. Calculate ΔE for this annihilation reaction in joules.

55. If a neutron escapes from a sample undergoing a chain reaction, it may disintegrate into a proton plus an electron. Calculate ΔE for this process in joules per mole. The masses are as follows: 1.00728 u for a proton, 0.00055 u for an electron, and 1.00866 u for a neutron.

Use this table for the following problems.

Particle	Mass (u)
Proton	1.00728
Neutron	1.00866

56. Calculate ΔE for the following reaction. The mass of a Mo-98 nucleus is 97.88236 u, and that of a Mo-99 nucleus is 98.88467 u.

$$^{98}\text{Mo} + \text{n} \rightarrow {}^{99}\text{Mo} + \gamma$$

57. Calculate ΔE for the following reaction. The mass of a N-14 nucleus is 13.99923 u, and that of a C-14 nucleus is 13.99995 u.

$$^{14}\text{N} + \text{n} \rightarrow {}^{14}\text{C} + \text{p}$$

58. Calculate ΔE for the following reaction. The mass of a He-3 nucleus is 3.01493 u, and that of a H-3 nucleus is 3.01550 u.

$$^{3}\text{He} + \text{n} \rightarrow {}^{3}\text{H} + \text{p}$$

59. Calculate ΔE for the following reaction. The mass of a He-3 nucleus is 3.01493 u, and that of a He-4 nucleus is 4.00151 u.

$$2\,{}^{3}\text{He} + \text{n} \rightarrow {}^{4}\text{He} + 2\,\text{p}$$

20.7 Nuclear Binding Energy

Use this table for the following problems.

Particle	Mass (u)
Proton	1.00728
Neutron	1.00866

60. Calculate the nuclear binding energy per nucleon of a ^{208}Pb nucleus, which has a mass of 207.93172 u.

61. Calculate the nuclear binding energy per nucleon of a ^{209}Pb nucleus, which has a mass of 208.93612 u.

62. Use your answers for the previous two problems to predict the relative stabilities of lead-208 and lead-209.

63. Calculate the nuclear binding energy per nucleon of a ^{36}Cl nucleus, which has a mass of 35.95898 u.

64. Calculate the nuclear binding energy per nucleon of a ^{37}Cl nucleus, which has a mass of 36.95657 u.

65. Use your answers for the previous two problems to predict the relative stabilities of chlorine-36 and chlorine-37.

66. Calculate the nuclear binding energy per nucleon of a ^{105}Cd nucleus, which has a mass of 104.88317 u.

67. Calculate the nuclear binding energy per nucleon of a ^{106}Cd nucleus, which has a mass of 105.88017 u.

68. Use your answers for the previous two problems to predict the relative stabilities of cadmium-105 and cadmium-106.

Putting It Together

69. The isotope ^{207}Tl disintegrates by beta emission with a half-life of 4.79 min to give the stable isotope ^{207}Pb. Calculate the approximate mass of the entire system 4.79 min after 0.100 g of ^{207}Tl starts decaying.

70. Classify these nuclear reactions as decay, fission, or fusion.
    a. $^{1}\text{H} + {}^{2}\text{H} \rightarrow {}^{3}\text{He} + {}^{0}\gamma$
    b. $^{220}\text{Rn} \rightarrow \alpha + {}^{216}\text{Po}$
    c. $\text{n} + {}^{235}\text{U} \rightarrow {}^{90}\text{Sr} + {}^{143}\text{Xe} + 3\,\text{n}$

71. Which of the following reactions represent natural radioactivity, and which are artificially induced?
    a. $^{218}\text{Po} \rightarrow {}^{214}\text{Pb} + \alpha$
    b. $^{14}\text{N} + \alpha \rightarrow {}^{17}\text{O} + {}^{1}\text{H}$
    c. $^{238}\text{U} + \text{n} \rightarrow {}^{239}\text{U} + \gamma$

72. Calculate the number of joules emitted by the complete conversion of 1.00 u of matter to energy.

73. Using your answer to the previous problem as a conversion factor, calculate the binding energy per nucleon for deuterium, which has a mass defect of 0.00239 u.

74. The isotope ^{148}Gd disintegrates by alpha emission with a half-life of 130 years to give the stable isotope ^{144}Sm. Calculate the energy emitted by the system in the 130 years after 1.00 kg of ^{148}Gd starts decaying. The isotopic masses are $^{148}\text{Gd} = 147.9177$ u, $^{144}\text{Sm} = 143.9117$ u, and $^{4}\text{He} = 4.00260$ u.

75. Some texts use the equation $N = N_0(\frac{1}{2})^n$ for half-life problems, where n is the number of half-lives.
    a. Show that this is equivalent to $\ln(N_0/N) = (\ln 2/t_{1/2})t$ using the following mathematical rules:
        - $\ln(x \cdot y) = \ln x + \ln y$
        - $\ln(x/y) = \ln x - \ln y$
        - $\ln x^y = y \cdot \ln x$
    b. Redo problem 26 using $N = N_0(\frac{1}{2})^n$.

PRACTICE PROBLEM SOLUTIONS

Practice Problem 20.1 Solution

Thorium, Th, is element 90 in the periodic table, so $^{234}_{90}\text{Th}$ is the parent nuclide. In beta decay, the parent nuclide produces a daughter nuclide and a beta particle, $^{0}_{-1}\beta$. Based on this information, write a preliminary equation for the reaction:

$$^{234}_{90}\text{Th} \rightarrow {}^{0}_{-1}\beta + {}^{?}_{?}?$$

To balance the mass numbers (the superscripts) of the reactant and products, the daughter isotope must have a mass number of 234 because 234 = 0 + 234. To balance the nuclear charges (the subscripts), the daughter isotope must have an atomic number of 91 because 90 = −1 + 91. Element 91 is protactinium, Pa, so the balanced equation for the radioactive decay is

$$^{234}_{90}\text{Th} \rightarrow {}^{0}_{-1}\beta + {}^{234}_{91}\text{Pa}$$

Practice Problem 20.2 Solution

a. The daughter isotope has $Z = 11$, so it is sodium. The charge on the emitted particle must be +1 to balance the charge, and the only particle emitted in radioactive decay with a +1 charge is a positron, which has a mass number of 0. As a result, the mass number of the daughter isotope must be the same as that of the parent.

$$^{23}_{12}\text{Mg} \rightarrow {}^{23}_{11}\text{Na} + {}^{0}_{+1}\beta \qquad \text{Positron emission}$$

b. The atomic number of uranium is 92, so the difference in nuclear charge between the parent and daughter isotopes is equal to 2. The particle with $Z = 2$ is an alpha particle. Because an alpha particle was emitted, the mass number of the daughter isotope must be 4 less than that of the parent. The daughter isotope has an atomic number of 90, which means it is thorium.

$$^{238}_{92}\text{U} \rightarrow {}^{234}_{90}\text{Th} + {}^{4}_{2}\text{He} \qquad \text{Alpha decay}$$

c. The mass numbers of the parent and daughter isotopes are the same, so the mass number of the unknown particle must be 0. To balance the charge between the parent and the daughter, the unknown particle must have a charge of −1. The unknown particle has a mass number of 0 and a charge of −1, so it is an electron. Adding an electron to the parent means this decay is electron capture.

$$^{40}_{19}\text{K} + {}^{0}_{-1}\text{e} \rightarrow {}^{40}_{18}\text{Ar} \qquad \text{Electron capture}$$

d. Atomic number 82 (parent) is lead, and atomic number 83 (daughter) is bismuth. To balance the equation, a particle must be emitted that has a mass number of 0 and a charge of −1, so the emitted particle is an electron (a beta particle).

$$^{211}_{82}\text{Pb} \rightarrow {}^{211}_{83}\text{Bi} + {}^{0}_{-1}\beta \qquad \text{Beta decay}$$

Practice Problem 20.3 Solution

Alpha decay is ruled out for all of these isotopes because none has $Z > 82$.

a. The average atomic mass of nickel in the periodic table is 58.693 u. Nickel-63 is heavier than that, meaning it is *above* the belt of stability and will decay by converting a neutron to a proton via *beta decay*.

b. The average atomic mass of phosphorus is 30.974 u. Phosphorus-30 is just a little lighter than that, so it is *below* the belt of stability and will decay by converting a proton to a neutron via *positron emission* or *electron capture*.

c. Nitrogen-13 is lighter than the average atomic mass of nitrogen (14.007 u), so it will decay by converting a proton to a neutron via *positron emission* or *electron capture*.

d. Strontium-90 is heavier than the average atomic mass of strontium (87.62 u), so it will decay by converting a neutron to a proton via *beta decay*.

Practice Problem 20.4 Solution

According to Table 20.4, the half-life of ^{140}La is 40 hours. If the scientist is gone for 5 days, then 5 days × 24 hours/day = 120 hours will pass.

$$120 \text{ hours} \times \frac{1 \text{ half-life}}{40 \text{ hours}} = 3 \text{ half-lives}$$

After three half-lives, the amount remaining will be

$$10.0 \text{ mg} \times \left(\frac{1}{2}\right)^3 = 1.25 \text{ mg}$$

Practice Problem 20.5 Solution

The fraction of the original sample remaining is

$$\frac{8.10 \text{ g}}{64.8 \text{ g}} = 0.125 = \frac{1}{8}$$

The isotope in the sample has disintegrated to one-eighth of its original mass, which takes three half-lives. The time necessary is therefore 3(29.8 s) = 89.4 s.

Practice Problem 20.6 Solution

The time required to reduce the sample to a given fraction can be calculated using Equation 20.2.

$$\ln\left(\frac{N_0}{N}\right) = \left(\frac{\ln 2}{t_{1/2}}\right)t$$

The time (t) can be isolated by multiplying both sides of the equation by $\left(\frac{t_{1/2}}{\ln 2}\right)$.

$$t = \ln\left(\frac{N_0}{N}\right)\left(\frac{t_{1/2}}{\ln 2}\right)$$

Plug the known variables into the equation to solve it. Because N is 1/5 of N_0, $\frac{N_0}{N} = \frac{1}{\frac{1}{5}} = 5$.

$$t = \ln(5)\left(\frac{6.79 \text{ y}}{\ln 2}\right) = 15.8 \text{ y}$$

The time (15.8 y) is a little more than two half-lives, and slightly less than 1/4 of the isotope remains, so this answer is reasonable.

Practice Problem 20.7 Solution

a. Solve for t using Equation 20.2.

$$\ln\left(\frac{N_0}{N}\right) = \left(\frac{\ln 2}{t_{1/2}}\right)t$$

The time (t) can be isolated by multiplying both sides of the equation by $\left(\frac{t_{1/2}}{\ln 2}\right)$.

$$t = \ln\left(\frac{N_0}{N}\right)\left(\frac{t_{1/2}}{\ln 2}\right)$$

Plug the known variables into the equation: $N_0 = 1.77 \times 10^{15}$ atoms, $N = 5.59 \times 10^{14}$, and $t_{1/2} = 47.2$ y.

$$t = \ln\left(\frac{1.77 \times 10^{15}}{5.59 \times 10^{14}}\right)\left(\frac{47.2 \text{ y}}{\ln 2}\right) = 78.5 \text{ y}$$

The time, 78.5 y, is between one and two half-lives, so the amount remaining should be between 1/2 and 1/4 of the original sample. The amount left is about 32%, so this answer for t is reasonable.

b. Solving for N_0 means you will have to take the inverse natural log of both sides of the equation, so first plug in the known values for t and $t_{1/2}$, and simplify the right side of the equation.

$$\ln\left(\frac{N_0}{N}\right) = \left(\frac{\ln 2}{47.2 \text{ y}}\right)112 \text{ y} = 1.64$$

To extract N_0 from the natural log term, take the inverse natural log of both sides of the equation (Section 0.5):

$$e^{\ln\left(\frac{N_0}{N}\right)} = e^{1.64}$$

The e and ln functions cancel each other out, leaving

$$\frac{N_0}{N} = 5.2$$

Multiply both sides by N to solve for N_0:

$$N_0 = (5.2)(1.77 \times 10^{15} \text{ atoms}) = 9.2 \times 10^{15} \text{ atoms}$$

Practice Problem 20.8 Solution

This problem provides information about the *mass* of the isotope rather than the number of atoms. Because the mass of the isotope is directly proportional to the number of atoms of the isotope, the ratio of m_0/m can be used in place of N_0/N, as shown in Equation 20.3.

$$\ln\left(\frac{m_0}{m}\right) = \left(\frac{\ln 2}{t_{1/2}}\right)t$$

The mass remaining (m) is 75% of the initial mass (m_0), and the elapsed time (t) is 10.0 years:

$$\ln\left(\frac{100}{75.0}\right) = \left(\frac{\ln 2}{t_{1/2}}\right)(10.0 \text{ years})$$

$$0.2877 = \left(\frac{\ln 2}{t_{1/2}}\right)(10.0 \text{ years})$$

Rearranging gives

$$t_{1/2} = \left(\frac{\ln 2}{0.2877}\right)(10.0 \text{ years}) = 24.1 \text{ years}$$

This answer is reasonable because when 75% of the isotope remains, less than one half-life has passed (and 10.0 y < 24.1 y).

Practice Problem 20.9 Solution

The number of atoms of ^{40}K originally present was

$$N_0 = 2.57 \times 10^{17} + 7.71 \times 10^{16}$$

$$= 3.341 \times 10^{17} \text{ atoms} \ln\left(\frac{N_0}{N}\right)$$

$$= \left(\frac{\ln 2}{t_{1/2}}\right)t$$

Isolate t by multiplying both sides of the equation by $\left(\frac{t_{1/2}}{\ln 2}\right)$.

$$t = \ln\left(\frac{N_0}{N}\right)\left(\frac{t_{1/2}}{\ln 2}\right)$$

Plug the known variables into the equation to solve it.

$$t = \ln\left(\frac{3.341 \times 10^{17}\ \text{atoms}}{2.57 \times 10^{17}\ \text{atoms}}\right)\left(\frac{1.3 \times 10^{9}\ \text{y}}{\ln 2}\right)$$
$$= 4.9 \times 10^{8}\ \text{y}$$

Practice Problem 20.10 Solution

Initial mass of $^{40}_{19}\text{K}$ present $= m_0 = 9.61\ \text{g} + 1.04\ \text{g} = 10.65\ \text{g}$.

$$\ln\left(\frac{m_0}{m}\right) = \left(\frac{\ln 2}{t_{1/2}}\right)t$$

Isolate t by multiplying both sides of Equation 20.3 by $\left(\frac{t_{1/2}}{\ln 2}\right)$.

$$t = \ln\left(\frac{m_0}{m}\right)\left(\frac{t_{1/2}}{\ln 2}\right)$$

Plug the known variables into the equation to solve for t.

$$t = \ln\left(\frac{10.65\ \text{g}}{9.61\ \text{g}}\right)\left(\frac{1.3 \times 10^{9}\ \text{y}}{\ln 2}\right) = 1.9 \times 10^{8}\ \text{y}$$

Practice Problem 20.11 Solution

Use Equation 20.4 to solve for A. $A_0 = 15.3\ d/\text{min} \cdot \text{g}$ (Example 20.11) and $t_{1/2} = 5730$ y (Table 20.4).

$$\ln\left(\frac{A_0}{A}\right) = \left(\frac{\ln 2}{t_{1/2}}\right)t$$

Because you are solving for A in the ln term, it is easiest to evaluate the right side of the equation first, then take the inverse natural log of both sides:

$$\ln\left(\frac{A_0}{A}\right) = \left(\frac{\ln 2}{5730\ \text{y}}\right)(1018\ \text{y})$$
$$\ln\left(\frac{A_0}{A}\right) = 0.1231$$
$$e^{\ln\left(\frac{A_0}{A}\right)} = e^{0.1231}$$
$$\frac{A_0}{A} = 1.131$$
$$A = \frac{A_0}{1.131} = \frac{15.3\ \frac{d}{\text{min} \cdot \text{g}}}{1.131} = 13.5\ d/\text{min} \cdot \text{g}$$

Practice Problem 20.12 Solution

a. As with all nuclear equations, the sum of the superscripts and subscripts on each side must be balanced. The subscripts are already balanced (92 on each side). To balance the superscripts, set up an equation where x is the missing coefficient.

$$235 + 1 = 137 + 97 + x(1)$$
$$236 = 234 + x$$
$$x = 2$$

The balanced equation is

$$^{235}_{92}\text{U} + {}^{1}_{0}\text{n} \rightarrow {}^{137}_{52}\text{Te} + {}^{97}_{40}\text{Zr} + 2\,{}^{1}_{0}\text{n}$$

b. The first reaction produces 2 neutrons, which each initiate a second round of reactions, producing $2^2 = 4$ neutrons.

Practice Problem 20.13 Solution

Use the values given in the table to determine the difference in mass, Δm, between the products and the reactants. The products are Ba-140, Kr-94, and two neutrons. The reactants are U-235 and one neutron.

$$\text{Products} = 139.87988\ \text{u} + 93.91439\ \text{u} + (2 \times 1.00866)\ \text{u} = 235.81159\ \text{u}$$
$$\text{Reactants} = 234.99343\ \text{u} + 1.00866\ \text{u} = 236.00209\ \text{u}$$
$$\Delta m = m_{\text{products}} - m_{\text{reactants}}$$
$$= 235.81159\ \text{u} - 236.00209\ \text{u} = -0.19050\ \text{u}$$

Convert Δm to kilograms per mole, and substitute this value into Equation 20.6.

$$\Delta m = -0.19050\ \text{u}\left(\frac{1\ \text{g/mol}}{1\ \text{u}}\right)\left(\frac{1\ \text{kg}}{1000\ \text{g}}\right)$$
$$= -1.9050 \times 10^{-4}\ \text{kg/mol}$$
$$\Delta E = \Delta mc^2$$
$$= (-1.9050 \times 10^{-4}\ \text{kg/mol})(2.998 \times 10^{8}\ \text{m/s})^2$$
$$= -1.711 \times 10^{13}\ \text{J/mol}$$

The amount of energy released is 1.711×10^{13} J/mol.

Practice Problem 20.14 Solution

First, find the difference in mass, Δm, between the products and the reactants. The products are Si-28 and He-4. The reactants are two oxygen-16 atoms.

$$\text{Products} = 27.96925\ \text{u} + 4.00151\ \text{u} = 31.97076\ \text{u}$$
$$\text{Reactants} = 2 \times 15.99052\ \text{u} = 31.98104\ \text{u}$$
$$\Delta m = m_{\text{products}} - m_{\text{reactants}}$$
$$= 31.97076\ \text{u} - 31.98104\ \text{u} = -0.01028\ \text{u}$$

Convert Δm to kilograms per mole, and substitute this value into Equation 20.6.

$$\Delta m = -0.01028\ \text{u}\left(\frac{1\ \text{g/mol}}{1\ \text{u}}\right)\left(\frac{1\ \text{kg}}{1000\ \text{g}}\right)$$
$$= -1.028 \times 10^{-5}\ \text{kg/mol}$$

$$\Delta E = \Delta mc^2$$
$$= (-1.028 \times 10^{-5}\ \text{kg/mol})(2.998 \times 10^8\ \text{m/s})^2$$
$$= -9.240 \times 10^{11}\ \text{J}$$

Practice Problem 20.15 Solution

${}^{15}_{8}O$ is made up of eight protons and seven neutrons: ${}^{15}_{8}O \rightarrow 8\,{}^{1}_{1}p + 7\,{}^{1}_{0}n$.

$$\text{Mass of } {}^{15}_{8}O \text{ nucleus} = 14.99868\ \text{u}$$
$$\text{Sum of its particles} = 8(1.00728\ \text{u}) + 7(1.00866\ \text{u}) = 15.11886\ \text{u}$$
$$\Delta m = 15.11886\ \text{u} - 14.99868\ \text{u} = 0.12018\ \text{u}$$

Convert Δm to kilograms and apply Equation 20.6.

$$\Delta m = 0.12018\ \text{u}\left(\frac{1\ \text{g}}{6.022 \times 10^{22}\ \text{u}}\right)\left(\frac{1\ \text{kg}}{1000\ \text{g}}\right)$$
$$= 1.996 \times 10^{-28}\ \text{kg}$$
$$\Delta E = \Delta mc^2$$
$$= (1.996 \times 10^{-28}\ \text{kg})(2.998 \times 10^8\ \text{m/s})^2$$
$$= 1.794 \times 10^{-11}\ \text{J}$$

The total number of nucleons is 8 protons + 7 neutrons = 15 nucleons (equal to the mass number).

$$\text{Binding energy per nucleon} = \frac{1.794 \times 10^{-11}\ \text{J}}{15\ \text{nucleons}}$$
$$= 1.196 \times 10^{-12}\ \text{J per nucleon}$$

Repeat the same calculation for ${}^{16}_{8}O$, which has eight protons and eight neutrons: ${}^{16}_{8}O \rightarrow 8\,{}^{1}_{1}H + 8\,{}^{1}_{0}n$.

$$\text{Mass of } {}^{16}_{8}O = 15.99052\ \text{u}$$
$$\text{Sum of its particles} = 8(1.00728\ \text{u}) + 8(1.00866\ \text{u}) = 16.12752\ \text{u}$$
$$\Delta m = 16.12752\ \text{u} - 15.99052\ \text{u} = 0.13700\ \text{u}$$

Convert Δm to kilograms and apply Equation 20.6.

$$\Delta m = 0.13700\ \text{u}\left(\frac{1\ \text{g}}{6.022 \times 10^{23}\ \text{u}}\right)\left(\frac{1\ \text{kg}}{1000\ \text{g}}\right)$$
$$= 2.275 \times 10^{-28}\ \text{kg}$$
$$\Delta E = \Delta mc^2$$
$$= (2.275 \times 10^{-28}\ \text{kg})(2.998 \times 10^8\ \text{m/s})^2$$
$$= 2.045 \times 10^{-11}\ \text{J}$$

The total number of nucleons is 8 protons + 8 neutrons = 16 nucleons (equal to the mass number).

$$\text{Binding energy per nucleon} = \frac{2.045 \times 10^{-11}\ \text{J}}{16\ \text{nucleons}}$$
$$= 1.278 \times 10^{-12}\ \text{J per nucleon}$$

The binding energy per nucleon is much greater for ${}^{16}O$ (1.278×10^{-12} J) than it is for ${}^{15}O$ (1.196×10^{-12} J), indicating that ${}^{16}O$ is a more stable nucleus. In fact, ${}^{16}O$ is stable, whereas ${}^{15}O$ is radioactive. The ${}^{16}O$ nucleus is unusually stable, in part because it is an even–even nucleus (even numbers of protons and neutrons) and because its number of protons and its number of neutrons are both magic numbers (8; Section 20.2).

Practice Problem 20.16 Solution

a. According to the periodic table, Pu has an atomic number of 94. Radioactive isotopes with $Z > 82$ tend to decay by alpha decay.

$$^{238}_{94}\text{Pu} \rightarrow {}^{?}_{?}? + {}^{4}_{2}\alpha$$

The missing mass number must be 234 because 238 = 234 + 4. The missing nuclear charge must be 92 because 94 = 92 + 2. The element with atomic number 92 is uranium.

$$^{238}_{94}\text{Pu} \rightarrow {}^{234}_{92}\text{U} + {}^{4}_{2}\alpha$$

b. There are two different ways (method 1 and method 2) you can approach this part.

Method 1: Convert the mass of ${}^{238}Pu$ to atoms of ${}^{238}Pu$, then use Equation 20.2 to determine how many ${}^{238}Pu$ atoms remain after exactly 100 years. From that, you can calculate how many atoms of ${}^{234}U$ were formed, and using the molar mass of ${}^{234}U$, calculate the mass of ${}^{234}U$ present.

$$N_0 = 8.59\ \text{kg}\left(\frac{10^3\ \text{g}}{1\ \text{kg}}\right)\left(\frac{1\ \text{mol}}{238\ \text{g}}\right)\left(\frac{6.022 \times 10^{23}\ \text{atoms}}{1\ \text{mol}}\right)$$
$$= 2.17 \times 10^{25}\ \text{atoms}$$

Solve for N using Equation 20.2:

$$\ln\left(\frac{N_0}{N}\right) = \left(\frac{\ln 2}{t_{1/2}}\right)t$$

Solving for N means you will have to take the inverse natural log of both sides of the equation, so first plug in the known values for t and $t_{1/2}$, and simplify the right side of the equation.

$$\ln\left(\frac{N_0}{N}\right) = \left(\frac{\ln 2}{87.7\ \text{y}}\right)100\ \text{y}$$
$$\ln\left(\frac{N_0}{N}\right) = 0.790$$

To extract N from the natural log term, take the inverse natural log of both sides (Section 0.5).

$$e^{\ln\left(\frac{N_0}{N}\right)} = e^{0.790}$$

The e and ln functions cancel each other out, leaving

$$\frac{N_0}{N} = 2.20$$

Rearrange the equation algebraically to isolate and solve for N.

$$N = \frac{2.17 \times 10^{25} \text{ atoms}}{2.20} = 9.86 \times 10^{24} \text{ atoms}$$

The number of ^{238}Pu atoms that decayed is $N_0 - N = 2.17 \times 10^{25} - 9.86 \times 10^{24} = 1.18 \times 10^{25}$ atoms. Convert this number of ^{234}U atoms to a mass of U in kilograms.

$$m = 1.18 \times 10^{25} \text{ } ^{234}\text{U atoms}\left(\frac{1 \text{ mol}}{6.022 \times 10^{23} \text{ atoms}}\right)\left(\frac{234 \text{ g}}{1 \text{ mol}}\right)\left(\frac{1 \text{ kg}}{1000 \text{ g}}\right)$$
$$= 4.59 \text{ kg } ^{234}\text{U}$$

Method 2: Use Equation 20.3 (the m_0/m version of Equation 20.2) to determine the mass of ^{238}Pu remaining, then calculate the mass of ^{238}Pu that decayed and multiply that mass by the ratio of atomic masses to determine how many kilograms of ^{234}U were formed.

Initial mass of $^{238}_{94}$Pu present $= m_0 = 8.59$ kg. Equation 20.3 is

$$\ln\left(\frac{m_0}{m}\right) = \left(\frac{\ln 2}{t_{1/2}}\right)t$$

Solving for m means you will have to take the inverse natural log of both sides of the equation, so first plug in the known values for t and $t_{1/2}$, and simplify the right side of the equation.

$$\ln\left(\frac{m_0}{m}\right) = \left(\frac{\ln 2}{87.7 \text{ y}}\right)100 \text{ y}$$

$$\ln\left(\frac{m_0}{m}\right) = 0.790$$

To extract m from the natural log term, take the inverse natural log of both sides (Section 0.5).

$$e^{\ln\left(\frac{m_0}{m}\right)} = e^{0.790}$$

The e and ln functions cancel each other out.

$$\frac{m_0}{m} = 2.20$$

Rearrange the equation algebraically to isolate and solve for m.

$$m = \frac{8.59 \text{ kg}}{2.20} = 3.90 \text{ kg}$$

The mass of ^{238}Pu atoms that decayed is $m_0 - m = 8.59 \text{ kg} - 3.90 \text{ kg} = 4.69 \text{ kg } ^{238}\text{Pu}$.

This can be converted to a mass of ^{234}U by multiplying by the mass ratio of the two isotopes.

$$4.69 \text{ kg } ^{238}\text{Pu}\left(\frac{234 \text{ kg } ^{234}\text{U}}{238 \text{ kg } ^{238}\text{Pu}}\right) = 4.61 \text{ kg } ^{234}\text{U}$$

c. The unbalanced equation for the alpha decay of the daughter isotope is

$$^{234}_{92}\text{U} \rightarrow {}^{?}_{?}? + {}^{4}_{2}\alpha$$

Find the missing mass and charge, then locate the appropriate element in the periodic table.

$$^{234}_{92}\text{U} \rightarrow {}^{230}_{90}\text{Th} + {}^{4}_{2}\alpha$$

The granddaughter isotope, thorium-230, has an atomic number of 90. There are no elements above atomic number 82 that have stable isotopes, so that alone indicates that $^{230}_{90}$Th is radioactive.

CHAPTER 21

Organic Chemistry

The Lyda Hill Texas Collection of Photographs in Carol M. Highsmith's America Project, Library of Congress, Prints and Photographs Division

Crude oil, a type of petroleum, is processed in oil refineries such as the one shown here. Crude oil is a mixture of many organic compounds—mainly hydrocarbons containing varying numbers of carbon atoms per molecule.

Chapter Outline

GOALS

- Identify, name, and write formulas and reactions for saturated hydrocarbons.
- Describe the properties of saturated hydrocarbons.
- Identify, name, and write formulas and reactions for unsaturated hydrocarbons.
- Describe the properties of unsaturated hydrocarbons.
- Identify and write formulas for structural isomers.
- Identify, name, and write formulas and reactions for organic halides, alcohols, ethers, and amines.
- Identify, name, and write formulas and reactions for aldehydes, ketones, carboxylic acids, esters, and amides.
- Write equations for the formation of polymers.
- Describe the properties of the compounds polymers comprise.

21.1 Introduction to Hydrocarbons

GOALS

- Identify, name, and write formulas and reactions for saturated hydrocarbons.
- Describe the properties of saturated hydrocarbons.

Organic chemistry is the chemistry of compounds that contain carbon. There are a vast number of **organic compounds**, and they are found everywhere from fossil fuels to plastics to living organisms. Carbon is unique in its ability to form long chains. The lengths and shapes of these chains affect the physical properties of the compound, as shown in Figure 12.9 and Figure 12.10.

Hydrocarbons are compounds that contain only carbon and hydrogen atoms. They have important uses, especially as fuels such as gasoline, but they also form the foundation of all the other classes of organic compounds. This section discusses how to name and write formulas for hydrocarbons, as well as a few of their simple reactions. The number of possible hydrocarbons is immense because carbon atoms can bond to other carbon atoms in vast combinations, provided each carbon atom has no more than four bonds total. A hydrocarbon consisting of an eight-carbon chain (octane, chemical formula C_8H_{18}) is shown in Figure 21.1. Compounds with much longer carbon chains are discussed in Section 21.6.

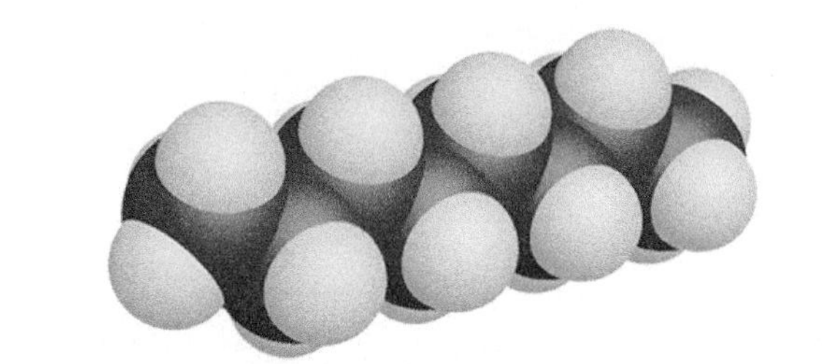

FIGURE 21.1 Octane, an Eight-Carbon Unbranched Hydrocarbon

NOTE: You need to be online to access this activity.
This space-filling model of an octane molecule, C_8H_{18}, consists of a central chain of 8 carbon atoms surrounded by 18 hydrogen atoms. *Click the molecule to open the interactive view.*

When a carbon atom is connected to four other atoms by single bonds, those bonds are oriented toward the corners of a tetrahedron (Figure 21.2). The angle between any two of the bonds is 109.5 degrees, and each sp^3-hybridized carbon atom (Section 11.3) has a tetrahedral geometry (Table 11.1). A chain of these atoms in a hydrocarbon can assume a zigzag shape (review the model of octane shown in Figure 21.1).

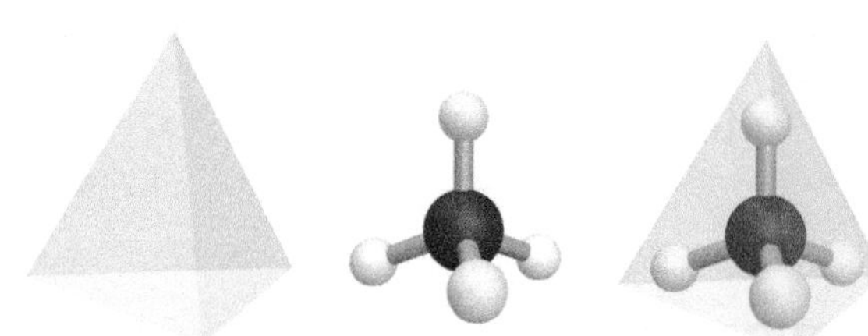

(a) (b) (c)

FIGURE 21.2 Tetrahedral Nature of the Carbon Atom

NOTE: You need to be online to access this activity.
(a) A tetrahedron has four triangular sides (including the base). (b) In methane, CH_4, the carbon atom is at the center and is bonded to four hydrogen atoms. (c) Superimposing the tetrahedron on the ball-and-stick model of CH_4 demonstrates how the four C–H bonds point toward the corners of the tetrahedron. *Click each image to open the interactive view.*

TABLE 21.1 Different Representations of the Same Organic Molecule

Name	Representation	Description
Space-filling model		Most realistic three-dimensional representation. *Click the molecule to open the interactive view.*
Ball-and-stick model	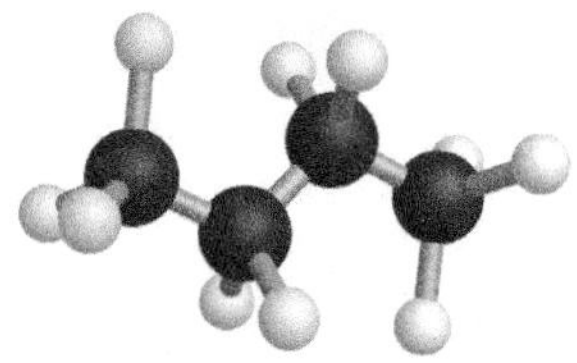	Three-dimensional representation with more distance between atoms, making it easier to see the bond angles. *Click the molecule to open the interactive view.*
Structural formula (with bond angles)	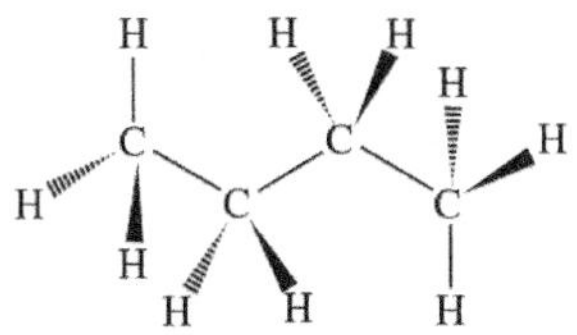	Two-dimensional representation with information about bond angles. Lines are in the plane of the page. Dashed lines angle away from you into the page. Solid wedges angle toward you out of the page.
Structural formula	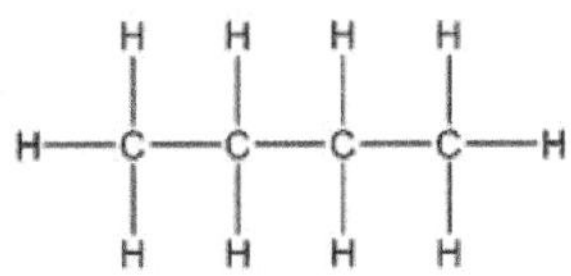	Two-dimensional representation that does not depict bond angles. Similar to a Lewis structure but omits lone pairs (if present).
Condensed structural formula	$CH_3CH_2CH_2CH_3$ or $CH_3(CH_2)_2CH_3$	Depicts some aspects of the structure based on groupings of atoms.
Molecular formula	C_4H_{10}	Each element is listed only once.

Organic molecules are usually represented in one of the six different ways shown in Table 21.1.

A space-filling model is the most realistic representation of the relative sizes of the atoms and how far apart they are. The space-filling model makes it possible to visualize the overall shape of the molecule, although some parts of the molecule are often hidden from view. A ball-and-stick model more clearly shows the bond angles between the atoms, but it is not as realistic as the space-filling model because it puts too much space between the atoms. **Structural formulas**, often just referred to as *structures,* are the most similar to Lewis structures (Chapter 10), except that lone pairs are typically omitted. It is possible to depict the bond angles in a structural formula using wedge and dash bonds, where wedges angle toward you, dashes angle away from you, and regular lines are in the plane of the page. A **condensed structural formula**, or *condensed structure,* is written on a single line, with groups of atoms that are connected within the molecule written together. This representation is easier to write than a structural formula, but it requires the reader to infer more about the bonding of the atoms in the molecule.

Finally, a **molecular formula** is the easiest to write, but it provides the least structural information of all. In organic chemistry, one molecular formula often represents more than one compound.

A variation of the condensed structural formula further condenses a formula such as $CH_3CH_2CH_2CH_3$ to $CH_3(CH_2)_2CH_3$. Another situation in which you may see parentheses in a condensed structural formula is with branches on a carbon chain. For example, both $CH_3CH(CH_3)_2$ and $CH(CH_3)_3$ represent the following branched hydrocarbon.

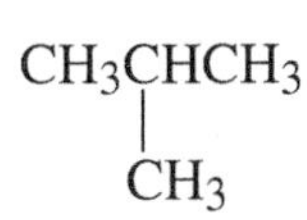

ALKANES

Hydrocarbons can be classified as alkanes, alkenes, alkynes, or aromatic hydrocarbons, depending on their unique structural characteristics.

Alkanes have only *single* covalent bonds within their molecules. They are also referred to as **saturated hydrocarbons** because their carbon backbones cannot

TABLE 21.2 The First 10 Unbranched Alkanes

Name	Molecular Formula	Condensed Structural Formula
Methane	CH_4	CH_4
Ethane	C_2H_6	CH_3CH_3
Propane	C_3H_8	$CH_3CH_2CH_3$
Butane	C_4H_{10}	$CH_3CH_2CH_2CH_3$
Pentane	C_5H_{12}	$CH_3CH_2CH_2CH_2CH_3$
Hexane	C_6H_{14}	$CH_3CH_2CH_2CH_2CH_2CH_3$
Heptane	C_7H_{16}	$CH_3CH_2CH_2CH_2CH_2CH_2CH_3$
Octane	C_8H_{18}	$CH_3CH_2CH_2CH_2CH_2CH_2CH_2CH_3$
Nonane	C_9H_{20}	$CH_3CH_2CH_2CH_2CH_2CH_2CH_2CH_2CH_3$
Decane	$C_{10}H_{22}$	$CH_3CH_2CH_2CH_2CH_2CH_2CH_2CH_2CH_2CH_3$

TABLE 21.3 Names of Common Alkyl Groups

Condensed Structural Formula	Name	Condensed Structural Formula	Name
$—CH_3$	Methyl	$—CHCH_3$ | CH_3	Isopropyl
$—CH_2CH_3$	Ethyl	$—CH_2CHCH_3$ | CH_3	Isobutyl
$—CH_2CH_2CH_3$	Propyl	$—CHCH_2CH_3$ | CH_3	*sec*-Butyl
$—CH_2CH_2CH_2CH_3$	Butyl	CH_3 | $—CCH_3$ | CH_3	*tert*-Butyl

bond to any more hydrogen atoms. Their molecular formulas all conform to the general formula C_nH_{2n+2}, where $n = 1, 2, 3, \ldots$. If $n = 4$, for example, the formula is C_4H_{10}, and if $n = 6$, the formula is C_6H_{14}. The names and formulas of the first 10 unbranched alkanes are listed in Table 21.2. The unbranched hydrocarbons are sometimes called "straight-chain" hydrocarbons, despite their actual zigzag geometries (see the model of octane in Figure 21.1).

Each of the alkanes has a name that ends in *–ane.* The names of the C_5 through C_{10} alkanes have Greek or Latin prefixes for the numbers that correspond to the numbers of carbon atoms in these molecules. For example, a molecule of *pent*ane has *five* carbon atoms, and a molecule of *oct*ane has *eight*.

Any atom or group that would take the place of a hydrogen atom in a hydrocarbon is called a **substituent**. Branches on a hydrocarbon chain, sometimes called side chains, are a type of substituent called an **alkyl group**. The names of some common alkyl groups are listed in Table 21.3.

Naming branched alkanes follows a set of rules:

- Rule 1: The name is based on the longest continuous chain of carbon atoms in the molecule, using the names in Table 21.2. This is the **parent name** of the compound.
- Rule 2: Branches on alkanes are additional carbon chains that are attached to one of the carbons of the main chain. Branches that are made up of a hydrocarbon molecule with one hydrogen atom removed are named according to Table 21.2, but with the *–ane* suffix replaced by *–yl* (Table 21.3). Thus, a one-carbon branch coming off the main chain of the molecule, $-CH_3$, is called a methyl group.
- Rule 3: When necessary, the position of a branched group on the main chain is identified with a number, which is the number of that carbon atom counting from the *nearer end* of the chain. That is, the main chain is numbered to give the first branch point the lowest possible number.
- The following molecule is named 2-methylpentane, *not* 4-methylpentane, because numbering the main chain from the right gives the methyl group (the first and only branch point) the lowest possible number (2 instead of 4).

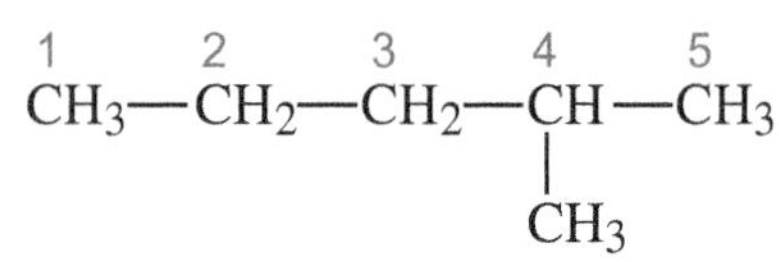

~~4-Methylpentane~~
(Incorrect)

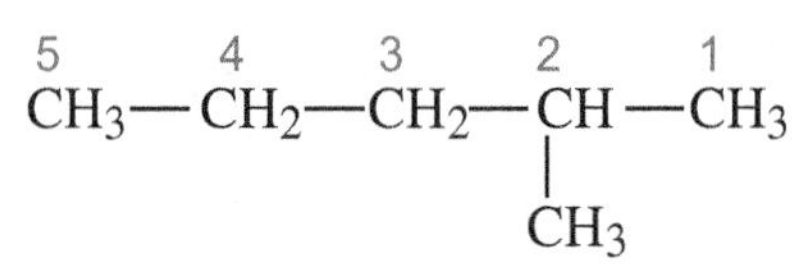

2-Methylpentane
(Correct)

- Rule 4: If two or more of the same substituents are present on the hydrocarbon, then the appropriate prefix (*di–* for two, *tri–* for three, *tetra–* for four, etc.) is used.

For example, consider the structural formulas in Figure 21.3. The longest continuous chain of the alkane in Figure 21.3a has six carbon atoms, so this compound is named as a *hexane* (see Table 21.2). The

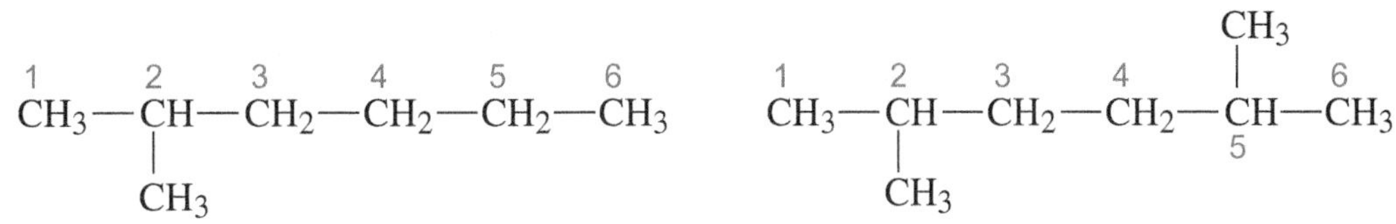

(a) (b)

FIGURE 21.3 Naming Alkanes

According to the alkane naming rules, compound (a) is 2-methylhexane and compound (b) is 2,5-dimethylhexane.

methyl group (CH_3—) is attached to carbon 2 (not carbon 4) because that carbon is the *second* from the *nearer* end of the chain. The name, then, is 2-methylhexane. The number 2 in 2-methylhexane identifies *where* it is located on the carbon chain—it does *not* mean that there are two methyl groups in the structure. Figure 21.3b has a six-carbon (hexane) chain with two methyl groups.

Example 21.1

Name the following organic compounds.

a. 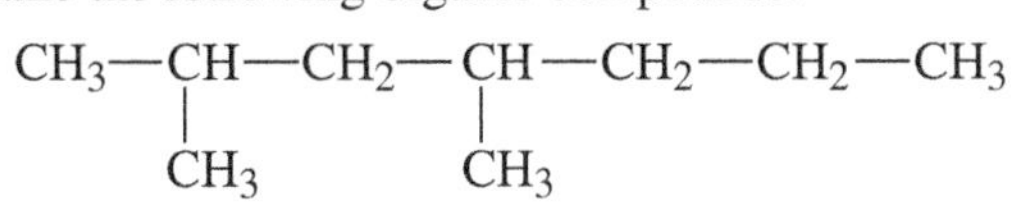

b. 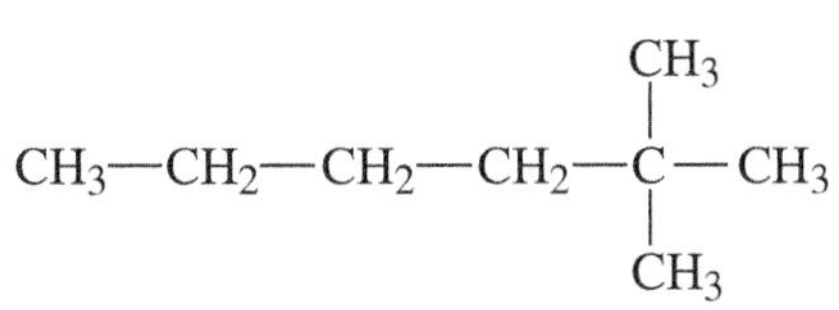

Solution

a. The longest continuous carbon chain has seven atoms, so this compound is a heptane (Table 21.2).

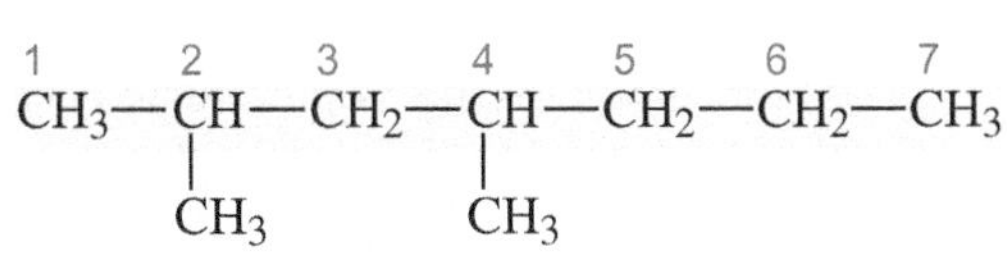

Numbering the chain from left to right puts the two methyl groups on carbons 2 and 4 (instead of 4 and 6). The name of the compound is 2,4-dimethylheptane.

b. The longest continuous carbon chain has six atoms, so this compound is a hexane (Table 21.2).

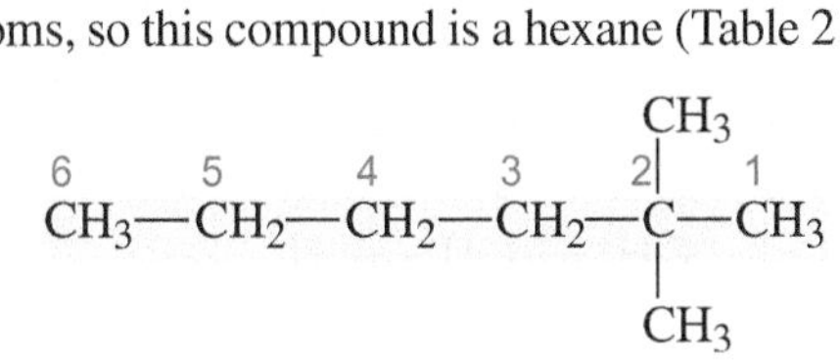

Numbering the chain from right to left puts the two methyl groups on carbon 2 (instead of carbon 5). The name of the compound is 2,2-dimethylhexane.

PRACTICE PROBLEM 21.1

Name the following organic compounds.

a. 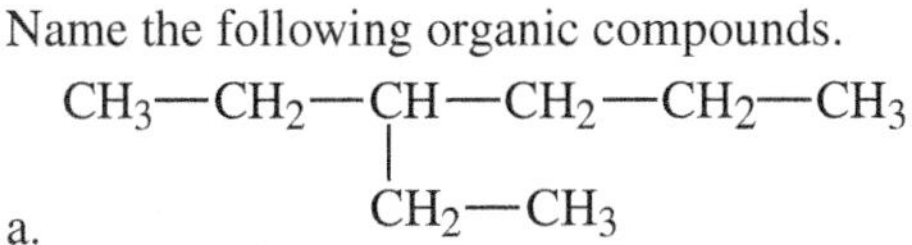

b. 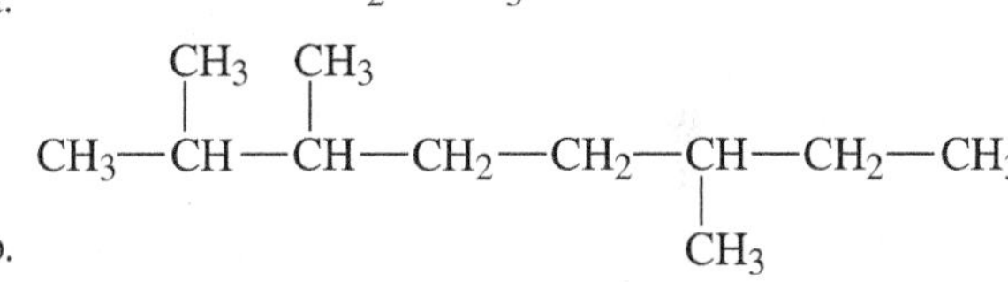

Hint: First, determine the longest continuous carbon chain and use Table 21.2 to determine the name associated with that parent chain. Number the chain to give the first substituent the lowest possible number. Then, use Table 21.3 to determine the names of the substituents.

- Rule 5: Note that if a methyl (or other straight-chain carbon group) is attached to either carbon atom at the end of the chain, a longer continuous chain is formed. The following compound is butane, *not* 1-methylpropane.

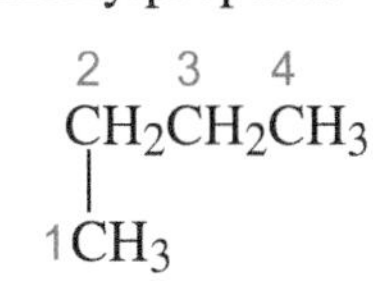

Organic compounds containing a halogen such as chlorine are named in an analogous manner, so the following molecule is 2,3-dichloropentane. The 2 and 3 indicate that the chlorines are located on carbons 2 and 3, and the prefix *di–* indicates that there are two chlorine atoms. The prefixes *tri–*, *tetra–*, and the like are used to indicate three, four, and so on of the same groups, respectively.

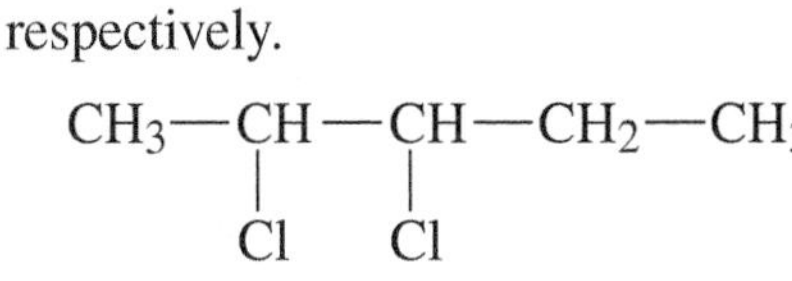

2,3-Dichloropentane

- Rule 6: When an unambiguous name can be assigned to a compound without numbers indicating the location of the substituents, then the numbers are often omitted. For example, the following compound is typically called methylpropane, not 2-methylpropane, because there is only one carbon atom (i.e., carbon 2) where a branch may occur.

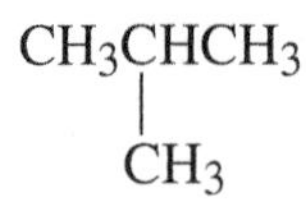

Note that some sources (e.g., the International Union of Pure and Applied Chemistry, IUPAC), recommend including the numbering, even when it is not necessary. In this text, both versions are acceptable.

Remember that even though these formulas are written in a straight line or with 90 degree angles, they are not really that shape; the bonds are tetrahedrally oriented around each carbon atom with 109.5 degree bond angles.

- Rule 7: When a hydrocarbon contains two or more substituents, they should be listed in alphabetical order in the name (e.g., *e*thyl before *m*ethyl before *p*ropyl). If two or more of the same substituents are present on the hydrocarbon, then the appropriate prefix (*di–* for two, *tri–* for three, *tetra–* for four, etc.) is *not* used to determine the alphabetical order (e.g., tri*e*thyl before *m*ethyl). In the following compound,

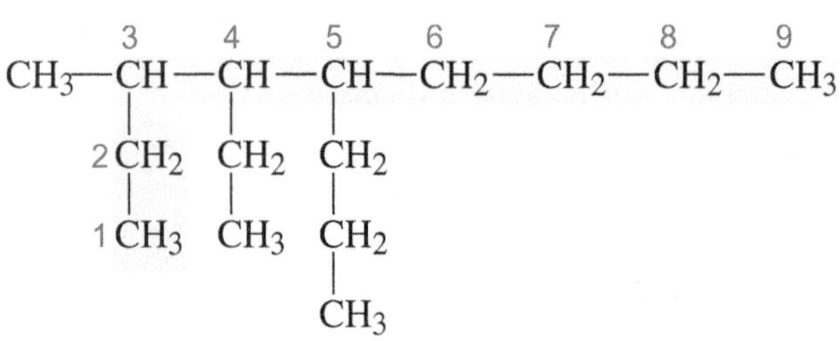

the longest continuous chain contains nine carbon atoms, so it is named as a nonane. The carbon chain is numbered from the bottom left up to the right because that numbering gives the first substituent the lowest value. The first substituent encountered is the methyl group at carbon 3 (3-methyl), then comes the ethyl group at carbon 4 (4-ethyl) and the propyl group at carbon 5 (5-propyl). Alphabetically, ethyl comes before methyl, which comes before propyl, so the name of the compound is 4-ethyl-3-methyl-5-propylnonane.

Example 21.2

Name the following organic compounds.

a. 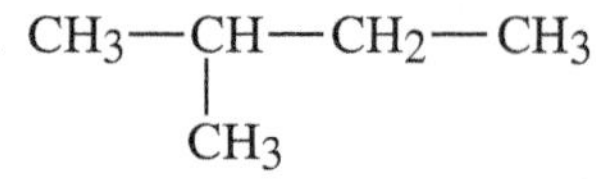

b. 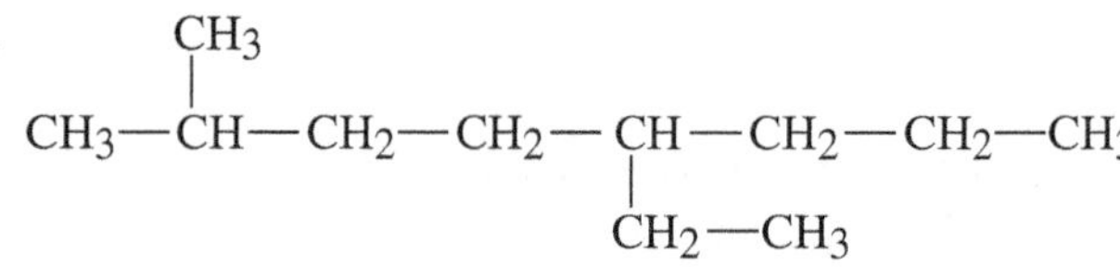

Solution

a. The longest continuous carbon chain has four atoms, so this compound is a butane (Table 21.2).

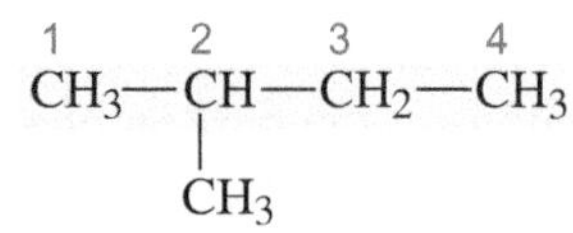

The numbering that results in the lowest number for the methyl groups is left to right, which puts the methyl group on carbon 2, so the compound can be called 2-methylbutane. However, this compound can also be called methylbutane. Notice that "3-methylbutane" is the same compound (prove this to yourself). Therefore, specifying the position of the methyl group is acceptable but not strictly necessary.

b. The longest continuous carbon chain has eight atoms, so this compound is an octane (Table 21.2).

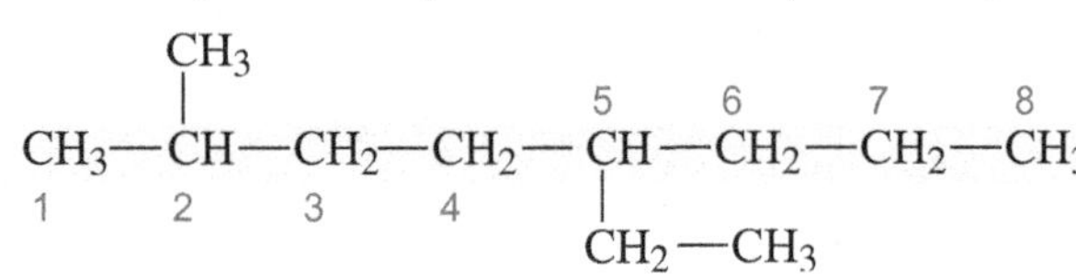

The numbering that results in the lowest numbers for the branch points is left to right, which puts the first branch point (the methyl group) on carbon 2. This is preferable because numbering from right to left would place the first branch point (the ethyl group) on carbon 4. Naming alphabetically, ethyl comes before methyl, so the compound is 5-ethyl-2-methyloctane.

PRACTICE PROBLEM 21.2

Name the following organic compounds.

a. 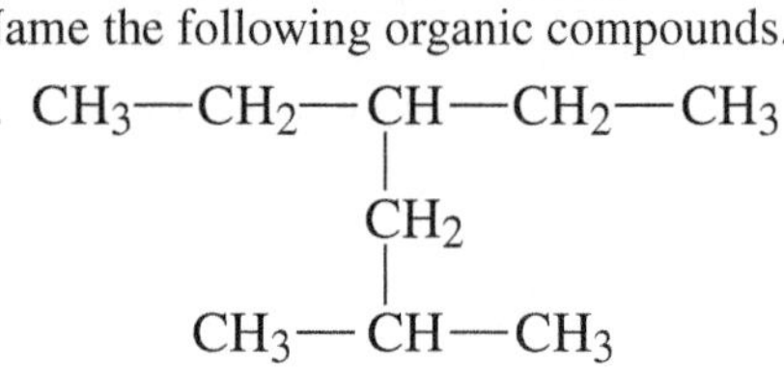

b. 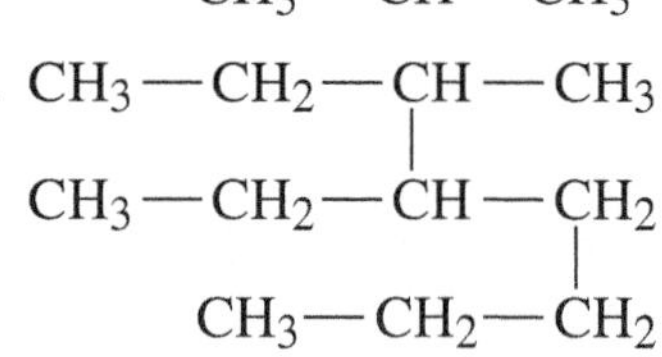

Hint: First, determine the longest continuous carbon chain, and use Table 21.2 to determine the name associated with that parent chain. Number the chain to give the first substituent the lowest possible number. Then, use Table 21.3 to determine the names of the substituents.

RULES FOR NAMING ALKANES

1. Find the longest continuous chain of carbon atoms in the molecule, and use the name in Table 21.2 for that chain.
2. Name any hydrocarbon branches off the main chain according to Table 21.3. The names of the branches are similar to those in Table 21.2 but with the *–ane* suffix replaced by *–yl*.
3. The position of a branched group on the main chain is identified with a number, which is the number of that carbon atom counting from the *nearer end* of the chain. That is, the main chain is numbered to give the first branch point the lowest possible number.
4. If two or more of the same substituents are present on the hydrocarbon, then the appropriate prefix (di– for two, tri– for three, tetra– for four, etc.) is used.
5. If an apparent branch is attached to the carbon atom at the end of the chain, it is not actually a branch but rather part of the main chain.
6. When an unambiguous name can be assigned to a compound without numbers indicating the location of the substituents, then the numbers may be omitted.
7. When a hydrocarbon contains two or more substituents, they are listed in alphabetical order. Prefixes are used if more than one of the same substituent is present, but the prefixes do not determine the alphabetical order.

REACTIONS OF ALKANES

At high temperatures, alkanes react with excess oxygen to yield carbon *di*oxide and water in combustion reactions (Section 4.2).

$$2\,C_2H_6(g) + 7\,O_2(g,\text{ excess}) \xrightarrow{\text{heat}} 4\,CO_2(g) + 6\,H_2O(g)$$

When oxygen is limited, however, the combustion of alkanes yields carbon *mon*oxide and water.

$$2\,C_2H_6(g) + 5\,O_2(g,\text{ limited supply}) \xrightarrow{\text{heat}} 4\,CO(g) + 6\,H_2O(g)$$

Alkanes are widely used as fuels: methane is the main component of natural gas, propane is used as bottled gas and as a fuel for welding torches, and butane is used in blowtorches and cigarette lighters. Despite the octane rating listed on gasoline pumps, octane itself is a fairly small fraction of the overall mixture that makes up gasoline. The octane rating is a measure of how much compression the fuel can withstand before exploding, and it is unrelated to the actual octane content of the gasoline.

Alkanes also react with elemental halogens at high temperatures to produce halogenated hydrocarbons in substitution reactions.

$$CH_4(g) + Br_2(g,\text{ limited supply}) \xrightarrow{\text{heat}} CH_3Br(g) + HBr(g)$$

$$CH_4(g) + 4\,Br_2(g,\text{ excess}) \xrightarrow{\text{heat}} CBr_4(l) + 4\,HBr(g)$$

The reactions of all the alkanes are similar. For example, all alkanes will react with excess bromine at high temperatures, replacing their hydrogen atoms with bromine atoms and generating HBr as a product. That fact makes the study of the alkanes the study of a single class of compounds rather than the millions of individual compounds that make up the class.

Example 21.3

Write balanced equations for the reaction of

a. propane with oxygen in limited supply and
b. ethane with bromine in limited supply.

You may omit the phases of the reactants and products.

Solution

a. When an alkane reacts with a limited supply of O_2, the products are CO and H_2O.

$$2\,C_3H_8 + 7\,O_2 \rightarrow 6\,CO + 8\,H_2O$$

b. When an alkane reacts with a limited supply of Br_2, the products are HBr and a halogenated hydrocarbon in which one H has been replaced by Br.

$$C_2H_6 + Br_2 \rightarrow C_2H_5Br + HBr$$

PRACTICE PROBLEM 21.3

Write balanced equations for the reaction of

a. butane with excess oxygen and
b. propane with excess bromine.

You may omit the phases of the reactants and products.

Hint: What products are obtained when a hydrocarbon reacts with excess oxygen or Br_2?

EVERYDAY CONNECTION

Crude oil, a type of petroleum, is processed in oil refineries such as the one shown in the opening image of this chapter. Crude oil is a mixture of many compounds—mainly hydrocarbons containing varying numbers of carbon atoms per molecule. Hydrocarbons with more than 12 carbon atoms per molecule are oily, greasy, or waxy substances. To produce smaller molecules, which are characteristic of hydrocarbons used as fuels, oil companies *crack* the petroleum by heating it in the absence of air. The heating causes some of the carbon–carbon bonds to break, thus producing a range of smaller molecules. Cracking in the presence of certain catalysts optimizes the yield of those compounds that are useful as fuels. The cracking process is followed by distillation, in which various types of petroleum products are separated from one another by means of their different boiling points (Section 12.4).

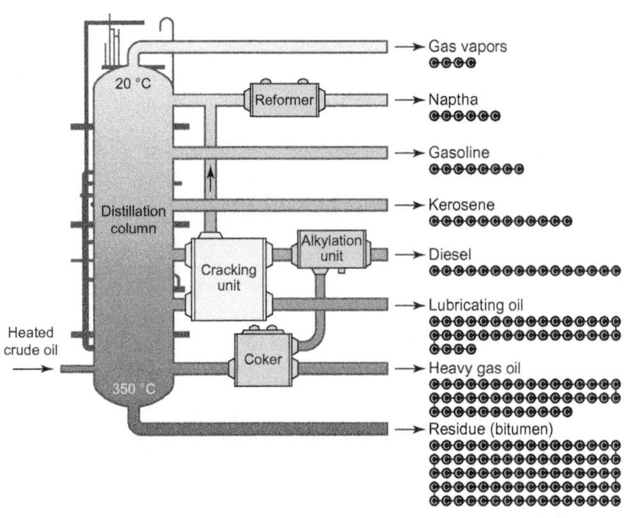

SECTION REVIEW

- Carbon has a unique ability to form long chains with many branches. This allows carbon to form a vast number of different compounds, which can be classified based on their structures. The compounds within each group react similarly but not always identically.
- Hydrocarbons are made up entirely of carbon and hydrogen atoms and are the simplest type of organic molecule.
- The following rules are used to name alkanes:
  - Find the longest continuous chain of carbon atoms in the molecule, and use the name in Table 21.2 for that chain.
  - Name any hydrocarbon branches off the main chain according to Table 21.3.
  - The position of a branched group on the main chain is identified with a number.
  - If two or more of the same substituents are present on the hydrocarbon, then the appropriate prefix (di– for two, tri– for three, tetra– for four, etc.) is used.
  - If an apparent branch is attached to the carbon atom at the end of the chain, it is not actually a branch but rather part of the main chain.
  - When an unambiguous name can be assigned to a compound without numbers indicating the location of the substituents, then the numbers may be omitted.
  - When a hydrocarbon contains two or more substituents, they are listed in alphabetical order. Prefixes are used if more than one of the same substituent is present, but the prefixes do not determine the alphabetical order.
- Alkanes react with O_2 at high temperatures in combustion reactions and with halogens at high temperatures in substitution reactions.

21.2 Unsaturated Hydrocarbons

GOALS

- Identify, name, and write formulas and reactions for unsaturated hydrocarbons.
- Describe the properties of unsaturated hydrocarbons.

Background Review

Chapter 11 Molecular Shape and Bonding Theories: Section 11.1—VSEPR and Molecular Geometry

ALKENES

An **alkene** is a hydrocarbon that has one or more carbon–carbon double bond. The simplest alkene is ethene (Figure 21.4).

An alkene has two fewer hydrogen atoms than that of the corresponding alkane with the same number of carbon atoms. Alkenes are therefore said to be **unsaturated hydrocarbons**, and their general molecular formula is C_nH_{2n}. The two carbon atoms involved in the double bond are sp^2 hybridized (Section 11.3),

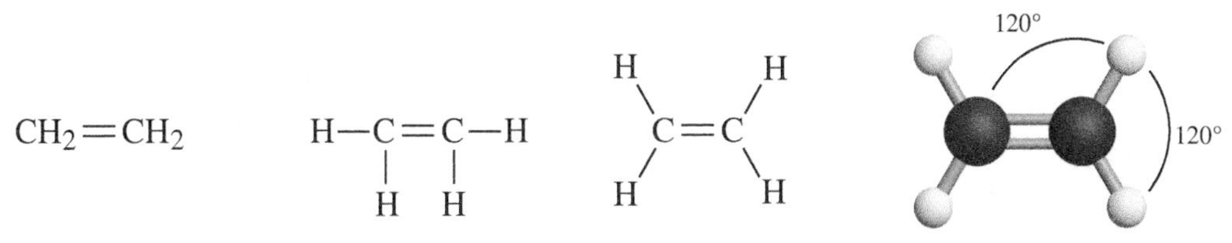

(a) (b) (c) (d)

FIGURE 21.4 Different Representations of Ethene

Here are several valid representations of ethene, C_2H_4. Part (a) shows the condensed structural formula, (b) is the structural formula, (c) is the structural formula showing bond angles, and (d) is the ball-and-stick model.

so the bond angles around those carbon atoms are 120 degrees, which gives the carbon atoms trigonal planar geometries (Table 11.1).

Alkenes, like alkanes, are named systematically:

- Find the longest continuous carbon chain that includes both carbon atoms of the double bond. The parent name of the compound will be similar to those in Table 21.2, but with the *–ane* suffix replaced by *–ene*. For example, the following compound is named as a four-carbon alkene (a butene), not as a five-carbon alkane (a pentane).

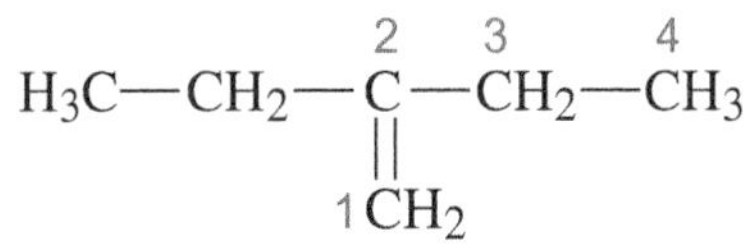

- The location of the double bond is indicated with a number when necessary. Of the *two* carbon atoms involved in the double bond, use the number of the carbon closer to the nearer end of the longest chain in the name, thus giving the double bond the lowest number possible. For example, the preceding compound is numbered with the double bond in the 1 position, not the 3 position.

This compound is called 2-ethyl-1-butene. The suffix *–ene* means that this compound contains a carbon–carbon double bond. The prefix *but–* indicates that there are four carbon atoms in the main chain, and the number 1 indicates that the double bond is between carbon 1 and carbon 2. Finally, the name indicates that this compound contains an ethyl group that branches off at position 2 in the main chain.

> The formulas $CH_3CH{=}CH_2$ and $CH_2{=}CHCH_3$ both represent propene. They are simply written in the opposite order. The double bond in propene must always be between carbon 1 and carbon 2, so although the name 1-propene is acceptable, you will more commonly see it called propene, without the number.

TABLE 21.4 The First Four Unbranched Alkenes

Systematic Name	Molecular Formula	Structural Formula	Condensed Structural Formula
Ethene	C_2H_4	H—C=C—H H H	$CH_2{=}CH_2$
Propene	C_3H_6	H H—C=C—C—H H H H	$CH_2{=}CHCH_3$
1-Butene	C_4H_8	H H H—C=C—C—C—H H H H H	$CH_2{=}CHCH_2CH_3$
2-Butene	C_4H_8	H H H—C—C=C—C—H H H H H	$CH_3CH{=}CHCH_3$

The names and formulas of the first four unbranched alkenes are listed in Table 21.4. Common names are often used for the smallest members of each class. Ethene (ethylene) and propene (propylene) are the raw materials used in the manufacture of the well-known plastics polyethylene and polypropylene.

Example 21.4

Name the following alkenes.

a. $CH_3CH{=}CHCH_2CH_3$
b. $CH_3CH_2CH_2CH_2CH{=}CH_2$
c. $CH_2{=}CH_2$

Solution

a. The double bond has the lowest possible number when it is assigned to position 2. There are five carbon atoms in the main chain, so this compound is 2-pentene.
b. The double bond has the lowest possible number when it is assigned to position 1. There are six carbon atoms in the main chain, so this is 1-hexene.

c. There are only two carbon atoms, so the double bond has to be in position 1 and no number is needed to identify where it is. The compound is ethene, the simplest possible alkene.

PRACTICE PROBLEM 21.4

Draw condensed structural formulas for the following alkenes.

a. 3,4-dimethyl-2-hexene
b. 3-ethyl-2,4-dimethyl-2-hexene

Hint: Use the parent name to determine the number of carbon atoms in the longest continuous chain and where in that chain the double bond appears. Place the double bond where the number in the name indicates it is supposed to be. Then determine where the substituent groups belong on the main chain.

REACTIONS OF ALKENES

Alkenes undergo **addition reactions** at room temperature, making alkenes much more reactive than alkanes. In an addition reaction, new groups, such as the atoms from halogen molecules or hydrogen halides, are added to the starting material. When an alkene reacts with Br_2,

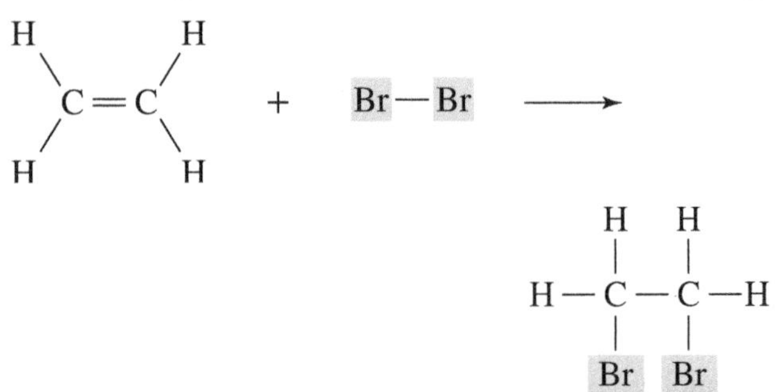

the Br—Br bond and one of the bonds involved in the double bond are broken and two new C—Br bonds are formed. The line formula equation for this reaction is as follows (pay attention to how the Br atoms are written in the product):

$$CH_2{=}CH_2(g) + Br_2(l) \rightarrow CH_2BrCH_2Br(l)$$

When an alkene reacts with a hydrogen halide such as HBr,

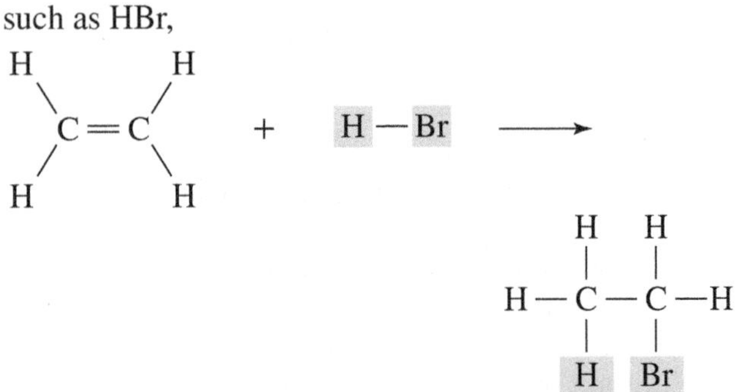

$$CH_2 = CH_2(g) + HBr(g) \rightarrow CH_3CH_2Br(l)$$

the H—Br bond and one of the bonds involved in the double bond are broken and two new bonds (C—H and C—Br) are formed.

Alkenes can also undergo addition reactions with water to form alcohols—a process called hydration.

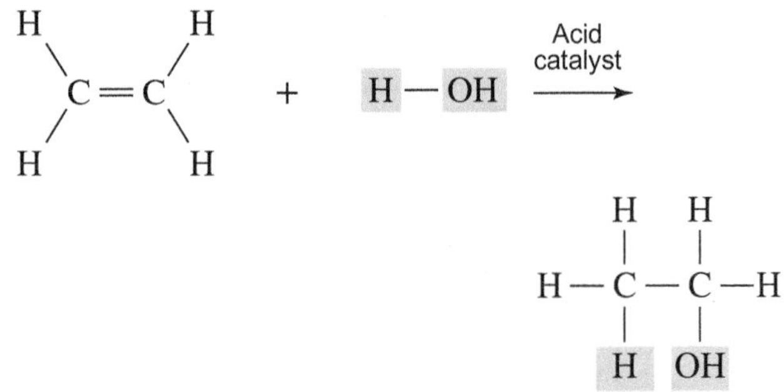

$$CH_2 = CH_2(g) + H_2O(l) \rightarrow CH_3CH_2OH(l)$$

Alcohols are discussed in greater detail in Section 21.3.

Finally, alkenes can undergo addition reactions with hydrogen molecules to form alkanes—a process called hydrogenation.

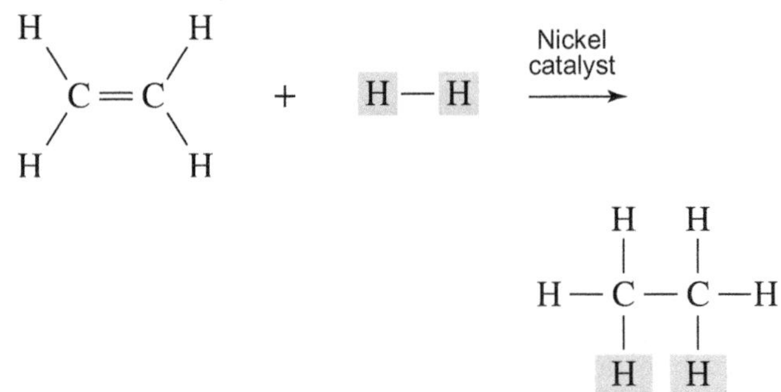

$$CH_2 = CH_2(g) + H_2(g) \rightarrow CH_3CH_3(g)$$

ALKYNES

An **alkyne** is a hydrocarbon that contains one or more carbon–carbon triple bond. For alkynes that contain just one triple bond, the general molecular formula is C_nH_{2n-2}. The simplest alkyne is called ethyne, C_2H_2, but is commonly known as acetylene (Figure 21.5).

Acetylene is used as a fuel in high-temperature welding torches. Each carbon atom in acetylene is *sp*-hybridized (Section 11.3). The overall geometry of the molecule is linear, with 180-degree bond angle (Table 11.1).

The alkynes are named the same way as alkenes, but with the suffix *–yne* instead of *–ene.*

Like alkenes, alkynes are unsaturated and more reactive than alkanes. Alkynes undergo addition

CH≡CH

(a)

H—C≡C—H

(b)

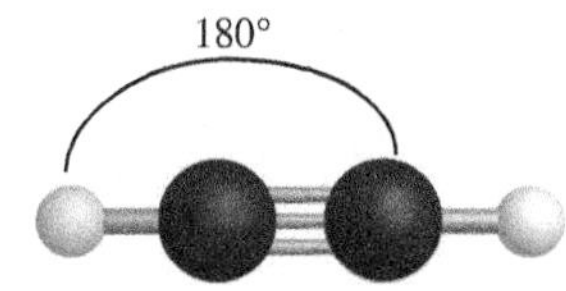

(c)

FIGURE 21.5 Different Representations of Ethyne (Acetylene)

NOTE: You need to be online to access this activity.

Here are several valid representations of ethyne, C_2H_2, also known as acetylene. Part (a) shows the condensed structural formula, (b) is the structural formula, and (c) is the ball-and-stick model. *Click the image to open the interactive view.*

reactions like alkenes, but alkynes can add two molecules of a halogen or hydrogen molecule across the triple bond:

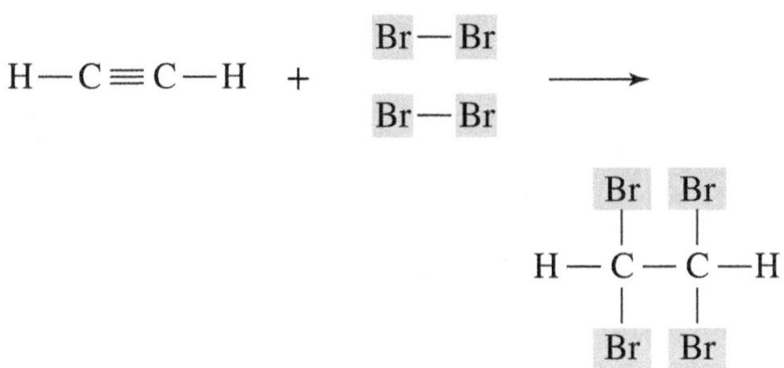

$$CH{\equiv}CH(g) + 2\,Br_2(g) \rightarrow CHBr_2CHBr_2(g)$$

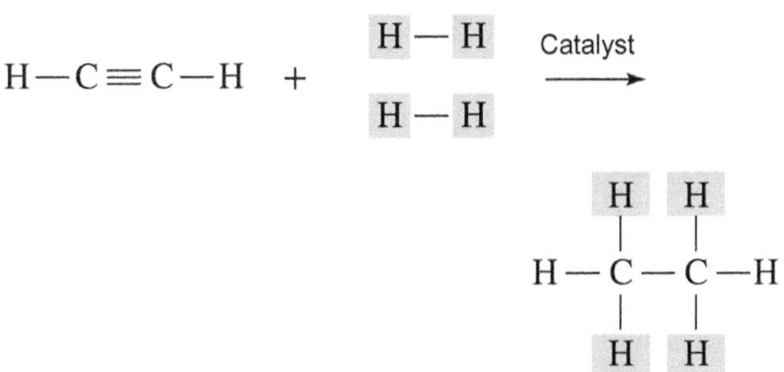

$$CH{\equiv}CH(g) + 2\,H_2(g) \rightarrow CH_3CH_3(g)$$

Figure 21.6 shows how to draw structures of alkenes and alkynes given the name, and name them based on their structure.

Steve Lemon, Macmillan Learning

FIGURE 21.6 Video Tutorial: Alkyne Reactions

NOTE: You need to be online to access this video.

This video shows how to draw and name the products of an addition reaction.

Example 21.5

Name the following unsaturated hydrocarbons. Then write condensed structures for the products formed when 1 mole of each reacts with 1 mole of Br_2.

a. $CH_3CH{=}CH_2$
b. $CH_3CH_2CH_2C{\equiv}CCH_3$

Solution

a. The longest continuous chain that contains the double bond is three carbons long, so this is a propene. Numbering the chain from right to left gives the double bond the lowest possible number. The name of the compound is simply propene, though, not 1-propene, because the only place the double bond can go is between carbons 1 and 2.

The reaction of 1 mole propene with 1 mole of Br_2 is

$$CH_3CH{=}CH_2 + Br_2 \rightarrow CH_3CHBrCH_2Br$$

The longest continuous chain in the product is three carbons long, so this is a propane. Numbering the chain from right to left again gives the first Br substituent the lowest possible number (i.e., 1, not 2). The second Br substituent is then on carbon 2 (instead of carbon 3). The name of the product is 1,2-dibromopropane.

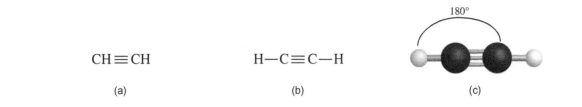

b. The longest continuous chain that contains the triple bond is six carbons long, so this is a hexyne. Numbering the chain from right to left gives the triple bond the lowest possible number (2 instead of 4). The name of the compound is 2-hexyne.

The reaction of 1 mole of 2-hexyne with 1 mole of Br_2 yields a halogenated alkene:

$$CH_3CH_2CH_2C{\equiv}CCH_3 + Br_2 \rightarrow CH_3CH_2CH_2CBr{=}CBrCH_3$$

The longest continuous chain that contains the double bond is six carbons long, so this is a hexene. Numbering the chain from right to left again gives the double bond the lowest possible number (2 instead of 4). Using this same numbering scheme, the two Br substituents are on carbons 2 and 3. The name of this product is 2,3-dibromo-2-hexene.

When 1 mole of an alkyne reacts with 1 mole of a halogen, the halogen is added across the triple bond to give a halogenated alkene. If 2 moles of halogen had reacted with 1 mole of 2-hexyne, the product would have been the unsaturated brominated alkane $CH_3CH_2CH_2CBr_2CBr_2CH_3$. The name of this unsaturated product is 2,2,3,3-tetrabromohexane.

PRACTICE PROBLEM 21.5

Name the following unsaturated hydrocarbons. Then write condensed structures for the products formed when 1 mole of each reacts with 1 mole of H_2 in the presence of a nickel catalyst.

a. $CH_3CH{=}CHCH_2CH_3$
b. $CH_3CH_2CH_2C{\equiv}CH$

Hint: First, determine the longest continuous carbon chain that contains the multiple bond. Then, number the main chain so that the multiple bond has the lowest possible number. Finally, add one molecule of H_2 across 1 carbon–carbon multiple bond, thus eliminating one of those bonds.

AROMATIC HYDROCARBONS

Aromatic hydrocarbons constitute the fourth and final class of hydrocarbons. The simplest aromatic hydrocarbon is **benzene**, C_6H_6 (Figure 21.7), which consists of a ring of six carbon atoms. Alternating single and double bonds and a bond to a single H atom give each carbon four bonds. All other aromatic hydrocarbons have at least one benzene ring included in their structures, and many have groups other than H bonded to their rings.

Alternating double and single bonds yield two possible resonance structures (Section 10.3) that obey the octet rule, but aromatic hydrocarbons have more stability than is expected for compounds that have ordinary double bonds. Although the octet rule leads to structures with alternating single and double bonds, the carbon–carbon bonds in an aromatic hydrocarbon are all identical and are more like one-and-a-half strength bonds than they are single or double bonds. Lewis structures are unable to depict a one-and-a-half bond, so the benzene ring is often represented as a hexagon with a circle drawn in the middle (Figure 21.7c) to indicate the identical bonds throughout. This uniform bonding throughout the molecule is referred to as delocalized double bonding

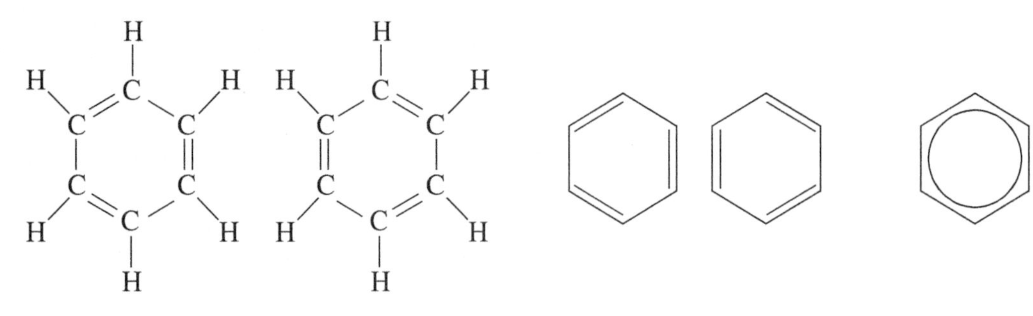

(a) (b) (c)

FIGURE 21.7 Different Representations of Benzene

(a) Benzene has two resonance structures (Section 10.3) because the alternating double and single bonds can be in different locations. (b) Organic structures, particularly rings, are often represented by only their carbon-carbon bonds—that is, the letters representing the carbon and hydrogen atoms are omitted, as are the bonds to H. (c) The circle represents the averaged locations of the double bonds—that is, it is meant to suggest delocalized double bonds in the resonance hybrid.

(Section 10.3) and is responsible for the special stability of benzene and its derivatives. The delocalized electrons also give benzene a planar, or flat, structure (Figure 21.8).

One indication of this special stability is that benzene reacts with a halogen molecule by substitution not addition—that is, benzene reacts in a manner that is more like an alkane than an alkene:

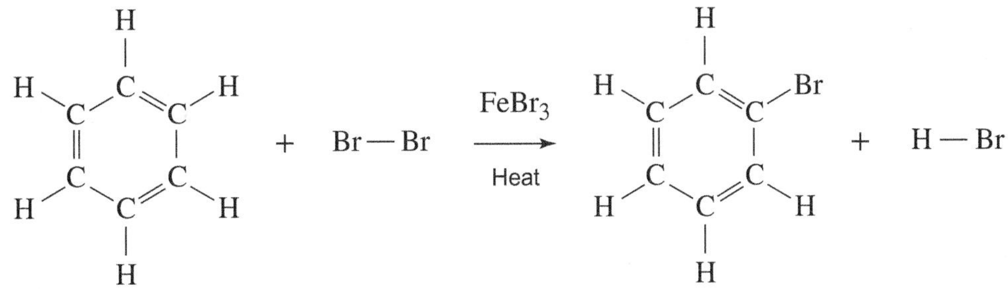

$$C_6H_6 + Br_2 \xrightarrow[\text{Heat}]{FeBr_3} C_6H_5Br + HBr$$

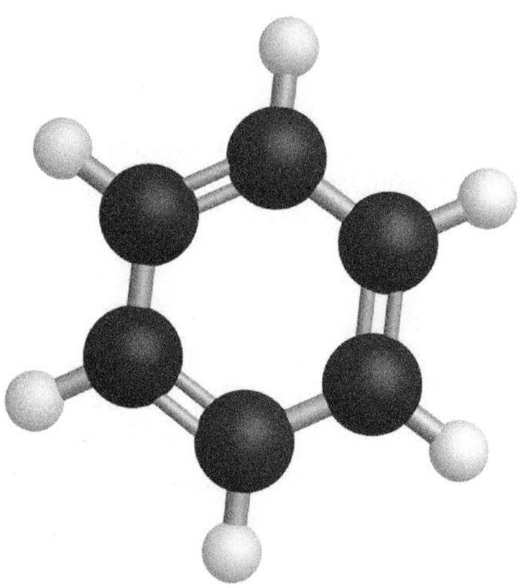

FIGURE 21.8 Benzene Is a Planar Molecule

NOTE: You need to be online to access this activity.

Due to the delocalization of its electrons, benzene has a planar (flat) structure. *Click on the molecule to open the interactive view.*

Note that the carbon–carbon double bonds remain intact during this reaction. Iron is a necessary catalyst in this reaction.

NAMING SUBSTITUTED BENZENE DERIVATIVES

In *monosubstituted* benzene derivatives, one of the hydrogens on the benzene ring has been replaced with another group. They are named by using the group name as the prefix and *benzene* as the suffix:

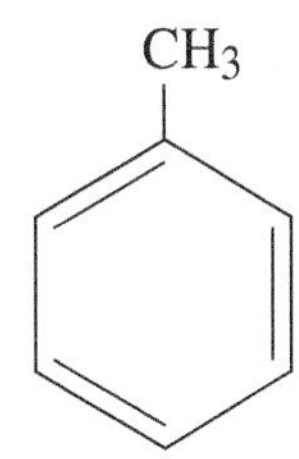

Methylbenzene

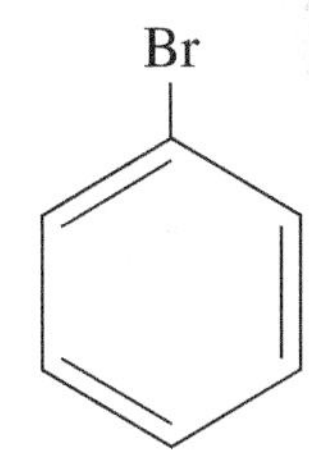

Bromobenzene

When more than one of the same *type* of group is substituted onto a benzene ring, multiple isomers can exist, as shown for the following *disubstituted* bromobenzene compounds (Figure 21.9).

For structures such as the ones in Figure 21.9, a systematic numbering system is used to distinguish between them. This system numbers their relative positions on the ring and uses prefixes such as *di–* and *tri–* to indicate the number of substituents. There is also an older naming system that uses the prefixes *ortho–* (*o–*), *meta–* (*m–*), and *para–* (*p–*) corresponding to the 1,2-, 1,3-, and 1,4- configurations, respectively.

When *different types* of groups are present, the groups are named alphabetically. The first substituent in alphabetical order is assigned position 1 (Figure 21.10).

Example 21.6

Draw the structure of chlorobenzene.

Solution

The structure of chlorobenzene is similar to the structure of benzene in Figure 21.7 but with

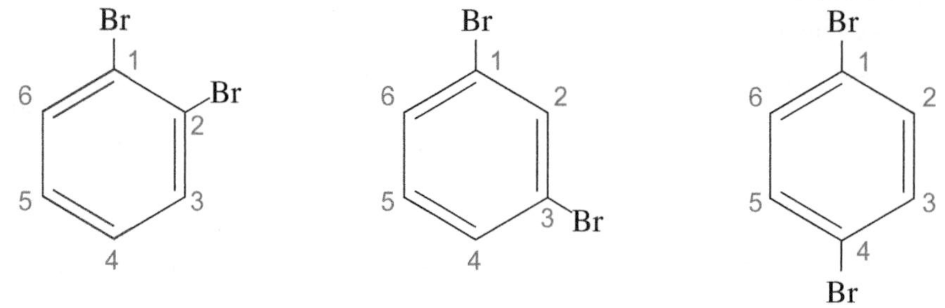

1,2-Dibromobenzene
ortho-Dibromobenzene
o-Dibromobenzene
(a)

1,3-Dibromobenzene
meta-Dibromobenzene
m-Dibromobenzene
(b)

1,4-Dibromobenzene
para-Dibromobenzene
p-Dibromobenzene
(c)

FIGURE 21.9 Nomenclature for Disubstituted Benzene Compounds

There are three ways to name each of these compounds. (a) The 1,2- configuration of substituents is also known as *ortho*– or *o*–. (b) The 1,3- configuration is also known as *meta*– or *m*–. (c) The 1,4- configuration is also known as *para*– or *p*–.

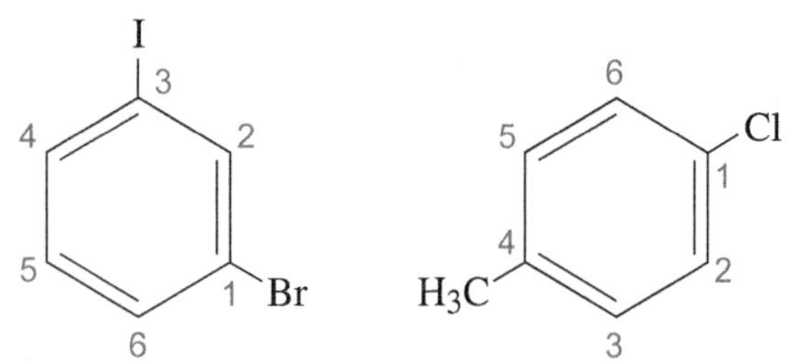

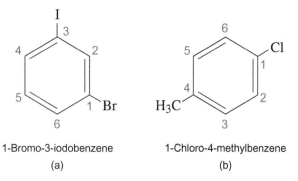

1-Bromo-3-iodobenzene
(a)

1-Chloro-4-methylbenzene
(b)

FIGURE 21.10 Numbering the Benzene Ring Based on the Alphabetical Order of Substituent Names

(a) Since bromo comes before iodo alphabetically, the carbon atom with the bromo substituent is designated as number 1. Thereafter the numbering follows consecutively in the direction that gives the other substituent the lower number. (b) Since chloro comes before methyl alphabetically, the carbon atom with the chloro substituent is designated as number 1. Thereafter the numbering follows consecutively in either direction, since the other substituent is at carbon number 4 either way.

one hydrogen atom replaced with a chlorine atom:

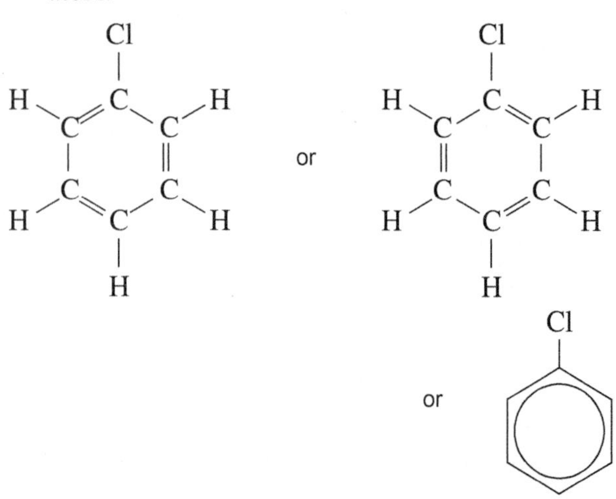

PRACTICE PROBLEM 21.6

Determine the number of hydrogen atoms in a 1,4-dichlorobenzene molecule.

Hint: Draw the structure of 1,4-dichlorobenzene, then count the hydrogen atoms.

Example 21.7

Name the following benzene derivatives.

a.

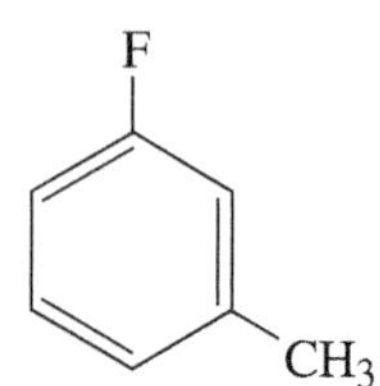

b.

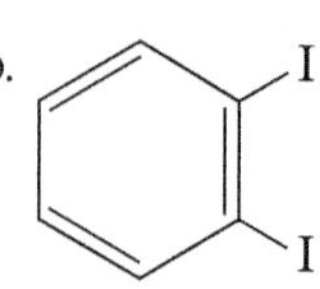

Solution

a. Two different types of groups, fluoro and methyl, are located in the 1,3- (*meta*-) configuration, so they are named alphabetically. The first substituent in alphabetical order (i.e., fluoro) is assigned position 1. This compound is 1-fluoro-3-methylbenzene.

b. The two iodo groups are in the 1,2- (*ortho*-) arrangement, so this compound is 1,2-diiodobenzene, *ortho*-diiodobenzene, or *o*-diiodobenzene.

PRACTICE PROBLEM 21.7

Name the following benzene derivatives.

a.

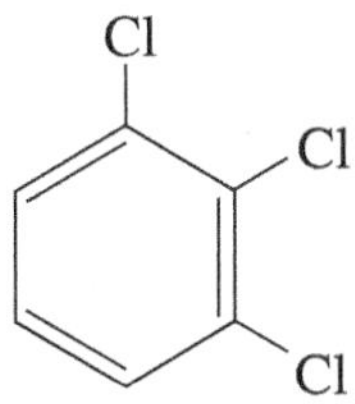

b.

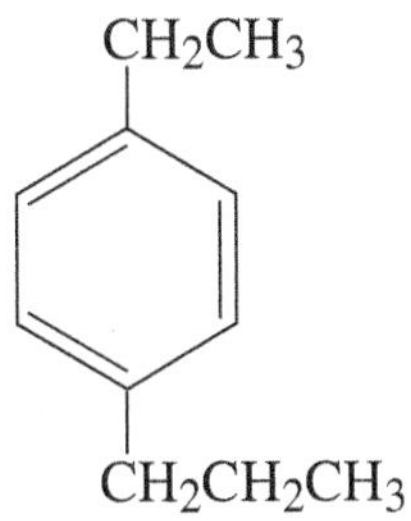

Hint: Benzene derivatives that have more than one of the same type of substituent are named by numbering their relative positions on the ring and using prefixes such as *di–* and *tri–* to indicate the number of substituents. When a benzene derivative has different types of groups, the groups are named alphabetically, with the first group assigned to position 1.

SECTION REVIEW

- Unsaturated hydrocarbons consist of three classes:
  - alkenes, which contain one or more C=C double bond
  - alkynes, which contain one or more C≡C triple bond
  - aromatic hydrocarbons, which have benzene ring structures with delocalized bonding within the ring.
- Alkenes and alkynes are much more reactive than alkanes (Section 21.1). Alkenes and alkynes react with halogens and hydrogen halides at room temperature in addition reactions.
- Aromatic hydrocarbons do not undergo addition reactions like alkenes or alkynes, but they do undergo some substitution reactions like alkanes.
- Alkenes and alkynes are named in a manner similar to alkanes, except that the double or triple bond is given the lowest possible number.
- Benzene derivatives are named using the substituent group name as the prefix and *–benzene* as the suffix. When more than one of the *same* type of group is present, the groups are numbered by their relative positions and a prefix is used to indicate the number of groups. An older system uses *ortho–*, *meta–*, and *para–* to give the relative positions of two groups that are present. When more than one *different* type of group is present on a benzene ring, the groups are named alphabetically, and the first group is assigned position 1 on the ring.

21.3 Introduction to Isomerism

GOAL

- Identify and write formulas for structural isomers.

For hydrocarbons with at least four carbon atoms, more than one compound may exist with a given molecular formula. For example, there are two isomers with the formula C_4H_{10} (Figure 21.11).

Compounds that have identical molecular formulas but the atoms are arranged differently are called **isomers** of each other. Butane and methylpropane are isomers of each other. Each is a unique compound, but both have the same molecular formula, C_4H_{10}.

Isomers such as butane and methylpropane often have different physical properties. For example, the boiling point of butane is 0°C, while the boiling point of methylpropane is −12°C.

Three classes of isomers—namely, structural isomers, cis–trans isomers, and stereoisomers—are discussed in this section. Butane and methylpropane are structural isomers.

STRUCTURAL ISOMERS

Structural isomers, such as butane and methylpropane, have the same number and type of atoms connected in different ways.

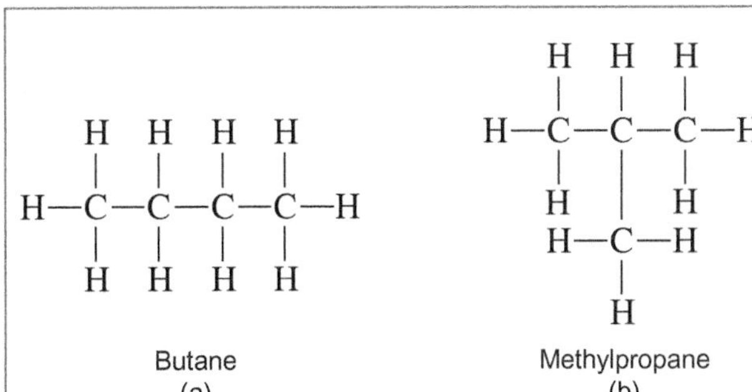

FIGURE 21.11 Isomers of C_4H_{10}

Butane (a) and methylpropane (b) are isomers of each other because they have the same molecular formula, C_4H_{10}, but different arrangements of atoms.

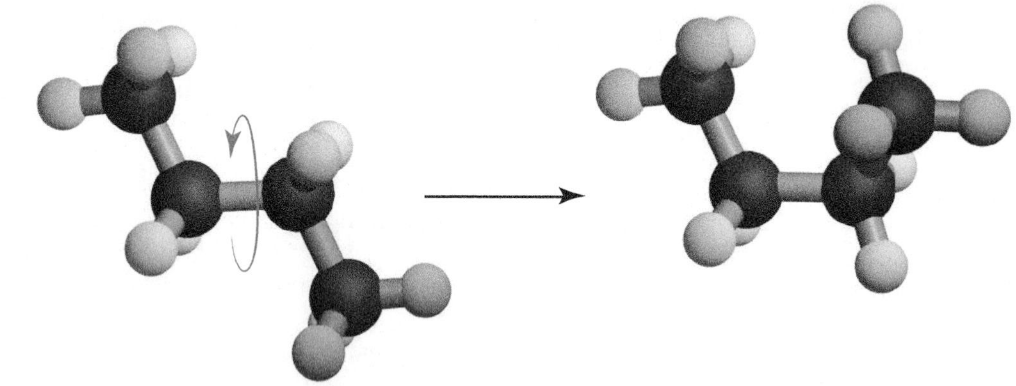

FIGURE 21.12 Two Different Orientations of Butane

NOTE: You need to be online to access this activity.

Although these models appear to have a different shape, the carbon atoms are still connected in a continuous, unbranched chain. The apparent difference is a result of rotating the right side of the molecule so that the fourth carbon sticks up instead of down. This rotation does not break any bonds or connect any atoms differently, so the models show the same molecule in different orientations. In other words, these are *not* isomers. *Click the image to open an interactive view.*

In an alkane, one part of the molecule can rotate about one or more of the carbon–carbon single bonds to assume different shapes (Figure 21.12). These different orientations are different forms of the *same* molecule, not isomers. Example 21.8 can help you learn how to determine when two molecules are different orientations of the same compound and when they are isomers.

Example 21.8

Determine whether the following sets of molecules are isomers or the same compounds.

a.

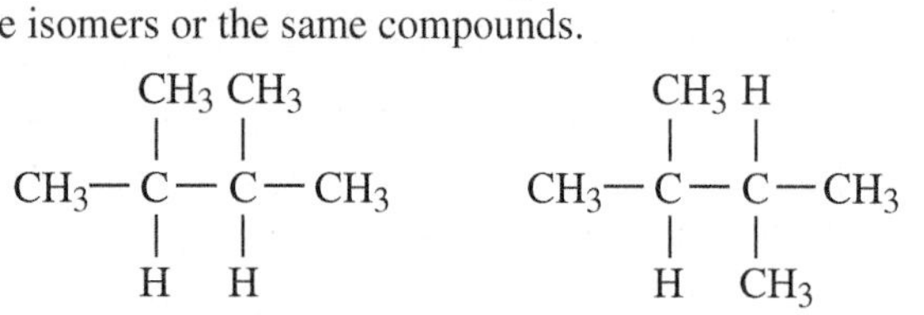

b.

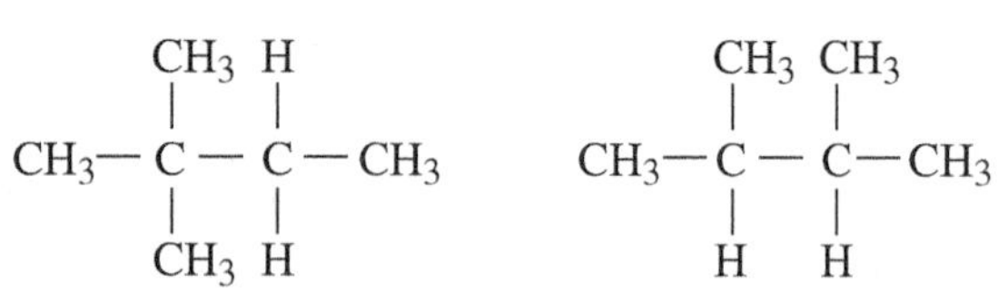

Solution

a. These two molecules are the same because all of the atoms are connected in the same way. If the bond between carbons 2 and 3 of the molecule on the left is rotated 180 degrees, you get the molecule on the right.

b. These two molecules are structural isomers because their formulas are the same but the connectivities around carbons 2 and 3 are different.

In the compound on the left, carbon 2 is bonded to three methyl groups and carbon 3 is bonded to two hydrogen atoms and one methyl group. In the compound on the right, both carbons 2 and 3 are bonded to two methyl groups and one hydrogen atom.

PRACTICE PROBLEM 21.8

Determine whether the following sets of molecules are isomers or the same compounds.

a.

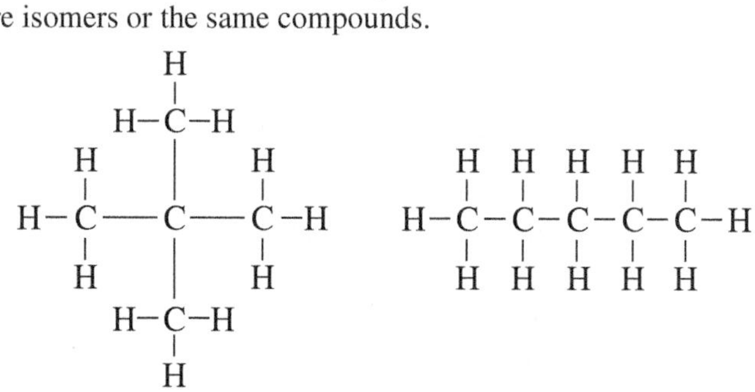

b.

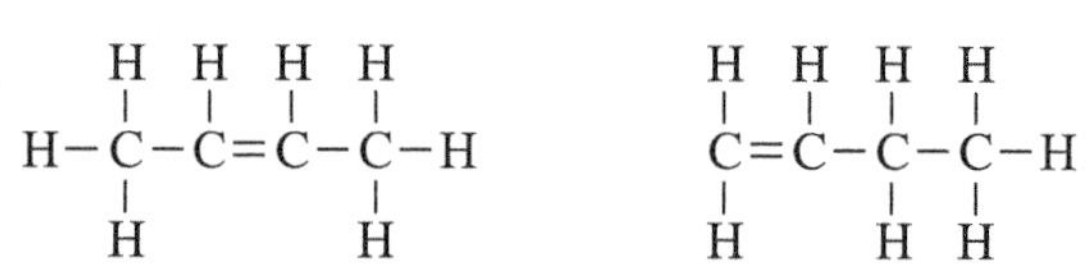

Hint: Structural isomers have the same molecular formulas, but their atoms are connected in different ways. Different compounds have different molecular formulas.

Example 21.9

Draw condensed structural formulas for three compounds with the molecular formula C_5H_{12}. Name these three compounds.

Solution

The general formula for C_5H_{12} is C_nH_{2n+2}, where $n = 5$. This is the general formula for an alkane, so C_5H_{12} is an alkane. Begin with the one straight-chain isomer of C_5H_{12} (pentane), and then draw two different branched isomers that have the same molecular formula.

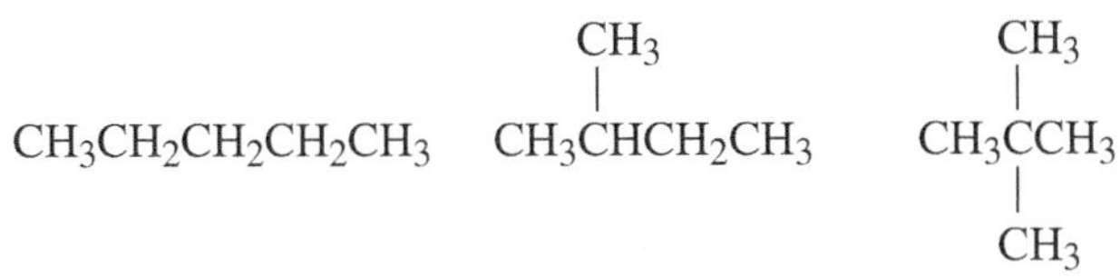

Pentane | Methylbutane | Dimethylpropane

PRACTICE PROBLEM 21.9

Draw condensed structural formulas for two compounds with the molecular formula C_5H_{10} that have the five carbon atoms in a continuous chain. Name these two compounds.

Hint: Use the general formula of C_5H_{10}—namely, C_nH_{2n}—to determine whether it is an alkane, alkene, or alkyne.

Example 21.10

Write condensed structural formulas for all of the alkynes with the molecular formula C_4H_6. Name these compounds.

Solution

There are two alkynes with the molecular formula C_4H_6: $CH{\equiv}CCH_2CH_3$ and $CH_3C{\equiv}CCH_3$. The names of these compounds are 1-butyne and 2-butyne, respectively.

PRACTICE PROBLEM 21.10

Draw a condensed structural formula for a branched unsaturated isomer of C_4H_8. Name the compound.

Hint: This molecule has the general formula C_nH_{2n}, where $n = 4$. Is it an alkane, alkene, or alkyne?

EVERYDAY CONNECTION

The octane rating of gasoline is based on the degree of engine "knocking," where higher numbers indicate slower and more efficient combustion. The rating gets its name from *isooctane*, which is the common name for 2,2,4-trimethylpentane, an isomer of C_8H_{18}. 2,2,4-trimethylpentane has an octane rating of 100, whereas straight-chain octane, a different isomer of C_8H_{18}, has an octane rating of −10.

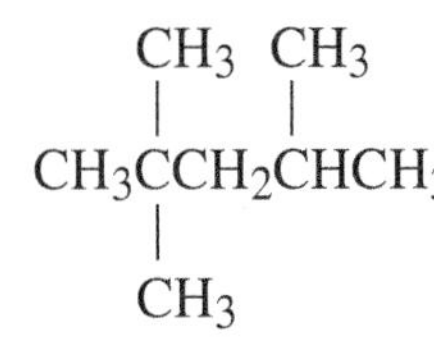

2,2,4-Trimethylpentane
(isooctane)

$CH_3CH_2CH_2CH_2CH_2CH_2CH_2CH_3$

Octane

Gasoline is a mixture of hydrocarbons. "Regular" gasoline has an octane rating of approximately 87, whereas "premium" gasoline typically has an octane rating of 91 or higher.

Daniel Korzeniewski/Shutterstock.com

CIS–TRANS ISOMERS

The carbon–carbon single bonds in an alkane rotate freely, as shown previously in Figure 21.12. Rotation about the carbon–carbon double bond of an alkene is restricted (unfavorable), however, because it takes energy to break the C=C π bond (Section 11.4) and re-form it in the opposite orientation. Thus, the orientation of the groups around the C=C bond of an alkene is static at room temperature (Figure 21.13).

Due to this lack of rotation about the double bond, 2-butene (Figure 21.14) can exist as two different **cis–trans isomers** (also known as geometric isomers). Cis–trans isomers have the same molecular formulas and same connections between the atoms, but the atoms have different orientations in space. In a cis isomer such as *cis*-2-butene, the alkyl groups are on the same side of the double bond; in a trans isomer such as *trans*-2-butene, the alkyl groups are on opposite sides of the double bond. Cis–trans isomers can also occur with other types of molecules, some of which are described more fully in Section 22.5.

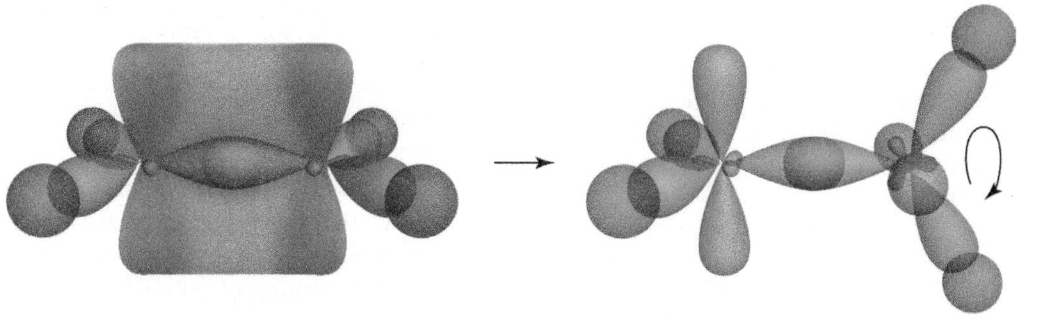

FIGURE 21.13 Rotation about a Double Bond Is Energetically Unfavorable
Rotation about a C=C double bond breaks the π bond.

cis-2-Butene *trans*-2-Butene

FIGURE 21.14 Cis–trans Isomers of 2-Butene
In the cis isomer of 2-butene, the alkyl groups—methyl groups, in this case—are on the same side of the double bond. In the trans isomer, the alkyl groups are on opposite sides of the double bond.

Cis–trans isomers are one type of stereoisomer. **Stereoisomers** are molecules with the same atom connectivities but a different spatial arrangement of atoms.

Example 21.11

Determine whether the following compounds are in the cis or trans configuration.

a. 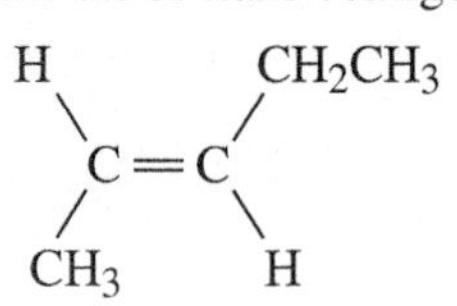

b. 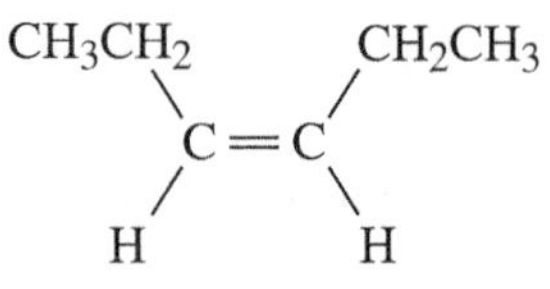

Solution

a. The alkyl groups are on opposite sides of the double bond, so the compound is in the trans configuration. (Its name is *trans*-2-pentene.)
b. The alkyl groups are on the same side of the double bond, so the compound is in the cis configuration. (Its name is *cis*-3-hexene.)

PRACTICE PROBLEM 21.11

Draw the structure of *cis*-2,3-dibromo-2-hexene.

Hint: In the cis isomer, the alkyl groups are on the same side of the double bond.

OPTICAL ISOMERS

Optical isomers are a second type of stereoisomer. Your hands are similar to optical isomers, in the sense that the fingers and thumb on one hand have the same connectivities as the ones on the other hand, but their spatial arrangements on each hand are different. Your hands are mirror images of one another (Figure 21.15a), but they are not *superimposable* mirror images. You can prove this to yourself by placing your hands on top of one another with both palms pointed downward. When your hands are held in this way, the thumbs of each hand are on opposite sides. As a result, a pair of hands are *nonsuperimposable mirror images* of one another and are *not* equivalent, which is why your left hand fits so awkwardly into a right-handed glove (and vice versa). This property is known as *chirality*. A pair of molecules that are **chiral** (i.e., that are nonsuperimposable mirror images of one another) are a type of stereoisomer known as **optical isomers** or enantiomers.

Optical isomers can be differentiated from one another by the way that they rotate plane-polarized light. When light is passed through a polarizing filter, the electric field of the light is confined to a single plane. This plane of polarization of the resulting light is rotated in different directions by different optical isomers of a given compound. Two tetrahedral complexes that contain the same set of four unique groups (Figure 21.15b) are nonsuperimposable mirror images of each other. These two complexes are optical isomers.

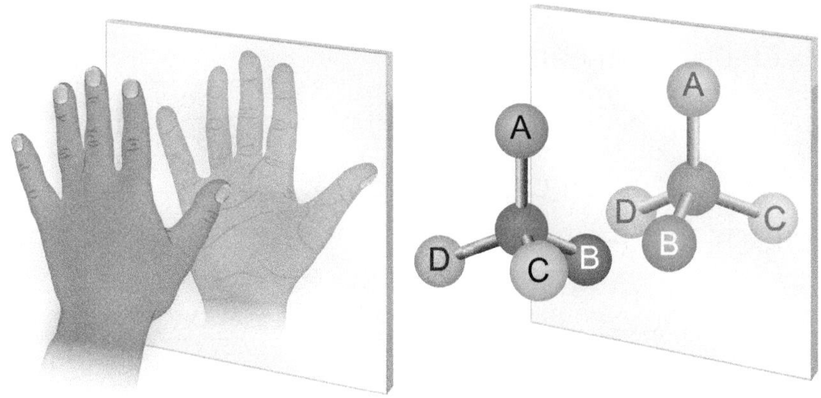

(a) (b)

FIGURE 21.15 Examples of Chiral Objects

(a) Your hands are nonsuperimposable mirror images of one another. (b) Two tetrahedral molecules that contain the same set of four unique groups are nonsuperimposable mirror images of one another.

Steve Lemon, Macmillan Learning

FIGURE 21.16 Video Tutorial: Isomers

NOTE: You need to be online to access this video.
This video shows how to recognize and classify isomers.

Compounds with carbon atoms that are bonded to four different groups can exist as optical isomers.

Figure 21.16 demonstrates how to recognize and classify isomers.

Example 21.12

Determine whether the following sets of molecules are structural isomers, cis–trans isomers, or the same molecule. If they appear to be the same molecule, can they exist as optical isomers?

a.

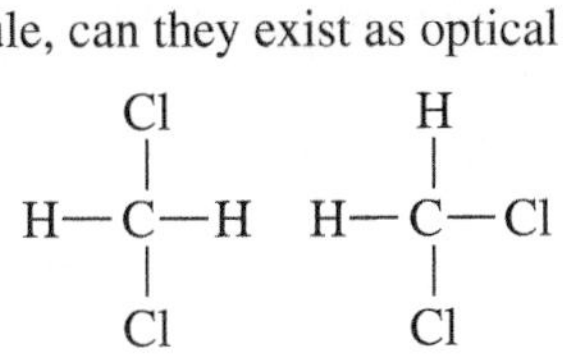

b.

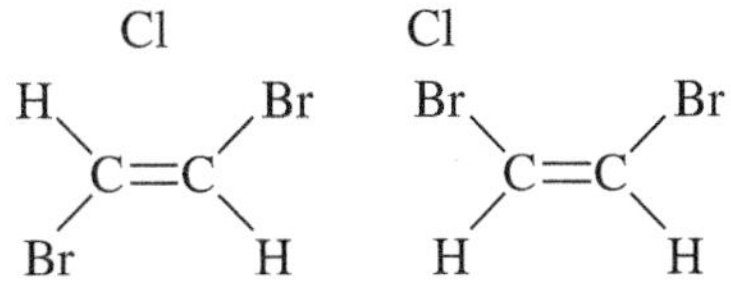

c.

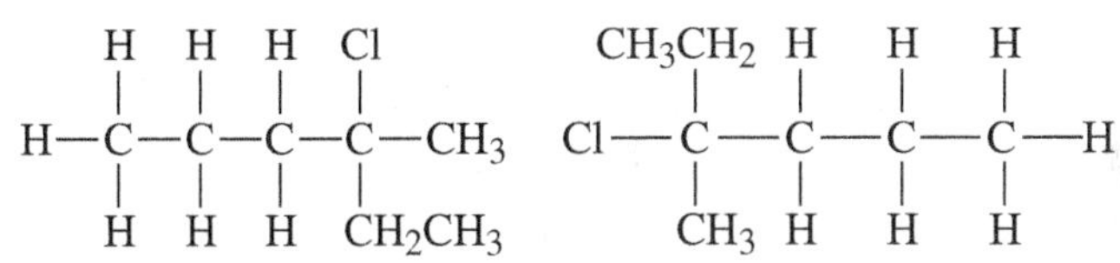

Solution

a. These two molecules are the same. They cannot exist as stereoisomers, though, because their central carbon atoms are only bonded to two different groups, not the four needed to exist as optical isomers. They are not cis–trans isomers, either, because no carbon–carbon double bond exists.

b. These two molecules are cis–trans isomers because the two bromo groups in each compound are on different sides of the carbon–carbon double bond. The compound on the left is the trans isomer, and the one on the right is the cis isomer.

c. These two molecules are the same. They *can* exist as optical isomers, though, because the carbon atoms circled in the following structures are bonded to four different groups: Cl, CH_3, CH_3CH_2, and $CH_3CH_2CH_2$:

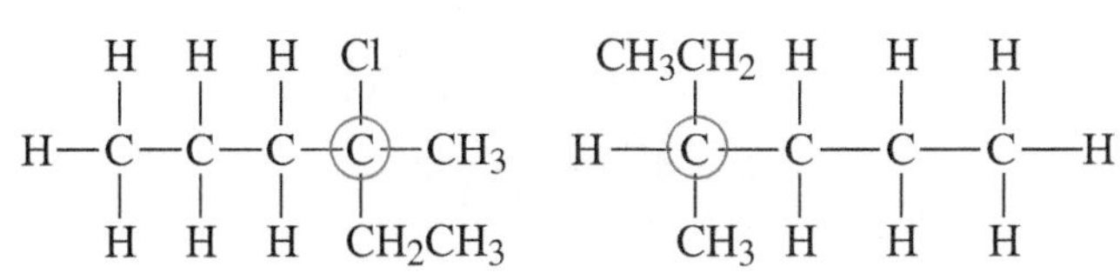

PRACTICE PROBLEM 21.12

Determine whether the following sets of molecules are structural isomers, cis–trans isomers, different molecules, or the same molecule. If they appear to be the same molecule, can they exist as optical isomers?

a. 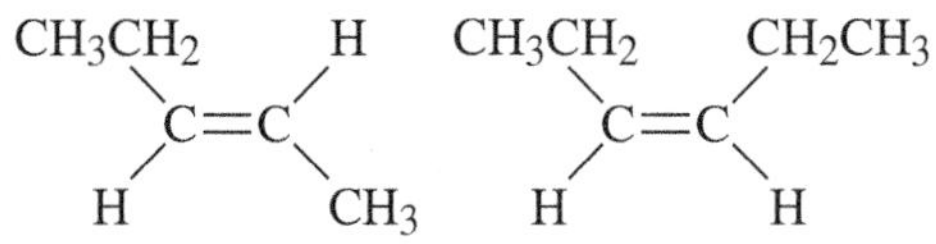

b. 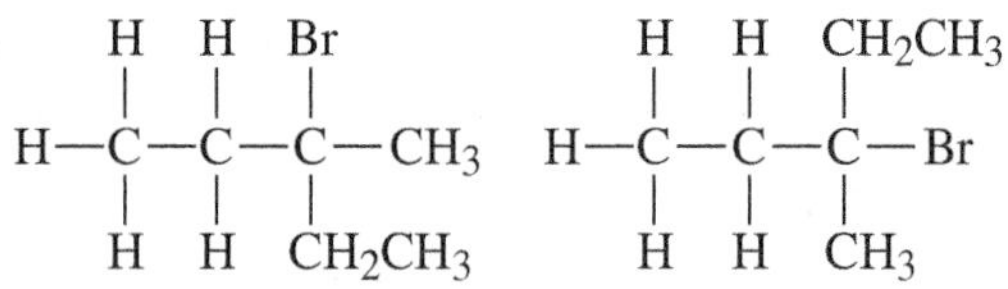

Hint: Structural isomers have the same molecular formulas but different atom connectivities. Cis–trans isomers have unique groups on different sides of the carbon–carbon double bond. Optical isomers are nonsuperimposable mirror images of one another and contain at least one carbon atom that is bonded to four different groups.

SECTION REVIEW

- Isomers are two or more compounds that have the same molecular formula but different arrangements of or connections between atoms.
- Structural isomers of hydrocarbons result from differences in the positions of carbon atoms, multiple bonds, or both. Structural isomers have the same molecular formulas but different names.
- Stereoisomers have the same molecular formulas and atom connectivities but a different spatial arrangement of atoms. Stereoisomers include cis–trans isomers and optical isomers.
- Cis–trans isomers have the same molecular formulas and connections between atoms, but the alkyl groups are on different sides of the carbon–carbon double bond. Cis–trans isomers have the same name except for the prefix *cis–* or *trans–*.
- Optical isomers are nonsuperimposable mirror images of one another. Compounds with at least one carbon atom that is bonded to four different groups can exist as optical isomers.

21.4 Organic Halides, Alcohols, Ethers, and Amines

GOAL

- Identify, name, and write formulas and reactions for organic halides, alcohols, ethers, and amines.

TABLE 21.5 The Total Bond Orders of Atoms in Uncharged Organic Molecules

Atom	Total Bond Order
C	4
H	1
O	2
S	2
N	3
P	3
X*	1

*X refers to any halogen atom: F, Cl, Br, or I.

A wide variety of organic compounds contain at least one other element in addition to carbon and hydrogen. Most of the other elements commonly found in organic compounds are nonmetals, such as oxygen, nitrogen, fluorine, chlorine, bromine, iodine, sulfur, and phosphorus. The total bond order (Section 11.5) of an atom is its number of bonding electron pairs (in effect, the bond order is also the number of bonds attached to an atom). Just as a hydrogen atom always shares one electron pair to form one covalent bond and a carbon atom shares four electron pairs in organic compounds (as four single bonds, two double bonds, two single bonds and one double bond, or one single bond and one triple bond), these other elements also have characteristic total bond orders in neutral molecules (Table 21.5). The carbon atoms in CH_3CH_3 and $CH_2{=}CH_2$ both have bond orders of four. In CH_3CH_3, each carbon atom has four single bonds. In $CH_2{=}CH_2$, each carbon atom has two single bonds and one double bond, for a total of four bonds. Knowing these characteristic total numbers of bonds is essential to interpreting condensed structural formulas correctly.

> Bond order is typically equal to the number of electrons an atom needs to gain to achieve a full valence shell. For most elements, the bond order is eight minus its valence number.

In organic structures, the lone-pair electrons on atoms that have a bond order of less than four (e.g., oxygen, sulfur, nitrogen, and phosphorus) are often omitted for the sake of simplicity. Keep in mind that they are still there, even if they are not shown.

Example 21.13

Complete the following structure by adding all necessary hydrogen atoms.

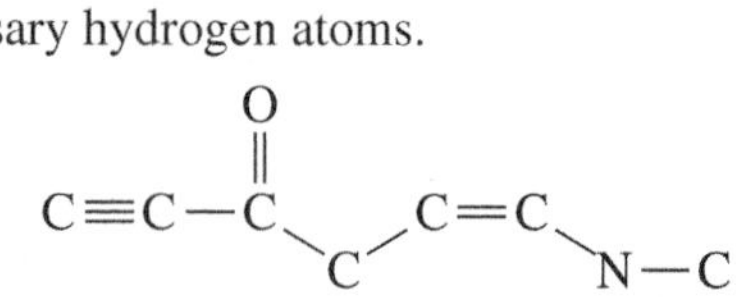

Solution

Carbon has a bond order of four, so each carbon atom must make four bonds to other atoms. For the carbon atoms that do not already contain four bonds, hydrogens are added to them to bring the total number of bonds to four. Oxygen has a bond order of two and, in the given structure, is already double-bonded to a carbon atom, so no hydrogens should be added. Nitrogen has a bond order of three and is bonded to only two other atoms here, so one hydrogen must be bonded to the nitrogen.

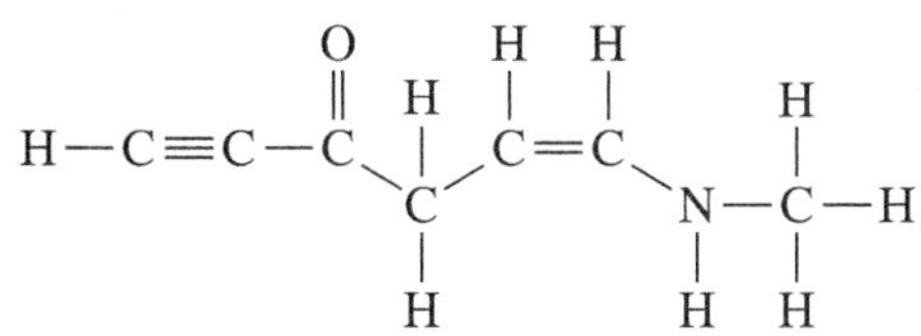

PRACTICE PROBLEM 21.13

Complete the following structure by adding all necessary hydrogen atoms.

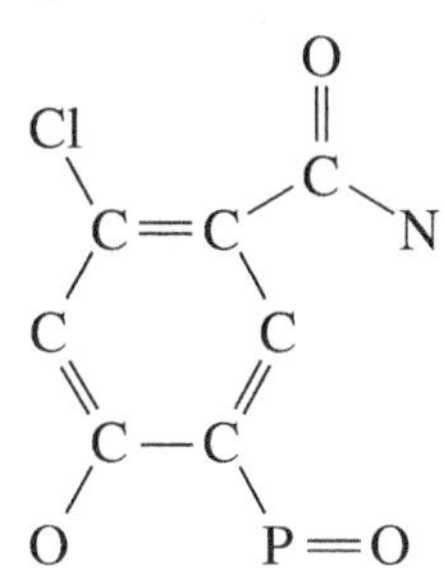

Hint: Consult Table 21.5 to determine the bond order of each element. If an atom in the given structure has fewer bonds than its bond order, add the appropriate number of hydrogen atoms.

FUNCTIONAL GROUPS

The **functional group** of a molecule is an atom or group of atoms that has characteristic physical and chemical properties. A functional group consists of a **heteroatom** (an atom other than carbon or hydrogen) and/or an unsaturated carbon atom (a carbon atom with a double or triple bond). Any hydrogen atoms attached to the heteroatom or unsaturated carbon atom are also considered part of the functional group. Because the alkane portion of a molecule is relatively unreactive, functional groups form the centers of reactions in molecules. The alkane portion is called an *alkyl group* and is often represented by the symbol R and referred to informally as an **R group**. The alkyl group is essentially the parent alkane with one hydrogen atom removed. The R group can be any number of carbon and hydrogen atoms in any arrangement, so a structural formula that contains an R group can actually represent hundreds or thousands of different compounds. If a molecule contains multiple R groups, they are often designated as R, R′, R″, and so on to indicate that they are not necessarily the same. For example, $CH_3OCH_2CH_3$ can be represented as R—O—R′, where R is CH_3— and R′ is $-CH_2CH_3$.

Organic molecules can be classified based on their functional groups. You have encountered two functional groups already—namely, the double and triple bond of alkenes and alkynes, respectively. When alkenes and alkynes react, the reactions take place at their functional groups (their double and triple bonds; Section 21.1), not at their R groups (the alkyl portions of the compounds).

Example 21.14

Identify the functional groups and R groups in these molecules.

a. CH_3-OH

b. $CH_2=CH-CH_3$

c. $CH_3-C(=O)-CH_3$

Solution

A functional group consists of a heteroatom (an atom other than carbon or hydrogen) and/or an unsaturated carbon atom (a carbon atom with a double or triple bond). Any hydrogen atoms attached to the heteroatom or unsaturated carbon atom are also considered part of the functional group. The rest of the molecule is the R group or groups. Recall that R groups are saturated hydrocarbon groups (consisting of only carbon and hydrogen, connected with only single bonds).

a. The —OH portion of the molecule is the functional group. The rest is the R group.

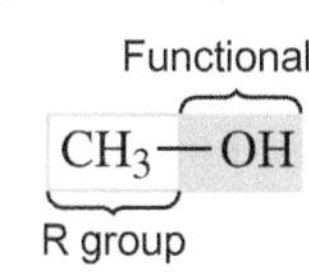

b. The unsaturated ($CH_2=CH-$) portion of the molecule is the functional group. The rest is the R group.

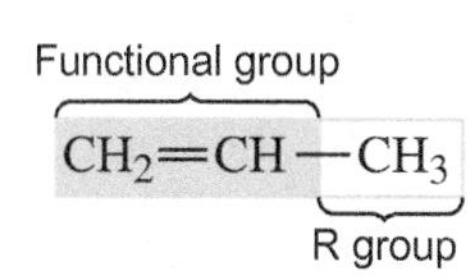

c. The portion of the molecule that contains the oxygen and the double-bonded carbon is the functional group. The other two portions are R groups.

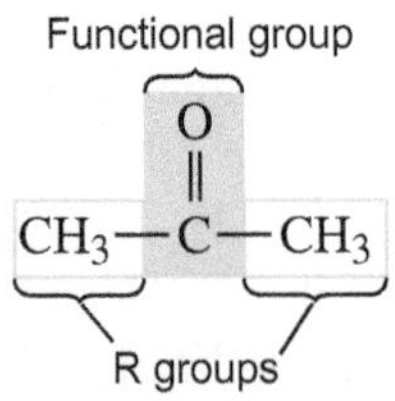

PRACTICE PROBLEM 21.14

Identify the functional groups and R groups in these molecules.

a. $CH_3—CH—C(=O)—OH$

b. $CH_3—CH_2—CH=CH—CH_2—C(=O)—OH$

c. $CH_3—CH_2—O—CH_2—CH_2—NH_2$

Hint: The functional groups contain atoms other than carbon and hydrogen, and/or multiple bonds to carbon. The R groups are the alkane portions of the molecule.

The subsections that follow briefly describe nine different classes of organic compounds: organic halides, alcohols, ethers, aldehydes, ketones, organic acids, esters, amines, and amides. A summary of the functional group for each class of compound, along with general formula and name, can be found in Table 21.7, presented later in the chapter.

ORGANIC HALIDES

An **organic halide** or alkyl halide is a hydrocarbon with at least one F, Cl, Br, or I substituent. The halogen atom is bonded with a single covalent bond to one carbon atom, as in CH_3Cl or CH_3CH_2Br.

When naming organic halides, the halide's *–ide* suffix is replaced with *–o*. For example, the name of the following compound is 2-chloropropane:

$$CH_3CHClCH_3$$

Organic halides can be produced by the reaction of an elemental halogen (X_2, where X = Cl, Br, or I) with a hydrocarbon or by the reaction of a hydrogen halide (HX) with an unsaturated hydrocarbon.

$$X_2 + CH_4 + \text{heat} \rightarrow CH_3X + HX \quad (X = Cl, Br, \text{ or } I)$$
$$HX + CH_2{=}CH_2 \rightarrow CH_3CH_2X$$

EVERYDAY CONNECTION

DDT is a chlorinated hydrocarbon that has had widespread success in controlling mosquitoes and preventing thousands of deaths from malaria. The insecticide is not easily decomposed in the environment, however, and finds its way into the food chain of higher animals, with harmful results. For this reason, its use has been banned in the United States.

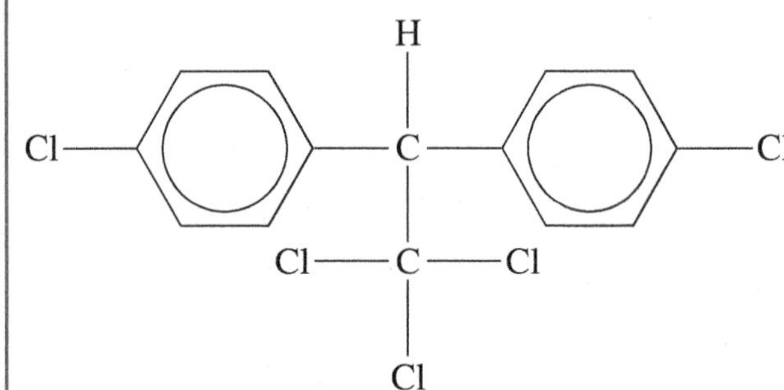

The official name of this compound is 1,1-di(4-chlorophenyl)-2,2,2-trichloroethane. This name uniquely describes its structure, including the position of each Cl. This name is so cumbersome, though, that it was informally referred to as *d*ichloro*d*iphenyl*t*richloroethane, and it is from this name that the abbreviation DDT is derived.

Reaction of excess halogen with an alkane can replace more than one hydrogen atom:

$$2\,X_2 + CH_4 \rightarrow CH_2X_2 + 2\,HX$$
$$3\,X_2 + CH_4 \rightarrow CHX_3 + 3\,HX$$
$$4\,X_2 + CH_4 \rightarrow CX_4 + 4\,HX$$

ALCOHOLS AND ETHERS

The —OH group, known as a hydroxyl group, consists of a hydrogen atom covalently bonded to an oxygen atom. The bond order of oxygen is two, so the oxygen of the —OH group can form one more bond. **Alcohols** are a class of organic compounds in which a hydroxyl group is bonded to a carbon atom. The simplest alcohol is methanol, CH_3OH. Alcohols can be formed by reacting alkenes with water (Section 21.1).

The —OH group does not ionize, and alcohols do not act as bases. In this way, the covalent hydroxyl group (—OH) is different from the ionic hydroxide anion (OH^-).

EVERYDAY CONNECTION

Chlorofluorocarbons (CFCs) are organic halides in which fluorine and chlorine atoms are substituted for all the hydrogen atoms of methane or ethane. An example is Freon 12, CCl_2F_2. CFCs were used as refrigerants for many years because they were relatively inert, they boiled in a suitable temperature range, and they had a relatively high heat of vaporization (Section 12.3). The CFC was allowed to evaporate in the coils in the inner part of the refrigerator, and the evaporation process absorbed thermal energy, resulting in cooling. The CFC was then pumped as a gas to coils outside the food compartment, where it was compressed back to the liquid state. The liquefaction gives off heat, which was discharged. The process was repeated continuously. The refrigeration process is an example of thermal energy being moved from a cold place to a warmer place. This is opposite of its spontaneous flow, so energy is required to accomplish this change.

The escape of CFCs into Earth's atmosphere has contributed to the destruction of the stratospheric ozone layer. For this reason, CFCs are no longer used in aerosol cans for spray paint, shaving cream, hairspray, and other products, and they have been phased out of refrigeration systems.

showcake/Shutterstock

The systematic name of an alcohol is formed from the name of the parent hydrocarbon by changing the suffix to *–ol*. Thus, CH_3CH_2OH is ethan*ol*, the alcohol in alcoholic beverages. When necessary, the position of the hydroxyl group is indicated with the lowest possible number (Figure 21.17).

An older naming system used the name of the alkyl group (the name of the parent hydrocarbon with the *–yl* suffix) plus the word *alcohol*. Thus, ethanol is also known as ethyl alcohol. 2-Propanol is also known informally as isopropyl alcohol (the alcohol in rubbing alcohol).

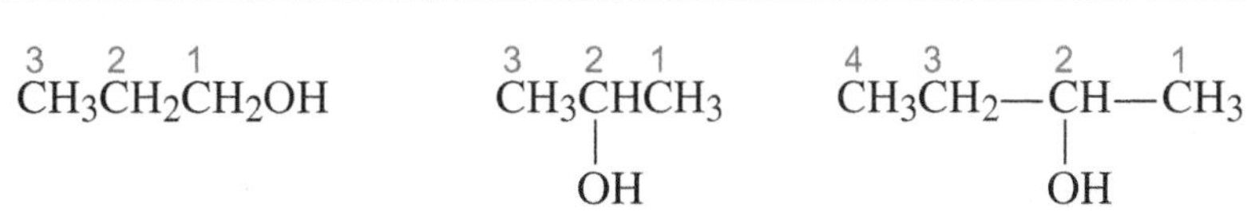

1-Propanol (a) | 2-Propanol (b) | 2-Butanol (c)

FIGURE 21.17 Naming Alcohols

Structure (a) is named 1-propanol, not 3-propanol, because the carbon chain should be numbered in the direction that gives the functional group the lower number. Structure (b) is 2-propanol no matter which direction the chain is numbered. Structure (c) is 2-butanol, not 3 butanol.

The general structure of an alcohol is ROH, where R represents the alkyl portion of the molecule and OH represents the hydroxyl group—the functional group. The alkyl portion of a molecule is not very reactive and the R groups of similar hydrocarbons have similar properties, so the characteristic properties of alcohols come from the —OH functional group. Methanol (CH_3OH) and 1-propanol ($CH_3CH_2CH_2OH$), for example, have chemical properties very similar to those of ethanol (CH_3CH_2OH).

Caution: The physiological effects of drinking ethanol are different from those of other alcohols. Ethanol should be consumed with caution, but the other alcohols are much more toxic and can cause blindness or death if ingested.

Most alcohols react in a similar way:

- Alcohols react with very active metals, such as sodium, to produce hydrogen and the corresponding organic salt.

$$2\,ROH(l) + 2\,Na(s) \rightarrow 2\,RONa(s) + H_2(g)$$

- Alcohols react when heated in the presence of a dehydrating agent, such as concentrated H_2SO_4, to produce ethers. **Ethers** are a class of organic compounds in which two R groups are connected by a central oxygen atom. The general structure of an ether is ROR, where the two R groups may be the same or different. The term *dehydrating agent* refers to the fact that water is a product of the reaction.

$$ROH + HOR \xrightarrow{H_2SO_4} ROR + H_2O$$

$$\underset{\text{Ethanol}}{CH_3CH_2OH} + \underset{\text{Ethanol}}{HOCH_2CH_3} \xrightarrow{H_2SO_4} \underset{\text{Ethoxyethane}}{CH_3CH_2OCH_2CH_3} + H_2O$$

If two different alcohols combine, a mixed ether is formed:

$$ROH + HOR' \xrightarrow{H_2SO_4} ROR' + H_2O$$

$$\underset{\text{Methanol}}{CH_3OH} + \underset{\text{Ethanol}}{HOCH_2CH_3} \xrightarrow{H_2SO_4} \underset{\text{Methoxyethane}}{CH_3OCH_2CH_3} + H_2O$$

Ethers are named by first identifying the shorter alkyl substituent and giving it an *–oxy* suffix. The longer alkyl substituent simply uses the alkane base name. Thus, $CH_3OCH_2CH_3$ is methoxyethane. An older naming system that is still frequently encountered uses the format *alkyl alkyl ether*. Using this system, methoxyethane would be called "ethyl methyl ether."

TABLE 21.6 Ether and Alcohol Isomers

Name	Molecular Formula	Condensed Structural Formula	Ball-and-Stick Model
Methoxymethane	C_2H_6O	CH_3OCH_3	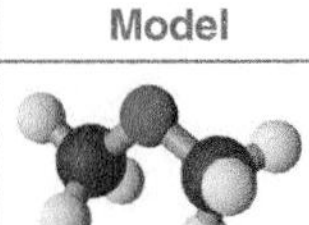
Ethanol	C_2H_6O	CH_3CH_2OH	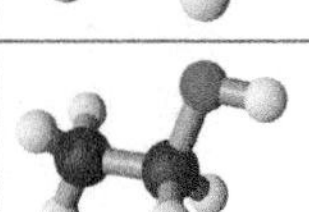

Ethers and alcohols, such as methoxymethane and ethanol, can be structural isomers of each other because both classes have the general molecular formula $C_nH_{2n+2}O$, as shown in Table 21.6.

Example 21.15

Give the structural formula and name of the organic compound formed by the following reaction:

$$CH_3CH_2OH(l) + HOCH_2CH_2CH_3(l) \xrightarrow{H_2SO_4} ?$$

Solution

In the presence of H_2SO_4, two alcohols react to form an ether and water.

$$\underset{\text{Ethanol}}{CH_3CH_2OH(l)} + \underset{\text{1-Propanol}}{HOCH_2CH_2CH_3(l)} \xrightarrow{H_2SO_4}$$

$$\underset{\text{Ethoxypropane}}{CH_3CH_2OCH_2CH_2CH_3(l)} + H_2O(l)$$

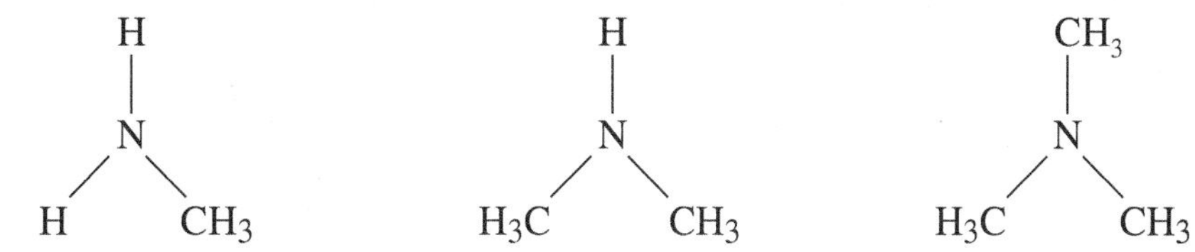

CH_3NH_2	$(CH_3)_2NH$	$(CH_3)_3N$
Methylamine	Dimethylamine	Trimethylamine
A primary amine	A secondary amine	A tertiary amine
(a)	(b)	(c)

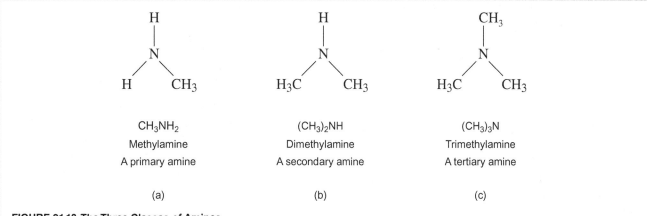

FIGURE 21.18 The Three Classes of Amines

(a) Primary amines have one alkyl group bonded to the nitrogen atom, (b) secondary amines have two alkyl groups bonded to the nitrogen, and (c) tertiary amines have three alkyl groups bonded to the nitrogen. Although the alkyl groups shown here are all the same, they need not be.

The ether formed in this reaction is ethoxypropane. The name of the smaller alkyl group (ethane) is given the *–oxy* suffix, and the name of the longer group (propane) is given the alkane base name.

PRACTICE PROBLEM 21.15

Give the condensed formula and name of the organic compound formed by the following reaction:

$$CH_3(CH_2)_3OH(l) + HO(CH_2)_3CH_3(l) \xrightarrow{H_2SO_4} ?$$

Hint: This reaction forms an ether and water. Ethers are named by first identifying the shorter alkyl substituent and giving it an *–oxy* suffix. The longer alkyl substituent simply uses the alkane base name.

AMINES

Amines are organic nitrogen compounds that can be formed by replacing one or more of the hydrogen atoms of ammonia (NH_3) with R groups. Replacing one H atom produces a *primary* amine, replacing two produces a *secondary* amine, and replacing all three produces a *tertiary* amine (Figure 21.18).

Like ammonia, amines act as weak bases in aqueous solution by removing H^+ from water, which produces OH^-.

$$CH_3NH_2(aq) + H_2O(l) \rightleftharpoons CH_3NH_3^+(aq) + OH^-(aq)$$

SECTION REVIEW

- Organic molecules are classified based on their functional groups.
- All of the compounds of a particular class react similarly because the functional group is the reactive portion of the compounds.
- The name of each type of organic molecule has a suffix, such as *–ane*, *–ene*, *–ol*, and so forth, which indicates what class of compound it belongs to.
- Organic halides are formed from the reactions of alkanes and alkenes with halogens.
- Ethers are formed from the reactions of two alcohols in the presence of an acid.
- Ethers are named by first identifying the shorter alkyl substituent and giving it an *–oxy* suffix. The longer alkyl substituent simply uses the alkane base name. The name of the ether is the combination of the alkoxy name and the alkane base name.
- Amines are nitrogen-containing organic compounds that act as weak bases.

21.5 Aldehydes, Ketones, Carboxylic Acids, Esters, and Amides

GOAL

- Identify, name, and write formulas and reactions for aldehydes, ketones, carboxylic acids, esters, and amides.

ALDEHYDES AND KETONES

The functional group of both aldehydes and ketones is the carbonyl group. A **carbonyl group** consists of a carbon atom double-bonded to an oxygen atom and single-bonded to two additional atoms:

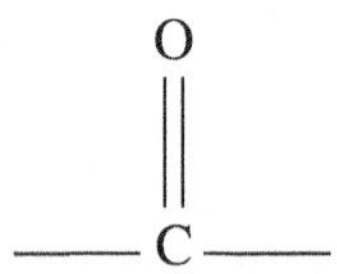

For an **aldehyde**, the two groups bonded to the carbon of the carbonyl group are a hydrocarbon (R) and H; for a **ketone**, the two groups (R and R′) are both hydrocarbons and are not necessarily the same.

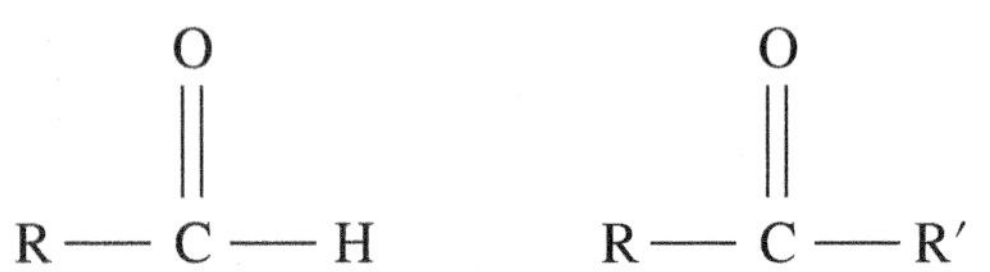

Aldehyde Ketone

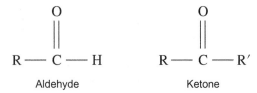

The systematic names of *al*dehydes end in *–al*, whereas the systematic names of ket*ones* end in *–one*. The simplest aldehyde—methanal (also known as formaldehyde)—was once routinely used as a preservative for biological specimens. The simplest ketone—propanone (known commonly as acetone)—is used as nail polish remover. When naming ketones, the carbon atom of the carbonyl group (C═O) should be given the lowest possible number. For aldehydes, the functional group is always located at carbon 1, so it does not need to be specified.

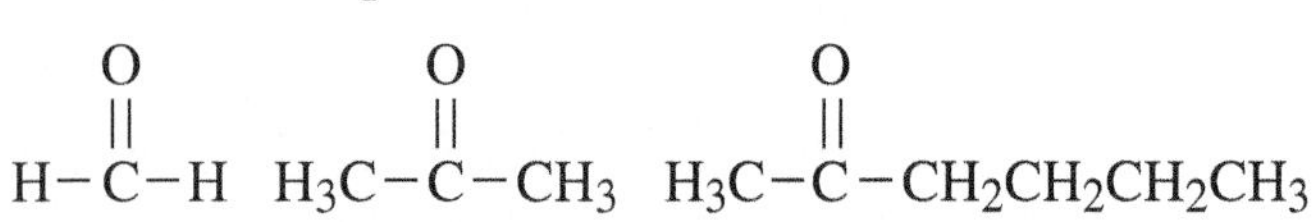

Methanal Propanone 2-Hexanone

Example 21.16

Name the following compounds.

a. 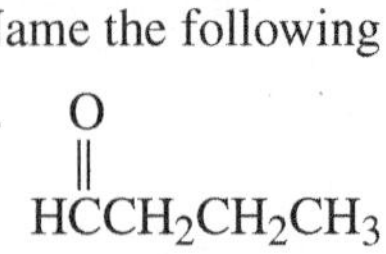

b. 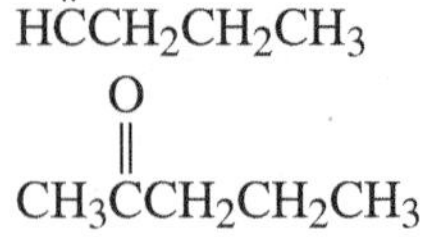

c. 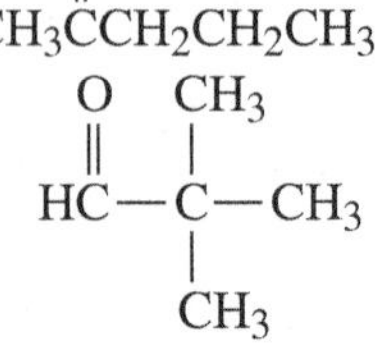

Solution

The compounds in parts (a) and (c) contain aldehyde functional groups (they have the general formula RCHO). The compound in part (b) contains a ketone group (RCOR′).

a. The parent hydrocarbon is butane, so the name of this aldehyde is butanal.
b. The parent hydrocarbon is pentane. The carbonyl group is on the second carbon atom, so the name of this ketone is 2-pentanone.
c. The longest continuous chain is propane, with two methyl groups on the second carbon atom. In other words, the parent hydrocarbon is 2,2-dimethylpropane. The name of this aldehyde is 2,2-dimethylpropanal.

PRACTICE PROBLEM 21.16

Name the following compounds.

a. 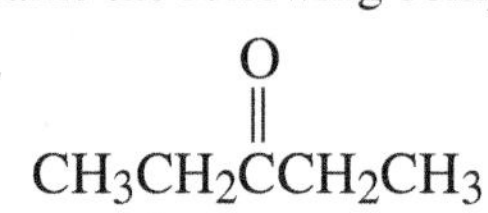

b. 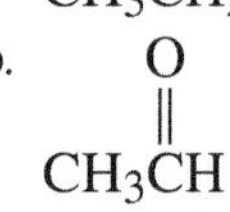

c. 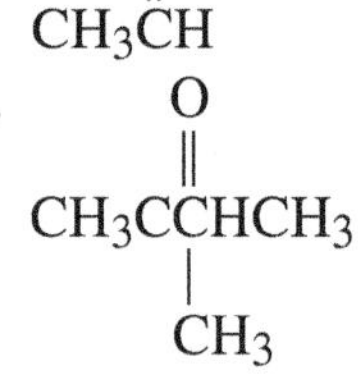

Hint: First, determine whether the compound is an aldehyde or a ketone. The systematic naming of an aldehyde is formed from the name of the parent hydrocarbon by changing the suffix to *–al*. The systematic name of a ketone is formed from the name of the parent hydrocarbon by changing the suffix to *–one*.

Aldehydes and ketones are produced by the mild oxidation of alcohols. The oxidation of organic compounds can be described either as increasing the number of carbon–oxygen bonds or as decreasing the number of carbon–hydrogen bonds (Figure 21.19). Reduction, then, increases the number of C—H bonds or decreases the number of C—O bonds.

When an alcohol is oxidized to an aldehyde or ketone, one carbon–oxygen double bond is formed, and one C—H bond is eliminated. If the —OH group of the alcohol is on a terminal carbon atom, in what is known as a *primary alcohol*, oxidation produces an aldehyde (Figure 21.19a). In the oxidation of a *secondary alcohol*, where the —OH group is attached to a carbon atom that is bonded to two other carbon atoms, a ketone is produced (Figure 21.19b). *Tertiary alcohols*, where the —OH group is attached to a carbon atom bonded to three other carbon atoms, *cannot* be oxidized to ketones (Figure 21.19c).

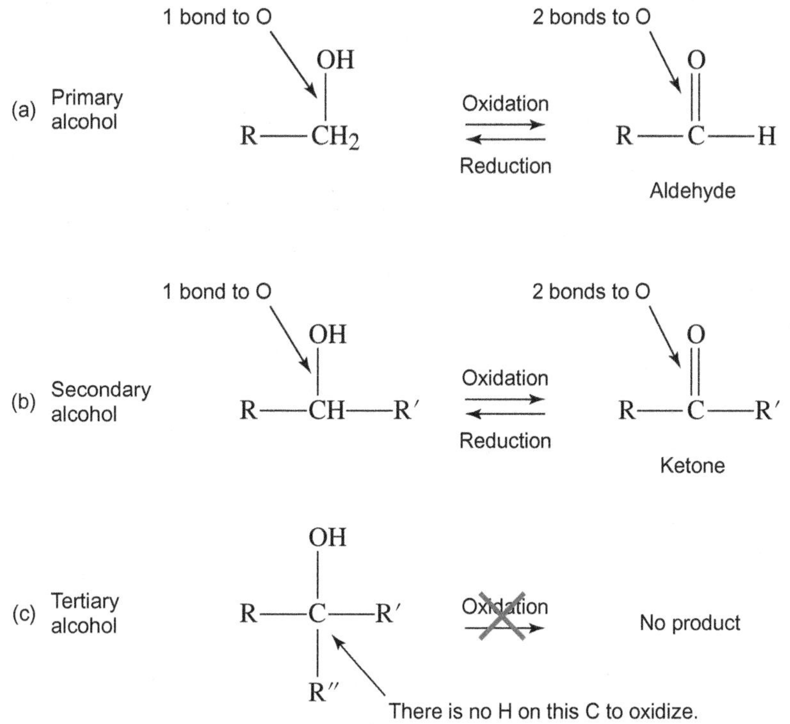

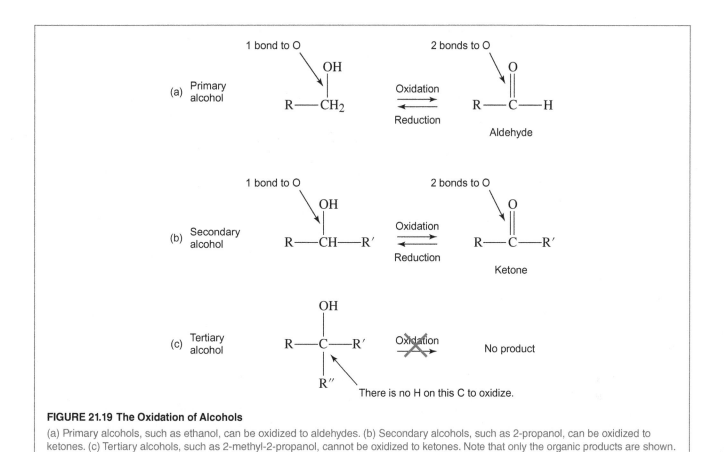

FIGURE 21.19 The Oxidation of Alcohols

(a) Primary alcohols, such as ethanol, can be oxidized to aldehydes. (b) Secondary alcohols, such as 2-propanol, can be oxidized to ketones. (c) Tertiary alcohols, such as 2-methyl-2-propanol, cannot be oxidized to ketones. Note that only the organic products are shown.

A primary alcohol can be oxidized to an aldehyde (Figure 21.19a) or to another class of compound known as a carboxylic acid with an oxidizing agent such as $Na_2Cr_2O_7$ in sulfuric acid.

$$\underset{\text{Alcohol}}{CH_3CH_2CH_2OH} \xrightarrow[Na_2Cr_2O_7]{H_2SO_4} \underset{\text{Aldehyde}}{CH_3CH_2COH} \xrightarrow[Na_2Cr_2O_7]{H_2SO_4} \underset{\text{Carboxylic acid}}{CH_3CH_2COOH}$$

The oxidation stops at the aldehyde stage if an excess of alcohol is used and if the aldehyde product is removed from the reaction mixture as it is formed. If an excess of $Na_2Cr_2O_7$ is used, however, then the primary alcohol is oxidized to the aldehyde and the aldehyde is further oxidized to the carboxylic acid.

CARBOXYLIC ACIDS AND ESTERS

A **carboxylic acid**, also known as an organic acid, has the functional group —COOH:

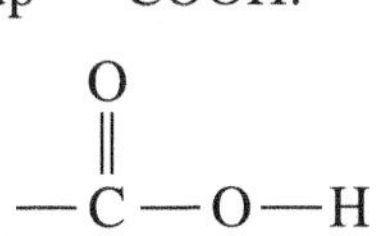

The —OH group in a carboxylic acid ionizes to give H^+ in aqueous solution, *not* OH^-. Although the ionizable hydrogen atom (Section 3.5 and Section 16.8) of an organic acid is part of an —OH group, the —COOH group in a carboxylic acid is a separate functional group from an alcohol (—OH) or a carbonyl (C=O), and it is different from a hydroxide ion (OH^-), which is a base. The —COOH group contains a carbon atom double-bonded to one oxygen atom and single-bonded to another oxygen atom.

> Molecules with covalently bonded —OH groups, such as alcohols and carboxylic acids, are *not* bases.

The systematic name of a carboxylic acid replaces the *–ane* suffix of the parent alkane (Table 21.2) with *–oic acid.* For example, a carboxylic acid that contains one carbon atom is *methanoic acid*, and one that contains five carbon atoms is *pentanoic acid.* Like aldehydes, the carbon atom that is part of the carboxylic acid functional group is on the end of the molecule and is always carbon 1. As a result, the position of the carboxylic acid functional group does not have to be specified when naming the molecule.

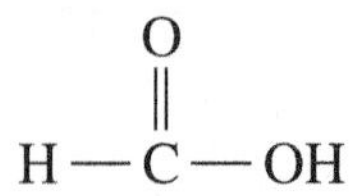

Methanoic acid

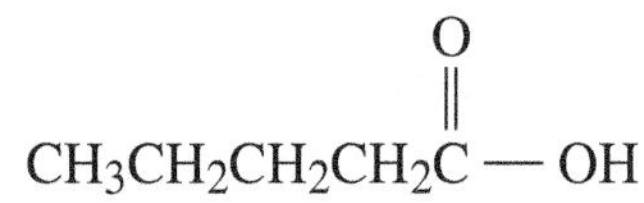

Pentanoic acid

Example 21.17

Draw condensed structural formulas for the following:

a. heptanoic acid
b. 5-methyloctanoic acid

Solution

a. Heptanoic acid contains a linear chain of seven carbon atoms:

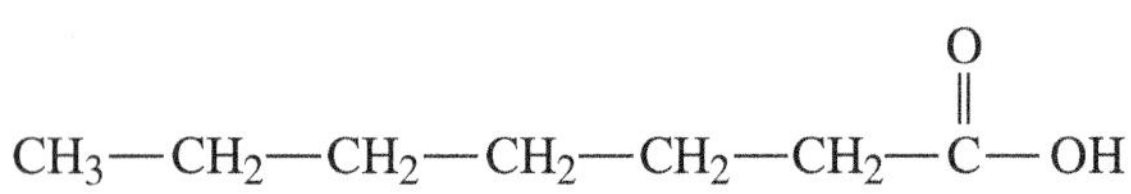

Heptanoic acid

b. The longest continuous chain in octanoic acid is eight carbon atoms. Number the chain to place the carboxylic acid functional group at carbon 1 (the lowest possible number). Place a methyl group on carbon 5:

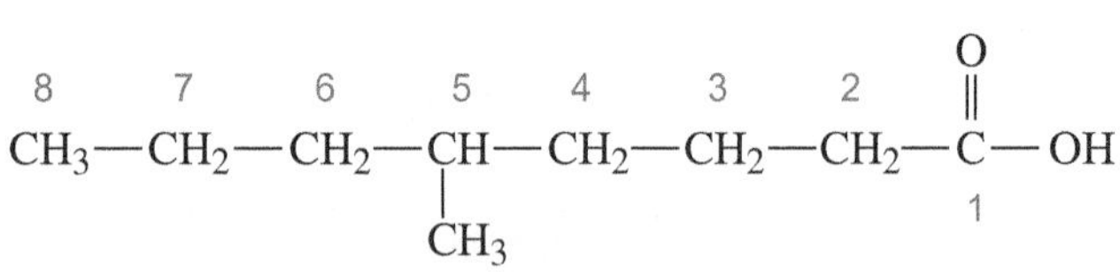

5-Methyloctanoic acid

PRACTICE PROBLEM 21.17

Name the following carboxylic acids.

a.

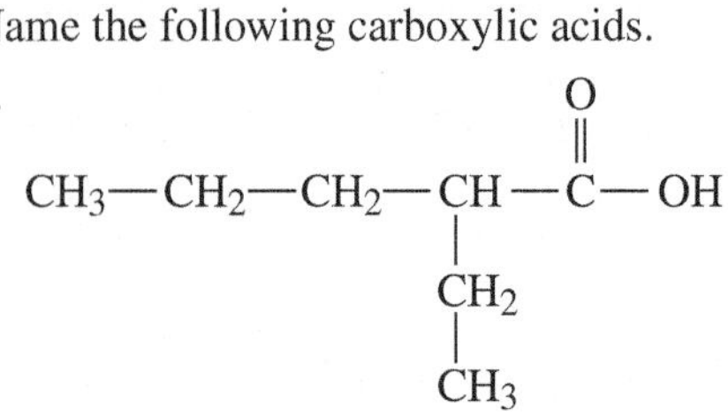

b.

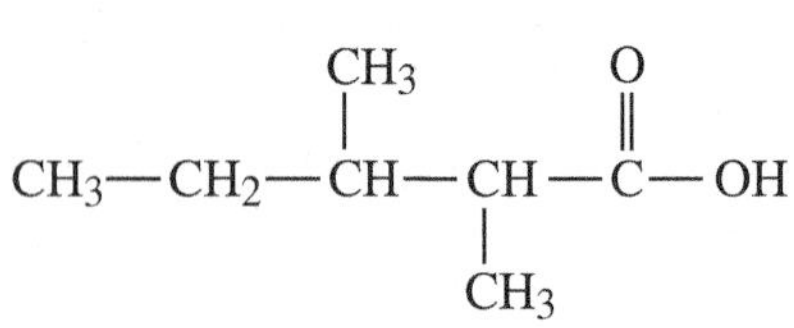

Hint: The systematic name of a carboxylic acid replaces the *–ane* suffix of the parent alkane (Table 21.2) with *–oic acid*. The longest continuous chain of carbon atoms should be numbered so that the carbon atom of the carboxylic acid functional group is carbon 1 (the lowest possible number).

The hydrogen atom of the carboxylic acid functional group ionizes to a slight extent in water, so carboxylic acids are weak acids (Chapter 16). The ionizable hydrogen is not necessarily written first in formulas for organic acids, and writing hydrogen first in organic compounds does not necessarily indicate that the compound is an acid. Ethanoic acid (also called acetic acid), which is denoted by $HC_2H_3O_2$ in previous chapters of this book, has the following structural and condensed structural formulas:

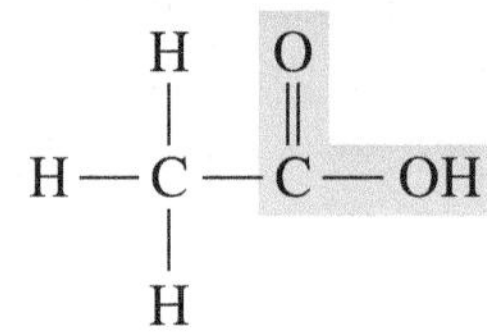

CH_3COOH

Throughout most of this text, acetic acid is written as $HC_2H_3O_2$ to emphasize that it is an acid, but in an organic chemistry context, it is frequently written as CH_3COOH to emphasize its carboxylic acid functional group.

Acetic acid is the most abundant acid in vinegar. Its equilibrium reaction with water can be written as follows (Chapter 16):

$$CH_3COOH(aq) + H_2O(l) \rightleftharpoons CH_3COO^-(aq) + H_3O^+(aq)$$

The resulting anion (i.e., the conjugate base) is CH_3COO^-, the acetate ion. Previously in this text it has been written using its molecular formula, $C_2H_3O_2^-$. In organic chemistry, though, it is more common to use its condensed structural formula, CH_3COO^-.

Organic acids react with alcohols to produce *esters* and water:

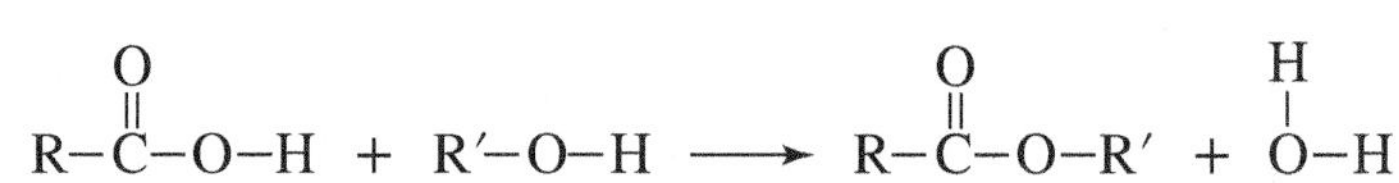

Acid Alcohol Ester Water

This is known as a **condensation reaction**. In a condensation reaction, two or more organic molecules form a covalent bond and release a small molecule such as water. The functional group of an **ester** is related to that of the carboxylic acid, with the hydrogen atom replaced by a carbon atom:

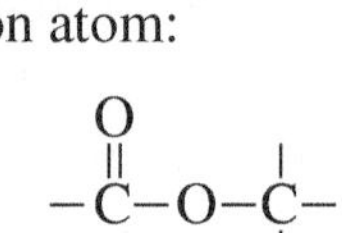

The name of an ester is a combination of the name of the hydrocarbon group of the alcohol plus the name of the parent acid with its suffix changed to *–oate.* The ester of *methanol* and *ethanoic acid* is *methyl ethanoate.*

> Ethanoic acid is also called acetic acid, so another name for methyl ethanoate is methyl acetate.

Many simple esters have pleasant odors. Ethyl acetate is used to provide an odor to artificial fruits, as a solvent for lacquers and varnishes, and as the solvent in nonacetone nail polish remover, among other uses. Many esters occur naturally; their sweet odors are responsible for the fragrances of flowers and fruits. Esters, especially those containing more than one ester linkage in a molecule, are components of many polymers (Section 21.6).

Figure 21.20 demonstrates how to draw and name the product of a condensation reaction between a carboxylic acid and an alcohol.

FIGURE 21.20 Video Tutorial: Ester Formation

NOTE: You need to be online to access this video.
This video shows how to draw and name the product of the reaction of a carboxylic acid with an alcohol.

Example 21.18

Use condensed structural formulas to write an equation for the reaction of 1-propanol with acetic acid. Name the products.

Solution

The structure of acetic acid (ethanoic acid) consists of two carbon atoms, and 1-propanol contains three carbon atoms. A carboxylic acid reacts with an alcohol to form an ester and water. The name of the compound is a combination of the name of the hydrocarbon group of the alcohol (propyl) plus the name of the parent acid (ethanoic) with its suffix changed to *–oate.*

$$\underset{\text{Ethanoic acid (acetic acid)}}{CH_3\overset{O}{\overset{\|}{C}}-OH} + \underset{\text{1-Propanol}}{HO-CH_2CH_2CH_3} \rightleftharpoons \underset{\text{Propyl ethanoate (propyl acetate)}}{CH_3\overset{O}{\overset{\|}{C}}-OCH_2CH_2CH_3} + H_2O$$

This equation is written with equilibrium arrows because it does not go to completion unless the water is removed as it is formed (Le Châtelier's principle, Section 15.6).

PRACTICE PROBLEM 21.18

Write an equation for the reaction of ethanol with butanoic acid, and name the products.

Hint: A carboxylic acid (butanoic acid) reacts with an alcohol (ethanol) to form an ester and water. The name of the ester is a combination of the name of the hydrocarbon group of the alcohol (ethyl) plus the name of the parent acid (butanoic) with its suffix changed to *–oate.*

AMIDES

When amines (Section 21.4) are not in aqueous solution, they can react with carboxylic acids to produce another class of organic compounds called **amides**. Amides are formed by the reaction of organic acids with ammonia or primary or secondary amines:

$$\underset{\text{Acid}}{R-\overset{O}{\overset{\|}{C}}-OH} + \underset{\text{Amine}}{H-\overset{R''}{\overset{|}{N}}-R'} \longrightarrow \underset{\text{Amide}}{R-\overset{O}{\overset{\|}{C}}-\overset{R''}{\overset{|}{N}}-R'} + H_2O$$

Like ester formation from a carboxylic acid and an alcohol, amide formation from a carboxylic acid and an amine is also a condensation reaction where water is produced. Here R, R', and R''' on the amide represent alkyl groups that may or may not be the same; any or all of them can be hydrogen atoms instead. Unlike the product of the reaction of an acid and a base, an amide is covalently bonded and is therefore not categorized as a salt. If the reaction conditions are changed, the reverse reaction, known as hydrolysis, can occur. The functional group that characterizes an amide is

$$-\overset{O}{\overset{\|}{C}}-\overset{|}{N}-$$

EVERYDAY CONNECTION

Salicylic acid, obtained from willow bark, has been used since the fifth century BCE to reduce pain and fever. Unfortunately, its acidity irritates the mouth, esophagus, and stomach. Conversion of the alcohol group of salicylic acid to an ester results in acetylsalicylic acid, which proved to be less acidic and irritable. Acetylsalicylic acid is widely known today as aspirin. *Click on the structure to open a three-dimensional view of an aspirin molecule.*

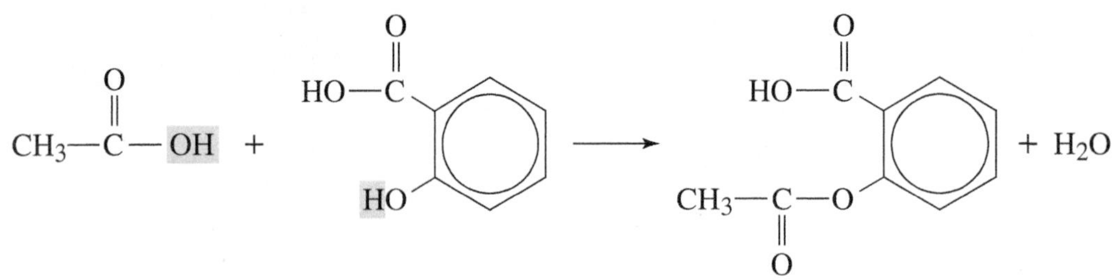

Acetic acid Salicylic acid Acetylsalicylic acid (aspirin)

The first synthesis of aspirin is often credited to German chemist Felix Hoffman (1868–1946) in 1897, though his former colleague Arthur Eichengrün has claimed that the work was done under his instruction.

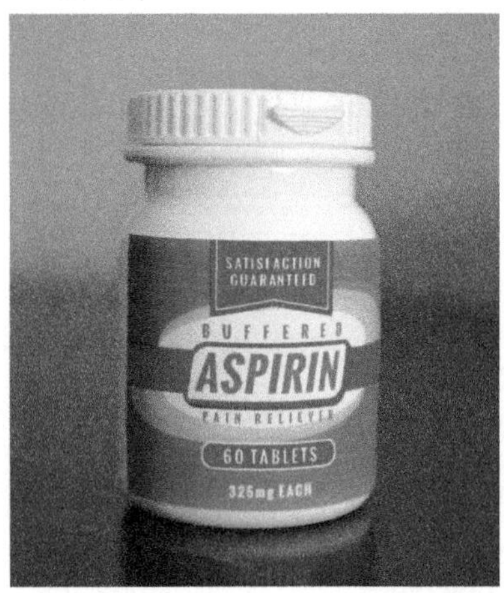

Thomas Turner, Macmillan Learning

Amides are named from the acid and amine from which they are prepared, similarly to esters. The characteristic name suffix is *–amide*, which replaces the *–oic acid* of the parent acid:

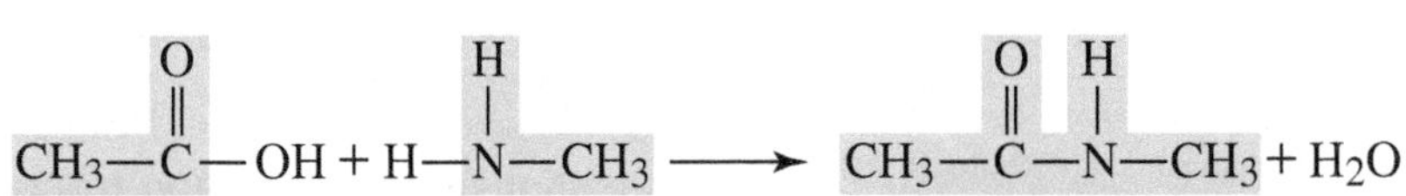

Ethanoic acid Methyl amine Methyl ethanamide

The classes of organic compounds introduced in Section 21.4 and Section 21.5 are summarized in Table 21.7.

SECTION REVIEW

- Aldehydes are formed from the oxidation of primary alcohols, while ketones are formed from the oxidation of secondary alcohols. The oxidation of tertiary alcohols does not form either an aldehyde or a ketone.
- The naming of aldehydes uses the suffix *–al*, and the naming of ketones uses the suffix *–one*.
- Carboxylic acids can be formed by the reaction of primary alcohols with excess oxidizing agent. When naming carboxylic acids, the suffix *–oic acid* is used.
- Esters are formed by the condensation reaction of carboxylic acids with alcohols. The name of an ester is a combination of the name of the

TABLE 21.7 Classes of Organic Compounds

Class	Functional Group	General Formula*	Suffix for Name	Example
Organic halides	—X	RX	*-o*	CH_3Cl, chloromethane
Alcohols	—OH	ROH	*-ol*	CH_3CH_2OH, ethanol (ethyl alcohol)
Ethers	—O—	ROR′	*-oxy*	CH_3OCH_3, methoxymethane (dimethyl ether)
Aldehydes	$-\underset{\substack{\vert \\ H}}{C}=O$	RCHO	*-al*	CH_3CHO, ethanal
Ketones	$-\underset{\vert}{C}=O$	$R\underset{\substack{\vert \\ R'}}{C}=O$	*-one*	CH_3COCH_3, propanone (acetone)
Organic acids	$-\underset{\substack{\Vert \\ O}}{C}-OH$	$R\underset{\substack{\Vert \\ O}}{C}-OH$	*-oic acid*	CH_3COOH, ethanoic acid (acetic acid)
Esters	$-\underset{\substack{\Vert \\ O}}{C}-O-$	$R\underset{\substack{\Vert \\ O}}{C}=O-R'$	*-oate*	$CH_3\underset{\substack{\Vert \\ O}}{C}-OCH_3$ methyl ethanoate (methyl acetate)
Amines	$-NH_2$	RNH_2	amine	CH_3NH_2, methylamine
Amides	$-\underset{\substack{\Vert \\ O}}{C}-N-$	$R\underset{\substack{\Vert \\ O}}{C}-\underset{\substack{\vert \\ R''}}{N}-R'$	amide	$CH_3\underset{\substack{\Vert \\ O}}{C}=NHCH_3$ methyl ethanamide

*The groups designated R, R′, and R″ may or may not be the same.

hydrocarbon group of the alcohol plus the name of the parent acid with its suffix changed to *–ate*.

- Amides are formed by the condensation reaction of carboxylic acids with amines (Section 21.4).

21.6 Polymers

GOALS

- Write equations for the formation of polymers.
- Describe the properties of the compounds polymers comprise.

Common polymers consist of plastics and **synthetic fibers**, such as Teflon, polyethylene, nylon, and polyester. Two main types of polymerization reactions are discussed in this section: condensation polymerization and addition polymerization.

In the condensation reactions that form esters and amides (Section 21.5), two organic molecules (each containing one functional group) combine to form a new molecule whose size is approximately that of the two reacting molecules combined (minus the small molecule, H_2O, that is expelled). What happens, then, if an organic molecule has two functional groups that can react with each other? It turns out that each functional group acts more or less independently of the other. For example, when $NH_2(CH_2)_6NH_2$, which has an amine functional group on each end, reacts with $HOCO(CH_2)_4COOH$, which has an organic acid functional group on each end, the amines react with the organic acids to form amides (Section 21.5):

$$NH_2(CH_2)_6NH_2 + HO-\underset{\substack{\Vert \\ O}}{C}-(CH_2)_4-\underset{\substack{\Vert \\ O}}{C}-OH + NH_2(CH_2)_6NH_2 + HO-\underset{\substack{\Vert \\ O}}{C}-(CH_2)_4-\underset{\substack{\Vert \\ O}}{C}-OH \longrightarrow$$

$$-\!\!\left[NH_2(CH_2)_6NHCO(CH_2)_4CONH(CH_2)_6NHCO(CH_2)_4CO\right]_n\!\!- \quad + 2n\ H_2O$$

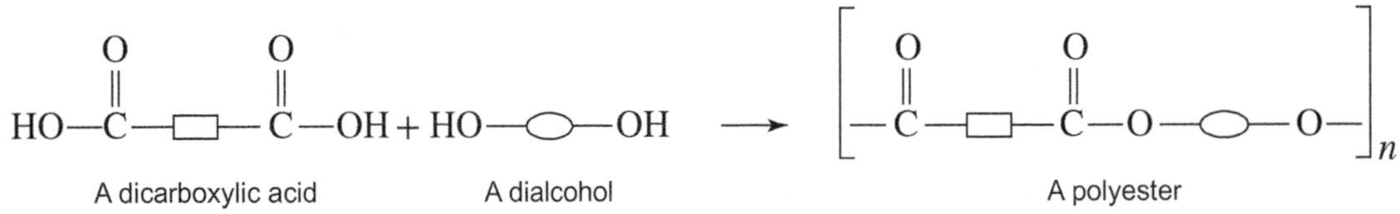

FIGURE 21.21 Polyester Formation

Polyesters are formed via numerous condensation reactions between dicarboxylic acids and dialcohols. The number of condensation reactions is represented by the *n* subscript in the polyester structure.

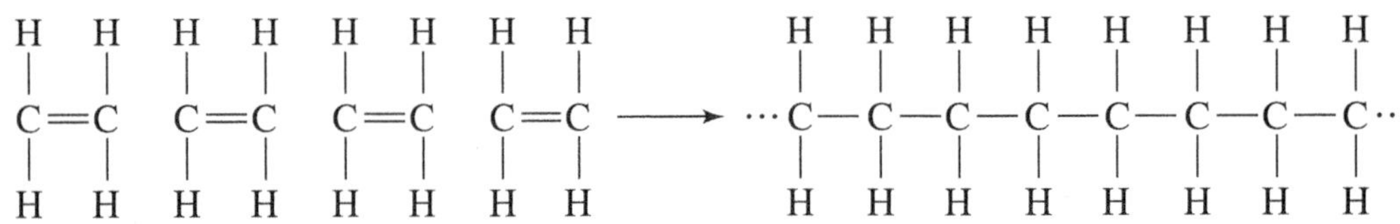

FIGURE 21.22 Polyethylene Formation

Polyethylene is formed via the addition polymerization of ethene (ethylene) molecules.

The product of this reaction still has functional groups on both ends and is capable of further reaction, which leads to an even larger molecule. This kind of reaction can continue until the supply of reactant molecules, called **monomers**, is exhausted. The large molecule that is the product of such a reaction is called a **polymer** (from the Greek words *poly*, meaning "many," and *mer*, meaning "parts"). A polymer can have a molecular mass of hundreds of thousands of atomic mass units (u) or even more. The polymer formed in the preceding reaction is called **nylon**. In the image, the squiggled lines on each end of the molecule represent the units that continue to repeat themselves at either end of the central group. The formation of nylon is an example of a **condensation polymerization**.

A polymerization reaction similar to the one that forms nylon can take place between molecules containing two organic acid groups (a dicarboxylic acid) and molecules containing two alcohol groups (a dialcohol). The product that results is a **polyester**, which is widely used in clothing manufacturing (Figure 21.21). The oval and rectangular shapes depicted in these molecules represent R groups that can be the same but in practice are usually different. This is another condensation reaction, where water is formed as a by-product.

The portion of the polyester molecule that is in square brackets is the repeating unit of the polyester. Each unit can be considered to be one link in a chain that is *n* links long.

The polymerization reactions described so far are examples of condensation reactions. The other type of polymerization discussed here is **addition polymerization**, where the monomer molecules add together by shifting electrons from their double bonds to form new carbon–carbon single bonds. An example of addition polymerization is the formation of polyethylene from ethene (also known as ethylene; Figure 21.22).

In this polymerization process, hundreds or thousands of ethylene molecules combine to form one large polymer molecule. Several commercial polymers that form by addition polymerization are listed in Table 21.8. Notice that all of the monomers contain a C=C double bond. In fluorinated polymers, such as Teflon, the fluorine atoms in place of all the hydrogen

TABLE 21.8 Commercial Polymers Formed by Addition Polymerization

Name* and Formula of Monomer	Polymer	Common Uses
Ethylene $CH_2{=}CH_2$	Polyethylene	Milk jugs, trash bags
Propylene $CH_3CH{=}CH_2$	Polypropylene	Plastic bins, heat-resistant plastics
Vinyl chloride $CH_2{=}CHCl$	Polyvinylchloride (PVC)	Raincoats, bottles, pipes
Styrene $C_6H_5CH{=}CH_2$	Polystyrene	Styrofoam, molded plastic insulation
Tetrafluoroethylene $CF_2{=}CF_2$	Polytetrafluoroethylene (PTFE), Teflon	Chemical- and heat-resistant plastics

*In industry, the common names of these monomers are often used instead of their systematic names.

atoms makes the polymer nonflammable and much more resistant to oxidation and thermal decomposition, which is why Teflon is used in nonstick cookware.

Example 21.19

The polymer polyvinyl acetate is formed by addition polymerization.

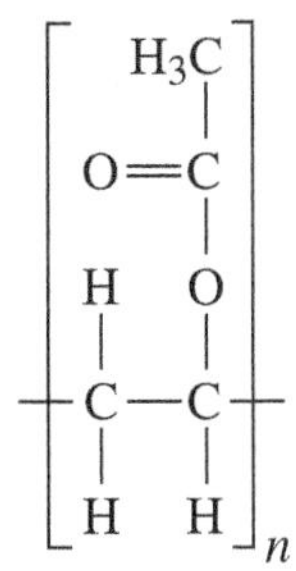

Draw the structure of the monomer used to prepare polyvinyl acetate.

Solution

Polyvinyl acetate is an addition polymer that is formed in an analogous manner to polyethylene. Thus, the monomer must contain a C=C double bond.

Hint: In a condensation reaction, water is released. Remove —H from one molecule and —OH from the other to form water, then combine the remaining structures to form the polymer.

SECTION REVIEW

- The reactions of one or more functional groups on small monomer molecules can yield very long-chain products called polymers. Polymers can consist of tens to hundreds of thousands of monomer units.

PRACTICE PROBLEM 21.19

If one hydrogen atom on ethylene is replaced with a $-CH_3$ group, what is the name of the polymer that results from the addition polymerization of this new monomer?

Hint: Determine the structure of the new monomer. It must be similar to ethylene, but with a $-CH_3$ group in place of a hydrogen atom.

Example 21.20

Use the structure of vinyl chloride (Table 21.8) to draw one repeat unit of polyvinyl chloride (PVC), which is formed by addition polymerization.

Solution

Polyvinyl chloride is formed by addition polymerization, which means that the C=C double bond in the monomer becomes a C—C single bond, allowing each of those C atoms to bond with another monomer unit.

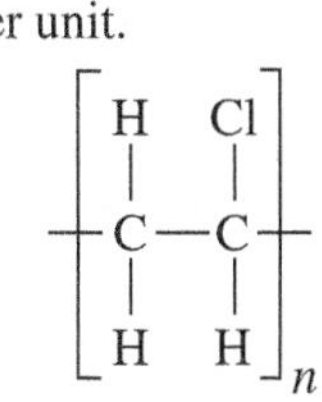

PRACTICE PROBLEM 21.20

PET polyester (polyethylene terephthalate) is formed by the condensation polymerization of the monomers terephthalic acid and ethylene glycol. Draw one repeating unit of PET polyester.

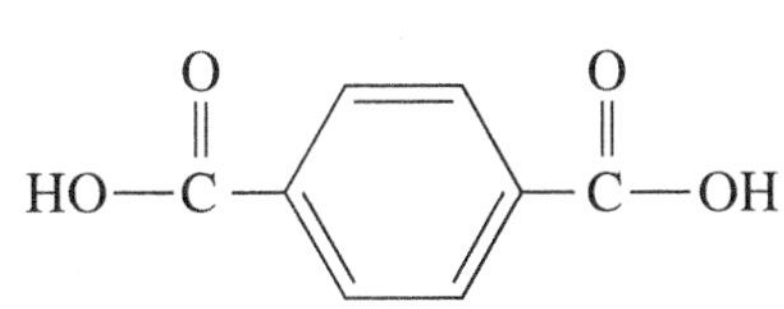

Terephthalic acid

$$HO-CH_2-CH_2-OH$$

Ethylene glycol

- The two main classes of polymers are those formed by condensation reactions and those formed by addition reactions.

Putting It Together

The example problems in earlier sections of this chapter focus on the new skills acquired in that section, but homework and exam questions in chemistry often require more than just one skill at a time. In fact, you will likely be expected to apply knowledge from throughout the chapter, or even multiple chapters in a single problem. This final example problem is meant to help you prepare for these types of multi-concept questions. Additional examples can be found in the end of chapter exercises.

Example 21.21

a. Name the following compound: $CH_3CH_2CH_2—OH$.

b. An excess of the compound in part (a) reacts with $Na_2Cr_2O_7$, and the product is removed from the reaction mixture as it is formed. Draw the condensed structural formula of the product, and give its name.

c. The compound in part (a) reacts with an excess of $Na_2Cr_2O_7$. Draw the condensed structural formula of the product, and give its name.

d. The compound in part (a) is a primary alcohol. Draw the condensed structural formula of a structural isomer of this compound that is a secondary alcohol. What is the name of this isomer?

e. The compound in part (d) reacts with $Na_2Cr_2O_7$. Draw the condensed structural formula of the product, and give its name.

Solution

a. The —OH group means this compound is an alcohol (its name will have the suffix *–ol*). The longest continuous chain that contains the —OH group has three carbons, so this compound has a propane backbone. Numbering the chain to give the carbon attached to the —OH group the lowest possible number places the functional group on carbon 1. The name of the compound is 1-propanol.

b. 1-Propanol is a primary alcohol. When an excess of a primary alcohol reacts with a limiting amount of $Na_2Cr_2O_7$ and the product is removed from the reaction as it is formed, the —OH group of the alcohol is oxidized to an aldehyde (RCHO).

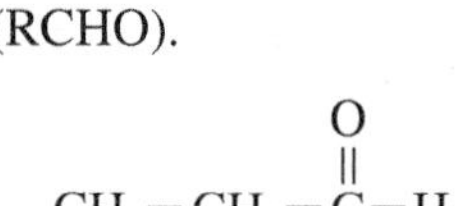

The name of this compound is similar to that of the alcohol, but the *–ol* suffix is replaced with *–al*. The name is propanal.

c. When a primary alcohol reacts with an excess of $Na_2Cr_2O_7$, an aldehyde forms initially, but it is immediately oxidized further to a carboxylic acid.

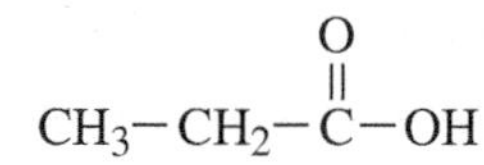

The name of this compound is similar to that of the alcohol, but the *–ol* suffix is replaced with *–oic acid*. The name is propanoic acid.

d. The structural isomer of 1-propanol is 2-propanol, a secondary alcohol:

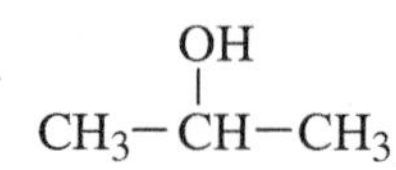

e. Secondary alcohols react with $Na_2Cr_2O_7$ to give ketones:

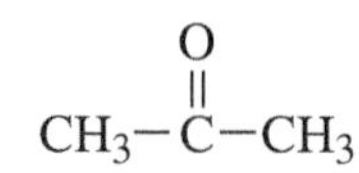

The name of this compound is similar to that of 2-propanol, but the *–ol* suffix is replaced with *–one*. The name is propanone. No number identifying the location of the carbonyl carbon is needed because carbon 2 is the only place it can appear in a three-carbon ketone.

PRACTICE PROBLEM 21.21

Use the following hydrocarbon to solve parts (a)–(f).

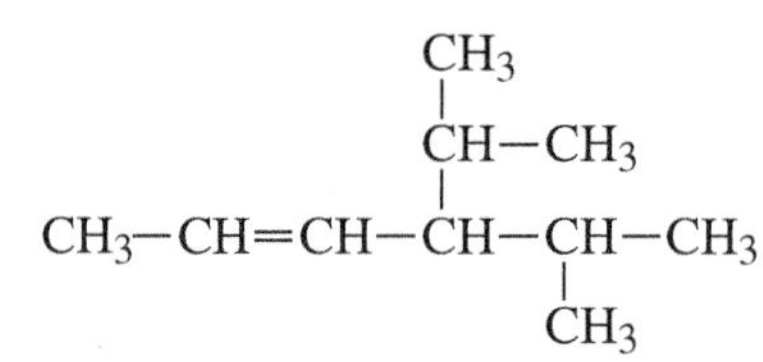

a. Name this compound.

b. Draw the condensed structural formulas of the two cis–trans isomers of the compound. Name each geometric isomer.

c. Draw the product of the reaction of 1 mole of this compound with 1 mole of Br_2.

d. Draw the alkyne equivalent of the compound named in part (a). Name this alkyne.

e. Determine the reaction product of 1 mole of the alkyne formed in part (d) with 1 mole of Br_2. Name the compound.

f. Draw the possible cis–trans isomers of the product formed in part (e). (*Hint:* The cis isomer has the bromo groups on the same side of the double bond.)

Hint: Determine the length of the longest continuous chain that contains both carbons of the double bond; give the first carbon of the double bond the lowest possible number. The names of common branched substituents are given in Table 21.2. The alkyl groups of the cis geometric isomer are on the same side of the double bond, while the alkyl groups of the trans geometric isomer are on opposite sides of the double bond. Finally, bromine adds across the double bond of an alkene or alkyne.

Key Terms, Symbols, and Equations

KEY TERMS

addition polymerization (21.6): A polymerization of molecules that proceeds via addition reactions.

addition reaction (21.2): A type reaction in which substituents are added across a double or triple bond.

alcohol (21.4): An organic compound with the hydroxyl (—OH) functional group.

aldehyde (21.5): An organic compound with the —CHO functional group.

alkane (21.1): A hydrocarbon containing only C—C and C—H single bonds.

alkene (21.2): A hydrocarbon containing one or more carbon–carbon double bond per molecule.

alkyl group (21.1): A portion of an alkane formed by loss of one hydrogen atom.

alkyne (21.2): A hydrocarbon containing at least one carbon–carbon triple bond.

amide (21.5): An organic compound with the —CONH— functional group.

amine (21.4): An organic compound with the $—NR_2$ functional group, in which either or both R groups can be hydrogen atoms.

aromatic hydrocarbon (21.2): A hydrocarbon containing one or more benzene rings.

benzene (21.2): The simplest aromatic hydrocarbon, which consists of six carbon atoms in a hexagonal ring with alternating double and single bonds.

carbonyl group (21.5): A functional group made up of a carbon atom double-bonded to an oxygen atom: C=O.

carboxylic acid (21.5): An organic acid containing the functional group —COOH.

chiral (21.3): Describes an object that cannot be superimposed on its mirror image (e.g., a carbon atom bonded to four unique groups).

cis–trans isomers (21.3): A type of stereoisomer in which the groups are located on the same (cis) or opposite (trans) side of the double bond of an alkene.

condensation polymerization (21.6): A polymerization of molecules that proceeds via condensation reactions.

condensation reaction (21.5): A reaction in which two or more organic molecules form a covalent bond and release a small molecule such as water.

condensed structural formula (21.1): A formula that shows bonded groups of atoms in a molecule rather than the total number of each type of atom.

ester (21.5): An organic compound with the —COO—R functional group.

ether (21.4): An organic compound with the —O— functional group; the general formula of an ether is ROR′, where R and R′ may or may not be the same.

functional group (21.4): The characteristic group of atoms attached to an R group that gives a class of organic compounds its characteristic properties.

heteroatom (21.4): An atom other than carbon or hydrogen in an organic molecule.

hydrocarbon (21.1): A compound consisting of only carbon and hydrogen.

isomers (21.3): Different compounds with the same molecular formula but a different arrangement of atoms.

ketone (21.5): A class of organic compounds with the carbonyl functional group; the general formula of a ketone is RCOR′, where R and R′ may or may not be the same.

molecular formula (21.1): A formula for an organic compound where each element is listed only once.

monomer (21.6): A molecule that is capable of reacting with other similar molecules to form a polymer.

nylon (21.6): A polymer of a six-carbon diacid and a six-carbon diamine.

optical isomers (21.3): Stereoisomers that are nonsuperimposable mirror images of one another; also known as enantiomers.

organic compound (21.1): A compound that contains carbon.

organic halide (21.4): An organic compound that has at least one halogen atom per molecule.

parent name (21.1): The name of an unbranched alkane that serves as the basis of the name of another compound with the same number of carbon atoms in its longest continuous carbon chain.

polyester (21.6): A polymer of a diacid and a dialcohol.

polymer (21.6): A molecule built from many (thousands or even more) smaller molecules (monomers) or parts of molecules.

R group (21.4): A section of an organic molecule (usually an alkane) that typically has no functional group. R is often used as an abbreviation when writing molecular structures to represent a nonreactive portion of the molecule.

saturated hydrocarbon (21.1): A compound containing only carbon and hydrogen linked by only single bonds; an alkane.

stereoisomers (21.3): Compounds with the same molecular formulas and connectivities but a different arrangement of the atoms in space.

structural formula (21.1): Similar to a Lewis structure, but lone pairs are omitted.

structural isomers (21.3): Compounds with the same molecular formula but a different structural arrangement of their atoms.

substituent (21.1): An atom or group of atoms that takes the place of a hydrogen atom on an unbranched hydrocarbon.

synthetic fiber (21.6): A polymer, such as nylon, that has the form of a fiber.

unsaturated hydrocarbon (21.2): A compound containing only carbon and hydrogen and having one or more multiple bonds per molecule.

SYMBOLS

R (alkyl group) (21.4)

R′ (different alkyl group) (21.4)

X (halogen) (21.4)

Chapter Summary

Organic compounds contain at least one carbon–carbon or carbon–hydrogen bond. Hydrocarbons are compounds that contain only carbon and hydrogen atoms. The simplest hydrocarbons are the alkanes, which have only C—C and C—H single bonds. Their systematic names end in *–ane,* and their general molecular formula is C_nH_{2n+2}. Alkanes are not very reactive but can undergo combustion reactions with oxygen and substitution reactions with halogens (Section 21.1).

Unsaturated hydrocarbons include the alkenes, alkynes, and aromatic hydrocarbons. Alkenes contain at least one carbon–carbon double bond per molecule, and alkynes contain at least one carbon–carbon triple bond per molecule. Their systematic names begin just like the names of the corresponding alkanes, but they end with *–ene* or *–yne*, respectively. When the location of the multiple bond has to be specified in the name, the carbons in the main chain are numbered so that the first carbon of the multiple bond has the lowest possible number. Alkenes and alkynes are much more reactive than alkanes; for example, alkenes and alkynes undergo addition reactions with halogens to form halogenated hydrocarbons under much less severe conditions than are required for the reactions of alkanes with halogens. Alkenes and alkynes also undergo addition reactions with water (hydration) to form alcohols.

Aromatic hydrocarbons contain a benzene ring. The ring structure and special bonding in benzene give the aromatic hydrocarbons added stability. Benzene derivatives are named by using the substituent group name as the prefix and *–benzene* as the suffix. When more than one of the *same* type of group is present, the groups are numbered by their relative positions and a prefix is used to give the number of groups. An older system uses *ortho–*, *meta–*, and *para–* to identify the relative positions of two groups that are present. When more than one *different* type of group is present on a benzene ring, the groups are named alphabetically, and the first group is assigned position 1 on the ring (Section 21.2).

Molecules with the same molecular formulas but different atom connectivities are structural isomers of one another. They are different compounds with different properties and different names. Structural isomers exist because different points of attachment are possible for the groups on a chain of carbon atoms or because the multiple bonds are located between different carbons in the chain. Cis–trans isomers have the same formulas and atom connectivities, but they have different arrangements of the atoms in space. Optical isomers also have the same formulas and atom connectivities, but they are nonsuperimposable mirror images of one another. Optical isomers typically contain at least one carbon atom that is bonded to four different groups (Section 21.3).

In addition to hydrocarbons, other important classes of organic compounds that are discussed include organic halides, alcohols, ethers, and amines. The hydrocarbon-like part of such molecules is called the alkyl (R) group, and the reactive part is called the functional group. The functional groups of these compounds largely govern their reactivity. Organic halides are formed by the reaction of hydrocarbons with halogens, while ethers are formed by the condensation reaction of two alcohols (Section 21.4).

Organic compounds with the carbonyl functional group include aldehydes, ketones, organic acids, esters, and amides. Aldehydes are formed by the oxidation of primary alcohols, whereas ketones are formed by the oxidation of secondary alcohols. Carboxylic acids can be formed by reacting a primary alcohol with excess oxidizing agent. Esters are formed by the condensation reaction of a carboxylic acid with an alcohol, and amides are formed by the condensation reaction of an alcohol with an amine (Section 21.5).

Some small molecules (called monomers) can react to form very large molecules (called polymers). The two major classes of polymers are condensation polymers and addition polymers. Nylon, polyester, and polyethylene are common polymers (Section 21.6).

END OF CHAPTER QUESTIONS

21.1 Introduction to Hydrocarbons

1. What is a hydrocarbon?
2. What is the general molecular formula of an alkane?
3. Write the structural formula, condensed structural formula, and molecular formula for heptane.
4. Draw structural formulas of the following compounds.
   a. 2-methylpentane
   b. 2,4-dimethylpentane
   c. 3-ethyl-2-methyloctane
   d. isopropane
5. Draw structural formulas of the following compounds.
   a. 2-butene
   b. 2,3,4-trimethyloctane
   c. 2,2-dimethyl-5-propyldecane
   d. isobutane
6. Draw condensed structural formulas for the compounds from question 4.
7. Draw condensed structural formulas for the compounds from question 5.
8. Name the following compounds.
   a. 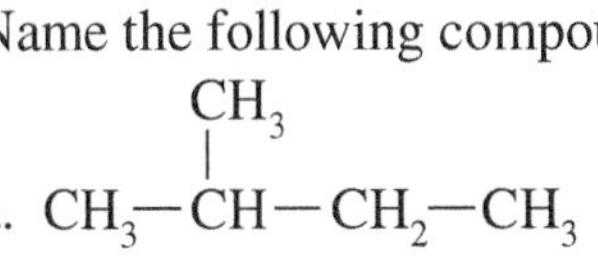
   b. 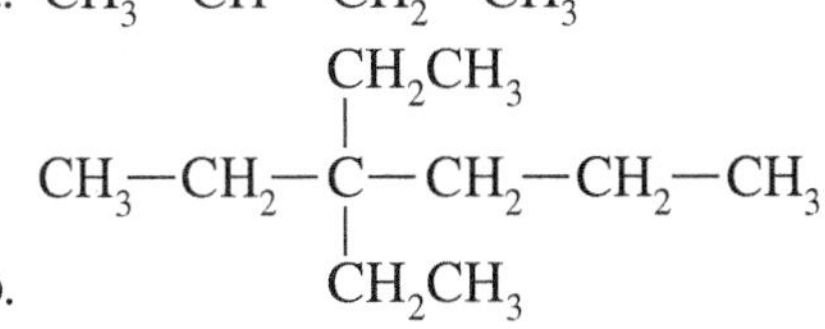
   c. 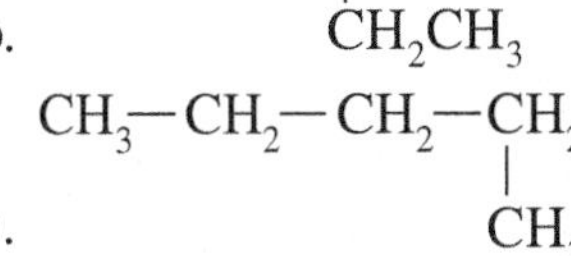
9. Name the following compounds.
   a. 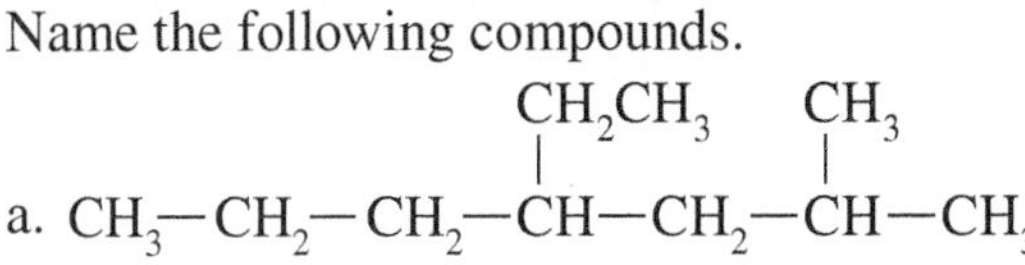

b. 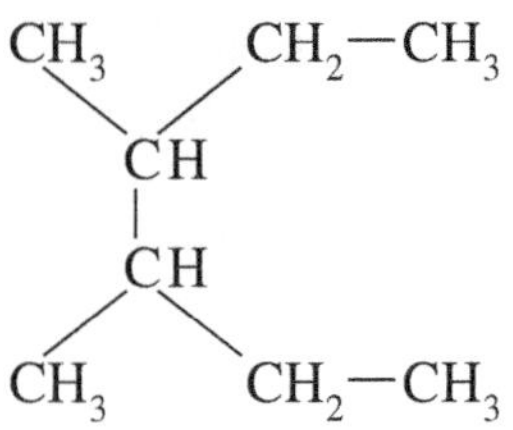

c. 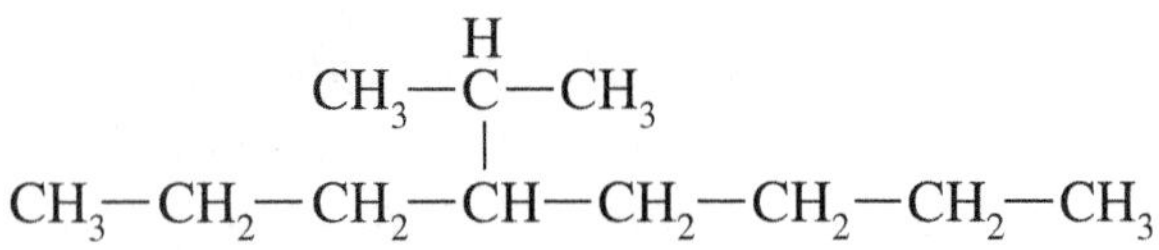

10. Name the following compounds.
   a. 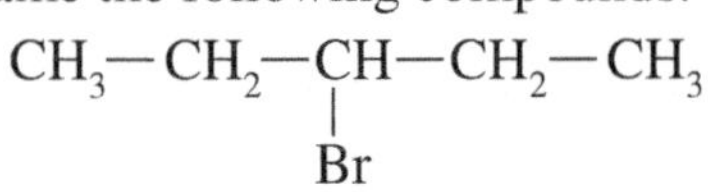
   b. 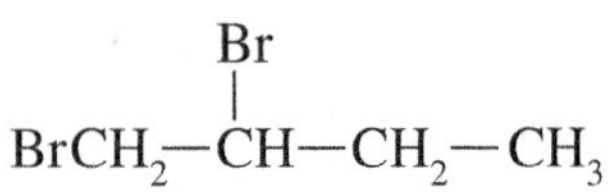
   c. 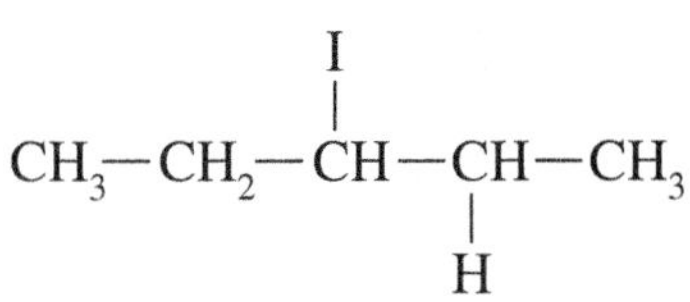

11. Write the products of the following reactions, and balance the equations.
   a. $C_4H_{10}(g) + O_2(g, \text{limited supply}) \rightarrow$
   b. $C_4H_{10}(g) + O_2(g, \text{excess}) \rightarrow$

12. Write the products of the following reactions, and balance the equations.
   a. $C_5H_{12}(g) + Cl_2(g, \text{limited supply}) \rightarrow$
   b. $C_5H_{12}(g) + Cl_2(g, \text{excess}) \rightarrow$

21.2 Unsaturated Hydrocarbons

13. What is the difference between a saturated and an unsaturated hydrocarbon?

14. Write the general molecular formula for each of the following:
   a. an alkene
   b. an alkyne

15. What is the hybridization of a carbon atom attached to the following?
   a. A double bond
   b. A triple bond

16. Draw structural formulas of the following compounds.
   a. An alkene with the formula C_6H_{12}
   b. An alkyne with the formula C_6H_{10}
   c. An aromatic compound with the formula C_6H_6

17. Draw structural formulas of the following compounds.
   a. an alkene with the formula C_4H_8
   b. an alkyne with the formula C_4H_6

18. Draw structural formulas of the following compounds.
   a. 1-nonene
   b. 1-nonyne

19. Draw structural formulas of the following compounds.
   a. 2-heptyne
   b. 3-heptyne

20. Draw condensed structural formulas for the compounds from question 18.

21. Draw condensed structural formulas for the compounds from question 19.

22. Name the following compounds.
   a. $CH_2{=}CH{-}CH_2{-}CH_2{-}CH_3$
   b. $CH_3{-}CH{=}CH{-}CH_2{-}CH_2{-}CH_3$
   c. 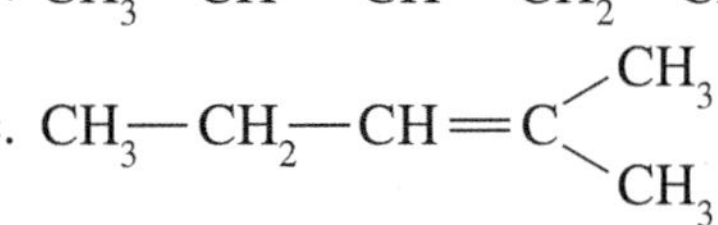

23. Name the following compounds.
   a. $CH{\equiv}C{-}CH_2{-}CH_3$
   b. 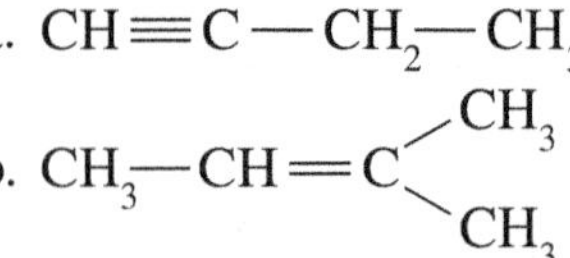
   c. 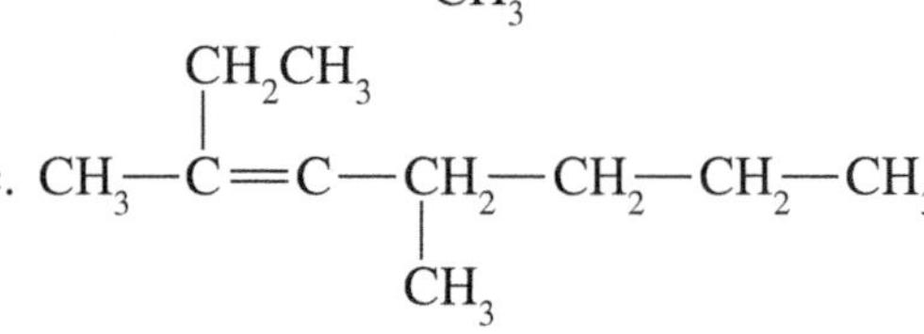

24. Write the products of the following reactions, and name the products.
   a. $CH_3CH{=}CHCH_3(g) + Cl_2(g) \rightarrow$
   b. $HC{\equiv}CCH_2CH_3(g) + Cl_2(g) \rightarrow$

25. Write the products of the following reactions, and name the products.
   a. $HC{\equiv}CCH_2CH_3(g) + 2\,Cl_2(g) \rightarrow$
   b. $CH_3CH{=}CHCH_2CH_3(g) + H_2(g) \rightarrow$

26. Name the following compounds.
   a. 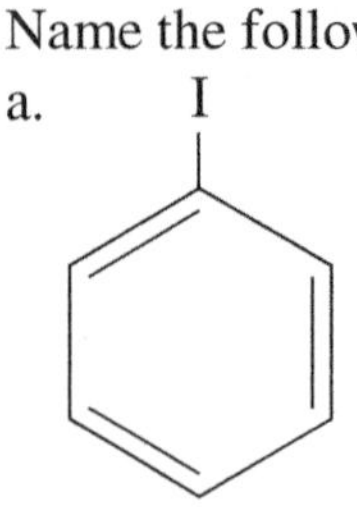

b. 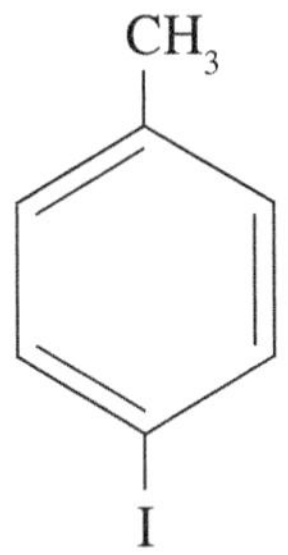

c. 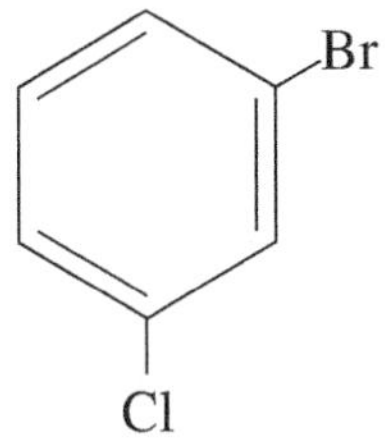

21.3 Introduction to Isomerism

27. What are structural isomers?

28. Do structural isomers of propane exist? Explain.

29. Draw all the structural isomers of C_4H_{10}.

30. Draw all the structural isomers of C_5H_{12}.

31. Name all the molecules from the previous two problems.

32. Determine whether the following sets of compounds are isomers or if they are the same compound. If they are isomers, identify the type of isomer.
a. $HC{\equiv}C{-}CH_2{-}CH_3$ $\quad$ $CH_3{-}CH_2{-}C{\equiv}CH$
b. 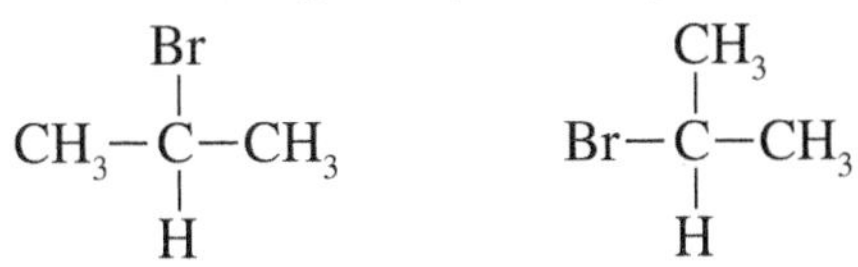

33. Determine whether the compounds in each set are isomers or if they are the same compound. If they are isomers, identify the type of isomer.
a. $CH_3{-}CH{=}CH{-}CH_2{-}CH_2{-}CH_3$
$CH_3{-}CH_2{-}CH{=}CH{-}CH_2{-}CH_3$
b. 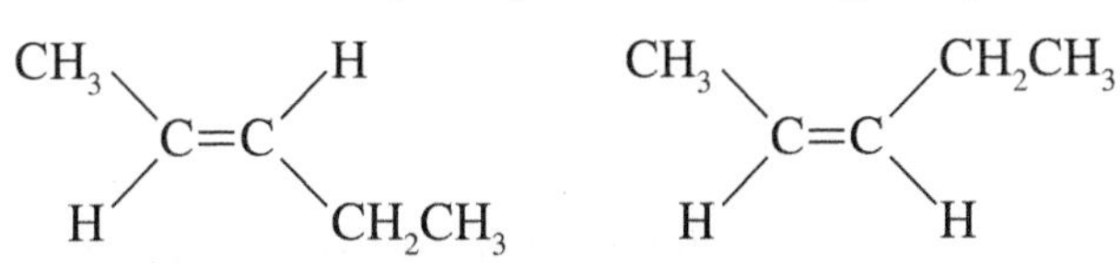

34. Determine whether the compounds in each set are isomers or if they are the same compound. If they are isomers, identify the type of isomer.
a. 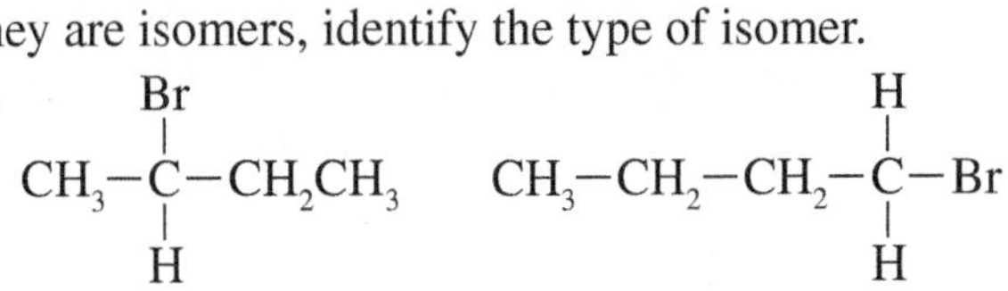
b. 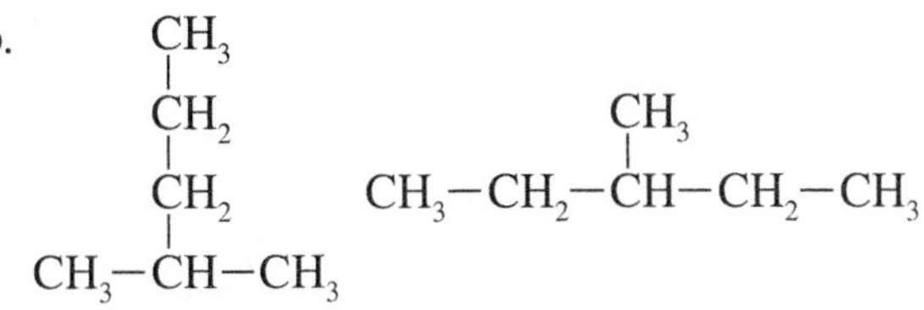

35. Cis–trans isomers and optical isomers are both stereoisomers but in a fundamentally different way. Explain.

36. How do structural isomers and optical isomers differ with regard to physical properties?

37. Can a hydrocarbon with only an alkyne functional group exhibit cis–trans isomerism? Explain.

38. Explain how the π bonding in alkenes and alkynes affects the ability of multiply bonded carbon atoms to rotate about their bonds.

39. Which of the following molecules are chiral and can exist as optical isomers?
a. $CH_2{=}CH{-}CH_3$
b. 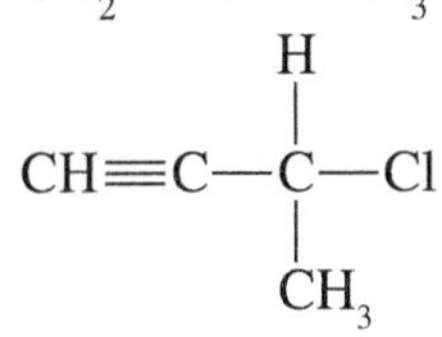
c. 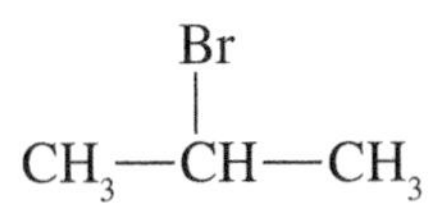

40. Which of the following molecules are chiral and can exist as optical isomers?
a. 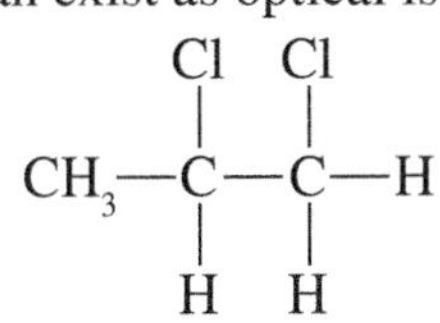
b. 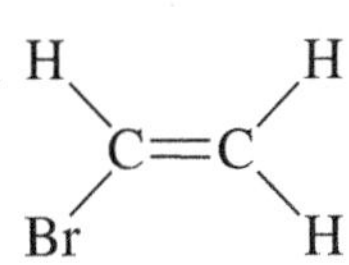
c. 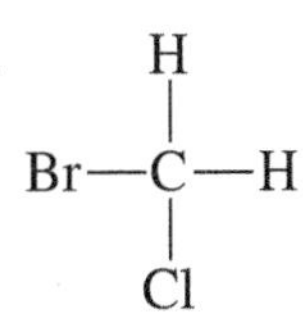

21.4 Organic Halides, Alcohols, Ethers, and Amines

41. Complete the following structures by adding all necessary hydrogen atoms.
a. $C{=}C{-}C$
b. $C{\equiv}C{-}C{-}O$

42. Complete the following structures by adding all necessary hydrogen atoms.

a. 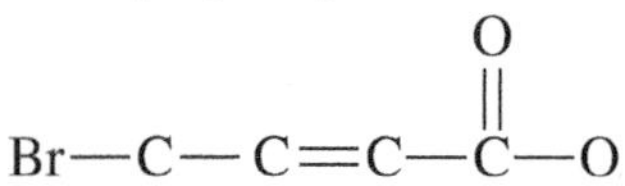

b. 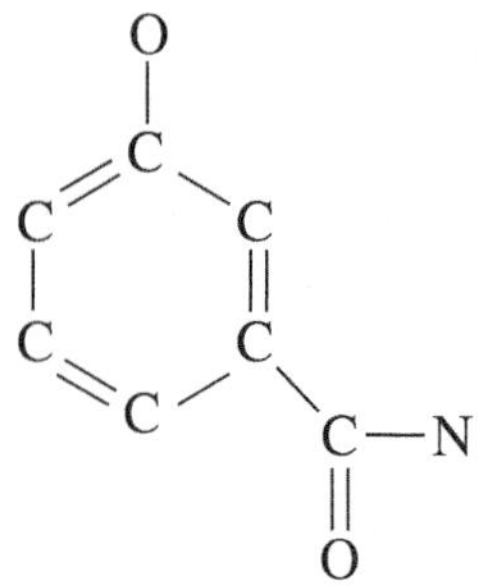

43. Circle the functional groups on the following molecules.

a. $CH_3-C\equiv C-CH_2-\overset{O}{\overset{\|}{C}}-H$

b. $HO-CH_2-CH_2-\overset{O}{\overset{\|}{C}}-NH_2$

44. Give the products of the following reactions.
   a. $Br_2(g) + CH_3CH_3(g) + \text{heat} \rightarrow$
   b. $2\ Br_2(g) + CH_3CH_3(g) + \text{heat} \rightarrow$
   c. $4\ Br_2(g) + CH_3CH_3(g) + \text{heat} \rightarrow$
   d. $6\ Br_2(g) + CH_3CH_3(g) + \text{heat} \rightarrow$

45. Give the products of the following reactions.
   a. $HCl(g) + CH_2{=}CHCH_3(g) + \text{heat} \rightarrow$
   b. $HCl(g) + CH_2{=}CHCH{=}CH_2(g) + \text{heat} \rightarrow$
   c. $HCl(g) + CH_2{=}CHCH{=}CH_2(g) + \text{heat} \rightarrow$

46. Name the following alcohols.
   a. $HO-CH_2-CH_2-CH_3$
   b. $CH_3-CH_2-CH_2-OH$
   c. $CH_3-CH_2-CH_2-\overset{OH}{\overset{|}{C}H}-CH_3$
   d. $CH_3-CH_2-CH_2-\overset{OH}{\overset{|}{C}H}-CH_2-CH_2-CH_3$

47. Name the following ethers.
   a. $CH_3-CH_2-O-CH_2-CH_2-CH_3$
   b. $CH_3-CH_2-O-CH_2-CH_3$

48. Draw condensed structural formulas for the following:
   a. ethoxymethane
   b. butoxybutane
   c. methoxypropane

49. Give the products of the following reaction, then give the correct name for each reactant and product.

$$CH_3CH_2CH_2OH + CH_3CH_2CH_2OH \xrightarrow{H_2SO_4}$$

50. Name the following amines.
   a. $(CH_3CH_2)NH_2$
   b. $(CH_3CH_2CH_2)_2NH$
   c. $(CH_3CH_2)_3N$

21.5 Aldehydes, Ketones, Carboxylic Acids, Esters, and Amides

51. When naming aldehydes, the position of the carbonyl group on the carbon chain is never given. Explain why.

52. Name the following compounds.
   a. $CH_3\overset{O}{\overset{\|}{C}}CH_3$
   b. $CH_3CH_2\overset{O}{\overset{\|}{C}}CH_3$
   c. $H\overset{O}{\overset{\|}{C}}CH_2\overset{CH_3}{\overset{|}{C}}HCH_3$

53. Draw structural formulas for the following molecules.
   a. methanal
   b. 3-ethyl-2-heptanone
   c. 2-methylbutanal

54. Draw structural formulas for the following molecules.
   a. hexanoic acid
   b. 2-methylbutanoic acid
   c. 2-ethyl-3-methylpentanoic acid

55. Draw condensed structural formulas for the molecules in question 53.

56. Draw condensed structural formulas for the molecules in question 54.

57. Draw the products of the following oxidation reactions. If no reaction occurs, write "no reaction." Give the correct name for each reactant and product.
   a. oxidation of 1-butanol with $Na_2Cr_2O_7$ in H_2SO_4, where 1-butanol is in excess
   b. oxidation of methanal with $Na_2Cr_2O_7$ in H_2SO_4
   c. oxidation of 2-methyl-2-butanol with $Na_2Cr_2O_7$ in H_2SO_4, where 2-methyl-2-butanol is in excess

58. Esters are formed between which two classes of organic compounds? What is the by-product of this reaction?

59. Give the products of the following reactions, then give the correct name for each reactant and product.

    a. $H-\overset{O}{\overset{\|}{C}}-OH + CH_3-OH \rightleftharpoons$

    b. $CH_3CH_2CH_2CH_2CH_2-OH + CH_3CH_2\overset{O}{\overset{\|}{C}}-OH \rightleftharpoons$

60. Amides are formed between which two classes of organic compounds? What is the by-product of this reaction?

61. Give the products of the following reactions, then give the correct name for each reactant and product.

    a. $CH_3CH_2-\overset{O}{\overset{\|}{C}}-OH + NH_3 \rightleftharpoons$

    b. $CH_3-\overset{O}{\overset{\|}{C}}-OH + (CH_3)_2NH_3 \rightleftharpoons$

62. Draw structural formulas for the following compounds.
    a. propyl methanamide
    b. butyl propanoate
    c. methyl hexanamide
    d. isopropyl pentanoate

63. Draw condensed structural formulas for the compounds in question 62.

21.6 Polymers

64. What is the difference between an addition polymerization reaction and a condensation polymerization reaction?

65. Name the three functional groups that are present in all peptides and proteins.

66. Use the following structure of styrene to draw one repeat of a polystyrene unit.

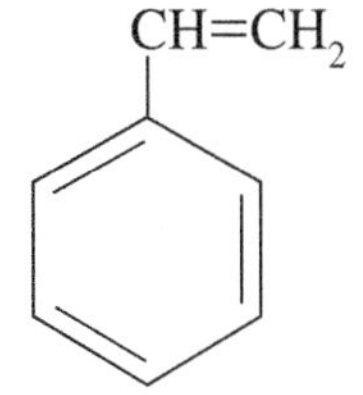

67. Use Table 21.8 to draw one repeat of a polypropylene unit.

68. Polytetrafluoroethylene (PTFE) is an addition polymer. Draw the structure of the monomer used to prepare PTFE.

69. Aramid is a strong, heat-resistant synthetic fiber that is formed by a condensation reaction. The reactants are shown here, and the by-product of this reaction is HCl. Draw one repeat of an Aramid unit.

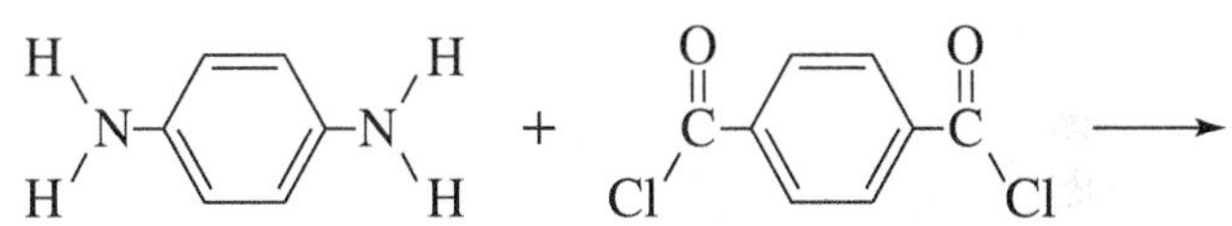

70. The following polymer was formed via a condensation reaction, where water is formed as a by-product. Draw the structures of the two reactants.

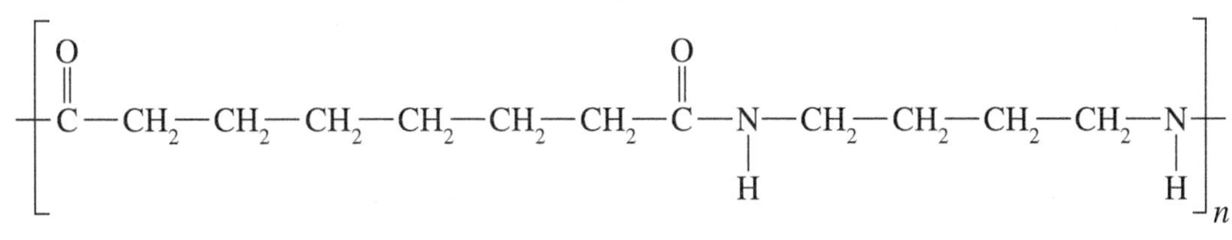

Putting It Together

71. Cis–trans isomers can have different physical properties, but optical isomers cannot. Explain why.

72. Methylamine ($pK_b = 3.43$) is dissolved in pure water.
    a. Write the balanced chemical equation for the ionization reaction that occurs.
    b. Write the equilibrium constant expression.
    c. If the initial concentration of methylamine is 0.100 M, determine the pH of the solution at equilibrium.

73. The "alcohol" in alcoholic beverages is ethanol. Ethanol is metabolized (broken down) by the body in two steps. The first is the oxidation of ethanol to ethanal by two molecules named nicotinamide adenine dinucleotide (NAD^+) and alcohol dehydrogenase. Ethanal is toxic and results

in symptoms commonly associated with a "hangover." Ethanal can be removed from the body once it is oxidized to ethanoic acid via a molecule known as aldehyde dehydrogenase. Write the chemical equations for these two steps, omitting NAD^+, alcohol dehydrogenase, aldehyde dehydrogenase, and their respective by-product.

74. Name two compounds that could react to form dimethyl propanamide.

75. Could trimethylamine react with a carboxylic acid to form an amide? Explain why or why not.

76. Amides and esters can both undergo hydrolysis. Give the hydrolysis products of the following compounds.
   a. ethanamide
   b. methyl propanoate

77. Aldehydes and ketones can be reduced (Section 4.6) to alcohols with H_2 and a metal catalyst such as nickel or palladium combined with carbon. Determine the products of the following reactions, write the balanced equations, and name the reaction products.
   a. reduction of methanal with H_2 and a Pd/C catalyst
   b. reduction of 3-pentanone with H_2 and a Ni catalyst

78. Draw the structures of and name three alcohols that are structural isomers of 3-pentanone.

79. Draw one repeat of an addition polymer formed from isobutylene, shown here.

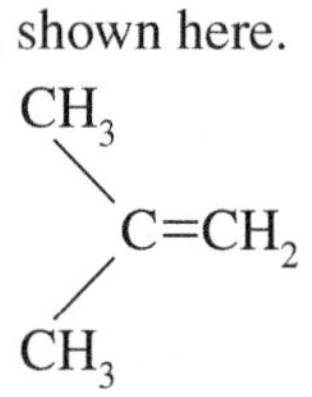

80. Draw structural formulas for
   a. pentane
   b. 1-pentene
   c. 2-pentyne
   d. 3-pentanol
   e. 1,3-dibromopentane

81. Draw structural formulas for
   a. pentanal
   b. pentanoic acid
   c. 2-pentanone
   d. ethoxypropane
   e. ethyl propanoate

PRACTICE PROBLEM SOLUTIONS

Practice Problem 21.1 Solution

a. The longest continuous carbon chain is six atoms, so this compound is a hexane (Table 21.2).

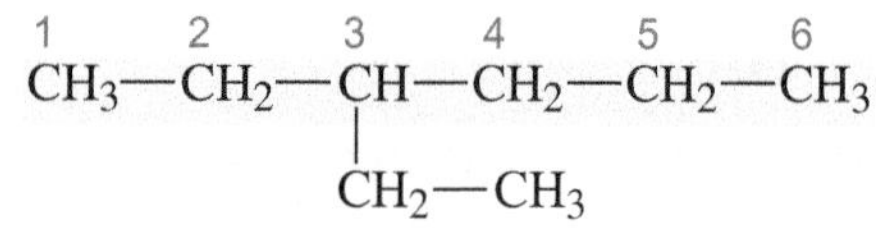

Numbering the chain as shown gives the ethyl group the lowest possible number (3 instead of 4). This compound is 3-ethylhexane.

b. The longest continuous carbon chain is eight atoms, so this compound is an octane (Table 21.2).

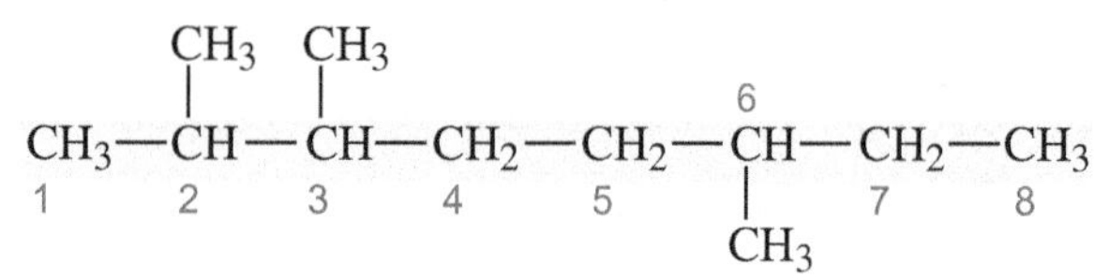

Numbering the chain as shown gives the first methyl group the lowest possible number (2 instead of 3). The other two methyl groups are thus on carbons 3 and 6 (instead of 6 and 7). This compound is 2,3,6-trimethyloctane.

Practice Problem 21.2 Solution

a. The longest continuous carbon chain is six atoms, so this compound is a hexane (Table 21.2).

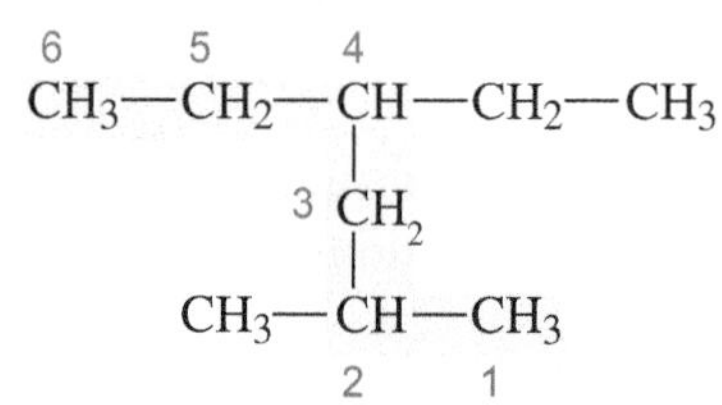

Numbering the chain as shown gives the first branch point the lowest possible number (the methyl group on carbon 2 instead of the ethyl group on carbon 3). If the methyl group is on carbon 2, then the ethyl group is on carbon 4. Ethyl must appear in the name before methyl, so this compound is 4-ethyl-2-methylhexane.

b. The longest continuous carbon chain is eight atoms, so this compound is an octane (Table 21.2).

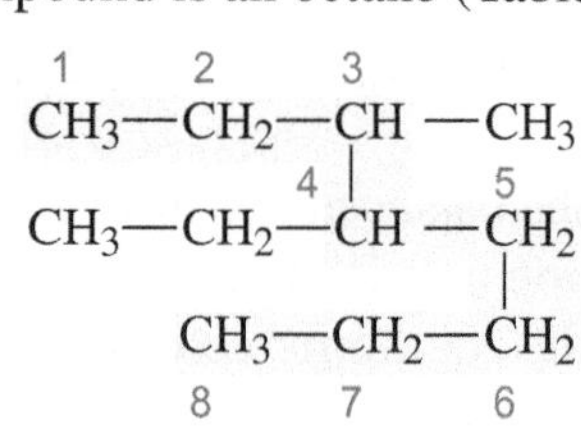

Numbering the chain as shown gives the first branch point the lowest possible number (the methyl group on carbon 3 instead of the ethyl group on carbon 5). If the methyl group is on carbon 3, then the ethyl group is on carbon 4. Ethyl must appear in the name before methyl, so this compound is 4-ethyl-3-methyloctane.

Practice Problem 21.3 Solution

a. When an alkane reacts with excess O_2, the products are CO_2 and H_2O.

$$2\,C_4H_{10} + 13\,O_2 \rightarrow 8\,CO_2 + 10\,H_2O$$

b. When an alkane reacts with excess Br_2, the products are HBr and a halogenated hydrocarbon in which each H has been replaced by Br.

$$C_3H_8 + 8\,Br_2 \rightarrow C_3Br_8 + 8\,HBr$$

Practice Problem 21.4 Solution

a. The parent name is 2-hexene, so the longest continuous chain that contains the double bond is six carbons long, and the double bond appears between carbons 2 and 3. Placing methyl groups on carbons 3 and 4 gives the following structure (after adding enough hydrogen atoms so that each carbon has a total of four bonds).

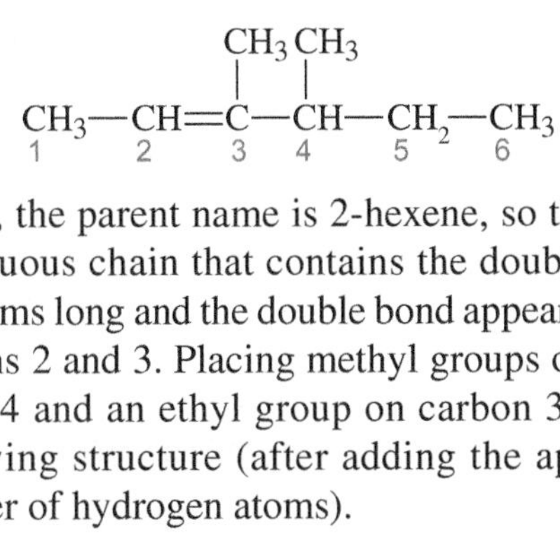

b. Again, the parent name is 2-hexene, so the longest continuous chain that contains the double bond is six atoms long and the double bond appears between carbons 2 and 3. Placing methyl groups on carbons 2 and 4 and an ethyl group on carbon 3 gives the following structure (after adding the appropriate number of hydrogen atoms).

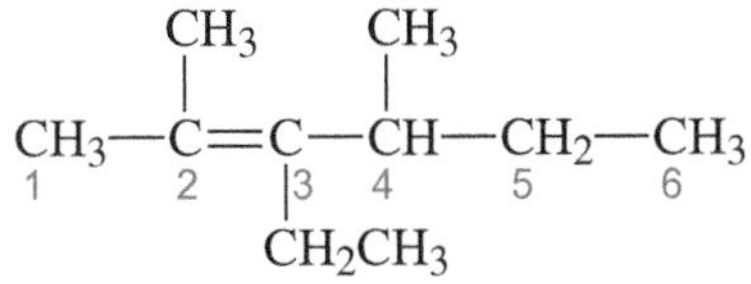

Practice Problem 21.5 Solution

a. The longest continuous chain that contains the double bond is five carbons long, so this is a pentene. Numbering the carbon atoms from left to right gives the double bond the lowest possible number (2 instead of 3).

The reaction of 1 mole of 2-pentene with 1 mole of H_2 is a hydrogenation. For each molecule of 2-pentene, 1 molecule of H_2 is added across the double bond to yield an alkane:

$$CH_3CH{=}CHCH_2CH_3 + H_2 \rightarrow CH_3CH_2CH_2CH_2CH_3$$

b. The longest continuous chain that contains the triple bond is five carbons long, so this is a pentyne. Numbering the carbon atoms from right to left gives the triple bond the lowest possible number (1 instead of 4).

The reaction of 1 mole of 1-pentyne with 1 mole of H_2 yields an alkene:

$$CH_3CH_2CH_2C{\equiv}CH + H_2 \rightarrow CH_3CH_2CH_2CH{=}CH_2$$

(At least 2 moles of H_2 would be needed to convert 1 mole of 1-pentyne into 1 mole of pentane.)

Practice Problem 21.6 Solution

1,4-Dichlorobenzene, also known as *para*-dichlorobenzene, contains two chlorine atoms, leaving four positions on the benzene ring for hydrogen atoms.

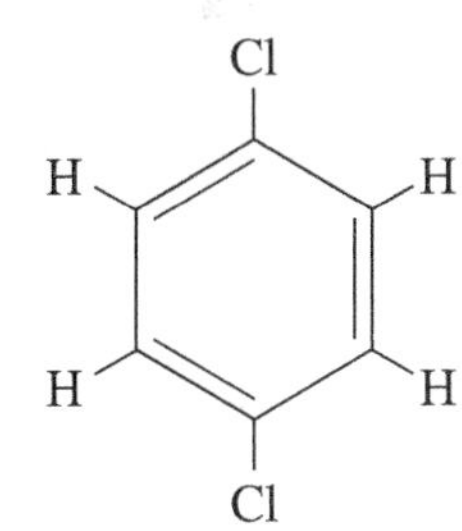

1,4-Dichlorobenzene

1,4-Dichlorobenzene is used as a disinfectant and an insecticide. It is often used as the active ingredient in mothballs.

Practice Problem 21.7 Solution

a. All three substituents are chloro groups, so their relative positions are assigned numbers on the ring and the prefix *tri*– must appear in the name. This compound is 1,2,3-trichlorobenzene.

b. Two different types of groups—ethyl and propyl—are located in the 1,4- (*para*-) configuration, so they are named alphabetically, and the first substituent in alphabetical order (i.e., ethyl) is assigned position 1. This compound is 1-ethyl-4-propylbenzene.

Practice Problem 21.8 Solution

a. These two molecules are structural isomers. They have the same formula (C_5H_{12}), but their atoms are connected differently.

b. These two molecules are structural isomers, too. They have the same molecular formula (C_4H_8), but their double bonds are located in different places along the main chain. For the compound on the left, the double bond is between carbons 2 and 3; for the compound on the right, it is between carbons 1 and 2.

Practice Problem 21.9 Solution

The molecular formula C_5H_{10} is represented by the general formula C_nH_{2n}, where $n = 5$. This is the general formula of an alkene, so the two compounds are isomers of pentene.

The condensed structural formulas of these two compounds are $CH_2{=}CHCH_2CH_2CH_3$ and $CH_2CH{=}CHCH_2CH_3$. The names of these compounds are 1-pentene and 2-pentene, respectively.

Practice Problem 21.10 Solution

The general formula of this compound is C_nH_{2n}, which makes it an alkene with $n = 4$. A branched alkene with four total carbon atoms must have a straight chain of three carbon atoms with a methyl group on the second carbon:

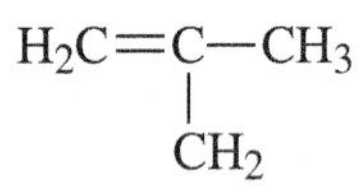

The name of the compound is methylpropene.

Practice Problem 21.11 Solution

This compound is a 2-hexene, so the main chain has six carbon atoms and the double bond is between carbons 2 and 3. Because it is in the cis configuration, the alkyl groups are on one side of the double bond and the bromo groups are on the opposite side.

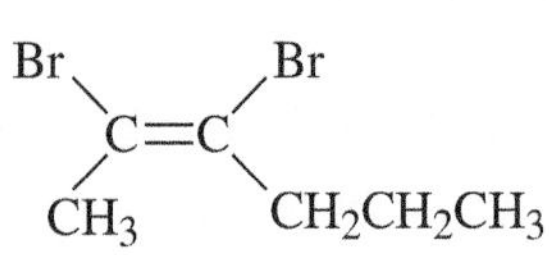

Practice Problem 21.12 Solution

a. These two molecules are different. The compound in the left is *trans*-2-pentene, and the one on the right is *cis*-3-hexene.

b. These two molecules are the same. They cannot exist as optical isomers, however, because the carbon atoms circled in the following structures are only bonded to three different groups: Br, CH_3, and *two* CH_3CH_2:

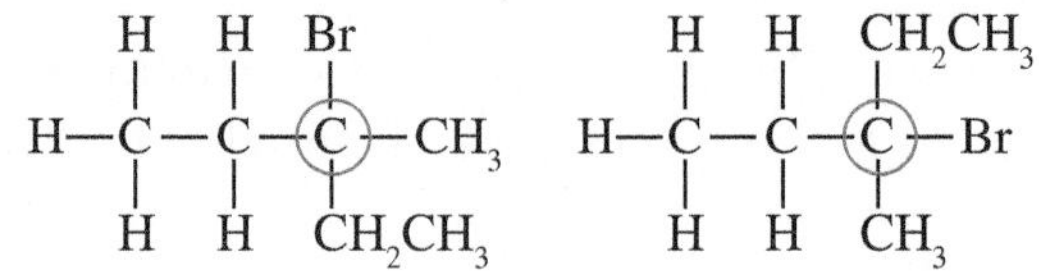

Practice Problem 21.13 Solution

Carbon has a bond order of four, so each carbon atom must have four bonds. Two carbon atoms of the benzene ring contain only three bonds, so one hydrogen must be added to each of them. Oxygen has a bond order of two, so two of the three oxygen atoms need no additional hydrogen atoms. The one bonded to the benzene ring, though, has only one bond. It needs a single hydrogen atom. Nitrogen has a bond order of three and the nitrogen in the structure contains only one bond, so two hydrogens must be added to the nitrogen. Phosphorus also has a bond order of three, but it is already connected to three bonds. No hydrogen atoms need to be added to the phosphorus atom. Chlorine has a bond order of one and is bonded to a carbon atom, so no hydrogen atoms need to be added to the chlorine atom.

The complete structure is as follows:

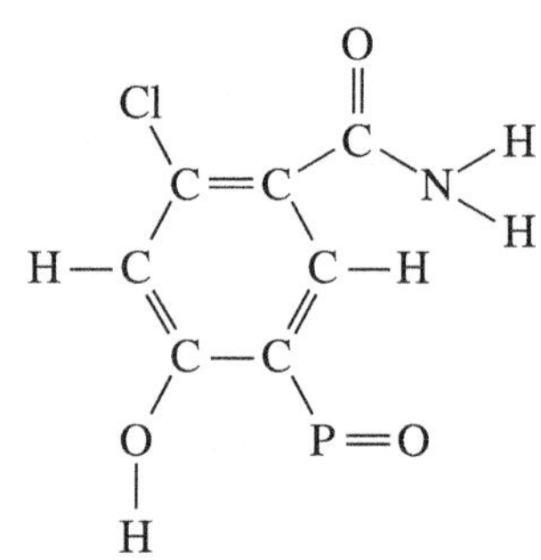

Practice Problem 21.14 Solution

A functional group consists of a heteroatom (an atom other than carbon or hydrogen) and/or an unsaturated carbon atom (a carbon atom with a double or triple bond). Any hydrogen atoms attached to the heteroatom or unsaturated carbon atom are also considered part of the functional group. The rest of the molecule is the R group or groups. Recall that R groups are saturated hydrocarbon groups (consisting of only carbon and hydrogen, connected with only single bonds).

a. The CH_3CH_2— portion of the molecule is the R group, and the rest of the molecule is the functional group.

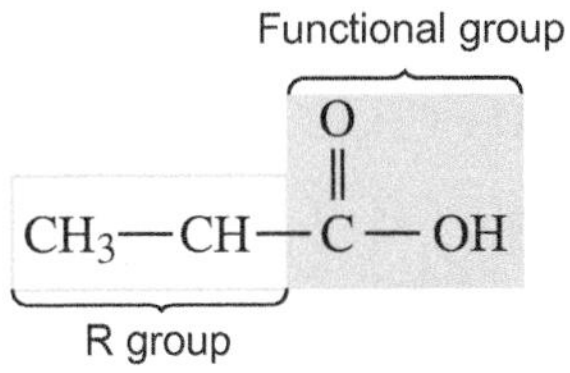

b. The double bond (—CH=CH—) and CO_2H groups are the functional groups. The other portions of the molecule are the R groups.

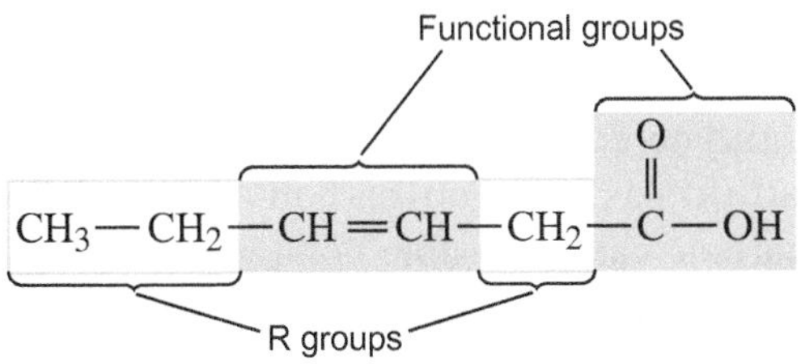

c. The oxygen atom and —NH_2 groups are the functional groups. The other portions of the molecule are the R groups.

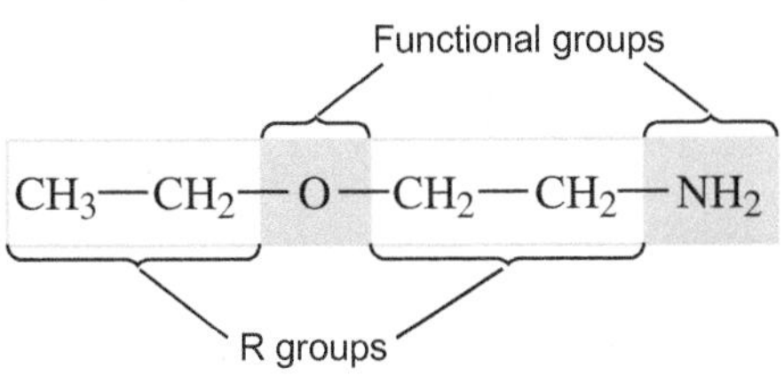

Practice Problem 21.15 Solution

In the presence of H_2SO_4, two alcohols react to form an ether and water. In this case, 2 moles of 1-butanol react. The name of the ether formed is butoxybutane.

$$\underset{\text{1-Butanol}}{CH_3(CH_2)_3OH(l)} + \underset{\text{1-Butanol}}{HO(CH_2)_3CH_3(l)} \xrightarrow{H_2SO_4} \underset{\text{Butoxybutane}}{CH_3(CH_2)_3O(CH_2)_3CH_3} + H_2O$$

Practice Problem 21.16 Solution

The compounds in parts (a) and (c) are ketones (they have the general form RCOR′). The molecule in part (b) is an aldehyde (RCHO).

a. The parent hydrocarbon is pentane. The carbonyl group is on carbon 3, so the name of this ketone is 3-pentanone.

b. The parent hydrocarbon is ethane, so the name of this aldehyde is ethanal.

c. The longest continuous chain is butane. The chain is numbered to give the carbonyl group the lower number, 2, so the methyl branch is on carbon 3. The name of this ketone is 3-methyl-2-butanone.

Practice Problem 21.17 Solution

The systematic name of a carboxylic acid replaces the *-ane* suffix of the parent alkane (Table 21.2) with *-oic acid*. The longest continuous chain of carbon atoms in both parts (a) and (b) is five carbons, so the parent compound for both is pentanoic acid. Numbering the chain so that the carbon atom of the carboxylic acid functional group is carbon 1 gives the following names:

a. 2-ethylpentanoic acid

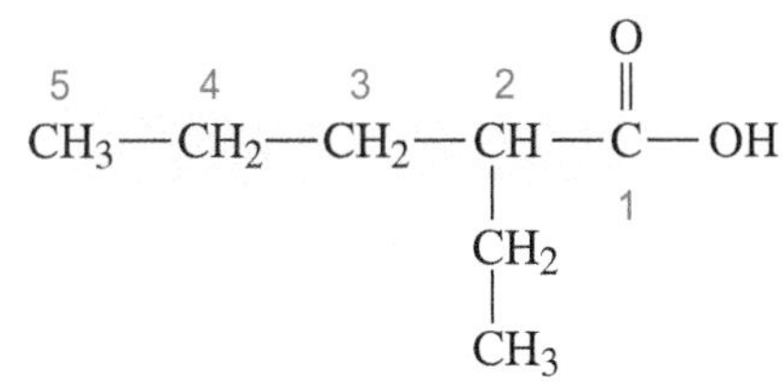

b. 2,3-dimethylpentanoic acid

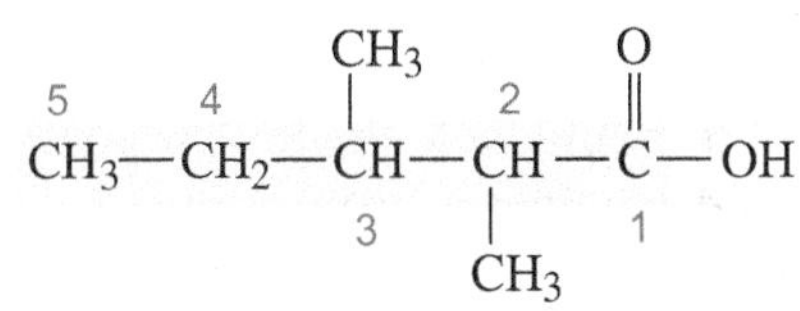

Practice Problem 21.18 Solution

Ethanol (an alcohol) contains two carbon atoms, and butanoic acid (a carboxylic acid) contains four carbon atoms. Ethanol reacts with butanoic acid to form ethyl butanoate and water.

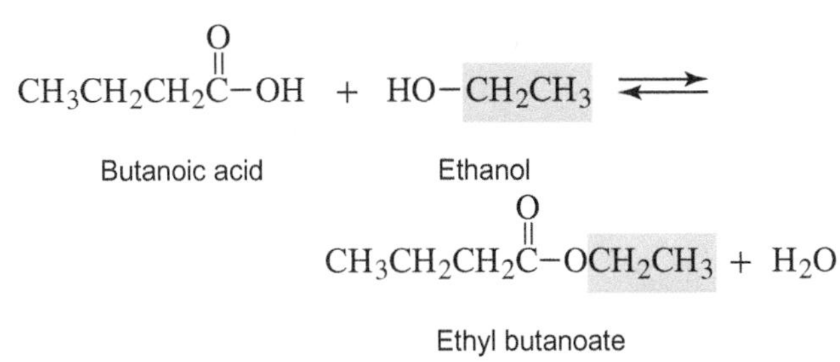

Practice Problem 21.19 Solution

Replacing one hydrogen atom on ethylene (ethene) with a —CH_3 group yields propene (also known as propylene). According to Table 21.8, the addition polymer made from propylene is called polypropylene.

Practice Problem 21.20 Solution

In a condensation reaction, two molecules combine to form a larger molecule and water. In the case of PET polyester, the water molecule consists of the H from the $-COOH$ group of terephthalic acid and the $—OH$ group from ethylene glycol:

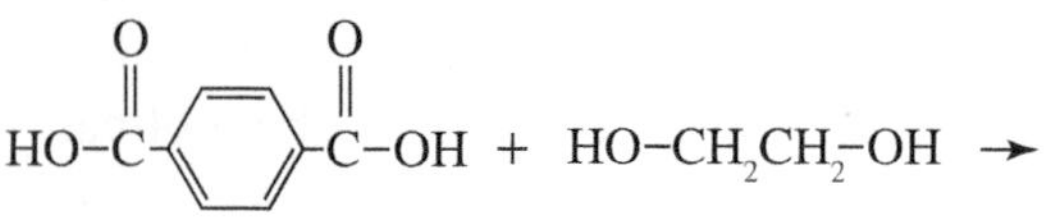

Terephthalic acid Ethylene glycol

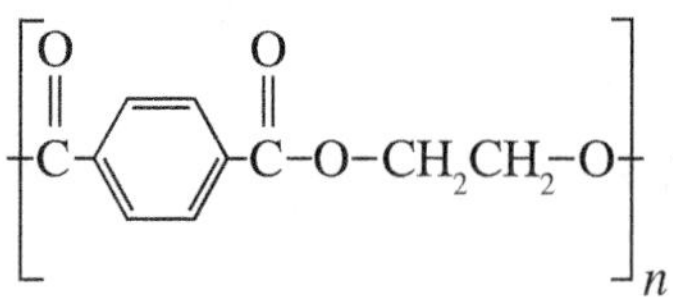

PET polymer

Practice Problem 21.21 Solution

a. The longest continuous chain in this compound that includes the double bond is six carbon atoms long. According to Table 21.2, the branched substituent group is an isopropyl group. The first carbon of the double bond should have the lowest possible number, and the substituent groups must be named in alphabetical order (i.e., isopropyl before methyl). Therefore, the name is 4-isopropyl-5-methyl-2-hexene.

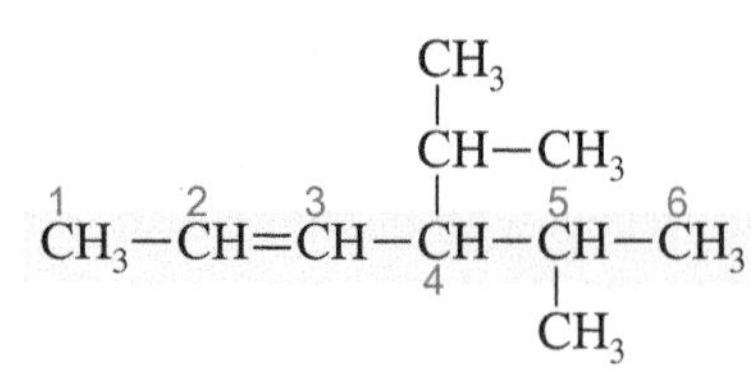

b. The cis isomer of an alkene has the alkyl groups on the same side of the double bond, whereas the trans isomer has the alkyl groups on opposite sides. The structures of *cis*- and *trans*-4-isopropyl-5-methyl-2-hexene are

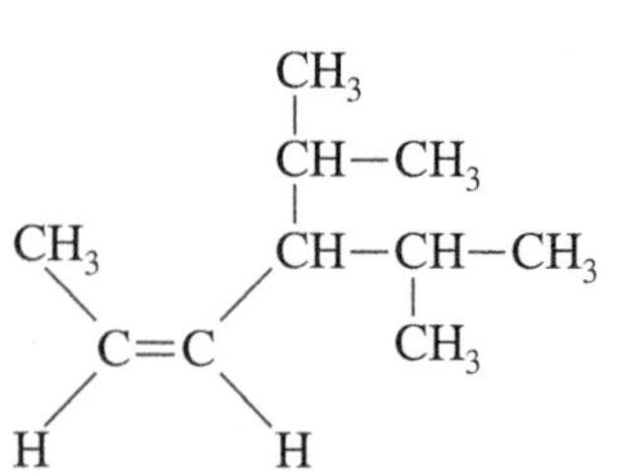

cis-4-Isopropyl-5-methyl-2-hexene

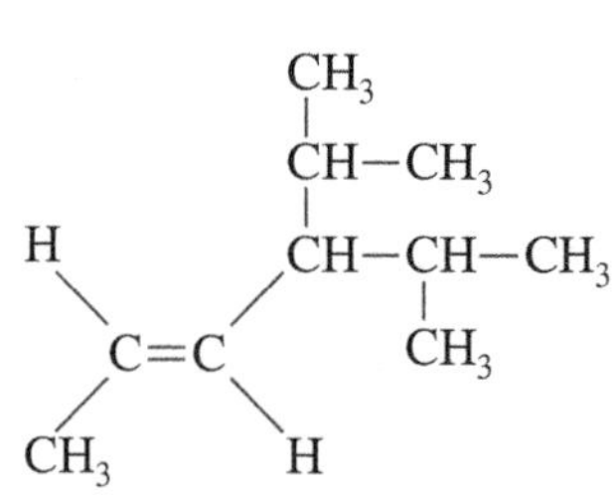

trans-4-Isopropyl-5-methyl-2-hexene

c. One mole of Br_2 adds across the double bonds in 1 mole of 4-isopropyl-5-methyl-2-hexene as follows:

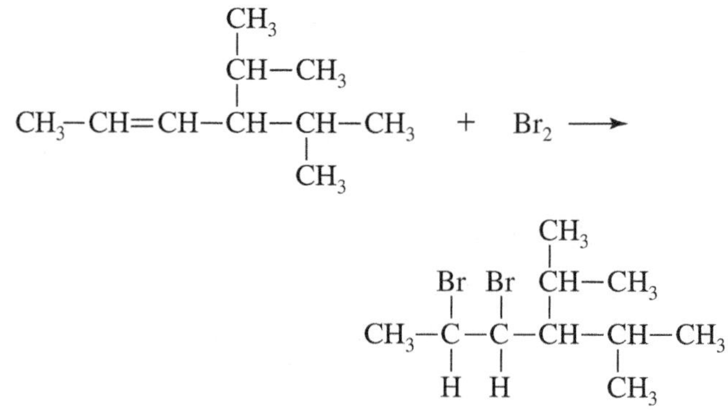

d. The alkyne equivalent of the compound named in part (a) has a carbon–carbon triple bond where the carbon–carbon double bond was. Carbon has a bond order of four, however, so a hydrogen atom must be removed from each of the carbons in the triple bond.

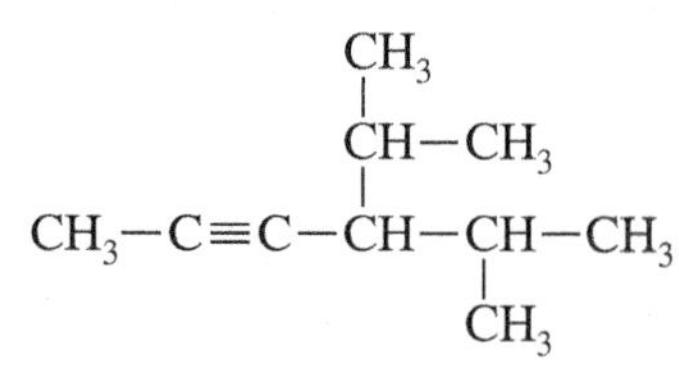

The name of this alkyne is 4-isopropyl-5-methyl-2-hexyne.

e. One mole of the alkyne in part (d) reacts with 1 mole of Br_2 to give the following brominated alkene:

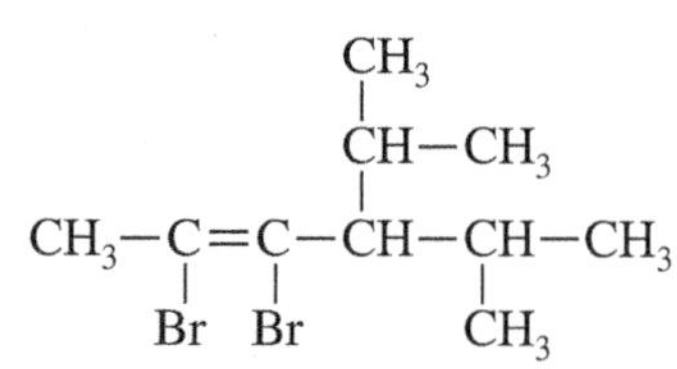

The name of this compound is 2,3-dibromo-4-isopropyl-5-methyl-2-hexene.

f. The cis isomer has the bromo groups on the same side of the double bond, whereas the trans isomer has them on opposite sides.

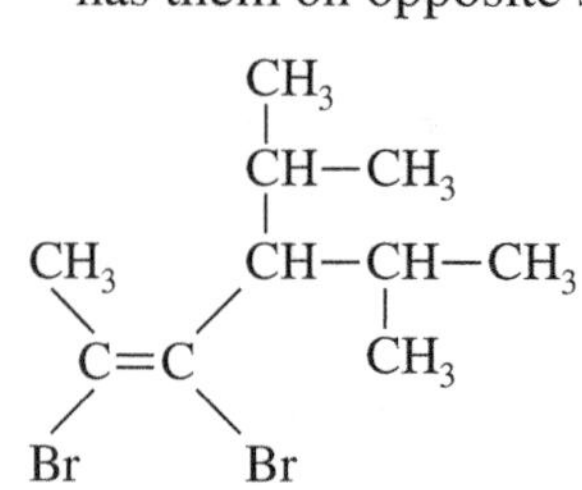

Cis

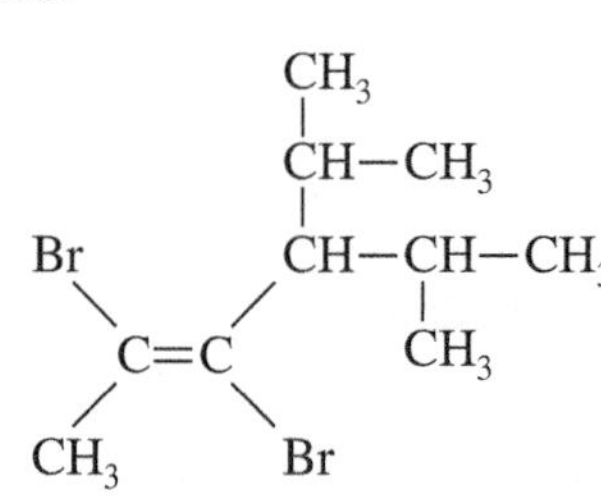

Trans

CHAPTER 22

Coordination Chemistry

Sara Egner, Macmillan Learning

Chlorophyll, essential for photosynthesis in plants, is a coordination compound. As you will learn in this chapter, a characteristic of all coordination compounds is the presence of a metal atom or ion. In chlorophyll, the metal is magnesium. In the chlorophyll molecule shown here, Mg^{2+} is at the center of the large cluster of atoms. When it was discovered that chlorophyll contained magnesium in 1906, it was the first time magnesium had ever been detected in living tissue.

Chapter Outline

GOALS

- Identify the oxidation state of transition metals within ionic compounds.
- Identify the electron configurations and physical properties of transition metals.
- Differentiate the electron configurations and physical properties of transition metals from those of main group elements.
- Define and identify a coordination sphere.
- Define and identify coordinate covalent bonds.
- Identify common ligands and their role in coordination chemistry.
- Apply the systematic rules for naming coordination compounds.
- Define, explain, and identify four major types of isomerism in coordination compounds.
- Use crystal field theory to identify high-spin and low-spin complexes.
- Apply crystal field theory to explain the effects of a coordination compound's ligands on its color and magnetic properties.

22.1 Review of Using Oxidation States in Naming Compounds

GOAL

- Identify the oxidation state of transition metals within ionic compounds.

Background Review

Chapter 3 Compounds and the Mole: Section 3.3—Formulas for Ionic Compounds; Section 3.4—Naming Ionic Compounds.

Chapter 9 Periodicity and Ionic Bonding: Section 9.4—Ionic Bonding

In Chapter 3, the charges on monoatomic ions were used to distinguish between different ions of the same element. For example, Cu^{+} and Cu^{2+} are named copper(I) and copper(II), respectively. However, the Roman numeral actually represents the oxidation state of the metal, not the charge. For monoatomic ions, the charge is equal to the oxidation state (Section 4.6); however, for polyatomic cations, it is important to make the distinction between oxidation state and charge. For example, Hg_2^{2+} is called mercury(I), even though its ionic charge is $+2$, because the oxidation state of *each* of the two mercury atoms is $+1$. It will be important for you to be able to identify both the charges and oxidation states of metal ions in this chapter.

In Chapter 3, the suffixes *-ate* and *-ite* for oxyanions (and the corresponding *-ic* and *-ous* suffixes for oxyacids) were explained in terms of the relative number of oxygen atoms; however, they can also be explained in terms of the relative oxidation state of the central atom. The suffix *-ous* corresponds to the oxoacid in which the

EVERYDAY CONNECTION

Ferric oxide is another name for iron(III) oxide (rust), and *stannous fluoride* is another name for tin(II) fluoride (the active ingredient in some toothpastes).

Africa Studio/Shutterstock

These names come from an older naming system that used the *-ous* and *-ic* suffixes instead of Roman numerals. This older naming system was also used for covalent compounds, where the suffix was based on the oxidation state (Section 4.6) of the element. For example, N_2O, the laughing gas anesthetic used in dentists' offices, is still commonly known as *nitrous oxide*, and the highly reactive air pollutant NO is still known as *nitric oxide*. The older naming system is now obsolete and is not used in this text, but it lingers on in the common names of a few compounds.

central atom has a lower oxidation state than that of the -*ic* acid; for example, the nitrogen, N, in nitrous acid, HNO_2, has an oxidation state of $+3$, whereas N in nitric acid, HNO_3, has an oxidation state of $+5$.

The Stock system (i.e., Roman numerals) is the preferred method among scientists for naming variable-charge cations and is used exclusively in this text.

Example 22.1

Give the charge and oxidation state of chromium, Cr, in each compound.

a. CrO
b. $NaCrO_4$
c. $Na_2Cr_2O_7$

Solution

From Section 3.3, recall that the overall charge of the compound is the sum of the charges of its constituent ions.

a. The oxide ion has a charge of -2. To balance the charge of the oxide ion, Cr has a charge of $+2$. The oxidation state of Cr is $+2$.
b. The sodium ion has a charge of $+1$, and each of the four oxide ions has a charge of -2. The charge of chromium, x, is calculated as follows.

$$\begin{aligned} 1(+1) + x + 4(-2) &= 0 \\ 1 + x + (-8) &= 0 \\ x &= +7 \end{aligned}$$

The charge of the chromium ion is $+7$. Since there is only one chromium ion in the compound, the oxidation state of chromium is $+7$.
c. The sodium ions each have a charge of $+1$, and the seven oxide ions each have a charge of -2. The charge of the two chromium ions, $2x$, is calculated as follows.

$$\begin{aligned} 2(+1) + 2x + 7(-2) &= 0 \\ 2 + 2x + (-14) &= 0 \\ 2x &= +12 \\ x &= +6 \end{aligned}$$

The charge of each chromium ion is $+6$, and the two Cr^{6+} ions combine for a total charge of $+12$. The oxidation state of chromium is $+6$.

PRACTICE PROBLEM 22.1

Give the charge and oxidation state of the indicated metal in each compound.

a. Co in $Co(OH)_3$
b. Mn in $KMnO_4$
c. Mn in K_2MnO_4

Hint: Recall that the overall charge of an ionic compound (zero) is the sum of the charges of each ion in the compound. Set up an equation where the quantity and charges of each of the known ions, as well as the unknown ion, are added and the equation is set equal to zero. Solve for the charge of the unknown ion, and recall the relationship between charge and oxidation state.

SECTION REVIEW

- Oxidation states are represented by Roman numerals when naming ions of metals that have more than one possible charge.
- This system, known as the Stock system, is the preferred method for naming variable-charge metal cations.

22.2 The Properties of Transition Metals

GOALS

- Identify the electron configurations and physical properties of transition metals.
- Differentiate the electron configurations and physical properties of transition metals from those of main group elements.

Background Review

Chapter 8 The Quantum Model of the Atom: Section 8.3—Electron Shells, Subshells, and Orbitals; Section 8.4—Energy-Level Diagrams; Section 8.5—Electron Configurations

ELECTRON CONFIGURATIONS OF THE *d*-BLOCK ELEMENTS AND IONS

Section 8.5 discussed the periodicity of electron configurations. As shown in Table 22.1, the outer electrons of period 4 transition metals occupy the 3*d* subshell. Similarly, the outer electrons of period 5 transition metals occupy the 4*d* subshell. In general, the valence *d* orbitals of a transition metal of period *n* are located in the $(n-1)d$ subshell. Electron configurations in Table 22.1 are given using noble gas shorthand notation (Section 8.5).

TABLE 22.1 *d*-Block Electron Configurations for Periods 4–6

Period 4 (3*d*)			Period 5 (4*d*)			Period 6 (5*d*)		
Z	Element	Electron Configuration	*Z*	Element	Electron Configuration	*Z*	Element	Electron Configuration
21	Sc	$[Ar]4s^2 3d^1$	39	Y	$[Kr]5s^2 4d^1$	57	La	$[Xe]6s^2 5d^1$
22	Ti	$[Ar]4s^2 3d^2$	40	Zr	$[Kr]5s^2 4d^2$	72	Hf	$[Xe]6s^2 4f^{14} 5d^2$
23	V	$[Ar]4s^2 3d^3$	41	Nb	$[Kr]5s^1 4d^4$	73	Ta	$[Xe]6s^2 4f^{14} 5d^3$
24	Cr	$[Ar]4s^1 3d^5$	42	Mo	$[Kr]5s^1 4d^5$	74	W	$[Xe]6s^2 4f^{14} 5d^4$
25	Mn	$[Ar]4s^2 3d^5$	43	Tc	$[Kr]5s^2 4d^5$	75	Re	$[Xe]6s^2 4f^{14} 5d^5$
26	Fe	$[Ar]4s^2 3d^6$	44	Ru	$[Kr]5s^1 4d^7$	76	Os	$[Xe]6s^2 4f^{14} 5d^6$
27	Co	$[Ar]4s^2 3d^7$	45	Rh	$[Kr]5s^1 4d^8$	77	Ir	$[Xe]6s^2 4f^{14} 5d^7$
28	Ni	$[Ar]4s^2 3d^8$	46	Pd	$[Kr]5s^0 4d^{10}$	78	Pt	$[Xe]6s^1 4f^{14} 5d^9$
29	Cu	$[Ar]4s^1 3d^{10}$	47	Ag	$[Kr]5s^1 4d^{10}$	79	Au	$[Xe]6s^1 4f^{14} 5d^{10}$
30	Zn	$[Ar]4s^2 3d^{10}$	48	Cd	$[Kr]5s^2 4d^{10}$	80	Hg	$[Xe]6s^2 4f^{14} 5d^{10}$

Section 8.5 and Table 22.1 show electron configurations written in *periodic table order* where the *ns* subshell comes before the $(n-1)d$. It is important to note, however, that the outer *s* electrons of transition metals (beginning with scandium) are lost during ionization before the outer *d* electrons. For example, the electron configuration of cobalt, Co, is $[Ar]4s^2 3d^7$ and the electron configuration of cobalt(II), Co^{2+}, is $[Ar]3d^7$. The correct electron configuration of iron(II), Fe^{2+}, is $[Ar]3d^6$, rather than $[Ar]4s^2 3d^4$, because electrons are lost from the outer *s* orbital first. Similarly, the electron configuration of iron(III), Fe^{3+}, is $[Ar]3d^5$.

For most transition metals, the outer *s* electrons ionize before the outer *d* electrons.

FIGURE 22.1 Video Tutorial: Counting *d* Electrons in Transition Metal Ions

NOTE: You need to be online to access this video.
This video shows how to write electron configurations for Co(II) and Cr(III) and determine their numbers of *d* electrons.

For the sake of correctly predicting the electron configurations of the majority of the transition metal ions, it is useful to start by writing the electron configuration of the neutral atom as usual (i.e., periodic table order), and then preferentially remove the outermost *s* electrons when forming the ion. For example, for titanium(II), Ti^{2+}, start by writing the configuration of titanium, Ti, as usual, $[Ar]4s^2 3d^2$. For Ti^{2+}, the two outer *s* electrons are removed, giving a correct electron configuration of $[Ar]3d^2$.

The periodic table is a powerful predictive tool, but it does have some limitations as described previously. Chromium and copper have electron configurations that are different than what would be predicted (Section 8.5). Chromium, Cr, has an electron configuration of $[Ar]4s^1 3d^5$, rather than $[Ar]4s^0 3d^6$. Copper, Cu, has an electron configuration of $[Ar]4s^1 3d^{10}$, rather than $[Ar]4s^2 3d^9$. As shown in Table 22.1, there are several other *d*-block elements with s^1 or s^0 in their outer electron configurations, rather than s^2 as would be predicted.

The video in Figure 22.1 shows how to write electron configurations and count the number of *d* electrons in transition metal ions.

Example 22.2

Give the electron configurations of the following atoms or ions.

a. V(0)
b. V(III)
c. Mo(IV)

Solution

a. Vanadium(0) has 23 total electrons and its electron configuration has an argon core of 18 electrons, leaving five outer electrons. Two electrons occupy the 4*s* orbital, and the remaining three electrons occupy the 3*d* subshell. The electron configuration of V(0) is $[Ar]4s^23d^3$.

b. The electron configuration of V(0) from part a is $[Ar]4s^23d^3$. For V(III), the three highest-energy electrons, the two 4*s* electrons and one of the 3*d* electrons, are removed to give the +3 ion. The electron configuration of V(III) is $[Ar]3d^2$.

c. First, determine the electron configuration of Mo(0). Molybdenum has 42 total electrons, and its electron configuration has a krypton core of 36 electrons. Two electrons occupy the 5*s* orbital and four electrons occupy the 4*d* subshell. The electron configuration of Mo(0) is $[Kr]5s^24d^4$.

For Mo(IV), the two 5*s* electrons and two of the 4*d* electrons are removed to give the +4 ion. The electron configuration of Mo(IV) is $[Kr]4d^2$.

PRACTICE PROBLEM 22.2

Give the electron configurations of the following atoms or ions.

a. Sc(0)

b. Sc(II)

Hint: Determine the total number of electrons, and use the nearest noble gas to determine the abbreviated electron configuration (Section 8.5). Recall that for transition metals, the outer *s* electrons are ionized before the outer *d* electrons.

COMMON OXIDATION STATES

Common oxidation states for period 4 transition metals are shown in Table 22.2. Note that the +2 oxidation state, resulting from the loss of both electrons in the outer *s* orbital, is common for most of these elements. This is because electrons in *s* orbitals are relatively easy to remove. For a given element, the variety of oxidation states peaks halfway across the *d* block (Mn can exhibit six different oxidation states) and decreases again toward the end of the block. A major reason for the decrease is an increase in effective nuclear charge, which makes it harder to remove *d* electrons. In other words, going from left to right across the *d* block, the outer *d* electrons of transition metals are not as well *shielded* (Section 9.2) from the positive charge of their nuclei. For example, it is relatively difficult to ionize nickel and copper to the +3 oxidation state, and zinc compounds with an oxidation state other than +2 are unknown.

Transition metals of the fifth and sixth periods, which possess 4*d* and 5*d* electrons, respectively, are able to achieve higher common oxidation states because the outer *d* orbitals are more diffuse and are located farther from the positive charge of the nucleus. Oxidation states of +8 are achievable in elements such as ruthenium and osmium. It is also relatively easy to oxidize 4*d* and 5*d* transition metals on the right side of the *d* block past the +2 state. For example, many stable Pd(IV) and Pt(IV) compounds exist. Several stable Au(III) compounds are also known.

TABLE 22.2 Oxidation States of Period 4 (3*d*) Transition Metals

	+1	+2	+3	+4	+5	+6	+7
Sc			Common				
Ti		Uncommon	Uncommon	Common			
V		Uncommon	Uncommon	Common	Common		
Cr		Uncommon	Common	Uncommon	Uncommon	Common	
Mn		Common	Uncommon	Common	Uncommon	Uncommon	Common
Fe		Common	Common	Uncommon	Uncommon	Uncommon	
Co		Common	Common	Uncommon			
Ni		Common	Uncommon	Uncommon			
Cu	Uncommon	Common	Uncommon				
Zn		Common					

Empty cells indicate an extremely rare or nonexistent oxidation state for that element.

Example 22.3

Of the metals Sc, Cr, and Zn, select

a. the one that is most likely to exist with a stable +6 oxidation state.

b. the one in which it is most difficult to remove electrons from *d* orbitals.

Solution

a. The likelihood of higher oxidation states peaks halfway across the *d* block, as shown in Table 22.2. Chromium is closer to the middle of the *d* block than scandium or zinc. Therefore, Cr is most likely to exist with a stable oxidation state of +6.

b. The nuclear charge of the transition metals increases from left to right across the *d* block. Therefore, of the three given metals, zinc's outer electrons experience the greatest degree of nuclear charge and are the most difficult to remove. In fact, the only stable oxidation state of zinc, Zn(II), is formed by the removal of only *s* electrons.

PRACTICE PROBLEM 22.3

Determine whether Sc, Co, or Ir is likely to be most stable in the +4 oxidation state, and explain your reasoning.

Hint: Recall the periodic trends that support high oxidation states and the types of orbitals that are most likely to lose electrons.

ATOMIC RADIUS

As discussed in Section 9.2, the atomic radius of the main group elements generally decreases from left to right across a period. Going from left to right across a period, the outer electrons of the elements become less shielded from the charge of their respective nuclei. However, this trend is only followed by the first few elements of the *d* block. The atomic radii of elements from the middle to right-hand side of the *d* block generally do not change much (Figure 22.2). This is because the number of electrons in the outer *s* orbital is two for most elements. In most cases, all added electrons go into the outer *d* orbital, which has a lower quantum number and is lower in energy. Because these added electrons shield the outer *s* electrons by approximately the same degree, transition metals do not experience as pronounced a contraction of their radii across the *d* block as the main group elements experience across the *p* block.

The atomic radii of transition metals also differ from the atomic radii of main group elements when moving down groups. Section 9.2, noted that the atomic radii of main group elements increase moving down a given group. As shown in Figure 22.2, this trend is seen only between the period 4 (3*d*) and period 5 (4*d*) transition metals. The difference in radii between period 5 (4*d*) and period 6 (5*d*) transition metals is minimal. The reason the radii do not change

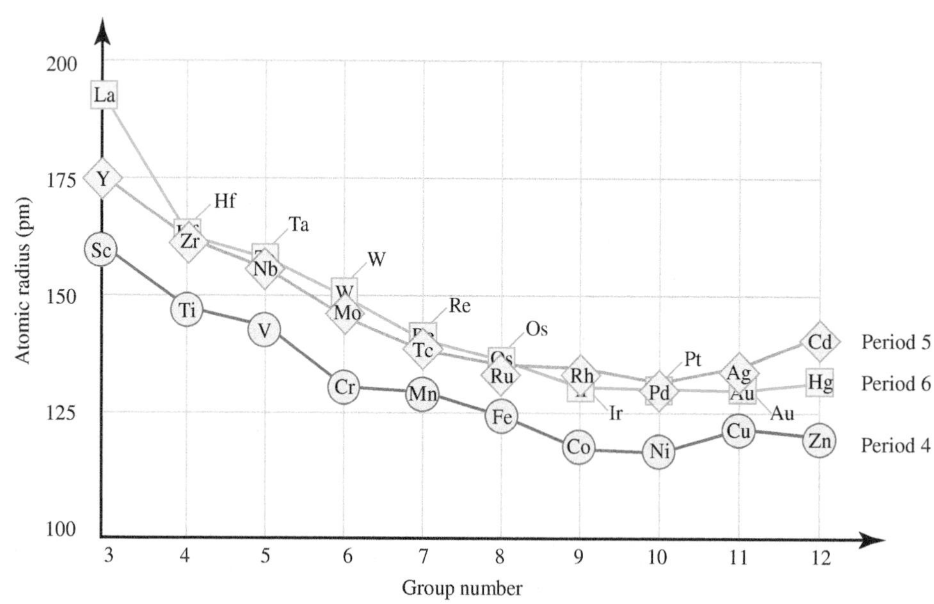

FIGURE 22.2 The Atomic Radii of the *d*-Block Elements

After the elements in groups 3 and 4, the atomic radii do not change much going from left to right across the *d* block, due to a relative lack of change in shielding from the nuclear charge. The poor shielding of electrons in the 4*f* orbitals results in similar radii between transition metals of a given group in periods 5 and 6, a phenomenon known as the lanthanoid contraction.

much is similar to why the radii change so little across a *d*-block period. Beginning with element 57, electrons are placed into the 4*f* orbitals—which are lower in energy than the 5*d* and 6*s* electrons—*and* do not shield the outer electrons as well as *s*, *p*, and *d* orbitals. The filling of electrons into the poorly shielding 4*f* subshell and concurrent increase in nuclear charge results in the 6*s* electrons experiencing a stronger effective nuclear charge. The resulting lack of the expected increase in atomic radius is known as the **lanthanoid contraction**. For a given row, the atomic radii of transition metals between periods 5 and 6 are similar (see Figure 22.2).

Example 22.4

Predict whether Y, Ru, or Cd has the largest atomic radius.

Solution

In a given period, the elements on the left side of the *d* block generally have the largest atomic radius because their outer electrons are better shielded from the charge of their respective nuclei than are the elements in the middle and right side of the *d* block. Yttrium, ruthenium, and cadmium are all period 5 transition metals, and yttrium is in group 1. Therefore, Y is expected to have the largest radii of the three given metals. Figure 22.2 confirms the prediction.

PRACTICE PROBLEM 22.4

Predict which pair of elements has the most similar atomic radii.

a. Sc and Y
b. La and Hg
c. Mo and W

Hint: Recall how the lanthanoid contraction and the positions of elements on the periodic table (see Figure 22.2) affect the difference in radii between two elements.

IONIZATION ENERGY

Like main group elements (Section 9.3), the first ionization energies of transition metals increase from left to right across a period. This is due to an increase in effective nuclear charge. However, in the same way that the atomic radius does not decrease as expected across the *d* block, ionization energy increases more modestly than expected across the *d* block. The reason is largely the same: going from left to right, electrons added to *d* orbitals shield the outer *s* electrons by a similar amount, and this mitigates the increase in ionization energy that is expected. While the ionization energies of main group elements generally decrease down a group, the ionization energies of the periods 4 and 5 (3*d* and 4*d*) transition metals are relatively similar (Figure 22.3). However, the period 6 (5*d*) transition metals have higher first ionization

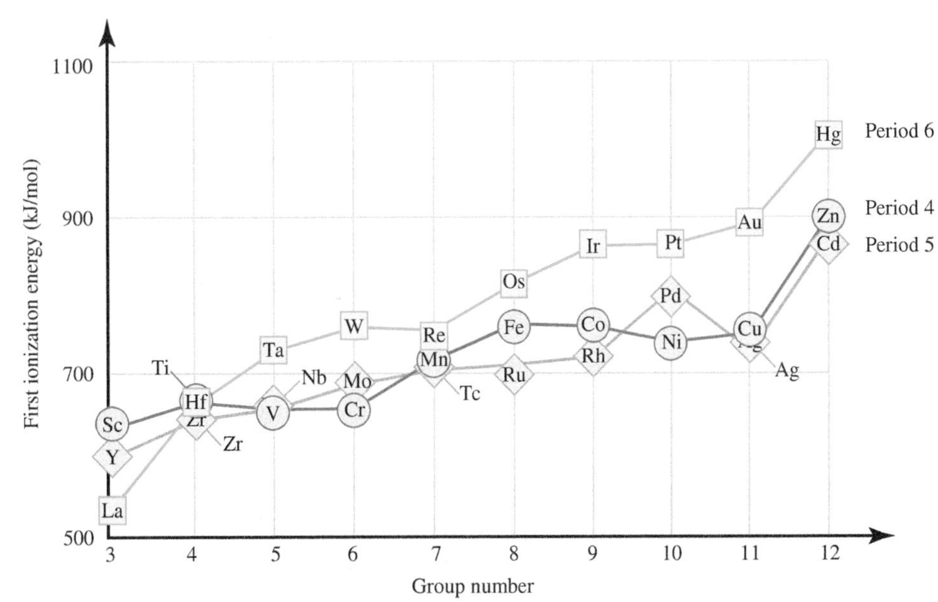

FIGURE 22.3 The First Ionization Energies of the *d*-Block Elements

The ionization first energies of the transition metals increase modestly from left to right across the *d* block. The ionization energies from the periods 4 and 5 transition metals are similar, but the lanthanoid contraction results in an increase in ionization energy between period 5 and period 6 transition metals.

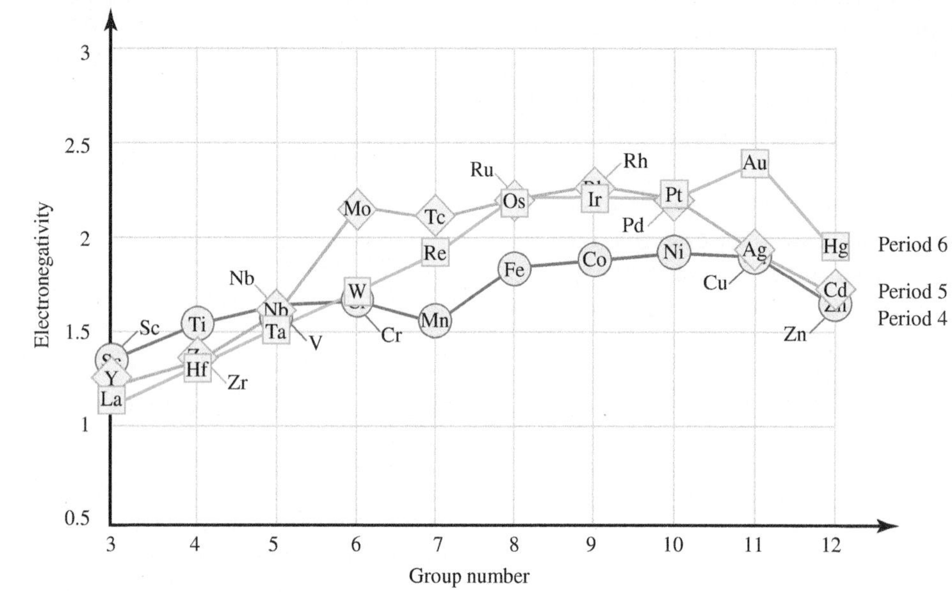

FIGURE 22.4 The Electronegativities of the *d*-Block Elements

The electronegativity of the transition metals increases modestly from left to right across the *d* block. Electronegativity increases going down a group from period 4 to period 5, but the electronegativities of period 5 and period 6 transition metals are very similar.

energies than those in periods 4 and 5. As explained earlier, the lanthanoid contraction renders the atomic radii of 5*d* transition metals similar to the radii of 4*d* transition metals. Given that period 6 metals experience a stronger effective nuclear charge than those in period 5, electrons in the 6*s* orbital are more difficult to remove than would be expected.

ELECTRONEGATIVITY

As discussed in Section 10.3, the electronegativity of main group elements generally increases from left to right across a period and from bottom to top of a group. The electronegativity of the transition metals (Figure 22.4) also increases modestly from left to right across the *d* block. Going down a given group, there is an increase in electronegativity between period 4 and period 5 transition metals. This is due in large part to poor shielding from the relatively diffuse *d* orbitals and the resulting relatively small change in atomic radius between period 4 and period 5 transition metals. However, as shown in Figure 22.4, there is little difference in electronegativity between the elements in period 5 and period 6, and the reason for this is not easily explained.

Example 22.5

a. Predict whether Ti, Rh, or Ir has the highest first ionization energy.
b. Predict whether Fe, Cu, or Pd is the most electronegative.

Solution

a. Figure 22.3 shows that period 6 transition metals tend to have higher first ionization energies than periods 4 and 5 transition metals. As shown in the figure, iridium does indeed have a higher first ionization energy than rhodium and titanium.
b. Electronegativities of periods 5 and 6 transition metals are similar and tend to be higher than those of period 4 transition metals. Iron and copper are both period 4 transition metals, while palladium is a period 5 transition metal. As shown in Figure 22.4, palladium is more electronegative than any of the period 4 transition metals.

PRACTICE PROBLEM 22.5

a. Predict whether Sc, Cu, or Fe has the lowest first ionization energy.
b. Place the elements Mo, Y, and Ru in increasing order of electronegativity.

Hint: The general trend for both first ionization energy and electronegativity is that they increase from left to right across the *d* block.

SECTION REVIEW

- Most transition metals lose their outer *s* electrons before their outer *d* electrons when they are ionized.

- An oxidation state of +2 is common for many transition metals, with the +3 oxidation state being common for many others. Transition metals near the middle of the *d* block tend to have the highest stable oxidation states.
- The shielding effect of lower quantum number *d* electrons prevents transition metals from experiencing the same radius contraction across the *d* block that main group elements experience across the *p* block.
- The filling of electrons into the poorly shielding 4*f* subshell and the concurrent increase in nuclear charge results in 5*d* transition metals having approximately the same atomic radius as 4*d* transition metals. This observation is known as the lanthanoid contraction.
- The first ionization energies of transition metals increase across a period, but do so less drastically than the main group elements.
- Due to the lanthanoid contraction, 5*d* transition metals have higher ionization energies than 4*d* transition metals.
- The electronegativities of the transition metals increase from left to right across a period and from bottom to top within a group, but the increase is less drastic than the corresponding trends for the main group elements.

22.3 Introduction to Coordination Compounds

GOALS

- Define and identify a coordination sphere.
- Define and identify coordinate covalent bonds.
- Identify common ligands and their role in coordination chemistry.

Background Review

Chapter 3 Compounds and the Mole:
Section 3.3—Formulas for Ionic Compounds;
Section 3.4—Naming Ionic Compounds.

Chapter 9 Periodicity and Ionic Bonding:
Section 9.4—Ionic Bonding

Chapter 10 Covalent Bonding:
Section 10.1—Formation of Covalent Bonds

Chapter 16 Acid–Base Theory:
Section 16.9—Lewis Acids and Bases

Chapter 17 Aqueous Equilibria:
Section 17.10—Complex Ion Equilibria, K_f

Chapter 18 Chemical Thermodynamics:
Section 18.1—Entropy and Spontaneity;
Section 18.2—Entropy Changes

COORDINATION COMPOUNDS

Section 17.10 introduced complex ions and the formation constant, K_f. Complex ions consist of transition metals (Lewis acids) that are bonded to **ligands** (Lewis bases). Examples of complex ions include $Ni(NH_3)_6{}^{2+}$ and $Fe(CN)_6{}^{3-}$. Complex ions can associate with *counterions*, ions of opposite charge, to form neutral compounds. Examples include $[Ni(NH_3)_6]Cl_2$ and $K_3[Fe(CN)_6]$, where the chloride and potassium ions, respectively, act as counterions. In this text, the term **coordination compound** is used to describe any complex ion or neutral compound that contains a metal that is complexed by ligands.

The counterions in coordination compounds associate electrostatically with the complex ion. The counterions do not covalently bond to the complex. For example, in the case of $[Co(NH_3)_6]Cl_3$ in Figure 22.5, the six NH_3 ligands covalently bond to Co^{3+}, so they constitute what is known as the **primary coordination sphere**. Ligands inside the brackets are part of the primary coordination sphere. The **coordination number** is the number of atoms that are bonded directly to the metal. In the case of $[Co(NH_3)_6]Cl_3$, the coordination number is six (because the nitrogen atoms of the six NH_3 ligands bond to Co^{3+}). The chloride ions are the counterions, so they are part of the **secondary coordination sphere**. The secondary coordination sphere need not consist of ions. Solvent molecules or portions of large ligands, such as a protein, can interact via intermolecular forces with either the metal ion or the ligands. The structure of $[Co(NH_3)_6]Cl_3$ was first proposed by Swiss chemist Alfred Werner in 1893. Werner's evidence for the three Cl^- ions being weakly associated with $[Co(NH_3)_6]^{3+}$ was substantiated by his precipitation of AgCl when aqueous $AgNO_3$ was added to aqueous $[Co(NH_3)_6]Cl_3$. Precipitation of AgCl would have been more difficult if the Cl^- ions were ligands that were bonded directly to Co^{3+}. Werner was the first person to suggest the two types of interactions that we now refer to as the primary and secondary coordination spheres.

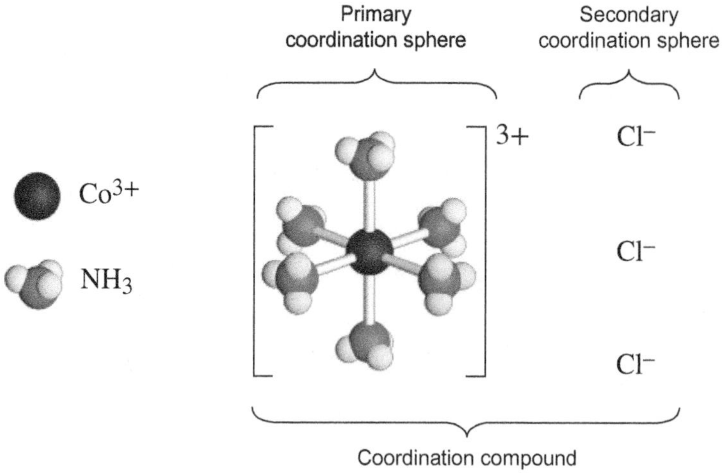

FIGURE 22.5 The Primary and Secondary Coordination Spheres of $[Co(NH_3)_6]Cl_3$

The six NH_3 ligands bond to the Co^{3+} ion via coordinate covalent bonds. The Cl^- ions associate electrostatically (ionically bond) with the positively charged $[Co(NH_3)_6]^{3+}$ complex.

Ions can also act as ligands by bonding to the metal in the primary coordination sphere. In $CoCl_2(NH_3)_4$, both chloride groups are ligands and are part of the primary coordination sphere. Unless an ion or molecule is located outside of a pair of brackets, you should assume that it bonds to the metal center.

> When a coordination compound is written with brackets, groups located inside of the brackets are ligands and part of the primary coordination sphere. Groups located outside of the brackets are part of the secondary coordination sphere. If the compound is written without brackets, all groups are assumed to be ligands and, therefore, part of the primary coordination sphere.

Example 22.6

Determine the coordination number of each coordination compound, and determine which groups are in the primary and secondary coordination spheres.

a. $Cu(H_2O)_6^{2+}$
b. $Pt(NH_3)_2Cl_2$
c. $K_2[PtCl_6]$

Solution

a. $Cu(H_2O)_6^{2+}$ has a coordination number of six. No brackets are shown, so all six H_2O groups are bonded to Cu^{2+} and, therefore, are in the primary coordination sphere.
b. $Pt(NH_3)_2Cl_2$ has a coordination number of four. No brackets are shown, so all NH_3 and Cl^- groups are bonded to Pt^{2+} and, therefore, are in the primary coordination sphere.
c. $K_2[PtCl_6]$ has a coordination number of six. The six Cl^- groups are inside the brackets and, therefore, constitute the primary coordination sphere. The two potassium ions that are outside of the brackets are part of the secondary coordination sphere.

PRACTICE PROBLEM 22.6

Determine the coordination number of each coordination compound, and determine which groups are in the primary and secondary coordination spheres.

a. $[Fe(NH_3)_6](NO_3)_3$
b. $Rh(H_2O)_2Br_2$

Hint: Recall that groups that are outside of the primary coordination sphere are shown outside of the brackets of the complex. If the complex does not contain brackets, you can assume that all of the ligands are in the primary coordination sphere.

BONDING IN COORDINATION COMPOUNDS

Complexes are formed when metals and metal ions act as Lewis acids by accepting electron density from Lewis base ligands. An example is shown in Figure 22.6, where four ammonia molecules coordinate a Zn^{2+} ion via the lone-pair electrons on the nitrogen atoms of each ammonia molecule. These types of bonds are known as **coordinate covalent bonds** or dative bonds. What makes a coordinate

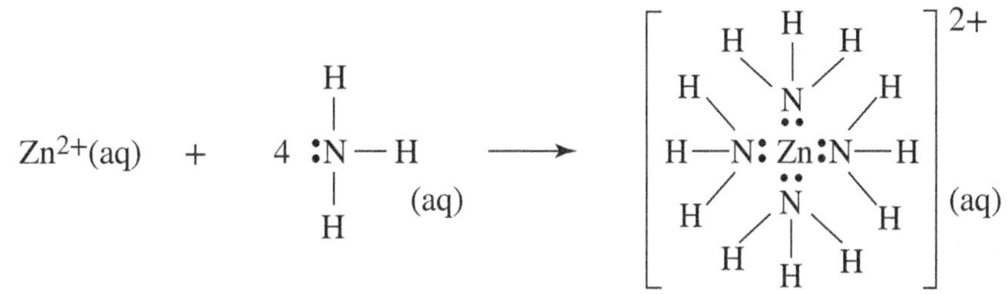

FIGURE 22.6 The Coordinate Covalent Bonds of $[Zn(NH_3)_4]^{2+}$

Zn^{2+} acts as a Lewis acid and four NH_3 ligands act as Lewis bases to form the complex ion $[Zn(NH_3)_4]^{2+}$. Nitrogen, N, is the donor atom in each ligand.

covalent bond different from a covalent bond is that only one atom donates all the shared electrons. Ligands in coordination compounds all have at least one lone pair of electrons that is available for bonding. The atoms within a ligand that donate a lone pair are called **donor atoms**.

Table 22.3 shows the formulas of ligands commonly found in coordination compounds. Some ligands, such as NH_3, can form only one bond to a metal, whereas others have multiple donor atoms with lone-pair electrons that can bond to the metal. Ligands that can form only one bond with a metal atom are known as **monodentate** (this term is a combination of Greek and Latin meaning "one tooth"). Ligands that can form more than one bond to a metal are known as **polydentate**. For example, oxalate ion (ox) and ethylenediamine (en), each with two donor atoms, are **bidentate**. Ethylenediaminetetraacetate (EDTA), with six donor atoms, is **hexadentate**.

TABLE 22.3 Some Common Ligands

Molecule or Ion	Ligand Name*	Coordination	Donor Atom(s)
NH_3	Ammine	Monodentate	N
H_2O	Aqua	Monodentate	O
N^{3-}	Azido	Monodentate	N
Br^-	Bromido	Monodentate	Br
CO_3^{2-}	Carbonato	Bidentate	O and O
CO	Carbonyl	Monodentate	C
Cl^-	Chlorido	Monodentate	Cl
CN^-	Cyanido	Monodentate	C
$NH_2CH_2CH_2NH_2$ (en)	Ethylenediamine	Bidentate	N and N
$EDTA^{4-}$	Ethylenediaminetetraacetato	Hexadentate	Four O and two N
F^-	Fluorido	Monodentate	F
OH^-	Hydroxido	Monodentate	O
I^-	Iodido	Monodentate	I
NO_2^-	Nitrito	Monodentate	N or O
NO^+	Nitrosyl	Monodentate	N
$C_2O_4^{2-}$	Oxalato	Bidentate	O and O
O^{2-}	Oxido	Monodentate	O
PH_3	Phosphane	Monodentate	P

*Alternate names exist for many ligands. This text uses International Union of Pure and Applied Chemistry (IUPAC) recommendations, except for en and EDTA, for which the common names persist in most textbooks.

Example 22.7

Predict whether these ligands are monodentate, bidentate, and so on.

a. F^-
b. bis(dimethylphosphino)ethane,

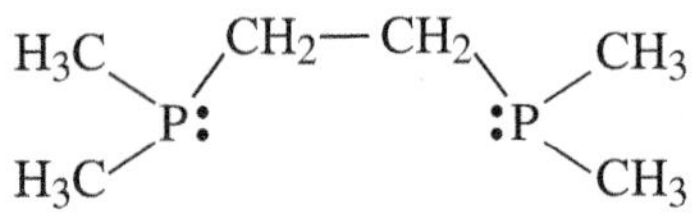

Solution

Count the number of atoms with at least one lone pair. These are the potential donor atoms. The number of donor atoms is equal to the number of coordinate covalent bonds a ligand can make.

a. If you draw the Lewis structure of fluoride ion, you will see that it contains four lone-pair electrons. However, all of these are located on the same atom, so only one lone pair can form a bond to a metal. Fluoride is monodentate.
b. Bis(dimethylphosphino)ethane contains lone-pair electrons on two different phosphorus atoms. Both of these phosphorus atoms can act as Lewis bases and form bonds to a metal. Bis(dimethylphosphino)ethane is bidentate.

EVERYDAY CONNECTION

Polyethylene is the plastic found in milk jugs and plastic bags. Transition metal coordination compounds are widely used in the industrial synthesis of polyethylene, which is a polymer (Section 21.6). The catalyst shown above the reaction arrow is dichloridobis(cyclopentadienyl)titanium(IV), $[Cp_2TiCl_2]$, where Cp^- is the cyclopentadienyl ligand, $C_5H_6^-$, shown as a five-membered ring. Chloridodiethylaluminum, $[Et_2AlCl]$, which mediates the insertion of the reactant molecules into the polymer, is also a coordination compound, where Et is the ethyl ligand, CH_3CH_2. The catalyst converts the small molecule ethylene, $CH_2{=}CH_2$, to the very long hydrocarbon polyethylene.

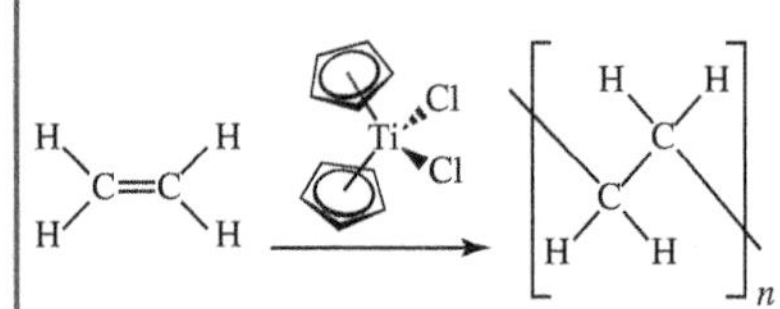

Ethylene $[Et_2AlCl]$ Polyethylene

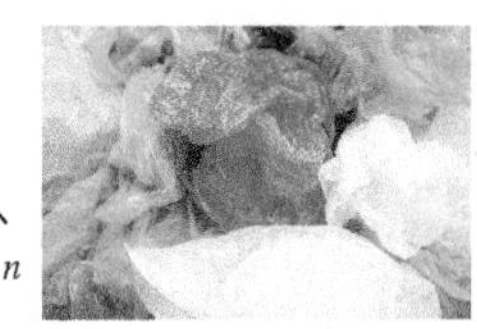

daizuoxin/iStock/Getty Images

PRACTICE PROBLEM 22.7

Predict whether these ligands are monodentate, bidentate, and so on.

a. acetylacetone
b. pyridine

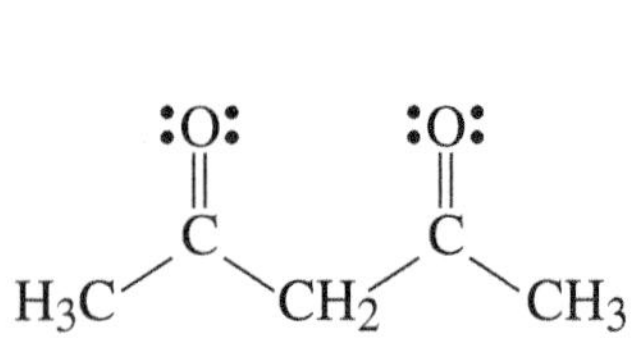

Acetylacetone
(a)

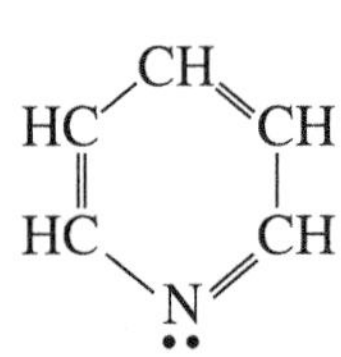

Pyridine
(b)

Hint: Count the number of atoms with at least one lone pair.

Bidentate and polydentate ligands are also known as **chelating agents**. Chelating agents are known for their unusually stable complexes with metals. As explained in Section 17.10, the formation constant, K_f, of a coordination complex is an indication of its thermodynamic stability. As K_f increases, so does the stability of the complex. Compare the reactions of $[Ni(H_2O)_6]^{2+}$ with pyridine (py), a monodentate ligand, and bipyridine (bipy), a bidentate chelating ligand.

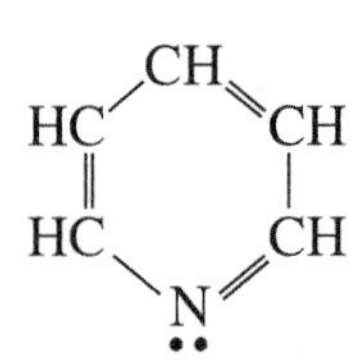

Pyridine (py)

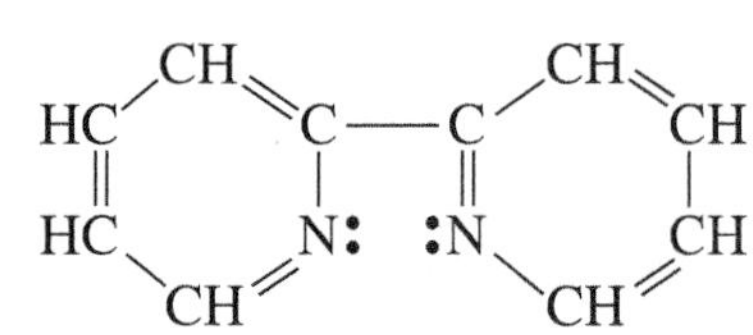

Bipyridine (bipy)

$$[Ni(H_2O)_6]^{2+}(aq) + 6\,py(aq) \rightleftharpoons [Ni(py)_6]^{2+}(aq) + 6\,H_2O(l) \quad K_f = 6.3 \times 10^9$$

$$[Ni(H_2O)_6]^{2+}(aq) + 3\,bipy(aq) \rightleftharpoons [Ni(bipy)_3]^{2+}(aq) + 6\,H_2O(l) \quad K_f = 2.0 \times 10^9$$

The reaction of the chelating ligand bipyridine with $[Ni(H_2O)_6]^{2+}$ has a formation constant that is 3×10^9 greater than the corresponding reaction

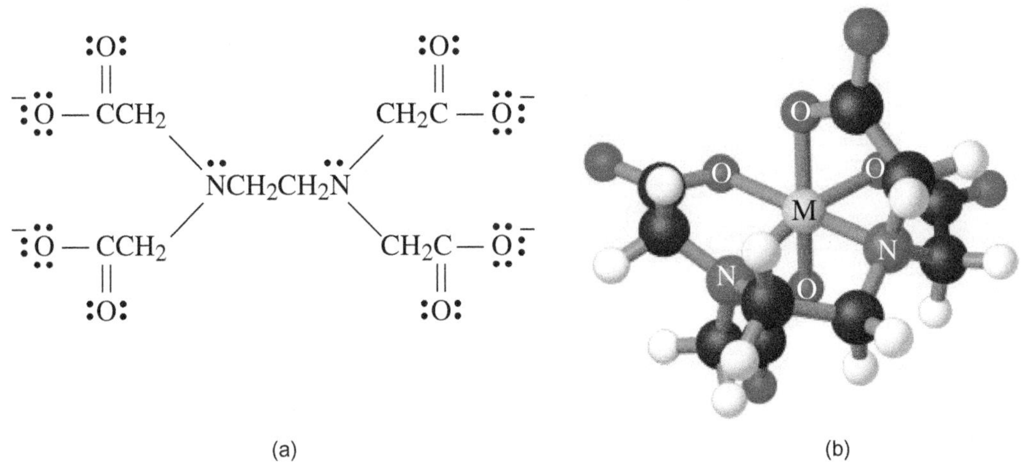

FIGURE 22.7 EDTA^{4-} Structure

(a) Lewis structure of ethylenediaminetetraacetate, EDTA, a hexadentate ligand with a −4 charge. (b) Ball-and-stick model of an EDTA complex where M is a generic metal.

with pyridine. The greater general stability of coordination compounds with chelating ligands versus those with monodentate ligands is known as the **chelate effect**. The chelate effect is largely explained in terms of the differences in entropy change, ΔS. Section 18.1 explained that entropy is the measure of disorder within a system. A chemical reaction that has more moles of products than reactants generally exhibits an increase in entropy. In the reaction of $[Ni(H_2O)_6]^{2+}$ with pyridine, 7 moles of reactants produces 7 moles of products. There is no change in entropy. However, in the reaction of $[Ni(H_2O)_6]^{2+}$ with bipyridine, 4 moles of reactants produces 7 moles of products. In this case, there is a net increase of 3 moles. The thermodynamic favorability of this increase in entropy renders $[Ni(bipy)_3]^{2+}$ a more thermodynamically stable complex than $[Ni(py)_6]^{2+}$.

The polydentate ligand ethylenediaminetetraacetate, $EDTA^{4-}$ (Figure 22.7), can form up to six bonds with a single transition metal ion, with K_f values typically in large excess of 10^{10}. EDTA is often used to bond to a metal ion that interferes with a chemical reaction or analysis.

Many biological molecules also chelate transition metal ions. Transferrin is a large biomolecule known as a glycoprotein that regulates the concentration of iron(III), Fe^{3+}, in biological fluids. Iron is chelated by four amino acid ligands from the protein backbone of transferrin and, interestingly, two oxygen atoms from a free CO_3^{2-} ion. Transferrin binds iron(III) very strongly, with a K_f on the order of 10^{20}.

EVERYDAY CONNECTION

EDTA is sometimes used to treat lead or mercury poisoning. Since EDTA bonds to lead and mercury, it prevents these heavy metals from interacting with bodily systems in other, harmful ways. The EDTA is usually administered in the form of a calcium complex, and the heavy metal displaces the calcium.

$$[Ca(EDTA)]^{2-}(aq) + Hg^{2+}(aq) \rightleftharpoons [Hg(EDTA)]^{2-}(aq) + Ca^{2+}(aq)$$

In this way, the heavy metal is biologically detoxified and allowed to be excreted rather than absorbed by the body.

COMMON GEOMETRIES OF COORDINATION COMPOUNDS

Some common geometries of coordination compounds are shown in Table 22.4. Compounds with coordination numbers of two have linear geometries. Some coordination compounds with coordination numbers of four have tetrahedral geometries, while others have square planar geometries. Coordination compounds with d^{10} configurations in their outer d subshell, such as Cu(I) and Zn(II), tend to be tetrahedral. Four-coordinate complexes that have metals with d^8 electron configurations, such as Pt(II) and Pd(II), are typically square planar. Most six-coordinate complexes have an octahedral geometry.

TABLE 22.4 Common Geometries of Coordination Compounds

Coordination Number	Geometry	Model
2	Linear	
4	Square planar	
	Tetrahedral	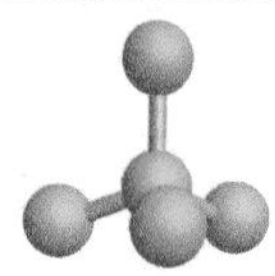
6	Octahedral	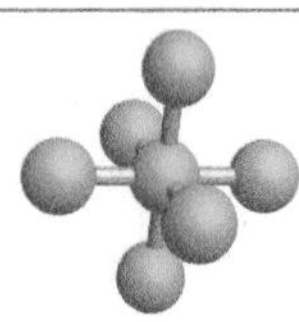

Example 22.8

Determine the likely geometry of the following coordination compounds.

a. $[Ag(H_2O)_2]^+$
b. $[Pd(NH_3)_4]^{2+}$

Solution

a. $[Ag(H_2O)_2]^+$ contains two monodentate ligands, so it has a coordination number of two. It has a linear geometry.
b. $[Pd(NH_3)_4]^{2+}$ contains four monodentate ligands. With a coordination number of four, the complex could be either square planar or tetrahedral. If the electron configuration of the metal is d^8, assume the complex is square planar. If the electron configuration of the metal is d^{10}, assume the complex is tetrahedral. Pd(II) has a d^8 electron configuration, so $[Pd(NH_3)_4]^{2+}$ has a square planar geometry rather than a tetrahedral geometry.

PRACTICE PROBLEM 22.8

Determine the likely geometry of the following coordination compounds.

a. $[CoCl_6]^{3-}$
b. $[Cd(NH_3)_4]^{2+}$

Hint: For coordination numbers two and six, the geometries can be assumed to be linear and octahedral, respectively. With a coordination number of four, the complex could be either square planar or tetrahedral. In this situation, if the electron configuration of the metal is d^8, assume the complex is square planar, and if the electron configuration of the metal is d^{10}, assume the complex is tetrahedral.

SECTION REVIEW

- A coordination compound is any complex ion or neutral compound that contains a metal that is complexed by ligands via coordinate covalent bonds.
- The metal center and covalently bound ligands constitute the coordination compound's primary coordination sphere. The coordination number is the number of atoms that covalently bond to the metal.
- Other groups that interact with the metal or ligands via intermolecular forces are part of the secondary coordination sphere.
- Ligands are classified as monodentate (one bond), bidentate (two bonds), and polydentate (three or more bonds) based on the number of atoms on each ligand that bond to the metal.
- Bidentate and polydentate ligands, known as chelating agents, form coordination compounds with unusually high K_f values, due in large part to a thermodynamically favorable increase in entropy.
- Common geometries of coordination compounds include linear (two-coordinate), tetrahedral (four-coordinate), square planar (four-coordinate), and octahedral (six-coordinate).

22.4 Nomenclature of Coordination Compounds

GOAL

- Apply the systematic rules for naming coordination compounds.

Background Review

Chapter 3 Compounds and the Mole: Section 3.2—Naming Binary Covalent Compounds; 3.4—Naming Ionic Compounds

Chapter 4 Chemical Reactions and Aqueous Solutions: Section 4.6—Oxidation States and Redox Reactions

As discussed in Section 3.4, to name an ionic compound, you name first the cation and then the anion. To name a complex cation or anion, you must be able to determine the oxidation state of the metal. As discussed in Section 4.6,

Steve Lemon, Macmillan Learning

FIGURE 22.8 Video Tutorial: Oxidation State of Metal in a Coordination Compound

NOTE: You need to be online to access this video.
This video shows how to find the oxidation state of Ni in $Na_2[Ni(CN)_4]$ and Cr in $[Cr(H_2O)_4(OH)_2](NO_3)_2$.

the overall charge of any compound or ion is the sum of the individual oxidation states. In the case of a complex ion, the overall charge is the sum of the charge of the metal ion and the charges of all the ligands. If the charges of each ligand and the overall charge of the complex are known, the charge, and thus oxidation state of the metal ion, can be determined. For $[CoCl_6]^{3-}$, the overall charge of the complex is -3. Table 22.3 shows that each Cl ligand has a charge of -1. The combined charge of the ligands is -6, and the overall charge of the complex is -3, so the oxidation state of Co, denoted as x below, must be $+3$.

$$[CoCl_6]^{3-}$$
$$x + 6(-1) = -3$$
$$x - 6 = -3$$
$$x = +3$$

Figure 22.8 demonstrates how to find the oxidation state of the central metal in coordination compounds.

Example 22.9

Determine the oxidation state of the metal in each compound or ion.

a. $[Pd(CN)_6]^{2-}$
b. $[Ni(CO)_4]$
c. $[MnCl_5(NH_3)]NO_3$

Solution

a. The overall charge of the complex is -2. As shown in Table 22.3, the charge of the CN ligand is -1. If x represents the oxidation state of Pd, then

$$x + 6(-1) = -2$$
$$x = +4$$

That is, the oxidation state of Pd is $+4$.

b. The overall charge of the complex is 0. Table 22.3 shows that the CO ligand has no charge. If x represents the oxidation state of Ni, then

$$x + 4(0) = 0$$
$$x = 0$$

That is, the oxidation state of Ni is 0. *(While most coordination compounds consist of metal ions, it is important to note that some do contain metals in their 0 oxidation states.)*

c. The overall charge of the complex is 0. There are three different types of ligands in this complex. From Table 22.3, Cl has a charge of -1, NH_3 has a charge of 0, and NO_3 has a charge of -1. If x represents the oxidation state of Mn, then

$$x + 5(-1) + 1(0) + 1(-1) = 0$$
$$x = +6$$

The oxidation state of Mn is $+6$. Note that although NO_3^- is in the secondary coordination sphere of the complex and technically not a ligand, its -1 charge still contributes to the overall charge of the coordination compound. As an alternative method, you could omit the NO_3^- ion and calculate the oxidation state of Mn in $[MnCl_5(NH_3)]^+$. You would arrive at the same result: the oxidation state of Mn is $+6$.

PRACTICE PROBLEM 22.9

Determine the oxidation state of the metal in each compound.

a. $[RhCl(NH_3)_3]^+$
b. $[NiCl_4]^{2-}$

Hint: Consider that halide ligands have a -1 charge and that NH_3 is neutral in charge (see Table 22.3). The charge of an ionic compound is the sum of the charges of each ligand and ion in the compound. Set up an equation where the quantity and charges of each of the known ions, as well as the unknown ion, are added and the equation is set equal to the overall complex charge. Solve for the charge of the unknown ion, and recall the relationship between charge and oxidation state.

SYSTEMATIC NAMING RULES

Here are the rules for naming the primary coordination sphere in a coordination compound.

1. Name the ligands first.
   - For anionic ligands, the ending *–e* changes to *–o*. For example, chloride becomes chlorido, carbonate becomes carbonato, and nitrite becomes nitrito.

   - Neutral ligands often have special names (see Table 22.3) (e.g., H_2O is aqua and NH_3 is ammine).
2. If multiple ligands exist in a coordination compound, list them alphabetically by name. For example, aqua (H_2O) is named before bromido (Br^-).
3. Add prefixes to indicate the number (if greater than one) of a particular type of ligand.
   - Use Greek prefixes (*di–*, *tri–*, *tetra–*, *penta–*, *hexa–*) for most ligands. For example, four Cl^- ligands are named tetrachlorido.
   - In cases where the ligand name itself already contains a Greek prefix, such as triphenylphosphine, use alternate prefixes *bis–*, *tris–*, *tetrakis–*, *pentakis–*, *hexakis–*, and so forth to specify quantity. Additionally, enclose the name of the ligand in parentheses. For example, bis(triphenylphospine) denotes the presence of two triphenyphosphine ligands.
   - Do not consider the prefixes when listing ligands alphabetically. For example, *tetraaqua* comes before *dibromido* because *aqua* comes before *bromido* alphabetically.
4. Name the metal last.
   - If the complex is positive or neutral, the metal is named as normal. For example, in a complex cation, Fe^{3+} uses the name iron(III).
   - If the complex is negative, the metal name ends in *–ate*. For example, in a complex anion, Co^{2+} is named cobaltate(II). Additionally, the Latin root is used for some metals (e.g., ferrate for iron), as shown in Table 22.5.

What is the name of the complex ion $[Co(NH_3)_6]^{3+}$? According to Table 22.3, NH_3 is neutral, so the $+3$ charge of the complex is the oxidation state of copper. Table 22.3 also shows that, when part of a coordination complex, NH_3 is named *ammine*. Using the prefix for the number six, $[Co(NH_3)_6]^{3+}$ is named hexamminecobalt(III). Note that the *–ate* suffix is not appended to cobalt because the overall complex charge is positive.

What, then, is the name of the neutral coordination compound $[Co(NH_3)_6]Cl_3$? The Cl^- groups are anions, not ligands, so you simply append the word *chloride* to the previously named complex ion. $[Co(NH_3)_6]Cl_3$ is hexamminecobalt(III) chloride.

$K_2[Pt(CN)_4]$ is made up of potassium cations and the $[Pt(CN)_4]^{2-}$ anion. The CN^- ligands are given the name *cyanido* (see Table 22.3). The oxidation state of Pt is $+2$ and, because the complex $[Pt(CN)_4]^{2-}$ is negative, platinum(II) becomes *platinate(II)* (see Table 22.5). $K_2[Pt(CN)_4]$ is potassium tetracyanidoplatinate(II).

For $[Cu(H_2O)_4Cl]Br$, the H_2O ligands are given the name *aqua* (see Table 22.3), and the Cl^- ligand is *chlorido*. Given that the Cl^- ligand and the Br^- anion both have charges of -1 and H_2O is neutral, the oxidation state of Cu is $+2$. Naming the ligands in alphabetical order, but ignoring any Greek prefixes when doing so, $[Cu(H_2O)_4Cl]Br$ is tetraaquachloridocopper(II) bromide.

TABLE 22.5 Names of Some Common Metals Found in Anionic Coordination Complexes

Name	Symbol	Name in Complex Anion
Chromium	Cr	Chromate
Cobalt	Co	Cobaltate
Copper	Cu	Cuprate
Gold	Au	Aurate
Iron	Fe	Ferrate
Lead	Pb	Plumbate
Manganese	Mn	Manganate
Nickel	Ni	Nickelate
Platinum	Pt	Platinate
Vanadium	V	Vanadate
Zinc	Zn	Zincate

Example 22.10

Name the following coordination compounds.

a. $Na_2[Ni(CN)_4]$
b. $[Fe(en)_3]Cl_2$

Solution

a. This compound is made up of Na^+ cations and the $[Ni(CN)_4]^{2-}$ anion. The CN^- ligands are named *cyanido* (see Table 22.3). Given the combined -4 charge of the ligands, Ni must have an oxidation state of $+2$ to give $[Ni(CN)_4]^{2-}$ an overall charge of -2. As part of an anionic complex, nickel should be named *nickelate* (see Table 22.5). Therefore, $Na_2[Ni(CN)_4]$ is named sodium tetracyanidonickelate(II).
b. Table 22.3 indicates that ethylenediamine, en, is a neutral molecule. Therefore, the oxidation state of Fe is the same as the complex ion charge, which is $+2$ to balance the charge of the two Cl^- anions. Recall that when a ligand contains a Greek prefix, the alternative naming system is used to denote the number of those ligands. Therefore, the name *tris(ethylenediamine)* describes the en ligands. The full name of $[Fe(en)_3]Cl_2$ is tris(ethylenediamine) iron(II) chloride.

PRACTICE PROBLEM 22.10

Name the following coordination compounds.

a. $[Cr(H_2O)_4(OH)_2](NO_3)_2$

b. $K_3[Co(C_2O_4)_3]$

Hint: Start by identifying the names and charges of the ligands, using Table 22.3 as a reference as needed. Then use the charges of the ligands and counterions to determine the oxidation state of the metal in the complex. Finally, piece together the names of the components according to the systematic naming rules.

SECTION REVIEW

- The oxidation states of coordination compounds are determined in an analogous manner to the oxidation states of ionic compounds (Section 4.6).
- A systematic method is used to name coordination compounds.

22.5 Isomerism in Coordination Compounds

GOAL

- Define, explain, and identify four major types of isomerism in coordination compounds.

Background Review

Chapter 11 Molecular Shape and Bonding Theories: Section 11.1—VSEPR and Molecular Geometry

Chapter 21 Organic Chemistry: Section 21.3—Introduction to Isomerism

Isomers are compounds that have the same chemical formula but a different arrangement of atoms (Section 21.3). This section discusses the structural isomers and stereoisomers of coordination compounds. As discussed in Section 21.3, structural isomers are compounds with the same chemical formula but with different atom connectivities, whereas stereoisomers have the same atom connectivities but a different arrangement of atoms in space.

STRUCTURAL ISOMERS

As shown in the flowchart in Figure 22.9, the two main types of structural isomers that will be discussed are coordination isomers and linkage isomers. **Coordination isomers**, also sometimes called *ionization isomers*, are two compounds that differ in the types of groups that are located inside and outside the primary coordination sphere. For example, $[Co(NH_5)Cl]Br$ and $[Co(NH_3)_5Br]Cl$ are coordination isomers. In the first compound, Cl^- is a ligand in the primary coordination sphere and

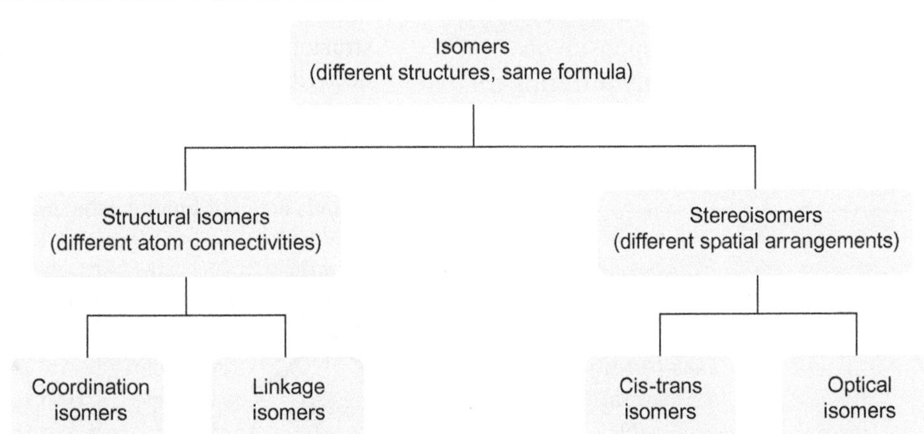

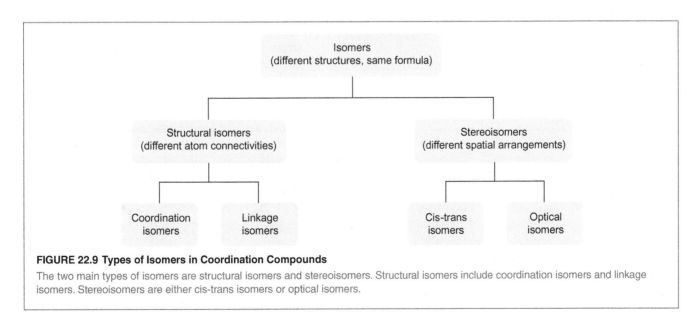

FIGURE 22.9 Types of Isomers in Coordination Compounds

The two main types of isomers are structural isomers and stereoisomers. Structural isomers include coordination isomers and linkage isomers. Stereoisomers are either cis-trans isomers or optical isomers.

Br^- is an anion in the secondary coordination sphere. In the second, Br^- is a ligand and Cl^- is an anion in the secondary coordination sphere.

Linkage isomers are two coordination compounds that share a common ligand that bonds to the metal through different groups. Given that the number of ligands that can bond to a metal via multiple groups is limited, linkage isomers are relatively uncommon. A classic example of a ligand that can bond through different groups is SCN^-. As a ligand, SCN^- can be either the thiocyano group, $[S{-}C{\equiv}N]^-$, which bonds to the metal through the sulfur atom, or the iso thiocyanato group, $[N{=}C{=}S]^-$, which bonds to the metal through the nitrogen atom. The atom that bonds to the metal (the donor atom) is typically underlined. For example, $[Pd(NH_3)_2Cl(\underline{S}CN)]$ has a thiocyanato linkage, while $[Pd(NH_3)_2Cl(\underline{N}CS)]$ has an isothiocyanato linkage.

STEREOISOMERS

Stereoisomers differ from structural isomers in that their atom connectivities are the same, but the spatial arrangement of atoms is different (Section 21.3). Cis-trans isomers, sometimes referred to as geometric isomers, of coordination compounds describe two compounds that have a different spatial arrangement of ligands around the central metal atom. This relationship can be seen in the square planar anticancer drug cisplatin, *cis*-$[Pt(NH_3)_2Cl_2]$, and its isomer transplatin, *trans*-$[Pt(NH_3)_2Cl_2]$. In this case, the *cis*- prefix refers to the same ligands occupying positions adjacent to one another and the *trans*- prefix refers to the same ligands occupying positions across from one another. As shown in Figure 22.10, the ammine and chlorido ligands are adjacent to one another in *cis*-$[Pt(NH_3)_2Cl_2]$, whereas they are located opposite one another in *trans*-$[Pt(NH_3)_2Cl_2]$. Given this differing spatial arrangement of groups, cisplatin and transplatin are cis-trans isomers of one another.

cis-$[Pt(NH_3)_2Cl_2]$
cisplatin
(a)

trans-$[Pt(NH_3)_2Cl_2]$
transplatin
(b)

FIGURE 22.10 Structures of Cisplatin and Transplatin

(a) Cisplatin and (b) transplatin are an example of cis-trans isomers.

The geometries of cisplatin and transplatin explain why cisplatin has anticancer properties and transplatin does not. The close proximity of the ammine ligands in cisplatin allows the complex to bind to cellular DNA molecules, causing the two DNA strands to crosslink. This ultimately causes the cell to die because it cannot properly replicate itself. Cisplatin's activity toward DNA allows it to be used to treat certain forms of cancer. Conversely, transplatin's ammine ligands are located far enough apart that they do not effectively bind DNA, so transplatin does not have the same therapeutic properties.

As discussed in Section 21.3, molecules that are chiral (nonsuperimposable mirror images of one another) are stereoisomers known as optical isomers or enantiomers. Your hands are an example of optical isomers, as are two tetrahedral molecules with four unique groups (Figure 21.10). Most coordination compounds that exist as optical isomers are octahedral and contain two or more bidentate ligands. An example of optical isomers containing ethylenediamine ligands is shown in Figure 22.11.

Example 22.11

Classify each of the following compounds as structural isomers, stereoisomers, or not isomers. If they are isomers, classify them as either coordination isomers, linkage isomers, cis-trans isomers, or optical isomers.

a. $[Fe(NH_3)_5F]Cl_2$ and $[Fe(NH_3)_5Cl]FCl$
b. *cis*-$[Ni(CO)_2(CN)_2]$ and *trans*-$[Ni(CO)_2(CN)_2]$
c. $[Co(en)_2Cl_2]NO_3$ and $[Co(en)_2Cl_2]OH$

Solution

a. In the first set of compounds, the atom connectivity differs, so the two compounds are structural isomers. The difference in atom connectivity is that the fluorido ligand in the first compound is replaced by a chlorido ligand in the second compound. The rest of the ligands and anions are the same. Therefore, these compounds are coordination isomers.

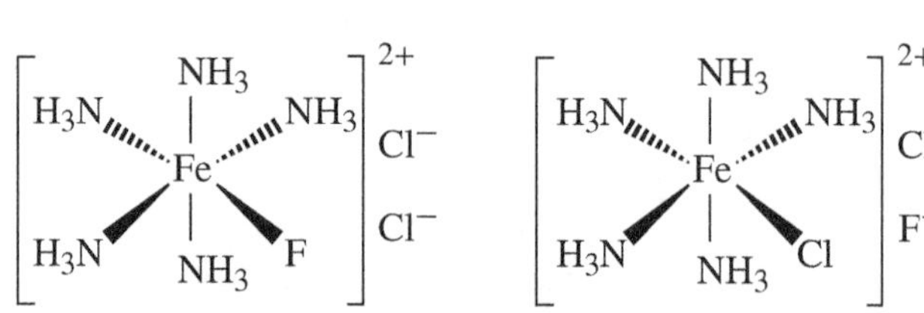

b. The atom connectivities of these two compounds are the same, so they are stereoisomers. Because the two CN^- ligands give nickel an oxidation state of $+2$, the two compounds are d^8

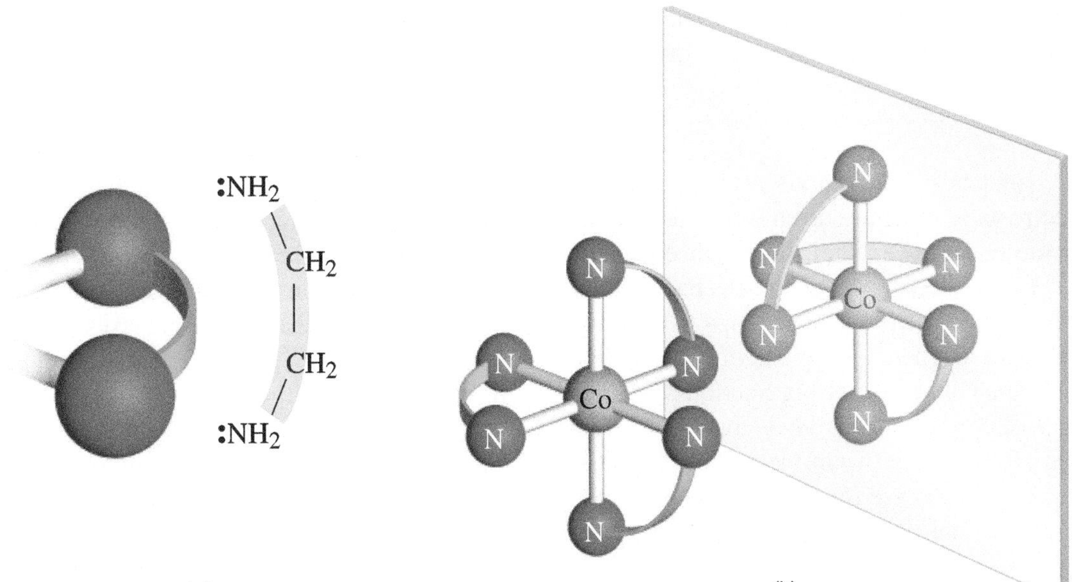

FIGURE 22.11 Optical Isomers of $[Co(en)_3]^{3+}$
(a) Ethylenediamine, $NH_2CH_2CH_2NH_2$ (en), is a bidentate ligand that is sometimes represented as two spheres connected by a ribbon. (b) When two or more bidentate ligands are bonded to the central metal atom of an octahedral complex, the complex is chiral, meaning it cannot be superimposed onto its mirror image.

and square planar. The compounds are not mirror images of each other, so they cannot be chiral. Therefore, the cis and trans isomers of these two compounds are cis-trans isomers.

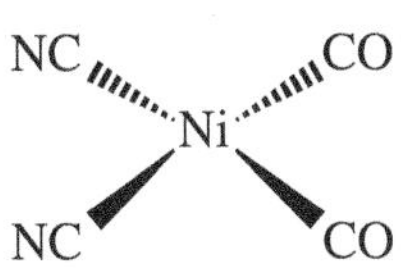

cis

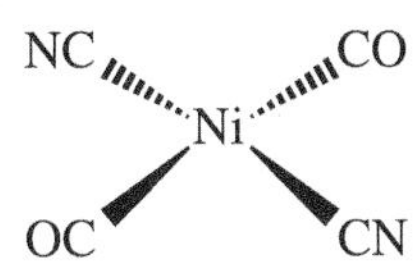

trans

c. These two compounds have different chemical formulas, so they are not isomers.

PRACTICE PROBLEM 22.11

Classify each of the following compounds as structural isomers or stereoisomers. If they are isomers, classify them as either coordination isomers, linkage isomers, cis-trans isomers, or optical isomers.

a. $[Fe(NH_3)_5(\underline{O}NO)]NO_3$ and $[Fe(NH_3)_5(O\underline{N}O)]NO_3$

b. *cis*-$[Pd(NH_3)_2Br_2]$ and *trans*-$[Pd(NH_3)_2Cl_2]$

Hint:

a. In potentially ambiguous cases, an underline indicates which atom is the donor atom within a ligand.

b. Keep in mind that isomers have the same chemical formula.

SECTION REVIEW

- Isomers are compounds that have the same chemical formula but a different arrangement of atoms.
- Structural isomers have the same chemical formula but different atom connectivities. Two main classes of structural isomers are coordination isomers and linkage isomers.
- Stereoisomers differ from structural isomers in that their atom connectivities are the same, but the spatial arrangement of atoms is different. Two main classes of stereoisomers are cis-trans isomers and optical isomers.

22.6 Crystal Field Theory

GOAL

- Use crystal field theory to identify high-spin and low-spin complexes.

Background Review

Chapter 8 The Quantum Model of the Atom: Section 8.3—Electron Shells, Subshells, and Orbitals; Section 8.4—Energy-Level Diagrams

Chapter 11 Molecular Shape and Bonding Theories: Section 11.3—Valence Bond Theory: Hybrid Orbitals and Bonding; Section 11.4—Using Valence Bond Theory

The interactions between metals and ligands are strongly electrostatic in nature, even when the ligands are neutral molecules (i.e., their lone-pair electrons are attracted to the electropositive metal, particularly if it is an ion). **Crystal field theory** helps to describe the electronic and magnetic properties of coordination compounds, which are discussed in Section 22.7. The basic premise of crystal field theory is that, despite the electrostatic attraction between metals and ligands, the *d* orbitals of metals are repelled by the electrons of the ligands. Crystal field theory describes only the effect of ligands on the metal's *d* orbitals, and not how the *d* orbitals bond to the ligands. Ligand field theory, which is an application of molecular orbital theory (Section 11.5) to coordination compounds, addresses bonding, but it is beyond the scope of this text. While crystal field theory is simplified in comparison to ligand field theory, it still accurately predicts many of the spectroscopic and magnetic properties of coordination compounds that the molecular orbital–based theories also predict. The remainder of this chapter focuses on how crystal field theory describes the energy of *d* orbitals in coordination complexes and how the identity of the ligands influences the spectroscopic and magnetic properties of these complexes.

d ORBITALS IN OCTAHEDRAL COMPLEXES

The shapes of the 3*d* orbitals are shown in Figure 22.12a. When a metal or metal ion is not coordinated to a ligand in close proximity to a molecule or ion, these five orbitals are said to be *degenerate*, meaning that they all have the same energy. The transition metal or metal ion is located at the center, where the *x*, *y*, and *z* axes intersect. The electron densities in two of the orbitals, d_{z^2} and $d_{x^2} - d_{y^2}$, are located along the *x*-, *y*-, and *z*-axes, where the ligands bond (see Figure 22.12b). In the other three orbitals—d_{xy}, d_{xz}, and d_{yz}—the electron densities are located between the axes of the metal–ligand bonds.

The location of electron density in relation to the metal–ligand bonding axes is important. Recall that, in crystal field theory, electrons from the ligand repel the *d* electrons of the metal. When the ligands approach a metal ion, as shown in Figure 22.12b, they electrostatically repel the *d* orbitals and the orbitals split into two sets of energy levels (see Figure 22.13). Given that the ligands of an octahedral complex are located along the *x*-, *y*-, and *z*-axes, the d_{z^2} and $d_{x^2} - d_{y^2}$ orbitals are most strongly repelled by the ligands because their electron densities are along these axes. Therefore, these orbitals experience an increase in energy. The d_{xy}, d_{xz}, and d_{yz} orbitals, in contrast, are located *between* the metal–ligand axes, so they are less strongly repelled by the ligands. Therefore, as shown in Figure 22.13, their increase in energy is more modest.

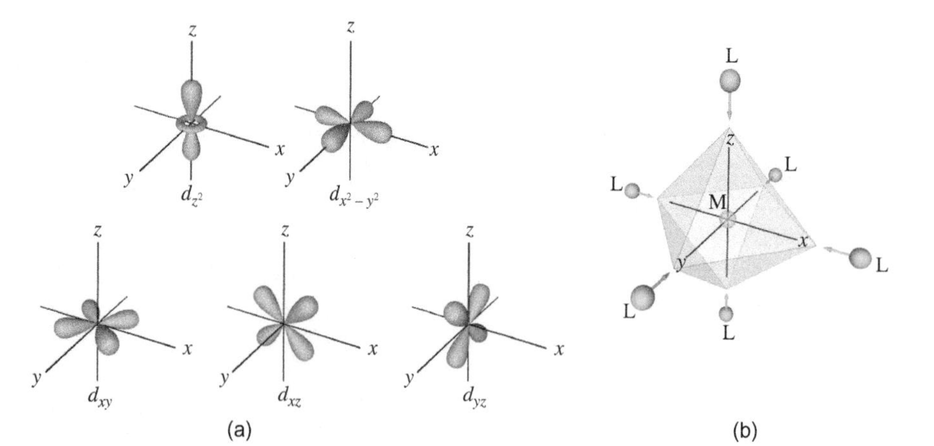

FIGURE 22.12 *d* Orbitals and Ligands in an Octahedral Complex

(a) The $d_{x^2} - d_{y^2}$ and d_{z^2} orbitals have electron densities along the axes (*x*, *y*, and *z*). The electron densities of the d_{xy}, d_{xz}, and d_{yz} orbitals are located in between the axes. (b) In an octahedral complex, ligands, L, approach the metal, M, along the axes, resulting in stronger repulsion of the $d_{x^2} - d_{y^2}$ and d_{z^2} orbitals and the splitting shown in Figure 22.13.

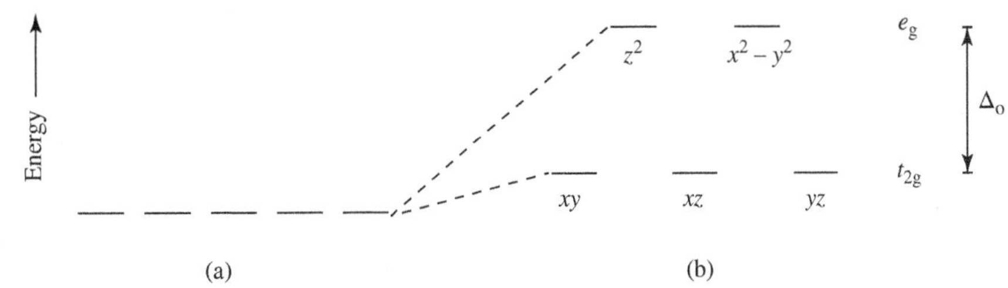

FIGURE 22.13 Splitting of *d* Orbitals in an Octahedral Complex

(a) In a free metal atom, the *d* orbitals are degenerate. (b) In an octahedral complex, the *d* orbitals split into the e_g and t_{2g} sets. The d_{z^2} and $d_{x^2} - d_{y^2}$ orbitals (the e_g set) are more strongly repelled by the ligands than the d_{xy}, d_{xz}, and d_{yz} orbitals (the t_{2g} set). The difference in energy is Δ_o, the crystal field splitting energy for an octahedral complex.

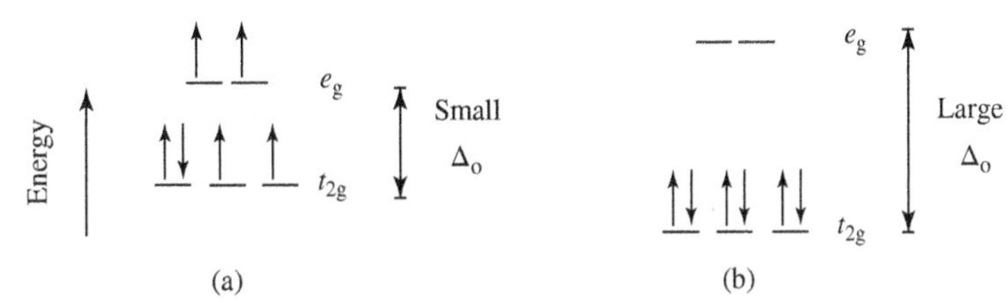

FIGURE 22.14 High-Spin and Low-Spin Octahedral d^6 Complexes

(a) In the high-spin configuration, Δ_o is small, so electrons occupy the e_g set while there are still unpaired electrons in t_{2g}. (b) In the low-spin configuration, Δ_o is large, so electrons do not occupy the e_g set until the t_{2g} orbitals are filled.

The difference in energy between the d_{z^2} and $d_{x^2} - d_{y^2}$ orbitals, known as the e_g set, and the d_{xy}, d_{xz}, and d_{yz} orbitals, known as the t_{2g} set, is the **crystal field splitting energy**, Δ. For an octahedral complex, the crystal field splitting energy is denoted as Δ_o. The magnitude of Δ_o influences how the *d* orbitals fill with electrons. When Δ_o is small for an octahedral d^6 complex (Figure 22.14a), electrons can occupy both the lower-energy t_{2g} orbitals and the higher-energy e_g orbitals. This **high-spin** configuration is favored when the energy needed to promote an electron from a t_{2g} orbital to an e_g orbital is less than the energy needed to pair two electrons in the same t_{2g} orbital. The term *high spin* is used because the electrons all have the same $+\frac{1}{2}$ spin, and the sum of these spins is the maximum number possible (+2 in this case, with four unpaired electrons and two paired electrons). If Δ_o is larger than the electron-pairing energy, however, then the fourth, fifth, and sixth electrons in a d^6 complex pair with the first three electrons in the lower-energy t_{2g} orbitals (Figure 22.14b). This electron configuration is known as **low-spin** because the total electron spin is the lowest possible number (zero in the d^6 case, because all six electrons are paired).

In the high-spin complex (see Figure 22.14a), Δ_o is less than the electron-pairing energy, so the electrons occupy as many different orbitals as possible. In the low-spin complex (see Figure 22.14b), Δ_o is greater than the pairing energy, so as many electrons as possible occupy the lower-energy t_{2g} orbitals. Figure 22.15 shows all of the high- and low-spin configurations of octahedral complexes.

Example 22.12

Write electron configurations for the *d* orbitals in the following types of octahedral complexes, and give the number of unpaired electrons in each.

a. low-spin d^4
b. high-spin d^4
c. a Cu(II) complex
d. a Ni(II) complex

Solution

a. In a low-spin complex, the total electron spin is minimized by pairing as many electrons as possible. Therefore, a low-spin d^4 complex has the configuration $t_{2g}{}^4 e_g{}^0$ with two electrons paired

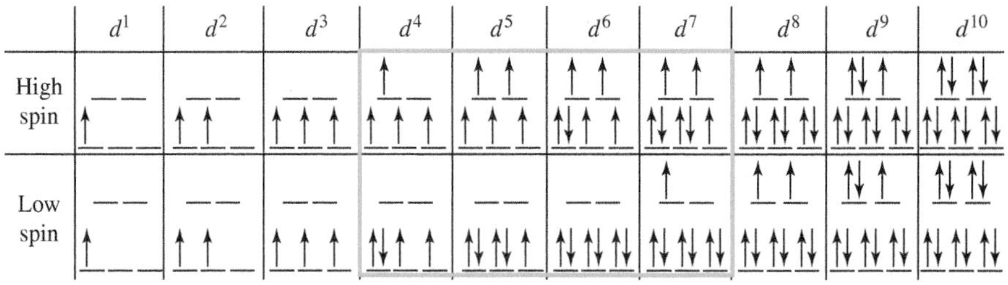

FIGURE 22.15 Configurations of Octahedral Complexes

In the high-spin configuration, pairing of electrons is minimized. In the low-spin configuration, the number of electrons in higher-energy orbitals is minimized. The resulting electron arrangements differ only for d^4 through d^7.

in one t_{2g} orbital and two unpaired electrons in each of the other two t_{2g} orbitals.

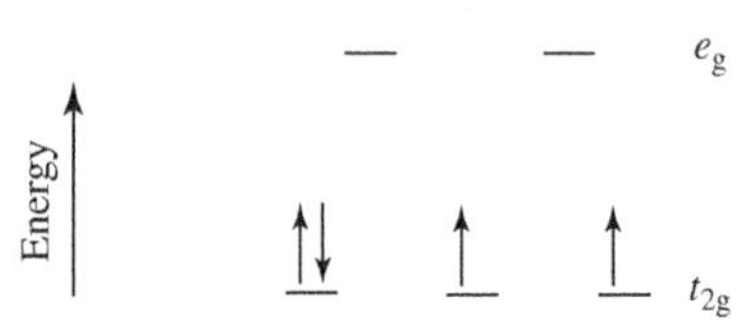

b. In a high-spin complex, the total electron spin is maximized by placing as many electrons as possible into different orbitals. Therefore, a high-spin d^4 complex has the configuration $t_{2g}{}^3e_g{}^1$ with unpaired electrons in each of the three t_{2g} orbitals and one unpaired electron in an e_g orbital. This gives a total of four unpaired electrons.

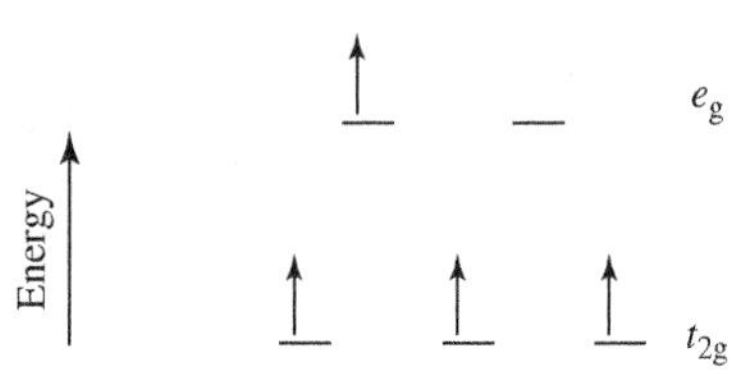

c. A Cu(II) complex has a d^9 configuration, which has only one possible configuration: $t_{2g}{}^6e_g{}^3$. The three t_{2g} orbitals contain six paired electrons, and one of the e_g orbitals contains two paired electrons. The other e_g orbital contains one unpaired electron.

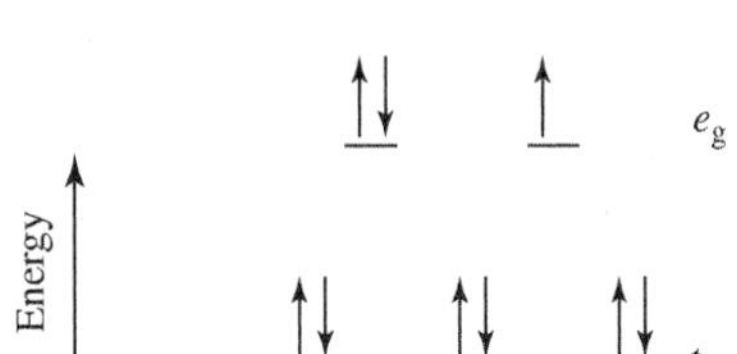

d. A Ni(II) complex has a d^8 configuration. Placing one electron into each degenerate e_g orbital is energetically favorable. Therefore, a d^8 complex has an electron configuration of $t_{2g}{}^6e_g{}^2$ and two unpaired electrons.

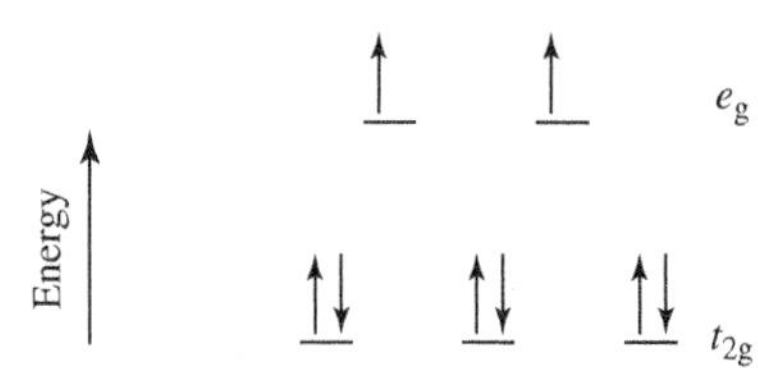

PRACTICE PROBLEM 22.12

Identify the number of d electrons in each of the following ions in an octahedral complex. Then write electron configurations for the d orbitals, and give the number of unpaired electrons in each.

a. A high-spin Co(II) complex
b. A low-spin Co(II) complex
c. A Cr(III) complex

Hint: In the case of high-spin complexes, the pairing of electrons into single orbitals is minimized. In low-spin complexes, pairing is maximized. Also consider that at least one electron must occupy each of the three t_{2g} orbitals before electrons can be placed into an e_g orbital.

d ORBITALS IN TETRAHEDRAL AND SQUARE PLANAR COMPLEXES

Most four-coordinate coordination compounds adopt tetrahedral geometries. As shown in Figure 22.16, the ligands of a tetrahedral coordination complex bond to the metal between the x-, y-, and z-axes. Therefore, the orbitals that most strongly interact with ligands in a

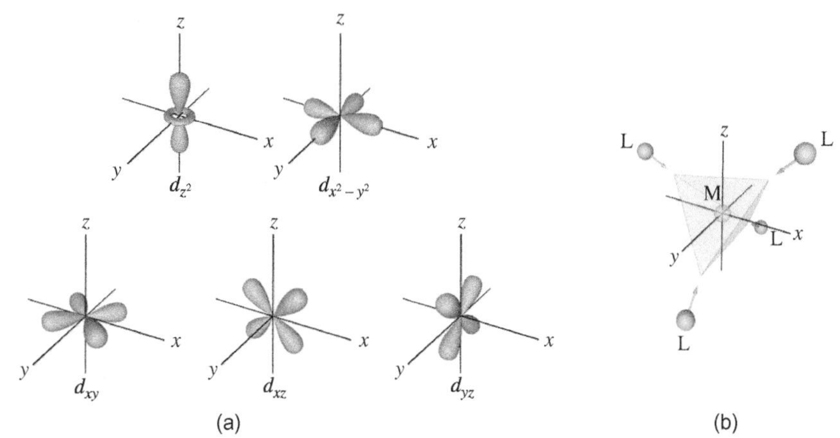

FIGURE 22.16 *d* Orbitals and Ligands in a Tetrahedral Complex

(a) The $d_{x^2} - d_{y^2}$ and d_{z^2} orbitals have electron densities along the axes. The electron densities of the d_{xy}, d_{xz}, and d_{yz} orbitals are located in between the axes. (b) In tetrahedral complexes, ligands, L, approach the metal, M, between the axes resulting in stronger repulsion of the d_{xy}, d_{xz}, and d_{yz} orbitals and the splitting shown in Figure 22.17.

tetrahedral coordination compound are those in the t_{2g} set—namely, d_{xy}, d_{xz}, and d_{yz}. The orbitals with electron density along the *x*-, *y*-, and *z*-axes (i.e., d_{z^2} and $d_{x^2} - d_{y^2}$) are repelled to a lesser degree. The result is that tetrahedral complexes exhibit *d* orbital splitting (Figure 22.17) that is the opposite of that seen in octahedral complexes.

Tetrahedral complexes differ from octahedral complexes in additional ways. The two orbitals that have electron density along the *x*-, *y*-, and *z*-axes are named the *e* set, rather than the e_g set, and the other set of three orbitals is named the t_2 set, rather than the t_{2g} set. Also, there are fewer ligands and less electron–electron repulsion in tetrahedral complexes, so the energy between the *e* and t_2 sets, Δ_t, is significantly less than Δ_o in an octahedral complex. In tetrahedral complexes, Δ_t is almost always less than the pairing energy needed to place two electrons in the same orbital, so tetrahedral complexes are usually high spin.

In square planar complexes, the ligands bond to the metal along the *x*- and *y*-axes (Figure 22.18). Therefore, the $d_{x^2} - d_{y^2}$ orbitals are most strongly repelled by the ligands (Figure 22.19). The d_{xy} orbital, with electron density between the axes of the bonding ligands, is also repelled appreciably due to its proximity to the ligands. The d_{z^2} orbitals have a small amount of electron density within the *xy* plane and are split at a slightly higher energy than the d_{xz} and d_{yz} orbitals.

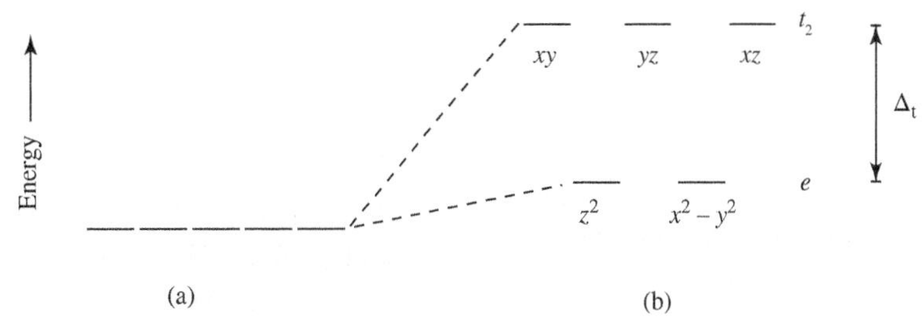

FIGURE 22.17 Splitting of *d* Orbitals in a Tetrahedral Complex

(a) In a free metal atom, the *d* orbitals are degenerate. (b) Because ligands approach the metal *between* the *x*-, *y*-, and *z*-axes, the d_{xy}, d_{xz}, and d_{yz} orbitals are repelled the most. Note that the orbital set labels, t_2 and *e*, are different than the labels for octahedral complexes, and the difference is symbolized as Δ_t.

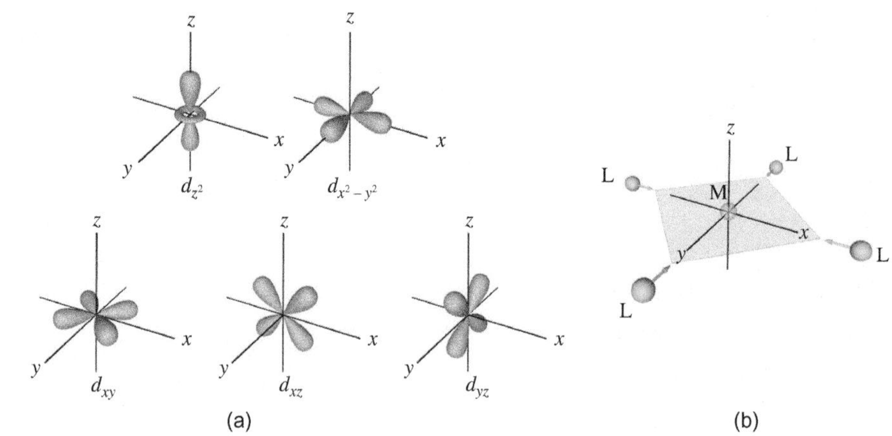

FIGURE 22.18 *d* Orbitals and Ligands in a Square Planar Complex
(a) The $d_{x^2} - d_{y^2}$ and d_{xy} orbitals have all their electron density in the *xy* plane, with $d_{x^2} - d_{y^2}$ being oriented along the axes. The d_{z^2} orbital has some electron density in the *xy* plane. (b) In square planar complexes, ligands approach the metal along the *x*- and *y*-axes, resulting in the splitting shown in Figure 22.19.

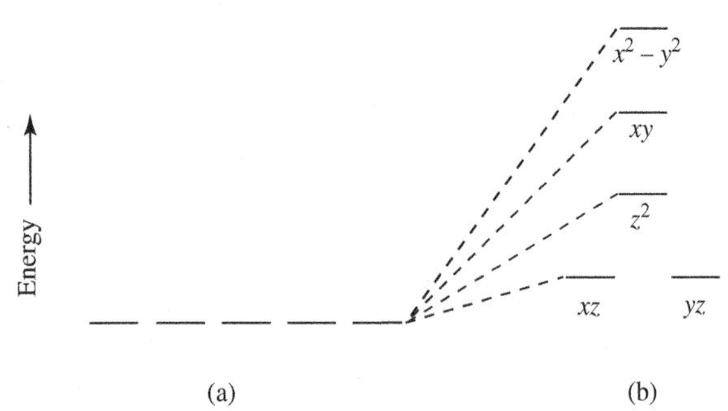

FIGURE 22.19 Splitting of *d* Orbitals in a Square Planar Complex
(a) In a free metal atom, the *d* orbitals are degenerate.
(b) Because ligands in square planar complexes bond along the *xy* plane, the $d_{x^2} - d_{y^2}$, d_{xy}, and d_{z^2} orbitals are repelled the most. Square planar complexes are typically observed with heavier d^8 transition metals with higher crystal field splitting energies, such as Rh(I), Pt(II), Pd(III), and Au(III). Period 4 d^8 complexes, such as Ni(II), have lower crystal field splitting energies and tend to favor tetrahedral geometries.

SECTION REVIEW

- Crystal field theory describes the splitting of *d* orbitals to higher energy levels when they are electrostatically repelled by ligands. The energy between two sets of split orbitals is known as the crystal field splitting energy.
- Octahedral complexes are split into three degenerate t_{2g} orbitals and two higher-energy, degenerate e_g orbitals. Depending on the crystal field splitting energy, Δ_o, either low-spin or high-spin configurations are possible.
- Tetrahedral complexes are split into two degenerate *e* orbitals and three higher-energy t_2 orbitals. The crystal field splitting energies of tetrahedral complexes, Δ_t, are typically small, so most tetrahedral complexes are high spin.
- The *d* orbitals of square planar compounds are split into four different energy levels. Square planar geometries are typically adopted by period 5 and period 6 d^8 complexes.

22.7 The Spectrochemical Series, Color, and Magnetism

GOAL

- Apply crystal field theory to explain the effects of a coordination compound's ligands on its color and magnetic properties.

Background Review

Chapter 8 The Quantum Model of the Atom: Section 8.3—Electron Shells, Subshells, and Orbitals; Section 8.4—Energy-Level Diagrams

As discussed in Section 22.6, the *d* orbitals of metals in coordination complexes are split into sets of orbitals with differing energies. Consequently, electrons can adopt either a high-spin or low-spin configuration, depending on the magnitude of the crystal field splitting energy (Δ) in comparison to the energy necessary to pair two electrons into a single orbital. In this section, you will learn how to predict which configuration a given coordination complex is likely to adopt and how this affects the compound's spectroscopic and magnetic properties. For the sake of simplicity, the discussion is limited to octahedral complexes.

THE SPECTROCHEMICAL SERIES

The crystal field splitting energy of an octahedral complex, Δ_o, depends strongly on the identity of the ligand. For example, an aqueous Co(II) complex with Cl^- ligands exhibits a different color than an aqueous Co(II) complex with CN^- ligands. Additionally, the energy of light absorbed by the complex with chlorido ligands is lower than the energy of light absorbed by the complex with the cyano ligands. These results imply that the CN^- ligands impart a larger Δ_o to the *d* orbitals of Co(II) than Cl^-. Recall from Section 22.6 that a larger Δ_o equates to a larger energy difference between the degenerate sets of orbitals (e_g and t_{2g}, in the case of an octahedral complex). The effect of ligands on the magnitude of the crystal field splitting energy of a coordination compound is summarized in a list in order according to Δ, known as the **spectrochemical series**.

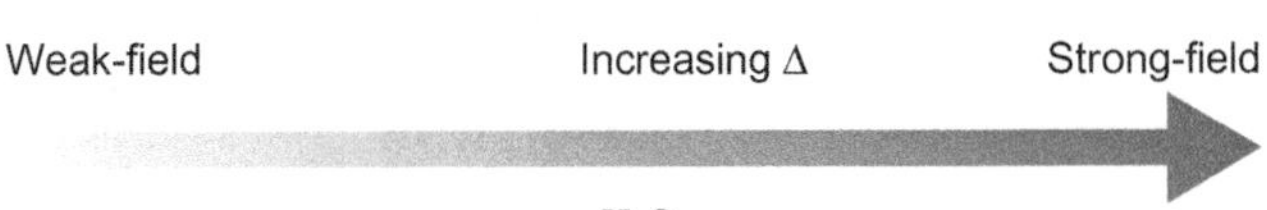

$I^- < Br^- < Cl^- < N_3^- < F^- < OH < H_2O,\ Cr_2O_4^{2-} < py < NH_3 < en < NO_2^- < CN^-,\ CO$

Ligands that form coordination compounds with relatively high Δ values, such as CO and CN^-, are known as **strong-field ligands**, whereas ligands that form coordination compounds with relatively small Δ values, such as I^- and Cl^-, are known as **weak-field ligands**. The spectrochemical series predicts that strong-field ligands give complexes with the highest Δ values and that weak-field ligands give complexes with the lowest Δ values.

> Strong-field ligands tend to produce low-spin complexes, while weak-field ligands typically produce high-spin complexes.

Example 22.13

Using the spectrochemical series, predict the number of unpaired *d* electrons in each of the following octahedral complexes.

a. $[CoBr_6]^{4-}$
b. $[Mn(CO)_6]^{2+}$
c. $[Cu(H_2O)_6]^{2+}$

Solution

a. According to the spectrochemical series, Br^- is a weak-field ligand, so Δ_o will be relatively small and the complex will most likely be high spin. The six Br^- ligands and the overall charge of −4 on the complex mean that the oxidation state of Co is +2. Co^{2+} has a d^7 configuration. The *d* electron configuration for a high-spin d^7 octahedral complex is $t_{2g}^5e_g^2$. In this configuration, two of the t_{2g} orbitals contain two electrons and the other t_{2g} orbital contains one electron. $[CoBr_6]^{4-}$, therefore, is predicted to contain three unpaired electrons.

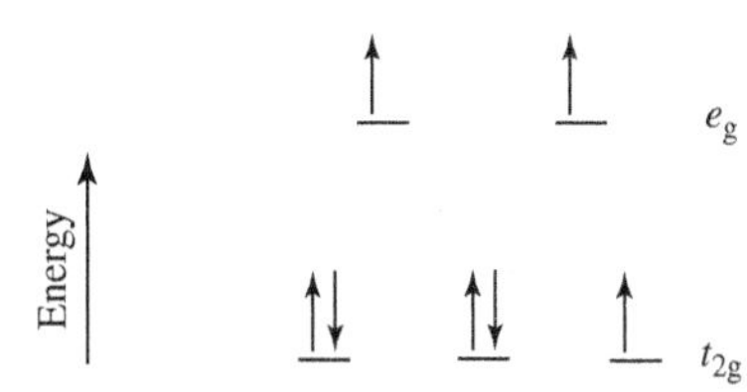

b. According to the spectrochemical series, CO is a strong-field ligand, so Δ_o will be relatively large and the complex will most likely be low spin. The six neutral CO ligands and the overall charge of +2 on the complex mean that the oxidation state of Mn is +2. Mn^{2+} has a d^5 configuration. The *d* electron configuration for a low-spin d^5 octahedral complex is $t_{2g}^5e_g^0$. In this configuration, two of the t_{2g} orbitals contain two electrons, and one t_{2g} orbital contains one electron. $[Mn(CO)_6]^{2+}$, therefore, is predicted to contain one unpaired electron.

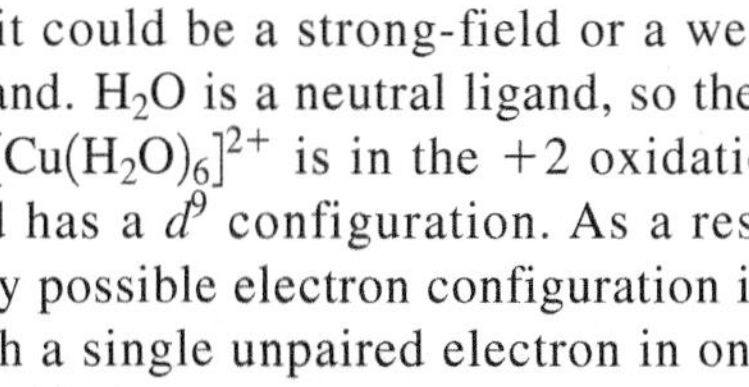

c. The aqua (H_2O) ligand is approximately in the middle of the spectrochemical series, so it could be a strong-field or a weak-field ligand. H_2O is a neutral ligand, so the copper in $[Cu(H_2O)_6]^{2+}$ is in the +2 oxidation state and has a d^9 configuration. As a result, the only possible electron configuration is $t_{2g}^6e_g^3$, with a single unpaired electron in one of the e_g orbitals.

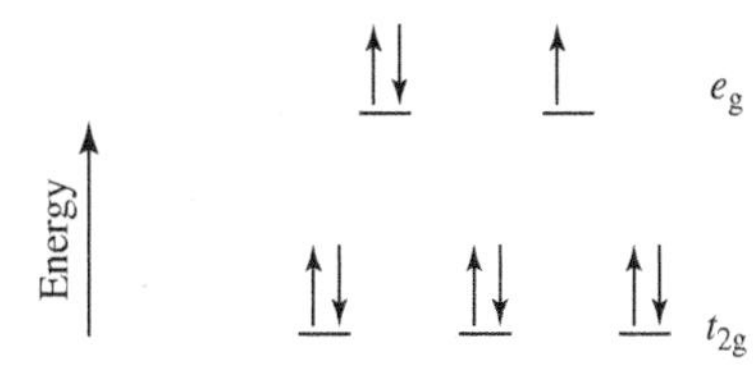

PRACTICE PROBLEM 22.13

Using the spectrochemical series, predict the number of unpaired d electrons in each of the following octahedral complexes.

a. $[Fe(CN)_6]^{3-}$
b. $[Cr(NH_3)_6]^{3+}$

Hint: Consult the spectrochemical series to determine whether a ligand is strong field (high Δ) or weak field (low Δ). A high Δ results in a low-spin complex, where electrons do not populate the higher-energy orbitals until the lower-energy orbitals are full. A low Δ results in a high-spin complex, where electrons fill as if the orbitals were degenerate.

THE COLOR OF COORDINATION COMPOUNDS

As discussed in Chapter 8, the wavelength of light, λ, is related to the energy of light, E, by the following equation, where h is Planck's constant and c is the speed of light.

$$E = \frac{hc}{\lambda}$$

According to this equation, the wavelength of light is inversely proportional to its energy. The crystal field splitting energy, Δ, is the energy needed to promote an electron from a lower-energy d orbital to a higher-energy d orbital. As a result, Δ is inversely proportional to the wavelength of the light needed to promote an electron in a t_{2g} orbital to an e_g orbital.

Example 22.14

An aqueous solution of $[Cr(H_2O)_6]^{3+}$ absorbs energy at a wavelength of 575 nm. Calculate the energy, in joules, associated with an electron transitioning from the t_{2g} energy level of Cr(III) to its e_g energy level. Planck's constant, h, is $6.626 \times 10^{-34}\ \text{J} \cdot \text{s}$, and the speed of light, c, is $2.998 \times 10^8\ \text{m/s}$.

Solution

The equation used to calculate the energy of Δ_o is

$$E = \frac{hc}{\lambda}$$

$$E = \frac{(6.626 \times 10^{-34}\ \text{J} \cdot \text{s})\left(2.998 \times 10^8\ \frac{\text{m}}{\text{s}}\right)}{575 \times 10^{-9}\ \text{m}}$$

$$E = \Delta_o = 3.45 \times 10^{-19}\ \text{J}$$

PRACTICE PROBLEM 22.14

An aqueous solution of $[MnCl_6]^{4-}$ has $\Delta_o = 1.49 \times 10^{-19}$ J. Calculate the wavelength, in nanometers, associated with this Δ_o value. Planck's constant, h, is $6.626 \times 10^{-34}\ \text{J} \cdot \text{s}$, and the speed of light, c, is $2.998 \times 10^8\ \text{m/s}$.

Hint: Use the equation that relates energy to wavelength, the speed of light, and Planck's constant, $E = hc/\lambda$.

Example 22.15

Two separate Cr(III) complexes absorb light at 465 nm and 730 nm. Based on Example 22.14, determine which complex is $[CrCl_6]^{3-}$ and which is $[Cr(NH_3)_6]^{3+}$.

Solution

From Example 22.14, $[Cr(H_2O)_6]^{3+}$ absorbs energy at a wavelength of 575 nm. Aquo ligands fall very near the middle of the spectrochemical series, whereas chlorido ligands are weak field (Δ_o is low) and ammine ligands are relatively strong field (Δ_o is high). Consequently, $[CrCl_6]^{3-}$ would be expected to absorb lower-energy light than $[Cr(NH_3)_6]^{3+}$. The wavelength of light absorbed is inversely proportional to the energy of Δ_o, so $[CrCl_6]^{3-}$ should absorb energy with a longer wavelength than $[Cr(NH_3)_6]^{3+}$. Therefore, $[CrCl_6]^{3-}$ absorbs light at 730 nm, and $[Cr(NH_3)_6]^{3+}$ absorbs light at 465 nm.

PRACTICE PROBLEM 22.15

Suppose that two theoretical iron(III) complexes, $[FeX_6]^{3+}$ and $[FeY_6]^{3+}$, are present in a solution. One complex absorbs light at 410 nm, and the other absorbs light at 680 nm. If X is a strong-field ligand and Y is a weak-field ligand, then which complex most likely absorbs light at 410 nm and which absorbs light at 680 nm?

Hint: Complexes with strong-field ligands tend to have larger Δ_o values than complexes with weak-field ligands. Consider the relationship between Δ_o (energy) and wavelength.

Coordination compounds that absorb light in the visible range (approximately 400–750 nm) also reflect light in the visible range. This means that coordination compounds that absorb light in this range will have a color that is discernable to the human eye. There is an important relationship between the color of light absorbed by the compound and the color of light that you see.

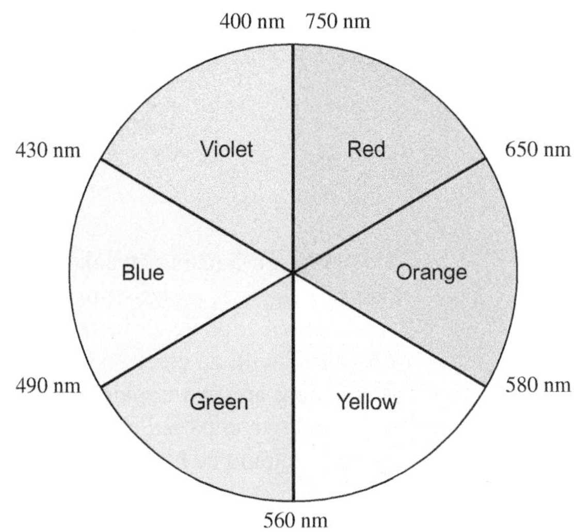

FIGURE 22.20 The Color Wheel

The complementary color of a given color is located on the opposite side of the wheel. For example, the complementary color of red is green.

> The color of light absorbed by a compound is the complementary color of the light that is reflected by the compound.

The color wheel shown in Figure 22.20 offers a good way to determine the complementary color of a compound.

Figure 22.21 shows an absorption spectrum of the copper-containing protein plastocyanin, which is found in plants. Plastocyanin absorbs light at approximately 595 nm. That wavelength falls in the orange region of the color wheel in Figure 22.20. The side of the wheel opposite orange light is blue light. Therefore, a solution of plastocyanin reflects blue light and appears blue in color.

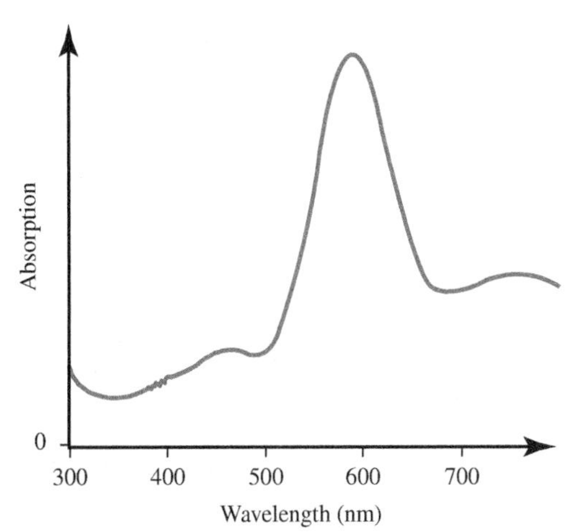

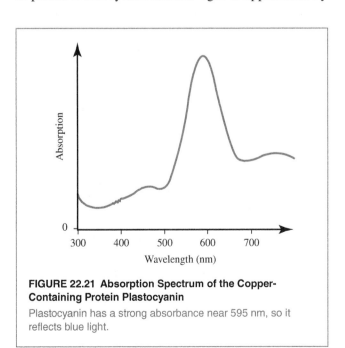

FIGURE 22.21 Absorption Spectrum of the Copper-Containing Protein Plastocyanin

Plastocyanin has a strong absorbance near 595 nm, so it reflects blue light.

EVERYDAY CONNECTION

Colorful coordination compounds are frequently encountered in biology. For example, the oxygen-transport protein hemoglobin is present in the red blood cells of most vertebrates. Hemoglobin contains four iron-binding heme groups, shown below. Four nitrogen atoms of each heme ligand bond to iron. Iron is also coordinated to a fifth nitrogen atom (not shown) from an amino acid located elsewhere on the protein. When the heme groups of hemoglobin are bound to iron, hemoglobin absorbs yellowish green light near 560 nm, giving red blood cells a dark red color. When hemoglobin is transporting oxygen, an O_2 molecule also coordinates to iron, oxidizing it to Fe^{3+}. Oxygen-containing hemoglobin absorbs light near 540 and 570 nm, so it has a brighter red color than oxygen-free hemoglobin.

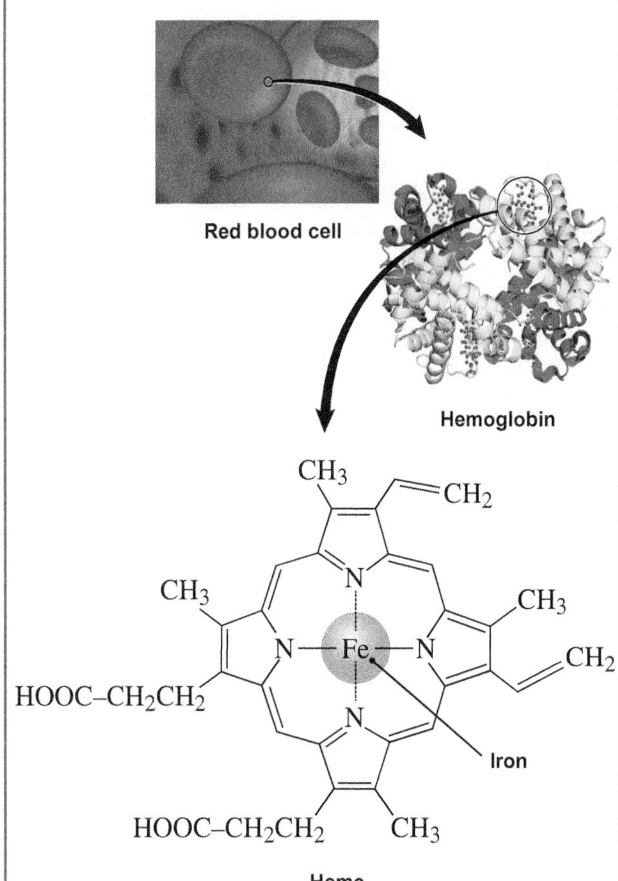

Example 22.16

An aqueous solution of a coordination compound is yellow. Use the color wheel in Figure 22.20 to determine the approximate wavelength range over which the compound absorbs light in the visible region.

Solution

From the color wheel, the complementary color of yellow is violet. Based on the wavelength range of violet, the coordination compound would be expected to absorb light somewhere between 400 and 430 nm.

PRACTICE PROBLEM 22.16

An aqueous solution of a coordination compound absorbs light at 520 nm. Use the color wheel in Figure 22.20 to determine the color of the compound to the human eye.

Hint: For a given color of light absorbed, the color of light reflected is located on the opposite side of the color wheel.

THE MAGNETISM OF COORDINATION COMPOUNDS

As discussed in the last few sections of this chapter, many coordination complexes have unpaired electrons. Recall from Section 11.5 that compounds with unpaired electrons are attracted to an electric field. Compounds with unpaired electrons are said to be *paramagnetic*. In contrast, *diamagnetic* compounds have no unpaired electrons and are not attracted to electric fields. Crystal field theory can be used to predict whether a compound is paramagnetic or diamagnetic.

Example 22.17

Predict whether the following compounds are paramagnetic or diamagnetic.

a. $[Fe(en)_3]^{2+}$
b. $[FeI_6]^{4-}$
c. $ZrCl_4$

Solution

a. Ethylenediamine (en) is a neutral, strong-field ligand. Therefore, $[Fe(en)_3]^{2+}$ is a low-spin octahedral complex. Given that Fe is in the +2 oxidation state, it is d^6 with an electron configuration of $t_{2g}^6e_g^0$. There are no unpaired electrons, so $[Fe(en)_3]^{2+}$ should be diamagnetic.

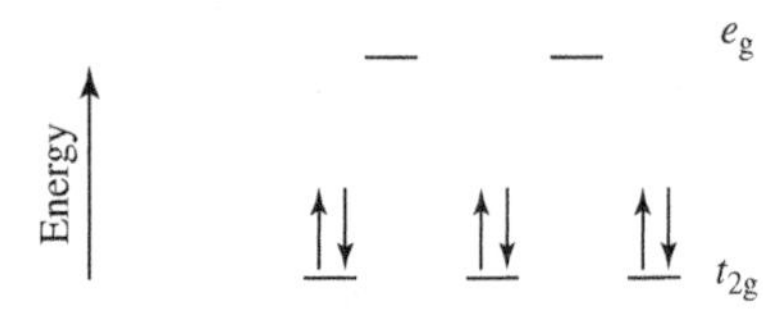

b. Iodido has a −1 charge and is a weak-field ligand. Therefore, $[FeI_6]^{4-}$ is a high-spin octahedral complex. Given that Fe is in the +2 oxidation state, it is d^6 with an electron configuration of $t_{2g}^4e_g^2$. There are two unpaired electrons in the t_{2g} set and two unpaired electrons in the e_g set, so $[FeI_6]^{4-}$ should be paramagnetic.

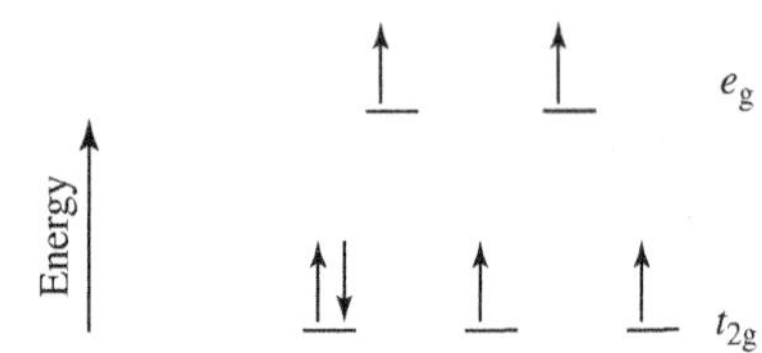

c. The zirconium in $ZrCl_4$ has a +4 oxidation state, so it is d^0. Since there are no unpaired electrons in its *d* orbitals, $ZrCl_4$ should be diamagnetic.

PRACTICE PROBLEM 22.17

Predict whether the following compounds are paramagnetic or diamagnetic.

a. $K_4[Fe(CN)_6]$
b. $[Zn(NH_3)_4]^{2+}$
c. $[Ni(NH_3)_4]^{2+}$

Hint: Determine the *d* electron configuration of each complex, and then determine whether the ligand of each complex is strong field (low-spin) or weak field (high-spin) by consulting the spectrochemical series.

SECTION REVIEW

- The spectrochemical series shows how coordination compound ligands vary in their contribution to the size of the crystal field splitting energy. The spectrochemical series can be used to predict the color of coordination compounds.
- Crystal field theory can be used to predict the magnetism of coordination compounds. Coordination compounds that contain unpaired *d* electrons are predicted to be paramagnetic, whereas coordination compounds with all paired *d* electrons are predicted to be diamagnetic.

Putting It Together

The example problems in earlier sections of this chapter focus on just the new skills acquired in that section, but homework and exam questions in chemistry often require more than just one skill at a time. In fact, you will likely be expected to apply knowledge from across the entire chapter, or even multiple chapters, in a single problem. This final example problem is meant to help you prepare for these types of multi-concept questions. Additional examples can be found in the end-of-chapter exercises.

Example 22.18

Consider the coordination compounds $K_3[Fe(CN)_6]$ and $K_3[CrCl_6]$.

a. Name the compounds.
b. Determine the likely geometries of these compounds.
c. Determine the electron configurations of the metal in each of these compounds.

Solution

a. Both compounds have three K^+ ions in the secondary coordination sphere and six ligands of -1 charge in their primary coordination spheres. The compounds are both neutral overall. The charge of each metal, x, is the oxidation state of the metal.

$$3(+1) + x + 6(-1) = 0$$
$$3 + x - 6 = 0$$
$$x = +3$$

The oxidation states of Fe and Cr are both +3.

Use the nomenclature rules in Section 22.4 and the information in Table 22.3 and Table 22.5.

$K_3[Fe(CN)_6]$ = potassium hexacyanidoferrate(III)

$K_3[CrCl_6]$ = potassium hexachloridoferrate(III)

b. Each compound contains six ligands inside the primary coordination sphere. From Table 22.4, compounds with a coordination number of six are most likely octahedral.

c. $K_3[Fe(CN)_6]$ is an Fe(III) compound with the electron configuration of $[Ar]3d^5$. $K_3[CrCl_6]$ is a Cr(III) compound with the electron configuration of $[Ar]3d^3$.

PRACTICE PROBLEM 22.18

Consider the coordination compounds in Example 22.18.

a. Determine whether each compound is paramagnetic or diamagnetic.
b. Suppose that the compounds are dissolved in aqueous solution to give $[Fe(CN)_6]^{3-}$ and $[CrCl_6]^{3-}$. Determine which compound absorbs light at 286 nm and which absorbs light at 730 nm.
c. Based on your answer to part b, calculate Δ_o for each compound.

Hint: Draw the t_{2g} and e_g orbital sets for each of the two complexes, and consider the type of ligand (strong-field versus weak-field) in each case. Also consider the relationship between wavelength and energy.

Key Terms, Symbols, and Equations

KEY TERMS

bidentate (22.3): Describes a ligand that forms two coordinate covalent bonds to a metal.

chelate effect (22.3): The unusually large thermodynamic stability of coordination compounds that contain polydentate ligands instead of monodentate ligands.

chelating agent (22.3): The name given to bidentate and polydentate ligands.

coordinate covalent bond (22.3): The bond that is formed between a Lewis base ligand and the Lewis acid metal of a coordination compound.

coordination compound (22.3): Any complex ion or neutral compound that contains a metal that is complexed by ligands.

coordination isomers (22.5): Compounds that have the same chemical formula but differ in the types of groups that are located inside and outside of the primary coordination sphere.

coordination number (22.3): The number of atoms that are bonded directly to the metal in a coordination compound.

crystal field splitting energy (22.6): The energy difference between sets of d orbitals in the central metal of a coordination compound.

crystal field theory (22.6): A model of bonding in coordination compounds where the d orbitals of the central metal are repelled by the electrons of the ligands and are split into different energy levels.

donor atom (22.3): The atom or atoms in a ligand that donate a lone pair of electrons to a coordinate covalent bond.

hexadentate (22.3): Describes a ligand that forms six coordinate covalent bonds to a metal.

high spin (22.6): A configuration of *d* electrons in a coordination compound that maximizes the number of unpaired electrons.

lanthanoid contraction (22.2): The smaller-than-expected atomic radius of period 6 transition metals, due to the poor shielding of the outer electrons by the electrons in the 4*f* orbitals.

ligand (22.3): A Lewis base that forms a coordinate covalent bond to a metal or metal ion.

linkage isomers (22.5): Coordination compounds that have the same chemical formula but share a common ligand that bonds to the metal through different groups.

low spin (22.6): A configuration of *d* electrons in a coordination compound that minimizes the number of unpaired electrons.

monodentate (22.3): Describes a ligand that forms one coordinate covalent bond to a metal.

polydentate (22.3): Describes a ligand that forms more than one coordinate covalent bond to a metal.

primary coordination sphere (22.3): The molecules or ions that are covalently bonded to the metal in a coordination compound.

secondary coordination sphere (22.3): The molecules or ions outside the primary coordination sphere of a coordination compound that interact with the metal or ligands via intermolecular forces.

spectrochemical series (22.7): A list of coordination compound ligands that vary in their contribution to the size of the crystal field splitting energy.

strong-field ligand (22.7): A ligand that contributes to a large crystal field splitting energy in a coordination compound.

weak-field ligand (22.7): A ligand that contributes to a small crystal field splitting energy in a coordination compound.

SYMBOLS AND ABBREVIATIONS

c (speed of light) (22.7)

Δ (crystal field splitting energy) (22.6)

Δ_o (crystal field splitting energy of an octahedral complex) (22.6)

Δ_t (crystal field splitting energy of a tetrahedral complex) (22.6)

e (two degenerate *d* orbitals in a tetrahedral complex) (22.6)

e_g (two degenerate *d* orbitals in an octahedral complex) (22.6)

h (Planck's constant) (22.7)

K_f (formation constant) (22.3)

λ (wavelength) (22.7)

t_2 (three degenerate *d* orbitals in a tetrahedral complex) (22.6)

t_{2g} (three degenerate *d* orbitals in an octahedral complex) (22.6)

Chapter Summary

Oxidation states are represented by Roman numerals in naming ions of metals with ions of more than one possible charge. This system, known as the Stock system, is the most commonly used and is preferred over the older system of using prefixes and suffixes to indicate oxidation state (Section 22.1).

For most transition metals, the outer *s* orbital is populated with electrons before the outer *d* orbital. One important consequence is that the transition metals lose their *s* electrons before their *d* electrons when they are ionized. An oxidation state of +2 is common for many transition metals.

The shielding effect of lower quantum number *d* electrons prevents transition metals from experiencing the same radius contraction across the *d* block that main group elements experience across the *p* block. The filling of electrons into the poorly shielding 4*f* subshell and concurrent increase in nuclear charge results in 5*d* transition metals having approximately the same atomic radius as 4*d* transition metals. This observation is known as the lanthanoid contraction. The lanthanoid contraction also explains the increase in ionization energies between period 5 and period 6 transition metals. The electronegativities of the transition metals increase from left to right across a period and from bottom to top in a group, but the variations are less drastic than in the main group elements (Section 22.2).

A coordination compound is any complex ion or neutral compound that contains a metal that is complexed by ligands via coordinate covalent bonds. The metal center and covalently bound ligands constitute the coordination compound's primary coordination sphere. The coordination number is the number of atoms that covalently bond to the metal. Other groups that interact with the metal or ligands via electrostatic forces are part of the secondary coordination sphere.

Ligands are classified as monodentate (one bond), bidentate (two bonds), and polydentate (more than two bonds) based on the number of ligand atoms that bond to the metal. Bidentate and polydentate ligands, known as chelating agents, form coordination compounds with unusually high K_f values, due in large part to a thermodynamically favorable increase in entropy. Common geometries of coordination compounds include linear (two-coordinate), tetrahedral (four-coordinate), square planar (four-coordinate), and octahedral (six-coordinate) (Section 22.3).

The oxidation states of coordination compounds are determined in an analogous manner to the oxidation states of ionic compounds. A systematic method is used to name coordination compounds (Section 22.4).

Isomers are compounds that have the same chemical formula but a different arrangement of atoms. The two main types of isomers in coordination chemistry are structural isomers and stereoisomers. Structural isomers have the same chemical formula but different atom connectivities. Two main classes of structural isomers are coordination isomers and linkage isomers. Stereoisomers isomers differ from structural isomers in that their atom connectivities are the same but the spatial arrangement of atoms is different. Two main classes of stereoisomers are cis-trans isomers and optical isomers (Section 22.5).

Crystal field theory describes the splitting of some *d* orbitals to higher energy levels when they are electrostatically repelled by ligands. The energy between two sets of split orbitals is known as the crystal field splitting energy. Octahedral complexes are split into three degenerate, lower-energy t_{2g} orbitals and two degenerate, higher-energy e_g orbitals. Depending on the crystal field splitting energy, either low-spin or high-spin configurations are possible.

Tetrahedral complexes are split into two degenerate, lower-energy *e* orbitals and three degenerate, higher-energy t_2 orbitals. The crystal field splitting energies of tetrahedral complexes are typically small, so most tetrahedral complexes are high spin. The *d* orbitals of square planar compounds are split into four different energy levels. Square planar geometries are typically adopted by period 5 and period 6 d^8 complexes (Section 22.6).

The spectrochemical series shows how coordination compound ligands vary in their contribution to the size of the crystal field splitting energy. The spectrochemical series can be used to predict the color and magnetism of coordination compounds. The magnetism of coordination compounds can be predicted by crystal field theory. Coordination compounds that contain unpaired *d* electrons are predicted to be paramagnetic, and those that lack unpaired *d* electrons are predicted to be diamagnetic (Section 22.7).

END OF CHAPTER QUESTIONS

22.1 Review of Using Oxidation States in Naming Compounds

1. Give the oxidation state and charge of the *d*-block metal in each of the following.
   a. CuCl
   b. FeS
   c. Hg_2Cl_2
   d. CrO_3
   e. $[CrOCl_4]^-$

2. Give the oxidation state of the *d*-block metal in each of the following.
   a. $W(CN)_6$
   b. Fe_2O_3
   c. K_3MnO_4
   d. Li_2ZrF_6
   e. $[MnO_3]^+$

3. Give the oxidation state of the *d*-block metal in each of the following.
   a. $IrBr_3$
   b. $LiRuO_4$
   c. K_2OsCl_6
   d. $CsVOF_4$
   e. $[OsO_3F_3]^-$

22.2 The Properties of Transition Metals

4. Give the electron configurations for the following.
   a. Fe(0)
   b. Fe(II)
   c. Ni(0)
   d. Ni(III)

5. Give the electron configurations for the following.
   a. Pt(II)
   b. Cr(IV)
   c. Cr(VI)
   d. Os(IV)

6. Determine the highest possible oxidation state for each of the following elements.
   a. Sc
   b. Zr
   c. W
   d. Ir

7. Explain why +2 is such a common oxidation state for transition metals.

8. Explain why elements in the middle of the *d* block tend to have higher stable oxidation states than elements on the left or right sides of the *d* block.

9. Identify which of these elements is most likely to have a stable +6 oxidation state.
   a. Y
   b. Hf
   c. W
   d. Pd

10. Explain why the atomic radii of transition metals do not decrease as much going from left to right across the *d* block as the radii of main group elements do going from left to right across the *p* block.

11. What is the lanthanoid contraction?

12. For each of the following sets of three elements, identify the two that have the most similar atomic radii.
    a. Ti, Zr, Hf
    b. V, Nb, Ta
    c. Sc, Mn, Co
    d. Y, Zr, Ru

13. The first ionization energy of tantalum, Ta, is significantly higher than that those of vanadium, V, and niobium, Nb. Explain why.

14. For each of the following sets of three elements, identify the element that is most electronegative.
    a. Y, Zr, Ru
    b. Hf, Zr, Ti
    c. V, Au, Mn

22.3 Introduction to Coordination Compounds

15. Compare and contrast covalent bonds with coordinate covalent bonds.

16. Describe the difference between the type of bonding found the primary coordination sphere of coordination compounds with the type of bonding found in the secondary coordination sphere.

17. Determine the coordination number of each coordination compound, and determine which groups are in the primary and secondary coordination spheres.
    a. $[Cu(NH_3)_4]^{2+}$
    b. $[Cr(H_2O)_6]Cl_3$
    c. $Fe(CN)_6^{3-}$
    d. $K_2[Co(H_2O)_2Cl_4]$

18. Determine the coordination number of each coordination compound, and determine which groups are in the primary and secondary coordination spheres.
   a. $[Fe(SCN)_3]Cl$
   b. $Li_3[IrCl_6]$
   c. $[Cr(SCN)_4]F_2$
   d. $[Fe(H_2O)_6](ClO_4)_2$

19. Explain the role of entropy as a thermodynamic driving force in the chelate effect.

20. Consider the following reactions of $Co^{2+}(aq)$ with ammonia, NH_3; ethylenediamine, en; and ethylenediaminetetraacetic acid, EDTA.

$$Co^{2+}(aq) + 6\,NH_3(aq) \rightleftharpoons [Co(NH_3)_6]^{2+}(aq)$$
$$Co^{2+}(aq) + 3\,en(aq) \rightleftharpoons [Co(en)_3]^{2+}(aq)$$
$$Co^{2+}(aq) + EDTA(aq) \rightleftharpoons [Co(EDTA)]^{2+}(aq)$$

   Rank the expected formation constants, K_f, for the complex ions, from lowest to highest. You may want to consult Table 22.3.

21. Name one factor that determines whether a ligand is mondentate, bidentate, or polydentate.

22. Consider the SCN^- ion. Which atoms of SCN^- could bond to a metal ion?

23. Determine the coordination number and likely geometry of the following coordination compounds.
   a. $[Cu(H_2O)_6]^{2+}$
   b. $[CoF_6]Cl_2$
   c. $Ni(CO)_4$

24. Determine the coordination number and likely geometry of the following coordination compounds.
   a. $[VCl_6]^{2-}$
   b. Na_3CuCl_4
   c. $[Pt(NH_3)_4]^{2+}$

22.4 Nomenclature of Coordination Compounds

25. Determine the oxidation number of the transition metal in each of the following.
   a. $[Cu(NH_3)_4]^{2+}$
   b. $[Cr(H_2O)_6]Br_3$
   c. $Fe(CN)_6{}^{3-}$
   d. $K_2[Co(H_2O)_2Cl_4]$

26. Determine the oxidation number of the transition metal in each of the following.
   a. $[IrCl_6]^{3-}$
   b. $[CoCl_6](SCN)_3$
   c. $[CrCl_2(H_2O)_4]Br_2$
   d. $V(CO)_2(NH_3)_2Cl$

27. Name the following.
   a. $Cu(NH_3)_6{}^{2+}$
   b. $Pt(NH_3)_4{}^{2+}$
   c. $[Cr(H_2O)_6]Br_3$
   d. $Na_2[NiCl_4]$

28. Name the following.
   a. $[Fe(H_2O)_6]Cl_3$
   b. $Na[V(CO)_6]$
   c. $Fe(H_2O)_4Cl_2$
   d. $[Fe(H_2O)_4Cl_2]Br$

29. Give the formula for the following.
   a. hexaaquanickel(II) sulfate
   b. bis(ethylenediamine)cadmium(II)
   c. pentaamminenitritocobalt(III)
   d. potassium hexacyanidoferrate(II)

30. Give the formula for the following.
   a. dichloridobis(ethylenediamine)chromium(III) chloride
   b. sodium carbonyltricyanidocobaltate(II)
   c. pentaamminebromidorhodium(III)
   d. pentaauqoxidoiron(III)

22.5 Isomerism in Coordination Compounds

31. Describe the difference between structural isomers and stereoisomers.

32. Of the geometries shown in Table 22.4, which would potentially exhibit cis-trans isomerism?

33. Classify each of the following compounds as structural isomers, stereoisomers, or not isomers. If isomers, classify them as either coordination isomers, linkage isomers, cis-trans isomers, or optical isomers.
   a. *cis*-$[Pd(NH_3)Br_2]$ and *trans*-$Pd(NH_3)Br_2]$
   b. $Na_4[CuCl_6]$ and $K_4[CuCl_6]$
   c. $[Co(NH_3)_5(\underline{S}CN)]ClO_4$ and $[Co(NH_3)_5(\underline{N}CS)]ClO_4$

34. Classify each of the following compounds as structural isomers, stereoisomers, or not isomers. If isomers, classify them as either coordination isomers, linkage isomers, cis-trans isomers, or optical isomers.
   a. *cis*-$[Pd(NH_3)_2Br_2]$ and *trans*-$Pd(NH_3)_2Br_2]$
   b. $[CuCl_6]Br_4$ and $[CuCl_6]F_4$
   c. $[Co(NH_3)_5(\underline{S}CN)]ClO_4$ and $[Co(NH_3)_5(\underline{N}CS)]ClO_4$

35. Classify each of the following compounds as structural isomers, stereoisomers, or not isomers. If isomers, classify them as either coordination isomers, linkage isomers, cis-trans isomers, or optical isomers.
 a. $[Co(en)_2Cl_2]Br_2$ and $[Co(en)_2Br_2]Cl_2$
 b. *cis*-$[Ni(NH_3)_2Cl_2]$ and *trans*-$Ni(NH_3)_2Br_2]$
 c. $[Cr(H_2O)_5Cl]Br_2$ and $[Cr(H_2O)_5Br]ClBr$

36. Draw cis-trans isomers of $[Pd(CN)_2Cl_2]^{2-}$.

37. Draw two linkage isomers of $[Mo(NH_3)_5NO_2]^{4+}$.

38. Draw optical isomers of $[Cr(bipy)_3]^{3+}$. The structure of bipyridine (bipy) is shown here.

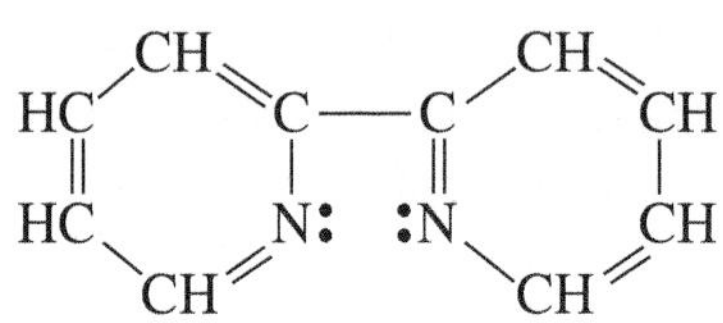

Bipyridine (bipy)

39. Draw all possible isomers of the octahedral $[Pd(H_2O)_2(OH)_2Br_2]^{2-}$ complex.

22.6 Crystal Field Theory

40. In an octahedral complex (Figure 22.12), which *d* orbitals have electron density along the axes where ligands bond to the metal? Which *d* orbitals have electron density *between* the axes where the ligands bond to the metal?

41. In a square planar complex (Figure 22.18), which *d* orbitals have electron density along the axes where ligands bond to the metal? Which *d* orbitals have electron density *between* the axes where the ligands bond to the metal?

42. In an octahedral complex, which set of *d* orbitals is higher in energy than the other set? Use crystal field theory to explain why. Hint: See Figure 22.12 and Figure 22.13.

43. In a tetrahedral complex, which set of *d* orbitals is higher in energy than the other set? Contrast your answer to the *d* orbital splitting in an octahedral complex and use crystal field theory to explain the difference. Hint: See Figure 22.16 and Figure 22.17.

44. Write electron configurations for the *d* orbitals of the following.
 a. a high-spin octahedral d^5 complex
 b. a low-spin octahedral d^5 octahedral complex
 c. a high-spin octahedral Cr(III) complex
 d. an octahedral Mo(III) complex

45. Write electron configurations for the *d* orbitals of the following.
 a. a high-spin octahedral d^4 complex
 b. a low-spin octahedral Fe(III) complex
 c. a high-spin octahedral Ir(II) complex
 d. an octahedral Zr(IV) complex

46. Identify the *d* electron configurations for octahedral complexes in which separate high-spin and low-spin configurations are *not* possible. Explain why only one ground-state electron configuration is possible in these cases.

47. Explain why high-spin and low-spin octahedral d^8 complexes have the same *d* electron configurations.

48. Draw crystal field splitting diagrams for the following.
 a. a high-spin octahedral Rh(III) complex
 b. a low-spin square planar $[NiBr_4]^{2-}$ complex
 c. a tetrahedral Zn(II) complex

49. Determine the likely geometries of the following coordination compounds and then draw crystal field splitting diagrams for each.
 a. $[TiF_6]^{2-}$
 b. $[CuCl_4]^{3-}$
 c. $[Cu(en)_3]^{2+}$

22.7 The Spectrochemical Series, Color, and Magnetism

50. Write the likely electron configurations for the *d* orbitals of the following octahedral complexes.
 a. $[Ru(CN)_6]^{3-}$
 b. $[CoF_6]^{2-}$
 c. $Cr(CO)_6$

51. Write the likely electron configurations for the *d* orbitals of the following octahedral complexes.
 a. $[Mn(NH_3)_6]^{2+}$
 b. $[Rh(en)_3]^{3+}$
 c. $[Ni(H_2O)_6]^{2+}$

52. Consider the following octahedral complex ions: $[Cr(CN)_6{}^{3-}]$, $[CrCl_6]^{3-}$, and $[Cr(H_2O)_6]^{3+}$. Arrange these in terms of their expected Δ_o values, from smallest to largest.

53. Consider the following tetrahedral complex ions: $[Zr(H_2O)_4]^{2+}$, $[Zr(CN)_4]^{3-}$, and $[Zr(OH)_4]^{2-}$. Arrange these in terms of their expected Δ_t values, from smallest to largest.

54. Determine whether the following octahedral complexes are likely paramagnetic or diamagnetic.
a. $[FeCl_6]^{4-}$
b. $W(CO)_6$
c. $[Cu(NH_3)_6]^{2+}$

55. Determine whether the following complexes are likely paramagnetic or diamagnetic.
a. $[Co(en)_3]^{3+}$
b. $[PtBr_4]^{2-}$
c. $[Ni(H_2O)_6]^{2+}$

56. Which of the following complexes would be expected to *absorb* light at the highest wavelength? Which would be expected to absorb light at the lowest wavelength?
a. $[Co(H_2O)_6]^{3+}$
b. $[Co(CN)_6]^{3-}$
c. $[CoBr_6]^{3-}$

57. Which of the following complexes would be expected to *reflect* light at the highest wavelength? Which would be expected to reflect light at the lowest wavelength?
a. $[Cr(en)_3]^{3+}$
b. $[Cr(NH_3)_6]^{3+}$
c. $[Cr(C_2O_4)_3]^{3-}$

58. A coordination complex exhibits an orange color. At which of the following wavelengths is it most likely to absorb light?
a. 620 nm
b. 520 nm
c. 450 nm
d. 420 nm

59. A coordination complex absorbs light at 420 nm. Which of the following colors best describes its appearance to the human eye?
a. violet
b. blue
c. yellow
d. orange

60. A chemist prepares three solutions containing various manganese complexes, but forgets to label them. He determines that one solution absorbs light at 1330 nm, another at 1180 nm, and the third at 333 nm. Match the wavelength to the likely Mn(II) complex.
a. $[Mn(CN)_6]^{4-}$
b. $[Mn(H_2O)_6]^{2+}$
c. $[MnCl_6]^{4-}$

61. $[RhCl_6]^{4-}$ absorbs light at 490 nm. Calculate its Δ_o value in units of joules.

62. $[Rh(CN)_6]^{4-}$ has a Δ_o value of 9.03×10^{-19} J. Calculate the wavelength, in nanometers, at which it absorbs light.

Putting It Together

63. Give the *d* electron configuration of $[PtCl_4]^{2-}$ and draw its crystal field splitting diagram. Assume that the electrons are in a high-spin configuration.

64. The hydrates introduced in Chapter 3 are actually coordination compounds. For example, copper sulfate pentahydrate, $CuSO_4 \cdot 5\,H_2O$ (Figure 3.13), is a coordination compound of copper, with aqua ligands in the primary coordination sphere and the sulfate ion in the secondary coordination sphere. Rewrite the name and formula of this compound as a coordination compound.

65. A particular coordination compound of cobalt(III) has four NH_3 ligands and three Cl^- ions, but suppose you are unsure which of those Cl^- ions are ligands and which are counterions in the secondary coordination sphere.
a. Write three possible formulas for this coordination compound where at least one of the chloride ions is in the secondary coordination sphere.
b. When 0.0420 mol of this compound is dissolved in 375 mL of water at 25°C, the resulting osmotic pressure is 5.48 atm. Identify the correct formula and name for this compound.

66. Write the K_f expression associated with each of these complexes.
a. $[Ni(H_2O)_6]^{2+}$
b. $[Zn(OH)_4]^{2-}$

67. Aluminum hydroxide is an example of an amphoteric hydroxide. An amphoteric hydroxide can react with an acid in a double-replacement reaction or with a base to produce a complex ion where all the OH^- ions are hydroxido ligands.
a. Write the reaction of aluminum hydroxide with HCl.
b. Write the reaction of aluminum hydroxide with NaOH. The resulting complex has a coordination number of four.

68. The addition of Fe^{3+} ions to water will create an acidic solution because they form a complex

ion, $[Fe(H_2O)_6]^{3+}$, which then partially ionizes to produce H_3O^+ (Section 16.7).

a. Write the balanced equation for the formation of $[Fe(H_2O)_6]^{3+}$ from Fe^{3+} and water.
b. Write the balanced equation for the ionization of $[Fe(H_2O)_6]^{3+}$ to produce an acidic solution. Hint: One of the aqua ligands becomes a hydroxido ligand.

69. Consider the coordination compound $Na[Co(en)_2Br_2]$.
    a. Name this compound.
    b. Assuming a low-spin electron configuration, draw the crystal field splitting diagram of this compound.
    c. Draw all of the possible isomers of this compound.

70. Consider the following coordination compounds: $[Cu(NH_3)_5(H_2O)]Cl$ and $[Cu(NH_3)_5Cl](H_2O)]$.
    a. Are these compounds isomers? If so, name the type of isomer.
    b. Using Table 4.5, describe a precipitation reaction that can be used to distinguish between these two compounds.

71. $K_3[Fe(CN)_6]$ exhibits a bright red color. Determine the number of unpaired electrons in the *d* orbitals of Fe.

72. $[CoBr_4]^{2-}$ is tetrahedral. Determine the number of unpaired electrons in the *d* orbitals of Co.

PRACTICE PROBLEM SOLUTIONS

Practice Problem 22.1 Solution

The overall charge of the compound is the sum of the charges of its constituent ions.

a. Each hydroxide ion has a charge of −1. To balance the charge of the hydroxide ions (−3), Co has a charge of +3. The oxidation state of Co is +3.

b. The potassium ion has a charge of +1, and each of the four oxygens has a charge of −2. The charge of manganese, *x*, is calculated as follows.

$$1(+1) + x + 4(-2) = 0$$
$$1 + x + -8 = 0$$
$$x = +7$$

The charge of the manganese ion is +7. Since there is only one manganese ion in the compound, the oxidation state of manganese is +7.

c. Each potassium ion has a charge of +1, and each of the four oxygens has a charge of −2. The charge of manganese, *x*, is calculated as follows.

$$2(+1) + x + 4(-2) = 0$$
$$2 + x + -8 = 0$$
$$x = +6$$

The charge of the manganese ion is +6. Since there is only one manganese ion in the compound, the oxidation state of manganese is +6.

Practice Problem 22.2 Solution

a. Scandium(0) has 21 total electrons, and its electron configuration has an argon core of 18 electrons. Two electrons occupy the 4*s* orbital, and the remaining electron occupies the 3*d* subshell. The electron configuration of Sc(0) is $[Ar]4s^2 3d^1$.

b. The electron configuration of Sc(0) from part a is $[Ar]4s^2 3d^1$. For Sc(II), the two 4*s* electrons are removed to give the +2 ion. The electron configuration of Sc(II) is $[Ar]3d^1$.

Practice Problem 22.3 Solution

Scandium is unlikely to be stable in the +4 oxidation state because only its two 4*s* electrons and one 3*d* electron are relatively easy to remove. The removal of a fourth electron to achieve a +4 oxidation state would require the removal of a 3*p* electron, which would break up a noble gas configuration. This is energetically unfavorable. Cobalt and iridium are located closer to the center of the *d* block than scandium and would both be more stable in the +4 oxidation state than scandium. Between the two, iridium is likely to be more stable with a +4 oxidation state because it is in period 6, whereas cobalt is in period 4. The electrons in iridium's outer *d* orbitals are located farther from the positive charge of its nucleus than the electrons in cobalt's outer *d* orbitals. Therefore, it is easier to remove iridium's outer *d* electrons than it is to remove cobalt's outer *d* electrons. Iridium is most likely to be most stable in the +4 oxidation state.

Practice Problem 22.4 Solution

Recall that the lanthanoid contraction describes the similar atomic radii of transition metals between periods 5 and 6. Scandium and yttrium are in periods 4 and 5, respectively, and there is still a substantial difference between their atomic radii (see Figure 22.2). Lanthanum and mercury are at the opposite ends of the *d* block in period 6, and there is a great deal of difference between their atomic radii. Molybdenum and tungsten are in periods 5 and 6, respectively, and are both in group 6. As shown in Figure 22.2, their atomic radii are much more similar than the atomic radii of the other two pairs of elements.

Practice Problem 22.5 Solution

a. First ionization energies increase from left to right across the *d* block. Since all three elements are in period 4, scandium has the lowest first ionization energy. Figure 22.3 confirms this prediction.

b. Transition metal electronegativity generally increases from left to right across a period. The three given elements are all in period 5, so you would predict their relative electronegativities to be Y < Mo < Ru. Figure 22.4 confirms this prediction.

Practice Problem 22.6 Solution

a. $[Fe(NH_3)_6](NO_3)_3$ has a coordination number of six. The six NH_3 ligands are inside the brackets and, therefore, are part of the primary coordination sphere. The three NO_3^- ions outside the brackets are part of the secondary coordination sphere.

b. $Rh(H_2O)_2Br_2$ has a coordination number of four. The two H_2O ligands and two Br^- ions are part of the primary coordination sphere, as no brackets are shown.

Practice Problem 22.7 Solution

a. Acetylacetone has two oxygen atoms, each of which contains two lone pairs of electrons. Each of these oxygen atoms can form coordinate covalent bonds to a metal. Acetylacetone is bidentate.

b. Pyridine contains a nitrogen atom with a lone pair of electrons. No other atoms contain lone-pair electrons. Pyridine is monodentate.

Practice Problem 22.8 Solution

a. $[CoCl_6]^{3-}$ contains six monodentate ligands, so it has a coordination number of six. It has an octahedral geometry.

b. $[Cd(NH_3)_4]^{2+}$ contains four monodentate ligands. Cd(II) has a d^{10} electron configuration, so $[Cd(NH_3)_4]^2$ has a tetrahedral geometry rather than a square planar geometry.

Practice Problem 22.9 Solution

a. The overall charge of the complex is +1. From Table 22.3, Cl has a charge of −1, and NH_3 has a charge of 0. If x represents the oxidation state of Rh, then

$$x + 1(-1) + 3(0) = +1$$
$$x = +2$$

The oxidation state of Rh is +2.

b. The overall charge of the complex is −2, and Cl has a charge of −1. If x represents the oxidation state of Ni, then

$$x + 4(-1) = -2$$
$$x = +2$$

The oxidation state of Ni is +2.

Practice Problem 22.10 Solution

a. From Table 22.3, OH^- is the *hydroxido* ligand. The nitrate and hydroxido ions each contribute a charge of −1 to the complex, so the oxidation state of Cr is +4. Using alphabetical order to name the ligands, but ignoring any Greek prefixes when doing so, the full name of $[Cr(H_2O)_4(OH)_2](NO_3)_2$ is tetraaquadihydroxidochromium(IV) nitrate.

b. From Table 22.3, the $C_2O_4^{2-}$ ligand is named *oxalato*. From Table 22.5, cobalt as an anion in a coordination compound is named *cobaltate*. The total charge from the oxalate ligands is −6, and the total charge from the potassium cations is +3. Therefore, the oxidation state of Co is +3. The full name of $K_3[Co(C_2O_4)_3]$ is potassium trioxalatocobaltate(III).

Practice Problem 22.11 Solution

a. These compounds differ only in the donor atom within a ligand. Since the atom connectivity differs, the two compounds are structural isomers. In one complex, an oxygen of NO_2^- bonds to Fe^{2+}, whereas the nitrogen of NO_2^- bonds to Fe^{2+} in the other. These two compounds are linkage isomers.

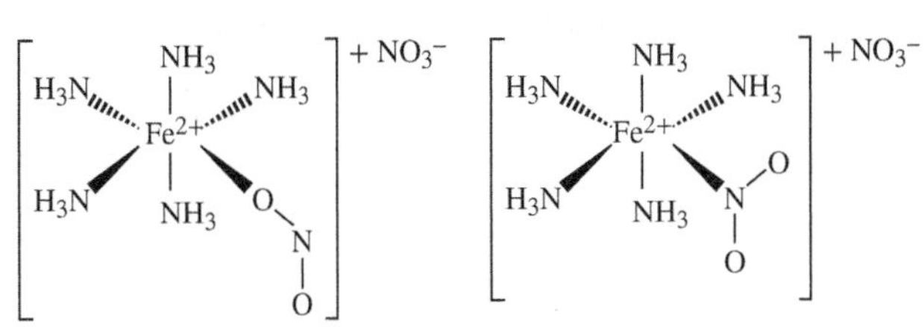

b. These two compounds have different chemical formulas (Br^- versus Cl^- ligands), so they are not isomers.

Practice Problem 22.12 Solution

a. A Co(II) complex is d^7. In a high-spin complex, the total electron spin is maximized by placing as many electrons as possible into different orbitals. Therefore, a high-spin d^7 complex has the configuration $t_{2g}{}^5e_g{}^2$ with one unpaired electron in one of the t_{2g} orbitals and unpaired electrons in each of the e_g orbitals. This gives a total of three unpaired electrons.

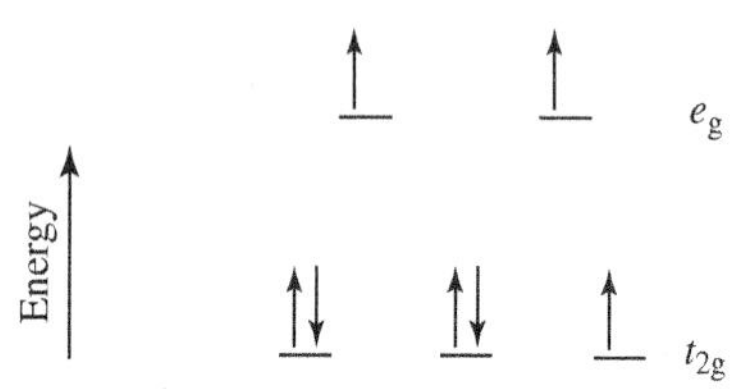

b. In a low-spin complex, the total electron spin is minimized by pairing as many electrons as possible. Therefore, a low-spin d^7 complex has the configuration $t_{2g}{}^6e_g{}^1$ with zero unpaired electrons in the t_{2g} orbitals and one unpaired electron in an e_g orbital.

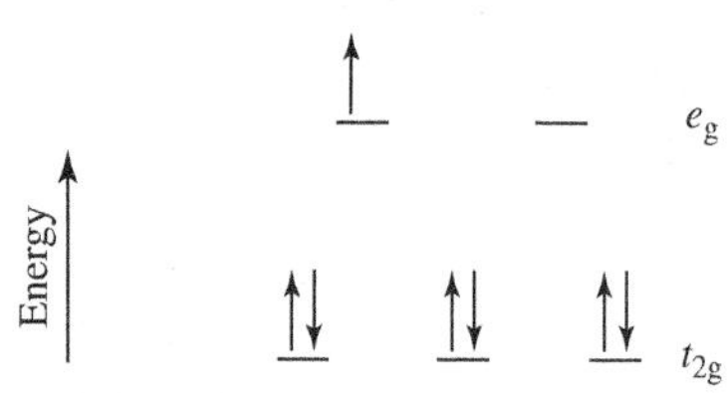

c. A Cr(III) complex is d^3. It is more energetically favorable to place each electron into separate (degenerate) t_{2g} orbitals than to expend pairing energy by placing two of them into the same orbital. Therefore, the Cr(III) complex has an electron configuration of $t_{2g}{}^3e_g{}^0$, with three unpaired electrons.

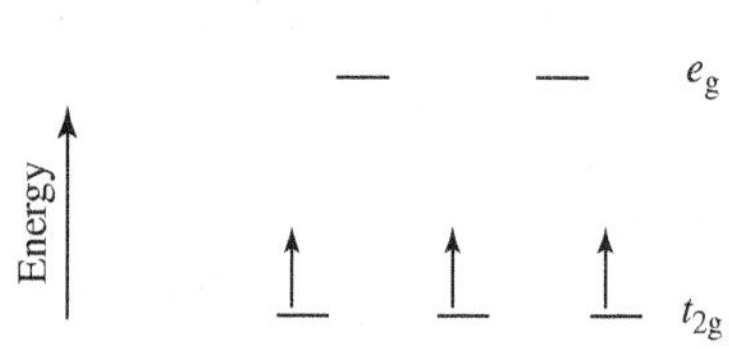

Practice Problem 22.13 Solution

a. According to the spectrochemical series, CN^- is a strong-field ligand, so Δ_o will be relatively large and the complex will most likely be low spin. The six CN^- ligands and the overall charge of -3 on the complex mean that the oxidation state of Fe is $+3$. Fe^{3+} has a d^5 configuration. The d electron configuration for a low-spin d^5 octahedral complex is $t_{2g}{}^5e_g{}^0$. In this configuration, two of the t_{2g} orbitals contain two electrons, and one contains one electron. $[Fe(CN)_6]^{3-}$, therefore, should contain one unpaired electron.

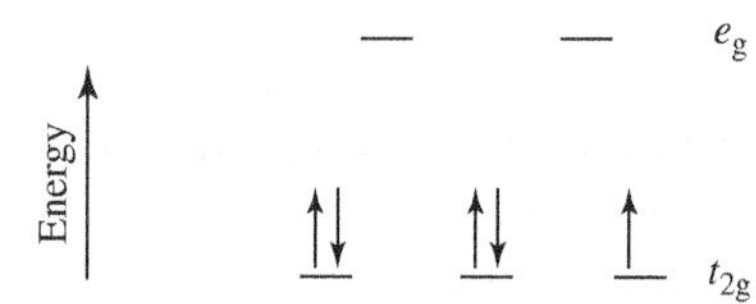

b. In the spectrochemical series, the NH_3 ligand is closer to the strong-field end of the spectrum than the weak-field end. You should assume, then, that NH_3 is a strong-field ligand and that Δ_o will be relatively large for this complex. The six neutral NH_3 ligands and the overall charge of $+3$ on the complex mean that the oxidation state of Cr is $+3$. Cr^{3+} has a d^3 configuration. The d electron configuration of a d^3 octahedral complex is $t_{2g}{}^3e_g{}^0$. Regardless of whether a d^3 complex has strong-field or weak-field ligands, the most stable d electron configuration consists of a single electron in each of the t_{2g} orbitals. Therefore, $[Cr(NH_3)_6]^{3+}$ has three unpaired d electrons.

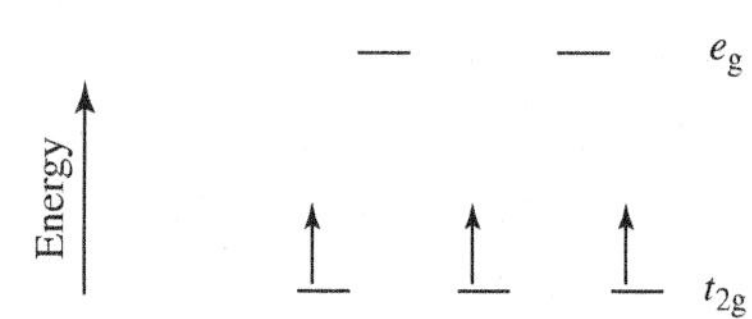

Practice Problem 22.14 Solution

The equation used to calculate the energy of Δ_o is

$$\lambda = \frac{hc}{\Delta_o} = \frac{(6.626 \times 10^{-34}\,\text{J} \cdot \text{s})\left(2.998 \times 10^{8}\,\frac{\text{m}}{\text{s}}\right)}{1.49 \times 10^{-19}\,\text{J}}$$

$$= 1.33 \times 10^{-6}\,\text{m}$$

$$1.33 \times 10^{-6}\,\text{m}\left(\frac{1\,\text{nm}}{10^{-9}\,\text{m}}\right) = 1330\,\text{nm}$$

Practice Problem 22.15 Solution

Complexes with strong-field ligands typically have larger Δ_o values than complexes with weak-field ligands. The wavelength of light absorbed is inversely proportional to the energy of Δ_o, so the iron(III) complex with the strong-field ligands will absorb light at a shorter wavelength than the iron(III) complex with the weak-field ligands. Therefore, $[FeX_6]^{3+}$ most likely absorbs light at 410 nm, and $[FeY_6]^{3+}$ most likely absorbs light at 680 nm.

Practice Problem 22.16 Solution

From the color wheel, the color of light absorbed at 520 nm is green. The complementary color of green is red, so the solution will appear to be red to the human eye.

Practice Problem 22.17 Solution

a. Cyanido has a −1 charge and is a strong-field ligand. Therefore, $K_4[Fe(CN)_6]$ is a low-spin octahedral complex. Given that Fe is in the +2 oxidation state, it is d^6 with an electron configuration of $t_{2g}{}^6e_g{}^0$. There are no unpaired electrons, so $K_4[Fe(CN)_6]$ should be diamagnetic.

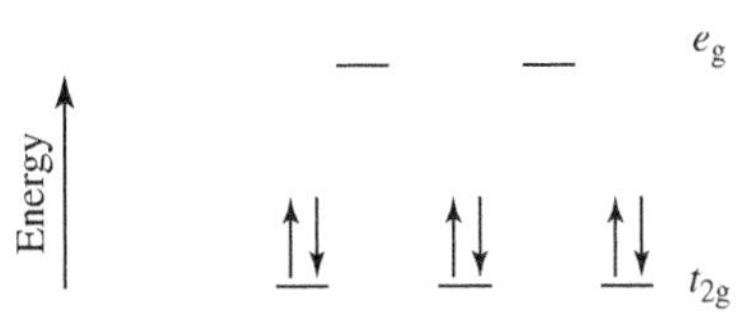

b. Zn^{2+} is d^{10}, so all of the d orbitals of $[Zn(NH_3)_4]^{2+}$ are full—they contain zero unpaired d electrons. Therefore, the compound should be diamagnetic.

c. While NH_3 is a relatively strong-field ligand, $[Ni(NH_3)_4]^{2+}$ has tetrahedral geometry because it is a period 4 d^8 complex. Therefore, it is likely to be high spin. That said, $[Ni(NH_3)_4]^{2+}$ will contain unpaired electrons whether its d electrons are in the low-spin or high-spin configuration. Ni is in the +2 oxidation state and is d^8. Both low- and high-spin tetrahedral d^8 complexes have the electron configuration of $e^4t_2{}^4$, with two unpaired electrons in the t_2 set. Therefore, $[Ni(NH_3)_4]^{2+}$ should be paramagnetic.

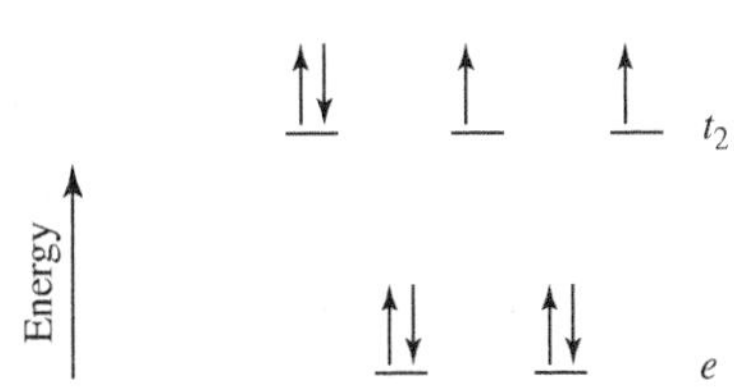

Practice Problem 22.18 Solution

a. As determined in Example 22.18c, $K_3[Fe(CN)_6]$ is a d^5 compound. The spectrochemical series shows that CN^- is a strong-field ligand, which will maximize Δ_o and result in a low-spin complex. This compound has one unpaired electron in the t_{2g} set and is paramagnetic.

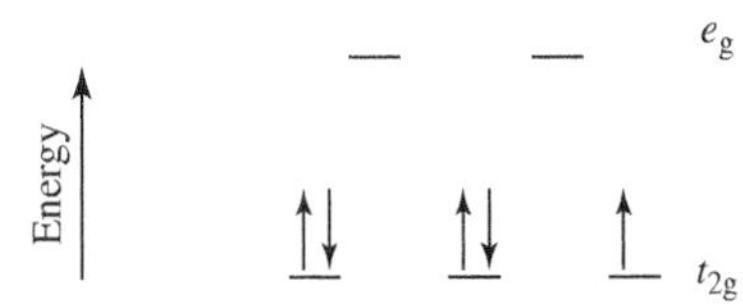

From Example 22.18c, $K_3[CrCl_6]$ is a d^3 compound. Since only three d electrons are present, all reside in separate orbitals of the t_{2g} set. $K_3[CrCl_6]$ is paramagnetic with three unpaired electrons.

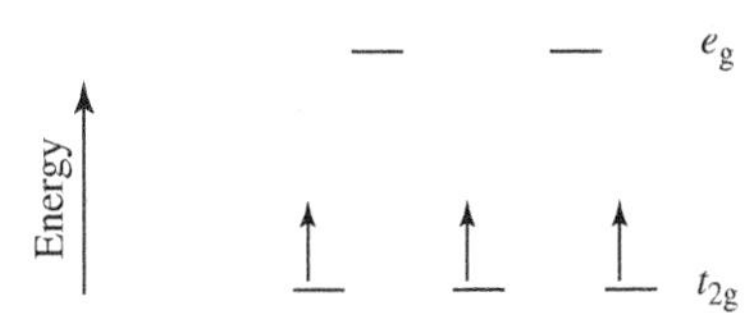

b. Recall that the energy of Δ_o is inversely proportional to the wavelength of light absorbed (Section 22.7). Therefore, the complex with the highest Δ_o, $[Fe(CN)_6]^{3-}$, absorbs energy at the lower wavelength (286 nm). $[CrCl_6]^{3-}$ has weak-field Cl^- ligands and a smaller Δ_o value. Therefore, $[CrCl_6]^{3-}$ absorbs light at the higher wavelength (730 nm).

c. The relationship between Δ_o and λ is $\Delta_o = \frac{hc}{\lambda}$.

For $[Fe(CN)_6]^{3-}$:

$$\Delta_o = \frac{hc}{\lambda} = \frac{(6.626 \times 10^{-34}\ \text{J} \cdot \text{s})\left(2.998 \times 10^8\ \frac{\text{m}}{\text{s}}\right)}{286 \times 10^{-9}\ \text{m}}$$
$$= 6.95 \times 10^{-19}\ \text{J}$$

For $[CrCl_6]^{3-}$:

$$\Delta_o = \frac{hc}{\lambda} = \frac{(6.626 \times 10^{-34}\ \text{J} \cdot \text{s})\left(2.998 \times 10^8\ \frac{\text{m}}{\text{s}}\right)}{730 \times 10^{-9}\ \text{m}}$$
$$= 2.72 \times 10^{-19}\ \text{J}$$

As expected, the complex with the lower wavelength, $[Fe(CN)_6]^{3-}$ has the larger (higher energy) Δ_o value.

CHAPTER 23 Biochemistry

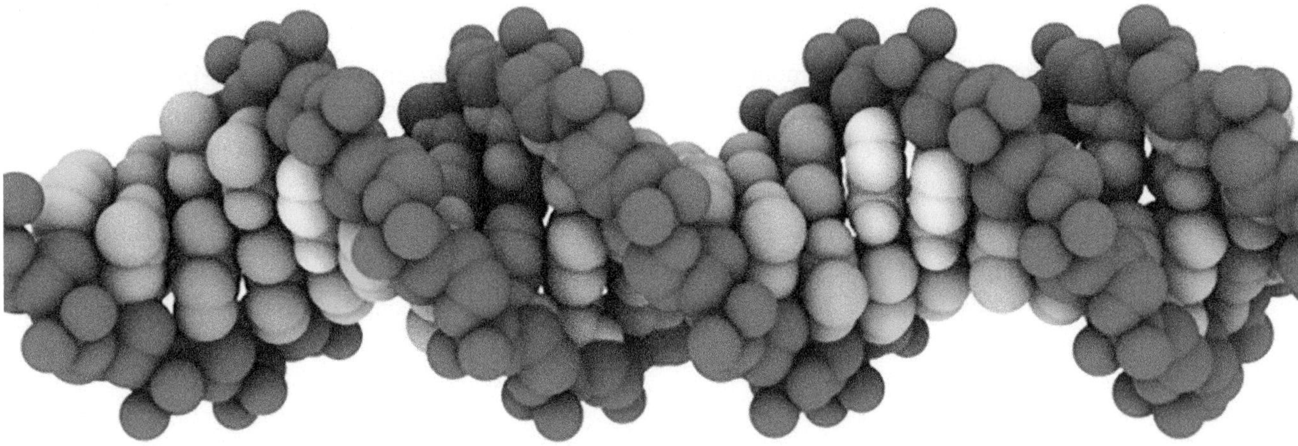

Like all matter, biological matter (such as proteins and DNA) is made up of atoms that bond and interact in the same ways that have been discussed throughout this book. One difference, however, is that biological molecules tend to be extremely large and made up of thousands and thousands of atoms. For example, in just the small portion of a DNA molecule shown here, each sphere is an atom. The main skeleton of the molecule is held together with covalent bonds (Chapter 10), but the overall spiral shape of DNA, called a double helix, is the result of hydrogen bonds (Chapter 12). Since different parts of the same long molecule are attracted to each other, the molecule folds over on itself.

Chapter Outline

GOALS

- Define *biochemistry*.
- Recognize and classify biomolecules.
- Describe the role of carbohydrates in living things.
- Compare and contrast the structures of monosaccharides, disaccharides, and polysaccharides.
- Explain the differences in the properties of carbohydrates based on their structures.
- Describe the role of lipids in living things.
- Compare and contrast the structures of triglycerides, phospholipids, steroids, and prostaglandins.
- Apply intermolecular forces to explain the solubility of lipids and their role in membranes.
- Describe the role of proteins in living things.
- Draw the structures of amino acids and peptides.
- Identify the four levels of protein structure and explain the forces that stabilize them.
- Describe the role and structure of the nucleic acids DNA and RNA, including how they differ.
- Describe the processes of DNA replication, transcription, and translation.
- Use the genetic code to predict peptide sequences from DNA and RNA sequences.

23.1 Introduction to Biomolecules

GOALS

- Define *biochemistry*.
- Recognize and classify biomolecules.

Background Review

Chapter 21 Organic Chemistry: Section 21.4—Organic Halides, Alcohols, Ethers, and Amines; Section 21.5—Aldehydes, Ketones, Carboxylic Acids, Esters, and Amides; Section 21.6—Polymers

Biochemistry is the chemistry of living things and, because the molecules that make up living things are primarily organic compounds, biochemistry is closely related to organic chemistry. Until 1828, when Friedrich Wöhler synthesized urea from silver cyanate and ammonia, scientists thought that carbon-containing compounds could only be made by living organisms. In the almost 200 years since then, scientists have learned to synthesize hundreds of thousands of organic compounds in the laboratory and have learned how to harness cellular mechanisms to manufacture biomolecules, such as the protein antigens needed to make effective vaccines.

Biomolecules cover a vast array of substances. One way to categorize them is by their size—that is, to separate the small biomolecules from the large. The many small molecules involved in metabolism—the chemical reactions that sustain life in organisms—are carbon-based molecules that contain the same functional groups first discussed in Section 21.3. These **biomolecules** undergo redox, synthesis, decomposition, substitution, and polymerization reactions in the metabolic processes of cells, just like the reactions discussed in Chapter 4, Chapter 19, and Chapter 21. Some biomolecules are broken down in oxidation reactions to release energy, while others are combined in synthesis reactions to form the materials needed for growth and repair processes. Small biomolecules can also have functions outside of metabolism; **neurotransmitters**, for example, are small molecules that transmit signals between cells of the nervous systems of animals.

The major focus of this chapter is on large biomolecules—namely, **carbohydrates**, **lipids**, **proteins**, and **nucleic acids**, which include substances composed of many smaller molecules. Table 23.1 gives examples of the roles of these biomolecules in organisms.

Carbohydrates are primarily involved with energy metabolism and energy storage, although carbohydrates on cell surfaces play a role in communication within an organism. Some lipids are also involved in energy metabolism and storage, but others play an important role in the structures of cells and communication between cells. Proteins have many functions, including structure, transport, catalysis, communication, and defense. Nucleic acids store information in genes, transmit information to future generations, and help to put the information to use, primarily to synthesize proteins.

TABLE 23.1 Examples of Biomolecules and Their Importance in Living Things

Biomolecule	Examples	Importance
Carbohydrates (Section 23.2)	Glucose (monosaccharide) Short chains of sugar molecules on cell surfaces	Energy metabolism in all living things Antigens identifying blood and tissue types in mammals
	Amylose and amylopectin Glycogen Cellulose Other polysaccharides	Energy storage in plants (seeds, tubers, fruits) Energy storage in animals Structure of cell walls in plants and fungi Structure of cell walls in bacteria
Lipids (Section 23.3)	Triglycerides	Energy storage in plants and animals
	Steroids, prostaglandins	Communication in mammals (hormones)
	Phospholipids	Structure of cell membranes in all living things
Proteins (Section 23.4)	Enzymes	Catalysis in metabolism of all living things
	Hemoglobin	Oxygen transport
	Collagen	Structure of skin in mammals
	Immunoglobulins	Protection (immune system)
	Peptide hormones	Communication
Nucleic acids (Section 23.5)	DNA	Stores genetic information
	RNA	Uses genetic information to synthesize proteins

Large biomolecules form by condensation reactions between functional groups of smaller molecules, resulting in the release of water molecules, a process sometimes referred to as **dehydration synthesis**. Use the Biomolecules activity (Figure 23.1) to simulate dehydration synthesis by combining generic monomers to create a polymer. The formation of each connection between monomers of biomolecules requires an enzyme catalyst (Section 14.6). Catalysis is one of the many functions of proteins in cells.

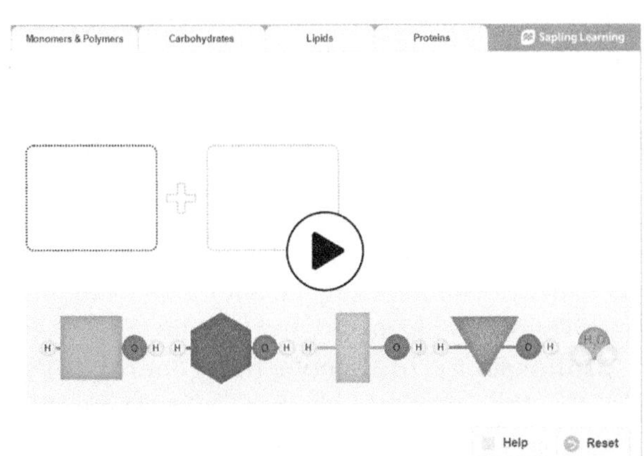

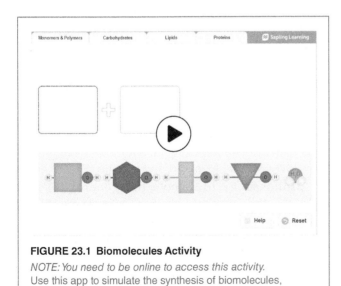

FIGURE 23.1 Biomolecules Activity

NOTE: You need to be online to access this activity.
Use this app to simulate the synthesis of biomolecules, including carbohydrates, proteins, and nucleic acids.

Example 23.1

Draw the products of a condensation reaction involving the highlighted functional groups on the following reactants.

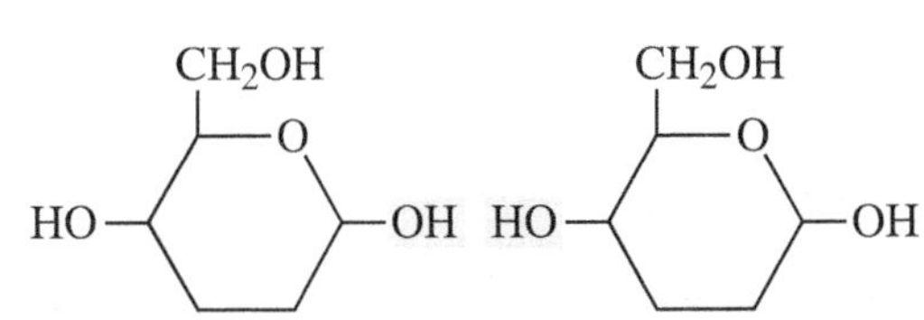

Solution

Once the atoms needed for a molecule of water are removed, connect the two molecules via the remaining O atom.

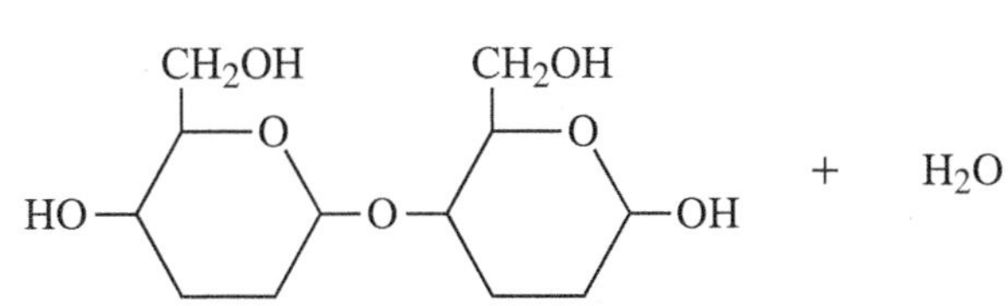

PRACTICE PROBLEM 23.1

Draw the products of a condensation reaction involving the highlighted functional groups on the following reactants.

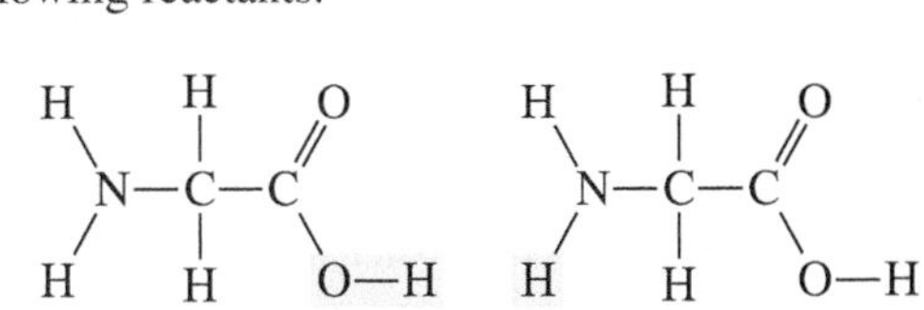

Hint: What small molecule can be made from the highlighted functional groups? What bond results once that small molecule is removed?

Example 23.2

Categorize the biomolecule represented by each of the following as a carbohydrate, lipid, protein, or nucleic acid:

a. a gene containing the information to produce brown pigment in eyes
b. the amylopectin stored in wheat seeds, which can be ground to make flour for bread and pasta
c. a substance that catalyzes the oxidation of glucose, a type of sugar

Solution

There are four categories of biomolecules: carbohydrates, lipids, proteins, and nucleic acids. Compare the descriptions to the functions of each category, as shown in Table 23.1.

a. Genetic information is stored in nucleic acids.
b. Wheat seeds are ground up to make bread flour, so amylopectin is a carbohydrate.
c. The most common biological catalysts are enzymes, which are proteins.

PRACTICE PROBLEM 23.2

Categorize the biomolecule represented by each of the following as a carbohydrate, lipid, protein, or nucleic acid:

a. a substance that transports oxygen throughout the bodies of mammals
b. a substance that hibernating animals such as bears store to survive the winter
c. a message sent between cells to trigger changes in metabolism

Hint: Review the functions of the four categories of biomolecules.

SECTION REVIEW

- Biomolecules are organic molecules found in living things, and, during metabolism, they undergo typical chemical reactions.
- Large biomolecules can be categorized as carbohydrates, lipids, proteins, or nucleic acids.
- Many biomolecules are composed of smaller molecules and form via condensation reactions catalyzed by enzymes that release a water molecule for each new connection.

23.2 Carbohydrates

GOALS

- Describe the role of carbohydrates in living things.
- Compare and contrast the structures of monosaccharides, disaccharides, and polysaccharides.
- Explain the differences in the properties of carbohydrates based on their structures.

Background Review

Chapter 11 Molecular Shape and Bonding Theories: Section 11.2—Polar and Nonpolar Molecules

Chapter 13 Solutions: Section 13.1—The Solution Process

Chapter 21 Organic Chemistry: Section 21.3—Introduction to Isomerism

Chapter 22 Coordination Chemistry: Section 22.5—Isomerism in Coordination Compounds

Several examples of carbohydrates and their roles in the biological world were presented in Table 23.1. Living things use **sugars**, which are carbohydrates, and **fats** and **oils** (Section 23.3), which are lipids, as energy sources. Photosynthetic organisms make their own sugar using the energy of sunlight and then metabolize those sugars to carry out the organism's metabolic processes. Other organisms consume the carbohydrates produced by plants. These sugars then undergo oxidation reactions to release energy, which is used to drive metabolic reactions for other life processes, such as movement, growth, neural transmission, and temperature regulation.

Sugars are the simplest carbohydrates and can be single-unit sugars, called **monosaccharides**, or two-unit sugars, called **disaccharides**. These small biomolecules, which contain many alcohol functional groups, are **polyhydroxy** aldehydes and ketones (Figure 23.2).

Monosaccharides have the general formula $C_nH_{2n}O_n$. The name *carbohydrate* is based on the relationship between the number of carbon atoms and the number of H and O atoms in that general formula. To the scientists who first studied these compounds, it appeared that an H_2O molecule was present for each carbon atom, in which case these sugars were thought to be *hydrates of carbon* (carbohydrates). Later

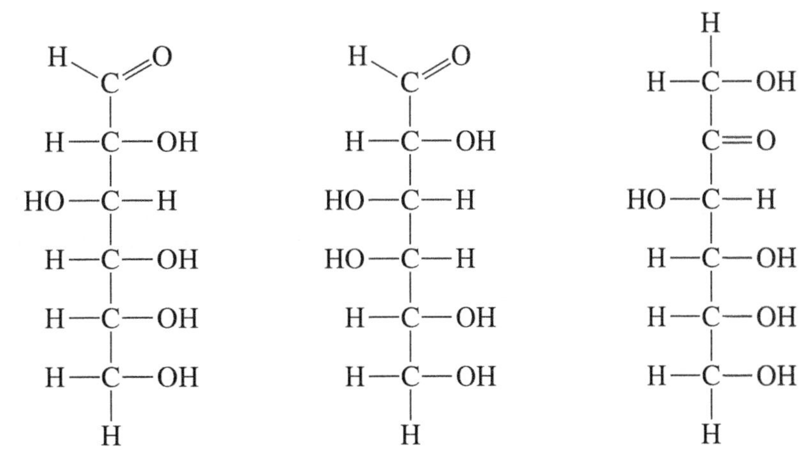

Glucose (a) | Galactose (b) | Fructose (c)

FIGURE 23.2 Monosaccharide Structures

Simple sugars, also known as monosaccharides, are aldehydes or ketones that contain many alcohol functional groups. The three sugars shown here contain six carbon atoms, so they are further categorized as hexoses. (a) Glucose and (b) galactose have aldehyde functional groups, making them aldohexoses, whereas (c) fructose has a ketone functional group, making it a ketohexose.

research showed that this was a poor description of their structures, but, by then, the name *carbohydrate* was in common usage.

MONOSACCHARIDES

Monosaccharides, such as glucose and galactose (Figure 23.2), contain aldehyde functional groups, so they are called **aldoses**; those that have ketone functional groups, such as fructose, are called **ketoses**. Aldoses and ketoses are further classified by the number of carbon atoms into **triose**, **tetrose**, **pentose**, and **hexose** sugars, which contain three, four, five, and six carbon atoms, respectively. These terms can be combined to describe glucose and galactose as aldohexoses and fructose as a ketohexose.

Example 23.3

Classify each monosaccharide by its functional group and number of carbon atoms:

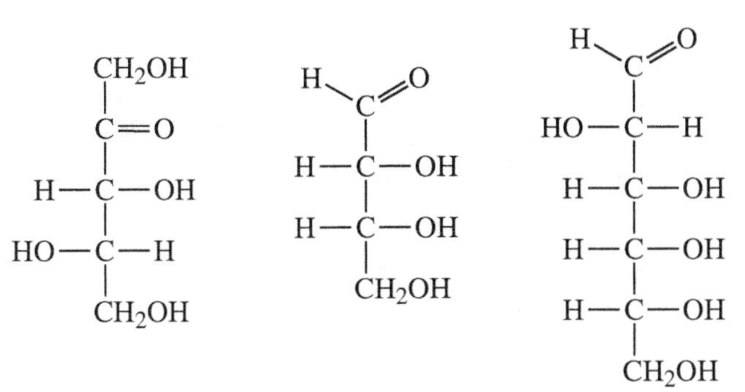

(a) (b) (c)

Solution

Determine whether the carbonyl group is part of an aldehyde or ketone, and then count the number of carbons to determine the correct description for each monosaccharide.

a. A ketone functional group and five carbon atoms overall make this a ketopentose.
b. aldehyde + 4C = aldotetrose
c. aldehyde + 6C = aldohexose

PRACTICE PROBLEM 23.3

Classify each monosaccharide by its functional group and number of carbon atoms:

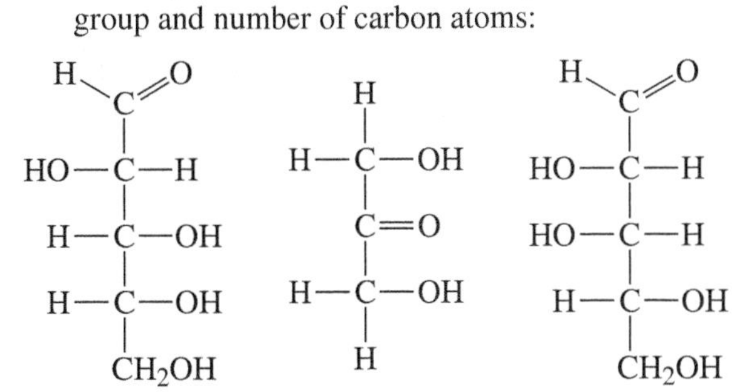

(a) (b) (c)

Hint: Is the carbonyl group part of an aldehyde or a ketone functional group? How many total carbon atoms are there in the structure?

Tetrahedral complexes with four unique ligands are chiral centers with two possible optical isomers (Section 22.3). A carbon atom bonded to four unique groups is tetrahedral and a chiral center. Fructose (Figure 23.3a)

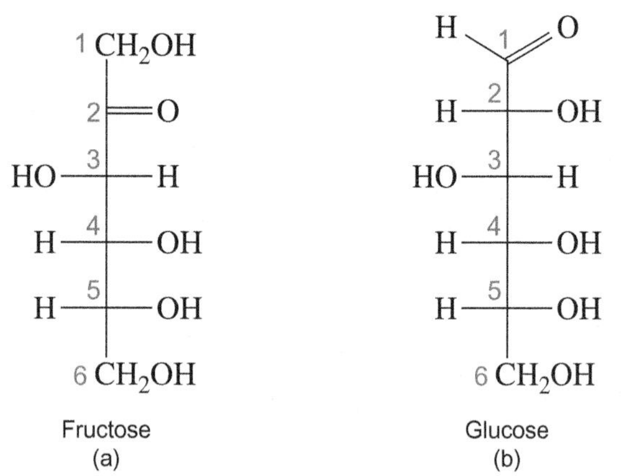

FIGURE 23.3 The Chiral Centers of Fructose and Glucose

Carbon atoms are implied at the intersections of lines.
(a) Fructose has chiral centers at C3, C4, and C5. (b) Glucose has chiral centers at C2, C3, C4, and C5.

has three chiral centers (C3, C4, and C5), whereas glucose (Figure 23.3b) has four (C2, C3, C4, and C5).

The structures shown in Figure 23.2, Example 23.3, and again in Figure 23.3 are called **Fischer projections**. Fischer projections indicate the three-dimensional arrangement of each of the chiral centers without using dash and wedge bonds (Section 21.2). Each vertical bond in a Fischer projection points backward (away from the viewer), like the dash bonds, while each horizontal bond points forward (toward the viewer), like the wedge bonds, thus making it possible to designate the three-dimensional arrangement of the bonds at each carbon.

Although Fischer projections are commonly used to compare the structures of different monosaccharides, they are not accurate representations of monosaccharides in aqueous solution. When dissolved in water, pentose and hexose molecules undergo an intramolecular reaction of the carbonyl group with an alcohol group on the fifth or sixth carbon, forming a cyclic structure that contains an oxygen atom as part of the ring (Figure 23.4).

This reaction also forms a new chiral center, called the **anomeric carbon**, because the carbonyl group has been transformed into a carbon atom bonded to four unique substituents. That is, the C1 aldehyde group of glucose (the carbonyl group) reacts with the C5 hydroxyl group to create the cyclic structure. C1 is now bonded to four atoms: the O in the ring structure, a —OH group that formed from the original carbonyl oxygen, a H atom, and C2. The bonds that point to the right in the Fischer projection (vertical structure) point

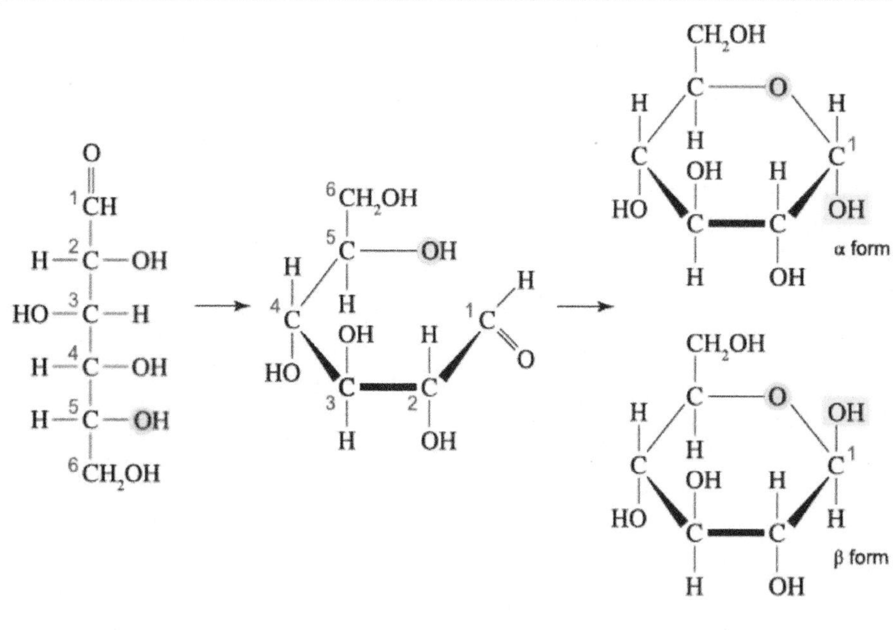

FIGURE 23.4 Formation of the Cyclic Form of Glucose

NOTE: You need to be online to access this video.

In aqueous solution, glucose molecules undergo an intramolecular reaction to form more stable cyclic structures. The *carbonyl carbon* (i.e., the carbon of the C=O group; Section 21.5) reacts with a hydroxyl group on C5 to form an ether group. This closes the ring, while the carbonyl oxygen becomes a new hydroxyl group. With this new hydroxyl group, C1 has become a new chiral center because it has four unique substituents. This new chiral center, which is referred to as the *anomeric carbon*, has two different forms. The —OH group points *down* (as compared to the position of C6) in the alpha anomer and points *up* in the beta anomer of the cyclic structure of glucose.

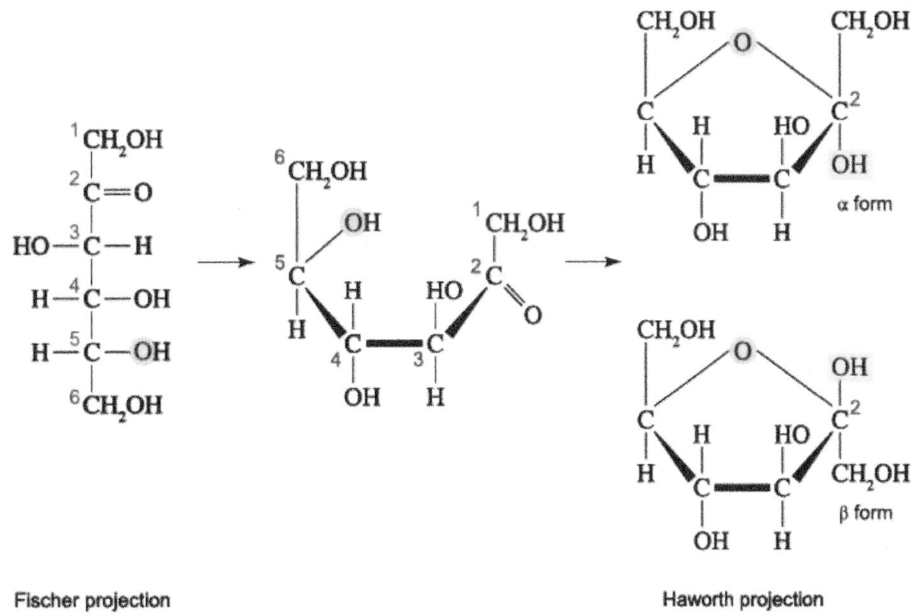

FIGURE 23.5 Formation of the Cyclic Form of Fructose

NOTE: You need to be online to access this video.

Fructose is a ketohexose, in which case C2 is the carbonyl carbon. In aqueous solution, fructose molecules undergo an intramolecular reaction to form a cyclic structure when the carbonyl carbon reacts with the C5 hydroxyl group. This forms a five-membered ring with a new hydroxyl group at C2. This new hydroxyl group can point down or up with respect to the $-CH_2OH$ group bonded to C5 of the ring, creating α and β anomers.

down in the **Haworth projection** (ring structure). Because C1, the carbon bonded to both the ring O atom and a hydroxyl group, is now a chiral center, there are two possible ways for the cyclic structure to form, with the newly formed hydroxyl group pointing in the same direction as or in the opposite direction of the bond between C5 and C6. These two possible versions of the ring structure are called **anomers**. In the α anomer, the newly formed hydroxyl group on C1 points in the *opposite* direction of the $-CH_2OH$ group bonded to C5. In the β anomer, the newly formed hydroxyl group on C1 points in the *same* direction as the $-CH_2OH$ group bonded to C5. Commonly, these two anomers are drawn as shown in Figure 23.4, with the bond to the C1 hydroxyl pointing down for the α anomer and up for the β anomer. In aqueous solution, ~64% of glucose molecules are in the β anomer form, ~36% are in the α anomer form, and less than 1% are in the open-chain form. Ketose sugars, such as fructose, form cyclic structures, too, in which the carbonyl carbon (C2) becomes the anomeric carbon (Figure 23.5).

Example 23.4

Identify the following monosaccharides as hexoses or pentoses, and determine whether they are α or β anomers.

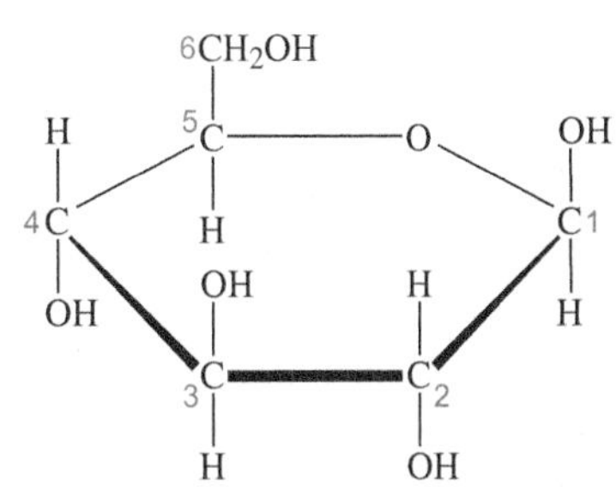

(a)

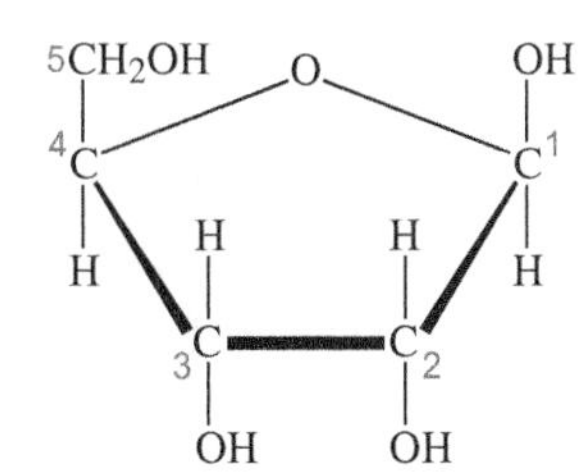

(b)

Solution

Count the number of carbon atoms in each monosaccharide to determine whether it is a hexose or a pentose. Then, locate the anomeric carbon, which was the carbonyl carbon in the open-chain form and, in this case, is C1 in both cyclic forms. It is bonded to the O atom in the ring *and* a $-OH$ group. Use the α designation when the $-OH$ group points down relative to the $-CH_2OH$ group bonded to the ring and the β designation when it points up.

a. This monosaccharide has six total carbon atoms, and the $-OH$ group of the anomeric carbon (C1) points in the same direction as the $-CH_2OH$ group bonded to C5, so this is a β-hexose.
b. Here there are five total carbon atoms, and the anomeric $-OH$ is up (the same direction as the $-CH_2OH$ group bonded to C5); this monosaccharide is a β-pentose.

PRACTICE PROBLEM 23.4

Identify the following monosaccharides as hexoses or pentoses, and determine whether they are α or β anomers.

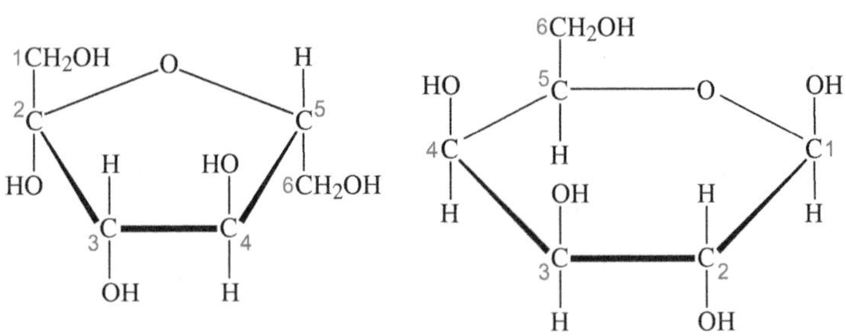

(a) (b)

Hint: The number of carbon atoms indicates whether the monosaccharide is a hexose or pentose. The orientation of the —OH group on the anomeric carbon (i.e., down or up with respect to the —CH_2OH group bonded to the ring at C5 or C6) determines whether it is α or β, respectively.

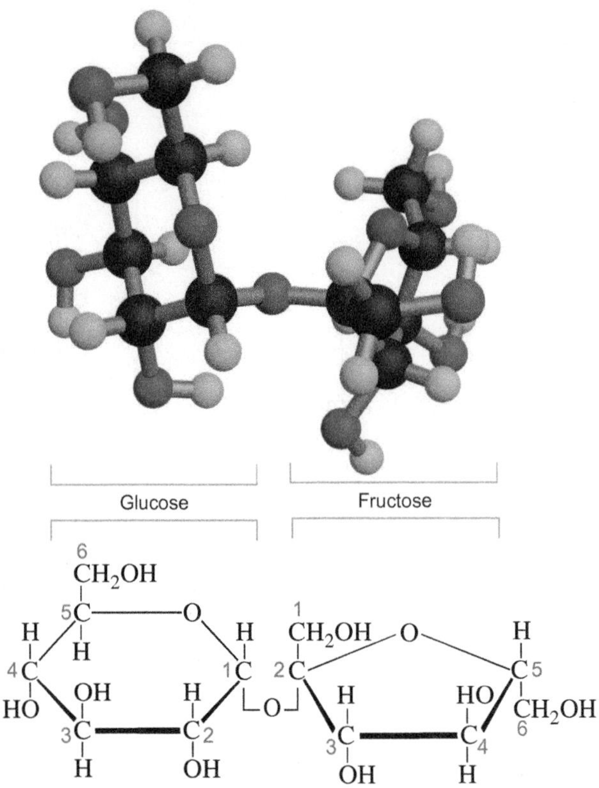

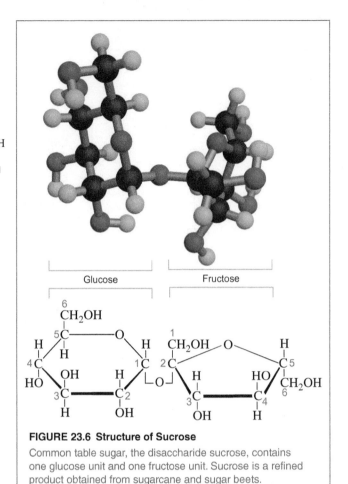

FIGURE 23.6 Structure of Sucrose

Common table sugar, the disaccharide sucrose, contains one glucose unit and one fructose unit. Sucrose is a refined product obtained from sugarcane and sugar beets.

DISACCHARIDES

Two monosaccharides combine in condensation reactions to form disaccharides. Sucrose (Figure 23.6) is a disaccharide made up of the monosaccharides glucose and fructose. Use the "Carbohydrates" tab of the Biomolecules activity (Figure 23.1) to form the common disaccharides maltose, sucrose, and lactose. In each case, a carbon on one molecule reacts with a hydroxyl group on another to form an ether functional group, while a molecule of water is eliminated.

In a disaccharide, the monosaccharides are linked by **glycosidic bonds**, also known as glycosidic linkages. To form maltose (Figure 23.7), the α-hydroxyl group of C1 of one glucose molecule reacts with the C4 of a second glucose molecule. This creates what is called an α-1,4 linkage, because the link from C1 points down (α) with respect to the ring and connects, via an O atom, to C4 of the second glucose molecule. Since C4 is not anomeric in this case, it does not have the α or β designation in the linkage notation.

Disaccharides are characterized by the identity of the two monosaccharides and by the details of the glycosidic bond. Some disaccharides, such as maltose, have an unreacted anomeric carbon. This makes additional linkages possible, leading to trisaccharides and other short-chain sugars known as **oligosaccharides**. Oligosaccharides on the surfaces of mammalian cells help to determine cell and tissue types and are involved in many important metabolic processes.

Example 23.5

The following equation depicts the formation of sucrose from glucose and fructose.

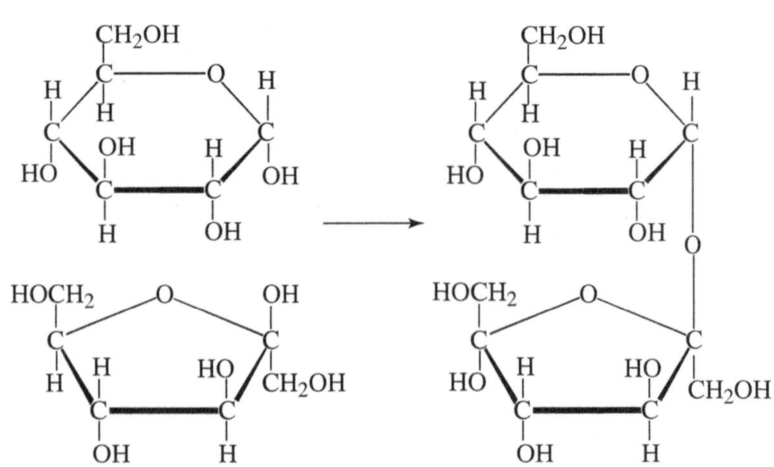

Identify the type of glycosidic bond using the "α/β-number" notation.

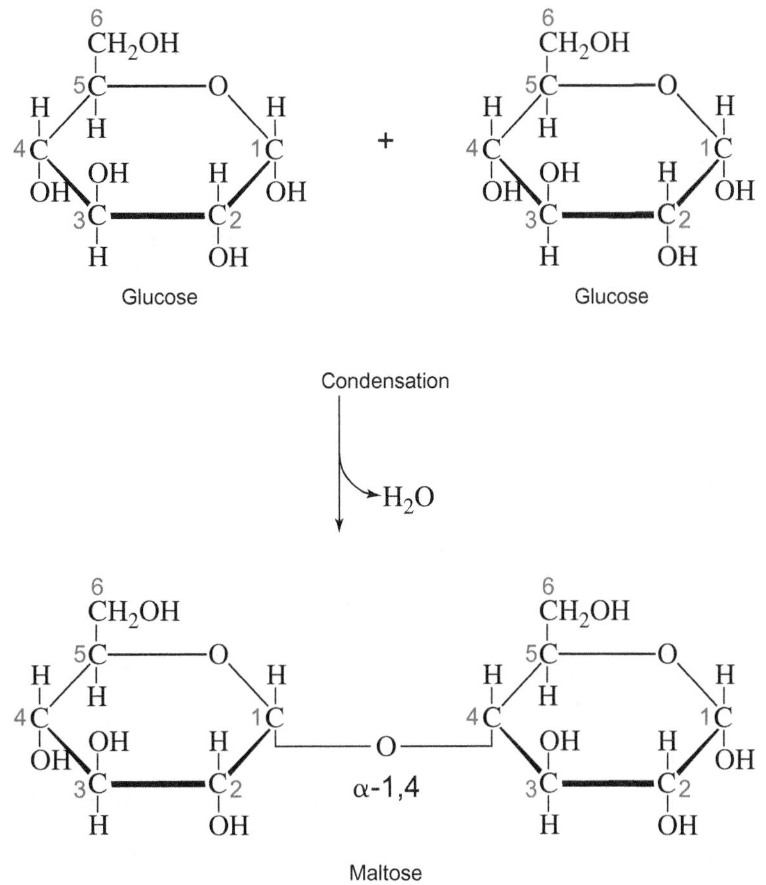

FIGURE 23.7 Formation of Maltose

Two glucose molecules combine via an α-1,4 linkage to form the disaccharide maltose. The α-1,4 linkage forms between C1 of one glucose and C4 of the other.

Solution

Start by numbering the carbon atoms. The glycosidic bond forms between C1 of glucose and C2 of fructose (a ketohexose). From the information so far, you can describe the linkage as 1,2.

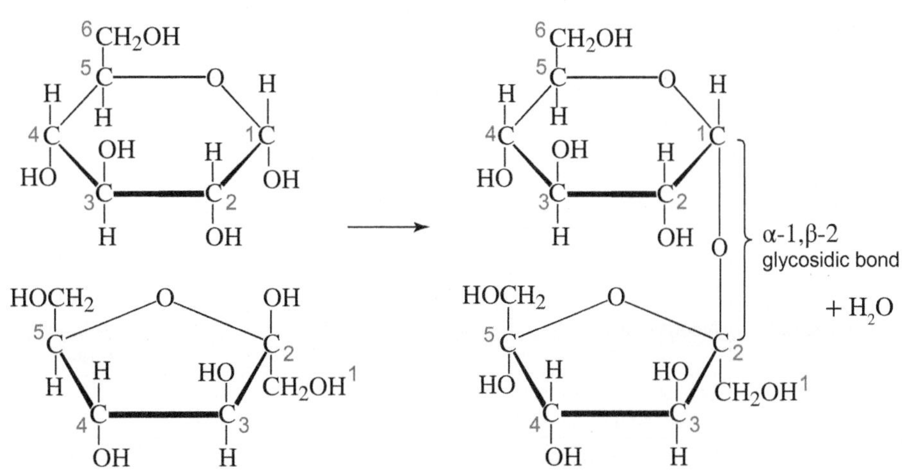

Both of these carbon atoms are anomeric, so classify each as α or β. C1 in glucose is in the α position, whereas C2 in fructose is in the β position. Thus, the exact description of the glycosidic linkage between monosaccharide units in sucrose is α-1,β-2.

EVERYDAY CONNECTION

Lactose, a disaccharide formed from the hexose sugars galactose and glucose (Practice Problem 23.5), is found in mammalian milk. Infants produce the enzyme *lactase* that enables them to digest lactose. However, many adults no longer make that enzyme and therefore are unable to digest lactose. This is known as lactose intolerance.

fcafotodigital/Getty Images

Adults who are lactose intolerant can consume lactase supplements along with dairy products to aid in digestion.

PRACTICE PROBLEM 23.5

Lactose is a disaccharide found in mammalian milk. It consists of the monosaccharides galactose and glucose.

Identify the type of glycosidic bond using the "α/β-number" notation.

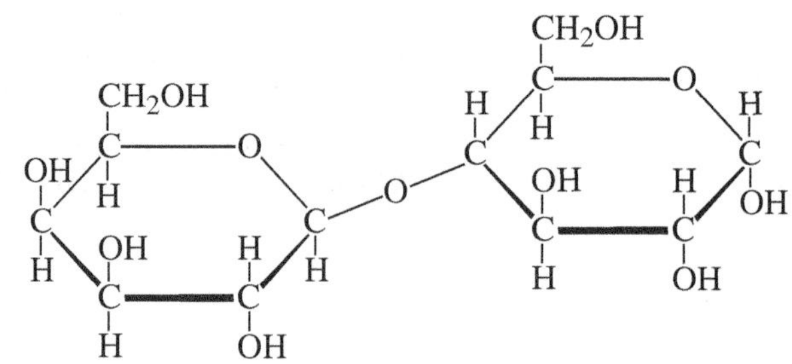

Hint: Start by numbering the carbon atoms. In this case, C1 is on the right side of each ring. The notation for the bond type should identify the two carbon atoms involved in the glycosidic bond by their number. If the carbon atom is anomeric, then it also requires the α or β designation.

The identities and structures of the monosaccharides and disaccharides discussed here are summarized in Table 23.2.

POLYSACCHARIDES

Anywhere from hundreds to thousands (or more) molecules of glucose, the most common carbohydrate, combine to form the polysaccharides **starch**, **cellulose**, and **glycogen**. The sizes and structures of these common polysaccharides are summarized in Table 23.3.

Cellulose, as a primary component of plant structure, makes up most of the biomass in the world. Cellulose is a linear polymer of thousands of β-glucose molecules, linked to each other via β-1,4 glycosidic linkages (Figure 23.8). For simplicity, it is common to

TABLE 23.2 Common Monosaccharides and Disaccharides

Name		Structure	Other Names	Source
Monosaccharides	Glucose	Aldohexose	Dextrose, corn sugar, invert sugar	Most common carbohydrate; makes up most of the biomass on Earth
	Fructose	Ketohexose	Fruit sugar	Found in fruit juices and honey
	Galactose	Aldohexose	–	Found in avocados and other plants
Disaccharides	Maltose	Two glucose units with α-1,4 linkage	–	Formed when starches hydrolyze
	Sucrose	Glucose and fructose with α-1,β-2 linkage	Cane sugar, beet sugar, table sugar	Found in sugarcane and sugar beets
	Lactose	Galactose and glucose with β-1,4 linkage	Milk sugar	Found in mammalian milk

TABLE 23.3 Polysaccharide Size and Structure

Polysaccharide	Source/Use	Glucose Units	Structure	Linkages
Cellulose	Plants/structure	300–3000	Linear	β-1,4
Amylose (starch)	Plants/energy storage	250–4000	Linear	α-1,4
Amylopectin (starch)	Plants/energy storage	2000–200,000	Branched	α-1,4, α-1,6 (branches)
Glycogen	Animals/energy storage	Up to 10^6	Highly branched	α-1,4, α-1,6 (branches)

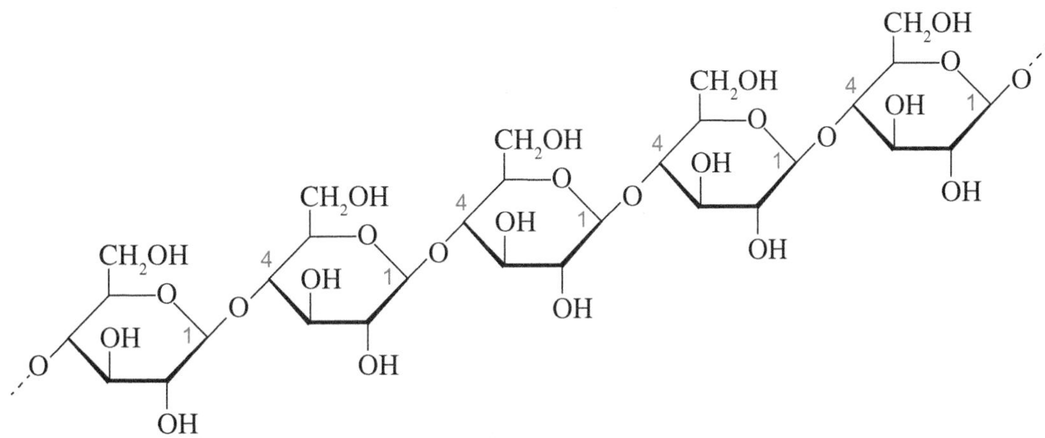

FIGURE 23.8 Cellulose

Cellulose, a major component of plant cell walls, contains thousands of glucose molecules linked to each other via β-1,4 glycosidic linkages. A carbon atom is implied at each vertex of a ring, as is the hydrogen atom attached to each of those carbon atoms.

omit the letter C at each vertex in a ring, as well as each H attached to the ring (Section 21.2).

Starch, which is produced by plants for energy storage, is found in two forms, called **amylose** and **amylopectin** (Figure 23.9).

Both are polymers of glucose. Amylose is a linear polymer with α-1,4 glycosidic bonds, whereas amylopectin is a branched polymer. Within each chain of amylopectin, the glucose units are linked via α-1,4, while the branches connect to the main chain via an α-1,6 link.

Cellulose and amylose have similar structures, differing only in the glycosidic bonds, yet humans use cellulose from wood to make paper and amylose from grains to make bread. The difference lies in the enzymes needed to catalyze the hydrolysis of the different glycosidic linkages to separate the polysaccharides into glucose units. Animals make amylase, an enzyme that catalyzes the hydrolysis of the α-1,4 glycosidic linkage in starches, but only certain bacteria and fungi can make cellulase, the enzyme needed to catalyze the hydrolysis of the β-1,4 links in cellulose. Thus, animals can digest the starches in the seeds and tubers of plants but not the cellulose in wood.

SECTION REVIEW

- Simple sugars, also called monosaccharides, are aldehydes or ketones with many alcohol groups. Monosaccharides combine through dehydration reactions to produce disaccharides and polysaccharides, all of which constitute the class of biomolecules known as carbohydrates.
- Monosaccharides are categorized by the number of carbon atoms and the presence of aldehyde or ketone functional groups.
- Hexoses and pentoses form cyclic structures in water and are present as either α or β anomers.
- Maltose, sucrose, and galactose are common disaccharides characterized by the identity of their constituent monosaccharides and by the type of glycosidic linkage.

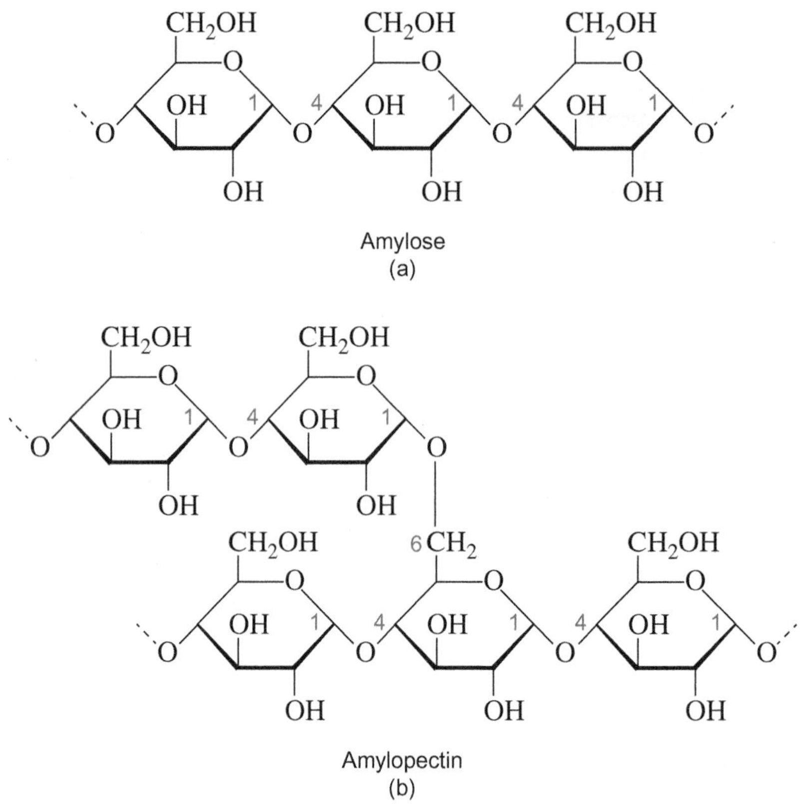

FIGURE 23.9 Amylose and Amylopectin

The starches amylose and amylopectin are large polymers consisting of varying numbers of glucose monomers. (a) Amylose is an unbranched chain of glucose units connected by α-1,4 glycosidic bonds. (b) Amylopectin is branched with α-1,4 bonds within each chain and α-1,6 bonds at the branch points.

- Polysaccharides are polymers of monosaccharides (commonly glucose); they make up most of the biomass on Earth.
- Amylose, amylopectin (in plants), and glycogen (in animals) are used for energy storage, while cellulose forms structural material in plants.

23.3 Lipids

GOALS

- Describe the role of lipids in living things.
- Compare and contrast the structures of triglycerides, phospholipids, steroids, and prostaglandins.
- Apply intermolecular forces to explain the solubility of lipids and their role in membranes.

Background Review

Chapter 12 Liquids and Solids: Section 12.1—Intermolecular Forces

Chapter 21 Organic Chemistry: Section 21.1—Introduction to Hydrocarbons; Section 21.2—Unsaturated Hydrocarbons

TRIGLYCERIDES

The term *lipid* is used to describe all molecules of biological origin that are insoluble in water. Consequently, lipids include a broad range of substances, including fats and oils, steroids, phospholipids, and prostaglandins. Fats and oils are not polymers like polysaccharides, but rather they are **triglycerides**, also known as triacylglycerols (Figure 23.10), which form when **glycerol**, a three-carbon tri-alcohol, undergoes condensation reactions with three long-chain carboxylic acids, known as **fatty acids**, to create three

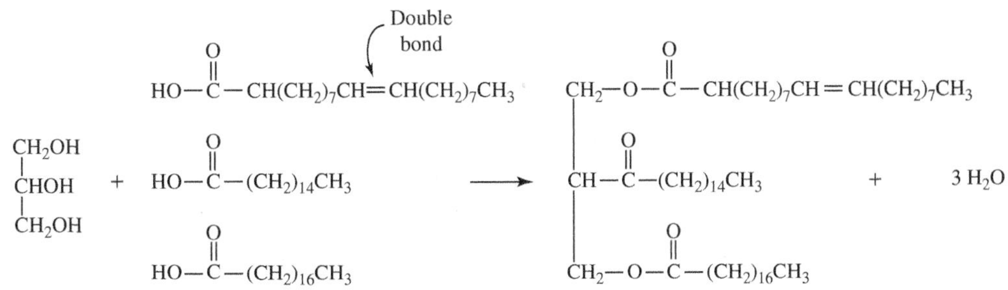

Glycerol Three fatty acids Triglyceride

FIGURE 23.10 Triglyceride Structure of Fats and Oils

Glycerol reacts with three fatty acid molecules to form a triglyceride, a molecule with three ester functional groups, while releasing three molecules of water. Triglycerides containing mostly saturated fatty acids (no carbon–carbon double bonds) are fats, while those composed of higher amounts of unsaturated fatty acids (those containing C=C bonds) are oils. The three fatty acids in a triglyceride may or may not be the same.

(a) $CH_3CH_2CH_2CH_2CH_2CH_2CH_2CH_2CH_2CH_2CH_2CH_2CH_2CH_2CH_2COOH$

or

$CH_3(CH_2)_{14}COOH$

(b)

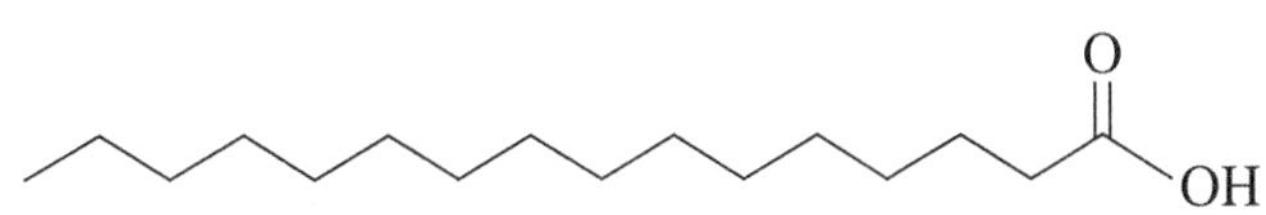

FIGURE 23.11 Two Ways to Depict Palmitic Acid, a Fatty Acid

(a) The condensed structure of palmitic acid shows all of the atoms but omits the bonds. (b) In the line-angle diagram, most of the atoms are omitted. (The zigzag line implies a carbon chain.)

ester functional groups. Fatty acids are said to be unsaturated (Section 21.1) if they contain one or more carbon–carbon double bonds and saturated if they have no C=C bonds. You can simulate the formation of triglycerides using the "Lipids" tab of the Biomolecules activity (Figure 23.1).

It is tedious to draw the structures of large carbon-containing molecules that include all of the atoms and bonds. Chemists use two different approaches to minimize the work of drawing structures and to still communicate the important parts of the structures. In Figure 23.11a, the structure of a fatty acid is shown as a condensed structure (Section 21.1), which emphasizes all of the atoms that are present but not the bonds. In Figure 23.11b, the same fatty acid is shown in a line-angle structure, which emphasizes the bonds but not the atoms. In the line-angle structure, a C atom exists at the end of each bond where no other element is shown explicitly, and sufficient bonds to H atoms are assumed so that each C atom has four bonds.

Fats, which generally contain high levels of saturated fatty acids, tend to be derived from animal sources, whereas oils, which generally contain some unsaturated fatty acids, tend to be derived from plants. Fats are typically solids at room temperature because of the strength of the dispersion forces (Section 13.6) that form between the long chains of the saturated fatty acids. The majority of naturally occurring fatty acids contain double bonds in the cis geometry (Section 21.2), which creates a kink in the structure that results in weaker dispersion forces and, therefore, lower melting points (Figure 23.12).

Thus, oils, with their higher concentrations of unsaturated fatty acids, are liquids at room temperature. A tiny percentage of naturally occurring fatty acids include double bonds with trans geometry. However, trans fats can be produced when foods that

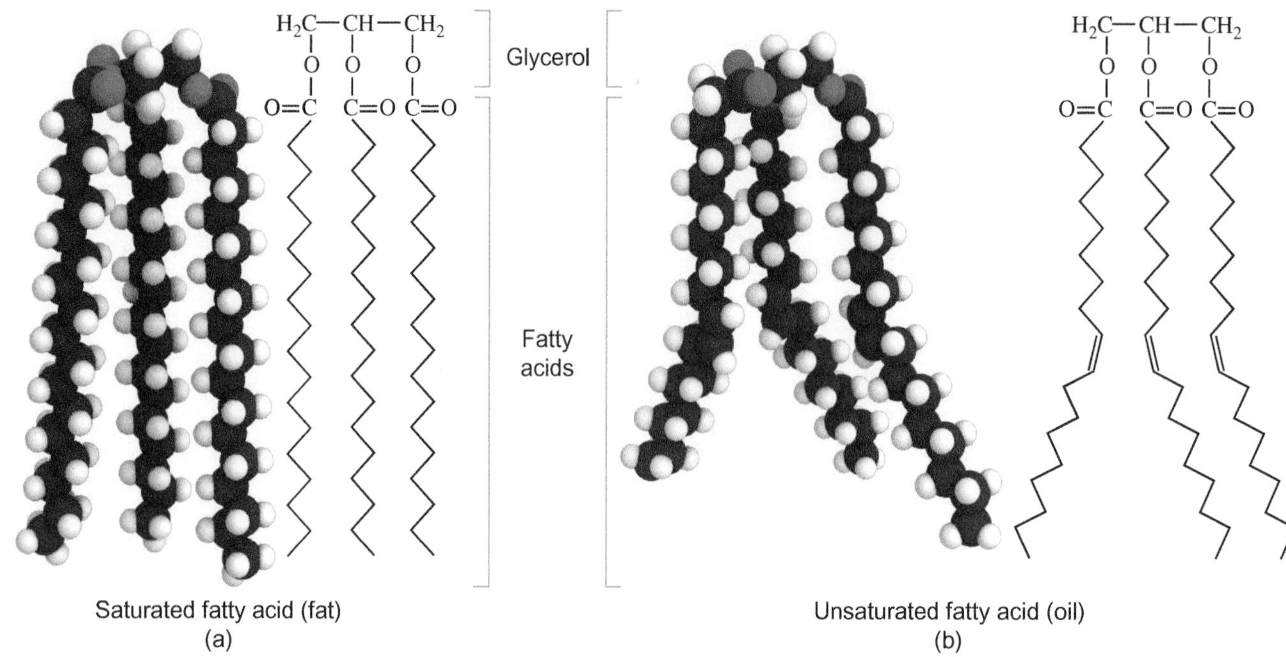

FIGURE 23.12 Structures of Fats and Oils

(a) In fats, the zigzag structure of the *saturated* fatty-acid hydrocarbon chains allows strong dispersion forces to form between triglyceride molecules. These relatively strong intermolecular forces result in higher melting points. (b) Oils contain a higher percentage of *unsaturated* fatty acids. A cis geometry of the double bond causes a kink in the chain, making it harder for strong dispersion forces to form. These relatively weak overall intermolecular forces result in a lower melting point.

TABLE 23.4 Melting Points and Percentage of Unsaturated Fatty Acids in Selected Fats and Oils

Source	% Unsaturated Fatty Acids	Melting Point, °C
Butter	33	35
Coconut oil	9	25
Canola oil	92	−10
Soybean oil	89	−16
Olive oil	86	−16

contain oils are processed to be more stable and to have a longer shelf life (Figure 23.13).

Partial hydrogenation of unsaturated fats produces the more stable saturated fats and, under certain conditions, can also cause the double bonds to rearrange from the cis to the trans configuration. The United States Food and Drug Administration (FDA) ruled that trans fats must be eliminated from commercial foods by 2018.

Table 23.4 lists the composition of unsaturated fatty acids and melting temperatures for some common fats and oils. Notice that the fats and oils in the table fall into two categories—one with *low* percentages of unsaturated fatty acids ($<40\%$) and another with *high* percentages of unsaturated fatty acids ($>85\%$). Butter and coconut, with lower concentrations of unsaturated fatty acids, have melting points higher than room temperature. In contrast, the oils that have higher concentrations of unsaturated fatty acids, such as canola, soybean, and olive oils, have melting points so low that they would remain liquid in your kitchen freezer.

Why, though, does canola oil, with a slightly *higher* percentage of unsaturated fatty acids, have a *higher* melting temperature than soybean oil? The unsaturated fatty acids in most oils are a mixture of monounsaturated (one double bond) and polyunsaturated (more than one double bond) fatty acids. Each double bond creates a kink in the chain of the fatty acid, and more kinks lead to weaker dispersion forces between triglyceride molecules. Soybean oil contains a higher percentage of polyunsaturated fatty acids than canola oil, which accounts for its lower melting point.

Example 23.6

Fish oil harvested from salmon contains approximately 80% unsaturated fatty acids, whereas fish oil from trout contains approximately 72% unsaturated fatty acids.

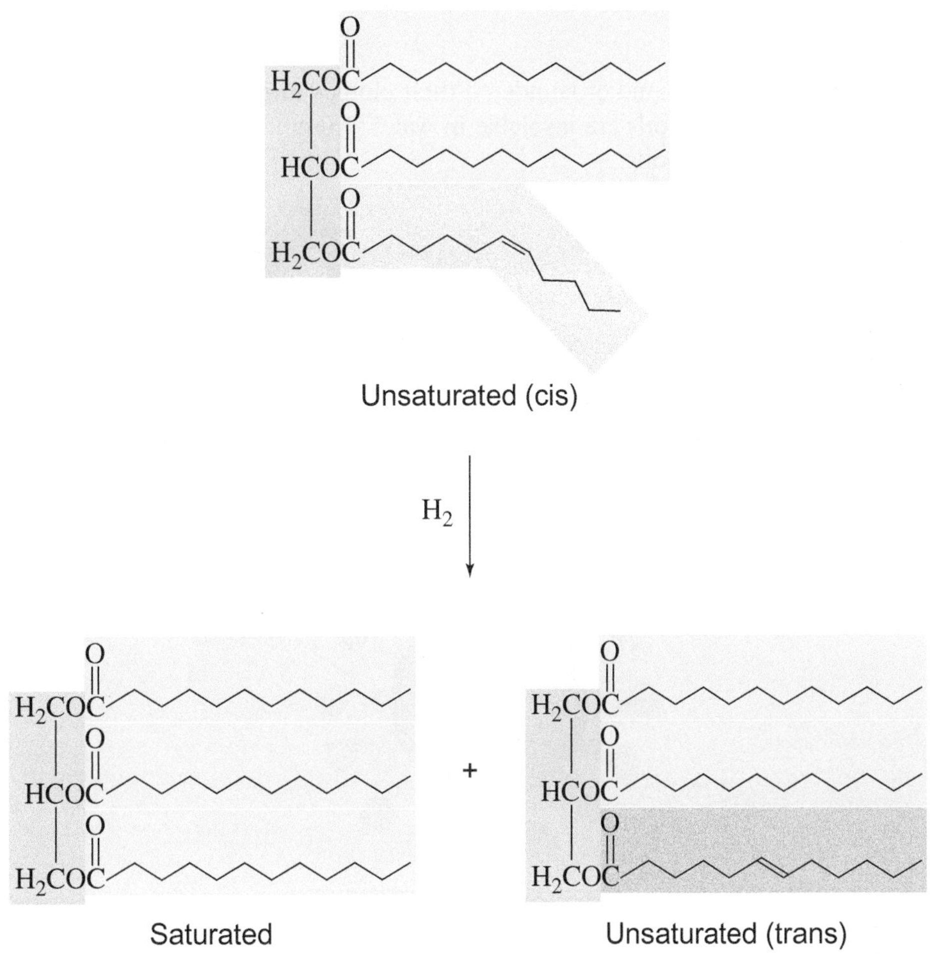

FIGURE 23.13 Production of Trans Fats

Unsaturated fatty acids in fats and oils are more likely to oxidize and change the odor of packaged foods over time. The processing of packaged foods frequently involves hydrogenating vegetable oils to reduce some of the double bonds to single bonds, a process known as partial hydrogenation. If the conditions are not chosen correctly, a second reaction may occur in which the cis double bonds rearrange to form trans double bonds. Fats that include these trans double bonds are referred to as trans fats.

a. Would you expect these fish oils to be liquids or solids at room temperature?
b. Which oil is likely to have the higher melting temperature?
c. Give a rough estimate of the melting points of these two oils.

Solution

a. High percentages of unsaturated fatty acids, such as 72% and 80%, are associated with weak intermolecular forces between triglyceride molecules. These two oils should be liquids at room temperature.
b. Based solely on the percentages of unsaturated fatty acids (salmon > trout), you would predict that the fish oil from trout would have the *higher* melting point. However, if the fish oil from trout contains more polyunsaturated fatty acids than the salmon oil, the trout oil may have a *lower* melting temperature.
c. These two fish oils have slightly lower percentages of unsaturated fatty acids than canola, olive, and soybean oils and much higher percentages than butter and coconut oil. Therefore, the melting temperatures of the fish oils should be lower but close to the melting temperatures of canola, olive, and soybean oils. A reasonable estimate for the melting point of the fish oils is between 0 and -10°C.

PRACTICE PROBLEM 23.6

The fatty acid content of palm oil is 50% unsaturated, whereas that of chicken fat is 65% unsaturated.

a. Would you expect these substances to be liquids or solids at room temperature?

EVERYDAY CONNECTION

Anyone who has washed dishes by hand or laundered their clothes knows that grease is difficult to remove with water. This is because fats and oils are insoluble in water. To remove grease using water, you must also use soap, which is made from fats or oils.

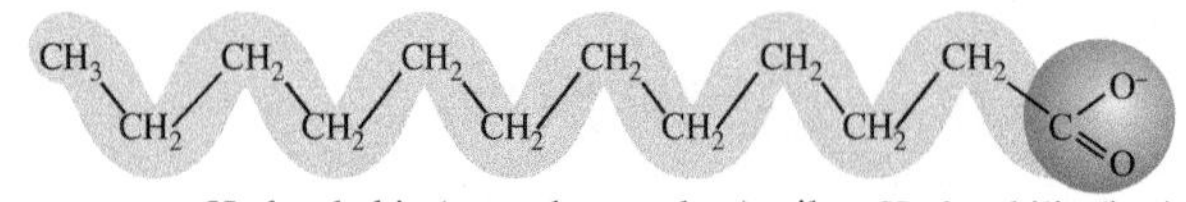

In the soap molecule shown above, the ionic end forms ion–dipole interactions with water molecules, while the long carbon chain forms dispersion forces with other nonpolar molecules, such as those in greasy dirt. When soapy water encounters grease, the nonpolar, **hydrophobic** tails of the soap dissolve in the grease, surrounding it with the charged, **hydrophilic** ends of the soap. This process forms a small sphere called a micelle and allows the grease to be suspended in water and washed away.

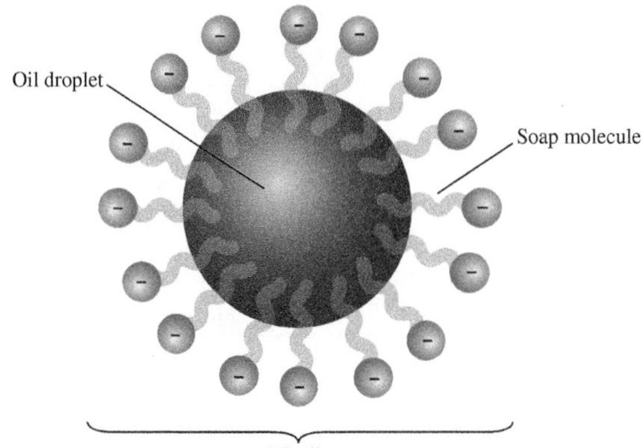

b. Which substance is likely to have the higher melting temperature?
c. Give a rough estimate of the melting points of these two substances.

Hint: How is the percentage of unsaturated fatty acids related to the strength of the intermolecular forces between triglyceride molecules? To estimate the melting temperatures, compare the data in the problem with the data in Table 23.4.

PHOSPHOLIPIDS

The structures of **phospholipids** (Figure 23.14) are closely related to those of triglycerides, because they consist of a glycerol molecule bonded to two fatty acid molecules via ester functional groups.

A highly polar molecule containing a phosphate group occupies the third position, instead of a fatty acid. This highly polar region of a phospholipid, known as the polar head, interacts with water, while the region with the nonpolar tails (the fatty acid chains) does not. In living organisms, these molecules form the phospholipid bilayer (Figure 23.15) found in cell membranes, which surround the cell and control transport in and out of the cell.

OTHER LIPIDS

Steroids and **prostaglandins** each represent a family of lipid compounds. Steroids contain the following standard backbone (often called the steroid nucleus) of four interconnected rings:

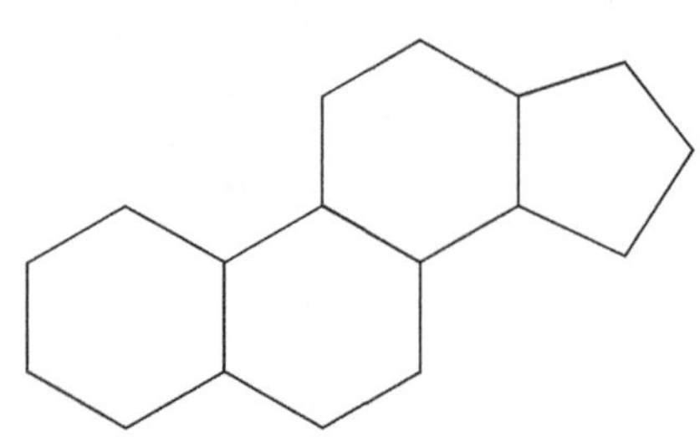

Each steroid is identified by a unique set of substituents bonded to the carbon atoms of that steroid nucleus. The steroid **cholesterol** (Figure 23.16) is another lipid component of cell membranes and a component of the **lipoproteins** that transport lipids throughout the bloodstream of mammals.

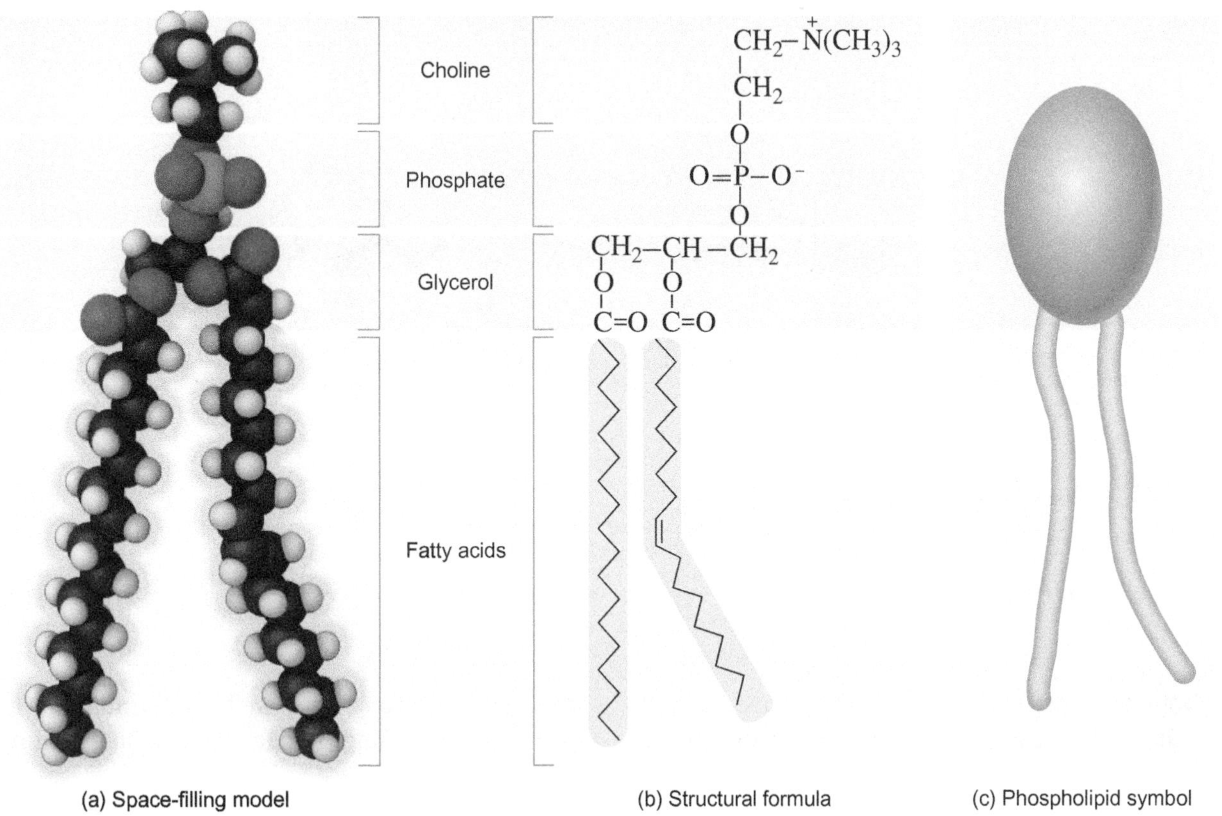

FIGURE 23.14 Structure of Phosphatidylcholine

Phospholipids, important components of cell membranes, are similar in structure to a triglyceride with the third fatty acid replaced by a polar group containing phosphorus. Different phospholipids contain different polar groups. The phospholipid shown here contains choline bonded to the phosphate group, giving rise to its name—phosphatidylcholine.

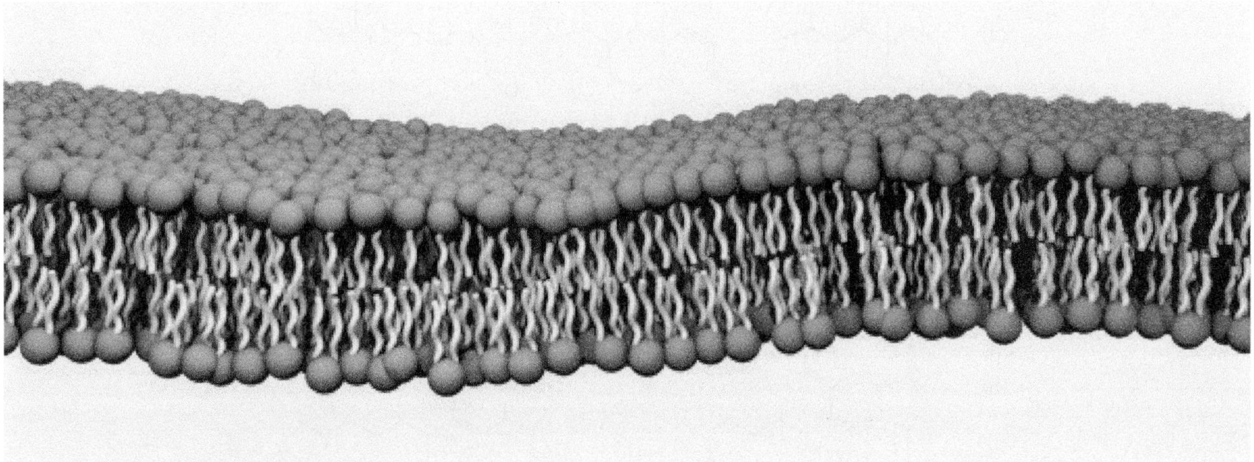

FIGURE 23.15 Phospholipid Bilayer

In the presence of water, phospholipids form a two-layer structure with the nonpolar, hydrophobic tails buried within the layers and the polar, hydrophilic heads on both the inner and outer surfaces. In living things, this bilayer, along with many proteins, other lipids, and, to a lesser extent, carbohydrates, forms the basic structure of cell membranes.

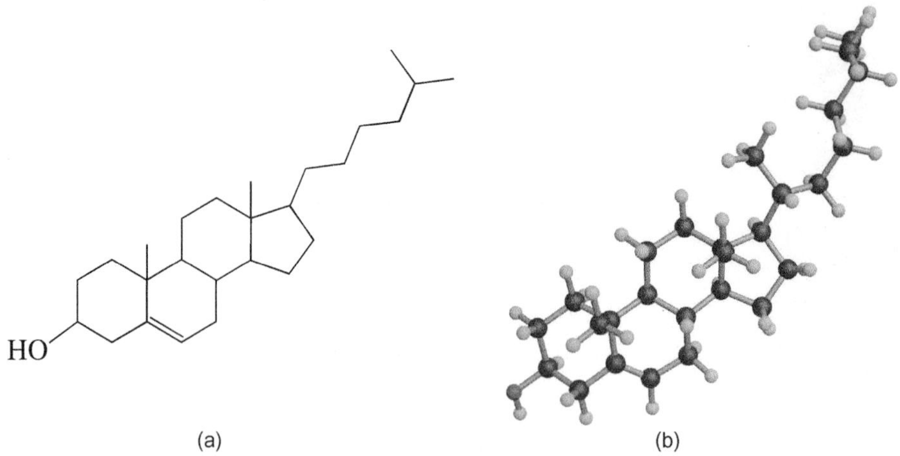

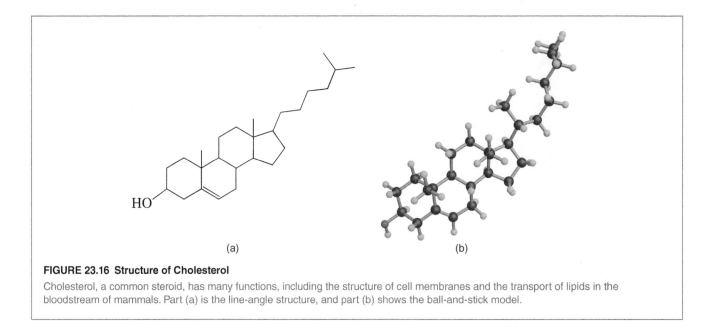

FIGURE 23.16 Structure of Cholesterol

Cholesterol, a common steroid, has many functions, including the structure of cell membranes and the transport of lipids in the bloodstream of mammals. Part (a) is the line-angle structure, and part (b) shows the ball-and-stick model.

Other steroids (Figure 23.17) are hormones that communicate between cells within complex organisms and play many roles in metabolism, including growth, reproduction, and the immune system. Prostaglandins, which contain a single five-membered ring plus two long-chain substituents, are hormones that also have multiple functions, such as maintaining blood pressure, controlling stomach acidity, and eliciting the inflammatory response to injury.

Table 23.5 summarizes the structures and roles of the various categories of lipids discussed in this section.

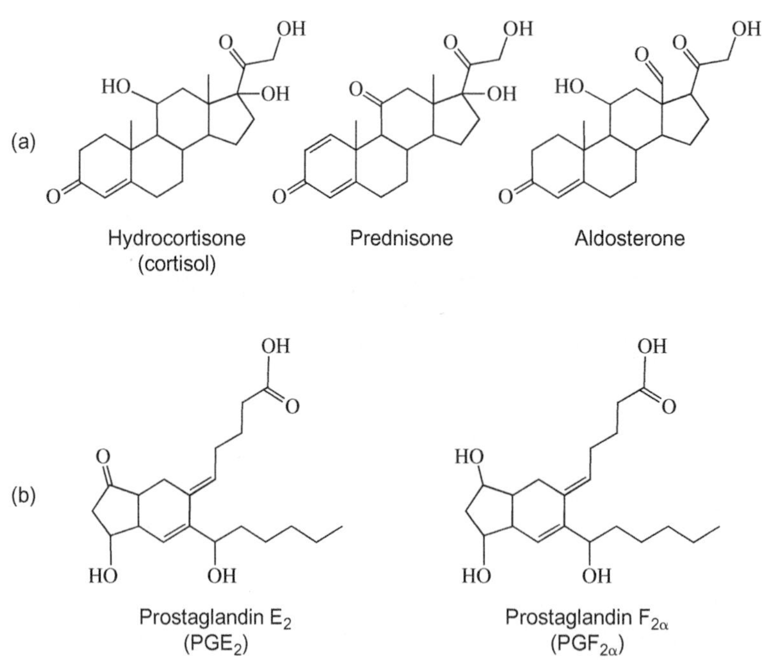

FIGURE 23.17 Examples of Lipid Hormones

(a) Different groups bonded to the steroid nucleus give rise to the various steroid hormones. (b) Prostaglandin hormones typically contain only a single cyclic structure and, in animals, are synthesized from unsaturated fats in the diet.

TABLE 23.5 Summary of Lipid Types

Category	General Structure	Role in Living Things
Triglycerides	Glycerol + three fatty acids linked via ester functional groups; fatty acids may be saturated or unsaturated	Energy storage and insulation
Phospholipids	Glycerol + two fatty acids linked via ester functional groups + polar/charged group on C3 of glycerol	Structure of cell membranes
Steroids	Contains characteristic four-ring structure with unique substituents for each steroid	Hormones: regulation of growth, immune response, inflammation, etc. Cholesterol: transport of fatty acids and structure of cell membranes
Prostaglandins	Five-membered ring with two long-chain substituents and other variable substituents	Hormones: regulation of blood pressure, stomach acidity, inflammation, etc.

Example 23.7

Classify these lipids as triglyceride, phospholipid, steroid, or prostaglandin. If it is a triglyceride, is it saturated or unsaturated?

a.

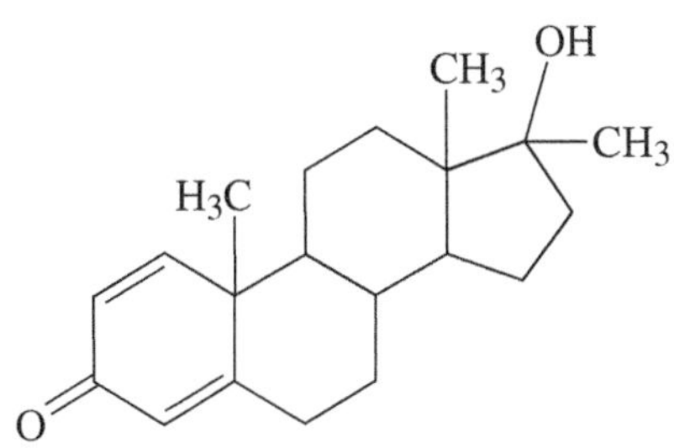

b.

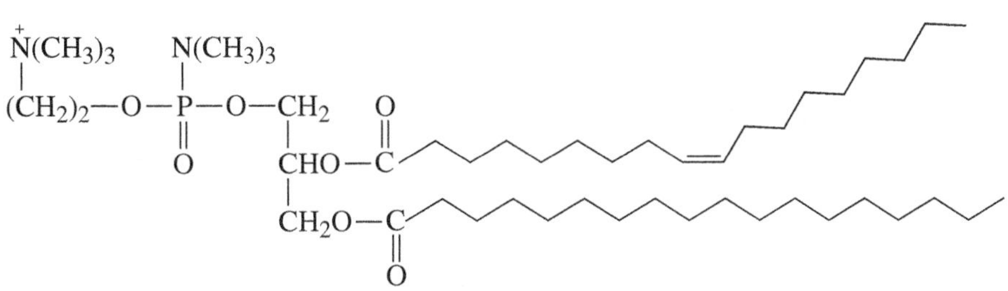

c.

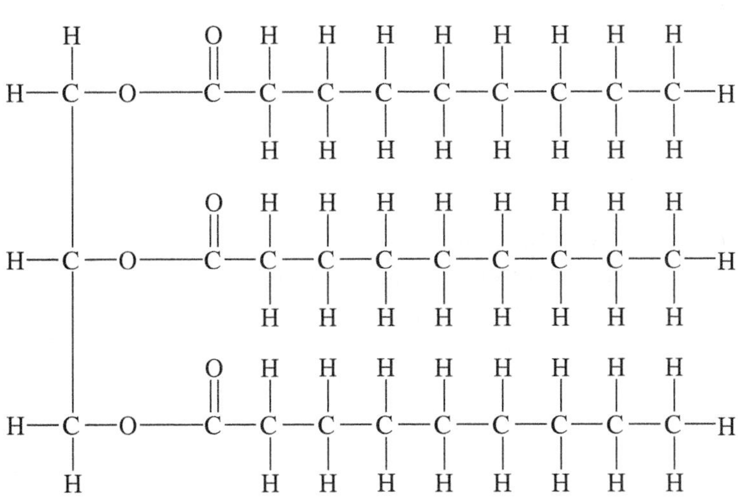

Solution

a. The structure contains the four interconnected rings that are characteristic of a steroid. This particular steroid happens to be methandienone, an anabolic steroid used by some athletes to increase muscle mass and improve endurance. Use of this compound could cause an athlete to be disqualified from national and international competitions such as the Olympics.

b. The structure consists of a glycerol molecule bonded to *two* fatty acid molecules via ester functional groups. A highly polar molecule containing a phosphate group occupies the third position, instead of a fatty acid. This compound is a phospholipid.

c. The structure consists of a glycerol molecule bonded to *three* long-chain fatty acid molecules via ester functional groups. This compound is a triglyceride. More specifically, it is a *saturated* triglyceride because none of the fatty acid chains contains carbon–carbon double bonds.

PRACTICE PROBLEM 23.7

Classify these lipids as triglyceride, phospholipid, steroid, or prostaglandin. If it is a triglyceride, is it saturated or unsaturated?

a.

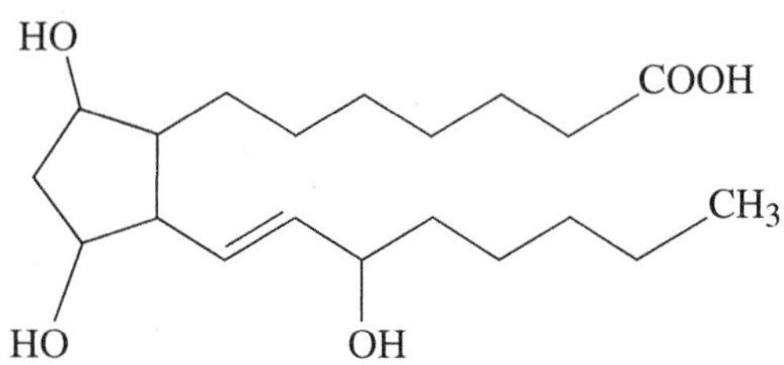

b.

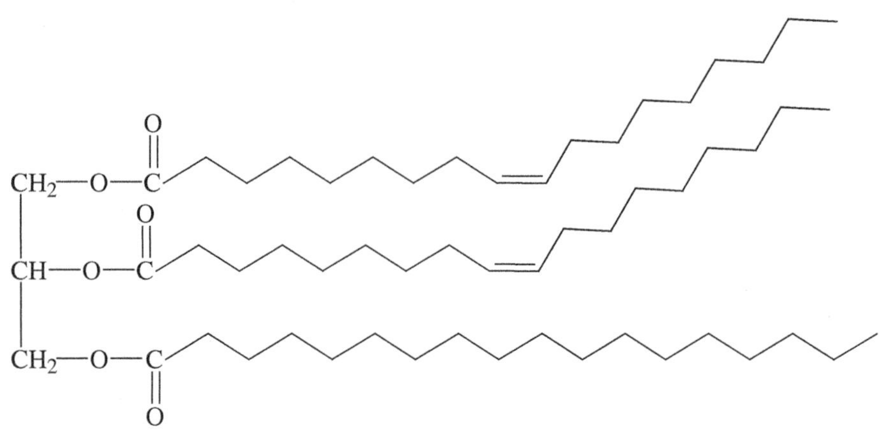

Hint: Compare these structures to the examples of lipids provided in this section.

SECTION REVIEW

- Lipids are a diverse group of biomolecules that are insoluble in water.
- Triglycerides, another energy source for living things, are lipids and are composed of a glycerol molecule linked via ester functional groups to three fatty acids.
- Triglycerides containing unsaturated fatty acids have lower melting points and are more likely to be liquids at room temperature than those containing saturated fatty acids.
- Other physiologically important lipids are the membrane phospholipids, steroids, and prostaglandins.

23.4 Amino Acids, Peptides, and Proteins

GOALS

- Describe the role of proteins in living things.
- Draw the structures of amino acids and peptides.
- Identify the four levels of protein structure and explain the forces that stabilize them.

Background Review

Chapter 12 Liquids and Solids: Section 12.1—Intermolecular Forces

Organisms contain thousands of different proteins that serve a variety of functions from catalysis (Section 14.6) and transport to support and protection (Table 23.6).

Proteins are polymers composed of small molecules called **amino acids**, which include both an amine functional group (sometimes called an amino group) and a carboxyl functional group bonded to the same carbon, called the **α-carbon**. A third group bonded to the α-carbon is referred to as the R group (Section 21.4) and varies in structure. The general structure of an amino acid is shown in Figure 23.18, with the functional groups given in the form present at physiological pH.

The amine group of an amino acid is a weak base and is protonated at neutral pH, whereas the carboxyl

TABLE 23.6 Biological Function of Proteins

Function	Description	Example
Catalysis (Section 14.6)	Enzymes are proteins that catalyze metabolic reactions.	Lactase, amylase, and lipase catalyze hydrolysis reactions to separate lactose, amylose, and triglycerides, respectively, into their component molecules.
Regulation	Peptide hormones communicate between cells of complex organisms.	Insulin and glucagon regulate the levels of sugar in the blood by causing cells either to take up glucose to synthesize glycogen or to break down glycogen and release glucose into the blood.
Transport	Proteins move ions and molecules across membranes or between cells.	Hemoglobin moves oxygen from lungs to all peripheral tissues. Glucose, a polar molecule, is transported across nonpolar membranes by a glucose transporter protein.
Storage	Proteins store essential nutrients.	Ferritin stores iron ions, ovalbumin stores nitrogen for developing bird embryos, and casein in milk stores nitrogen for developing mammalian infants.
Movement	Contractile and motile proteins provide movement.	Actin and myosin are proteins involved in the contraction of skeletal muscles, while tubulin and other motor proteins provide movement for materials within cells.
Structure	Proteins provide physical protection and support.	Skin and hair are composed of α-keratin, and the connective tissue that holds bones to other bones and muscles to bones is primarily composed of collagen.
Protection	Proteins are active in cellular defense systems.	Antibodies target invading pathogens, and clotting factors trigger the formation of blood clots after injuries.

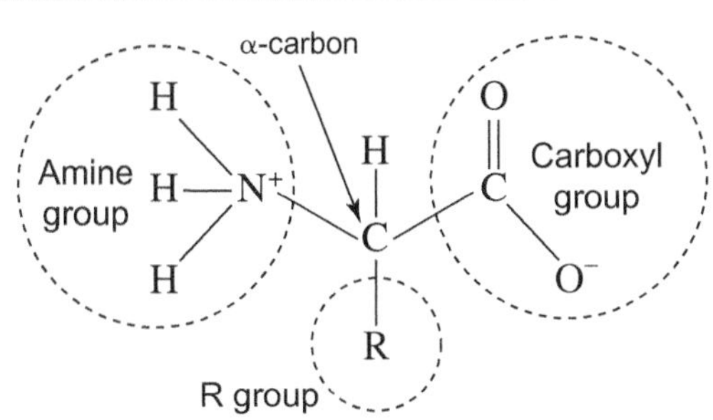

FIGURE 23.18 General Structure of an Amino Acid

The α-carbon of amino acids, the monomers that make up proteins, is bonded to three groups: an amine group, a carboxyl group, and a variable R group. For most amino acids, the fourth position on the α-carbon is bonded to a hydrogen atom.

group is a weak acid and is ionized at neutral pH. The result is a form, known as a **zwitterion**, that has two charged regions but is neutral overall.

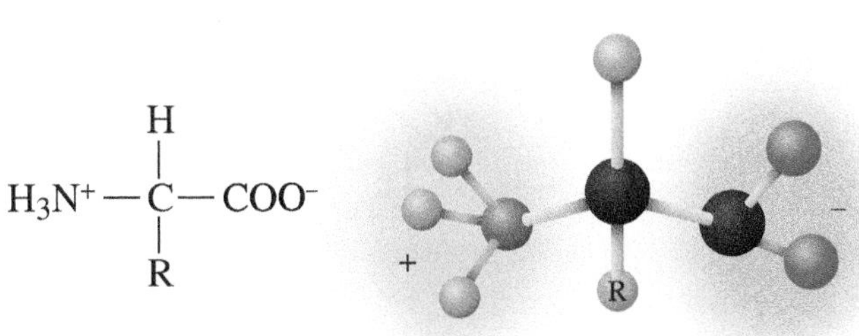

Certain R groups also act as acids and bases and are charged or neutral depending on the pH. Structures of the 20 common amino acids are shown in Table 23.7 along with their three-letter abbreviations.

The R groups are quite varied, but they can be generally categorized as nonpolar (hydrophobic); polar, but uncharged; acidic and negatively charged at neutral pH; and basic and positively charged at neutral pH. The polar, acidic, and basic amino acids are hydrophilic.

Amino acids combine to form peptides when the carboxyl group of one amino acid reacts with the amine group of another to form an amide functional group that is known as a **peptide bond** (Figure 23.19).

The formation of peptides from amino acids is another example of a condensation reaction because a molecule of water is released for each peptide bond formed. Use the "Proteins" tab of the Biomolecules activity (Figure 23.1) to simulate the formation of a peptide. Notice that any two amino acids, A and B, can form two different dipeptides, designated AB and BA, because the two ends of each amino acid are different. Thus, the first amino acid has an unreacted amine group, known as the **N-terminal end**, whereas the second amino acid has an unreacted carboxyl group, called the **C-terminal end**. A dipeptide composed of serine at the N-terminal end and asparagine at the C-terminal end is named *serylasparagine*. A dipeptide containing the same two amino acids with their positions reversed is *asparagylserine*. These two dipeptides may also be described using the three-letter abbreviations as Ser-Asn and Asn-Ser. The video in Figure 23.20 demonstrates how to draw and name a dipeptide from its component amino acids.

TABLE 23.7 The 20 Amino Acids

Category	Structure and Name (abbreviation)	Structure and Name (abbreviation)	Structure and Name (abbreviation)
Nonpolar	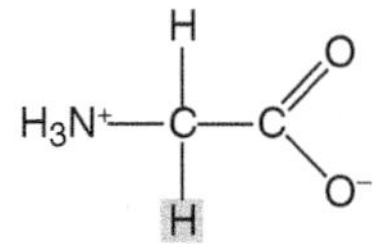 Glycine (Gly)	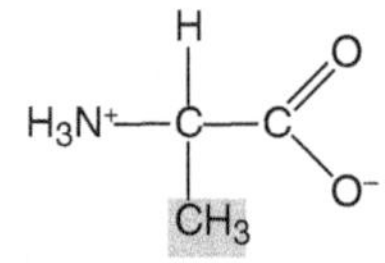 Alanine (Ala)	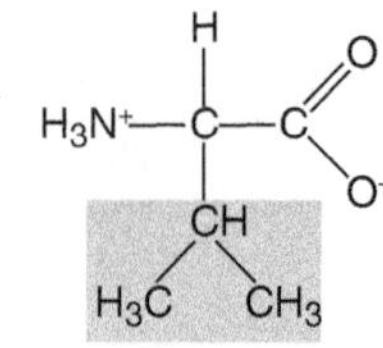 Valine (Val)
	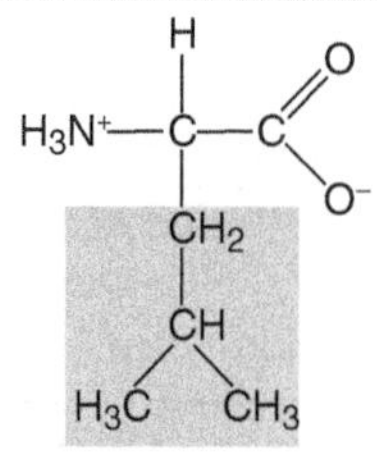 Leucine (Leu)	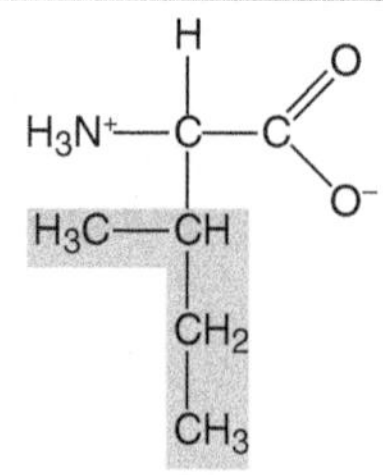 Isoleucine (Ile)	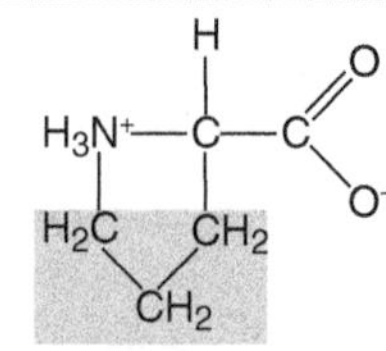 Proline (Pro)
	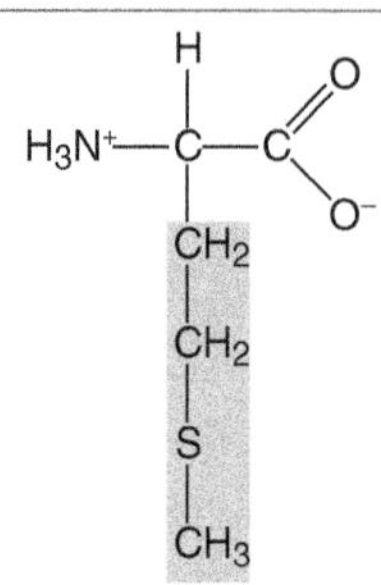 Methionine (Met)	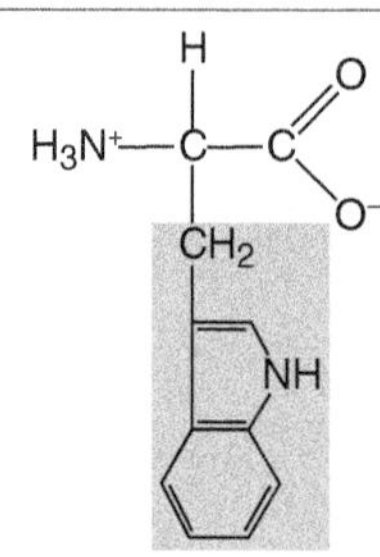 Tryptophan (Trp)	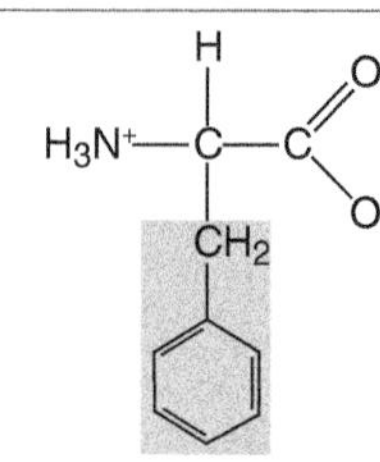 Phenylalanine (Phe)
Polar	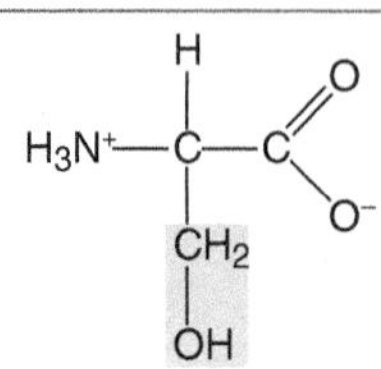 Serine (Ser)	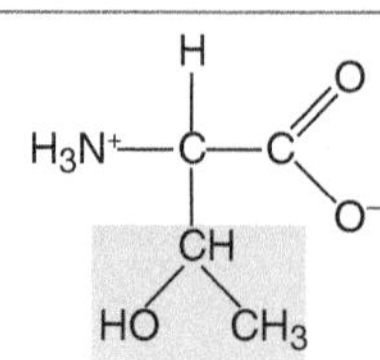 Threonine (Thr)	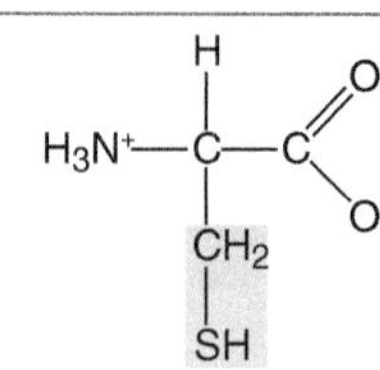 Cysteine (Cys)
	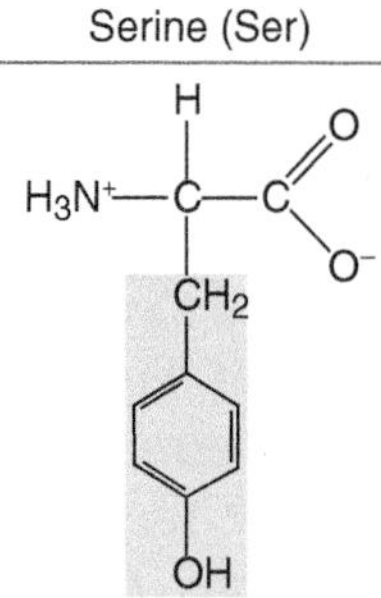 Tyrosine (Tyr)	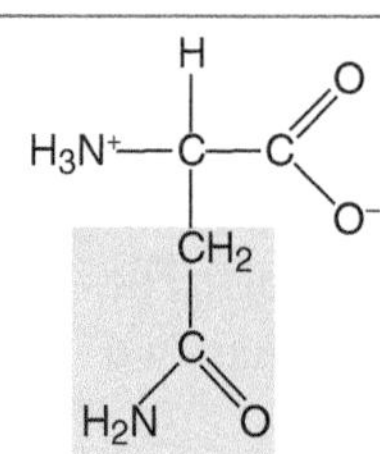 Asparagine (Asp)	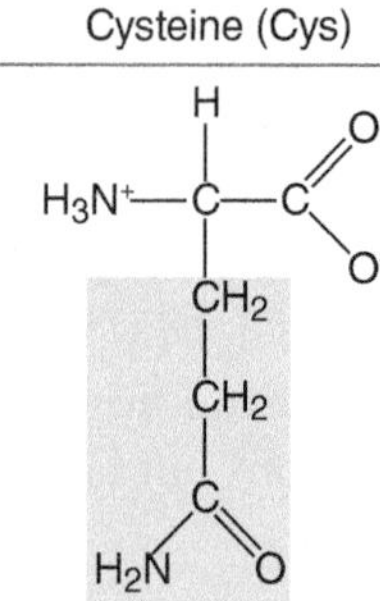 Glutamine (Gln)
Acidic	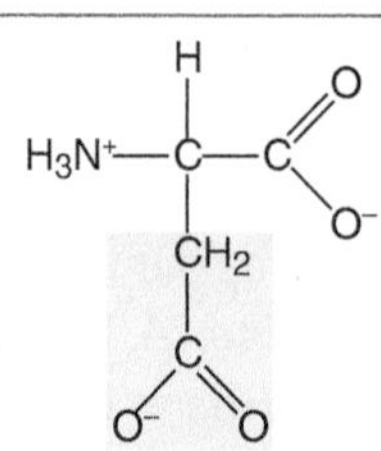 Aspartic acid (Asp)	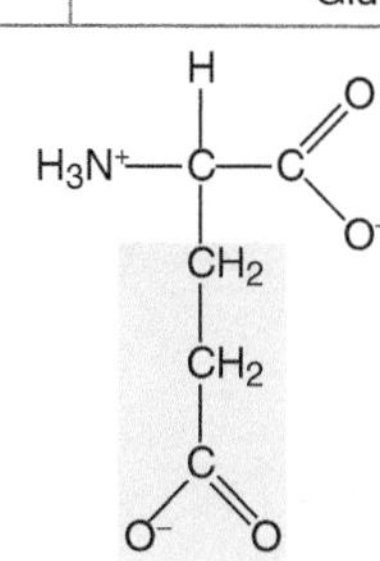 Glutamic acid (Glu)	

TABLE 23.7 The 20 Amino Acids (*Continued*)

Category	Structure and Name (abbreviation)	Structure and Name (abbreviation)	Structure and Name (abbreviation)
Basic	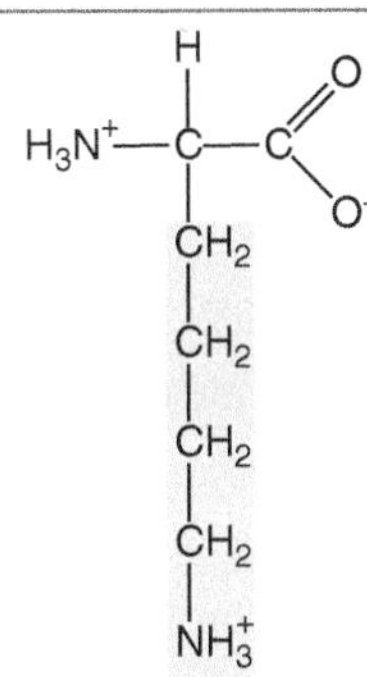 Lysine (Lys)	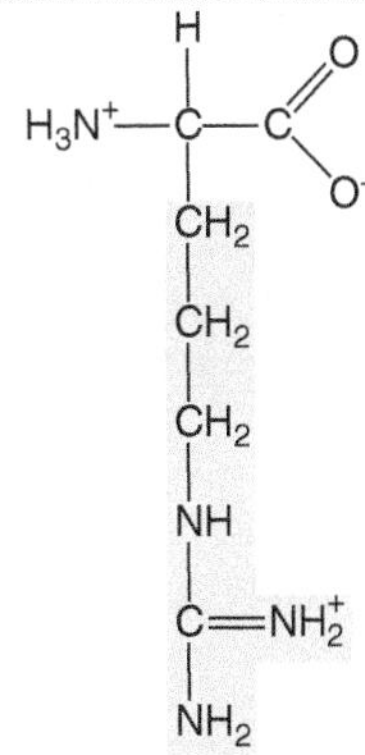 Arginine (Arg)	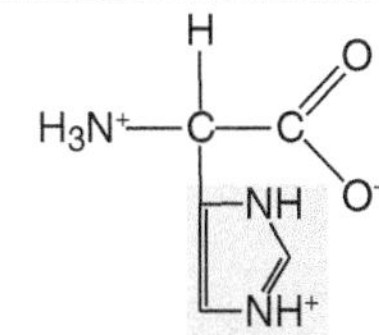 Histidine (His)

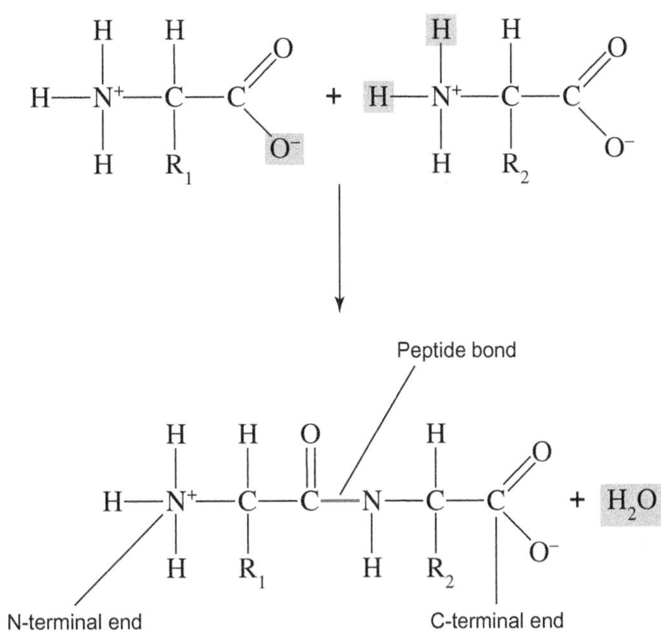

FIGURE 23.19 Formation of a Peptide Bond

The carboxyl group of one amino acid reacts with the amine group of the second to form an amide linkage called a peptide bond. The end of the peptide with an unreacted amine group is called the N-terminal end, and the other end, with the unreacted carboxyl group, is the C-terminal end.

FIGURE 23.20 Video Tutorial: Dipeptide Structure

NOTE: You need to be online to access this video.
This video shows how to draw and name the possible dipeptides formed from glycine and leucine.

Example 23.8

Identify the N-terminal end, the C-terminal end, and the three amino acids in the following tripeptide. Show the sequence using the three-letter abbreviations, and name the peptide.

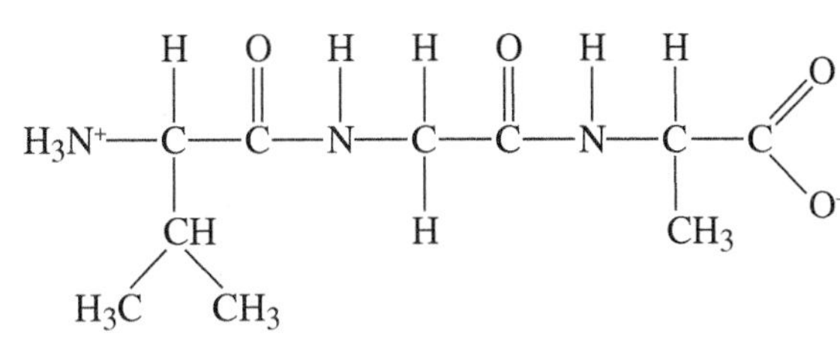

Solution

The amino acid with an unreacted amine group is the N-terminal end of the peptide, and the amino acid with the unreacted carboxyl group is the C-terminal end. Using Table 23.7 as a guide, identify the amino acids based on their R group. The N-terminal amino acid is valine, the middle amino acid is glycine, and the C-terminal amino acid is alanine, Val-Gly-Ala. The name of this tripeptide is valylglycylalanine.

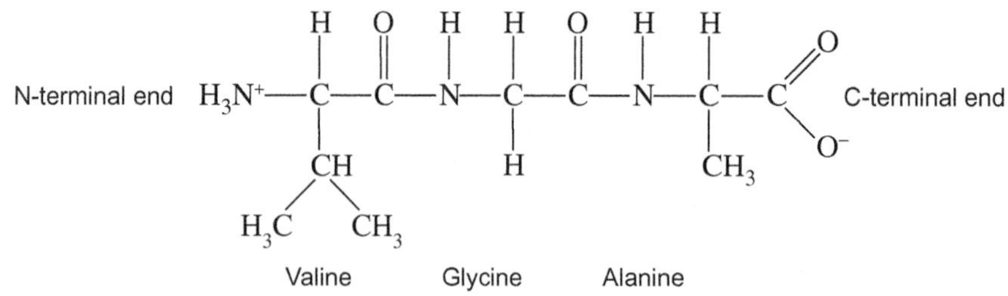

PRACTICE PROBLEM 23.8

Identify the N-terminal end, the C-terminal end, and the three amino acids in the following tripeptide. Show the sequence using the three-letter abbreviations, and name the peptide.

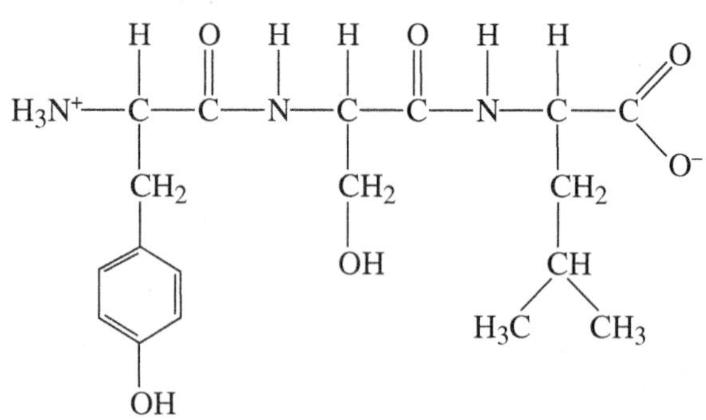

Hint: The amino acid with an unreacted amine group is at the N-terminal end of the peptide, and the amino acid with the unreacted carboxyl group is the C-terminal end. Use Table 23.7 to identify the amino acids, and name the peptide.

Example 23.9

a. Draw the structure of a generic tetrapeptide using R_1, R_2, R_3, and R_4 to indicate the R groups of the four different amino acids.

b. Draw the structure of the tetrapeptide alanylglycylcysteinylaspartate (Ala-Gly-Cys-Asp). Refer to Table 23.7 for the structures of the 20 common amino acids.

Solution

a. A tetrapeptide consists of four amino acids connected by peptide bonds. Draw the structure starting with an amino acid with an unreacted amine group on the left (the N-terminal end) and ending with an amino acid with an unreacted carboxyl group on the right (the C-terminal end).

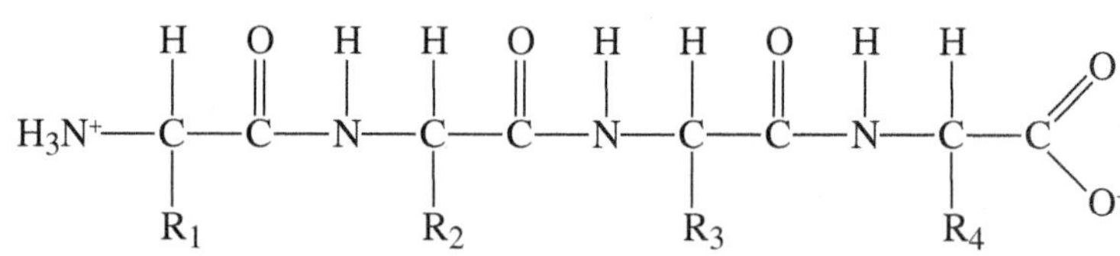

b. The structure of alanylglycylcysteinylaspartate is the same as the generic peptide (both are tetrapeptides), except R_1 through R_4 must be replaced with the specific structures of the R groups for alanine (N-terminal end), glycine, cysteine, and aspartic acid (C-terminal end), respectively, because peptides are named from the N-terminal end to the C-terminal end. Table 23.7 provides the structures of the four amino acids.

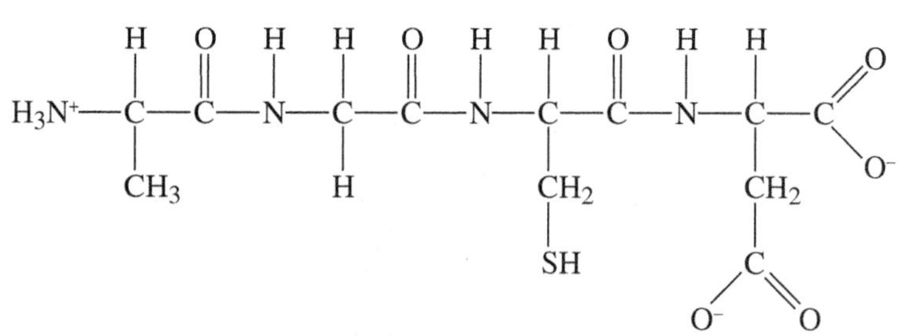

PRACTICE PROBLEM 23.9

a. Draw the structure of a generic tripeptide using R_1, R_2, and R_3 to indicate the R groups of the different amino acids.

b. Draw the structure of the tripeptide valylglutamylmethionine (Val-Glu-Met).

Hint: Glutamic acid becomes glutamyl when naming a peptide, whereas glutamine becomes glutaminyl.

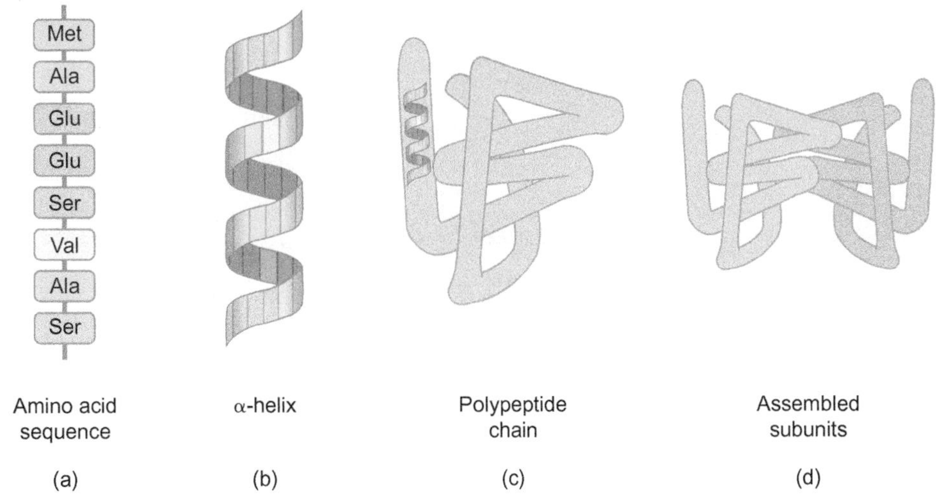

FIGURE 23.21 Levels of Protein Structure

The complex structure of proteins consists of four levels: (a) primary structure is the sequence of amino acids in the molecule; (b) secondary structure describes any repeated orientations of the polypeptide backbone; (c) tertiary structures describes how the polypeptide chain folds back on itself to form the three-dimensional shape of the protein; and (d) quaternary structure describes how different polypeptide chains combine to form a functional unit.

Proteins containing hundreds of amino acids in their **polypeptide** chains are synthesized from information coded in the organism's DNA. This information indicates how potentially hundreds of amino acids should be placed in a specific sequence to form a different protein for each function. For a protein to function properly, it must be in a specific three-dimensional shape, determined by many factors, including its sequence of amino acids and the environment of the protein. Proteins adopt different shapes if they are in aqueous solution versus the hydrophobic regions of a membrane and if a change in the pH results in different charges on its acidic and basic R groups. As a protein is synthesized in the cell, intermolecular forces form between different parts of the polypeptide chain to create the functional shape of the protein.

The overall structure of a molecule with thousands of atoms and bonds is difficult to describe. Consequently, scientists have chosen to distinguish four levels of protein structure (Figure 23.21). The first level, referred to as **primary structure**, is the sequence of amino acids in the protein, which can be described by simply listing the names of the amino acids in the polypeptide, starting at the N-terminal end and continuing through to the C-terminal end. The primary structure of the peptide in Example 23.9b, for example, is alanine-glycine-cysteine-aspartic acid.

Secondary structure (Figure 23.21b) describes how the polypeptide backbone adopts repeating shapes, such as the α-helix and the β-sheet. In an **α-helix** configuration (Figure 23.22), the polypeptide backbone atoms form a coil in which the atoms of one peptide bond to form hydrogen bonds to the atoms of other peptide bonds located in the coils directly above and below. Specifically, hydrogen bonds form between the carbonyl O atom of one amino acid and the amide H atom of an amino acid in the coil below it. The coiled structure is commonly found in membrane and structural proteins, and many catalytic and transport proteins contain small regions of α-helix.

In the **β-sheet** (Figure 23.23), segments of the protein chain are in a parallel arrangement. These parallel portions are held in place again by hydrogen bonds between the peptide bond atoms.

In proteins, interactions between the R groups and between the R groups and the external environment (hydrophilic or hydrophobic) cause the long polypeptide chain to fold into lower energy three-dimensional shapes, referred to as **tertiary structure** (Figure 23.21c). The interactions that maintain tertiary structure are summarized in Figure 23.24.

Example 23.10

Classify the following amino acids by whether they are more likely folded into the interior or found on the exterior of a protein in an aqueous environment. Explain your answer.

a. asparagine
b. isoleucine
c. glutamic acid
d. phenylalanine

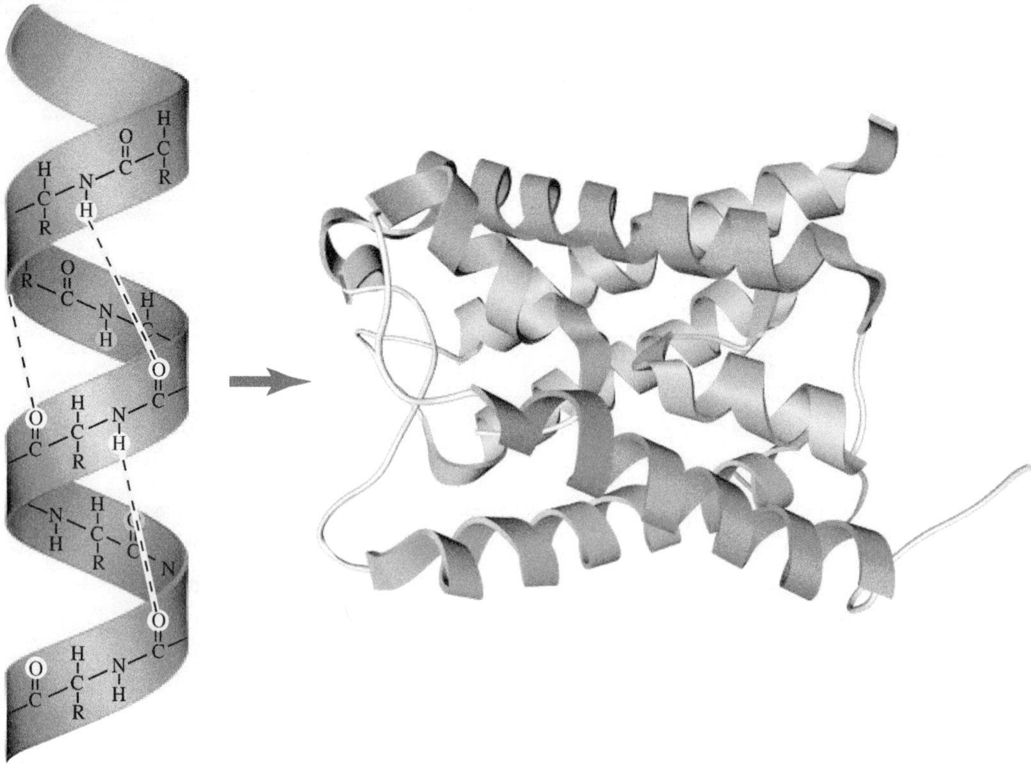

(a) (b)

FIGURE 23.22 α-Helix Protein Secondary Structure

A common structure in proteins occurs when the polypeptide chain adopts a coiled structure known as an α-helix. (a) The coil is held in place by the formation of hydrogen bonds between peptide bond atoms, as shown by the dotted lines. (b) In complex polypeptide structures, such as large proteins, α-helix regions are generally shown using a coiled ribbon to represent the polypeptide chain.

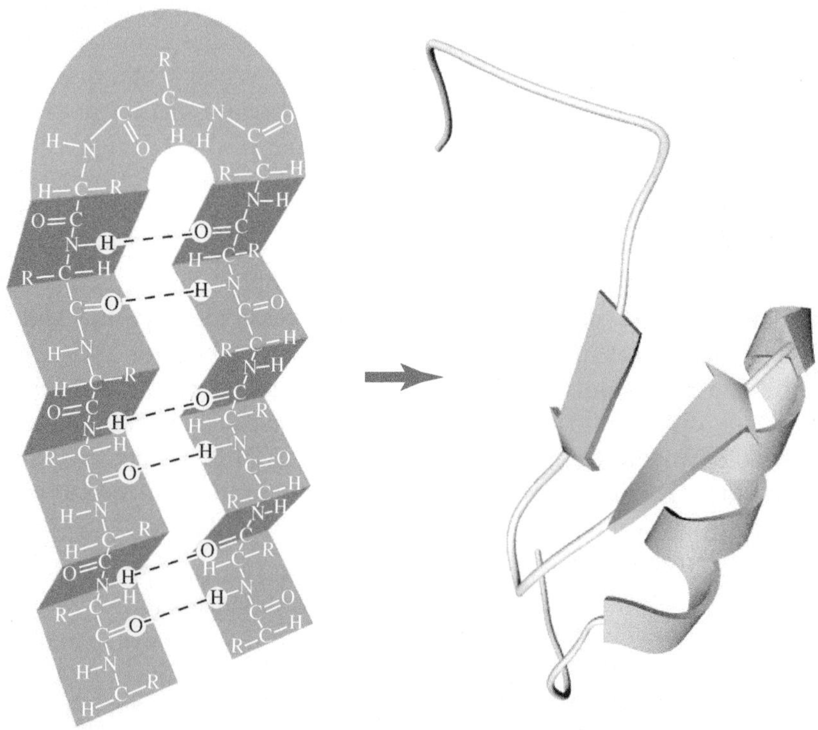

(a) (b)

FIGURE 23.23 β-Sheet Secondary Protein Structure

A common structure in proteins occurs when the polypeptide chain adopts a parallel structure known as a β-sheet. (a) The parallel strands of the chain are held in place by the formation of hydrogen bonds between peptide bond atoms, as shown by the dotted lines. (b) In complex polypeptide structures, such as large proteins, β-sheets region are generally shown using arrows to represent the polypeptide chain.

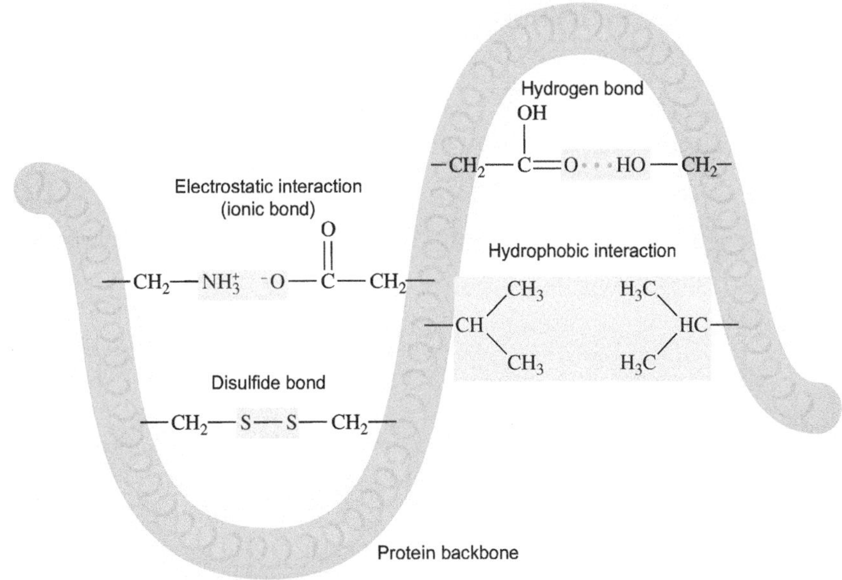

FIGURE 23.24 Interactions between R Groups Maintain Tertiary Structure

Proteins fold into a low-energy three-dimensional shape that is maintained by interactions between R groups. These interactions include hydrophobic interactions (dispersion forces) between nonpolar R groups, hydrogen bonding and dipole–dipole interactions between polar R groups, ionic interactions between oppositely charged R groups, and covalent bonds in the case of disulfide bonds.

EVERYDAY CONNECTION

When you cook food that contains protein (such as meat or eggs), the heat causes the proteins to become denatured, which means their tertiary structure is altered. This affects the taste and texture of the food.

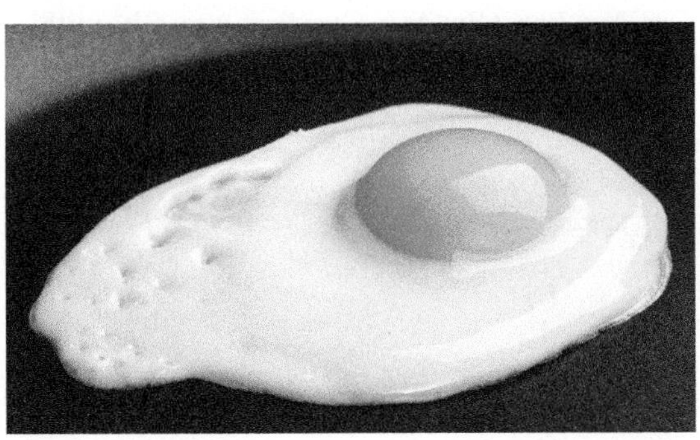

Valentina Proskurina/Shutterstock

Polypeptide chains forming in an aqueous (hydrophilic) environment fold so that the nonpolar R groups are in the interior of the structure, with the polar and charged R groups on the surface, where they can form hydrogen bonds, ion–dipole, and dipole–dipole interactions with water molecules. Conversely, a protein forming in a lipid (hydrophobic) environment would be lower in energy if the polar R groups were sequestered on the inside and the nonpolar R groups were on the surface.

Solution

In an aqueous environment, proteins fold to place hydrophobic (nonpolar) amino acids on the inside and hydrophilic (polar or charged) amino acids on the surface. Use Table 23.7 to identify which of these amino acids are hydrophilic and which are hydrophobic.

a. The R group of asparagine is $-CH_2CONH_2$ (an amide group), which can form a hydrogen bond with water. Asparagine is likely to be on the surface of the protein.

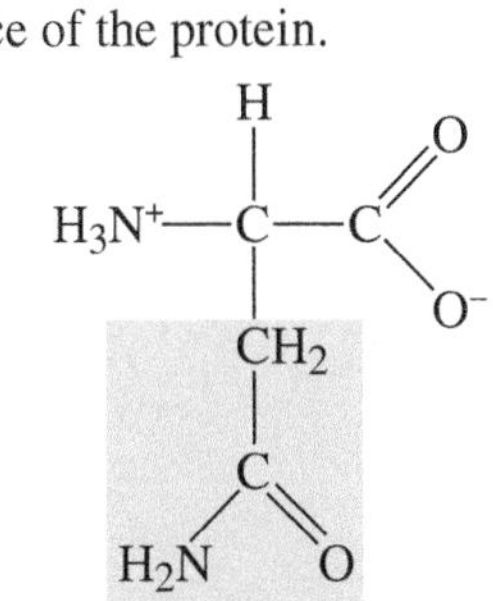

b. The R group of isoleucine is $-CH_2CH(CH_3)_2$ (a hydrocarbon), which is nonpolar and hydrophobic. Isoleucine is likely to be folded to the inside of the protein.

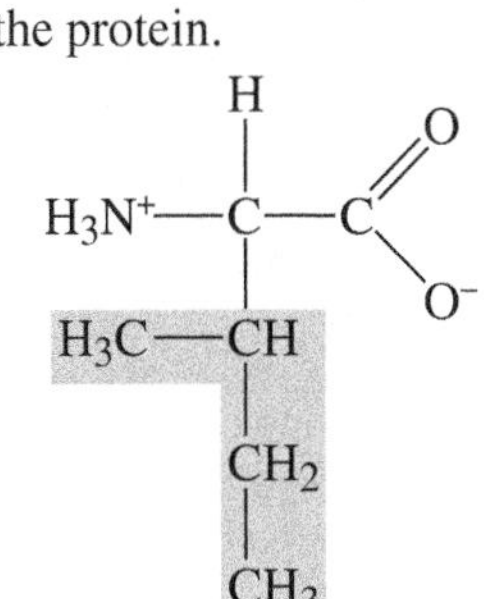

c. The R group of glutamic acid is $—CH_2CH_2COOH$ (a carboxyl group), which is charged at neutral pH becoming $—CH_2CH_2COO^-$. In this form, it is often called glutamate. The $—COO^-$ group can form an ion–dipole interaction with water, so glutamate is likely to be on the surface of the protein.

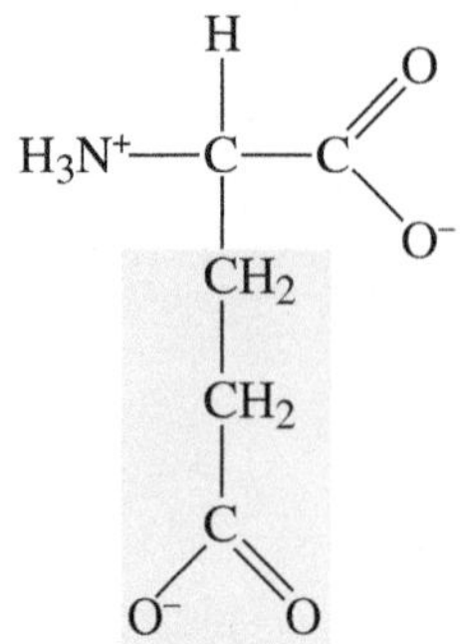

d. The R group of phenylalanine is $—CH_2C_6H_5$ (an aromatic hydrocarbon), which is nonpolar and hydrophobic. Phenylalanine is likely to be folded to the inside of the protein.

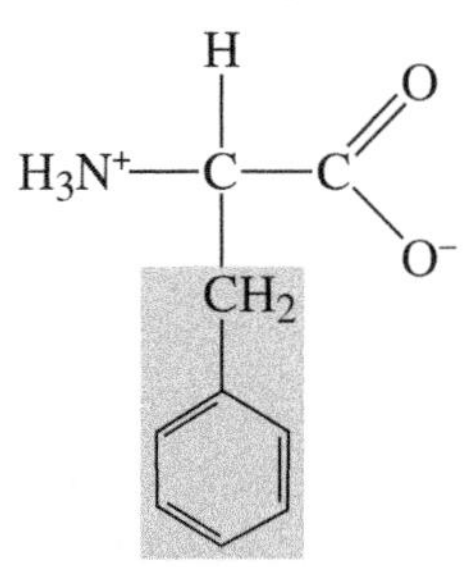

PRACTICE PROBLEM 23.10

Classify the following amino acids by whether they are more likely folded into the interior or found on the exterior of a protein in a lipid environment. Explain your answer.

a. lysine
b. methionine
c. valine
d. glutamine

Hint: Use Table 23.7 to identify which of these amino acids are hydrophilic and which are hydrophobic.

Another very important interaction between R groups is the formation of a covalent bond. The R group of cysteine is $—CH_2SH$, which can form a covalent bond, called a **disulfide bond**, with the $—CH_2SH$ group of another cysteine as shown in Figure 23.25.

The structures of the peptide hormones vasopressin and oxytocin (Figure 23.26) depend on disulfide bonds to achieve the overall shape they need to function properly. These two hormones trigger changes within cells by binding to specific receptor proteins.

Example 23.11

How does the presence of the disulfide bond affect the three-dimensional shape of vasopressin (Figure 23.26a)?

Solution

Disulfide bonds bring two parts of the peptide chain close to each other. Vasopressin has the sequence Cys-Tyr-Phe-Glu-Asp-Cys-Pro-Arg-Gly with a

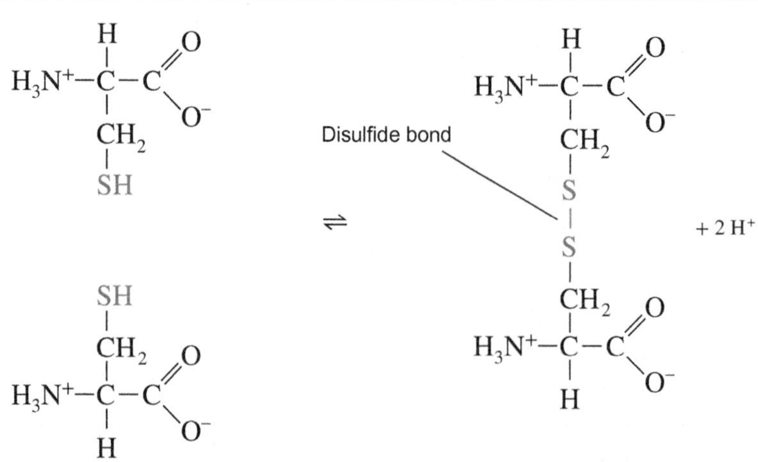

FIGURE 23.25 Formation of a Disulfide Bond

The R groups of two cysteine units can react together to form a new covalent bond that will link different sections of the polypeptide chain. The —SH groups (called thiol functional groups) readily oxidize to produce disulfide bonds. Under acidic conditions, —S—S— can be reduced back to —SH groups.

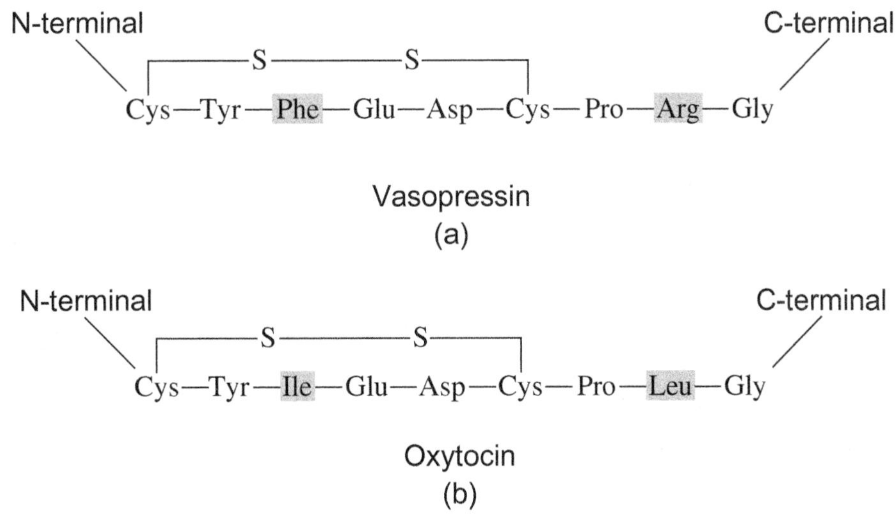

FIGURE 23.26 Structures of Two Peptide Hormones

Vasopressin (a) and oxytocin (b) are peptide hormones containing a disulfide bond between two cysteines in the primary structure. Despite their similar structures, which differ only by the highlighted groups, their functions are quite different. Vasopressin is an antidiuretic, triggering the kidneys to excrete less water, while oxytocin triggers the onset of labor in pregnancy, among other actions.

disulfide bond between the two Cys R groups. For the disulfide bond to form, the two CH_2SH groups of the two cysteine residues must be close together. Thus, the peptide chain must curve or fold back on itself to create a ring structure that is held in place by the disulfide bond.

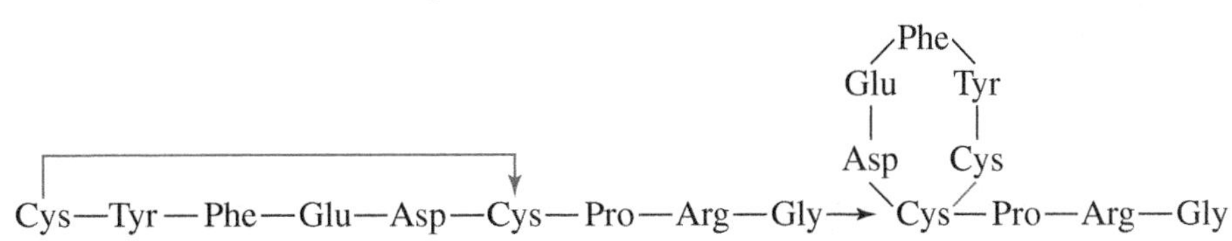

PRACTICE PROBLEM 23.11

What would happen to the shape of oxytocin (Figure 23.26b) if alanine replaced the cysteine molecule as amino acid 6? Would this molecule be likely to have the same function as normal oxytocin?

Hint: Think about the role that cysteine plays in the structure of oxytocin.

Many proteins can be completely described using the primary, secondary, and tertiary levels of structure. In some cases, a functional protein requires more than one polypeptide chain. **Quaternary structure** (Figure 23.21d) describes how the tertiary units of the individual polypeptide chains interact to form the functioning protein. The different polypeptide chains are held together by the same types of interactions that hold tertiary structures in place. Examples of proteins with a quaternary structure are the ion channel proteins (Figure 23.27a), composed of four polypeptide chains, and collagen (Figure 23.27b), composed of three strands of α-helical polypeptide chains.

In addition to amino acids, proteins may also require additional components, or **cofactors**, to be functional. These cofactors may be metal ions such as zinc(II) ions (Figure 23.28) or small, organic molecules, many of which derive from vitamins in the diet.

Proteins that bind to DNA often include a region of amino acids forming a shape known as a zinc finger, which is stabilized by the formation of coordinate covalent bonds between R groups and a zinc(II) ion. Proteases, which are enzymes that break down proteins, often require zinc(II) ions for their catalytic activity.

Table 23.8 summarizes the four levels of protein structure.

SECTION REVIEW

- Proteins carry out many functions in cells involving structure, catalysis, communication, movement, storage, regulation, and protection.
- Proteins are polymers of amino acids, which consist of an α-carbon bonded to an amine group, a carboxyl group, a variable R group, and H.

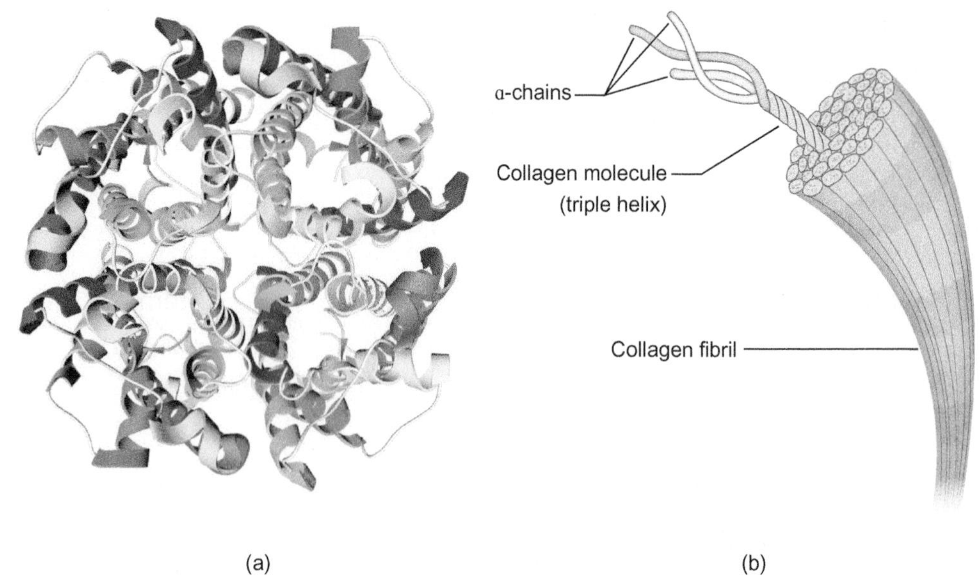

FIGURE 23.27 Examples of Quaternary Structure

(a) Aquaporin is a membrane protein that facilitates the rapid movement of water across cell membranes. This protein is composed of four polypeptide chains. (b) Collagen, a common protein in the connective tissues of animals, is composed of three strands of α-helical polypeptide chains.

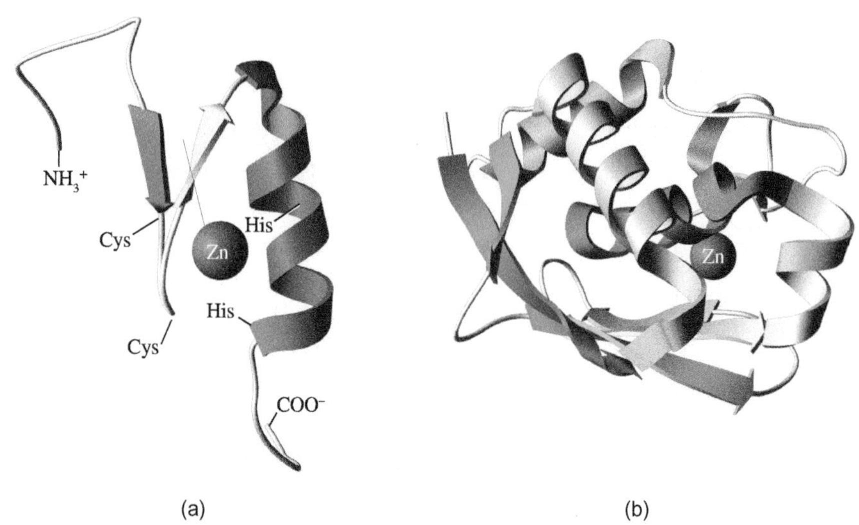

FIGURE 23.28 Zinc(II) Ions as Cofactors in Proteins

Zinc ions play an important role in the structure and reactivity of many proteins. Image (a) shows a "zinc finger," a portion of a DNA binding protein in which zinc(II) ions interact with the R groups of four amino acids, creating a specific three-dimensional shape capable of attaching to DNA molecules. Image (b) shows the entire structure of a zinc protease enzyme with the zinc(II) ion participating in the catalytic action of the enzyme.

- There are 20 common amino acids with R groups that are classified as nonpolar, polar, weak acids, and weak bases.
- At neutral pH, amino acids exist as zwitterions (doubly charged species).
- The amine group on one amino acid undergoes a condensation reaction with the carboxylic acid group of another amino acid to form peptides in which the identities of the amino acids are listed from N-terminal end to C-terminal end.
- The structures of proteins consist of four levels:
  - Primary structure is held together by the covalent bonds in the peptide bond; it consists of the sequence of amino acids.

EVERYDAY CONNECTION

Hemoglobin, the molecule responsible for transporting oxygen from the lungs to the peripheral tissues of mammals, is an example of a protein containing an organic cofactor. It consists of four polypeptide chains, two alpha subunits with 141 amino acids in a particular sequence and two beta subunits with 146 amino acids in a specific sequence. Parts of the subunits coil into alpha helices, which fold into specific three-dimensional shapes. In addition to the polypeptide chains, each subunit also contains a cofactor called heme. Heme is composed of an organic molecule called porphyrin and an iron(II) ion and is held to the protein by interaction with R groups on the protein.

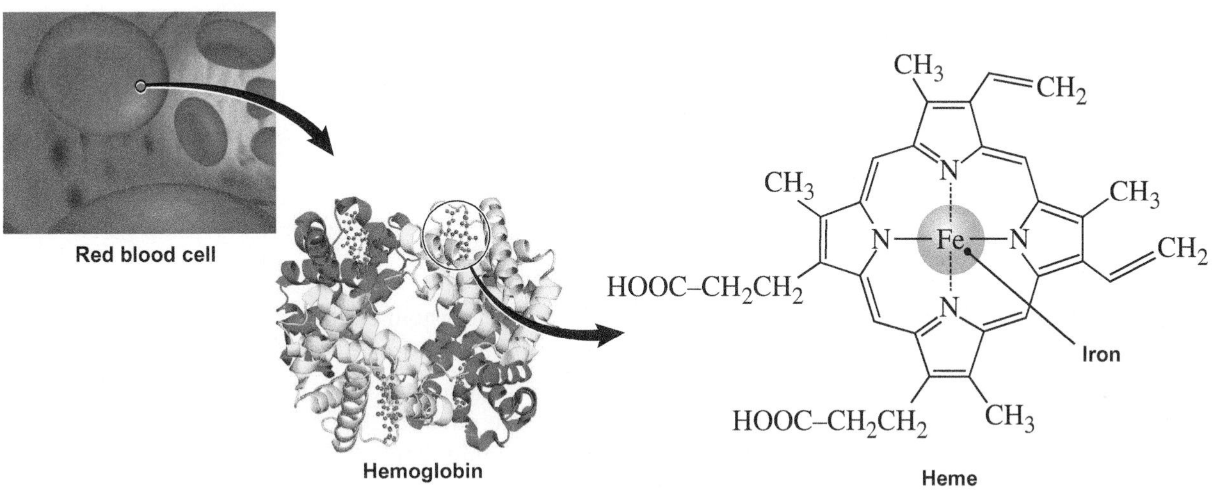

TABLE 23.8 The Four Levels of Protein Structure

Level	Description	Stabilizing Forces
Primary	The sequence of amino acids from N-terminal end to C-terminal end	Covalent bonds
Secondary	Repeating patterns of the polypeptide bond atoms, including α-helix and β-sheet	Hydrogen bonds forming between atoms of different peptide bonds
Tertiary	How the polypeptide chain folds back on itself to form its overall three-dimensional shape	Intermolecular forces between R groups and between R groups and the protein's environment; covalent disulfide bonds between Cys R groups; may involve cofactors
Quaternary	Interaction of more than one polypeptide chain to form a functional unit	Intermolecular forces between R groups of different polypeptide chains; may involve cofactors

- Secondary structure describes any repeated orientations of the polypeptide chain, such as α-helices or β-sheet structures; they are held together by hydrogen bonding.
- Tertiary structure describes how the polypeptide chain folds back upon itself to create a three-dimensional shape held in place by interactions between R groups and between R groups and molecules in the external environment of the protein (aqueous or lipid).
- Quaternary structure describes how more than one polypeptide chain interacts to form a functional protein.

23.5 Nucleic Acids and Protein Synthesis

GOALS

- Describe the role and structure of the nucleic acids DNA and RNA, including how they differ.
- Describe the processes of DNA replication, transcription, and translation.
- Use the genetic code to predict peptide sequences from DNA and RNA sequences.

STRUCTURE OF NUCLEIC ACIDS

Deoxyribonucleic acid (DNA) and ribonucleic acid (RNA) are the nucleic acids, which store and use genetic information in organisms. Nucleic acids are

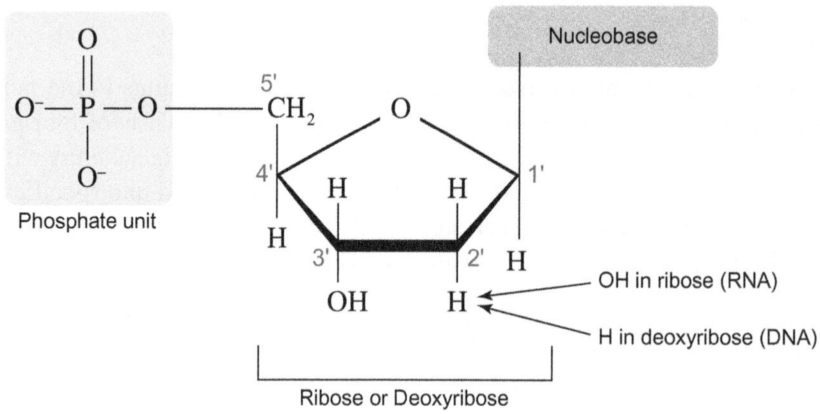

FIGURE 23.29 General Nucleotide Structure

Nucleotides are the monomers that make up the nucleic acid polymers DNA and RNA. Each nucleotide monomer consists of a nucleobase (which is a cyclic structure containing nitrogen), a five-carbon sugar molecule (deoxyribose for DNA; ribose for RNA), and a phosphate group.

polymers made up of **nucleotide** monomers. Each nucleotide has a nitrogen-containing ring structure known as a **nucleobase**, a five-carbon monosaccharide, and a phosphate group (Figure 23.29).

Within a nucleotide, the nucleobase can be either adenine (A), thymine (T), guanine (G), cytosine (C), or uracil (U), whose structures are shown in Figure 23.30. DNA nucleotides contain the bases A, G, C, and T, and the sugar deoxyribose. RNA nucleotides contain A, G, C, and U, and the sugar ribose.

Use the Biomolecules activity (Figure 23.1) to simulate how nucleotides form nucleic acid polymers. Notice that the connection forms between the phosphate group of one nucleotide and the sugar portion of the next nucleotide, releasing a molecule of water in the process. The linkage between the nucleotides is a new functional group, called a **phosphodiester** group.

In nucleic acid chemistry, the carbon atoms in the sugar are given separate numbers to distinguish these carbon atoms from the carbon atoms in the nucleobase. The carbon atoms in ribose and deoxyribose are numbered from 1′ to 5′ (read as "from one prime to five prime"). Using this numbering system, the phosphate in a nucleotide is bonded to the 5′ carbon. When two nucleotides form a dinucleotide, the 5′ phosphate of the one nucleotide reacts with the 3′ hydroxyl group of the second nucleotide. In the dinucleotide product, the first nucleotide has an unreacted 3′ hydroxyl group, while the second nucleotide has an unreacted phosphate on the 5′ carbon. Additional nucleotides are always added to the 3′ end of the growing polymer. Notice in Figure 23.31 that the connection between nucleotides is between a 5′ phosphate and a 3′ carbon.

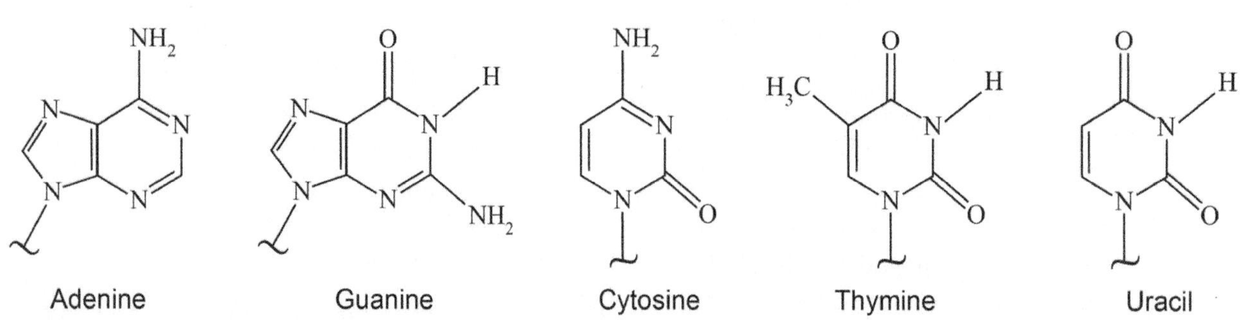

FIGURE 23.30 Nucleobase Structures

There are five nucleobases, designated A, G, C, T, and U for adenine, guanine, cytosine, thymine, and uracil, respectively. A, G, C, and T are found in DNA, whereas A, G, C, and U are found in RNA.

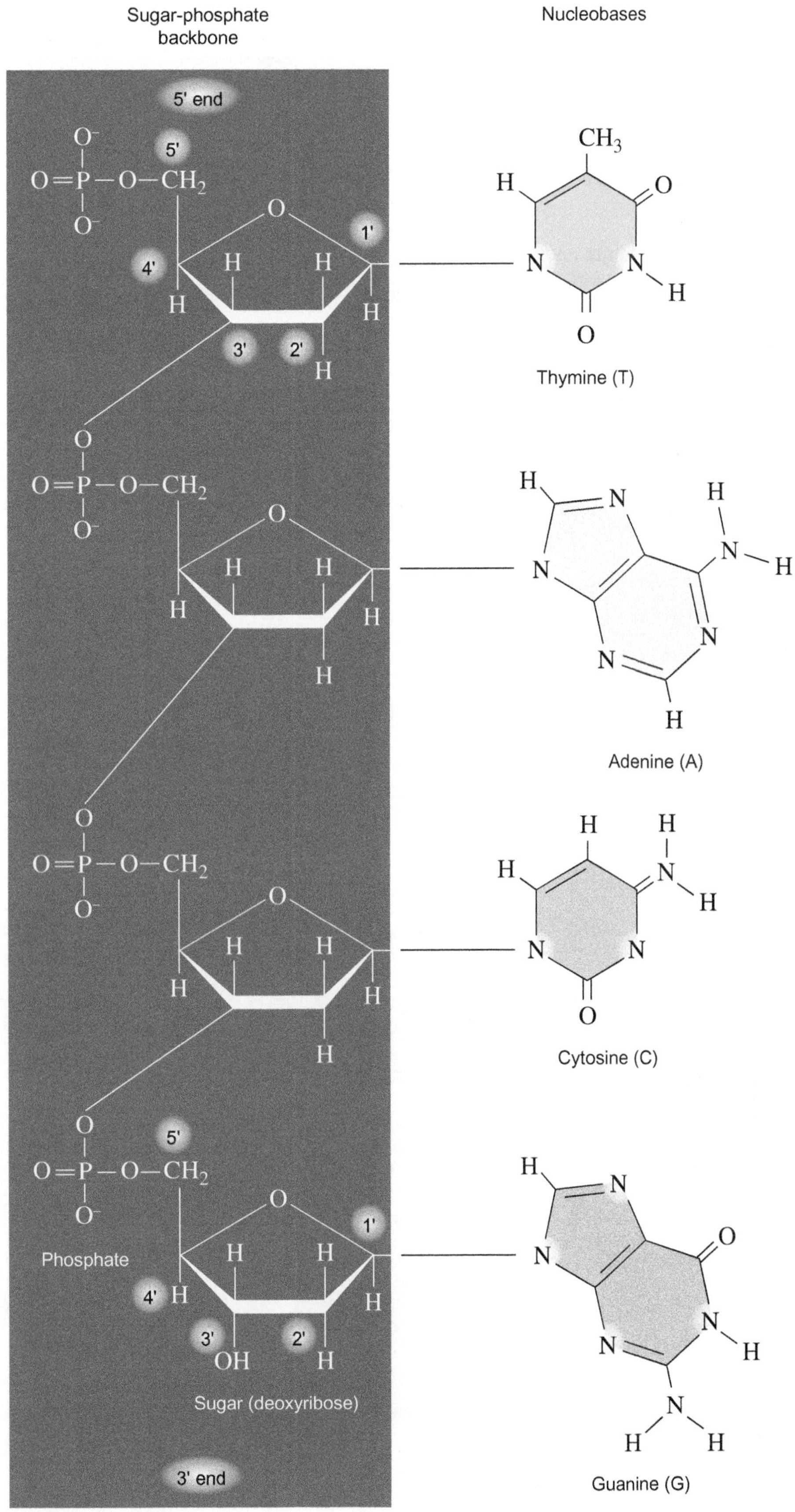

FIGURE 23.31 Nucleic Acid Structure

In a nucleic acid such as DNA and RNA, individual nucleotides connect to each other by way of the phosphate groups. The phosphate group of each nucleotide is attached to the 5′ carbon of the sugar. A new phosphodiester bond forms between that phosphate group and the 3′ carbon of the sugar portion of the next nucleotide.

Example 23.12

How would the structure in Figure 23.31 differ if this were a strand of RNA?

Solution

There are two major differences in the nucleotides of DNA and RNA. All DNA nucleotides contain deoxyribose, whereas all RNA nucleotides contain ribose. In RNA, moreover, uracil replaces thymine as one of the four bases. To convert the nucleotides in Figure 23.31 from DNA to RNA, the H below the ring on each C2′ would need to be OH instead (this would convert deoxyribose to ribose), and the thymine base at the top of the structure would need to be replaced by uracil (i.e., replace the CH_3 group of thymine with H).

PRACTICE PROBLEM 23.12

What sequence of nucleotides would result from the addition of G, C, and T to the structure in Figure 23.31?

Hint: Additional nucleotides are added to the 3′ end of the nucleic acid chain.

STORING AND REPLICATING GENETIC INFORMATION

DNA is a double-stranded molecule present mainly in the nucleus of cells. The two chains of nucleic acid are attracted by hydrogen bonds between the nitrogen-containing bases, as shown in Figure 23.32.

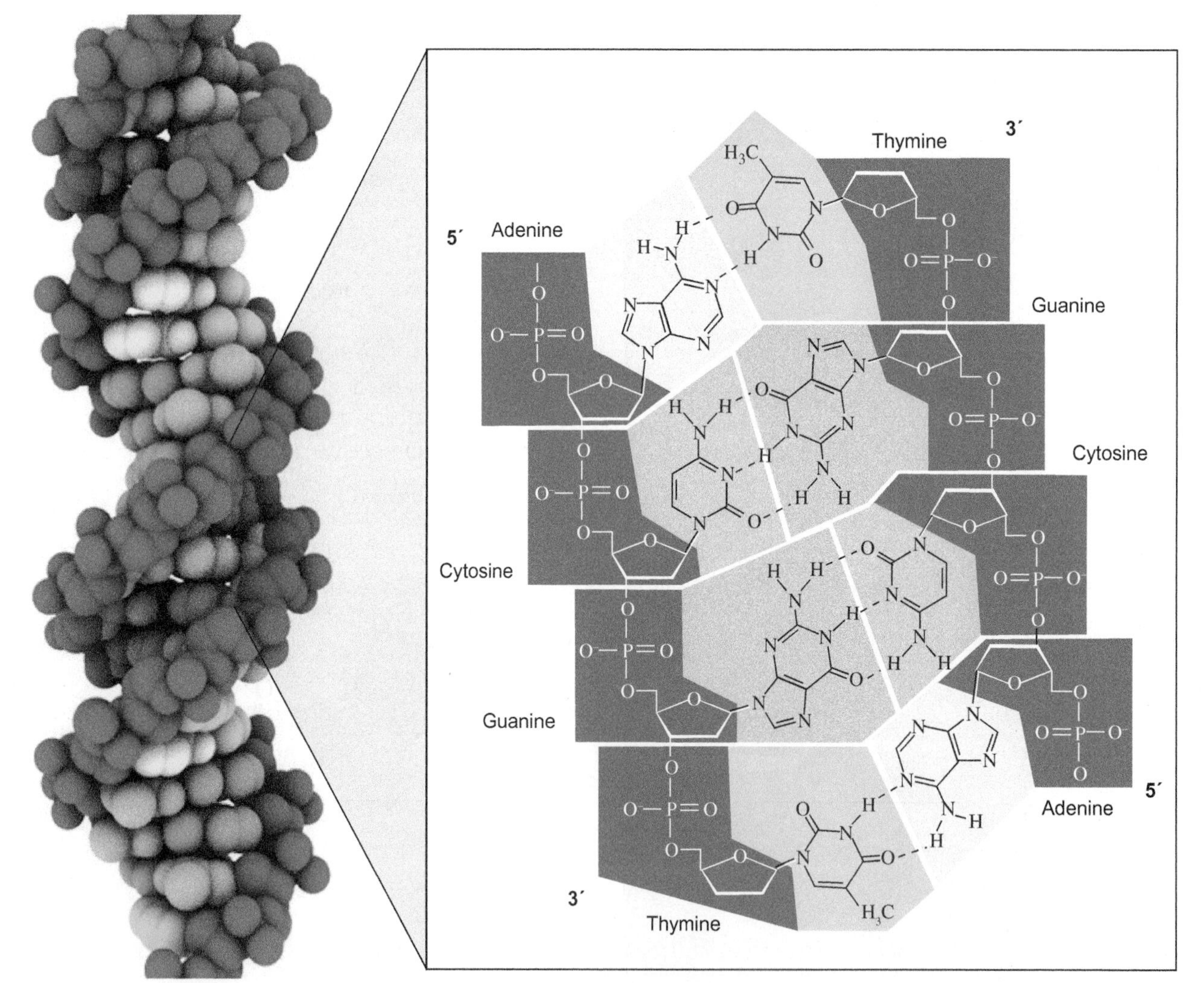

FIGURE 23.32 DNA Double Helix and Hydrogen Bonding between Base Pairs

DNA is a double-stranded nucleic acid in the form of a twisted ladder or helix. This structure is held together in part by hydrogen bonding between complementary nucleotides. Adenine nucleotides pair with thymine nucleotides, whereas guanine nucleotides pair with cytosine nucleotides.

These two very long, connected strands twist to form the DNA **double helix**. DNA structure is often compared to a ladder, with the sides of the ladder made up of the alternating sugar and phosphate units and with the nitrogen bases making up the rungs of the ladder. Adenine nucleotides always pair with thymine nucleotides. These A-T **base pairs** are connected by *two* hydrogen bonds. Guanine nucleotides always pair with cytosine nucleotides. These G-C base pairs are connected by *three* hydrogen bonds. Other forces, including dispersion forces and dipole–dipole forces, as well as the hydrogen bonds between base pairs, help to stabilize the DNA helix. The two strands of DNA are antiparallel—that is, one strand runs from its 3′ end to its 5′ end, whereas the other strand runs in the opposite direction (5′ to 3′). Starting at the top of Figure 23.32, the strand on the left is in the 5′ to 3′ direction, and the strand on the right is in the 3′ to 5′ direction.

Example 23.13

If the nucleotide sequence of one strand of DNA is 3′GTTAACCG5′, what must the sequence of the other strand be?

Solution

You can predict the sequence of the other strand by knowing that A always pairs with T, G always pairs with C, and the two strands are antiparallel:

5′CAATTGGC3′

PRACTICE PROBLEM 23.13

RNA is synthesized from a DNA template in an antiparallel fashion, using RNA nucleotides, and substituting U for T. What DNA sequence provided the template for the following RNA sequence?

3′GUCCAAUGGUAA5′

Hint: U in RNA pairs with A in DNA.

Prior to cell division, cells replicate their DNA to provide a complete copy of the genetic material for the two new cells present after cell division, a process known as DNA **replication**. The two strands of DNA unwind and separate, and each strand becomes a template to create a new strand (Figure 23.33). When the replication process is complete, two new molecules of DNA are present, each with one original strand and one newly replicated strand.

USING THE STORED GENETIC INFORMATION

The information stored in DNA directs the synthesis of proteins. This information is used by the cell during the processes of **transcription** and **translation** (Figure 23.34).

The cell copies the entire DNA molecule during replication, while only a portion of the DNA sequence is copied during transcription, and that copy is made using RNA nucleotides. In transcription, the portion of DNA that contains the information for a specific protein unwinds to allow one strand to serve as a template for the synthesis of **messenger RNA** (mRNA) in an antiparallel fashion, just as DNA is replicated. Each sequence of three nucleotides in the mRNA, referred to as a **codon**, specifies one of the 20 common amino acids (Table 23.7). In Figure 23.35, the **genetic code**, you can identify the codon sequences that specify each of the 20 amino acids plus the three codons that serve as start and stop codons.

One codon, AUG, which codes for methionine, indicates the start of a coding sequence. The messenger RNA carries the information to the cellular organelles responsible for protein synthesis, called **ribosomes**, which are composed of **ribosomal RNA** (rRNA) and proteins. A third type of RNA molecule, called **transfer RNA** (tRNA), binds to specific amino acids, bringing them to the ribosome for protein synthesis. Each tRNA contains an **anticodon** region complementary to the codon sequence designating that amino acid. During translation, these tRNA molecules form base pairs between their anticodon regions and the codons on the mRNA, bringing the designated amino acids into place. Enzymes then catalyze the formation of peptide bonds between the amino acids to synthesize the polypeptide chain. New amino acids continue to be added to the growing polypeptide chain until reading the stop codon, when the now complete polypeptide is released from the ribosomes.

Example 23.14

Use this short sequence of template DNA to answer the questions that follow.

3′TACGCCTTACGGTTCTCA5′

a. What mRNA sequence results from the transcription of the template DNA?
b. What is the primary structure of the polypeptide chain that results from the translation of the mRNA sequence in part (a)?

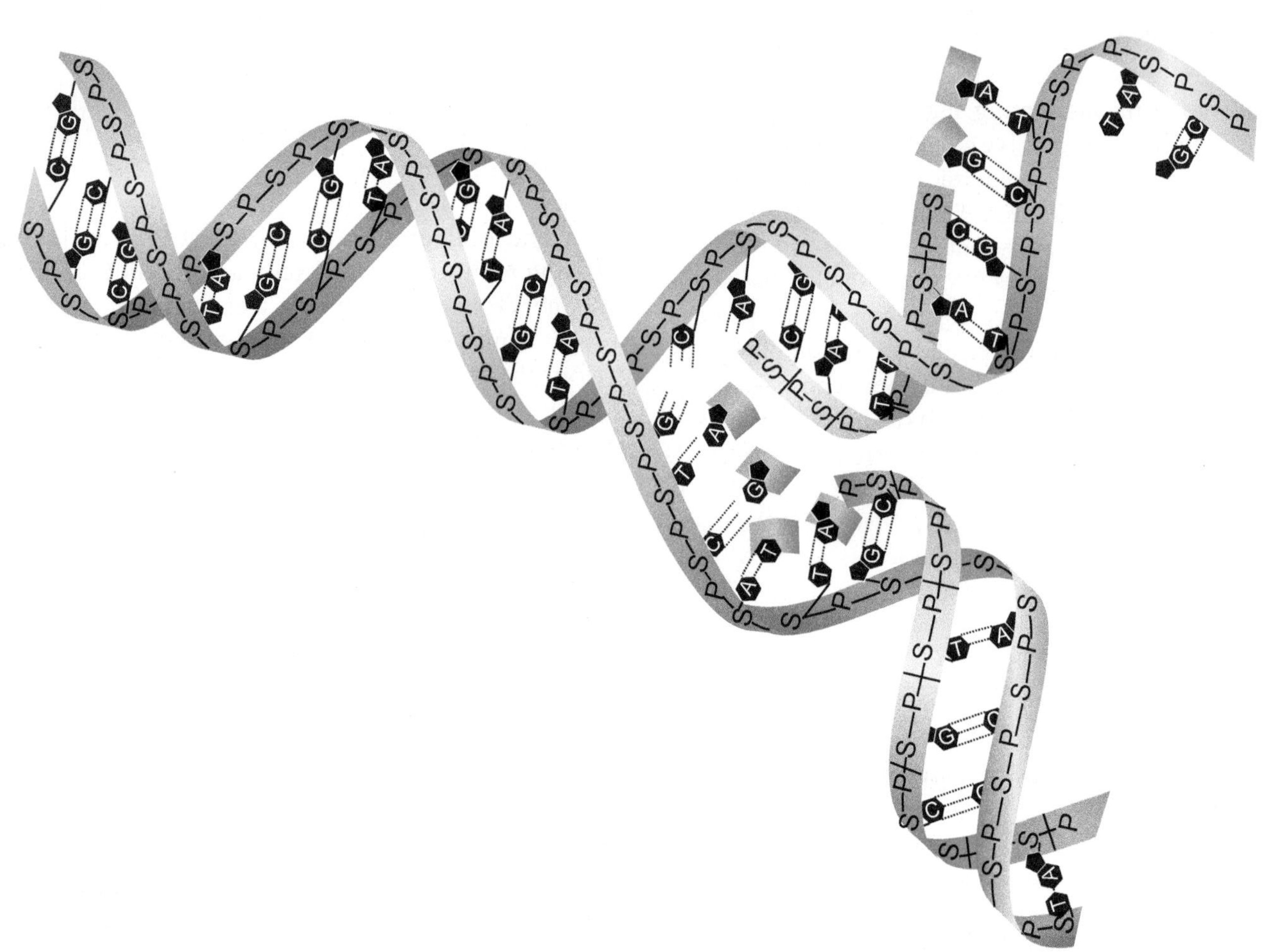

FIGURE 23.33 DNA Replication

During DNA replication, the double helix unwinds, and the two nucleic acid strands separate. DNA nucleotides form base pairs with the exposed bases and then form two new nucleic acid strands complementary to the original strands. The process of unwinding and base pairing continues until both strands of the original DNA molecule are replicated.

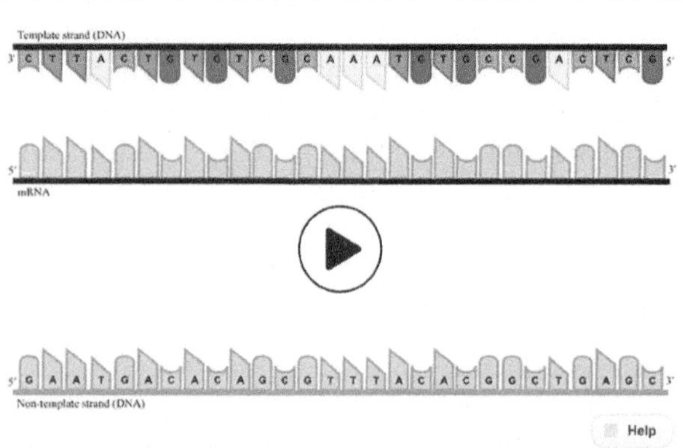

FIGURE 23.34 Transcription/Translation Activity

NOTE: You need to be online to access this activity.

Information stored in DNA is copied onto mRNA during transcription and is used to direct the sequence of amino acids in the synthesis of proteins during translation.

Solution

a. The template DNA is written from the 3′ end to the 5′ end. During transcription, the nucleotides of the mRNA are assembled in an antiparallel fashion, just as in replication, so the mRNA sequence will be written from the 5′ end to the 3′ end. As with all RNA molecules, U in mRNA pairs with A in DNA:

5′AUGCGGAAUGCCAAGAGU3′

b. Primary structure is the identity and order of the amino acids in the protein. Divide the mRNA sequence into codons, and then use the genetic code in Figure 23.35 to identify the amino acids in the peptide.

5′AUG CGG AAU GCC AAG AGU3′

AUG is the codon for methionine.
CGG is the codon for arginine.

First Position	Second Position: U	Second Position: C	Second Position: A	Second Position: G	Third Position
U	UUU Phenylalanine	UCU Serine	UAU Tyrosine	UGU Cysteine	U
	UUC Phenylalanine	UCC Serine	UAC Tyrosine	UGC Cysteine	C
	UUA Leucine	UCA Serine	UAA Stop	UGA Stop	A
	UUG Leucine	UCG Serine	UAG Stop	UGG Tryptophan	G
C	CUU Leucine	CCU Proline	CAU Histidine	CGU Arginine	U
	CUC Leucine	CCC Proline	CAC Histidine	CGC Arginine	C
	CUA Leucine	CCA Proline	CAA Glutamine	CGA Arginine	A
	CUG Leucine	CCG Proline	CAG Glutamine	CGG Arginine	G
A	AUU Isoleucine	ACU Threonine	AAU Asparagine	AGU Serine	U
	AUC Isoleucine	ACC Threonine	AAC Asparagine	AGC Serine	C
	AUA Isoleucine	ACA Threonine	AAA Lysine	AGA Arginine	A
	AUG Methionine	ACG Threonine	AAG Lysine	AGG Arginine	G
G	GUU Valine	GCU Alanine	GAU Aspartic acid	GGU Glycine	U
	GUC Valine	GCC Alanine	GAC Aspartic acid	GGC Glycine	C
	GUA Valine	GCA Alanine	GAA Glutamic acid	GGA Glycine	A
	GUG Valine	GCG Alanine	GAG Glutamic acid	GGG Glycine	G

FIGURE 23.35 The Genetic Code

The genetic code is made up of sequences of three nucleotides in mRNA that specify the identity and order of amino acids in protein synthesis.

AAU is the codon for asparagine.
GCC is the codon for alanine.
AAG is the codon for lysine
AGU is the codon for serine.

Thus, the primary structure of this hexapeptide is methionine-arginine-asparagine-alanine-lysine-serine.

PRACTICE PROBLEM 23.14

Give (a) an mRNA sequence and (b) a DNA template sequence that would result in the formation of the following tetrapeptide: valine-aspartic acid-isoleucine-cysteine.

Hint: Use the genetic code table (Figure 23.35) to determine which codons correspond to each amino acid (more than one may apply). Write the mRNA sequence from those codons in the 5′ to 3′ direction, and write the corresponding template DNA sequence in the 3′ to 5′ direction.

A summary of the types and roles of nucleic acids appears in Table 23.9.

TABLE 23.9 Types of Nucleic Acids

Type of Nucleic Acid	Description	Role in Living Things
DNA (deoxyribonucleic acid)	Double stranded, contains A, T, G, and C nucleotides and deoxyribose	Stores genetic information, undergoes replication, is transcription template
mRNA (messenger ribonucleic acid)	Single stranded, contains A, U, G, and C nucleotides and ribose	Produced by transcription, directs amino acid placement in translation
rRNA (ribosomal ribonucleic acid)	Single stranded, contains A, U, G, and C nucleotides and ribose	Forms part of ribosomal structure (translation site)
tRNA (transfer ribonucleic acid)	Single stranded, contains A, U, G, and C nucleotides and ribose	Brings appropriate amino acids to mRNA during translation

SECTION REVIEW

- The nucleic acids DNA and RNA are polymers composed of nucleotide monomers. Nucleotides are composed of a nucleobase, a sugar, and a phosphate group. They undergo dehydration synthesis to form phosphodiester bonds between the phosphate group of one nucleotide and the 3′ hydroxyl group of the sugar portion of the next nucleotide.
- Nucleotides can form base pairs by hydrogen bonding between the nitrogen-containing bases of adjacent strands of nucleic acid; A pairs with T or U, and G pairs with C.
- The DNA double helix contains two strands of DNA aligned in an antiparallel fashion and connected by nucleotide base pairs.

- During DNA replication, the double-stranded DNA unwinds and forms base pairs with new nucleotides.
- Transcription copies the information contained in the DNA nucleotide sequence into the nucleotide sequence of mRNA, which carries the information to the ribosomes, where the sequence of nucleotides in mRNA determines the order of amino acids in protein synthesis.

Putting It Together

The example problems in earlier sections of this chapter focus on just the new skills acquired in that section, but homework and exam questions in chemistry often require more than just one skill at a time. In fact, you will likely be expected to apply knowledge from across the entire chapter, or even multiple chapters in a single problem. This final example problem is meant to help you prepare for these types of multi-concept questions. Additional examples can be found in the end of chapter exercises.

Example 23.15

At neutral pH, amino acids are in their zwitterion form, with *both* the amine and carboxyl groups in their ionized states ($-NH_3^+$ and $-COO^-$) rather than their neutral states ($-NH_2$ and $-COOH$).

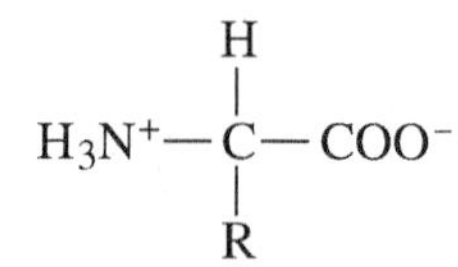

Which of the following forms would the amino acid take at very high pH?

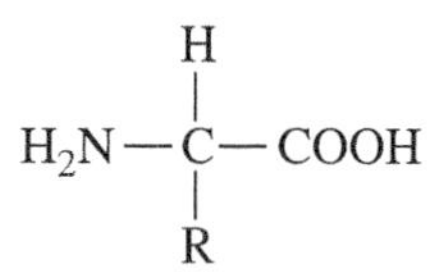

(a)

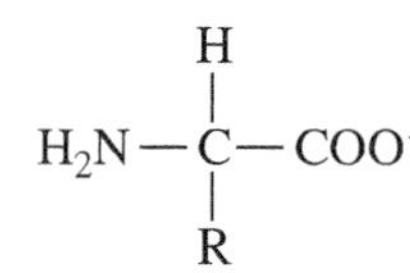

(b)

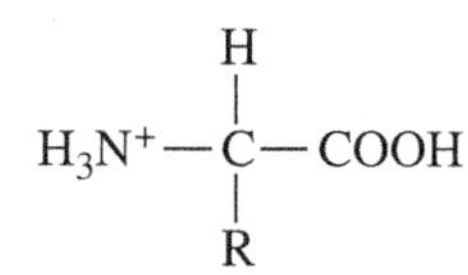

(c)

Solution

As pH increases, [H^+] decreases, which drives the ionization equilibrium of each group toward its unprotonated form according to Le Châtelier's principle.

$$-NH_3^+ \rightleftharpoons -NH_2 + H^+$$

$$-COOH \rightleftharpoons -COO^- + H^+$$

Thus, at very high pH, the amino acid will be in form (b).

PRACTICE PROBLEM 23.15

At neutral pH, amino acids are in their zwitterion form, with *both* the amine and carboxyl groups in their ionized states ($-NH_3^+$ and $-COO^-$) rather than their neutral states ($-NH_2$ and $-COOH$).

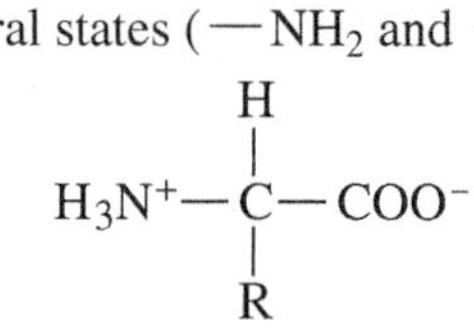

Which of the following forms would the amino acid take at very low pH?

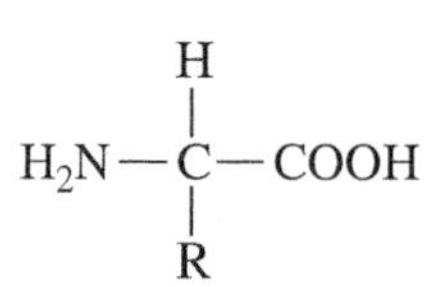

(a)

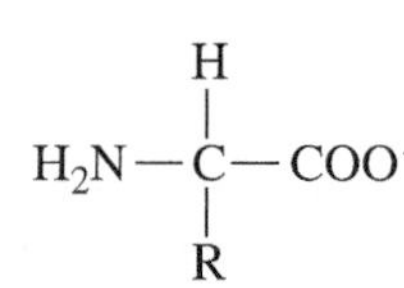

(b)

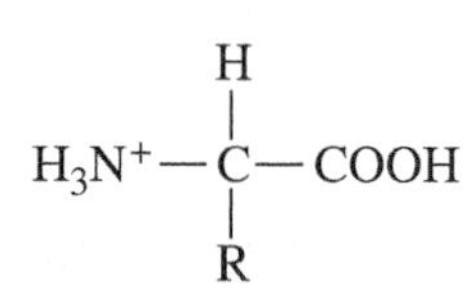

(c)

Hint: Use Le Châtelier's principle to predict how the equilibrium between $-NH_3^+$ and $-NH_2$ or between $-COO^-$ and $-COOH$ would shift as a result of an increase in [H^+].

Key Terms, Symbols, and Equations

KEY TERMS

aldose (23.2): A monosaccharide with an aldehyde functional group.

α-carbon (23.4): The carbon in an amino acid that is bonded to the amine functional group, the carboxy functional group, the R group, and H.

α-helix (23.4): The spiral-shaped secondary protein structure formed by hydrogen bonds between the amide NH group of one amino acid and the carbonyl group on another amino acid further along on the chain.

amino acid (23.4): A small molecule with both amine and carboxylic acid functional groups; a protein monomer.

amylopectin (23.2): A branched polymer of glucose.

amylose (23.2): An unbranched polymer of glucose.

anomer (23.2): One of two forms of the cyclic structures of monosaccharides that differ only in the position of the hydroxyl group that forms during the reaction that produces the cyclic structure.

anomeric carbon (23.2): The new chiral carbon formed when monosaccharides form a cyclic structure; it is derived from the carbonyl carbon in the Fischer projection.

anticodon (23.5): The site on tRNA that is complementary to the codons in mRNA.

base pair (23.5): The combination of two nucleotides in different nucleic acids that form hydrogen bonds to each other; A-T, G-C, and A-U.

β-sheet (23.4): A zigzag-shaped secondary protein structure formed by parallel strands of polypeptide that are held in place by hydrogen bonds between amide NH and carbonyl groups on different amino acids.

biochemistry (23.1): The chemistry of living things.

biomolecules (23.1): Molecules found in living things.

carbohydrates (23.1): Biomolecules involved in energy metabolism and storage; includes monosaccharides, disaccharides, and polysaccharides.

cellulose (23.2): A polysaccharide made by plants as a structural material; a polymer of glucose.

cholesterol (23.3): A steroid; classified as a lipid.

codons (23.5): A sequence of three consecutive nucleotides that specifies an amino acid.

cofactor (23.4): A metal ion or small organic molecule required for a protein's structure and function.

C-terminal end (23.4): The end of a polypeptide with an unreacted carboxyl group.

dehydration synthesis (23.1): The synthesis reaction in which a molecule of water is formed; common in the formation of larger biomolecules; a type of condensation reaction.

disaccharides (23.2): Two-unit carbohydrates, such as sucrose or lactose.

disulfide bond (23.4): A covalent bond between two organic compounds containing SH groups (R–S–S–R); it typically refers to the covalent bond that forms between two cysteine R groups in a peptide.

double helix (23.5): The twisted ladder shape of DNA.

fats (23.2): Triglycerides that are solids at room temperature with higher levels of saturated fatty acids; typically of animal origin.

fatty acid (23.3): A long-chain carboxylic acid.

Fischer projection (23.2): A two-dimensional diagram of monosaccharide structures that specifies the specific three-dimensional shape at each carbon atom; vertical bonds point away from the viewer, and horizontal bonds point toward the viewer.

genetic code (23.5): The list of codons and the amino acids they specify.

glycerol (23.3): A three-carbon tri-alcohol compound.

glycogen (23.2): A highly branched polysaccharide made by animals for energy.

glycosidic bond (23.2): The bond formed between the carbonyl carbon of one monosaccharide and a hydroxyl group of another.

Haworth projection (23.2): A diagram depicting monosaccharides and monosaccharide units in polysaccharides showing carbon atoms in ring structure; downward-pointing bonds represent right-pointing bonds in Fischer projection.

hexose (23.2): A monosaccharide containing six carbon atoms.

hydrophilic (23.3): Capable of interacting with water; refers to polar and charged species or polar and charged regions of large structures.

hydrophobic (23.3): Incapable of interacting with water; refers to nonpolar species or nonpolar regions of large structures.

ketose (23.2): A monosaccharide with a ketone functional group.

lipids (23.1): Biomolecules that are insoluble in water; lipids include fats, oils, phospholipids, steroids, and prostaglandins.

lipoprotein (23.3): A biologically important compound consisting of both protein and lipid components.

messenger RNA (23.5): The RNA molecule that carries information from DNA to the ribosome for protein synthesis; also known as mRNA.

monosaccharides (23.2): Single-unit carbohydrates, such as glucose or fructose.

neurotransmitters (23.1): Small biomolecules that transmit nerve signals between cells.

N-terminal end (23.4): The end of a polypeptide with an unreacted amine group.

nucleic acids (23.1): Biomolecules composed of nucleotide monomers; nucleic acids are involved in information storage and usage.

nucleobase (23.5): The nitrogen-containing bases in nucleotides.

nucleotide (23.5): The nucleic acid monomer consisting of a nucleobase, a five-carbon sugar, and a phosphate group.

oils (23.2): Triglycerides that are liquids at room temperature with higher levels of unsaturated fatty acids; typically of plant origin.

oligosaccharide (23.2): A short-chain carbohydrate composed of more than two monosaccharides.

pentose (23.2): A monosaccharide containing five carbon atoms.

peptide bond (23.4): The amide group formed when amino acids react to form peptides.

phosphodiester (23.5): The bond between two nucleotides in a nucleic acid, extending from the phosphate group of one nucleotide to a hydroxyl group of another.

phospholipid (23.3): The family of lipids with both polar and nonpolar components; phospholipids play important roles in the structure of cell membranes.

polyhydroxy (23.2): A compound containing many hydroxyl groups; a characteristic of carbohydrates.

polypeptide (23.4): A chain of many amino acids connected by peptide bonds.

primary structure (23.4): The sequence of amino acids in the structure of a polypeptide from the N-terminal end to the C-terminal end.

prostaglandin (23.3): The family of lipids with a characteristic five-membered ring and many physiological functions.

proteins (23.1): Biomolecules with many important functions; proteins are composed of hundreds of amino acids.

quaternary structure (23.4): The structure resulting when more than one polypeptide chain is needed to form a functional protein unit.

replication (23.5): The process by which DNA is copied prior to cell division.

ribosomal RNA (23.5): A nucleic acid component of ribosomes; also called rRNA.

ribosome (23.5): A cellular organelle that is the site of protein synthesis.

secondary structure (23.4): Any repeating shapes formed by the polypeptide chain, such as the α-helix and β-sheet structures.

starch (23.2): A polysaccharide made by plants for energy storage, such as amylose and amylopectin.

steroid (23.3): The family of lipids with a characteristic four-ring structure and many physiological functions.

sugars (23.2): Mono- and disaccharides.

tertiary structure (23.4): The description of how a polypeptide chain folds to create its overall three-dimensional shape; tertiary structure is held in place by interactions between R groups and between R groups and the polypeptide environment.

tetrose (23.2): A monosaccharide containing four carbon atoms.

transcription (23.5): The process by which the nucleotide sequence on a small part of the DNA is copied using RNA nucleotides to form mRNA, which is later used to specify the order of the amino acids in protein synthesis.

transfer RNA (23.5): The molecule responsible for bringing the correct amino acids into place during protein synthesis; also referred to as tRNA.

translation (23.5): The process by which information in mRNA is used to synthesize a protein.

triglyceride (23.3): The family of lipids consisting of glycerol linked to three fatty acids via ester functional groups.

triose (23.2): A monosaccharide containing three carbon atoms.

zwitterion (23.4): A molecule that has two charged regions but is neutral overall.

SYMBOLS AND ABBREVIATIONS

3′ (unreacted 3′ end of a nucleic acid) (23.5)

5′ (unreacted 5′ end of a nucleic acid) (23.5)

A (adenine) (23.5)

C (cytosine) (23.5)

G (guanine) (23.5)

mRNA (messenger RNA) (23.5)

rRNA (ribosomal RNA) (23.5)

T (thymine) (23.5)

tRNA (transfer RNA) (23.5)

U (uracil) (23.5)

Chapter Summary

Biomolecules are organic molecules found in living things, and, during metabolism, they undergo typical chemical reactions. Large biomolecules can be categorized as carbohydrates, lipids, proteins, or nucleic acids, most of which are polymers composed of smaller molecules. These smaller molecules combine via condensation reactions that are catalyzed by enzymes and release a water molecule for each new connection formed (Section 23.1).

Carbohydrates are a family of biomolecules made up of the simple sugars and the polysaccharides. Simple sugars (monosaccharides) are aldehydes or ketones with many alcohol groups. These combine to produce disaccharides and polysaccharides, all of which constitute the carbohydrates. Monosaccharides are categorized by the number of carbon atoms and the presence of aldehyde or ketone functional groups. Although it is convenient to draw monosaccharide structures in a linear format known as a Fischer projection, hexose and pentose sugars undergo an intramolecular reaction in water to form two cyclic structures, known as α and β anomers. Maltose, sucrose, and galactose are common disaccharides characterized by the identity of their monosaccharides and the linkage between them. Polysaccharides are polymers of glucose and make up the majority of the biomass on Earth. Amylose, amylopectin in plants, and glycogen in animals are used for energy storage, while cellulose is a structural material in plants (Section 23.2).

Lipids are a diverse group of biomolecules that are insoluble in water. They include the triglycerides, phospholipids, steroids, and prostaglandins. Triglycerides, another energy source for living things, are composed of a glycerol molecule linked via ester functional groups to three fatty acids. Triglycerides containing unsaturated fatty acids have lower melting points and are more likely to be liquids at room temperature than those containing saturated fatty acids. Phospholipids contain both polar and nonpolar regions and are a major component of cell membranes. Both steroids and prostaglandins play a role in communication between cells in complex organisms (Section 23.3).

Proteins carry out many functions in cells involving structure, catalysis, communication, movement, storage, regulation, and protection. Proteins are composed of amino acid monomers connected via peptide bonds. Each amino acid consists of an α-carbon bonded to an amine group, a carboxyl group, a variable R group, and H. There are 20 common amino acids with R groups that can be classified as nonpolar, polar, weak acids, and weak bases. At neutral pH, amino acids exist as zwitterions—neutral species in which both the amine group and the carboxyl group are ionized. The sequence of amino acids in peptides is specified from the N-terminal end (the unreacted amine group) to the C-terminal end (the unreacted carboxyl group). The structures of proteins consist of four levels. Primary structure consists of the sequence of amino acids. Secondary structure describes any repeated orientations of the polypeptide chain, such as α-helices or β-sheet structures. These structures are held in place by hydrogen bonds between the NH group of one amino acid and the C=O group of another. Tertiary structure describes how the polypeptide chain folds back upon itself to create its three-dimensional shape. Tertiary structure is held in place by interactions between R groups and between R groups and molecules in the external environment of the protein (aqueous or lipid). Quaternary structure describes how multiple polypeptide chains interact to form a functional protein (Section 23.4).

Nucleotides are composed of a nitrogen-containing base, a sugar, and a phosphate group. Nucleotide monomers combine to form the nucleic acids DNA and RNA. Nucleotides form base pairs by hydrogen bonding between the nitrogen-containing bases of adjacent strands of nucleic acid. Adenine nucleotides pair with thymine or uracil nucleotides via the formation of two hydrogen bonds. Guanine nucleotides pair with cytosine nucleotides via the formation of three hydrogen bonds. The DNA double helix contains two strands of DNA aligned in an antiparallel fashion and held together by nucleotide base pairs. DNA replication occurs by the separation of DNA strands and the formation of base pairs with new nucleotides. Protein synthesis occurs in two major steps: transcription, which copies the information in DNA into mRNA (which carries the information to the ribosomes), and translation, where the sequence of mRNA nucleotides directs the correct ordering of amino acids to form the polypeptide (Section 23.5).

END OF CHAPTER QUESTIONS

23.1 Introduction to Biomolecules

1. Marathon runners store far more glycogen in their muscle cells than the average person does. Glycogen is broken down to glucose to power muscles. Is glycogen a protein, carbohydrate, lipid, or nucleic acid?

2. Bodybuilders increase their nutritional intake of amino acids to provide the raw materials to increase and maintain muscle mass. Is muscle mass protein, carbohydrate, lipid, or nucleic acid?

3. Gene therapy involves the introduction of functional genes into patients who lack the instructions to make or regulate the production of a specific protein. Are genes carbohydrates, proteins, lipids, or nucleic acids?

4. Lecithin is an important component of cell membranes and is also found in the yolks of eggs. It is insoluble in water. Is lecithin a protein, carbohydrate, lipid, or nucleic acid?

23.2 Carbohydrates

5. Describe the general structure of a monosaccharide.

6. Identify the most important intermolecular forces for monosaccharides and explain your reasoning.

7. Classify the following molecules as triose, tetrose, pentose, or hexose monosaccharides.

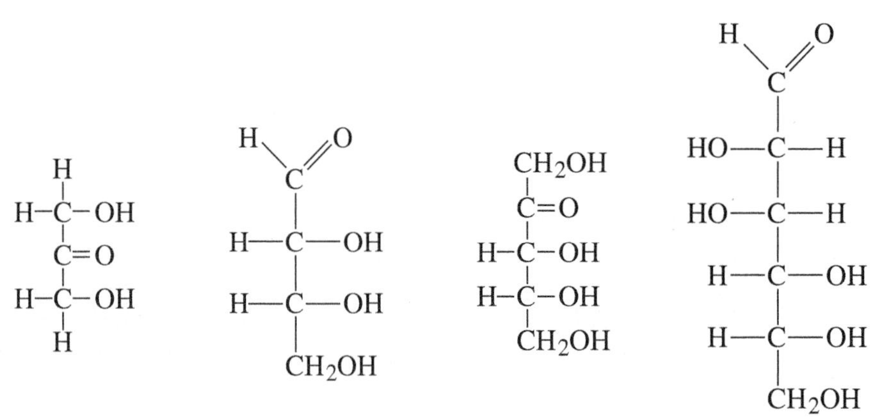

(a) (b) (c) (d)

8. Classify the molecules in the previous problem as aldose or ketose monosaccharides.

9. Classify the following monosaccharides as a ketopentose, a ketohexose, an aldotriose, or an aldotetrose.

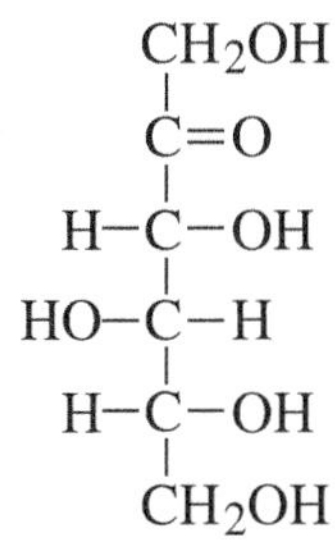
(a)

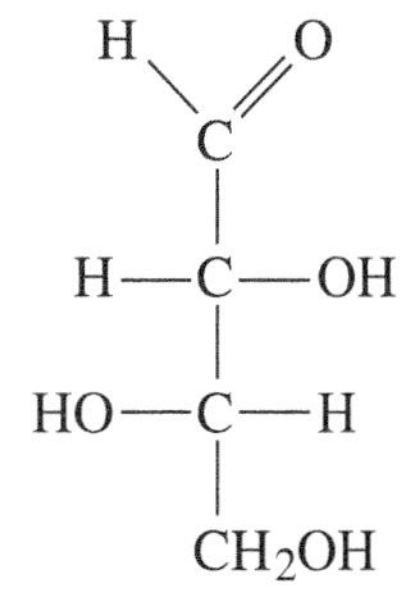
(b)

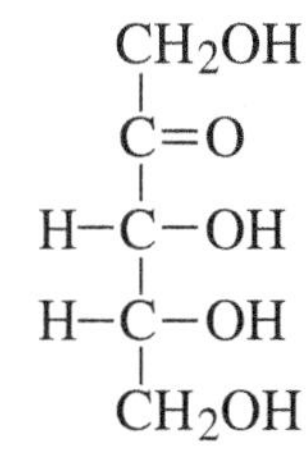
(c)

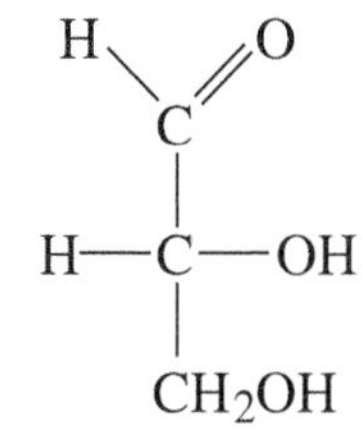
(d)

10. Identify the chiral centers in the monosaccharide ribose.

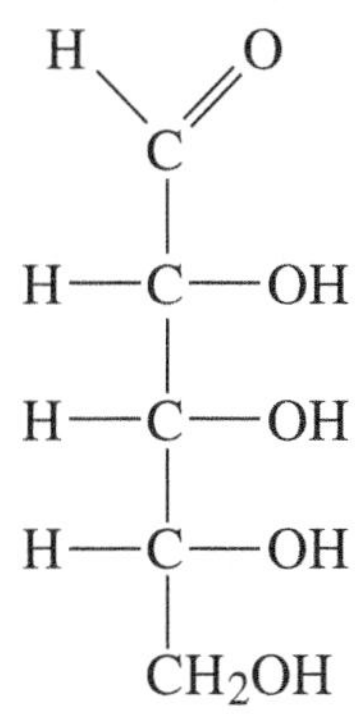

11. Identify the chiral centers in the monosaccharide mannose.

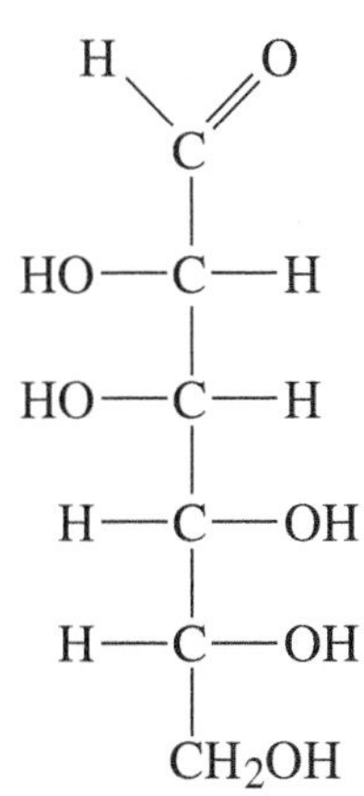

12. Identify the linkage in the following disaccharides.

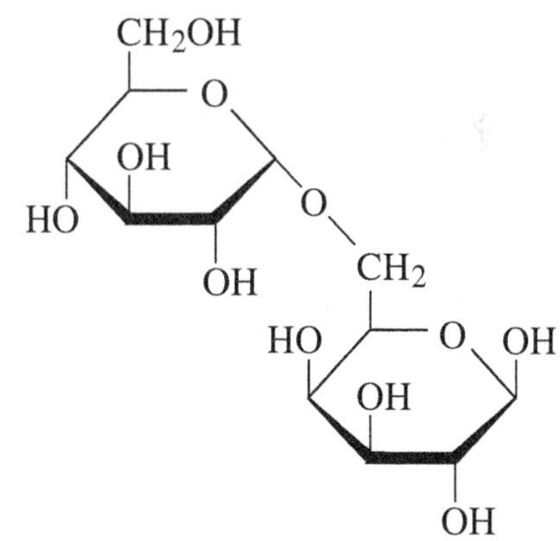
(a)

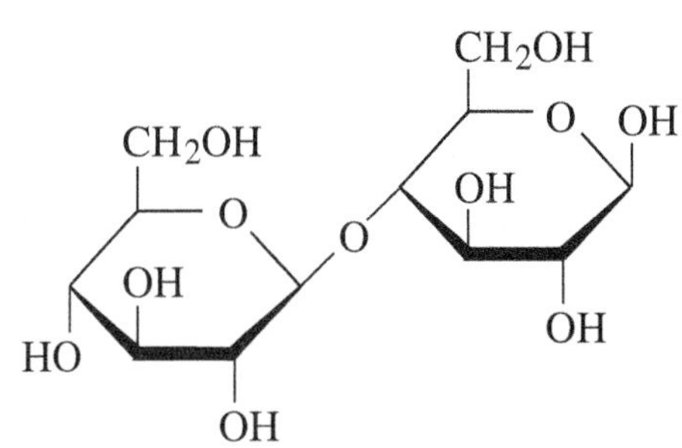
(b)

13. Carbohydrates have many roles in living organisms. The structure in (a) is a portion of a cell surface antigen, whereas the structure in (b) is chondroitin, which is found in connective tissue. While these structures have additional functional groups associated with them, they are basically disaccharides. Identify the type of linkage present in each.

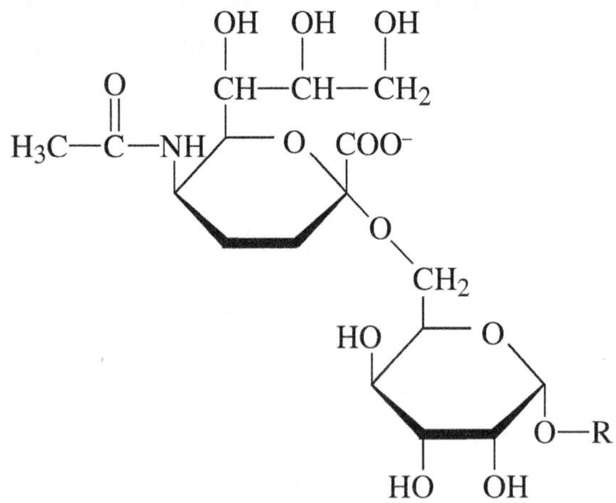

(a)

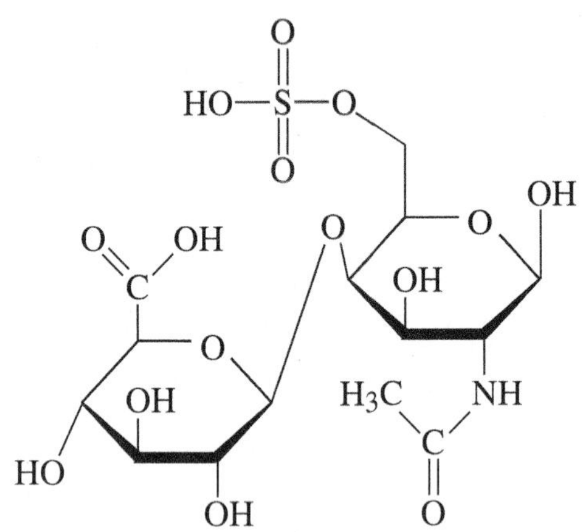

(b)

14. Draw a disaccharide composed of two glucose molecules connected by the following linkages.
   a. α-1,4
   b. β-1,4
   c. α-1,6
   d. β-1,6
15. Draw a disaccharide composed of one glucose molecule and one galactose molecule connected by the following linkages.
   a. α-1,4
   b. β-1,4
   c. α-1,6
   d. β-1,6
16. Match these descriptions with the appropriate polysaccharide.
   a. unbranched chain of glucose units with α-1,4 glycosidic links
   b. highly branched chain of glucose units found in animal cells
   c. unbranched chain of glucose units with β-1,4 glycosidic links
17. Compare and contrast the structures of amylose and cellulose (Table 23.3).
18. Compare and contrast the structures of amylopectin and glycogen (Table 23.3).

23.3 Lipids

19. What components make up a triglyceride?
20. What intermolecular forces are most important for triglycerides? Explain your answer.
21. Draw a reaction showing the formation of a triglyceride composed of three saturated fatty acids, each of which contains 18 carbon atoms.
22. Draw a reaction showing the formation of a triglyceride composed of three saturated fatty acids, each of which contains 16 carbon atoms.
23. Consider triglyceride molecules containing three identical fatty acids chosen from the fatty acids listed below. Rank these triglycerides from lowest to highest melting point. Explain your reasoning.
   a. stearic acid: $CH_3(CH_2)_{16}COOH$
   b. oleic acid: $CH_3(CH_2)_7CH{=}CH(CH_2)_7COOH$
   c. linoleic acid: $CH_3(CH_2)_4CH{=}CHCH_2CH{=}CH(CH_2)_7COOH$
24. Coconut oil contains more than 90% saturated fatty acids, whereas lard contains a bit more than 40% saturated fatty acids.
   a. Which would you expect to have the higher melting temperature?
   b. Would you expect these to be solids or liquids at room temperature?
25. Categorize the following molecule as a triglyceride, phospholipid, steroid, or prostaglandin.

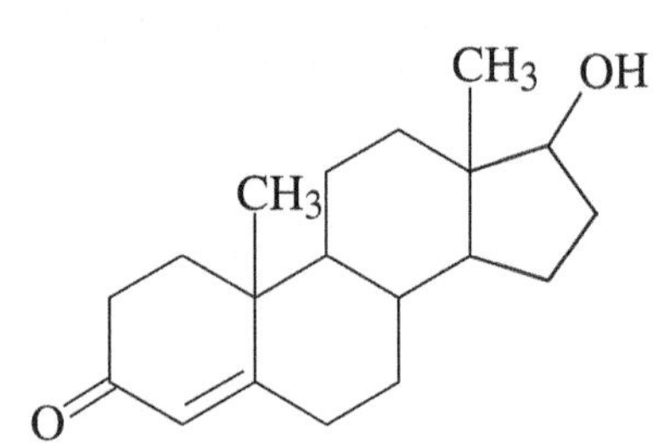

26. Categorize the following molecule as a triglyceride, phospholipid, steroid, or prostaglandin.

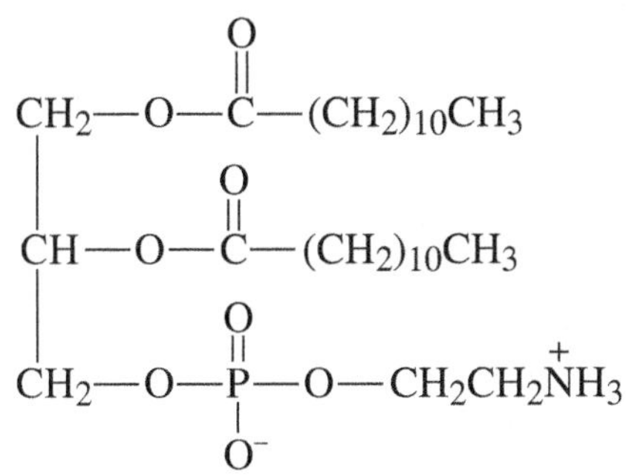

27. Categorize the following molecule as a triglyceride, phospholipid, steroid, or prostaglandin.

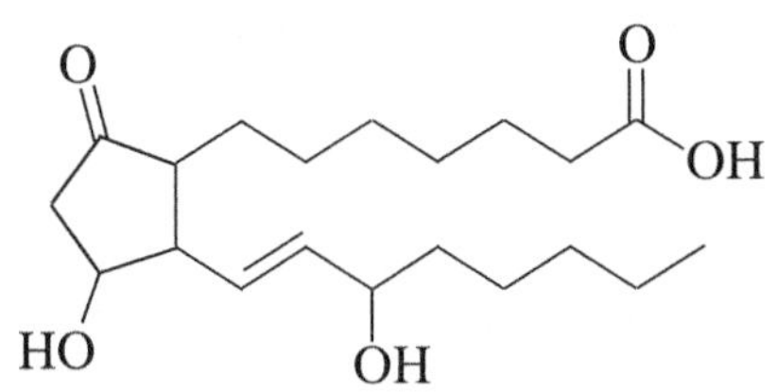

28. In humans, bile acids help digest fats in the small intestine. Bile acids are produced from a particular category of lipids. Use this structure of a bile acid to identify the lipid category that produces bile acids.

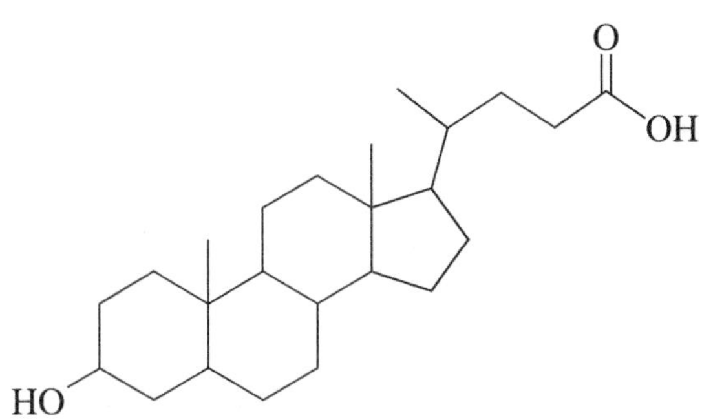

23.4 Amino Acids, Peptides, and Proteins

29. Identify the alpha carbon, the carboxylic acid and amino functional groups, and the R group in the following structure of phenylalanine.

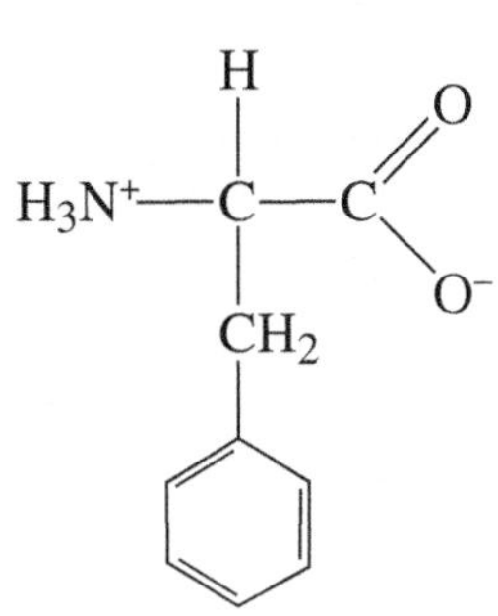

30. Identify the alpha carbon, the carboxylic acid and amino functional groups, and the R group in the following structure of isoleucine.

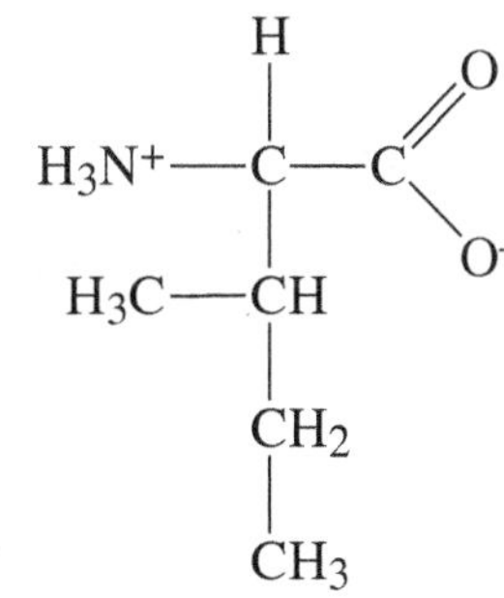

31. Draw the possible dipeptides formed by serine and glutamic acid.

32. Draw the possible dipeptides formed by valine and tyrosine.

33. Name the dipeptides from problem 31.

34. Name the dipeptides from problem 32.

35. How many different tripeptides would be possible to make from three different amino acids?

36. Are the R groups of the following amino acids nonpolar, polar, acidic, or basic?

a.

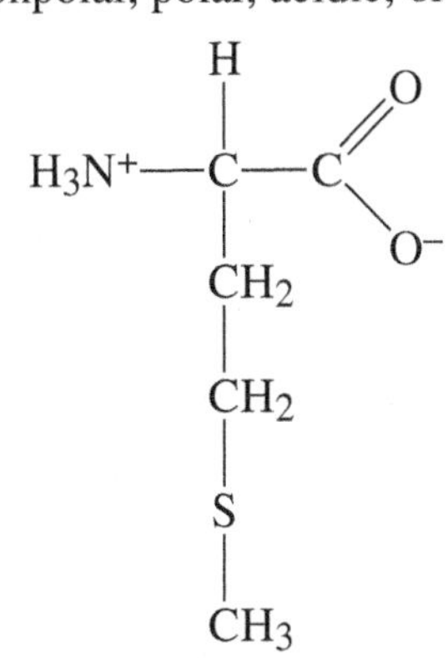

b.

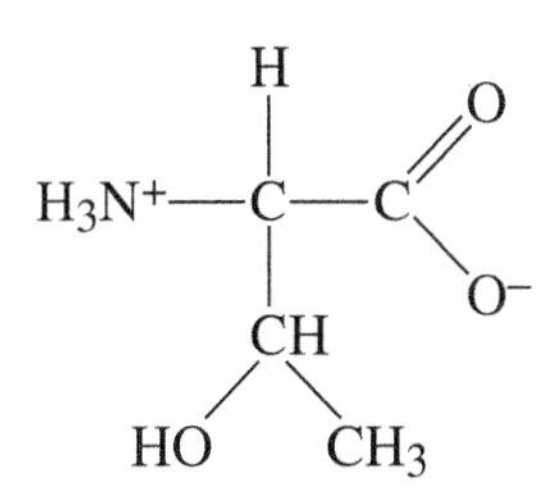

c.

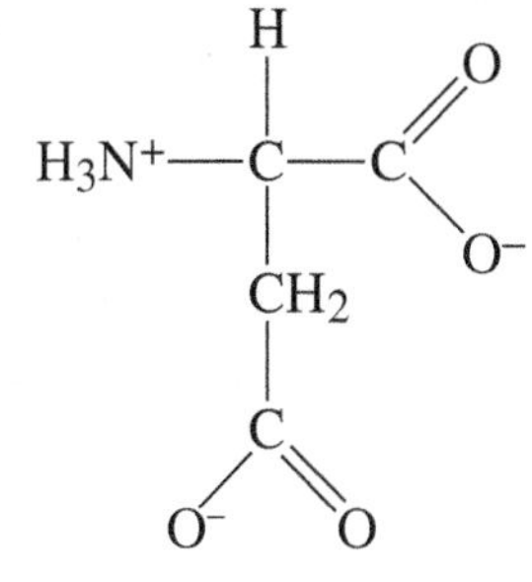

37. Are the R groups of the following amino acids nonpolar, polar, acidic, or basic?

a.

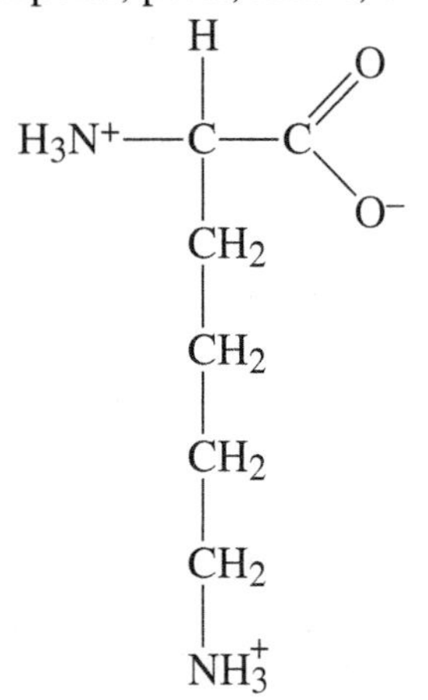

b.

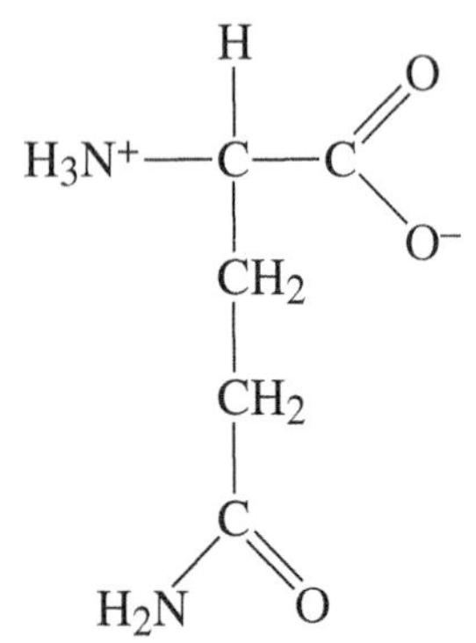

c.

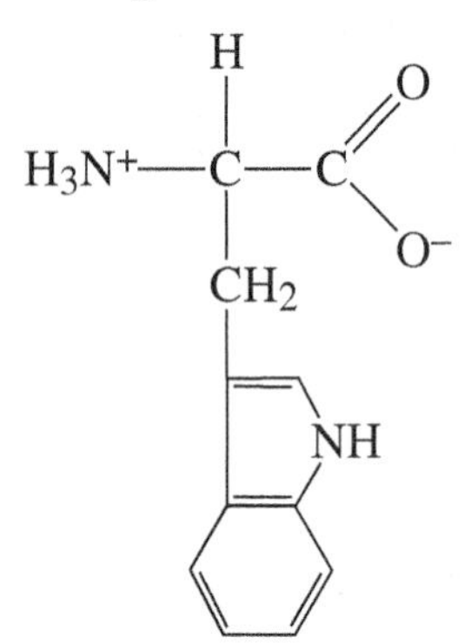

38. Amino acids combine to form a peptide via a condensation reaction. How many water molecules are produced in the formation of one molecule of
    a. a dipeptide?
    b. a tripeptide?
    c. a tetrapeptide?

39. Hydrolysis is the reverse of condensation. How many water molecules are needed to break a tripeptide molecule into its component amino acids by hydrolysis?

40. Draw the tripeptide Val-Lys-Ser and identify the N-terminal and C-terminal ends.

41. Draw the tripeptide glycylisoleucyltyrosine and identify the N-terminal and C-terminal ends.

42. Draw the tripeptide alanylseryltryptophan and identify the N-terminal and C-terminal ends.

43. Define or describe primary protein structure.

44. Define or describe secondary protein structure.

45. Define or describe tertiary protein structure.

46. Define or describe quaternary protein structure.

47. The reaction in Figure 23.25 shows the oxidation of two thiol molecules to form the disulfide functional group.
    a. How is this related to protein structure?
    b. Write a chemical reaction for the addition of H^+ to vasopressin (Figure 23.36).

48. Identify the levels of protein structure evident in the image of zinc protease in Figure 23.28b.

49. Identify the levels of protein structure evident in hemoglobin (see the Everyday Connection in Section 23.4).

23.5 Nucleic Acids and Protein Synthesis

50. In the following nucleotide structure:
    a. label the components (nucleobase, sugar, and phosphate).
    b. identify the name of the specific nucleobase present.
    c. identify the name of the specific sugar present.

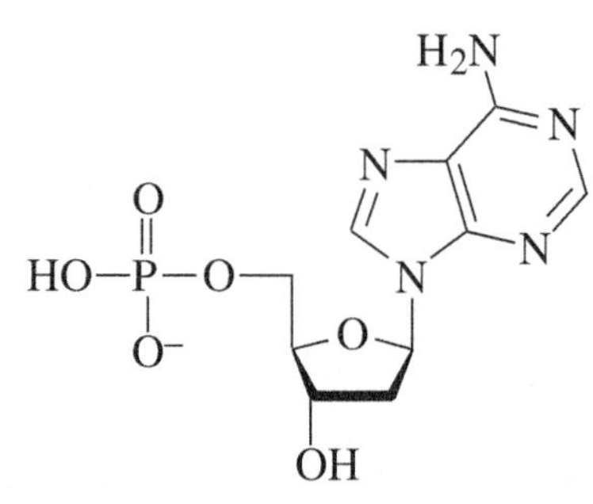

51. In the following nucleotide structure:
    a. label the components (nucleobase, sugar, and phosphate).
    b. identify the name of the specific nucleobase present.
    c. identify the name of the specific sugar present.

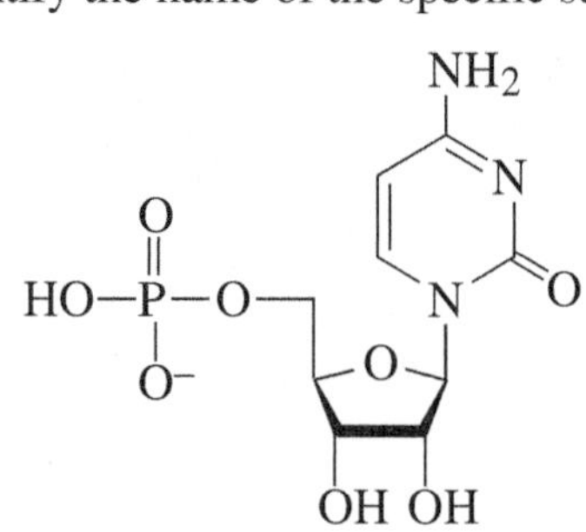

52. Draw the product of the condensation reaction between the nucleotides from the previous two problems, and label the phosphodiester bond.

53. Indicate where the hydrogen bonds form between A and T using the structures found in Figure 23.30.

54. Indicate where the hydrogen bonds form between G and C using the structures found in Figure 23.30.

55. Is it possible for hydrogen bonds to form between other pairs of nucleotides, such as between A and G and between T and C? Use the information in Figure 23.30 to predict how the formation of these unusual base pairs might affect the double helix structure of DNA.

56. Describe the process of transcription and its purpose.

57. Describe the process of translation and its purpose.

58. Describe the process of replication and its purpose.

59. Define or give a brief description of each of the following terms:
   a. genetic code
   b. codon
   c. anticodon

60. Define or give a brief description of each of the following terms:
   a. mRNA
   b. tRNA
   c. rRNA

61. Answer the questions based on the nucleotide sequence of the following *template* strand of DNA: CGG AAT TTC GGG AAT TTA GAG CAC GAC
   a. What is the sequence of the complementary strand of DNA?
   b. What is the corresponding mRNA sequence?
   c. What is the corresponding amino acid sequence?

62. Answer the questions based on the nucleotide sequence of the following *template* strand of DNA: TTA CGG GAA TTT ACG GAA TGA GCA
   a. What is the sequence of the complementary strand of DNA?
   b. What is the corresponding mRNA sequence?
   c. What is the corresponding amino acid sequence?

63. Answer the questions based on the nucleotide sequence of the following *template* strand of DNA: GAA TTT CGG GAA TTT AGA GCA CGA
   a. What is the sequence of the complementary strand of DNA?
   b. What is the corresponding mRNA sequence?
   c. What is the corresponding amino acid sequence?

64. Answer the questions based on the nucleotide sequence of the following *template* strand of DNA: ATT TAG AGC ACG ACC GGA ATT TCG TGG
   a. What is the sequence of the complementary strand of DNA?
   b. What is the corresponding mRNA sequence?
   c. What is the corresponding amino acid sequence?

Putting It Together

65. The metabolic reaction that releases energy from glucose is

$$C_6H_{12}O_6(aq) + 6\,O_2(g) \rightarrow 6\,CO_2(g) + 6\,H_2O(l)$$

Classify this reaction as one of the five reaction types from Table 4.2.

66. Consider the reverse of the reaction from the previous problem. This reaction, called photosynthesis, is how plants produce glucose.

$$6\,CO_2(g) + 6\,H_2O(l) \xrightarrow{\text{light}} C_6H_{12}O_6(aq) + 6\,O_2(g)$$

How many liters of CO_2 (at 1.00 atm and 25°C) are needed to produce 1.00 g of glucose?

67. For each hydrogen bond shown in Figure 12.7, identify the hydrogen-bond donor and the hydrogen-bond acceptor.

68. Which amino acids are chiral?

69. At pH = 7, the carboxyl group of an amino acid is in its ionized form ($-COO^-$). Is the pK_a of a carboxyl group greater than or less than 7?

70. At pH = 7, the amine group of an amino acid is in its ionized form ($-NH_3^+$). Is the pK_a of an amine group greater than or less than 7?

PRACTICE PROBLEM SOLUTIONS

Practice Problem 23.1 Solution

Remove the elements that make up a molecule of water from the highlighted functional groups and connect the two molecules by forming a bond between them.

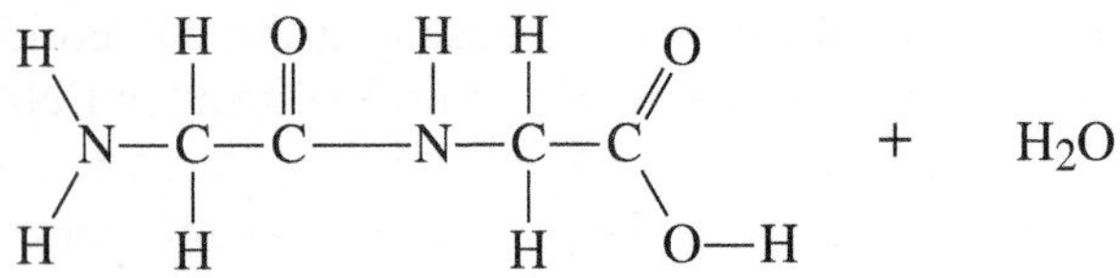

Practice Problem 23.2 Solution

Refer to Table 23.1 to identify the likely biomolecule for each function.

a. Transport is one of the many functions of proteins.
b. Energy storage is a function of both carbohydrates and lipids, but lipids are generally used for longer term energy storage in animals.
c. Communication between cells may be carried out by certain proteins and lipids, as well as smaller biomolecules.

Practice Problem 23.3 Solution

The location of the carbonyl group determines if the monosaccharide is an aldose (C1) or a ketose (C2). The number of carbon atoms in the monosaccharide provides the rest of the classification: triose, tetrose, pentose, or hexose for C3, C4, C5, or C6, respectively.

a. An aldehyde functional group and five carbon atoms overall make this an aldopentose.
b. ketone + 3C = ketotriose
c. aldehyde + 5C = aldopentose

Practice Problem 23.4 Solution

a. This monosaccharide has six carbon atoms total, making it a hexose. The anomeric carbon is bonded to the O group in the ring, a $-CH_2OH$ group, and an $-OH$ group and is located on the left side of the image. The $-OH$ group points down in this image, which is in the same direction as the $-CH_2OH$ group bonded to C5, so this is a β-hexose.
b. This monosaccharide has six carbon atoms total, making it a hexose, too. The anomeric carbon is bonded to the O group in the ring, $-H$, and an $-OH$ group. The $-OH$ group points up (the same direction as the $-CH_2OH$ group bonded to C5), so this is a β-hexose.

Practice Problem 23.5 Solution

Number the carbon atoms in each ring. In this case, the anomeric carbon is C1 for both monosaccharide units.

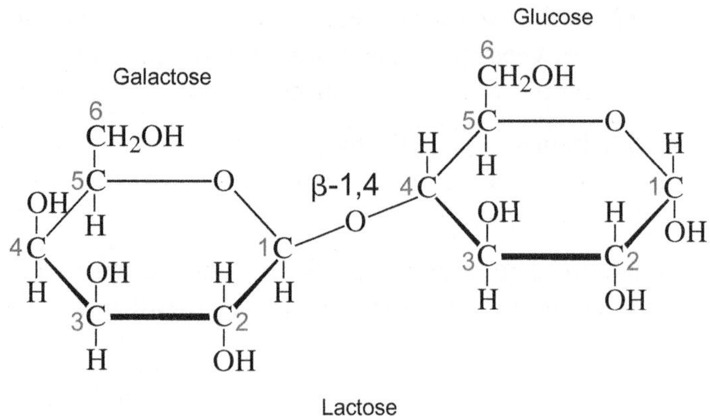

The glycosidic bond forms between C1 of galactose and C4 of glucose, so it is a 1,4 linkage. C1 of galactose is anomeric, so it requires the α or β distinction. What used to be the OH group on C1 of galactose points up (the same direction as the CH_2OH group on C5), indicating the β position. C4 of glucose is not anomeric, so it does not get classified as α or β in the linkage notation. Thus, the glycosidic bond is β-1,4.

Practice Problem 23.6 Solution

a. High percentages of unsaturated fatty acids are associated with weak intermolecular forces between triglyceride molecules and low melting temperatures. The 50% and 65% unsaturated contents are higher than those of butter and coconut oil but much lower than those of canola, olive, and soybean oils. Butter, however, melts quite readily at slightly higher than room temperature, so palm oil and chicken fat are probably liquids at room temperature.
b. Based solely on the percentages of unsaturated fatty acids (chicken fat > palm oil), you would predict that the palm oil would have the *higher* melting point. However, if the chicken fat contains more polyunsaturated fatty acids than the palm oil, the palm oil may have a *lower* melting temperature.
c. Based on the reasons outlined in part (a), the melting points of both oils should be below room temperature—perhaps between 10°C and 20°C.

Practice Problem 23.7 Solution

a. This structure contains a single five-membered ring plus two long-chain substituents. This is a prostaglandin.
b. This structure consists of a glycerol molecule bonded to *three* long-chain fatty acid molecules

via ester functional groups. This compound is a triglyceride. More specifically, the fatty acid chains contain carbon–carbon double bonds, so this an *unsaturated* triglyceride.

Practice Problem 23.8 Solution

According to Figure 23.19, the amino acid with the unreacted amine group (the N-terminal end) is tyrosine, the one with the unreacted carboxyl group (the C-terminal end) is leucine, and the one in between is serine, Tyr-Ser-Leu. Peptides are named from the N-terminal end to the C-terminal end, so this one is tyrosylserylleucine.

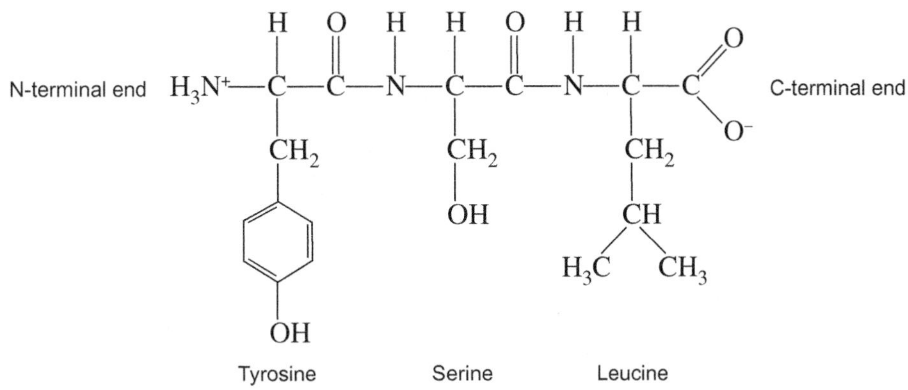

Practice Problem 23.9 Solution

a. A tripeptide consists of three amino acids connected by peptide bonds. The amino acid with the unreacted amino group (the N-terminal end) should be on the left, and the amino acid with the unreacted carboxyl group (the C-terminal end) should be on the right. Amino acids are connected by peptide bonds (Figure 23.19). Table 23.7 shows the structures of the 20 common amino acids. Draw the structure starting with an amino acid with an unreacted amino group on the left (the N-terminal end) and ending with an amino acid with an unreacted carboxyl group on the right (the C-terminal end).

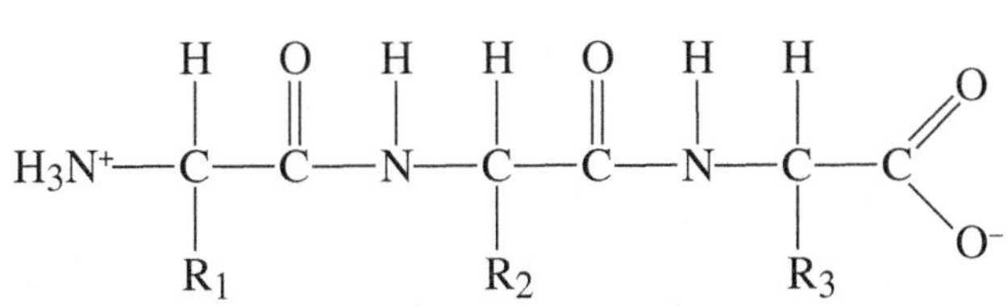

b. The structure of valylglutamylmethionine is the same as the generic peptide, except R_1 through R_3 must be replaced with the specific structures of the R groups for valine (N-terminal end), glutamic acid, and methionine (C-terminal end), respectively. Table 23.7 provides the structures of the three amino acids.

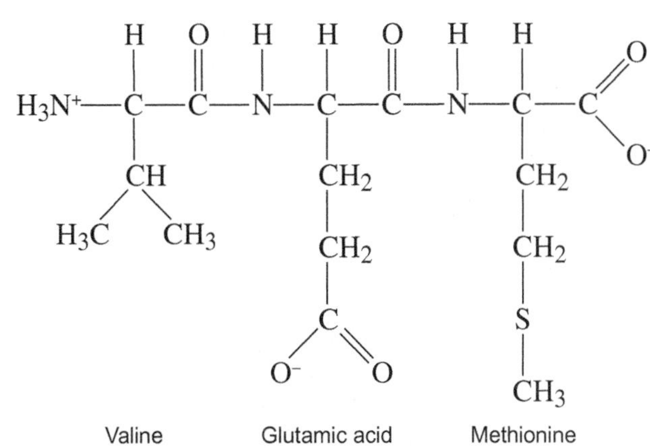

Practice Problem 23.10 Solution

In a lipid environment, proteins fold so as to place polar amino acids on the inside and nonpolar amino acids on the surface.

a. According to Table 23.7, the R group of lysine is $-(CH_2)_4NH_2$ (an amine group), which is charged at neutral pH. This charged, hydrophilic group means that lysine is likely to be folded into the interior of the protein.

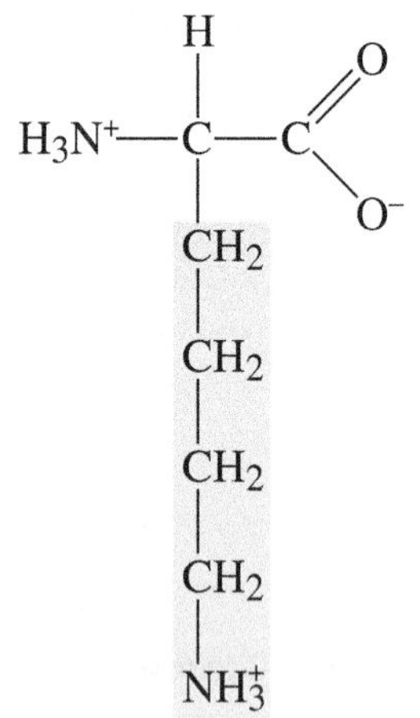

b. The R group of methionine is $—CH_2CH_2SCH_3$, which is nonpolar. Methionine is likely to be on the surface of a protein in a lipid environment.

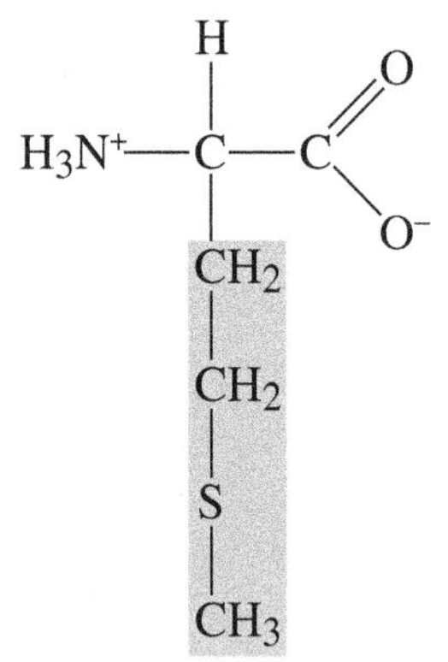

c. The R group of valine is $—CH(CH_3)_2$ (nonpolar). Valine is likely to be on the surface of the protein.

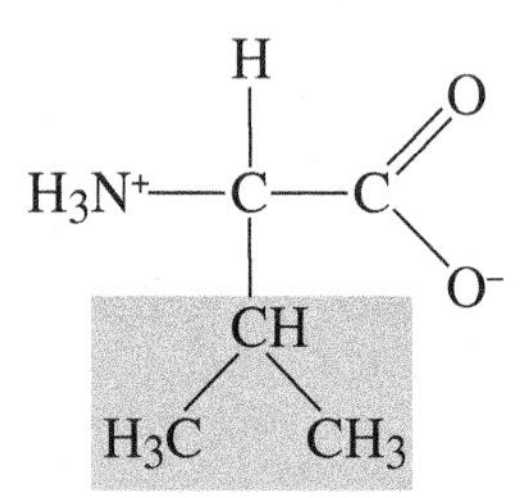

d. The R group of glutamine is $—CH_2CH_2CONH_2$ (an amide group), which is charged at neutral pH. With a polar R group, glutamine is likely to be folded into the interior of the protein.

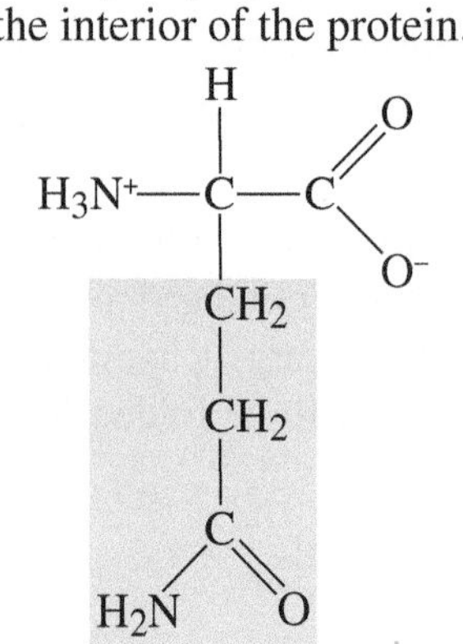

Practice Problem 23.11 Solution

The primary structure of oxytocin contains nine amino acids, Cys-Tyr-Ile-Glu-Asp-Cys-Pro-Leu-Gly with a disulfide bond between the two Cys R groups, forming a loop structure. If amino acid 6 was alanine, then there would be no disulfide bond. The resulting peptide would not contain the loop structure present in normal oxytocin, so it is unlikely to have the same physiological function.

Practice Problem 23.12 Solution

Starting with the 5′ end (top) of the image in Figure 23.31, the existing sequence is TACG. Adding G, C, and T to the 3′ end (bottom) gives the following sequence of seven nucleotides: 5′TACGGCT3′.

Practice Problem 23.13 Solution

Because RNA is synthesized in an antiparallel fashion, the DNA sequence will run from 5′ to 3′. G, C, A, and U in RNA pair with C, G, T, and A in DNA, respectively:

5′CAGGTTACCATT3′

Practice Problem 23.14 Solution

a. There are four possible codons for valine (GUU, GUC, GUA, and GUG), two for aspartic acid (GAU and GAC), two for isoleucine (AUU and AUC), and two for cysteine (UGU and UGC). Selecting the first codon option listed for each amino acid gives the following mRNA sequence:

5′GUUGAUAUUUGU3′

b. Remember that U in RNA base pairs with A in DNA, so the corresponding template DNA sequence is

3′CAACTATAAACA5′

Practice Problem 23.15 Solution

As pH decreases, $[H^+]$ increases, which drives the ionization equilibrium of each group toward its protonated form according to Le Châtelier's principle.

$$—NH_2 + H^+ \rightleftharpoons —NH_3^+$$
$$—COO^- + H^+ \rightleftharpoons —COOH$$

Thus, at very low pH, the amino acid will be in form (c).

Appendix

Appendix Outline

A.1 Periodic Table of the Elements

metal | metalloid | nonmetal

	1 1A	2 2A	3 3B	4 4B	5 5B	6 6B	7 7B	8	9 8B	10	11 1B	12 2B	13 3A	14 4A	15 5A	16 6A	17 7A	18 8A
1	1 H 1.008																	2 He 4.0026
2	3 Li 6.94	4 Be 9.0122											5 B 10.81	6 C 12.011	7 N 14.007	8 O 15.999	9 F 18.998	10 Ne 20.18
3	11 Na 22.99	12 Mg 24.305											13 Al 26.982	14 Si 28.085	15 P 30.974	16 S 32.06	17 Cl 35.45	18 Ar 39.948
4	19 K 39.098	20 Ca 40.078	21 Sc 44.956	22 Ti 47.867	23 V 50.942	24 Cr 51.996	25 Mn 54.938	26 Fe 55.845	27 Co 58.933	28 Ni 58.693	29 Cu 63.546	30 Zn 65.38	31 Ga 69.723	32 Ge 72.63	33 As 74.922	34 Se 78.971	35 Br 79.904	36 Kr 83.798
5	37 Rb 85.468	38 Sr 87.62	39 Y 88.906	40 Zr 91.224	41 Nb 92.906	42 Mo 95.95	43 Tc (98)	44 Ru 101.07	45 Rh 102.91	46 Pd 106.42	47 Ag 107.87	48 Cd 112.41	49 In 114.82	50 Sn 118.71	51 Sb 121.76	52 Te 127.6	53 I 126.9	54 Xe 131.29
6	55 Cs 132.91	56 Ba 137.33	57 La 138.91	72 Hf 178.49	73 Ta 180.95	74 W 183.84	75 Re 186.21	76 Os 190.23	77 Ir 192.22	78 Pt 195.08	79 Au 196.97	80 Hg 200.59	81 Tl 204.38	82 Pb 207.2	83 Bi 208.98	84 Po (209)	85 At (210)	86 Rn (222)
7	87 Fr (223)	88 Ra (226)	89 Ac (227)	104 Rf (267)	105 Db (268)	106 Sg (271)	107 Bh (270)	108 Hs (269)	109 Mt (278)	110 Ds (281)	111 Rg (282)	112 Cn (285)	113 Nh (286)	114 Fl (289)	115 Mc (289)	116 Lv (293)	117 Ts (294)	118 Og (294)

Lanthanoids	58 Ce 140.12	59 Pr 140.91	60 Nd 144.24	61 Pm (145)	62 Sm 150.36	63 Eu 151.96	64 Gd 157.25	65 Tb 158.93	66 Dy 162.5	67 Ho 164.93	68 Er 167.26	69 Tm 168.93	70 Yb 173.05	71 Lu 174.97
Actinoids	90 Th 232.04	91 Pa 231.04	92 U 238.03	93 Np (237)	94 Pu (244)	95 Am (243)	96 Cm (247)	97 Bk (247)	98 Cf (251)	99 Es (252)	100 Fm (257)	101 Md (258)	102 No (259)	103 Lr (266)

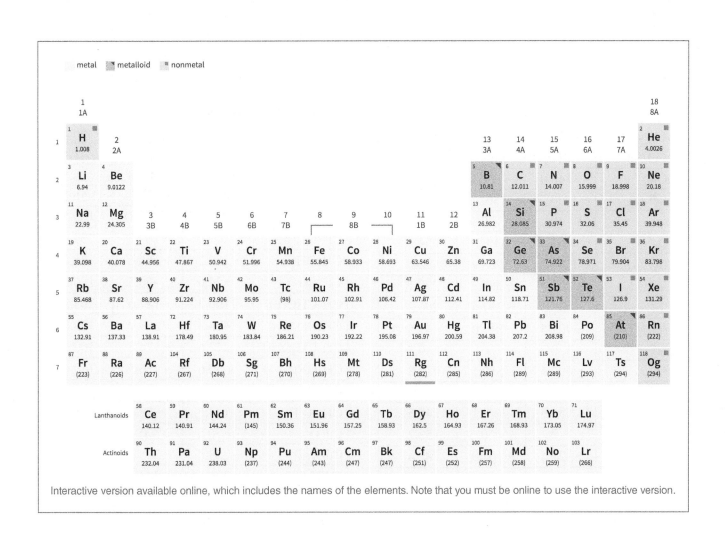

Interactive version available online, which includes the names of the elements. Note that you must be online to use the interactive version.

A.2 Thermodynamic Properties at 298 K

Substance	ΔH_f° kJ/mol	ΔG_f° kJ/mol	S° J/mol · K
Ag(s)	0	0	42.6
$Ag^+(aq)$	105.8	77.107	73.4
$Ag_2O(s)$	−31.1	−11.2	121.3
$Ag_2S(s)$	−32.6	−40.7	144.0
AgBr(s)	−100.4	−96.9	107.1
AgCl(s)	−127.0	−109.8	96.3
AgI(s)	−61.8	−66.2	115.5
$AgNO_3(s)$	−124.4	−33.4	140.9
Al(s)	0	0	28.3
$Al_2O_3(s)$	−1675.7	−1582.3	50.9
$AlCl_3(s)$	−704.2	−628.8	109.3
Ar(g)	0	0	154.843
As(s)	0	0	35.1
$As_2O_5(s)$	−924.9	−782.3	105.4
$AsCl_3(l)$	−305.0	−259.4	216.3
Au(s)	0	0	47.4
Ba(s)	0	0	62.5
$BaCl_2(s)$	−855.0	−806.7	123.7
$BaCO_3(s)$	−1213.0	−1134.4	112.1
BaO(s)	−548.0	−520.3	72.1
$BaSO_4(s)$	−1473.2	−1362.2	132.2
B(s)	0	0	5.9
$B_2O_3(s)$	−1273.5	−1194.3	54.0
$H_3BO_3(s)$	−1094.3	−968.9	90.0
$BCl_3(g)$	−403.8	−388.7	290.1
$BCl_3(l)$	−427.2	−387.4	206.3
$Be(OH)_2(s)$	−902.5	−815.0	45.5
Be(s)	0	0	9.5
BeO(s)	−609.4	−580.1	13.8
Br(g)	111.9	82.4	175.0
$Br_2(g)$	30.9	3.1	245.5
$Br_2(l)$	0	0	152.2
$Br^-(aq)$	−121.4	−104.0	82.4
$BrO^-(aq)$	−94.1	−33.4	42
$BrF_3(g)$	−255.6	−229.4	292.5
C(diamond)	1.9	2.9	2.4
C(g)	716.7	671.3	158.1

Substance	ΔH_f° kJ/mol	ΔG_f° kJ/mol	S° J/mol · K
C(graphite)	0	0	5.7
$CCl_4(l)$	−139	−68.6	214.4
$CH_4(g)$	−74.6	−50.5	186.3
$C_2H_2(g)$	227.4	209.9	200.9
$C_2H_4(g)$	52.4	68.4	219.3
$C_2H_5OH(g)$	−234.8	−167.9	281.6
$C_2H_5OH(l)$	−277.6	−174.8	160.7
$C_2H_6(g)$	−84.0	−32.0	229.2
$C_3H_6(g)$ (propene)	20.0	74.62	226.9
$C_3H_8(g)$	−103.8	−23.4	270.3
$C_6H_6(l)$	49.1	124.5	173.4
Ca(g)	177.8	144	154.9
$Ca(OH)_2(s)$	−985.2	−897.5	83.4
Ca(s)	0	0	41.6
$Ca^{2+}(aq)$	−543.0	−553.6	−56.2
$Ca_3(PO_4)_2(s)$	−4120.8	−3884.7	236.0
$CaC_2(s)$	−59.8	−64.9	70.0
$CaCl_2(s)$	−795.4	−748.8	108.4
$CaCO_3(s)$	−1207.6	−1129.1	91.7
$CaF_2(s)$	−1228.0	−1175.6	68.5
$CaH_2(s)$	−181.5	−142.5	41.4
CaO(s)	−634.9	−603.3	38.1
CaS(s)	−482.4	−477.4	56.5
$CaSO_4(s)$	−1434.5	−1322.0	106.5
$CH_3OH(g)$	−201.0	−162.3	239.9
$CH_3OH(l)$	−239.2	−166.6	126.8
$CH_4(g)$	−74.6	−50.5	186.3
$CH_3CHO(g)$	−166.2	−127.6	263.8
$CH_3CO_2H(l)$	−484.3	−389.9	159.8
$CH_3CH_2OH(l)$	−277.6	−174.8	160.7
$CH_3CN(l)$	40.6	86.5	149.6
$CHCl_3(g)$	−102.7	6.0	295.7
$CHCl_3(l)$	−134.1	−73.7	201.7
Cd(s)	0	0	51.8
CdO(s)	−258.4	−228.7	54.8
$CdCl_2(s)$	−391.5	−343.9	115.3
$Cl_2(g)$	0	0	223.1
Cl(g)	121.3	105.3	165.2
$Cl^-(aq)$	−167.1	−131.0	56.60

Substance	ΔH_f° kJ/mol	ΔG_f° kJ/mol	S° J/mol · K
$ClO^-(aq)$	−107.1	−36.8	42
$ClO_2^-(aq)$	−67	17	101
$ClO_3^-(aq)$	−104	−3	162
$ClO_4^-(aq)$	−128.1	−8.52	184.0
$ClO(g)$	101.8	98.1	226.6
$ClO_2(g)$	102.5	120.5	256.8
$CO(g)$	−110.5	−137.2	197.7
$CO_2(g)$	−393.5	−394.4	213.8
$COCl_2(g)$	−219.1	−204.9	283.5
$Cr(s)$	0	0	23.8
$Cr_2O_3(s)$	−1139.7	−1058.1	81.2
$CrCl_3(s)$	−556.5	−486.1	123.1
$Co(s)$	0	0	30.0
$CoO(s)$	−237.9	−214.2	53.0
$CoCl_2(s)$	−312.5	−269.8	109.2
$Cs(s)$	0	0	85.2
$CS_2(g)$	116.7	67.1	237.8
$CS_2(l)$	89.0	64.6	151.3
$CsCl(s)$	−443.0	−414.5	101.2
$Cu(s)$	0	0	33.2
$CuO(s)$	−157.3	−129.7	42.6
$CuS(s)$	−53.1	−53.6	66.5
$CuCl_2(s)$	−220.1	−175.7	108.1
$CuCl(s)$	−137.2	−119.9	86.2
$CuBr(s)$	−104.6	−100.8	96.1
$CuI(s)$	−67.8	−69.5	96.7
$CuSO_4(s)$	−771.4	−662.2	109.2
$F(g)$	79.4	62.3	158.8
$F_2(g)$	0	0	202.8
$F^-(g)$	−335.4	−278.79	−13.8
$Fe(s)$	0	0	27.3
$Fe_2O_3(s)$	−824.2	−742.2	87.4
$FeO(s)$	−272.0	−251.4	60.8
$Fe_3O_4(s)$	−1118.4	−1015.4	146.4
$Fe(OH)_3(s)$	−823.0	−696.5	106.7
$FeCl_2(s)$	−341.8	−302.3	118.0
$FeCl_3(s)$	−399.5	−334.0	142
$FeSO_4(s)$	−928.4	−820.8	107.5
$FeS(s)$	−100.0	−100.4	60.3
$FeS_2(s)$	−178.2	−166.9	52.9

Substance	ΔH_f° kJ/mol	ΔG_f° kJ/mol	S° J/mol · K
$Ga(s)$	0	0	40.8
$Ga_2O_3(s)$	−1089.1	−998.3	85.0
$Ge(s)$	0	0	31.1
$GeO(s)$	−261.9	−237.2	50.0
$GeCl_4(g)$	−495.8	−457.3	347.7
$GeO_2(s)$	−580.0	−521.4	39.7
$H^+(aq)$	0	0	0
$H_2(g)$	0	0	130.7
$H_2O(g)$	−241.8	−228.6	188.8
$H_2O(l)$	−285.8	−237.1	70.0
$H_3O^+(aq)$	−285.83	−237.1	69.95
$H_2O_2(l)$	−187.8	−120.4	109.6
$H_2S(g)$	−20.6	−33.4	205.8
$H_2SO_4(l)$	−814	−690.0	156.9
$H_3PO_4(l)$	−1271.7	−1123.6	150.8
$H_3PO_4(aq)$	−1288.34	−1142.54	158.2
$HBr(g)$	−36.3	−53.4	198.7
$HCl(g)$	−92.3	−95.3	186.9
$HCN(g)$	135.1	124.7	201.8
$HF(g)$	−273.3	−275.4	173.8
$HNO_3(l)$	−174.1	−80.7	155.6
$HNO_3(g)$	−133.9	−73.5	266.9
$H_2Se(g)$	29.7	15.9	219.0
$Hg(l)$	0	0	75.9
$Hg(g)$	61.4	31.8	175.0
$HgO(s)$	−90.8	−58.5	70.3
$HgS(s)$	−58.2	−50.6	82.4
$HgCl_2(s)$	−224.3	−178.6	146.0
$Hg_2Cl_2(s)$	−265.4	−210.7	191.6
$HI(g)$	26.5	1.7	206.6
$He(g)$	0	0	126.153
$I_2(g)$	62.4	19.3	260.7
$I_2(s)$	0	0	116.1
$I^-(aq)$	−56.78	−51.57	106.5
$K(s)$	0	0	64.7
$K^+(aq)$	−252.1	−283.7	101.2
$KO_2(s)$	−284.9	−239.4	116.7
$KOH(s)$	−424.6	−378.9	78.9
$KBr(s)$	−393.8	−380.7	95.9

(Continued)

Substance	ΔH_f° kJ/mol	ΔG_f° kJ/mol	S° J/mol · K
KCl(s)	−436.5	−408.5	82.6
$KClO_3$(s)	−397.7	−296.3	143.1
KF(s)	−567.3	−537.8	66.6
KI(s)	−327.9	−324.9	106.3
Kr(g)	0	0	164.085
Li(s)	0	0	29.1
Li^+(aq)	−278.47	−293.31	12.2
Li_2O(s)	−597.9	−561.2	37.6
LiOH(s)	−484.9	−439.0	42.8
LiCl(s)	−408.6	−384.4	59.3
Mg(s)	0	0	32.7
Mg^{2+}(aq)	−467.0	−454.8	−137
$Mg(OH)_2$(s)	−924.5	−833.5	63.2
$MgCl_2$(s)	−641.3	−591.8	89.6
MgF_2(s)	−1124.2	−1071.1	57.2
$MgCO_3$(s)	−1095.8	−1012.1	65.7
MgO(s)	−601.6	−569.3	27.0
$MgSO_4$(s)	−1284.9	−1170.6	91.6
Mn(s)	0	0	32.0
MnO(s)	−385.2	−362.9	59.7
MnO_2(s)	−520.0	−465.1	53.1
$MnCl_2$(s)	−481.3	−440.5	118.2
$MnCO_3$(s)	−894.1	−816.7	85.8
$MnSO_4$(s)	−1065.25	−957.36	112.1
N_2(g)	0	0	191.6
N_2H_4(l)	50.6	149.3	121.2
N_2O(g)	81.6	103.7	220.0
N_2O_4(g)	11.1	99.8	304.4
N_2O_5(g)	13.3	117.1	355.7
NH_3(g)	−45.9	−16.4	192.8
NH_3(aq)	−80.29	−26.50	111.3
NH_4^+(aq)	−133.3	−79.31	111.2
NH_4Cl(s)	−314.4	−202.9	94.6
NH_4NO_3(s)	−365.6	−183.9	151.1
$(NH_2)_2CO$(s)	−333.1	−198	105
Na(s)	0	0	51.3
Na^+(aq)	−240.3	−261.905	58.5
Na_2CO_3(s)	−1130.7	−1044.4	135.0
NaCl(s)	−411.2	−384.1	72.1
NaF(s)	−576.6	−546.3	51.1

Substance	ΔH_f° kJ/mol	ΔG_f° kJ/mol	S° J/mol · K
NaBr(s)	−361.1	−349.0	86.8
NaI(s)	−287.8	−286.1	98.5
$NaNO_3$(s)	−467.9	−367.0	116.5
NaOH(s)	−425.8	−379.7	64.4
Na_2O(s)	−414.2	−375.5	75.1
Ne(g)	0	0	146.328
Ni(s)	0	0	29.9
NiO(s)	−239.7	−211.7	37.99
$NiCl_2$(s)	−305.3	−259.0	97.7
NO(g)	91.3	87.6	210.8
NO_2(g)	33.2	51.3	240.1
O(g)	249.2	231.7	161.1
O_2(g)	0	0	205.2
O_3(g)	142.7	163.2	238.9
OH^-(aq)	−230.0	−157.244	−10.9
OPb(s) (massicot)	−217.3	−187.9	68.7
O_2Te(s)	−322.6	−270.3	79.5
OTl_2(s)	−178.7	−147.3	126.0
P(s, white)	0	0	41.1
P(s, red)	−17.6	−12.1	22.8
P_4(g)	58.9	24.4	280.0
PH_3(g)	5.4	13.4	210.2
P_4O_{10}(s)	−2984.0	−2697.7	228.86
PCl_3(g)	−287.0	−267.8	311.8
PCl_5(g)	−374.9	−305.0	364.6
Pb(s)	0	0	64.8
$PbCl_2$(s)	−359.4	−314.1	136.0
PbO(s)	−217.3	−187.9	68.7
PbO_2(s)	−277.4	−217.3	68.6
PbS(s)	−100.4	−98.7	91.2
Sb(s)	0	0	45.7
Sb_4O_6(s)	−1417.1	−1253.0	246.0
Se(s)	0	0	42.7
Si(s)	0	0	18.8
SiH_4(g)	34.3	56.9	204.6
SiO_2(s)	−910.7	−856.3	41.5
$SiCl_4$(l)	−687.0	−619.8	239.7
SiC(s)	−65.3	−62.8	16.6
Sn(s, white)	0	0	51.2
Sn(s, gray)	−2.1	0.13	44.1

Substance	ΔH_f° kJ/mol	ΔG_f° kJ/mol	S° J/mol · K
$SnO(s)$	−280.7	−251.9	57.2
$SnO_2(s)$	−577.6	−515.8	49.0
$SnCl_4(s)$	−511.3	−440.1	258.6
$Sr(s)$	0	0	55.0
$SrO(s)$	−592.0	−561.9	54.4
$SrCl_2(s)$	−828.9	−781.1	114.9
$S_8(s)$	0	0	31.80
$S_8(g)$	102.30	49.63	430.23
$SO_2(g)$	−296.8	−300.1	248.2
$SO_3(g)$	−395.7	−371.1	256.8
$SO_4^{2-}(aq)$	−909.3	−744.53	18.5
$SF_6(g)$	−1220.5	−1116.5	291.5
$Te(s)$	0	0	49.7
$TeO_2(s)$	−322.6	−270.3	79.5
$Ti(s)$	0	0	30.7
$TiCl_4(l)$	−804.2	−737.2	252.3
$TiCl_4(g)$	−763.2	−726.3	353.2
$TiO_2(s)$	−944.0	−888.8	50.6
$Tl(s)$	0	0	64.2
$U(s)$	0	0	50.2
$UO_2(s)$	−1085.0	−1031.8	77.0
$UF_6(g)$	−2147.4	−2063.7	377.9
$Xe(g)$	0	0	169.685
$XeF_4(s)$	−261.5	−138	316
$Zn(s)$	0	0	41.63
$ZnO(s)$	−350.5	−320.5	43.7
$ZnCl_2(s)$	−415.1	−369.4	111.5
$ZnS(s)$	−206.0	−201.3	57.7

Reference: *CRC Handbook of Chemistry and Physics*, 2007

A.3 Ionization Constants for Acids and Bases

ACIDS

Acid	Formula	Ionization Constant K_a
Acetic	CH_3COOH	1.8×10^{-5}
Arsenic	H_3AsO_4	5.5×10^{-3}
Ascorbic	$H_2C_6H_6O_6$	$K_{a1} = 8.0 \times 10^{-5}$ > $K_{a2} = 1.6 \times 10^{-12}$
Benzoic	C_6H_5COOH	6.3×10^{-5}
Boric	H_3BO_3	5.4×10^{-10}
Butanoic	C_3H_7COOH	1.5×10^{-5}
Carbonic	H_2CO_3	$K_{a1} = 4.5 \times 10^{-7}$ $K_{a2} = 4.7 \times 10^{-11}$
Chloroacetic	$ClCH_2COOH$	1.4×10^{-3}
Chlorous	$HClO_2$	1.1×10^{-2}
Chromic	H_2CrO_4	$K_{a1} = 1.8 \times 10^{-1}$ $K_{a2} = 3.2 \times 10^{-7}$
Citric	$H_3C_6H_5O_7$	$K_{a1} = 7.4 \times 10^{-4}$ $K_{a2} = 1.7 \times 10^{-5}$
Cyanic	$HCNO$	3.5×10^{-4}
Formic	$HCOOH$	1.8×10^{-4}
Hydrazoic	HN_3	2.5×10^{-5}
Hydrocyanic	HCN	6.2×10^{-10}
Hydrofluoric	HF	6.3×10^{-4}
Hydrogen peroxide	H_2O_2	2.4×10^{-12}
Hydrosulfuric	H_2S	$K_{a1} = 8.9 \times 10^{-8}$ $K_{a2} = 1.0 \times 10^{-19}$
Hypobromous	$HBrO$	2.8×10^{-9}
Hypochlorous	$HClO$	4.0×10^{-8}
Hypoiodous	HIO	3.2×10^{-11}
Iodic	HIO_3	1.7×10^{-1}
Nitrous	HNO_2	5.6×10^{-4}
Oxalic	$C_2H_2O_4$	$K_{a1} = 5.6 \times 10^{-2}$ $K_{a2} = 1.5 \times 10^{-4}$
Paraperiodic	H_5IO_6	2.8×10^{-2}
Pentanoic	C_4H_9COOH	1.5×10^{-5}
Periodic	HIO_4	7.3×10^{-2}
Phenol	HC_6H_5O	1.3×10^{-10}
Phosphoric	H_3PO_4	$K_{a1} = 6.9 \times 10^{-3}$ $K_{a2} = 6.2 \times 10^{-8}$ $K_{a3} = 4.8 \times 10^{-13}$

(Continued)

Acid	Formula	Ionization Constant K_a
Phosphorous	H_3PO_3	$K_{a1} = 5.0 \times 10^{-2}$ $K_{a2} = 2.0 \times 10^{-7}$
Propanoic	C_2H_5COOH	1.3×10^{-5}
Sulfuric	H_2SO_4	K_{a1} = very large $K_{a2} = 1.2 \times 10^{-2}$
Sulfurous	H_2SO_3	$K_{a1} = 1.4 \times 10^{-2}$ $K_{a2} = 6.3 \times 10^{-8}$
Trichloroacetic	Cl_3CCOOH	2.2×10^{-1}

BASES

Base	Formula	Ionization Constant K_b
Ammonia	NH_3	1.8×10^{-5}
Methylamine	CH_3NH_2	5.0×10^{-4}
Dimethylamine	$(CH_3)_2NH$	5.4×10^{-4}
Diethylamine	$(C_2H_5)_2NH$	6.9×10^{-4}
Trimethylamine	$(CH_3)_3N$	6.3×10^{-5}
Triethylamine	$(C_2H_5)_3N$	5.6×10^{-4}
Ethylamine	$CH_3CH_2NH_2$	6.3×10^{-4}
Ethylenediamine	$(CH_2NH_2)_2$	8.3×10^{-5}
Pyridine	C_5H_5N	1.7×10^{-9}
Hydroxylamine	NH_2OH	8.7×10^{-9}
Aniline	$C_6H_5NH_2$	7.4×10^{-10}
Hydrazine	H_2NNH_2	1.3×10^{-6}

Reference: *CRC Handbook of Chemistry and Physics*, 2007

A.4 Solubility–Product Constants at 298 K

Compound	Formula	K_{sp}
Aluminum hydroxide	$Al(OH)_3$	4.6×10^{-33}
Aluminum phosphate	$AlPO_4$	9.84×10^{-21}
Antimony sulfide	Sb_2S_3	1.6×10^{-93}
Arsenic sulfide	As_2S_3	1×10^{-16}
Barium bromate	$Ba(BrO_3)_2$	2.43×10^{-4}
Barium carbonate	$BaCO_3$	2.58×10^{-9}
Barium chromate	$BaCrO_4$	1.17×10^{-10}
Barium fluoride	BaF_2	1.84×10^{-7}
Barium hydroxide octahydrate	$Ba(OH)_2 \cdot 8H_2O$	2.55×10^{-4}
Barium iodate	$Ba(IO_3)_2$	4.01×10^{-9}
Barium iodate monohydrate	$Ba(IO_3)_2 \cdot H_2O$	1.67×10^{-9}
Barium molybdate	$BaMoO_4$	3.54×10^{-8}
Barium nitrate	$Ba(NO_3)_2$	4.64×10^{-3}
Barium phosphate	$Ba_3(PO_4)_2$	3.40×10^{-23}
Barium selenate	$BaSeO_4$	3.40×10^{-8}
Barium sulfate	$BaSO_4$	1.08×10^{-10}
Barium sulfite	$BaSO_3$	5.0×10^{-10}
Beryllium hydroxide	$Be(OH)_2$	6.92×10^{-22}
Bismuth arsenate	$BiAsO_4$	4.43×10^{-10}
Bismuth iodide	BiI	7.71×10^{-19}
Cadmium arsenate	$Cd_3(AsO_4)_2$	2.2×10^{-33}
Cadmium carbonate	$CdCO_3$	1.0×10^{-12}
Cadmium fluoride	CdF_2	6.44×10^{-3}
Cadmium hydroxide	$Cd(OH)_2$	7.2×10^{-15}
Cadmium iodate	$Cd(IO_3)_2$	2.5×10^{-8}
Cadmium oxalate trihydrate	$CdC_2O_4 \cdot 3H_2O$	1.42×10^{-8}
Cadmium phosphate	$Cd_3(PO_4)_2$	2.53×10^{-33}
Cadmium sulfide	CdS	1×10^{-27}
Caesium perchlorate	$CsClO_4$	3.95×10^{-3}
Caesium periodate	$CsIO_4$	5.16×10^{-6}
Calcium carbonate (calcite)	$CaCO_3$	3.36×10^{-9}
Calcium carbonate (aragonite)	$CaCO_3$	6.0×10^{-9}
Calcium fluoride	CaF_2	3.45×10^{-11}
Calcium hydroxide	$Ca(OH)_2$	5.02×10^{-6}
Calcium iodate	$Ca(IO_3)_2$	6.47×10^{-6}
Calcium iodate hexahydrate	$Ca(IO_3)_2 \cdot 6H_2O$	7.10×10^{-7}
Calcium molybdate	$CaMoO$	1.46×10^{-8}

Compound	Formula	K_{sp}
Calcium oxalate monohydrate	$CaC_2O_4 \cdot H_2O$	2.32×10^{-9}
Calcium phosphate	$Ca_3(PO_4)_2$	2.07×10^{-33}
Calcium sulfate	$CaSO_4$	4.93×10^{-5}
Calcium sulfate dihydrate	$CaSO_4 \cdot 2H_2O$	3.14×10^{-5}
Calcium sulfate hemihydrate	$CaSO_4 \cdot 0.5H_2O$	3.1×10^{-7}
Chromium(III) hydroxide	$Cr(OH)_3$	3×10^{-29}
Cobalt(II) arsenate	$Co_3(AsO_4)_2$	6.80×10^{-29}
Cobalt(II) carbonate	$CoCO_3$	1.4×10^{-13}
Cobalt(II) hydroxide (blue)	$Co(OH)_2$	5.92×10^{-15}
Cobalt(III) hydroxide	$Co(OH)_3$	1.6×10^{-44}
Cobalt(II) iodate dihydrate	$Co(IO_3)_2 \cdot 2H_2O$	1.21×10^{-2}
Cobalt(II) phosphate	$Co_3(PO_4)_2$	2.05×10^{-35}
Cobalt(II) sulfide	CoS	4.0×10^{-21}
Copper(I) bromide	CuBr	6.27×10^{-9}
Copper(II) carbonate	$CuCO_3$	1.4×10^{-10}
Copper(I) chloride	CuCl	1.72×10^{-7}
Copper(I) cyanide	CuCN	3.47×10^{-20}
Copper(I) hydroxide	CuOH	2×10^{-15}
Copper(I) iodide	CuI	1.27×10^{-12}
Copper(I) thiocyanate	CuSCN	1.77×10^{-13}
Copper(II) arsenate	$Cu_3(AsO_4)_2$	7.95×10^{-36}
Copper(II) hydroxide	$Cu(OH)_2$	1.1×10^{-15}
Copper(II) iodate monohydrate	$Cu(IO_3)_2 \cdot H_2O$	6.94×10^{-8}
Copper(II) oxalate	CuC_2O_4	4.43×10^{-10}
Copper(II) phosphate	$Cu_3(PO_4)_2$	1.40×10^{-37}
Copper(II) sulfide	CuS	6.3×10^{-26}
Copper(I) sulfide	Cu_2S	2.5×10^{-48}
Europium(III) hydroxide	$Eu(OH)_3$	9.38×10^{-27}

Compound	Formula	K_{sp}
Gallium(III) hydroxide	$Ga(OH)_3$	7.28×10^{-36}
Iron(II) carbonate	$FeCO_3$	3.13×10^{-11}
Iron(II) fluoride	FeF_2	2.36×10^{-6}
Iron(II) hydroxide	$Fe(OH)_2$	4.87×10^{-17}
Iron(II) sulfide	FeS	1.6×10^{-19}
Iron(III) hydroxide	$Fe(OH)_3$	2.79×10^{-39}
Iron(III) phosphate dihydrate	$FePO_4 \cdot 2H_2O$	9.91×10^{-16}
Lanthanum iodate	$La(IO_3)_3$	7.50×10^{-12}
Lead(II) bromide	$PbBr_2$	6.60×10^{-6}
Lead(II) carbonate	$PbCO_3$	7.40×10^{-14}
Lead(II) chloride	$PbCl_2$	1.70×10^{-5}
Lead(II) chromate	$PbCrO_4$	3×10^{-13}
Lead(II) fluoride	PbF_2	3.3×10^{-8}
Lead(II) hydroxide	$Pb(OH)_2$	1.43×10^{-20}
Lead(II) iodate	$Pb(IO_3)_2$	3.69×10^{-13}
Lead(II) iodide	PbI_2	9.8×10^{-9}
Lead(II) oxalate	PbC_2O_4	8.5×10^{-9}
Lead(II) selenate	$PbSeO_4$	1.37×10^{-7}
Lead(II) sulfate	$PbSO_4$	2.53×10^{-8}
Lead(II) sulfide	PbS	8.9×10^{-29}
Lithium carbonate	Li_2CO_3	8.15×10^{-4}
Lithium fluoride	LiF	1.84×10^{-3}
Lithium phosphate	Li_3PO_4	2.37×10^{-11}
Magnesium ammonium phosphate	$MgNH_4PO_4$	3×10^{-13}
Magnesium carbonate	$MgCO_3$	6.82×10^{-6}
Magnesium carbonate trihydrate	$MgCO_3 \cdot 3H_2O$	2.38×10^{-6}
Magnesium carbonate pentahydrate	$MgCO_3 \cdot 5H_2O$	3.79×10^{-6}
Magnesium fluoride	MgF_2	5.16×10^{-11}
Magnesium hydroxide	$Mg(OH)_2$	5.61×10^{-12}

(Continued)

Compound	Formula	K_{sp}
Magnesium oxalate dihydrate	$MgC_2O_4 \cdot 2H_2O$	4.83×10^{-6}
Magnesium phosphate	$Mg_3(PO_4)_2$	1.04×10^{-24}
Manganese(II) carbonate	$MnCO_3$	2.24×10^{-11}
Manganese(II) iodate	$Mn(IO_3)_2$	4.37×10^{-7}
Manganese(II) hydroxide	$Mn(OH)_2$	2×10^{-13}
Manganese(II) oxalate dihydrate	$MnC_2O_4 \cdot 2H_2O$	1.70×10^{-7}
Manganese(II) sulfide	MnS	4.6×10^{-14}
Mercury(I) bromide	Hg_2Br_2	6.40×10^{-23}
Mercury(I) carbonate	Hg_2CO_3	3.6×10^{-17}
Mercury(I) chloride	Hg_2Cl_2	1.43×10^{-18}
Mercury(I) fluoride	Hg_2F_2	3.10×10^{-6}
Mercury(I) iodide	Hg_2I_2	5.2×10^{-29}
Mercury(I) oxalate	$Hg_2C_2O_4$	1.75×10^{-13}
Mercury(I) sulfate	Hg_2SO_4	6.5×10^{-7}
Mercury(I) thiocyanate	$Hg_2(SCN)_2$	3.2×10^{-20}
Mercury(II) bromide	$HgBr_2$	6.2×10^{-20}
Mercury(II) hydroxide	$Hg(OH)_2$	3.6×10^{-26}
Mercury(II) iodide	HgI_2	2.9×10^{-29}
Mercury(II) sulfide	HgS	4×10^{-53}
Mercury(I) sulfide	Hg_2S	1.0×10^{-47}
Neodymium carbonate	$Nd_2(CO_3)_3$	1.08×10^{-33}
Nickel(II) carbonate	$NiCO_3$	1.42×10^{-7}
Nickel(II) hydroxide	$Ni(OH)_2$	5.48×10^{-16}
Nickel(II) iodate	$Ni(IO_3)_2$	4.71×10^{-5}

Compound	Formula	K_{sp}
Nickel(II) phosphate	$Ni_3(PO_4)_2$	4.74×10^{-32}
Nickel(II) sulfide	NiS	1.1×10^{-21}
Palladium(II) thiocyanate	$Pd(SCN)_2$	4.39×10^{-23}
Potassium hexachloroplatinate	K_2PtCl_6	7.48×10^{-6}
Potassium perchlorate	$KClO_4$	1.05×10^{-2}
Potassium periodate	KIO_4	3.71×10^{-4}
Praseodymium hydroxide	$Pr(OH)_3$	3.39×10^{-24}
Radium iodate	$Ra(IO_3)_2$	1.16×10^{-9}
Radium sulfate	$RaSO_4$	3.66×10^{-11}
Rubidium perchlorate	$RbClO_4$	3.00×10^{-3}
Scandium fluoride	ScF_3	5.81×10^{-24}
Scandium hydroxide	$Sc(OH)_3$	2.22×10^{-31}
Silver(I) acetate	$AgCH_3COO$	1.94×10^{-3}
Silver(I) arsenate	Ag_3AsO_4	1.03×10^{-22}
Silver(I) bromate	$AgBrO_3$	5.38×10^{-5}
Silver(I) bromide	$AgBr$	5.35×10^{-13}
Silver(I) carbonate	Ag_2CO_3	8.46×10^{-12}
Silver(I) chloride	$AgCl$	1.77×10^{-10}
Silver(I) chromate	Ag_2CrO_4	1.12×10^{-12}
Silver(I) cobalticyanide	$Ag_3Co(CN)_6$	3.9×10^{-26}
Silver(I) cyanide	$AgCN$	5.97×10^{-17}
Silver(I) iodate	$AgIO_3$	3.17×10^{-8}
Silver(I) iodide	AgI	8.52×10^{-17}
Silver(I) oxalate	$Ag_2C_2O_4$	5.40×10^{-12}
Silver(I) phosphate	Ag_3PO_4	8.89×10^{-17}
Silver(I) sulfate	Ag_2SO_4	1.20×10^{-5}
Silver(I) sulfite	Ag_2SO_3	1.50×10^{-14}
Silver(I) sulfide	Ag_2S	3.3×10^{-50}
Silver(I) thiocyanate	$AgSCN$	1.03×10^{-12}

Compound	Formula	K_{sp}
Strontium arsenate	$Sr_3(AsO_4)_2$	4.29×10^{-19}
Strontium carbonate	$SrCO_3$	5.60×10^{-10}
Strontium fluoride	SrF_2	4.33×10^{-9}
Strontium iodate	$Sr(IO_3)_2$	1.14×10^{-7}
Strontium iodate monohydrate	$Sr(IO_3)_2 \cdot H_2O$	3.77×10^{-7}
Strontium iodate hexahydrate	$Sr(IO_3)_2 \cdot 6H_2O$	4.55×10^{-7}
Strontium oxalate	SrC_2O_4	5×10^{-8}
Strontium phosphate	$Sr_3(PO_4)_2$	1×10^{-31}
Strontium sulfate	$SrSO_4$	3.44×10^{-7}
Thallium(I) bromate	$TlBrO_3$	1.10×10^{-4}
Thallium(I) bromide	$TlBr$	3.71×10^{-6}
Thallium(I) chloride	$TlCl$	1.86×10^{-4}
Thallium(I) chromate	Tl_2CrO_4	8.67×10^{-13}
Thallium(I) hydroxide	$Tl(OH)_3$	1.68×10^{-44}
Thallium(I) iodate	$TlIO_3$	3.12×10^{-6}
Thallium(I) iodide	TlI	5.54×10^{-8}
Thallium(I) thiocyanate	$TlSCN$	1.57×10^{-4}
Thallium(I) sulfide	Tl_2S	6×10^{-22}
Tin(II) hydroxide	$Sn(OH)_2$	5.45×10^{-27}
Tin(II) sulfide	SnS	3.2×10^{-28}
Tin(IV) sulfide	SnS_2	1×10^{-70}
Yttrium carbonate	$Y_2(CO_3)_3$	1.03×10^{-31}
Yttrium fluoride	YF_3	8.62×10^{-21}
Yttrium hydroxide	$Y(OH)_3$	1.00×10^{-22}
Yttrium iodate	$Y(IO_3)_3$	1.12×10^{-10}
Zinc arsenate	$Zn_3(AsO_4)_2$	2.8×10^{-28}
Zinc carbonate	$ZnCO_3$	1.46×10^{-10}
Zinc carbonate monohydrate	$ZnCO_3 \cdot H_2O$	5.42×10^{-11}
Zinc fluoride	ZnF	3.04×10^{-2}
Zinc hydroxide	$Zn(OH)_2$	3×10^{-17}
Zinc iodate dihydrate	$Zn(IO_3)_2 \cdot 2H_2O$	4.1×10^{-6}
Zinc oxalate dihydrate	$ZnC_2O_4 \cdot 2H_2O$	1.38×10^{-9}
Zinc selenide	$ZnSe$	3.6×10^{-26}
Zinc selenite monohydrate	$ZnSe \cdot H_2O$	1.59×10^{-7}
Zinc sulfide (alpha)	ZnS	2×10^{-25}
Zinc sulfide (beta)	ZnS	3×10^{-23}

References: *CRC Handbook of Chemistry and Physics*, 2007
Chemistry, 5th edition, by John Olmsted and Greg Williams

A.5 Standard Reduction Potentials at 298 K

Reduction Half-Reaction	Standard Potential E°_{red}(V)
$F_2(g) + 2\,e^- \rightarrow 2\,F^-(aq)$	+2.87
$O_3(g) + 2\,H_3O^+(aq) + 2\,e^- \rightarrow O_2(g) + 3\,H_2O(l)$	+2.076
$Co^{3+}(aq) + e^- \rightarrow Co^{2+}(aq)$	+1.92
$H_2O_2(aq) + 2\,H_3O^+(aq) + 2\,e^- \rightarrow 2\,H_2O(l)$	+1.776
$N_2O(g) + 2\,H_3O^+(aq) + 2\,e^- \rightarrow N_2(g) + 3\,H_2O(l)$	+1.766
$Ce^{4+}(aq) + e^- \rightarrow Ce^{3+}(aq)$	+1.72
$PbO_2(s) + SO_4^{2-}(aq) + 4\,H_3O^+(aq) + 2\,e^- \rightarrow PbSO_4(s) + 6\,H_2O(l)$	+1.6913
$MnO_4^-(aq) + 4\,H_3O^+(aq) + 3\,e^- \rightarrow MnO_2(s) + 6\,H_2O(l)$	+1.679
$NiO_2(s) + 4\,H_3O^+(aq) + 2\,e^- \rightarrow Ni^{2+}(aq) + 6\,H_2O(l)$	+1.678
$HClO_2(aq) + 2\,H_3O^+(aq) + 2\,e^- \rightarrow HClO(aq) + 3\,H_2O(l)$	+1.645
$2\,HClO_2(aq) + 6\,H_3O^+(aq) + 6\,e^- \rightarrow Cl_2(g) + 10\,H_2O(l)$	+1.628
$2\,HClO(aq) + 2\,H_3O^+(aq) + 2\,e^- \rightarrow Cl_2(g) + 4\,H_2O(l)$	+1.611

(Continued)

Reduction Half-Reaction	Standard Potential E°_{red}(V)
$H_5IO_6(s) + H_3O^+(aq) + 2e^- \rightarrow IO_3^-(aq) + 4H_2O(l)$	+1.601
$RuO_4^-(aq) + 4H_3O^+(aq) + 2e^- \rightarrow RuO_2^+(aq) + 6H_2O(l)$	+1.6
$2NO(g) + 2H_3O^+(aq) + 2e^- \rightarrow N_2O(g) + 3H_2O(l)$	+1.591
$IO_4^-(aq) + 2H_3O^+(aq) + 2e^- \rightarrow IO_3^-(aq) + 3H_2O(l)$	+1.589
$MnO_4^-(aq) + 8H_3O^+(aq) + 5e^- \rightarrow Mn^{2+}(aq) + 12H_2O(l)$	+1.507
$RuO_2^+(aq) + 2H_3O^+(aq) + e^- \rightarrow Ru(OH)_2^{2+}(aq) + 2H_2O(l)$	+1.5
$Au^{3+}(aq) + 3e^- \rightarrow Au(s)$	+1.498
$2ClO_3^-(aq) + 12H_3O^+(aq) + 10e^- \rightarrow Cl_2(g) + 18H_2O(l)$	+1.47
$PbO_2(s) + 4H_3O^+(aq) + 2e^- \rightarrow Pb^{2+}(aq) + 6H_2O(l)$	+1.455
$ClO_3^-(aq) + 6H_3O^+(aq) + 6e^- \rightarrow Cl^-(aq) + 9H_2O(l)$	+1.451
$BrO_3^-(aq) + 6H_3O^+(aq) + 5e^- \rightarrow \frac{1}{2}Br_2(l) + 9H_2O(l)$	+1.482
$HOI(aq) + H_3O^+(aq) + e^- \rightarrow \frac{1}{2}I_2(s) + 2H_2O(l)$	+1.430
$RuO_4(aq) + 6H_3O^+(aq) + 4e^- \rightarrow Ru(OH)_2^{2+}(aq) + 8H_2O(l)$	+1.40
$2ClO_4^-(aq) + 16H_3O^+(aq) + 14e^- \rightarrow Cl_2(g) + 24H_2O(l)$	+1.39
$ClO_4^-(aq) + 8H_3O^+(aq) + 8e^- \rightarrow Cl^-(aq) + 12H_2O(l)$	+1.389
$Cl_2(g) + 2e^- \rightarrow 2Cl^-(aq)$	+1.36
$ClO_4^-(aq) + 6H_3O^+(aq) + 6e^- \rightarrow ClO^-(aq) + 9H_2O(l)$	+1.36
$HBrO(aq) + H_3O^+(aq) + 2e^- \rightarrow Br^- + 2H_2O(l)$	+1.331
$IO_4^-(aq) + 8H_3O^+(aq) + 7e^- \rightarrow \frac{1}{2}I_2(s) + 12H_2O(l)$	+1.318
$ClO_2(aq) + H_3O^+(aq) + e^- \rightarrow HClO_2(aq) + H_2O(l)$	+1.277

Reduction Half-Reaction	Standard Potential E°_{red}(V)
$Zn(OH)_2(s) + 2e^- \rightarrow Zn(s) + 2OH^-(aq)$	+1.249
$Cr_2O_7^{2-}(aq) + 14H_3O^+(aq) + 6e^- \rightarrow 2Cr^{3+}(aq) + 21H_2O(l)$	+1.232
$O_2(g) + 4H^+(aq) + 4e^- \rightarrow 2H_2O(l)$	+1.23
$MnO_2(s) + 4H_3O^+(aq) + 2e^- \rightarrow Mn^{2+}(aq) + 6H_2O(l)$	+1.224
$ClO_3^-(aq) + 3H_3O^+(aq) + 2e^- \rightarrow HClO_2(aq) + 4H_2O(l)$	+1.214
$2IO_3^-(aq) + 12H_3O^+(aq) + 10e^- \rightarrow I_2(s) + 18H_2O(l)$	+1.195
$ClO_4^-(aq) + 2H_3O^+(aq) + 2e^- \rightarrow ClO_3^-(aq) + 3H_2O(l)$	+1.189
$Pt^{2+}(aq) + 2e^- \rightarrow Pt(s)$	+1.18
$IO_3^-(aq) + 5H_3O^+(aq) + 4e^- \rightarrow HOI(aq) + 7H_2O(l)$	+1.154
$ClO_3^-(aq) + 2H_3O^+(aq) + e^- \rightarrow ClO_2(aq) + 3H_2O(l)$	+1.152
$Br_2(aq) + 2e^- \rightarrow 2Br^-(aq)$	+1.0873
$Br_2(l) + 2e^- \rightarrow 2Br^-(aq)$	+1.07
$RuO_4(aq) + 8H_3O^+(aq) + 8e^- \rightarrow Ru(s) + 12H_2O(l)$	+1.04
$NO_2(g) + 2H_3O^+(aq) + 2e^- \rightarrow NO(g) + 3H_2O(l)$	+1.03
$RuO_4(aq) + e^- \rightarrow RuO_4^-(aq)$	+1.00
$NO_3^-(aq) + 4H_3O^+(aq) + 3e^- \rightarrow NO(g) + 6H_2O(l)$	+0.957
$2Hg^{2+}(aq) + 2e^- \rightarrow Hg_2^{2+}(aq)$	+0.920
$Ru(OH)_2^{2+}(aq) + 2H_3O^+(aq) + e^- \rightarrow Ru^{3+}(aq) + 4H_2O(l)$	0.86
$Hg^{2+}(aq) + 2e^- \rightarrow Hg(l)$	+0.851
$ClO^-(aq) + H_2O(l) + 2e^- \rightarrow Cl^-(aq) + 2OH^-(aq)$	+0.81
$Ag^+(aq) + e^- \rightarrow Ag(s)$	+0.80
$Hg_2^{2+}(aq) + 2e^- \rightarrow 2Hg(l)$	+0.7973
$Fe^{3+}(aq) + e^- \rightarrow Fe^{2+}(aq)$	+0.771
$Ni(OH)_2(s) + 2e^- \rightarrow Ni(s) + 2OH^-(aq)$	+0.72
p − benzoquinone + $H_3O^+(aq)$ + $2e^- \rightarrow$ hydroquinone + $H_2O(l)$	+0.6992

Reduction Half-Reaction	Standard Potential E°_{red}(V)
$O_2(g) + 2\ H_3O^+(aq) + 2\ e^- \rightarrow H_2O_2(l) + 2\ H_2O(l)$	+0.695
$Ru(OH)_2^{2+}(aq) + 2\ H_3O^+(aq) + 4\ e^- \rightarrow Ru(s) + 4\ H_2O(l)$	+0.68
$MnO_4^-(aq) + 2\ H_2O(l) + 3\ e^- \rightarrow MnO_2(s) + 4\ OH^-(aq)$	+0.595
$I_2(s) + 2\ e^- \rightarrow 2\ I^-(aq)$	+0.54
$I_3^-(aq) + 2\ e^- \rightarrow 3\ I^-(aq)$	+0.536
$Cu^+(aq) + e^- \rightarrow Cu(s)$	+0.52
$Ru^{2+}(aq) + 2\ e^- \rightarrow Ru(s)$	+0.455
$O_2(g) + 2\ H_2O(l) + 4\ e^- \rightarrow 4\ OH^-(aq)$	+0.401
$Fe(CN)_6^{3-}(aq) + e^- \rightarrow Fe(CN)_6^{4-}(aq)$	+0.358
$Cu^{2+}(aq) + 2\ e^- \rightarrow Cu(s)$	+0.34
$Hg_2Cl_2(s) + 2\ e^- \rightarrow 2\ Hg(l) + 2\ Cl^-(aq)$	+0.26808
$Ru^{3+}(aq) + e^- \rightarrow Ru^{2+}(aq)$	+0.249
$HAsO_2(s) + 3\ H_3O^+(aq) + 3\ e^- \rightarrow As(s) + 5\ H_2O$	+0.248
$AgCl(s) + e^- \rightarrow Ag(s) + Cl^-(aq)$	+0.22233
$Cu^{2+}(aq) + e^- \rightarrow Cu^+(aq)$	+0.153
$Sn^{4+}(aq) + 2\ e^- \rightarrow Sn^{2+}(aq)$	+0.151
$S(s) + 2\ H_3O^+(aq) + 2\ e^- \rightarrow H_2S(s) + 2\ H_2O(l)$	+0.14
$NO_3^-(aq) + 2\ H_2O(l) + 3\ e^- \rightarrow NO(g) + 4\ OH^-(aq)$	+0.109
$N_2(g) + 8\ H_3O^+(aq) + 6\ e^- \rightarrow 2\ NH_4^+(aq) + 8\ H_2O(l)$	+0.092
$S_4O_6^{2-}(aq) + 2\ e^- \rightarrow 2\ S_2O_3^{2-}(aq)$	+0.08
$AgBr(s) + e^- \rightarrow Ag(s) + Br^-(aq)$	+0.07133
$2\ H^+(aq) + 2\ e^- \rightarrow H_2(g)$	0.00
$Fe^{3+}(aq) + 3\ e^- \rightarrow Fe(s)$	−0.04
$[Co(NH_3)_6]^{3+}(aq) + e^- \rightarrow [Co(NH_3)_6]^{2+}(aq)$	−0.108
$Pb^{2+}(aq) + 2\ e^- \rightarrow Pb(s)$	−0.13
$Sn^{2+}(aq) + 2\ e^- \rightarrow Sn(s)$	−0.14
$O_2(g) + 2\ H_2O(l) + 2\ e^- \rightarrow H_2O_2(l) + 2\ OH^-(aq)$	−0.146
$AgI(s) + e^- \rightarrow Ag(s) + I^-(aq)$	−0.15224

Reduction Half-Reaction	Standard Potential E°_{red}(V)
$CO_2(g) + 2\ H_3O^+(aq) + 2\ e^- \rightarrow HCO_2H(s) + 2\ H_2O(l)$	−0.199
$Cu(OH)_2(s) + 2\ e^- \rightarrow Cu(s) + 2\ OH^-(aq)$	−0.222
$Ni^{2+}(aq) + 2\ e^- \rightarrow Ni(s)$	−0.26
$Co^{2+}(aq) + 2\ e^- \rightarrow Co(s)$	−0.28
$PbSO_4(s) + 2\ e^- \rightarrow Pb(s) + SO_4^{2-}(aq)$	−0.3588
$SeO_3^{2-}(aq) + 3\ H_2O(l) + 4\ e^- \rightarrow Se(aq) + 6\ OH^-(aq)$	−0.366
$Cd^{2+}(aq) + 2\ e^- \rightarrow Cd(s)$	−0.403
$Cr^{3+}(aq) + e^- \rightarrow Cr^{2+}(aq)$	−0.407
$Fe^{2+}(aq) + 2\ e^- \rightarrow Fe(s)$	−0.44
$NO_2^-(g) + H_2O(l) + 3\ e^- \rightarrow NO(g) + 2\ OH^-(aq)$	−0.46
$S(s) + 2\ e^- \rightarrow S^{2-}(aq)$	−0.48
$2\ CO_2(g) + 2\ H_3O^+(aq) + 2\ e^- \rightarrow H_2C_2O_4(s) + H_2O(l)$	−0.49
$TiO_2(s) + 4\ H_3O^+(aq) + 2\ e^- \rightarrow Ti^{2+}(aq) + 6\ H_2O(l)$	−0.502
$Au(CN)_2^-(aq) + e^- \rightarrow Au(s) + 2\ CN^-(aq)$	−0.60
$Cr^{3+}(aq) + 3\ e^- \rightarrow Cr(s)$	−0.74
$Zn^{2+}(aq) + 2\ e^- \rightarrow Zn(s)$	−0.76
$Cd(OH)_2(s) + 2\ e^- \rightarrow Cd(s) + 2\ OH^-(aq)$	−0.809
$2\ H_2O(l) + 2\ e^- \rightarrow H_2(g) + 2\ OH^-(aq)$	−0.83
$Ti^{3+}(aq) + e^- \rightarrow Ti^{2+}(aq)$	−0.85
$H_3BO_3(s) + 3\ H_3O^+(aq) + 3\ e^- \rightarrow B(s) + 6\ H_2O(l)$	−0.8698
$Cr^{2+}(aq) + 2\ e^- \rightarrow Cr(s)$	−0.91
$SO_4^{2-}(aq) + H_2O(l) + 2\ e^- \rightarrow SO_3^{2-}(aq) + 2\ OH^-(aq)$	−0.93
$CNO^-(aq) + H_2O(l) + 2\ e^- \rightarrow CN^-(aq) + 2\ OH^-(aq)$	−0.970
$[Zn(NH_3)_4]^{2+}(aq) + 2\ e^- \rightarrow Zn(s) + 4\ NH_3(aq)$	−1.04
$Mn^{2+}(aq) + 2\ e^- \rightarrow Mn(s)$	−1.185

(Continued)

Reduction Half-Reaction	Standard Potential E°_{red}(V)
$Cr(OH)_3(s) + 3\ e^- \rightarrow Cr(s) + 3\ OH^-(aq)$	−1.48
$Ti^{2+}(aq) + 2\ e^- \rightarrow Ti(s)$	−1.630
$Al^{3+}(aq) + 3\ e^- \rightarrow Al(s)$	−1.66
$Al(OH)_3(s) + 3\ e^- \rightarrow Al(s) + 3\ OH^-(aq)$	−2.31
$Mg^{2+}(aq) + 2\ e^- \rightarrow Mg(s)$	−2.38
$Mg(OH)_2(s) + 2\ e^- \rightarrow Mg(s) + 2\ OH^-(aq)$	−2.69
$Na^+(aq) + e^- \rightarrow Na(s)$	−2.71

Reduction Half-Reaction	Standard Potential E°_{red}(V)
$Ca^{2+}(aq) + 2\ e^- \rightarrow Ca(s)$	−2.87
$Ba^{2+}(aq) + 2\ e^- \rightarrow Ba(s)$	−2.912
$K^+(aq) + e^- \rightarrow K(s)$	−2.931
$Ba(OH)_2(s) + 2\ e^- \rightarrow Ba(s) + 2\ OH^-(aq)$	−2.99
$Ca(OH)_2(s) + 2\ e^- \rightarrow Ca(s) + 2\ OH^-(aq)$	−3.02
$Cs^+(aq) + e^- \rightarrow Cs(s)$	−3.026
$Li^+(aq) + e^- \rightarrow Li(s)$	−3.04

Reference: *CRC Handbook of Chemistry and Physics*, 2007

Glossary

α-carbon (23.4): The carbon in an amino acid that is bonded to the amine functional group, the carboxy functional group, the R group, and H.

α-helix (23.4): The spiral-shaped secondary protein structure formed by hydrogen bonds between the amide NH group of one amino acid and the carbonyl group on another amino acid further along on the chain.

absorbance spectrum (8.1): The specific wavelengths of light that are absorbed by an atom when it gains energy.

accuracy (1.6): The closeness of a measurement or set of measurements to the correct or known value.

acid (3.5): A compound that produces H^+ ions in solution.

acid (4.2): A compound that ionizes in solution to produce H^+ ions.

acid ionization constant, K_a (16.5): The equilibrium constant that describes the extent of ionization of a weak acid in water.

acid strength (16.2): The tendency for a certain percentage of acid molecules to ionize in water; the higher the acid strength, the higher the percentage of ionization.

acid–base reaction (4.2): The reaction of an acid and a base to produce a salt and usually water; also called a neutralization reaction.

acidic (16.3): A solution in which the H_3O^+ concentration is greater than the OH^- concentration.

activation energy, E_a (14.4): The minimum amount of energy needed for the reactant to reach the transition state; also called barrier energy.

active metal (4.7): A metal that is easily oxidized.

activity series (4.7): A list of metals showing the relative level of activity, with most active (most readily oxidized) at the top and the least active (least readily oxidized) at the bottom.

activity, A (20.1): The number of disintegrations per unit time in a sample of a radioactive substance. The activity is proportional to the decay rate and to the number of atoms of the isotope in the sample.

actual yield (5.4): The amount of product that is actually obtained from a chemical reaction.

addition polymerization (21.6): A polymerization of molecules that proceeds via addition reactions.

addition reaction (21.2): A type reaction in which substituents are added across a double or triple bond.

adhesion (12.2): Attraction to different particles.

alcohol (21.4): An organic compound with the hydroxyl (—OH) functional group.

aldehyde (21.5): An organic compound with the —CHO functional group.

aldose (23.2): A monosaccharide with an aldehyde functional group.

algebra (0.4): A method for rearranging the numbers and variables in a mathematical equation to simplify the equation or make it easier to solve.

alkali metal (2.6): A metal in group 1 (1A) of the periodic table—Li, Na, K, Rb, Cs, or Fr.

alkaline earth metal (2.6): A metal in group 2 (2A) of the periodic table—Be, Mg, Ca, Sr, Ba, or Ra.

alkane (21.1): A hydrocarbon containing only C—C and C—H single bonds.

alkene (21.2): A hydrocarbon containing one or more carbon–carbon double bond per molecule.

alkyl group (21.1): A portion of an alkane formed by loss of one hydrogen atom.

alkyne (21.2): A hydrocarbon containing at least one carbon–carbon triple bond.

allotrope (3.1): One of two or more forms of an uncombined element; for example, diamond and graphite are allotropes of carbon.

alloy (13.1): A homogeneous mixture of two or more metals; an example of a solid–solid solution.

alpha decay (20.1): A form of radioactive decay in which a nucleus emits an alpha particle and often a gamma ray.

alpha particle, α (20.1): A particle made up of two protons and two neutrons that is ejected from a radioactive atom's nucleus in alpha decay. Alpha particles eventually pick up two electrons from their surroundings and become helium atoms.

amide (21.5): An organic compound with the —CONH— functional group.

amine (21.4): An organic compound with the $—NR_2$ functional group, in which either or both R groups can be hydrogen atoms.

amino acid (23.4): A small molecule with both amine and carboxylic acid functional groups; a protein monomer.

ammonia (3.2): The binary covalent compound NH_3.

amorphous solid (12.6): A solid whose structure consists of irregular arrangements of the constituent particles.

ampere, A (19.9): A unit of electrical current; $1\ A = 1\ C/s$.

amphiprotic (16.2): The ability of a molecule or ion to act as both a proton donor and a proton acceptor. This definition is specific to Brønsted acids and bases.

amphoteric (16.2): The ability of a molecule or ion to act as an acid or as a base. This is a general term that is used in any acid–base theory.

amylopectin (23.2): A branched polymer of glucose.

amylose (23.2): An unbranched polymer of glucose.

analyte (17.3): A solution of unknown concentration, to which titrant is added during a titration.

angular momentum quantum number, ℓ (8.6): The number that corresponds to a particular subshell within the atom.

anhydrous (3.4): Without water; for example, anhydrous $CuSO_4$ results from the loss of water from $CuSO_4 \cdot 5\ H_2O$.

anion (2.4): A negatively charged ion.

anion (3.3): A negatively charged ion.

anode (19.4): The electrode at which the oxidation half-reaction occurs.

anomer (23.2): One of two forms of the cyclic structures of monosaccharides that differ only in the position of the hydroxyl group that forms during the reaction that produces the cyclic structure.

anomeric carbon (23.2): The new chiral carbon formed when monosaccharides form a cyclic structure; it is derived from the carbonyl carbon in the Fischer projection.

antibonding orbital (11.5): A higher-energy molecular orbital resulting from the subtractive combination of atomic orbitals, designated by *.

anticodon (23.5): The site on tRNA that is complementary to the codons in mRNA.

antilog (0.5): The inverse of the logarithm function in which 10 is raised to the power of the original number. Also known as an inverse logarithm.

aqueous solution (1.1): A solution in water.

aqueous solution (4.1): A homogeneous mixture of a pure substance dissolved in water.

area (1.5): The amount of space occupied by a two-dimensional object.

aromatic hydrocarbon (21.2): A hydrocarbon containing one or more benzene rings.

Arrhenius acid (16.1): A compound that releases H^+ into solution.

Arrhenius base (16.1): A compound that releases OH^- into solution.

Arrhenius equation (14.4): An equation relating the rate constant, activation energy, frequency of collisions, orientation, and temperature.

Arrhenius theory (16.1): The acid–base theory that defines acids as compounds that increase the H^+ concentration when dissolved in water, and bases as compounds that increase the OH^- concentration when dissolved in water.

atmosphere, atm (7.1): A unit of pressure equal to 760 torr that is the pressure of the atmosphere on a "normal" day at sea level; the envelope of air surrounding Earth.

atmospheric pressure (7.1): The pressure of the atmosphere.

atom (1.1): A single particle of any element—the smallest possible amount of an element that retains the properties of that element.

atom (2.3): The smallest particle that retains the characteristic composition of an element.

atomic bomb (20.5): A nuclear weapon that uses a fission reaction to release energy.

atomic mass (2.5): The weighted average of the masses of the naturally occurring mixture of isotopes of an element, compared with one-twelfth of the mass of a ^{12}C atom.

atomic mass (3.8): The mass of an individual atom, expressed in units of atomic mass units, u.

atomic mass scale (2.5): A relative scale of masses based on the mass of ^{12}C being the standard and having a mass defined as exactly 12 u.

atomic mass unit, u (2.5): A mass equal to one-twelfth of the mass of a ^{12}C atom; also abbreviated as amu.

atomic mass units, u (3.8): A unit of mass used for expressing the masses of individual atoms or molecules. One atomic mass unit, 1 u, = 1.66×10^{-24} g.

atomic number, *Z* (2.4): The number of protons in the nucleus of each atom of an element.

atomic weight (3.8): Another term for atomic mass.

aufbau principle (8.4): When filling the subshells of an atom with electrons, the electrons always fill the lowest-energy subshell available before any electrons are added to higher-energy subshells.

autoionization (16.3): A reaction of two molecules of a single substance to produce both positive and negative ions; for example, water can autoionize to turn two H_2O molecules into one H_3O^+ and one OH^-.

average kinetic energy (7.10): The total kinetic energy of all the molecules of a sample, divided by the number of molecules; the average kinetic energy depends on temperature only.

average rates (14.2): Reaction rates determined by measuring the concentration at two different times and dividing the change in concentration by the change in time.

Avogadro's law (7.5): Equal volumes of gas, at the same temperature and pressure, contain an equal number of gas particles (atoms or molecules): $\frac{V_1}{n_1} = \frac{V_2}{n_2}$.

Avogadro's number, N_A (3.7): 6.022×10^{23}—the number of atomic mass units in exactly 1 g.

β-sheet (23.4): A zigzag-shaped secondary protein structure formed by parallel strands of polypeptide that are held in place by hydrogen bonds between amide NH and carbonyl groups on different amino acids.

balanced equation (4.1): A chemical equation in which the number and type of atoms in the reactants are equal to the number and type of atoms in the products.

barometer (7.1): An instrument for measuring the pressure of a gas, especially the atmosphere.

barometric pressure (7.1): The pressure of the atmosphere.

base (0.2): The number that is being multiplied by itself in an exponential expression. In scientific notation, the base is always 10.

base (4.2): A compound that ionizes in solution to produce OH^- ions.

base ionization constant, K_b (16.5): The equilibrium constant that describes the extent of ionization of a weak base in water.

base pair (23.5): The combination of two nucleotides in different nucleic acids that form hydrogen bonds to each other; A-T, G-C, and A-U.

base strength (16.2): The tendency for a certain percentage of molecules of a base to ionize in water; the higher the base strength, the greater the percent ionization.

base units (1.5): The fundamental SI quantities (i.e., length, mass, time, electric current, temperature, amount of substance, and luminous intensity) that can be combined to describe every other quantity.

basic (16.3): A solution in which the OH^- concentration is greater than the H_3O^+ concentration.

belt of stability (20.2): The area showing the stable isotopes within the plot of the number of neutrons versus the number of protons for all isotopes.

bent (11.1): A molecular geometry associated with three electron domains with one lone pair, or four electron domains with two lone pairs.

benzene (21.2): The simplest aromatic hydrocarbon, which consists of six carbon atoms in a hexagonal ring with alternating double and single bonds.

beta decay (20.1): A form of radioactive decay in which a nucleus emits a beta particle and often a gamma ray, turning a neutron into a proton.

beta particle, β (20.1): An electron that is ejected from a radioactive atom's nucleus in beta decay as a neutron in the nucleus is transformed into a proton.

bidentate (22.3): Describes a ligand that forms two coordinate covalent bonds to a metal.

binary compound (3.2): A compound composed of exactly two elements.

binding energy (20.7): The energy required to separate an atomic nucleus into its component protons and neutrons.

biochemistry (23.1): The chemistry of living things.

biomolecules (23.1): Molecules found in living things.

body-centered cubic, bcc, unit cell (12.7): A cubic unit cell with one atom in the center of the cell and atoms at the eight corners.

Bohr model (8.2): The first model of the atom to propose that electrons in atoms were in definite energy levels.

boiling-point elevation, ΔT_b (13.4): An increase in the boiling point of a solution compared to the pure solvent, due to the presence of a solute.

Boltzmann constant, k (18.1): The proportionality constant relating entropy to the natural log of the number of microstates for the system; equal to 1.38×10^{-23} J/K.

bomb calorimeter (6.6): Instrument used to measure the heat of combustion of a reaction.

bond energy, BE (9.5): The energy needed to break a mole of a specific type of bond; also called bond enthalpy.

bond enthalpy (10.6): The enthalpy change, ΔH, associated with breaking a specific bond in one mole of gaseous molecules.

bond order (11.5): Measure of the stability of the molecule, calculated from the MO diagram as: bond order = $\frac{1}{2}$(bonding e^- − antibonding e^-).

bonding orbital (11.5): Lower energy molecular orbital resulting from the additive combination of atomic orbitals.

Born–Haber cycle (9.5): A thermodynamic cycle that uses Hess's law, ionization energy, electron affinity, and the energies of other processes to calculate the lattice energy of an ionic compound.

Boyle's law (7.2): At constant temperature, the volume of a given sample of gas is inversely proportional to its pressure: $P_1V_1 = P_2V_2$.

Brønsted acid (16.2): A substance that can donate H^+ to another substance.

Brønsted base (16.2): A substance that can accept H^+ from another substance.

Brønsted–Lowry theory (16.2): A theory of acids and bases based on the exchange of H^+ ions between two species. In Brønsted–Lowry theory, anytime an acid is in solution, by definition there must also be a base, and vice versa.

buffer capacity (17.2): The ability of a buffer solution to resist a change in pH when an acid or base is added.

buffer solution (17.1): A solution consisting of a weak acid and its conjugate base (or a weak base and its conjugate acid) that resists changes in pH.

building-up principle (8.4): Another name for the aufbau principle.

buret (5.9): A piece of laboratory glassware calibrated for measuring the volume of liquid delivered.

C-terminal end (23.4): The end of a polypeptide with an unreacted carboxyl group.

calorie, cal (6.1): A unit of energy that is equal to 4.184 J; the amount of energy required to raise the temperature of 1 g of water 1°C.

Calorie, Cal (6.1): A unit of energy used in the field of nutrition that is equal to exactly 1000 cal, 1 kcal, 4184 J, or 4.184 kJ.

calorimetry (6.6): The study of heat transfer between substances by measuring the temperature changes of the substances involved.

capillary action (12.2): The ability to flow against gravity up a narrow tube.

carbohydrates (23.1): Biomolecules involved in energy metabolism and storage; includes monosaccharides, disaccharides, and polysaccharides.

carbonyl group (21.5): A functional group made up of a carbon atom double-bonded to an oxygen atom: C=O.

carboxylic acid (21.5): An organic acid containing the functional group —COOH.

catalyst (14.1): A substance that provides an alternate, lower-energy path for a reaction to occur but is not consumed by the reaction.

cathode (19.4): The electrode at which the reduction half-reaction occurs.

cathode ray (2.3): A beam of electrons.

cathodic protection (19.8): Protecting a metal structure by creating an electrochemical cell in which a more active metal is the anode and the metal structure that needs to be protected is the cathode.

cation (2.4): A positively charged ion.

cation (3.3): A positively charged ion.

cellulose (23.2): A polysaccharide made by plants as a structural material; a polymer of glucose.

Celsius scale (1.9): The temperature scale in which the freezing point of water is defined as 0°C and the normal boiling point of water is defined as 100°C; formerly the centigrade scale.

chain reaction (20.5): In nuclear fission, a reaction that requires one neutron to trigger fission, but the fission process produces two or more neutrons, thereby continuing, and accelerating the rate of, the reaction.

Charles's law (7.3): At constant pressure, the volume of a given sample of gas is directly proportional to its absolute temperature: $\frac{V_1}{T_1} = \frac{V_2}{T_2}$.

chelate effect (22.3): The unusually large thermodynamic stability of coordination compounds that contain polydentate ligands instead of monodentate ligands.

chelating agent (22.3): The name given to bidentate and polydentate ligands.

chemical bond (1.1): An attraction between any two atoms that holds them together.

2): A chemical reaction. The products of a …e different materials than the reactants.

…uation (4.1): A symbolic description of a chemi- …on using chemical formulas for reactants and products …ing coefficients to indicate the proportions of reactants and …oducts.

chemical formula (3.1): A combination of symbols, subscripts, and possibly superscripts that identifies the composition of an element, compound, or ion.

chemical nomenclature (3.1): The systematic naming of chemical substances.

chemical property (1.2): A property having to do with possible changes in the composition of a substance.

Chemical thermodynamics (18.1): The study of how heat and work are involved in chemical reactions and in physical changes, such as changes of state.

chemistry (1.1): The study of the interaction of matter and energy and the changes that matter undergoes.

chiral (21.3): Describes an object that cannot be superimposed on its mirror image (e.g., a carbon atom bonded to four unique groups).

cholesterol (23.3): A steroid; classified as a lipid.

cis–trans isomers (21.3): A type of stereoisomer in which the groups are located on the same (cis) or opposite (trans) side of the double bond of an alkene.

Clausius–Clapeyron equation (12.4): The relationship among vapor pressure, temperature, and enthalpy of vaporization.

close-packing (12.7): A packing arrangement that uses space efficiently.

codons (23.5): A sequence of three consecutive nucleotides that specifies an amino acid.

coefficient (0.2): A number by which a quantity is multiplied. In a scientific notation, the coefficient is the number that comes before $\times 10^x$.

coefficient (4.1): A number, usually an integer, placed before a chemical formula in a chemical equation to indicate the ratio or proportion of reactant and product in a chemical change.

cofactor (23.4): A metal ion or small organic molecule required for a protein's structure and function.

cohesion (12.2): Attraction to like particles.

coinage metal (2.6): An element of periodic group 11 (1B)—Cu, Ag, or Au.

colligative properties (13.4): Properties of a liquid that change when a solute is dissolved in a pure solvent to create a solution. The four most common colligative properties are vapor-pressure lowering, freezing-point depression, boiling-point elevation, and osmotic pressure.

collision theory (14.4): Theory that describes chemical reactions as occurring when reactants collide with sufficient energy and in the correct orientation.

combination (4.2): A chemical reaction in which simple reactants combine to form a more complex product; also called synthesis.

combined gas law (7.4): For a given sample of gas, the volume is directly proportional to the absolute temperature and inversely proportional to the pressure.

combustion (4.2): A chemical reaction involving the rapid combination of a substance with oxygen; also called burning.

combustion analysis (3.12): A laboratory technique which allows masses of carbon and hydrogen in a compound to be calculated by first converting the carbon and hydrogen to CO_2 and H_2O and then measuring the masses of the CO_2 and H_2O.

common-ion effect (17.1): A phenomenon whereby the addition of a strong electrolyte containing a common ion suppresses the ionization of a weak electrolyte.

completion (5.3): The condition a reaction has reached when the limiting quantity of reactant has been consumed.

complex fractions (0.4): Fractions that contain other fractions within them.

complex ion (17.10): A compound consisting of a metal ion that is bound to one or more ligands.

compound (1.1): A chemical combination of elements that has a definite composition and its own set of properties.

concentrated solution (5.5): A solution that has a relatively large amount of solute per volume of solvent.

concentration (5.5): The quantity of solute per unit volume of solution or per unit mass of solvent.

concentration cell (19.7): An electrochemical cell in which the half-cells undergo the same reaction but differ in ion concentrations, thus leading to a spontaneous reaction.

condensation (12.3): The transition from gas to liquid phase.

condensation polymerization (21.6): A polymerization of molecules that proceeds via condensation reactions.

condensation reaction (21.5): A reaction in which two or more organic molecules form a covalent bond and release a small molecule such as water.

condensed structural formula (21.1): A formula that shows bonded groups of atoms in a molecule rather than the total number of each type of atom.

conformation (11.4): Various shapes possible for larger molecules due to rotation around single bonds.

conjugate acid (16.2): The Brønsted weak acid that results from the gain of a proton by a weak base.

conjugate acid–base pair (16.2): A Brønsted weak acid and weak base that are related by the gain or loss of one proton.

conjugate base (16.2): The Brønsted weak base that results from the loss of a proton by a weak acid.

constant-volume calorimetry (6.6): Science of measuring changes in heat transfer between substances by measuring the temperature changes of the substances involved.

constructive interference (11.5): Waves combine in phase to increase peaks and decrease troughs.

control rod (20.5): A rod made of a material that can absorb neutrons without causing a reaction. Control rods are used in fission reactors to absorb neutrons and slow the reaction down if too much heat is being generated.

conversion factor (1.7): A ratio equal to 1 that can be multiplied by a quantity to change the form of the quantity without changing its value.

coordinate covalent bond (16.9): A covalent bond in which both shared electrons come from the same atom.

coordinate covalent bond (22.3): The bond that is formed between a Lewis base ligand and the Lewis acid metal of a coordination compound.

coordinate covalent bonds (11.3): Covalent bond in which both electrons in the shared pair is supplied by one of the atoms.

coordination compound (22.3): Any complex ion or neutral compound that contains a metal that is complexed by ligands.

coordination isomers (22.5): Compounds that have the same chemical formula but differ in the types of groups that are located inside and outside of the primary coordination sphere.

coordination number (12.7): The number of nearest neighbors for each atom in a crystalline structure.

coordination number (22.3): The number of atoms that are bonded directly to the metal in a coordination compound.

core electron (8.5): An electron in an atom that is in a lower energy level than is a valence electron; any electron in an atom that is not a valence electron.

core electrons (9.1): The electrons in the shells of an atom or ion that are lower in energy (principal quantum number $n - 1$ or lower) than the highest occupied shell (n); all electrons that are not valence electrons.

corrosion (19.8): The oxidation of a metal object in soil or water that is accelerated by the unintentional formation of a voltaic cell.

coulomb, C (19.6): A unit of charge; $1\ C = 1\ J/V$.

counterion (16.1): The ion that accompanies another ion of opposite charge in an ionic compound.

covalent compound (3.1): A compound that contains only nonmetals and/or metalloids bonded together; also called a molecular compound.

covalent-network solid (12.6): A solid whose constituent particles are atoms that interact via covalent bonds. Also called a macromolecular solid.

critical mass (20.5): The minimum mass of a fissionable isotope necessary to sustain a chain reaction. If less than the critical mass is present, neutrons are able to escape the sample and the reaction will eventually stop.

critical point (12.5): The pressure and temperature above which a substance no longer exists as either a liquid or a gas.

critical pressure (12.5): The pressure above which a substance no longer exists as either a liquid or a gas.

critical temperature (12.5): The temperature above which a substance no longer exists as either a liquid or a gas.

crystal field splitting energy (22.6): The energy difference between sets of *d* orbitals in the central metal of a coordination compound.

crystal field theory (22.6): A model of bonding in coordination compounds where the *d* orbitals of the central metal are repelled by the electrons of the ligands and are split into different energy levels.

crystalline solid (12.6): A solid whose structure consists of regular repeating arrangements of the constituent particles.

cubic close-packing, ccp (12.7): A three-layer, efficient packing arrangement that forms a face-centered cubic unit cell.

cubic unit cell (12.7): A unit cell with equal length edges and 90° angles.

Dalton's atomic theory (2.3): The theory that matter is made of small particles (atoms) that have properties characteristic of a element.

Dalton's law of partial pressures (7.7): The total pressure of a gas mixture is equal to the sum of the partial pressures of its components: $P_{total} = P_1 + P_2 + \cdots + P_n$.

daughter nuclide (20.1): The product isotope that is formed as a result of a radioactive decay process.

debye (D) (10.5): The unit of dipole moment measurement, where $1\ D = 3.34 \times 10^{-30}\ C \cdot m$.

decomposition (4.2): A chemical reaction in which a reactant breaks down into less complex products.

definite composition (1.1): The given ratio by mass of each element in a compound to any other element in the compound.

degenerate (8.4): Having the same energy.

dehydration synthesis (23.1): The synthesis reaction in which a molecule of water is formed; common in the formation of larger biomolecules; a type of condensation reaction.

delocalized bond (10.3): Multiple bonds in resonance structures that are spread out over more than one location.

density, *d* (1.8): The mass per unit volume of a sample of matter.

dependent variable (0.7): The quantity that changes in response to the dependent variable and is measured on the *y*-axis.

deposition (12.3): The transition between gas and solid phase.

derived units (1.5): The product or powers of one or more base units.

destructive interference (11.5): Waves combine out of phase to cancel peaks and troughs.

deuterium (20.5): An isotope of hydrogen that has one proton and one neutron in the nucleus instead of the usual lone proton.

deuteron (20.5): A particle made up of one proton and one neutron (the nucleus of a deuterium atom).

diamagnetism (11.5): Very slight repulsion for a magnetic field; property of molecules with all paired electrons.

diatomic molecule (3.1): A molecule containing two atoms.

dibasic (16.1): Describes an Arrhenius strong base, such as $Ba(OH)_2$, that releases two OH^- ions per formula unit.

diffusion (7.11): The spreading out of gas particles by random motion and collisions to occupy an entire volume.

dilute solution (5.5): A solution that has a relatively low amount of solute per volume of solvent.

dilution (5.5): The process of adding more solvent to decrease the concentration of solute in a solution.

dimensional analysis (1.7): A system that involves the use of units to indicate the proper arithmetic operation to perform; also called unit analysis or the factor label method.

dipole (10.5): A bond that exhibits separate areas of opposite charge of equal magnitude.

dipole moment, μ (10.5): Measurable quantity related to the magnitude of the charge, q, and the distance between the charges, r, and is reported in debye units, D: $\mu = qr$.

dipole–dipole attraction (12.1): The temporary attraction between polar molecules.

diprotic acid (16.6): An acid with two ionizable hydrogen atoms.

(0.8): Two quantities with a fixed quotient. ... increases, the other will also increase by the ... vice versa.

...des (23.2): Two-unit carbohydrates, such as sucrose ...se.

...crete energy level (8.2): An atomic energy level that has specific energy.

disintegration (20.1): A single nuclear decay event, such as alpha decay, beta decay, electron capture, or positron emission.

dispersion forces (12.1): The temporary, weak attraction between an instantaneous dipole and an induced dipole. Also called London forces or London dispersion forces.

displacement (4.2): A chemical reaction in which an element reacts with a compound, replacing one of the elements in the compound to produce a new compound and a new element; also called single-replacement and single-displacement reactions.

disproportionation (19.1): A reaction in which one reactant acts as both the oxidizing and reducing agent.

dissociate (4.3): To separate into ions; applies to ionic compounds dissolved in water.

dissolve (1.2): To go into solution, thus making a homogeneous mixture.

distillation (12.4): The process of vaporizing a liquid and collecting its vapors.

disulfide bond (23.4): A covalent bond between two organic compounds containing SH groups (R–S–S–R); it typically refers to the covalent bond that forms between two cysteine R groups in a peptide.

donor atom (22.3): The atom or atoms in a ligand that donate a lone pair of electrons to a coordinate covalent bond.

double bond (10.1): A bond consisting of two atoms sharing two pairs of electrons and shown as two short lines in Lewis structures.

double helix (23.5): The twisted ladder shape of DNA.

double-displacement (4.2): A chemical reaction in which two ionic compounds exchange ions to form two new ionic compounds; also called double-replacement or metathesis.

double-replacement (4.2): A chemical reaction in which two ionic compounds exchange ions to form two new ionic compounds; also called metathesis or double-displacement.

driving force (4.2): The reason that a reaction happens; what causes a reaction to occur.

dry cell (19.8): A sealed voltaic cell containing the mobile ions in a paste or gel form rather than an aqueous solution; commonly referred to as a battery.

ductile (12.6): Able to be drawn into a thin wire.

ductile (2.6): Capable of being drawn into a wire.

duet rule (10.1): Hydrogen forms only one bond in covalent compounds, filling its 1*s* valence shell.

dynamic state (15.1): A state in which two opposite processes occur at equal rates.

effective nuclear charge (9.2): The net positive charge from the nucleus that a valence electron experiences.

effusion (7.11): The movement of gas particles through a tiny opening without collisions.

electrical circuit (19.4): The circular connection for the free flow of electrons and ions.

electrochemical cell (19.4): A system composed of two half-cells connected by a salt bridge and a wire, thus allowing for electron transfer.

electrochemistry (19.1): The branch of chemistry that studies the relationship between electricity and chemistry.

electrode (19.4): A half-cell in an electrochemical cell; sometimes it requires an inert wire or carbon rod to make electrical connection to the half-cell.

electrolysis (19.9): The process of applying an electrical current to a cell to cause a nonspontaneous reaction to occur.

electrolyte (4.3): A substance that dissolves in water to produce hydrated ions and a solution capable of conducting electricity; typically, an ionic compound, acid, or base.

electrolytic cell (19.4): An electrochemical cell in which an electrical current is used to cause a nonspontaneous redox reaction to occur.

electromagnetic radiation (20.1): A general term for light of all wavelengths, from radio waves to gamma rays. The gamma particles released in nuclear reactions are a form of electromagnetic radiation.

electromagnetic radiation (8.1): A collective term for light of all wavelengths in the electromagnetic spectrum.

electromagnetic spectrum (8.1): The complete collection of electromagnetic waves, including visible light, infrared, ultraviolet, X-rays, gamma rays, and microwaves.

electron (2.3): A negatively charged subatomic particle found outside the nucleus; a fundamental particle of nature.

electron affinity, EA (9.3): The energy liberated when an electron is added to a gaseous atom to form a gaseous anion.

electron capture (20.1): A form of radioactive decay in which a nucleus captures an electron from one of the inner shells of the atom, turning a proton into a neutron.

electron configuration (8.5): The arrangement of the electrons in the shells and subshells of an atom, or the shorthand notation used to represent this arrangement.

electron domain (11.1): A charge cloud around a central atom that can be: lone pairs, single unshared electrons, single bond, double bond, or triple bond.

electron geometry (11.1): Shape determined by the number of electron domains.

electron pair acceptor (16.9): A Lewis acid.

electron pair donor (16.9): A Lewis base.

electron-sea model (12.6): The model in which the valence electrons of atoms in a metallic solid form a sea of mobile electrons surrounding the metal cations.

electronegativity (10.3): Measure of the electron-attracting ability of an atom in a covalent bond.

electroplating (19.9): The process of using an electrical current to cause a protective or cosmetic layer of metal to form on the surface of a metal object.

electrorefining (19.9): The process of using an electrical current to remove impurities from a metal sample.

electrostatic attraction (9.4): The forces of attraction between oppositely charged species.

element (1.1): A substance that cannot be broken down into simpler substances by chemical means; one of the basic building blocks of which all matter is composed.

elementary step (14.5): An individual molecular event with a transition state and rate law, typically part of a series that makes up a reaction mechanism.

emission spectrum (8.2): The specific wavelengths of light that are emitted by an atom when it releases stored energy.

empirical formula (3.10): The simplest chemical formula for a compound that shows the ratio of elements in the compound but does not necessarily show the actual number of each type of atom in the compound.

end point (5.9): The point in a titration at which the indicator signals that the reaction is complete.

endothermic process (6.4): A process in which heat is absorbed from outside the system and ΔH is positive.

energy (1.3): The capacity to do work.

energy (6.1): The capacity to do work or transfer heat.

energy-level diagram (8.4): A diagram in which horizontal lines represent the orbitals of an atom, those with higher energies toward the top, in which arrows may be used to represent electrons.

enthalpy of fusion, ΔH_{fus} (12.3): The energy required for the fusion or melting of 1 mol of a solid.

enthalpy of sublimation, ΔH_{sub} (12.3): The energy required for the sublimation of 1 mol of a solid.

enthalpy of vaporization, ΔH_{vap} (12.3): The energy required for the vaporization of 1 mol of a liquid.

enthalpy, H (6.4): The sum of internal energy of a system and the product of its pressure and volume change.

entropy (13.1): A measure of the randomness or disorder in a system.

entropy, S (18.1): The degree of disorder or randomness of a system's energy.

equilibrium (12.4): The dynamic situation in which two opposing processes occur at the same rate, resulting in no net change.

equilibrium (15.1): The situation in which the forward and reverse reactions are occurring *at the same rate.*

equilibrium constant expression (15.2): The ratio of the product of the concentrations of the products divided by the product of the concentrations or partial pressures of the reactants, each raised to the power corresponding to its coefficient in the balanced equation. Also referred to as an equilibrium expression.

equilibrium constant, K (15.2): A constant that tells how far a reaction will proceed until it reaches equilibrium.

equivalence point (5.9): The point in a titration at which the ratio of moles of reactants is the same as the ratio in the balanced equation.

Erlenmeyer flask (5.9): A flask designed to allow swirling of the liquid contents without spillage.

ester (21.5): An organic compound with the —COO—R functional group.

ether (21.4): An organic compound with the —O— functional group; the general formula of an ether is ROR′, where R and R′ may or may not be the same.

excess (5.3): The quantity of a reactant that exceeds that which can react with the limiting quantity of another reactant.

excited state (8.2): The state of an atom that has more er than does its lowest energy state.

exothermic process (6.4): A process in which heat is transferre from the system to the surroundings and the change in enthalpy is negative.

expanded valence shell (10.4): Elements from periods 3–7 can form more than four bonds when making compounds, expanding beyond the octet rule.

exponent (0.2): A superscript that represents repeated multiplication of the same number.

extensive property (1.2): A characteristic that depends on the quantity of the sample.

extrapolation (0.7): Determining a value from a graph when that value lies outside the range of the data plotted on the graph.

face-centered cubic, fcc, unit cell (12.7): The cubic unit cell with an atom on each of the six faces and an atom at each of the eight corners.

Fahrenheit scale (1.9): A temperature scale in which the freezing point of water is defined as 32°F and the normal boiling point of water is defined as 212°F.

family (2.6): In the periodic table, a column that includes elements with similar chemical properties; a periodic group.

Faraday constant, F (19.6): The charge, in coulombs, of a mole of electrons; $F = 96{,}485\ C/mol$.

fats (23.2): Triglycerides that are solids at room temperature with higher levels of saturated fatty acids; typically of animal origin.

fatty acid (23.3): A long-chain carboxylic acid.

first law of thermodynamics (6.2): The energy of the universe is constant.

first order (14.2): A type of reaction in which the rate depends upon a reactant's concentration raised to the first power.

Fischer projection (23.2): A two-dimensional diagram of monosaccharide structures that specifies the specific three-dimensional shape at each carbon atom; vertical bonds point away from the viewer, and horizontal bonds point toward the viewer.

fissionable (20.5): The property of an isotope that makes it capable of undergoing fission when triggered with a low-energy neutron.

flash point (11.1): Temperature at which vapors of a liquid fuel can be ignited.

force (7.1): A push or a pull.

formal charge (10.3): Compares an atom's electron status within a molecule to the number of valence electrons of the atom.

$$\text{Formal charge} = \#\text{ valence e}^- - \left(\frac{\#\text{ shared e}^-}{2} + \#\text{ unshared e}^-\right)$$

formation constant, K_f (17.10): The equilibrium constant for the formation of a complex ion.

formula (2.1): A combination of symbols, subscripts, and possibly superscripts that identifies the composition of an element, compound, or ion.

formula mass (3.8): The mass of one formula unit of an atom, molecule, or ionic compound, expressed in units of u. The formula mass of an atom is also called the atomic mass, and the formula mass of a molecule is also called the molecular mass.

formula unit (3.1): The collection of atoms described by a chemical formula—an atom or molecule of an uncombined element, a molecule of a molecular compound, or the set of ions in the formula of an ionic compound.

formula weight (3.8): Another term for formula mass.

freezing (12.3): The transition from liquid to solid phase.

freezing-point depression, ΔT_f (13.4): A decrease in the freezing point of a solution compared to the pure solvent, due to the presence of a solute.

frequency factor (14.4): Indicates the number of correctly oriented reactions per unit time.

frequency, v (8.1): The number of times a wave crest passes a certain point per second.

fuel cell (19.8): A voltaic cell with continuous inflow of fuel (usually hydrogen) and outflow of products (usually water) used to generate electricity.

functional group (21.4): The characteristic group of atoms attached to an R group that gives a class of organic compounds its characteristic properties.

fusion (12.3): The transition from solid to liquid phase (melting).

gamma particle (20.1): A photon of high-energy gamma radiation emitted from the nucleus in a nuclear reaction.

gas (7.1): A state of matter; a sample of matter that has its volume and shape determined by the volume and shape of its container.

Gay-Lussac's law of combining volumes (7.9): At equal temperatures and equal pressures, the volumes of separate gases involved in a chemical reaction are directly proportional to their coefficients in the balanced chemical equation.

Geiger counter (20.1): A device that captures the charged particles emitted by the decay of a radioactive sample and generates an electrical current to indicate the activity of the radioactive sample.

genetic code (23.5): The list of codons and the amino acids they specify.

Gibbs free energy, G (18.4): A state function defined in terms of the enthalpy, entropy, and temperature of the system, and used to determine if a process is spontaneous.

glycerol (23.3): A three-carbon tri-alcohol compound.

glycogen (23.2): A highly branched polysaccharide made by animals for energy.

glycosidic bond (23.2): The bond formed between the carbonyl carbon of one monosaccharide and a hydroxyl group of another.

Graham's law of effusion (7.11): The ratio of rates of effusion of two gases, $\frac{r_1}{r_2}$, is equal to the square root of the inverse ratio of their molar masses, $\sqrt{\frac{\mathcal{M}_2}{\mathcal{M}_1}}$.

gram, g (1.5): The primary unit of mass in the metric system; one-thousandth of the kilogram, the SI standard unit of mass.

ground state (8.2): The lowest energy state of the set of electrons in an atom.

group (2.6): In the periodic table, a column that includes elements with similar chemical properties; a family.

half-cell (19.4): One section of an electrochemical cell in which either the oxidation or the reduction reaction occurs.

half-life (14.3): The time needed for one-half of the reactant to be consumed by a reaction.

half-life, $t_{1/2}$ (20.3): The amount of time required for one-half of a radioactive isotope to decay.

half-reaction (19.1): A chemical equation for just the oxidation or reduction component of a redox reaction.

halogen (2.6): An element of periodic group 17 (7A)—F, Cl, Br, I, or At.

Haworth projection (23.2): A diagram depicting monosaccharides and monosaccharide units in polysaccharides showing carbon atoms in ring structure; downward-pointing bonds represent right-pointing bonds in Fischer projection.

heat of vaporization (12.4): The energy required for the vaporization of 1 mol of a liquid.

heat, q (6.2): The flow of energy that causes a temperature change in an object or its surroundings.

heating curve (12.3): A graph showing how the temperature and phase change as energy is added to a pure substance.

Heisenberg uncertainty principle (8.2): The accuracies with which the position and the velocity of an electron can be measured are inversely related.

Henderson–Hasselbalch equation (17.2): An equation that relates the pH of a buffer solution to the pK_a of the weak acid and the concentrations of its acidic and basic components.

Henry's law (13.2): The solubility of a gas in a liquid is directly proportional to its partial pressure above the liquid.

Hess's law (6.7): When two or more processes combine to give a resulting process, their enthalpy changes add to give the enthalpy change for the resulting process.

heteroatom (21.4): An atom other than carbon or hydrogen in an organic molecule.

heterogeneous catalyst (14.6): A catalyst in a different phase than the reactants.

heterogeneous equilibrium (15.2): An equilibrium in which the species are in different phases.

heterogeneous mixture (1.1): A physical combination of substances that is not uniform throughout, so different samples taken from the same mixture might have different compositions from one another.

hexadentate (22.3): Describes a ligand that forms six coordinate covalent bonds to a metal.

hexagonal close-packing, hcp (12.7): A two-layer, efficient packing arrangement that forms a hexagonal unit cell.

hexose (23.2): A monosaccharide containing six carbon atoms.

high spin (22.6): A configuration of *d* electrons in a coordination compound that maximizes the number of unpaired electrons.

homogeneous catalyst (14.6): A catalyst in the same phase as the reactants.

homogeneous mixture (1.1): A physical combination of substances that is uniform throughout, so different samples taken from the same mixture always have identical compositions; a solution.

Hund's rule (8.4): The electrons in a partially filled subshell in an atom spread out to occupy the orbitals singly as much as possible.

hybrid orbitals (11.3): Mathematical combinations of the standard atomic orbitals that result in maximal overlap of orbitals in bonds.

hydrate (3.4): An ionic compound that has water molecules bonded to it.

hydrated ion (4.3): An ion surrounded by water molecules; formed when electrolytes dissolve in water.

hydration energy (13.1): The amount of energy given off when 1 mole of a substance is solvated in water. Another term for hydration energy is enthalpy of hydration.

hydrocarbon (21.1): A compound consisting of only carbon and hydrogen.

hydrocarbon (4.2): A category of chemical compounds containing only carbon and hydrogen; commonly used as fuels, they produce carbon dioxide and water if excess oxygen is present.

hydrogen bomb (20.5): A nuclear bomb that uses a fusion reaction to release energy; also known as a thermonuclear bomb or H-bomb.

hydrogen bond (12.1): The unusually strong dipole–dipole attraction formed between partially positive hydrogen atoms and a highly electronegative atom (fluorine, oxygen, or nitrogen) with a lone pair of electrons.

hydrogen bond acceptor (12.1): A molecule containing a highly electronegative atom (fluorine, oxygen, or nitrogen) with a lone pair of electrons.

hydrogen bond donor (12.1): A molecule containing an H—N, H—O, or H—F bond.

hydrolysis (16.1): The breaking up of water into H^+ and OH^-. One of these ions ends up bonded to the species doing the hydrolysis, and the other ion is released into solution, potentially changing the pH of the solution.

hydronium ion (16.1): H_3O^+, a water molecule that has accepted an H^+. In this text *hydronium ion* is used synonymously with *hydrogen ion*.

hydrophilic (23.3): Capable of interacting with water; refers to polar and charged species or polar and charged regions of large structures.

hydrophobic (23.3): Incapable of interacting with water; refers to nonpolar species or nonpolar regions of large structures.

hypothesis (1.4): A proposed explanation for a body of observed facts.

ICE table (15.5): A table that shows the initial, change, and equilibrium values of the species in an equilibrium.

ideal gas (7.6): Hypothetical gas whose behavior is predicted by the gas laws and explained by kinetic molecular theory.

ideal gas constant (7.6): $R = 0.08206 \frac{L \cdot atm}{mol \cdot K}$ or $R = 8.3145 \frac{J}{K \cdot mol}$. R is the same for all gases.

ideal gas law (7.6): The pressure, volume, number of moles, and temperature of a sample of gas are related by the equation $PV = nRT$, where $R = 0.08206 \frac{L \cdot atm}{mol \cdot K}$.

ideal solution (13.4): A solution that obeys Raoult's law exactly.

immiscible (13.2): Describes two liquids that do not mix to form a solution, such as oil and water, because they have different intermolecular forces between their particles.

independent variable (0.7): The quantity that is being controlled and is measured on the x-axis.

indicator (5.9): A compound that has different colors in solutions of different acidities and is used to signal the end of a titration.

induced dipole (12.1): A temporarily uneven distribution of electrons caused by the proximity of a spontaneous dipole.

initial rate (14.2): The instantaneous rate measured at time zero.

inner transition elements (2.6): A collective term for the lanthanoids and actinoids.

insoluble (4.3): Unable to dissolve.

instantaneous dipole (12.1): A temporarily uneven distribution of electrons caused by a spontaneous shift in electron density.

instantaneous rates (14.2): Reaction rates determined by graphing concentration versus time, drawing a tangent to the curve, and determining the slope of the tangent.

integrated rate law (14.3): Version of the rate law that allows for the calculation of changes in reactant concentration over time and for graphical determination of the rate constant.

intensive property (1.2): A characteristic, such as color, that does *not* depend on the quantity of material present.

intermediate (14.5): A high-energy, unstable species formed by one intermediate step and consumed by the next intermediate step in a reaction mechanism.

intermolecular force (12.1): An attractive force that forms between particles in the liquid and solid phases.

internal energy, *U* (6.2): The sum of all kinetic and potential energies of a system.

International System of Units, SI (1.5): Système International d'Unités; the modern form of the metric system.

interpolation (0.7): Determining a value from a graph when that value lies between two of the plotted data points.

inverse logarithm (0.5): The inverse of the logarithm function in which 10 is raised to the power of the original number. Also known as an antilog.

inversely proportional (0.8): Two quantities with a fixed product. When one quantity increases, the other will decrease by the same factor, and vice versa.

ion (2.4): A charged atom or molecule that has either lost or gained one or more electrons.

ion (3.3): An atom or group of atoms that has gained or lost electrons and therefore has a net negative or positive charge.

ion pair (13.5): Two oppositely charged ions in solution that feel a sufficiently strong attraction toward one another that they behave as one larger solute particle instead of as two separate solute particles.

ion-selective electrode (19.7): An electrochemical probe that works like concentration cells to measure the concentration of specific ions.

ion–dipole attraction (12.1): The temporary attraction between ions and a polar molecule; important in the formation of solutions.

ionic character (10.5): Measured as percent comparing the observed charge separation to 100% charge separation: % ionic character = $(\mu_{measured}/\mu_{calculated})(100\%)$.

ionic compound (3.1): A compound made up of metal atoms bonded to nonmetal atoms.

ionic equation (4.4): A chemical equation in which any strong electrolytes in aqueous solution are written as hydrated ions.

ionic solid (12.6): A solid whose constituent particles are ions that interact via ionic bonds.

ionizable hydrogen atom (3.5): Any of the hydrogen atoms in an acid that are capable of reacting with water to form H^+ ions.

ionization constant (16.5): A generic term that can mean either an acid ionization constant (K_a) or a base ionization constant (K_b).

ionization energy, IE (9.3): The energy required to remove an electron from a gaseous atom to produce a gaseous cation.

ionize (4.3): To become an ion or ions; applies to acids and weak bases dissolved in water.

isoelectronic (8.5): Having the same electron configuration.

isomers (11.1): Different compounds with the same molecular formula.

isomers (21.3): Different compounds with the same molecular formula but a different arrangement of atoms.

isothermal process (18.3): A process or reaction for which the temperature of the surroundings does not change.

isotope (2.4): A form of an element whose atoms have the same number of protons but different numbers of neutrons.

joule, J (6.1): The SI unit of energy; it takes 4.184 J to raise the temperature of 1 g of water 1°C.

Kelvin scale (1.9): The temperature scale with 273.15 K as the freezing point of water and 373.15 K as the normal boiling point of water; the scale required for gas law and many other scientific calculations.

ketone (21.5): A class of organic compounds with the carbonyl functional group; the general formula of a ketone is RCOR′, where R and R′ may or may not be the same.

ketose (23.2): A monosaccharide with a ketone functional group.

kilogram, kg (1.5): 1000 g; the standard SI unit of mass.

kinetic energy, KE (6.1): The energy of motion.

kinetic molecular theory (7.10): The theory that explains the gas laws (and other phenomena) in terms of the motions and characteristics of the molecules of a gas.

labile hydrogen atom (16.8): An ionizable hydrogen atom on an acid.

lanthanoid contraction (22.2): The smaller-than-expected atomic radius of period 6 transition metals, due to the poor shielding of the outer electrons by the electrons in the 4*f* orbitals.

lattice energy (9.5): The energy released when gas-phase ions combine to form a solid ionic compound.

lattice structure (3.1): A three-dimensional framework containing alternating positive and negative ions, in which the ions are bonded to multiple different ions of the opposite charge in all directions.

law of conservation of energy (1.3): Energy can be neither created nor destroyed in any chemical or physical process.

law of conservation of energy (6.2): Energy cannot be created or destroyed.

law of conservation of mass (1.4): The amount of mass present at the end of a chemical or physical change is equal to the amount of mass present before the change.

law of constant composition (2.2): The composition of a compound is fixed; also called *law of definite proportions*.

law of definite proportions (2.2): The composition of a compound is fixed; also called *law of constant composition*.

law of mass action (15.2): The ratio of products to reactants in the equilibrium constant expression does *not* change as long as the system is at equilibrium.

law of multiple proportions (2.2): When two or more elements combine to form more than one compound, for a fixed mass of one element, the masses of each of the other elements in the compounds occur in a small, whole-number ratio.

Le Châtelier's principle (15.6): When a stress is applied to a system at equilibrium, the reaction shifts in a direction to relieve that stress.

Lewis acid (16.9): In Lewis acid–base theory, a species that does not have a filled outer valence electron shell and is capable of forming a coordinate covalent bond by accepting an electron pair from an atom in another substance. Also called an electron pair acceptor.

Lewis adduct (16.9): The product formed in a Lewis acid–base reaction in which the acid and base are bonded together via a coordinate covalent bond.

Lewis base (16.9): In Lewis acid–base theory, a species that has a nonbonding electron pair in its outer valence shell and is capable of forming a coordinate covalent bond by sharing its electron pair with an atom in another substance. Also called an electron pair donor.

Lewis structure (10.1): Diagram of a molecule or polyatomic ion showing shared pairs or bonds as straight lines and unshared or lone pairs as dots.

Lewis theory (16.9): An expanded theory of acid–base chemistry in which an acid is a substance that accepts an electron pair from a base, forming a Lewis adduct as the product.

ligand (17.10): A Lewis base that bonds to the metal ion of a complex ion.

ligand (22.3): A Lewis base that forms a coordinate covalent bond to a metal or metal ion.

light (8.1): In general, any electromagnetic radiation; specifically, visible light—the wave motion that is visible to the human eye.

light absorption (8.1): The process in which the energy of certain wavelengths of light increases the energy of electrons in atoms.

light emission (8.1): The process in which light of specific wavelengths is produced when electrons in atoms fall to lower energy levels.

limiting quantity (5.3): The quantity of the reactant that will be completely consumed first in a chemical reaction, limiting the quantity of product(s) that can be produced.

limiting reactant (5.3): The reactant that runs out first when a chemical reaction is carried out. The reaction stops at that point, and no more product is formed.

line spectrum (8.2): The emission spectrum of an element when it appears as a series of discrete lines.

linear (0.7): Describes a data set in which the points form a straight line when plotted on a graph.

linear (11.1): An electron geometry associated with two electron domains. Also a molecular geometry resulting from two bonded groups at a 180° bond angle, which occurs with two electron domains with no lone pairs, and five electron domains with three lone pairs.

linkage isomers (22.5): Coordination compounds that have the same chemical formula but share a common ligand that bonds to the metal through different groups.

lipids (23.1): Biomolecules that are insoluble in water; lipids include fats, oils, phospholipids, steroids, and prostaglandins.

lipoprotein (23.3): A biologically important compound consisting of both protein and lipid components.

liquid (7.1): A state of matter; a sample of matter that has a definite volume but assumes the shape of its container.

litmus (16.4): An acid–base indicator that is pink in acidic solution and blue in basic solution. Litmus paper is often used to make a quick assessment of whether a solution is acidic or basic.

lobe (8.3): One portion of an atomic orbital.

logarithm (0.5): The exponent of 10 that would be equal to the original number.

lone pair (10.1): Unshared pairs of electrons in molecules or polyatomic ions.

low spin (22.6): A configuration of *d* electrons in a coordination compound that minimizes the number of unpaired electrons.

macrostate (18.1): A set of energetically equivalent microstates.

magic number (20.2): A specific number of protons or neutrons commonly found in stable atoms.

magnetic quantum number, m_ℓ (8.6): The number that represents an individual orbital within a subshell.

main group element (2.6): An element in groups 1, 2, and 13–18 (1A–8A) in the periodic table.

malleable (12.6): Able to bend or change shape without breaking when force is applied.

malleable (1.2): Capable of being pounded into various shapes.

mass defect (20.7): The difference in mass between an atomic nucleus and the total mass of the protons and neutrons that make up that nucleus. The nucleus always has less mass than the sum of the constituent particles.

mass number, *A* (2.4): The sum of the number of protons and the number of neutrons in an atom; the distinguishing difference among isotopes of a given element.

mass, *m* (1.3): A measure of how much matter is in a sample. When a mass is acted on by an attracting force like gravity, the downward force exerted by the mass is measured as weight.

matter (1.1): Anything that has mass and occupies space.

mean free path (7.11): The average distance traveled by a gas particle between collisions.

mechanical energy (6.1): Energy in an object that is attributable to its motion, position, or both.

messenger RNA (23.5): The RNA molecule that carries information from DNA to the ribosome for protein synthesis; also known as mRNA.

metal (2.6): An element on the left of the stepped line in the periodic table, or a mixture of such elements. Metals tend to be solids at room temperature, conduct heat and electricity, and are malleable and ductile.

metallic solid (12.6): A solid whose constituent particles are metal atoms that are loosely held by their valence electrons.

metalloid (2.6): An element near the stepped line between metals and nonmetals in the periodic table. Metalloids have some properties of both metals and nonmetals.

metathesis (4.2): Another name for a double-replacement reaction.

meter, m (1.5): The primary unit of length in the metric system and SI.

microstate (18.1): A specific energetic state possible for a system.

miscible (13.2): Describes two liquids that readily mix in any proportion to form a solution, such as ethanol and water, because they have very similar intermolecular forces between their particles.

mixture (1.1): A physical combination of substances that has a nondefinite composition and properties characteristic of its components.

molal, *m* or mol/kg (13.3): The unit of molality.

molality, *m* (13.3): A measure of solute concentration defined as the number of moles of solute per kilogram of solvent.

molar, M (5.5): The unit of molarity.

molar mass (3.8): The mass in grams of 1 mol of a substance.

molar solubility (17.6): The number of moles of a substance that can dissolve into 1 L of solution.

molarity, *M* (5.5): A measure of concentration defined as the number of moles of solute per liter of solution.

mole fraction (7.7): The number of moles of a component in a mixture divided by the total number of moles in the mixture, $X_i = n_i/n_t$.

mole fraction, *X* (13.3): The ratio of the number of moles of a component of a solution to the total number of moles of all components in the solution.

mole, mol (3.7): The chemical unit of quantity for any substance; equal to 6.02×10^{23} individual atoms, molecules, or formula units of the substance.

molecular compound (3.1): A compound made up of only nonmetals bonded together; also called a covalent compound.

molecular dipole (11.2): Molecule with uneven electron distribution; polar molecule.

molecular formula (21.1): A formula for an organic compound where each element is listed only once.

molecular formula (3.11): The formula of a molecular substance that gives the ratio of atoms of each element to the substance's molecules.

molecular geometry (11.1): Three-dimensional shape of molecule.

molecular mass (3.8): The mass of a molecule of a substance expressed in atomic mass units.

molecular orbital, MO (11.5): A type of orbital resulting from the combination of atomic orbitals in a molecule.

molecular orbital, MO, diagram (11.5): Similar to an atomic orbital diagram; shows the relative energy levels and electron population of the molecular orbital; used to predict properties.

molecular orbital, MO, theory (11.5): Theory that explains bonding by the combination of atomic orbitals to form bonding molecular orbitals and antibonding molecular orbitals.

molecular solid (12.6): A solid whose constituent particles are molecules that interact via intermolecular forces.

molecular weight (3.8): Another term for molecular mass.

molecularity (14.5): Identifies the number of reactant molecules in an elementary step.

molecule (2.3): A group of atoms bonded by shared electrons.

molecule (3.1): An uncharged, covalently bonded group of atoms.

monatomic ion (3.3): An ion consisting of a single atom that has gained or lost one or more electrons.

monodentate (22.3): Describes a ligand that forms one coordinate covalent bond to a metal.

monomer (21.6): A molecule that is capable of reacting with other similar molecules to form a polymer.

monoprotic acid (3.5): An acid that has only one ionizable hydrogen atom per formula unit.

monosaccharides (23.2): Single-unit carbohydrates, such as glucose or fructose.

N-terminal end (23.4): The end of a polypeptide with an unreacted amine group.

natural logarithm (0.5): A type of logarithm with base *e*.

natural radioactivity (20.1): The spontaneous release of energy and particles from the nucleus of an atom.

negative electrode (19.4): The anode in a voltaic cell; the cathode in an electrolytic cell.

Nernst equation (19.7): The equation used to calculate cell potential under nonstandard conditions.

net ionic equation (4.4): A chemical equation in which only the ions that undergo change during the reaction are present.

neurotransmitters (23.1): Small biomolecules that transmit nerve signals between cells.

neutral (2.4): Neither positively nor negatively charged.

neutral solution (16.3): A solution in which $[H_3O^+] = [OH^-]$. A neutral solution is neither acidic nor basic.

neutralization (4.2): A subcategory of double-replacement reactions in which an acid reacts with a base to form an ionic compound and water; also called an acid–base reaction.

neutron (2.3): A subatomic particle found in the nucleus that has no charge and a mass slightly greater than 1 u.

noble gas (2.6): An element in the far-right column of the periodic table, group 18 (8A)—He, Ne, Ar, Kr, Xe, or Rn.

nonbonding orbitals (11.5): Orbitals occupied by lone pairs in MO diagrams.

nonelectrolyte (4.3): A substance that dissolves in water as molecules, not as hydrated ions.

nonmetal (2.6): Hydrogen or any element to the right of the stepped line in the periodic table. When nonmetals are solid at room temperature, they tend to be brittle and nonconducting. Many nonmetals are gases at room temperature.

nonpolar molecule (11.2): Molecule with symmetric electron distribution; no dipole.

nonvolatile (12.4): Refers to a substance that does not easily vaporize.

nonvolatile (13.4): Not easily vaporized.

normal boiling point (12.4): The boiling point of a liquid at a pressure of 1.00 atm.

nuclear (20.1): Pertaining to the nucleus of an atom.

nuclear fission (20.5): The breaking of a large nuclide into two smaller nuclides. Fission is triggered by striking the parent nuclide with a low-energy neutron.

nuclear fusion (20.5): The combining of two smaller nuclides into one larger one. Fusion requires extreme temperatures.

nuclear radiation (20.1): The energy and particles that are given off by radioactive isotopes.

nuclear transmutation (20.1): The transformation of one element into another via a nuclear reaction.

nucleic acids (23.1): Biomolecules composed of nucleotide monomers; nucleic acids are involved in information storage and usage.

nucleobase (23.5): The nitrogen-containing bases in nucleotides.

nucleons (20.2): The particles found in the nucleus of an atom (i.e., protons and neutrons).

nucleotide (23.5): The nucleic acid monomer consisting of a nucleobase, a five-carbon sugar, and a phosphate group.

nucleus (2.3): The center (core) of an atom, consisting of the protons and neutrons. It accounts for almost all of the mass, but almost none of the volume, of an atom.

nuclide (20.1): The nucleus of an isotope. In this chapter, *isotope* and *nuclide* are used synonymously.

nylon (21.6): A polymer of a six-carbon diacid and a six-carbon diamine.

octahedral (11.1): An electron geometry associated with six electron domains. Also a molecular geometry if all six domains are bonded groups; symmetrical shape consisting of eight triangular faces and 90° and 180° bond angles.

octet rule (10.1): Atoms gain, lose, or share electrons to achieve a stable noble-gas electron configuration, ns^2np^6 (8 electrons), for elements in periods 2 especially and, with expanded valence exceptions, for elements in periods 3–7.

oils (23.2): Triglycerides that are liquids at room temperature with higher levels of unsaturated fatty acids; typically of plant origin.

oligosaccharide (23.2): A short-chain carbohydrate composed of more than two monosaccharides.

optical isomers (21.3): Stereoisomers that are nonsuperimposable mirror images of one another; also known as enantiomers.

orbit (8.2): As described by Bohr and later revised, the circular path for electrons in an atom, the most important characteristic of which is its energy.

orbital (8.3): A region of space in an atom that makes up part or all of a subshell and can hold a maximum of two electrons.

order of operations (0.3): Indicates the order in which you should evaluate multiple steps within a mathematical expression.

organic compound (21.1): A compound that contains carbon.

organic halide (21.4): An organic compound that has at least one halogen atom per molecule.

orientation (14.4): The arrangement of molecules as they approach for a collision, where the proximity of certain atoms dictates whether the reaction can occur.

osmosis (13.4): The movement of solvent molecules through a semipermeable membrane from a pure liquid or a lower concentration solution into a higher concentration solution.

osmotic pressure, Π (13.4): The amount of pressure required to maintain a constant concentration of solution when it is separated from a pure solvent by a semipermeable membrane.

overall reaction order (14.2): The sum of the reaction orders for the individual reactants.

oxidation number (4.6): A type of electron bookkeeping used to keep track of the electrons transferred in redox reactions; assigned according to a set of rules or guidelines; also called oxidation state.

oxidation state (4.6): A type of electron bookkeeping used to keep track of the electrons transferred in redox reactions; assigned according to a set of rules or guidelines; also called oxidation number.

oxidation–reduction (4.2): A reaction involving a transfer of electrons from a higher energy state to a lower energy state; a driving force in many types of reactions; also called redox.

oxidizing agent (4.6): A substance that accepts electrons (is reduced) in a redox reaction.

oxyacid (3.5): An acid of a nonmetal covalently bonded to one or more oxygen atoms, such as $HClO_3$.

oxyanion (3.4): An anion containing oxygen covalently bonded to another element, such as ClO_3^-.

ozone (3.1): O_3, an allotrope of oxygen.

packing (12.7): How layers of atoms are arranged in a crystalline solid.

packing efficiency (12.7): The fraction of the volume of the unit cell occupied by atoms.

paramagnetism (11.5): Weak attraction to a magnetic field; property of molecules with unpaired electrons.

parent name (21.1): The name of an unbranched alkane that serves as the basis of the name of another compound with the same number of carbon atoms in its longest continuous carbon chain.

parent nuclide (20.1): The radioactive atom that undergoes radioactive decay to generate a new isotope (the daughter nuclide).

partial pressure (7.7): The pressure of one gas in a mixture of gases.

particle accelerator (20.5): A large magnetic track designed for accelerating small electrically charged particles in order to make them impact one another at high speeds.

path function (6.3): A function that is dependent on the sequence of steps that move the system from its initial state to its final state.

Pauli exclusion principle (8.6): No two electrons in the same atom can have the same four quantum numbers.

pentose (23.2): A monosaccharide containing five carbon atoms.

peptide bond (23.4): The amide group formed when amino acids react to form peptides.

percent (0.6): The amount of a certain component in 100 units of the total.

percent (2.2): Parts per hundred parts.

percent by mass (13.3): One hundred percent times the mass of the solute divided by the mass of the entire solution.

percent composition (3.9): The percentage by mass of each element in a compound.

percent yield (5.4): The ratio of actual yield to theoretical yield, expressed as a percentage.

perfectly elastic collision (7.10): A collision that occurs with no loss of kinetic energy.

period (2.6): One of the seven horizontal rows of the periodic table.

periodic table (2.6): An organization of elements by increasing atomic number, with elements having similar chemical properties being aligned in vertical columns.

pH paper (16.4): Paper that has been infused with universal indicator so that it can be used to make quick assessments of the approximate pH of a solution. pH paper provides more information about the pH of a solution than litmus paper.

pH scale (16.4): A scale of acidity that typically goes from 1 to 14, with 7 indicating a neutral solution. $pH < 7$ indicates an acidic solution, and $pH > 7$ indicates a basic solution. Mathematically equal to the negative logarithm of the hydrogen ion concentration.

phase diagram (12.5): A graph showing the phase of a substance under all possible pressure and temperature combinations.

phosphodiester (23.5): The bond between two nucleotides in a nucleic acid, extending from the phosphate group of one nucleotide to a hydroxyl group of another.

phospholipid (23.3): The family of lipids with both polar and nonpolar components; phospholipids play important roles in the structure of cell membranes.

photoelectric effect (8.1): An experiment that demonstrates the particle nature of light.

photoelectron (8.1): An electron that is emitted from a surface as a result of an interaction between the surface and a photon.

photon (8.1): A particle of light.

physical change (1.2): A process in which no change in chemical composition occurs.

physical property (1.2): Property unrelated to possible changes in the chemical composition of a substance.

pi, π, bond (11.3): Bond formed by side-on overlap of unhybridized *p* orbitals above and below the internuclear axis; found in double and triple bonds.

polar covalent bond (10.5): A bond resulting from uneven sharing of electrons and characterized by a separation of partial charges.

polar molecule (11.2): A molecule with asymmetric electron distribution; molecular dipole.

polarizability (12.1): The measure of how readily an electron cloud can become asymmetric.

polyatomic ion (10.2): Connected by covalent bonds that carry a charge, allowing them to form ionic compounds.

polyatomic ion (3.3): An ion composed of two or more atoms bonded together.

polydentate (22.3): Describes a ligand that forms more than one coordinate covalent bond to a metal.

polyester (21.6): A polymer of a diacid and a dialcohol.

polyhydroxy (23.2): A compound containing many hydroxyl groups; a characteristic of carbohydrates.

polymer (21.6): A molecule built from many (thousands or even more) smaller molecules (monomers) or parts of molecules.

polypeptide (23.4): A chain of many amino acids connected by peptide bonds.

polyprotic acid (16.6): An acid that has more than one ionizable proton per molecule.

polyprotic acid (3.5): An acid that has two or more ionizable hydrogen atoms per formula unit.

positive electrode (19.4): The cathode in a voltaic cell; the anode in an electrolytic cell.

positron emission (20.1): A form of radioactive decay in which a nucleus emits a positron and often a gamma ray, turning a proton into a neutron.

positron, β^+ (20.1): An antimatter particle that is identical to an electron in all its properties except that it has a $+1$ charge instead of a -1 charge.

potential energy (6.1): The energy of an object that is related to its position.

potential, *E* (19.4): The tendency of an electrochemical reaction or half-reaction to proceed.

power (0.2): Another word for exponent, also used to identify the value of the exponent, as in "2^3 is two to the third power".

precipitate (4.2): The insoluble product of a double-replacement reaction.

precipitation (4.2): The formation of a new solid; a driving force in certain double-replacement reactions.

precision (1.6): The degree to which measurements are reproducible.

pressure (7.1): Force divided by area.

pressure–volume work (6.4): The work done on or by a system when there is a volume change against an external pressure.

primary coordination sphere (22.3): The molecules or ions that are covalently bonded to the metal in a coordination compound.

primary structure (23.4): The sequence of amino acids in the structure of a polypeptide from the N-terminal end to the C-terminal end.

principal energy level (8.3): Another term for an electron shell.

principal quantum number, *n* (8.6): The number that identifies the principal energy level in which the electron can be found.

product (1.2): The substance or substances that result from a chemical or physical change.

product (4.1): The substance present at the end of a chemical change; the result of the reaction.

property (1.2): A characteristic of a substance.

proportion (2.2): The ratio of the number of a certain item divided by the total number of items (compare to percent).

prostaglandin (23.3): The family of lipids with a characteristic five-membered ring and many physiological functions.

proteins (23.1): Biomolecules with many important functions; proteins are composed of hundreds of amino acids.

proton (16.1): In the context of acid–base chemistry, a proton refers only to a hydrogen atom that has been stripped of its electron, and not to any of the protons in the nucleus of a larger atom.

proton (2.3): A subatomic particle found in the nucleus with a mass slightly greater than 1 u and a charge of 1+.

proton acceptor (16.2): A Brønsted base.

proton donor (16.2): A Brønsted acid.

pure substance (1.1): A substance in which all of the particles that make up that substance are of exactly the same kind. Elements and compounds are pure substances, but mixtures are not.

quadratic equation (0.10): An algebraic equation involving a variable raised to the second power.

quadratic formula (0.10): A formula used to solve for the variables in quadratic equations: $x = \dfrac{-b \pm \sqrt{b^2 - 4ac}}{2a}$.

qualitative (1.6): Without a numeric measurement of any kind. A qualitative description might include things like color and shape, or subjective terms like *heavy* or *tall* that do not involve making a numeric measurement.

qualitative analysis (17.9): The determination of the identity of chemical species present in a sample.

quantitative (1.6): Based on a numerical measurement of some kind.

quantitative analysis (17.9): The determination of the amounts of chemical species present in a sample.

quantum number (8.6): One of four numbers that is assigned to each electron in an atom that identifies the electron based on its location and energy.

quaternary structure (23.4): The structure resulting when more than one polypeptide chain is needed to form a functional protein unit.

R group (21.4): A section of an organic molecule (usually an alkane) that typically has no functional group. R is often used as an abbreviation when writing molecular structures to represent a nonreactive portion of the molecule.

radical (10.4): A molecule or ion with an unpaired electron in its Lewis structure.

radioactive (20.1): The property of an unstable isotope that makes it eject particles from the nucleus.

radioactive decay (20.1): A process in which an unstable nucleus of an atom releases energy by ejecting a particle from the nucleus or by capturing an electron from the atom's inner shells.

radioactive series (20.1): A series of sequential radioactive decays from one radioactive isotope to another, ending with a stable isotope.

radioactivity (2.3): The emission of particles during nuclear decay.

radiocarbon dating (20.4): Radiometric dating that uses the activity of carbon-14 to determine the age of a sample; also called carbon dating.

radiometric dating (20.4): A method of determining the age of a sample by comparing the ratios of parent and daughter isotopes in the sample (such as potassium-argon dating) or by comparing the activity of a radioactive isotope in the sample to the activity of the same isotope in a modern sample (such as carbon-14 dating).

random motion (7.10): Motion of molecules in arbitrary directions.

Raoult's law (13.4): The vapor pressure of a solute in a solution (P_A) is equal to its mole fraction in the solution times the vapor pressure of the pure solute: $P_A = X_A P_A^\circ$.

rate (14.1): In a chemical reaction, the change in the concentration of a reactant or product per unit time.

rate constant, *k* (14.2): A proportionality constant used in the rate law.

rate law (14.2): A mathematical expression for the relationship between reaction rate and the concentrations of reactants that includes a proportionality constant.

rate-determining step (14.5): The slowest elementary step in a reaction mechanism.

reactant (1.2): The starting material that undergoes a change in a physical or chemical change.

reactant (4.1): The substance present at the beginning of a chemical reaction that undergoes a chemical change.

reacting ratio (5.1): A ratio of coefficients from a balanced equation, which represents the ratio of moles of any reactant or product to any other reactant or product in the reaction.

reaction mechanism (14.5): A series of elementary steps that make up a chemical reaction.

reaction order, *n* (14.2): The power to which a reactant's concentration is raised in a rate law.

reaction quotient, *Q* (15.4): The ratio of the products to the reactants, where each species is raised to its stoichiometric coefficient, at any time in an equilibrium.

reaction rate (14.1): The change in the concentration of a reactant or product per unit time.

recrystallization (13.2): A purification process carried out by dissolving a substance in a solvent at one temperature and then reducing the temperature so that the (purified) substance crystallizes out, leaving impurities in the solution.

redox (4.2): A reaction involving electron transfer; also called oxidation–reduction.

reducing agent (4.6): A substance that donates electrons (is oxidized) in a redox reaction.

relative scale (2.5): A scale based on an arbitrarily chosen standard; the atomic mass scale is a relative scale of masses based on the mass of ^{12}C.

replication (23.5): The process by which DNA is copied prior to cell division.

resonance (10.3): The property of having resonance structures.

resonance hybrid (10.3): A single structure with delocalized bonds that represents the average of the separate resonance structures.

resonance structures (10.3): Multiple, equivalent, or close-to-equivalent Lewis structures for a molecule or ion that differ only in the placement of multiple bonds and lone pairs.

ribosomal RNA (23.5): A nucleic acid component of ribosomes; also called rRNA.

ribosome (23.5): A cellular organelle that is the site of protein synthesis.

root-mean-square speed, v_{rms} (7.11): A measure of the average speed of a gas particle: $v_{rms} = \sqrt{\frac{3RT}{\mathcal{M}}}$.

rounding (1.6): Reducing the number of digits in a calculated result to the proper number of significant digits.

Rydberg constant, R_H (8.2): A mathematical constant in the Rydberg equation.

Rydberg equation (8.2): An equation that predicts the wavelengths of all hydrogen atomic emission lines.

sacrificial anode (19.8): A more active metal that is purposely allowed to be oxidized to prevent corrosion of a metal structure.

salt (4.2): An ionic compound that does not contain H^+ or OH^-.

salt bridge (19.4): The physical connection between half-cells in both voltaic and electrolytic cells that allows for movement of ions to complete the electrical circuit.

saturated hydrocarbon (21.1): A compound containing only carbon and hydrogen linked by only single bonds; an alkane.

saturated solution (13.2): A solution that holds as much dissolved solute as it is capable of holding stably at a given temperature.

Schrödinger wave equation (8.3): A mathematical formula that produces a distribution map for the probable position of an electron in an atom.

scientific calculator (0.1): A type of electronic calculator with keys for functions, such as scientific notation, logarithms, and exponents, that are necessary for solving problems in science and related disciplines.

scientific law (1.4): A scientific observation that is always seen to be that way, with no exceptions.

scientific method (1.4): A process that combines observation, hypothesis, and experimentation.

scientific notation (0.2): A format that uses powers of 10 to consolidate very large or very small numbers into a more manageable form.

second ionization energy (9.3): The energy required to remove an electron from the +1 gaseous ion.

second law of thermodynamics (18.1): All spontaneous changes result in an increase in the entropy of the universe.

second order (14.2): A type of reaction in which the rate depends upon a reactant's concentration raised to the second power.

secondary coordination sphere (22.3): The molecules or ions outside the primary coordination sphere of a coordination compound that interact with the metal or ligands via intermolecular forces.

secondary structure (23.4): Any repeating shapes formed by the polypeptide chain, such as the α-helix and β-sheet structures.

see-saw (11.1): A molecular geometry associated with five electron domains with one lone pair.

semipermeable membrane (13.4): A membrane that allows some types of molecules to pass through but not others, often based on their size. Typically a semipermeable membrane allows solvent molecules to freely pass through in either direction but blocks solute particles.

shell (8.3): A set of energy levels for electrons in an atom, made up of one or more subshells.

sigma, σ, bond (11.3): A type of bond formed by head-to-head overlap of orbitals along the internuclear axis; found in all covalent bonds.

significant digit (1.6): Any digit that reflects the precision with which a measurement was made.

significant figure (1.6): A significant digit.

simple cubic unit cell (12.7): The simplest form of cubic unit cell, with one atom at each corner. Also called a primitive unit cell.

single bond (10.1): A bond consisting of two atoms sharing one pair of electrons and shown as a short, straight line in Lewis structures.

single-displacement (4.2): A chemical reaction in which an element reacts with a compound, replacing one of the elements in the compound to produce a new compound and a new element; also called single-replacement or displacement.

single-replacement (4.2): A chemical reaction in which an element reacts with a compound, replacing one of the elements in the compound to produce a new compound and a new element; also called single-displacement or displacement.

Slater's rules (9.2): A set of rules that provides a numerical value for the shielding constant S when calculating effective nuclear charge.

slope, *m* (0.7): The steepness of a line on a straight-line graph. A higher slope is a steeper line, and a lower slope is a flatter line.

solid (7.1): A state of matter; a sample of matter that has a definite shape and volume.

solubility (13.2): The concentration of a saturated solution at a given temperature.

solubility guidelines (4.4): A series of rules or guidelines used to help predict the solubility of an ionic compound.

solubility product constant, K_{sp} (17.6): The equilibrium constant for the dissolution of an ionic compound. It is a measure of the compound's solubility and is equal to the product of that compound's ion concentrations in a saturated solution, each raised to the power of its coefficient in the balanced chemical equation.

soluble (1.2): Able to be dissolved.

soluble (4.3): Able to dissolve.

solute (5.5): The component of a solution that is dissolved in another component (the solvent).

solute (13.1): The substance that is dissolved in another substance to create a solution.

solution (1.1): A homogenous mixture.

solvation (13.1): The process of forming solute–solvent attractions.

solvent (13.1): The substance that has another substance dissolved in it to create a solution.

solvent (5.5): The component of a solution that does the dissolving.

***sp* hybrid orbitals** (11.3): Hybrid orbitals formed from one *s* orbital and one *p* orbital; associated with linear electron geometry.

sp^2 hybrid orbitals (11.3): Hybrid orbitals formed from one *s* orbital and two *p* orbitals; associated with trigonal planar electron geometry.

sp^3 hybrid orbitals (11.3): Hybrid orbitals formed from one *s* orbital and three *p* orbitals; associated with tetrahedral electron geometry.

specific heat, c (6.5): The quantity of heat required to raise the temperature of 1 g of a substance by 1°C.

spectator ion (4.4): An ion that does not change during a chemical reaction; the ion is omitted from a net ionic equation.

spectrochemical series (22.7): A list of coordination compound ligands that vary in their contribution to the size of the crystal field splitting energy.

spin quantum number, m_s (8.6): The number that represents the two allowed spin angular momentum states of an electron, commonly referred to as "spin up" or "spin down" and assigned values of either $+\frac{1}{2}$ or $-\frac{1}{2}$, respectively.

spontaneous process (18.1) A process or reaction that occurs.

square planar (11.1): A molecular geometry associated with six electron domains with two lone pairs.

square pyramidal (11.1): A molecular geometry associated with six electron domains with one lone pair.

standard enthalpy of formation, ΔH_f° (6.8): The enthalpy change in the formation of 1 mol of a compound from its elements in their standard states.

standard format (0.10): An arrangement of a quadratic equation that provides coefficient values to solve for the variable: $ax^2 + bx + c = 0$.

standard free energy of formation, ΔG_f° (18.4) The free-energy change in the formation of a substance from its elements in their standard states.

standard hydrogen electrode, SHE (19.5): A half-cell composed of hydrogen gas and a platinum electrode in 1 M hydrogen ion solution that is assigned a voltage of zero; it is used to measure the standard reduction potentials of other half-reactions.

standard molar entropy, ΔS_f° (18.2) The entropy of 1 mol of substance under standard conditions.

standard reduction potential (19.5): The voltage of a half-reaction under standard conditions measured against the standard hydrogen electrode.

standard solution (5.9): An aqueous solution whose concentration is known precisely.

standard state (6.8): The state in which the substance is most stable at 25°C (298 K) and 1 atm pressure.

standard temperature and pressure, STP (7.1): Standard temperature and pressure, usually defined as 0°C and 100 kPa pressure (1 bar).

starch (23.2): A polysaccharide made by plants for energy storage, such as amylose and amylopectin.

state (4.1): The physical state of matter, shown as an abbreviation in parentheses after a chemical formula in a chemical equation: solid (s), liquid (l), gas (g), or aqueous solution (aq).

state function (6.3): A function that is independent of the path taken to achieve its value.

stereoisomers (21.3): Compounds with the same molecular formulas and connectivities but a different arrangement of the atoms in space.

steroid (23.3): The family of lipids with a characteristic four-ring structure and many physiological functions.

Stock system (3.4): The nomenclature system for inorganic compounds in which the oxidation state (or charge for a monatomic cation) is represented as a Roman numeral in the name of the compound.

stoichiometry (5.1): The determination of how much product a reactant can produce or how much of a product can be produced from a given quantity of another substance in a reaction.

strong acid (4.3): A molecular compound that ionizes 100% in water to produce H^+ and an aqueous anion.

strong base (4.3): An ionic compound containing hydroxide ion, OH^-, that dissolves and dissociates 100% in water.

strong electrolyte (4.3): A substance that produces ions when dissolved in water.

strong-field ligand (22.7): A ligand that contributes to a large crystal field splitting energy in a coordination compound.

structural formula (21.1): Similar to a Lewis structure, but lone pairs are omitted.

structural isomers (21.3): Compounds with the same molecular formula but a different structural arrangement of their atoms.

subatomic particle (2.4): A proton, neutron, or electron.

sublimation (12.3): The direct transition from solid phase to gas phase.

sublimation (9.5): The phase change from solid to gas.

subscript (3.1): A number following the symbol of an element (or a closing parenthesis) that denotes the number of atoms of the element (or the number of groups) in the formula unit.

subshell (8.3): The portion of a shell characterized by the same energy level and the same orbital type (*s*, *p*, *d*, or *f*).

substituent (21.1): An atom or group of atoms that takes the place of a hydrogen atom on an unbranched hydrocarbon.

sugars (23.2): Mono- and disaccharides.

supercritical fluid (12.5): The fourth phase of matter, existing at pressures and temperatures above the critical point.

supersaturated solution (13.2): A solution holding more dissolved solute than it can hold stably at a given temperature.

surface tension (12.2): The tendency of a liquid to minimize its surface area.

surroundings (6.2): The part of the universe that is separate from a system of study.

symbol (2.1): The abbreviation for an element consisting of a capital letter, which may sometimes be followed by a lowercase letter.

synthesis (4.2): A chemical reaction in which simple reactants combine to form a more complex product; also called combination.

synthetic fiber (21.6): A polymer, such as nylon, that has the form of a fiber.

system (6.2): A specified portion of the universe that is studied.

T-shaped (11.1): A molecular geometry associated with five electron domains with two lone pairs.

termolecular (14.5): Elementary steps with three reactant molecules.

tertiary structure (23.4): The description of how a polypeptide chain folds to create its overall three-dimensional shape; tertiary structure is held in place by interactions between R groups and between R groups and the polypeptide environment.

tetrahedral (11.1): An electron geometry associated with four electron domains. Also a molecular geometry if all four electron domains are bonded groups; having the shape of a tetrahedron; 109.5° bond angles.

tetrahedron (11.1): Symmetric three-dimensional shape consisting of four equilateral triangular faces.

tetrose (23.2): A monosaccharide containing four carbon atoms.

theoretical yield (5.4): The calculated quantity of product that would result from a chemical reaction based on the stoichiometry of the reaction.

theory (1.4): An explanation that has been thoroughly tested and widely accepted.

thermochemistry (6.1): The study of heat and energy in chemical reactions.

thermonuclear weapon (20.5): A nuclear bomb that generates energy through a fusion reaction rather than through fission; also called a hydrogen bomb or H-bomb.

third ionization energy (9.3): The energy required to remove an electron from the +2 gaseous ion.

third law of thermodynamics (18.2) The entropy of a pure, perfectly ordered, crystalline substance at 0 *K* is 0.

threshold frequency (8.1): The minimum frequency of light required to eject an electron from the surface of a metal in the photoelectric effect.

titrant (17.3): A solution of known concentration, typically delivered via buret in a titration.

titrant (5.9): The solution that is dispensed from the buret in a titration.

titration (5.9): An experimental technique used to determine the concentration of a solution of unknown concentration or the number of moles in an unknown sample of a substance.

titration curve (17.3): A plot of pH versus volume of titrant added over the course of a titration.

torr (7.1): A unit of pressure equal to 1 mmHg or $\frac{1}{760}$ atm.

total equation (4.4): The overall, balanced chemical equation that shows the formulas of the reactants and products and their states of matter.

tracer (20.1): A radioactive isotope that is added to a medicine or procedure (often medical) so that the movement of the isotope through a system can be monitored using a Geiger counter or other means.

transcription (23.5): The process by which the nucleotide sequence on a small part of the DNA is copied using RNA nucleotides to form mRNA, which is later used to specify the order of the amino acids in protein synthesis.

transfer RNA (23.5): The molecule responsible for bringing the correct amino acids into place during protein synthesis; also referred to as tRNA.

transition element (2.6): Any element in groups 3–12 that start in the fourth period of the periodic table, having atomic numbers 21–30, 39–48, 57, 72–80, or 104–112, and designated with B in the classical group naming system.

transition metal (2.6): Another term for transition element, because all of the transition elements are metals.

transition state (14.4): A high-energy state associated with rearrangement of bonds that occurs during chemical reactions; also called activated complex.

translation (23.5): The process by which information in mRNA is used to synthesize a protein.

triglyceride (23.3): The family of lipids consisting of glycerol linked to three fatty acids via ester functional groups.

trigonal bipyramidal (11.1): An electron geometry associated with five electron domains consisting of two three-sided pyramids sharing a base. Also a molecular geometry if all five electron domains are bonded groups; 90°, 120°, and 180° bond angles.

trigonal planar (11.1): An electron geometry associated with three electron domains. Also a molecular geometry if all three electron domains are bonded groups; 120° bond angles.

trigonal pyramidal (11.1): Molecular geometry associated with four electron domains with one lone pair; a three-sided pyramid.

triose (23.2): A monosaccharide containing three carbon atoms.

triple bond (10.1): A bond consisting of two atoms sharing three pairs of electrons and shown as three short lines in Lewis structures.

triple point (12.5): The pressure and temperature at which all three phases of the substance are in equilibrium.

triprotic acid (16.6): An acid with three ionizable hydrogen atoms.

tritium (20.5): A radioactive isotope of hydrogen that has two neutrons and one proton in the nucleus.

triton (20.5): A particle made up of one proton and two neutrons (a tritium nucleus).

unit (1.7): A standard division of measure having a certain value; for example, the meter is the SI base unit of length.

unit cell (12.7): The simplest repeating unit of a crystal structure.

universal indicator (16.4): A mixture of acid–base indicators that results in a different color for each pH from 1 to 14 and can therefore be used to provide a rough estimate of the pH of a solution.

unsaturated hydrocarbon (21.2): A compound containing only carbon and hydrogen and having one or more multiple bonds per molecule.

unsaturated solution (13.2): A solution that contains less dissolved solute than it can hold stably at a given temperature.

valence bond, VB, theory (11.3): Theory that explains bonding by the overlap of atomic orbitals and hybridization of atomic orbitals.

valence electron (8.5): An electron in the highest occupied shell (principal quantum number *n*) of an atom or ion. A valence electron is an electron that takes part in chemical reactions and chemical bonding.

valence electrons (9.1): The electrons in the highest occupied shell (principal quantum number *n*) of an atom or ion.

valence shell electron pair repulsion, VSEPR, model (11.1): Model that uses the number of electron domains around a central atom to predict the most stable shape occupied by the domain due to repulsion.

van der Waals equation (7.12): A modification of the ideal gas law to account for the finite volumes of particles and intermolecular forces between particles: $\left[P + a\left(\frac{n}{V}\right)^2\right](V - nb) = nRT$.

van der Waals forces (12.1): Sometimes used as a general term for any intermolecular force and sometimes used as a synonym for dispersion forces.

van't Hoff factor, *i* (13.5): The number of particles produced when one formula unit of a substance is dissolved in solution. For nonelectrolytes, $i = 1$, and for strong electrolytes $i =$ the number of ions the electrolyte breaks into.

vapor (12.3): A gas in contact with its liquid phase.

vapor pressure (7.7): The pressure of the vapor in equilibrium with its liquid (or solid).

vapor-pressure lowering, ΔP (13.4): A decrease in the vapor pressure of a solution compared to that of the pure solvent due to the presence of a solute.

vaporization (12.3): The transition from liquid to gas phase (evaporation).

viscosity (12.2): The resistance to flow of a liquid.

visible light (8.1): The narrow range of the electromagnetic spectrum that can be detected by the human eye. Visible light corresponds to a wavelength range of approximately 400 nm to 750 nm.

volatile (12.4): Refers to a substance that can easily vaporize.

volatile (13.4): Easily vaporized.

volt, V (19.4): The unit used to measure electrical potential; $1\ V = 1\ J/C$.

voltaic cell (19.4): An electrochemical cell in which a spontaneous redox reaction is used to create an electrical current.

volume ratio (7.9): The ratio of volumes of separate gases involved in a chemical reaction.

volume, *V* (1.5): The extent of space occupied by a sample of matter.

water ionization constant, K_w (16.3): The equilibrium constant describing the autoionization of water into H_3O^+ and OH^-.

waters of hydration (3.4): Water molecules incorporated into the crystal lattice structure of some ionic compounds, indicated in the chemical formula by a centered dot after the ionic formula, followed by the number of waters of hydration per formula unit; for example, $CuSO_4 \cdot 5\ H_2O$.

wavelength, λ (8.1): The length of a single wave, measured from one crest to the next or one trough to the next or any point to the next corresponding point.

weak acid (4.3): A molecular compound that dissolves in water primarily as a molecule but ionizes to a small degree, thus producing aqueous H^+ and an aqueous anion.

weak base (4.3): A molecular compound that dissolves in water primarily as a molecule but ionizes to a small degree, thus producing aqueous OH^- and an aqueous cation.

weak electrolyte (4.3): A substance that dissolves in water primarily as a molecule but ionizes to a small degree, thus producing small percentages of hydrated ions.

weak-field ligand (22.7): A ligand that contributes to a small crystal field splitting energy in a coordination compound.

weighted average (0.9): The average value of several types of items, taking into account the number of individual items of each type.

weighted average (2.5): The average value of several types of items, taking into account the number of individual items of each type.

work function, Φ (8.1): The minimum amount of energy required to eject an electron from the surface of a material in a vacuum.

work, *w* (6.2): The energy resulting from a force acting on an object over a distance.

y-intercept, *b* (0.7): The value of the *y* variable on a graph when the value of the *x* variable is 0.

zero order (14.2): A type of reaction in which the rate does not depend upon a reactant's concentration.

zwitterion (23.4): A molecule that has two charged regions but is neutral overall.

Index

Note: Page numbers followed by f and t refer to figures and tables, respectively.